Hoover's MasterList of U.S. Companies

2011

Hoover's Business Press
Austin, Texas

Hoover's MasterList of U.S. Companies is intended to provide readers with accurate and authoritative information about the enterprises covered in it. The information contained herein is as accurate as we could reasonably make it. In many cases we have relied on third-party material that we believe to be trustworthy but were unable to independently verify. We do not warrant that the book is absolutely accurate or without error. Readers should not rely on any information contained herein in instances where such reliance might cause financial loss. The publisher, the editors, and their data suppliers specifically disclaim all warranties, including the implied warranties of merchantability and fitness for a specific purpose. This book is sold with the understanding that neither the publisher, the editors, nor any content contributors are engaged in providing investment, financial, accounting, legal, or other professional advice.

Morningstar, Inc., provided financial data for most public companies in this book. For private companies and historical information on public companies prior to their becoming public, we obtained information directly from the companies or from third-party material that we believe to be trustworthy. Hoover's, Inc., is solely responsible for the presentation of all data.

Many of the names of products and services mentioned in this book are the trademarks or service marks of the companies manufacturing or selling them and are subject to protection under U.S. law. Space has not permitted us to indicate which names are subject to such protection, and readers are advised to consult with the owners of such marks regarding their use. Hoover's is a trademark of Hoover's, Inc.

10 9 8 7 6 5 4 3 2 1

Publishers Cataloging-in-Publication Data

Hoover's MasterList of U.S. Companies 2011, Vol. 1

    Includes indexes.

    ISBN: 978-1-57311-142-3

    ISSN 1549-6457

    1. Business enterprises — Directories. 2. Corporations — Directories.

HF3010 338.7

Hoover's Company Information is also available on the Internet at Hoover's Web site (www.hoovers.com). A catalog of Hoover's products is available on the Internet at www.hooversbooks.com.

This book was produced for Hoover's Business Press by:

Sycamore Productions, Inc.
5808 Balcones Drive, Suite 205
Austin, Texas 78731
info@sycamoreproductions.com

Cover design is by Jim Neeley. Electronic prepress and printing are by Yurchak Printing Inc. of Landisville, PA.

U.S. AND WORLD BOOK SALES

Hoover's, Inc.
5800 Airport Blvd.
Austin, TX 78752
Phone: 512-374-4500
Fax: 512-374-4538
e-mail: orders@hoovers.com
Web: www.hooversbooks.com

EUROPEAN BOOK SALES

William Snyder Publishing Associates
5 Five Mile Drive
Oxford OX2 8HT
England
Phone & fax: +44-186-551-3186
e-mail: snyderpub@aol.com

Hoover's, Inc.

Founder: Gary Hoover
President: Hyune Hand
VP Technology: Mamie Jones
VP Business Excellence: Jeff Cross
VP Product Management and Development: Ken Maranian
Interim VP Marketing: James Rogers
VP Product Development, D&B Digital: Gregory (Greg) Stern
VP Advertising Sales and Operations: Mark Walters
VP Sales: Tom Wickersham
Director Acquisitions: Amy Bible
Senior Director Account Services: Ron M. Chipman
Leader Strategy and Customer Insights: Katherine (Katie) Bullard

(For the latest updates on Hoover's, please visit: http://hoovers.com/global/corp)

EDITORIAL

Managing Editor: Margaret L. Harrison
Senior Editors: Adrianne Argumaniz, Larry Bills, Jason Cother, Barbara-Anne Mansfield, Greg Perliski, Barbara Redding, Dennis Sutton
Team Leads: Danny Cummings and Matt Saucedo
Editors: Chelsea Adams, Adam Anderson, Victoria Bernard, Alex Biesada, Joe Bramhall, James Bryant, Ryan Caione, Jason Cella, Catherine Colbert, Tami Conner, Nancy Daniels, Bobby Duncan, Lesley Epperson, Rachel Gallo, Chris Hampton, Stuart Hampton, Jim Harris, Laura Huchzermeyer, Chris Huston, Jessica Jimenez, Linnea Anderson Kirgan, Sylvia Lambert, Anne Law, Josh Lower, John MacAyeal, Kathryn Mackenzie, Rebecca Mallett, Erin McInnis, Michael McLellan, Barbara Murray, Nell Newton, Lynett Oliver, Tracey Panek, Rachel Pierce, David Ramirez, Diane Ramirez, Mark Richardson, Melanie Robertson, Patrice Sarath, Amy Schein, Nikki Sein, Seth Shafer, Lee Simmons, Anthony Staats, Tracy Uba, Vanessa Valencia, Randy Williams, David Woodruff
QA Editors: Carrie Geis, Rosie Hatch, Diane Lee, John Willis
Editorial Customer Advocates: Adi Anand and Kenny Jones

HOOVER'S BUSINESS PRESS

Distribution Manager: Rhonda Mitchell
Customer Support and Fulfillment Manager: Michael Febonio

ABOUT HOOVER'S, INC.

Hoover's, a D&B company, provides its customers the fastest path to business with insight and actionable information about companies, industries and key decision makers, along with the powerful tools to find and connect to the right people to get business done. Hoover's provides this information for sales, marketing, business development, and other professionals who need intelligence on U.S. and global companies, industries, and the people who lead them. Hoover's unique combination of editorial expertise and one-of-a-kind data collection with user-generated and company-supplied content gives customers a 360-degree view and competitive edge. This information, along with powerful tools to search, sort, download and integrate the content, is available through Hoover's (http://www.hoovers.com), the company's premier online service. Hoover's is headquartered in Austin, Texas.

Abbreviations

AFL-CIO – American Federation of Labor and Congress of Industrial Organizations
AMA – American Medical Association
AMEX – American Stock Exchange
ARM – adjustable-rate mortgage
ASP – application services provider
ATM – asynchronous transfer mode
ATM – automated teller machine
CAD/CAM – computer-aided design/computer-aided manufacturing
CD-ROM – compact disc – read-only memory
CD-R – CD-recordable
CEO – chief executive officer
CFO – chief financial officer
CMOS – complementary metal oxide silicon
COO – chief operating officer
DAT – digital audiotape
DOD – Department of Defense
DOE – Department of Energy
DOS – disk operating system
DOT – Department of Transportation
DRAM – dynamic random-access memory
DSL – digital subscriber line
DVD – digital versatile disc/digital video disc
DVD-R – DVD-recordable
EPA – Environmental Protection Agency
EPROM – erasable programmable read-only memory
EPS – earnings per share
ESOP – employee stock ownership plan
EU – European Union
EVP – executive vice president
FCC – Federal Communications Commission
FDA – Food and Drug Administration
FDIC – Federal Deposit Insurance Corporation
FTC – Federal Trade Commission
FTP – file transfer protocol
GATT – General Agreement on Tariffs and Trade
GDP – gross domestic product
HMO – health maintenance organization
HR – human resources
HTML – hypertext markup language
ICC – Interstate Commerce Commission
IPO – initial public offering
IRS – Internal Revenue Service
ISP – Internet service provider
kWh – kilowatt-hour
LAN – local-area network
LBO – leveraged buyout
LCD – liquid crystal display

LNG – liquefied natural gas
LP – limited partnership
Ltd. – limited
mips – millions of instructions per second
MW – megawatt
NAFTA – North American Free Trade Agreement
NASA – National Aeronautics and Space Administration
NASDAQ – National Association of Securities Dealers Automated Quotations
NATO – North Atlantic Treaty Organization
NYSE – New York Stock Exchange
OCR – optical character recognition
OECD – Organization for Economic Cooperation and Development
OEM – original equipment manufacturer
OPEC – Organization of Petroleum Exporting Countries
OS – operating system
OSHA – Occupational Safety and Health Administration
OTC – over-the-counter
PBX – private branch exchange
PCMCIA – Personal Computer Memory Card International Association
P/E – price to earnings ratio
RAID – redundant array of independent disks
RAM – random-access memory
R&D – research and development
RBOC – regional Bell operating company
RISC – reduced instruction set computer
REIT – real estate investment trust
ROA – return on assets
ROE – return on equity
ROI – return on investment
ROM – read-only memory
S&L – savings and loan
SCSI – Small Computer System Interface
SEC – Securities and Exchange Commission
SEVP – senior executive vice president
SIC – Standard Industrial Classification
SOC – system on a chip
SVP – senior vice president
USB – universal serial bus
VAR – value-added reseller
VAT – value-added tax
VC – venture capitalist
VP – vice president
VoIP – Voice over Internet Protocol
WAN – wide-area network
WWW – World Wide Web

CONTENTS

Volume 1

Volume 2

About *Hoover's MasterList of U.S. Companies 2011*

This seventeenth edition of *Hoover's MasterList of U.S. Companies* is packed with information, and we believe, represents a true value for the information seeker. We have worked hard to ensure that this edition of the *MasterList* retains its position as one of the most comprehensive, but still affordable, sources for information on the vast array of enterprises that power the U.S. economy.

In this two-volume set, we feature our capsule summaries for each company. Additionally, we have included lists of the Top 500 companies in this book, organized by sales, employees, five-year annualized sales growth, and market value.

Hoover's MasterList of U.S. Companies 2011 contains essential information on about 10,000 companies taken from our internal database. We supplemented and expanded that database by obtaining sales information on most public companies from Morningstar, Inc.

In our selection process, we have endeavored to cover all US companies traded on the major stock exchanges and the largest and most important private enterprises in the US, as well as many other organizations that contribute to our economy, including government-owned enterprises (the United States Postal Service), foundations (the Bill & Melinda Gates Foundation), and major subsidiaries of US and non-US corporations.

We selected companies using the following criteria:

Public Companies (5,261)

We've included all US companies that trade on the New York Stock Exchange (NYSE), the NYSE Alternext, and the NASDAQ Global (NASDAQ GM) and Global Select Markets (NASDAQ GS), as well as many of the companies in Hoover's database that trade on the NASDAQ Capital Market (NASDAQ CM), OTC, or Pink Sheets.

Private and Other Enterprises (4,769)

Our coverage of privately held businesses and other non-public entities includes:

- the largest privately held companies in the US;
- hundreds of the largest mutual insurance companies, agricultural co-ops, foundations, sports teams and leagues, universities, and not-for-profits;
- major subsidiaries of US and non-US corporations that have strong identities independent of the parent organizations;
- major government-owned enterprises.

INFORMATION PROVIDED ABOUT THE COMPANIES

Each entry contains a description of the company's products and operations, ownership, and market position if available, as well as the basic information that most people need to locate, communicate with, and evaluate a company. We have included each company's legal name at the top of the entry (or in the text if it is too long), and if available:

- The street address, phone number, fax number, and Web site address;
- The names of the chief executive officer (CEO), chief financial officer (CFO), and human resources (HR) contact;
- The company's status (privately held, public, subsidiary, etc.).

Headquarters for companies that are incorporated in Bermuda, but whose operational headquarters are in the

US, are listed under their US address. The same applies for companies with joint US and non-US headquarters (such as KPMG International).

For public companies, we have provided trading symbols and exchanges. Sales numbers are provided for all companies, if available, with generally two major exceptions: Corporate parents do not break out sales for many subsidiaries or business segments, and venture capital firms and investment bankers do not provide revenue numbers. Sales for private companies are the most recent available; some are estimated or approximate, as the companies would not divulge exact figures. (Estimated sales numbers are identified as such.)

Some companies have joint CEOs or even no one with the title CEO, although there is someone who functions as the chief executive. In these cases, we have listed after the CEO heading the name of the person who appears first in the company's materials. In smaller companies, sometimes no one individual has the official title of CFO. In those cases, we have listed after the CFO heading the name of the principal financial officer (i.e., the officer who signs off on the company's financial statements).

INDEXES

To help readers easily locate information, we have included three indexes: companies by headquarters location, by industry, and by stock exchange symbol. The indexes for the two volumes are combined and are located at the end of Volume 2.

OTHER HOOVER'S RESOURCES

Companies in *Hoover's MasterList of U.S. Companies* that have more in-depth coverage on Hoover's Online (www.hoovers.com) are indicated by this symbol:

Many of these in-depth profiles are also available in the Hoover's Handbook series, including *Hoover's Handbook of American Business* and *Hoover's Handbook of Emerging Companies*. Information on non-US and private companies can be found in *Hoover's Handbook of World Business* and *Hoover's Handbook of Private Companies*. For more information about these or other Hoover's products, call us at 800-486-8666, e-mail us at orders@hoovers.com, or check out www.hooversbooks.com.

The best suggestions we receive come from our readers. If you would like to see any additional information included in future editions of this book, we invite your comments via telephone (512-374-4500), fax (512-374-4538), mail (5800 Airport Blvd., Austin, TX 78752), or e-mail (info@hoovers.com).

As always, we hope you find our books useful.

The Editors
Hoover's, Inc.
August 2010

Hoover's MasterList of U.S. Companies

of U.S. Companies

Company Rankings

Top 500 Companies by Sales in
Hoover's MasterList of U.S. Companies 2011

Rank	Company	Headquarters	Sales ($ mil.)	Rank	Company	Headquarters	Sales ($ mil.)
1	Wal-Mart Stores, Inc.	Bentonville, AR	408,214.0	51	Safeway Inc.	Pleasanton, CA	40,850.7
2	Exxon Mobil Corporation	Irving, TX	310,586.0	52	SUPERVALU INC.	Eden Prairie, MN	40,597.0
3	Chevron Corporation	San Ramon, CA	171,636.0	53	Kraft Foods Inc.	Northfield, IL	40,386.0
4	General Electric Company	Fairfield, CT	156,783.0	54	Federal Home Loan Mortgage Corporation	McLean, VA	37,614.0
5	ConocoPhillips	Houston, TX	152,840.0	55	SYSCO Corporation	Houston, TX	36,853.3
6	Bank of America Corporation	Charlotte, NC	150,450.0	56	Apple Inc.	Cupertino, CA	36,537.0
7	AT&T Inc.	Dallas, TX	123,018.0	57	The Walt Disney Company	Burbank, CA	36,149.0
8	Ford Motor Company	Dearborn, MI	118,308.0	58	Cisco Systems, Inc.	San Jose, CA	36,117.0
9	Cargill, Incorporated	Wayzata, MN	116,579.0	59	Comcast Corporation	Philadelphia, PA	35,756.0
10	JPMorgan Chase & Co.	New York, NY	115,632.0	60	FedEx Corporation	Memphis, TN	35,497.0
11	Hewlett-Packard Company	Palo Alto, CA	114,552.0	61	Intel Corporation	Santa Clara, CA	35,127.0
12	Berkshire Hathaway Inc.	Omaha, NE	112,493.0	62	Aetna Inc.	Hartford, CT	34,764.1
13	McKesson Corporation	San Francisco, CA	108,702.0	63	Northrop Grumman Corporation	Los Angeles, CA	33,755.0
14	Citigroup Inc.	New York, NY	108,006.0	64	Prudential Financial, Inc.	Newark, NJ	32,688.0
15	Verizon Communications Inc.	New York, NY	107,808.0	65	Caterpillar Inc.	Peoria, IL	32,396.0
16	General Motors Company	Detroit, MI	104,589.0	66	Sprint Nextel Corporation	Overland Park, KS	32,260.0
17	Cardinal Health, Inc.	Dublin, OH	99,512.4	67	The Allstate Corporation	Northbrook, IL	32,013.0
18	CVS Caremark Corporation	Woonsocket, RI	98,729.0	68	General Dynamics Corporation	Falls Church, VA	31,981.0
19	Wells Fargo & Company	San Francisco, CA	98,636.0	69	Sunoco, Inc.	Philadelphia, PA	31,312.0
20	American International Group, Inc.	New York, NY	96,004.0	70	The Coca-Cola Company	Atlanta, GA	30,990.0
21	International Business Machines	Armonk, NY	95,758.0	71	Humana Inc.	Louisville, KY	30,960.4
22	UnitedHealth Group Incorporated	Minnetonka, MN	87,138.0	72	Honeywell International Inc.	Morristown, NJ	30,908.0
23	The Procter & Gamble Company	Cincinnati, OH	79,029.0	73	Abbott Laboratories	Abbott Park, IL	30,764.7
24	The Kroger Co.	Cincinnati, OH	76,733.0	74	News Corporation	New York, NY	30,423.0
25	AmerisourceBergen Corporation	Chesterbrook, PA	71,760.0	75	Morgan Stanley	New York, NY	30,070.0
26	Costco Wholesale Corporation	Issaquah, WA	71,422.0	76	HCA Inc.	Nashville, TN	30,052.0
27	Archer Daniels Midland Company	Decatur, IL	69,207.0	77	Hess Corporation	New York, NY	29,569.0
28	The Boeing Company	Chicago, IL	68,281.0	78	Ingram Micro Inc.	Santa Ana, CA	29,515.4
29	Valero Energy Corporation	San Antonio, TX	68,144.0	79	Federal National Mortgage Association	Washington, DC	29,065.0
30	The Home Depot, Inc.	Atlanta, GA	66,176.0	80	Johnson Controls, Inc.	Milwaukee, WI	28,497.0
31	Target Corporation	Minneapolis, MN	65,357.0	81	Delta Air Lines, Inc.	Atlanta, GA	28,063.0
32	WellPoint, Inc.	Indianapolis, IN	65,028.1	82	American Express Company	New York, NY	26,730.0
33	Walgreen Co.	Deerfield, IL	63,335.0	83	Tyson Foods, Inc.	Springdale, AR	26,704.0
34	Johnson & Johnson	New Brunswick, NJ	61,897.0	84	PricewaterhouseCoopers International	New York, NY	26,171.0
35	Medco Health Solutions, Inc.	Franklin Lakes, NJ	59,804.2	85	E. I. du Pont de Nemours and Company	Wilmington, DE	26,109.0
36	Microsoft Corporation	Redmond, WA	58,437.0	86	Deloitte Touche Tohmatsu	New York, NY	26,100.0
37	Marathon Oil Corporation	Houston, TX	54,139.0	87	Time Warner Inc.	New York, NY	25,785.0
38	United Technologies Corporation	Hartford, CT	52,920.0	88	Rite Aid Corporation	Camp Hill, PA	25,669.1
39	Dell Inc.	Round Rock, TX	52,902.0	89	Enterprise GP Holdings L.P.	Houston, TX	25,510.9
40	The Goldman Sachs Group, Inc.	New York, NY	51,673.0	90	Enterprise Products Partners L.P.	Houston, TX	25,510.9
41	Pfizer Inc.	New York, NY	50,009.0	91	Philip Morris International Inc.	New York, NY	25,035.0
42	Best Buy Co., Inc.	Richfield, MN	49,694.0	92	Raytheon Company	Waltham, MA	24,881.0
43	Lowe's Companies, Inc.	Mooresville, NC	47,220.0	93	Express Scripts, Inc.	St. Louis, MO	24,748.9
44	United Parcel Service, Inc.	Atlanta, GA	45,297.0	94	The Hartford Financial Services Group, Inc.	Hartford, CT	24,701.0
45	Lockheed Martin Corporation	Bethesda, MD	45,189.0	95	The Travelers Companies, Inc.	New York, NY	24,680.0
46	The Dow Chemical Company	Midland, MI	44,875.0	96	Amazon.com, Inc.	Seattle, WA	24,509.0
47	Sears Holdings Corporation	Hoffman Estates, IL	44,043.0	97	Staples, Inc.	Framingham, MA	24,275.5
48	PepsiCo, Inc.	Purchase, NY	43,232.0	98	Google Inc.	Mountain View, CA	23,650.6
49	Bunge Limited	White Plains, NY	41,926.0	99	Macy's, Inc.	Cincinnati, OH	23,489.0
50	MetLife, Inc.	New York, NY	41,058.0	100	International Paper Company	Memphis, TN	23,366.0

Top 500 Companies by Sales in
Hoover's MasterList of U.S. Companies 2011 (continued)

Rank	Company	Headquarters	Sales ($ mil.)	Rank	Company	Headquarters	Sales ($ mil.)
101	Oracle Corporation	Redwood City, CA	23,252.0	151	General Mills, Inc.	Minneapolis, MN	14,691.3
102	Accenture plc	New York, NY	23,171.0	152	Arrow Electronics, Inc.	Melville, NY	14,684.1
103	3M Company	St. Paul, MN	23,123.0	153	Halliburton Company	Houston, TX	14,675.0
104	Deere & Company	Moline, IL	23,112.4	154	Amgen Inc.	Thousand Oaks, CA	14,642.0
105	McDonald's Corporation	Oak Brook, IL	22,744.7	155	Medtronic, Inc.	Minneapolis, MN	14,599.0
106	Schlumberger Limited	Houston, TX	22,702.0	156	The Progressive Corporation	Mayfield Village, OH	14,563.6
107	New York Life Insurance Company	New York, NY	22,246.0	157	The Gap, Inc.	San Francisco, CA	14,197.0
108	Tech Data Corporation	Clearwater, FL	22,099.9	158	Union Pacific Corporation	Omaha, NE	14,143.0
109	Motorola, Inc.	Schaumburg, IL	22,044.0	159	The AES Corporation	Arlington, VA	14,119.0
110	Fluor Corporation	Irving, TX	21,990.3	160	Loews Corporation	New York, NY	14,117.0
111	Eli Lilly and Company	Indianapolis, IN	21,836.0	161	EMC Corporation	Hopkinton, MA	14,025.9
112	Coca-Cola Enterprises Inc.	Atlanta, GA	21,645.0	162	Coventry Health Care, Inc.	Bethesda, MD	13,903.5
113	DIRECTV	El Segundo, CA	21,565.0	163	Illinois Tool Works Inc.	Glenview, IL	13,877.1
114	Emerson Electric Co.	St. Louis, MO	20,915.0	164	Viacom Inc.	New York, NY	13,619.0
115	The TJX Companies, Inc.	Framingham, MA	20,288.4	165	Toys "R" Us, Inc.	Wayne, NJ	13,568.0
116	AMR Corporation	Fort Worth, TX	19,917.0	166	American Electric Power Company, Inc.	Columbus, OH	13,489.0
117	U.S. Bancorp	Minneapolis, MN	19,490.0	167	PG&E Corporation	San Francisco, CA	13,399.0
118	The PNC Financial Services Group, Inc.	Pittsburgh, PA	19,231.0	168	Carnival Corporation	Miami, FL	13,157.0
119	NIKE, Inc.	Beaverton, OR	19,176.1	169	Consolidated Edison, Inc.	New York, NY	13,032.0
120	Kimberly-Clark Corporation	Irving, TX	19,115.0	170	The Chubb Corporation	Warren, NJ	13,016.0
121	Murphy Oil Corporation	El Dorado, AR	19,012.4	171	CBS Corporation	New York, NY	13,014.6
122	Bristol-Myers Squibb Company	New York, NY	18,808.0	172	FirstEnergy Corp.	Akron, OH	12,967.0
123	Plains All American Pipeline, L.P.	Houston, TX	18,520.0	173	Sara Lee Corporation	Downers Grove, IL	12,881.0
124	Alcoa Inc.	New York, NY	18,439.0	174	ConAgra Foods, Inc.	Omaha, NE	12,731.2
125	CIGNA Corporation	Philadelphia, PA	18,414.0	175	Duke Energy Corporation	Charlotte, NC	12,731.0
126	Aflac Incorporated	Columbus, GA	18,254.0	176	National Oilwell Varco, Inc.	Houston, TX	12,712.0
127	Time Warner Cable Inc.	New York, NY	17,868.0	177	Continental Airlines, Inc.	Houston, TX	12,586.0
128	J. C. Penney Company, Inc.	Plano, TX	17,556.0	178	Kellogg Company	Battle Creek, MI	12,575.0
129	Exelon Corporation	Chicago, IL	17,318.0	179	Baxter International Inc.	Deerfield, IL	12,562.0
130	Tyco International Ltd.	Princeton, NJ	17,237.0	180	Smithfield Foods, Inc.	Smithfield, VA	12,487.7
131	Kohl's Corporation	Menomonee Falls, WI	17,178.0	181	Public Service Enterprise Group	Newark, NJ	12,406.0
132	Whirlpool Corporation	Benton Harbor, MI	17,099.0	182	Edison International	Rosemead, CA	12,361.0
133	Tesoro Corporation	San Antonio, TX	16,872.0	183	Qwest Communications International	Denver, CO	12,311.0
134	Altria Group, Inc.	Richmond, VA	16,824.0	184	ARAMARK Corporation	Philadelphia, PA	12,297.9
135	UAL Corporation	Chicago, IL	16,335.0	185	PPG Industries, Inc.	Pittsburgh, PA	12,239.0
136	The Goodyear Tire & Rubber Company	Akron, OH	16,301.0	186	Office Depot, Inc.	Boca Raton, FL	12,144.5
137	Avnet, Inc.	Phoenix, AZ	16,229.9	187	Community Health Systems, Inc.	Franklin, TN	12,107.6
138	Computer Sciences Corporation	Falls Church, VA	16,128.0	188	KBR, Inc.	Houston, TX	12,105.0
139	Manpower Inc.	Milwaukee, WI	16,038.7	189	Eaton Corporation	Cleveland, OH	11,873.0
140	Capital One Financial Corporation	McLean, VA	15,950.7	190	Dollar General Corporation	Goodlettsville, TN	11,796.4
141	Southern Company	Atlanta, GA	15,743.0	191	Waste Management, Inc.	Houston, TX	11,791.0
142	Health Net, Inc.	Woodland Hills, CA	15,713.2	192	Monsanto Company	St. Louis, MO	11,724.0
143	NextEra Energy, Inc.	Juno Beach, FL	15,643.0	193	Omnicom Group Inc.	New York, NY	11,720.7
144	L-3 Communications Holdings, Inc.	New York, NY	15,615.0	194	Jabil Circuit, Inc.	St. Petersburg, FL	11,684.5
145	Constellation Energy Group, Inc.	Baltimore, MD	15,598.8	195	DISH Network Corporation	Englewood, CO	11,664.2
146	Occidental Petroleum Corporation	Los Angeles, CA	15,531.0	196	TRW Automotive Holdings Corp.	Livonia, MI	11,614.0
147	Colgate-Palmolive Company	New York, NY	15,327.0	197	Navistar International Corporation	Warrenville, IL	11,569.0
148	Xerox Corporation	Norwalk, CT	15,179.0	198	Jacobs Engineering Group Inc.	Pasadena, CA	11,467.4
149	Dominion Resources, Inc.	Richmond, VA	15,131.0	199	World Fuel Services Corporation	Miami, FL	11,295.2
150	Freeport-McMoRan Copper & Gold Inc.	Phoenix, AZ	15,040.0	200	Tennessee Valley Authority	Knoxville, TN	11,255.0

Top 500 Companies by Sales in
Hoover's MasterList of U.S. Companies 2011 (continued)

Rank	Company	Headquarters	Sales ($ mil.)	Rank	Company	Headquarters	Sales ($ mil.)
201	Nucor Corporation	Charlotte, NC	11,190.3	251	Catholic Healthcare West	San Francisco, CA	8,957.9
202	Danaher Corporation	Washington, DC	11,184.9	252	Praxair, Inc.	Danbury, CT	8,956.0
203	Dean Foods Company	Dallas, TX	11,158.4	253	NRG Energy, Inc.	Princeton, NJ	8,952.0
204	ONEOK, Inc.	Tulsa, OK	11,111.7	254	Automatic Data Processing, Inc.	Roseland, NJ	8,867.1
205	Liberty Global, Inc.	Englewood, CO	11,080.2	255	Principal Financial Group, Inc.	Des Moines, IA	8,849.1
206	United States Steel Corporation	Pittsburgh, PA	11,048.0	256	Weatherford International Ltd.	Houston, TX	8,826.9
207	Marriott International, Inc.	Bethesda, MD	10,908.0	257	The Great Atlantic & Pacific Tea Company	Montvale, NJ	8,813.6
208	ITT Corporation	White Plains, NY	10,904.5	258	Sutter Health	Sacramento, CA	8,772.0
209	SAIC, Inc.	McLean, VA	10,846.0	259	eBay Inc.	San Jose, CA	8,727.4
210	YUM! Brands, Inc.	Louisville, KY	10,836.0	260	Assurant, Inc.	New York, NY	8,700.5
211	BB&T Corporation	Winston-Salem, NC	10,818.0	261	Limited Brands, Inc.	Columbus, OH	8,632.0
212	Cummins Inc.	Columbus, IN	10,800.0	262	Nordstrom, Inc.	Seattle, WA	8,627.0
213	AutoNation, Inc.	Fort Lauderdale, FL	10,757.8	263	Apache Corporation	Houston, TX	8,614.8
214	Entergy Corporation	New Orleans, LA	10,745.7	264	Lincoln National Corporation	Radnor, PA	8,499.0
215	Textron Inc.	Providence, RI	10,500.0	265	CNA Financial Corporation	Chicago, IL	8,472.0
216	Marsh & McLennan Companies, Inc.	New York, NY	10,493.0	266	Reynolds American Inc.	Winston-Salem, NC	8,419.0
217	US Airways Group, Inc.	Tempe, AZ	10,458.0	267	Liberty Interactive Group	Englewood, CO	8,305.0
218	Texas Instruments Incorporated	Dallas, TX	10,427.0	268	CenterPoint Energy, Inc.	Houston, TX	8,281.0
219	SunTrust Banks Inc.	Atlanta, GA	10,420.0	269	The Bank of New York Mellon	New York, NY	8,279.0
220	QUALCOMM Incorporated	San Diego, CA	10,416.0	270	Air Products and Chemicals, Inc.	Allentown, PA	8,256.2
221	Avon Products, Inc.	New York, NY	10,382.8	271	The Williams Companies, Inc.	Tulsa, OK	8,255.0
222	Southwest Airlines Co.	Dallas, TX	10,350.0	272	Smith International, Inc.	Houston, TX	8,218.6
223	Parker Hannifin Corporation	Cleveland, OH	10,309.0	273	Republic Services, Inc.	Phoenix, AZ	8,199.1
224	The Mosaic Company	Plymouth, MN	10,298.0	274	Boston Scientific Corporation	Natick, MA	8,188.0
225	BJ's Wholesale Club, Inc.	Natick, MA	10,187.0	275	Sempra Energy	San Diego, CA	8,106.0
226	Liberty Starz	Englewood, CO	10,158.0	276	Ashland Inc.	Covington, KY	8,106.0
227	H. J. Heinz Company	Pittsburgh, PA	10,148.1	277	Owens & Minor, Inc.	Mechanicsville, VA	8,037.6
228	Thermo Fisher Scientific Inc.	Waltham, MA	10,109.7	278	Whole Foods Market, Inc.	Austin, TX	8,031.6
229	Unum Group	Chattanooga, TN	10,091.0	279	Devon Energy Corporation	Oklahoma City, OK	8,015.0
230	Genuine Parts Company	Atlanta, GA	10,057.5	280	DTE Energy Company	Detroit, MI	8,014.0
231	Progress Energy, Inc.	Raleigh, NC	9,885.0	281	National Football League	New York, NY	8,000.0
232	R.R. Donnelley & Sons Company	Chicago, IL	9,857.4	282	Discover Financial Services	Riverwoods, IL	7,985.7
233	Seagate Technology LLC	Scotts Valley, CA	9,805.0	283	Norfolk Southern Corporation	Norfolk, VA	7,969.0
234	Starbucks Corporation	Seattle, WA	9,774.6	284	Crown Holdings, Inc.	Philadelphia, PA	7,938.0
235	Lear Corporation	Southfield, MI	9,739.6	285	Icahn Enterprises L.P.	New York, NY	7,865.0
236	Baker Hughes Incorporated	Houston, TX	9,664.0	286	Bed Bath & Beyond Inc.	Union, NJ	7,828.8
237	Xcel Energy Inc.	Minneapolis, MN	9,644.3	287	Ameriprise Financial, Inc.	Minneapolis, MN	7,805.0
238	Penske Automotive Group, Inc.	Bloomfield Hills, MI	9,523.1	288	Masco Corporation	Taylor, MI	7,792.0
239	EmblemHealth, Inc.	New York, NY	9,519.7	289	Cablevision Systems Corporation	Bethpage, NY	7,773.3
240	Fifth Third Bancorp	Cincinnati, OH	9,450.0	290	Huntsman Corporation	Salt Lake City, UT	7,763.0
241	State Street Corporation	Boston, MA	9,362.0	291	SYNNEX Corporation	Fremont, CA	7,719.2
242	Pepco Holdings, Inc.	Washington, DC	9,259.0	292	Newmont Mining Corporation	Greenwood Village, CO	7,705.0
243	URS Corporation	San Francisco, CA	9,249.1	293	Chesapeake Energy Corporation	Oklahoma City, OK	7,702.0
244	Regions Financial Corporation	Birmingham, AL	9,087.0	294	Guardian Life Insurance Company	New York, NY	7,693.0
245	GameStop Corp.	Grapevine, TX	9,078.0	295	Eastman Kodak Company	Rochester, NY	7,606.0
246	Genworth Financial, Inc.	Richmond, VA	9,069.0	296	Aon Corporation	Chicago, IL	7,595.0
247	XTO Energy Inc.	Fort Worth, TX	9,064.0	297	Campbell Soup Company	Camden, NJ	7,586.0
248	CSX Corporation	Jacksonville, FL	9,041.0	298	C.H. Robinson Worldwide, Inc.	Eden Prairie, MN	7,577.2
249	Tenet Healthcare Corporation	Dallas, TX	9,014.0	299	PPL Corporation	Allentown, PA	7,556.0
250	Anadarko Petroleum Corporation	The Woodlands, TX	9,000.0	300	Integrys Energy Group, Inc.	Chicago, IL	7,499.8

Top 500 Companies by Sales in
Hoover's MasterList of U.S. Companies 2011 (continued)

Rank	Company	Headquarters	Sales ($ mil.)	Rank	Company	Headquarters	Sales ($ mil.)
301	CarMax, Inc.	Richmond, VA	7,470.2	351	DaVita Inc.	Denver, CO	6,108.8
302	Quest Diagnostics Incorporated	Madison, NJ	7,455.2	352	Virgin Media Inc.	New York, NY	6,058.9
303	Western Digital Corporation	Lake Forest, CA	7,453.0	353	MeadWestvaco Corporation	Richmond, VA	6,049.0
304	Family Dollar Stores, Inc.	Matthews, NC	7,400.6	354	New York City Health and Hospitals	New York, NY	6,036.9
305	Winn-Dixie Stores, Inc.	Jacksonville, FL	7,367.0	355	The Interpublic Group of Companies	New York, NY	6,027.6
306	Ball Corporation	Broomfield, CO	7,345.3	356	Peabody Energy Corporation	St. Louis, MO	6,012.4
307	The Estée Lauder Companies Inc.	New York, NY	7,323.8	357	Symantec Corporation	Mountain View, CA	5,985.0
308	The Shaw Group Inc.	Baton Rouge, LA	7,279.7	358	MGM MIRAGE	Las Vegas, NV	5,978.6
309	V.F. Corporation	Greensboro, NC	7,220.3	359	The First American Financial Corporation	Santa Ana, CA	5,972.8
310	Darden Restaurants, Inc.	Orlando, FL	7,217.5	360	Avery Dennison Corporation	Pasadena, CA	5,952.7
311	OfficeMax Incorporated	Naperville, IL	7,212.0	361	The McGraw-Hill Companies, Inc.	New York, NY	5,951.8
312	Ross Stores, Inc.	Pleasanton, CA	7,184.2	362	Ecolab Inc.	St. Paul, MN	5,900.6
313	Becton, Dickinson and Company	Franklin Lakes, NJ	7,160.9	363	Royal Caribbean Cruises Ltd.	Miami, FL	5,889.8
314	Hertz Global Holdings, Inc.	Park Ridge, NJ	7,101.5	364	KeyCorp	Cleveland, OH	5,830.0
315	The Sherwin-Williams Company	Cleveland, OH	7,094.2	365	Fidelity National Financial, Inc.	Jacksonville, FL	5,828.4
316	Ameren Corporation	St. Louis, MO	7,090.0	366	Global Partners LP	Waltham, MA	5,818.4
317	Pilgrim's Pride Corporation	Pittsburg, TX	7,088.1	367	Dover Corporation	New York, NY	5,775.7
318	PACCAR Inc	Bellevue, WA	7,076.7	368	UGI Corporation	King of Prussia, PA	5,737.8
319	Reinsurance Group of America	Chesterfield, MO	7,066.8	369	Enbridge Energy Partners, L.P.	Houston, TX	5,731.8
320	Owens-Illinois, Inc.	Perrysburg, OH	7,066.5	370	Gannett Co., Inc.	McLean, VA	5,613.0
321	Gilead Sciences, Inc.	Foster City, CA	7,011.4	371	Stanford University	Stanford, CA	5,602.0
322	Kinder Morgan Energy Partners, L.P.	Houston, TX	7,003.4	372	Newell Rubbermaid Inc.	Atlanta, GA	5,577.6
323	Visa Inc.	Foster City, CA	6,911.0	373	Smurfit-Stone Container Corporation	Chicago, IL	5,574.0
324	WellCare Health Plans, Inc.	Tampa, FL	6,878.2	374	Pitney Bowes Inc.	Stamford, CT	5,569.2
325	AutoZone, Inc.	Memphis, TN	6,816.8	375	EMCOR Group, Inc.	Norwalk, CT	5,547.9
326	Western Refining, Inc.	El Paso, TX	6,807.4	376	Dr Pepper Snapple Group, Inc.	Plano, TX	5,531.0
327	Commercial Metals Company	Irving, TX	6,793.4	377	Weyerhaeuser Company	Federal Way, WA	5,528.0
328	Charter Communications, Inc.	St. Louis, MO	6,755.0	378	Precision Castparts Corp.	Portland, OR	5,486.6
329	Stryker Corporation	Kalamazoo, MI	6,723.1	379	The Clorox Company	Oakland, CA	5,450.0
330	Fortune Brands, Inc.	Deerfield, IL	6,694.7	380	Northeast Utilities	Berlin, CT	5,439.4
331	Goodrich Corporation	Charlotte, NC	6,685.6	381	Mattel, Inc.	El Segundo, CA	5,430.8
332	Visteon Corporation	Van Buren Township, MI	6,685.0	382	Sunoco Logistics Partners L.P.	Philadelphia, PA	5,429.7
333	NiSource Inc.	Merrillville, IN	6,649.4	383	PartnerRe Ltd.	Bermuda	5,418.3
334	AGCO Corporation	Duluth, GA	6,630.4	384	Energy Transfer Partners, L.P.	Dallas, TX	5,417.3
335	Calpine Corporation	Houston, TX	6,564.0	385	Energy Transfer Equity, L.P.	Dallas, TX	5,417.3
336	Henry Schein, Inc.	Melville, NY	6,538.3	386	Advance Auto Parts, Inc.	Roanoke, VA	5,412.6
337	Hormel Foods Corporation	Austin, MN	6,533.7	387	Advanced Micro Devices, Inc.	Sunnyvale, CA	5,403.0
338	Core-Mark Holding Company, Inc.	South San Francisco, CA	6,531.6	388	Corning Incorporated	Corning, NY	5,395.0
339	ONEOK Partners, L.P.	Tulsa, OK	6,474.5	389	Mohawk Industries, Inc.	Calhoun, GA	5,344.0
340	Yahoo! Inc.	Sunnyvale, CA	6,460.3	390	PetSmart, Inc.	Phoenix, AZ	5,336.4
341	The Pantry, Inc.	Cary, NC	6,390.1	391	Federal-Mogul Corporation	Southfield, MI	5,330.0
342	American Family Mutual Insurance	Madison, WI	6,360.1	392	Reliance Steel & Aluminum Co.	Los Angeles, CA	5,318.1
343	Dillard's, Inc.	Little Rock, AR	6,226.6	393	The Hershey Company	Hershey, PA	5,298.7
344	W.W. Grainger, Inc.	Lake Forest, IL	6,222.0	394	Oshkosh Corporation	Oshkosh, WI	5,295.2
345	CMS Energy Corporation	Jackson, MI	6,205.0	395	YRC Worldwide Inc.	Overland Park, KS	5,282.8
346	McDermott International, Inc.	Houston, TX	6,193.1	396	Lorillard, Inc.	Greensboro, NC	5,233.0
347	Omnicare, Inc.	Covington, KY	6,166.2	397	Dollar Tree, Inc.	Chesapeake, VA	5,231.2
348	SLM Corporation	Reston, VA	6,144.7	398	Dana Holding Corporation	Maumee, OH	5,228.0
349	Sonic Automotive, Inc.	Charlotte, NC	6,131.7	399	Cameron International Corporation	Houston, TX	5,223.2
350	AECOM Technology Corporation	Los Angeles, CA	6,119.5	400	Nash-Finch Company	Minneapolis, MN	5,212.7

Top 500 Companies by Sales in
Hoover's MasterList of U.S. Companies 2011 (continued)

Rank	Company	Headquarters	Sales ($ mil.)	Rank	Company	Headquarters	Sales ($ mil.)
401	Pacific Mutual Holding Company	Newport Beach, CA	5,211.0	451	Las Vegas Sands Corp.	Las Vegas, NV	4,563.1
402	Universal Health Services, Inc.	King of Prussia, PA	5,202.4	452	Spectra Energy Corp	Houston, TX	4,552.0
403	AMERIGROUP Corporation	Virginia Beach, VA	5,188.1	453	Group 1 Automotive, Inc.	Houston, TX	4,525.7
404	Sanmina-SCI Corporation	San Jose, CA	5,177.5	454	Genzyme Corporation	Cambridge, MA	4,515.5
405	Jarden Corporation	Rye, NY	5,152.6	455	Allergan, Inc.	Irvine, CA	4,503.6
406	Tutor Perini Corporation	Sylmar, CA	5,152.0	456	Everest Re Group, Ltd.	Bermuda	4,498.6
407	Avis Budget Group, Inc.	Parsippany, NJ	5,131.0	457	Broadcom Corporation	Irvine, CA	4,490.3
408	MasterCard Incorporated	Purchase, NY	5,098.7	458	Agilent Technologies, Inc.	Santa Clara, CA	4,481.0
409	Mylan Inc.	Canonsburg, PA	5,092.8	459	Rockwell Collins, Inc.	Cedar Rapids, IA	4,470.0
410	The Western Union Company	Englewood, CO	5,083.6	460	White Mountains Insurance Group, Ltd.	Hanover, NH	4,448.1
411	Celanese Corporation	Dallas, TX	5,082.0	461	Transatlantic Holdings, Inc.	New York, NY	4,445.7
412	Cooper Industries plc	Houston, TX	5,069.6	462	W. R. Berkley Corporation	Greenwich, CT	4,431.2
413	Eastman Chemical Company	Kingsport, TN	5,047.0	463	The Charles Schwab Corporation	San Francisco, CA	4,414.0
414	Telephone and Data Systems, Inc.	Chicago, IL	5,020.7	464	Dick's Sporting Goods, Inc.	Coraopolis, PA	4,412.8
415	Applied Materials, Inc.	Santa Clara, CA	5,013.6	465	FMC Technologies, Inc.	Houston, TX	4,405.4
416	Harris Corporation	Melbourne, FL	5,005.0	466	NII Holdings, Inc.	Reston, VA	4,397.6
417	Booz Allen Hamilton Inc.	McLean, VA	5,000.0	467	General Cable Corporation	Highland Heights, KY	4,385.2
418	Anixter International Inc.	Glenview, IL	4,982.4	468	Biogen Idec Inc.	Cambridge, MA	4,377.3
419	Polo Ralph Lauren Corporation	New York, NY	4,978.9	469	Flowserve Corporation	Irving, TX	4,365.3
420	CenturyTel, Inc.	Monroe, LA	4,974.2	470	CA, Inc.	Islandia, NY	4,353.0
421	Atmos Energy Corporation	Dallas, TX	4,969.1	471	CNO Financial Group, Inc.	Carmel, IN	4,341.4
422	Universal American Corp.	Rye Brook, NY	4,963.5	472	Rockwell Automation, Inc.	Milwaukee, WI	4,332.5
423	Ryder System, Inc.	Miami, FL	4,887.3	473	American Financial Group, Inc.	Cincinnati, OH	4,320.6
424	Foot Locker, Inc.	New York, NY	4,854.0	474	Kelly Services, Inc.	Troy, MI	4,314.8
425	SPX Corporation	Charlotte, NC	4,850.8	475	Spectrum Group International, Inc.	Irvine, CA	4,293.3
426	O'Reilly Automotive, Inc.	Springfield, MO	4,847.1	476	Activision Blizzard, Inc.	Santa Monica, CA	4,279.0
427	Holly Corporation	Dallas, TX	4,834.3	477	RadioShack Corporation	Fort Worth, TX	4,276.0
428	Alliant Techsystems Inc.	Minneapolis, MN	4,807.7	478	Kindred Healthcare, Inc.	Louisville, KY	4,270.0
429	Owens Corning	Toledo, OH	4,803.0	479	Con-way Inc.	San Mateo, CA	4,269.2
430	Micron Technology, Inc.	Boise, ID	4,803.0	480	Sealed Air Corporation	Elmwood Park, NJ	4,242.8
431	EOG Resources, Inc.	Houston, TX	4,787.0	481	Frontier Oil Corporation	Houston, TX	4,237.2
432	Harley-Davidson, Inc.	Milwaukee, WI	4,781.9	482	SCANA Corporation	Columbia, SC	4,237.0
433	Big Lots, Inc.	Columbus, OH	4,726.8	483	United States Cellular Corporation	Chicago, IL	4,214.6
434	Starwood Hotels & Resorts Worldwide, Inc.	White Plains, NY	4,712.0	484	Electronic Arts Inc.	Redwood City, CA	4,212.0
435	United Stationers Inc.	Deerfield, IL	4,710.3	485	Gerdau Ameristeel Corporation	Tampa, FL	4,195.7
436	BlackRock, Inc.	New York, NY	4,700.0	486	Franklin Resources, Inc.	San Mateo, CA	4,194.1
437	TravelCenters of America LLC	Westlake, OH	4,699.8	487	Northern Trust Corporation	Chicago, IL	4,193.1
438	Laboratory Corporation of America	Burlington, NC	4,694.7	488	Live Nation Entertainment, Inc.	Beverly Hills, CA	4,181.0
439	Casey's General Stores, Inc.	Ankeny, IA	4,687.9	489	MDU Resources Group, Inc.	Bismarck, ND	4,176.5
440	NYSE Euronext	New York, NY	4,687.0	490	CB Richard Ellis Group, Inc.	Los Angeles, CA	4,165.8
441	St. Jude Medical, Inc.	St. Paul, MN	4,681.3	491	Host Hotels & Resorts, Inc.	Bethesda, MD	4,158.0
442	Tenneco Inc.	Lake Forest, IL	4,649.0	492	Insight Enterprises, Inc.	Tempe, AZ	4,136.9
443	El Paso Corporation	Houston, TX	4,631.0	493	Wisconsin Energy Corporation	Milwaukee, WI	4,127.9
444	WESCO International, Inc.	Pittsburgh, PA	4,624.0	494	ArvinMeritor, Inc.	Troy, MI	4,108.0
445	CONSOL Energy Inc.	Canonsburg, PA	4,621.9	495	Centene Corporation	St. Louis, MO	4,102.9
446	Health Management Associates, Inc.	Naples, FL	4,617.1	496	Graphic Packaging Holding Company	Marietta, GA	4,095.8
447	NCR Corporation	Duluth, GA	4,612.0	497	Targa Resources Partners LP	Houston, TX	4,095.6
448	Unisys Corporation	Blue Bell, PA	4,597.7	498	Zimmer Holdings, Inc.	Warsaw, IN	4,095.4
449	The Lubrizol Corporation	Wickliffe, OH	4,586.3	499	Expeditors International	Seattle, WA	4,092.3
450	The Washington Post Company	Washington, DC	4,569.7	500	PulteGroup, Inc.	Bloomfield Hills, MI	4,084.4

Top 500 Companies by Employees in
Hoover's MasterList of U.S. Companies 2011

Rank	Company	Headquarters	Employees	Rank	Company	Headquarters	Employees
1	Wal-Mart Stores, Inc.	Bentonville, AR	2,100,000	51	The Gap, Inc.	San Francisco, CA	135,000
2	Kelly Services, Inc.	Troy, MI	487,900	52	H&R Block, Inc.	Kansas City, MO	133,700
3	United Parcel Service, Inc.	Atlanta, GA	408,000	53	Kohl's Corporation	Menomonee Falls, WI	133,000
4	International Business Machines	Armonk, NY	399,409	54	Johnson Controls, Inc.	Milwaukee, WI	130,000
5	McDonald's Corporation	Oak Brook, IL	385,000	55	Emerson Electric Co.	St. Louis, MO	129,000
6	Target Corporation	Minneapolis, MN	351,000	56	Honeywell International Inc.	Morristown, NJ	122,000
7	YUM! Brands, Inc.	Louisville, KY	350,000	57	Northrop Grumman Corporation	Los Angeles, CA	120,700
8	The Kroger Co.	Cincinnati, OH	334,000	58	Tyson Foods, Inc.	Springdale, AR	117,000
9	Sears Holdings Corporation	Hoffman Estates, IL	322,000	59	Pfizer Inc.	New York, NY	116,500
10	The Home Depot, Inc.	Atlanta, GA	317,000	60	Johnson & Johnson	New Brunswick, NJ	115,500
11	General Electric Company	Fairfield, CT	304,000	61	Comcast Corporation	Philadelphia, PA	107,000
12	Hewlett-Packard Company	Palo Alto, CA	304,000	62	Tyco International Ltd.	Princeton, NJ	106,000
13	CVS Caremark Corporation	Woonsocket, RI	295,000	63	Rite Aid Corporation	Camp Hill, PA	97,500
14	Bank of America Corporation	Charlotte, NC	284,000	64	Kraft Foods Inc.	Northfield, IL	97,000
15	AT&T Inc.	Dallas, TX	282,720	65	Dell Inc.	Round Rock, TX	96,000
16	Wells Fargo & Company	San Francisco, CA	281,000	66	American International Group, Inc.	New York, NY	96,000
17	Citigroup Inc.	New York, NY	269,000	67	Chevron Corporation	San Ramon, CA	95,500
18	Berkshire Hathaway Inc.	Omaha, NE	257,000	68	Computer Sciences Corporation	Falls Church, VA	94,000
19	ARAMARK Corporation	Philadelphia, PA	255,000	69	Caterpillar Inc.	Peoria, IL	93,813
20	Lowe's Companies, Inc.	Mooresville, NC	239,000	70	Microsoft Corporation	Redmond, WA	93,000
21	Walgreen Co.	Deerfield, IL	238,000	71	The Coca-Cola Company	Atlanta, GA	92,800
22	Verizon Communications Inc.	New York, NY	222,900	72	Limited Brands, Inc.	Columbus, OH	92,100
23	JPMorgan Chase & Co.	New York, NY	222,316	73	General Dynamics Corporation	Falls Church, VA	91,700
24	General Motors Company	Detroit, MI	217,000	74	Staples, Inc.	Framingham, MA	91,095
25	United Technologies Corporation	Hartford, CT	206,700	75	ABM Industries Incorporated	New York, NY	91,000
26	PepsiCo, Inc.	Purchase, NY	203,000	76	Oracle Corporation	Redwood City, CA	86,000
27	Ford Motor Company	Dearborn, MI	198,000	77	Carnival Corporation	Miami, FL	84,800
28	HCA Inc.	Nashville, TN	192,000	78	Delta Air Lines, Inc.	Atlanta, GA	81,106
29	Safeway Inc.	Pleasanton, CA	186,000	79	Exxon Mobil Corporation	Irving, TX	80,700
30	Best Buy Co., Inc.	Richfield, MN	180,000	80	Abercrombie & Fitch Co.	New Albany, OH	80,000
31	Darden Restaurants, Inc.	Orlando, FL	179,000	81	UnitedHealth Group Incorporated	Minnetonka, MN	80,000
32	Accenture plc	New York, NY	177,000	82	Dollar General Corporation	Goodlettsville, TN	79,800
33	Deloitte Touche Tohmatsu	New York, NY	168,651	83	Intel Corporation	Santa Clara, CA	79,800
34	Robert Half International Inc.	Menlo Park, CA	166,900	84	Community Health Systems, Inc.	Franklin, TN	79,214
35	PricewaterhouseCoopers International	New York, NY	163,545	85	AMR Corporation	Fort Worth, TX	78,900
36	SFN Group, Inc.	Fort Lauderdale, FL	161,000	86	Cognizant Technology Solutions	Teaneck, NJ	78,400
37	Macy's, Inc.	Cincinnati, OH	161,000	87	Philip Morris International Inc.	New York, NY	77,300
38	SUPERVALU INC.	Eden Prairie, MN	160,000	88	Brinker International, Inc.	Dallas, TX	77,100
39	Cargill, Incorporated	Wayzata, MN	159,000	89	Schlumberger Limited	Houston, TX	77,000
40	The Boeing Company	Chicago, IL	157,100	90	Raytheon Company	Waltham, MA	75,000
41	The TJX Companies, Inc.	Framingham, MA	154,000	91	Lear Corporation	Southfield, MI	75,000
42	J. C. Penney Company, Inc.	Plano, TX	154,000	92	3M Company	St. Paul, MN	74,835
43	Starwood Hotels & Resorts Worldwide	White Plains, NY	145,000	93	Abbott Laboratories	Abbott Park, IL	73,000
44	The Walt Disney Company	Burbank, CA	144,000	94	Coca-Cola Enterprises Inc.	Atlanta, GA	70,000
45	Costco Wholesale Corporation	Issaquah, WA	142,000	95	Eaton Corporation	Cleveland, OH	70,000
46	Starbucks Corporation	Seattle, WA	142,000	96	The Goodyear Tire & Rubber Company	Akron, OH	69,000
47	Lockheed Martin Corporation	Bethesda, MD	140,000	97	Toys "R" Us, Inc.	Wayne, NJ	68,000
48	FedEx Corporation	Memphis, TN	140,000	98	Wendy's/Arby's Group, Inc.	Atlanta, GA	67,500
49	Marriott International, Inc.	Bethesda, MD	137,000	99	L-3 Communications Holdings, Inc.	New York, NY	67,000
50	The Procter & Gamble Company	Cincinnati, OH	135,000	100	Whirlpool Corporation	Benton Harbor, MI	67,000

Top 500 Companies by Employees in
Hoover's MasterList of U.S. Companies 2011 (continued)

Rank	Company	Headquarters	Employees	Rank	Company	Headquarters	Employees
101	Cracker Barrel Old Country Store	Lebanon, TN	66,000	151	Time Warner Cable Inc.	New York, NY	47,000
102	Cisco Systems, Inc.	San Jose, CA	65,550	152	SYSCO Corporation	Houston, TX	47,000
103	TRW Automotive Holdings Corp.	Livonia, MI	63,600	153	UAL Corporation	Chicago, IL	47,000
104	Omnicom Group Inc.	New York, NY	63,000	154	Danaher Corporation	Washington, DC	46,600
105	MGM MIRAGE	Las Vegas, NV	62,000	155	Bob Evans Farms, Inc.	Columbus, OH	46,495
106	Morgan Stanley	New York, NY	61,388	156	SAIC, Inc.	McLean, VA	46,200
107	Jabil Circuit, Inc.	St. Petersburg, FL	61,000	157	Western Digital Corporation	Lake Forest, CA	45,991
108	Royal Caribbean Cruises Ltd.	Miami, FL	60,300	158	Res-Care, Inc.	Louisville, KY	45,700
109	Catholic Healthcare West	San Francisco, CA	60,000	159	V.F. Corporation	Greensboro, NC	45,700
110	Convergys Corporation	Cincinnati, OH	60,000	160	Ross Stores, Inc.	Pleasanton, CA	45,600
111	AutoZone, Inc.	Memphis, TN	60,000	161	The Great Atlantic & Pacific Tea Company	Montvale, NJ	45,000
112	The Brink's Company	Richmond, VA	59,400	162	Automatic Data Processing, Inc.	Roseland, NJ	45,000
113	Regis Corporation	Minneapolis, MN	59,000	163	Hyatt Hotels Corporation	Chicago, IL	45,000
114	GameStop Corp.	Grapevine, TX	59,000	164	PetSmart, Inc.	Phoenix, AZ	45,000
115	Alcoa Inc.	New York, NY	59,000	165	URS Corporation	San Francisco, CA	45,000
116	Illinois Tool Works Inc.	Glenview, IL	59,000	166	TeleTech Holdings, Inc.	Englewood, CO	45,000
117	American Express Company	New York, NY	58,300	167	O'Reilly Automotive, Inc.	Springfield, MO	44,822
118	U.S. Bancorp	Minneapolis, MN	58,229	168	Fresh Del Monte Produce Inc.	Cayman Islands	44,000
119	E. I. du Pont de Nemours and Company	Wilmington, DE	58,000	169	Union Pacific Corporation	Omaha, NE	43,531
120	Tenet Healthcare Corporation	Dallas, TX	57,613	170	Waste Management, Inc.	Houston, TX	43,400
121	R.R. Donnelley & Sons Company	Chicago, IL	56,800	171	EMC Corporation	Hopkinton, MA	43,200
122	International Paper Company	Memphis, TN	56,100	172	AECOM Technology Corporation	Los Angeles, CA	43,200
123	Kimberly-Clark Corporation	Irving, TX	56,000	173	United States Steel Corporation	Pittsburgh, PA	43,000
124	The PNC Financial Services Group, Inc.	Pittsburgh, PA	55,820	174	Quest Diagnostics Incorporated	Madison, NJ	43,000
125	News Corporation	New York, NY	55,000	175	Icahn Enterprises L.P.	New York, NY	42,368
126	Dollar Tree, Inc.	Chesapeake, VA	54,480	176	The Bank of New York Mellon	New York, NY	42,200
127	Kindred Healthcare, Inc.	Louisville, KY	54,100	177	Prudential Financial, Inc.	Newark, NJ	41,943
128	MetLife, Inc.	New York, NY	54,000	178	Burger King Holdings, Inc.	Miami, FL	41,320
129	Xerox Corporation	Norwalk, CT	53,600	179	Dillard's, Inc.	Little Rock, AR	41,300
130	Apollo Group, Inc.	Phoenix, AZ	53,498	180	Continental Airlines, Inc.	Houston, TX	41,300
131	Motorola, Inc.	Schaumburg, IL	53,000	181	Pilgrim's Pride Corporation	Pittsburg, TX	41,240
132	Whole Foods Market, Inc.	Austin, TX	52,500	182	Office Depot, Inc.	Boca Raton, FL	41,000
133	Smithfield Foods, Inc.	Smithfield, VA	52,400	183	Sara Lee Corporation	Downers Grove, IL	41,000
134	The Dow Chemical Company	Midland, MI	52,195	184	Bed Bath & Beyond Inc.	Union, NJ	41,000
135	Marsh & McLennan Companies, Inc.	New York, NY	52,000	185	West Corporation	Omaha, NE	41,000
136	Weatherford International Ltd.	Houston, TX	52,000	186	Avon Products, Inc.	New York, NY	41,000
137	Parker Hannifin Corporation	Cleveland, OH	51,639	187	Medtronic, Inc.	Minneapolis, MN	41,000
138	Deere & Company	Moline, IL	51,300	188	The Jones Financial Companies	Des Peres, MO	40,500
139	KBR, Inc.	Houston, TX	51,000	189	WellPoint, Inc.	Indianapolis, IN	40,500
140	Halliburton Company	Houston, TX	51,000	190	Eli Lilly and Company	Indianapolis, IN	40,360
141	Winn-Dixie Stores, Inc.	Jacksonville, FL	50,000	191	ITT Corporation	White Plains, NY	40,200
142	Baxter International Inc.	Deerfield, IL	49,700	192	Sprint Nextel Corporation	Overland Park, KS	40,000
143	Sykes Enterprises, Incorporated	Tampa, FL	49,200	193	The Interpublic Group of Companies	New York, NY	40,000
144	Advance Auto Parts, Inc.	Roanoke, VA	49,000	194	PPG Industries, Inc.	Pittsburgh, PA	39,900
145	Nordstrom, Inc.	Seattle, WA	48,000	195	Universal Health Services, Inc.	King of Prussia, PA	39,900
146	Sutter Health	Sacramento, CA	48,000	196	American Eagle Outfitters, Inc.	Pittsburgh, PA	39,400
147	Blockbuster Inc.	Dallas, TX	48,000	197	Federal-Mogul Corporation	Southfield, MI	39,000
148	Hanesbrands Inc.	Winston-Salem, NC	47,400	198	Jacobs Engineering Group Inc.	Pasadena, CA	38,900
149	Seagate Technology LLC	Scotts Valley, CA	47,000	199	Foot Locker, Inc.	New York, NY	38,764
150	Family Dollar Stores, Inc.	Matthews, NC	47,000	200	Sanmina-SCI Corporation	San Jose, CA	38,602

Top 500 Companies by Employees in
Hoover's MasterList of U.S. Companies 2011 (continued)

Rank	Company	Headquarters	Employees	Rank	Company	Headquarters	Employees
201	Colgate-Palmolive Company	New York, NY	38,100	251	ConocoPhillips	Houston, TX	30,000
202	Sunrise Senior Living, Inc.	McLean, VA	37,600	252	Stream Global Services, Inc.	Wellesley, MA	30,000
203	National Oilwell Varco, Inc.	Houston, TX	36,802	253	General Mills, Inc.	Minneapolis, MN	30,000
204	The Allstate Corporation	Northbrook, IL	36,800	254	Collective Brands, Inc.	Topeka, KS	30,000
205	Apple Inc.	Cupertino, CA	36,800	255	Regions Financial Corporation	Birmingham, AL	30,000
206	Ruby Tuesday, Inc.	Maryville, TN	36,700	256	Cardinal Health, Inc.	Dublin, OH	29,600
207	RadioShack Corporation	Fort Worth, TX	36,700	257	Visteon Corporation	Van Buren Township, MI	29,500
208	Jones Lang LaSalle Incorporated	Chicago, IL	36,600	258	Dover Corporation	New York, NY	29,300
209	Aon Corporation	Chicago, IL	36,200	259	CIGNA Corporation	Philadelphia, PA	29,300
210	Fluor Corporation	Irving, TX	36,152	260	The Sherwin-Williams Company	Cleveland, OH	29,220
211	YRC Worldwide Inc.	Overland Park, KS	36,000	261	Becton, Dickinson and Company	Franklin Lakes, NJ	29,116
212	Jack in the Box Inc.	San Diego, CA	35,700	262	Genuine Parts Company	Atlanta, GA	29,000
213	Avery Dennison Corporation	Pasadena, CA	35,700	263	CB Richard Ellis Group, Inc.	Los Angeles, CA	29,000
214	Big Lots, Inc.	Columbus, OH	35,600	264	McDermott International, Inc.	Houston, TX	29,000
215	Thermo Fisher Scientific Inc.	Waltham, MA	35,400	265	Marathon Oil Corporation	Houston, TX	28,855
216	Masco Corporation	Taylor, MI	35,400	266	Norfolk Southern Corporation	Norfolk, VA	28,593
217	Gannett Co., Inc.	McLean, VA	35,000	267	Freeport-McMoRan Copper & Gold Inc.	Phoenix, AZ	28,400
218	Aetna Inc.	Hartford, CT	35,000	268	Cooper Industries plc	Houston, TX	28,255
219	Cummins Inc.	Columbus, IN	34,900	269	Archer Daniels Midland Company	Decatur, IL	28,200
220	Southwest Airlines Co.	Dallas, TX	34,726	270	Humana Inc.	Louisville, KY	28,100
221	Barrett Business Services, Inc.	Vancouver, WA	34,725	271	SunTrust Banks Inc.	Atlanta, GA	28,001
222	Baker Hughes Incorporated	Houston, TX	34,400	272	Universal Corporation	Richmond, VA	28,000
223	NIKE, Inc.	Beaverton, OR	34,300	273	Manpower Inc.	Milwaukee, WI	28,000
224	Health Management Associates, Inc.	Naples, FL	33,700	274	Weight Watchers International, Inc.	New York, NY	28,000
225	Pitney Bowes Inc.	Stamford, CT	33,004	275	Laboratory Corporation of America	Burlington, NC	28,000
226	DaVita Inc.	Denver, CO	32,500	276	Capital One Financial Corporation	McLean, VA	28,000
227	H. J. Heinz Company	Pittsburgh, PA	32,500	277	The Shaw Group Inc.	Baton Rouge, LA	28,000
228	McKesson Corporation	San Francisco, CA	32,500	278	The Hartford Financial Services Group, Inc.	Hartford, CT	28,000
229	The Goldman Sachs Group, Inc.	New York, NY	32,500	279	Bristol-Myers Squibb Company	New York, NY	28,000
230	BB&T Corporation	Winston-Salem, NC	32,400	280	Cablevision Systems Corporation	Bethpage, NY	27,940
231	Amphenol Corporation	Wallingford, CT	32,200	281	The Bon-Ton Stores, Inc.	York, PA	27,600
232	Textron Inc.	Providence, RI	32,000	282	Con-way Inc.	San Mateo, CA	27,400
233	The Travelers Companies, Inc.	New York, NY	32,000	283	Mohawk Industries, Inc.	Calhoun, GA	27,400
234	The Estée Lauder Companies Inc.	New York, NY	31,300	284	Dean Foods Company	Dallas, TX	27,157
235	US Airways Group, Inc.	Tempe, AZ	31,300	285	The AES Corporation	Arlington, VA	27,000
236	Freeman Decorating Services, Inc.	Dallas, TX	31,200	286	Las Vegas Sands Corp.	Las Vegas, NV	27,000
237	OfficeMax Incorporated	Naperville, IL	31,000	287	Monsanto Company	St. Louis, MO	27,000
238	Texas Roadhouse, Inc.	Louisville, KY	31,000	288	State Street Corporation	Boston, MA	27,000
239	Cintas Corporation	Cincinnati, OH	31,000	289	Mattel, Inc.	El Segundo, CA	27,000
240	Fidelity National Information Services, Inc.	Jacksonville, FL	31,000	290	Charming Shoppes, Inc.	Bensalem, PA	27,000
241	Time Warner Inc.	New York, NY	31,000	291	Texas Instruments Incorporated	Dallas, TX	26,584
242	Republic Services, Inc.	Phoenix, AZ	31,000	292	Praxair, Inc.	Danbury, CT	26,164
243	The First American Financial Corporation	Santa Ana, CA	30,922	293	Southern Company	Atlanta, GA	26,112
244	Kellogg Company	Battle Creek, MI	30,900	294	P.F. Chang's China Bistro, Inc.	Scottsdale, AZ	26,000
245	Six Flags, Inc.	New York, NY	30,580	295	American Greetings Corporation	Cleveland, OH	26,000
246	Newmont Mining Corporation	Greenwood Village, CO	30,400	296	Boston Scientific Corporation	Natick, MA	26,000
247	Qwest Communications International Inc.	Denver, CO	30,138	297	Williams-Sonoma, Inc.	San Francisco, CA	26,000
248	CSX Corporation	Jacksonville, FL	30,088	298	Bunge Limited	White Plains, NY	25,945
249	Sun Healthcare Group, Inc.	Irvine, CA	30,029	299	Ecolab Inc.	St. Paul, MN	25,931
250	The Cheesecake Factory Incorporated	Calabasas Hills, CA	30,000	300	Unisys Corporation	Blue Bell, PA	25,600

Top 500 Companies by Employees in
Hoover's MasterList of U.S. Companies 2011 (continued)

Rank	Company	Headquarters	Employees	Rank	Company	Headquarters	Employees
301	ConAgra Foods, Inc.	Omaha, NE	25,600	351	Tenneco Inc.	Lake Forest, IL	21,000
302	CBS Corporation	New York, NY	25,580	352	Chiquita Brands International, Inc.	Cincinnati, OH	21,000
303	Molex Incorporated	Lisle, IL	25,240	353	Valero Energy Corporation	San Antonio, TX	20,920
304	Regal Entertainment Group	Knoxville, TN	25,226	354	Cinemark Holdings, Inc.	Plano, TX	20,700
305	Dick's Sporting Goods, Inc.	Coraopolis, PA	25,200	355	Borders Group, Inc.	Ann Arbor, MI	20,600
306	EMCOR Group, Inc.	Norwalk, CT	25,000	356	Crown Holdings, Inc.	Philadelphia, PA	20,500
307	Ruddick Corporation	Charlotte, NC	24,800	357	Bemis Company, Inc.	Neenah, WI	20,400
308	The Progressive Corporation	Mayfield Village, OH	24,661	358	Nucor Corporation	Charlotte, NC	20,400
309	Wyndham Worldwide Corporation	Parsippany, NJ	24,600	359	Eastman Kodak Company	Rochester, NY	20,250
310	DISH Network Corporation	Englewood, CO	24,500	360	CenturyTel, Inc.	Monroe, LA	20,200
311	Amazon.com, Inc.	Seattle, WA	24,300	361	Service Corporation International	Houston, TX	20,176
312	Fortune Brands, Inc.	Deerfield, IL	24,248	362	Jarden Corporation	Rye, NY	20,000
313	Red Robin Gourmet Burgers, Inc.	Greenwood Village, CO	24,038	363	Fiserv, Inc.	Brookfield, WI	20,000
314	O'Charley's Inc.	Nashville, TN	24,000	364	Biglari Holdings Inc.	Indianapolis, IN	20,000
315	Dana Holding Corporation	Maumee, OH	24,000	365	MeadWestvaco Corporation	Richmond, VA	20,000
316	Goodrich Corporation	Charlotte, NC	24,000	366	Medical Staffing Network Holdings	Boca Raton, FL	19,950
317	The Children's Place Retail Stores, Inc.	Secaucus, NJ	23,600	367	Landry's Restaurants, Inc.	Houston, TX	19,850
318	BJ's Wholesale Club, Inc.	Natick, MA	23,500	368	Google Inc.	Mountain View, CA	19,835
319	Brookdale Senior Living, Inc.	Brentwood, TN	23,500	369	Harsco Corporation	Camp Hill, PA	19,600
320	Corning Incorporated	Corning, NY	23,500	370	Newell Rubbermaid Inc.	Atlanta, GA	19,500
321	DIRECTV	El Segundo, CA	23,300	371	PG&E Corporation	San Francisco, CA	19,425
322	Liberty Starz	Englewood, CO	23,075	372	Technitrol, Inc.	Trevose, PA	19,400
323	Liberty Interactive Group	Englewood, CO	23,073	373	Exelon Corporation	Chicago, IL	19,329
324	Liberty Capital Group	Englewood, CO	23,073	374	Rockwell Collins, Inc.	Cedar Rapids, IA	19,300
325	Hertz Global Holdings, Inc.	Park Ridge, NJ	23,050	375	Edison International	Rosemead, CA	19,244
326	Psychiatric Solutions, Inc.	Franklin, TN	23,000	376	Vanguard Health Systems, Inc.	Nashville, TN	19,200
327	Liberty Global, Inc.	Englewood, CO	23,000	377	Rockwell Automation, Inc.	Milwaukee, WI	19,000
328	Hewitt Associates, Inc.	Lincolnshire, IL	23,000	378	Polo Ralph Lauren Corporation	New York, NY	19,000
329	Ryder System, Inc.	Miami, FL	22,900	379	Dr Pepper Snapple Group, Inc.	Plano, TX	19,000
330	DineEquity, Inc.	Glendale, CA	22,900	380	Smurfit-Stone Container Corporation	Chicago, IL	19,000
331	Medco Health Solutions, Inc.	Franklin Lakes, NJ	22,850	381	Air Products and Chemicals, Inc.	Allentown, PA	18,900
332	Avis Budget Group, Inc.	Parsippany, NJ	22,700	382	Wynn Resorts, Limited	Las Vegas, NV	18,900
333	Select Medical Holdings Corporation	Mechanicsburg, PA	22,500	383	AnnTaylor Stores Corporation	New York, NY	18,800
334	Sally Beauty Holdings, Inc.	Denton, TX	22,410	384	Casey's General Stores, Inc.	Ankeny, IA	18,780
335	DynCorp International Inc.	Falls Church, VA	22,300	385	Campbell Soup Company	Camden, NJ	18,700
336	Vishay Intertechnology, Inc.	Malvern, PA	22,300	386	Duke Energy Corporation	Charlotte, NC	18,680
337	Chipotle Mexican Grill, Inc.	Denver, CO	22,250	387	Ingles Markets, Incorporated	Black Mountain, NC	18,600
338	Five Star Quality Care, Inc.	Newton, MA	22,000	388	Hormel Foods Corporation	Austin, MN	18,600
339	Booz Allen Hamilton Inc.	McLean, VA	22,000	389	Stryker Corporation	Kalamazoo, MI	18,582
340	Owens-Illinois, Inc.	Perrysburg, OH	22,000	390	Leggett & Platt, Incorporated	Carthage, MO	18,500
341	LifePoint Hospitals, Inc.	Brentwood, TN	22,000	391	Loews Corporation	New York, NY	18,500
342	Smith International, Inc.	Houston, TX	21,931	392	Nabors Industries Ltd.	Bermuda	18,390
343	Fifth Third Bancorp	Cincinnati, OH	21,901	393	RehabCare Group, Inc.	St. Louis, MO	18,200
344	American Electric Power Company, Inc.	Columbus, OH	21,673	394	Amkor Technology, Inc.	Chandler, AZ	18,200
345	NCR Corporation	Duluth, GA	21,500	395	Micron Technology, Inc.	Boise, ID	18,200
346	The Washington Post Company	Washington, DC	21,500	396	Precision Castparts Corp.	Portland, OR	18,100
347	CKE Restaurants, Inc.	Carpinteria, CA	21,300	397	Cameron International Corporation	Houston, TX	18,100
348	Jo-Ann Stores, Inc.	Hudson, OH	21,135	398	Alliant Techsystems Inc.	Minneapolis, MN	18,000
349	The McGraw-Hill Companies, Inc.	New York, NY	21,077	399	W.W. Grainger, Inc.	Lake Forest, IL	18,000
350	Hostess Brands, Inc.	Irving, TX	21,000	400	AutoNation, Inc.	Fort Lauderdale, FL	18,000

Top 500 Companies by Employees in
Hoover's MasterList of U.S. Companies 2011 (continued)

Rank	Company	Headquarters	Employees	Rank	Company	Headquarters	Employees
401	Navistar International Corporation	Warrenville, IL	17,900	451	Flowserve Corporation	Irving, TX	15,000
402	Dominion Resources, Inc.	Richmond, VA	17,900	452	Vail Resorts, Inc.	Broomfield, CO	14,960
403	The Pep Boys - Manny, Moe & Jack	Philadelphia, PA	17,718	453	Weyerhaeuser Company	Federal Way, WA	14,900
404	AMERCO	Reno, NV	17,700	454	Penn National Gaming, Inc.	Wyomissing, PA	14,772
405	Corrections Corporation of America	Nashville, TN	17,425	455	Neiman Marcus, Inc.	Dallas, TX	14,700
406	Emeritus Corporation	Seattle, WA	17,409	456	Ashland Inc.	Covington, KY	14,700
407	Rent-A-Center, Inc.	Plano, TX	17,400	457	TravelCenters of America LLC	Westlake, OH	14,680
408	Symantec Corporation	Mountain View, CA	17,400	458	Quanta Services, Inc.	Houston, TX	14,673
409	Life Time Fitness, Inc.	Chanhassen, MN	17,400	459	California Pizza Kitchen, Inc.	Los Angeles, CA	14,600
410	Emergency Medical Services Corporation	Greenwood Village, CO	17,276	460	Molson Coors Brewing Company	Denver, CO	14,540
411	Fidelity National Financial, Inc.	Jacksonville, FL	17,200	461	Columbia University	New York, NY	14,520
412	Amgen Inc.	Thousand Oaks, CA	17,200	462	Ball Corporation	Broomfield, CO	14,500
413	Express Parent LLC	Columbus, OH	17,000	463	Zale Corporation	Irving, TX	14,500
414	New York Life Insurance Company	New York, NY	17,000	464	AGCO Corporation	Duluth, GA	14,500
415	Agilent Technologies, Inc.	Santa Clara, CA	16,800	465	Principal Financial Group, Inc.	Des Moines, IA	14,487
416	CEC Entertainment, Inc.	Irving, TX	16,800	466	Aéropostale, Inc.	New York, NY	14,460
417	AMC Entertainment Inc.	Kansas City, MO	16,800	467	Coventry Health Care, Inc.	Bethesda, MD	14,400
418	Amedisys, Inc.	Baton Rouge, LA	16,700	468	Career Education Corporation	Hoffman Estates, IL	14,383
419	Charter Communications, Inc.	St. Louis, MO	16,700	469	Express Scripts, Inc.	St. Louis, MO	14,270
420	Stanley Black & Decker, Inc.	New Britain, CT	16,700	470	M&T Bank Corporation	Buffalo, NY	14,226
421	KeyCorp	Cleveland, OH	16,698	471	J.B. Hunt Transport Services, Inc.	Lowell, AR	14,171
422	The Timken Company	Canton, OH	16,667	472	Sonic Corp.	Oklahoma City, OK	14,150
423	Weis Markets, Inc.	Sunbury, PA	16,600	473	The Dress Barn, Inc.	Suffern, NY	14,100
424	Sonoco Products Company	Hartsville, SC	16,500	474	St. Jude Medical, Inc.	St. Paul, MN	14,000
425	eBay Inc.	San Jose, CA	16,400	475	Airgas, Inc.	Radnor, PA	14,000
426	Diebold, Incorporated	North Canton, OH	16,397	476	Buffalo Wild Wings, Inc.	Minneapolis, MN	14,000
427	Pier 1 Imports, Inc.	Fort Worth, TX	16,200	477	Urban Outfitters, Inc.	Philadelphia, PA	14,000
428	Chico's FAS, Inc.	Fort Myers, FL	16,200	478	NBTY, Inc.	Ronkonkoma, NY	13,950
429	Sealed Air Corporation	Elmwood Park, NJ	16,200	479	Penske Automotive Group, Inc.	Bloomfield Hills, MI	13,950
430	QUALCOMM Incorporated	San Diego, CA	16,100	480	Genesco Inc.	Nashville, TN	13,900
431	A. O. Smith Corporation	Milwaukee, WI	16,067	481	Yahoo! Inc.	Sunnyvale, CA	13,900
432	Papa John's International, Inc.	Louisville, KY	16,000	482	Sempra Energy	San Diego, CA	13,839
433	Owens Corning	Toledo, OH	16,000	483	CA, Inc.	Islandia, NY	13,800
434	The Men's Wearhouse, Inc.	Houston, TX	15,900	484	Ingram Micro Inc.	Santa Ana, CA	13,750
435	Terex Corporation	Westport, CT	15,900	485	The Hershey Company	Hershey, PA	13,700
436	Raley's	West Sacramento, CA	15,800	486	The Pantry, Inc.	Cary, NC	13,694
437	Carrols Restaurant Group, Inc.	Syracuse, NY	15,700	487	NII Holdings, Inc.	Reston, VA	13,673
438	Consolidated Edison, Inc.	New York, NY	15,541	488	Commercial Metals Company	Irving, TX	13,586
439	Energizer Holdings, Inc.	St. Louis, MO	15,500	489	Hospira, Inc.	Lake Forest, IL	13,500
440	Mylan Inc.	Canonsburg, PA	15,500	490	CarMax, Inc.	Richmond, VA	13,439
441	Harris Corporation	Melbourne, FL	15,400	491	Hallmark Cards, Incorporated	Kansas City, MO	13,400
442	Multi-Fineline Electronix, Inc.	Anaheim, CA	15,400	492	FirstEnergy Corp.	Akron, OH	13,379
443	Boyd Gaming Corporation	Las Vegas, NV	15,400	493	Cabela's Incorporated	Sidney, NE	13,300
444	Regal Beloit Corporation	Beloit, WI	15,300	494	Tractor Supply Company	Brentwood, TN	13,300
445	Omnicare, Inc.	Covington, KY	15,200	495	Hess Corporation	New York, NY	13,300
446	PACCAR Inc	Bellevue, WA	15,200	496	ArvinMeritor, Inc.	Troy, MI	13,200
447	Brunswick Corporation	Lake Forest, IL	15,003	497	Pentair, Inc.	Golden Valley, MN	13,150
448	SPX Corporation	Charlotte, NC	15,000	498	Stage Stores, Inc.	Houston, TX	13,100
449	Assurant, Inc.	New York, NY	15,000	499	The Manitowoc Company, Inc.	Manitowoc, WI	13,100
450	Entergy Corporation	New Orleans, LA	15,000	500	Graphic Packaging Holding Company	Marietta, GA	13,100

Top 500 Companies by Sales Growth in
Hoover's MasterList of U.S. Companies 2011

Rank	Company	Headquarters	Five-Year Annualized Sales Growth	Rank	Company	Headquarters	Five-Year Annualized Sales Growth
1	Cheniere Energy Partners, L.P.	Houston, TX	2,678.7%	51	Spectrum Pharmaceuticals, Inc.	Irvine, CA	182.1%
2	Alexza Pharmaceuticals, Inc.	Mountain View, CA	1,800.0%	52	LecTec Corporation	Texarkana, TX	180.9%
3	Synta Pharmaceuticals Corp.	Lexington, MA	1,335.3%	53	Maiden Holdings, Ltd.	Bermuda	179.8%
4	Advanced Life Sciences Holdings, Inc.	Woodridge, IL	1,300.0%	54	Cheniere Energy, Inc.	Houston, TX	178.7%
5	Boise Inc.	Boise, ID	1,279.2%	55	Trubion Pharmaceuticals, Inc.	Seattle, WA	178.3%
6	Chimera Investment Corporation	New York, NY	823.5%	56	HSW International, Inc.	Atlanta, GA	176.9%
7	EnerJex Resources, Inc.	Overland Park, KS	700.0%	57	Stream Global Services, Inc.	Wellesley, MA	176.6%
8	Thompson Creek Metals Company Inc.	Littleton, CO	681.7%	58	The Amacore Group, Inc.	Maitland, FL	175.5%
9	First Physicians Capital Group, Inc.	Beverly Hills, CA	647.4%	59	SkyTerra Communications, Inc.	Reston, VA	175.4%
10	Green Plains Renewable Energy, Inc.	Omaha, NE	634.1%	60	Bridgepoint Education, Inc.	San Diego, CA	174.5%
11	Solera Holdings, Inc.	San Diego, CA	626.7%	61	Massachusetts Higher Education Assistance	Boston, MA	173.7%
12	Synthesis Energy Systems, Inc.	Houston, TX	600.0%	62	Ardea Biosciences, Inc.	San Diego, CA	171.8%
13	MAKO Surgical Corp.	Fort Lauderdale, FL	599.3%	63	Transcept Pharmaceuticals, Inc.	Point Richmond, CA	168.5%
14	Hughes Communications, Inc.	Germantown, MD	540.5%	64	Evergreen Energy Inc.	Denver, CO	166.8%
15	Hatteras Financial Corp.	Winston-Salem, NC	522.7%	65	Information Services Group, Inc.	Stamford, CT	165.0%
16	Rand Logistics, Inc.	New York, NY	505.3%	66	Champions Biotechnology, Inc.	Arlington, VA	164.3%
17	Amicus Therapeutics, Inc.	Cranbury, NJ	498.1%	67	FiberTower Corporation	San Francisco, CA	164.1%
18	Affymax, Inc.	Palo Alto, CA	482.2%	68	American Capital Agency Corp.	Bethesda, MD	163.0%
19	Validus Holdings, Ltd.	Bermuda	451.1%	69	CytRx Corporation	Los Angeles, CA	162.5%
20	Medivation, Inc.	San Francisco, CA	450.0%	70	Contango Oil & Gas Company	Houston, TX	158.1%
21	Insulet Corporation	Bedford, MA	406.9%	71	First Solar, Inc.	Tempe, AZ	156.0%
22	MaxLinear, Inc.	Carlsbad, CA	340.5%	72	Keryx Biopharmaceuticals, Inc.	New York, NY	154.6%
23	BioCryst Pharmaceuticals, Inc.	Birmingham, AL	339.5%	73	Meru Networks, Inc.	Sunnyvale, CA	150.9%
24	Alexion Pharmaceuticals, Inc.	Cheshire, CT	333.0%	74	Primus Guaranty, Ltd.	New York, NY	150.9%
25	Ener1, Inc.	Fort Lauderdale, FL	331.9%	75	TC PipeLines, LP	Omaha, NE	148.0%
26	Lighting Science Group Corporation	Dallas, TX	321.0%	76	Helicos BioSciences Corporation	Cambridge, MA	146.6%
27	Waytronx, Inc.	Tualatin, OR	312.3%	77	Echo Global Logistics, Inc.	Chicago, IL	144.2%
28	Opko Health	Miami, FL	304.7%	78	Genoptix, Inc.	Carlsbad, CA	144.0%
29	Graymark Healthcare, Inc.	Oklahoma City, OK	304.6%	79	BMP Sunstone Corporation	Plymouth Meeting, PA	143.2%
30	Jamba, Inc.	Emeryville, CA	276.6%	80	DexCom, Inc.	San Diego, CA	138.1%
31	Pacific Office Properties Trust, Inc.	Santa Monica, CA	267.0%	81	Entropic Communications, Inc.	San Diego, CA	136.8%
32	Summer Infant, Inc.	Woonsocket, RI	261.4%	82	St. Bernard Software, Inc.	San Diego, CA	135.3%
33	Javelin Pharmaceuticals, Inc.	Cambridge, MA	245.5%	83	Cogdell Spencer Inc.	Charlotte, NC	135.2%
34	Cardiovascular Systems, Inc.	St. Paul, MN	244.7%	84	Healthy Fast Food, Inc.	Henderson, NV	135.1%
35	Halozyme Therapeutics, Inc.	San Diego, CA	242.1%	85	Tix Corporation	Studio City, CA	134.6%
36	A123 Systems, Inc.	Watertown, MA	237.7%	86	Genomic Health, Inc.	Redwood City, CA	131.6%
37	Command Center, Inc.	Post Falls, ID	237.0%	87	American Home Food Products, Inc.	New York, NY	131.1%
38	Insmed Incorporated	Richmond, VA	219.3%	88	BioFuel Energy Corp.	Denver, CO	131.0%
39	Artificial Life, Inc.	Santa Monica, CA	209.4%	89	Airvana, Inc.	Chelmsford, MA	130.2%
40	Constellation Energy Partners LLC	Houston, TX	209.0%	90	EGPI Firecreek, Inc.	Scottsdale, AZ	128.9%
41	The Orchard Enterprises, Inc.	New York, NY	207.1%	91	SXC Health Solutions Corp.	Lisle, IL	127.1%
42	Radient Pharmaceuticals Corporation	Tustin, CA	204.5%	92	Rentech, Inc.	Los Angeles, CA	124.5%
43	Homeland Security Capital Corporation	Arlington, VA	202.3%	93	NxStage Medical, Inc.	Lawrence, MA	123.1%
44	Santa Fe Financial Corporation	Los Angeles, CA	202.3%	94	NovaBay Pharmaceuticals, Inc.	Emeryville, CA	118.7%
45	Portsmouth Square, Inc.	Los Angeles, CA	200.9%	95	Kodiak Oil & Gas Corp.	Denver, CO	118.0%
46	Franklin Wireless Corp.	San Diego, CA	199.1%	96	PokerTek, Inc.	Matthews, NC	117.4%
47	BioDelivery Sciences International, Inc.	Raleigh, NC	197.7%	97	GeneLink, Inc.	Longwood, FL	115.3%
48	Infinera Corporation	Sunnyvale, CA	194.7%	98	LogMeIn, Inc.	Woburn, MA	114.7%
49	Hallador Petroleum Company	Denver, CO	192.0%	99	Targacept, Inc.	Winston-Salem, NC	113.9%
50	Procera Networks, Inc.	Los Gatos, CA	186.1%	100	pSivida Corp.	Watertown, MA	112.3%

Top 500 Companies by Sales Growth in
Hoover's MasterList of U.S. Companies 2011 (continued)

Rank	Company	Headquarters	Five-Year Annualized Sales Growth	Rank	Company	Headquarters	Five-Year Annualized Sales Growth
101	TranS1 Inc.	Wilmington, NC	111.1%	151	ANTs Software Inc.	San Francisco, CA	84.6%
102	Lyris, Inc.	Wilmington, DE	110.6%	152	GlobalOptions Group, Inc.	New York, NY	83.5%
103	Force Protection, Inc.	Ladson, SC	110.6%	153	Global Telecom & Technology, Inc.	McLean, VA	82.9%
104	EnerNOC, Inc.	Boston, MA	110.0%	154	Osiris Therapeutics, Inc.	Columbia, MD	82.6%
105	SunPower Corporation	San Jose, CA	109.8%	155	Targa Resources Partners LP	Houston, TX	82.6%
106	Energy XXI (Bermuda) Limited	Bermuda	109.6%	156	Synergetics USA, Inc.	O'Fallon, MO	82.3%
107	Flint Telecom Group, Inc.	Henderson, NV	108.9%	157	Ambient Corporation	Newton, MA	82.1%
108	Redpoint Bio Corporation	Ewing, NJ	108.8%	158	Oragenics, Inc.	Alachua, FL	81.7%
109	Wave Systems Corp.	Lee, MA	108.5%	159	Access Plans, Inc.	Norman, OK	81.5%
110	Quicksilver Gas Services LP	Fort Worth, TX	108.0%	160	Inova Technology Inc.	Las Vegas, NV	81.1%
111	Cornerstone Therapeutics Inc.	Cary, NC	105.0%	161	Acorda Therapeutics, Inc.	Hawthorne, NY	81.0%
112	Alnylam Pharmaceuticals, Inc.	Cambridge, MA	104.9%	162	Universal Insurance Holdings, Inc.	Fort Lauderdale, FL	80.8%
113	Dune Energy, Inc.	Houston, TX	104.6%	163	A.P. Pharma, Inc.	Redwood City, CA	80.3%
114	Riverbed Technology, Inc.	San Francisco, CA	103.7%	164	Accuray Incorporated	Sunnyvale, CA	79.7%
115	New World Brands, Inc.	McKinney, TX	103.5%	165	ISTA Pharmaceuticals, Inc.	Irvine, CA	79.3%
116	Jaguar Mining Inc.	Concord, NH	101.7%	166	SIRIUS XM Radio Inc.	New York, NY	78.7%
117	Multiband Corporation	New Hope, MN	100.9%	167	Sirona Dental Systems, Inc.	Long Island City, NY	78.5%
118	Aruba Networks, Inc.	Sunnyvale, CA	100.2%	168	GeoResources, Inc.	Houston, TX	78.0%
119	TeleNav, Inc.	Sunnyvale, CA	100.1%	169	Concho Resources Inc.	Midland, TX	77.5%
120	Access Pharmaceuticals, Inc.	Dallas, TX	100.0%	170	L-1 Identity Solutions, Inc.	Stamford, CT	77.1%
121	Millennium Bankshares Corporation	Reston, VA	100.0%	171	Lithium Technology Corporation	Plymouth Meeting, PA	76.2%
122	Aircastle Limited	Stamford, CT	99.5%	172	ONEOK Partners, L.P.	Tulsa, OK	75.8%
123	ReachLocal, Inc.	Woodland Hills, CA	99.4%	173	NYSE Euronext	New York, NY	75.6%
124	NeoGenomics, Inc.	Fort Myers, FL	98.5%	174	Cytokinetics, Incorporated	South San Francisco, CA	74.0%
125	American CareSource Holdings, Inc.	Dallas, TX	98.5%	175	Williams Partners L.P.	Tulsa, OK	73.6%
126	Advanced Battery Technologies, Inc.	New York, NY	97.3%	176	Illumina, Inc.	San Diego, CA	73.5%
127	M & F Worldwide Corp.	New York, NY	96.6%	177	Converted Organics Inc.	Boston, MA	73.3%
128	NextWave Wireless Inc.	San Diego, CA	95.8%	178	Encore Energy Partners LP	Fort Worth, TX	72.7%
129	Lime Energy Co.	Elk Grove Village, IL	95.0%	179	Sangamo BioSciences, Inc.	Richmond, CA	72.6%
130	Human Genome Sciences, Inc.	Rockville, MD	94.9%	180	Constant Contact, Inc.	Waltham, MA	72.1%
131	SecureAlert, Inc.	Salt Lake City, UT	93.4%	181	Gramercy Capital Corp.	New York, NY	71.6%
132	PTS, Inc.	Las Vegas, NV	93.4%	182	Impax Laboratories, Inc.	Hayward, CA	70.6%
133	Patriot Coal Corporation	St. Louis, MO	93.1%	183	Eagle Rock Energy Partners, L.P.	Houston, TX	69.7%
134	Idera Pharmaceuticals, Inc.	Cambridge, MA	92.7%	184	Clearwire Corporation	Kirkland, WA	69.2%
135	ThermoEnergy Corporation	Little Rock, AR	91.1%	185	Argan, Inc.	Rockville, MD	69.0%
136	Depomed, Inc.	Menlo Park, CA	90.3%	186	AeroGrow International, Inc.	Boulder, CO	69.0%
137	Cleveland BioLabs, Inc.	Buffalo, NY	89.9%	187	EXCO Resources, Inc.	Dallas, TX	68.8%
138	Deep Down, Inc.	Houston, TX	89.1%	188	John D. Oil and Gas Company	Mentor, OH	68.2%
139	Global Geophysical Services, Inc.	Missouri City, TX	88.6%	189	Immunomedics, Inc.	Morris Plains, NJ	67.6%
140	Compellent Technologies, Inc.	Eden Prairie, MN	88.6%	190	3PAR Inc.	Fremont, CA	66.9%
141	BioMarin Pharmaceutical Inc.	Novato, CA	88.5%	191	Cinedigm Digital Cinema Corp.	Morristown, NJ	66.9%
142	Prospect Capital Corporation	New York, NY	87.7%	192	Blueknight Energy Partners, L.P.	Tulsa, OK	66.5%
143	Terra Nova Financial Group, Inc.	Chicago, IL	86.1%	193	Iconix Brand Group, Inc.	New York, NY	66.5%
144	U.S. Energy Corp.	Riverton, WY	86.1%	194	Elite Pharmaceuticals, Inc.	Northvale, NJ	66.4%
145	Pressure BioSciences, Inc.	South Easton, MA	86.1%	195	JMP Group Inc.	San Francisco, CA	66.3%
146	Digital Ally, Inc.	Overland Park, KS	86.0%	196	BGC Partners, Inc.	New York, NY	66.0%
147	GigOptix, Inc.	Palo Alto, CA	86.0%	197	Patient Safety Technologies, Inc.	Temecula, CA	65.5%
148	SuccessFactors, Inc.	San Mateo, CA	85.2%	198	Zoom Telephonics, Inc.	Boston, MA	64.9%
149	Atrinsic, Inc.	New York, NY	85.0%	199	Endologix, Inc.	Irvine, CA	64.8%
150	GT Solar International, Inc.	Merrimack, NH	84.7%	200	Manitex International, Inc.	Bridgeview, IL	64.7%

Top 500 Companies by Sales Growth in
Hoover's MasterList of U.S. Companies 2011 (continued)

Rank	Company	Headquarters	Five-Year Annualized Sales Growth	Rank	Company	Headquarters	Five-Year Annualized Sales Growth
201	Raser Technologies, Inc.	Provo, UT	64.6%	251	Isilon Systems, Inc.	Seattle, WA	55.7%
202	Epoch Holding Corporation	New York, NY	64.1%	252	NuStar Energy L.P.	San Antonio, TX	55.5%
203	KIT digital, Inc.	New York, NY	63.6%	253	ICx Technologies, Inc.	Arlington, VA	55.5%
204	AMAG Pharmaceuticals, Inc.	Lexington, MA	63.6%	254	Document Security Systems, Inc.	Rochester, NY	55.3%
205	XenoPort, Inc.	Santa Clara, CA	63.5%	255	Regeneron Pharmaceuticals, Inc.	Tarrytown, NY	54.7%
206	Wireless Ronin Technologies, Inc.	Minneapolis, MN	63.5%	256	Hologic, Inc.	Bedford, MA	54.4%
207	Medidata Solutions, Inc.	New York, NY	63.2%	257	Geron Corporation	Menlo Park, CA	54.3%
208	Legacy Reserves LP	Midland, TX	63.1%	258	Life Partners Holdings, Inc.	Waco, TX	54.0%
209	Codexis, Inc.	Redwood City, CA	62.8%	259	Caraco Pharmaceutical Laboratories	Detroit, MI	53.8%
210	AvStar Aviation Group, Inc.	Houston, TX	62.7%	260	Antigenics Inc.	New York, NY	53.1%
211	Nuvilex, Inc.	Cherry Hill, NJ	62.7%	261	The Providence Service Corporation	Tucson, AZ	53.1%
212	Research Frontiers Incorporated	Woodbury, NY	62.7%	262	Linn Energy, LLC	Houston, TX	53.1%
213	ARIAD Pharmaceuticals, Inc.	Cambridge, MA	62.2%	263	Amylin Pharmaceuticals, Inc.	San Diego, CA	52.4%
214	Archipelago Learning, Inc.	Dallas, TX	61.8%	264	Celera Corporation	Alameda, CA	52.4%
215	Conspiracy Entertainment Holdings, Inc.	Santa Monica, CA	61.8%	265	OmniComm Systems, Inc.	Fort Lauderdale, FL	52.0%
216	Lucas Energy, Inc.	Houston, TX	61.7%	266	Raptor Networks Technology, Inc.	Santa Ana, CA	52.0%
217	Applied Nanotech Holdings, Inc.	Austin, TX	61.7%	267	Real Goods Solar, Inc.	Louisville, CO	51.8%
218	Dynasil Corporation of America	West Berlin, NJ	61.2%	268	Seattle Genetics, Inc.	Bothell, WA	51.8%
219	GeoEye, Inc.	Dulles, VA	60.7%	269	Smith Micro Software, Inc.	Aliso Viejo, CA	51.6%
220	El Paso Pipeline Partners, L.P.	Houston, TX	60.5%	270	American Public Education, Inc.	Charles Town, WV	51.6%
221	Boots & Coots International Well Control	Houston, TX	60.4%	271	XOMA Ltd.	Berkeley, CA	51.5%
222	NPS Pharmaceuticals, Inc.	Bedminster, NJ	60.1%	272	XELR8 Holdings, Inc.	Denver, CO	51.4%
223	Santarus, Inc.	San Diego, CA	59.7%	273	CyberSource Corporation	Mountain View, CA	51.4%
224	Echo Therapeutics, Inc.	Franklin, MA	59.7%	274	VMware, Inc.	Palo Alto, CA	51.2%
225	Dice Holdings, Inc.	New York, NY	59.5%	275	Cavium Networks, Inc.	Mountain View, CA	51.1%
226	Hercules Technology Growth Capital	Palo Alto, CA	59.4%	276	Rosetta Stone Inc.	Arlington, VA	51.1%
227	eMagin Corporation	Bellevue, WA	59.3%	277	Terremark Worldwide, Inc.	Miami, FL	51.1%
228	IntercontinentalExchange, Inc.	Atlanta, GA	58.9%	278	InnerWorkings, Inc.	Chicago, IL	51.1%
229	Crimson Exploration, Inc.	Houston, TX	58.7%	279	IntelliCheck Mobilisa, Inc.	Port Townsend, WA	50.8%
230	SyntheMed, Inc.	Iselin, NJ	58.7%	280	Progenics Pharmaceuticals, Inc.	Tarrytown, NY	50.6%
231	Arrowhead Research Corporation	Pasadena, CA	58.6%	281	Full House Resorts, Inc.	Las Vegas, NV	50.5%
232	Icahn Enterprises L.P.	New York, NY	58.0%	282	EasyLink Services International	Norcross, GA	50.4%
233	Questcor Pharmaceuticals, Inc.	Union City, CA	57.9%	283	Rick's Cabaret International, Inc.	Houston, TX	50.1%
234	American Electric Technologies, Inc.	Houston, TX	57.9%	284	Discovery Communications, Inc.	Silver Spring, MD	50.0%
235	Conceptus, Inc.	Mountain View, CA	57.8%	285	Grand Canyon Education, Inc.	Phoenix, AZ	50.0%
236	Sigma Designs, Inc.	Milpitas, CA	57.7%	286	Pacific WebWorks, Inc.	Salt Lake City, UT	49.9%
237	Limelight Networks, Inc.	Tempe, AZ	57.7%	287	Loral Space & Communications Inc.	New York, NY	49.8%
238	Hampton Roads Bankshares, Inc.	Norfolk, VA	57.7%	288	Celgene Corporation	Summit, NJ	49.6%
239	Evergreen Solar, Inc.	Marlboro, MA	57.7%	289	Enviro Voraxial Technology, Inc.	Fort Lauderdale, FL	49.5%
240	KapStone Paper and Packaging	Northbrook, IL	56.9%	290	StemCells, Inc.	Palo Alto, CA	49.5%
241	Chart Industries, Inc.	Garfield Heights, OH	56.9%	291	Quick-Med Technologies, Inc.	Boca Raton, FL	49.5%
242	Neutral Tandem, Inc.	Chicago, IL	56.7%	292	Green Mountain Coffee Roasters, Inc.	Waterbury, VT	49.3%
243	Pacific Sands, Inc.	Racine, WI	56.5%	293	Wendy's/Arby's Group, Inc.	Atlanta, GA	49.0%
244	Simtrol, Inc.	Norcross, GA	56.5%	294	GMX Resources Inc.	Oklahoma City, OK	48.9%
245	ZBB Energy Corporation	Menomonee Falls, WI	56.5%	295	Ladenburg Thalmann Financial Services	Miami, FL	48.8%
246	Jazz Pharmaceuticals, Inc.	Palo Alto, CA	56.5%	296	Celldex Therapeutics, Inc.	Needham, MA	48.8%
247	NuVasive, Inc.	San Diego, CA	56.5%	297	GateHouse Media, Inc.	Fairport, NY	48.7%
248	American Superconductor	Devens, MA	56.3%	298	Arena Resources, Inc.	Tulsa, OK	48.7%
249	Crocs, Inc.	Niwot, CO	56.2%	299	Duff & Phelps Corporation	New York, NY	48.7%
250	Windstream Corporation	Little Rock, AR	56.0%	300	Hansen Medical, Inc.	Mountain View, CA	48.3%

Top 500 Companies by Sales Growth in
Hoover's MasterList of U.S. Companies 2011 (continued)

Rank	Company	Headquarters	Five-Year Annualized Sales Growth	Rank	Company	Headquarters	Five-Year Annualized Sales Growth
301	Allis-Chalmers Energy Inc.	Houston, TX	48.1%	351	Allegiant Travel Company	Las Vegas, NV	43.2%
302	Walter Investment Management Corp.	Tampa, FL	47.8%	352	Telkonet, Inc.	Milwaukee, WI	43.2%
303	AIMS Worldwide, Inc.	Fairfax, VA	47.6%	353	Golden Star Resources Ltd.	Littleton, CO	43.1%
304	Pinnacle Financial Partners, Inc.	Nashville, TN	47.6%	354	Oplink Communications, Inc.	Fremont, CA	43.0%
305	Convio, Inc.	Austin, TX	47.6%	355	SolarWinds, Inc.	Austin, TX	42.9%
306	Mariner Energy, Inc.	Houston, TX	47.4%	356	Catalyst Health Solutions, Inc.	Rockville, MD	42.9%
307	Cardica, Inc.	Redwood City, CA	47.4%	357	ArcSight, Inc.	Cupertino, CA	42.7%
308	ICOP Digital, Inc.	Lenexa, KS	47.0%	358	Medifast, Inc.	Owings Mills, MD	42.6%
309	Accretive Health, Inc.	Chicago, IL	47.0%	359	Caspian Services, Inc.	Salt Lake City, UT	42.5%
310	EnergySolutions, Inc.	Salt Lake City, UT	47.0%	360	Bridgeline Digital, Inc.	Woburn, MA	42.5%
311	Cubist Pharmaceuticals, Inc.	Lexington, MA	46.9%	361	Medical Properties Trust, Inc.	Birmingham, AL	42.5%
312	Global Partners LP	Waltham, MA	46.9%	362	Isramco, Inc.	Houston, TX	42.4%
313	Smart Balance, Inc	Paramus, NJ	46.9%	363	OpenTable, Inc.	San Francisco, CA	42.4%
314	Intuitive Surgical, Inc.	Sunnyvale, CA	46.7%	364	NorthStar Realty Finance Corp.	New York, NY	42.3%
315	Vitacost.com, Inc.	Boca Raton, FL	46.6%	365	Nuance Communications, Inc.	Burlington, MA	42.2%
316	Cano Petroleum, Inc.	Fort Worth, TX	46.6%	366	Stifel Financial Corp.	St. Louis, MO	42.2%
317	Bucyrus International, Inc.	South Milwaukee, WI	46.5%	367	Cumberland Pharmaceuticals Inc.	Nashville, TN	42.0%
318	Hercules Offshore, Inc.	Houston, TX	46.5%	368	DineEquity, Inc.	Glendale, CA	42.0%
319	Vanguard Natural Resources, LLC	Houston, TX	46.4%	369	Mylan Inc.	Canonsburg, PA	42.0%
320	Molecular Insight Pharmaceuticals, Inc.	Cambridge, MA	46.3%	370	Ebix, Inc.	Atlanta, GA	41.9%
321	NetSuite Inc.	San Mateo, CA	46.2%	371	Pain Therapeutics, Inc.	San Mateo, CA	41.8%
322	Clarient, Inc.	Aliso Viejo, CA	46.1%	372	Bioheart, Inc.	Sunrise, FL	41.4%
323	Inverness Medical Innovations, Inc.	Waltham, MA	46.1%	373	Solitario Exploration & Royalty Corp.	Wheat Ridge, CO	41.4%
324	CardioNet, Inc.	Conshohocken, PA	46.1%	374	Helix BioMedix, Inc.	Bothell, WA	41.4%
325	Allscripts-Misys Healthcare Solutions	Chicago, IL	46.0%	375	Aldagen, Inc.	Durham, NC	41.4%
326	Rackspace Hosting, Inc.	San Antonio, TX	45.9%	376	Jacobs Financial Group, Inc.	Charleston, WV	41.4%
327	Global Traffic Network, Inc.	New York, NY	45.7%	377	Torvec, Inc.	Rochester, NY	41.4%
328	Annaly Capital Management, Inc.	New York, NY	45.6%	378	Equinix, Inc.	Foster City, CA	41.3%
329	Tower Group, Inc.	New York, NY	45.4%	379	NewStar Financial, Inc.	Boston, MA	41.2%
330	Virtual Radiologic Corporation	Minnetonka, MN	45.4%	380	Amedisys, Inc.	Baton Rouge, LA	41.1%
331	Diamond Hill Investment Group, Inc.	Columbus, OH	45.2%	381	Myriad Genetics, Inc.	Salt Lake City, UT	41.1%
332	Preferred Voice, Inc.	Dallas, TX	45.2%	382	Inspire Pharmaceuticals, Inc.	Durham, NC	41.0%
333	Emerging Vision, Inc.	New York City, NY	45.1%	383	BlackRock, Inc.	New York, NY	40.9%
334	Exterran Holdings, Inc.	Houston, TX	45.0%	384	Almost Family, Inc.	Louisville, KY	40.9%
335	Compass Diversified Holdings	Westport, CT	44.8%	385	LivePerson, Inc.	New York, NY	40.7%
336	Southern National Bancorp of Virginia	McLean, VA	44.8%	386	Acme Packet, Inc.	Burlington, MA	40.7%
337	Energy Recovery, Inc.	San Leandro, CA	44.8%	387	Akeena Solar, Inc.	Los Gatos, CA	40.7%
338	Synutra International, Inc.	Rockville, MD	44.7%	388	The NASDAQ OMX Group, Inc.	New York, NY	40.3%
339	Axcess International Inc.	Carrollton, TX	44.5%	389	Natus Medical Incorporated	San Carlos, CA	40.3%
340	Buckeye GP Holdings L.P.	Breinigsville, PA	44.3%	390	GTx, Inc.	Memphis, TN	40.2%
341	Buckeye Partners, L.P.	Breinigsville, PA	44.3%	391	TransMontaigne Partners L.P.	Denver, CO	40.2%
342	BioSante Pharmaceuticals, Inc.	Lincolnshire, IL	44.3%	392	NexCen Brands, Inc.	New York, NY	40.1%
343	Tidelands Bancshares, Inc.	Mt. Pleasant, SC	44.1%	393	Google Inc.	Mountain View, CA	40.1%
344	Alkermes, Inc.	Cambridge, MA	44.0%	394	Thermo Fisher Scientific Inc.	Waltham, MA	40.0%
345	FairPoint Communications, Inc.	Charlotte, NC	43.9%	395	Penwest Pharmaceuticals Co.	Danbury, CT	40.0%
346	Salary.com, Inc.	Waltham, MA	43.6%	396	Auxilium Pharmaceuticals, Inc.	Malvern, PA	39.9%
347	Craft Brewers Alliance, Inc.	Portland, OR	43.5%	397	PAA Natural Gas Storage, LLC	Houston, TX	39.9%
348	Comverge, Inc.	East Hanover, NJ	43.3%	398	HMS Holdings Corp.	New York, NY	39.8%
349	Wynn Resorts, Limited	Las Vegas, NV	43.3%	399	Evolution Petroleum Corporation	Houston, TX	39.7%
350	salesforce.com, inc.	San Francisco, CA	43.3%	400	ICF International, Inc.	Fairfax, VA	39.7%

Top 500 Companies by Sales Growth in
Hoover's MasterList of U.S. Companies 2011 (continued)

Rank	Company	Headquarters	Five-Year Annualized Sales Growth	Rank	Company	Headquarters	Five-Year Annualized Sales Growth
401	ShoreTel, Inc.	Sunnyvale, CA	39.6%	451	Western Gas Partners, LP	The Woodlands, TX	36.0%
402	Antares Pharma, Inc.	Ewing, NJ	39.4%	452	Stereotaxis, Inc.	St. Louis, MO	35.9%
403	Aviat Networks, Inc.	Morrisville, NC	39.4%	453	Pacific Biomarkers, Inc.	Seattle, WA	35.9%
404	First Clover Leaf Financial Corp.	Edwardsville, IL	39.3%	454	Brocade Communications Systems, Inc.	San Jose, CA	35.8%
405	Broadview Institute, Inc.	Woodbury, MN	39.2%	455	VIVUS, Inc.	Mountain View, CA	35.8%
406	Bruker Corporation	Billerica, MA	39.1%	456	XATA Corporation	Eden Prairie, MN	35.6%
407	LKQ Corporation	Chicago, IL	39.1%	457	Spirit AeroSystems Holdings, Inc.	Wichita, KS	35.6%
408	IBERIABANK Corporation	Lafayette, LA	39.0%	458	The Dolan Company	Minneapolis, MN	35.5%
409	Auxilio, Inc.	Mission Viejo, CA	38.9%	459	Fidelity National Information Services, Inc.	Jacksonville, FL	35.5%
410	Lattice Incorporated	Pennsauken, NJ	38.8%	460	ev3 Inc.	Plymouth, MN	35.4%
411	Cognizant Technology Solutions	Teaneck, NJ	38.7%	461	MetroPCS Communications, Inc.	Richardson, TX	35.3%
412	Nutrition 21, Inc.	Purchase, NY	38.7%	462	McMoRan Exploration Co.	New Orleans, LA	35.3%
413	K12 Inc.	Herndon, VA	38.7%	463	Atlas Energy, Inc.	Moon Township, PA	35.2%
414	Cal Dive International, Inc.	Houston, TX	38.7%	464	Premier Exhibitions, Inc.	Atlanta, GA	35.2%
415	Online Vacation Center Holdings Corp.	Plantation, FL	38.6%	465	McDermott International, Inc.	Houston, TX	35.1%
416	Globe Specialty Metals, Inc.	New York, NY	38.6%	466	Orion Energy Systems, Inc.	Manitowoc, WI	35.1%
417	CombinatoRx, Incorporated	Cambridge, MA	38.5%	467	Atwood Oceanics, Inc.	Houston, TX	35.1%
418	Argo Group International Holdings, Ltd.	San Antonio, TX	38.5%	468	ATSI Communications, Inc.	San Antonio, TX	35.0%
419	AVEO Pharmaceuticals, Inc.	Cambridge, MA	38.4%	469	NRG Energy, Inc.	Princeton, NJ	34.8%
420	Titan Machinery Inc.	Fargo, ND	38.4%	470	Vonage Holdings Corp.	Holmdel, NJ	34.8%
421	AVI BioPharma, Inc.	Portland, OR	38.4%	471	Hallmark Financial Services, Inc.	Fort Worth, TX	34.8%
422	WellCare Health Plans, Inc.	Tampa, FL	38.3%	472	Radiant Logistics, Inc.	Bellevue, WA	34.7%
423	Monarch Financial Holdings, Inc.	Chesapeake, VA	38.2%	473	Hansen Natural Corporation	Corona, CA	34.5%
424	Peregrine Pharmaceuticals, Inc.	Tustin, CA	38.1%	474	LHC Group, Inc.	Lafayette, LA	34.5%
425	VSE Corporation	Alexandria, VA	38.0%	475	ANSYS, Inc.	Canonsburg, PA	34.5%
426	HealthSpring, Inc.	Franklin, TN	37.9%	476	DG FastChannel, Inc.	Irving, TX	34.5%
427	Pacific Ethanol, Inc.	Sacramento, CA	37.9%	477	National CineMedia, Inc.	Centennial, CO	34.4%
428	RadNet, Inc.	Los Angeles, CA	37.8%	478	Micrus Endovascular Corporation	San Jose, CA	34.4%
429	Freeport-McMoRan Copper & Gold Inc.	Phoenix, AZ	37.7%	479	WidePoint Corporation	Oakbrook Terrace, IL	34.3%
430	Pharmasset, Inc.	Princeton, NJ	37.7%	480	Cypress Bioscience, Inc.	San Diego, CA	34.3%
431	IEC Electronics Corp.	Newark, NY	37.3%	481	Genco Shipping & Trading Limited	New York, NY	34.2%
432	American Campus Communities, Inc.	Austin, TX	37.2%	482	Community Health Systems, Inc.	Franklin, TN	34.2%
433	Netezza Corporation	Marlborough, MA	37.1%	483	AngioDynamics, Inc.	Queensbury, NY	34.1%
434	PharMerica Corporation	Louisville, KY	37.0%	484	Masimo Corporation	Irvine, CA	34.1%
435	athenahealth, Inc.	Watertown, MA	37.0%	485	VCG Holding Corp.	Lakewood, CO	34.1%
436	Trico Marine Services, Inc.	The Woodlands, TX	37.0%	486	Powell Industries, Inc.	Houston, TX	34.1%
437	The InterGroup Corporation	Los Angeles, CA	36.9%	487	eHealth, Inc.	Mountain View, CA	34.0%
438	Blue Coat Systems, Inc.	Sunnyvale, CA	36.8%	488	KMG Chemicals, Inc.	Houston, TX	34.0%
439	instaCare Corp.	Westlake Village, CA	36.8%	489	Avantair Inc.	Clearwater, FL	33.8%
440	Advanced Cell Technology, Inc.	Worcester, MA	36.8%	490	Tennessee Commerce Bancorp, Inc.	Franklin, TN	33.7%
441	PURE Bioscience	El Cajon, CA	36.8%	491	ZymoGenetics, Inc.	Seattle, WA	33.7%
442	International Assets Holding	Altamonte Springs, FL	36.8%	492	United Therapeutics Corporation	Silver Spring, MD	33.7%
443	Xfone, Inc.	Lubbock, TX	36.8%	493	ForeverGreen Worldwide Corporation	Orem, UT	33.6%
444	Syntroleum Corporation	Tulsa, OK	36.5%	494	Emerald Dairy, Inc.	Reston, VA	33.5%
445	Eyeblaster, Inc.	New York, NY	36.4%	495	Southwestern Energy Company	Houston, TX	33.5%
446	MedAssets, Inc.	Alpharetta, GA	36.4%	496	Tessera Technologies, Inc.	San Jose, CA	33.3%
447	Gilead Sciences, Inc.	Foster City, CA	36.4%	497	Assured Guaranty Ltd.	Bermuda	33.3%
448	Concur Technologies, Inc.	Redmond, WA	36.3%	498	Gladstone Commercial Corporation	McLean, VA	33.3%
449	Acacia Technologies Group	Newport Beach, CA	36.1%	499	TowerStream Corporation	Middletown, RI	33.2%
450	Eagle Bulk Shipping Inc.	New York, NY	36.1%	500	Sourcefire, Inc.	Columbia, MD	33.2%

Top 500 Companies by Market Value in
Hoover's MasterList of U.S. Companies 2011

Rank	Company	Headquarters	Mkt. Value* ($ mil.)	Rank	Company	Headquarters	Mkt. Value ($ mil.)
1	Exxon Mobil Corporation	Irving, TX	320,360	51	Altria Group, Inc.	Richmond, VA	40,881
2	Microsoft Corporation	Redmond, WA	208,316	52	Colgate-Palmolive Company	New York, NY	40,291
3	Wal-Mart Stores, Inc.	Bentonville, AR	198,207	53	Gilead Sciences, Inc.	Foster City, CA	38,507
4	Google Inc.	Mountain View, CA	197,455	54	Target Corporation	Minneapolis, MN	37,759
5	Johnson & Johnson	New Brunswick, NJ	177,647	55	EMC Corporation	Hopkinton, MA	35,911
6	Apple Inc.	Cupertino, CA	168,657	56	Caterpillar Inc.	Peoria, IL	35,775
7	International Business Machines	Armonk, NY	167,859	57	Medtronic, Inc.	Minneapolis, MN	35,249
8	JPMorgan Chase & Co.	New York, NY	165,792	58	Baxter International Inc.	Deerfield, IL	35,000
9	AT&T Inc.	Dallas, TX	165,629	59	Apache Corporation	Houston, TX	34,796
10	Berkshire Hathaway Inc.	Omaha, NE	162,756	60	Freeport-McMoRan Copper & Gold Inc.	Phoenix, AZ	34,737
11	General Electric Company	Fairfield, CT	161,536	61	UnitedHealth Group Incorporated	Minnetonka, MN	34,646
12	Chevron Corporation	San Ramon, CA	154,645	62	Ford Motor Company	Dearborn, MI	34,066
13	Bank of America Corporation	Charlotte, NC	151,096	63	The Bank of New York Mellon Corporation	New York, NY	33,926
14	The Procter & Gamble Company	Cincinnati, OH	147,163	64	MasterCard Incorporated	Purchase, NY	33,485
15	Pfizer Inc.	New York, NY	146,723	65	Time Warner Inc.	New York, NY	33,211
16	Wells Fargo & Company	San Francisco, CA	140,622	66	Walgreen Co.	Deerfield, IL	33,149
17	The Coca-Cola Company	Atlanta, GA	131,502	67	Devon Energy Corporation	Oklahoma City, OK	32,847
18	Cisco Systems, Inc.	San Jose, CA	125,702	68	Union Pacific Corporation	Omaha, NE	32,341
19	Intel Corporation	Santa Clara, CA	113,506	69	Exelon Corporation	Chicago, IL	32,282
20	Hewlett-Packard Company	Palo Alto, CA	111,298	70	The Dow Chemical Company	Midland, MI	31,910
21	Oracle Corporation	Redwood City, CA	98,324	71	Texas Instruments Incorporated	Dallas, TX	31,851
22	PepsiCo, Inc.	Purchase, NY	98,053	72	Lowe's Companies, Inc.	Mooresville, NC	31,249
23	Citigroup Inc.	New York, NY	95,923	73	Anadarko Petroleum Corporation	The Woodlands, TX	30,882
24	Verizon Communications Inc.	New York, NY	93,650	74	eBay Inc.	San Jose, CA	30,753
25	Philip Morris International Inc.	New York, NY	89,242	75	E. I. du Pont de Nemours and Company	Wilmington, DE	30,506
26	The Goldman Sachs Group, Inc.	New York, NY	86,917	76	DIRECTV	El Segundo, CA	30,309
27	Abbott Laboratories	Abbott Park, IL	83,337	77	Emerson Electric Co.	St. Louis, MO	30,187
28	Schlumberger Limited	Houston, TX	77,640	78	Corning Incorporated	Corning, NY	30,138
29	ConocoPhillips	Houston, TX	76,008	79	Honeywell International Inc.	Morristown, NJ	30,034
30	QUALCOMM Incorporated	San Diego, CA	73,784	80	Medco Health Solutions, Inc.	Franklin Lakes, NJ	29,197
31	McDonald's Corporation	Oak Brook, IL	67,173	81	MetLife, Inc.	New York, NY	28,992
32	Occidental Petroleum Corporation	Los Angeles, CA	66,070	82	Lockheed Martin Corporation	Bethesda, MD	27,955
33	United Technologies Corporation	Hartford, CT	64,765	83	The PNC Financial Services Group, Inc.	Pittsburgh, PA	27,770
34	Amazon.com, Inc.	Seattle, WA	59,952	84	NIKE, Inc.	Beaverton, OR	27,709
35	3M Company	St. Paul, MN	58,949	85	News Corporation	New York, NY	27,701
36	Visa Inc.	Foster City, CA	58,036	86	Southern Company	Atlanta, GA	27,474
37	United Parcel Service, Inc.	Atlanta, GA	56,824	87	Halliburton Company	Houston, TX	27,240
38	Amgen Inc.	Thousand Oaks, CA	54,191	88	XTO Energy Inc.	Fort Worth, TX	27,190
39	The Walt Disney Company	Burbank, CA	53,782	89	Carnival Corporation	Miami, FL	26,651
40	American Express Company	New York, NY	48,675	90	Kimberly-Clark Corporation	Irving, TX	26,374
41	Comcast Corporation	Philadelphia, PA	47,572	91	General Dynamics Corporation	Falls Church, VA	26,295
42	Kraft Foods Inc.	Northfield, IL	47,388	92	Celgene Corporation	Summit, NJ	25,661
43	The Home Depot, Inc.	Atlanta, GA	47,067	93	Dell Inc.	Round Rock, TX	25,255
44	Monsanto Company	St. Louis, MO	45,761	94	WellPoint, Inc.	Indianapolis, IN	24,901
45	CVS Caremark Corporation	Woonsocket, RI	43,834	95	The Travelers Companies, Inc.	New York, NY	24,698
46	Bristol-Myers Squibb Company	New York, NY	43,422	96	EOG Resources, Inc.	Houston, TX	24,632
47	U.S. Bancorp	Minneapolis, MN	43,149	97	Praxair, Inc.	Danbury, CT	24,571
48	Morgan Stanley	New York, NY	41,375	98	Danaher Corporation	Washington, DC	24,413
49	Eli Lilly and Company	Indianapolis, IN	41,179	99	The Mosaic Company	Plymouth, MN	24,363
50	The Boeing Company	Chicago, IL	41,087	100	Illinois Tool Works Inc.	Glenview, IL	24,114

*Market value at the latest available fiscal year-end

Top 500 Companies by Market Value in
Hoover's MasterList of U.S. Companies 2011 (continued)

Rank	Company	Headquarters	Mkt. Value ($ mil.)	Rank	Company	Headquarters	Mkt. Value ($ mil.)
101	Express Scripts, Inc.	St. Louis, MO	23,683	151	Air Products and Chemicals, Inc.	Allentown, PA	16,474
102	Accenture plc	New York, NY	23,430	152	Alcoa Inc.	New York, NY	16,459
103	Yahoo! Inc.	Sunnyvale, CA	23,241	153	Tyco International Ltd.	Princeton, NJ	16,392
104	Dominion Resources, Inc.	Richmond, VA	23,198	154	Applied Materials, Inc.	Santa Clara, CA	16,388
105	Prudential Financial, Inc.	Newark, NJ	23,188	155	YUM! Brands, Inc.	Louisville, KY	16,346
106	Simon Property Group, Inc.	Indianapolis, IN	23,068	156	Waste Management, Inc.	Houston, TX	16,331
107	Newmont Mining Corporation	Greenwood Village, CO	22,872	157	Becton, Dickinson and Company	Franklin Lakes, NJ	16,275
108	Franklin Resources, Inc.	San Mateo, CA	22,870	158	The Allstate Corporation	Northbrook, IL	16,159
109	Duke Energy Corporation	Charlotte, NC	22,599	159	The Chubb Corporation	Warren, NJ	16,071
110	The Charles Schwab Corporation	San Francisco, CA	22,462	160	Broadcom Corporation	Irvine, CA	15,622
111	Costco Wholesale Corporation	Issaquah, WA	22,457	161	The TJX Companies, Inc.	Framingham, MA	15,507
112	Marathon Oil Corporation	Houston, TX	22,151	162	Entergy Corporation	New Orleans, LA	15,490
113	CME Group Inc.	Chicago, IL	22,069	163	Kohl's Corporation	Menomonee Falls, WI	15,462
114	NextEra Energy, Inc.	Juno Beach, FL	21,903	164	Reynolds American Inc.	Winston-Salem, NC	15,438
115	State Street Corporation	Boston, MA	21,845	165	Best Buy Co., Inc.	Richfield, MN	15,399
116	Aflac Incorporated	Columbus, GA	21,717	166	Starbucks Corporation	Seattle, WA	15,386
117	Kellogg Company	Battle Creek, MI	20,251	167	Loews Corporation	New York, NY	15,212
118	Enterprise Products Partners L.P.	Houston, TX	20,080	168	BlackRock, Inc.	New York, NY	14,936
119	Stryker Corporation	Kalamazoo, MI	19,982	169	Nucor Corporation	Charlotte, NC	14,701
120	Hess Corporation	New York, NY	19,865	170	Time Warner Cable Inc.	New York, NY	14,672
121	Raytheon Company	Waltham, MA	19,632	171	Biogen Idec Inc.	Cambridge, MA	14,284
122	Thermo Fisher Scientific Inc.	Waltham, MA	19,572	172	FirstEnergy Corp.	Akron, OH	14,160
123	Norfolk Southern Corporation	Norfolk, VA	19,398	173	Juniper Networks, Inc.	Sunnyvale, CA	14,032
124	Deere & Company	Moline, IL	19,351	174	The Kroger Co.	Cincinnati, OH	13,849
125	Allergan, Inc.	Irvine, CA	19,160	175	Public Storage	Glendale, CA	13,833
126	Viacom Inc.	New York, NY	19,132	176	Sempra Energy	San Diego, CA	13,827
127	CSX Corporation	Jacksonville, FL	18,874	177	T. Rowe Price Group, Inc.	Baltimore, MD	13,822
128	National Oilwell Varco, Inc.	Houston, TX	18,475	178	Activision Blizzard, Inc.	Santa Monica, CA	13,820
129	Adobe Systems Incorporated	San Jose, CA	18,467	179	Diamond Offshore Drilling, Inc.	Houston, TX	13,683
130	Motorola, Inc.	Schaumburg, IL	18,035	180	Boston Scientific Corporation	Natick, MA	13,647
131	Precision Castparts Corp.	Portland, OR	18,018	181	Cognizant Technology Solutions	Teaneck, NJ	13,573
132	McKesson Corporation	San Francisco, CA	17,836	182	Symantec Corporation	Mountain View, CA	13,523
133	Automatic Data Processing, Inc.	Roseland, NJ	17,826	183	Avon Products, Inc.	New York, NY	13,495
134	BB&T Corporation	Winston-Salem, NC	17,559	184	Aetna Inc.	Hartford, CT	13,469
135	Capital One Financial Corporation	McLean, VA	17,504	185	SYSCO Corporation	Houston, TX	13,299
136	American Tower Corporation	Boston, MA	17,399	186	Spectra Energy Corp	Houston, TX	13,290
137	Baker Hughes Incorporated	Houston, TX	17,368	187	Weatherford International Ltd.	Houston, TX	13,265
138	FedEx Corporation	Memphis, TN	17,360	188	PACCAR Inc	Bellevue, WA	13,235
139	Archer-Daniels-Midland-Company	Decatur, IL	17,214	189	Jaguar Mining Inc.	Concord, NH	13,175
140	VMware, Inc.	Palo Alto, CA	17,205	190	Genzyme Corporation	Cambridge, MA	13,079
141	Johnson Controls, Inc.	Milwaukee, WI	17,194	191	Consolidated Edison, Inc.	New York, NY	12,810
142	Staples, Inc.	Framingham, MA	17,124	192	Vornado Realty Trust	New York, NY	12,723
143	General Mills, Inc.	Minneapolis, MN	16,980	193	Northern Trust Corporation	Chicago, IL	12,673
144	Chesapeake Energy Corporation	Oklahoma City, OK	16,846	194	The Western Union Company	Englewood, CO	12,670
145	Synthes, Inc.	West Chester, PA	16,834	195	Kinder Morgan Energy Partners, L.P.	Houston, TX	12,642
146	Public Service Enterprise Group	Newark, NJ	16,823	196	Noble Energy, Inc.	Houston, TX	12,437
147	Northrop Grumman Corporation	Los Angeles, CA	16,822	197	The Gap, Inc.	San Francisco, CA	12,413
148	Southwestern Energy Company	Houston, TX	16,686	198	The Williams Companies, Inc.	Tulsa, OK	12,316
149	American Electric Power Company, Inc.	Columbus, OH	16,660	199	Lorillard, Inc.	Greensboro, NC	12,264
150	PG&E Corporation	San Francisco, CA	16,625	200	PPL Corporation	Allentown, PA	12,232

Top 500 Companies by Market Value in
Hoover's MasterList of U.S. Companies 2011 (continued)

Rank	Company	Headquarters	Mkt. Value ($ mil.)	Rank	Company	Headquarters	Mkt. Value ($ mil.)
201	Peabody Energy Corporation	St. Louis, MO	12,152	251	CBS Corporation	New York, NY	9,553
202	The Progressive Corporation	Mayfield Village, OH	12,061	252	Valero Energy Corporation	San Antonio, TX	9,472
203	CA, Inc.	Islandia, NY	12,060	253	Life Technologies Corporation	Carlsbad, CA	9,443
204	St. Jude Medical, Inc.	St. Paul, MN	12,019	254	Boston Properties, Inc.	Boston, MA	9,324
205	Omnicom Group Inc.	New York, NY	12,017	255	Intuit Inc.	Mountain View, CA	9,323
206	Zimmer Holdings, Inc.	Warsaw, IN	11,988	256	DISH Network Corporation	Englewood, CO	9,302
207	Marsh & McLennan Companies, Inc.	New York, NY	11,951	257	Bunge Limited	White Plains, NY	9,201
208	Intuitive Surgical, Inc.	Sunnyvale, CA	11,884	258	Cummins Inc.	Columbus, IN	9,199
209	Progress Energy, Inc.	Raleigh, NC	11,777	259	Weyerhaeuser Company	Federal Way, WA	9,129
210	International Paper Company	Memphis, TN	11,692	260	ITT Corporation	White Plains, NY	9,127
211	Xerox Corporation	Norwalk, CT	11,667	261	HCP, Inc.	Long Beach, CA	8,978
212	TD AMERITRADE Holding Corporation	Omaha, NE	11,572	262	Delta Air Lines, Inc.	Atlanta, GA	8,960
213	First Solar, Inc.	Tempe, AZ	11,548	263	Mead Johnson Nutrition Company	Glenview, IL	8,937
214	Crown Castle International Corp.	Houston, TX	11,339	264	Virgin Media Inc.	New York, NY	8,866
215	Edison International	Rosemead, CA	11,332	265	Fidelity National Information Services, Inc.	Jacksonville, FL	8,827
216	CONSOL Energy Inc.	Canonsburg, PA	11,240	266	NVIDIA Corporation	Santa Clara, CA	8,806
217	Marvell Technology Group Ltd.	Santa Clara, CA	11,234	267	Discovery Communications, Inc.	Silver Spring, MD	8,720
218	Bed Bath & Beyond Inc.	Union, NJ	10,954	268	Vertex Pharmaceuticals	Cambridge, MA	8,664
219	Sprint Nextel Corporation	Overland Park, KS	10,911	269	Agilent Technologies, Inc.	Santa Clara, CA	8,613
220	H. J. Heinz Company	Pittsburgh, PA	10,885	270	Energy Transfer Partners, L.P.	Dallas, TX	8,600
221	CenturyTel, Inc.	Monroe, LA	10,878	271	Southwest Airlines Co.	Dallas, TX	8,509
222	Quest Diagnostics Incorporated	Madison, NJ	10,864	272	Hospira, Inc.	Lake Forest, IL	8,460
223	Republic Services, Inc.	Phoenix, AZ	10,810	273	Discover Financial Services	Riverwoods, IL	8,408
224	Sears Holdings Corporation	Hoffman Estates, IL	10,715	274	Computer Sciences Corporation	Falls Church, VA	8,405
225	Eaton Corporation	Cleveland, OH	10,663	275	Molson Coors Brewing Company	Denver, CO	8,383
226	Coca-Cola Enterprises Inc.	Atlanta, GA	10,609	276	Polo Ralph Lauren Corporation	New York, NY	8,350
227	The AES Corporation	Arlington, VA	10,586	277	IntercontinentalExchange, Inc.	Atlanta, GA	8,304
228	The McGraw-Hill Companies, Inc.	New York, NY	10,572	278	ConAgra Foods, Inc.	Omaha, NE	8,283
229	Campbell Soup Company	Camden, NJ	10,558	279	Safeway Inc.	Pleasanton, CA	8,273
230	Noble Corporation	Sugar Land, TX	10,413	280	Stanley Black & Decker, Inc.	New Britain, CT	8,262
231	Ecolab Inc.	St. Paul, MN	10,404	281	Coach, Inc.	New York, NY	8,201
232	Murphy Oil Corporation	El Dorado, AR	10,378	282	salesforce.com, inc.	San Francisco, CA	8,179
233	priceline.com Incorporated	Norwalk, CT	10,362	283	The Hershey Company	Hershey, PA	8,133
234	The Hartford Financial Services Group, Inc.	Hartford, CT	10,330	284	V.F. Corporation	Greensboro, NC	8,064
235	Aon Corporation	Chicago, IL	10,330	285	Fluor Corporation	Irving, TX	8,050
236	Invesco Ltd.	Atlanta, GA	10,248	286	Goodrich Corporation	Charlotte, NC	8,043
237	Cameron International Corporation	Houston, TX	10,208	287	Amphenol Corporation	Wallingford, CT	8,015
238	SunTrust Banks Inc.	Atlanta, GA	10,143	288	Rockwell Collins, Inc.	Cedar Rapids, IA	7,996
239	L-3 Communications Holdings, Inc.	New York, NY	10,064	289	M&T Bank Corporation	Buffalo, NY	7,951
240	Ameriprise Financial, Inc.	Minneapolis, MN	9,997	290	Range Resources Corporation	Fort Worth, TX	7,947
241	Paychex, Inc.	Rochester, NY	9,881	291	Cardinal Health, Inc.	Dublin, OH	7,943
242	Las Vegas Sands Corp.	Las Vegas, NV	9,865	292	United States Steel Corporation	Pittsburgh, PA	7,903
243	Marriott International, Inc.	Bethesda, MD	9,846	293	The Clorox Company	Oakland, CA	7,863
244	Apollo Group, Inc.	Phoenix, AZ	9,829	294	Williams Partners L.P.	Tulsa, OK	7,845
245	CIGNA Corporation	Philadelphia, PA	9,758	295	Laboratory Corporation of America	Burlington, NC	7,783
246	Xcel Energy Inc.	Minneapolis, MN	9,752	296	Dover Corporation	New York, NY	7,771
247	C.H. Robinson Worldwide, Inc.	Eden Prairie, MN	9,743	297	Fifth Third Bancorp	Cincinnati, OH	7,749
248	PPG Industries, Inc.	Pittsburgh, PA	9,737	298	Citrix Systems, Inc.	Fort Lauderdale, FL	7,729
249	Annaly Capital Management, Inc.	New York, NY	9,711	299	Principal Financial Group, Inc.	Des Moines, IA	7,686
250	Equity Residential	Chicago, IL	9,558	300	Host Hotels & Resorts, Inc.	Bethesda, MD	7,681

Top 500 Companies by Market Value in
Hoover's MasterList of U.S. Companies 2011 (continued)

Rank	Company	Headquarters	Mkt. Value ($ mil.)	Rank	Company	Headquarters	Mkt. Value ($ mil.)
301	Analog Devices, Inc.	Norwood, MA	7,637	351	Unum Group	Chattanooga, TN	6,497
302	Ultra Petroleum Corp.	Houston, TX	7,588	352	Liberty Interactive Group	Englewood, CO	6,475
303	Nordstrom, Inc.	Seattle, WA	7,530	353	CNA Financial Corporation	Chicago, IL	6,458
304	Lincoln National Corporation	Radnor, PA	7,526	354	Sara Lee Corporation	Downers Grove, IL	6,454
305	Humana Inc.	Louisville, KY	7,470	355	CF Industries Holdings, Inc.	Deerfield, IL	6,450
306	C. R. Bard, Inc.	Murray Hill, NJ	7,408	356	Newfield Exploration Company	Houston, TX	6,434
307	Expeditors International	Seattle, WA	7,402	357	International Game Technology	Reno, NV	6,403
308	Fiserv, Inc.	Brookfield, WI	7,399	358	Clearwire Corporation	Kirkland, WA	6,392
309	DTE Energy Company	Detroit, MI	7,341	359	Moody's Corporation	New York, NY	6,352
310	Qwest Communications International Inc.	Denver, CO	7,310	360	ONEOK Partners, L.P.	Tulsa, OK	6,349
311	Expedia, Inc.	Bellevue, WA	7,308	361	McAfee, Inc.	Santa Clara, CA	6,330
312	Continental Resources, Inc.	Enid, OK	7,290	362	AmerisourceBergen Corporation	Chesterbrook, PA	6,323
313	Mattel, Inc.	El Segundo, CA	7,288	363	New York Community Bancorp, Inc.	Westbury, NY	6,318
314	Questar Corporation	Salt Lake City, UT	7,279	364	Regions Financial Corporation	Birmingham, AL	6,308
315	Hudson City Bancorp, Inc.	Paramus, NJ	7,230	365	NetApp, Inc.	Sunnyvale, CA	6,307
316	Plains All American Pipeline, L.P.	Houston, TX	7,195	366	Micron Technology, Inc.	Boise, ID	6,306
317	Wynn Resorts, Limited	Las Vegas, NV	7,180	367	EQT Corporation	Pittsburgh, PA	6,306
318	AutoZone, Inc.	Memphis, TN	7,180	368	People's United Financial, Inc.	Bridgeport, CT	6,258
319	Warner Chilcott plc	Rockaway, NJ	7,179	369	Nabors Industries Ltd.	Bermuda	6,243
320	Cooper Industries plc	Houston, TX	7,143	370	Cliffs Natural Resources Inc.	Cleveland, OH	6,242
321	Constellation Energy Group, Inc.	Baltimore, MD	7,093	371	Limited Brands, Inc.	Columbus, OH	6,185
322	W.W. Grainger, Inc.	Lake Forest, IL	7,058	372	Plum Creek Timber Company, Inc.	Seattle, WA	6,154
323	FMC Technologies, Inc.	Houston, TX	7,033	373	Fastenal Company	Winona, MN	6,139
324	Xilinx, Inc.	San Jose, CA	6,983	374	Sigma-Aldrich Corporation	St. Louis, MO	6,136
325	SAIC, Inc.	McLean, VA	6,965	375	Garmin Ltd.	Olathe, KS	6,115
326	Dr Pepper Snapple Group, Inc.	Plano, TX	6,953	376	DaVita Inc.	Denver, CO	6,103
327	Starwood Hotels & Resorts Worldwide	White Plains, NY	6,930	377	Rockwell Automation, Inc.	Milwaukee, WI	6,075
328	Parker Hannifin Corporation	Cleveland, OH	6,918	378	Western Digital Corporation	Lake Forest, CA	6,073
329	El Paso Corporation	Houston, TX	6,918	379	Whirlpool Corporation	Benton Harbor, MI	6,059
330	BMC Software, Inc.	Houston, TX	6,898	380	NRG Energy, Inc.	Princeton, NJ	6,028
331	Scripps Networks Interactive, Inc.	Cincinnati, OH	6,896	381	Genuine Parts Company	Atlanta, GA	6,028
332	Ventas, Inc.	Louisville, KY	6,861	382	Electronic Arts Inc.	Redwood City, CA	5,942
333	Brown-Forman Corporation	Louisville, KY	6,830	383	Harley-Davidson, Inc.	Milwaukee, WI	5,933
334	Altera Corporation	San Jose, CA	6,826	384	J. C. Penney Company, Inc.	Plano, TX	5,866
335	Energy Transfer Equity, L.P.	Dallas, TX	6,818	385	PartnerRe Ltd.	Greenwich, CT	5,842
336	AvalonBay Communities, Inc.	Alexandria, VA	6,814	386	Wisconsin Energy Corporation	Milwaukee, WI	5,825
337	Cerner Corporation	Kansas City, MO	6,777	387	Leucadia National Corporation	New York, NY	5,788
338	The Sherwin-Williams Company	Cleveland, OH	6,765	388	Boardwalk Pipeline Partners, LP	Houston, TX	5,783
339	Smith International, Inc.	Houston, TX	6,752	389	Waters Corporation	Milford, MA	5,759
340	Vulcan Materials Company	Birmingham, AL	6,726	390	Jacobs Engineering Group Inc.	Pasadena, CA	5,745
341	Macy's, Inc.	Cincinnati, OH	6,724	391	Liberty Global, Inc.	Englewood, CO	5,732
342	SanDisk Corporation	Milpitas, CA	6,667	392	Human Genome Sciences, Inc.	Rockville, MD	5,729
343	Ameren Corporation	St. Louis, MO	6,660	393	CenterPoint Energy, Inc.	Houston, TX	5,723
344	Forest Laboratories, Inc.	New York, NY	6,640	394	Mylan Inc.	Canonsburg, PA	5,692
345	NYSE Euronext	New York, NY	6,603	395	Ross Stores, Inc.	Pleasanton, CA	5,628
346	Fortune Brands, Inc.	Deerfield, IL	6,580	396	NII Holdings, Inc.	Reston, VA	5,617
347	ProLogis	Denver, CO	6,524	397	Pride International, Inc.	Houston, TX	5,604
348	Advanced Micro Devices, Inc.	Sunnyvale, CA	6,518	398	Pioneer Natural Resources Company	Irving, TX	5,584
349	Cablevision Systems Corporation	Bethpage, NY	6,517	399	Genworth Financial, Inc.	Richmond, VA	5,551
350	The Estée Lauder Companies Inc.	New York, NY	6,502	400	McDermott International, Inc.	Houston, TX	5,534

Top 500 Companies by Market Value in
Hoover's MasterList of U.S. Companies 2011 (continued)

Rank	Company	Headquarters	Mkt. Value ($ mil.)	Rank	Company	Headquarters	Mkt. Value ($ mil.)
401	Health Care REIT, Inc.	Toledo, OH	5,501	451	Pitney Bowes Inc.	Stamford, CT	4,723
402	Kimco Realty Corporation	New Hyde Park, NY	5,488	452	Cephalon, Inc.	Malvern, PA	4,693
403	SLM Corporation	Reston, VA	5,474	453	The J. M. Smucker Company	Orrville, OH	4,693
404	Verisk Analytics, Inc.	Jersey City, NJ	5,469	454	Legg Mason, Inc.	Baltimore, MD	4,689
405	Autodesk, Inc.	San Rafael, CA	5,459	455	SCANA Corporation	Columbia, SC	4,688
406	Royal Caribbean Cruises Ltd.	Miami, FL	5,434	456	Kinder Morgan Management, LLC	Houston, TX	4,674
407	Enterprise GP Holdings L.P.	Houston, TX	5,424	457	Stericycle, Inc.	Lake Forest, IL	4,669
408	Owens-Illinois, Inc.	Perrysburg, OH	5,422	458	The Macerich Company	Santa Monica, CA	4,664
409	Artio Global Investors Inc.	New York, NY	5,376	459	Hasbro, Inc.	Pawtucket, RI	4,663
410	Urban Outfitters, Inc.	Philadelphia, PA	5,332	460	Energizer Holdings, Inc.	St. Louis, MO	4,646
411	Airgas, Inc.	Radnor, PA	5,310	461	Iron Mountain Incorporated	Boston, MA	4,627
412	Flowserve Corporation	Irving, TX	5,300	462	Magellan Midstream Partners, L.P.	Tulsa, OK	4,625
413	Red Hat, Inc.	Raleigh, NC	5,291	463	R.R. Donnelley & Sons Company	Chicago, IL	4,594
414	O'Reilly Automotive, Inc.	Springfield, MO	5,265	464	Beckman Coulter, Inc.	Brea, CA	4,588
415	Alpha Natural Resources, Inc.	Abingdon, VA	5,252	465	Bucyrus International, Inc.	South Milwaukee, WI	4,566
416	Teradata Corporation	Miamisburg, OH	5,246	466	The Blackstone Group L.P.	New York, NY	4,556
417	Linear Technology Corporation	Milpitas, CA	5,234	467	Northeast Utilities	Berlin, CT	4,539
418	Enbridge Energy Partners, L.P.	Houston, TX	5,232	468	Cabot Oil & Gas Corporation	Houston, TX	4,529
419	Comerica Incorporated	Dallas, TX	5,214	469	EXCO Resources, Inc.	Dallas, TX	4,510
420	Varian Medical Systems, Inc.	Palo Alto, CA	5,205	470	CarMax, Inc.	Richmond, VA	4,505
421	Whole Foods Market, Inc.	Austin, TX	5,194	471	Manpower Inc.	Milwaukee, WI	4,469
422	Joy Global Inc.	Milwaukee, WI	5,189	472	CNX Gas Corporation	Canonsburg, PA	4,458
423	Hyatt Hotels Corporation	Chicago, IL	5,183	473	Cimarex Energy Co.	Denver, CO	4,443
424	Tiffany & Co.	New York, NY	5,164	474	MDU Resources Group, Inc.	Bismarck, ND	4,440
425	DENTSPLY International Inc.	York, PA	5,147	475	VeriSign, Inc.	Mountain View, CA	4,424
426	Textron Inc.	Providence, RI	5,141	476	Allegheny Technologies Incorporated	Pittsburgh, PA	4,412
427	Seagate Technology LLC	Scotts Valley, CA	5,099	477	Quanta Services, Inc.	Houston, TX	4,387
428	Darden Restaurants, Inc.	Orlando, FL	5,085	478	NVR, Inc.	Reston, VA	4,383
429	Everest Re Group, Ltd.	Liberty Corner, NJ	5,048	479	Alexion Pharmaceuticals, Inc.	Cheshire, CT	4,374
430	Celanese Corporation	Dallas, TX	5,029	480	CB Richard Ellis Group, Inc.	Los Angeles, CA	4,366
431	FLIR Systems, Inc.	Wilsonville, OR	5,019	481	Akamai Technologies, Inc.	Cambridge, MA	4,361
432	Windstream Corporation	Little Rock, AR	5,018	482	Eastman Chemical Company	Kingsport, TN	4,361
433	H&R Block, Inc.	Kansas City, MO	4,985	483	Nuance Communications, Inc.	Burlington, MA	4,357
434	The Lubrizol Corporation	Wickliffe, OH	4,976	484	Dolby Laboratories, Inc.	San Francisco, CA	4,332
435	Och-Ziff Capital Management Group LLC	New York, NY	4,956	485	Massey Energy Company	Richmond, VA	4,325
436	Masco Corporation	Taylor, MI	4,954	486	AMB Property Corporation	San Francisco, CA	4,297
437	Watson Pharmaceuticals, Inc.	Corona, CA	4,934	487	KLA-Tencor Corporation	Milpitas, CA	4,292
438	Roper Industries, Inc.	Sarasota, FL	4,921	488	Church & Dwight Co., Inc.	Princeton, NJ	4,285
439	Edwards Lifesciences Corporation	Irvine, CA	4,921	489	Cincinnati Financial Corporation	Fairfield, OH	4,277
440	Hertz Global Holdings, Inc.	Park Ridge, NJ	4,908	490	NiSource Inc.	Merrillville, IN	4,267
441	MeadWestvaco Corporation	Richmond, VA	4,891	491	The Dun & Bradstreet Corporation	Short Hills, NJ	4,251
442	Calpine Corporation	Houston, TX	4,887	492	Hologic, Inc.	Bedford, MA	4,233
443	KeyCorp	Cleveland, OH	4,879	493	Equinix, Inc.	Foster City, CA	4,224
444	Hormel Foods Corporation	Austin, MN	4,873	494	Nationwide Health Properties, Inc.	Newport Beach, CA	4,214
445	Henry Schein, Inc.	Melville, NY	4,806	495	Dollar Tree, Inc.	Chesapeake, VA	4,200
446	Ball Corporation	Broomfield, CO	4,773	496	Helmerich & Payne, Inc.	Tulsa, OK	4,180
447	Tyson Foods, Inc.	Springdale, AR	4,761	497	Newell Rubbermaid Inc.	Atlanta, GA	4,176
448	Maxim Integrated Products, Inc.	Sunnyvale, CA	4,744	498	Federal Realty Investment Trust	Rockville, MD	4,155
449	ONEOK, Inc.	Tulsa, OK	4,738	499	Crown Holdings, Inc.	Philadelphia, PA	4,144
450	McCormick & Company, Incorporated	Sparks, MD	4,727	500	The NASDAQ OMX Group, Inc.	New York, NY	4,127

Hoover's MasterList of U.S. Companies

of U.S. Companies

**Company
Listings**

1-800 CONTACTS, INC.

66 E. Wadsworth Park Dr., 3rd Fl.
Draper, UT 84020
Phone: 801-924-9800
Fax: 801-924-9905
Web: www.1800contacts.com

CEO: Jonathan C. Coon
CFO: Robert G. Hunter
HR: Max Neves
FYE: December 31
Type: Private

Lose a contact? If you can still find your telephone or computer, you can get replacement lenses from 1-800 CONTACTS. Through its website and over the phone, the company offers contact lenses from major manufacturers and distributors. Its most popular brands include Acuvue, Air Optix, Biomedics, Focus, FreshLook, and Proclear. To ensure order accuracy, 1-800 CONTACTS verifies prescription information with eye doctors. The company was founded in 1995 by entrepreneurs Jonathan Coon and John Nichols; it was acquired and taken private by affiliates of New York-based equity firm Fenway Partners in 2007.

	Annual Growth	12/04	12/05	12/06	12/07	12/08
Est. sales ($ mil.)	—	—	—	—	—	248.7
Employees	—	—	—	—	—	1,135

1-800-FLOWERS.COM, INC.

NASDAQ (GS): FLWS

1 Old Country Rd., Ste. 500
Carle Place, NY 11514
Phone: 516-237-6000
Fax: 516-237-6060
Web: www.1800flowers.com

CEO: James F. (Jim) McCann
CFO: William E. Shea
HR: —
FYE: June 30
Type: Public

Some say it's all in the name, but 1-800-FLOWERS.COM does more than just peddle petunias. The flower company sells fresh flowers and plants primarily through its toll-free number and websites, but it also markets products via its branded catalogs, TV and radio advertising, and third-party online affiliates. Through its subsidiaries, 1-800-FLOWERS.com offers gift baskets, gourmet foods, chocolates and candies, cookies, popcorn, and wine. Inspired by the emergence of toll-free calling, founder and CEO James F. McCann launched the flower business in 1976 and over time established a national brand that was further fueled by the evolution of the Internet.

	Annual Growth	6/05	6/06	6/07	6/08	6/09
Sales ($ mil.)	1.6%	670.7	781.7	912.6	919.4	714.0
Net income ($ mil.)	—	7.8	3.2	17.1	21.1	(98.4)
Market value ($ mil.)	(27.7%)	448.8	367.8	601.1	411.1	122.4
Employees	(6.4%)	3,000	3,700	4,000	4,000	2,300

1800MATTRESS.COM

31-10 48th Ave.
Long Island City, NY 11101
Phone: 718-472-1200
Fax: 718-482-6561
Web: www.mattress.com

CEO: Napoleon Barragan
CFO: William A. Johnson
HR: Kathy Desmond
FYE: December 31
Type: Private

Some bedding dealers may leave you hot and bothered, but 1800Mattress.com hopes to leave you comfy and well-rested. The firm offers mattresses from Sealy, Serta, Simmons, King Koil, and Tempur-Pedic, as well as its own private-label brand. Customers can order over the phone or on the Internet, 24 hours a day. Those who prefer to feel the merchandise before buying, however, can visit 1800Mattress.com's more than 100 showrooms in California, Connecticut, Maryland, New Jersey, and New York. It also ships products throughout the US and internationally. Founded in 1976, the company was originally named Dial-A-Mattress. In 2009 rival retailer Sleepy's acquired 1800Mattress.com out of bankruptcy for $25 million.

1MAGE SOFTWARE, INC.

384 Inverness Pkwy., Ste. 206
Englewood, CO 80112
Phone: 800-844-1468
Fax: 303-796-0587
Web: www.1mage.com

CEO: David R. DeYoung
CFO: Susan Bulloch
HR: Mary Anne DeYoung
FYE: December 31
Type: Private

For 1mage Software, images are everything. 1mage helps organizations manage their paper and electronic files by providing software that captures, stores, and displays documents as electronic images. The company's software handles a wide range of documents, including e-mails, scanned forms, memos, letters, spreadsheets, databases, multimedia documents, faxes, and maps. Add-on modules include tools for faxing, printing, workflow, searching, reporting, and remote access. 1mage licenses its software to a wide range of clients including energy, manufacturing, transportation, and real estate firms, as well as government agencies and organizations.

1ST COLONIAL BANCORP, INC.

OTC: FCOB

1040 Haddon Ave.
Collingswood, NJ 08108
Phone: 856-858-1100
Fax: 856-858-9255
Web: www.1stcolonial.com

CEO: Gerard M. (Gerry) Banmiller
CFO: Robert C. Faix
HR: —
FYE: December 31
Type: Public

1st Colonial Bancorp is the holding company for 1st Colonial National Bank. Founded in 2000, the bank serves Camden County in southern New Jersey through branches in the communities of Cinnaminson, Collingswood, and Westville. With an emphasis on personalized service, it caters to small and mid-sized businesses, professional practices, and local government entities, as well as consumers. The bank provides traditional deposit products such as checking, savings, and money market accounts and certificates of deposit. Additional services include check cards, online banking, and safe deposit boxes.

	Annual Growth	12/05	12/06	12/07	12/08	12/09
Assets ($ mil.)	13.9%	164.2	184.8	218.3	232.8	276.6
Net income ($ mil.)	(8.1%)	0.7	0.8	0.9	0.6	0.5
Employees	0.0%	27	27	—	—	—

1ST CONSTITUTION BANCORP

NASDAQ (GM): FCCY

2650 Rte. 130
Cranbury, NJ 08512
Phone: 609-655-4500
Fax: 609-655-5653
Web: www.1stconstitution.com

CEO: Robert F. Mangano
CFO: Joseph M. Reardon
HR: Beverly Tindall
FYE: December 31
Type: Public

In order to "secure the blessings of liberty," the founding fathers established the US Constitution. As for promoting the general welfare, some banks share the same dedication to "We the people." 1st Constitution Bancorp is the parent of 1st Constitution Bank, which serves consumers, small businesses, and not-for-profits through about a dozen branches in Middlesex, Mercer, and Somerset counties in New Jersey. Services and products include demand, savings, and time deposits, as well as loans and mortgages. Commercial mortgages, business loans, and construction loans make up more than 60% of the company's lending portfolio. Directors and executive offices of 1st Constitution Bancorp own about 15% of the company.

	Annual Growth	12/05	12/06	12/07	12/08	12/09
Assets ($ mil.)	16.2%	372.5	392.7	429.2	546.3	678.0
Net income ($ mil.)	(13.3%)	4.6	5.3	5.4	2.8	2.6
Market value ($ mil.)	(22.5%)	74.6	72.7	62.0	41.5	26.9
Employees	8.7%	91	102	112	117	127

1ST FRANKLIN FINANCIAL CORPORATION

213 E. Tugalo St.
Toccoa, GA 30577
Phone: 706-886-7571
Fax: 706-886-7953
Web: www.1ffc.com

CEO: Ben F. Cheek III
CFO: A. Roger Guimond
HR: C. Michael Haynie
FYE: December 31
Type: Private

Benjamin Franklin was known for doling out sage financial advice to "common folk." Today, 1st Franklin Financial is known for doling out direct cash loans and first and second home mortgages to a similar demographic. Secured direct cash loans make up the lion's share (more than 85%) of the company's loan portfolio. 1st Franklin Financial also buys and services sales finance contracts from retailers and offers credit insurance to borrowers. The firm operates through around 250 branch offices in the Southeast. Chairman and CEO Ben Cheek III and his family own more than 90% of the company.

1ST NRG CORP

OTC: FNRC

1730 LaBounty Rd. #213
Ferndale, WA 98248
Phone: 360-384-4390
Fax: —
Web: www.1stnrg.com

CEO: Charles A. Kohlhaas
CFO: Edward D. Renyk
HR: —
FYE: December 31
Type: Public

A development-stage company, 1st NRG formerly sought to develop gold properties in Canada, but the company relinquished its gold-related mineral interests in 2003. In 2006 the company changed its name from Naptau Gold and began to explore other business opportunities, including specialty fuel production. 1st NRG is seeking to invest in oil and gas production and vertically integrate those assets into midstream operations. The company is reviewing initial projects in the midwestern US, Argentina, and Guatemala. In 2008 it announced plans that it would explore specialty fuel opportunities in China. However, that year 1st NRG also announced that it was facing heavy debt, and posted going concern warnings.

	Annual Growth	12/04	12/05	12/06	12/07	*12/08
Sales ($ mil.)	—	—	—	—	—	0.1
Employees	—					1

*Most recent year available

1ST SECURITY BANCORP, INC.

6920 220th St. SW, Ste. 200
Mountlake Terrace, WA 98043
Phone: 425-771-8840
Fax: —
Web: www.fsbwa.com

CEO: Joseph C. Adams
CFO: T. Bradford (Brad) Canfield
HR: —
FYE: December 31
Type: Private

1st Security Bancorp was formed in 2008 to be the holding company for 1st Security Bank of Washington, which operates about a dozen branches in the Puget Sound region. The bank provides standard deposit products such as checking and savings accounts, CDs, and IRAs to area businesses and consumers. Its lending activities are focused on consumer loans (about half of its portfolio), including home improvement and automobile loans. The bank also writes business and construction loans and commercial and residential mortgages. 1st Security Bancorp filed for an IPO in 2008 as the global credit meltdown was in its nascent stages; it has since shelved the offering.

1ST SOURCE CORPORATION

NASDAQ (GS): SRCE

100 N. Michigan St.
South Bend, IN 46601
Phone: 574-235-2000
Fax: 574-235-2882
Web: www.1stsource.com

CEO: Christopher J. (Chris) Murphy III
CFO: Larry E. Lentych
HR: —
FYE: December 31
Type: Public

Need a bank? Don't give it a 2nd thought. Contact 1st Source Corporation, parent of 1st Source Bank, which provides commercial and consumer banking services through more than 75 branches in northern Indiana and southwestern Michigan. The bank offers deposit accounts; business, agricultural, and consumer loans; residential and commercial mortgages; credit cards; and trust services. Its specialty finance group provides financing for aircraft, automobile fleets, trucks, and construction and environmental equipment through about two-dozen offices nationwide; such loans account for approximately half of 1st Source's portfolio. Subsidiaries offer insurance and investment advisory services.

	Annual Growth	12/05	12/06	12/07	12/08	12/09
Assets ($ mil.)	6.6%	3,511.3	3,807.3	4,447.1	4,464.2	4,542.1
Net income ($ mil.)	(6.8%)	33.8	39.3	30.5	33.4	25.5
Market value ($ mil.)	(8.4%)	555.3	780.3	420.4	573.9	390.8
Employees	(0.6%)	1,200	1,200	1,350	1,280	1,170

1SYNC, INC.

Princeton Pike Corporate Center, 1009 Lenox Dr., Ste. 115
Lawrenceville, NJ 08648
Phone: 312-463-4000
Fax: 609-620-4601
Web: www.1sync.org

CEO: Robert (Bob) Noe
CFO: Kumar Yegneswaran
HR: —
FYE: December 31
Type: Subsidiary

1SYNC hopes to help you synchronize all sorts of trading relationships and product information. The company provides collaborative software used to synchronize data in multiple locations, formats, and languages. 1SYNC's products are used for functions such as supply chain management, business intelligence, collaborating with trading partners, and managing catalog and pricing information. The company also offers services such as consulting, implementation, maintenance, support, and training. Its customers include manufacturers, membership organizations, and retailers. The company was formed in 2005 when the operations of Transora and UCCnet were combined. 1SYNC is a not-for-profit subsidiary of GS1 US.

II-VI INCORPORATED

NASDAQ (GS): IIVI

375 Saxonburg Blvd.
Saxonburg, PA 16056
Phone: 724-352-4455
Fax: 724-352-5284
Web: www.ii-vi.com

CEO: Francis J. Kramer
CFO: Craig A. Creaturo
HR: —
FYE: June 30
Type: Public

II-VI sees the world through amber-colored lenses — at least while it is focusing CO2 laser light. The company (pronounced "two-six") makes lenses, mirrors, prisms, and other infrared optical components used to manipulate laser beams. Additionally, it produces selenium and tellurium metals and chemicals, and silicon carbide substrates. II-VI's clients — drawn from the aerospace, health care, industrial, military, and telecommunications equipment sectors — employ these components in lasers for precision manufacturing, fiber-optic transmission and reception, and other applications. Subsidiary VLOC makes laser and sensing system parts and materials. The company gets about 47% of its sales outside the US.

	Annual Growth	6/05	6/06	6/07	6/08	6/09
Sales ($ mil.)	10.8%	194.0	232.5	263.2	316.2	292.2
Net income ($ mil.)	10.4%	24.8	10.8	38.0	64.3	36.8
Market value ($ mil.)	4.9%	566.0	563.3	836.3	1,074.8	684.2
Employees	5.4%	1,548	1,690	2,138	2,342	1,913

3C SOFTWARE

1300 Parkwood Cir., Ste. 300	CEO: Matthew Smith
Atlanta, GA 30339	CFO: Joan Hayden
Phone: 770-956-7744	HR: —
Fax: 770-956-0612	FYE: December 31
Web: www.3csoftware.com	Type: Private

3C Software keeps a close eye on the bottom line. The company provides software used to manage a variety of manufacturing and production processes. Its Impact:ECS platform aggregates information used by process manufacturers to analyze, monitor, and manage costs. Clients come from diverse industries such as paper, metals and mining, textiles, semiconductor, and food and beverage. 3C also offers a variety of professional services including consulting, training, and support. The company was originally founded in 1988 as Computer Concepts Corporation.

	Annual Growth	12/04	12/05	12/06	12/07	12/08
Est. sales ($ mil.)	—	—	—	—	—	3.1
Employees	—	—	—	—	—	30

3D SYSTEMS CORPORATION

NASDAQ (GM): TDSC

333 Three D Systems Circle	CEO: Abraham N. (Abe) Reichental
Rock Hill, SC 29730	CFO: Damon J. Gregoire
Phone: 803-326-3900	HR: Robert M. (Bob) Grace Jr.
Fax: 803-324-8810	FYE: December 31
Web: www.3dsystems.com	Type: Public

3D Systems helps product designers and engineers bring their concepts to life. The company's stereolithography apparatuses (SLAs) and other machines create 3-D prototypes of everything from toys to airplane parts. Its SLAs rapidly produce 3-D objects designed in CAD/CAM software in a process called solid imaging, which uses a laser to sculpt plastic resin materials into physical models. Its ThermoJet solid object printer also fabricates plastic models using a modified ink jet printing system. Additionally, 3D Systems sells the raw plastic and metal consumable material used in its machinery. Customers have included General Electric, Hasbro, and Texas Instruments. The company does business in Europe, the US, and Asia.

	Annual Growth	12/05	12/06	12/07	12/08	12/09
Sales ($ mil.)	(5.2%)	139.7	134.8	156.5	138.9	112.8
Net income ($ mil.)	(42.6%)	10.1	(29.3)	(6.7)	(6.2)	1.1
Market value ($ mil.)	(11.0%)	414.2	367.3	355.3	182.7	260.0
Employees	2.5%	351	341	332	331	387

3DLABS INC., LTD.

1901 McCarthy Blvd.	CEO: C. Hock Leow
Milpitas, CA 95035	CFO: —
Phone: 408-432-6700	HR: —
Fax: 408-432-6702	FYE: June 30
Web: www.3dlabs.com	Type: Subsidiary

When you want 3-D graphics in your hand, 3Dlabs has a product for you. 3Dlabs' three-dimensional graphics accelerator products are intended for the portable handheld device market. The company's Embedded Graphics and IP Cores division supplies graphics chips and flexible intellectual property cores for embedded applications. Customers include the BBC, Jaguar, Stargate Digital, and Trek Bicycle. 3Dlabs is a subsidiary of computer board maker Creative Technology. The company has shifted its product emphasis, introducing the DMS-02 media processor in late 2006 for applications in automotive infotainment systems, mobile handsets, navigation systems, portable media players, and videoconferencing equipment.

3E COMPANY, INC.

1905 Aston Ave.	CEO: Robert S. Christie
Carlsbad, CA 92008	CFO: Kevin O'Hare
Phone: 760-602-8700	HR: —
Fax: 760-602-8852	FYE: December 31
Web: www.3ecompany.com	Type: Private

3E won't touch your hazardous materials, but the company will tell you what you need to know about them. 3E provides environmental, health, and safety (EH&S) information management services to help customers respond to emergencies and comply with federal regulations. The company maintains databases containing information about materials used at more than 75,000 of its customers' facilities, and it provides around-the-clock telephone access to hazardous materials experts. Customers include companies and governmental bodies such as Bostik, Southwest Airlines, Costco Wholesale, and the City of Amarillo.

3H TECHNOLOGY L.L.C.

1767 Business Center Dr., Ste. 100	CEO: David Riggs
Reston, VA 20190	CFO: —
Phone: 703-521-5200	HR: —
Fax: 703-521-5201	FYE: December 31
Web: www.3ht.com	Type: Subsidiary

3H Technology can think of more than three ways in which to improve your information technology (IT) operations. The company provides IT services such as custom software development, network design and integration, computer-based training, and website design. The company's clients have included the US Navy, General Services Administration, the Department of Health & Human Services, and the Department of Treasury, as well as local governments and commercial businesses. 3H also offers software for implementing and managing corporate portals as well as applications for document imaging. QinetiQ acquired the company in 2007 for about $52 million.

3M COMPANY

NYSE: MMM

3M Center	CEO: George W. Buckley
St. Paul, MN 55144	CFO: Patrick D. (Pat) Campbell
Phone: 651-733-1110	HR: Angela S. Lalor
Fax: 651-733-9973	FYE: December 31
Web: www.mmm.com	Type: Public

Loath to be stuck on one thing, 3M makes everything from masking tape to asthma inhalers. The diversified company makes products through six operating segments: consumer and office; display and graphics; electro and communications; health care (through 3M Health Care); industrial and transportation; and safety, security, and protection services. Well-known brands include Post-it Notes, Scotch tapes, Scotchgard fabric protectors, Scotch-Brite scouring pads, and Filtrete home air filters. 3M has operations in more than 60 countries. About two-thirds of its sales are made outside of the US. It sells products directly to users and through numerous wholesalers, retailers, distributors, and dealers worldwide.

	Annual Growth	12/05	12/06	12/07	12/08	12/09
Sales ($ mil.)	2.2%	21,167.0	22,923.0	24,462.0	25,269.0	23,123.0
Net income ($ mil.)	(0.3%)	3,234.0	3,851.0	4,096.0	3,460.0	3,193.0
Market value ($ mil.)	1.6%	55,262.8	55,569.4	60,125.9	41,029.9	58,949.3
Employees	1.9%	69,315	75,333	76,239	79,183	74,835

3PAR INC.

NYSE Arca: PAR

4209 Technology Dr.
Fremont, CA 94538
Phone: 510-413-5999
Fax: 510-413-5699
Web: www.3par.com

CEO: David C. Scott
CFO: Adriel G. Lares
HR: Jeannette Robinson
FYE: March 31
Type: Public

3PAR has taken a swing at the high-end storage market. The company's storage servers and software let large enterprises pool their storage assets across multiple departments or lines of business, consolidating data management while allowing differentiated service levels. Its customers include midsized and large corporations and government agencies worldwide. Target sectors for 3PAR include cloud computing service providers, consumer-oriented Web companies, and financial services firms. 3PAR counts eHarmony.com, Hilton Grand Vacations, Thomas Weisel Partners, and the US Army among its clients.

	Annual Growth	3/05	3/06	3/07	3/08	3/09
Sales ($ mil.)	66.9%	23.8	38.2	66.2	118.0	184.7
Net income ($ mil.)	—	(17.4)	(16.3)	(15.5)	(10.1)	(1.0)
Market value ($ mil.)	(4.5%)	—	—	—	427.1	407.8
Employees	16.9%	—	370	352	451	591

3SG CORPORATION

344 Cramer Creek Ct.
Dublin, OH 43017
Phone: 614-761-8394
Fax: 614-761-2716
Web: www.3sg.com

CEO: K. A. (Ranjan) Manoranjan
CFO: Anton Rasiah
HR: —
FYE: December 31
Type: Private

Drowning in documents? 3SG Corp. wants businesses to throw out their file cabinets and let it convert their paper, microfiche, and microfilm documents to digital images. The firm provides document imaging and conversion, management solutions, and business process outsourcing services to some 400 clients in state and local government, and industries such as insurance, education, and health care. Other services include data entry and processing, custom software development, and HIPAA compliance services. Founded in 2000, 3SG's business plan was to provide its clients with the three S's: software, service, and solutions. Today 3SG focuses on helping clients cope in a digital age.

	Annual Growth	12/04	12/05	12/06	12/07	12/08
Est. sales ($ mil.)	—	—	—	—	—	10.7
Employees	—	—	—	—	—	302

4 STAR ELECTRONICS, INC.

930 Calle Negocio, Ste. C
San Clemente, CA 92673
Phone: 949-240-8500
Fax: 949-240-8503
Web: www.4starelectronics.com

CEO: Duane Wilson
CFO: Josh Wilson
HR: —
FYE: December 31
Type: Private

Shopping for electronics? 4 Star Electronics scores the "bling." The electronic components distributor specializes in obsolete and hard-to-find components. 4 Star Electronics' online catalog includes semiconductors, military components, integrated circuits, transistors, and capacitors as well as connectors, switches, relays, and hard drives. The company also deals in excess inventory and liquidation lot bids, and even sells goods on consignment. Customers from Boeing to NASA can access millions of parts from a global network of manufacturers including Motorola, National Semiconductor, and Texas Instruments brands. Founded in 2001, the company is led by father and son CEO Duane Wilson and marketing guru Jake.

	Annual Growth	12/04	12/05	12/06	12/07	12/08
Est. sales ($ mil.)	—	—	—	—	—	2.9
Employees	—	—	—	—	—	22

4KIDS ENTERTAINMENT, INC.

NYSE: KDE

1414 Avenue of the Americas
New York, NY 10019
Phone: 212-758-7666
Fax: —
Web: www.4kidsentertainmentinc.com

CEO: Alfred R. (Al) Kahn
CFO: Bruce R. Foster
HR: —
FYE: December 31
Type: Public

If your youth are into *Yu-Gi-Oh!*, thank (or blame) 4Kids Entertainment. The company makes money by licensing rights to third-party entertainment properties for use in cartoons, games, toys, and apparel. Its five-year partnership with The CW Network allows it to program Saturday morning shows, beginning with the 2008-2009 season. 4Kids is responsible for ad sales and content for *The CW4Kids* lineup, which showcases such 4Kids properties as *Winx Club* and *Yu-Gi-Oh!*. Other youth-oriented properties include *Cabbage Patch Kids*, *Dinosaur King*, and *Viva Piñata*; in addition, 4Kids handles licensing for the American Kennel Club, the Cat Fanciers' Association, and the UK's Royal Air Force.

	Annual Growth	12/05	12/06	12/07	12/08	12/09
Sales ($ mil.)	(19.3%)	86.7	71.8	55.6	63.7	36.8
Net income ($ mil.)	—	5.1	(1.0)	(23.3)	(36.8)	(42.1)
Market value ($ mil.)	(43.6%)	209.5	243.3	175.6	26.2	21.2
Employees	(17.4%)	238	209	233	214	111

4LIFE RESEARCH, LLC

9850 S. 300 West
Sandy, UT 84070
Phone: 801-256-3102
Fax: 801-562-3611
Web: www.4life.com

CEO: David Lisonbee
CFO: Mark Ostler
HR: —
FYE: December 31
Type: Private

Whether man or man's best friend, 4Life Research wants to protect the health of bipeds and quadrupeds alike. The multilevel marketing company manufactures nutritional supplements for humans and animals and sells them through its global network of independent distributors. The company's flagship product is Transfer Factor, a supplement made from egg yolks and cow colostrum that is meant to enhance the body's immune system. The firm makes Transfer Factor formulations for humans, dogs, cats, horses, and livestock. The privately held company was founded in 1998 by CEO David Lisonbee, who had previous experience with multilevel marketing organizations.

5.11 INC.

4300 Spyres Way
Modesto, CA 95356
Phone: 209-527-4511
Fax: 209-527-1511
Web: 511tactical.com

CEO: Dan Costa
CFO: Jeff Hamilton
HR: —
FYE: December 31
Type: Private

5.11 outfits some of the toughest folks on the block. The company, more commonly known as 5.11 Tactical, makes a variety of clothing for law enforcement personnel and public safety officers, including the military and firefighters. Its products include tactical apparel, uniforms, outerwear, footwear, and accessories such as eyewear, knives, tactical gear, and holsters. The company's signature 5.11 tactical pants were originally designed for rock-climbing enthusiasts. It also sells leisure wear and children's clothing. 5.11 was founded in 2003.

An in-depth profile of this company is available to Hoover's Online members at hoovers.com.

7-ELEVEN, INC.

1722 Routh St., Ste. 1000
Dallas, TX 75201
Phone: 972-828-0711
Fax: 972-828-7848
Web: www.7-eleven.com

CEO: Joseph M. (Joe) DePinto
CFO: Stanley W. (Stan) Reynolds
HR: Cynthia Noren
FYE: December 31
Type: Subsidiary

"If convenience stores are open 24 hours, why the locks on their doors?" If anyone knows, it's 7-Eleven. The North American subsidiary of Seven-Eleven Japan, 7-Eleven operates about 6,800 company-owned or franchised stores in the US and Canada under the 7-Eleven name. The retailer also has an interest in more than 1,000 stores in Mexico. Globally, 7-Eleven operates, franchises, or licenses more than 37,500 stores worldwide. The US's leading convenience store chain was taken private in late 2005 by its largest shareholder, the Japanese retail conglomerate Seven & I Holdings, the holding company for Seven-Eleven Japan, Ito-Yokado, Denny's restaurants, and other businesses.

	Annual Growth	12/04	12/05	12/06	12/07	12/08
Est. sales ($ mil.)	—	—	—	—	—	15,471.1
Employees	—	—	—	—	—	27,748

8X8, INC.

NASDAQ (CM): EGHT

810 W. Maude Ave.
Sunnyvale, CA 94085
Phone: 408-727-1885
Fax: —
Web: www.8x8.com

CEO: Bryan R. Martin
CFO: Daniel (Dan) Weirich
HR: —
FYE: March 31
Type: Public

8x8 hopes that Internet telephony usage continues to multiply. The company offers software, services, and equipment that enable voice and video communication over Internet Protocol (IP) networks. Through its software and related services, 8x8 allows subscribers to make phone calls and perform other broadband networking functions using Voice over IP (VoIP) technology, enabling features such as voice mail, caller ID, call waiting, call forwarding, and three-way conferencing. The company sells its products directly and through resellers, distributors, and retailers. Its clients include residential customers, businesses, government agencies, and educational institutions.

	Annual Growth	3/06	3/07	3/08	3/09	3/10
Sales ($ mil.)	18.7%	31.9	53.1	61.6	64.7	63.4
Net income ($ mil.)	—	(24.1)	(9.9)	0.0	(2.5)	3.9
Market value ($ mil.)	(4.6%)	111.3	92.8	62.3	36.2	92.2
Employees	8.4%	175	195	197	244	242

10-K WIZARD TECHNOLOGY, LLC

3232 McKinney St., Ste. 750
Dallas, TX 75204
Phone: 214-800-4560
Fax: 214-800-4567
Web: www.10kwizard.com

CEO: Martin X. Zacarias
CFO: —
HR: —
FYE: December 31
Type: Subsidiary

Need a little magic to sort through SEC filings? Having access to a wizard certainly helps. 10-K Wizard Technology, through its Morningstar Document Research product, provides subscription-based online access to SEC filings, as well as searching and parsing tools to sort through the information. Users can search by company name, ticker, SIC code, industry type, or keyword. The company's services are powered by its data mining technology, which can be applied to complex information such as news feeds. The company also delivers personal custom e-mail alerts of new filings, and uses its technology to power the SEC portions of websites. 10-K Wizard is a subsidiary of global investment research firm Morningstar.

21ST CENTURY HOLDING COMPANY

NASDAQ (GM): TCHC

3661 W. Oakland Park Blvd., Ste. 300
Lauderdale Lakes, FL 33311
Phone: 954-581-9993
Fax: 954-316-9201
Web: www.21stcenturyholding.com

CEO: Michael H. Braun
CFO: Peter J. Prygelski III
HR: —
FYE: December 31
Type: Public

Trashed trailer, crashed car, damaged dwelling? 21st Century can help. Through Federated National Insurance and other subsidiaries, the company underwrites a variety of personal property/casualty insurance lines in Florida. Products include homeowners, flood, liability, and nonstandard automobile coverage. Through its American Vehicle Insurance subsidiary, the company offers commercial general liability insurance in nearly a dozen primarily southeastern states. 21st Century underwrites policies and handles claims for third-party insurers through its Assurance MGA and Superior Adjusting subsidiaries. The company distributes its products through independent agents and its Insure-Link agency.

	Annual Growth	12/05	12/06	12/07	12/08	12/09
Assets ($ mil.)	(8.6%)	290.2	212.1	219.4	197.1	202.9
Net income ($ mil.)	—	12.1	13.9	21.3	(2.5)	(10.3)
Market value ($ mil.)	(30.4%)	136.0	188.7	106.8	36.8	31.9
Employees	(2.7%)	135	122	100	110	121

21ST CENTURY INSURANCE GROUP

3 Beaver Valley
Wilmington, DE 19803
Phone: 800-443-3100
Fax: —
Web: www.21st.com

CEO: Anthony J. (Tony) DeSantis
CFO: Glenn A. Pfeil
HR: Laura Rock
FYE: December 31
Type: Subsidiary

Cutting out the middleman — that's how 21st Century Insurance Group grew in the 20th century. The company's primary subsidiaries provide inexpensive auto and personal umbrella insurance for customers by selling directly (through direct-mail, print, and radio advertising) rather than through brokers, which eliminates the cost of agents and commissions. 21st Century Insurance limits sales of its auto policies to preferred-risk applicants (good drivers). The company has historically been most active in California but has been actively expanding into other states, including Texas. American International Group (AIG) sold the company to Zurich Financial Services in 2009.

22SQUARED, INC.

1170 Peachtree St. Northeast, 15th Fl.
Atlanta, GA 30309
Phone: 404-347-8700
Fax: 404-347-8800
Web: www.22squared.com

CEO: Richard Ward
CFO: Tom Fuller
HR: —
FYE: December 31
Type: Private

For this agency, advertising + marketing = 22squared. Formerly known as Westwayne, 22squared provides strategic marketing and creative services across multiple industries. Marketing services include media buying and planning, direct marketing, event marketing, interactive, and public relations delivered from its two offices in Atlanta, Georgia and Tampa, Florida. The agency's campaigns ultimately aim to turn consumers into brand advocates. The independent agency serves clients across the Southeast, including such notable brands as Shoe Carnival, Stein Mart, and SunTrust Banks. 22squared traces its roots back to 1922 when it was founded as Westwayne.

	Annual Growth	12/04	12/05	12/06	12/07	12/08
Est. sales ($ mil.)	—	—	—	—	—	450.0
Employees	—	—	—	—	—	225

24 HOUR FITNESS WORLDWIDE, INC.

12647 Alcosta Blvd., Ste. 500	CEO: Carl C. Liebert III
San Ramon, CA 94583	CFO: Jeffrey N. (Jeff) Boyer
Phone: 925-543-3100	HR: —
Fax: 925-543-3200	FYE: December 31
Web: www.24hourfitness.com	Type: Private

If you're holding too much weight, 24 Hour Fitness Worldwide has the solution. It owns and operates more than 400 fitness centers that offer aerobic, cardiovascular, and weight lifting activities to the company's more than 3.5 million members. Some facilities also feature squash, racquetball, and basketball courts; swimming pools; steam and sauna rooms; tanning rooms; and whirlpools. It is one of the only fitness chains open 24 hours a day. The centers are located in more than 15 states in the US, as well as throughout Asia. (It has some 15 clubs in Hong Kong, Malaysia, Singapore, and Taiwan). Forstmann Little & Co owns 24 Hour Fitness, which was founded in 1983.

24 SEVEN INC.

120 Wooster St., 4th Fl.	CEO: Celeste Gudas
New York, NY 10012	CFO: Anthony Donnarumma
Phone: 212-966-4426	HR: Ernie Buffalino
Fax: 212-966-2313	FYE: December 31
Web: www.24seveninc.com	Type: Private

When it comes to recruiting creative talent, 24 Seven never sleeps. The company (not to be confused with advertising firm 24/7 Real Media) provides staffing services to clients in the beauty, entertainment, fashion, home furnishings, marketing, advertising, and retail industries. It identifies candidates and performs interviews and background checks on the way to filling freelance and full-time positions in fields such as creative services, design, merchandising, production, and purchasing. Clients have included Ann Taylor, Kenneth Cole, Neutrogena, and Target. 24 Seven operates from about half a dozen offices in the US and the UK. The company was founded in 2000.

24/7 REAL MEDIA, INC.

132 W. 31st St.	CEO: Jonathan K. (Jon) Hsu
New York, NY 10001	CFO: Kristopher Heinrichs
Phone: 212-231-7100	HR: —
Fax: 212-760-1774	FYE: December 31
Web: www.247realmedia.com	Type: Subsidiary

Keeping it real — 24/7. 24/7 Real Media provides key elements in the rapidly changing Internet advertising arena: search marketing services, software to host and manage ads, and a network of websites that run the ads. The company's Media Solutions segment provides advertisers access to its network of websites and permission-based e-mail marketing database. 24/7 also offers search engine optimization services. Technology offerings revolve around the company's ad delivery and management software, which allows advertisers to plan, manage, and measure their online campaigns. Owning almost 20 offices across 12 countries, 24/7 is a subsidiary of global communications conglomerate WPP.

84 LUMBER COMPANY

1019 Rte. 519	CEO: Joseph A. Hardy Sr.
Eighty Four, PA 15330	CFO: Dan Wallach
Phone: 714-222-8600	HR: Jim Guest
Fax: 724-222-1078	FYE: December 31
Web: www.84lumber.com	Type: Private

With its utilitarian stores (most don't have heat or A/C), 84 Lumber has built itself up to be a leading low-cost provider of lumber, building materials, and services. Through about 290 stores in 35 states, the company (which is the nation's largest privately held building materials retailer) sells lumber, siding, drywall, windows, and other supplies, as well as plans to construct decks, garages, and houses. Stores are mainly located in the Northeast, Midwest, and South. Its 84 Components subsidiary operates five plants that make floor and roof trusses and wall panels. In addition, 84 Lumber provides insurance, travel, and professional installation services. CEO Joseph Hardy Sr. founded 84 Lumber in 1956.

	Annual Growth	12/04	12/05	12/06	12/07	12/08
Sales ($ mil.)	(11.7%)	3,460.0	4,000.0	3,920.0	3,100.0	2,100.0
Employees	(13.4%)	8,000	10,500	9,500	7,000	4,500

99 CENTS ONLY STORES

NYSE: NDN

4000 Union Pacific Ave.	CEO: Eric Schiffer
Commerce, CA 90023	CFO: Robert (Rob) Kautz
Phone: 323-980-8145	HR: Dan Abfalter
Fax: 323-980-8160	FYE: March 31
Web: www.99only.com	Type: Public

Pass the buck, get a penny back. 99 Cents Only Stores sells closeout and regular general merchandise for 99 cents or less. With about 275 stores, the company sells name-brand and private-label food and beverages, health and beauty aids, household goods, hardware, toys, and more. Though about 200 of its stores are in California, the company also operates locations in Arizona, Nevada, and Texas. The firm's Bargain Wholesale unit distributes discounted merchandise to retailers, distributors, and exporters. The Gold family owns about 35% of the company and is actively involved in running it. Chairman David Gold is the founder, and his son Jeff is president; son-in-law Eric Schiffer is the firm's CEO.

	Annual Growth	3/06	3/07	3/08	3/09	3/10
Sales ($ mil.)	7.3%	1,023.6	1,104.7	1,199.4	1,302.9	1,355.2
Net income ($ mil.)	51.7%	11.4	9.8	2.9	8.5	60.4
Market value ($ mil.)	4.7%	944.3	1,025.7	688.7	643.4	1,135.1
Employees	4.8%	9,690	10,000	11,700	11,500	11,700

123GREETINGS.COM, INC.

1674 Broadway, Ste. 403	CEO: Sharad Kajaria
New York, NY 10019	CFO: Manish Saraf
Phone: 212-246-0044	HR: —
Fax: 212-202-4738	FYE: December 31
Web: www.123greetings.com	Type: Private

Sending an electronic greeting is easier than counting to three. 123Greetings.com seems to think so, anyway. With an offering of more than 20,000 free e-mail cards, the company's greetings run the gamut, offering a variety of religious cards (for Buddhist, Christian, Hindi, Islamic, Shinto, Sikh, and Jewish holidays and observances, among others), as well cards celebrating secular occasions (birthdays, anniversaries, and the other usual suspects plus unique holidays such as Fluffernutter Day and Fly a Kite Day). 123Greetings.com also provides a wireless service that allows subscribers to access, personalize, and send greeting cards through their mobile phones. IntraSoft Technologies owns the company.

	Annual Growth	12/04	12/05	12/06	12/07	12/08
Est. sales ($ mil.)	—	—	—	—	—	6.0
Employees	—	—	—	—	—	5

An in-depth profile of this company is available to Hoover's Online members at hoovers.com.

29

170 SYSTEMS, INC.

36 Crosby Dr.	CEO: David J. (Dave) Ellenberger
Bedford, MA 01730	CFO: Paul G. Smith Jr.
Phone: 781-743-1900	HR: —
Fax: 781-743-2200	FYE: June 30
Web: www.170systems.com	Type: Subsidiary

170 Systems hopes to find more than a few ways to help you get a complete view of all your business operations. Its 170 MarkView software is a document management and imaging system that captures and manages data used in core business functions such as accounts payable and receivable, expense management, purchasing, project management, records management, order management, and contract management. 170 Systems also offers services such as consulting, installation, maintenance, support, and training. Its clients come from a wide range of industries, including financial services, retail, and manufacturing. In 2009 the company was acquired by Kofax for about $33 million, minus cash held by 170 Systems.

	Annual Growth	6/04	6/05	6/06	6/07	6/08
Est. sales ($ mil.)	—	—	—	—	—	28.0
Employees	—	—	—	—	—	150

180S, INC.

701 E. Pratt St., Ste. 180	CEO: Emile Giliotti
Baltimore, MD 21202	CFO: —
Phone: 410-534-6320	HR: —
Fax: 410-534-6321	FYE: December 31
Web: www.180s.com	Type: Private

Cold weather sports fanatics ought to thank their lucky stars for 180s, Inc. The company designs apparel, ear warmers, sunglasses, and gloves to aid athletes in battling the rigors of outdoor training and exercise. It also makes all-weather performance wear for sports fans (team-branded ear warmers, scarves); tradesmen and laborers (work hats, gloves); and soldiers (combat jackets). 180s products are sold at sporting goods and department stores nationwide, as well as online. Military orders account for about 10% of its revenue. 180s was founded by Ron Wilson II and Brian Le Gette in 1995. The two were classmates at the University of Pennsylvania, where they began selling ear warmers on campus.

	Annual Growth	12/04	12/05	12/06	12/07	12/08
Est. sales ($ mil.)	—	—	—	—	—	40.0
Employees	—	—	—	—	—	41

360I LLC

1 Peachtree Pointe, 1545 Peachtree St., Ste. 450	CEO: Bryan Wiener
Atlanta, GA 30309	CFO: —
Phone: 404-876-6007	HR: —
Fax: 404-876-9097	FYE: March 31
Web: www.360i.com	Type: Subsidiary

If you are ready for a revolution in your online marketing campaign, keep this company on your short list. 360i provides search engine optimization, paid placement management, and performance analytics services for US and international clients including H&R Block, NBC Universal, and Office Depot. In addition to turning Web searches into marketing opportunities (through optimization and paid placement) the company also provides development and management services for targeted marketing campaigns using banner ads, e-mails, and websites. A subsidiary of Innovation Interactive, 360i got off the ground in 1998. In 2010, Innovation Interactive was acquired by Japanese advertising conglomerate Dentsu.

	Annual Growth	3/05	3/06	3/07	3/08	3/09
Est. sales ($ mil.)	—	—	—	—	—	25.5
Employees	—	—	—	—	—	74

454 LIFE SCIENCES

20 Commercial St.	CEO: Christopher K. (Chris) McLeod
Branford, CT 06405	CFO: Peter J. Dacey
Phone: 203-871-2300	HR: —
Fax: 203-481-2075	FYE: December 31
Web: www.454.com	Type: Subsidiary

454 Life Sciences wants to give drug developers and other gene researchers the 411 on entire genomes. The company has developed a computer-controlled instrument and related software that enable scientists to analyze whole genomes in one fell swoop, rather than a few hundred genes at a time. Parent company Roche Diagnostics distributes 454 Life Sciences' Genome Sequencing Systems to clinical laboratories, research departments of drugmakers, and other customers worldwide. Research fields include cancer and infectious disease, drug discovery, and paleontology. The company's 454 Sequencing Center provides sequencing services directly. The firm, founded in 2000, is led by CEO Christopher McLeod.

800-JR CIGAR, INC.

301 Rte. 10 East	CEO: Lewis (Lew) Rothman
Whippany, NJ 07981	CFO: Wanda Rosella
Phone: 973-884-9555	HR: Karen D'Alessandro
Fax: 973-884-9556	FYE: December 31
Web: www.jrcigars.com	Type: Subsidiary

800-JR Cigar would like to give that man (or woman) a cigar. The company that began as a small Manhattan cigar shop is now a leading distributor and retailer of premium cigars. It also sells pipe tobacco, lighters, humidors, and other smoking accessories, as well as coffee and such specialty items as Montecristo golf clubs. 800-JR Cigar's retail operations include three discount outlet stores in North Carolina, a mail-order catalog, and an e-commerce site. The company's website also features regular auctions and a section titled JR Cigar University, where tobacco aficionados can read up on all things stogie related. 800-JR Cigar is a subsidiary of Altadis, itself owned by Imperial Tobacco Group.

911 AIR CARGO, INC.

30 Hidden Valley Airpark	CEO: Madlin Mangrum
Denton, TX 76208	CFO: Tommy James
Phone: 940-321-9110	HR: —
Fax: 940-321-9114	FYE: December 31
Web: www.911aircargo.com	Type: Private

911 Air Cargo wants to help companies solve their freight transportation emergencies. The company specializes in arranging flights for time-sensitive cargo or cargo requiring special handling. Its business ranges from auto manufacturers and suppliers needing parts in a hurry, to disaster relief charters for the USAID, to flying seven dolphins and their veterinarians to a children's aquatic therapy center in Mexico. The company doesn't own or operate any aircraft; instead, it acts as a broker of air charter services. 911 Air Cargo arranges flights within the US, between the US and Mexico, and between the US and Canada. The company was founded in 1999 by president and CEO Madlin Mangrum.

	Annual Growth	12/04	12/05	12/06	12/07	12/08
Est. sales ($ mil.)	—	—	—	—	—	0.9
Employees	—	—	—	—	—	12

1105 MEDIA, INC.

9121 Oakdale Ave., Ste. 101
Chatsworth, CA 91311
Phone: 818-734-1520
Fax: 818-734-1522
Web: www.101com.com

CEO: Neal Vitale
CFO: Richard Vitale
HR: Michael J. (Mike) Valenti
FYE: December 31
Type: Private

1105 Media has a myriad of ways to distribute business-to-business information. Its products and operations include publications (*Redmond Magazine* for the Microsoft IT community), e-newsletters (*Federal Employees News Digest*), websites (EduHound.com), and conferences and events (Web Design World). The company covers markets such as Government, Education, Enterprise Computing, Business Technology, Office Equipment, Industrial Health & Safety, Security, and Home Medical Equipment. 1105 Media was founded in 2006 by Nautic Partners, Alta Communications, and publishing and marketing executive Neal Vitale, who serves as president and CEO.

A. DUIE PYLE INC.

650 Westtown Rd.
West Chester, PA 19381
Phone: 610-696-5800
Fax: 610-696-3768
Web: www.aduiepyle.com

CEO: Stephen M. (Steve) O'Kane
CFO: Kurt V. Christensen
HR: —
FYE: December 31
Type: Private

A. Duie Pyle has piled up a collection of transportation-related businesses. The company's services include less-than-truckload (LTL) and truckload freight hauling, warehousing, third-party logistics, and equipment leasing. A. Duie Pyle's LTL business operates primarily in the eastern US and in Canada from a network of about a dozen terminals. (LTL carriers consolidate freight from multiple shippers into a single trailer.) The LTL unit maintains a fleet of about 780 tractors and 1,685 trailers; another 280 tractors are devoted to heated truckload hauling. The company offers service outside its core region through alliances with other carriers. A. Duie Pyle maintains about 2 million sq. ft. of warehouse space.

2929 ENTERTAINMENT LP

2425 Olympic Blvd., Ste. 6040W
Santa Monica, CA 90404
Phone: 310-309-5701
Fax: 310-309-5716
Web: www.2929entertainment.com

CEO: Todd R. Wagner
CFO: Sky Hansen
HR: —
FYE: —
Type: Private

It doesn't hurt to name an entertainment firm after a few lucky numbers. 2929 Entertainment is owned by business partners Mark Cuban (owner of the Dallas Mavericks) and Todd Wagner, who struck gold when they sold their Broadcast.com business to Yahoo! for more than $5 billion at the height of the dot-com boom. (2929 Entertainment is named after Broadcast.com's address at 2929 Elm St.) The company has ownership stakes in movie distribution firms (Magnolia Pictures), high-definition television networks (HDNet and HDNet Movies); and movie exhibition (Landmark Theatres). 2929 Entertainment also partners with movie studios such as Warner Bros. to release various film and TV projects.

A. EICOFF & COMPANY

401 N. Michigan Ave.
Chicago, IL 60611
Phone: 312-527-7100
Fax: 312-527-7192
Web: www.eicoff.com

CEO: Ronald L. (Ron) Bilwas
CFO: —
HR: Cathy Watt
FYE: December 31
Type: Subsidiary

This firm's business is getting couch potatoes to take action. A. Eicoff & Company is a leading advertising agency specializing in direct response television marketing. It helps create TV spots and campaigns that not only highlight a product or brand but also urge consumers to call, write, or log onto the Internet for more information. In addition to creative work, A. Eicoff provides monitoring and measuring services to track the effectiveness of its campaigns, and it offers planning services to help its clients target specific consumer groups. The company was founded in 1965 by Alvin Eicoff and now operates as part of OgilvyOne, the marketing services arm of global advertising agency network Ogilvy & Mather.

A. DUDA & SONS, INC.

1200 Duda Tr.
Oviedo, FL 32765
Phone: 407-365-2111
Fax: 407-365-2010
Web: www.duda.com

CEO: Joseph A. Duda
CFO: Barton (Bart) Weeks
HR: Angelo Toro
FYE: August 31
Type: Private

DUDA has been around the block — er, the vegetable chopping block. In business for some 80 years, A. Duda & Sons (DUDA) grows and markets fresh fruits and vegetables, as well as value-added produce products. The company sells its produce to retail and foodservice customers through it shipping and import/export operations. Its main offerings include celery (DUDA is one of the world's largest celery producers), radishes, lettuce, onions, and sweet corn, as well as citrus fruits, all sold under the DANDY label. DUDA also grows and processes sugarcane and sod and has cattle operations. Its Viera division develops and manages commercial and residential properties in Florida.

	Annual Growth	8/04	8/05	8/06	8/07	8/08
Est. sales ($ mil.)	—	—	—	—	—	494.5
Employees	—	—	—	—	—	1,600

A. FINKL & SONS COMPANY

2011 N. Southport Ave.
Chicago, IL 60614
Phone: 773-975-2510
Fax: 773-348-5347
Web: www.finkl.com

CEO: Bruce C. Liimatainen
CFO: Joe Curci
HR: Steve Denten
FYE: January 31
Type: Private

Thanks to Mrs. O'Leary's cow, A. Finkl & Sons has chiseled a niche for itself in the steel industry. The company was founded in 1879 when Anton Finkl developed a chisel to clean bricks rescued from buildings destroyed in the Great Chicago Fire. Since then Finkl has forged ahead to become a leading global supplier of forging die steels. (A forging die is a steel block used in a hammer or press for shaping metal.) The firm also produces plastic mold steels, die casting tool steels, and custom open-die forging. German steel company SCHMOLZ+BICKENBACH owns Finkl.

	Annual Growth	1/04	1/05	1/06	1/07	1/08
Est. sales ($ mil.)	—	—	—	—	—	250.0
Employees	—	—	—	—	—	350

An in-depth profile of this company is available to Hoover's Online members at hoovers.com.

31

A. SCHULMAN, INC.

NASDAQ (GS): SHLM

3550 W. Market St.
Akron, OH 44333
Phone: 330-666-3751
Fax: 330-668-7204
Web: www.aschulman.com

CEO: Joseph M. (Joe) Gingo
CFO: Paul F. DeSantis
HR: Nancy Lauwers
FYE: August 31
Type: Public

A. Schulman adds color to plastic resins but keeps them from getting red hot. Schulman adds chemicals to basic plastics such as polypropylene, polyethylene, and PVC to give them color and desired characteristics like flexibility or the ability to retard flame. Its products include color and additive concentrates, engineered compounds (such as reinforced plastics), and value-added PVC. Customers include makers of plastics and auto parts, with more than a third of its sales to packaging manufacturers. At the end of 2009 the company acquired ICO in a deal that valued the plastics maker at $190 million. The deal was designed to expand both Schulman's global presence and its masterbatch and molding businesses.

	Annual Growth	8/05	8/06	8/07	8/08	8/09
Sales ($ mil.)	(2.8%)	1,435.6	1,616.4	1,787.1	1,984.0	1,279.2
Net income ($ mil.)	—	32.1	32.7	22.6	18.0	(2.8)
Market value ($ mil.)	2.5%	480.5	622.0	568.4	639.1	530.2
Employees	(4.4%)	2,399	2,480	2,471	2,200	2,000

A2D TECHNOLOGIES

2345 Atascocita Rd.
Humble, TX 77396
Phone: 281-319-4944
Fax: 281-319-4945
Web: www.tgsnopec.com

CEO: H. H. (Hank) Hamilton III
CFO: Arne Helland
HR: Michelle Hobbs
FYE: December 31
Type: Subsidiary

Less talkative than *Star Wars'* R2-D2, A2D Technologies nevertheless communicates well, by providing digital well log data, interpretive software, and data management services. A2D's LOG-LINE system allows geoscientists to access and download well log data from their workstations. Customers use its well log data to calibrate seismic data to known geologic conditions in well bores. A2D Technologies has data coverage worldwide, including the US, Canada, the Gulf of Mexico, offshore Northwest Europe, Russia, West Africa, and Madagascar. Parent TGS-NOPEC Geophysical is one of the largest owners of digital well log data in North America.

A123 SYSTEMS, INC.

NASDAQ (GM): AONE

321 Arsenal St.
Watertown, MA 02472
Phone: 617-778-5700
Fax: 617-778-5749
Web: www.a123systems.com

CEO: David P. (Dave) Vieau
CFO: Michael Rubino
HR: Andew Cole
FYE: December 31
Type: Public

A123 Systems wants to give the Energizer Bunny a run for his money. And it plans to use rechargeable lithium-ion batteries to do it. The vertically integrated company designs, makes, and sells rechargeable batteries and battery systems used primarily in the electricity and portable power markets. Portable power, for home appliances, power tools, and consumer electronics, makes up a majority of sales, but A123 is targeting the fast-growing electric and hybrid electric vehicle market. It also participates with AES to develop multi-megawatt battery systems that would take the fluctuations out of the electricity grid and provide backup power during shortages.

	Annual Growth	12/05	12/06	12/07	12/08	12/09
Sales ($ mil.)	237.7%	0.7	34.3	41.3	68.5	91.0
Net income ($ mil.)	—	(14.3)	(15.7)	(31.0)	(80.4)	(85.8)
Market value ($ mil.)	—	—	—	—	—	2,341.4
Employees	18.4%			1,160	1,672	1,627

AAA COOPER TRANSPORTATION

1751 Kinsey Rd.
Dothan, AL 36302
Phone: 334-793-2284
Fax: 334-794-3353
Web: www.aaacooper.com

CEO: G. Mack Dove
CFO: Steve Roy
HR: —
FYE: December 31
Type: Private

They might not give you a map like that other AAA, but AAA Cooper Transportation can freight your cargo from point A to point B. A regional less-than-truckload (LTL) freight hauler, AAA Cooper operates in the southeastern US and Puerto Rico; it also maintains facilities in Chicago, and a few other industrial crossroads. (LTL carriers combine freight from multiple shippers into a single truckload.) AAA Cooper Transportation operates close to 80 terminals, and the company's fleet includes about 2,000 tractors and 6,000 trailers. AAA Cooper Transportation also offers freight brokerage services and dedicated contract carriage. Chairman and CEO Mack Dove owns the company, which was founded by his father in 1955.

	Annual Growth	12/04	12/05	12/06	12/07	12/08
Est. sales ($ mil.)	—	—	—	—	—	519.3
Employees	—	—	—	—	—	4,625

AAC GROUP HOLDING CORP.

7211 Circle S Rd.
Austin, TX 78745
Phone: 512-444-0571
Fax: 512-443-5213
Web: www.cbi-rings.com

CEO: Alyce Alston
CFO: Kris G. Radhakrishnan
HR: Theresa Ann Broome
FYE: June 30
Type: Subsidiary

AAC Group, which does business as American Achievement, wants you to show off its class ring, sign its yearbook, and wear its jacket. The firm manufactures and supplies those items of high school and college memorabilia, as well as graduation products such as caps and gowns, diplomas, letter jackets, and announcements. Its ring brands include ArtCarved, Balfour, Keystone, Master Class, and R. Johns. While scholastic products account for most of the company's sales, American Achievement also makes commemorative jewelry for families, sports fans, employee awards, and professional sporting events such as the World Series, Super Bowl, and Stanley Cup. The company is owned by Fenway Partners.

AAF-MCQUAY INC.

10300 Ormsby Park Place, #600
Louisville, KY 40223
Phone: 502-637-0011
Fax: 502-637-0452
Web: www.aafmcquay.com

CEO: Katsuhiko Takagi
CFO: Yasuhisa Kumada
HR: Dan Long
FYE: June 30
Type: Subsidiary

AAF-McQUAY is into AC. The company, a part of Daikin Industries, makes and markets commercial air-conditioning and air-filtration products and systems for commercial, institutional, and industrial clients worldwide. Its AAF International division makes air-filtration products under the AAF and AmericanAir-Filter brands. Products include replacement filters and environmental products (air pollution-control products and systems, machinery filtration products, and acoustical systems). The McQuay International arm produces commercial air-conditioning and refrigeration equipment (chiller products, air handling systems, applied terminal systems, and industrial refrigeration). The company operates plants worldwide.

	Annual Growth	6/04	6/05	6/06	6/07	6/08
Est. sales ($ mil.)	—	—	—	—	—	1,491.4
Employees	—	—	—	—	—	5,300

AAI CORPORATION

124 Industry Ln.	CEO: Ellen Lord
Hunt Valley, MD 21030	CFO: —
Phone: 410-666-1400	HR: Anna-Maria Gonzalez Palmer
Fax: 410-628-3968	FYE: December 31
Web: www.aaicorp.com	Type: Subsidiary

AAI flies high, with or without pilots. The company, once the primary subsidiary of United Industrial and now a part of Textron, makes unmanned aerial vehicle (UAV) systems for the US military and other customers. Other AAI products include automatic test equipment for avionics, electronic warfare test and training systems, and training simulators for combat systems and aircraft maintenance. It also provides engineering, logistics, and maintenance services related to its products. The US military accounts for most of AAI's sales; other customers include foreign militaries and commercial aviation companies. After Textron acquired United Industrial in 2007, AAI became a part of Textron Systems Corporation.

	Annual Growth	12/04	12/05	12/06	12/07	12/08
Est. sales ($ mil.)	—	—	—	—	—	564.0
Employees	—	—	—	—	—	1,625

A & E STORES, INC.

1000 Huyler St.	CEO: Alan Ades
Teterboro, NJ 07608	CFO: Herb Bernstein
Phone: 201-393-0600	HR: —
Fax: 201-393-0233	FYE: December 31
Web: www.aestores.com	Type: Private

Working women who have never heard of A & E Stores are more likely to be familiar with its Strawberry and Bolton's retail apparel chains. The company operates about 30 Bolton's and 25 Strawberry stores that sell junior and women's career and casual apparel, shoes, and accessories. The stores are concentrated in prime office districts in Manhattan and elsewhere in New York City. A & E's third chain, Pay/Half, operates some 45 discount family clothing stores in about a half-dozen northeastern states and the Chicago area. Founded in 1973, A & E Stores also owns Rugby Realty, a real estate investment firm.

A&E TELEVISION NETWORKS, LLC

235 E. 45th St.	CEO: Abbe Raven
New York, NY 10017	CFO: —
Phone: 212-210-1400	HR: —
Fax: 212-210-1308	FYE: December 31
Web: www.aetn.com	Type: Joint venture

You might say this company gives viewers a lifetime dose of television. A&E Television Networks (AETN) owns and operates a leading portfolio of cable television channels, including its flagship A&E and Lifetime networks. Reaching nearly 100 million US homes, A&E offers a mix of reality-based programming and documentaries. Lifetime, operated through subsidiary Lifetime Entertainment, is the #1 network aimed at women with lifestyle and entertainment programming. AETN's portfolio also includes Bio, the History Channel, and History International. Its networks reach about 230 million homes in more than 140 countries. The company is a joint venture between Hearst, Walt Disney, and NBC Universal (NBCU).

A & L, INC.

4201 State Rte. 51	CEO: Louis D. (Lou) Ruscitto
Belle Vernon, PA 15012	CFO: Michelle Herron
Phone: 724-929-2125	HR: —
Fax: 724-929-3011	FYE: September 30
Web: www.alconstruction.com	Type: Private

An alternate way to spell heavy civil and highway construction might be A & L. The company provides construction management, site development, and demolition services for such projects as airports, bridges, dams, roads, tunnels, manufacturing facilities, railways, toll plazas, and water treatment plants. Clients run the gamut from businesses to school districts to government agencies and include CONSOL Energy, US Steel, Volkswagen, Westinghouse, and the Pittsburgh Zoo. Its largest contracts are for the construction or rehabilitation of highways and public transportation systems. A & L, which was founded in 1963 by president Louis Ruscitto, operates offices in Illinois, New York, and Pennsylvania.

A&R LOGISTICS, INC.

8440 S. Tabler Rd.	CEO: James E. Bedeker
Morris, IL 60450	CFO: Brian Reichert
Phone: 815-941-5200	HR: —
Fax: 800-406-5703	FYE: December 31
Web: www.artransport.com	Type: Private

Through its subsidiaries, A&R Logistics offers a diverse menu of transportation and logistics services, mainly for companies in the plastics and chemicals industries. Trucker A&R Transport hauls dry and liquid bulk commodities from about 25 terminals throughout the US; its fleet includes about 950 tractors and 3,000 trailers. A&R Global Logistics (formerly Alliance Logistics) arranges freight transportation through a network of independent carriers, and A&R Packaging & Distribution operates warehouses and provides freight handling services. UTC Overseas arranges international shipments. Investment firm FdG Associates owns a controlling stake in A&R Logistics.

A&W RESTAURANTS, INC.

1900 Colonel Sanders Ln.	CEO: Ben Butler
Louisville, KY 40213	CFO: Cheryl Balkenhol
Phone: 502-874-3000	HR: Ruth Melchior
Fax: 502-874-8848	FYE: December 31
Web: www.awrestaurants.com	Type: Subsidiary

The old-fashioned root beer stand lives on thanks to this business. A subsidiary of fast-food giant YUM! Brands, A&W Restaurants franchises more than 630 quick-service restaurants in the US and about 10 other countries. The eateries, many of which still offer drive-up service in addition to dine-in seating, offer a menu featuring hamburgers, hot dogs, onion rings, and fries, along with its signature root beer. A&W traces its roots back to a California root beer stand business started by Roy Allen in 1919. YUM! Brands is the world's largest fast-food franchisor and owns such chains as KFC, Pizza Hut, and Taco Bell.

An in-depth profile of this company is available to Hoover's Online members at hoovers.com.

33

AAON, INC.

NASDAQ (GS): AAON

2425 S. Yukon Ave.	CEO: Norman H. (Norm) Asbjornson
Tulsa, OK 74107	CFO: Kathy I. Sheffield
Phone: 918-583-2266	HR: Robert G. (Bob) Fergus
Fax: 918-583-6094	FYE: December 31
Web: www.aaon.com	Type: Public

Whichever way the thermostat turns, it generates cool cash for AAON. Through subsidiaries, the company manufactures rooftop air-conditioning and heating equipment for commercial and industrial uses primarily in the US. AAON produces five types of rooftop air-conditioning products with cooling sizes ranging from two tons to 230 tons. (Typical commercial buildings require one ton of cool air for every 300 to 400 sq. ft.) The company estimates that it has a 13% share of the rooftop market. AAON also makes air handlers, condensing units, chillers, coils, and boilers. It serves the new construction and replacement markets.

	Annual Growth	12/05	12/06	12/07	12/08	12/09
Sales ($ mil.)	7.3%	185.2	231.5	262.5	279.7	245.3
Net income ($ mil.)	24.6%	11.5	17.1	23.2	28.6	27.7
Market value ($ mil.)	13.1%	204.1	300.0	339.3	357.5	333.7
Employees	(4.4%)	1,413	1,441	1,391	1,360	1,178

AAR CORP.

NYSE: AIR

1100 N. Wood Dale Rd.	CEO: David P. Storch
Wood Dale, IL 60191	CFO: Richard J. (Rick) Poulton
Phone: 630-227-2000	HR: Timothy O. Skelly
Fax: 630-227-2039	FYE: May 31
Web: www.aarcorp.com	Type: Public

With much more than a wing and a prayer, AAR provides a wide range of products and services for the aerospace and defense industries. The company's aviation supply chain unit (over 40% of sales) buys and sells a variety of engine and airframe parts and components and offers inventory management services. Other AAR units manufacture containers, pallets, and in-plane cargo loading and handling systems; provide maintenance, repair, and overhaul (MRO) of commercial and military aircraft and components; and sell and lease used commercial jet aircraft. Customers include airlines, business aircraft operators, cargo carriers, aviation OEMs, and militaries. The US Department of Defense accounts for over 35% of sales.

	Annual Growth	5/05	5/06	5/07	5/08	5/09
Sales ($ mil.)	17.5%	747.8	897.3	1,061.2	1,384.9	1,424.0
Net income ($ mil.)	50.1%	15.5	35.2	58.7	75.1	78.7
Market value ($ mil.)	(2.2%)	626.0	939.7	1,268.3	752.4	573.7
Employees	19.5%	2,600	3,300	3,900	5,400	5,300

AARON BROTHERS, INC.

1221 S. Beltline Rd., Ste. 500	CEO: James O. King
Coppell, TX 75019	CFO: Elaine D. Crowley
Phone: 214-492-6200	HR: Shawn Hearn
Fax: —	FYE: January 31
Web: www.aaronbros.com	Type: Subsidiary

Aaron Brothers has its hand in custom-framing and crafting. The company opened its first shop in Los Angeles in 1946; today it operates some 160 stores in about 10 states. Its stores are located mostly in Texas and in the western US, but also reach to Georgia and Virginia. Aaron Brothers stores offer ready-made frames and mattes, art supplies, and custom framing services. A subsidiary of big brother hobby-retailer Michaels Stores, Aaron Brothers stores average about 5,500 sq. ft. and offer its customers some 5,700 products. Parent company Michaels Stores was taken private in 2006 by a pair of private equity firms (Bain Capital Partners and The Blackstone Group).

	Annual Growth	1/04	1/05	1/06	1/07	1/08
Est. sales ($ mil.)	—	—	—	—	—	111.1
Employees	—	—	—	—	—	1,700

THE AARON GROUP, LLC

31-00 47th Ave., Ste. 4	CEO: Robert Kempler
Long Island City, NY 11101	CFO: Richard Katz
Phone: 718-392-5454	HR: —
Fax: 718-786-2748	FYE: —
Web: www.samuelaaron.com	Type: Private

The Aaron Group supplies rocks to those who dig bling. The diamond and gemstone jewelry manufacturer fills two niches — it makes low- to moderately priced pieces (sold to mass merchandisers, department stores, jewelry chains, and direct marketers) and high-end fashion designs. Retail customers have included Helzberg Diamonds, Macy's, QVC, Wal-Mart, and Zale. The Aaron Group is also a major exporter, through its Thailand division Thai Link, to Asian, Australian, European, and South American markets. It has sourcing and manufacturing operations in Costa Rica, Hong Kong, and India. The business was founded in 1950 as Samuel Aaron International.

AARON INDUSTRIES, INC.

28966 Hwy. 76 East	CEO: James L. Medford
Clinton, SC 29325	CFO: David Meek
Phone: 864-833-0178	HR: Kathy Harding
Fax: 864-833-5493	FYE: December 31
Web: www.aaronindustriesinc.com	Type: Private

Aaron Industries makes a lot of medicines you might be acquainted with, but under less-familiar names. The pharmaceutical company makes approximately 70 different branded and private-label OTC products, including a broad line of cold, cough, and pain relief medicines. It also produces antacids, laxatives, isopropyl alcohol, and hydrogen peroxide, and well as electrolyte drinks and food-grade chemicals. Brands include Tussin, Triacting, and Peptic Relief. Aaron Industries provides contract manufacturing services to other drug and consumer care product makers, and it offers planning, ordering, and logistics services. The company operates two manufacturing facilities, one in California and one in South Carolina.

AARON'S, INC.

NYSE: AAN

309 E. Paces Ferry Rd. NE	CEO: Robert C. Loudermilk Jr.
Atlanta, GA 30305	CFO: Gilbert L. Danielson
Phone: 404-231-0011	HR: D. Chad Strickland
Fax: 678-402-3560	FYE: December 31
Web: www.aaronrents.com	Type: Public

For all those customers who desire a desk, seek a sofa, or wish for a washer, Aaron's rents — and sells — all of the above and more. One of the leading furniture rental and rent-to-own companies in the US (behind industry leader Rent-A-Center), Aaron's purveys home and office furnishings, electronics, computers, and appliances through more than 1,675 eponymous stores in the US, Puerto Rico, and Canada. Its MacTavish Furniture Industries unit makes most of the firm's furniture and bedding at a dozen plants in the US. In addition, Aaron's leases tires, rims, and wheels through its RIMCO chain of about 20 locations. Founded in 1955, the firm changed its name from Aaron Rents to Aaron's in 2009.

	Annual Growth	12/05	12/06	12/07	12/08	12/09
Sales ($ mil.)	11.7%	1,125.5	1,326.6	1,494.9	1,592.6	1,752.8
Net income ($ mil.)	18.0%	58.0	78.6	80.3	90.2	112.6
Market value ($ mil.)	7.1%	1,145.1	1,563.4	1,045.2	1,446.1	1,506.4
Employees	7.1%	7,600	8,400	9,600	9,600	10,000

AARP

601 E St. NW	CEO: A. Barry Rand
Washington, DC 20049	CFO: Robert R. Hagans Jr.
Phone: 202-434-7700	HR: Ellie Hollander
Fax: 202-434-7710	FYE: December 31
Web: www.aarp.org	Type: Not-for-profit

Turn 50 and the doors of the AARP will open for you, as they have for 40 million current members. On behalf of its members, the not-for-profit AARP acts as an advocate on public policy issues, such as health care and financial security, publishes information (the monthly *AARP Bulletin* and the bimonthly *AARP The Magazine,* and through Spanish language media), promotes community service, and works with business partners to offer products and services (including discounts on insurance and travel). The group is organized into some 2,400 local chapters throughout the US. Royalties from businesses eager to reach AARP members account for about 50% of the group's revenue; membership dues account for about 20%.

	Annual Growth	12/04	12/05	12/06	12/07	12/08
Sales ($ mil.)	9.4%	877.6	935.7	1,009.6	1,255.1	1,257.0
Net income ($ mil.)	—	—	—	(30.8)	107.5	98.5
Employees	12.3%	—	—	1,849	1,867	2,330

AASTRA INTECOM INC.

2811 Internet Blvd.	CEO: Hugues Scholaert
Frisco, TX 75034	CFO: —
Phone: 469-365-3237	HR: —
Fax: 469-365-3533	FYE: December 31
Web: www.aastraintecom.com	Type: Subsidiary

Aastra Intecom, also known as Aastra USA, is the US division of Canada's Aastra Technologies. The company provides IP telephony systems and contact center services to enterprise and government customers. Its products include the Clearspan line of IP communications equipment, as well as its Centergy virtual contact center for managing agents across multiple sites. The company also offers professional services such as project management, system installation, and technical support. It targets such industry sectors as education, government, health care, and insurance.

AASTROM BIOSCIENCES, INC.   NASDAQ (CM): ASTM

Domino's Farms, Lobby K, 24 Frank Lloyd Wright Dr.	CEO: Timothy M. (Tim) Mayleben
Ann Arbor, MI 48106	CFO: Timothy M. (Tim) Mayleben
Phone: 734-930-5555	HR: Kris M. Maly
Fax: 734-665-0485	FYE: June 30
Web: www.aastrom.com	Type: Public

Aastrom Biosciences brings new life to dying tissue. Its proprietary Tissue Repair Cell (TRC) technology uses a patient's own cells (harvested from bone marrow) to manufacture treatments for a number of chronic diseases. The new cells, created through a sterile, automated process, are then used in tissue regeneration therapies for the donor patient. The US-based company's ongoing development activities are primarily focused on applying TRC technology to cardiovascular applications including cardiomyopathy (weakening of the heart muscle) and critical limb ischemia (severe obstruction of the arteries).

	Annual Growth	6/05	6/06	6/07	6/08	6/09
Sales ($ mil.)	(31.3%)	0.9	0.9	0.7	0.5	0.2
Net income ($ mil.)	—	(11.8)	(16.5)	(17.6)	(20.1)	(15.9)
Market value ($ mil.)	(39.3%)	705.3	300.6	302.9	83.6	95.5
Employees	(0.5%)	49	59	67	45	48

A. B. BOYD COMPANY

600 S. McClure Rd.	CEO: Mitchell F. (Mitch) Aiello
Modesto, CA 95357	CFO: Kurt Wetzel
Phone: 209-236-1111	HR: —
Fax: 209-236-0154	FYE: December 31
Web: www.boydcorp.com	Type: Private

A. B. Boyd Company puts a little zip in rubber manufacturing. Originally a zipper distributor, the company has evolved to operate as Boyd Corporation and manufacture rubber, plastic, and fiber products that offer environmental sealing and energy-efficient solutions. The custom designed and manufactured products meet requirements for acoustic, thermal, shock, and shielding systems, among others. Boyd uses a range of specialized materials from silicone to Mylar, polypropylene, copper and aluminum foils, and coated fabrics to deliver a low-cost, engineered lineup. Boyd caters to OEMs in aerospace, electronics, medical equipment, telecommunications, and transportation. It is held by Stonebridge Partners Management.

A.B. WATLEY GROUP INC.   Pink Sheets: ABWG

50 Broad St., Ste. 1728	CEO: Steven (Steve) Malin
New York, NY 10004	CFO: —
Phone: 646-753-9301	HR: —
Fax: 212-202-5204	FYE: September 30
Web: www.abwatley.com	Type: Public

A.B. Watley Group wants you to trade up. Through A.B. Watley Direct, it provides online trading and related services to individual and corporate customers. The firm's institutional sales and trading desk handles anonymous, off-exchange, large-block transactions for mutual and pension funds, insurance companies, banks, corporations, and independent fund managers. A.B. Watley operates through the UltimateTrader (targeting individuals) and WatleyTrader (targeting institutional and large-volume traders). In 2009 former management of now-defunct daytrading subsidiary A.B. Watley, Inc. were convicted of conspiring to violate securities laws.

ABARTA, INC.

1000 Gamma Dr., Ste. 500	CEO: John F. Bitzer III
Pittsburgh, PA 15238	CFO: —
Phone: 412-963-6226	HR: Frank Nowak
Fax: 412-968-1084	FYE: —
Web: www.abarta.com	Type: Private

ABARTA sure didn't put all its eggs in one basket. The diverse holding company has subsidiaries in soft drinks, frozen food, newspaper publishing, and oil and gas exploration and development. ABARTA owns four Coca-Cola bottling companies, Kahiki Foods, ABARTA Oil & Gas, and the South Jersey Publishing Company, which publishes *The Press of Atlantic City*. ABARTA's Beverage Group is the country's eighth-largest bottler, selling 16 million cases a year from its four plants in Buffalo, New York; Cleveland, Ohio; Coatesville, Pennsylvania; and Lehigh Valley, Pennsylvania.

ABATIX CORP.

Pink Sheets: ABIX

2400 Skyline Dr., Ste. 400
Mesquite, TX 75149
Phone: 214-381-0322
Fax: 214-381-9513
Web: www.abatix.com

CEO: Terry W. Shaver
CFO: Frank J. Cinatl IV
HR: Andrea Staub
FYE: December 31
Type: Public

Abatix helps companies clean up. The company supplies more than 30,000 personal protection and safety products to environmental contractors, construction companies, and industrial safety companies. Abatix's products are used by workers involved in cleanup projects such as asbestos and lead abatement and mold remediation. Products include sheeting and bags, fire retardant and disposable clothing, and asbestos and lead abatement and restoration equipment. Abatix serves some 6,000 customers located throughout the US. It operates nine distribution centers in Dallas, Houston, Las Vegas, Los Angeles, Phoenix, San Diego, San Francisco, Seattle, and Jacksonville, Florida.

ABAXIS, INC.

NASDAQ (GS): ABAX

3240 Whipple Rd.
Union City, CA 94587
Phone: 510-675-6500
Fax: 510-441-6150
Web: www.abaxis.com

CEO: Clinton H. (Clint) Severson
CFO: Alberto R. Santa Ines
HR: —
FYE: March 31
Type: Public

Abaxis makes a praxis of analyzing blood. Its two types of point-of-care blood analyzers (one for humans and one for animals) can each perform more than a dozen types of tests. The analyzers are portable, require little training, provide on-the-spot results, and offer built-in quality control and calibration. The company also sells reagent discs used to perform common blood tests. Abaxis markets the systems under the VetScan name in the veterinary market (where it makes most of its sales) and Piccolo in the human medical market. It is developing a wider range of tests to penetrate the human diagnostic market. Abaxis sells its products to veterinarians, hospitals, managed care organizations, and the military.

	Annual Growth	3/05	3/06	3/07	3/08	3/09
Sales ($ mil.)	18.9%	52.8	68.9	86.2	100.6	105.6
Net income ($ mil.)	25.1%	4.9	7.5	10.1	12.5	12.0
Market value ($ mil.)	18.1%	195.4	500.8	538.1	511.6	380.7
Employees	16.5%	184	217	265	321	339

ABB INC.

12040 Regency Pkwy.
Cary, NC 27518
Phone: 203-750-2200
Fax: 203-750-2263
Web: www.abb.us

CEO: Enrique Santacana
CFO: Ismo Haka
HR: Don Allen
FYE: December 31
Type: Subsidiary

When robots take over the world, you can blame ABB Inc. The US operations of global manufacturing conglomerate ABB have built a presence in dozens of industries. Like its Swiss parent company, ABB Inc. operates in two main areas — automation technologies and power technologies — and serves customers in the power utilities, chemicals, oil and gas, and industrial process industries. ABB Inc.'s products include controls and instrumentation, robotics, switches, motors, transformers, and power electronics. It also offers various consulting, repair, and outsourcing services. Although ABB Inc. has acted independently in the past, its parent has brought it under the umbrella of a central management structure.

ABBOTT DIABETES CARE, INC.

1360 S. Loop Rd.
Alameda, CA 94502
Phone: 510-749-5400
Fax: 510-749-5401
Web: www.abbottdiabetescare.com

CEO: Heather L. Mason
CFO: —
HR: —
FYE: December 31
Type: Subsidiary

Abbott Diabetes Care cares about diabetics. The unit of Abbott Labs makes glucose monitoring equipment and supplies for use by diabetics at home or by medical professionals in hospitals and other care facilities throughout the US in retail stores and online. Its monitoring systems are sold under the FreeStyle and Precision Xtra brands. Its diabetes data management systems are sold under the CoPilot and Precision Link brands and are designed to be used in conjunction with its monitoring systems. The company also offers insulin pumps including its CoZmonitor which is a combination of insulin pump and blood glucose monitoring system.

⊞ ABBOTT LABORATORIES

NYSE: ABT

100 Abbott Park Rd.
Abbott Park, IL 60064
Phone: 847-937-6100
Fax: 847-937-9555
Web: www.abbott.com

CEO: Miles D. White
CFO: Thomas C. (Tom) Freyman
HR: Stephen R. (Steve) Fussell
FYE: December 31
Type: Public

Filling baby bottles and soothing aching joints are habit for Abbott. Abbott Laboratories is one of the US's top health care products makers. The company's pharmaceuticals include HIV treatment Norvir, rheumatoid arthritis therapy Humira, and Depakote to treat epilepsy and bipolar disorder. Its nutritional products division makes such well-known brands as Similac infant formula and the Ensure line of nutrition supplements. Abbott also makes diagnostic instruments and tests, including the FreeStyle diabetes care line, as well as vascular medical devices such as its Xience drug-eluting stents. The company sells its products in about 130 countries through affiliates and distributors.

	Annual Growth	12/05	12/06	12/07	12/08	12/09
Sales ($ mil.)	8.3%	22,337.8	22,476.3	25,914.2	29,527.6	30,764.7
Net income ($ mil.)	14.3%	3,372.1	1,716.8	3,606.3	4,880.7	5,745.8
Market value ($ mil.)	8.2%	60,862.8	75,187.0	86,671.2	82,380.1	83,337.1
Employees	5.1%	59,735	66,663	68,000	69,000	73,000

ABBOTT MEDICAL OPTICS, INC.

1700 E. St. Andrew Place
Santa Ana, CA 92705
Phone: 714-247-8200
Fax: 714-247-8672
Web: www.amo-inc.com

CEO: James V. (Jim) Mazzo
CFO: Brian Durkin
HR: Chris Darragh
FYE: December 31
Type: Subsidiary

On a vision quest? Those wanting to see more clearly might benefit from products made by Abbott Medical Optics (formerly Advanced Medical Optics). The subsidiary of Abbott Labs makes eye care products in three key segments: corneal, refractive, and cataract. The company's corneal products include contact lens solutions and eyedrops for consumers. Its refractive and cataract product lines focus on professional devices, equipment, and accessories used in laser vision correction procedures and cataract surgery; it is the global leader in LASIK surgical devices. Surgery products are marketed to eye surgeons and surgery centers worldwide through a direct sales force.

ABBOTT NUTRITION

625 Cleveland Ave.
Columbus, OH 43215
Phone: 614-624-7677
Fax: —
Web: www.abbottnutrition.com

CEO: Miles D. White
CFO: Don Edwards
HR: —
FYE: December 31
Type: Subsidiary

Abbott Nutrition is a calorie king. The company makes and markets nutritional products and devices for customers big and small around the world. A long-held division of Abbott Laboratories, over the years it has acquired a portfolio of brands that serve niches of the nutritional supplement market. Its infant products include Isomil, PediaSure, Pedialyte, and Similac. Abbott Nutrition makes adult and diabetic products under brand names such as Ensure, Glucerna, and ProSure. The company also boasts a lengthy list of enteral (feeding) products. Abbott Nutrition sells its products to consumers via online retailers and bricks-and-mortar retail stores. Hospitals and other institutions order directly from the company.

ABC HOME FURNISHINGS, INC.

888 Broadway
New York, NY 10003
Phone: 212-473-3000
Fax: 212-505-3125
Web: www.abchome.com

CEO: Paulette Cole
CFO: David E. Lauber
HR: —
FYE: September 30
Type: Private

Do your ABCs start with armoires, beds, and carpets? Then ABC Home Furnishings (aka ABC Carpet & Home) is the store for you. The specialty home furnishings retailer operates four stores in the US, plus a store in Harrods in London, offering high-quality furniture, electronics, linens, window treatments, mattresses, rugs, and related accessories. It provides solar power to homes and offices in New York and New Jersey through ABC Real Goods Solar, operated in collaboration with Gaiam's Real Goods division. The company is owned by CEO and creative director Paulette Cole, the daughter of ABC's founder, Jerry Weinrib, who started the company as a single carpet store in 1961.

ABC CABLE NETWORKS GROUP

3800 W. Alameda Ave.
Burbank, CA 91505
Phone: 818-569-7500
Fax: —
Web: www.disneyabctv.com

CEO: Anne M. Sweeney
CFO: —
HR: —
FYE: September 30
Type: Subsidiary

ABC Cable Networks Group wants to work a little magic on the television dial. The unit of Disney-ABC Television Group owns and operates a portfolio of cable television networks including entertainment channels ABC Family and SOAPnet. It also owns Disney Channels Worldwide, which operates kids' networks the Disney Channel and Disney XD; other kids' programming is distributed under the Jetix name. (Through ABC Family, ABC Cable Networks owns animation distributor Jetix Europe.) In addition, ABC Cable Networks holds a 42% stake in A&E Television. Disney-ABC Television Group oversees the television broadcasting, production, and distribution operations of media giant Walt Disney.

⊞ ABC, INC.

77 W. 66th St.
New York, NY 10023
Phone: 212-456-7777
Fax: 212-456-1424
Web: abc.go.com

CEO: Anne M. Sweeney
CFO: James L. (Jim) Hedges
HR: Sandy Hooper
FYE: September 30
Type: Subsidiary

Some *Desperate Housewives*, a *Modern Family*, and a group of doctors schooled in *Grey's Anatomy* call this network home. ABC operates the #3 television network in the US (behind CBS and FOX), with more than 230 affiliates (including 10 corporate-owned stations). ABC also owns an 80% stake in ESPN, a leader in cable sports broadcasting with a stable of channels, including ESPN2, ESPN Classic, and ESPN News, as well as its flagship channel. (Publisher Hearst owns the remaining 20% of ESPN.) In addition, the company operates mass-market publisher Hyperion. ABC is the cornerstone of Disney-ABC Television Group, the TV division of parent Walt Disney.

ABC FINANCIAL SERVICES, INC.

8320 Hwy. 107
North Little Rock, AR 72124
Phone: 501-515-5000
Fax: 501-992-0801
Web: www.abcfinancial.com

CEO: James A. (Jim) Bottin
CFO: Bob Whisnant
HR: Julianne Loum
FYE: December 31
Type: Private

Health club owners can get fiscally fit with ABC Financial Services. Founded in 1981 by CEO Jim Bottin, the company provides management products and services to fitness club owners across the country. Services include payment processing, funds transfer, and accounts receivable management for member accounts, as well as customized sales, marketing, and loyalty programs aimed at attracting and retaining club members. ABC Financial Services' DataTrak software facilitates club operations by centralizing data, tracking sales and inventory, managing member access, and collecting information on prospective members.

ABCO LABORATORIES, INC.

2450 S. Watney Way
Fairfield, CA 94533
Phone: 707-432-2200
Fax: 707-432-2240
Web: www.abcolabs.com

CEO: Allen Baron
CFO: Jessica Chua
HR: Jessica Chua
FYE: December 31
Type: Private

ABCO Laboratories knows the ABCs of ingredients. The company offers custom, contract, and private-label ingredient manufacturing for the food, nutritional, OTC pharmaceutical, cosmetic, and homeopathic industries. It provides ingredient custom blending, packaging, and encapsulation. Its food products include seasonings, herbs, and marinades. In addition to the ingredients themselves, ABCO offers services such as product development, physical and sensory laboratory analyses, and microbiological testing. It can test for yeast, mold, *E. coli* and other coliforms, *salmonella*, and other pathogens.

	Annual Growth	12/04	12/05	12/06	12/07	12/08
Est. sales ($ mil.)	—	—	—	—	—	14.3
Employees	—	—	—	—	—	100

ABENGOA BIOENERGY CORPORATION

16150 Main Circle Dr., Ste. 300
Chesterfield, MO 63017
Phone: 636-728-0508
Fax: 636-728-1148
Web: www.abengoabioenergy.com

CEO: Javier Salgado Leirado
CFO: Ignacio García
HR: —
FYE: June 30
Type: Subsidiary

Among the world's largest producers of ethanol, Abengoa Bioenergy is the only global ethanol producer, with about a dozen plants in the US, Europe, and South America. The plants have a production capacity of about 450 gallons a year. The company's primary product is fuel-grade ethanol, which, when blended with gasoline, raises oxygen levels and reduces exhaust emissions of pollutants such as carbon monoxide. Its research and development unit works in partnership with universities and other companies to develop improved processing technology for ethanol. Abengoa Bioenergy has been a part of Spanish engineering firm Abengoa, which owns about 80% of the company, since 2002.

	Annual Growth	6/04	6/05	6/06	6/07	6/08
Est. sales ($ mil.)	—	—	—	—	—	300.0
Employees	—	—	—	—	—	165

ABERCROMBIE & FITCH CO.

NYSE: ANF

6301 Fitch Path
New Albany, OH 43054
Phone: 614-283-6500
Fax: 614-283-6710
Web: www.abercrombie.com

CEO: Michael S. (Mike) Jeffries
CFO: Jonathan E. Ramsden
HR: Ron Grzymkowski
FYE: January 31
Type: Public

Trading on its century-old name, Abercrombie & Fitch (A&F) sells upscale men's, women's, and kids' casual clothes and accessories — quite a change from when the company outfitted Ernest Hemingway and Teddy Roosevelt for safaris. A&F operates some 1,100 stores in the US, Canada, and Europe, and also sells via its catalog and online. Its carefully selected college-age sales staff and use of 20-something models imbue its stores with an upscale fraternity house feel. A&F runs a fast-growing chain of some 525 teen stores called Hollister Co., and a chain targeted at boys and girls ages seven to 14 called abercrombie kids. Its new just-for-women brand, Gilly Hicks, launched in 2008 and has about 15 stores.

	Annual Growth	1/06	1/07	1/08	1/09	1/10
Sales ($ mil.)	1.3%	2,784.7	3,318.2	3,749.8	3,540.3	2,928.6
Net income ($ mil.)	(82.7%)	334.0	422.2	475.7	272.3	0.3
Market value ($ mil.)	(17.0%)	5,853.7	7,013.1	7,017.6	1,573.9	2,780.9
Employees	1.3%	76,100	86,400	99,000	83,000	80,000

ABERCROMBIE & KENT, INC.

1411 Opus Place, Executive Towers West II, Ste. 300
Downers Grove, IL 60515
Phone: 630-725-3400
Fax: 630-725-3401
Web: www.abercrombiekent.com

CEO: Geoffrey J. W. Kent
CFO: —
HR: —
FYE: December 31
Type: Private

When you want to commune with lions and elephants without roughing it, you go with A&K. Founded as a safari company in Kenya, Abercrombie & Kent today provides luxury travel packages including safaris, cruises, and train travel through nearly 60 offices worldwide in places like the Galapagos Islands, Antarctica, and Bhutan. Escorted travelers are accompanied by local guides who are employees, not subcontractors. The company also has a private vacation option called the Marco Polo Club which offers discounts and other perks. The company is operated by chairman and CEO Geoffrey Kent and executive vice chairman Jorie Butler Kent.

ABERDEEN GROUP, INC.

260 Franklin St., Ste. 260
Boston, MA 02110
Phone: 617-723-7890
Fax: 617-723-7897
Web: www.aberdeen.com

CEO: Andrew Boyd
CFO: —
HR: Jayson Saba
FYE: December 31
Type: Subsidiary

Aberdeen Group provides market research for information technology vendors and buyers. The company provides decision-making executives with research and analysis regarding technology strategy, trends, and products affecting businesses. Its services include benchmarking data from more than 25,000 companies; it also offers market assessments, sales acceleration programs, and conferences for executives from such clients as IBM, Intel, and Unisys. Aberdeen maintains an online research library featuring thousands of publications, performance indicators, and metrics across all vertical markets. The group was founded in 1988 and is a subsidiary of direct marketing giant Harte-Hanks.

	Annual Growth	12/04	12/05	12/06	12/07	12/08
Est. sales ($ mil.)	—	—	—	—	—	1.3
Employees	—	—	—	—	—	115

ABF FREIGHT SYSTEM, INC.

3801 Old Greenwood Rd.
Fort Smith, AR 72903
Phone: 479-785-6000
Fax: 800-599-2810
Web: www.abfs.com

CEO: Wesley B. (Wes) Kemp
CFO: —
HR: —
FYE: December 31
Type: Subsidiary

ABF Freight System knows the ABCs of freight transportation. The primary subsidiary of Arkansas Best, ABF Freight System specializes in national and regional long-haul, less-than-truckload (LTL) transportation of general commodities such as apparel, appliances, chemicals, food, furniture, plastics, rubber, and textiles. (LTL carriers combine freight from multiple shippers into a single truckload.) ABF Freight System operates from a network of about 280 terminals throughout the US and Canada and in Puerto Rico. It maintains a fleet of some 4,000 tractors and 17,000 trailers. The company, which traces its origins to 1923, offers service in Mexico through arrangements with Mexican carriers.

	Annual Growth	12/04	12/05	12/06	12/07	12/08
Est. sales ($ mil.)	—	—	—	—	—	1,770.7
Employees	—	—	—	—	—	11,560

ABINGTON BANCORP, INC.

NASDAQ (GS): ABBC

180 Old York Rd.
Jenkintown, PA 19046
Phone: 215-887-3200
Fax: 215-887-4100
Web: www.abingtonbankonline.com

CEO: Robert W. White
CFO: Jack J. Sandoski
HR: —
FYE: December 31
Type: Public

Abington Bancorp is young, but its bank is old. Formed in 2004, the holding company (formerly Abington Community Bancorp) owns Abington Bank, which was established in 1867. The community bank has about 20 branches in southeastern Pennsylvania, north of Philadelphia. The bank offers such standard products as checking and savings accounts, debit cards, and loans. Residential mortgages account for more than half of the company's loan portfolio, which also includes construction loans, commercial and multifamily real estate loans, and home equity lines of credit.

	Annual Growth	12/05	12/06	12/07	12/08	12/09
Assets ($ mil.)	10.1%	844.1	925.2	1,079.7	1,189.8	1,238.1
Net income ($ mil.)	—	6.3	6.8	7.1	2.1	(7.2)
Market value ($ mil.)	(14.6%)	270.4	399.9	196.0	192.9	143.7
Employees	4.4%	144	148	170	177	171

ABINGTON MEMORIAL HOSPITAL

1200 Old York Rd.
Abington, PA 19001
Phone: 215-481-2000
Fax: 215-481-3619
Web: www.amh.org

CEO: Laurence M. Merlis
CFO: Michael Walsh
HR: Meghan Patton
FYE: June 30
Type: Not-for-profit

Abington Memorial Hospital brings health care to residents of southeastern Pennsylvania. Serving Montgomery, Bucks, and Philadelphia counties, the not-for-profit community hospital has some 670 beds. In addition to general medical and surgical care, the hospital offers specialized care centers for cancer and cardiovascular conditions, operates high-tech orthopedic and neurological surgery units, and serves as a regional trauma care facility. It also runs an inpatient pediatric unit in affiliation with The Children's Hospital of Philadelphia. Abington Memorial, also known as Abington Health, operates the neighboring 125-bed Lansdale Hospital and several area outpatient facilities.

ABIOMED, INC.

NASDAQ (GM): ABMD

22 Cherry Hill Dr.
Danvers, MA 01923
Phone: 978-777-5410
Fax: 978-777-8411
Web: www.abiomed.com

CEO: Michael R. Minogue
CFO: Robert L. (Bob) Bowen
HR: —
FYE: March 31
Type: Public

ABIOMED is no heartless company. On the contrary, it helps troubled hearts regain their vigor with its BVS 5000 and AB5000 ventricular assist devices. The FDA-approved products temporarily take over the heart's pumping function and improve circulatory flow in patients with acute heart failure, thus allowing their hearts to rest and recover. The company has also developed a battery-powered, implantable replacement heart system called AbioCor, which has received Humanitarian Device Exemption approval from the FDA. The device can be used to extend life for dying patients who aren't eligible for a heart transplant. ABIOMED markets its products through both a direct sales force and distributors.

	Annual Growth	3/06	3/07	3/08	3/09	3/10
Sales ($ mil.)	18.3%	43.7	50.6	58.9	73.2	85.7
Net income ($ mil.)	—	(29.4)	(27.9)	(40.9)	(31.6)	(19.0)
Market value ($ mil.)	(5.4%)	482.9	511.3	491.9	183.4	386.3
Employees	5.0%	300	324	377	386	365

ABLE ENERGY, INC.

Pink Sheets: ABLE

198 Green Pond Rd.
Rockaway, NJ 07866
Phone: 973-625-1012
Fax: 973-586-9866
Web: www.ableenergy.com

CEO: Gregory D. Frost
CFO: John F. O'Brien
HR: Colleen Harrington
FYE: June 30
Type: Public

An able consolidator in the fragmented heating-oil and motor fuels markets, Able Energy provides retail distribution of heating oil and other fuels to more than 30,000 residential and commercial customers in Florida, New Jersey, New York, and Pennsylvania through its Able Oil subsidiary. Able Energy also installs and repairs HVAC equipment and markets gasoline and other refined petroleum products and natural gas. Moving into the travel plaza business (motor fuels and food), in 2007 Able acquired All American Plazas' truck stops in return for a 75% stake in Able, making AAP Able's largest shareholder.

	Annual Growth	6/04	6/05	6/06	6/07	*6/08
Sales ($ mil.)	59.3%	42.9	62.0	75.1	93.6	276.4
Net income ($ mil.)	—	(0.1)	(2.1)	(6.2)	(6.6)	(12.9)
Employees	54.9%	87	95	77	645	501

*Most recent year available

ABLESTIK LABORATORIES

20021 Susana Rd.
Rancho Dominguez, CA 90221
Phone: 310-764-4600
Fax: 310-764-2545
Web: www.ablestik.com

CEO: Jeff Gausepohl
CFO: —
HR: Cindy Reina
FYE: December 31
Type: Subsidiary

Semiconductors need help sticking to business too, and that's where Ablestik Laboratories comes in. A part of global chemicals titan Henkel, Ablestik manufactures tape and film adhesives, thermally and electrically conductive paste, and underfill encapsulants. They are used in microelectronics, optoelectronics, image sensors, semiconductor assemblies, and semiconductor packaging. Ablestik Laboratories maintains sales and service centers throughout Asia and in the UK in addition to its locations in the US. The company had been a part of Imperial Chemical Industries (ICI) until the beginning of 2008.

ABM INDUSTRIES INCORPORATED

NYSE: ABM

551 5th Ave., Ste. 300
New York, NY 10176
Phone: 212-297-0200
Fax: 212-297-0375
Web: www.abm.com

CEO: Henrik C. Slipsager
CFO: James S. Lusk
HR: Erin M. Andre
FYE: October 31
Type: Public

Many businesses hope to clean up, but diversified facilities services contractor ABM Industries counts on it. Through its primary business unit, ABM Janitorial, the company offers cleaning services to owners and operators of office buildings, hospitals, manufacturing plants, schools, shopping centers, and transportation facilities throughout the US and in Canada and Puerto Rico. Through other units, ABM Industries provides security services and maintains mechanical, electrical, and plumbing systems. Ampco System Parking operates more than 1,800 parking lots and garages, mainly at airports across 35 states, while ABM Security Services provides security officers and security systems monitoring services.

	Annual Growth	10/05	10/06	10/07	10/08	10/09
Sales ($ mil.)	7.7%	2,587.8	2,792.7	2,842.8	3,623.6	3,481.8
Net income ($ mil.)	(1.6%)	57.9	93.2	52.4	45.4	54.3
Market value ($ mil.)	(1.2%)	1,024.3	1,031.1	1,221.1	847.8	975.0
Employees	5.7%	73,000	75,000	107,000	100,000	91,000

ABOUT, INC.

249 W. 17th St.
New York, NY 10011
Phone: 212-204-4000
Fax: 212-204-1521
Web: www.about.com

CEO: Cella M. Irvine
CFO: Darline Jean
HR: —
FYE: December 31
Type: Subsidiary

Prepositionally inclined About wants to be your online guru. The About Group's flagship About.com offers a network of topic-specific websites grouped into channels such as arts, hobbies, shopping, and sports on more than 70,000 topics. The site features content (some 2 million pieces) created by 770 human guides, or "topical advisors" — which About describes as the "heart and soul" of its business. A free site, About.com generates revenue from advertisers trying to reach the 60 million people worldwide that visit the site monthly. In addition to About.com, the company operates the ConsumerSearch.com, UCompareHealthCare.com, and Caloriecount.about.com sites. The New York Times Company owns the About Group.

An in-depth profile of this company is available to Hoover's Online members at hoovers.com.

39

ABOVENET, INC.
NYSE: ABVT

360 Hamilton Ave.
White Plains, NY 10601
Phone: 914-421-6700
Fax: 914-421-6777
Web: www.above.net

CEO: William G. (Bill) LaPerch
CFO: Joseph P. Ciavarella
HR: —
FYE: December 31
Type: Public

AboveNet wants to light the way to faster communications. The company operates metro and long-haul fiber-optic networks, providing service to more than a dozen metropolitan markets in the US. It leases dark fiber and provides managed network services to communications carriers and government agencies, as well as high-usage enterprise customers in such industries as financial services, health care, media, and retail. The company also operates a Tier 1 IP network over its metro and long-haul infrastructure that provides customers in North America, Europe, and Japan with data transport and virtual private network (VPN) services.

	Annual Growth	12/05	12/06	12/07	12/08	12/09
Sales ($ mil.)	13.1%	219.7	236.7	253.6	319.9	360.1
Net income ($ mil.)	—	(8.4)	46.4	13.8	42.3	281.6
Market value ($ mil.)	46.2%	358.1	753.9	980.1	364.4	1,634.4
Employees	9.8%	444	—	549	615	646

ABP CORPORATION

1 Au Bon Pain Way
Boston, MA 02210
Phone: 617-423-2100
Fax: 617-423-7879
Web: www.aubonpain.com

CEO: Susan (Sue) Morelli
CFO: Michael Lynch
HR: Kris Broe
FYE: September 30
Type: Private

To make dough in the bistro business, it helps to start with good bread. ABP Corporation operates the Au Bon Pain bakery cafe chain, with more than 250 company-owned and franchised locations in the US, Kuwait, Japan, Thailand, South Korea, and Taiwan. The bistros offer a wide range of sandwiches, soups, salads, and baked goods, as well as coffee and other cafe beverages. Most of the restaurants are located in urban areas, but ABP also has on-site locations in airports, shopping malls, and on university campuses. The Au Bon Pain chain was started in 1978 by Louis Kane. ABP is controlled by LNK Partners, a Boston-based private equity firm.

ABRAXAS PETROLEUM CORPORATION
NASDAQ (CM): AXAS

18803 Meisner Dr.
San Antonio, TX 78258
Phone: 210-490-4788
Fax: 210-490-8837
Web: www.abraxaspetroleum.com

CEO: Robert L. G. (Bob) Watson
CFO: Chris E. Williford
HR: Carol O'Brien
FYE: December 31
Type: Public

Abraxas is a mythical Gnostic symbol that represents the number 365 in Greek, and Abraxas Petroleum is working hard as a 365-days-a-year oil and gas company. The independent energy company is engaged in natural gas and crude oil exploration, development, and production. It operates primarily in Texas (along the Gulf Coast and in the Permian Basin), the Rocky Mountains, and the Mid-Continent, and in 2008 the company reported estimated proved reserves of 108.4 billion cu. ft. of natural gas and 7 million barrels of oil. Abraxas Petroleum also owns interests in more than 160,100 net acres, primarily in mature fields and in more than 1,800 producing wells.

	Annual Growth	12/05	12/06	12/07	12/08	12/09
Sales ($ mil.)	2.1%	48.6	51.7	48.3	100.3	52.8
Net income ($ mil.)	—	19.1	1.2	56.7	(52.4)	(18.8)
Market value ($ mil.)	(22.3%)	402.6	235.6	294.3	54.9	146.4
Employees	9.9%	48	50	61	65	70

ABRAXIS BIOSCIENCE INC.
NASDAQ (GS): ABII

11755 Wilshire Blvd., 20th Fl.
Los Angeles, CA 90025
Phone: 310-883-1300
Fax: 310-998-8553
Web: www.abraxisbio.com

CEO: Bruce J. Wendel
CFO: Richard J. (Rick) Rodgers
HR: —
FYE: December 31
Type: Public

Cancer patients will hopefully get a helpful shot in the arm thanks to Abraxis BioScience. The company's oncology and research division is developing a line of injectable drugs starting with Abraxane, its patented version of cancer drug paclitaxel that is approved to treat breast cancer. Abraxane is approved for marketing in about 40 countries, and Abraxis BioScience is working to get it on the market in others. It uses a direct sales force and independent representatives to market the drug to oncologists and cancer centers around the globe. Chairman Patrick Soon-Shiong holds more than 80% of the company.

	Annual Growth	12/05	12/06	12/07	12/08	12/09
Sales ($ mil.)	27.5%	135.7	182.3	333.7	345.3	359.0
Net income ($ mil.)	—	(12.7)	(124.6)	(41.6)	(276.8)	(103.1)
Market value ($ mil.)	(23.2%)	—	—	2,777.4	2,662.3	1,637.7
Employees	(12.2%)	1,488	1,864	615	734	885

ABT ASSOCIATES INC.

55 Wheeler St.
Cambridge, MA 02138
Phone: 617-492-7100
Fax: 617-492-5219
Web: www.abtassociates.com

CEO: Kathleen Flanagan
CFO: Richard Small
HR: Shawn Mood
FYE: March 31
Type: Private

Abt Associates offers a wide array of research-based consulting services to government agencies, businesses, and other organizations worldwide. The firm specializes in issues related to social, economic, and health policy; clinical research; and international development. Its services include consulting, implementation, and technical assistance; research and evaluation; survey data collection, management, and analysis; and strategy, planning, and policy. Abt Associates has served the US Departments of Agriculture, Commerce, Education, Energy, and Defense and does business from seven US offices and from about 40 project sites around the globe. Employees own the company, which was founded in 1965 by Clark Abt.

ABT ELECTRONICS, INC.

1200 N. Milwaukee Ave.
Glenview, IL 60025
Phone: 847-967-8830
Fax: 847-544-2270
Web: www.abt.com

CEO: Robert J. (Bob) Abt
CFO: —
HR: Jennifer Guzman
FYE: December 31
Type: Private

Looking for a $10,000 loudspeaker or just a moderately priced clothes dryer? Abt Electronics & Appliance is apt to have it. Abt has just one location — a massive 37-acre megastore with a parking lot that accommodates 1,000 cars in suburban Chicago, where the natives tend to incorrectly call the store "A-B-T." One of the country's largest independent retailers of electronics and appliances, the company carries mostly name brands and targets affluent Chicagoans with high-end products such as Bang & Olufsen audio systems and Sub-Zero refrigerators. It also markets products through its website and services everything sold. Founded in 1936 by David and Jewel Abt, the company is still family owned.

ABVIVA, INC.

OTC: ABVV

10940 Wilshire Blvd., Ste. 600
Los Angeles, CA 90024
Phone: 310-443-4102
Fax: 310-443-4103
Web: www.abviva.com

CEO: Douglas Lane
CFO: —
HR: —
FYE: December 31
Type: Public

Abviva aims to bring better diagnostics to the fight against breast cancer. The drug developer (formerly known as Genesis Bioventures) is working on proteomics-based cancer diagnostics and therapeutics. Its wholly owned subsidiary Biomedical Diagnostics has developed a blood test, called the Mammastatin Serum Assay, which assesses a person's risk for developing breast cancer. Abviva also has a significant stake in Prion Developmental Laboratories, a developer of diagnostic tools for Mad Cow Disease and a similar neurodegenerative disorder that affects deer and elk called Chronic Wasting Disease.

	Annual Growth	12/04	12/05	12/06	12/07	*12/08
Sales ($ mil.)	—	—	—	—	—	1.3
Employees	—	—	—	—	—	17

*Most recent year available

A.C. MOORE ARTS & CRAFTS, INC.

NASDAQ (GS): ACMR

130 A.C. Moore Dr.
Berlin, NJ 08009
Phone: 856-768-4930
Fax: 856-753-4723
Web: www.acmoore.com

CEO: Joseph A. (Joe) Jeffries
CFO: David Stern
HR: Jennifer Roelke
FYE: December 31
Type: Public

Some are content to merely collect and dust their tchotchkes, but others are compelled to make them. A.C. Moore Arts & Crafts is eager to serve them all (focusing on women 35 and older). The chain's 135 superstores (up from just 17 in 1997) sell crafts and art and scrapbooking supplies, which account for more than 50% of sales, as well as yarn, seasonal items, fashion crafts, home decor and picture frames, and everything else needed to glue, paint, or arrange. A.C. Moore also offers in-store arts-and-crafts classes for children and adults. Its stores are located in more than 15 states along the East Coast. The company was founded in 1985 by its former chairman William Kaplan and ex-CEO Jack Parker.

	Annual Growth	12/05	12/06	12/07	12/08	12/09
Sales ($ mil.)	(3.4%)	539.4	589.5	559.7	534.7	468.9
Net income ($ mil.)	—	10.0	2.4	3.8	(26.6)	(25.9)
Market value ($ mil.)	(33.0%)	363.2	540.9	343.2	34.9	73.4
Employees	(3.6%)	5,090	4,941	5,459	4,391	4,400

ACA FINANCIAL GUARANTY CORPORATION

Pink Sheets: ACAH

140 Broadway, 47th Fl.
New York, NY 10005
Phone: 212-375-2000
Fax: 212-375-2100
Web: www.aca.com

CEO: Raymond J. Brooks
CFO: Philip Sam Sherman
HR: Eileen Hackett
FYE: December 31
Type: Public

ACA Financial Guaranty provides financial guaranty insurance for municipal and other public finance bonds. Previously, the company also provided asset management services for collateralized debt obligations (CDOs) built by pooling fixed-income assets, including bonds, loans, and credit swaps; investors in the company's CDOs included banks, money managers, hedge funds, and insurance companies. While the company's guaranty business was sound, its other services led to its distress. When the US subprime mortgage market tanked, the company was forced to reorganize and place its municipal bond guaranty business into run-off. ACA is now tending to its existing obligations; it is no longer writing new policies.

	Annual Growth	12/05	12/06	12/07	12/08	12/09
Assets ($ mil.)	(46.8%)	5,792.2	6,038.2	698.5	441.0	463.5
Net income ($ mil.)	14.1%	28.8	58.7	4.8	(238.6)	48.8
Employees	12.7%	102	115	—	—	—

ACACIA RESEARCH CORPORATION

NASDAQ (GM): ACTG

500 Newport Center Dr., 7th Fl.
Newport Beach, CA 92660
Phone: 949-480-8300
Fax: 949-480-8301
Web: www.acaciaresearch.com

CEO: Paul R. Ryan
CFO: Clayton J. Haynes
HR: —
FYE: December 31
Type: Public

It's the stuff you'd expect to see in a George Orwell novel. Acacia Research acquires, develops, licenses, and protects patented technologies for individual inventors and small companies that have limited resources to protect against infringement. The company owns or controls the rights to more than 140 patent portfolios and about 50 technology license programs in the US and abroad. It typically buys portfolios and pays its clients an upfront fee or becomes the exclusive licensing agent and doles out royalties. It has out-licensed to such companies as 3M, Dell, IBM, Texas Instruments, and Walt Disney Company. Acacia Research primarily operates through its Acacia Technologies subsidiary.

	Annual Growth	12/05	12/06	12/07	12/08	12/09
Sales ($ mil.)	36.1%	19.6	34.8	52.6	48.2	67.3
Net income ($ mil.)	—	(6.3)	(5.5)	(15.4)	(13.8)	(11.3)
Market value ($ mil.)	7.2%	233.0	451.8	303.3	102.7	307.6
Employees	(16.8%)	92	33	45	41	44

ACACIA TECHNOLOGIES GROUP

500 Newport Center Dr., 7th Fl.
Newport Beach, CA 92660
Phone: 949-480-8300
Fax: 949-480-8301
Web: www.acaciatechnologies.com

CEO: Paul R. Ryan
CFO: Clayton J. Haynes
HR: —
FYE: December 31
Type: Subsidiary

Acacia Technologies offers shade to more than 100 patent portfolios. The company (which is the primary subsidiary of Acacia Research) acquires and licenses patent rights to various technologies related to digital audio-on-demand and video-on-demand transmission. It markets many of these patents under the DMT brand to makers of electronics gear, who incorporate the technologies into applications for cable, satellite, and Internet distribution of digital content. Acacia Technologies has reached licensing agreements with Fujitsu, Pioneer, Sony, and Union Pacific, among other companies.

ACADEMY CORPORATION

5520 Midway Park Place NE
Albuquerque, NM 87109
Phone: 505-345-1805
Fax: 505-342-5543
Web: www.academycorp.com

CEO: Keith Philippi
CFO: Robert Middleton
HR: —
FYE: December 31
Type: Subsidiary

There's gold in them there scrap heaps, or there can be, and that's where Academy comes in. The Academy Group refines precious metals, including silver and gold, from leftovers such as flake, scrap, sludges, sweepings, filings, and buffings. Academy manufactures bullion, provides materials (sheet, wire, and casting grain products) for jewelry makers and silversmiths, and operates silver-recovery equipment for the photo processing, medical, and graphic arts industries. It operates half a dozen locations throughout the US, including its refinery in New Mexico. Brush Engineered Materials bought Academy in early 2010 for about $25 million; it will operate the company as a wholly owned subsidiary.

An in-depth profile of this company is available to Hoover's Online members at hoovers.com.

41

ACADEMY, LTD.

1800 N. Mason Rd.
Katy, TX 77449
Phone: 281-646-5200
Fax: 281-646-5000
Web: www.academy.com

CEO: David Gochman
CFO: Rodney (Rod) Faldyn
HR: —
FYE: January 31
Type: Private

Academy is near the head of the class among sporting goods retailers. It is one of the leading full-line sporting goods chains in the US with about 120 Academy Sports + Outdoors stores in Texas and some 10 other states in the Southeast. Academy's low-frills stores carry clothing, shoes, and equipment for almost any sport and outdoor activity, including camping, golf, hunting, fishing, and boating. The company, which also operates a catalog and e-commerce site, dates back to a San Antonio tire shop opened by Max Gochman in 1938. The business moved into military surplus items and during the 1980s began focusing on sports and outdoor goods. The Gochman family still owns Academy and is run by CEO David Gochman.

ACADIA PHARMACEUTICALS INC.

NASDAQ (GM): ACAD

3911 Sorrento Valley Blvd.
San Diego, CA 92121
Phone: 858-558-2871
Fax: 858-558-2872
Web: www.acadia-pharm.com

CEO: Uli Hacksell
CFO: Thomas H. Aasen
HR: Natasha Bowman
FYE: December 31
Type: Public

ACADIA Pharmaceuticals puts genes and drugs together to fight disease. The development-stage company uses its proprietary R-SAT technology to identify genomic targets for its small-molecule (chemical) drug therapies, primarily for central nervous system disorders. ACADIA hopes its lead drug candidate pimavanserin (under development with Biovail) will effectively treat psychosis in patients with Parkinson's disease. In partnership with eye-care heavyweight Allergan, ACADIA is also developing therapies for glaucoma and chronic pain. Other development targets include neurological indications such as insomnia and schizophrenia.

	Annual Growth	12/05	12/06	12/07	12/08	12/09
Sales ($ mil.)	(12.7%)	11.0	8.1	7.6	1.6	6.4
Net income ($ mil.)	—	(34.1)	(45.1)	(56.4)	(64.2)	(45.1)
Market value ($ mil.)	(39.5%)	377.6	337.0	424.4	34.5	50.6
Employees	(29.9%)	112	138	143	63	27

ACADIA REALTY TRUST

NYSE: AKR

1311 Mamaroneck Ave., Ste. 260
White Plains, NY 10605
Phone: 914-288-8100
Fax: 914-428-2760
Web: www.acadiarealty.com

CEO: Kenneth F. Bernstein
CFO: Michael L. Nelsen
HR: Joseph M. Napolitano
FYE: December 31
Type: Public

A self-managed real estate investment trust (REIT), Acadia Realty acquires, redevelops, and manages retail properties in the Northeast, Mid-Atlantic, and Midwest. The REIT specializes in community shopping centers and mixed-use properties in urban areas; it owns or has interests in some 85 properties — mostly shopping centers anchored by a grocery store, drug store, or big box store — that contain more than 7 million sq. ft. of leasable space. It also has investments in self-storage properties, mortgage loans, and other real estate interests. The company's largest tenants include A&P, SUPERVALU, and The TJX Companies.

	Annual Growth	12/05	12/06	12/07	12/08	12/09
Sales ($ mil.)	15.3%	83.3	102.7	101.6	140.7	147.3
Net income ($ mil.)	(11.4%)	20.6	39.0	23.6	27.5	12.7
Market value ($ mil.)	(4.2%)	804.4	1,003.8	1,027.5	572.5	676.8
Employees	(7.0%)	158	130	142	135	118

ACCEL PARTNERS

428 University Ave.
Palo Alto, CA 94301
Phone: 650-614-4800
Fax: 650-614-4880
Web: www.accel.com

CEO: Arthur C. Patterson
CFO: —
HR: —
FYE: December 31
Type: Private

How fast can you make money? Venture capital firm Accel Partners hopes to accelerate that. Founded in 1983, the firm traditionally has made early-stage investments in two sectors, software and networking, and has some $3 billion under management. The company's investment history includes a who's who of tech powerhouses such as Macromedia, Riverbed, and Facebook. Based in Silicon Valley, Accel also has offices in China, London, and India. Accel looks to invest in companies that were founded by entrepreneurs but are run by experienced management teams. It provides strategic financing, recruiting, and business development, among other services.

	Annual Growth	12/04	12/05	12/06	12/07	12/08
Est. sales ($ mil.)	—	—	—	—	—	0.6
Employees	—	—	—	—	—	5

ACCELLENT INC.

100 Fordham Rd.
Wilmington, MA 01887
Phone: 978-570-6900
Fax: 978-657-0878
Web: www.accellent.com

CEO: Donald J. Spence Jr.
CFO: Jeremy A. Friedman
HR: Tricia M. McCall
FYE: December 31
Type: Private

Accellent provides the nuts and bolts for the medical device industry. The company offers outsourced design, engineering, and manufacturing of custom components, subassemblies, and completed devices, primarily for medical device firms. Its customers include such industry leaders as Medtronic, Abbott Labs, Stryker, and Johnson & Johnson. Accellent specializes in equipment used for cardiac rhythm management, interventional cardiology, neurology, and orthopedics, as well as urology and minimally invasive procedures (especially in the field of endoscopy). It also offers its customers complete supply chain management. The company has about 25 locations in North America and Europe.

	Annual Growth	12/04	12/05	12/06	12/07	12/08
Est. sales ($ mil.)	—	—	—	—	—	525.5
Employees	—	—	—	—	—	3,289

ACCELR8 TECHNOLOGY CORPORATION

NYSE Amex: AXK

7000 N. Broadway, Bldg. 3, Unit 307
Denver, CO 80221
Phone: 303-863-8088
Fax: 303-863-1218
Web: www.accelr8.com

CEO: Thomas V. Geimer
CFO: Thomas V. Geimer
HR: —
FYE: July 31
Type: Public

Accelr8 Technology wants to speed up your lab results. Using its BACcel technology, the company is working on quicker methods for identifying bacterial infections. Its BACcelr8r system is being designed for use in clinical settings to provide bacterial identification within two hours. If successful, the system will be an improvement over existing methods which depend upon identifying bacteria in a culture grown over two to five days from a patient sample. Instead, BACcelr8r will look directly at the sample itself, sort through the tens of thousands of bacterial cells to identify any pathogenic bacteria, and determine if any are resistant to antibiotics.

	Annual Growth	7/05	7/06	7/07	7/08	7/09
Sales ($ mil.)	27.0%	0.5	0.2	0.2	0.5	1.3
Net income ($ mil.)	—	(2.1)	(3.0)	(1.9)	(1.7)	(0.7)
Market value ($ mil.)	(3.3%)	31.6	24.4	24.0	45.2	27.6
Employees	(14.8%)	19	18	14	7	10

ACCELRYS, INC.

NASDAQ (GM): ACCL

10188 Telesis Ct., Ste. 100
San Diego, CA 92121
Phone: 858-799-5000
Fax: 858-799-5100
Web: www.accelrys.com

CEO: Scipio M. (Max) Carnecchia
CFO: Michael A. Piraino
HR: Judith Ohrn Hicks
FYE: March 31
Type: Public

Accelrys knows nothing can accelerate research like good software. It develops scientific business intelligence software that clients use to accelerate the discovery and development of new drugs and technologies. Its software and services are used to collect, aggregate, and analyze scientific data and include tools for reporting and collaboration. While its customers are primarily involved in the pharmaceutical, life sciences, and biotech industries, Accelrys also counts clients involved in industries with significant R&D efforts, such as aerospace, consumer packaged goods, and energy. In 2010 Accelrys set plans to merge with rival Symyx Technologies in a stock-swap transaction.

	Annual Growth	3/05	3/06	3/07	3/08	3/09
Sales ($ mil.)	3.9%	69.6	82.0	81.0	79.7	81.0
Net income ($ mil.)	—	(24.6)	(7.7)	(1.5)	1.3	0.1
Market value ($ mil.)	(9.5%)	164.0	201.0	176.4	151.5	110.1
Employees	(8.7%)	525	479	372	379	364

ACCENT MARKETING SERVICES, L.L.C.

400 Missouri Ave., Ste. 107
Jeffersonville, IN 47130
Phone: 812-206-6200
Fax: 812-206-6201
Web: www.accentonline.com

CEO: Kevin Foley
CFO: Chris Dauk
HR: Laura Carpenter
FYE: December 31
Type: Subsidiary

ACCENT Marketing Services provides customer relationship marketing (CRM) services with an emphasis on contact center support. Among ACCENT's services are inbound and outbound call support, mail, e-mail, and Web chat. The company also offers loyalty marketing programs and customer satisfaction tracking. It has call centers in Arkansas, Florida, Indiana, and Missouri, as well as in the Caribbean and the Philippines. The company was founded in 1993 and serves a variety of industries from telecommunications to financial services to automotive. It is owned by marketing communications services firm MDC Partners.

	Annual Growth	12/04	12/05	12/06	12/07	12/08
Est. sales ($ mil.)	—	—	—	—	—	120.0
Employees	—	—	—	—	—	3,100

ACCENTIA BIOPHARMACEUTICALS, INC.

Pink Sheets: ABPIQ

324 S. Hyde Park Ave., Ste. 350
Tampa, FL 33606
Phone: 813-864-2554
Fax: 813-258-6912
Web: www.accentia.net

CEO: Francis E. O'Donnell Jr.
CFO: Alan M. Pearce
HR: Kristy Duffy
FYE: September 30
Type: Public

Accentia Biopharmaceuticals emphasizes runny noses. The company acquires and develops treatments for respiratory conditions, as well as other ailments. Its development-stage drugs include sinus inflammation treatment SinuNase, multiple sclerosis drug Revimmune, and BiovaxID, a possible vaccine for non-Hodgkin's lymphoma being developed by majority-owned subsidiary Biovest International. Accentia also develops cell production instruments, including the AutovaxID system, and offers pharmaceutical consulting services. The company and its subsidiaries (including Biovest) filed for Chapter 11 bankruptcy protection in late 2008.

ACCENTURE PLC

NYSE: ACN

1345 Avenue of the Americas
New York, NY 10105
Phone: 917-452-4400
Fax: 917-527-9915
Web: www.accenture.com

CEO: William D. (Bill) Green
CFO: Pamela J. Craig
HR: Jill B. Smart
FYE: August 31
Type: Public

For Accenture, the accent is on trying to help businesses improve their performance. The world's largest consulting firm, Accenture offers management consulting, information technology and systems integration, and business process outsourcing (BPO) services to customers around the globe. The company divides its practices into five main operating groups — communications and high technology, financial services, public service, products, and resources — that encompass more than 15 industries. Accenture, which is domiciled in Dublin but headquartered in New York, operates from more than 200 locations in about 50 countries.

	Annual Growth	8/05	8/06	8/07	8/08	8/09
Sales ($ mil.)	7.9%	17,094.4	18,228.4	21,452.7	25,313.8	23,171.0
Net income ($ mil.)	14.0%	940.5	973.3	1,243.1	1,691.8	1,590.0
Market value ($ mil.)	7.8%	17,323.7	21,058.3	29,258.6	29,365.1	23,429.6
Employees	9.5%	123,000	140,000	170,000	186,000	177,000

ACCESS BUSINESS GROUP, LLC

7575 Fulton St. East
Ada, MI 49355
Phone: 616-787-6000
Fax: —
Web: www.accessbusinessgroup.com

CEO: Steve Van Andel
CFO: —
HR: —
FYE: August 31
Type: Subsidiary

Somehow all those Amway products have to get from factories to salespeople. That's where Access Business Group comes in. The company manages supply chains for Amway and online retailer Quixtar. (Amway, Quixtar, and Access Business Group are units of Alticor.) Access Business Group operates more than half a dozen distribution centers with an overall capacity of more than 1.7 million sq. ft. In addition to distribution, the company provides contract manufacturing of cosmetics, nutritional supplements, and personal care products for its affiliates and other clients; it also offers printing and packaging services. More than 500 scientists and engineers work in the company's research and development labs worldwide.

	Annual Growth	8/04	8/05	8/06	8/07	8/08
Est. sales ($ mil.)	—	—	—	—	—	2,162.8
Employees	—	—	—	—	—	3,600

ACCESS COMMUNICATIONS

101 Howard St., 2nd Fl.
San Francisco, CA 94105
Phone: 415-904-7070
Fax: 415-904-7055
Web: www.accesspr.com

CEO: Susan G. Butenhoff
CFO: Colleen Brandon
HR: —
FYE: December 31
Type: Subsidiary

Access Communications opens the lines of communication between its clients and their selected audiences. The agency serves business customers in such industries as consumer products, e-commerce, health care, and telecommunications. Core offerings include brand building, communication strategy and counsel, media relations, opinion leader activities, spokesperson and speaker support, and design services. The company has worked with such clients as Google, Intuit, Johnson & Johnson, and LeapFrog Enterprises. Founded in 1991, Access Communications operates offices on both US coasts. In late 2008 it was acquired by Ketchum, a leading public relations firm owned by Omnicom.

An in-depth profile of this company is available to Hoover's Online members at hoovers.com.

43

ACCESS NATIONAL CORPORATION

NASDAQ (GM): ANCX

1800 Robert Fulton Dr., Ste. 310
Reston, VA 20191
Phone: 703-871-2100
Fax: 703-766-3386
Web: www.accessnationalbank.com

CEO: Michael W. (Mike) Clarke
CFO: Charles Wimer
HR: —
FYE: December 31
Type: Public

Enabling easy access to your money is Access National's aim. The holding company for Access National Bank, a thrift founded in 1999, serves the Washington, DC, area. It offers standard services including checking and savings accounts, IRAs, CDs, and loans to consumers and small to midsized businesses. Bank subsidiary Access National Mortgage originates residential real estate loans. Commercial real estate loans make up more than 40% of the company's portfolio; residential real estate accounts for about another third. Consumer, home equity, real estate construction, and business loans round out its lending activities.

	Annual Growth	12/05	12/06	12/07	12/08	12/09
Assets ($ mil.)	5.6%	537.0	644.8	622.4	702.3	666.9
Net income ($ mil.)	12.9%	5.9	7.6	3.7	4.7	9.6
Market value ($ mil.)	(19.8%)	151.3	101.5	64.1	50.8	62.6
Employees	7.9%	242	253	203	285	328

ACCESS PHARMACEUTICALS, INC.

OTC: ACCP

2600 N. Stemmons Fwy., Ste. 176
Dallas, TX 75207
Phone: 214-905-5100
Fax: 214-905-5101
Web: www.accesspharma.com

CEO: Jeffrey B. Davis
CFO: Stephen B. Thompson
HR: —
FYE: December 31
Type: Public

Access Pharmaceuticals is looking for ways to provide drugs direct and effective access to the parts of the body that need treatment. The company develops drug-delivery systems for application in cancer treatment. Oral treatment MuGard, which is used to reduce mouth inflammation in chemotherapy patients, has received marketing approval from the FDA. Its lead development product is ProLindac, a polymer platinate chemotherapy drug designed to target tumors. Other products in development include oral delivery systems and treatments for diabetes and cancer. The company added several anti-cancer candidates, including a monoclonal antibody, with the 2008 acquisition of Somanta Pharmaceuticals.

	Annual Growth	12/05	12/06	12/07	12/08	12/09
Sales ($ mil.)	100.0%	—	—	0.1	0.3	0.4
Net income ($ mil.)	—	—	—	(21.9)	(17.2)	(17.3)
Market value ($ mil.)	0.6%	—	—	50.2	15.3	50.8
Employees	(18.4%)	—	—	15	9	10

ACCESS PLANS, INC.

OTC: APNC

900 36th Ave. NW, Ste. 105
Norman, OK 73072
Phone: 405-579-8525
Fax: —
Web: www.accessplans.com

CEO: Danny C. Wright
CFO: Brett Wimberley
HR: —
FYE: September 30
Type: Public

Access Plans (formerly Alliance HealthCard) is an ally for people without health insurance. The company provides health care savings programs, serving individuals and families with limited health benefits or no insurance. Its membership programs offer access to hospitals, doctors, dentists, mental health services, pharmacies, physical therapy, and outpatient clinics at discounted rates for an annual fee. In addition, subsidiary Benefit Marketing Solutions (BMS) provides grocery, entertainment, auto, and rent-to-own membership programs, and BMS Insurance Agency provides leased property and other insurance coverage. Access Plans markets its service through retailers and financial services partners.

	Annual Growth	9/05	9/06	9/07	9/08	9/09
Sales ($ mil.)	81.5%	3.6	3.3	17.6	20.9	39.1
Net income ($ mil.)	43.6%	0.8	0.6	1.4	2.7	3.4
Market value ($ mil.)	6.8%	15.2	10.9	37.6	13.8	19.8
Employees	47.4%	18	17	4	—	85

⊞ ACCESS TO MONEY, INC.

OTC: AEMI

1101 Kings Highway N, Ste. G100
Cherry Hill, NJ 08034
Phone: 856-414-9100
Fax: —
Web: www.accesstomoney.com

CEO: Richard B. Stern
CFO: Michael J. Dolan
HR: —
FYE: December 31
Type: Public

Access to Money (formerly TRM Corporation) traded in paper for plastic. Originally in the photocopier business, the company expanded into the ATM (automatic teller machine) business, partially through the 2004 acquisition of 15,000 ATMs from eFunds Corporation. The company now offers supermarkets, convenience stores, malls, pharmacies, restaurants, and other retailers in the US the chance to increase foot traffic and consumer impulse buys by providing ATMs to their customers. Access to Money sells or rents the machines and provides maintenance and processing services to major merchant customers, such as The Pantry (25% of sales) and Cumberland Farms (10% of sales).

	Annual Growth	12/05	12/06	12/07	12/08	12/09
Sales ($ mil.)	(30.3%)	124.7	45.5	33.7	31.9	29.4
Net income ($ mil.)	—	(8.9)	(120.1)	(8.4)	(26.1)	(6.6)
Market value ($ mil.)	(51.3%)	166.2	47.7	10.0	2.5	9.4
Employees	(37.5%)	451	364	39	61	69

ACCESSORY NETWORK GROUP

350 5th Ave., 4th Fl.
New York, NY 10118
Phone: 212-842-3000
Fax: 212-842-3242
Web: www.accessorynetwork.com

CEO: Abe Chehebar
CFO: —
HR: —
FYE: December 31
Type: Private

To this company's customers, accessories are the spice of life. Accessory Network Group (ANG) makes and markets private-label, licensed, and branded fashion bags, small leather goods, stationery, and accessories for women, men, and children. ANG, founded in 1984, makes licensed products under such brand names as Vera Wang, Calvin Klein, and Cynthia Rowley. It owns the Ghurka leather-goods brand. It sells its items in department, discount, and specialty stores in the US, Canada, South America, Europe, and Australia. ANG distributes from facilities in New Jersey, California, and Canada. Its Brand Science unit acquired handbag maker LeSportsac through an alliance with ITOCHU Corporation in 2006.

ACCLARENT, INC.

1525 O'Brien Dr., Ste. B
Menlo Park, CA 94025
Phone: 650-687-5888
Fax: 650-687-5889
Web: www.acclarent.com

CEO: William M. Facteau
CFO: George A. Harter Jr.
HR: —
FYE: December 31
Type: Private

Acclarent's medical technology helps people breathe easy without surgery. The company created the Balloon Sinuplasty, a minimally invasive device used to treat patients with chronic sinusitis. The Balloon Sinuplasty opens blocked sinuses by inflating a balloon in the sinus cavity instead of cutting away bone and tissue, and patients can return to work as soon as the next day. The device received FDA approval in 2005 and is marketed directly to ear, nose, and throat (ENT) doctors in the US and the UK. Acclarent was acquired by Ethicon, a Johnson & Johnson subsidiary and a leading maker of medical equipment, in 2010.

ACCLIVITY LLC

300 Roundhill Dr., Ste. 2
Rockaway, NJ 07866
Phone: 973-586-2200
Fax: 973-586-2229
Web: www.myob-us.com

CEO: Tom Nash
CFO: John Burke
HR: —
FYE: December 31
Type: Subsidiary

Acclivity (formerly MYOB US) helps you mind your own business, providing accounting and financial management software for small and midsized businesses. Its products include MYOB AccountEdge (for tracking sales and purchases), MYOB FirstEdge (for the very small one or two-person businesses), and MYOB BusinessEssentials (for small businesses). The company also provides services and tools for functions such as managing credit card processing, payrolls, and vendor payments. In 2005 Acclivity acquired the company (and the rights to use the MYOB brand) from MYOB Limited; in 2008 the company purchased MYOB's US-based development operations.

	Annual Growth	12/04	12/05	12/06	12/07	12/08
Est. sales ($ mil.)	—	—	—	—	—	1.2
Employees	—	—	—	—	—	12

ACCO BRANDS CORPORATION

NYSE: ABD

300 Tower Pkwy.
Lincolnshire, IL 60069
Phone: 847-541-9500
Fax: 847-484-4492
Web: www.accobrands.com

CEO: Robert J. (Bob) Keller
CFO: Neal V. Fenwick
HR: David L. Kaput
FYE: December 31
Type: Public

Reach into the recesses of your desk drawer for that trusty box of staples or paperclips, and you've entered the realm of ACCO Brands. The company is a leading manufacturer and marketer of office supplies and computer products, including Swingline staplers, Kensington-branded keyboards and iPhone chargers, Wilson Jones binders and ledger paper, and Day-Timer personal organizers. It also produces private-label supplies. ACCO's goods are sold worldwide through office and computer product retailers, mass merchandisers, warehouse clubs, wholesalers, mail-order and Internet catalogs, and educational institutions. Staples and Office Depot are the firm's biggest customers, together accounting for about 25% of sales.

	Annual Growth	12/05	12/06	12/07	12/08	12/09
Sales ($ mil.)	(3.8%)	1,487.5	1,951.0	1,938.9	1,578.2	1,272.5
Net income ($ mil.)	—	56.2	7.2	(0.9)	(339.2)	(126.1)
Market value ($ mil.)	(26.2%)	1,342.6	1,450.5	879.0	189.1	398.9
Employees	(14.3%)	7,770	6,846	6,000	5,100	4,200

ACCO ENGINEERED SYSTEMS, INC.

6265 San Fernando Rd.
Glendale, CA 91201
Phone: 818-244-6571
Fax: 818-247-6533
Web: www.accoair.com

CEO: John Aversano
CFO: John G. Petersen
HR: —
FYE: —
Type: Private

ACCO Engineered Systems doesn't break a sweat to keep you cool. The company provides design, construction, and maintenance of mechanical systems, including heating, ventilation, air-conditioning, refrigeration, piping, plumbing, engineering, and building controls. The employee-owned company is licensed in nearly 20 states across the US, with operations mainly on the West Coast. Subsidiary Sunbelt Controls serves Southern California and installs automated building systems. ACCO's projects include office buildings, shopping malls, hospitals, hotels, clean rooms, factories, theaters, stadiums, and more. Clients include Boeing, Disney, Microsoft, Sun Microsystems, and Universal Studios, as well as the government.

ACCOR NORTH AMERICA

4001 International Pkwy.
Carrollton, TX 75007
Phone: 972-360-9000
Fax: 972-716-6590
Web: www.accor-na.com

CEO: Olivier Poirot
CFO: Didier Bosc
HR: Sherry Vidal-Brown
FYE: December 31
Type: Business segment

This company is keeping the light on for budget-minded travelers. Accor North America, a division of global hotel giant Accor, is a leading operator and franchisor of economy hotels, with more than 1,000 properties. Its flagship chain, Motel 6, caters primarily to vacationing families in the US and Canada with a limited menu of amenities. It also operates economy extended-stay lodging chain Studio 6 in the US and Canada, as well as the luxury Sofitel and upscale Novotel brands. (Accor's operations in Mexico fall under a separate Latin American business unit.)

	Annual Growth	12/04	12/05	12/06	12/07	12/08
Est. sales ($ mil.)	—	—	—	—	—	1,145.4
Employees	—	—	—	—	—	650

ACCOUNTING PRINCIPALS, INC.

1 Independent Dr.
Jacksonville, FL 32202
Phone: 904-360-2400
Fax: 904-360-2394
Web: www.accountingprincipals.com

CEO: John L. Marshall III
CFO: —
HR: —
FYE: December 31
Type: Subsidiary

Accounting Principals provides temporary, temp-to-hire, and permanent placement staffing services in the areas of accounting, finance, mortgage, and banking. Positions filled range from high-level CFOs to data entry clerks. The company's executive direct hire division, Parker & Lynch, executes searches for companies seeking high-level financial officers. The firm has more than 30 locations throughout the US, with concentrations in California, Texas, Florida, and Virginia. It works closely with another accounting staffing firm, Garelli Wong. Accounting Principals was a division of MPS Group, which was acquired by global staffing rival Adecco in 2010.

ACCREDO HEALTH, INCORPORATED

1640 Century Center Pkwy.
Memphis, TN 38134
Phone: 901-385-3688
Fax: 901-385-3689
Web: www.accredo.com

CEO: Steven R. (Steve) Fitzpatrick
CFO: Kenneth J. Bodmer
HR: Tara Wolckenhauer
FYE: December 30
Type: Subsidiary

Accredo Health is one pharmacy where you won't be able to pick up a bottle of aspirin. As the specialty pharmacy segment of pharmacy benefits manager Medco Health, Accredo dispenses high-tech injectable and infusion drugs for chronic and serious illnesses such as cancer, multiple sclerosis, hemophilia, pulmonary arterial hypertension (PAH), and certain autoimmune disorders. Under contracts with managed care organizations and drugmakers, it delivers drugs and related supplies in temperature-controlled packaging to patient homes or clinics. It also provides consulting and monitoring services to make sure patients are complying with their drug regimens, and it files claims on behalf of patients and doctors.

An in-depth profile of this company is available to Hoover's Online members at hoovers.com.

45

ACCRETIVE HEALTH, INC.
NYSE: AH

401 N. Michigan Ave., Ste. 2700
Chicago, IL 60611
Phone: 312-324-7820
Fax: —
Web: www.accretivehealth.com

CEO: Mary A. Tolan
CFO: John T. Staton
HR: —
FYE: December 31
Type: Public

You could say Accretive Health makes sure hospitals don't leave money on the *operations* table. The company provides its own employees and management systems to improve back-office operations for health care providers and specializes in maximizing profits while reducing costs. Typical customers are hospital systems, independent medical centers and clinics, and physician practice groups. Former clients include Ascension Health, the Henry Ford Health System, and Dartmouth-Hitchcock Medical Center. Accretive, founded in 2003 by chairman J. Michael Cline and CEO Mary Tolan, completed an initial public offering in 2010.

	Annual Growth	12/05	12/06	12/07	12/08	12/09
Sales ($ mil.)	47.0%	—	160.7	240.7	398.5	510.2
Net income ($ mil.)	—	—	(7.3)	0.8	1.2	14.6
Employees	24.4%	—	—	—	1,305	1,623

ACCRETIVE SOLUTIONS, INC.

888 Veterans Hwy., Ste. 440
Hauppauge, NY 11788
Phone: 631-348-9100
Fax: 631-348-7788
Web: www.accretivesolutions.com

CEO: Mike G. Reinecke
CFO: Dirk D. Hobgood
HR: —
FYE: December 31
Type: Private

Accretive Solutions helps build businesses' growth. The company provides a variety of consulting services including financial advisory, corporate restructuring, accounting, risk management, and data management. It also handles executive searches. The firm targets the energy, financial services, health care, and telecommunications industries. Its client list has included ConocoPhillips, Trinity Health, and Cisco Systems. Accretive Solutions was founded in 1999 to, well, accrete the strengths of former member firms Horn Murdock Cole (auditing, accounting, and consulting) and Dickson Allan (search and interim management services).

ACCUMED, INC.

2572 Brunswick Pike
Lawrenceville, NJ 08648
Phone: 609-883-1818
Fax: 609-883-2288
Web: www.accumed.org

CEO: Burgise Palkhiwala
CFO: Jeff Kase
HR: Archana Khanna
FYE: December 31
Type: Private

AccuMed believes in both medicine and the power of accuracy. The company develops and manufactures private-label (store brand), over-the-counter (OTC) pharmaceutical products. Its offerings come in tablet, liquid, powder, and other oral medication forms. AccuMed's products address a variety of conditions and ailments, including constipation, indigestion, skin conditions, bad breath, and nose and throat soreness. The company's products are sold in drug stores, grocery chains, convenience stores, and wholesale locations. AccuMed also provides contract manufacturing services to branded consumer product and pharmaceutical companies in the US and abroad.

	Annual Growth	12/04	12/05	12/06	12/07	12/08
Est. sales ($ mil.)	—	—	—	—	—	27.2
Employees	—	—	—	—	—	222

ACCURAY INCORPORATED
NASDAQ (GM): ARAY

1310 Chesapeake Terrace
Sunnyvale, CA 94089
Phone: 408-716-4600
Fax: 408-716-4601
Web: www.accuray.com

CEO: Euan S. Thomson
CFO: Derek A. Bertocci
HR: Theresa L. Dadone
FYE: June 30
Type: Public

Accuray's CyberKnife radiosurgery system zaps solid tumors with precisely aimed, high-dose radiation. The system, approved for use in the US, the EU, and several Asian countries, improves upon older radiosurgery systems that have limited mobility and are mostly used to treat brain tumors. Doctors can use CyberKnife to treat tumors anywhere in the body; the system tracks and adjusts for movement in real time, allowing for patient and tumor movement. Procedures with CyberKnife require no anesthesia and can be performed on an outpatient basis. More than 170 of the systems have been installed in hospitals around the world, over 100 of them in the US.

	Annual Growth	6/05	6/06	6/07	6/08	6/09
Sales ($ mil.)	79.7%	22.4	52.9	140.5	210.4	233.6
Net income ($ mil.)	—	(25.2)	(33.7)	(6.5)	5.4	0.6
Market value ($ mil.)	(45.3%)	—	—	1,286.2	422.9	385.2
Employees	5.9%	364	386	449	504	458

ACCURIDE CORPORATION
OTC: ACUZ

7140 Office Cir.
Evansville, IN 47715
Phone: 812-962-5000
Fax: 812-962-5400
Web: www.accuridecorp.com

CEO: William M. (Bill) Lasky
CFO: James H. (Jim) Woodward Jr.
HR: James T. (Jim) Maniatis
FYE: December 31
Type: Public

If you're driving a big rig, Accuride offers the goods to keep you rolling — or to stop you in your tracks. The company is a leading manufacturer of steel and forged aluminum wheels for commercial trucks and trailers, pickups, and military vehicles. It also makes truck body and chassis parts, brake systems, seating assemblies, aftermarket components, and non-powered farm equipment. Customers include commercial vehicle OEMs (Daimler Trucks North America), trailer manufacturers (Great Dane and Wabash National), and automakers (General Motors). Accuride's brands include Accuride, Bostrom, Brillion, Fabco, Gunite, Imperial, and Sisu. In 2009 Accuride filed for bankruptcy protection; it emerged in February 2010.

	Annual Growth	12/05	12/06	12/07	12/08	12/09
Sales ($ mil.)	(17.5%)	1,229.3	1,408.2	1,013.7	931.4	570.2
Net income ($ mil.)	—	51.2	65.1	(8.6)	(328.3)	(140.1)
Market value ($ mil.)	(60.0%)	1,629.2	1,422.1	992.7	29.0	41.7
Employees	(15.2%)	4,745	4,622	3,500	2,980	2,450

ACCURIDE INTERNATIONAL INC.

12311 Shoemaker Ave.
Santa Fe Springs, CA 90670
Phone: 562-903-0200
Fax: 562-903-0208
Web: www.accuride.com

CEO: Scott Jordan
CFO: Larry Campbell
HR: —
FYE: December 31
Type: Private

Slides rule at Accuride International. Accuride International designs and makes ball bearing slides for such uses as drawers in residential and office furniture, appliances, and enclosures for servers and telecommunications. The company's slides are also found in automotive accessories, including storage units and arm rests, and industrial equipment, such as cash registers and assembly lines. Accuride International builds and maintains its own tools and machinery for manufacturing its products. The company was founded in 1962 by Fred Jordan. It is still owned and operated by the Jordan family.

ACCU-TECH CORPORATION

200 Hembree Park Dr.
Roswell, GA 30076
Phone: 770-740-2240
Fax: 770-740-2260
Web: www.accu-tech.com

CEO: Edward R. (Ed) Ellis
CFO: Alison Santoro
HR: —
FYE: December 31
Type: Subsidiary

Waiting for a ride on the information super highway? Accu-Tech is your shuttle for voice, data, and security services. The company distributes a slate of copper and fiber-optic cabling to a telecommunications, commercial, institutional, and defense customer base. The company resells networking products and also maintains a staff of systems engineers ready to make product recommendations. Accu-Tech's portfolio ranges from cable assemblies and fasteners to fuses and breakers by top suppliers including 3M, Belden, Corning Cable Systems, and Tyco Electronics. More than 25 Accu-Tech sales and stocking centers dot the US. Founded in 1984, Accu-Tech is a subsidiary of Anixter International.

ACE INA HOLDINGS INC.

436 Walnut St.
Philadelphia, PA 19106
Phone: 215-640-1000
Fax: 215-640-2489
Web: www.ace-ina.com

CEO: Brian E. Dowd
CFO: —
HR: —
FYE: December 31
Type: Subsidiary

ACE INA holds the international property/casualty insurance and reinsurance operations of ultimate parent Swiss firm ACE Limited (it holds some domestic operations, too). ACE USA, one of its largest subsidiaries, provides specialty insurance products in the US and Canada through units such as ACE Accident & Health, ACE Casualty Risk, and ACE Financial Solutions. ACE INA also contains the ACE European Holdings, which is a major property/casualty insurance provider in Europe. In addition, ACE INA holds ACE group subsidiaries operating in the Asia/Pacific region, South America, Africa, and the Middle East.

[H] ACE CASH EXPRESS, INC.

1231 Greenway Dr., Ste. 600
Irving, TX 75038
Phone: 972-550-5000
Fax: —
Web: www.acecashexpress.com

CEO: Jay B. Shipowitz
CFO: Douglas A. Lindsay
HR: James E. Gibbs
FYE: June 30
Type: Private

ACE Cash Express really has a bankless job. The company owns a chain of financial services outlets that target the underbanked and bankless populations. For a fee, customers can cash checks, obtain short-term unsecured loans ("payday loans"), purchase money orders, pay bills, and set up pre-paid debit cards. There are more than 1,800 ACE Cash Express and ACE Cash Advance stores throughout the US, about 10% of which are franchised locations. ACE stores are typically found in strip malls, in free-standing buildings on busy streets, and in kiosks within retail stores. Private equity firm JLL Partners took ACE private in 2006 in a deal worth some $455 million.

	Annual Growth	6/04	6/05	6/06	6/07	6/08
Est. sales ($ mil.)	—	—	—	—	—	479.2
Employees	—	—	—	—	—	4,000

ACER AMERICA CORPORATION

333 W. San Carlos St., Ste. 1500
San Jose, CA 95110
Phone: 408-533-7700
Fax: 408-533-4555
Web: www.acer.us

CEO: Rudi Schmidleithner
CFO: Ming Wang
HR: Lenny Pollak
FYE: December 31
Type: Subsidiary

Whether it's monitors in the Midwest or servers in Saskatchewan, Acer America has North America covered. The company, a subsidiary of Taiwanese computer giant Acer, sells to businesses, government agencies, schools, and individual consumers. Its offerings include desktop, notebook, and tablet PCs. Other products include servers, flat-panel LCD monitors, and digital projectors. Acer is deep into the netbook market with its Aspire line; netbooks are ultralight, portable computers capable of checking online e-mail and surfing the Web. The company sells through resellers and online retail partners. Established in 1977, Acer America serves the Canadian market with its Acer Canada division.

[H] ACE HARDWARE CORPORATION

2200 Kensington Ct.
Oak Brook, IL 60523
Phone: 630-990-6600
Fax: 630-990-6838
Web: www.acehardware.com

CEO: Ray A. Griffith
CFO: Dorvin D. Lively
HR: Jimmy Alexander
FYE: December 31
Type: Cooperative

Luckily, Ace has John Madden up its sleeve. Despite the growth of warehouse-style competitors, Ace Hardware has remained a household name, thanks to ads featuring Madden, a former Oakland Raiders football coach and retired TV commentator. By sales the company is the #1 hardware cooperative in the US, ahead of Do It Best. Ace dealer-owners operate about 4,600 Ace Hardware stores, home centers, and lumber and building materials locations in all 50 US states and about 60 other countries. From about 15 warehouses Ace distributes such products as electrical and plumbing supplies, garden equipment, hand tools, housewares, and power tools. Its paint division is also a major paint manufacturer in the US.

	Annual Growth	12/04	12/05	12/06	12/07	12/08
Sales ($ mil.)	4.1%	3,288.7	3,466.0	3,770.0	3,970.6	3,864.2
Net income ($ mil.)	(4.2%)	101.9	100.4	107.4	86.9	85.8
Employees	(1.0%)	5,000	4,976	5,000	4,800	4,800

[H] ACETO CORPORATION

NASDAQ (GS): ACET

1 Hollow Ln.
Lake Success, NY 11042
Phone: 516-627-6000
Fax: 516-627-6093
Web: www.aceto.com

CEO: Vincent G. Miata
CFO: Douglas Roth
HR: Terry Steinberg
FYE: June 30
Type: Public

Distributor Aceto (pronounced "a-seat-o") is getting bigger through chemicals — namely generic drugs. The company sources and distributes roughly 1,000 chemicals through three segments. Its largest segment is health sciences, which sources and distributes bulk generic drugs, advanced pharmaceutical intermediates (APIs), and nutritionals. Aceto's other business units include chemicals and colorants (which distributes intermediates and chemicals for coatings, inks, and electronics) and crop protection (herbicides, insecticides, and fungicides). Aceto sources about two-thirds of its products from Asia, mostly China and India, and sells more than half of them in the US.

	Annual Growth	6/05	6/06	6/07	6/08	6/09
Sales ($ mil.)	0.7%	313.4	297.1	313.5	359.6	322.6
Net income ($ mil.)	(3.7%)	10.0	9.2	10.2	13.5	8.6
Market value ($ mil.)	(2.8%)	190.1	175.8	235.6	194.1	169.5
Employees	(2.2%)	242	216	224	227	221

[H] An in-depth profile of this company is available to Hoover's Online members at hoovers.com.

47

ACF INDUSTRIES LLC

101 Clark St.
St. Charles, MO 63301
Phone: 636-949-2399
Fax: 636-949-2825
Web: www.acfindustries.com

CEO: James E. Bowles
CFO: —
HR: —
FYE: December 31
Type: Private

After more than a century, ACF Industries is still on track making railcars and railcar components. ACF (originally The American Car and Foundry Co.) manufactures and fabricates an array of transportation equipment for the new railcar and repair railcar markets, as well as custom steel parts for non-rail customers. Operations include facilities in Pennsylvania and West Virginia, which churn out related products, such as weld sub-assemblies, pressure vessels, and wheel and axle machining and mounting. ACF is owned by financier Carl Icahn, who serves as chairman. Icahn is a major stockholder and chairman of American Railcar Industries and American Railcar Leasing, trade affiliates of ACF railcar components.

ACH FOOD COMPANIES, INC.

7171 Goodlett Farms Pkwy.
Memphis, TN 38016
Phone: 901-381-3000
Fax: 901-381-2968
Web: www.achfood.com

CEO: Richard Rankin
CFO: Jeffrey A. (Jeff) Atkins
HR: Sarah Blankenship
FYE: September 30
Type: Subsidiary

ACH Food Companies is ACH-ing to help the cook. It's products include edible oils, shortenings, and other oil-based products, as well as food ingredients such as cornstarch, syrup, spices, and cake decorations. The company has two divisions (consumer products and commercial products) that serve the retail, industrial food, and foodservice markets. Its brands include the well-known Mazola Corn Oil, Argo Corn Starch, and Karo Corn Syrup. The company also offers private-label and customized product services. ACH sells its products to customers in Canada, Mexico, and the US. It is a subsidiary of UK food, ingredient, and retail giant Associated British Foods, which purchased ACH in 1995.

ACHESON COLLOIDS COMPANY

1600 Washington Ave.
Port Huron, MI 48060
Phone: 810-984-5581
Fax: 810-984-1446
Web: www.achesoncolloids.com

CEO: Jim Vorderbrueggen
CFO: —
HR: —
FYE: December 31
Type: Subsidiary

Not to say that Acheson Colloids likes a drink every now and then, but the company is well lubed. Acheson Colloids manufactures lubricants, specialty coatings, and electronic materials, which it sells to the electronics, automotive, and aerospace industries. The lubricants are used for cast and forged products. Its coatings fight friction and protect from weather damage and are applied to everything from gaskets to injection seats in jets. Founded in 1908, Acheson is a part of German adhesives titan Henkel. It had joined with Ablestik Laboratories to make up National Starch and Chemical's Electronic and Engineering Materials division until a 2008 deal led to the breakup of National Starch's parent company, ICI.

	Annual Growth	12/04	12/05	12/06	12/07	12/08
Est. sales ($ mil.)	—	—	—	—	—	11.8
Employees	—	—	—	—	—	206

ACHIEVEGLOBAL INC.

8875 Hidden River Pkwy., Ste. 400
Tampa, FL 33637
Phone: 813-631-5799
Fax: 813-631-5796
Web: www.achieveglobal.com

CEO: Sharon M. Daniels
CFO: John Graves
HR: Myron A. Harmon
FYE: December 31
Type: Subsidiary

AchieveGlobal provides consulting and training services throughout the world to help companies improve workers' "soft skills" in areas such as customer service, leadership development, and sales effectiveness. It offers in-person and online programs. The company maintains a network of offices in more than 40 countries around the globe, primarily in Europe and the Asia/Pacific region but also in North and South America. AchieveGlobal, which offers training programs in more than 30 different languages, is part of The Institute for International Research, a group of training and conference-planning companies that itself is a unit of UK-based publishing powerhouse Informa.

	Annual Growth	12/04	12/05	12/06	12/07	12/08
Est. sales ($ mil.)	—	—	—	—	—	75.0
Employees	—	—	—	—	—	375

ACHILLION PHARMACEUTICALS, INC.

NASDAQ (GM): ACHN

300 George St.
New Haven, CT 06511
Phone: 203-624-7000
Fax: 203-624-7003
Web: www.achillion.com

CEO: Michael D. Kishbauch
CFO: Mary Kay Fenton
HR: —
FYE: December 31
Type: Public

Achillion Pharmaceuticals is looking for the Achilles heel of infectious disease. The firm is developing treatments for infectious diseases, including antiviral treatments for HIV infection and hepatitis C, as well as antibacterials for fighting drug-resistant hospital-based infections. Lead candidate elvucitabine is in late-stage clinical trials for the treatment of HIV; the drug is designed specifically for patients who have become resistant to existing antiviral drugs. Achillion is also focused on the development of three hepatitis C treatments (one of which it is developing in collaboration with biotech firm Gilead Sciences). Another candidate is aimed at combating staph and other drug-resistant infections.

	Annual Growth	12/05	12/06	12/07	12/08	12/09
Sales ($ mil.)	—	8.5	3.3	4.0	(0.2)	(0.3)
Net income ($ mil.)	—	(13.6)	(24.1)	(28.1)	(28.2)	(25.9)
Market value ($ mil.)	(42.2%)	—	620.6	192.2	26.2	119.8
Employees	(9.1%)	63	66	60	54	43

[H] ACI WORLDWIDE, INC.

NASDAQ (GS): ACIW

120 Broadway, Ste. 3350
New York, NY 10271
Phone: 646-348-6700
Fax: 212-470-4000
Web: www.aciworldwide.com

CEO: Philip G. (Phil) Heasley
CFO: Scott W. Behrens
HR: —
FYE: December 31
Type: Public

ACI Worldwide helps money go mobile. The company develops e-payment and electronic funds transfer (EFT) software for companies around the world. Customers use its software to process transactions involving ATMs, credit and debit cards, online banking and payment processing, point-of-sale terminals, smart cards, and wire transfers. ACI also makes network integration software, and it offers services such as design, implementation, and facilities management. Company sales representatives, along with some outside distributors, sell its software. Clients, more than 800 in about 90 countries, include banks (Bank of America, ING), retailers (Hy-Vee), and third-party transaction processors (EVERTEC).

	Annual Growth	9/05	9/06	9/07	*12/08	12/09
Sales ($ mil.)	6.7%	313.2	347.9	366.2	417.7	405.8
Net income ($ mil.)	(17.9%)	43.2	55.4	(9.1)	10.6	19.6
Market value ($ mil.)	(11.4%)	947.2	1,166.2	760.1	540.8	583.3
Employees	6.0%	1,674	1,960	2,186	2,154	2,114
						*Fiscal year change

ACMAT CORPORATION

Pink Sheets: ACMT

233 Main St.
New Britain, CT 06050
Phone: 860-229-9000
Fax: 860-229-1111
Web: www.acmatcorp.com

CEO: Henry W. Nozko Jr.
CFO: Michael P. Cifone
HR: —
FYE: December 31
Type: Public

ACMAT does its part to wipe out asbestos. Originally a contracting firm focused on asbestos abatement, the company moved into the insurance industry when it was dropped by its own insurer. Through its ACSTAR Insurance subsidiary the company handles liability insurance and supplies bonds to customers such as general, specialty trade, environmental, and asbestos and lead abatement contractors. ACMAT's insurance products are sold nationwide. AMCAT still provides design and construction contracting services for commercial and government customers through its ACMAT Contracting division.

ACME MARKETS, INC.

75 Valley Stream Pkwy.
Malvern, PA 19355
Phone: 610-889-4000
Fax: 610-889-3039
Web: www.acmemarkets.com

CEO: Dan Sanders
CFO: —
HR: —
FYE: February 28
Type: Subsidiary

Acme Markets operates about 125 supermarkets under the Acme and Acme Sav-on banners mostly in and around Philadelphia and in Delaware, Maryland, and New Jersey. The company is the #1 food and drug retailer in the competitive Philly market, where it competes with local chains, including Wakefern Food-owned ShopRite and A&P's Super Fresh and Pathmark chains. In addition to its bricks-and-mortar operations, Acme offers online grocery ordering for shoppers in Delaware, New Jersey, and Pennsylvania. Founded in 1891, Acme Markets is owned by SUPERVALU, which acquired it from Albertsons in 2006. Acme's strong market position made it one of Albertsons' more valuable properties.

ACME BRICK COMPANY

3101 Bryant Irvin Rd. South
Fort Worth, TX 76109
Phone: 817-332-4101
Fax: 817-390-2404
Web: www.brick.com

CEO: Dennis Knautz
CFO: Judy B. Hunter
HR: Ben P. Muro
FYE: December 31
Type: Subsidiary

Troy Aikman doesn't lob bricks, but the former Cowboys quarterback does pitch products for Acme Brick. The Berkshire Hathaway subsidiary produces and distributes more than a billion bricks annually for its construction customers in a variety of colors, shapes, and sizes. It also makes all-brick wood burning fireplace systems. Bricks are churned out from more than 20 brick manufacturing plants. Acme Brick holds a family of companies, including Acme-Ochs Brick and Stone, offering brick and natural stone; American Tile Supply, distributing residential and commercial stone tiles; Featherlite, masonry materials; IBP Glass Block Grid System, custom aluminum glass block grids; and Texas Quarries, supplying limestone.

	Annual Growth	12/04	12/05	12/06	12/07	12/08
Est. sales ($ mil.)	—	—	—	—	—	450.0
Employees	—	—	—	—	—	2,602

ACME PACKET, INC.

NASDAQ (GS): APKT

71 3rd Ave.
Burlington, MA 01803
Phone: 781-328-4400
Fax: 781-425-5077
Web: www.acmepacket.com

CEO: Andrew (Andy) Ory
CFO: Peter J. Minihane
HR: —
FYE: December 31
Type: Public

Acme Packet brings networks together. The company makes communications equipment designed to ensure that advanced network services span multiple Internet protocol-based networks. Acme's family of Net-Net session border controllers (SBCs) are used to connect networks operated by service providers and enterprise customers. SBCs handle interactive services, including VoIP. Acme Packet also provides multiservice security gateways and session routing proxies. The company markets directly and through distribution partnerships with vendors including Ericsson and Sonus Networks. It counts Charter Communications, China Unicom, and Telstra among its customers.

	Annual Growth	12/05	12/06	12/07	12/08	12/09
Sales ($ mil.)	40.7%	36.1	84.1	113.1	116.4	141.5
Net income ($ mil.)	—	0.0	28.9	19.6	11.6	17.1
Market value ($ mil.)	(18.9%)	—	1,253.2	764.4	319.4	667.9
Employees	18.1%	231	247	322	381	450

ACME COMMUNICATIONS, INC.

Pink Sheets: ACME

2101 E. 4th St., Ste. 202A
Santa Ana, CA 92705
Phone: 714-245-9499
Fax: 714-245-9494
Web: www.acmecommunications.com

CEO: Jamie Kellner
CFO: Thomas D. (Tom) Allen
HR: —
FYE: December 31
Type: Public

ACME Communications' relationship with Warner Bros. has nothing to do with a wily coyote, rockets, or any other explosives. The company owns and operates a half-dozen television stations in midsized markets in five states, most of which are affiliated with The CW Network, a joint venture between Time Warner's Warner Bros. Entertainment and CBS Corporation. It also has one station that is affiliated with MyNetworkTV, a sister network to FOX (News Corporation). In addition to its stations, ACME Communications produces a syndicated morning program called *The Daily Buzz* that airs on about 160 TV stations throughout the country.

	Annual Growth	12/04	12/05	12/06	12/07	*12/08
Sales ($ mil.)	(8.3%)	46.9	40.9	34.8	32.0	33.2
Net income ($ mil.)	—	(17.5)	(15.9)	(4.2)	15.3	(32.7)
Employees	(14.9%)	229	195	186	141	—

*Most recent year available

ACME UNITED CORPORATION

NYSE Amex: ACU

60 Round Hill Road
Fairfield, CT 06824
Phone: 203-254-6060
Fax: 203-254-6019
Web: www.acmeunited.com

CEO: Walter C. Johnsen
CFO: Paul G. Driscoll
HR: —
FYE: December 31
Type: Public

Acme United has taken measures to trim its business. It sold its medical equipment division to focus on its core products: scissors, rulers, and first-aid kits. Its products are used in schools, offices, and homes. (The kits come complete with bandages, gloves, and over-the-counter medications.) Its name brands include Westcott, Clauss, and PhysiciansCare. Acme sells its products to stationery and school supply distributors, office supply stores, and mass merchants, such as Staples, Office Max, and United Stationers. Its operations span Canada, Germany, Hong Kong, China, and the US (which contributes most of sales). President and CEO Walter Johnsen owns about 20% of company stock.

	Annual Growth	12/05	12/06	12/07	12/08	12/09
Sales ($ mil.)	4.3%	49.9	56.9	63.2	68.7	59.1
Net income ($ mil.)	(0.9%)	2.9	3.9	4.0	4.5	2.8
Market value ($ mil.)	(9.9%)	44.3	45.7	45.2	22.4	29.2
Employees	3.7%	116	120	126	137	134

An in-depth profile of this company is available to Hoover's Online members at hoovers.com.

49

ACNB CORPORATION

OTC: ACNB

16 Lincoln Sq.
Gettysburg, PA 17325
Phone: 717-334-3161
Fax: 717-334-9319
Web: www.acnb.com

CEO: Thomas A. Ritter
CFO: David W. Cathell
HR: Sandra A. Deaner
FYE: December 31
Type: Public

Seven score and a few years ago, ACNB Corporation's fathers brought forth a small-town bank. Now ACNB is dedicated to the proposition of being the holding company for Adams County National Bank, operating more than 20 branches in the Gettysburg and Newville areas of Pennsylvania. It is altogether fitting and proper that the bank offers traditional retail banking services. The world may long note and remember that the bank also provides residential mortgage (about 60% of the portfolio), commercial real estate, consumer, and business loans. In addition, ACNB gives a full measure of devotion to insurance products; provides trust services; and hopes that community banking shall not perish from the earth.

	Annual Growth	12/05	12/06	12/07	12/08	12/09
Assets ($ mil.)	0.4%	945.1	964.8	926.7	976.7	961.9
Net income ($ mil.)	(0.7%)	7.4	7.3	7.9	6.7	7.2
Market value ($ mil.)	(8.0%)	107.0	112.6	90.1	73.5	76.8
Employees	8.2%	203	260	266	269	278

ACO HARDWARE, INC.

23333 Commerce Dr.
Farmington Hills, MI 48335
Phone: 248-471-0100
Fax: 248-615-2696
Web: www.acohardware.com

CEO: Terry Shoenberger
CFO: —
HR: —
FYE: February 28
Type: Private

ACO Hardware can provide both the food and the supplies if you want to get your floor clean enough to eat off of. The company's outlets sell automotive supplies, electrical goods, food and beverages, hardware, housewares, paint, lawn and garden necessities, patio furniture, and tools. It also rents equipment for carpet cleaning, plumbing, and home maintenance. ACO Hardware operates about 70 stores in southeastern Michigan, primarily in the Detroit area. Customers can view weekly specials and find hardware tips on the company's website. Founded in 1946 by Ted Traskos and his four brothers, ACO Hardware is still owned by the Traskos family.

ACORDA THERAPEUTICS, INC.

NASDAQ (GM): ACOR

15 Skyline Dr.
Hawthorne, NY 10532
Phone: 914-347-4300
Fax: 914-347-4560
Web: www.acorda.com

CEO: Ron Cohen
CFO: David Lawrence
HR: Denise J. Duca
FYE: December 31
Type: Public

Acorda Therapeutics hopes its products really get on your nerves. The company is developing therapeutics that aim to restore neurological function for patients with spinal cord injury and other central nervous system disorders. The company markets and sells muscle relaxant Zanaflex in the US. Its lead drug development candidate is Fampridine-SR, which enhances conduction in the myelin layer of nerves damaged by blunt trauma or from multiple sclerosis (MS). The drug uses a sustained-release delivery system developed by and licensed from Elan Corporation. Acorda's other drug candidates include potential therapies for MS, brain damage, and spinal cord injuries.

	Annual Growth	12/05	12/06	12/07	12/08	12/09
Sales ($ mil.)	81.0%	5.1	27.4	39.5	47.8	54.7
Net income ($ mil.)	—	(35.5)	(24.5)	(38.0)	(74.3)	(83.9)
Market value ($ mil.)	16.7%	—	613.3	850.3	794.2	975.8
Employees	32.8%	80	126	144	174	249

ACORN ENERGY, INC.

NASDAQ (GM): ACFN

4 W. Rockland Rd.
Montchanin, DE 19710
Phone: 302-656-1707
Fax: 302-994-3086
Web: www.acornfactor.com

CEO: John A. Moore
CFO: Michael Barth
HR: —
FYE: December 31
Type: Public

Acorn Energy is nuts about its investments. The company, formerly known as Data Systems & Software, is a holding company that maintains controlling or equity positions in a variety of companies, including Comverge, Paketeria, and dsIT Solutions. Comverge is a demand response company that enables utilities, industry, and consumers to better manage peak electricity usage. Paketeria combines five service businesses, including eBay dropshops, shipping services, photo processing, and photocopying and printer cartridge refilling. dsIT Solutions offers software consulting and development related to port security, oncology treatment, health-care billing, real-time and embedded systems, and information technology.

	Annual Growth	12/05	12/06	12/07	12/08	12/09
Sales ($ mil.)	9.3%	21.9	4.1	5.7	20.7	31.3
Net income ($ mil.)	—	(1.3)	(6.1)	32.5	(7.9)	(5.8)
Market value ($ mil.)	45.9%	23.2	49.3	84.6	19.8	104.9
Employees	19.2%	94	70	86	156	190

ACOSTA, INC.

6600 Corporate Center Pkwy.
Jacksonville, FL 32216
Phone: 904-281-9800
Fax: 904-281-9966
Web: www.acosta.com

CEO: Robert Hill Jr.
CFO: Gregory (Greg) Delaney
HR: Rebecca (Becky) Steele
FYE: October 31
Type: Private

Acosta spends a lot of time thinking about which products are top-shelf. The company (which does business as Acosta Sales and Marketing Company) offers sales and marketing services that reach consumers at the shelves of retail food service and grocery businesses. Some 1,000 US consumer products manufacturers (that have included Coca-Cola and Pepsi) call on Acosta to help them position their products in grocery and convenience stores, drug stores, and mass merchandisers in the US and Canada. Acosta specializes in inventory and merchandising services and business consulting for promotions, marketing campaigns, and sales. Established in 1927, Acosta is owned by private equity firm AEA Investors LLC.

ACOUSTICAL MATERIAL SERVICES, INC.

10200 Pioneer Blvd., Ste. 500
Santa Fe Springs, CA 90670
Phone: 562-447-2900
Fax: 562-906-9817
Web: www.a-m-s.com

CEO: Ruben Mendoza
CFO: John Gorey
HR: —
FYE: April 30
Type: Subsidiary

Acoustical Material Services (AMS) sells the materials builders need to put a roof over your head — not to mention hold your whole house together. The company provides acoustical ceiling products, lath and plaster, drywall, doors, and frames, as well as other construction supplies. Customers include large and small contractors, subcontractors, building owners, and dealers. AMS distributes products from about 20 locations in Arizona, California, Hawaii, Nevada, and Utah, as well as Mexico (via AMS De México). It also exports to markets in Guam, Hong Kong, the Philippines, and Taiwan. Chairman Max Gondon founded AMS in 1969. The company was acquired in 2007 by CRH, an Ireland-based building materials maker.

	Annual Growth	4/04	4/05	4/06	4/07	4/08
Est. sales ($ mil.)	—	—	—	—	—	68.4
Employees	—	—	—	—	—	550

ACRONIS, INC.

23 3rd Ave.
Burlington, MA 01803
Phone: 781-222-0920
Fax: 781-222-0919
Web: www.acronis.com

CEO: Jason Donahue
CFO: —
HR: —
FYE: —
Type: Private

Acronis' software takes a hard line on security. The company's storage management and disaster recovery products safeguard the computer infrastructures of home offices, as well as small, midsized, and *FORTUNE* 500 businesses in the banking, government, health care, retail, and technology markets. Its backup and recovery products create an exact copy of a PC hard disk or entire Windows and Linux servers for full or partial data backup. Acronis products are also used to restore systems after a server crash and to migrate systems between servers. With offices in the US, Europe, and Asia, Acronis sells its products directly, through resellers, and in retail stores in more than 150 countries.

ACT, INC.

500 ACT Dr.
Iowa City, IA 52243
Phone: 319-337-1000
Fax: 319-339-3021
Web: www.act.org

CEO: Richard L. Ferguson
CFO: Thomas J. Goedken
HR: Jim Friel
FYE: August 31
Type: Not-for-profit

Those three little letters strike fear in the hearts of high-school students across the US. ACT most famously develops and administers the national college admission exam that bears its name (some 1 million high-school seniors take it each year), but the company also designs educational assessment and workforce development programs for people of all ages around the world. Its EXPLORE program, for example, helps students determine how prepared they are for college. Its Workforce Solutions division provides assessment, training, and consulting to employers. Founded in 1959 as The American College Testing Program, ACT has offices across the US and in Australia, China, Indonesia, South Korea, Singapore, and Spain.

	Annual Growth	8/04	8/05	8/06	8/07	8/08
Est. sales ($ mil.)	—	—	—	—	—	190.0
Employees	—	—	—	—	—	1,200

ACT TELECONFERENCING, INC.

Pink Sheets: ACTT

1526 Cole Blvd., Ste. 300
Golden, CO 80401
Phone: 303-233-3500
Fax: 303-238-0096
Web: www.acttel.com

CEO: Peter E. Salas
CFO: Fran Ross
HR: Jennie McQuade
FYE: December 31
Type: Public

ACT Teleconferencing helps its customers get their acts together over communications lines. The company provides audio-, video-, and Web-conferencing services, including operator-assisted and unattended conferencing. The company also offers video conferencing equipment and facility rental services. Its video event services include technical support and production services such as lighting and staging. With office in nine countries, ACT serves customers in North America, Europe, the Middle East, and Asia. The company targets clients in a broad range of industries, including finance, health care, investor relations, legal, government, manufacturing, and technology.

ACTAVIS U.S.

60 Columbia Rd., Bldg. B
Morristown, NJ 07960
Phone: 973-993-4500
Fax: 973-993-4303
Web: www.actavis.us

CEO: Doug Boothe
CFO: Mark Keatley
HR: Gunnar A. Beinteinsson
FYE: December 31
Type: Subsidiary

Keeping its parent active in the US is Actavis U.S. As its name implies, the company is the US manufacturing and marketing unit of global generics firm Actavis. As such it makes a variety of generic equivalents of both prescription and OTC drugs, in a number of forms, including liquids, tablets, creams, and suppositories. Among other consumer and specialty drugs, it makes anxiety, depression, and pain medications. Actavis US has manufacturing facilities in Maryland, New Jersey, and North Carolina, from which it ships its own products and provides contract manufacturing services to third parties. Overseeing the US market for its parent is no small feat, since it comprises about one-third of Actavis' sales.

ACTEL CORPORATION

NASDAQ (GM): ACTL

2061 Stierlin Ct.
Mountain View, CA 94043
Phone: 650-318-4200
Fax: 650-318-4600
Web: www.actel.com

CEO: John C. East
CFO: Maurice E. Carson
HR: Barbara L. McArthur
FYE: December 31
Type: Public

Actel acts to design and sell programmable chips. The company makes field-programmable gate arrays (FPGAs), a type of integrated circuit that can be programmed by users for specific functions. Actel sells FPGAs to a broad range of manufacturers in the telecommunications, military, industrial equipment, computer, consumer electronics, and automotive industries. Actel makes high-speed, anti-fuse FPGAs, as well as flash-based FPGAs; it also offers design software and programming hardware used to configure and test its chips. The fabless semiconductor company's customers include Boeing, Cisco Systems, Magna Electronics, and Siemens. The US represents about half of sales.

	Annual Growth	12/05	12/06	12/07	12/08	12/09
Sales ($ mil.)	1.5%	179.4	191.5	197.0	218.4	190.6
Net income ($ mil.)	—	7.0	(2.2)	(2.9)	(11.7)	(46.2)
Market value ($ mil.)	(1.7%)	334.1	476.6	358.5	307.6	311.8
Employees	(0.9%)	565	574	584	550	—

ACTIVANT SOLUTIONS INC.

7683 Southfront Rd.
Livermore, CA 94551
Phone: 925-449-0606
Fax: —
Web: www.activant.com

CEO: Pervez A. Qureshi
CFO: Kathleen M. (Kathy) Crusco
HR: Iain W. Paterson Jr.
FYE: September 30
Type: Private

Activant Solutions wants all parts of a business holding hands, singing in perfect harmony. The company provides enterprise resource planning (ERP) software for more than 14,000 small and midsized businesses in the automotive parts aftermarket, hardware and home center, wholesale trade, and lumber and building materials industries. Activant's software automates functions such as inventory management, parts selection, general accounting, and point-of-sale analysis. Customers include members of the Ace Hardware and True Value cooperatives, and CF Supply. The company gets most of its sales in the US. Activant Solutions is owned by Hellman & Friedman, JMI Equity, Thoma Bravo, and members of its management.

	Annual Growth	9/04	9/05	9/06	9/07	9/08
Est. sales ($ mil.)	—	—	—	—	—	426.4
Employees	—	—	—	—	—	2,000

ACTIVE HEALTH MANAGEMENT, INC.

102 Madison Ave.
New York, NY 10016
Phone: 212-651-8200
Fax: 212-448-0096
Web: www.activehealthmanagement.com

CEO: Gregory (Greg) Steinberg
CFO: John A. Budnick III
HR: —
FYE: December 31
Type: Subsidiary

Employers active in improving employee health care might turn to Active Health Management (ActiveHealth). The health management and data analytics company uses proprietary technology to gather detailed, claims-driven information collected across a patient's care spectrum and then generates a comprehensive personal health record. Its ultimate goal is to help reduce medical errors and expenses and identify gaps in care. Clients include employers, health insurance firms, and Medicare and Medicaid providers. ActiveHealth was founded in 1998 and acquired by Aetna in 2005. It continues to operate as a branded, standalone business headquartered in New York.

	Annual Growth	12/04	12/05	12/06	12/07	12/08
Est. sales ($ mil.)	—	—	—	—	—	17.2
Employees	—	—	—	—	—	500

ACTIVE MEDIA SERVICES, INC.

1 Blue Hill Plaza
Pearl River, NY 10965
Phone: 845-735-1700
Fax: 845-735-0717
Web: www.activeinternational.com

CEO: Alan S. Elkin
CFO: Richard E. Vendig
HR: Tom Ruderman
FYE: June 30
Type: Private

Take a pawn shop, cross it with a factoring service, and you have Active Media Services. Doing business as Active International, the corporate trading firm acquires underperforming assets including surplus inventory, capital equipment, real estate, and receivables. It exchanges these for cash and/or trade credit, which is used to offset expenses or purchase such services as advertising, freight, printing, shipping, event planning, and travel. Clients may also barter future manufacturing capacity for services. Active International operates in 11 countries; it acquires assets in one part of the world and remarkets them in another. CEO Alan Elkin and president Art Wagner founded the employee-owned company in 1984.

THE ACTIVE NETWORK, INC.

10182 Telesis Ct., Ste. 100
San Diego, CA 92121
Phone: 858-964-3800
Fax: 858-551-7619
Web: www.theactivenetwork.com

CEO: David (Dave) Alberga
CFO: Scott Mendel
HR: Sheryl Roland
FYE: December 31
Type: Private

Thinking about enrolling for a marathon or adventure race? The first step is to get fit, but the second one might involve The Active Network. The company makes software used to build websites that help participants find and register for sports events online. Using Active.com, organizers can administer online registration, promotion, and fundraising efforts. Other platforms include Active Team Sports, which facilitates communication within teams, leagues, and camps; and RecWare, targeted at parks, recreation agencies, and universities. The Active Network has international operations in Australia, Canada, China, and the UK. Investors include Austin Ventures, Canaan Partners, and Jefferies & Company.

ACTIVE POWER, INC.

NASDAQ (GM): ACPW

2128 W. Braker Ln., Bldg. 12
Austin, TX 78758
Phone: 512-836-6464
Fax: 512-836-4511
Web: www.activepower.com

CEO: James A. (Jim) Clishem
CFO: John K. Penver
HR: John K. Penver
FYE: December 31
Type: Public

Active Power keeps the juices flowing. The company's CleanSource DC and CleanSource UPS (uninterruptible power system) are designed to replace conventional UPS products that use lead-acid batteries. The CleanSource DC/UPS products use a flywheel that stores kinetic energy by spinning. When a power quality problem is detected, the products convert the kinetic energy into electricity. The CleanSource UPS was developed in partnership with heavy equipment maker Caterpillar (40% of sales), which markets the product with its generator sets. CleanSource is marketed to Internet service providers, as well as telecommunications, industrial, and commercial customers. US customers provide more than half of sales.

	Annual Growth	12/05	12/06	12/07	12/08	12/09
Sales ($ mil.)	22.7%	17.8	25.0	33.6	43.0	40.3
Net income ($ mil.)	—	(22.9)	(21.1)	(20.5)	(13.4)	(11.0)
Market value ($ mil.)	(27.6%)	306.9	208.8	175.4	25.5	84.5
Employees	(2.4%)	164	145	155	149	149

ACTIVIDENTITY CORPORATION

NASDAQ (GM): ACTI

6623 Dumbarton Cir.
Fremont, CA 94555
Phone: 510-574-0100
Fax: 510-574-0101
Web: www.actividentity.com

CEO: Grant Evans
CFO: Jacques D. Kerrest
HR: —
FYE: September 30
Type: Public

ActivIdentity isn't passive when it comes to security. The company provides a variety of authentication and user management products, including smart cards, biometric readers, tokens, and USB keys. Its products are used to control and monitor access to intranets, extranets, and the Internet, enabling businesses to authenticate and manage the digital identities of employees, customers, and trading partners. The company's customers include Citibank, Novell, and Oracle. It markets its products worldwide; more than half of its sales outside of North America. ActivIdentity also offers professional services, such as consulting, support, and training.

	Annual Growth	9/05	9/06	9/07	9/08	9/09
Sales ($ mil.)	10.2%	42.2	53.4	59.6	59.0	62.3
Net income ($ mil.)	—	(47.9)	(22.5)	(9.3)	(76.5)	(5.5)
Market value ($ mil.)	(10.6%)	208.2	226.0	248.1	108.7	133.2
Employees	(8.4%)	313	313	322	260	220

⊞ ACTIVISION BLIZZARD, INC.

NASDAQ (GS): ATVI

3100 Ocean Park Blvd.
Santa Monica, CA 90405
Phone: 310-255-2000
Fax: 310-255-2100
Web: www.activisionblizzard.com

CEO: Robert A. (Bobby) Kotick
CFO: Thomas Tippl
HR: Ann E. Weiser
FYE: December 31
Type: Public

Video game maker Activision Blizzard is a firm believer that action speaks louder than words. The video game publisher is best known for title franchises such as *World of Warcraft*, *Guitar Hero*, *Tony Hawk*, and *Call of Duty*. It also makes games based on licensed properties from LucasArts (*Star Wars*), Marvel (*Spider-Man* and *X-Men*), and DreamWorks Animation (*Shrek*). Its titles are produced for console game systems and handheld devices from Sony, Microsoft, and Nintendo, as well as games for Apple's iPhone. Vivendi acquired a majority stake in the company in a deal valued at $9.8 billion; it then combined Activision with Vivendi Games (and its Blizzard Entertainment division) to form Activision Blizzard.

	Annual Growth	3/06	3/07	3/08	*12/08	12/09
Sales ($ mil.)	30.7%	1,468.0	1,513.0	2,898.1	3,026.0	4,279.0
Net income ($ mil.)	28.1%	41.9	85.8	344.9	(107.0)	113.0
Market value ($ mil.)	12.7%	8,576.7	11,779.8	16,985.5	10,747.3	13,819.8
Employees	34.3%	2,149	2,125	2,640	7,000	7,000
						*Fiscal year change

An in-depth profile of this company is available to Hoover's Online members at hoovers.com. ⊞

ACTIVX BIOSCIENCES, INC.

11025 N. Torrey Pines Rd., Ste. 120
La Jolla, CA 92037
Phone: 858-558-5558
Fax: 858-587-4878
Web: www.activx.com

CEO: John W. Kozarich
CFO: Yoh Ito
HR: —
FYE: March 31
Type: Subsidiary

ActivX Biosciences figures that the more you know about protein kinases, the easier it will be to inhibit them. That's the basis of its main product: a platform to profile protein kinases — enzymes that regulate cells' signaling pathways. Its KiNativ platform has been launched for use by pharmaceutical and biotechnology companies as they develop the kinase inhibitors expected to make drug breakthroughs. The company also has its own pipeline of drug candidates in development, including one in trials for the treatment of Type-2 diabetes. Japanese drugmaker Kyorin Pharmaceutical, with whom ActivX had collaborated since 2002, bought the company in 2005 for $21 million.

	Annual Growth	3/04	3/05	3/06	3/07	3/08
Est. sales ($ mil.)	—	—	—	—	—	12.0
Employees	—	—	—	—	—	43

ACTS RETIREMENT-LIFE COMMUNITIES, INC.

375 Morris Rd.
West Point, PA 19486
Phone: 215-661-8330
Fax: 215-661-8320
Web: www.actsretirement.com

CEO: Marvin Mashner
CFO: Gerald T. Grant
HR: Warren Johnson
FYE: December 31
Type: Not-for-profit

No acting here! ACTS is serious about providing seniors with the opportunity to live independently, but with a helping hand when needed. ACTS develops, owns, and operates continuing-care retirement communities in eight US states along the Eastern Seaboard. The company's properties feature resort-style amenities in Christian environments (ACTS comes from a Biblical reference). It owns about two dozen properties located in Alabama, Delaware, Florida, Georgia, Maryland, North Carolina, Pennsylvania, and South Carolina. The not-for-profit organization was founded as Open Door Estates by a group of Pennsylvania church members in 1971.

	Annual Growth	12/04	12/05	12/06	12/07	12/08
Est. sales ($ mil.)	—	—	—	—	—	304.4
Employees	—	—	—	—	—	5,375

⊞ ACTUANT CORPORATION

NYSE: ATU

13000 W. Silver Spring Dr.
Butler, WI 53007
Phone: 414-352-4160
Fax: —
Web: www.actuant.com

CEO: Robert C. (Bob) Arzbaecher
CFO: Andrew G. (Andy) Lampereur
HR: Susan S. Korthase
FYE: August 31
Type: Public

Actual results may vary, but Actuant consistently produces a range of tools and equipment. It makes electrical and industrial tools, such as wire connectors, switches, transformers, and tools, for wholesale and retail distribution under such brand names as Acme Electric, Gardner Bender, and Kopp. Actuant's engineered solutions product line includes Power-Packer brand drive systems for hydraulic cab-tilt systems for heavy-duty trucks and automotive convertible top systems. The company also offers cable, synthetic rope, pipeline connectors, and equipment rental for the energy industry. Caterpillar, BorgWarner, BP, Petrofac, and West Marine are among its customers. Actuant has operations in about 30 countries.

	Annual Growth	8/05	8/06	8/07	8/08	8/09
Sales ($ mil.)	6.2%	976.1	1,201.2	1,458.7	1,663.9	1,239.8
Net income ($ mil.)	(33.8%)	71.3	92.6	105.0	122.5	13.7
Market value ($ mil.)	(9.6%)	1,440.0	1,531.7	2,071.3	2,143.0	959.7
Employees	0.2%	5,850	6,300	7,400	7,500	5,900

⊞ ACTUATE CORPORATION

NASDAQ (GM): ACTU

2207 Bridgepointe Pkwy., Ste. 500
San Mateo, CA 94404
Phone: 650-645-3000
Fax: 650-645-3700
Web: www.actuate.com

CEO: Peter I. (Pete) Cittadini
CFO: Daniel A. (Dan) Gaudreau
HR: —
FYE: December 31
Type: Public

Actuate accentuates reporting. The company provides enterprise reporting and analytics software that corporations use to analyze business data and design, publish, and distribute report content through company networks and the Internet. Actuate's customers, which include Bank of America, Dell, Johnson & Johnson, and Lockheed Martin, use the company's software to publish financial statements, performance metrics, manufacturing and distribution reports, and customer account information; that information is pulled from databases and displayed in easily digestible, interactive Web pages, Excel spreadsheets, and other formats. Actuate gets nearly three-quarters of its sales in North America.

	Annual Growth	12/05	12/06	12/07	12/08	12/09
Sales ($ mil.)	2.9%	106.4	128.6	140.6	131.0	119.3
Net income ($ mil.)	1.3%	11.6	13.8	20.2	13.6	12.2
Market value ($ mil.)	8.1%	142.4	269.4	352.3	134.2	194.1
Employees	0.3%	491	582	581	533	497

ACUITY, A MUTUAL INSURANCE COMPANY

2800 S. Taylor Dr.
Sheboygan, WI 53081
Phone: 920-458-9131
Fax: 920-458-1618
Web: www.acuity.com

CEO: Benjamin M. (Ben) Salzmann
CFO: Wendy Schuler
HR: John Signer
FYE: December 31
Type: Mutual company

For Acuity, A Mutual Insurance Company, keeping an eye on the prize means meeting its customers' insurance needs. The company writes a variety of personal and commercial property/casualty insurance plans for policyholders in nearly 20 states, primarily in the Midwest. Its products include automobile, homeowners, liability, marine, umbrella, and workers' compensation coverage. Acuity provides policies for such businesses as construction contractors, manufacturers, and small service businesses. Some 900 independent agents sell the company's policies. Acuity was founded in 1925 as Mutual Auto Insurance Company of the Town of Herman. As a mutual insurance firm, the company is owned by its policyholders.

	Annual Growth	12/04	12/05	12/06	12/07	12/08
Est. sales ($ mil.)	—	—	—	—	—	745.7
Employees	—	—	—	—	—	730

ACUITY BRANDS, INC.

NYSE: AYI

1170 Peachtree St. NE, Ste. 2400
Atlanta, GA 30309
Phone: 404-853-1400
Fax: 404-853-1411
Web: www.acuitybrands.com

CEO: Vernon J. (Vern) Nagel
CFO: Richard K. (Ricky) Reece
HR: —
FYE: August 31
Type: Public

And God said, "Let there be light," and there was Acuity Brands. Acuity Brands, through its subsidiaries, manufactures and distributes residential and commercial lighting fixtures and controls, as well as the high-mast systems for lighting highways and parking lots. It touts such brands as MetalOptics, Gotham, and Lithonia. Subsidiary Acuity Brands Technology Services (ABTS) makes SAERIS (lighting for commercial projects) and ROAM (wireless and network control-based lighting and security systems). The company's 14 plants in the US and Mexico, and two in Europe, turn out some 100,000 fixtures a day! About 90% of sales are made in the US, through multiple channels; The Home Depot accounts for more than 10%.

	Annual Growth	8/05	8/06	8/07	8/08	8/09
Sales ($ mil.)	(6.5%)	2,172.9	2,393.1	2,530.7	2,026.6	1,657.4
Net income ($ mil.)	12.9%	52.2	106.6	148.1	148.3	84.9
Market value ($ mil.)	6.9%	1,069.4	1,547.5	1,902.8	1,892.5	1,396.6
Employees	(12.0%)	10,000	10,600	10,000	6,500	6,000

ACUNETX, INC.
OTC: ANTX

2301 W. 205th St., Ste. 102
Torrance, CA 90501
Phone: 310-328-0477
Fax: 310-328-0697
Web: www.acunetx.com

CEO: Robert S. (Bob) Corrigan
CFO: Robert S. (Bob) Corrigan
HR: —
FYE: December 31
Type: Public

If you find yourself humming "Catch me now, I'm falling" then AcuNetx can help. The company's IntelliNetx division markets patented medical devices that assist in the diagnosis of dizziness and vertigo, and rehabilitate those in danger of falling as a result of balance disorders. Through its majority-owned VisioNetx subsidiary, AcuNetx makes diagnostic equipment that can tell employers and police if someone is impaired by alcohol, some other substance, or by fatigue or illness. The company's OrthoNetx unit is a medical subsidiary which provides surgery devices that create new bone in order to correct deformities and deficiencies of the skeleton.

	Annual Growth	12/05	12/06	12/07	12/08	12/09
Sales ($ mil.)	(10.5%)	1.4	2.2	2.6	1.1	0.9
Net income ($ mil.)	—	(0.4)	(8.2)	(0.9)	(0.7)	(0.3)
Market value ($ mil.)	(51.5%)	11.8	4.0	5.6	0.1	0.7
Employees	(13.1%)	7	4	6	5	4

ACURA PHARMACEUTICALS, INC.
NASDAQ (CM): ACUR

616 N. North Ct.
Palatine, IL 60067
Phone: 847-705-7709
Fax: 847-705-5399
Web: acurapharm.com

CEO: Andrew D. (Andy) Reddick
CFO: Peter A. Clemens
HR: James F. (Jim) Emigh
FYE: December 31
Type: Public

Acura Pharmaceuticals is working to provide accurate drug dosages without allowing for abuse. The company has developed a technology to add abuse-deterring agents to commonly abused pharmaceuticals. If a drug with these agents (what Acura calls Aversion Technology) is taken in excess, the ingredients cause unpleasant symptoms shortly after ingestion. If a tablet is crushed and inhaled other ingredients will cause nasal irritation; and if an abuser attempts to dissolve the powder, it will form a non-injectable gel. Lead product candidate Acurox combines Aversion Technology with the commonly abused opioid painkiller oxycodone HCl.

	Annual Growth	12/05	12/06	12/07	12/08	12/09
Sales ($ mil.)	(22.9%)	—	—	6.4	44.4	3.8
Net income ($ mil.)	—	—	—	(4.3)	14.5	(15.8)
Market value ($ mil.)	(6.5%)	—	—	266.7	321.0	233.1
Employees	3.5%	—	—	14	15	15

ACUSHNET COMPANY

333 Bridge St.
Fairhaven, MA 02719
Phone: 508-979-2000
Fax: 508-979-3927
Web: www.acushnet.com

CEO: Walter R. (Wally) Uihlein
CFO: William C. Burke Sr.
HR: Dennis D. Doherty
FYE: December 31
Type: Subsidiary

Acushnet stays teed off all the time. Owned by Fortune Brands, the company is a top maker of golf balls, clubs, shoes, gloves, and other golfing equipment and accessories. Its Titleist golf balls and FootJoy golf shoes and gloves are #1 sellers in the US. The firm also makes value-priced Pinnacle golf balls, Cobra and Titleist golf clubs, Scotty Cameron putters, and Vokey Design wedges, as well as golf bags and outerwear. Products are sold through golf pro shops, specialty sporting goods stores, and mass merchants worldwide. PGA players who have used Acushnet's equipment include Adam Scott, Davis Love III, Geoff Ogilvy, Mark O'Meara, and Steve Stricker. PUMA purchased Acushnet's Cobra Golf business in 2010.

ACUSPHERE, INC.
NASDAQ (GM): ACUS

500 Arsenal St.
Watertown, MA 02472
Phone: 617-648-8800
Fax: 617-926-4750
Web: www.acusphere.com

CEO: Sherri Carroll Oberg
CFO: —
HR: —
FYE: December 31
Type: Public

Acusphere micromanages its products, but then how else would you handle microparticles? Acusphere uses proprietary technology to create porous microparticles smaller than red blood cells to develop cardiovascular drugs for the detection of coronary artery disease. Its lead injectable candidate, Imagify, is in clinical trials. The company has granted the European development and marketing rights for Imagify to Nycomed Danmark ApS. It intends to seek a similar marketing partnership in the US. Additional candidates in Acusphere's pipeline include two separate drug delivery systems designed to enhance the formulation of certain cancer drugs and improve the delivery of certain asthma treatments.

ACXIOM CORPORATION
NASDAQ (GS): ACXM

601 E. 3rd St.
Little Rock, AR 72201
Phone: 501-342-1000
Fax: 501-342-3913
Web: www.acxiom.com

CEO: John A. Meyer
CFO: Christopher W. (Chris) Wolf
HR: Cindy K. Childers
FYE: March 31
Type: Public

Acxiom will help you make sense of customer information. The provider of data and software used for direct marketing and customer relationship management (CRM) collects and maintains a storehouse of consumer information covering nearly every household in the US. It has real estate records on about 60 million properties that it offers to clients needing contact and demographics for direct mail and telemarketing. Acxiom helps companies manage customer data and integrate that information into marketing systems. It draws clients from various sectors including financial services, packaged goods, automotive, health care, and telecommunications. Acxiom has operations in the US, Canada, Europe, China, and Australia.

	Annual Growth	3/06	3/07	3/08	3/09	3/10
Sales ($ mil.)	(4.7%)	1,332.6	1,395.1	1,384.1	1,276.6	1,099.2
Net income ($ mil.)	(8.7%)	64.1	70.7	(7.8)	37.5	44.5
Market value ($ mil.)	(8.7%)	2,059.1	1,704.5	945.9	589.7	1,429.8
Employees	(1.4%)	6,765	7,100	6,610	6,400	6,400

ADA-ES, INC.
NASDAQ (CM): ADES

8100 SouthPark Way, Unit B
Littleton, CO 80120
Phone: 303-734-1727
Fax: 303-734-0330
Web: www.adaes.com

CEO: Michael D. (Mike) Durham
CFO: Mark H. McKinnies
HR: Beth Turner-Graziano
FYE: December 31
Type: Public

ADA-ES is trying to make "clean coal" more than just a marketing term. The company, which was spun off from Earth Sciences in 2003, makes environmental technology systems and specialty chemicals that reduce emissions at coal-burning power plants. It offers integrated mercury control systems, as well as flue gas conditioning and combustion aid chemicals. ADA-ES provides consulting and testing services and mercury measurement equipment. ADA-ES also participates in a joint venture with NexGen Refined Coal to market proprietary coal technology that reduces emissions of nitrogen oxides and mercury from some treated coals.

	Annual Growth	12/05	12/06	12/07	12/08	12/09
Sales ($ mil.)	16.3%	11.0	15.5	19.2	16.2	20.1
Net income ($ mil.)	—	0.7	0.4	0.2	(4.1)	(8.8)
Market value ($ mil.)	(24.0%)	135.2	120.1	56.1	23.0	45.2
Employees	14.0%	32	42	58	64	54

A.D.A.M., INC.

NASDAQ (CM): ADAM

1600 RiverEdge Pkwy., Ste. 100
Atlanta, GA 30328
Phone: 770-980-0888
Fax: 770-955-3088
Web: www.adam.com

CEO: Mark B. Adams
CFO: Christopher (Chris) Joe
HR: —
FYE: December 31
Type: Public

A.D.A.M. has prescribed itself a healthy dose of information distribution. The company provides health information and services for consumers, media companies, employees, and health care professionals. A.D.A.M offers Web-based interactive information on diseases, symptoms, treatments, surgical procedures, and specialty medicine and topics. Its library features medical illustrations, color graphics, animation, 3D models, video content, and printed reference guides. It also offers more than 3,600 health reference articles. A.D.A.M.'s Broker and Employer Solutions segment provides benefits-related services to the human resources market. A.D.A.M. stands for Animated Dissection of Anatomy for Medicine.

	Annual Growth	12/05	12/06	12/07	12/08	12/09
Sales ($ mil.)	29.3%	10.1	16.5	27.9	28.9	28.2
Net income ($ mil.)	—	7.1	2.5	3.9	0.0	(13.3)
Market value ($ mil.)	(15.0%)	80.2	60.5	83.3	39.8	41.8
Employees	24.8%	40	108	112	118	97

ADAMIS PHARMACEUTICALS CORPORATION

OTC: ADMP

2658 Del Mar Heights Rd., No. 555
Del Mar, CA 92014
Phone: 858-401-3984
Fax: —
Web: www.adamispharmaceuticals.com

CEO: Dennis J. Carlo
CFO: Robert O. Hopkins
HR: Bethany Banner
FYE: March 31*
Type: Public

Adamis Pharmaceuticals adamantly develops and markets specialty prescription drugs for respiratory ailments, allergies, viral infections, and other medical conditions. Subsidiary Adamis Labs develops and markets allergy, respiratory, and pediatric prescription medicines to physicians in the US. Its products include a pre-filled epinephrine syringe for severe allergic reactions dubbed Epi PFS. Adamis Viral Therapies is developing vaccine technologies for ailments such as influenza and hepatitis. The company is also developing Savvy, a contraceptive gel.

	Annual Growth	12/04	12/05	12/06	12/07	†12/08
Sales ($ mil.)	—	—	—	—	—	0.0
Net income ($ mil.)	—	—	—	—	—	(1.5)
Market value ($ mil.)	—	—	—	—	—	15.5
Employees	—	—	—	—	—	14

*Fiscal year change †Most recent year available

ADAMS EXPRESS COMPANY

NYSE: ADX

7 St. Paul St., Ste. 1140
Baltimore, MD 21202
Phone: 410-752-5900
Fax: 410-659-0080
Web: www.adamsexpress.com

CEO: Douglas G. (Doug) Ober
CFO: Brian S. Hook
HR: —
FYE: December 31
Type: Public

The Adams Express Company will be quick to tell you it administers a closed-end fund (an investment fund similar to a mutual fund, except with a limited number of shares). A conservative investor that strives for capital preservation and low-risk returns, the firm maintains a portfolio that focuses on such sectors as consumer products (PepsiCo, Procter & Gamble, Unilever); technology (Microsoft, Oracle); and oil and related services (ConocoPhillips, Schlumberger). Adams Express shares its headquarters and most of its executives with fellow closed-end fund Petroleum & Resources (also its largest holding); its largest non-affiliated holding is General Electric.

ADAMS GOLF, INC.

NASDAQ (CM): ADGF

2801 E. Plano Pkwy.
Plano, TX 75074
Phone: 972-673-9000
Fax: 972-398-8818
Web: www.adamsgolf.com

CEO: Oliver G. (Chip) Brewer III
CFO: Pamela J. (Pam) High
HR: Ann Neff
FYE: December 31
Type: Public

Like any golfer, Adams Golf believes the problem isn't in the swing, it's in the clubs. The company's Tight Lies fairway woods are designed to quickly lift a golf ball from any lie — even from bunkers, rough, or divots — and achieve longer distance. Adams Golf also makes drivers, wedges, irons, and accessories (such as golf bags and hats). Its Women's Golf Unlimited subsidiary caters to the ladies with clubs, balls, and other gear. Sales to specialty retailers, mass merchants, pro shops, and sporting goods stores account for about 80% of Adams' sales. In addition to endorsing Adams Golf's products, pro golfer Tom Watson assists in design and testing. The firm was founded by chairman Barney Adams in 1987.

	Annual Growth	12/05	12/06	12/07	12/08	12/09
Sales ($ mil.)	7.8%	56.4	76.0	94.6	91.5	76.1
Net income ($ mil.)	—	3.2	9.0	9.4	(1.5)	(12.2)
Market value ($ mil.)	(11.5%)	33.6	55.1	62.9	21.0	20.6
Employees	(0.8%)	124	147	155	144	120

ADAMS RESOURCES & ENERGY, INC.

NYSE Amex: AE

4400 Post Oak Pkwy., Ste. 2700
Houston, TX 77027
Phone: 713-881-3600
Fax: 713-881-3491
Web: www.adamsresources.com

CEO: K. S. (Bud) Adams Jr.
CFO: Richard B. (Rick) Abshire
HR: —
FYE: December 31
Type: Public

Bud Adams may have moved his football team to Tennessee years ago, but his Adams Resources & Energy remains a Houston oiler. Subsidiary Gulfmark Energy buys crude oil at the wellhead for transport to refiners and other customers via more than 110 trucks, and the company's Ada Resources subsidiary markets refined petroleum products such as gasoline and diesel fuel. With exploration and production mainly in Texas and Louisiana, Adams Resources boasts proved reserves of 6.4 billion cu. ft. of natural gas and 230,000 barrels of oil. The company's primary operations are all within a 1,000-mile radius of Houston. Chairman and CEO Adams, owner of the NFL's Tennessee Titans, controls 49.3% of the company.

	Annual Growth	12/05	12/06	12/07	12/08	12/09
Sales ($ mil.)	(4.8%)	2,364.8	2,246.6	2,636.2	4,159.7	1,943.1
Net income ($ mil.)	(30.5%)	17.6	10.5	17.1	(5.6)	4.1
Market value ($ mil.)	(0.9%)	96.3	127.0	108.4	71.7	93.0
Employees	(2.3%)	745	748	742	806	679

ADAPTEC, INC.

NASDAQ (GM): ADPT

691 S. Milpitas Blvd.
Milpitas, CA 95035
Phone: 408-945-8600
Fax: 408-262-2533
Web: www.adaptec.com

CEO: John J. Quicke
CFO: Mary L. Dotz
HR: —
FYE: March 31
Type: Public

Connection is in the cards for Adaptec. The company provides adapters, controllers, and related hardware and software that facilitate the transfer of data by connecting computers to storage devices. Adaptec sells its products, which include such devices as RAID controllers and host bus adapters (HBAs), directly and through resellers and distributors to OEMs, retailers, and systems integrators. Its products are sold under its own brand and the brands of its OEM customers. Adaptec outsources the manufacturing of its products primarily through a partnership with Sanmina-SCI. The company's top customers include Hewlett-Packard, IBM (17% of sales), Intel, and Super Micro Computer.

	Annual Growth	3/06	3/07	3/08	3/09	3/10
Sales ($ mil.)	(30.2%)	310.1	255.2	167.4	114.8	73.7
Net income ($ mil.)	—	(148.4)	30.8	(9.6)	(10.2)	(17.4)
Market value ($ mil.)	(12.3%)	665.8	465.9	354.0	289.0	393.7
Employees	(36.2%)	1,128	598	391	232	187

An in-depth profile of this company is available to Hoover's Online members at hoovers.com.

55

ADB AIRFIELD SOLUTIONS LLC

977 Gahanna Pkwy.	CEO: Steve Rauch
Columbus, OH 43230	CFO: Mike Morrow
Phone: 614-861-1304	HR: —
Fax: 614-864-2069	FYE: September 30
Web: www.adb-airfield.com	Type: Business segment

ADB Airfield Solutions (formerly Siemens Airfield Solutions) can shed some light on landings, takeoffs, and other aircraft endeavors. The company makes products that illuminate approach zones, aprons, main runways, and taxiways. From the largest freight hub in the world to small regional airports, ADB's products can be found in virtually any airport. Other products include externally lighted wind cones, guidance and control monitoring systems, and cables and connectors. ADB also acts as a turnkey contractor for a variety of airport projects. Montagu Private Equity acquired ADB in November 2009 for €45 million ($60 million) from German giant Siemens AG, which had owned the airfield lighting business since 1987.

ADC TELECOMMUNICATIONS, INC.
NASDAQ (GS): ADCT

13625 Technology Dr.	CEO: Robert E. (Bob) Switz
Eden Prairie, MN 55344	CFO: James G. (Jim) Mathews
Phone: 952-938-8080	HR: —
Fax: 952-917-1717	FYE: September 30
Web: www.adc.com	Type: Public

The transmission overhauls ADC Telecommunications performs don't leave grease stains on the driveway. The company provides broadband data access and infrastructure equipment. Its products — central office service platforms, broadband switches and routers, and wireless gear — are used to transmit voice and data signals and connect communications providers with their subscribers. ADC also provides network management software and integration services. The company caters to local, long-distance, and wireless telephone and cable TV providers; it also sells to distributors and other equipment makers. Customers include AT&T, Ciena, Graybar Electric, Time Warner Cable, and Verizon Communications.

	Annual Growth	10/05	10/06	10/07	10/08	*9/09
Sales ($ mil.)	(3.9%)	1,169.2	1,281.9	1,322.2	1,456.4	996.7
Net income ($ mil.)	—	110.7	72.1	106.3	(41.9)	(474.3)
Market value ($ mil.)	(16.9%)	1,692.5	1,387.9	1,813.7	614.9	808.7
Employees	2.5%	8,200	8,600	9,050	10,600	9,050

*Fiscal year change

ADCARE HEALTH SYSTEMS, INC.
NYSE Amex: ADK

5057 Troy Rd.	CEO: Gary L. Wade
Springfield, OH 45502	CFO: Scott Cunningham
Phone: 937-964-8974	HR: —
Fax: 937-964-8961	FYE: December 31
Web: www.adcarehealth.com	Type: Public

Retirement keeps AdCare Health Systems working. The company manages about 15 assisted-living facilities, nursing homes, and independent retirement communities in Alabama and Ohio with a total of about 850 residences. It owns all or part of about half of its facilities, including the Hearth & Home assisted living facilities. Services include Alzheimer's and subacute care. AdCare also operates a home health care business, Assured Health Care, which offers nursing, therapy, and living assistance services, as well as administrative services for insurance coordination and caregiver hiring.

	Annual Growth	12/05	12/06	12/07	12/08	12/09
Sales ($ mil.)	5.1%	21.9	22.5	23.7	24.8	26.7
Net income ($ mil.)	—	(0.9)	(2.4)	(0.2)	(1.1)	0.4
Market value ($ mil.)	12.0%	—	15.2	4.3	5.8	21.4
Employees	(0.1%)	850	934	898	906	846

ADDUS HOMECARE CORPORATION
NASDAQ (GM): ADUS

2401 S. Plum Grove Rd.	CEO: Mark S. Heaney
Palatine, IL 60067	CFO: Francis J. (Frank) Leonard
Phone: 847-303-5300	HR: Paul Diamond
Fax: 847-303-5376	FYE: December 31
Web: www.addus.com	Type: Public

When caregivers need a little respite, Addus is there. Addus HomeCare provides home health care and related services such as rehabilitation and disease management. The company offers long-term home care for the elderly, which primarily includes in-home support services such as bathing, dressing, medication assistance, and other social activities. Additional offerings include short-term skilled home nursing and therapy (for patients recovering from a health condition) and adult day care. Addus serves more than 20,000 patients from around 120 offices in 16 states. Investment firm Eos Capital Partners owns a controlling stake in Addus HomeCare, which completed an IPO in 2009.

	Annual Growth	12/04	12/05	12/06	12/07	*12/08
Sales ($ mil.)	15.2%	—	—	178.2	194.6	236.3
Net income ($ mil.)	(12.3%)	—	—	5.2	0.2	4.0
Employees	13.4%	—	—	9,440	10,797	12,137

*Most recent year available

ADDVANTAGE TECHNOLOGIES GROUP, INC.
NASDAQ (GM): AEY

1221 E. Houston St.	CEO: Kenneth A. (Ken) Chymiak
Broken Arrow, OK 74012	CFO: Scott A. Francis
Phone: 918-251-9121	HR: —
Fax: —	FYE: September 30
Web: www.addvantagetech.com	Type: Public

ADDvantage Technologies uses change to its advantage. The company took its present form in 1999, when it bought Oklahoma-based cable TV parts and services provider TULSAT in a deal that gave TULSAT's owners control over the company. ADDvantage sells new and remanufactured cable TV equipment and provides repair services to cable operators. Its products include headend equipment (satellite receivers, amplifiers, and antennas), fiber products (couplers, optical transmitters), and distribution gear (directional taps, line extenders). ADDvantage gets most of its sales in the US, with a small portion in Central America and South America.

	Annual Growth	9/05	9/06	9/07	9/08	9/09
Sales ($ mil.)	(4.3%)	50.3	52.5	65.6	56.4	42.2
Net income ($ mil.)	(15.2%)	5.8	4.8	7.4	4.7	3.0
Market value ($ mil.)	(12.3%)	39.5	42.6	82.4	27.3	23.3
Employees	(3.1%)	159	167	167	152	140

ADEPT TECHNOLOGY, INC.
NASDAQ (GM): ADEP

3011 Triad Dr.	CEO: John Dulchinos
Livermore, CA 94551	CFO: Lisa M. Cummins
Phone: 925-245-3400	HR: Sue Lim
Fax: 925-960-0452	FYE: June 30
Web: www.adept.com	Type: Public

Adept Technology makes "intelligent automation hardware," or, for the sci-fi fan in all of us: robots. Its robots are designed to handle, assemble, test, inspect, and package products in the electronics, food processing, automotive component, and pharmaceutical industries. Adept Technology's line of robots replicate the movements of human shoulders, elbows, and wrists. The company also makes vision guidance and inspection systems, as well as software that allows operators to control robots from a PC. Adept Technology targets Global 1000 companies, selling its products through more than 200 system integrators, a direct sales force, and OEMs.

	Annual Growth	6/05	6/06	6/07	6/08	6/09
Sales ($ mil.)	(4.8%)	50.5	57.6	48.7	60.8	41.5
Net income ($ mil.)	—	1.3	0.5	(11.5)	3.6	(13.1)
Market value ($ mil.)	(25.5%)	68.9	120.0	54.7	81.5	21.2
Employees	(6.3%)	174	175	157	158	134

ADESA, INC.

13085 Hamilton Crossing Blvd.	CEO: Thomas J. (Tom) Caruso
Carmel, IN 46032	CFO: Paul Lips
Phone: 317-815-1100	HR: —
Fax: 317-249-4600	FYE: December 31
Web: www.adesa.com	Type: Subsidiary

ADESA (Auto Dealers Exchange Services of America) doesn't sell cars, it sells fleets of cars to dealers. The firm offers used- and salvage-vehicle redistribution services to automakers, lessors, and dealers in the US, Canada, and Mexico. ADESA operates about 60 whole car auction sites; it also offers such ancillary services as logistics, inspections, evaluation, titling, and settlement administration. The company collects fees from buyers and sellers on each auction and from its extra services. Its AFC (Automotive Finance Corporation) unit offers dealer floorplan financing services from more than 85 locations. ADESA was acquired by KAR Auction Services in 2007. KAR, a holding company, went public in late 2009.

	Annual Growth	12/04	12/05	12/06	12/07	12/08
Sales ($ mil.)	65.8%	—	—	—	677.7	1,123.4
Net income ($ mil.)	60.7%	—	—	—	81.6	131.1
Employees	0.0%	—	—	—	11,000	11,000

ADESTA, LLC

1299 Farnam St., 1200 Landmark Center, Ste. 1300	CEO: Robert (Bob) Sommerfeld
Omaha, NE 68102	CFO: Jim Kawamoto
Phone: 402-233-7700	HR: Mark Berner
Fax: 402-233-7650	FYE: December 31
Web: www.adestagroup.com	Type: Subsidiary

Adesta is adept at piecing together communications systems. Specializing in systems integration, the company brings together disparate components to create communications networks and electronic security systems. Adesta provides design, construction, management, and maintenance of stand-alone or integrated networks, including work with SONET, Internet protocol/Ethernet, ATM, wireless, last-mile, and broadband networks. The company serves clients in the commercial security, critical infrastructure, public safety, and telecommunications industries. Adesta has completed projects in Asia, Central America, Europe, and the Middle East, in addition to the US. In 2010 G4S plc acquired the company for $66 million in cash.

	Annual Growth	12/04	12/05	12/06	12/07	12/08
Est. sales ($ mil.)	—	—	—	—	—	92.1
Employees	—	—	—	—	—	333

ADHEREX TECHNOLOGIES INC.

NYSE Amex: ADH

4620 Creekstone Dr., Ste. 200	CEO: Rosty Raykov
Durham, NC 27703	CFO: Robert Andrade
Phone: 919-484-8484	HR: —
Fax: 919-484-8001	FYE: December 31
Web: www.adherex.com	Type: Public

Working nimbly with a very sticky subject, Adherex Technologies researches and develops cancer treatments. One of its lead drug candidates targets a tumor's blood supply and makes those blood vessels weak and leaky by disrupting a key protein. Other potential therapies could make cancer cells more vulnerable to anti-cancer drugs or help prevent hearing loss in children undergoing certain types of chemotherapy. Adherex Technologies' pipeline is strongly based on compounds that disrupt cadherins, proteins that adhere similar molecules together in cell adhesion. Southpoint Capital Advisors own a controlling stake in the company.

	Annual Growth	12/05	12/06	12/07	12/08	12/09
Sales ($ mil.)	—	—	—	—	0.0	0.0
Net income ($ mil.)	—	—	—	—	(13.6)	(3.0)
Market value ($ mil.)	0.0%	—	—	—	13.9	13.9
Employees	(83.3%)	—	—	—	18	3

ADM ALLIANCE NUTRITION, INC.

1000 N. 30th St.	CEO: Terry Myers
Quincy, IL 62301	CFO: —
Phone: 217-222-7100	HR: —
Fax: 217-222-4069	FYE: June 30
Web: www.admani.com	Type: Subsidiary

ADM Alliance Nutrition is located in the animal-food aisle in the "supermarket to the world." A subsidiary of the "supermarket to the world" Archer Daniels Midland (ADM), ADM Alliance Nutrition supplies feed for beef and dairy cattle, swine, sheep, poultry, and horses, as well as for game birds, deer and elk, goats, and rabbits. It also makes show feeds for various animals. Alliance also makes animal-health products, including dewormers, probiotics, insecticides, and vitamin-enhanced and medicated pellets and crumbles. Although many of the company's products are made for domestic farm animals, the company doesn't forget the family pet — ADM Alliance makes dog and cat food, under the Proud Paws brand name.

	Annual Growth	6/04	6/05	6/06	6/07	6/08
Est. sales ($ mil.)	—	—	—	—	—	241.9
Employees	—	—	—	—	—	1,200

ADM TRONICS UNLIMITED, INC.

OTC: ADMT

224-S Pegasus Ave.	CEO: Andre' A. DiMino
Northvale, NJ 07647	CFO: Andre' A. DiMino
Phone: 201-767-6040	HR: —
Fax: 201-784-0620	FYE: March 31
Web: www.admtronics.com	Type: Public

ADM Tronics has had its own Industrial Revolution. While the company previously focused on the making of medical devices, ADM has shifted its main focus to water-based chemical products for industrial use. These products include coatings, resins, primers, and additives, primarily for the printing and packaging industries. The firm licenses many of its medical products, which include the Sonotron line of devices (used to treat osteoarthritis and inflammatory joint ailments with radio waves). Its Pros-Aide unit makes adhesives used in professional makeup products. ADM spun off Ivivi Technologies in 2006 but still owns about a third of the company. The founding DiMino family owns nearly half of ADM Tronics.

	Annual Growth	3/05	3/06	3/07	3/08	3/09
Sales ($ mil.)	1.7%	1.4	1.7	1.5	1.9	1.5
Net income ($ mil.)	—	(2.3)	(7.2)	(8.2)	(2.9)	(8.9)
Market value ($ mil.)	(52.1%)	21.6	14.6	12.9	8.6	1.1
Employees	(6.9%)	16	23	16	25	12

⊞ ADMINISTAFF, INC.

NYSE: ASF

19001 Crescent Springs Dr.	CEO: Paul J. Sarvadi
Kingwood, TX 77339	CFO: Douglas S. (Doug) Sharp
Phone: 281-358-8986	HR: Betty L. Collins
Fax: 281-348-3718	FYE: December 31
Web: www.administaff.com	Type: Public

Administaff handles the payroll so you don't have to. The company is one of the leading professional employer organizations (PEOs) in the US, providing small and midsized companies such services as payroll and benefits administration, workers' compensation programs, personnel records management, and employee recruiting. As a PEO, it is a co-employer of its clients' workers. Administaff also offers Web-based services through its Employee Service Center and operates a business-to-business e-commerce site. Most of its client companies are engaged in the administration, financial, consulting, and computer services industries.

	Annual Growth	12/05	12/06	12/07	12/08	12/09
Sales ($ mil.)	9.0%	1,169.6	1,389.5	1,570.0	1,724.4	1,653.1
Net income ($ mil.)	(13.8%)	30.0	46.5	47.5	45.8	16.6
Market value ($ mil.)	(13.5%)	1,100.0	1,118.9	739.8	567.1	617.1
Employees	(61.5%)	88,780	104,325	117,301	2,060	1,950

⌂ ADOBE SYSTEMS INCORPORATED

NASDAQ (GS): ADBE

345 Park Ave.
San Jose, CA 95110
Phone: 408-536-6000
Fax: 408-537-6000
Web: www.adobe.com

CEO: Shantanu Narayen
CFO: Mark S. Garrett
HR: Donna Morris
FYE: November 30
Type: Public

Adobe Systems' role as a leading desktop publishing software provider is well documented. The company offers the ubiquitous Acrobat Reader (distributed free of charge), a tool that displays portable document format (PDF) files on the Internet. The company's Web and print publishing products include Photoshop, Illustrator, and PageMaker. Adobe's offerings also include print technology geared toward manufacturers, as well as Web design (Dreamweaver) and electronic book publishing software. Its InDesign publishing package provides professional layout and design applications. Adobe's Professional Services group offers implementation, training, and support.

	Annual Growth	11/05	11/06	11/07	11/08	11/09
Sales ($ mil.)	10.6%	1,966.3	2,575.3	3,157.9	3,579.9	2,945.9
Net income ($ mil.)	(10.5%)	602.8	505.8	723.8	871.8	386.5
Market value ($ mil.)	1.8%	17,166.7	21,141.1	22,183.5	12,192.0	18,466.9
Employees	10.9%	5,734	6,082	6,959	7,335	8,660

ADOLOR CORPORATION

NASDAQ (GM): ADLR

700 Pennsylvania Dr.
Exton, PA 19341
Phone: 484-595-1500
Fax: 484-595-1520
Web: www.adolor.com

CEO: Michael R. Dougherty
CFO: Stephen W. Webster
HR: Denise Kerton
FYE: December 31
Type: Public

If you haven't got time for the pain, or some of the unwanted side effects brought on by painkillers, Adolor hopes to help. In keeping with the movement toward improved pain management (including the increased use of opioids like hydrocodone), the company is developing drugs that alleviate some of the side effects of certain pain treatments. Adolor's only marketed product, Entereg, is used as a treatment for postoperative ileus (POI), or bowel dysfunction in patients following bowel resection surgery; the condition is associated with the use of opioids (like morphine) used to treat post-operative pain.

	Annual Growth	12/05	12/06	12/07	12/08	12/09
Sales ($ mil.)	24.2%	15.7	15.1	9.1	49.5	37.4
Net income ($ mil.)	—	(56.8)	(69.7)	(48.4)	(30.1)	(47.9)
Market value ($ mil.)	(43.8%)	676.7	348.6	213.2	76.9	67.7
Employees	(10.7%)	179	129	109	129	114

ADP TOTALSOURCE GROUP, INC.

10200 Sunset Dr.
Miami, FL 33173
Phone: 305-630-1000
Fax: 305-630-3006
Web: www.adptotalsource.com

CEO: Mark Benjamin
CFO: Sergio Fernandez
HR: —
FYE: June 30
Type: Subsidiary

ADP TotalSource wants to share your paperwork pain. The professional employer organization (PEO) giant provides small and midsized businesses with staffing-related services. It establishes a co-employer relationship with clients by providing services in such areas as human resources, regulatory compliance and tax administration, employee benefits, payroll tax, and risk management. The PEO's offerings also include corporate training seminars covering such topics as employment law, conflict management, and communication skills. ADP TotalSource has about 45 regional offices in more than 20 US states. The company is a unit of Automatic Data Processing, a leading payroll and tax processing services firm.

ADS MEDIA GROUP, INC.

OTC: AMGU

12758 Cimarron Path, Ste. B-128
San Antonio, TX 78249
Phone: 210-655-6613
Fax: 210-655-6269
Web: www.adsmediagroup.com

CEO: Clark R. (Dub) Doyal
CFO: Clark R. (Dub) Doyal
HR: —
FYE: December 31
Type: Public

ADS Media Group through its Alternative Delivery Solutions subsidiary specializes in direct marketing for businesses in the US, Canada, Mexico, and Puerto Rico. The company focuses on door-to-door delivery of promotional products to homes, apartments, and businesses in North America. ADS can target its marketing efforts down to the neighborhood level, delivering materials to households based on specific demographic information. One key branded product is its La Canasta de Valores campaign, a door-delivered package containing advertising inserts and promotional material geared toward the Hispanic consumer. The company was founded in 2001.

ADSTAR, INC.

Pink Sheets: ADST

4553 Glencoe Ave., Ste. 300
Marina del Rey, CA 90292
Phone: 310-577-8255
Fax: 310-577-8266
Web: www.adstar.com

CEO: Leslie Bernhard
CFO: Jim Linesch
HR: —
FYE: December 31
Type: Public

Adstar deals with matters that are strictly classified. More than 70 publishers use Adstar's technology, which enables advertisers to compose, format, schedule, and submit newspaper classified ads electronically. Adstar also provides mobile advertising solutions through a partnership with Relevantis, a provider of software used to measure advertising effectiveness in the mobile advertising and mobile video games sectors. Through subsidiary Edgil Associates, Adstar markets and sells credit card payment processing software. Leslie Bernhard (president and CEO) and Eli Rousso (EVP and chief technology officer) co-founded the company in 1986.

ADT SECURITY SERVICES, INC.

1 Town Center Rd.
Boca Raton, FL 33486
Phone: 561-988-3600
Fax: 561-988-3601
Web: www.adt.com

CEO: John B. Koch
CFO: —
HR: Andrea Kane
FYE: September 30
Type: Subsidiary

ADT Security Services has come a long way since it was founded as American District Telegraph in 1874. ADT provides services such as fire protection, access control, alarm monitoring, medical alert system monitoring, video surveillance, and intrusion detection. The security services company has commercial, residential, and government customers in North America. All total, it has sales and service offices in some 200 communities throughout North America. The company offers services to certain residential customers through its authorized dealer network. ADT Security Services is part of ADT Worldwide, itself a unit of conglomerate Tyco International.

ADT WORLDWIDE

1 Town Center Rd.
Boca Raton, FL 33486
Phone: 561-988-3600
Fax: 561-988-3673
Web: www.adt.com

CEO: Naren K. Gursahaney
CFO: —
HR: Rich Lovely
FYE: September 30
Type: Subsidiary

ADT Worldwide, formerly Tyco Fire & Security, provides electronic security systems and services to more than 5 million residential customers, as well as 2 million additional commercial buildings worldwide. A division of Tyco International, the company operates in North America through its ADT Security Services subsidiary. It also has a presence in Africa, Asia, Australia, Europe, and South America. The company's security systems are primarily marketed under the ADT and Sensormatic brands, and are designed to detect intrusion as well as react to hazards such as fire, smoke, flooding, and other environmental conditions.

⊞ ADTRAN, INC.

NASDAQ (GS): ADTN

901 Explorer Blvd.
Huntsville, AL 35806
Phone: 256-963-8000
Fax: 256-963-8030
Web: www.adtran.com

CEO: Thomas R. Stanton
CFO: James E. (Jim) Matthews
HR: —
FYE: December 31
Type: Public

ADTRAN turns copper into gold. The company offers more than 1,700 network access products and systems used to enable Internet access, telephony, data transport, and video over voice and data networks, from traditional copper wire to optical. ADTRAN sells its switches, routers, and multiplexing systems to wireline and wireless carriers and service providers, such as AT&T (22% of sales), Qwest (19%), Sprint, and Verizon (11%). Its enterprise networking equipment ranges from modems to larger integrated access devices intended for multiple users, access routers, multiplexers, firewalls, and radio equipment. The company sells directly and through a network of distributors. Almost all sales are in the US.

	Annual Growth	12/05	12/06	12/07	12/08	12/09
Sales ($ mil.)	(1.4%)	513.2	472.7	476.8	500.7	484.2
Net income ($ mil.)	(7.5%)	101.2	78.3	76.3	78.6	74.2
Market value ($ mil.)	(6.7%)	1,846.6	1,410.9	1,328.9	924.9	1,401.6
Employees	(0.9%)	1,628	1,601	1,611	1,606	1,571

ADVANCE AMERICA, CASH ADVANCE CENTERS, INC.

NYSE: AEA

135 N. Church St.
Spartanburg, SC 29306
Phone: 864-342-5600
Fax: 864-342-5612
Web: www.advanceamerica.net

CEO: Kenneth E. (Ken) Compton
CFO: J. Patrick O'Shaughnessy
HR: —
FYE: December 31
Type: Public

Advance America, Cash Advance Centers is one of the nation's leading payday advance firms. To cover unexpected expenses, customers visit one of the lender's approximately 2,700 locations in more than 30 states, show two forms of ID, bank statement, paycheck stub, and personal check, and the company loans them from $50 to $1,000 until payday. Advance America also offers money orders, pre-paid debit cards, and money transfer services. Its customers are primarily middle-income working individuals whose average age is 40 and whose median household income is about $40,000. Nearly 90% of them have high school degrees, and some 45% are homeowners. Advance America also has about 10 centers in Canada and 20 in the UK.

	Annual Growth	12/05	12/06	12/07	12/08	12/09
Assets ($ mil.)	0.6%	436.4	525.1	471.7	447.0	446.2
Net income ($ mil.)	(3.7%)	63.0	70.2	54.4	38.5	54.2
Market value ($ mil.)	(18.2%)	771.2	911.1	631.9	117.5	345.8
Employees	(1.6%)	6,500	7,000	7,000	6,700	6,100

ADVANCE AUTO PARTS, INC.

NYSE: AAP

5008 Airport Rd.
Roanoke, VA 24012
Phone: 540-362-4911
Fax: 540-561-1448
Web: corp.advanceautoparts.com

CEO: Darren R. Jackson
CFO: Michael A. (Mike) Norona
HR: —
FYE: December 31
Type: Public

Advance Auto Parts (AAP) has turned auto parts retailing into less of a one-company race. Comfortably in 2nd place (AutoZone is #1), AAP operates more than 3,200 stores under the Advance Auto Parts, Advance Discount Auto Parts, and Western Auto banners in about 40 states, Puerto Rico, and the Virgin Islands, as well as an e-commerce site. Its stores carry brand-name replacement parts, batteries, maintenance items, and automotive chemicals. AAP's Autopart International (AI) unit operates about 150 locations and primarily serves commercial customers, including garages, service stations, and auto dealers. Commercial customers account for about 30% of AAP's revenues while do-it-yourselfers generate the balance.

	Annual Growth	12/05	12/06	12/07	12/08	12/09
Sales ($ mil.)	6.1%	4,265.0	4,616.5	4,844.4	5,142.3	5,412.6
Net income ($ mil.)	3.6%	234.7	231.3	238.3	238.0	270.4
Market value ($ mil.)	(1.8%)	4,009.7	3,280.8	3,505.0	3,104.6	3,734.7
Employees	3.7%	42,427	43,772	44,065	47,582	49,000

ADVANCE BRANDS, LLC

3540 S. Boulevard St., Ste. 225
Edmond, OK 73013
Phone: 405-562-1500
Fax: 405-562-1664
Web: www.advancebrands.com

CEO: Tom Harpenau
CFO: Brian Thompson
HR: —
FYE: December 31
Type: Joint venture

Advance Brands knows its customers have precious little time. That's why it spends its time manufacturing more than 150 fully-cooked, frozen, convenience meat products for hurried, harried, and hungry customers. Its Fast Fixin', Fast Fixin' Restaurant Style, and Steak-EZE brands of value-added meat items are made using beef, chicken, pork, turkey, and veal. Varieties include breakfast sausage links, sausage patties, and sausage biscuits with gravy. Advance's brands are available at food retailers throughout the US. The company is a privately owned joint venture between Cargill's Excel division and Advance Food.

	Annual Growth	12/04	12/05	12/06	12/07	12/08
Est. sales ($ mil.)	—	—	—	—	—	190.0
Employees	—	—	—	—	—	625

ADVANCE DISPLAY TECHNOLOGIES, INC.

OTC: ADTI

7334 S. Alton Way, Ste. F
Centennial, CO 80112
Phone: 303-267-0111
Fax: 303-267-0330
Web: www.advancedisplaytechnologies.com

CEO: Matthew W. (Matt) Shankle
CFO: Matthew W. (Matt) Shankle
HR: —
FYE: June 30
Type: Public

Advance Display Technologies develops large-screen fiber-optic video displays. The company, doing business as ADTIMedia, plans to license or sell its intellectual property assets. After a brief foray into theater operations, ADT is looking to raise capital and restructure its debt in order to continue development of its displays. It has also acquired the rights to light-emitting diode (LED) technologies that are patented and have patents pending. These LED display technologies are trademarked as SkyNet. The company's auditor issued a "going concern" warning about ADTI's ability to continue operations. Including convertible notes and preferred stock, director Lawrence DeGeorge owns about 79% of ADTI.

	Annual Growth	6/05	6/06	6/07	6/08	6/09
Sales ($ mil.)	—	0.1	0.1	0.0	0.0	0.0
Net income ($ mil.)	—	(0.8)	(1.2)	(2.1)	(5.4)	(5.6)
Market value ($ mil.)	14.4%	1.1	4.5	3.2	9.6	1.9
Employees	62.7%	4	5	6	15	28

⊞ An in-depth profile of this company is available to Hoover's Online members at hoovers.com.

59

ADVANCE FOOD COMPANY, INC.

301 W. Broadway   CEO: Greg Allen
Enid, OK 73701   CFO: Frank Merritt
Phone: 580-237-6656   HR: Brian Hayden
Fax: 580-213-4707   FYE: December 31
Web: www.advf.com   Type: Private

Advance Food Company helps restaurants and cafeterias prepare their food in advance. The company manufactures some 2,000 portion-controlled, processed beef, pork, poultry, lamb, and veal products, as well as bakery items for foodservice customers in the restaurant industry. In addition to restaurants, its other clients include convenience stores, health-care facilities, and the US military, along with colleges, universities, and schools. The company's brands include Steak-EZE Philly steaks and 54th Street Bakery. Advance Food's products are available throughout the US and in several foreign countries.

	Annual Growth	12/04	12/05	12/06	12/07	12/08
Est. sales ($ mil.)	—	—	—	—	—	525.0
Employees	—	—	—	—	—	2,200

⊞ ADVANCE PUBLICATIONS, INC.

950 Fingerboard Rd.   CEO: Samuel I. (Si) Newhouse Jr.
Staten Island, NY 10305   CFO: Thomas S. (Tom) Summer
Phone: 718-981-1234   HR: —
Fax: 718-981-1456   FYE: December 31
Web: www.advance.net   Type: Private

The drumbeat urging this company forward is the drone of printing presses. Advance Publications is a leading newspaper and magazine publisher with several dozen titles. Its portfolio of about 20 newspapers includes *The Star-Ledger* (New Jersey), *The Cleveland Plain Dealer*, and namesake *Staten Island Advance*, as well as more than 40 weekly titles published by American City Business Journals. Through Condé Nast, Advance Publications owns a bevy of magazines including *The New Yorker, Vanity Fair*, and *Wired*. Other operations and interests include online content (Condé Nast Digital) and cable television. Patriarch Sam Newhouse started the family-owned business with the purchase of the *Staten Island Advance* in 1922.

	Annual Growth	12/04	12/05	12/06	12/07	12/08
Est. sales ($ mil.)	1.4%	—	7,315.0	7,700.0	7,970.0	7,630.0
Employees	(3.2%)	—	30,000	28,000	29,100	27,200

ADVANCED ANALOGIC TECHNOLOGIES

NASDAQ (GS): AATI

3230 Scott Blvd.   CEO: Richard K. Williams
Santa Clara, CA 95054   CFO: Brian R. McDonald
Phone: 408-330-1400   HR: —
Fax: 408-737-4611   FYE: December 31
Web: www.analogictech.com   Type: Public

Advanced Analogic Technologies Incorporated tries to take an advanced approach to analog chip technology. The company, known as AnalogicTech, provides specialized power management semiconductors for use in a variety of computing, communications, and consumer electronics applications. AnalogicTech's chips go into digital audio players, digital still cameras, netbook and notebook computers, and wireless handsets. The company's investors include Samsung Electronics. Another Korean company, LG Electronics, accounts for one-quarter of sales; Samsung and its contract manufacturers, 36%. AnalogicTech gets most of its revenues from Asian customers.

	Annual Growth	12/05	12/06	12/07	12/08	12/09
Sales ($ mil.)	6.1%	68.3	81.2	109.6	90.3	86.5
Net income ($ mil.)	—	2.1	(2.1)	1.9	(18.4)	(12.7)
Market value ($ mil.)	(27.0%)	595.6	231.8	485.1	129.9	169.4
Employees	8.7%	200	252	295	281	279

ADVANCED BATTERY TECHNOLOGIES, INC.

NASDAQ (CM): ABAT

15 W. 39th St., 14th Fl.   CEO: Zhiguo Fu
New York, NY 10018   CFO: Sharon Tang
Phone: 212-391-2752   HR: —
Fax: 212-391-2751   FYE: December 31
Web: www.abat.com.cn   Type: Public

Advanced Battery Technologies, through its operating subsidiary ZQ Power-Tech, hopes to ride the rising wave of electric and hybrid-electric vehicle sales all the way to the bank. The company produces rechargeable polymer lithium-ion batteries used in cars, buses, cell phones, digital cameras, and other modern gadgets. Its batteries can be as thin as one-tenth of an inch or as large as 500 pounds (for commuter buses). ZQ makes lamps used on miners' helmets, but most of its products are sold to OEMs for use in their finished goods. Customers for vehicle battery components include Aiyingsi, ZAP, and Beijing Guoqiang Global Technology Development Co. Chairman and CEO Zhiguo Fu formed the company in 2002.

	Annual Growth	12/05	12/06	12/07	12/08	12/09
Sales ($ mil.)	97.3%	4.2	16.3	31.9	45.2	63.6
Net income ($ mil.)	—	(0.2)	6.0	10.2	16.1	21.4
Market value ($ mil.)	69.9%	32.9	43.2	322.4	182.4	274.3
Employees	(14.8%)	1,621	1,264	1,262	909	854

ADVANCED BIONICS CORPORATION

28515 Westinghouse Place   CEO: Jeffrey H. (Jeff) Greiner
Valencia, CA 91355   CFO: Russ Ramanayake
Phone: 661-362-1400   HR: —
Fax: 661-362-1500   FYE: December 31
Web: www.advancedbionics.com   Type: Subsidiary

No, the Six Million Dollar Man isn't working at hearing technology firm Advanced Bionics. The company has the technology not to make a person "better, faster, and stronger," but instead to help people with severe to profound hearing loss to hear. A leading provider of cochlear hearing devices, Advanced Bionics makes the Harmony HiResolution Bionic Ear System, which includes a cochlear implant, sound processor, and other equipment that together can restore hearing to the deaf. The company provides mentoring and support services to implant customers worldwide. Advanced Bionics was acquired by global hearing aid manufacturer Sonova for $489 million in early 2010.

ADVANCED CELL TECHNOLOGY, INC.

OTC: ACTC

381 Plantation St.   CEO: William M. (Bill) Caldwell IV
Worcester, MA 01605   CFO: —
Phone: 508-756-1212   HR: —
Fax: 508-756-4468   FYE: December 31
Web: www.advancedcell.com   Type: Public

No need to choose between embryonic and adult stem cells — Advanced Cell Technology (ACT) works with both to develop cellular therapies designed to regenerate human tissue. The company has developed three product platforms based on stem-cell technology. They are retinal pigment epithelial therapy (RPE) for the treatment of degenerative retinal disease; myoblast stem cell therapy to treat chronic heart failure and other heart problems; and the hemangioblast platform (HG) for the treatment of blood and cardiovascular diseases. Though the company is focused on bringing the clinical-stage technologies to market, it is also continuing to conduct research for other regenerative medicine treatments.

	Annual Growth	12/05	12/06	12/07	12/08	12/09
Sales ($ mil.)	36.8%	0.4	0.4	0.6	0.8	1.4
Net income ($ mil.)	—	(9.4)	(18.7)	(13.2)	(33.9)	(36.8)
Market value ($ mil.)	(53.7%)	1,795.3	520.6	148.1	29.6	82.6
Employees	(21.6%)	37	40	48	12	14

ADVANCED DRAINAGE SYSTEMS, INC.

4640 Trueman Blvd.
Hilliard, OH 43026
Phone: 614-658-0050
Fax: 614-658-0204
Web: www.ads-pipe.com

CEO: Joseph A. (Joe) Chlapaty
CFO: Mark B. Sturgeon
HR: Erick Piscopo
FYE: December 31
Type: Private

Work at Advanced Drainage Systems (ADS) isn't going down the drain, it *is* the drain. ADS manufactures high-density polyethylene (HDPE) pipes for storm and sanitary sewers, agricultural drainage, road and highway construction, and residential and commercial development. The corrugated HDPE lineup runs from culverts to drains, fittings, grates, grease interceptors, and leaching chambers. ADS even offers a green building mix of products. Customers are mining and timber operators as well as engineers in highway construction and waste management systems. ADS products lie under fabled US athletic turf and recreation sites such as Augusta National, Dodger Stadium, and Lambeau Field. ADS is an employee-owned company.

	Annual Growth	12/04	12/05	12/06	12/07	12/08
Sales ($ mil.)	0.0%	—	1,200.0	1,200.0	1,200.0	1,200.0
Employees	1.7%	—	3,800	3,900	4,000	4,000

ADVANCED EQUITIES FINANCIAL CORPORATION

311 S. Wacker Dr., Ste. 1650
Chicago, IL 60606
Phone: 312-377-5300
Fax: 312-377-5314
Web: www.advancedequities.com

CEO: Dwight Badger
CFO: Gregg S. Glaser
HR: —
FYE: December 31
Type: Private

Advanced Equities Financial is in the business of equity advancement. Through First Allied Securities and other business units, the company provides investment management and retail brokerage services for high-net-worth individuals. Its products include separately managed accounts, 401(k) retirement plans, exchange-traded funds, and insurance programs; it also offers investment services tailored specifically for doctors. Advanced Equities' investment banking practice specializes in private equity placements, particularly late-stage venture capital for emerging companies in technology-related fields, and makes such investments available to its wealthy clientele.

	Annual Growth	12/04	12/05	12/06	12/07	12/08
Est. sales ($ mil.)	—	—	—	—	—	299.0
Employees	—	—	—	—	—	589

⊞ ADVANCED ENERGY INDUSTRIES, INC.　　NASDAQ (GM): AEIS

1625 Sharp Point Dr.
Fort Collins, CO 80525
Phone: 970-221-0108
Fax: 970-407-6550
Web: www.advanced-energy.com

CEO: Hans-Georg Betz
CFO: Lawrence D. (Larry) Firestone
HR: —
FYE: December 31
Type: Public

Advanced Energy Industries advances ordinary electrical power to the head of the high-tech class. The company's power conversion and control products transform raw electricity, making it uniform enough to ensure consistent production in high-precision manufacturing. Top clients include semiconductor equipment makers Applied Materials (20% of sales), Axcelis, Lam Research, Novellus, and ULVAC. Advanced Energy's gear also is used in the production of data storage devices (including hard disks, CD-ROMs, and DVDs) and flat-panel displays, and for a variety of industrial processes, such as applying coatings to eyeglasses, solar panels, and windows. The company gets more than half of its sales outside the US.

	Annual Growth	12/05	12/06	12/07	12/08	12/09
Sales ($ mil.)	(13.0%)	325.5	410.7	384.7	328.9	186.4
Net income ($ mil.)	—	12.8	88.3	34.4	(1.8)	(102.7)
Market value ($ mil.)	6.3%	498.5	795.1	551.1	419.2	635.4
Employees	(3.6%)	1,527	1,583	1,611	1,679	1,316

ADVANCED LIFE SCIENCES HOLDINGS, INC.　　OTC: ADLS

1440 Davey Rd.
Woodridge, IL 60517
Phone: 630-739-6744
Fax: 630-739-6754
Web: www.advancedlifesciences.com

CEO: Michael T. Flavin
CFO: John L. Flavin
HR: —
FYE: December 31
Type: Public

Seeking to advance life through science, Advanced Life Sciences is a biopharmaceutical company that develops clinical and preclinical drug candidates for infectious disease, cancer, and respiratory diseases. Its lead candidate Restanza (cethromycin), an antibiotic for treatment of respiratory infections and pneumonia, has been submitted to the FDA for approval. Restanza is also being studied for use in the biodefense sector to treat pathogens such as anthrax. The biopharmaceutical company's other drug candidates include treatments for metastatic melanoma and acute respiratory distress. Advanced Life Sciences has licensed the development and commercialization rights to cethromycin from Abbott Laboratories.

	Annual Growth	12/05	12/06	12/07	12/08	12/09
Sales ($ mil.)	1,300.0%	—	—	—	0.2	2.8
Net income ($ mil.)	—	—	—	—	(22.8)	(9.2)
Market value ($ mil.)	(52.8%)	—	—	—	36.1	17.1
Employees	(36.7%)	—	—	—	30	19

ADVANCED ENVIRONMENTAL RECYCLING　　OTC: AERT

914 N. Jefferson St.
Springdale, AR 72764
Phone: 479-756-7400
Fax: 479-756-7410
Web: www.aertinc.com

CEO: Joe G. Brooks
CFO: J. R. Brian Hanna
HR: –
FYE: December 31
Type: Public

It may not turn straw into gold, but Advanced Environmental Recycling Technologies, Inc. (AERT), does practice a kind of alchemy by turning waste wood fiber and recycled plastics into building materials for homes. Its products are mainly used in residential renovation by individual homeowners, homebuilders, and contractors as a more environmentally conscious alternative to traditional wood and plastic products used to make decking, railing, and trim. AERT markets its products under such names as ChoiceDek and MoistureShield; they are sold to do-it-yourself retailers like Lowe's through Weyerhaeuser (some three-quarters of sales). The founding Brooks family owns about 30% of AERT.

	Annual Growth	12/05	12/06	12/07	12/08	12/09
Sales ($ mil.)	(5.0%)	87.3	97.8	82.2	87.4	71.1
Net income ($ mil.)	—	8.0	1.8	(8.9)	(35.9)	(4.2)
Market value ($ mil.)	(35.0%)	88.7	100.1	36.2	8.4	15.9
Employees	(8.9%)	670	664	662	514	462

⊞ ADVANCED MATERIALS GROUP, INC.　　Pink Sheets: ADMG

2364 Merritt Dr., Ste. A
Garland, TX 75041
Phone: 469-246-4100
Fax: —
Web: www.ami4.com

CEO: Marty Lehman
CFO: —
HR: —
FYE: November 30
Type: Public

Advanced Materials Group (AM) has a cushy job. Through its principal subsidiary Advanced Materials, Inc. (AMI), the company converts raw materials (foam, foil, film, adhesive components) into an array of medical and consumer products. FXI-Foamex Innovations is a key materials supplier for AM's lineup, which includes padding for helmets, luggage, and neck braces; foam inserts and inking felts for printer cartridges; air-conditioner insulation; water and dust seals; and consumer fashion accessories. AM serves customers in aerospace, medical, automotive, consumer, and technology industries. A plunge in earnings forced AM and subsidiary AMI to file for Chapter 11 bankruptcy relief in July 2009.

ADVANCED MICRO DEVICES, INC.
NYSE: AMD

1 AMD Place
Sunnyvale, CA 94088
Phone: 408-749-4000
Fax: —
Web: www.amd.com

CEO: Derrick R. (Dirk) Meyer
CFO: Thomas J. Seifert
HR: Allen Sockwell
FYE: December 31
Type: Public

Advanced Micro Devices (AMD) made some advances in its battle against Intel but hasn't capitalized on those gains. AMD ranks #2 in PC and server microprocessors, far behind its archrival. Though Intel commands about three-quarters of the world processor market, AMD at times eroded that market share thanks to the popularity of its Athlon and Opteron processor families. The company also makes embedded processors and other chips for communications and networking applications. Hewlett-Packard is AMD's biggest customer, and Chinese OEMs account for nearly half of the company's sales. In 2009 AMD split its operations, spinning off a manufacturing venture.

	Annual Growth	12/05	12/06	12/07	12/08	12/09
Sales ($ mil.)	(2.0%)	5,847.6	5,649.0	6,013.0	5,808.0	5,403.0
Net income ($ mil.)	15.3%	165.5	(166.0)	(3,379.0)	(3,098.0)	293.0
Market value ($ mil.)	(25.0%)	20,605.0	13,703.0	5,050.2	1,454.5	6,518.2
Employees	1.3%	9,860	16,500	16,420	14,700	10,400

ADVANCED PHOTONIX, INC.
NYSE Amex: API

2925 Boardwalk
Ann Arbor, MI 48104
Phone: 734-864-5600
Fax: 734-998-3474
Web: www.advancedphotonix.com

CEO: Richard D. (Rick) Kurtz
CFO: Robin F. (Rob) Risser
HR: —
FYE: March 31
Type: Public

Advanced Photonix, Inc. (API) senses more with light. The company makes devices that detect light and radiation, including photodiodes, photodetectors, and optoelectronic assemblies, which are used by manufacturers in analysis and imaging equipment for applications ranging from missile guidance and satellite positioning to baggage scanning and blood analysis. API's large-area avalanche photodiodes (LAAPDs) are used to sense low levels of light and radiation. Its FILTRODE technology applies optical coatings to photodiode chips to filter out bright background light. Most of API's sales are to customers located in the US.

	Annual Growth	3/05	3/06	3/07	3/08	3/09
Sales ($ mil.)	19.0%	14.8	23.6	23.6	23.2	29.7
Net income ($ mil.)	—	5.3	(3.5)	(4.6)	(9.6)	(2.0)
Market value ($ mil.)	(26.0%)	58.1	66.4	48.3	32.6	17.4
Employees	(0.5%)	156	152	162	140	153

ADVANCED PROTEOME THERAPEUTICS INC.
TSX Venture: APC

650 Albany St., Ste. 113
Boston, MA 02118
Phone: 617-638-0340
Fax: 617-638-0341
Web: www.advancedproteome.com

CEO: Alexander A. (Allen) Krantz
CFO: Kenneth C. (Ken) Phillippe
HR: —
FYE: July 31
Type: Public

Advanced Proteome Therapeutics (APT) has the technology to help biopharmaceutical developers place their therapeutic proteins in exactly the right spot. However, it's taking a while to find those developers and those right spots. One of its applications will enhance the usefulness of existing polyethylene glycol-based drug delivery technology. The company is housed with other research firms on the campus of Boston University, but is technically a Canadian company. APT's technology is based upon the work of its founder and CEO Dr. Allen Krantz.

	Annual Growth	7/05	7/06	7/07	7/08	7/09
Sales ($ mil.)	0.0%	—	—	0.1	0.1	0.1
Net income ($ mil.)	—	—	—	(1.9)	(1.1)	(1.0)
Market value ($ mil.)	13.6%	—	—	22.0	41.2	28.4
Employees	—	—	—	5	—	—

ADVANCED TECHNOLOGIES GROUP, LTD.
OTC: AVGG

921 Bergen Ave., Ste. 405
Jersey City, NJ 07306
Phone: 732-784-2801
Fax: 732-784-2850
Web: www.atgworld.com

CEO: Alex J. Stelmak
CFO: Alex J. Stelmak
HR: —
FYE: January 31
Type: Public

Advanced Technologies Group (ATG) is looking to enter the e-commerce software market. The company — which has a 25% interest in FX Direct Dealer, a developer of software for conducting online foreign currency exchange transactions — hopes to acquire and commercialize technologies for Internet-based marketplaces. The company also offers PromotionStat, a Web-based statistical and analytical traffic-monitoring tool, as well as online portals Promote4Free and LuxuryLounge.

	Annual Growth	1/06	1/07	1/08	1/09	1/10
Sales ($ mil.)	—	1.0	1.3	0.9	0.0	0.0
Net income ($ mil.)	—	(0.9)	(0.6)	(0.2)	16.6	17.1
Market value ($ mil.)	(35.6%)	—	13.9	1.5	0.6	3.7
Employees	(55.7%)	—	23	—	2	2

ADVANCED TECHNOLOGY SERVICES, INC.

8201 N. University St.
Peoria, IL 61615
Phone: 309-693-4000
Fax: 309-693-4164
Web: www.advancedtech.com

CEO: Richard W. (Dick) Blaudow
CFO: John L. (Jack) Rainey
HR: James W. Hefti
FYE: December 31
Type: Private

Advanced Technology Services (ATS) improves productivity and profitability on the factory floor by providing outsourced factory equipment maintenance, spare parts repair, calibration, and IT services. As part of its managed services approach, ATS will also place trained maintenance technicians and IT professionals on-site. It provides services primarily to manufacturers in the heavy equipment, auto, consumer appliance, health care, and aerospace industries. Customers include Caterpillar, Eaton, Honda, IBM, Johnson & Johnson, Motorola, and MasterBrand Cabinets. Founded in 1985, ATS has offices and service centers in China, Mexico, Puerto Rico, the UK, and the US.

ADVANSOURCE BIOMATERIALS CORPORATION
NYSE Amex: ASB

229 Andover St.
Wilmington, MA 01887
Phone: 978-657-0075
Fax: 978-657-0074
Web: www.cardiotech-inc.com

CEO: Michael F. Adams
CFO: David C. Volpe
HR: —
FYE: March 31
Type: Public

If artificial blood becomes a reality, the manufacturers can hook up with AdvanSource Biomaterials, maker of synthetic blood vessels. The company's products replace or bypass damaged and diseased arteries and provide access for dialysis needles in kidney disease patients undergoing hemodialysis. These man-made blood vessels, also called vascular grafts, are made of ChronoFlex, the company's polyurethane-based biomaterial. Its CardioPass product candidate is a synthetic coronary artery bypass graft. AdvanSource's HydroThane polymer-based biomaterial mimics living tissue and is marketed for use by other medical device makers.

	Annual Growth	3/05	3/06	3/07	3/08	3/09
Sales ($ mil.)	(37.6%)	21.8	22.4	21.2	3.2	3.3
Net income ($ mil.)	—	(1.6)	(5.1)	(3.0)	(6.1)	(2.5)
Market value ($ mil.)	(44.6%)	40.2	58.8	33.0	11.4	3.8
Employees	(41.3%)	168	206	153	22	20

ADVANSTAR COMMUNICATIONS INC.

6200 Canoga Ave., 2nd Fl.
Woodland Hills, CA 91367
Phone: 818-593-5000
Fax: 818-593-5020
Web: www.advanstar.com

CEO: Joseph (Joe) Loggia
CFO: Theodore S. (Ted) Alpert
HR: Nancy Nugent
FYE: December 31
Type: Private

Advanstar Communications offers a constellation of business-to-business publishing and marketing services related to fashion, life sciences, and powersports. The company has a portfolio of nearly 70 print publications and directories and some 270 electronic publications and websites. It also stages nearly 140 expositions, conferences, and other events annually. Titles include *Motor Age*, *Medical Economics*, and *Dermatology Times*; trade shows include apparel show MAGIC Marketplace; and marketing offerings include direct-mail services and custom publishing. A consortium of investors led by private-equity firm Veronis Suhler Stevenson owns Advanstar.

ADVANTAGE RENT A CAR

6660 1st Park Ten Blvd., Ste. 116
San Antonio, TX 78213
Phone: 210-344-4712
Fax: 210-679-2589
Web: www.arac.com

CEO: Mark P. Frissora
CFO: Elyse Douglas
HR: LeighAnne G. Baker
FYE: December 31
Type: Subsidiary

Advantage Rent A Car hopes to gain an advantage by focusing on happy leisure travelers. The company rents cars from about 20 locations in Arizona, California, Colorado, Florida, and Hawaii, and in about a half-dozen other top leisure markets in the US. It also offers its services through its own website and those operated by online travel sites, such as Expedia and Travelocity. Founded with a fleet of five cars by Kenneth and Helen Walker in 1963, the Walkers sold the business to Venture Holding in 2006. Advantage Rent A Car fell on hard times due to the slowdown in pleasure and business travel in 2008 and was acquired out of bankruptcy in 2009 by Hertz Global Holdings.

ADVANTAGE SALES AND MARKETING, LLC

18100 Von Karman Ave., Ste. 900
Irvine, CA 92612
Phone: 949-797-2900
Fax: 949-797-9112
Web: www.asmnet.com

CEO: Sonny King
CFO: Frank D. Martell
HR: Pamela James
FYE: December 31
Type: Private

Making consumer products is one thing, but selling them is another, and that's where Advantage Sales & Marketing (ASM) comes in. The company provides outsourced sales, merchandising, and marketing services to consumer goods and food product manufacturers and suppliers. It works to win optimal placement of clients' products at retail locations throughout the US and Canada, and it offers a variety of promotional programs aimed at boosting sales. Owning more than 65 offices in the US and Canada, ASM does merchandising for Wal-Mart, Target, Home Depot, and other major retailers. Investment firms Allied Capital, J.W. Childs Associates, and Merrill Lynch Global Private Equity own a controlling stake in the company.

ADVANT-E CORPORATION
OTC: ADVC

2680 Indian Ripple Rd.
Dayton, OH 45440
Phone: 937-429-4288
Fax: 937-429-4309
Web: www.advant-e.com

CEO: Jason K. Wadzinski
CFO: James E. Lesch
HR: —
FYE: December 31
Type: Public

Advant-e makes software that helps companies establish e-commerce websites. The company's EnterpriseEC platform is a building system for online business transactions and trading communities. In addition, Advant-e's subsidiary Edict Systems provides hosted trading community management software used to develop industry-specific business-to-business portals such as CPGSupplier.com, LogisticsEC.com, MfgEC.com, and RetailEC.com. Advant-e also provides consulting services, as well as professional services such as training, support, and maintenance.

	Annual Growth	12/05	12/06	12/07	12/08	12/09
Sales ($ mil.)	17.6%	4.5	5.4	7.2	8.9	8.6
Net income ($ mil.)	18.9%	0.6	0.9	1.0	1.1	1.2
Market value ($ mil.)	17.8%	9.3	13.9	13.3	9.0	18.0
Employees	11.3%	43	52	55	59	66

ADVANTEST AMERICA CORPORATION

3201 Scott Blvd.
Santa Clara, CA 95054
Phone: 408-988-7700
Fax: 408-987-0691
Web: www.advantest.com/aac

CEO: R. Keith Lee
CFO: Keith Hardwick
HR: —
FYE: March 31
Type: Subsidiary

Advantest America Corporation manufactures and distributes electronic measuring instruments and semiconductor test equipment used in the development and manufacture of computer and telecommunications products. Products include handlers, interconnect products, and testers. The company is the North American subsidiary of Advantest Corporation and was established to expand the automatic test equipment business (ATE) in the US. It has 13 offices throughout the US and an R&D Center located in California. The Japanese parent company gets about 15% of its annual sales from the Americas. Advantest established its first representative office in the States in 1973 and founded Advantest America in 1982.

	Annual Growth	3/04	3/05	3/06	3/07	3/08
Est. sales ($ mil.)	—	—	—	—	—	179.3
Employees	—	—	—	—	—	320

ADVENT INTERNATIONAL CORPORATION

75 State St.
Boston, MA 02109
Phone: 617-951-9400
Fax: 617-951-0566
Web: www.adventinternational.com

CEO: Peter A. Brooke
CFO: Janet L. Hennessy
HR: —
FYE: December 31
Type: Private

Buyout firm Advent International invests in middle-market companies in North America, Europe, Latin America, and Japan. It focuses on the business and financial services, health care, industrial, consumer, technology, and communications sectors. Portfolio companies in North America and Western Europe use the company's infusions of capital (up to $1.25 billion) for international expansion, restructuring, or to fuel growth. Advent International finances companies in developing markets like Central Europe, Brazil, Mexico, and Argentina to the tune of $50 million to $200 million per transaction. In 2008 it closed its sixth North American and Western European private equity fund, worth more than $10 billion.

An in-depth profile of this company is available to Hoover's Online members at hoovers.com.

63

ADVENT SOFTWARE, INC.

NASDAQ (GS): ADVS

600 Townsend St.
San Francisco, CA 94103
Phone: 415-543-7696
Fax: 415-543-5070
Web: www.advent.com

CEO: Stephanie G. DiMarco
CFO: James S. (Jim) Cox
HR: John P. Brennan
FYE: December 31
Type: Public

Advent Software manages investments from beginning to end. A provider of enterprise investment management software for investment advisors, banks, and corporations, Advent offers applications for managing everything from client relationships to trade order executions. The company's products are used for managing portfolio accounting, trading and order execution, hedge and venture fund allocation, securities clients, reconciliation, and other functions. Advent also offers services such as consulting, support, maintenance, systems integration, and installation.

	Annual Growth	12/05	12/06	12/07	12/08	12/09
Sales ($ mil.)	11.4%	168.7	184.1	215.3	264.8	259.5
Net income ($ mil.)	27.2%	14.1	82.6	12.6	18.9	36.9
Market value ($ mil.)	8.9%	745.9	909.5	1,394.3	514.7	1,049.7
Employees	7.9%	736	824	946	1,068	998

ADVENTIST HEALTH

2100 Douglas Blvd.
Roseville, CA 95661
Phone: 916-781-2000
Fax: 916-783-9909
Web: www.adventisthealth.org

CEO: Robert G. Carmen
CFO: Douglas E. Rebok
HR: Roy Wu
FYE: December 31
Type: Not-for-profit

Not content to wait around for the advent of good health, Adventist Health operates 17 hospital systems (with about 2,600 beds) in the western portion of the US. Its health care offerings — sprinkled throughout California, Hawaii, Oregon, and Washington — also include physicians' clinics and outpatient centers. Additionally, the not-for-profit organization runs more than a dozen home health care agencies and has established a handful of joint-venture nursing homes in California, Oregon, and Washington. Adventist Health maintains strong ties to the Seventh-Day Adventist Church but is independently owned. A sister organization, Adventist Health System, operates in the central and southern parts of the country.

	Annual Growth	12/04	12/05	12/06	12/07	12/08
Est. sales ($ mil.)	—	—	—	—	—	36.4
Employees	—	—	—	—	—	4,583

ADVENTIST HEALTH SYSTEM

111 N. Orlando Ave.
Winter Park, FL 32789
Phone: 407-647-4400
Fax: 407-975-1469
Web: www.adventisthealthsystem.com

CEO: Donald L. Jernigan
CFO: Terry D. Shaw
HR: Donald G. (Don) Jones
FYE: December 31
Type: Not-for-profit

Adventist Health's mission is to serve the community, and boy does it! One of the country's largest faith-based hospital systems, not-for-profit Adventist Health System runs about 40 hospitals and some 20 nursing homes, as well as nearly 30 home health care agencies. Its acute care hospitals have more than 6,500 beds combined, and its long-term care facilities offer about 2,000 beds. It operates in 12 states mostly in the Southeast, with Florida being its key market. The organization's Florida Hospital division includes 17 hospitals serving the state via more than 1,400 beds. The health system is sponsored by the Seventh-Day Adventist Church as part of that denomination's legacy of providing health care.

	Annual Growth	12/04	12/05	12/06	12/07	12/08
Sales ($ mil.)	5.8%	4,379.2	4,637.2	4,968.7	4,834.6	5,496.1
Net income ($ mil.)	(0.3%)	236.2	251.4	325.4	360.2	233.5
Employees	0.0%	—	43,000	43,000	43,000	43,000

ADVENTIST HEALTHCARE, INC.

1801 Research Blvd., Ste. 400
Rockville, MD 20850
Phone: 301-315-3030
Fax: 301-315-3043
Web: www.adventisthealthcare.com

CEO: William G. (Bill) Robertson
CFO: James G. Lee
HR: Elyse A. Kaplan
FYE: December 31
Type: Not-for-profit

From the newest newborn to the, um, most senior senior, Adventist HealthCare takes care of residents living throughout metro Washington DC. The not-for-profit network is home to three acute care hospitals, a range of specialty care facilities offering inpatient and outpatient mental health care, and more than a dozen home health, rehabilitation, skilled nursing, and senior care operations. Hospitals include Hackettstown Regional Medical Center, Shady Grove Adventist Hospital, and Washington Adventist Hospital. Combined, Adventist HealthCare's facilities have nearly 890 acute care, rehabilitation, and behavioral health beds. Founded in 1907, the system is affiliated with the Seventh-Day Adventist Church.

ADVENTRX PHARMACEUTICALS, INC.

NYSE Amex: ANX

6725 Mesa Ridge Rd., Ste. 100
San Diego, CA 92121
Phone: 858-552-0866
Fax: 858-552-0876
Web: www.adventrx.com

CEO: Brian M. Culley
CFO: Patrick L. Keran
HR: —
FYE: December 31
Type: Public

ADVENTRX Pharmaceuticals hopes to balance adventure with profits with its investigational drug treatments for cancer and infectious diseases. Its lead cancer candidates are improved formulations of existing treatments that aim to reduce the toxic side effects of most chemotherapies. The company is also developing CoFactor, which may enhance the effectiveness of popular chemotherapy 5-FU. Though its cancer programs are its main focus, ADVENTRX also owns the rights to a number of potential infectious disease compounds, including treatments for bacterial infections, HIV, and influenza. ADVENTRX has reduced its workforce by more than half and is exploring strategic options for the company.

	Annual Growth	12/05	12/06	12/07	12/08	12/09
Sales ($ mil.)	(22.5%)	—	—	0.5	0.5	0.3
Net income ($ mil.)	—	—	—	(22.1)	(26.6)	(11.3)
Market value ($ mil.)	(11.8%)	—	—	115.8	19.3	90.0
Employees	(64.6%)	—	—	32	14	4

ADVENTURELAND PARK

305 34th NW
Altoona, IA 50009
Phone: 515-266-2121
Fax: 515-266-9831
Web: www.adventureland-usa.com

CEO: Jan Krantz
CFO: Dan Bohner
HR: —
FYE: December 31
Type: Private

Adventureland is indeed a land within itself. The 180-acre family resort boasts an amusement park with more than 100 attractions (Adventureland Park), an inn (Adventureland Inn), and a full-service campground (Adventureland Campground). Rides range from roller coasters to kiddie-sized fun and shows include live music, magic, and musicals. The Adventureland Inn features a tropical themed pool and free shuttle service to and from the amusement park. Adventureland Campground offers its own pool along with RV and tent camping spots. The company opened a new water area, Adventure Island, in 2008. Former CEO John Krantz founded Adventureland in 1974. Krantz died in 2006.

	Annual Growth	12/04	12/05	12/06	12/07	12/08
Est. sales ($ mil.)	—	—	—	—	—	6.2
Employees	—	—	—	—	—	200

THE ADVISORY BOARD COMPANY

NASDAQ (GS): ABCO

2445 M St., NW
Washington, DC 20037
Phone: 202-266-5600
Fax: 202-266-5700
Web: www.advisoryboardcompany.com

CEO: Robert W. Musslewhite
CFO: Michael T. Kirshbaum
HR: —
FYE: March 31
Type: Public

Here's where a hospital might go for a second opinion. The Advisory Board Company specializes in providing best practices consulting to member-clients in the health care industry, including more than 2,800 hospitals, pharmaceutical companies, insurance firms, and medical device manufacturers in the US. The Advisory Board offers more than 40 programs in areas such as strategy, operations, and management. Members buy annual subscriptions to one or more programs and participate in the firm's research efforts. Programs typically include best practices research studies, seminars, customized reports, and decision-support tools. The company was founded in 1979 as the Research Council of Washington.

	Annual Growth	3/05	3/06	3/07	3/08	3/09
Sales ($ mil.)	12.9%	141.6	165.0	189.8	219.0	230.4
Net income ($ mil.)	(2.0%)	23.3	25.6	27.4	32.1	21.5
Market value ($ mil.)	(21.5%)	675.8	862.5	782.8	849.7	256.4
Employees	10.7%	681	768	855	910	1,021

ADVOCAT INC.

NASDAQ (CM): AVCA

1621 Galleria Blvd.
Brentwood, TN 37027
Phone: 615-771-7575
Fax: 615-771-7409
Web: www.irinfo.com/avc

CEO: William R. Council III
CFO: L. Glynn Riddle Jr.
HR: —
FYE: December 31
Type: Public

Spelling errors notwithstanding, Advocat strives to be an advocate for the elderly through its nursing homes and assisted-living facilities, most of which are located in the southeastern and southwestern US. The company operates 50 nursing homes and assisted-living centers with a total of some 5,800 beds. Advocat, which focuses on rural areas, offers a range of health care services including skilled nursing, recreational therapy, and social services, as well as nutritional support, respiratory treatments, rehabilitative therapy, and other specialized ancillary services. Payments from Medicare and Medicaid account for about 85% of the company's total revenues. Private and commercial payors comprise the rest.

	Annual Growth	12/05	12/06	12/07	12/08	12/09
Sales ($ mil.)	10.3%	203.7	216.8	245.1	288.8	302.0
Net income ($ mil.)	(43.4%)	25.3	21.9	9.4	5.7	2.6
Market value ($ mil.)	9.9%	30.1	91.9	63.0	17.1	44.0
Employees	5.5%	4,682	4,716	5,638	5,809	5,800

ADVOCATE HEALTH CARE

2025 Windsor Dr.
Oak Brook, IL 60523
Phone: 630-572-9393
Fax: 630-990-4752
Web: www.advocatehealth.com

CEO: James H. (Jim) Skogsbergh
CFO: Dominic J. Nakis
HR: Ben Grigaliunas
FYE: December 31
Type: Not-for-profit

Advocating wellness in Chicagoland from Palos Heights to Palatine, Advocate Health Care is an integrated health care network with more than 200 sites serving the Chicago area. Advocate's operations include about a dozen acute and specialty care hospitals (including Christ Medical Center, Hope Children's Hospital, and Lutheran General Hospital) with more than 3,300 beds, as well as community health clinics and home health care and hospice services. The health system includes the largest physician network of primary care physicians, specialists, and sub-specialists in the state. Advocate Health and BroMenn Healthcare System have announced they intend to merge.

	Annual Growth	12/04	12/05	12/06	12/07	12/08
Sales ($ mil.)	1.9%	2,779.7	2,973.9	3,268.3	3,456.8	3,000.0
Employees	0.0%	24,500	29,600	29,100	30,000	24,500

ADVOCATE LUTHERAN GENERAL HOSPITAL

1775 Dempster St.
Park Ridge, IL 60068
Phone: 847-723-2210
Fax: 847-696-2612
Web: www.advocatehealth.com/luth

CEO: David A. Stark
CFO: James Kelley
HR: —
FYE: December 31
Type: Not-for-profit

Advocate Lutheran General Hospital, also known simply as Lutheran General, provides acute and long-term medical and surgical care to the residents of Park Ridge, Illinois and the surrounding northern suburban Chicago area. As one of the largest hospitals in the region, Lutheran General has about 620 beds and a Level I trauma center. It also includes a complete children's hospital and pediatric critical care center. Lutheran General serves as a teaching hospital and its specialized programs include oncology, cardiology, women's health, emergency medicine, and hospice care. Lutheran General is part of the Advocate Health Care network.

AEA INVESTORS LP

65 E. 55th St.
New York, NY 10022
Phone: 212-644-5900
Fax: 212-888-1459
Web: www.aeainvestors.com

CEO: Vincent A. Mai
CFO: Kevin T. Seltzer
HR: Sandra L. (Sandy) Petruzzelli
FYE: December 31
Type: Private

AEA Investors is in business to make its group of rich investors even richer by buying midsize companies, improving their operations, and selling them a few years down the road. With an exclusive club-like reputation, the company has interests in more than a dozen firms in the consumer products, specialty chemicals, and industrial products sectors in the US, Asia, and Europe. It seeks out established firms with a strong management and competitive position. Holdings include roofing products manufacturer Henry Company, sales and marketing agency Acosta, and industrial insulation maker Unifrax. AEA Investors was founded in 1968 by the Rockefeller, Harriman, and Mellon industrial families and S.G. Warburg & Co.

AEARO TECHNOLOGIES INC.

5457 W. 79th St.
Indianapolis, IN 46268
Phone: 317-692-6666
Fax: 317-692-6772
Web: www.aearo.com

CEO: Michael A. McLain
CFO: —
HR: James M. Phillips
FYE: December 31
Type: Subsidiary

When the sparks fly, it helps to be under the aegis of Aearo Technologies. The company sells personal protection equipment in more than 70 countries under brand names such as AOSafety, E-A-R, Peltor, and SafeWaze. Products include earplugs, goggles, face shields, respirators, hard hats, safety clothing, first-aid kits, and communication headsets. Aearo also sells safety prescription eyewear and makes energy-absorbing foams that control noise, vibration, and shock. Bear Stearns Merchant Banking previously owned a controlling stake in Aearo, which in 2006 was acquired by private equity firm Permira for $765 million. 3M Company acquired Aearo in 2008.

An in-depth profile of this company is available to Hoover's Online members at hoovers.com.

65

AECOM TECHNOLOGY CORPORATION

NYSE: ACM

555 S. Flower St., Ste. 3700	CEO: John M. Dionisio
Los Angeles, CA 90071	CFO: Michael S. (Mike) Burke
Phone: 213-593-8000	HR: Ian R. MacLeod
Fax: 213-593-8730	FYE: September 30
Web: www.aecom.com	Type: Public

AECOM Technology means never having to say Architecture, Engineering, Consulting, Operations, and Maintenance. One of the world's leading engineering and design groups, AECOM provides planning, consulting, and construction management services for civil and infrastructure construction, primarily to governments and private industry. It is a top design firm, operating in Asia, Africa, Europe, the Middle East, and Australia/New Zealand. The group offers services through two divisions: Professional Technical Services and Management Support Services. AECOM Technology projects include project management for the Saadiyat Island Cultural District in Abu Dhabi and master planning for the 2012 London Olympics.

	Annual Growth	9/05	9/06	9/07	9/08	9/09
Sales ($ mil.)	26.4%	2,395.3	3,421.5	4,237.3	5,194.5	6,119.5
Net income ($ mil.)	37.0%	53.8	53.7	100.3	147.2	189.7
Market value ($ mil.)	(11.9%)	—	—	4,006.2	2,803.1	3,112.8
Employees	18.4%	22,000	27,300	32,000	43,000	43,200

AEGIS COMMUNICATIONS GROUP, INC.

8201 Ridgepoint Dr.	CEO: Aparup Sengupta
Irving, TX 75063	CFO: C. M. Sharma
Phone: 972-830-1879	HR: S. M. Gupta
Fax: 972-868-0220	FYE: December 31
Web: www.aegiscomgroup.com	Type: Subsidiary

This is not a pre-recorded message. Aegis Communications Group (which does business as Aegis BPO) provides outsourced telemarketing and customer care services through more than 30 facilities in the US and India. It handles both inbound and outbound calling services, order provisioning, and multilingual communications programs. Besides teleservices, Aegis offers online customer services such as e-mail responses, real-time chat, and data collection. Major clients have included AT&T, American Express, Qwest Communications, and Western Union. India-based investment firm Essar Group owns Aegis, which expanded in late 2008 when it acquired rival customer service provider PeopleSupport. Aegis was established in 1985.

	Annual Growth	12/04	12/05	12/06	12/07	12/08
Est. sales ($ mil.)	—	—	—	—	—	111.9
Employees	—	—	—	—	—	3,700

AEGIS CORPORATION

614 Dartmouth Terrace Ct.	CEO: Dai Wei Ma
Wildwood, MO 63011	CFO: —
Phone: 636-273-1011	HR: —
Fax: 636-273-1015	FYE: December 31
Web: www.goaegis.com	Type: Private

Aegis customers might consider themselves in good company. The company's primary product is AegisGuard, a leather case that protects against radiation and dangerous by-products of cordless and wireless telephones. "Aegis" was the word for a goatskin shield carried by the heroes of Greek mythology. Aegis also makes radiation shields for telephone headsets and a variety of other electronic equipment. The company additionally makes a line of laser products that include laser pointers, sound-activated laser light displays, and layout tools for construction and engineering applications. Aegis, which sells products online and through distributors, also provides custom manufacturing services to OEMs.

	Annual Growth	12/04	12/05	12/06	12/07	12/08
Est. sales ($ mil.)	—	—	—	—	—	910.0
Employees	—	—	—	—	—	4,300

AEGON USA, LLC

4333 Edgewood Rd. NE	CEO: Mark W. Mullin
Cedar Rapids, IA 52499	CFO: Darryl D. Button
Phone: 319-398-8511	HR: —
Fax: 319-369-2209	FYE: December 31
Web: www.aegonins.com	Type: Subsidiary

If AEGON USA was an Argonaut, its quest would be to conquer the US insurance market. The company, a subsidiary of Dutch insurance giant AEGON that operates under the AEGON Americas moniker, provides life insurance and accident and health insurance (such as cancer and long-term care policies) to some 30 million customers throughout the US. Its products include traditional whole life, universal life, variable universal life, and term life insurance for individuals and groups. AEGON USA also offers annuity and investment products, such as mutual funds, as well as asset management services. Subsidiaries include Monumental Life, Transamerica Life, and Western Reserve Life.

AEHR TEST SYSTEMS

NASDAQ (GM): AEHR

400 Kato Terrace	CEO: Rhea J. Posedel
Fremont, CA 94539	CFO: Gary L. Larson
Phone: 510-623-9400	HR: —
Fax: 510-623-9450	FYE: May 31
Web: www.aehr.com	Type: Public

Aehr Test Systems' products don't test air, but rather silicon. Aehr (pronounced "air") makes gear that tests logic and memory semiconductors to weed out defective devices. Its burn-in systems test chips' reliability under stress by exposing them to high temperatures and voltages. Aehr also makes massively parallel test systems for handling thousands of chips simultaneously, die carriers for testing unpackaged chips, custom-designed fixtures for test equipment, and other memory test products. Top customers include Spansion (about 80% of sales) and Texas Instruments. Aehr gets more than one-third of its business outside the US.

	Annual Growth	5/05	5/06	5/07	5/08	5/09
Sales ($ mil.)	7.4%	16.1	23.8	27.4	39.0	21.4
Net income ($ mil.)	—	(4.9)	0.8	2.4	10.6	(30.0)
Market value ($ mil.)	(25.5%)	26.0	55.3	52.0	74.8	8.0
Employees	(2.3%)	91	90	108	123	83

AEOLUS PHARMACEUTICALS, INC.

OTC: AOLS

26361 Crown Valley Parkway, Ste. 150	CEO: John L. McManus
Mission Viejo, CA 92691	CFO: John L. McManus
Phone: 949-481-9825	HR: —
Fax: 949-481-9829	FYE: September 30
Web: www.aeoluspharma.com	Type: Public

Aeolus Pharmaceuticals wants to put an end to free radicals' free-wheeling, cell-damaging fun. The development-stage company is focusing its attention on developing catalytic antioxidant drugs, which can neutralize free radicals. Aeolus' drug candidates could battle amyotrophic lateral sclerosis (ALS, better known as Lou Gehrig's disease), stroke, Parkinson's disease, and other neurodegenerative conditions. The company is also developing antioxidant drugs to treat respiratory conditions and protect healthy tissue from cancer-fighting radiation. Chairman David Cavalier controls about half of the company through investment company XMark Asset Management.

	Annual Growth	9/05	9/06	9/07	9/08	9/09
Sales ($ mil.)	—	—	—	—	—	0.0
Net income ($ mil.)	—	—	—	—	—	(2.3)
Market value ($ mil.)	—	—	—	—	—	18.8
Employees	—	—	—	—	—	2

AEP INDUSTRIES INC.

NASDAQ (GM): AEPI

125 Phillips Ave.
South Hackensack, NJ 07606
Phone: 201-641-6600
Fax: 201-807-2490
Web: www.aepinc.com

CEO: J. Brendan Barba
CFO: Paul M. Feeney
HR: Barbara Sweetman
FYE: October 31
Type: Public

Making plastic cling is its thing! AEP Industries manufactures plastic packaging films — more than 15,000 types — including stretch wrap for industrial pallets, packaging for foods and beverages, and films for agricultural uses, such as wrap for hay bales. AEP also makes dispenser boxed plastic wraps, which are sold to consumers as well as institutions, from schools to hospitals. Other industries courted by AEP are packaging, transportation, food, autos, chemicals, textiles, and electronics. The company underwent a multiyear restructuring program that drove divestiture of noncore businesses and consolidation of operations in Europe, Australia, and Asia. AEP's sales are concentrated in North America.

	Annual Growth	10/05	10/06	10/07	10/08	10/09
Sales ($ mil.)	0.4%	732.7	802.1	786.0	762.2	744.8
Net income ($ mil.)	—	(50.6)	62.9	30.1	12.2	31.5
Market value ($ mil.)	14.5%	139.0	360.8	273.0	134.0	238.9
Employees	4.1%	1,700	1,800	1,850	2,100	2,000

AERA ENERGY LLC

10000 Ming Ave.
Bakersfield, CA 93311
Phone: 661-665-5000
Fax: 661-665-5169
Web: www.aeraenergy.com

CEO: Gaurdie E. Banister Jr.
CFO: Kate Shae
HR: Robert C. (Bob) Alberstadt
FYE: December 31
Type: Joint venture

Aera Energy covers a large area of California. The state's leading oil and gas producer (accounting for 30% of California's total production), Aera Energy's properties extend from the Los Angeles Basin in the south to Coalinga in the north. It has daily production of 165,000 barrels of oil and 50 million cu. ft. of natural gas and boasts proved onshore and offshore reserves of 800 million barrels of oil equivalent. Aera Energy also has interests in real estate operations (in partnership with homebuilder Toll Brothers). The exploration and production company is a joint venture of affiliates of Exxon Mobil and Royal Dutch Shell.

	Annual Growth	12/04	12/05	12/06	12/07	12/08
Est. sales ($ mil.)	—	—	—	—	—	4,000.0
Employees	—	—	—	—	—	1,100

AEROCENTURY CORP.

NYSE Amex: ACY

1440 Chapin Ave., Ste. 310
Burlingame, CA 94010
Phone: 650-340-1888
Fax: 650-696-3929
Web: www.aerocentury.com

CEO: Neal D. Crispin
CFO: Toni M. Perazzo
HR: Toni M. Perazzo
FYE: December 31
Type: Public

With a high-flyin' inventory, AeroCentury leases used turboprop aircraft and engines to domestic and foreign regional airlines and other commercial customers. The company buys equipment from an airline, and then either leases it back to the seller, buys assets already under lease and assumes the obligations of the seller, or makes a purchase and then immediately enters into a new lease with a third party lessee (when it has a customer committed to a lease). Typically, lessees are responsible for any maintenance costs. AeroCentury owns over 40 aircraft, mainly deHavilland and Fokker models. Almost 90% of the company's lease revenues come from airlines headquartered outside the US.

	Annual Growth	12/05	12/06	12/07	12/08	12/09
Sales ($ mil.)	25.6%	13.5	18.3	23.8	31.8	33.6
Net income ($ mil.)	131.1%	0.2	0.8	3.8	3.3	5.7
Market value ($ mil.)	47.9%	5.1	10.0	35.8	14.2	24.3
Employees	—	0	0	0	0	—

AEROFLEX HOLDING CORP.

35 S. Service Rd.
Plainview, NY 11803
Phone: 516-694-6700
Fax: 516-694-0658
Web: www.aeroflex.com

CEO: Leonard (Len) Borow
CFO: John Adamovich Jr.
HR: —
FYE: June 30
Type: Private

Aeroflex flexes its high-tech muscle with aerospace and communications components. The company's diverse offerings include integrated circuits, radio-frequency (RF) components, and microwave assemblies used in military aircraft, satellites, and wireless communications networks. It also provides test equipment used in avionics, military, and mobile radio applications. The company's largest customers are the US government and its contractors (about one-third of sales); it sells to such blue-chip clients as Boeing, Cisco, and Lockheed Martin. In 2007 the company was acquired by Veritas Capital, Golden Gate Private Equity, and Goldman Sachs for about $1.1 billion in cash. Aeroflex filed to go public again in 2010.

AEROGROUP INTERNATIONAL, LLC

201 Meadow Rd.
Edison, NJ 08817
Phone: 732-985-6900
Fax: 732-985-3697
Web: www.aerosoles.com

CEO: Jules Schneider
CFO: Richard Morris
HR: —
FYE: June 30
Type: Private

Aerogroup International wants ladies to feel like they're walking on air or, at least, feel like buying a pair of its Aerosoles. The company designs women's footwear under the Aerosoles, What's What, A2, Aerology, Sole A, and Flexation brands. Its shoes are sold in more than 250 Aerosoles stores in the US and abroad, as well as by catalog, website, and through thousands of department and specialty stores (such as Kohl's, Macy's, and Boscov's). Originally a division of Kenneth Cole, CEO Jules Schneider got together a group of investors and took the business private in 1987.

AEROGROW INTERNATIONAL, INC.

OTC: AERO

6075 Longbow Dr., Ste. 200
Boulder, CO 80301
Phone: 303-444-7755
Fax: 303-444-0406
Web: www.aerogrow.com

CEO: Jack J. Walker
CFO: H. MacGregor (Greg) Clarke
HR: —
FYE: March 31
Type: Public

No time or space for a garden? AeroGrow may be able to cultivate your inner, indoor gardener self. The company develops and manufactures a line of indoor gardening products and seed kits. Using a self-contained light source and hydroponics technologies (water in place of soil), AeroGrow's products are capable of growing a variety of vegetables, herbs, flowers, and other plants without sunlight or frequent watering. Offering about a dozen different garden models and more than 50 seed kits, AeroGrow sells its products in the US through retailers such as Target, Kohl's, and Bed Bath & Beyond, as well as through its website. The company was founded in 2002 by former CEO and chairman Michael Bissonnette.

	Annual Growth	3/05	3/06	3/07	3/08	3/09
Sales ($ mil.)	69.0%	—	—	13.1	38.4	37.4
Net income ($ mil.)	—	—	—	(10.4)	(9.8)	(10.3)
Market value ($ mil.)	(81.7%)	—	—	74.4	37.1	2.5
Employees	(3.6%)	—	—	71	114	66

An in-depth profile of this company is available to Hoover's Online members at hoovers.com.

67

AEROJET-GENERAL CORPORATION

Highway 50 and Aerojet Road
Rancho Cordova, CA 95670
Phone: 916-355-4000
Fax: 916-351-8667
Web: www.aerojet.com

CEO: J. Scott Neish
CFO: —
HR: Elizabeth Zacharias
FYE: November 30
Type: Subsidiary

It *did* take a bunch of rocket scientists to come up with Aerojet-General. The company, a maker of missile and space propulsion systems, was founded by a professor and his colleagues at CIT. Aerojet's propulsion technologies are used in both defense- and space-related applications. The company's defense products include liquid, solid, and air-breathing propulsion systems for missiles and interceptors, as well as armament systems for tactical weapons and munitions. Among Aerojet's space products are liquid, solid, and electric propulsion systems for launch vehicles, transatmospheric vehicles, and spacecraft. Raytheon and Lockheed account for over 50% of sales. Aerojet is the primary subsidiary of GenCorp.

THE AEROSPACE CORPORATION

2350 E. El Segundo Blvd.
El Segundo, CA 90245
Phone: 310-336-5000
Fax: 310-336-7055
Web: www.aero.org

CEO: Wanda M. Austin
CFO: Dale E. Wallis
HR: B. Millado
FYE: September 30
Type: Not-for-profit

A not-for-profit company, The Aerospace Corporation provides space-related research, development, and advisory services, primarily for US government programs. Its chief sponsor is the US Air Force, and its main customers have included the Space and Missile Systems Center of Air Force Space Command and the National Reconnaissance Office. Other clients have included NASA and the National Oceanic and Atmospheric Administration, as well as commercial enterprises, universities, and international organizations. Areas of expertise include launch certification, process implementation, systems engineering, and technology application. The Aerospace Corporation was established in 1960 and operates through about 20 offices.

AÉROPOSTALE, INC.

NYSE: ARO

112 W. 34th St., 22nd Fl.
New York, NY 10120
Phone: 646-485-5410
Fax: —
Web: www.aeropostale.com

CEO: Thomas P. (Tom) Johnson
CFO: Michael J. Cunningham
HR: Kathy E. Gentilozzi
FYE: January 31
Type: Public

Aéropostale flies high in the world of youth fashion. The retailer operates about 950 mostly mall-based stores under the Aéropostale and P.S. from Aéropostale (for kids) banners in 49 states, Puerto Rico, and Canada. Aéropostale stocks the usual teen outerwear (jeans, T-shirts, accessories), mostly under the Aéropostale and Aéro names. It designs and sources its own merchandise so that it can quickly respond to trends. The Aéropostale name originated from a 1920s airmail firm, Compagnie Generale Aéropostale. The brand was created by R.H. Macy & Co. as a private label in the 1980s and later made into a specialty store concept. Macy's sold Aéropostale to its management and Bear Stearns Merchant Banking in 1998.

	Annual Growth	1/06	1/07	1/08	1/09	1/10
Sales ($ mil.)	16.7%	1,204.3	1,413.2	1,590.9	1,885.5	2,230.1
Net income ($ mil.)	28.6%	84.0	106.6	129.2	149.4	229.5
Market value ($ mil.)	13.0%	1,265.7	1,504.8	1,767.3	1,325.8	2,065.7
Employees	10.7%	9,621	22,310	11,155	14,689	14,460

AEROVIRONMENT, INC.

NASDAQ (GM): AVAV

181 W. Huntington Dr., Ste. 202
Monrovia, CA 91016
Phone: 626-357-9983
Fax: 626-359-9628
Web: www.avinc.com

CEO: Timothy E. Conver
CFO: Jikun Kim
HR: —
FYE: April 30
Type: Public

AeroVironment (AV) gives soldiers a birds-eye view of their mission. The company designs and manufactures a line of small unmanned aircraft systems (UAS) for the Department of Defense. Small enough for one-man transport and launch, and operable through a hand-held control, more than 10,000 AV UAS have provided intelligence, surveillance, and reconnaissance for small tactical units. Through its Efficient Energy Systems unit, AV produces PosiCharge fast-charge systems for industrial equipment batteries and electric vehicles (EV) as well as EV testing systems used by auto, defense, and utility markets. Adding to its efficient solutions, AV makes green energy systems, like small wind turbines, for commercial buildings.

	Annual Growth	4/05	4/06	4/07	4/08	4/09
Sales ($ mil.)	23.9%	105.2	139.4	173.7	215.7	247.7
Net income ($ mil.)	13.3%	14.7	11.4	20.7	21.4	24.2
Market value ($ mil.)	5.1%	—	—	463.3	517.6	512.2
Employees	10.1%	447	447	495	543	658

AEROSONIC CORPORATION

NYSE Amex: AIM

1212 N. Hercules Ave.
Clearwater, FL 33765
Phone: 727-461-3000
Fax: 727-447-5926
Web: www.aerosonic.com

CEO: Douglas J. Hillman
CFO: Kevin J. Purcell
HR: Sheryl Vaughn
FYE: January 31
Type: Public

Aerosonic helps pilots straighten up and fly right. The company makes a broad range of mechanical aircraft instruments, including altimeters, airspeed indicators, vertical speed indicators, mach airspeed gauges, artificial horizon indicators, cabin differential indicators, cabin altimeters, maximum allowable airspeed indicators, and stall warning systems. To ensure that everything's working before the wheels leave the ground, Aerosonic also makes aircraft instrument testing equipment. The company's customers include the US military and aircraft manufacturers.

	Annual Growth	1/06	1/07	1/08	1/09	1/10
Sales ($ mil.)	(2.8%)	34.8	31.3	25.4	20.5	31.1
Net income ($ mil.)	14.5%	2.5	0.6	(3.4)	(5.3)	4.3
Market value ($ mil.)	(13.4%)	26.1	26.2	18.7	3.2	14.7
Employees	(7.3%)	279	240	216	195	206

⊞ THE AES CORPORATION

NYSE: AES

4300 Wilson Blvd., 11th Fl.
Arlington, VA 22203
Phone: 703-522-1315
Fax: 703-528-4510
Web: www.aes.com

CEO: Paul T. Hanrahan
CFO: Victoria D. Harker
HR: —
FYE: December 31
Type: Public

The right place at the right time — Is it kismet? No, it's AES, one of the world's leading independent power producers. The company has interests in more than 120 generation facilities in about 30 countries throughout the Americas, Asia, Africa, Europe, and the Middle East that give it a combined net generating capacity of 43,000 MW. AES sells electricity to utilities and other energy marketers through wholesale contracts or on the spot market. AES also sells power directly to customers worldwide through its interests in distribution utilities, mainly in Latin America. In 2009 the company had 3,000 MW of power plants under development in ten countries.

	Annual Growth	12/05	12/06	12/07	12/08	12/09
Sales ($ mil.)	6.2%	11,086.0	12,299.0	13,588.0	16,070.0	14,119.0
Net income ($ mil.)	29.1%	632.0	240.0	(95.0)	1,234.0	1,755.0
Market value ($ mil.)	(4.2%)	12,590.8	17,530.1	17,013.1	6,553.9	10,586.5
Employees	(2.6%)	30,000	32,000	28,000	25,000	27,000

AESCULAP, INC.

3773 Corporate Pkwy.
Center Valley, PA 18034
Phone: 610-797-9300
Fax: 610-791-6880
Web: www.aesculapusa.com

CEO: Charles (Chuck) DiNardo
CFO: Mark Kilroy
HR: Denise Torcivia
FYE: December 31
Type: Subsidiary

Aesculapius, the god of medicine, won't be unleashing his wrath on this company anytime soon. Aesculap is the US-based unit of Aesculap AG & Company, a leading global supplier of surgical instruments, which itself is a subsidiary of German medical device manufacturer B. Braun. The company's products include handheld surgical instruments, implants, and sutures used in neurosurgery as well as laparoscopic, reconstructive, thoracic, and gynecological surgical procedures. Aesculap, Inc. also makes instruments used in minimally invasive spinal surgery, and it offers consulting, training, and supply chain management services.

	Annual Growth	12/04	12/05	12/06	12/07	12/08
Est. sales ($ mil.)	—	—	—	—	—	178.1
Employees	—	—	—	—	—	312

AETNA INC.

NYSE: AET

151 Farmington Ave.
Hartford, CT 06156
Phone: 860-273-0123
Fax: —
Web: www.aetna.com

CEO: Ronald A. (Ron) Williams
CFO: Joseph M. Zubretsky
HR: Elease E. Wright
FYE: December 31
Type: Public

Life, death, health, or injury — Aetna's got an insurance policy to cover it. The company, one of the largest health insurers in the US, also offers life, disability, and long-term care insurance, as well as retirement savings products. Its Health Care division offers HMO, PPO, point of service (POS), health savings account (HSA), and traditional indemnity coverage, along with dental, vision, behavioral health, and Medicare plans, to groups and individuals. The division covers some 19 million medical members. Aetna's Group Insurance segment sells life, disability, and long-term care insurance nationwide. And its Large Case Pensions segment offers pensions, annuities, and other retirement savings products.

	Annual Growth	12/05	12/06	12/07	12/08	12/09
Sales ($ mil.)	11.5%	22,491.9	25,145.7	27,599.6	30,950.7	34,764.1
Net income ($ mil.)	(6.0%)	1,634.5	1,701.7	1,831.0	1,384.1	1,276.5
Market value ($ mil.)	(9.5%)	20,036.2	18,347.2	24,529.5	12,109.7	13,469.3
Employees	5.5%	28,200	30,000	35,200	35,500	35,000

AETNA LIFE INSURANCE COMPANY

151 Farmington Ave.
Hartford, CT 06156
Phone: 860-273-0123
Fax: —
Web: www.aetna.com

CEO: Ronald A. (Ron) Williams
CFO: Joseph M. Zebretsky
HR: Elease E. Wright
FYE: December 31
Type: Subsidiary

Aetna thinks you oughta have some life insurance. As the life insurance subsidiary of health care giant Aetna, Aetna Life Insurance Company (ALIC) offers group life policies and select individual products throughout North America. ALIC was founded in 1853 as a spinoff of Aetna Insurance Company. After more than 150 years in operation, the company has more than 20,000 group life contracts in force. The parent company's operations are focused on accident and health insurance, while life insurance accounts for about 5% of total earned premiums.

AETRIUM INCORPORATED

NASDAQ (GM): ATRM

2350 Helen St.
North St. Paul, MN 55109
Phone: 651-770-2000
Fax: 651-770-7975
Web: www.aetrium.com

CEO: Joseph C. Levesque
CFO: Paul H. Askegaard
HR: Mary Kvall
FYE: December 31
Type: Public

Aetrium can attribute whatever success it reaps to its semiconductor testing equipment. The company makes systems used in testing integrated circuits (ICs) and other electronic components. Its main products are test handlers, which work with testers to thermally condition and sort ICs. Other product lines include automated IC handling products, reliability test systems, and gear for adapting test handlers to different types of IC packages. Aetrium's customers include analog chip maker Maxim Integrated Products (more than half of sales). The company gets about three-quarters of its sales outside the US, mostly in Asian nations.

	Annual Growth	12/05	12/06	12/07	12/08	12/09
Sales ($ mil.)	(14.9%)	16.4	28.2	28.0	17.2	8.6
Net income ($ mil.)	—	(1.9)	(0.6)	6.7	(0.6)	(6.7)
Market value ($ mil.)	(13.0%)	48.2	38.0	63.9	20.8	27.6
Employees	(7.4%)	91	74	78	69	67

AFC ENTERPRISES, INC.

NASDAQ (GM): AFCE

5555 Glendridge Connector NE, Ste. 300
Atlanta, GA 30342
Phone: 404-459-4450
Fax: —
Web: www.afce.com

CEO: Cheryl A. Bachelder
CFO: H. Melville (Mel) Hope III
HR: Stanley F. (Stan) Stout
FYE: December 31
Type: Public

This company's menu for success features fried chicken and biscuits. A leading fast-food company, AFC Enterprises operates the Popeyes restaurant chain, the #2 quick-service chain specializing in chicken behind YUM! Brands' KFC. Operating under the name Popeyes Louisiana Kitchen, the chain boasts about 1,950 locations in the US and in more than two dozen other countries. The restaurants feature Cajun-style fried chicken that is typically served with buttermilk biscuits and a variety of sides, including Cajun rice, coleslaw, mashed potatoes, or french fries. Customers can also select such items as chicken sandwiches, chicken strips, and fried fish and shrimp. About 40 Popeyes locations are company-owned.

	Annual Growth	12/05	12/06	12/07	12/08	12/09
Sales ($ mil.)	0.8%	143.4	153.0	167.3	166.8	148.0
Net income ($ mil.)	(40.5%)	149.6	22.4	23.1	19.4	18.8
Market value ($ mil.)	(14.3%)	386.4	451.6	289.3	119.9	208.6
Employees	(5.8%)	1,527	1,751	1,600	1,360	1,200

AFFILIATED COMPUTER SERVICES, INC.

2828 N. Haskell Ave.
Dallas, TX 75204
Phone: 214-841-6111
Fax: 214-821-8315
Web: www.acs-inc.com

CEO: Lynn R. Blodgett
CFO: Kevin Kyser
HR: Lora J. Villarreal
FYE: December 31*
Type: Subsidiary

Affiliated Computer Services (ACS) handles jobs its clients would rather hand off. The company provides business process outsourcing (BPO) services for commercial enterprises and government agencies, focusing on markets such as communications, health care, and transportation. As an outsourcer, ACS handles functions such as administration, including health care claims processing; finance and accounting; human resources; payment processing; sales, marketing, and customer care call centers; and supply chain management. BPO services account for most of the company's sales. ACS also offers information technology and systems integration services. In February 2010, ACS was acquired by Xerox for $6.4 billion.

	Annual Growth	6/05	6/06	6/07	6/08	6/09
Sales ($ mil.)	10.7%	4,351.2	5,353.7	5,772.5	6,160.5	6,523.2
Net income ($ mil.)	(4.2%)	415.9	358.8	253.1	329.0	349.9
Employees	9.2%	52,000	58,000	60,000	65,000	74,000

*Fiscal year change

An in-depth profile of this company is available to Hoover's Online members at hoovers.com.

69

AFFILIATED FOODS INC.

1401 W. Farmers Ave.
Amarillo, TX 79118
Phone: 806-372-3851
Fax: 806-372-3647
Web: www.afiama.com

CEO: George Lankford
CFO: Tammie Coffee
HR: —
FYE: September 30
Type: Cooperative

This company helps keep pantries stocked in the Panhandle and elsewhere. Affiliated Foods is a leading wholesale distribution cooperative that supplies more than 700 member grocery stores and restaurants in half a dozen states, including Texas, New Mexico, and Oklahoma. It distributes fresh produce, meat, and non-food products, as well as dairy products and beverages through its Plains Dairy unit. Its Tri State Baking Company supplies bread and other baked goods. In addition, Affiliated Foods owns a stake in private-label products supplier Western Family Foods. The company was founded in 1946 as Panhandle Associated Grocers, which merged with South Plains Associated Grocers to form Affiliated Foods in 1968.

	Annual Growth	9/04	9/05	9/06	9/07	9/08
Est. sales ($ mil.)	—	—	—	—	—	1,137.2
Employees	—	—	—	—	—	1,200

AFFILIATED FOODS MIDWEST COOPERATIVE, INC.

1301 Omaha Ave.
Norfolk, NE 68702
Phone: 402-371-0555
Fax: 402-371-1884
Web: afmidwest.com

CEO: Martin W. (Marty) Arter
CFO: Dwayne Severson
HR: Mike Murphy
FYE: June 30
Type: Cooperative

Affiliated Foods Midwest Cooperative is a wholesale food distribution cooperative that supplies more than 800 independent grocers in more than a dozen Midwestern states. From its three distribution centers in Kansas, Nebraska, and Wisconsin, the co-op distributes fresh produce, meats, deli products, baked goods, dairy items, and frozen foods, as well as general merchandise and equipment. It distributes goods under the Shurfine brand (from Topco Associates) and IGA labels. In addition to distribution, Affiliated Foods Midwest provides marketing, merchandising, and warehousing support services for its members. The cooperative was formed in 1931 to make wholesale purchases for a group of retailers in Nebraska.

	Annual Growth	6/04	6/05	6/06	6/07	6/08
Est. sales ($ mil.)	—	—	—	—	—	1,139.8
Employees	—	—	—	—	—	800

AFFILIATED MANAGERS GROUP, INC.   NYSE: AMG

600 Hale St.
Prides Crossing, MA 01965
Phone: 617-747-3300
Fax: 617-747-3380
Web: www.amg.com

CEO: Sean M. Healey
CFO: Darrell W. Crate
HR: —
FYE: December 31
Type: Public

AMG knows a good asset when it sees one — and it knows how to make the most of the ones it finds. Affiliated Managers Group (AMG) is an asset management company that owns interests in more than 30 boutique investment management firms in the US and Canada. The company typically acquires majority stakes of between 50% and 70% in its affiliates — firms that cater to institutional investors and wealthy individuals. Its structure lets affiliates retain partial ownership of their firms and operate with relative autonomy. AMG usually contracts to allocate a percentage of revenues to affiliates for operating expenses, such as compensation.

	Annual Growth	12/05	12/06	12/07	12/08	12/09
Assets ($ mil.)	9.9%	2,321.6	2,665.9	3,395.7	3,246.4	3,390.9
Net income ($ mil.)	(15.9%)	119.1	151.3	182.0	23.2	59.5
Market value ($ mil.)	(4.3%)	3,575.0	4,683.4	5,232.7	1,867.5	3,000.4
Employees	5.6%	1,270	1,275	1,580	1,680	1,580

AFFINIA GROUP INTERMEDIATE HOLDINGS INC.

1101 Technology Dr.
Ann Arbor, MI 48108
Phone: 734-827-5400
Fax: 734-827-5402
Web: www.affiniagroup.com

CEO: Terry R. McCormack
CFO: Thomas H. Madden
HR: Timothy J. Zorn
FYE: December 31
Type: Private

Affinia Group caters to those with an affinity for car parts. The company is a leading designer, manufacturer, and distributor of aftermarket vehicular components. "Aftermarket" refers to the network of vendors existing to sell vehicle components intended to replace the stock manufacturer's parts. Affinia's products, which are sold in 19 countries worldwide, consist of brake, filtration, steering, and suspension parts and are made for passenger cars; sport utility vehicles (SUVs); light, medium, and heavy trucks; and off-highway vehicles. Its brand names are well known in the industry and include AIMCO, McQuay-Norris, Nakata, Raybestos, and WIX.

	Annual Growth	12/04	12/05	12/06	12/07	12/08
Sales ($ mil.)	1.0%	2,089.0	2,132.0	2,160.0	2,138.0	2,178.0
Net income ($ mil.)	—	24.0	(30.0)	(5.0)	6.0	(3.0)
Employees	(3.9%)	12,400	11,678	10,497	9,507	10,576

AFFINION GROUP HOLDINGS, INC.

6 High Ridge Park
Stamford, CT 06905
Phone: 203-956-1000
Fax: —
Web: www.affiniongroup.com

CEO: Nathaniel J. Lipman
CFO: Todd H. Siegel
HR: —
FYE: December 31
Type: Private

Through its partners and affiliations, Affinion Group aims to make fans of its customers' customers. The company operates membership and loyalty programs on behalf of corporate clients seeking to strengthen their ties to consumers. It specializes in launching a variety of media services — through direct mail and the Internet — and packaging these benefits to its clients' customers. Programs overseen include AutoVantage, Buyers Advantage, and Travelers Advantage. Overall, the group offers its programs to more than 63 million members worldwide through more than 5,500 partners; it has offices in Europe, South Africa, and the US. In May 2010, Affinion Group filed for an initial public offering with the SEC.

	Annual Growth	12/05	12/06	12/07	12/08	12/09
Sales ($ mil.)	3.5%	1,198.7	1,137.7	1,321.0	1,409.9	1,376.9
Net income ($ mil.)	—	(89.0)	(452.6)	(191.1)	(88.7)	(66.4)
Employees	4.7%	3,000	3,000	3,300	3,550	3,600

AFFINITY GROUP, INC.

2575 Vista Del Mar
Ventura, CA 93001
Phone: 805-667-4100
Fax: 805-667-4419
Web: www.affinitygroup.com

CEO: Michael A. Schneider
CFO: Thomas F. Wolfe
HR: Laura A. James
FYE: December 31
Type: Private

Recreation is serious business for Affinity Group (AGI). The direct marketing firm sells goods and services through its membership and discount buyers clubs, such as Good Sam, Coast to Coast Resorts, Camp Club USA, and President's Club. It offers RV products (air conditioners, sanitation systems, furnishings) not usually found in general merchandise stores through about 80 Camping World specialty shops across the US, as well as via mail-order catalog and online. AGI also organizes related trade shows and publishes magazines and travel guides, from which it derives subscription fees and ad sales revenue. Chairman Steve Adams is the majority owner of both AGI and, through another entity, RV retailer FreedomRoads.

	Annual Growth	12/04	12/05	12/06	12/07	12/08
Sales ($ mil.)	3.2%	464.7	485.6	514.6	562.2	526.1
Net income ($ mil.)	—	10.3	10.7	(5,731.0)	18.9	(112.0)
Employees	0.2%	1,800	1,842	2,006	2,003	1,814

AFFINITY HEALTH PLAN, INC.

2500 Halsey St.
Bronx, NY 10461
Phone: 718-794-7700
Fax: 718-794-7800
Web: www.affinityplan.org

CEO: Maura Bluestone
CFO: Mark T. Corcoran
HR: —
FYE: December 31
Type: Not-for-profit

Affinity Health Plan has a knack for providing health care services to New York families. The not-for-profit company offers a variety of managed care services for low- and moderate-income residents of the New York metro area. The company serves more than 225,000 participants in its state-sponsored Child Health Plus, Family Health Plus, Medicaid, and Medicare programs. It also offers specialty programs for maternity, dental, and vision care services. Affinity Health's provider network includes 10,000 primary care and specialist physicians, as well as more than 80 hospitals. The company was established in 1986 as the Bronx Health Plan.

AFFIRMATIVE INSURANCE HOLDINGS, INC.   NASDAQ (GS): AFFM

4450 Sojourn Dr., Ste. 500
Addison, TX 75001
Phone: 972-728-6300
Fax: 972-991-0882
Web: www.affirmativeholdings.com

CEO: Kevin R. Callahan
CFO: Michael J. McClure
HR: Randy Smith
FYE: December 31
Type: Public

If you've got a bad driving record or let your insurance lapse, can you still get auto coverage? This company answers in the Affirmative. Affirmative Insurance Holdings, through its subsidiaries, writes and sells non-standard auto insurance policies — that is, coverage for drivers in high-risk categories due to their age, driving records, and other factors — in about a dozen states. It markets its own policies, as well as non-standard coverage from other insurers, through some 250 owned and franchised retail locations (including Driver's Choice, Yellow Key, and A-Affordable stores) and through independent brokers. Investment firm J.C. Flowers controls more than half of the company.

	Annual Growth	12/05	12/06	12/07	12/08	12/09
Assets ($ mil.)	8.4%	544.1	557.3	901.9	802.1	751.3
Net income ($ mil.)	—	18.3	9.7	9.7	1.4	(38.9)
Market value ($ mil.)	(27.3%)	224.9	250.8	160.0	22.4	62.9
Employees	(0.8%)	1,203	942	1,252	1,257	1,167

AFFYMAX, INC.   NASDAQ (GM): AFFY

4001 Miranda Ave.
Palo Alto, CA 94304
Phone: 650-812-8700
Fax: 650-424-0832
Web: www.affymax.com

CEO: Arlene M. Morris
CFO: Paul B. Cleveland
HR: Kay Slocum
FYE: December 31
Type: Public

Affymax is designing peptides to give red blood cells a pep talk. The biotechnology firm is researching and developing possible drugs based upon these biological process regulators. Its leading drug candidate, Hematide, is an erythropoietin (EPO) mimetic, designed to stimulate red blood cell production, like EPO itself. Hematide is being investigated as a possible treatment for anemia caused by chronic renal failure and chemotherapy. Affymax believes Hematide will be cheaper and longer lasting than the EPO stimulants currently used on dialysis patients.

	Annual Growth	12/05	12/06	12/07	12/08	12/09
Sales ($ mil.)	482.2%	0.1	11.7	44.3	82.9	114.9
Net income ($ mil.)	—	(32.6)	(48.3)	(43.1)	(86.5)	(76.5)
Market value ($ mil.)	(10.1%)	—	818.6	537.7	240.2	595.0
Employees	9.9%	98	105	151	147	143

AFFYMETRIX, INC.   NASDAQ (GS): AFFX

3420 Central Expwy.
Santa Clara, CA 95051
Phone: 408-731-5000
Fax: 408-731-5380
Web: www.affymetrix.com

CEO: Kevin M. King
CFO: Timothy C. Barabe
HR: Lori Ciano
FYE: December 31
Type: Public

Affymetrix detects the secrets of human genetics. Its GeneChip system and other products are used to identify, analyze, and manage genetic data in the development of new treatments for infectious diseases, cancer, and other ailments. Affymetrix sells its products directly to drugmakers, academic research labs, and government agencies in its key North American and European markets. It has partnerships and licensing agreements with such pharmaceutical companies as Life Technologies and Roche to develop new disease diagnostics and instrumentation systems.

	Annual Growth	12/05	12/06	12/07	12/08	12/09
Sales ($ mil.)	(2.9%)	367.6	355.3	371.3	410.2	327.1
Net income ($ mil.)	—	57.5	(13.7)	12.6	(307.9)	(23.9)
Market value ($ mil.)	(40.9%)	3,382.4	1,633.5	1,639.1	211.8	413.7
Employees	(2.6%)	1,101	1,128	1,141	1,128	989

AFLAC INCORPORATED   NYSE: AFL

1932 Wynnton Rd.
Columbus, GA 31999
Phone: 706-323-3431
Fax: 706-324-6330
Web: www.aflac.com

CEO: Daniel P. (Dan) Amos
CFO: Kriss Cloninger III
HR: Yosuke Miwa
FYE: December 31
Type: Public

Would you buy insurance from a duck? Aflac counts on it! To help clients lessen the financial losses during periods of disability or illness, Aflac sells supplemental health and life insurance policies, including coverage for accidents, intensive care, dental, vision, and short-term disability, as well as for specific conditions, primarily cancer. It is a leading supplier of supplemental insurance in the US and is an industry leader in Japan's cancer-insurance market (with 14 million policies in force). Aflac, which is marketed through — and is an acronym for — American Family Life Assurance Company, sells policies that pay cash benefits for hospital confinement, emergency treatment, and medical appliances.

	Annual Growth	12/05	12/06	12/07	12/08	12/09
Assets ($ mil.)	10.5%	56,361.0	59,805.0	65,805.0	79,331.0	84,106.0
Net income ($ mil.)	0.2%	1,483.0	1,483.0	1,634.0	1,254.0	1,497.0
Market value ($ mil.)	(0.1%)	21,797.1	21,599.9	29,408.7	21,524.8	21,717.3
Employees	3.7%	6,970	7,411	8,048	7,949	8,057

AFP IMAGING CORPORATION   Pink Sheets: AFPC

250 Clearbrook Rd.
Elmsford, NY 10523
Phone: 914-592-6100
Fax: 914-592-6148
Web: www.afpimaging.com

CEO: David Vozick
CFO: Elise Nissen
HR: Aida McKinney
FYE: June 30
Type: Public

Getting ready for a dental implant, or just wanting to look that gift horse in the mouth? AFP Imaging can assist you. The company makes imaging systems, for medical, dental, veterinary, and industrial markets. Products range from good old-fashioned film-based X-ray machines and film processors to digital computed tomography scanners and three-dimensional digital radiography systems (including both the sensors and software to display images on computer screens). Its digital radiography systems are designed for use in both human and animal dental diagnostics. In addition to selling its own products, AFP Imaging distributes imaging products from other manufacturers.

	Annual Growth	6/04	6/05	6/06	6/07	*6/08
Sales ($ mil.)	14.7%	19.8	23.1	25.0	28.7	34.3
Net income ($ mil.)	—	1.3	1.9	1.0	(4.7)	(11.0)
Market value ($ mil.)	(34.3%)	26.9	37.7	42.1	29.4	5.0
Employees	10.1%	83	84	83	115	122

*Most recent year available

An in-depth profile of this company is available to Hoover's Online members at hoovers.com.

71

AFTON CHEMICAL CORPORATION

500 Spring St.
Richmond, VA 23219
Phone: 804-788-5800
Fax: 804-788-5184
Web: www.aftonchemical.com

CEO: C. S. Warren Huang
CFO: —
HR: —
FYE: December 31
Type: Subsidiary

Performance enhancers aren't just the products advertised on late night TV and in the back of men's magazines. Afton Chemical manufactures additives that improve the effectiveness of fuels and lubricants. The company was formed in 2004 from the additives division of NewMarket, which had been called Ethyl before switching to a holding company structure and dividing its business into two operating subsidiaries: Afton and Ethyl. Afton divides its own products into fuel additives (which improve the refining process and boost the performance of gasoline and other fuels) and lubricant additives (which improve the performance, functionality, and durability of oils).

	Annual Growth	12/04	12/05	12/06	12/07	12/08
Est. sales ($ mil.)	—	—	—	—	—	78.7
Employees	—	—	—	—	—	555

田 AG PROCESSING INC., A COOPERATIVE

12700 W. Dodge Rd.
Omaha, NE 68154
Phone: 402-496-7809
Fax: 402-498-2215
Web: www.agp.com

CEO: Martin P. (Marty) Reagan
CFO: J. Keith Spackler
HR: Judith V. (Judy) Ford
FYE: August 31
Type: Cooperative

Soy far, soy good for Ag Processing (AGP), one of the largest soybean processors in the world — it processes 16,000 acres worth of soybeans at nine mills every day. AGP's chief soybean products are refined vegetable oil and commercial animal feed and feed additives. The cooperative provides grain marketing and transportation services for its 250,000 member/farmers, whose farms are located in Canada and 18 US states. It also offers corn-based ethanol and soybean-based bio-diesel. Consisting mostly of midwestern farmers, AGP's members are represented through 184 local and regional co-ops. AGP also owns Masterfeeds, a Canadian animal feed company and Proagro, a Venezuelan poultry processor.

A. G. SPANOS COMPANIES

10100 Trinity Pkwy., 5th Fl.
Stockton, CA 95219
Phone: 209-478-7954
Fax: 209-473-3703
Web: www.agspanos.com

CEO: Dean A. Spanos
CFO: Jeremiah T. Murphy
HR: —
FYE: September 30
Type: Private

Spanning the land from California to Florida, A. G. Spanos Companies bridges many operations — from building, managing, and selling multifamily housing units to constructing master-planned communities, as well as developing land and building commercial space. With divisions and operations in about 10 states, the firm has built about 2 million sq. ft. of office space properties, 120,000-plus apartment homes, and more than 400 developments. Other operations include mixed-use development and property management. Alex Spanos also owns the NFL's San Diego Chargers. He operates the companies with his sons Dean (president and CEO) and Michael Spanos (EVP).

AGA MEDICAL HOLDINGS, INC.

NASDAQ (GM): AGAM

5050 Nathan Lane North
Plymouth, MN 55442
Phone: 763-513-9227
Fax: 763-513-9226
Web: www.amplatzer.com

CEO: John R. Barr
CFO: Brigid A. Makes
HR: Larry Found
FYE: December 31
Type: Public

AGA Medical Holdings heals broken hearts. The company specializes in making medical devices for treating structural heart defects and vascular diseases. Its AMPLATZER occlusion devices use minimally invasive small catheters, which physicians can retrieve and position without the need for multiple devices or repetition of procedures. Approved for use in both Europe and the US, the company sells its devices in more than 100 countries through its own sales force and direct distributors. Its primary customers are pediatric cardiologists, radiologists, and vascular surgeons. Dr. Kurt Amplatz and director Franck Gougeon established AGA Medical Holdings in 1995.

	Annual Growth	12/05	12/06	12/07	12/08	12/09
Sales ($ mil.)	19.3%	98.1	127.5	147.3	166.9	198.7
Net income ($ mil.)	—	(48.8)	12.6	6.1	9.1	(1.1)
Market value ($ mil.)	—	—	—	—	—	740.6
Employees	22.2%	—	—	335	470	500

AGC AMERICA, INC.

2201 Water Ridge Pkwy., Ste. 400
Charlotte, NC 28217
Phone: 704-357-3631
Fax: 704-357-6328

CEO: Makoto Seki
CFO: Steve Hughes
HR: —
FYE: December 31
Type: Subsidiary

AGC America is a wholly owned subsidiary of Asahi Glass, the world's #1 maker of flat glass. AGC America is the holding company for Asahi's major subsidiaries in North America which include eight companies involved in the manufacture of products for the chemicals, glass, and electronics industries. AGC Flat Glass North America and its companies make architectural, automotive, flat, float, figured, and other processed glass. AGC Chemicals Americas manufactures and markets fluorochemicals, caustic soda, specialty chemicals, and soda ash for glass production. AGC Electronics America makes high-purity silicon carbide and synthetic quartz glass for semiconductors, and glass substrates for LCDs.

AGC FLAT GLASS NORTH AMERICA, INC.

11175 Cicero Dr., Ste. 400
Alpharetta, GA 30022
Phone: 404-446-4200
Fax: 404-446-4221
Web: www.na.agc-flatglass.com

CEO: Brad Kitterman
CFO: Ryan Vangorp
HR: —
FYE: December 31
Type: Subsidiary

In this company's line of work, if the boss catches you staring out the window, you can claim that you're doing research. AGC Flat Glass North America (formerly AFG Industries) boasts of being North America's largest manufacturer of construction/specialty glass, and the continent's second-largest maker of flat glass. AGC North America offers its coated, insulated, solar, laminated, store-front, and fire-rated glass products to customers in the residential/commercial building products, specialty, and automotive glass markets. AFG Industries was formed by the 1978 merger of Fourco Glass and ASG. AGC North America is a subsidiary of AGC America, which is itself a subsidiary of Japan's Asahi Glass.

AGCO CORPORATION

NYSE: AGCO

4205 River Green Pkwy.
Duluth, GA 30096
Phone: 770-813-9200
Fax: 770-813-6118
Web: www.agcocorp.com

CEO: Martin H. Richenhagen
CFO: Andrew H. (Andy) Beck
HR: Lucinda B. Smith
FYE: December 31
Type: Public

AGCO's annual harvests may be smaller than those of larger rivals John Deere and CNH Global, but it still reaps profits worldwide. AGCO makes tractors, combines, hay tools, sprayers, forage equipment, and replacement parts. It sells through a global network of about 2,800 dealers and distributors. It also makes diesel engines, gears, and generators through its AGCO Sisu Power unit. Brand names include Massey Ferguson, Challenger, Valtra (Finland-based), and Fendt (Germany-based). The company offers financing services to customers and dealers through a joint venture with Netherlands-based Rabobank. AGCO sells products in some 140 countries; more than 80% of sales are generated outside the US.

	Annual Growth	12/05	12/06	12/07	12/08	12/09
Sales ($ mil.)	5.0%	5,449.7	5,435.0	6,828.1	8,424.6	6,630.4
Net income ($ mil.)	44.0%	31.6	(64.9)	246.3	400.0	135.7
Market value ($ mil.)	18.2%	1,541.5	2,878.3	6,324.1	2,194.5	3,008.5
Employees	2.8%	13,000	12,800	13,700	15,600	14,500

AGFIRST FARM CREDIT BANK

1401 Hampton St.
Columbia, SC 29201
Phone: 803-799-5000
Fax: 803-254-1776
Web: www.agfirst.com

CEO: F. A. (Andy) Lowrey
CFO: Charl L. Butler
HR: —
FYE: December 31
Type: Cooperative

AgFirst puts farmers first. A large and growing agricultural lender, AgFirst Farm Credit Bank operates through 22 farmer-owned cooperatives in 15 eastern states and Puerto Rico. It offers more than $20 billion in loans to some 80,000 farmers, ranchers, rural homeowners, and agribusiness owners. The lender originates real estate, operating, and rural home mortgage loans. Additionally, it offers crop, life, and timber insurance; equipment leasing; tax services; record keeping; and other products and services designed to meet customers' business and personal needs. The bank does not accept deposits; it raises money by selling bonds and notes on the capital markets.

	Annual Growth	12/04	12/05	12/06	12/07	12/08
Assets ($ mil.)	15.4%	16,887.5	20,483.0	24,412.2	26,926.6	29,911.1
Net income ($ mil.)	4.8%	180.3	164.3	190.2	192.2	217.2
Employees	—	—	—	—	—	—

AGGREGATE INDUSTRIES MANAGEMENT INC.

7529 Standish Place, Ste. 200
Rockville, MD 20855
Phone: 301-284-3600
Fax: 301-284-3645
Web: www.aggregate-us.com

CEO: William (Will) Glusac
CFO: Al Stone
HR: —
FYE: December 31
Type: Subsidiary

Aggregate Industries Management, which does business as Aggregate Industries US, is a rock-solid supplier of building materials. The company produces aggregate products, such as crushed stone, sand and gravel, asphalt, ready-mix concrete, and recycled materials, used by the US construction industry. It also acts as an asphalt paving contractor. The firm's products and services are used in public infrastructure and commercial and residential development projects, from highways and bridges to buildings. A subsidiary of UK-based Aggregate Industries, Aggregate Industries US operates half a dozen regional businesses throughout the country, including Hardaway Concrete Company and Meyer Material Company.

	Annual Growth	12/04	12/05	12/06	12/07	12/08
Est. sales ($ mil.)	—	—	—	—	—	7.9
Employees	—	—	—	—	—	114

AGGREKO USA LLC

4607 W. Admiral Doyle Dr.
New Iberia, LA 70562
Phone: 337-365-5479
Fax: 337-369-3355
Web: www.aggreko.com/NorthAmerica

CEO: Rupert C. Soames
CFO: —
HR: —
FYE: December 31
Type: Subsidiary

Aggreko USA is an aggressive supplier of temporary power in the USA. The company is the US-based subsidiary of rental raja Aggreko plc, a world leader in the design and leasing of power generators, temperature control equipment, air compressors, and related equipment for the refrigeration, heat, and dehumidification needs of its many customers. Aggreko provides cooling, heating, and electrification services at natural disaster sites, as well as for more controlled events, such as the Super Bowl, the Olympic Games, and movie sets. Its products and services, however, are mostly used by utility, manufacturing, and construction companies.

AGILENT TECHNOLOGIES, INC.

NYSE: A

5301 Stevens Creek Blvd.
Santa Clara, CA 95051
Phone: 408-345-8886
Fax: 408-345-8474
Web: www.agilent.com

CEO: William P. (Bill) Sullivan
CFO: Didier Hirsch
HR: Jean M. Halloran
FYE: October 31
Type: Public

Agilent Technologies keeps scientists on their toes. A maker of scientific testing equipment, Agilent supplies a slew of bioanalytical and electronic measurement tools, including data generators, multimeters, and oscilloscopes. Operations straddle electronic test and measurement instruments (the largest in the world), bioanalytical measurement, and a semiconductor and board test business. The company offers centralized lab research, too. Agilent's 25,000 customers include global giants in communications, electronics, life sciences, and chemical analysis, such as Cisco, Dow Chemical, GlaxoSmithKline, Intel, Merck, and Samsung. Customers outside the US account for about two-thirds of sales.

	Annual Growth	10/05	10/06	10/07	10/08	10/09
Sales ($ mil.)	(3.4%)	5,139.0	4,973.0	5,420.0	5,774.0	4,481.0
Net income ($ mil.)	—	327.0	3,307.0	638.0	693.0	(31.0)
Market value ($ mil.)	(4.8%)	10,500.4	11,678.1	12,829.2	7,725.4	8,613.1
Employees	(5.4%)	21,000	18,700	19,400	19,600	16,800

AGILYSYS, INC.

NASDAQ (GS): AGYS

28925 Fountain Pkwy.
Solon, OH 44139
Phone: 440-519-8700
Fax: —
Web: www.agilysys.com

CEO: Martin F. Ellis
CFO: Kenneth J. Kossin Jr.
HR: Kathleen A. Weigand
FYE: March 31
Type: Public

Agilysys serves as an agile ally for systems procurement. The company provides IT services to enterprise and government customers. It implements hardware and software from partners, including EMC, Hewlett-Packard, IBM, and Oracle. The company's services range from disaster planning to document and storage management, and it provides industry-specific software tools, such as property management applications. Specializing in the retail and hospitality sectors, Agilysys also markets to the education, financial services, government, health care, manufacturing, and transportation industries. The company generates nearly all of its revenues from customers in North America.

	Annual Growth	3/05	3/06	3/07	3/08	3/09
Sales ($ mil.)	(18.1%)	1,622.9	1,742.5	474.6	781.0	730.7
Net income ($ mil.)	—	19.5	28.1	232.9	7.2	(284.1)
Market value ($ mil.)	(31.6%)	454.1	347.8	519.0	267.9	99.3
Employees	(2.5%)	1,386	1,483	996	1,328	1,250

AGL RESOURCES INC.

NYSE: AGL

10 Peachtree Place NE
Atlanta, GA 30309
Phone: 404-584-4000
Fax: 404-584-3714
Web: www.aglresources.com

CEO: John W. Somerhalder II
CFO: Andrew W. (Drew) Evans
HR: Melanie M. Platt
FYE: December 31
Type: Public

AGL Resources brings its resources to customers in several states through half a dozen utilities. Its Atlanta Gas Light unit delivers natural gas to 1.5 million customers in Georgia. AGL Resources also operates natural gas utilities in Tennessee (Chattanooga Gas) and Virginia (Virginia Natural Gas), and it has operations in Florida, Maryland, and New Jersey. Overall, the company distributes natural gas to 2.3 million customers. Through its nonregulated subsidiaries, AGL Resources markets natural gas to retail and wholesale customers, stores and transports gas, and offers asset and risk management services.

	Annual Growth	12/05	12/06	12/07	12/08	12/09
Sales ($ mil.)	(3.9%)	2,718.0	2,621.0	2,494.0	2,800.0	2,317.0
Net income ($ mil.)	3.6%	193.0	212.0	211.0	217.0	222.0
Market value ($ mil.)	1.2%	2,709.9	3,029.1	2,930.3	2,440.6	2,839.2
Employees	0.9%	2,385	2,369	2,332	2,389	2,469

AGREE REALTY CORPORATION

NYSE: ADC

31850 Northwestern Hwy.
Farmington Hills, MI 48334
Phone: 248-737-4190
Fax: 248-737-9110
Web: www.agreerealty.com

CEO: Richard Agree
CFO: Kenneth R. Howe
HR: —
FYE: December 31
Type: Public

Shopping sprees really agree with Agree Realty. The self-managed real estate investment trust (REIT) owns, develops, and manages retail real estate, primarily freestanding big-box properties. It owns nearly 75 retail properties in primarily midwestern states. A dozen of the REIT's properties are anchored strip malls. All told, Agree Realty owns a total of more than 3 million sq. ft. of leasable space. Its largest tenants include Borders, Kmart, and Walgreen. National tenants make up 90% of Agree's revenues. Agree considers acquisitions to diversify its portfolio and grow its stable of long-term tenants. The REIT was founded in 1971 by CEO Richard Agree.

	Annual Growth	12/05	12/06	12/07	12/08	12/09
Sales ($ mil.)	4.2%	31.6	32.9	34.5	35.7	37.3
Net income ($ mil.)	1.5%	16.0	14.0	15.5	21.5	17.0
Market value ($ mil.)	(5.3%)	281.9	335.3	293.6	176.8	227.2
Employees	5.7%	8	8	10	7	10

AGRIBANK, FCB

375 Jackson St.
St. Paul, MN 55101
Phone: 651-282-8800
Fax: 651-282-8666
Web: www.agribank.com

CEO: L. William (Bill) York
CFO: Brian J. O'Keane
HR: Sandi Schmiesing
FYE: December 31
Type: Cooperative

AgriBank puts the "green" in green acres. A financial intermediary, AgriBank provides wholesale lending and business services to Farm Credit System (FCS) associations in America's heartland. Established by Congress in 1916, the FCS is a nationwide network of cooperatives that provides loans and financial services for farmers, ranchers, agribusiness owners, timber producers, and rural homeowners. Farm Credit System's co-ops write loans for land, equipment, and other farm operating costs; they in turn own AgriBank. Formed in 1992, AgriBank also provides credit to rural electric, water, and telephone systems.

	Annual Growth	12/04	12/05	12/06	12/07	12/08
Assets ($ mil.)	15.0%	36,175.3	39,866.5	47,007.4	52,264.0	63,285.8
Net income ($ mil.)	20.3%	157.3	138.5	162.6	182.9	329.2
Employees	—	—	—	—	—	—

AGRI-MARK, INC.

100 Milk St.
Methuen, MA 01844
Phone: 978-689-4442
Fax: 978-794-8304
Web: www.agrimark.net

CEO: Paul P. Johnston
CFO: Margaret H. Bertolino
HR: Vince Candio
FYE: November 30
Type: Cooperative

Cheese lovers who make a habit of Cabot ought to know about Agri-Mark. The northeastern US dairy cooperative makes Cabot-brand Vermont cheddar cheese, butter, and cultured dairy products, as well as McCadam-branded and European cheeses. The co-op has more than 1,300 member-owners who operate farms throughout New England and New York, producing 300 million gallons of milk a year. Agri-Mark also sells milk to bottlers and manufacturers in the eastern US, and dairy ingredients to foodservice and industrial clients. It owns processing plants in Vermont, Massachusetts, and New York. The co-op was formed in 1916 as the New England Milk Producers Association and became Agri-Mark in 1980.

	Annual Growth	11/04	11/05	11/06	11/07	11/08
Est. sales ($ mil.)	—	—	—	—	—	203.1
Employees	—	—	—	—	—	900

AGRITEC SYSTEMS, INC.

TSX Venture: AGR

7720 Westview
Houston, TX 77055
Phone: 832-647-3287
Fax: 713-681-1114
Web: www.agritecsystems.com

CEO: Willy L. Verbrugghe
CFO: Greg R. Wellen
HR: —
FYE: July 31
Type: Public

AgriTec Systems converts nature's leftovers into a financially tasty main course. The company takes agricultural waste products and converts them into usable specialty chemicals. Its patented methods convert rice hull ash and other biomass materials into silicas, silicates, activated carbon, and related materials. Those products are used in food processing, air and water purification, semiconductor fabrication, and industrial manufacturing. AgriTech has several patented processes which it plans to commercialize on a global scale. One example is a fine-celled foam, manufactured and marketed through its subsidiary enviroLife, made from converted biomass materials for horticulture and agriculture applications.

	Annual Growth	7/05	7/06	7/07	7/08	7/09
Sales ($ mil.)	—	—	—	—	0.1	0.0
Net income ($ mil.)	—	—	—	—	(0.4)	(0.3)
Market value ($ mil.)	(58.3%)	—	—	—	2.4	1.0
Employees	—	—	—	—	—	—

AGRIUM U.S. INC.

4582 S. Ulster St., Ste. 1700
Denver, CO 80237
Phone: 303-804-4400
Fax: 303-804-4478
Web: www.agrium.com/company_profile/our_operations/retail.cfm

CEO: Michael M. (Mike) Wilson
CFO: Bruce G. Waterman
HR: James M. Grossett
FYE: December 31
Type: Subsidiary

Agrium U.S. operates south of the border for Canadian fertilizers manufacturer and distributor Agrium. The parent company produces and distributes four major crop nutrients: nitrogen, phosphate, potash, and sulfate fertilizers for the wholesale market. Agrium U.S. operates a network of about 800 retail farm centers in the US and Latin America, and is one of the largest independent retailers of fertilizers, seeds, and chemicals in North America. The US provides Agrium with about two-thirds of its sales. Agrium began originally as Cominco during the 1930s.

	Annual Growth	12/04	12/05	12/06	12/07	12/08
Est. sales ($ mil.)	—	—	—	—	—	3,294.0
Employees	—	—	—	—	—	2,500

AGT CRUNCH ACQUISITION LLC

22 W. 19th St., Fl. 4
New York, NY 10011
Phone: 212-993-0300
Fax: 212-367-0960
Web: www.crunch.com

CEO: Tim Miller
CFO: Michael R. Jacobs
HR: Daniel Espino
FYE: December 31
Type: Private

AGT Crunch Acquisition — operator of the Crunch Fitness chain — helps city folk stay in shape. The company operates about 30 physical fitness facilities in urban locations throughout the US. Crunch offers trendy workouts such as Cardio Go Go, Pole Dancing, and Hot Pilates. It also offers personal training sessions to its members. The company sells a variety of fitness-related products including apparel, exercise videos, books, and music-compilation CDs. With its base in New York City, Crunch has locations in cities such as New York, Los Angeles, Miami, Chicago, Atlanta, and San Francisco. AGT Crunch Acquisition filed for Chapter 11 bankruptcy protection in 2009.

	Annual Growth	12/04	12/05	12/06	12/07	12/08
Est. sales ($ mil.)	—	—	—	—	—	61.9
Employees	—	—	—	—	—	2,000

AGUSTA AEROSPACE CORPORATION

3050 Red Lion Rd.
Philadelphia, PA 19114
Phone: 215-281-1400
Fax: 215-281-0447
Web: www.agustausa.com

CEO: Bruno Cellemme
CFO: Thomas R. Hall
HR: Salvatore LoDico
FYE: December 31
Type: Subsidiary

Agusta Aerospace sells and services helicopters made by its parent, UK-based AgustaWestland. Agusta Aerospace offers sales support and services for customers in the US, Canada, and Central and South America. Services include airframe and sheet metal fabrication, inspections, pilot and mechanic training, component repair, overhaul, inventory support, and replacement services. Helicopters supported include the A109E, A119 KOALA, A109K2, A109C, A109MAX, and A109A. Customers come from the corporate, emergency medical, law enforcement, offshore, and utility markets.

	Annual Growth	12/04	12/05	12/06	12/07	12/08
Est. sales ($ mil.)	—	—	—	—	—	311.9
Employees	—	—	—	—	—	375

A. H. BELO CORPORATION

NYSE: AHC

400 S. Record St.
Dallas, TX 75202
Phone: 214-977-8200
Fax: 214-977-8201
Web: www.ahbelo.com

CEO: Robert W. Decherd
CFO: Alison K. Engel
HR: Sheila A. Hartley
FYE: December 31
Type: Public

This company gives the Big D a helping of news with breakfast. A. H. Belo is a leading newspaper publisher with a portfolio of three daily newspapers anchored by *The Dallas Morning News*, one of the country's top papers with a circulation of about 260,000. It also owns *The Press-Enterprise* (Riverside, California) and *The Providence Journal* (published in Rhode Island by subsidiary The Providence Journal Company). In addition to its flagship papers, A. H. Belo publishes the *Denton Record-Chronicle* (Texas) and several niche papers such as the Spanish-language paper Al Dia (Dallas), along with websites serving most of its publications. The company was spun off from TV station operator Belo Corp. in 2008.

	Annual Growth	12/05	12/06	12/07	12/08	12/09
Sales ($ mil.)	(10.9%)	822.3	817.7	738.7	637.3	518.3
Net income ($ mil.)	—	47.8	15.2	(347.0)	(62.3)	(107.9)
Market value ($ mil.)	164.2%	—	—	—	45.5	120.2
Employees	(17.6%)	—	—	3,800	3,350	2,580

AHOLD USA, INC.

1385 Hancock St., Quincy Center Plaza
Quincy, MA 02169
Phone: 781-380-8000
Fax: 617-770-8190
Web: www.ahold.com

CEO: Lawrence S. (Larry) Benjamin
CFO: —
HR: Enrique Boerboom
FYE: December 31
Type: Subsidiary

Ahold USA is the American arm of Netherlands-based Royal Ahold — one of the world's leading grocery retailers. The subsidiary oversees more than 730 supermarkets in four divisions: Stop & Shop New England, Stop & Shop Metro New York, Giant-Landover, and Giant-Carlisle, each with its own support business. Its online grocery delivery service Peapod serves Giant Food and Stop & Shop customers in select markets. Ahold USA's Dutch parent reorganized its US and European operations in 2010 to position them for growth. The reorganization led to speculation that the Dutch grocery chain, which has spent the better part of the past decade shedding businesses, may begin acquiring some on both sides of the Atlantic.

AIG AMERICAN GENERAL LIFE COMPANIES

2929 Allen Pkwy.
Houston, TX 77019
Phone: 713-522-1111
Fax: 713-620-6653
Web: www.aigag.com

CEO: Mary Jane B. Fortin
CFO: Don W. Cummings
HR: Debbie Runge
FYE: December 31
Type: Subsidiary

A-ten-shun! AIG American General is still among the top brass of US life insurance and financial services firms. It is the marketing name for the domestic life insurance companies and affiliates group of American International Group. AIG American General offers clients a variety of products to build their nest eggs, including fixed and variable annuities. Life insurance offerings include individual and group policies for families, businesses, and affiliation groups. Other products include accident and health insurance and worksite benefits programs. After approaching insolvency, parent firm AIG has announced that it will sell all of its US life insurance operations, including AIG American General.

AIG RETIREMENT SERVICES, INC.

1 SunAmerica Center, Century City
Los Angeles, CA 90067
Phone: 310-772-6000
Fax: 310-772-6574
Web: www.valic.com

CEO: Jay S. Wintrob
CFO: N. Scott Gillis
HR: —
FYE: December 31
Type: Subsidiary

AIG Retirement Services keeps its eyes on the future. The group is part of SunAmerica Financial Group, the domestic life and retirement services segment of insurance giant American International Group (AIG). Its subsidiaries sell a variety of investment products, including fixed annuities (Western National Life Insurance); group retirement services for education, health care, and not-for-profit organizations (VALIC); and variable annuities (SunAmerica Annuity and Life Assurance). SagePoint Financial provides broker/dealer services. Other units include AIG SunAmerica Asset Management and AIG SunAmerica Retirement Markets. Ailing parent AIG cancelled plans to sell its retirement businesses in 2009.

AIMCO PROPERTIES, L.P.

4582 S. Ulster Street Pkwy., Ste. 1100
Denver, CO 80237
Phone: 303-757-8101
Fax: —
Web: www.aimco.com

CEO: Terry Considine
CFO: David R. Robertson
HR: James G. Purvis
FYE: December 31
Type: Subsidiary

AIMCO Properties' aim is true. The company is the operating arm of multifamily real estate giant Apartment Investment and Management Company (AIMCO), which owns some 870 apartment properties throughout the US. AIMCO Properties holds most of its AIMCO's assets and manages its day-to-day operations, including property management and asset management. Its portfolio includes government-subsidized affordable housing properties, suburban apartment communities, and urban high-rise properties. Investment management operations include management of its own portfolio as well as services for affiliated partnerships. AIMCO controls more than 90% of AIMCO Properties.

	Annual Growth	12/04	12/05	12/06	12/07	12/08
Est. sales ($ mil.)	—	—	—	—	—	1,457.9
Employees	—	—	—	—	—	5,000

AIMS WORLDWIDE, INC.

OTC: AMWW

10400 Eaton Place, Ste. 450
Fairfax, VA 22030
Phone: 703-621-3875
Fax: 703-621-3865
Web: www.aimsworldwide.com

CEO: Gerald Garcia Jr.
CFO: Patrick J. Summers
HR: —
FYE: December 31
Type: Public

With a name like that, AIMS Worldwide has certainly set its sights sky-high. AIMS, which stands for Accurate Integrated Marketing Solutions, provides one-to-one marketing and consulting services through branded products such as AIMSolutions and its marketing model, One-2-One. The company operates via business segments that provide advertising, strategic planning, market research, public relations, training, and digital media services. AIMS expands its marketing services and widens its industry expertise by acquiring regional marketing and consulting agencies specializing in different industries.

	Annual Growth	12/05	12/06	12/07	12/08	12/09
Sales ($ mil.)	47.6%	1.2	1.7	2.1	14.0	5.7
Net income ($ mil.)	—	(1.9)	(3.2)	(3.2)	(1.3)	(2.1)
Market value ($ mil.)	(35.8%)	36.6	20.5	16.1	3.4	6.2
Employees	49.5%	5	5	25	25	25

AIR CRUISERS COMPANY, LLC

1740 State Rte. 34
Wall, NJ 07727
Phone: 732-681-3527
Fax: 732-681-9163
Web: www.aircruisers.com

CEO: John O'Donnell
CFO: John Melone
HR: Scott Ernst
FYE: August 31
Type: Subsidiary

Air Cruisers can be a pilot's best buddy if skies turn unfriendly. The company makes about 60% of the inflatable safety equipment — including life vests, life rafts, helicopter floats, and evacuation slides — used on the world's passenger planes, as well as many used on military and commercial aircraft. Its products were successfully deployed in the US Airways craft that landed on the Hudson River in 2009. Air Cruisers' lineup of rafts hold from four to nearly 60 people. A subsidiary of Zodiac Aerospace, the firm operates manufacturing facilities in the US, Mexico, and France; sales offices in the Asia/Pacific region, France, and the US; and service centers in France, Singapore, the UK, and the US.

AIR METHODS CORPORATION

NASDAQ (GS): AIRM

7301 S. Peoria St.
Englewood, CO 80112
Phone: 303-792-7400
Fax: 303-790-0499
Web: www.airmethods.com

CEO: Aaron D. Todd
CFO: Trent J. Carman
HR: Jackie Forker
FYE: December 31
Type: Public

Air Methods flies to the rescue for people needing intensive medical care. With a fleet of about 320 medically equipped aircraft, mainly helicopters, the company provides emergency medical air transportation services throughout the US. The company's community-based division, which accounts for most of Air Methods' sales, provides transportation and in-flight medical care from its own bases in more than 20 states. Its hospital-based division contracts with hospitals in more than 30 states to transport critically ill patients to trauma centers or tertiary care facilities; under the hospital-based model, the hospitals themselves provide in-flight medical personnel.

	Annual Growth	12/05	12/06	12/07	12/08	12/09
Sales ($ mil.)	10.9%	337.0	319.5	396.3	498.8	510.6
Net income ($ mil.)	25.2%	11.8	17.2	27.5	19.3	29.0
Market value ($ mil.)	18.1%	215.6	348.0	619.1	199.3	419.0
Employees	10.7%	1,961	2,155	3,133	2,976	2,942

⊞ AIR PRODUCTS AND CHEMICALS, INC.

NYSE: APD

7201 Hamilton Blvd.
Allentown, PA 18195
Phone: 610-481-4911
Fax: 610-481-5900
Web: www.airproducts.com

CEO: John E. McGlade
CFO: Paul E. Huck
HR: Lynn C. Minella
FYE: September 30
Type: Public

Much like Jumpin' Jack Flash, business at Air Products and Chemicals is a gas gas gas. The company provides gases such as argon, hydrogen, nitrogen, and oxygen to manufacturers, health care facilities, and other industries. Not all is light and airy, however. It also makes gas containers and equipment that separates air, purifies hydrogen, and liquefies gas. Air Products' largest segment is Merchant Gases, which manufactures atmospheric, process, and specialty gases delivered from tanker, truck and trailer or even directly for the customer through on-site plants. The company's Tonnage Gases segment serves the global refining and chemical industries. In 2010 the company made a $7 billion offer for rival Airgas.

	Annual Growth	9/05	9/06	9/07	9/08	9/09
Sales ($ mil.)	0.3%	8,143.5	8,850.4	10,037.8	10,414.5	8,256.2
Net income ($ mil.)	(3.0%)	711.7	729.6	1,035.6	909.7	631.3
Market value ($ mil.)	8.9%	11,709.1	14,093.9	20,759.6	14,544.0	16,474.3
Employees	(0.8%)	19,500	20,700	22,100	21,100	18,900

AIR SERV CORPORATION

3399 Peachtree Rd. NE, Ste. 1800
Atlanta, GA 30326
Phone: 404-926-4200
Fax: 404-267-2230
Web: www.airservcorp.com

CEO: Thomas J. (Tom) Marano
CFO: David L. Gamsey
HR: Megan Jones
FYE: December 31
Type: Private

Airlines hire Air Serv to provide the ground-based services that help passengers and cargo take to the skies. The company's offerings include cargo handling, ground transportation, passenger services (such as baggage handling and ticket verification), and ramp services. Air Serv operates at about 20 airports throughout the US; the company also does business in the UK. Customers have included Delta Air Lines, FedEx, and UAL's United Airlines. Air Serv was established in 2002 by chairman Frank Argenbright, who previously had founded Argenbright Security.

AIR SYSTEM COMPONENTS, INC.

1401 N. Plano Rd.
Richardson, TX 75081
Phone: 972-680-9126
Fax: 972-575-3372
Web: www.airsysco.com

CEO: Terry J. O'Halloran
CFO: Ron Dewey
HR: —
FYE: December 31
Type: Subsidiary

An air conditioner is nothing but a sum of its parts, with Air System Components (ASC) supplying the parts. The company manufactures components, such as grilles, registers, diffusers, and terminal devices for air conditioning, heating and ventilation systems, in addition to fans and other air distribution products. ASC's products are used in industrial facilities, institutions, and commercial and residential buildings, as well as the International Space Station. Brands include Titus, Krueger, Tuttle & Bailey, Reliable, Superior Rex, and PennBarry. Products are available worldwide through a network of wholesalers and distributors. ASC, which has about 10 manufacturing facilities, is a subsidiary of Tomkins.

AIR T, INC.

NASDAQ (CM): AIRT

3524 Airport Rd.
Maiden, NC 28650
Phone: 828-464-8741
Fax: 828-465-5281
Web: www.airt.net/home.html

CEO: Walter Clark
CFO: John Parry
HR: —
FYE: March 31
Type: Public

So FedEx can deliver for you, Air T flies for FedEx. Air T owns two overnight air cargo subsidiaries — Mountain Air Cargo and CSA Air — which operate under contracts with the express delivery giant. Mountain Air Cargo flies mainly in the southeastern US, the Caribbean, and South America; CSA Air operates primarily in the upper Midwest. The carriers' combined fleet consists of about 90 turboprop aircraft, nearly all of which are leased from FedEx. Air cargo operations account for about half of Air T's sales. The company's other businesses — Global Ground Support and Global Aviation Services — make de-icing and scissor-lift equipment used at airports and provide related maintenance services.

	Annual Growth	3/05	3/06	3/07	3/08	3/09
Sales ($ mil.)	6.7%	70.0	79.5	67.3	78.4	90.7
Net income ($ mil.)	20.3%	2.1	2.1	2.5	3.4	4.4
Market value ($ mil.)	(24.2%)	42.0	27.4	19.4	23.3	13.9
Employees	3.1%	414	390	392	460	467

AIR TRANSPORT SERVICES GROUP, INC.

NASDAQ (GM): ATSG

145 Hunter Dr.
Wilmington, OH 45177
Phone: 937-382-5591
Fax: 937-383-3838
Web: www.atsginc.com

CEO: Joseph C. (Joe) Hete
CFO: Quint O. Turner
HR: Debbie Loveless
FYE: December 31
Type: Public

Air Transport Services Group (ATSG) gets packages to their destination on time. Its main unit, cargo airline ABX Air, works for express delivery company DHL (USA) under an ACMI (aircraft, crew, maintenance, insurance) contract, providing international air transport. A hub services agreement with DHL to provide package sorting and other services expired in 2009. ABX Air also provides ACMI and charter services for customers not connected with DHL, including BAX/Schenker and the US military, primarily through airfreight carriers Air Transport International and Capital Cargo International Airlines. Sales from the DHL business, which accounted for 98% of sales in 2008, fell to about 45% in 2009.

	Annual Growth	12/05	12/06	12/07	12/08	12/09
Sales ($ mil.)	(13.4%)	1,464.4	1,260.4	1,174.5	1,610.7	823.5
Net income ($ mil.)	3.2%	30.3	90.1	19.6	(56.0)	34.4
Market value ($ mil.)	(23.8%)	500.6	442.0	266.6	11.5	168.4
Employees	(35.3%)	11,500	9,700	10,150	5,620	2,020

AIRBORNE, INC.

26811 S. Bay Dr., Ste. 300
Bonita Springs, FL 34134
Phone: 800-590-9794
Fax: 239-948-8551
Web: www.airbornehealth.com

CEO: Martha A. M. (Marti) Morfitt
CFO: Lucy Morris
HR: —
FYE: April 30
Type: Private

Airborne wants to keep users from being grounded. The company makes a dietary supplement that contains herbal extracts, vitamins, electrolytes, amino acids, and antioxidants meant to boost the immune system. The effervescent tablets come in four flavors and a powdered formulation to be added to water. The products are sold nationwide in pharmacies, supermarkets, and mass merchant retailers such as Costco, CVS Caremark, Target, and Wal-Mart. Airborne was established in 1997 by former second-grade teacher Victoria Knight-McDowell. Private equity investors GF Capital Management holds a majority of the company.

	Annual Growth	4/04	4/05	4/06	4/07	4/08
Est. sales ($ mil.)	—	—	—	—	—	120.0
Employees	—	—	—	—	—	23

AIRBUS AMERICAS, INC.

198 Van Buren St., Ste. 300
Herndon, VA 20170
Phone: 703-834-3400
Fax: 703-834-3340
Web: www.airbusnorthamerica.com

CEO: Barry Eccleston
CFO: —
HR: Robert N. Ehrenfeld
FYE: —
Type: Subsidiary

Airbus Americas, the US-based arm of France's Airbus S.A.S., serves the company's important North and South American customer base. It serves major passenger carriers, including Northwest Airlines and US Airways Group, as well as cargo carriers, startup airlines, and leading leasing companies. Airbus' single-aisle and wide-body jets can accommodate between 107 and more than 550 passengers. Its largest model, the A380, was delivered in 2007, while its A350 long-range jetliners continue to gain success in the Americas. The European Aeronautic Defence & Space Company (EADS) owns Airbus.

AIRCASTLE LIMITED

NYSE: AYR

300 First Stamford Pl., 5th Fl.
Stamford, CT 06902
Phone: 203-504-1020
Fax: 203-504-1021
Web: www.aircastle.com

CEO: Ron Wainshal
CFO: Michael J. Inglese
HR: —
FYE: December 31
Type: Public

Not to be confused with the inflatable palaces that parents rent for kids' birthday parties, Aircastle Limited is an aircraft leasing concern. The company owns a lineup of utility jet aircraft that it adds to, leases, and sells to passenger and cargo markets. Aircastle touts a portfolio of 130-plus aircraft, which are leased to about 60 different businesses. Lessees of Aircastle's aircraft maintain the planes, as well as pay operating and insurance expenses. The company's leases are managed from offices in Ireland, Singapore, and the US. Aircastle also invests in industry-related assets, such as financing vehicles secured by commercial aircraft. Its three largest customers are US Airways, Martinair, and Emirates.

	Annual Growth	12/05	12/06	12/07	12/08	12/09
Sales ($ mil.)	99.5%	36.0	189.3	381.1	582.6	570.6
Net income ($ mil.)	375.8%	0.2	51.2	127.3	115.3	102.5
Market value ($ mil.)	(30.6%)	—	2,346.4	2,094.3	380.2	783.5
Employees	26.4%	29	45	69	76	74

AIRCRAFT SERVICE INTERNATIONAL GROUP, INC.

201 S. Orange Ave., Ste. 1100-A
Orlando, FL 32801
Phone: 407-648-7373
Fax: 407-206-5391
Web: www.asig.com

CEO: Keith P. Ryan
CFO: Sami Teittinen
HR: —
FYE: December 31
Type: Subsidiary

Rather than soaring through the skies, Aircraft Service International Group (ASIG) takes care of planes when they're on the ground. The company provides fueling, ground handling, cargo handling, and related services to the commercial aviation industry. (Ground handling includes services such as baggage loading and unloading, cabin cleaning, and passenger check-in.) ASIG operates at more than 65 airports worldwide, primarily in the US and the UK but also elsewhere in Europe and in the Asia/Pacific region. Sister company Signature Flight Support serves the general aviation community as a leading fixed-base operator (FBO). ASIG was founded in 1947 and acquired by BBA Aviation in 2001.

AIRGAS, INC.

NYSE: ARG

259 N. Radnor-Chester Rd., Ste. 100
Radnor, PA 19087
Phone: 610-687-5253
Fax: 610-687-1052
Web: www.airgas.com

CEO: Peter McCausland
CFO: Robert M. McLaughlin
HR: Dwight T. Wilson
FYE: March 31
Type: Public

Airgas has floated to the top of the industrial gas distribution industry by buying up more than 400 companies since its founding in 1986. The company's North American network of more than 1,100 locations includes retail stores, gas fill plants, specialty gas labs, production facilities, and distribution centers. Airgas distributes argon, hydrogen, nitrogen, oxygen, and a variety of medical and specialty gases, as well as dry ice and protective equipment (hard hats, goggles). Its Merchant Gases unit operates air-separation plants that produce oxygen, nitrogen, and argon. It also sells welding machines and produces acetylene and nitrous oxide. Rival Air Products offered to buy Airgas for $7 billion in 2010.

	Annual Growth	3/06	3/07	3/08	3/09	3/10
Sales ($ mil.)	8.1%	2,829.6	3,205.1	4,017.0	4,349.5	3,864.0
Net income ($ mil.)	11.7%	126.1	154.4	223.3	261.1	196.3
Market value ($ mil.)	12.9%	3,262.9	3,518.3	3,795.4	2,822.1	5,310.4
Employees	8.0%	10,300	11,500	14,500	14,000	14,000

AIRSPAN NETWORKS INC.

Pink Sheets: AIRO

777 Yamato Rd., Ste. 310
Boca Raton, FL 33431
Phone: 561-893-8670
Fax: 561-893-8671
Web: www.airspan.com

CEO: Eric D. Stonestrom
CFO: David Brant
HR: —
FYE: December 31
Type: Public

Airspan Networks covers a lot of ground, mostly through the air. The company supplies equipment based on the WiMax wireless networking standard. Phone companies, ISPs, utility companies, and other network operators use Airspan's base stations and subscriber terminals to provide fixed and mobile broadband wireless access. The company's other products include Wi-Fi-based networking equipment, as well as voice-over-IP (VoIP) soft switches and gateways. Airspan sells directly and through OEMs, resellers and systems integrators to customers worldwide. The vast majority of the company's sales are to customers outside the US.

	Annual Growth	12/04	12/05	12/06	12/07	*12/08
Sales ($ mil.)	(7.1%)	94.6	111.0	127.8	95.0	70.4
Net income ($ mil.)	—	(10.0)	(15.1)	(29.2)	(30.5)	(49.8)
Market value ($ mil.)	(64.0%)	325.0	340.5	221.4	105.3	5.4
Employees	(1.6%)	221	118	292	295	207
						*Most recent year available

AIRTRAN HOLDINGS, INC.

NYSE: AAI

9955 AirTran Blvd.
Orlando, FL 32827
Phone: 407-318-5600
Fax: 407-318-5900
Web: www.airtran.com

CEO: Robert L. (Bob) Fornaro
CFO: Arne G. Haak
HR: Loral Blinde
FYE: December 31
Type: Public

Need to be transported by air with a low fare? AirTran Holdings may be the ticket. Through its main subsidiary, AirTran Airways, the company offers low-cost passenger transportation to more than 60 cities, mainly in the eastern US but also in Puerto Rico, Aruba, Mexico, and the Bahamas. The airline operates from its primary hub in Atlanta and secondary hubs in Baltimore, Milwaukee, and Orlando, Florida. AirTran maintains a fleet of about 140 Boeing aircraft, including the 717 and the 737. It is a leading carrier in the Atlanta market, behind Delta, which handles the largest share of the traffic at Hartsfield-Jackson Atlanta International Airport.

	Annual Growth	12/05	12/06	12/07	12/08	12/09
Sales ($ mil.)	12.7%	1,450.5	1,893.4	2,310.0	2,552.5	2,341.4
Net income ($ mil.)	198.4%	1.7	15.5	52.7	(273.8)	134.7
Market value ($ mil.)	(24.5%)	2,168.2	1,587.9	968.4	600.5	706.0
Employees	4.0%	6,900	7,700	8,500	8,000	8,070

AIRVANA, INC.

19 Alpha Rd.
Chelmsford, MA 01824
Phone: 978-250-3000
Fax: 978-250-3910
Web: www.airvana.com

CEO: Randall S. (Randy) Battat
CFO: Jeffrey D. (Jeff) Glidden
HR: —
FYE: December 31
Type: Private

Airvana can help you rock out to Nirvana. The company makes mobile broadband infrastructure products for wireless carriers. Its products enable wireless networks to deliver broadband multimedia services — such as Internet access, e-mail, music downloads, and video streaming — to cell phones, laptops, and other mobile devices. Customers include service providers such as Verizon Wireless in the US, TELUS in Canada, and Telstra in Australia; however, nearly all of its revenue was derived from sales to Nortel Networks (which filed for bankruptcy in 2009). Airvana was acquired in 2010 by 72 Mobile Holdings for about $540 million in cash. The company was taken private by its new owners.

	Annual Growth	12/05	12/06	12/07	12/08	12/09
Sales ($ mil.)	130.2%	2.3	170.3	305.8	138.2	64.6
Net income ($ mil.)	—	(63.0)	74.4	153.3	21.3	(25.0)
Employees	4.5%	504	491	560	555	600

AISIN U.S.A. MFG., INC.

1700 E. 4th St.
Seymour, IN 47274
Phone: 812-523-1969
Fax: 812-523-1984
Web: www.aisinusa.com

CEO: Shunzo (Sam) Hattori
CFO: Jim Hume
HR: Mark Handloser
FYE: March 31
Type: Subsidiary

Asia and the US come together in Aisin U.S.A. Mfg. A subsidiary of Japanese auto parts concern Aisin Seiki, the unit helps Japan's largest carmaker Toyota put its cars on the road in the US. The company makes a diverse line of components and systems, including door frame components, latching systems, seating, and trim molding. In addition to Toyota, Aisin U.S.A. Mfg. supplies parts to other Japanese carmakers (Honda, Mitsubishi, and Nissan) as well as to General Motors. The company's major plant is in Seymour, Indiana. It has another plant in Marion, Illinois.

	Annual Growth	3/04	3/05	3/06	3/07	3/08
Est. sales ($ mil.)	—	—	—	—	—	50.0
Employees	—	—	—	—	—	750

An in-depth profile of this company is available to Hoover's Online members at hoovers.com.

AISIN WORLD CORP. OF AMERICA

46501 Commerce Center Dr.	CEO: Don Whitsitt
Plymouth, MI 48170	CFO: —
Phone: 734-453-5551	HR: —
Fax: 734-453-4670	FYE: March 31
Web: www.aisinworld.com	Type: Private

The core of AISIN World Corp. of America's (AWA) business is automotive parts and systems. These include brake systems, suspensions, chassis components, engine parts, drivetrain components, body parts, and information devices. AWA's aftermarket products include clutch plates, water pumps, master cylinders, and brake pads. The company also makes lifestyle- and amenity-related products including home sewing and embroidery machines, and energy system-related products that include indoor and outdoor gas heat-pump air-conditioning systems. Automotive customers include Toyota Motor Engineering & Manufacturing North America, GM, Honda of America, and Johnson Controls. AWA's parent company is AISIN Seiki (Japan).

	Annual Growth	3/04	3/05	3/06	3/07	3/08
Est. sales ($ mil.)	—	—	—	—	—	964.1
Employees	—	—	—	—	—	1,278

AIT WORLDWIDE LOGISTICS, INC.

701 N. Rohlwing Rd.	CEO: Dan Lisowski
Itasca, IL 60143	CFO: —
Phone: 630-766-8300	HR: —
Fax: 630-766-0205	FYE: December 31
Web: www.aitworldwide.com	Type: Private

Arranging the transportation of its customers' cargo by air, land, and sea, AIT Worldwide Logistics provides domestic and international freight forwarding services, including customs brokerage. It also offers supply chain management, including information services that help customers keep track of their freight. Customers have come from a variety of industries; the company's specialties include service to government agencies and handling of perishable products. AIT Worldwide Logistics maintains about 40 offices in the US, and operates overseas through 330 global service centers and a network of agents. Steven Leturno and Dan Lisowski, who still advise the company, founded AIT Worldwide Logistics in 1979.

	Annual Growth	12/04	12/05	12/06	12/07	12/08
Est. sales ($ mil.)	—	—	—	—	—	56.9
Employees	—	—	—	—	—	600

AJILON CONSULTING

175 Broad Hollow Rd.	CEO: Jeff Rupp
Melville, NY 11747	CFO: Rob Stoia
Phone: 631-844-7800	HR: Marty Sylvester
Fax: 631-844-7363	FYE: December 31
Web: www.ajilonconsulting.com	Type: Subsidiary

Information technology staffing is just one of many things this company does for its clients. A unit of Switzerland-based global employment services giant Adecco, Ajilon Consulting provides IT consulting and technology services to both corporations and government agencies. The company specializes in such areas as custom software development, network management, and technology procurement. It also provides data management, software testing, and technical support outsourcing, among other services. Ajilon serves clients in a wide range of industries, including energy, finance, health care, and telecom. The company operates from about 60 locations in North America, Europe, and the Asia/Pacific region.

AJINOMOTO USA INC.

Country Club Plaza, 115 W. Century Rd.	CEO: Shinichi Suzuki
Paramus, NJ 07652	CFO: Hideki Nagano
Phone: 201-292-3200	HR: —
Fax: 201-261-7343	FYE: March 31
Web: www.ajinomotofoods.com	Type: Subsidiary

Ajinomoto USA knows the value of the most basic elements of flavors and wants to spread the joys of monosodium glutamate around the world. The company is the US-based distributor of one of East Asia's best-known companies (and brands), Ajinomoto. It manufactures and distributes Chinese-, Japanese-, and Korean-style food products, including stir-fry flavor packets, bottled seasonings, tamari (Japanese-style soy sauce), the aforementioned monosodium flavor enhancer, and its most well-known brand, Hon-Dashi — a fish and seaweed flavored broth that comes both dried and in shelf-stable packaging. Ajinomoto USA also makes frozen convenience foods such as potstickers and fried rice.

AJS BANCORP, INC.

OTC: AJSB

14757 S. Cicero Ave.	CEO: Thomas R. Butkus
Midlothian, IL 60445	CFO: Pamela N. Favero
Phone: 708-687-7400	HR: Jo Anne Cano
Fax: 708-687-7466	FYE: December 31
Web: www.ajsmithbank.com	Type: Public

There is no need for an alias: A. J. Smith Federal is the primary operating subsidiary of holding company AJS Bancorp. The bank serves customers in suburban Chicago from three branches in Midlothian and Orland Park, Illinois. Catering to area businesses and residents, A. J. Smith Federal offers checking and savings accounts, insurance and investments, and loans. One- to four-family residential mortgages make up more than two-thirds of the bank's loan portfolio; multifamily and commercial mortgages and home equity and consumer loans round out its lending activities. Arthur J. Smith founded A. J. Smith Federal in 1892 as a building and loan cooperative; it became a federally chartered savings bank in 1984.

	Annual Growth	12/05	12/06	12/07	12/08	12/09
Assets ($ mil.)	(0.8%)	257.9	266.5	248.3	244.0	249.3
Net income ($ mil.)	—	1.1	0.9	0.6	(2.1)	(2.4)
Market value ($ mil.)	(11.3%)	46.5	52.9	40.5	23.7	28.8
Employees	(3.2%)	74	64	58	67	65

⊞ AK STEEL HOLDING CORPORATION

NYSE: AKS

9227 Centre Pointe Dr.	CEO: James L. (Jim) Wainscott
West Chester, OH 45069	CFO: Albert E. Ferrara Jr.
Phone: 513-425-5000	HR: Lawrence F. Zizzo Jr.
Fax: 513-425-2676	FYE: December 31
Web: www.aksteel.com	Type: Public

Automobile sales help AK Steel's business keep rolling, though it has begun to branch out to the infrastructure and manufacturing industries. The company manufactures carbon, stainless, and electrical steel. It sells hot- and cold-rolled carbon steel to construction companies, steel distributors and service centers, and automotive and industrial machinery producers. AK Steel also sells cold-rolled and aluminum-coated stainless steel to automakers. The company produces electrical steels (iron-silicon alloys with unique magnetic properties) for makers of power transmission and distribution equipment. In addition, it makes carbon and stainless steel tubular products through AK Tube.

	Annual Growth	12/05	12/06	12/07	12/08	12/09
Sales ($ mil.)	(7.8%)	5,647.4	6,069.0	7,003.0	7,644.3	4,076.8
Net income ($ mil.)	—	(0.8)	12.0	387.7	4.0	(74.6)
Market value ($ mil.)	28.0%	873.8	1,857.4	5,082.1	1,024.3	2,346.5
Employees	(5.1%)	8,000	7,000	6,900	6,800	6,500

AKAMAI TECHNOLOGIES, INC.

NASDAQ (GS): AKAM

8 Cambridge Center
Cambridge, MA 02142
Phone: 617-444-3000
Fax: 617-444-3001
Web: www.akamai.com

CEO: Paul L. Sagan
CFO: J. Donald (J. D.) Sherman
HR: Debra Canner
FYE: December 31
Type: Public

Akamai Technologies offers an accelerated course on digital delivery. The company's technology enables corporations and government agencies to deliver content and applications, such as ads, business transaction tools, streaming video, and websites over the Internet. It also offers the EdgeControl suite of tools that supply network data feeds and website analytics to customers. Through its network of some 60,000 servers in about 70 countries, Akamai analyzes and manages Internet traffic, transmitting content from the server geographically closest to the end user. Akamai has about 20 global offices, but most sales are made in the US. Customers include Apple, Hitachi, NASDAQ, and the US Department of Defense.

	Annual Growth	12/05	12/06	12/07	12/08	12/09
Sales ($ mil.)	32.0%	283.1	428.7	636.4	790.9	859.8
Net income ($ mil.)	(18.3%)	328.0	57.4	101.0	145.1	145.9
Market value ($ mil.)	6.2%	3,430.3	9,142.9	5,955.3	2,597.3	4,361.5
Employees	22.2%	784	1,058	1,300	1,500	1,750

AKEENA SOLAR, INC.

NASDAQ (CM): AKNS

16005 Los Gatos Blvd.
Los Gatos, CA 95032
Phone: 408-395-7774
Fax: —
Web: www.akeena.net

CEO: Barry Cinnamon
CFO: Margaret R. Randazzo
HR: —
FYE: December 31
Type: Public

Ask anyone at Akeena about their company's name, and they'll tell you Akeena was the mistress of the Greek sun god Apollo. The company designs, markets, and sells solar power systems for residential and small commercial customers. It serves customers in six states: California, Colorado, Connecticut, New Jersey, New York, and Pennsylvania. Akeena was founded in 2001, and by early 2009 had installed more than 3,000 solar power systems at schools, wineries, restaurants, affordable housing developments, and other locations. It uses components (such as solar modules and inverters) from Sharp, Kyocera, and SunPower.

	Annual Growth	12/05	12/06	12/07	12/08	12/09
Sales ($ mil.)	40.7%	7.2	13.4	32.2	40.8	28.2
Net income ($ mil.)	—	0.0	(1.8)	(11.0)	(24.3)	(15.8)
Market value ($ mil.)	(21.7%)	—	97.4	298.2	64.4	46.8
Employees	(1.4%)	—	165	207	140	158

AKELA PHARMA INC.

Toronto: AKL

11501 Domain Dr.
Austin, TX 78758
Phone: 512-834-0449
Fax: 512-834-2105
Web: akelapharma.com

CEO: Gregory M. (Greg) McKee
CFO: Richard Martin
HR: —
FYE: December 31
Type: Public

Drug developer Akela Pharma is hoping to be there before the last dose of pain meds wears off and the next dose kicks in. The company's lead product candidate is Fentanyl Taifun, an inhaled formulation of cancer pain fighter fentanyl, to be used in conjunction with other drugs to manage severe pain. Akela Pharma is also working on research in areas not related to pain relief; it is developing a growth hormone stimulator to help treat frailty and malnutrition in patients with kidney failure. Akela Pharma's subsidiary PharmaForm provides contract drug development services and specializes in controlled-release drug delivery technology.

	Annual Growth	12/05	12/06	12/07	12/08	12/09
Sales ($ mil.)	(23.1%)	39.8	25.3	12.6	14.8	13.9
Net income ($ mil.)	—	(11.2)	(0.2)	(32.7)	(26.0)	(21.0)
Market value ($ mil.)	(60.3%)	211.9	194.6	101.9	3.1	5.3
Employees	(30.3%)	390	130	390	75	92

AKER CONSTRUCTION, INC.

701 Technology Dr.
Cannonsburg, PA 15317
Phone: 724-416-6900
Fax: —
Web: www.akersolutions.com

CEO: Steve Harker
CFO: Jerome Myron
HR: Robert C. (Bob) Hoover
FYE: December 31
Type: Subsidiary

Aker Construction is part of the North American union construction and maintenance division of Norway-based Aker Solutions, providing heavy and civil construction and renovation services for power generation plants and other industrial projects. (Non-union services are offered through Aker Industrial Constructors.) The company provides services such as prime contracting, electrical work, equipment setting, heavy mechanical contracting, steel erection, piping, and construction management. Customers have included AK Steel, BASF, and TransCanada.

AKERS BIOSCIENCES, INC.

London AIM: AKR

201 Grove Rd.
Thorofare, NJ 08086
Phone: 856-848-8698
Fax: 856-848-0269
Web: www.akersbiosciences.com

CEO: Thomas A. Nicolette
CFO: Robert J. (Bob) Paratore
HR: —
FYE: December 31
Type: Public

When there's no time to send a sample off to the lab, Akers Biosciences (ABI) steps up. The company manufactures a variety of point-of-care rapid diagnostic tests. In addition to tests for such diseases as malaria, it has produced screening tools to detect drug and enzyme levels in blood. ABI has also developed sniffing devices to detect breath alcohol as well as diseases such as lung disease and diabetes through breath analysis. Another product whiffs for biological warfare agents in the air. Its Tri-Cholesterol product is a home-use test kit. ABI customers include health care facilities (hospitals, physicians' offices) as well as the US military and aid organizations.

	Annual Growth	12/04	12/05	12/06	12/07	*12/08
Sales ($ mil.)	—	—	0.0	0.0	0.0	0.0
Net income ($ mil.)	—	—	(4.5)	(9.6)	(1.7)	(0.5)
Employees	—	—	—	—	—	—

*Most recent year available

AKG ACOUSTICS US

8400 Balboa Blvd.
Northridge, CA 91329
Phone: 818-920-3212
Fax: 818-920-3208
Web: www.akg.com

CEO: Doug MacCallum
CFO: —
HR: —
FYE: June 30
Type: Subsidiary

This business is definitely not a fan of lip synching. AKG Acoustics US is the American sales and marketing unit of leading pro audio equipment manufacturer AKG Acoustics. AKG markets a line of high-quality microphones used for both recording and live sound, as well as such applications as broadcasting, film production, and intercom systems. AKG is also a noted headphone manufacturer for both the professional and consumer markets. In addition, the company makes headsets, audio signal processors, and related accessories. AKG is a subsidiary of audio products manufacturer Harman International Industries.

AKIBIA, INC.

4 Technology Dr.
Westborough, MA 01581
Phone: 508-621-5100
Fax: 508-621-5205
Web: www.akibia.com

CEO: Thomas (Tom) Willson
CFO: Thomas (Tom) Tucker
HR: Karen Wall
FYE: March 31
Type: Private

Akibia provides information technology (IT) consulting, systems integration, and support services for UNIX, Linux, and Windows-based network computing environments. Its areas of specialty include data security, data center consolidation, desktop management, and infrastructure design and maintenance. The company also offers consulting related to customer relationship management (CRM) software installation and customization and network infrastructure planning and support. Akibia's outsourced services include technical support and training for corporate call centers. The company serves such industries as financial services, consumer electronics, and retail. Clients have included Bose, the Boston Red Sox, and Sepracor.

AKQA INC.

118 King St., 6th Fl.
San Francisco, CA 94107
Phone: 415-645-9400
Fax: 415-645-9420
Web: www.akqa.com

CEO: Tom Bedecarré
CFO: Lester Feintuck
HR: —
FYE: December 31
Type: Subsidiary

This alphabet soup-named agency helps get clients on the gravy train. AKQA, an independent Web design and interactive marketing agency, offers online and digital media development for branding, marketing, and e-commerce, as well as consulting services to help its customers use interactive technologies to their advantage. One such project was AKQA's design for the user interface for Microsoft's Xbox 360. AKQA's clients range from small companies to big names such as Nike, Coca-Cola, and McDonald's. The agency — which has offices in Amsterdam, London, New York, San Francisco, Shanghai, and Washington, DC — was founded in 1995. Private equity firm General Atlantic owns a majority stake in AKQA.

⊞ AKIN GUMP STRAUSS HAUER & FELD LLP

Robert S. Strauss Bldg., 1333 New Hampshire Ave. NW
Washington, DC 20036
Phone: 202-887-4000
Fax: 202-887-4288
Web: www.akingump.com

CEO: R. Bruce McLean
CFO: Janet L. Mourges
HR: Julie Dressing
FYE: December 31
Type: Partnership

Known for its work inside Washington's Beltway, law firm Akin Gump Strauss Hauer & Feld has a staff peppered with political insiders. Co-founder Robert Strauss is a former chairman of the Democratic National Committee who has advised several presidents. Overall, the firm has more than 800 attorneys in about a dozen offices, mainly in the US but also in the Asia/Pacific region and Europe. Beyond its work related to public policy and government contracts, Akin Gump maintains a wide range of practices, such as corporate finance and securities, energy, intellectual property, litigation, and project finance and development.

AKRION SYSTEMS LLC

6330 Hedgewood Dr., Ste. 150
Allentown, PA 18106
Phone: 610-391-9200
Fax: 610-391-1982
Web: www.akrion.com

CEO: Michael (Mike) Ioannou
CFO: W. James Whittle
HR: —
FYE: December 31
Type: Private

Akrion Systems takes a critical interest in the surface of semiconductor wafers. The company makes surface preparation equipment that readies semiconductor wafers for high-precision processes during manufacturing of microchips and other high-tech components. Akrion's tools are used in producing logic and memory parts, microelectromechanical system (MEMS) devices, photovoltaic solar cells, flat-panel displays, and photomasks. Its customers include Analog Devices, BAE SYSTEMS, Hewlett-Packard, Intel, MEMC Electronic Materials, Micron Technology, and Samsung Electronics. In 2008 Akrion's assets were acquired by Bayside Capital, an affiliate of H.I.G. Capital.

AKORN, INC.

1925 West Field Court, Ste. 300
Lake Forest, IL 60045
Phone: 847-279-6100
Fax: 800-943-3694
Web: www.akorn.com

NASDAQ (GM): AKRX
CEO: Raj Rai
CFO: Timothy A. (Tim) Dick
HR: Neill Shanahan
FYE: December 31
Type: Public

Akorn works hard to grow roots in several segments of the pharmaceutical industry. The company makes and sells specialty therapeutic and diagnostic pharmaceuticals in categories including ophthalmology, rheumatology, and anesthesia. Akorn's ophthalmic segment includes antibiotics, glaucoma treatments, lubricating ointments, diagnostic stains and dyes, and contact lens accessories. The firm's injectable segment includes drugs for rheumatoid arthritis and pain management. Akorn's products are sold nationally to hospitals, physicians, pharmacies, and wholesalers. Akorn also provides contract manufacturing services for other drugmakers. Chairman John Kapoor controls about a third of the company.

	Annual Growth	12/05	12/06	12/07	12/08	12/09
Sales ($ mil.)	14.3%	44.5	71.3	52.9	93.6	75.9
Net income ($ mil.)	—	(8.6)	(6.0)	(19.2)	(7.9)	(25.3)
Market value ($ mil.)	(20.8%)	420.9	576.8	677.4	212.3	165.2
Employees	0.2%	327	371	364	351	329

AKZO NOBEL INC.

525 W. Van Buren St., Ste. 1600
Chicago, IL 60607
Phone: 312-544-7000
Fax: 312-544-7137
Web: www.akzonobel.com

CEO: Philip Radtke
CFO: Alan D. Bensema
HR: —
FYE: December 31
Type: Subsidiary

Akzo Nobel Inc. works hard to create the right chemistry. The US and Canadian subsidiary of Dutch paints and chemicals giant Akzo Nobel N.V., the company develops and makes chemicals, coatings, and health care products. Its chemicals business includes catalysts, functional chemicals, polymers, pulp and paper chemicals, and surfactants. The coatings sector includes car refinishes, decorative coatings, and industrial coatings and finishes. While the parent company is the world's largest coatings maker, its American subsidiary traditionally has been driven by its chemicals business. Manufacturing in North America accounts for about a quarter of Akzo Nobel's total sales.

	Annual Growth	12/04	12/05	12/06	12/07	12/08
Est. sales ($ mil.)	—	—	—	—	—	2,306.1
Employees	—	—	—	—	—	8,210

AKZO NOBEL PAINTS LLC

15885 W. Sprague Rd.
Strongsville, OH 44136
Phone: 440-297-8000
Fax: 440-297-8900
Web: www.akzonobel.com/paints

CEO: Erik Bouts
CFO: Cathie McKinley
HR: Marguerite Walz
FYE: December 31
Type: Subsidiary

You might not readily recognize Akzo Nobel Paints by its name, but you likely know its brands. One of the largest North American makers of paints, the unit of Akzo Nobel is best known for Glidden paints and stores. Other well-known brands include Dulux, Ralph Lauren Paints, Fuller O'Brien, and Liquid Nails caulks and adhesives. Professionals are the primary buyers of its DeVoe industrial coatings and the Ultra-Hide line of primers and paints. While just about all of its sales come from architectural and decorative paints and coatings, the division also makes coatings for packaging (cans and closures). In 2008 Akzo Nobel acquired former parent company Imperial Chemical Industries (ICI).

ALA CARTE ENTERTAINMENT, INC.

2330 Hammond Dr., Ste. G
Schaumburg, IL 60173
Phone: 847-303-4400
Fax: 847-303-0112
Web: www.aceplaces.com

CEO: Fred Hoffman
CFO: —
HR: —
FYE: December 31
Type: Private

This company caters to many tastes with a varied menu of dining and drinking options. Ala Carte Entertainment (ACE) operates more than 20 nightspots in the Chicago area, including such popular night clubs as The Apartment and Excalibur. It also has several pub establishments, including The Celtic Crown and The Full Shilling in Wrigleyville, the area neighboring Wrigley Park. ACE's portfolio of restaurants includes Chandler's Chophouse and Moretti's Ristorante and Pizzeria. In addition to drinks and eats, ACE also provides catering services through several of its restaurants. Owner and company president Fred Hoffman started his dining empire in the early 1970s when he opened the Snuggery singles bar.

ALABAMA AIRCRAFT INDUSTRIES, INC.

Pink Sheets: AAII

1943 50th St. North
Birmingham, AL 35212
Phone: 205-592-0011
Fax: 205-592-6306
Web: www.alabamaaircraft.com

CEO: Ronald A. Aramini
CFO: Randall C. (Randy) Shealy
HR: —
FYE: December 31
Type: Public

Alabama Aircraft Industries (AAII) finds a sweet home maintaining aircraft. Formerly Pemco Aviation Group, AAII is busy with component repair and overhaul, airframe parts and systems modifications, and equipment logistics, primarily for the US government's behemoth air transport needs. Although AAII supports a slate of Programmed Depot Maintenance (PDM) activities, it pushes shop services, including sheet metal, piping, tubing, and hydraulics. Reframing its scope of work, AAII exited Pemco World Air Services in 2007, and Space Vector Corp. in 2009. Boeing, a US government subcontractor, accounts for nearly 90% of AAII's sales. Chairman Michael Tennenbaum controls a 55% stake in the company.

ALABAMA GAS CORPORATION

605 Richard Arrington Jr. Blvd. North
Birmingham, AL 35203
Phone: 205-326-2700
Fax: 205-326-2590
Web: www.alagasco.com

CEO: James T. McManus II
CFO: Charles W. (Chuck) Porter Jr.
HR: William K. (Bill) Bibb
FYE: December 31
Type: Subsidiary

With all the gas a customer could possibly need, Alagasco is THE gasco in Alabama. A unit of Birmingham, Alabama-based oil and gas company Energen, utility Alabama Gas Corporation (Alagasco) distributes natural gas to 413,150 residential and more than 33,900 commercial and industrial customers in about half of the counties in the state. The utility also provides gas transportation services to large end users who purchase wholesale gas from suppliers. Alagasgo has seven operating districts: Anniston, Birmingham, Gadsden, Montgomery, Opelika, Selma, and Tuscaloosa. The Alagasco distribution system includes 10,200 miles of main and more than 11,900 miles of service lines.

	Annual Growth	12/04	12/05	12/06	12/07	12/08
Est. sales ($ mil.)	—	—	—	—	—	654.8
Employees	—	—	—	—	—	1,530

ALAMO GROUP INC.

NYSE: ALG

1627 E. Walnut St.
Seguin, TX 78155
Phone: 830-379-1480
Fax: 830-372-9683
Web: www.alamo-group.com

CEO: Ronald A. (Ron) Robinson
CFO: Dan E. Malone
HR: —
FYE: December 31
Type: Public

Remember the Alamo Group for tractor-mounted mowing equipment — rotary, flail, and sickle-bar! The company designs, manufactures, and distributes a slew of right-of-way maintenance and agricultural equipment. Its branded lines, Alamo Industrial and Tiger hydraulically powered tractor-mounted mowers, serve US government agencies. Rhino Products and M&W Gear subsidiaries sell rotary cutters and other equipment to farmers for pasture upkeep. UK McConnel and Bomford, and France's S.M.A. subsidiaries market vegetation maintenance equipment, such as hydraulic boom-mounted hedge and grass mowers. Alamo Group operates 19 plants in North America, Europe, and Australia, garnering more than half of its sales in the US.

	Annual Growth	12/05	12/06	12/07	12/08	12/09
Sales ($ mil.)	4.9%	368.1	456.5	504.4	557.1	446.5
Net income ($ mil.)	10.9%	11.3	11.5	12.4	11.0	17.1
Market value ($ mil.)	(4.4%)	240.8	275.6	212.9	175.6	201.5
Employees	5.9%	1,862	2,215	2,347	2,460	2,340

ALAMO RENT A CAR, LLC

600 Corporate Park Dr.
St. Louis, MO 63105
Phone: 314-512-5000
Fax: 314-512-4706
Web: www.alamo.com

CEO: Greg R. Stubblefield
CFO: —
HR: —
FYE: —
Type: Subsidiary

Even if you're nowhere near Texas, this Alamo would like to be remembered as a car rental option. Alamo Rent A Car operates from more than 1,000 locations, mainly in the US and Canada, but also in Europe, Latin America, the Caribbean, Africa, and the Asia/Pacific region. The company markets its services primarily to leisure travelers. It also serves corporate customers and people who need vehicles for local use. Together with sister company National Car Rental, Alamo maintains a fleet of nearly 300,000 vehicles. Alamo and National are part of Enterprise Holdings, which was formed in 2009 following the integration of former parent Vanguard Car Rental Group. Vanguard was acquired by Enterprise Rent-A-Car in 2007.

ALANCO TECHNOLOGIES, INC.

NASDAQ (CM): ALAN

15575 N. 83rd Way, Ste. 3
Scottsdale, AZ 85260
Phone: 480-607-1010
Fax: 480-607-1515
Web: www.alanco.com

CEO: Robert R. Kauffman
CFO: John A. Carlson
HR: John A. Carlson
FYE: June 30
Type: Public

Having failed to strike gold in the pollution business and feeling fried, Alanco Technologies turned to location tracking. The company once made pollution control systems, owned gold mines, and made an unsuccessful foray into the restaurant fryer business. It now operates subsidiaries involved in radio-frequency identification (RFID) tracking devices for correctional facilities (Alanco/TSI PRISM, Inc.) and GPS tracking systems for the refrigerated transport industry (StarTrak Systems). StarTrak provides its tracking data services in North America on a subscription basis.

	Annual Growth	6/05	6/06	6/07	6/08	6/09
Sales ($ mil.)	27.6%	7.2	6.7	18.5	17.2	19.1
Net income ($ mil.)	—	(3.8)	(4.0)	(5.2)	(7.3)	(5.4)
Market value ($ mil.)	(35.4%)	85.1	66.1	85.9	50.7	14.8
Employees	(21.4%)	42	80	75	107	16

⊞ ALASKA AIR GROUP, INC.

NYSE: ALK

19300 International Blvd.
Seattle, WA 98188
Phone: 206-392-5040
Fax: 206-392-2804
Web: www.alaskaair.com

CEO: William S. (Bill) Ayer
CFO: Glenn S. Johnson
HR: Marne K. McCluskey
FYE: December 31
Type: Public

Whether you want to capture a Kodiak moment or down a daiquiri by the Sea of Cortez, an Alaska Air Group unit can fly you there. Through primary subsidiary, Alaska Airlines, and regional carrier Horizon Air, the group flies to about 90 destinations in the US (mainly western states including Alaska and Hawaii), Canada, and Mexico. The group has hubs in Seattle and Portland, Oregon. (Alaska Airlines has additional hubs in Los Angeles and Anchorage, Alaska, while Horizon also flies from Boise, Idaho.) Alaska Airlines has a fleet of some 115 Boeing 737 jets and Horizon Air operates some 20 jets and 40 turboprops.

	Annual Growth	12/05	12/06	12/07	12/08	12/09
Sales ($ mil.)	3.4%	2,975.3	3,334.4	3,506.0	3,662.6	3,399.8
Net income ($ mil.)	9.5%	84.5	(52.6)	125.0	(135.9)	121.6
Market value ($ mil.)	(0.8%)	1,277.6	1,412.8	894.5	1,046.2	1,236.1
Employees	(2.5%)	13,768	14,485	14,710	14,143	12,440

ALASKA COMMUNICATIONS SYSTEMS GROUP

NASDAQ (GS): ALSK

600 Telephone Ave.
Anchorage, AK 99503
Phone: 907-297-3000
Fax: 907-297-3100
Web: www.acsalaska.com

CEO: Liane J. Pelletier
CFO: David Wilson
HR: Nathan E. (Nate) Cagle Jr.
FYE: December 31
Type: Public

Alaska Communications Systems Group, Inc. (ACS Group), keeps customers in the largest US state connected. Through its subsidiaries, the facilities-based telecommunications carrier operates the leading local-exchange network in the state and provides wired local and long-distance voice services. It markets dial-up and DSL Internet access and wireless communications services under the "ACS" brand to retail, enterprise, and wholesale customers. Additional offerings include interexchange long-distance and Internet phone services. ACS Group has about 250,000 traditional phone access lines in service and about 150,000 wireless subscribers. The company makes sales to consumers in part through 15 retail stores and kiosks.

	Annual Growth	12/05	12/06	12/07	12/08	12/09
Sales ($ mil.)	1.5%	326.8	349.8	385.8	389.6	346.5
Net income ($ mil.)	—	(41.6)	20.0	144.1	(10.1)	(3.3)
Market value ($ mil.)	(5.9%)	452.8	676.9	668.5	418.0	355.6
Employees	(4.0%)	1,030	1,001	1,003	982	875

ALASKA PACIFIC BANCSHARES, INC.

OTC: AKPB

2094 Jordan Ave.
Juneau, AK 99801
Phone: 907-789-4844
Fax: 907-790-5110
Web: www.alaskapacificbank.com

CEO: Craig E. Dahl
CFO: Julie Pierce
HR: —
FYE: December 31
Type: Public

If you hail from Alaska, *Juneau* about Alaska Pacific Bancshares. It is the holding company for Alaska Pacific Bank, which serves the communities of Juneau, Ketchikan, and Sitka through about a half-dozen branches. The bank offers deposit products including checking and savings accounts, CDs, IRAs, and check cards. Single- to four-family residential mortgages and commercial real estate loans each account for about a quarter of the company's loan portfolio. The bank also originates construction, business, and consumer loans. Alaska Pacific Bank was founded in 1935.

	Annual Growth	12/05	12/06	12/07	12/08	12/09
Assets ($ mil.)	0.2%	177.2	178.9	187.5	190.9	178.3
Net income ($ mil.)	—	0.7	1.1	0.9	(2.3)	(2.2)
Market value ($ mil.)	(31.5%)	13.1	15.7	14.4	2.9	2.9
Employees	(2.2%)	72	71	73	70	66

ALBANY INTERNATIONAL CORP.

NYSE: AIN

1373 Broadway
Albany, NY 12204
Phone: 518-445-2200
Fax: 518-445-2265
Web: www.albint.com

CEO: Joseph G. Morone
CFO: Michael K. (Mike) Burke
HR: Ralph M. Polumbo
FYE: December 31
Type: Public

Albany International's products look good on paper and on papermaking machines. The company makes paper machine clothing (PMC, custom-made fabrics and belts that move paper stock through each phase of production). It markets these products to paper mills worldwide through a direct sales staff. Its five business segments, which cover diverse industries, include PMC, along with Albany Door Systems (ADS, industrial fabric doors, such as aircraft hangar and dock doors); Albany Engineered Composites (AEC, for aerospace and high-tech applications); Albany Engineered Fabrics (EF, woven/non-woven fabrics for paper/tannery/textile industries, and building products); and PrimaLoft (synthetic down insulation).

	Annual Growth	12/05	12/06	12/07	12/08	12/09
Sales ($ mil.)	(2.9%)	978.7	1,011.5	1,093.0	1,086.5	871.0
Net income ($ mil.)	—	71.9	58.0	17.8	(75.7)	(32.4)
Market value ($ mil.)	(11.2%)	1,239.3	1,127.9	1,271.5	440.1	769.8
Employees	(5.5%)	5,900	6,150	6,100	5,800	4,700

ALBANY MEDICAL CENTER

43 New Scotland Ave.
Albany, NY 12208
Phone: 518-262-3125
Fax: 518-262-3165
Web: www.amc.edu

CEO: James J. Barba
CFO: William C. Hasselbarth
HR: Catherine (Cathy) Halakan
FYE: December 31
Type: Not-for-profit

Albany Medical Center provides upscale medical care to the residents of upstate New York. Serving 25 counties in eastern New York and western New England, the health system has at its heart the 650-bed Albany Medical Center Hospital, a general medical-surgical facility that also provides specialty care in areas such as oncology, rehabilitation, and organ transplantation. Additionally, Albany Medical Center features a children's hospital, an outpatient surgery center, and a group medical practice. Its Albany Medical College, one of the nation's first private medical schools, offers undergraduate and graduate medical degrees and residency programs, as well as fellowships and continuing medical education.

	Annual Growth	12/04	12/05	12/06	12/07	12/08
Est. sales ($ mil.)	—	—	—	—	—	510.7
Employees	—	—	—	—	—	7,000

⊞ An in-depth profile of this company is available to Hoover's Online members at hoovers.com.

83

ALBANY MOLECULAR RESEARCH, INC.

NASDAQ (GS): AMRI

21 Corporate Circle
Albany, NY 12203
Phone: 518-464-0279
Fax: 518-464-0289
Web: www.albmolecular.com

CEO: Thomas E. D'Ambra
CFO: Mark T. Frost
HR: Brian D. Russell
FYE: December 31
Type: Public

Albany Molecular Research, dba AMRI, pushes drug development efforts along from start to finish. The company provides contract research and manufacturing services to pharmaceutical and biotechnology firms. The company's services run the gamut — from compound screening and other drug discovery services to the contract manufacturing of drugs and drug ingredients for clinical trials and commercial sale. In addition to its work for other drug companies, AMRI conducts some of its own research, with the goal of licensing its compounds to other firms for further development. The company has R&D locations and manufacturing plants in North America, Europe, and Asia.

	Annual Growth	12/05	12/06	12/07	12/08	12/09
Sales ($ mil.)	1.7%	183.9	179.8	192.5	229.3	196.4
Net income ($ mil.)	—	16.3	2.2	8.9	20.6	(16.7)
Market value ($ mil.)	(7.1%)	386.5	335.9	457.4	309.8	288.2
Employees	10.6%	847	1,015	1,226	1,357	1,266

ALBECCA INC.

3900 Steve Reynolds Blvd.
Norcross, GA 30093
Phone: 770-279-5200
Fax: 770-279-5297
Web: www.larsonjuhl.com

CEO: Stephen E. (Steve) McKenzie
CFO: R. Bradley Goodson
HR: Patrick R. Cronin
FYE: December 31
Type: Subsidiary

Albecca has a clear picture of the custom framing industry. Doing business as Larson-Juhl, the company makes and distributes framing products, including wood and metal molding, to art galleries, home decorating centers, and independent framers worldwide. Its moldings are sold under the Larson-Juhl Classic Collection and the Craig Ponzio Signature Collection names. Albecca also offers matboard and foam board, glass, and related supplies (such as joining machines and matboard cutters). The company operates about 25 facilities in the US as well as locations in some 15 other countries. Warren Buffett and his investment group, Berkshire Hathaway, bought the firm from designer Craig Ponzio and his wife in 2002.

ALBEMARLE CORPORATION

NYSE: ALB

Baton Rouge Tower, 451 Florida St.
Baton Rouge, LA 70801
Phone: 225-388-8011
Fax: 225-388-7686
Web: www.albemarle.com

CEO: Mark C. Rohr
CFO: Richard J. (Rich) Diemer Jr.
HR: Darian K. Rich
FYE: December 31
Type: Public

Albemarle has family chemistry. The company produces polymer additives, fine chemicals, and catalysts used by a variety of industries. Its polymer additives — flame retardants, stabilizers, and curatives — add desired properties to various plastics. Albemarle's catalysts segment makes polyolefin and refinery catalysts. The company ranks among the world's largest makers of hydroprocessing (HPC) catalysts and of fluidized catalytic cracking (FCC) catalysts. Its fine chemicals include bromine-based chemicals, agricultural chemicals, and bulk ibuprofen (used to make the pain reliever). Customers include chemical, plastics, pharmaceutical, petroleum, and paper companies.

	Annual Growth	12/05	12/06	12/07	12/08	12/09
Sales ($ mil.)	(1.2%)	2,107.5	2,368.5	2,336.2	2,467.1	2,005.4
Net income ($ mil.)	11.6%	114.9	143.0	229.7	194.2	178.4
Market value ($ mil.)	17.4%	1,752.5	3,281.1	3,770.1	2,038.1	3,324.1
Employees	1.6%	3,700	3,560	4,130	4,130	3,950

ALBERICI CORPORATION

8800 Page Ave.
St. Louis, MO 63114
Phone: 314-733-2000
Fax: 314-733-2001
Web: www.alberici.com

CEO: Gregory J. (Greg) Kozicz
CFO: Gregory T. (Greg) Hesser
HR: Denay Davis
FYE: December 31
Type: Private

Alberici helped shape the St. Louis skyline; it now sets its sights — or its construction sites — across North America. Alberici Corporation, parent of Alberici Constructors, encompasses a group of enterprises with a presence in North America, Central America, South America, and Europe. Operations include construction services, building materials, and steel fabrication and erection units. Alberici offers general contracting, design/build, construction management, demolition, and specialty contracting services. It also offers facilities management. The Alberici family still holds the largest share of the employee-owned firm, founded in 1918 by John S. Alberici.

	Annual Growth	12/04	12/05	12/06	12/07	12/08
Sales ($ mil.)	8.0%	—	1,033.0	1,030.0	1,150.0	1,300.0
Employees	(9.9%)	—	511	511	415	—

⊞ ALBERTO-CULVER COMPANY

NYSE: ACV

2525 Armitage Ave.
Melrose Park, IL 60160
Phone: 708-450-3000
Fax: 708-450-3409
Web: www.alberto.com

CEO: V. James Marino
CFO: Ralph J. Nicoletti
HR: —
FYE: September 30
Type: Public

From the bathroom to the kitchen to the laundry room, Alberto-Culver has you covered. The company makes products for hair care (Alberto VO5, Nexxus, TRESemmé), skin care (St. Ives, Noxzema), and personal care (FDS); sweeteners and seasonings (Sugar Twin, Mrs. Dash); home care (Kleen Guard); and laundry-care items (Static Guard). Alberto-Culver's products are developed, manufactured, and marketed in the US and in more than 100 other countries. The company also makes beauty products for other US companies under private label. Alberto-Culver's 2008 acquisition of the Noxzema brand from Procter & Gamble (P&G) has helped the company to ride out the recession.

	Annual Growth	9/05	9/06	9/07	9/08	9/09
Sales ($ mil.)	(20.2%)	3,531.2	3,772.0	1,541.6	1,443.5	1,434.0
Net income ($ mil.)	(13.3%)	210.9	205.3	78.3	228.2	119.4
Market value ($ mil.)	(7.9%)	3,794.5	4,289.7	2,441.9	2,683.2	2,726.6
Employees	(39.8%)	19,000	3,800	3,800	2,700	2,500

⊞ ALBERTSONS LLC

250 Parkcenter Blvd.
Boise, ID 83706
Phone: 208-395-6200
Fax: 208-395-6349
Web: albertsonsmarket.com

CEO: Robert G. (Bob) Miller
CFO: Richard J. (Rick) Navarro
HR: Andrew J. Scoggin
FYE: February 1
Type: Private

Call it the incredible shrinking grocery chain. Albertsons LLC (formerly Albertson's) runs some 245 Albertsons supermarkets in Arizona, Arkansas, Colorado, Florida, Louisiana, New Mexico, and Texas. That's all that remains of what was once the nation's #2 supermarket operator with about 2,500 stores. Stung by competition, the firm sold itself in 2006 to a consortium that included rival grocer SUPERVALU, drugstore chain CVS, investment firm Cerberus Capital Management, and Kimco Realty for about $9.7 billion. SUPERVALU and CVS cherry-picked the company's best supermarket and drugstore assets. Subsequent divestments, including 132 stores in Northern California and 50 stores in Florida, further shrunk the company.

ALCAN BALTEK CORPORATION

108 Fairway Ct.	CEO: Danny Wilmer
Northvale, NJ 07647	CFO: Bob Newmyer
Phone: 201-767-1400	HR: Robert Major
Fax: 201-387-6631	FYE: December 31
Web: www.alcanbaltek.com	Type: Subsidiary

Alcan Baltek (aka Baltek) makes composites and other materials that are used to manufacture yachts, aircraft, wind turbines, buses, and high-speed trains. The company, which is a division of Alcan Composites, supplies end-grain balsa core material, PVC foam products, and nonwoven polyester mats to manufacturers for use as lamination between fiberglass or metal skins in the production of fiberglass boats, aircraft flooring, and other applications. The hobby industry uses Baltek's balsa wood for model airplanes. Baltek and its sister company, Alcan Composites USA, make products under the Baltek, AIREX, Gator, and Dibond brands. In 2009 Rio Tinto sold Alcan Composites to Swiss group Schweiter Technologies.

	Annual Growth	12/04	12/05	12/06	12/07	12/08
Est. sales ($ mil.)	—	—	—	—	—	110.6
Employees	—	—	—	—	—	977

ALCAN CABLE

3 Ravinia Dr., Ste. 1600	CEO: Ian Hewett
Atlanta, GA 30346	CFO: —
Phone: 770-394-9886	HR: —
Fax: 770-395-9053	FYE: December 31
Web: www.cable.alcan.com	Type: Business segment

For this company, aluminum cable is the tie that binds. Alcan Cable is one of the largest US manufacturers of electrical aluminum cable. Its lines include bare and insulated conductors, rod and strip, and alloy feeder cable. Among the offerings, Alcan Cable's MODEX® modular wiring systems feature a variety of wiring assemblies for lower cost installation. The company caters to utilities and distributors, OEMs, and businesses in the building wire market — commercial and residential contractors and developers. Headquartered in Georgia, Alcan Cable owns and operates seven manufacturing plants in the US, Canada, and China. It is a division of Alcan Engineered Products, a business unit of aluminum giant Rio Tinto.

ALCAN COMPOSITES USA INC.

136 Fairview Rd., Ste. 300	CEO: Brendan Cooper
Mooresville, NC 28117	CFO: Barry Wyatt
Phone: 704-658-3522	HR: —
Fax: 704-658-3540	FYE: December 31
Web: www.graphicdisplayusa.com	Type: Subsidiary

Alcan Composites USA is a big supporter of the arts; graphic arts, that is. A manufacturer of lightweight composite materials, the company makes aluminum composite panels and extrusions, heavy-duty foam boards, and PVC boards used to create 2-D and 3-D graphic arts signs and displays (i.e. kiosks, large decorative props displayed at events, detailed replicas of statues, buildings, and other structures). It sells its products under the Omni-Flute, Fome-Cor, Sintra, Gator, Dibond, and Profiles brands and distributes its products globally. Alcan Composites USA is a subsidiary of Alcan Composites and a sister company of Alcan Baltek. Customers include advertisers, event organizers, and retailers, among others.

ALCATEL-LUCENT BELL LABS

600 Mountain Ave.	CEO: Ben Verwaayen
Murray Hill, NJ 07974	CFO: —
Phone: 908-582-8500	HR: —
Fax: 908-508-2576	FYE: September 30
Web: www.bell-labs.com	Type: Business segment

Alcatel-Lucent Bell Labs has a history of developing products that have shaped past and present technologies. Since its founding in 1925, the scientists at Bell Labs have been responsible for many groundbreaking technological achievements and have been awarded thousands of patents and several Nobel prizes for their efforts. Key "firsts" credited to Bell Labs include long-distance television transmission, fax transmission, touch-tone phone, communications satellite, and cellular telephone transmission. As the research and development arm of Alcatel-Lucent, Bell Labs' innovations include components of 3G mobile phone technology, telecommunications software, and nanotechnology for batteries, microphones, and lenses.

ALCATEL-LUCENT HOLDING INC.

3400 W. Plano Pkwy.	CEO: Ben Verwaayen
Plano, TX 75075	CFO: —
Phone: 972-519-3000	HR: —
Fax: 972-519-2240	FYE: December 31
Web: www.usa.alcatel.com	Type: Subsidiary

Alcatel-Lucent Holding, a regional US subsidiary of France-based Alcatel-Lucent, designs, develops, and builds communications networks. It supplies equipment, software applications, and related services to telecom carriers and network service providers, as well as enterprise and government customers. A leading supplier of broadband Internet access products, the company pioneered the development of digital subscriber line (DSL) technology for residential and small business end users. Alcatel-Lucent was formed from the 2006 merger of telecom rivals Alcatel and Lucent Technologies.

ALCOA INC.

	NYSE: AA
390 Park Ave.	CEO: Klaus Kleinfeld
New York, NY 10022	CFO: Charles D. (Chuck) McLane Jr.
Phone: 212-836-2600	HR: John D. (Jack) Bergen
Fax: 212-836-2815	FYE: December 31
Web: www.alcoa.com	Type: Public

Alcoa is among the world's top producers of alumina (aluminum's principal ingredient, processed from bauxite) and aluminum. Its vertically integrated operations include bauxite mining, alumina refining, and aluminum smelting; primary products include alumina and its chemicals, automotive components, and sheet aluminum for beverage cans. The company's non-aluminum products include fiber-optic cables. Major markets include the aerospace, automotive, and construction industries. A truly global company, Alcoa does about half of its business in the US; it operates in more than 30 countries, with Europe and Brazil being its largest international markets.

	Annual Growth	12/05	12/06	12/07	12/08	12/09
Sales ($ mil.)	(8.4%)	26,159.0	30,379.0	30,748.0	26,901.0	18,439.0
Net income ($ mil.)	—	1,235.0	2,248.0	2,564.0	(74.0)	(1,090.0)
Market value ($ mil.)	(14.1%)	30,191.6	30,640.8	37,318.3	11,496.7	16,458.8
Employees	(17.8%)	129,000	123,000	107,000	87,000	59,000

An in-depth profile of this company is available to Hoover's Online members at hoovers.com.

85

ALDAGEN, INC.

2810 Meridian Pkwy., Ste. 148
Durham, NC 27713
Phone: 919-484-2571
Fax: 919-484-8792
Web: www.aldagen.com

CEO: W. Thomas Amick
CFO: David Carberry
HR: —
FYE: December 31
Type: Private

Aldagen's work stems from the need for tissue repair. The biopharmaceutical company develops cell regeneration therapies using adult stem cells. It uses a proprietary technology that isolates an enzyme known as aldehyde dehydrogenase, or ALDH, which it believes can target a number of diseases. Aldagen hopes its products will be used to treat hereditary metabolic diseases in children, leukemia, and cardiovascular diseases; all its drugs are in the development stage. The company does its own manufacturing and plans to do its own marketing. Venture capital firm Intersouth Partners holds about 42% of Aldagen, which filed an IPO in late 2009. The company is led by CEO W. Thomas Amick.

	Annual Growth	12/05	12/06	12/07	12/08	12/09
Sales ($ mil.)	41.4%	0.1	0.1	0.2	0.2	0.4
Net income ($ mil.)	—	(7.1)	(5.8)	(6.7)	(10.2)	(9.0)
Employees	17.9%	—	—	18	24	25

ALDILA, INC.

Pink Sheets: ALDA

14145 Danielson St., Ste. B
Poway, CA 92064
Phone: 858-513-1801
Fax: 858-513-1870
Web: www.aldila.com

CEO: Peter R. Mathewson
CFO: Scott M. Bier
HR: Maryann Jacoub
FYE: December 31
Type: Public

Without Aldila, golf clubs just wouldn't look the same. Under the Aldila brand name, the company makes graphite golf club shafts for companies the likes of Callaway Golf, Ping, and Acushnet, which combine to represent more than 50% of Aldila's sales. The company's other customers include custom club builders, distributors, pro shops, and repair centers. Aldila is protecting itself against any erratic swings in the industry by producing its own graphite, and selling off the excess to other sporting goods manufacturers. The company makes its shafts in China, Mexico, and Vietnam.

	Annual Growth	12/05	12/06	12/07	12/08	12/09
Sales ($ mil.)	(10.3%)	77.0	72.4	69.1	53.6	49.8
Net income ($ mil.)	—	13.4	11.2	16.0	(2.5)	(0.2)
Market value ($ mil.)	(39.2%)	132.3	77.6	85.3	12.3	18.1
Employees	1.7%	1,274	1,366	1,399	1,303	1,364

ALE HOUSE MANAGEMENT INC.

612 N. Orange Ave., Ste. C-6
Jupiter, FL 33458
Phone: 561-743-2299
Fax: 561-744-3111
Web: www.millersalehouse.com

CEO: John W. (Jack) Miller
CFO: —
HR: —
FYE: December 31
Type: Private

Ale House Management operates more than 45 rustic-themed restaurants, mostly in Florida, under the name Miller's Ale House. The casual dining chain's menu features steak, seafood, and sandwiches, along with soups, salads, and desserts. Miller's Ale House locations also offer a wide selection of appetizers, including spiced chicken wings called Zingers, as well as full bar service and more than 75 varieties of beer. CEO Jack Miller opened the first Ale House with his wife, Claire, in 1988.

ALEGENT HEALTH

1010 N. 96th St., Ste. 200
Omaha, NE 68114
Phone: 402-343-4343
Fax: 402-343-4316
Web: www.alegent.com

CEO: Richard A. (Rick) Hachten II
CFO: Anthony L. Hatcher
HR: —
FYE: June 30
Type: Joint venture

Alegent Health has pledged allegiance to the residents of the Midwest. The not-for-profit health care system operates nine full-service hospitals in Omaha and surrounding communities in northeastern Nebraska and southwestern Iowa. At the heart of the vast network of acute care facilities, outpatient centers, and primary care clinics that comprise Alegent Health are two of its hospitals in Omaha — Bergan Mercy Medical Center (with 400 beds) and Immanuel Medical Center (360 beds). The health system has a total of more than 1,800 beds and provides general and specialized medical care from birth to old age, in specialties including cardiovascular disease, orthopedics, oncology, rehabilitation, and mental health.

ALERIS INTERNATIONAL, INC.

25825 Science Park Dr., Ste. 400
Beachwood, OH 44122
Phone: 216-910-3400
Fax: 216-910-3650
Web: www.aleris.com

CEO: Steven J. (Steve) Demetriou
CFO: Sean M. Stack
HR: Melissa A. Olmstead
FYE: December 31
Type: Private

Aleris International wants you to use that blue plastic recycling bin so that it can turn its world green. The company's rolled and extruded products unit makes alloy aluminum sheet from recycled metal, as well as extruded profiles for the construction and engineering markets. Aleris' recycling unit processes recycled aluminum and metal alloys. It operates more than 40 facilities in China, the Americas, and throughout Europe. Aleris emerged from Chapter 11 bankruptcy in 2010 as a privately held company. The company, now owned by funds managed by Oaktree Capital Management, closed on a $609 million rights offering as part of its reorganization.

ALEX LEE, INC.

120 4th St. SW
Hickory, NC 28602
Phone: 828-725-4424
Fax: 828-725-4435
Web: www.alexlee.com

CEO: Boyd L. George
CFO: Ronald W. Knedlik
HR: Robert Vipperman
FYE: September 30
Type: Private

Wholesale groceries are only part of the story for Alex Lee. The company is a leading distributor of food and other products to retailers and foodservice operators. Its Merchants Distributors, Inc. (MDI) subsidiary supplies food and general merchandise to more than 850 retailers in 10 states, and MDI's own Consolidation Services business provides warehousing and logistics services. The Institutional Food House unit is a foodservice supplier that serves customers in the hospitality industry. Alex Lee also operates Lowe's Food Stores, a chain of about 110 grocery stores in the Carolinas and Virginia. Alex and Lee George started the company in 1931. The George family continues to control Alex Lee.

ALEXANDER & BALDWIN, INC. NYSE: AXB

822 Bishop St.
Honolulu, HI 96813
Phone: 808-525-6611
Fax: 808-525-6652
Web: www.alexanderbaldwin.com

CEO: Stanley M. Kuriyama
CFO: Christopher J. (Chris) Benjamin
HR: Son-Jai Paik
FYE: December 31
Type: Public

Alexander & Baldwin (A&B) helps connect Hawaii with North America. The company's ocean transportation subsidiary, Matson Navigation, carries freight mainly between ports in Hawaii, Guam, China, Alaska, and Puerto Rico and the continental US. Its fleet of 15-plus vessels includes containerships and barges. Matson also provides intermodal services (arrangement of freight transportation by a combination of road and rail) and logistics services in North America. In addition to its transportation-related businesses, A&B has subsidiaries that engage in real estate development and property management, both in Hawaii and on the US mainland. Other units produce, market, and distribute sugar and coffee in Hawaii.

	Annual Growth	12/05	12/06	12/07	12/08	12/09
Sales ($ mil.)	(3.3%)	1,607.0	1,607.0	1,681.0	1,898.0	1,405.0
Net income ($ mil.)	(23.1%)	126.0	122.0	142.0	132.0	44.0
Market value ($ mil.)	(10.9%)	2,230.0	1,823.0	2,124.0	1,030.3	1,407.3
Employees	(0.8%)	2,177	2,197	2,255	2,160	2,110

ALEXANDER'S, INC. NYSE: ALX

210 Rte. 4 East
Paramus, NJ 07652
Phone: 201-587-8541
Fax: 201-708-6214
Web: www.alx-inc.com

CEO: Steven Roth
CFO: Joseph Macnow
HR: —
FYE: December 31
Type: Public

Alexander's knows what's great about real estate. The real estate investment trust (REIT) owns, manages, and leases a handful of properties totaling about 2.3 million sq. ft. in New York City and New Jersey. Once a department store chain, Alexander's held on to its property interests, including the site of its erstwhile flagship store — an entire block on Manhattan's Lexington Avenue. The REIT leases space at the mixed-use Lexington site to tenants such as Bloomberg, Citibank, The Home Depot, and The Container Store. The Lexington site is also home to about 100 condos. Bloomberg accounts for about a third of sales. Vornado Realty Trust owns 33% of the company and manages its real estate business.

	Annual Growth	12/05	12/06	12/07	12/08	12/09
Sales ($ mil.)	2.9%	201.9	251.6	235.3	226.3	226.4
Net income ($ mil.)	57.8%	21.3	(75.0)	114.3	76.3	132.2
Market value ($ mil.)	5.5%	1,253.5	2,142.7	1,803.7	1,301.5	1,554.3
Employees	(4.8%)	96	96	99	82	79

ALEXANDRIA REAL ESTATE EQUITIES, INC. NYSE: ARE

385 E. Colorado Blvd., Ste. 299
Pasadena, CA 91101
Phone: 626-578-0777
Fax: 626-578-0896
Web: www.labspace.com

CEO: Joel S. Marcus
CFO: Dean A. Shigenaga
HR: —
FYE: December 31
Type: Public

Alexandria Real Estate Equities sheds a little light on properties that can be useful to life science firms. The real estate investment trust (REIT) owns, develops, and operates offices and laboratories, with more than 150 properties in 10 states and about five additional properties in Canada. Biotechnology and pharmaceutical companies, universities, research institutions, government agencies, and similar tenants occupy its properties, which contain more than 11 million sq. ft. of rentable space. The properties are mainly located in high-tech hotbeds such as North Carolina's Research Triangle; the San Francisco Bay area; San Diego; Seattle; Washington, DC; and Boston.

	Annual Growth	12/05	12/06	12/07	12/08	12/09
Sales ($ mil.)	19.1%	244.1	316.8	405.4	460.7	491.4
Net income ($ mil.)	22.2%	63.4	73.4	93.7	122.9	141.6
Market value ($ mil.)	(5.5%)	3,566.0	4,447.5	4,503.7	2,672.9	2,847.9
Employees	11.2%	93	105	150	152	142

ALEXIAN BROTHERS HEALTH SYSTEM

3040 Salt Creek Ln.
Arlington Heights, IL 60005
Phone: 847-818-5100
Fax: 847-483-7039
Web: www.alexianhealthsystem.org

CEO: Thomas Keusenkothen
CFO: James J. Sances
HR: Bob Clark
FYE: December 31
Type: Not-for-profit

O brother, can you spare some health care? Alexian Brothers Health System — which follows the principles set forth by St. Alexius of Rome, the patron of beggars and pilgrims — runs two acute care medical centers, a psychiatric hospital, and a rehabilitation hospital. It also operates numerous occupational health and community health clinics in the northwestern suburbs of Chicago, as well as home health and hospice agencies. With some 800 beds, the system's hospitals emphasize such specialties as cardiology, obstetrics, orthopedics, and oncology. In Illinois, Missouri, Tennessee, and Wisconsin, the Roman Catholic brotherhood operates affiliated assisted-living residences and nursing facilities.

	Annual Growth	12/04	12/05	12/06	12/07	12/08
Est. sales ($ mil.)	—	—	—	—	—	44.7
Employees	—	—	—	—	—	1,771

ALEXION PHARMACEUTICALS, INC. NASDAQ (GS): ALXN

352 Knotter Dr.
Cheshire, CT 06410
Phone: 203-272-2596
Fax: 203-271-8198
Web: www.alexionpharm.com

CEO: Leonard Bell
CFO: Vikas Sinha
HR: Glenn R. Melrose
FYE: December 31
Type: Public

Alexion Pharmaceuticals can't suppress its enthusiasm for treating immune functions gone awry. The firm develops drugs that inhibit certain immune system functions that cause autoimmune disorders, cancers, and other diseases. The company's first marketed antibody product, Soliris, has won approval in the US, Canada, and the European Union for the treatment of a rare genetic blood disorder known as paroxysmal nocturnal hemoglobinuria (PNH). Alexion is developing the same antibody (eculizumab) used in Soliris as a potential treatment for other autoimmune and inflammatory conditions. The company has additional development programs for cancer-fighting antibodies.

	Annual Growth	7/05	*12/06	12/07	12/08	12/09
Sales ($ mil.)	333.0%	1.1	1.6	72.0	259.1	386.8
Net income ($ mil.)	—	(108.8)	(131.5)	(92.3)	33.1	295.2
Market value ($ mil.)	39.2%	1,166.4	1,809.2	3,360.8	3,242.1	4,373.6
Employees	29.3%	241	296	434	504	673

*Fiscal year change

ALEXZA PHARMACEUTICALS, INC. NASDAQ (GM): ALXA

2091 Stierlin Court
Mountain View, CA 94043
Phone: 650-944-7000
Fax: 650-944-7999
Web: www.alexza.com

CEO: Thomas B. King
CFO: August J. Moretti
HR: Emily Lee Kelley
FYE: December 31
Type: Public

Alexza Pharmaceuticals has found that some good can come out of smoking cigarettes. Though they deliver harmful chemicals, cigarettes deliver those chemicals almost instantly. That is the basis for Alexza Pharmaceutical's primary product, Staccato inhalers. The inhalers contain a heating element coated with a thin layer of medicine. Before use, the patient triggers the heating element, which vaporizes the medicine, allowing the patient to inhale it. The medicine is then rapidly absorbed through the lungs at a rate typically faster than oral and intravenous applications. Alexza Pharmaceuticals targets central nervous system conditions including acute pain and anxiety.

	Annual Growth	12/05	12/06	12/07	12/08	12/09
Sales ($ mil.)	1,800.0%	—	—	—	0.5	9.5
Net income ($ mil.)	—	—	—	—	(58.5)	(103.6)
Market value ($ mil.)	(24.3%)	—	—	—	167.6	126.9
Employees	(18.9%)	—	—	—	111	90

[H] An in-depth profile of this company is available to Hoover's Online members at hoovers.com.

87

ALFA CORPORATION

2108 E. South Blvd.
Montgomery, AL 36116
Phone: 334-288-3900
Fax: 334-613-4709
Web: www.alfains.com

CEO: Jerry A. Newby
CFO: Stephen G. Rutledge
HR: Thomas E. Bryant
FYE: December 31
Type: Private

Alfa Corporation wants to be the top dog in the Alabama insurance pack. As a subsidiary of the Alfa Mutual group of companies (Alfa Mutual Insurance, Alfa Mutual Fire Insurance, and Alfa Mutual General Insurance), Alfa Corporation provides personal property/casualty insurance in a dozen central and southeastern states. It also offers life insurance policies in Alabama, Georgia, and Mississippi. The company, which has 400 office locations, enjoys a pooling arrangement between all of the Alfa companies. President and chairman Jerry Newby is also president of the Alabama Farmers Federation, which founded the company in 1946.

ALFA LAVAL INC.

5400 International Trade Dr.
Richmond, VA 23231
Phone: 804-222-5300
Fax: 804-236-3672
Web: www.alfalaval.us

CEO: Alessandro Terenghi
CFO: Stephen Pratt
HR: —
FYE: December 31
Type: Subsidiary

There's a "whole lotta shakin' goin' on" at Alfa Laval Inc. The subsidiary of Sweden-based Alfa Laval AB makes separators (centrifuges), heat exchangers (evaporators and condensers), decanters, tank equipment, pumps, and valves under brand names Contherm, Merco, Sharples, and Tri-Clover, among others. Alfa Laval's products are used in a host of industries, from dairy and food processing to petrochemicals and steel manufacturing. The company also offers spare parts, reconditioned heat exchangers, and round-the-clock equipment-monitoring systems. The company has 14 locations in the US, including six manufacturing facilities, an international distribution center, and seven service and repair centers.

	Annual Growth	12/04	12/05	12/06	12/07	12/08
Est. sales ($ mil.)	—	—	—	—	—	323.2
Employees	—	—	—	—	—	632

ALFACELL CORPORATION

NASDAQ (CM): ACEL

300 Atrium Dr.
Somerset, NJ 08873
Phone: 732-652-4525
Fax: 732-652-4575
Web: www.alfacell.com

CEO: Charles Muniz
CFO: Charles Muniz
HR: —
FYE: July 31
Type: Public

Development-stage Alfacell is willing to kiss a few frogs in hopes one will transform into a princely product. The biotechnology firm has isolated proteins from Northern Leopard frog eggs and embryos as possible therapies for cancerous tumors that have become resistant to chemotherapy. The company's lead drug candidate, Onconase, is being studied as a possible treatment for a variety of cancers, including non-small cell lung cancer. Alfacell is researching applications for Onconase and other amphibian proteins for applications in other areas of oncology as well as infectious diseases.

	Annual Growth	7/05	7/06	7/07	7/08	7/09
Sales ($ mil.)	—	—	—	—	—	0.0
Net income ($ mil.)	—	—	—	—	—	(4.5)
Market value ($ mil.)	—	—	—	—	—	13.0
Employees	—	—	—	—	—	6

ALICO, INC.

NASDAQ (GS): ALCO

640 S. Main St.
La Belle, FL 33975
Phone: 863-675-2966
Fax: 863-675-6928
Web: www.alicoinc.com

CEO: Steven M. (Steve) Smith
CFO: Patrick W. Murphy
HR: Michael (Mike) Talaga
FYE: September 30
Type: Public

Alico is bullish on cattle, but citrus generates more revenue. The company, which owns some 135,000 acres of farm land in Florida, dabbles in sugarcane, citrus, vegetables, and sod production, as well as commercial land development. Alico's citrus is packed or processed with fruit from other growers through produce marketer Ben Hill Griffin. It has a breeding herd of approximately 10,000 cattle and it sells stock primarily to meat packing and processing plants. Alico's sugarcane is sold through a pooling agreement with a nearby sugar mill; sod is marketed through a US wholesaler. In addition, the company has real estate sales operations and leases some of its land for grazing, farming, recreation, and mining.

	Annual Growth	8/05	8/06	8/07	*9/08	9/09
Sales ($ mil.)	12.7%	55.5	77.4	134.8	116.4	89.5
Net income ($ mil.)	—	6.1	6.5	(13.8)	4.7	(3.6)
Market value ($ mil.)	(13.3%)	383.4	433.5	377.2	349.8	216.8
Employees	1.0%	155	215	228	203	161

*Fiscal year change

ALIGN TECHNOLOGY, INC.

NASDAQ (GM): ALGN

881 Martin Ave.
Santa Clara, CA 95050
Phone: 408-470-1000
Fax: 408-470-1010
Web: www.aligntech.com

CEO: Thomas M. Prescott
CFO: Kenneth B. (Ken) Arola
HR: —
FYE: December 31
Type: Public

Brace-face begone! Align Technology produces and sells the Invisalign System, which corrects malocclusion, or crooked teeth. Instead of using metal or ceramic mounts that are cemented on the teeth and connected by wires (traditional braces), the system involves using an array of clear and removable dental Aligners to move a patient's teeth into a desired tooth alignment. The company markets its products to orthodontists and dentists worldwide. Align also provides training for practitioners to model treatment schemes using its Internet-based application called ClinCheck, which simulates tooth movement and suggests the appropriate Aligner.

	Annual Growth	12/05	12/06	12/07	12/08	12/09
Sales ($ mil.)	10.8%	207.1	206.4	284.3	304.0	312.3
Net income ($ mil.)	—	1.4	(35.0)	35.7	80.0	(31.3)
Market value ($ mil.)	28.8%	489.6	1,057.2	1,262.3	662.2	1,348.6
Employees	14.6%	1,097	1,253	1,307	1,394	1,895

ALIMERA SCIENCES, INC.

NASDAQ (GM): ALIM

6120 Windward Pkwy., Ste. 290
Alpharetta, GA 30005
Phone: 678-990-5740
Fax: 678-990-5744
Web: www.alimerasciences.com

CEO: C. Daniel (Dan) Myers
CFO: Richard S. (Rick) Eiswirth Jr.
HR: —
FYE: December 31
Type: Public

Alimera Sciences wants to see clear into the future. The biopharmaceutical company specializes in prescription ophthalmic pharmaceuticals, particularly those aimed at treating ocular diseases affecting the retina. Alimera's most advanced product candidate, Iluvien, is an insert, smaller than a grain of rice, that slowly releases a drug to the back of the eye used in the treatment of diabetic macular edema (DME); DME, a retinal disease affecting diabetics, can lead to severe vision loss and blindness. Iluvien is effective for up to 36 months and may also have the potential to affect other ophthalmic diseases, such as retinal vein occlusion (RVO). Alimera Sciences went public through a $72 million IPO in 2010.

	Annual Growth	12/05	12/06	12/07	12/08	12/09
Sales ($ mil.)	—	0.0	0.0	0.0	0.0	0.0
Net income ($ mil.)	—	(13.6)	(13.0)	(5.7)	(61.5)	(44.2)
Employees	0.0%	—	—	21	21	21

ALION SCIENCE AND TECHNOLOGY CORPORATION

1750 Tysons Blvd., Ste. 1300
McLean, VA 22102
Phone: 703-918-4480
Fax: 703-714-6508
Web: www.alionscience.com

CEO: Bahman Atefi
CFO: Michael J. Alber
HR: —
FYE: September 30
Type: Private

Alion creates alliances between science and big government. Alion Science and Technology is a development and research company that provides consulting and technology services, primarily to federal agencies. Most of its revenues come from contracts with the US Department of Defense (DOD), especially the Navy. Alion specializes in areas including naval architecture and marine engineering, manufacturing engineering services, wargaming, lab support and chemical decontamination, military transformation analysis, and wireless communications engineering. The employee-owned firm has offices and facilities throughout the US, generally near government military bases and other installations. Alion was founded in 2002.

	Annual Growth	9/05	9/06	9/07	9/08	9/09
Sales ($ mil.)	21.4%	369.2	508.6	737.6	739.5	802.2
Net income ($ mil.)	—	(40.2)	(31.1)	(42.8)	(25.3)	(17.0)
Employees	7.7%	2,508	3,575	3,400	3,266	3,380

ALIXPARTNERS LLP

2000 Town Center, Ste. 2400
Southfield, MI 48075
Phone: 248-358-4420
Fax: 248-358-1969
Web: www.alixpartners.com

CEO: Frederick A. (Fred) Crawford
CFO: Douglas E. (Doug) Barnett
HR: Francis J. McKeon III
FYE: October 1
Type: Private

Company headed in the wrong direction? AlixPartners would like to try to help you turn things around. The consulting firm provides operational and financial advisory services to underperforming companies worldwide. Specialties include assistance with bankruptcy reorganizations and litigation. AlixPartners also offers performance improvement and strategic consulting services for healthy companies. The firm operates from more than a dozen offices, not only in the US but also in Europe and the Asia/Pacific region. Private equity firm Hellman & Friedman, together with AlixPartners employees, owns a controlling stake in the turnaround firm.

ALJ REGIONAL HOLDINGS, INC.

Pink Sheets: ALJJ

244 Madison Ave., PMB #358
New York, NY 10016
Phone: 212-883-0083
Fax: 212-622-7301

CEO: John Scheel
CFO: Rob Christ
HR: —
FYE: September 30
Type: Public

ALJ Regional Holdings owns a steel mini-mill in Kentucky, which it acquired in 2005. The mill is operated by Kentucky Electric Steel, which produces bar flat products that it sells to service centers as well as makers of truck trailers, steel springs, and cold drawn bars. Kentucky Electric Steel produces steel in both Merchant Bar Quality and Special Bar Quality.

ALKERMES, INC.

NASDAQ (GS): ALKS

88 Sidney St.
Cambridge, MA 02139
Phone: 617-494-0171
Fax: 617-494-9263
Web: www.alkermes.com

CEO: Richard F. Pops
CFO: James M. (Jim) Frates
HR: Madeline D. Coffin
FYE: March 31
Type: Public

Alkermes, whose name is Arabic for "magic potion," is working some biotech alchemy. The firm uses its proprietary drug-delivery systems to make fragile biotech compounds that require less frequent dosing or provide more targeted delivery. Focusing on widespread diseases like diabetes, central nervous system disorders, and addiction, it has a couple of drugs on the market that use its injectable extended-release technology, which lets patients take a drug once or twice a month, rather than once or twice a day. One such drug is Risperdal Consta, a long-acting version of Janssen's schizophrenia medication Risperdal. Another is Vivitrol, a treatment for alcohol dependence that the company markets itself.

	Annual Growth	3/05	3/06	3/07	3/08	3/09
Sales ($ mil.)	44.0%	76.1	166.6	240.0	240.7	326.8
Net income ($ mil.)	—	(73.9)	3.8	9.4	167.0	130.5
Market value ($ mil.)	4.0%	980.3	2,082.4	1,458.2	1,122.0	1,145.6
Employees	1.9%	528	760	830	610	570

ALL-AMERICAN SPORTPARK, INC

OTC: AASP

6730 S. Las Vegas Blvd.
Las Vegas, NV 89119
Phone: 702-798-7777
Fax: 702-739-9509

CEO: Ronald S. Boreta
CFO: Ronald S. Boreta
HR: —
FYE: December 31
Type: Public

If golf is your sport, then this company has a park for you. All-American SportPark operates Callaway Golf Center (CGC), a 42-acre golf practice facility located at the end of the famous Las Vegas Strip. Amenities include 110 driving stations in two tiers and a lighted nine-hole, par-three golf course called the Divine Nine. The center also features a restaurant and St. Andrews Golf Shop, where customers can buy golf equipment and related merchandise. The founding Boreta family owns more than 20% the company. Tennis pro Andre Agassi and partner Perry Rogers together also own almost 20% of All-American SportPark.

	Annual Growth	12/05	12/06	12/07	12/08	12/09
Sales ($ mil.)	(1.2%)	2.2	2.2	2.3	2.3	2.1
Net income ($ mil.)	—	(1.7)	(0.8)	(0.8)	0.1	(0.7)
Market value ($ mil.)	(18.2%)	1.0	0.6	0.9	0.5	0.5
Employees	11.0%	25	27	30	22	38

ALLEGHANY CORPORATION

NYSE: Y

7 Times Square Tower
New York, NY 10036
Phone: 212-752-1356
Fax: 212-759-8149
Web: www.alleghany.com

CEO: Weston M. Hicks
CFO: Roger B. Gorham
HR: —
FYE: December 31
Type: Public

After a spell as a conglomerate, with interests ranging from minerals to steel fasteners, Alleghany has found that it really prefers property/casualty insurance, with a smattering of good old real estate. Alleghany's subsidiaries include Capitol Transamerica (property/casualty, fidelity, and surety insurance) and RSUI Group, an underwriter of wholesale specialty insurance. It distributes its insurance products through independent insurance brokers in the US. Its Pacific Compensation Corp handles workers' compensation insurance in California. Alleghany also has commercial and residential real estate interests in California.

	Annual Growth	12/05	12/06	12/07	12/08	12/09
Assets ($ mil.)	1.2%	5,913.7	6,178.7	6,733.0	6,181.8	6,192.8
Net income ($ mil.)	50.9%	52.3	251.2	305.3	148.0	271.0
Market value ($ mil.)	1.3%	2,320.7	3,030.6	3,417.7	2,445.4	2,441.3
Employees	3.2%	676	713	951	807	768

ALLEGHENY ENERGY, INC.
NYSE: AYE

800 Cabin Hill Dr.
Greensburg, PA 15601
Phone: 724-837-3000
Fax: —
Web: www.alleghenyenergy.com

CEO: Paul J. Evanson
CFO: Kirk R. Oliver
HR: Edward (Ed) Dudzinski
FYE: December 31
Type: Public

Even when the Allegheny Moon isn't shining, Allegheny Energy (AE) can provide plenty of light. Its Allegheny Power unit provides electricity to more than 1.5 million customers in Maryland, Pennsylvania, West Virginia, and Virginia through regulated utilities Monongahela Power, Potomac Edison, and West Penn Power. Subsidiary Allegheny Energy Supply provides power to AE's utilities and sells electricity to wholesale and retail customers. Subsidiary Allegheny Ventures controls Allegheny Energy Solutions (energy consulting). It also has transmission line design and management units (Trans-Allegheny Interstate Line Company and PATH, LLC). In 2010 the company agreed to be bought by FirstEnergy in an $8.5 billion deal.

	Annual Growth	12/05	12/06	12/07	12/08	12/09
Sales ($ mil.)	3.1%	3,037.9	3,121.5	3,307.0	3,385.9	3,426.8
Net income ($ mil.)	54.5%	69.0	319.3	412.2	395.4	392.8
Market value ($ mil.)	(7.2%)	5,367.2	7,785.4	10,786.9	5,741.9	3,981.7
Employees	(0.4%)	4,460	4,362	4,355	4,455	4,383

ALLEGHENY TECHNOLOGIES INCORPORATED
NYSE: ATI

1000 Six PPG Pl.
Pittsburgh, PA 15222
Phone: 412-394-2800
Fax: 412-394-3034
Web: www.alleghenytechnologies.com

CEO: L. Patrick (Pat) Hassey
CFO: Richard J. (Rich) Harshman
HR: Jon D. Walton
FYE: December 31
Type: Public

Allegheny Technologies, Inc. (ATI) manufactures stainless and specialty steels, nickel- and cobalt-based alloys and superalloys, titanium and titanium alloys, tungsten materials, and such exotic alloys as niobium and zirconium. The company's flat-rolled products (sheet, strip, and plate) account for a great majority of its sales. Its high-performance metals unit produces metal bar, coil, foil, ingot, plate, rod, and wire. Allegheny Technologies' largest markets include aerospace, the chemical process, and oil and gas industries. Three-fourths of its sales are in the US.

	Annual Growth	12/05	12/06	12/07	12/08	12/09
Sales ($ mil.)	(3.6%)	3,539.9	4,939.6	5,452.5	5,309.7	3,054.9
Net income ($ mil.)	(45.6%)	361.8	571.9	747.1	565.9	31.7
Market value ($ mil.)	5.5%	3,555.4	8,935.7	8,514.0	2,515.8	4,411.7
Employees	(2.2%)	9,300	9,500	9,700	9,600	8,500

ALLEGHENY VALLEY BANCORP, INC.
OTC: AVLY

5137 Butler St.
Pittsburgh, PA 15201
Phone: 412-781-0318
Fax: 412-781-6474
Web: www.avbpgh.com

CEO: Andrew W. (Andy) Hasley
CFO: Jason W. Ross
HR: —
FYE: December 31
Type: Public

Allegheny Valley Bancorp is the holding company for Allegheny Valley Bank of Pittsburgh, which has about 10 branches in the Steel City and its suburbs. Founded in 1900, the bank offers standard services such as checking and savings accounts, CDs, IRAs, and debit cards. One- to four-family residential mortgages make up the largest portion of the bank's loan portfolio, followed by commercial mortgages, equipment leases, and business loans. The company's investment unit, AVB Advisors, provides financial planning, wealth management, insurance, and investment products. Another Western Pennsylvania bank holding company, S&T Bancorp, owns about 15% of Allegheny Valley Bancorp.

ALLEGIANT TRAVEL COMPANY
NASDAQ (GS): ALGT

8360 S. Durango Dr.
Las Vegas, NV 89113
Phone: 702-851-7300
Fax: 702-256-7209
Web: www.allegiantair.com

CEO: Maurice J. (Maury) Gallagher Jr.
CFO: Scott Sheldon
HR: —
FYE: December 31
Type: Public

Allegiant Travel pledges to serve the vacation needs of residents of more than 55 small US cities in more than 30 states. Through Allegiant Air, the company provides nonstop service to tourist destinations such as Las Vegas and Orlando, Florida, from places such as Cedar Rapids, Iowa; Fargo, North Dakota; and Toledo, Ohio. It maintains a fleet of about 45 MD-80 series aircraft. Besides scheduled service, Allegiant Air offers charter flights for casino operators Harrah's, MGM MIRAGE, and Wynn Resorts, in addition to other customers. Sister company Allegiant Vacations works with partners to allow customers to book hotel rooms and rental cars with their airline tickets.

	Annual Growth	12/05	12/06	12/07	12/08	12/09
Sales ($ mil.)	43.2%	132.5	243.4	360.6	504.0	557.9
Net income ($ mil.)	79.8%	7.3	8.7	31.5	35.4	76.3
Market value ($ mil.)	18.9%	—	558.9	640.1	967.4	939.5
Employees	30.6%	596	1,046	1,363	1,567	1,734

ALLEGIS GROUP, INC.

7301 Parkway Dr.
Hanover, MD 21076
Phone: 410-579-4800
Fax: 410-540-7556
Web: www.allegisgroup.com

CEO: James C. (Jim) Davis
CFO: Paul Bowie
HR: Neil Mann
FYE: December 31
Type: Private

Clients in need of highly skilled technical and other personnel might want to take the pledge of Allegis. One of the world's largest staffing and recruitment firms, Allegis Group has about 300 offices in North America and Europe. Among its companies are Aerotek (engineering, automotive, and scientific professionals), Stephen James Associates (recruitment for accounting, financial, and cash management positions), and TEKsystems (information technology staffing and consulting). Other Allegis units include sales support outsourcer MarketSource. Chairman Jim Davis helped found the company (originally known as Aerotek) in 1983 to provide contract engineering personnel to two clients in the aerospace industry.

	Annual Growth	12/04	12/05	12/06	12/07	12/08
Sales ($ mil.)	12.4%	3,600.0	4,400.0	5,000.0	5,570.0	5,740.0
Employees	9.1%	6,000	7,000	8,000	10,000	8,500

ALLEGRO MICROSYSTEMS, INC.

115 Northeast Cutoff
Worcester, MA 01606
Phone: 508-853-5000
Fax: 508-853-3353
Web: www.allegromicro.com

CEO: Dennis H. Fitzgerald
CFO: Mark A. Feragne
HR: Marybeth Perry
FYE: March 31
Type: Subsidiary

Allegro MicroSystems' chips do their jobs at a lively tempo. The company is one of the world's top makers of Hall-effect sensors. Automakers use these specialized components — named after an electromagnetic phenomenon called "the Hall effect" — in braking, steering, suspension, and other systems. Allegro also makes power integrated circuits (ICs) used in office machines and portable electronics, along with driver, controller, and power interface ICs used in a variety of applications. It sells directly and through distributors to OEMs worldwide. The company, a subsidiary of Sanken Electric, entered the chip business four decades ago as Sprague Semiconductor Group before taking the Allegro name in 1990.

ALLEN & COMPANY LLC

711 5th Ave., 9th Fl.
New York, NY 10022
Phone: 212-832-8000
Fax: 212-832-8023

CEO: Herbert A. (Herb) Allen III
CFO: —
HR: —
FYE: November 30
Type: Private

For Allen & Company, there's no business like financing show business. The investment bank serves variously as investor, underwriter, and broker to some of the biggest names in entertainment, technology, and information. Viewed as something of a secret society, the firm has had a quiet hand in such hookups as Seagram (now part of Vivendi) and Universal Studios, Hasbro and Galoob Toys, and Disney and Capital Cities/ABC. The notoriously secretive firm's famous annual retreat in Sun Valley, Idaho, attracts more moguls than a double-black ski run (Warren Buffett, Bill Gates, Oprah Winfrey, and former eBay CEO Meg Whitman have attended). Brothers Herbert and Charles Allen founded the company in 1922.

ALLEN SYSTEMS GROUP, INC.

1333 3rd Ave. South
Naples, FL 34102
Phone: 239-435-2200
Fax: 239-263-3692
Web: www.asg.com

CEO: Arthur L. (Art) Allen
CFO: Ernest J. Scheidemann
HR: Tom Romnios
FYE: December 31
Type: Private

When it comes to enterprise computing, Allen Systems Group (ASG) strives to make all systems go. The company provides a variety of software and services for enterprise performance, operations, and application management. Its products are used for functions such as migrating legacy data, business performance management, and developing business applications. ASG also offers business information portals and applications for identity and user access management, in addition to consulting, implementation, and training services. Customers have included Coca-Cola, General Electric, and Procter & Gamble.

ALLEN-EDMONDS SHOE CORPORATION

201 E. Seven Hills Rd.
Port Washington, WI 53074
Phone: 262-235-6000
Fax: 262-268-7427
Web: www.allenedmonds.com

CEO: Paul D. Grangaard
CFO: Jay Schauer
HR: Ellen Nickels
FYE: December 31
Type: Private

Allen-Edmonds' shoes stand their ground in the US. Maker of high-end men's dress and casual shoes, boots, belts, leather care goods, and hosiery, Allen-Edmonds makes most of its shoes in Maine and Wisconsin, resisting the trend of moving production abroad. Its shoes are handmade by skilled craftsmen, and Allen-Edmonds is known for its full range of shoe sizes for men. The company also offers a namesake cologne. Its products are sold in more than 25 company-owned stores in the US, Belgium, and Italy, as well as in department stores (Nordstrom), other specialty retailers, online and by catalog. Founded by Elbert Allen in 1922, the company was sold to Goldner Hawn Johnson & Morrison in 2006 for $123 million.

ALLENS, INC.

305 E. Main St.
Siloam Springs, AR 72761
Phone: 479-524-6431
Fax: 479-524-3291
Web: www.allencanning.com

CEO: Roderick L. Allen
CFO: Lori Sherrell
HR: —
FYE: December 31
Type: Private

He of the bulging biceps, Popeye himself, would definitely approve of Allens' business. Allens produces a full line of canned and frozen vegetables and beans (including the Popster's absolute fave — spinach). The Arkansas-based company's brands include Allens, Butterfield, Popeye, Royal Prince, Sunshine, and Trappey's, along with Freshlike and Veg·All. Its customers include US companies in the retail food, foodservice, and food-manufacturing sectors. Founded in 1926, Allens remains a family-owned and -operated business and is the largest privately owned vegetable company in the US.

ALLERGAN, INC.

NYSE: AGN

2525 Dupont Dr.
Irvine, CA 92612
Phone: 714-246-4500
Fax: 714-246-6987
Web: www.allergan.com

CEO: David E. I. Pyott
CFO: Jeffrey L. Edwards
HR: Douglas S. Ingram
FYE: December 31
Type: Public

Don't let the name fool you, Allergan can't help you with that runny nose. Instead, the company is a leading maker of eye care, skin care, and aesthetic products, including best-selling pharmaceutical Botox. Originally used to treat muscle spasms (as well as eye spasms and misalignment), Botox has found another, more popular application in diminishing facial wrinkles. Allergan's eye care products include medications for glaucoma, allergic conjunctivitis, and chronic dry eye. Skin care products include treatments for acne, wrinkles, and psoriasis. Allergan also sells implants used in breast augmentation and weight-loss surgery. Its products are sold in 100 countries via direct sales and distributors.

	Annual Growth	12/05	12/06	12/07	12/08	12/09
Sales ($ mil.)	18.0%	2,319.2	3,063.3	3,938.9	4,403.4	4,503.6
Net income ($ mil.)	12.8%	385.8	(127.4)	499.3	578.6	623.8
Market value ($ mil.)	3.9%	16,414.5	18,205.5	19,534.4	12,260.7	19,160.4
Employees	13.2%	5,055	6,772	7,886	8,740	8,300

ALLERGY RESEARCH GROUP, INC.

2300 North Loop Rd.
Alameda, CA 94502
Phone: 510-263-2000
Fax: 510-263-2100
Web: www.allergyresearchgroup.com

CEO: Stephen Levine
CFO: Laura Johnson
HR: —
FYE: December 31
Type: Subsidiary

You might only think about allergies once a year, but Allergy Research Group thinks about them every day. Through its Nutricology subsidiary, the company develops and markets hypoallergenic vitamins and nutritional supplements including amino acids, fatty acids, glandular tissue products, minerals, and multivitamins. It markets products directly to doctors, nutritionists, and other health care professionals under the Allergy Research Group label, and it distributes products to health food stores and pharmacies through its NutriCology label. The company was acquired by KI NutriCare, a subsidiary of Kikkoman Corporation, in 2008.

An in-depth profile of this company is available to Hoover's Online members at hoovers.com.

91

ALLETE, INC.

NYSE: ALE

30 W. Superior St.
Duluth, MN 55802
Phone: 218-279-5000
Fax: 218-720-2502
Web: www.allete.com

CEO: Alan R. Hodnik
CFO: Mark A. Schober
HR: Glen Porter
FYE: December 31
Type: Public

ALLETE provides light to the northern climes. Most of its business is classified within its regulated operations, which include electric, gas, and water utilities located in northeastern Minnesota and northwestern Wisconsin. Those operations are conducted through subsidiaries Minnesota Power (about 145,000 customers) and Superior Water, Light and Power (about 35,000 customers for its electric, gas, and water utilities). ALLETE's other segment includes coal mining operations, emerging technologies related to electric utilities, and a real estate business (large land tracts in Florida). Subsidiary BNI Coal operates a mine in North Dakota that supplies, primarily, two generating co-ops, Minnkota Power and Square Butte.

	Annual Growth	12/05	12/06	12/07	12/08	12/09
Sales ($ mil.)	0.7%	737.4	767.1	841.7	801.0	759.1
Net income ($ mil.)	46.3%	13.3	68.3	87.6	82.5	61.0
Market value ($ mil.)	(7.2%)	1,550.7	1,640.3	1,395.0	1,137.3	1,151.8
Employees	(0.4%)	1,500	1,500	15,000	1,529	1,474

ALLIANCE BANCORP, INC. OF PENNSYLVANIA

NASDAQ (GM): ALLB

541 Lawrence Rd.
Broomall, PA 19008
Phone: 610-353-2900
Fax: 610-359-6908
Web: www.allianceanytime.com

CEO: Dennis D. Cirucci
CFO: Peter J. Meier
HR: —
FYE: December 31
Type: Public

Alliance Bancorp, Inc. of Pennsylvania is the holding company for Alliance Bank (formerly Greater Delaware Valley Savings Bank). The bank has about 10 branch offices that serve individuals and local businesses in suburban Philadelphia's Delaware and Chester counties. It offers standard deposit products such as checking and savings accounts, money market accounts, CDs, and IRAs. Commercial real estate loans (more than 45% of the company's loan portfolio) and residential mortgages (more than 40%) comprise most of the bank's lending activities. Alliance Bancorp was formed in 2007 when the bank converted from mutual ownership to a mid-tier stock holding company structure.

	Annual Growth	12/05	12/06	12/07	12/08	12/09
Assets ($ mil.)	4.5%	389.0	410.3	424.5	424.1	464.2
Net income ($ mil.)	3.9%	1.2	1.4	1.1	0.6	1.4
Market value ($ mil.)	(9.6%)	84.2	72.1	49.0	50.2	56.3
Employees	1.0%	99	92	98	102	103

ALLIANCE BANKSHARES CORPORATION

NASDAQ (CM): ABVA

14200 Park Meadow Dr., Ste. 200 South
Chantilly, VA 20151
Phone: 703-814-7200
Fax: 703-378-7210
Web: www.alliancebankva.com

CEO: William E. (Bill) Doyle Jr.
CFO: Paul M. Harbolick Jr.
HR: —
FYE: December 31
Type: Public

Alliance Bankshares has enjoyed a healthy partnership with mortgages since 1996. The financial institution is the holding company for Alliance Bank and its home funding subsidiary, Alliance Mortgage Division. Alliance Bankshares operates branches and loan production offices in the DC suburbs of northern Virginia. The bank offers such services as checking and savings accounts, CDs, corporate credit cards, and cash management. Its lending activities mainly consist of residential and commercial mortgages, with business and consumer loans rounding out its portfolio.

	Annual Growth	12/05	12/06	12/07	12/08	12/09
Assets ($ mil.)	(1.5%)	611.5	644.4	541.3	572.8	576.3
Net income ($ mil.)	—	4.1	4.5	(2.8)	(9.0)	(4.4)
Market value ($ mil.)	(32.7%)	71.1	79.9	33.3	7.1	14.6
Employees	(8.4%)	115	115	105	107	81

ALLIANCE DATA SYSTEMS CORPORATION

NYSE: ADS

17655 Waterview Pkwy.
Dallas, TX 75252
Phone: 972-348-5100
Fax: 972-348-5335
Web: www.alliancedata.com

CEO: Edward J. (Ed) Heffernan
CFO: Charles L. Horn
HR: —
FYE: December 31
Type: Public

Hoping to forge an alliance between consumers and retailers, Alliance Data Systems provides private-label credit card financing, processing, and marketing services to more than 800 businesses. Its client base consists of retailers such as AnnTaylor, J. Crew, Pottery Barn, and Victoria's Secret, as well as supermarkets, gas stations, and hospitality, financial services, media, and pharmaceutical companies. Through its Epsilon unit, Alliance Data develops customer loyalty programs and performs marketing services for firms such as Visa and Capital One. LoyaltyOne operates the AIR MILES rewards and loyalty program in Canada. Almost all of Alliance Data's business is in North America.

	Annual Growth	12/05	12/06	12/07	12/08	12/09
Sales ($ mil.)	6.1%	1,552.4	1,998.7	2,291.2	2,025.3	1,964.3
Net income ($ mil.)	0.9%	138.7	189.6	164.1	217.4	143.7
Market value ($ mil.)	16.1%	1,899.3	3,332.8	4,000.8	2,482.4	3,445.9
Employees	(1.9%)	8,000	9,300	9,800	7,400	7,400

ALLIANCE ENTERTAINMENT, LLC

4250 Coral Ridge Dr.
Coral Springs, FL 33065
Phone: 954-255-4000
Fax: 954-255-4078
Web: www.aent.com

CEO: Alan Tuchman
CFO: George Campagna
HR: —
FYE: January 31
Type: Private

Alliance Entertainment rolls out the rock 'n' roll. The company distributes music and video items — CDs, DVDs, games, and related products — to more than 5,000 merchants, including Best Buy, Barnes and Noble, Borders, and Hastings Entertainment, as well as Internet retailers. Alliance Entertainment also provides e-commerce, marketing, distribution, and related support services through its IDN and AEC Direct divisions. Its NCircle Entertainment unit licenses and distributes family entertainment titles based on such characters as Super Mario Bros. and My Little Pony. The company is part of magazine and entertainment wholesaler Source Interlink.

ALLIANCE FIBER OPTIC PRODUCTS, INC.

NASDAQ (CM): AFOP

275 Gibraltar Dr.
Sunnyvale, CA 94089
Phone: 408-736-6900
Fax: 408-736-4882
Web: www.afop.com

CEO: Peter C. Chang
CFO: Anita K. Ho
HR: —
FYE: December 31
Type: Public

Alliance Fiber Optic Products (AFOP) unites with light. Communications equipment manufacturers incorporate AFOP's fiber-optic components into products used to build networks that connect cities, regions within cities, and telecommunications service providers with their individual customers. Its optical path integration and optical fiber amplifier components, which include attenuators, couplers, depolarizers, multiplexers, and splitters, account for most of sales. The company sells directly to telecom equipment makers, primarily in North America, where it gets about half of sales. AFOP has more than 200 customers.

	Annual Growth	12/05	12/06	12/07	12/08	12/09
Sales ($ mil.)	9.1%	21.0	26.8	33.8	38.8	29.8
Net income ($ mil.)	—	(2.6)	0.7	3.4	4.1	1.4
Market value ($ mil.)	0.4%	48.5	86.8	85.9	27.4	49.3
Employees	10.6%	581	684	691	769	870

ALLIANCE FINANCIAL CORPORATION

NASDAQ (GM): ALNC

120 Madison St., Tower 2, 18th Fl.
Syracuse, NY 13202
Phone: 315-475-2100
Fax: 315-475-4421
Web: www.alliancebankna.com

CEO: Jack H. Webb
CFO: J. Daniel Mohr
HR: Colleen K. Lefeve
FYE: December 31
Type: Public

Alliance Financial Corporation is the holding company for Alliance Bank, which operates about 30 branches in central New York state. Targeting individuals and small to midsized businesses, Alliance offers such retail banking products as checking and savings accounts, IRAs, and CDs. Its loan and lease portfolio mainly contains residential mortgages (about 30%), commercial loans (nearly 25%), and indirect auto loans (around 20%). The company provides commercial equipment leasing in more than 30 states through its Alliance Leasing subsidiary. Alliance Financial also operates a trust department that manages some $1 billion worth of investment assets.

	Annual Growth	12/05	12/06	12/07	12/08	12/09
Assets ($ mil.)	9.6%	980.4	1,273.0	1,307.3	1,367.4	1,417.2
Net income ($ mil.)	11.0%	7.5	7.3	9.5	10.4	11.4
Market value ($ mil.)	(4.1%)	149.6	148.6	121.2	110.5	126.6
Employees	5.8%	269	324	335	334	337

ALLIANCE HEALTHCARE SERVICES

NYSE: AIQ

100 Bayview Circle, Ste. 400
Newport Beach, CA 92660
Phone: 949-242-5300
Fax: —
Web: www.allianceimaging.com

CEO: Paul S. Viviano
CFO: Howard K. Aihara
HR: —
FYE: December 31
Type: Public

Alliance HealthCare Services has a lead apron ready for you. Through its primary imaging division, the company operates some 500 diagnostic imaging systems for more than 1,000 hospitals and other health care providers in more than 40 states. For most customers, the company (formerly Alliance Imaging) provides imaging systems and the staff to run and maintain them, as well as marketing and billing support. In addition to MRI equipment and services (its main revenue source), Alliance offers positron emission tomography (PET), computed tomography (CT), combination scanning, X-rays, and ultrasound, among other imaging services. The company also runs a handful of cancer centers providing radiation therapy.

	Annual Growth	12/05	12/06	12/07	12/08	12/09
Sales ($ mil.)	4.1%	430.8	455.8	444.9	495.8	505.5
Net income ($ mil.)	(60.1%)	19.8	19.3	16.2	16.5	0.5
Market value ($ mil.)	(1.0%)	313.9	350.8	507.5	420.5	301.2
Employees	(1.7%)	2,092	1,955	2,070	2,258	1,956

ALLIANCE HOLDINGS GP, L.P.

NASDAQ (GS): AHGP

1717 S. Boulder Ave.
Tulsa, OK 74119
Phone: 918-295-1415
Fax: 918-295-7361
Web: www.ahgp.com

CEO: Joseph W. Craft III
CFO: Brian L. Cantrell
HR: —
FYE: December 31
Type: Public

When it comes to coal mining, it takes more than one company to make an Alliance. Alliance Holdings GP owns Alliance Resource Management GP, which is the managing general partner of coal mining company Alliance Resource Partners, L.P. That company has eight coal mining complexes in Illinois, Indiana, Kentucky, and Maryland, plus other coal interests in West Virginia. Alliance Holdings GP generates revenue from its general partnership interest and its 42% ownership stake in Alliance Resource Partners, L.P. The Alliance companies have been assembled by Joseph Craft III, who is chairman, president, CEO, and majority owner of Alliance Holdings GP.

	Annual Growth	12/05	12/06	12/07	12/08	12/09
Sales ($ mil.)	10.1%	838.7	967.2	1,033.0	1,156.1	1,230.6
Net income ($ mil.)	74.2%	12.4	85.6	87.9	132.6	114.2
Market value ($ mil.)	11.5%	—	1,182.9	1,420.5	886.0	1,640.8
Employees	(0.8%)	2,300	2,500	2,600	2,955	2,230

ALLIANCE LAUNDRY HOLDINGS LLC

119 Shepard St.
Ripon, WI 54971
Phone: 920-748-3121
Fax: 920-748-4334
Web: www.comlaundry.com

CEO: Thomas F. (Tom) L'Esperance
CFO: Bruce P. Rounds
HR: —
FYE: December 31
Type: Private

Laundry day can't come often enough for Alliance Laundry Holdings (ALH). Through its wholly owned subsidiary, Alliance Laundry Systems, the company makes commercial laundry equipment used in Laundromats, multi-housing laundry facilities (such as apartments, dormitories, and military bases), and on-premise laundries (hotels, hospitals, and prisons). Its washers and dryers are made under the brands Speed Queen, UniMac, Huebsch, IPSO, and Cissell. They're sold primarily in the US and Canada, but also internationally. Investment firm Teachers' Private Capital (private equity arm of Ontario Teachers' Pension Plan) acquired more than 91% of ALH for about $450 million in 2005. The company was founded in 1908.

	Annual Growth	12/04	12/05	12/06	12/07	12/08
Sales ($ mil.)	13.1%	281.0	296.6	366.1	443.3	460.3
Net income ($ mil.)	7.1%	11.8	(0.7)	(3.4)	9.9	15.5
Employees	4.6%	1,312	1,312	1,517	1,653	1,572

ALLIANCE ONE INTERNATIONAL, INC.

NYSE: AOI

8001 Aerial Center Pkwy.
Morrisville, NC 27560
Phone: 919-379-4300
Fax: 919-379-4346
Web: www.aointl.com

CEO: Robert E. (Pete) Harrison
CFO: Robert A. Sheets
HR: Michael K. McDaniel
FYE: March 31
Type: Public

Alliance One International keeps one eye on the world's tobacco farmers and the other eye on the cigarette makers. The company is a leading global leaf-tobacco merchant, behind its slightly larger rival Universal Corporation. Alliance One buys leaf tobacco directly from growers in more than 45 countries. It also processes flue-cured, burley, and oriental tobaccos and sells them to large multinational cigarette and cigar manufacturers, including Philip Morris International (PMI) and Japan Tobacco, in some 90 countries. Alliance One was formed through the 2005 merger of tobacco processor DIMON and Standard Commercial.

	Annual Growth	3/05	3/06	3/07	3/08	3/09
Sales ($ mil.)	14.6%	1,311.4	2,112.7	1,979.1	2,011.5	2,258.2
Net income ($ mil.)	77.7%	13.3	(447.4)	(21.3)	16.9	132.6
Market value ($ mil.)	(11.5%)	605.9	471.1	894.8	585.5	372.3
Employees	1.2%	4,200	5,400	4,700	4,700	4,400

ALLIANCE PLASTICS, INC.

3123 Station Rd.
Erie, PA 16510
Phone: 814-899-7671
Fax: 814-898-1638
Web: www.allianceplastics.com

CEO: Mike Conley
CFO: Kevin McCann
HR: —
FYE: December 31
Type: Subsidiary

Alliance Plastics can get a grip, put a cap on it, and wrap things up. The company manufactures and distributes more than 6,000 injection and vinyl dip plastic protection and finishing components, from grips to caps and plugs, hose wraps, flange protectors, and netting, for a range of industries and heavy-duty applications. Its growth is based on emerging technologies, driving new products like high-temperature vinyl masking caps that offer chemical protection and heat resistance of up to 425°. Founded in 1968, it became a niche business of UK-based specialty plastic and bonded fiber products supplier Filtrona plc (formerly an arm of Bunzl plc) in 1987.

An in-depth profile of this company is available to Hoover's Online members at hoovers.com.

93

ALLIANCE RESIDENTIAL COMPANY

2415 E. Camelback Rd., Ste. 600
Phoenix, AZ 85016
Phone: 602-778-2800
Fax: 602-778-2850
Web: www.allresco.com

CEO: Bruce C. Ward
CFO: V. Jay Hiemenz
HR: —
FYE: December 31
Type: Private

Alliance Residential owns, manages, and redevelops apartment communities in about 20 metropolitan markets in Arizona, California, Colorado, Florida, Georgia, Nevada, New Mexico, Oregon, Texas, Utah, Virginia, and Washington. Alliance Residential manages some 140 apartment communities comprising more than 40,000 units; properties include garden-style complexes, mid-rises, high-rises, and student housing. Other services include construction rehabilitation of older complexes and upgrades of units; Alliance Residential has redeveloped nearly 60,000 additional units in the western and southern US.

ALLIANCE RESOURCE PARTNERS, L.P.

NASDAQ (GS): ARLP

1717 S. Boulder Ave., Ste. 600
Tulsa, OK 74119
Phone: 918-295-7600
Fax: 918-295-7358
Web: www.arlp.com

CEO: Joseph W. Craft III
CFO: Brian L. Cantrell
HR: —
FYE: December 31
Type: Public

Coal is the main resource of Alliance Resource Partners. The company has eight coal mining complexes (seven underground, one surface) in Illinois, Indiana, Kentucky, Maryland, Pennsylvania, and West Virginia. Alliance controls about 685 million tons of reserves. The company produces about 25 million tons of coal annually, nearly all of which is sold to electric utilities. President and CEO Joseph Craft III controls a more than 40% stake in Alliance Resource Partners. Craft, a coal industry veteran, owns his stake through Alliance Holdings GP, a company he controls that went public in 2006.

	Annual Growth	12/05	12/06	12/07	12/08	12/09
Sales ($ mil.)	10.1%	838.7	967.6	1,033.3	1,156.5	1,231.0
Net income ($ mil.)	4.7%	160.0	172.8	170.4	134.6	192.2
Market value ($ mil.)	3.9%	1,365.9	1,267.5	1,331.7	986.9	1,592.4
Employees	7.7%	2,300	2,500	2,600	2,955	3,090

ALLIANCEBERNSTEIN HOLDING L.P.

NYSE: AB

1345 Avenue of the Americas
New York, NY 10105
Phone: 212-969-1000
Fax: 212-969-2229
Web: www.alliancebernstein.com

CEO: Peter S. Kraus
CFO: John B. Howard
HR: Lori Massad
FYE: December 31
Type: Public

The *raison d'etre* of AllianceBernstein Holding is its more than 35% ownership of investment manager AllianceBernstein. (French insurer AXA, through its AXA Financial unit, owns a majority of the subsidiary.) AllianceBernstein, which has approximately $400 million of client assets under management, administers about 80 mutual funds, including value equity, growth equity, fixed income, index, and structured investments. The subsidiary mainly serves institutional clients such as pension funds, corporations, and not-for-profits, in addition to retail investors.

	Annual Growth	12/05	12/06	12/07	12/08	12/09
Assets ($ mil.)	8.6%	1,377.1	1,568.0	1,575.2	1,601.4	1,912.3
Net income ($ mil.)	(9.4%)	248.1	325.0	376.2	244.7	167.2
Market value ($ mil.)	(16.0%)	5,750.9	8,185.1	7,660.8	2,116.5	2,860.7
Employees	0.3%	4,312	4,914	5,580	4,997	4,369

◫ ALLIANCEBERNSTEIN L.P.

1345 Avenue of the Americas
New York, NY 10105
Phone: 212-969-1000
Fax: 212-969-2229
Web: www.alliancebernstein.com

CEO: Peter S. Kraus
CFO: John B. Howard
HR: Lori Massad
FYE: December 31
Type: Private

AllianceBernstein has tons of funds. As one of the world's largest investment managers, the company (formerly Alliance Capital Management) administers about 170 domestic and international mutual funds. Institutional customers, including public retirement funds, employee benefit plans, foundations, endowments, government entities, and insurance firms, account for a majority of the firm's approximately $400 billion in assets under management. For retail investors, the company provides private client services, managed accounts, annuities, retirement plans, and college savings plans. AllianceBernstein also owns money manager and research firm Sanford C. Bernstein.

	Annual Growth	12/05	12/06	12/07	12/08	12/09
Assets ($ mil.)	(6.6%)	9,490.5	10,601.1	9,368.8	8,503.4	7,214.9
Net income ($ mil.)	(10.5%)	868.3	1,108.6	1,260.4	839.2	556.1
Employees	0.3%	4,312	4,914	5,580	4,997	4,369

ALLIANT CREDIT UNION

11545 W. Touhy Ave.
Chicago, IL 60666
Phone: 773-462-2000
Fax: 773-462-2095
Web: www.alliantcreditunion.org

CEO: David W. Mooney
CFO: Mona Leung
HR: —
FYE: December 31
Type: Not-for-profit

Coffee, tea, or checking account? With about a dozen locations near major airports, Alliant Credit Union (formerly United Airlines Employees Credit Union), is one of the largest credit unions in the country with nearly $6.5 billion in assets and more than 250,000 members. Alliant offers a fleet of products and services, including checking and savings accounts, credit cards, investments, and insurance. Membership is open to all Chicagoland residents and workers, current and retired employees or members (and families) of United Airlines, Aflac, NAACP, Google, Kaiser Permanente, and over a hundred other qualifying companies and organizations. Alliant was founded by a group of United Airlines employees in 1935.

ALLIANT ENERGY CORPORATION

NYSE: LNT

4902 N. Biltmore Ln., Ste. 1000
Madison, WI 53718
Phone: 608-458-3311
Fax: 608-458-0100
Web: www.alliantenergy.com

CEO: William D. (Bill) Harvey
CFO: Patricia L. Kampling
HR: Wayne Reschke
FYE: December 31
Type: Public

Alliant would like you to increase your reliance on energy. Alliant Energy's utilities, Interstate Power and Light (IP&L) and Wisconsin Power and Light (WPL), provide electricity to 981,650 customers and natural gas to 411,640 customers in four states; the utility operations also own power plants that generate some 5,600 MW of capacity. Nonregulated operations include rail and marine transportation services, independent power production (including wind farms), and real estate. Alliant Energy also provides engineering, consulting, and management services.

	Annual Growth	12/05	12/06	12/07	12/08	12/09
Sales ($ mil.)	1.1%	3,279.6	3,359.4	3,437.6	3,681.7	3,432.8
Net income ($ mil.)	—	(7.7)	315.7	425.3	306.7	129.7
Market value ($ mil.)	1.9%	3,106.0	4,183.8	4,507.3	3,232.3	3,351.9
Employees	(1.4%)	5,239	5,151	5,179	5,318	4,957

ALLIANT TECHSYSTEMS INC.

NYSE: ATK

7480 Flying Cloud Dr.	CEO: Mark W. DeYoung
Minneapolis, MN 55344	CFO: John L. Shroyer
Phone: 952-351-3000	HR: Paula J. Patineau
Fax: 952-351-3009	FYE: March 31
Web: www.atk.com	Type: Public

Space is not the final frontier for Alliant Techsystems (ATK), as long as its aerospace offerings are paving new paths for the company's technological endeavors. ATK is a leading manufacturer of solid-propulsion rocket motors, force protection systems, laser warning systems, and strategic and defense missiles. ATK builds motors for unmanned space launch vehicles such as the Trident II and the Delta II. ATK is also a top supplier of ammunition — from small-caliber rounds to tank ammunition — to the US and its allies. Additional lethal offerings include anti-tank mines, aircraft weapons systems, and high-tech weapons components. The US government accounts for more than 60% of sales.

	Annual Growth	3/06	3/07	3/08	3/09	3/10
Sales ($ mil.)	10.6%	3,216.8	3,564.9	4,171.7	4,583.2	4,807.7
Net income ($ mil.)	16.0%	153.9	184.1	222.3	155.1	278.7
Market value ($ mil.)	1.3%	2,550.4	2,905.6	3,421.5	2,213.6	2,686.8
Employees	4.3%	15,200	16,000	17,000	19,000	18,000

ALLIANZ GLOBAL INVESTORS OF AMERICA L.P.

680 Newport Ctr. Dr., Ste. 250	CEO: Mohamed A. El-Erian
Newport Beach, CA 92660	CFO: —
Phone: 949-219-2200	HR: —
Fax: —	FYE: December 31
Web: www.allianzinvestors.com	Type: Subsidiary

Allianz Global Investors of America is the US arm of Allianz's asset management operations, Allianz Global Investors. Serving both institutional and individual investors, the company offers such products and services as mutual funds, exchange-traded closed-end funds, managed accounts, college savings plans, annuities, and financial advice. Its subsidiaries and affiliates include PIMCO, Nicholas-Applegate Capital Management, NFJ Investment Group, Oppenheimer Capital, and RCM Capital Management. All told, Allianz Global Investors of America has approximately $560 billion of assets under management.

ALLIANZ GLOBAL RISKS US INSURANCE COMPANY

2350 Empire Ave.	CEO: Wolfgang Schatz
Burbank, CA 91504	CFO: Randy Renn
Phone: 818-260-7500	HR: Daniel Barker
Fax: 818-260-7207	FYE: December 31
Web: www.allianzglobalrisks.com	Type: Subsidiary

International enterprise is a risky business, and that's where Allianz Global Risks US steps in. The company is the US arm of Allianz Global Risks, which provides international corporate insurance to large industrial clients of Munich-based mega-insurer Allianz SE. Allianz Global Risks US provides complex property/casualty insurance for US-based companies with global operations. The company's underwriters span about a dozen industries, including construction, energy, retail, power generation, public entities, real estate, and both standard and special industrial hazards. It also provides risk management services.

	Annual Growth	12/04	12/05	12/06	12/07	12/08
Est. sales ($ mil.)	—	—	—	—	—	104.0
Employees	—	—	—	—	—	425

ALLIANZ LIFE INSURANCE COMPANY OF NORTH AMERICA

5701 Golden Hills Dr.	CEO: Gary C. Bhojwani
Minneapolis, MN 55416	CFO: Giulio Terzariol
Phone: 763-765-6500	HR: Kirk Williams
Fax: —	FYE: December 31
Web: www.allianzlife.com	Type: Subsidiary

There's more to Allianz Life than life. The subsidiaries and affiliates of Allianz Life Insurance Company of North America (Allianz Life) offer a range of insurance, investment, and savings products to individuals throughout the US. Allianz Life boasts a network of more than 100,000 independent agents and financial planners selling such products as life insurance, variable and fixed life annuity products, and long-term care insurance. It offers mutual funds and other broker-dealer services through its Questar Capital affiliate. Allianz Life operates in New York through its Allianz Life Insurance Company of New York unit. Allianz Life became a subsidiary of Allianz SE in 1979.

	Annual Growth	12/04	12/05	12/06	12/07	12/08
Est. sales ($ mil.)	—	—	—	—	—	13,056.4
Employees	—	—	—	—	—	2,800

ALLIED BEVERAGE GROUP LLC

600 Washington Ave.	CEO: Jeffrey Altschuler
Carlstadt, NJ 07072	CFO: —
Phone: 201-842-6200	HR: Jeanette M. Valentin
Fax: 201-842-6327	FYE: January 31
Web: www.alliedbeverage.com	Type: Private

Allied Beverage Group is considered the largest New Jersey-based wine and spirits distributor and one of the 10 largest in the US. The company, which specializes in fine wines, sells beverages to restaurants and other establishments that serve alcohol. Among its divisions are Flagstaff Distributors, Meritage Wine Group, and J&J Distributing. Its Majestic Wine & Spirits is a brokerage and direct wholesale business in Pennsylvania. Allied Beverage, which is a distributor for Diageo, was created in 1996 from the merger of the Baxter Group, F&A Distributing Company, and Jaydor (companies that date back to the 1930s, just after the repeal of Prohibition).

	Annual Growth	1/04	1/05	1/06	1/07	1/08
Est. sales ($ mil.)	—	—	—	—	—	553.8
Employees	—	—	—	—	—	800

ALLIED BUILDING PRODUCTS CORP.

15 E. Union Ave.	CEO: Robert (Bob) Feury Jr.
East Rutherford, NJ 07073	CFO: Brian Reilly
Phone: 201-507-8400	HR: Christopher Gary
Fax: 201-507-3842	FYE: December 31
Web: www.alliedbuilding.net	Type: Subsidiary

Allied Building Products counts home builders and contractors among its circle of friends. Serving the commercial and residential construction markets, the company distributes exterior and interior building materials, including roofing, siding, drywall, and acoustical tile, from major manufacturers. It also markets products under its own brands: Cutting Edge and Tri-Bilt. Allied operates about 200 branches in some 30 US states and Mexico. It maintains a fleet of about 1,500 vehicles, including cranes and delivery trucks. The company is a subsidiary of Oldcastle (itself a subsidiary of CRH). Allied was founded in 1950 as a family-operated roofing and custom sheet metal fabrication business.

An in-depth profile of this company is available to Hoover's Online members at hoovers.com.

95

THE ALLIED DEFENSE GROUP, INC.

NYSE Amex: ADG

8000 Towers Crescent Dr., Ste. 260	CEO: John J. Marcello
Vienna, VA 22182	CFO: —
Phone: 703-847-5268	HR: —
Fax: 703-847-5334	FYE: December 31
Web: www.allieddefensegroup.com	Type: Public

Duck 'n cover — incoming! Allied Defense Group (ADG) designs, develops, manufactures, and sells defensive weapon direct fire and indirect fire ammunition for artillery, anti-tank, and anti-material weapons machinery; it also makes grenades and other pyrotechnic devices. Operating subsidiaries include Mecar S.A. (ammunition/mortars) and Mecar USA (sales/service). ADG also sells ammunition manufactured by other companies; it purchases and resells weapon systems and provides consulting on the development of manufacturing facilities. It has operating facilities in Belgium and the US. Saudi Arabia represents approximately 52% of revenues for 2008. Chemring Group agreed in 2010 to buy ADG for $59 million cash.

	Annual Growth	12/05	12/06	12/07	12/08	12/09
Sales ($ mil.)	6.1%	112.2	128.7	55.6	144.4	142.4
Net income ($ mil.)	—	(33.6)	(41.1)	(21.3)	(10.4)	(8.3)
Market value ($ mil.)	(32.3%)	186.1	173.7	47.2	50.7	39.0
Employees	(16.0%)	698	694	430	353	348

ALLIED ELECTRONICS, INC.

7151 Jack Newell Blvd. S.	CEO: Lee Davidson
Fort Worth, TX 76118	CFO: Mark McKone
Phone: 817-595-3500	HR: —
Fax: 817-595-6444	FYE: March 31
Web: www.alliedelec.com	Type: Subsidiary

Allied Electronics allies itself to customers looking for electronic gear. The company distributes test and measurement equipment (analyzers, meters, probes, and oscilloscopes), cable and wire assemblies, enclosure hardware, power supplies and transformers, switches, timers, passive components, and soldering equipment. It distributes components from such companies as Agilent, Honeywell, National Semiconductor, Panduit, Schneider Electric, and Vishay. Allied Electronics also offers services including assembly, labeling, packaging, and inventory management. The company, which was founded in 1928 as Allied Radio, is a subsidiary of UK-based Electrocomponents.

ALLIED FIRST BANCORP, INC.

OTC: AFBA

3201 Orchard Rd.	CEO: Kenneth L. Bertrand
Oswego, IL 60543	CFO: Brian K. Weiss
Phone: 630-554-8899	HR: —
Fax: 630-554-3311	FYE: June 30
Web: www.alliedfirst.com	Type: Public

Allied First Bancorp is the holding company for Allied First Bank, which has a single suburban Chicago location in Oswego, Illinois. The bank offers standard deposit products such as checking and savings accounts, money market accounts, and CDs, in addition to credit and debit cards. One- to four-family residential mortgages account for more than 60% of its loan portfolio; commercial and industrial loans, consumer loans, and commercial mortgages round out its lending activities. The bank offers insurance and investments through an agreement with Smith Barney, a unit of Citigroup.

ALLIED GROUP, INC.

1100 Locust St.	CEO: W. Kim Austen
Des Moines, IA 50391	CFO: —
Phone: 515-280-4211	HR: —
Fax: —	FYE: December 31
Web: www.alliedinsurance.com	Type: Subsidiary

ALLIED Group is central to many Midwesterners. A subsidiary of multiline insurer Nationwide, the company provides a variety of property/casualty insurance products including auto, farm, and homeowners policies. ALLIED Group also offers specialized commercial policies for small to midsized businesses, along with coverage for home-based businesses. The group includes such units as AMCO Insurance, Depositors Insurance, and Allied Property and Casualty Insurance, which work through independent agents and direct-response marketing in more than 30 states in the central and western US.

ALLIED HEALTHCARE INTERNATIONAL INC.

NASDAQ (GS): AHCI

245 Park Ave.	CEO: Alexander (Sandy) Young
New York, NY 10167	CFO: Paul D. J. Weston
Phone: 212-750-0064	HR: —
Fax: 212-750-7221	FYE: September 30
Web: www.alliedhealthcare.com	Type: Public

Allied Healthcare International (formerly Transworld HealthCare) offers temporary staffing services to the UK health care industry. The company operates through a network of about 100 branches across the UK. Allied Healthcare places its staff, which includes more than 11,000 nurses, nurses aides, and home health aides, in hospitals, nursing homes, care homes, and private homes. Customers affiliated with the British government, such as the UK National Health Service and local social service departments, account for more than two-thirds of the company's sales each year. Allied Healthcare International was established in 1981.

	Annual Growth	9/05	9/06	9/07	9/08	9/09
Sales ($ mil.)	(8.2%)	351.2	294.6	277.8	298.6	249.8
Net income ($ mil.)	(13.9%)	18.7	(123.8)	66.4	8.8	10.3
Market value ($ mil.)	(16.1%)	255.0	89.8	107.9	85.8	126.4
Employees	0.9%	980	960	821	900	1,015

⊞ ALLIED HEALTHCARE PRODUCTS, INC.

NASDAQ (GM): AHPI

1720 Sublette Ave.	CEO: Earl R. Refsland
St. Louis, MO 63110	CFO: Daniel C. Dunn
Phone: 314-771-2400	HR: —
Fax: 314-771-0650	FYE: June 30
Web: www.alliedhpi.com	Type: Public

Allied Healthcare Products helps medical workers get oxygen into those lungs. The medical equipment maker produces respiratory equipment used in hospitals, surgery centers, ambulances, and other medical facilities, as well as in patient homes. Its products include anesthesia equipment, oxygen cylinders and nebulizers used in home respiratory therapy, and emergency resuscitation products. It also makes medical gas system components installed in hospital walls during construction, as well as spine immobilization backboards and other items used in trauma situations. Allied Healthcare sells directly to hospitals and through equipment dealers in the US and abroad.

	Annual Growth	6/05	6/06	6/07	6/08	6/09
Sales ($ mil.)	(1.8%)	56.1	57.5	56.5	56.4	52.1
Net income ($ mil.)	—	2.3	1.6	1.6	0.9	(16.8)
Market value ($ mil.)	(3.3%)	39.7	46.9	52.8	57.1	34.8
Employees	(4.0%)	412	417	384	371	350

ALLIED MOTION TECHNOLOGIES INC.
NASDAQ (GM): AMOT

23 Inverness Way East, Ste. 150
Englewood, CO 80112
Phone: 303-799-8520
Fax: 303-799-8521
Web: www.alliedmotion.com

CEO: Richard S. (Dick) Warzala
CFO: Richard D. (Dick) Smith
HR: —
FYE: December 31
Type: Public

Allied Motion Technologies has the drive to put you in control of your own motions. The company makes specialized motors, optical encoders, and frequency converters used in mechanical motion control applications. Its products are incorporated into a number of end products, including high-definition printers, barcode scanners, dialysis systems, robotic systems, wheelchairs, and satellite tracking systems. Allied Motion targets applications in the aerospace and military, computer, industrial automation, medical equipment, and semiconductor manufacturing markets. The US accounts for more than half of sales.

	Annual Growth	12/05	12/06	12/07	12/08	12/09
Sales ($ mil.)	(4.7%)	74.3	82.8	84.6	86.0	61.2
Net income ($ mil.)	—	0.9	1.9	2.4	2.9	(12.4)
Market value ($ mil.)	(12.0%)	32.7	53.8	36.4	15.7	19.6
Employees	(9.1%)	515	517	505	425	351

ALLIED RESOURCES, INC.
OTC: ALOD

1403 E. 900 South
Salt Lake City, UT 84105
Phone: 801-582-9609
Fax: 801-582-9629
Web: www.allied-resources-inc.com

CEO: Ruairidh Campbell
CFO: Ruairidh Campbell
HR: —
FYE: December 31
Type: Public

Allied Resources has allied with Allstate Energy to get the most out of its Appalachian energy resources. The company is an oil and natural gas exploration and production enterprise with primary operations in West Virginia (in Calhoun and Ritchie counties). Allied Resources produces oil and natural gas from 145 wells, which are maintained and operated by Allstate Energy. The depth at which the wells produce ranges from 1,730 feet to more than 5,470 feet. The company also owns 13 gross wells in Goliad, Edwards, and Jackson counties, Texas. In 2008 Allied Resources reported proved reserves of 18,950 barrels of oil, and 1.4 billion cu. ft. of natural gas. CEO Ruairidh Campbell owns 27% of the company.

ALLIED SECURITY HOLDINGS LLC

3606 Horizon Dr.
King of Prussia, PA 19406
Phone: 610-239-1100
Fax: 610-239-1107
Web: www.alliedbarton.com

CEO: William C. (Bill) Whitmore Jr.
CFO: William A. (Bill) Torzolini
HR: Jim Gillece
FYE: December 31
Type: Subsidiary

Allied Security Holdings offers a secure ally for its customers. One of the largest private security firms in the US, the company does business as AlliedBarton Security Services, and primarily provides security guards for more than 3,000 clients, including shopping malls, industrial facilities, hospitals, residential communities, government facilities, and universities. The company, with more than 100 offices nationwide, also provides background verification and screening services through its HR Plus subsidiary (formerly VanElla). Allied Security began doing business as AlliedBarton Security Services after acquiring Barton Protective Services in 2004. It is owned by private equity firm Blackstone Group.

ALLIED SECURITY INNOVATIONS, INC.
Pink Sheets: ADSV

1709 Route 34, Ste. 2
Farmingdale, NJ 07727
Phone: 732-751-1115
Fax: 732-751-1130
Web: www.ddsi-cpc.com

CEO: Anthony R. (Tony) Shupin
CFO: Michael J. Pellegrino
HR: —
FYE: December 31
Type: Public

Allied Security Innovations (formerly Digital Descriptor Systems) sells computer-based image capture devices and management systems. Its Compu-Capture system incorporates such features as fingerprint matching and description text identifying aliases, hair color, facial scars, or physical deformities to law enforcement agencies and correctional facilities worldwide. Its Compu-Sketch product allows a person with no artistic ability to create composite sketches of potential suspects. The company's CGM Security Solutions subsidiary makes security seals, tapes, and related packaging security systems.

	Annual Growth	12/05	12/06	12/07	12/08	12/09
Sales ($ mil.)	(7.2%)	—	4.5	4.4	4.8	3.6
Net income ($ mil.)	—	—	(4.3)	(16.3)	(5.4)	(5.2)
Market value ($ mil.)	(77.1%)	—	11.8	35.3	11.8	0.1
Employees	(7.2%)	—	20	18	21	16

⊞ ALLIED SYSTEMS HOLDINGS, INC.

2302 Parklake Dr., Bldg. 15, Ste. 600
Atlanta, GA 30345
Phone: 404-373-4285
Fax: 404-370-4206
Web: www.alliedholdings.com

CEO: Mark Gendregske
CFO: Thomas H. (Tom) King
HR: Brenda Ragsdale
FYE: December 31
Type: Private

Carrying millions of cars, trucks, and SUVs every year, Allied Systems Holdings leads the North American automobile-hauling market. Subsidiary Allied Automotive Group moves vehicles with a fleet of about 3,400 tractor-trailer rigs, which it operates from about 90 terminals in the US and Canada. Vehicles are transported from manufacturing plants, railway distribution points, ports, and auctions to auto dealers and car rental companies. Automakers, including industry leaders such as Chrysler, Ford, General Motors, Honda, and Toyota, are the company's main customers. Investment firm Yucaipa Companies owns a controlling stake in Allied Systems Holdings.

ALLIED TUBE AND CONDUIT

16100 S. Lathrop Ave.
Harvey, IL 60426
Phone: 708-339-1610
Fax: 708-339-2399
Web: www.alliedtube.com

CEO: Ed Breen
CFO: Wes Tomaszek
HR: —
FYE: September 30
Type: Subsidiary

Allied wants to be your business' conduit to success. Allied Tube and Conduit manufactures over 400,000 tons of galvanized steel tubing a year for electrical conduit, mechanical tubing, fire sprinkler pipe, and chain-link fencing. The company's products include aluminum conduit, elbows and couplings, and PVC conduit and fittings. Allied builds metal framing, cable trays, and consumer products such as garage storage systems, too, sold under the brand name Off the Floor. A one-stop shop, the company offers contract manufacturing and steel coil processing services, along with tube and pipe fabrication. Allied caters to commercial and residential construction as well as to electrical, fire, and government security.

Ⓗ An in-depth profile of this company is available to Hoover's Online members at hoovers.com.

97

ALLIED WORLD ASSURANCE COMPANY HOLDINGS, LTD
NYSE: AWH

225 Franklin, 27th Fl.
Boston, MA 02110
Phone: 857-288-6000
Fax: 617-556-8060
Web: www.awac.com

CEO: Scott A. Carmilani
CFO: Joan H. Dillard
HR: Katherine Richardson
FYE: December 31
Type: Public

No doubt that large companies need some assurance that their holdings are safe. Bermuda-based Allied World Assurance Company Holdings aims to provide that. It offers insurance and reinsurance products internationally. Its insurance products include general property coverage, professional liability, and health care liability coverage in Bermuda, Europe, Hong Kong, and the US. Its US insurance operations target small and mid-market clients through regional offices while its Bermuda insurance operations serve larger US companies. In Europe its products are geared for large non-US based companies. Allied World's reinsurance segment operates out of its Bermuda, New York, and Swiss offices.

	Annual Growth	12/05	12/06	12/07	12/08	12/09
Assets ($ mil.)	9.9%	6,610.5	7,620.6	7,899.1	9,072.1	9,653.2
Net income ($ mil.)	—	(159.8)	442.8	469.2	183.6	606.9
Market value ($ mil.)	1.8%	—	2,201.9	2,531.9	2,049.0	2,325.0
Employees	30.4%	230	279	297	578	665

ALLIN CORPORATION
OTC: ALLN

381 Mansfield Ave., Ste. 400
Pittsburgh, PA 15220
Phone: 412-928-8800
Fax: 412-928-0887
Web: www.allin.com

CEO: Richard W. (Rich) Talarico
CFO: Dean C. Praskach
HR: —
FYE: December 31
Type: Public

Allin wants to be an all-in-one information technology (IT) provider on the high seas and dry land. The company (pronounced "all in") offers interactive media development and integration for cruise lines, technology infrastructure services, and systems integration. The company uses video equipment and services provided by On Command for its interactive TV operations. Formerly a provider of Microsoft-focused services, the company sold that business to PC maker Dell in 2009. With warrants, Pittsburgh investor Henry Posner controls just over 50% of Allin.

ALLINA HOSPITALS AND CLINICS

2925 Chicago Ave.
Minneapolis, MN 55407
Phone: 612-775-5000
Fax: 612-863-5667
Web: www.allina.com

CEO: Kenneth (Ken) Paulus
CFO: Duncan P. Gallagher
HR: —
FYE: December 31
Type: Not-for-profit

Allina Hospitals and Clinics is a not-for-profit health care system focused on protecting people's #1 asset — their good health. The health system owns and operates about a dozen hospitals, a network of nearly one hundred clinics and specialty centers, and 15 pharmacies. Its vast system of provider locations serve residents throughout Minnesota and western Wisconsin, providing disease prevention programs along with specialized inpatient and outpatient services. Allina's Aspen Medical Group division also operates a range of outpatient clinics providing primary and specialty care, as well as more than two dozen nursing homes. Allina is led by CEO Ken Paulus, who previously served as the system's COO.

	Annual Growth	12/04	12/05	12/06	12/07	12/08
Est. sales ($ mil.)	—	—	—	—	—	2,533.7
Employees	—	—	—	—	—	22,347

ALLION HEALTHCARE, INC.

1660 Walt Whitman Rd., Ste. 105
Melville, NY 11747
Phone: 631-547-6520
Fax: 631-249-5865
Web: www.allionhealthcare.com

CEO: Michael P. Moran
CFO: Russell J. (Russ) Fichera
HR: —
FYE: December 31
Type: Private

Allion Healthcare is a specialty drug distributor focusing on patients with HIV, AIDS, and other chronic conditions. Through subsidiaries MOMS Pharmacy and Biomed America, the company fills prescriptions at more than 15 distribution centers and delivers them to patients, doctors' offices, and clinics nationwide. Allion also provides ancillary drugs and nutritional supplies, and it offers consulting and drug packaging services (such as pre-filled pill boxes) to help patients stick with their medication regimens. Most of Allion's customers rely on Medicaid or state programs such as the AIDS Drug Assistance Program to pay for their prescriptions. Allion was taken private by H.I.G. Capital in early 2010.

	Annual Growth	12/04	12/05	12/06	12/07	12/08
Sales ($ mil.)	54.3%	60.1	123.1	209.5	246.7	340.7
Net income ($ mil.)	—	(2.7)	0.4	3.2	3.3	7.5
Employees	20.3%	140	170	222	226	293

ALLIS-CHALMERS ENERGY INC.
NYSE: ALY

5075 Westheimer, Ste. 890
Houston, TX 77056
Phone: 713-369-0550
Fax: 713-369-0555
Web: www.alchenergy.com

CEO: Munawar H. (Micki) Hidayatallah
CFO: Victor M. Perez
HR: Cassie Ramsay
FYE: December 31
Type: Public

This company knows the drill. Allis-Chalmers Energy provides drilling and oil field services to oil and gas exploration companies operating primarily in the western and southern US. It operates in three segments: Drilling and Completion; Oilfield Services (underbalanced drilling, directional drilling, tubular services, and production services); and Rental Services. Its Strata Directional Technology subsidiary offers drilling services to clients in Texas and Louisiana. Through its AirComp unit, Allis-Chalmers operates a fleet of 260 compressors, as well as a portfolio of full-time directional drillers, measurement-while-drilling tools, and downhole motors used for well production enhancement and completion.

	Annual Growth	12/05	12/06	12/07	12/08	12/09
Sales ($ mil.)	48.1%	105.3	307.3	571.0	675.9	506.3
Net income ($ mil.)	—	7.2	35.6	50.4	(39.5)	(21.2)
Market value ($ mil.)	(25.8%)	903.2	1,668.8	1,068.3	398.4	273.1
Employees	45.9%	700	2,567	3,050	3,580	3,174

ALLISON & PARTNERS, INC.

505 Sansome St., 7th Fl.
San Francisco, CA 94111
Phone: 415-217-7500
Fax: 415-217-7503
Web: www.allisonpr.com

CEO: Scott Allison
CFO: —
HR: —
FYE: December 31
Type: Subsidiary

Allison & Partners builds public relations and marketing communications campaigns. The firm offers expertise in corporate positioning, public affairs, media relations, trade show support, direct marketing, and interactive marketing services through about 10 nationwide offices including four in California. The firm serves clients in such industries as technology, travel, consumer products, professional services, entertainment, and health care. Clients have included YouTube, L'Oréal, and Best Western International. Allison & Partners was founded in 2001 by partners Scott Allison, Andy Hardie-Brown, and Scott Pansky. In May 2010 it was acquired by advertising and marketing communications giant MDC Partners.

ALLISON TRANSMISSION, INC.

4700 W. 10th St.
Indianapolis, IN 46222
Phone: 317-242-5000
Fax: —
Web: www.allisontransmission.com

CEO: Lawrence E. (Larry) Dewey
CFO: David S. Graziosi
HR: —
FYE: December 31
Type: Private

You can't have a tractor pull without Allison Transmission. The company builds automatic transmissions for commercial vehicles. Allison Transmission's customers include makers of everything from garbage trucks and city transit buses to military vehicles and dump trucks. Allison also makes a line of electric drives for use primarily on buses and shuttles, and remanufactures automatic transmissions for the commercial replacement aftermarket. Allison also builds transmissions for GM's Silverado HD and GMC Sierra HD pickups. In 2007 General Motors sold Allison to The Carlyle Group and Onex Corp. for $5.6 billion. GM kept one Allison plant that builds transmissions for its light trucks.

ALLOPTIC, INC.

2675 Collier Canyon Rd.
Livermore, CA 94551
Phone: 925-245-7600
Fax: 925-245-7601
Web: www.alloptic.com

CEO: Ric Johnsen
CFO: —
HR: —
FYE: December 31
Type: Private

Alloptic hopes to have all of your optical networking needs covered. The company provides network infrastructure equipment, software, and services to residential and commercial customers alike. Among its products are Gigabit Ethernet passive optical network (GEPON), fiber-to-the-premises (FTTP) equipment, deep fiber equipment, and central office equipment (T3/T1 interfaces, multiple Ethernet ports, etc.). Customers utilize Alloptic products to manage their own data, video, and voice services. The company was founded in 1999 and has received funding from venture capital firms, including Arcapita Ventures, GMG Capital Partners, and Ritchie Capital Management.

	Annual Growth	12/04	12/05	12/06	12/07	12/08
Est. sales ($ mil.)	—	—	—	—	—	11.6
Employees	—	—	—	—	—	70

ALLOS THERAPEUTICS, INC.

NASDAQ (GM): ALTH

11080 CirclePoint Rd., Ste. 200
Westminster, CO 80020
Phone: 303-426-6262
Fax: 303-426-4731
Web: www.allos.com

CEO: Paul L. Berns
CFO: David C. Clark
HR: Vicki Baca
FYE: December 31
Type: Public

Drug developer Allos Therapeutics is looking for the next big breakthrough in the fight against cancer. Its lead candidate PDX (pralatrexate) is undergoing clinical trials for a relatively rare blood cancer called peripheral T-cell lymphoma. Allos is also investigating the compound, a traditional small molecule drug, as a potential treatment for non-small cell lung cancer and additional blood cancers. Another candidate, RH1, is a chemotherapy in clinical trails for advanced solid tumors and non-Hodgkin's lymphoma. The company halted development of Efaproxyn in 2007, after it failed to outperform existing treatments in a key clinical trial.

	Annual Growth	12/05	12/06	12/07	12/08	12/09
Sales ($ mil.)	—	—	—	—	—	3.6
Net income ($ mil.)	—	—	—	—	—	(73.6)
Market value ($ mil.)	—	—	—	—	—	689.1
Employees	—	—	—	—	—	170

⊞ ALLOY, INC.

NASDAQ (GM): ALOY

151 W. 26th St., 11th Fl.
New York, NY 10001
Phone: 212-244-4307
Fax: 212-244-4311
Web: www.alloy.com

CEO: Matthew C. (Matt) Diamond
CFO: Joseph D. Frehe
HR: Kerry Gemza
FYE: January 31
Type: Public

Alloy has its eye on the next generation. The company, through its chief promotional division Alloy Media + Marketing, provides advertising and marketing services and produces content for online and print media, all designed to help customers reach people between the ages of 10 and 24. It helps customers place advertising in print and broadcast media focused on high school and college students and military personnel. In addition to its Channel One subsidiary, which broadcasts daily newscasts and educational videos at junior and senior high schools, Alloy's other media offerings include websites and social networks (alloy.com, TEEN.com), print publications, and display boards placed on school campuses.

	Annual Growth	1/06	1/07	1/08	1/09	1/10
Sales ($ mil.)	1.2%	195.3	196.1	199.1	216.9	205.1
Net income ($ mil.)	—	(35.5)	(7.2)	(70.1)	10.4	(4.9)
Market value ($ mil.)	(9.0%)	141.8	149.7	98.4	62.8	97.4
Employees	(14.4%)	2,723	601	674	619	1,460

ALLSCRIPTS-MISYS HEALTHCARE SOLUTIONS

NASDAQ (GS): MDRX

222 Merchandise Mart Plaza, Ste. 2024
Chicago, IL 60654
Phone: 866-358-6869
Fax: 312-506-1201
Web: www.allscripts.com

CEO: Glen E. Tullman
CFO: William J. (Bill) Davis
HR: Diane Adams
FYE: May 31
Type: Public

Jokes about doctors' handwriting may go the way of house calls thanks to Allscripts-Misys Healthcare Solutions, Inc. The company, which does business as Allscripts, provides prescription management software and services that let doctors enter prescription information over computer networks, including tools that give doctors access (via desktop or wireless handheld devices) to patient drug history, drug interactions, and generic alternatives. Other services include electronic document imaging and scanning and physician feedback services. In 2010 the company agreed to merge with Eclipsys in a deal valued at about $1.3 billion.

	Annual Growth	12/05	12/06	12/07	*5/08	5/09
Sales ($ mil.)	46.0%	120.6	228.0	281.9	383.8	548.4
Net income ($ mil.)	28.0%	9.7	11.9	20.6	25.4	26.0
Market value ($ mil.)	(0.9%)	1,958.6	3,945.0	2,838.5	1,816.8	1,887.0
Employees	60.6%	386	914	1,155	1,500	2,569
					*Fiscal year change	

⊞ THE ALLSTATE CORPORATION

NYSE: ALL

2775 Sanders Rd.
Northbrook, IL 60062
Phone: 847-402-5000
Fax: 866-532-3029
Web: www.allstate.com

CEO: Thomas J. Wilson II
CFO: Don Civgin
HR: James D. DeVries
FYE: December 31
Type: Public

Ya gotta hand it to Allstate. The "good hands" company has managed to work its way to the top of the insurance pile. The company is the second-largest personal lines insurer in the US, just behind rival State Farm. Its Allstate Protection segment sells auto, homeowners, property/casualty, and life insurance products in Canada and the US. Allstate Financial provides life insurance through subsidiaries Allstate Life, American Heritage Life, and Lincoln Benefit Life. It also provides investment products, targeting affluent and middle-income consumers. Allstate Motor Club provides emergency road service and, adding to its repertoire, the company also offers the nationwide online Allstate Bank.

	Annual Growth	12/05	12/06	12/07	12/08	12/09
Assets ($ mil.)	(4.0%)	156,072.0	157,554.0	156,408.0	134,798.0	132,652.0
Net income ($ mil.)	(16.4%)	1,752.0	4,900.0	4,636.0	(1,679.0)	854.0
Market value ($ mil.)	(13.7%)	29,084.4	35,022.9	28,094.7	17,621.7	16,158.6
Employees	(1.0%)	38,300	37,900	38,000	38,900	36,800

⊞ An in-depth profile of this company is available to Hoover's Online members at hoovers.com.

99

ALLY FINANCIAL INC.

200 Renaissance Center, P.O. Box 200
Detroit, MI 48265
Phone: 313-656-6278
Fax: 815-282-6156
Web: www.gmacfs.com

CEO: Michael A. (Mike) Carpenter
CFO: James G. Mackey
HR: James J. (Jim) Duffy
FYE: December 31
Type: Holding company

Ally Financial wants to be your friend in the financing business. The company (formerly GMAC Inc.) opted for its friendlier-sounding name in 2010 after it converted to a bank holding company and formed Ally Bank. Ally Financial provides auto financing for General Motors (GM) and Chrysler dealerships and their customers around the world. Its Residential Capital (ResCap) subsidiary issues residential mortgages in the US and Canada. Ally Financial also provides commercial financing services for large- and mid-market companies around the world through GMAC Commercial Finance. Although GM owns a stake in Ally, the lender was not included in GM's 2009 Chapter 11 bankruptcy reorganization.

	Annual Growth	12/04	12/05	12/06	12/07	12/08
Sales ($ mil.)	(0.4%)	—	—	35,723.0	31,490.0	35,445.0
Net income ($ mil.)	(6.2%)	—	—	2,125.0	(2,332.0)	1,868.0
Employees	(15.0%)	—	—	—	26,700	22,700

ALMOST FAMILY, INC.

NASDAQ (GS): AFAM

9510 Ormsby Station Rd., Ste. 300
Louisville, KY 40223
Phone: 502-891-1000
Fax: 502-891-8067
Web: www.almostfamily.com

CEO: William B. Yarmuth
CFO: C. Steven (Steve) Guenthner
HR: Mark Sutton
FYE: December 31
Type: Public

If you live in California and you're worried about Mom's failing faculties back in Florida, you could call Almost Family. With its home health nursing services, Almost Family offers senior citizens in 11 states (including Florida) an alternative to spending their days in nursing homes. The company operates through two segments: Its visiting nurse unit provides skilled nursing care under the Caretenders and Mederi-Caretenders names, while its personal care segment (operating under the Almost Family banner) offers custodial care, such as housekeeping, meal preparation, and medication management. The company has about 70 skilled nursing and 20 personal care branch locations.

	Annual Growth	12/05	12/06	12/07	12/08	12/09
Sales ($ mil.)	40.9%	75.6	91.8	132.1	212.6	297.8
Net income ($ mil.)	32.8%	7.9	4.2	7.6	16.3	24.6
Market value ($ mil.)	49.1%	73.3	200.6	177.9	411.9	362.0
Employees	17.6%	3,200	4,000	4,800	5,700	6,123

ALNYLAM PHARMACEUTICALS, INC.

NASDAQ (GM): ALNY

300 3rd St., 3rd Fl.
Cambridge, MA 02142
Phone: 617-551-8200
Fax: 617-551-8101
Web: www.alnylam.com

CEO: John M. Maraganore
CFO: Patricia L. Allen
HR: Eric Raichle
FYE: December 31
Type: Public

Call it *The Silence of the Genes*. Alnylam Pharmaceuticals runs interference with RNA to prevent disease. RNA interference (RNAi) technology developed by the biotech firm can selectively shut off harmful genes. The company is developing its own pipeline, including treatments for respiratory syncytial virus (RSV), a viral infection that is a leading cause of respiratory ailments in children and can be fatal in preemies and children with weak immune systems. Additional R&D programs target other viral infections, neurological disorders, and cancers. Alnylam has R&D alliances with companies including Roche, Novartis, and Takeda Pharmaceuticals, as well as licensing agreements with other biotechnology firms.

	Annual Growth	12/05	12/06	12/07	12/08	12/09
Sales ($ mil.)	104.9%	5.7	26.9	50.9	96.2	100.5
Net income ($ mil.)	—	(42.9)	(34.6)	(85.5)	(26.2)	(47.6)
Market value ($ mil.)	7.2%	560.6	898.0	1,220.2	1,037.7	739.4
Employees	17.3%	94	122	129	170	178

ALOETTE COSMETICS, INC.

3715 Northside Pkwy. NW, Bldg. 200, Ste. 200
Atlanta, GA 30327
Phone: 678-444-2563
Fax: 678-444-2564
Web: www.aloette.com

CEO: Jue Wong
CFO: —
HR: —
FYE: December 31
Type: Private

Aloette Cosmetics loves a good party. Best known for selling aloe vera-based skin care products, Aloette also markets cosmetics, fragrances, and other personal care items. Products are sold mainly through home parties held by Aloette's direct-sales network of more than 10,000 consultants in some 40 franchises in the US and Canada. The firm also markets its goods through an e-commerce site, catalog, and on television shopping channels. Founded in 1978, Aloette is part of Astral Health & Beauty, which also produces the Pür Minerals and CosMedix skin care brands.

ALON BRANDS, INC.

7616 LBJ Fwy., 3rd Fl.
Dallas, TX 75251
Phone: 972-367-3900
Fax: —
Web: www.alonbrands.com

CEO: Kyle C. McKeen
CFO: David Potter
HR: —
FYE: December 31
Type: Subsidiary

Alon Brands is gaining some independence, but it won't be going it alone in its new venture. Trading on the 7-Eleven and FINA brands, Alon Brands operates convenience stores and, through its wholesale marketing segment, provides motor fuels, supplies, and services to distributors in the southern US. The company is the largest 7-Eleven licensee in the US, with more than 300 convenience stores located in Texas and New Mexico. Alon Brands is also the sole licensee of the FINA brand for motor fuels in the south central and southwestern US. Alon USA Energy formed Alon Brands in 2008 as a holding company for its retail and wholesale marketing segments, with the intention of spinning the company off in an IPO.

ALON USA ENERGY, INC.

NYSE: ALJ

7616 LBJ Fwy., Ste. 300
Dallas, TX 75251
Phone: 972-367-3600
Fax: 972-367-3728
Web: www.alonusa.com

CEO: Jeff D. Morris
CFO: Shai Even
HR: —
FYE: December 31
Type: Public

Could anything be finer than FINA? Alon USA Energy is the driving force behind FINA-branded marketing and refining operations throughout the US Southwest. Alon USA Energy, a subsidiary of Alon Israel Oil, was formed in 2000 to acquire FINA Inc.'s downstream assets. The company provides fuel to more than 1,000 FINA-branded retail sites. It also owns or operates more than 300 convenience stores under the 7-Eleven and FINA brands. Alon USA Energy's refineries in Texas (one), California (two), Louisiana (one), and Oregon (one), have a combined throughput capacity of 250,000 barrels per day. Alon USA Energy is also a top asphalt producer. Alon Israel Oil owns 78% of Alon USA Energy.

	Annual Growth	12/05	12/06	12/07	12/08	12/09
Sales ($ mil.)	13.9%	2,328.5	3,198.1	4,542.2	5,156.7	3,915.7
Net income ($ mil.)	—	104.0	157.4	103.9	82.9	(93.7)
Market value ($ mil.)	(23.2%)	1,064.5	1,425.2	1,472.4	495.7	370.5
Employees	18.9%	1,415	2,029	2,697	2,760	2,825

ALORICA INC.

14726 Ramona Ave., 3rd Fl.
Chino, CA 91710
Phone: 909-606-3600
Fax: 909-606-7708
Web: www.alorica.com

CEO: Andy Lee
CFO: Jack Pollock
HR: —
FYE: December 31
Type: Private

Alorica is here to remedy your front- and back-office ailments. The company provides outsourced customer service operations through about 15 call centers located in the US and the Philippines. Alorica's contact center services include technical support, customer service, help desk, billing, and sales (inbound and outbound). The company also offers fulfillment and service logistics, including returns management, warranty support management, and field service dispatch. Alorica offers proprietary customer relationship management software, Helix by Alorica, that bridges the gap between call center agents and warehouse personnel. Clients have included USRobotics, Bose, and eMachines. Alorica was founded in 1999.

	Annual Growth	12/04	12/05	12/06	12/07	12/08
Est. sales ($ mil.)	—	—	—	—	—	250.0
Employees	—	—	—	—	—	8,000

ALPHA MEDIA GROUP INC.

1040 Ave. of the Americas
New York, NY 10018
Phone: 212-302-2626
Fax: 212-302-2631
Web: www.alphamediagroup.com

CEO: Stephen Duggan
CFO: —
HR: —
FYE: December 31
Type: Private

Alpha Media Group is vying for the spot of top dog in the magazine pack. The company publishes men's lifestyle magazine *Maxim* and its related website, as well as StuffMagazine.com. *Maxim* reaches "readers" each month through a mix of men's humor, information, and pictures of barely clothed women. After buying three titles from Dennis Publishing Limited in 2007 (*Blender*, the US edition of *Maxim*, and the gadget magazine *Stuff*) for some $250 million, private equity firm Quadrangle Capital Partners created Alpha Media Group and folded the operations of *Stuff* into *Maxim*. (The UK edition of *Maxim* is still published through Dennis Publishing.)

ALPHA NATURAL RESOURCES, INC.

NYSE: ANR

1 Alpha Place
Abingdon, VA 24212
Phone: 276-619-4410
Fax: —
Web: www.alphanr.com

CEO: Michael J. (Mike) Quillen
CFO: Eddie W. Neely
HR: Gary W. Banbury
FYE: December 31
Type: Public

Alpha Natural Resources doesn't mind going underground. The company produces steam and metallurgical coal at about 60 mines and 15 preparation plants, primarily in central and northern Appalachia and the Powder River Basin. Alpha's sales are divided fairly evenly between low-sulfur steam coal, which is used mainly for electricity generation, and metallurgical coal for industrial customers like steelmakers. The company produces about 100 million tons of coal annually. It sells about half of its product internationally. Alpha Natural Resources controls about 2.3 billion tons of proved and probable reserves. In 2009 Alpha made a big move when it bought miner Foundation Coal, creating a top three US coal producer.

	Annual Growth	12/05	12/06	12/07	12/08	12/09
Sales ($ mil.)	17.3%	1,316.9	1,470.3	1,489.7	1,690.1	2,495.5
Net income ($ mil.)	(10.1%)	88.9	31.4	32.6	11.6	58.0
Market value ($ mil.)	22.6%	2,325.7	1,722.8	3,932.3	1,960.1	5,251.9
Employees	15.5%	3,591	3,546	3,000	3,300	6,400

ALPHA-EN CORPORATION

OTC: ALPE

120 White Plains Rd.
Tarrytown, NY 10591
Phone: 914-631-5265
Fax: —

CEO: Jerome I. (Jerry) Feldman
CFO: Jerome I. (Jerry) Feldman
HR: —
FYE: December 31
Type: Public

alpha-En Corporation (formerly Avenue Entertainment) once brought entertainment to the street where you live. The company produced films such as *Closer* and *The Merchant of Venice*, and made-for-TV and cable movies, including *Angels in America* and *Path To Paradise: The Untold Story of the World Trade Center Bombing*, both for HBO. Its Wombat Productions created one-hour profiles of Hollywood celebrities, shown on networks such as PBS, A&E, and Bravo. The company halted production activities and sold its assets in 2007. It is seeking another business to acquire.

	Annual Growth	12/05	12/06	12/07	12/08	12/09
Sales ($ mil.)	—	—	0.0	0.0	0.0	0.0
Net income ($ mil.)	—	—	0.7	(0.1)	(0.2)	(0.1)
Market value ($ mil.)	62.0%	—	2.1	1.3	2.3	8.8
Employees	—	—	—	—	—	—

ALPHATEC HOLDINGS, INC.

NASDAQ (GM): ATEC

5818 El Camino Real
Carlsbad, CA 92008
Phone: 760-431-9286
Fax: 760-431-9823
Web: www.alphatecspine.com

CEO: Dirk Kuyper
CFO: Peter C. Wulff
HR: Susan L. Johnson
FYE: December 31
Type: Public

Alphatec Holdings aims to help people stand up straight and keep moving. The company develops and manufactures products used to treat spinal disorders including scoliosis and degenerating disks. Through its Alphatec Spine subsidiary, the company makes a variety of FDA-approved products primarily for the spine fusion market in the US. Its product line includes grafting materials, spinal implant systems, and surgical instruments. Alphatec markets its products to surgeons through a network of independent distributors, as well as a direct sales force. The company's Alphatec Pacific subsidiary sells spine fusion and orthopedic trauma devices in Japan.

	Annual Growth	12/05	12/06	12/07	12/08	12/09
Sales ($ mil.)	33.0%	42.3	74.0	80.0	101.3	132.2
Net income ($ mil.)	—	(14.1)	(25.8)	(20.2)	(29.3)	(13.3)
Market value ($ mil.)	12.7%	—	325.9	439.9	205.1	466.1
Employees	5.6%	241	295	263	290	300

ALPINE AIR EXPRESS, INC.

OTC: APNX

1177 Alpine Air Way
Provo, UT 84601
Phone: 801-373-1508
Fax: 801-377-3781
Web: www.alpine-air.com

CEO: Eugene R. (Gene) Mallette
CFO: Rick C. Wood
HR: —
FYE: October 31
Type: Public

Alpine Air Express flies the western skies to cart cargo for its customers. The air cargo company provides scheduled transportation of mail, packages, and other time-sensitive freight to more than 25 cities in the western half of the US mainland and in Hawaii. Its primary customers, the United States Postal Service and United Parcel Service, together account for more than 85% of sales. Alpine Air operates a fleet of about 25 Beechcraft turboprop planes from bases in Hawaii, Montana, and Utah. Along with its cargo operations, the company provides pilot training and aircraft maintenance services. CEO Eugene Mallette owns a controlling stake in Alpine Air.

	Annual Growth	10/05	10/06	10/07	10/08	10/09
Sales ($ mil.)	(2.4%)	22.6	20.2	18.4	19.8	20.5
Net income ($ mil.)	—	(2.3)	2.8	1.8	1.3	1.1
Market value ($ mil.)	(1.1%)	6.1	16.0	15.2	2.5	5.8
Employees	(7.6%)	147	56	118	122	107

ALPINE ELECTRONICS OF AMERICA, INC.

19145 Gramercy Place	CEO: Kaz Watanabe
Torrance, CA 90501	CFO: —
Phone: 310-326-8000	HR: —
Fax: 310-782-8127	FYE: March 31
Web: www.alpine-usa.com	Type: Subsidiary

Alpine prefers to be on top of the electronics market. Alpine Electronics of America, a subsidiary of Japanese electronics manufacturer Alps Electric, makes and distributes mobile electronics equipment to customers in Canada and the US. The company produces amplifiers, subwoofers, speakers, monitors, CD and DVD players, and security and navigation systems designed primarily for use in automobiles, but also in boats. Other products include adapters designed to connect Apple's iPod products to car stereos. It operates research and development facilities in Asia, Europe, and the US. Alpine Electronics was formed in 1978.

THE ALPINE GROUP, INC.

Pink Sheets: APNI

1 Meadowlands Plaza, Ste. 801	CEO: Steven S. Elbaum
East Rutherford, NJ 07073	CFO: Dana P. Sidur
Phone: 201-549-4400	HR: —
Fax: 201-549-4428	FYE: December 31
Web: www.alpine-group.net	Type: Public

The Alpine Group has experienced the peaks and valleys of various metals and wires businesses. The company's Exeon subsidiary specializes in the reclamation of metal and copper wires, and it produces copper chops. Other operations include subsidiary Posterloid (restaurant menuboard and signage systems) and majority-owned Synergy Cables (formerly Superior Cables, power and telecommunications cables). Alpine also holds a substantial stake in Wolverine Tube (small copper and alloy tubes). Company chairman and CEO Steven Elbaum controls nearly a quarter of the voting power in The Alpine Group.

	Annual Growth	12/05	12/06	12/07	12/08	12/09
Sales ($ mil.)	—	—	—	—	—	0.0
Net income ($ mil.)	—	—	—	—	—	1.7
Employees	—	—	—	—	—	410

ALPS AUTOMOTIVE, INC.

1500 Atlantic Blvd.	CEO: Akinori Ito
Auburn Hills, MI 48326	CFO: —
Phone: 248-391-9950	HR: —
Fax: 248-391-2500	FYE: March 31
Web: www.alps.com	Type: Subsidiary

Not really located in a Swiss mountain range, but rather the (Auburn) Hills of Michigan, Alps Automotive is part of Alps Electric Co., a Japanese supplier of electronic and electro-mechanical components. Alps Automotive designs and manufactures keyless entry systems, electronic control modules, interior switches, position sensors, connectors, potentiometers, steering controls, driver integration systems, and other electronic components and assemblies for use in automobiles. The company, established in 1977, operates from four sales and marketing offices in the US.

	Annual Growth	3/04	3/05	3/06	3/07	3/08
Est. sales ($ mil.)	—	—	—	—	—	403.4
Employees	—	—	—	—	—	230

ALR TECHNOLOGIES INC.

OTC: ALRT

3350 Riverwood Pkwy., Ste. 1900	CEO: Sidney Chan
Atlanta, GA 30339	CFO: Sidney Chan
Phone: 678-881-0002	HR: —
Fax: —	FYE: December 31
Web: www.alrt.com	Type: Public

ALR Technologies helps patients remember to take their medicine. The company makes medication compliance products and compliance home-monitoring and intervention systems. Its devices can be programmed to provide up to eight daily audio and visual alerts to indicate that it is time to take a medication. Its products target patients with diseases such as diabetes, COPD (chronic obstructive pulmonary disease), and congestive heart failure. ALR Technologies also makes pet medication reminders with alerts that can be set for every day or every month. In addition, the company provides reminder systems for contact lens replacement and nutritional programs.

	Annual Growth	12/05	12/06	12/07	12/08	12/09
Sales ($ mil.)	—	0.3	0.2	0.2	0.0	0.0
Net income ($ mil.)	—	(1.8)	(2.6)	(1.6)	(1.9)	(2.2)
Market value ($ mil.)	(6.9%)	16.9	8.5	40.2	10.6	12.7
Employees	(8.5%)	10	9	9	9	7

ALSCO, INC.

505 E. South Temple	CEO: Robert Steiner
Salt Lake City, UT 84102	CFO: Jim Kearns
Phone: 801-328-8831	HR: Tim Weiler
Fax: 801-363-5680	FYE: June 30
Web: www.alsco.com	Type: Private

Alsco tells its clients, "It pays to keep clean," and then provides the uniforms, linens, and related products to achieve that goal. Operating from some 120 sites in 10 countries worldwide, the company (whose name stands for American linen supply company) rents and sells uniforms, linens, towels, and clean room garments to more than 140,000 customers in North America. It also manages janitorial services, provides washroom supplies, and launders and sterilizes garments. Alsco serves the automotive, food processing, restaurant, medical, and IT industries, as well as the federal government. Founded in 1889 by George Steiner, the company is owned and operated by the Steiner family.

ALSERES PHARMACEUTICALS, INC.

Pink Sheets: ALSE

239 South St.	CEO: Peter G. Savas
Hopkinton, MA 01748	CFO: Kenneth L. (Ken) Rice Jr.
Phone: 508-497-2360	HR: —
Fax: 508-497-9964	FYE: December 31
Web: www.alseres.com	Type: Public

Unlike most people, the folks at Alseres Pharmaceuticals (formerly Boston Life Sciences) *want* to get on your nerves. The biotechnology company is developing therapies and diagnostics related to nervous system conditions, such as spinal cord injury, Parkinson's disease, and attention deficit hyperactivity disorder (ADHD). Its lead candidate is Altropane, a molecular imaging agent for diagnosing Parkinson's disease and ADHD. Another candidate, Cethrin, aims to repair nerve damage caused by spinal cord injury; Alseres licensed Cethrin from Canadian firm BioAxone Therapeutic in 2006.

	Annual Growth	12/05	12/06	12/07	12/08	12/09
Sales ($ mil.)	—	—	—	—	0.0	0.0
Net income ($ mil.)	—	—	—	—	(20.8)	(10.8)
Market value ($ mil.)	(84.0%)	—	—	—	33.8	5.4
Employees	(81.5%)	—	—	—	27	5

An in-depth profile of this company is available to Hoover's Online members at hoovers.com.

ALSTON & BIRD LLP

1 Atlantic Center, 1201 W. Peachtree St.	CEO: Richard R. Hays
Atlanta, GA 30309	CFO: Richard G. Levinson
Phone: 404-881-7000	HR: Cathy A. Benton
Fax: 404-881-7777	FYE: December 31
Web: www.alston.com	Type: Partnership

One of the South's leading law firms, Alston & Bird groups its 80-plus practices into four main areas: corporate and finance, intellectual property, litigation, and tax. The firm's intellectual property practice group is one of the nation's largest. Overall, Alston & Bird has about 900 attorneys, policy advisers, and patent agents. The firm serves a wide range of domestic and international clients, which have included Bank of America, Duke University, General Electric, and UPS. Besides its Atlanta home base, Alston & Bird has offices in California, North Carolina, New York, Texas, and Washington, DC. The firm traces its roots to a law practice founded in 1893.

ALSTYLE APPAREL, LLC

1501 E. Cerritos Ave.	CEO: Irshad Ahmad
Anaheim, CA 92805	CFO: Michael D. Magill
Phone: 714-765-0400	HR: —
Fax: 714-765-0450	FYE: July 31
Web: www.alstyle.com	Type: Subsidiary

Alstyle Apparel is all about style. The company makes clothing under several labels, including AAA Alstyle Apparel & Activewear, Gaziani, Diamond Star, Murina, A Classic, Tennessee River, D Drive, and Hyland Headware, as well as private labels. It makes more than 50 unique items, including fleece products, hats, pants, shorts, and T-shirts. Alstyle Apparel operates more than a handful of manufacturing facilities in the US (California) and Mexico, and distributes its products from locations in the US, Canada, and Mexico. Its customers include mass marketers, but also screen printers and embellishers. The company is a subsidiary of business forms maker Ennis.

	Annual Growth	7/04	7/05	7/06	7/07	7/08
Est. sales ($ mil.)	—	—	—	—	—	233.8
Employees	—	—	—	—	—	6,000

![H] ALTADIS U.S.A., INC.

5900 N. Andrews Ave., Ste. 1100	CEO: Gary R. Ellis
Fort Lauderdale, FL 33309	CFO: James M. Parnofiello
Phone: 954-772-9000	HR: Rick McKenzie
Fax: 954-267-1198	FYE: December 31
Web: www.altadisusa.com	Type: Subsidiary

The cigar-smoking fad may have lost some steam in other markets, but Altadis USA keeps rolling along. Created from the 2000 consolidation of HavaTampa Inc. and Consolidated Cigar Holdings, Altadis USA is a leading cigar maker nationwide that generates more than half of its parent Altadis, S.A.'s worldwide cigar sales. Altadis USA manufactures and markets both premium and mass-market cigars under well-known brand names such as Don Diego, El Producto, H. Upmann, and Montecristo. It also sells little cigars under the Dutch Treats and Supre Sweets brands, as well as humidors and cigar cases. Altadis USA's Spanish parent company was acquired by Britain's Imperial Tobacco Group in February 2008.

ALTAIR NANOTECHNOLOGIES INC.

NASDAQ (CM): ALTI

204 Edison Way	CEO: Terry M. Copeland
Reno, NV 89502	CFO: John C. Fallini
Phone: 775-856-2500	HR: Stephen A. (Steve) Balogh
Fax: 775-856-1619	FYE: December 31
Web: www.altairnano.com	Type: Public

When Altair Nanotechnologies paints the town, its pigment of choice is titanium dioxide (TiO2). The company produces titanium dioxide particles used in paints, coatings, and sensors. Altair intends to create new applications and products with its nanocrystalline technology. Its major development thus far has been its nano lithium Titanate battery materials, which offer superior performance, the company says, to other rechargeable batteries. The company tends to rely on just a few customers. Its largest in 2008 were the Office of Naval Research and the animal health unit of Eli Lilly, which combined accounted for more than half of Altair's sales that year.

	Annual Growth	12/05	12/06	12/07	12/08	12/09
Sales ($ mil.)	12.0%	2.8	4.3	9.1	5.7	4.4
Net income ($ mil.)	—	(9.9)	(17.2)	(31.5)	(29.1)	(21.3)
Market value ($ mil.)	(18.9%)	214.0	277.2	445.8	128.6	92.8
Employees	12.4%	62	77	105	98	99

ALTEC INDUSTRIES, INC.

210 Inverness Center Dr.	CEO: Lee J. Styslinger III
Birmingham, AL 35242	CFO: J. D. Williams
Phone: 205-991-7733	HR: —
Fax: 205-991-7747	FYE: December 31
Web: www.altec.com	Type: Private

Altec Industries is actually very little talk, but lots of action. Altec manufactures lift trucks, digger derricks, and specialty handling equipment used by electric utility, telecommunications, and forestry industries, and various government branches. After-sale services and parts are offered worldwide, as well. Altec's used equipment is sold through sister subsidiary National Utility Equipment Co., and rented through Global Rental Co., also in the Altec family. Altec offers financing, too, through Altec Capital Services. The equipment maker's production, assembly, and service facilities crisscross Canada and the US. Founded in 1929, Altec is owned and led by its founder's third generation, Lee Styslinger III.

ALTEGRITY, INC.

7799 Leesburg Pike, Ste. 1100 North	CEO: Michael G. (Mike) Cherkasky
Falls Church, VA 22043	CFO: Jeffrey S. Campbell
Phone: 703-448-0178	HR: Sean Joo
Fax: 703-448-1422	FYE: September 30
Web: www.altegrity.com	Type: Private

It doesn't take a great detective to find that this company is a leader in security services. Formerly US Investigations Services, Altegrity is one of the largest US providers of background investigations, employment screening, and related consulting services. Its flagship USIS unit offers a variety of security services for both government agencies and private sector clients, including investigations, training, and risk management services. Altegrity's HireRight subsidiary specializes in employment screening services, while its Explore Information Services offers database mining and other information services to insurance companies. Formed in 1996, the company is controlled by Providence Equity Partners.

	Annual Growth	9/04	9/05	9/06	9/07	9/08
Est. sales ($ mil.)	—	—	—	—	—	750.0
Employees	—	—	—	—	—	7,907

ALTERA CORPORATION

NASDAQ (GS): ALTR

101 Innovation Dr.
San Jose, CA 95134
Phone: 408-544-7000
Fax: 408-544-6408
Web: www.altera.com

CEO: John P. Daane
CFO: Ronald J. (Ron) Pasek
HR: Kevin H. Lyman
FYE: December 31
Type: Public

Altera is programmed to give you the gate — hundreds of thousands of logic gates per device. The fabless semiconductor company specializes in R&D of high-density programmable logic devices (PLDs) — integrated circuits that OEMs program to perform logic functions in electronic systems. PLDs are an alternative to custom-designed ICs, and offer a quick, reduced-cost chip. Altera outsources fabrication of the devices to top silicon foundry TSMC. Altera PLDs are used in communications network gear, consumer electronics, and industrial equipment. PLD sales rely heavily on a network of distributors; Arrow accounts for 45% of sales. Customers outside the US represent more than three-quarters of Altera's sales.

	Annual Growth	12/05	12/06	12/07	12/08	12/09
Sales ($ mil.)	1.6%	1,123.7	1,285.5	1,263.5	1,367.2	1,195.4
Net income ($ mil.)	(2.6%)	278.8	323.2	290.0	359.7	251.1
Market value ($ mil.)	5.1%	5,589.7	5,936.6	5,828.0	5,040.7	6,826.5
Employees	2.0%	2,361	2,654	2,651	2,760	2,551

ALTERNET SYSTEMS INC.

OTC: ALYI

1 Glen Royal Pkwy., Ste. 401
Miami, FL 33125
Phone: 786-265-1840
Fax: 786-513-2887
Web: www.alternetsystems.com

CEO: Henryk Dabrowski
CFO: Luz Villanueva
HR: —
FYE: December 31
Type: Public

Alternet Systems turns your mobile phone into a virtual wallet. The company provides mobile payment services to consumers, as well as banks and financial processing institutions, merchants and retailers, public transportation and utilities providers, telecommunications operators, and government customers throughout North America, Latin America, and the Caribbean. Its mobile commerce and e-ticketing products and services allow for cashless transactions, such as transferring and withdrawing funds, receiving overseas payments, and making point-of-sale purchases. Alternet Systems restructured its operations in 2008 after acquiring VoIP telecom company TekVoice Communications.

	Annual Growth	12/05	12/06	12/07	12/08	12/09
Sales ($ mil.)	—	0.0	0.0	3.2	0.7	0.3
Net income ($ mil.)	—	(0.3)	(1.0)	(0.3)	(2.0)	(0.7)
Market value ($ mil.)	(49.8%)	28.0	20.3	10.2	4.6	1.8
Employees	(55.9%)	35	35	35	3	

ALTERRA CAPITAL HOLDINGS LIMITED

NASDAQ (GS): ALTE

Alterra House, 2 Front St.
Hamilton, HM 11, Bermuda
Phone: 441-295-8800
Fax: 441-295-8899
Web: www.alterracap.com

CEO: W. Marston (Marty) Becker
CFO: Joseph W. Roberts
HR: —
FYE: December 31
Type: Public

Enjoying the tax-friendly climate in Bermuda, Alterra Capital Holdings (formerly Max Capital Group) provides property/casualty reinsurance and insurance, along with a sprinkling of life and annuities reinsurance, through its subsidiaries. The company specializes in reinsurance for workers' compensation, employers' liability, medical malpractice, property damage, and other casualty liability risks. Its insurance offerings include excess and surplus lines, such as liability, professional, and property coverage for large companies. The company's policies are sold through large brokerage and intermediary firms. Alterra changed its name in 2010 after acquiring another Bermuda-based reinsurer, Harbor Point Ltd.

	Annual Growth	12/05	12/06	12/07	12/08	12/09
Assets ($ mil.)	8.1%	5,373.6	5,849.0	6,537.2	7,252.0	7,339.7
Net income ($ mil.)	146.2%	6.7	216.9	303.2	(175.3)	246.2
Market value ($ mil.)	(3.7%)	1,479.8	1,414.3	1,594.9	1,008.6	1,270.7
Employees	48.1%	82	132	209	336	394

ALTEX INDUSTRIES, INC.

OTC: ALTX

217 S. Ridge Rd.
Breckenridge, CO 80424
Phone: 303-265-9312
Fax: 303-265-9312

CEO: Steven H. Cardin
CFO: Steven H. Cardin
HR: —
FYE: September 30
Type: Public

More OilRockies than AllTex(as), Altex Industries buys and sells oil and gas properties, participates in drilling exploratory wells, and sells oil and gas production to refineries, pipeline operators, and processing plants. The oil and gas exploration and production independent owns interests in two gross productive oil wells and 200 gross developed acres in Utah and Wyoming. Over the last few years Altex Industries has been forced to sell most of its oil and gas assets in order to pay down debt. CEO Steven Cardin holds a majority stake in the company.

	Annual Growth	9/05	9/06	9/07	9/08	9/09
Sales ($ mil.)	(43.8%)	1.0	0.3	0.0	0.0	0.1
Net income ($ mil.)	—	0.2	2.3	(0.2)	(0.3)	(0.3)
Market value ($ mil.)	(17.5%)	3.9	3.3	3.1	2.5	1.8
Employees	(9.6%)	3	2	2	2	2

ALTICOR INC.

7575 Fulton St. East
Ada, MI 49355
Phone: 616-787-1000
Fax: 616-682-4000
Web: www.alticor.com

CEO: Doug DeVos
CFO: Russell A. (Russ) Evans
HR: Kelly Savage
FYE: August 31
Type: Private

At the core of Alticor, there is Amway. Holding company Alticor operates direct-selling giant Amway International and North American Web sales affiliate Amway Corp., which does business as Amway Global. Its Access Business Group offers manufacturing and distribution services, primarily catering to the Amway units but also to contract clients. Outside the direct-sales realm, Alticor operates resort management firm Amway Hotel, upscale cosmetics maker Gurwitch Products (known for its Laura Mercier and ReVive brands), and health diagnostics developer Interleukin Genetics. Formed in 2000, Alticor is owned by Amway's founders, the DeVos and Van Andel families.

ALTIGEN COMMUNICATIONS, INC.

Pink Sheets: ATGN

410 E. Plumeria Dr.
San Jose, CA 95134
Phone: 408-597-9000
Fax: 408-597-9020
Web: www.altigen.com

CEO: Gilbert Hu
CFO: Philip M. (Phil) McDermott
HR: —
FYE: September 30
Type: Public

AltiGen Communications helps businesses find their calling on the Internet. The company provide voice-over-IP (VoIP) telephone systems and administration software. Its AltiServe Office phone systems utilize both the Internet and public telephone networks to transmit voice signals. AltiServe systems include voicemail, auto attendant menus, and other features of traditional business PBX systems; its AltiContact Manager product adds advanced call center functionality. The company also sells traditional analog telephones. AltiGen deals primarily through resellers and distributors.

	Annual Growth	9/05	9/06	9/07	9/08	9/09
Sales ($ mil.)	3.1%	15.4	17.9	17.9	18.9	17.4
Net income ($ mil.)	—	(0.3)	0.0	(0.9)	(3.9)	(4.7)
Market value ($ mil.)	(12.9%)	28.6	24.8	25.8	16.3	16.4
Employees	6.0%	91	88	109	121	115

ALTRA HOLDINGS, INC.

NASDAQ (GS): AIMC

300 Granite St., Ste. 201
Braintree, MA 02184
Phone: 781-917-0600
Fax: 781-843-0709
Web: www.altramotion.com

CEO: Carl R. Christenson
CFO: Christian Storch
HR: Chet Shubert
FYE: December 31
Type: Public

Altra Holdings brings things to a stop. The company, through its principal subsidiary Altra Industrial Motion, designs, makes, and markets mechanical power transmission and motion control products under several brand names including Warner Electric and Boston Gear. The company's industrial clutches and brakes, gear drives, couplings, and bearings are used in such assemblies as elevator braking systems and wheelchairs. Altra sells directly and through distributors to industrial equipment makers in material handling, mining, and transportation. Leveling the cyclical impact of any one industry, it also taps into energy, food processing, medical, and turf and garden. About 70% of its sales are from North America.

	Annual Growth	12/05	12/06	12/07	12/08	12/09
Sales ($ mil.)	5.6%	363.5	462.3	584.4	635.3	452.8
Net income ($ mil.)	—	2.5	8.9	11.5	6.5	(2.3)
Market value ($ mil.)	(4.2%)	—	376.6	445.7	212.0	331.0
Employees	(1.2%)	2,745	2,500	3,455	3,164	2,613

⊞ ALTRIA GROUP, INC.

NYSE: MO

6601 W. Broad St.
Richmond, VA 23230
Phone: 804-274-2200
Fax: 804-484-8231
Web: www.altria.com

CEO: Michael E. (Mike) Szymanczyk
CFO: David R. (Dave) Beran
HR: Charles (Charlie) Whitaker
FYE: December 31
Type: Public

The house the Marlboro Man built, Altria Group, is the largest cigarette company in the US. Altria operates its cigarette business through subsidiary Philip Morris USA, which sells Marlboro — the world's best-selling cigarette brand since 1972. Altria controls about half of the US tobacco market. It manufactures cigarettes under the Parliament, Virginia Slims, and Basic cigarette brands. While still firmly hooked on cigarettes, Altria is transitioning from primarily a cigarette manufacturer to a purveyor of a variety of tobacco products, including cigars and smokeless tobacco products. To that end, it has made a number of strategic acquisitions, including smokeless tobacco maker UST in 2009.

	Annual Growth	12/05	12/06	12/07	12/08	12/09
Sales ($ mil.)	(29.7%)	68,920.0	70,324.0	38,051.0	15,957.0	16,824.0
Net income ($ mil.)	(25.5%)	10,435.0	12,022.0	9,786.0	4,930.0	3,208.0
Market value ($ mil.)	3.2%	36,017.3	41,367.8	48,544.0	31,363.4	40,880.8
Employees	(52.7%)	199,000	175,000	84,000	10,400	10,000

ALVAREZ & MARSAL HOLDINGS, LLC

600 Lexington Ave., 6th Fl.
New York, NY 10022
Phone: 212-759-4433
Fax: 212-759-5532
Web: www.alvarezandmarsal.com

CEO: Antonio C. (Tony) Alvarez II
CFO: Susan Robinson
HR: Kevin Gregson
FYE: December 31
Type: Private

A&M specializes in M&A, along with restructuring, right-sizing, and other corporate turnaround processes. Alvarez & Marsal provides advisory and consulting services surrounding mergers and acquisitions, crisis and interim management, divestitures, performance improvement, restructuring, and strategic planning. The firm has served clients including U-Haul International parent AMERCO and underwear maker The Warnaco Group, but the biggest feather in its cap is the task of overseeing the dismantling of Lehman Brothers, which filed the largest bankruptcy filing in US history in 2008. Alvarez & Marsal has some 40 offices around the world. Co-CEOs Bryan Marsal and Tony Alvarez II started the firm in 1983.

ALYESKA PIPELINE SERVICE COMPANY

900 E. Benson St.
Anchorage, AK 99519
Phone: 907-787-8700
Fax: 907-787-8240
Web: www.alyeska-pipe.com

CEO: Kevin Hostler
CFO: Michael (Mike) Muckenthaler
HR: Kristi J. Acuff
FYE: December 31
Type: Consortium

Named after the Aleut word for mainland, The Alyeska Pipeline Service Company operates the 800-mile-long, 48-inch-diameter pipeline that transports crude oil from Alaska's North Slope to the marine oil terminal of Valdez in Prince William Sound. Founded in 1970 to make the newly discovered finds in Prudhoe Bay commercially accessible, the company was assigned the task of designing, building, operating, and maintaining the Trans-Alaska Pipeline System (TAPS). The $8 billion pipeline was completed in 1977. The volume of oil flowing through the pipeline averages about 1 million barrels per day. TAPS is owned by a consortium of oil and gas firms, including BP (47%), ConocoPhillips (28%), and Exxon Mobil (20%).

ALYESKA SEAFOODS INC.

303 NE Northlake Way
Seattle, WA 98105
Phone: 206-547-2100
Fax: 206-547-1808

CEO: Alec Brindle
CFO: —
HR: Karen Brindle
FYE: March 31
Type: Subsidiary

Alyeska Seafoods doesn't mind if you call it crabby. The Seattle-based company processes fresh and frozen seafood products, including Bristol Bay king crab and Bering Sea snow crab. Alyeska Seafoods is known for its large seafood operations in Dutch Harbor, Alaska. The company is a subsidiary of Japanese seafood giant Maruha Nichiro.

	Annual Growth	3/04	3/05	3/06	3/07	3/08
Est. sales ($ mil.)	—	—	—	—	—	34.3
Employees	—	—	—	—	—	340

A. M. CASTLE & CO.

NYSE: CAS

3400 N. Wolf Rd.
Franklin Park, IL 60131
Phone: 847-455-7111
Fax: 847-455-6930
Web: www.amcastle.com

CEO: Michael H. (Mike) Goldberg
CFO: Scott F. Stephens
HR: Kevin P. Fitzpatrick
FYE: December 31
Type: Public

Providing alloys for its allies, metals service company A. M. Castle distributes highly engineered metals and metal alloys to a broad range of industrial manufacturers. The company sells steel (alloy, carbon, and stainless), aluminum, copper, brass, and titanium in bar, sheet, plate, and tube form. A. M. Castle operates more than 50 steel service centers throughout North America, as well as in France, the UK, and China. Subsidiary Transtar distributes high-performance metals primarily to the aerospace and defense industries. The company also engages in industrial plastics distribution through subsidiary Total Plastics. Investor Patrick Herbert controls about a quarter of A. M. Castle.

	Annual Growth	12/05	12/06	12/07	12/08	12/09
Sales ($ mil.)	(4.1%)	959.0	1,177.6	1,420.4	1,501.0	812.6
Net income ($ mil.)	—	38.9	55.1	51.8	(17.1)	(26.9)
Market value ($ mil.)	(11.0%)	501.0	583.8	623.7	248.4	314.0
Employees	(0.4%)	1,604	2,016	1,945	1,923	1,576

AM GENERAL, LLC

105 N. Niles Ave.
South Bend, IN 46617
Phone: 574-237-6222
Fax: 574-284-2819
Web: www.amgeneral.com

CEO: Paul J. Kern
CFO: Paul J. Cafiero
HR: Gary L. Wuslich
FYE: October 31
Type: Subsidiary

AM General makes G.I. Joe's and Arnold Schwarzenegger's favorite rides — the Humvee and the HUMMER. Militaries use the High Mobility Multipurpose Wheeled Vehicle (Humvee) for battlefield transportation, but after the vehicles gained attention in Operation Desert Storm, AM General introduced a civilian version, the HUMMER H1, for General Motors. The unwieldy width of the H1 led to the more parking-space-friendly HUMMER H2 (and the even smaller HUMMER H3). AM General's General Engine Products subsidiary also makes 6.5-liter diesel engines for automotive, military, and marine OEM markets. Investor Ronald Perelman's MacAndrews & Forbes Holding owns about 70% of the company.

THE AMACORE GROUP, INC.

OTC: ACGI

485 N. Keller Rd., Ste. 450
Maitland, FL 32751
Phone: 407-805-8900
Fax: 407-805-0045
Web: www.amacoregroup.com

CEO: Jay Shafer
CFO: G. Scott Smith
HR: —
FYE: December 31
Type: Public

The Amacore Group wants you to be able to see a smaller optometry bill. Amacore is a provider of non-insurance based discount plans for eyewear and eyecare services, including surgery. Amacore Group's products are marketed to individuals, families, and businesses, as well as through the company's affiliations with insurance companies and other membership groups. The company has expanded its discount program offerings to include dental, hearing, chiropractic, and other health services. It also offers traditional health plans through partnerships with insurance providers.

	Annual Growth	12/05	12/06	12/07	12/08	12/09
Sales ($ mil.)	175.5%	0.5	0.4	4.3	29.5	28.8
Net income ($ mil.)	—	(4.4)	(1.7)	(21.2)	(33.9)	(10.7)
Market value ($ mil.)	(10.4%)	47.2	38.8	471.6	120.5	30.4
Employees	87.6%	8	9	76	103	99

AMADA AMERICA, INC.

7025 Firestone Blvd.
Buena Park, CA 90621
Phone: 714-739-2111
Fax: 714-739-4099
Web: www.amada.com

CEO: Mike Guerin
CFO: Koh Nakata
HR: Cathy Gonzalez
FYE: December 31
Type: Private

Amada America manufactures and sells sheet metal fabricating equipment, including CNC turret punch presses, lasers, press brakes, shears, flexible manufacturing systems, and related software. The company primarily sells its fabricating equipment to the aerospace, appliance, electronics, farm equipment, medical, and telecommunications industries. Through its Amada Capital Corporation subsidiary, Amada America finances and leases its equipment. Amada America was founded in 1971. Its parent company in Japan dates back to just after WWII and has about 80 affiliates and subsidiaries around the world. North America accounts for about 12% of the Amada Group's annual sales.

AMAG PHARMACEUTICALS, INC.

NASDAQ (GM): AMAG

100 Hayden Ave.
Lexington, MA 02421
Phone: 617-498-3300
Fax: 617-499-3361
Web: www.amagpharma.com

CEO: Brian J. G. Pereira
CFO: David A. Arkowitz
HR: —
FYE: December 31
Type: Public

AMAG Pharmaceuticals' magnetic technology doesn't make things stick, it makes things stick out. The company, formerly called Advanced Magnetics, uses its expertise in iron oxide nanoparticles to create organ-specific diagnostic contrast agents used in magnetic resonance imaging (MRI) tests. It has two products on the market: Feridex I.V. (for the diagnosis of liver lesions) and GastroMARK (used for delineating the bowel in abdominal imaging). The firm is developing Combidex as a contrast agent for the diagnosis of metastatic lymph nodes. Another product, Feraheme (ferumoxytol), received FDA approval as an iron replacement therapy for anemic patients in 2009.

	Annual Growth	9/05	9/06	*12/07	12/08	12/09
Sales ($ mil.)	63.6%	2.4	2.7	2.6	1.9	17.2
Net income ($ mil.)	—	(12.7)	(25.4)	(33.9)	(71.6)	(93.4)
Market value ($ mil.)	40.7%	204.0	716.5	1,263.4	753.3	799.1
Employees	67.4%	36	44	88	259	283

*Fiscal year change

AMALGAMATED LIFE INSURANCE COMPANY

333 Westchester Ave.
White Plains, NY 10604
Phone: 914-367-5000
Fax: —
Web: www.amalgamatedlife.com

CEO: David J. Walsh
CFO: Paul Mallen
HR: Leslie Bostic
FYE: December 31
Type: Private

Amalgamated Life Insurance has the back of the working man or woman. The company provides life insurance, retirement plans, and other benefits to members of some 30 different labor unions and other moderate income individuals. In addition to its group and individual products (life, accident, and disability), Amalgamated Life Insurance and its affiliates offer third party administration (TPA) and medical cost management to self-insured groups. The company is licensed in over 40 states and has offices nationwide. It provides coverage to some 800,000 customers.

THE AMALGAMATED SUGAR COMPANY LLC

3184 Elder St.
Boise, ID 83705
Phone: 208-383-6500
Fax: 208-383-6684
Web: www.amalgamatedsugar.com

CEO: Victor J. (Vic) Jaro
CFO: Wayne P. Neeley
HR: Paul Lemieux
FYE: December 31
Type: Cooperative

This fusion of beet growers makes for a sweet mix. A top US sugar producer, The Amalgamated Sugar Company (also known as the Snake River Sugar Company) processes sugar beets for its member/farmers. The cooperative manufactures granulated, coarse, powdered, and brown consumer sugar products marketed under the brand name White Satin. It also provides private-label products for retail grocery chains. In addition, Amalgamated Sugar produces beet pulp, molasses, and other beet byproducts for use by food and animal-feed manufacturers. The company, which dates back to 1915, became a grower-owned beet-sugar cooperative in 1997.

	Annual Growth	12/04	12/05	12/06	12/07	12/08
Est. sales ($ mil.)	—	—	—	—	—	605.3
Employees	—	—	—	—	—	1,500

AMANASU ENVIRONMENT CORPORATION

OTC: AMSU

115 East 57th St., 11th Fl.
New York, NY 10022
Phone: 646-274-1274
Fax: —

CEO: Atsushi Maki
CFO: Lina Lei
HR: —
FYE: December 31
Type: Public

Development stage environmental engineering company Amanasu Environment Corporation owns the licensing rights to produce and market high-temperature furnaces, hot-water boilers that extract heat energy from waste tires, a patented process for purifying seawater and removing hazardous pollutants from wastewater, and a range of solar panels. Amanasu Environment, however, has not developed any products for commercial sale, although it has developed prototypes. The firm was incorporated in 1999. Chairman and president Atsushi Maki owns about 73% of the company.

	Annual Growth	12/05	12/06	12/07	12/08	12/09
Sales ($ mil.)	—	0.5	0.5	0.5	0.2	0.0
Net income ($ mil.)	—	(0.6)	(1.1)	(1.1)	(0.6)	(0.3)
Market value ($ mil.)	(34.7%)	24.2	4.4	15.0	8.8	4.4
Employees	0.0%	2	2	2	2	—

AMARILLO BIOSCIENCES, INC.

OTC: AMAR

4134 Business Park Dr.
Amarillo, TX 79110
Phone: 806-376-1741
Fax: 806-376-9301
Web: www.amarbio.com

CEO: Joseph M. (Joe) Cummins
CFO: Bernard Cohen
HR: Chrystal Shelton
FYE: December 31
Type: Public

Amarillo — home to cattlemen, prairies, and . . . interferon? Amarillo Biosciences hopes its low-dose interferon alpha (IFNa), which modulates the immune system, will help those suffering from a range of maladies, including viral and autoimmune diseases. The company's interferon technology, which uses a low-dose dissolving tablet, potentially offers effective treatment with fewer side effects than injectable forms of the drug. Amarillo Biosciences is developing its interferon technology as a treatment for flu, oral warts in HIV patients, and chronic cough. Through research partners, it is also investigating the drug in relation to Behcet's disease (a severe inflammatory disorder) and hepatitis C.

	Annual Growth	12/05	12/06	12/07	12/08	12/09
Sales ($ mil.)	(15.9%)	0.2	0.1	0.1	0.1	0.1
Net income ($ mil.)	—	(0.7)	(2.8)	(2.5)	(1.9)	(3.0)
Market value ($ mil.)	(20.7%)	23.2	35.1	15.7	3.0	9.2
Employees	0.0%	5	5	7	6	5

⊞ AMAZON.COM, INC.

NASDAQ (GS): AMZN

1200 12th Ave. South, Ste. 1200
Seattle, WA 98144
Phone: 206-266-1000
Fax: —
Web: www.amazon.com

CEO: Jeffrey P. (Jeff) Bezos
CFO: Thomas J. (Tom) Szkutak
HR: —
FYE: December 31
Type: Public

What started as Earth's biggest bookstore has rapidly become Earth's biggest anything store. Expansion has propelled Amazon.com in innumerable directions. Its website offers millions of books, music, and movies (which account for most of its sales), not to mention auto parts, toys, electronics, home furnishings, apparel, health and beauty aids, prescription drugs, and groceries. Shoppers can download e-books, games, MP3s, and films to their computers or handheld devices, including Amazon's own portable reader, the Kindle. Amazon also offers products and services, such as self-publishing, online advertising, e-commerce platform, and a co-branded credit card. The firm acquired Zappos.com in 2009.

	Annual Growth	12/05	12/06	12/07	12/08	12/09
Sales ($ mil.)	30.3%	8,490.0	10,711.0	14,835.0	19,166.0	24,509.0
Net income ($ mil.)	28.3%	333.0	190.0	476.0	645.0	902.0
Market value ($ mil.)	30.0%	21,013.4	17,586.2	41,287.0	22,854.0	59,951.7
Employees	19.3%	12,000	13,900	17,000	20,700	24,300

AMB FINANCIAL CORP.

OTC: AMFC

8230 Hohman Ave.
Munster, IN 46321
Phone: 219-836-5870
Fax: 219-836-5883
Web: www.ambfinancial.com

CEO: Michael J. (Mike) Mellon
CFO: Steven A. Bohn
HR: —
FYE: December 31
Type: Public

AMB Financial is the holding company for American Savings, a thrift serving Lake County, Indiana, near the southern tip of Lake Michigan. It operates four offices in Dyer, Hammond, Munster, and Schererville. Catering to local families and businesses, the bank offers checking and savings accounts, money market accounts, certificates of deposit, and IRAs. It mainly uses these deposit funds to originate real estate, construction, consumer, commercial, land, and other loans. One- to four-family residential mortgages account for approximately three-quarters of its loan portfolio. American Savings offers financial planning services through its American Financial Services division.

	Annual Growth	12/04	12/05	12/06	12/07	*12/08
Assets ($ mil.)	3.5%	157.1	170.5	182.3	174.8	180.1
Net income ($ mil.)	—	0.9	0.9	0.6	0.0	(0.3)
Employees	1.4%	35	39	39	37	37

*Most recent year available

AMB PROPERTY CORPORATION

NYSE: AMB

Pier 1, Bay 1
San Francisco, CA 94111
Phone: 415-394-9000
Fax: 415-394-9001
Web: www.amb.com

CEO: Hamid R. Moghadam
CFO: Thomas S. Olinger
HR: Nancy J. Hemmenway
FYE: December 31
Type: Public

AMB Property knows the ABCs about property management. The company invests primarily in industrial properties in the Americas, Europe, and Asia. The real estate investment trust (REIT) owns, operates, and manages about 1,100 industrial buildings (and a handful of retail properties) totaling more than 160 million sq. ft. in nearly 50 major metropolitan areas. The company focuses on fast-paced, high-volume warehouse distribution facilities tied to global trade near ports, airports, and highways. Its portfolio is concentrated in and around Los Angeles, San Francisco, New York, Chicago, and Seattle. The US government, Deutsche Post, and powerhouse parcel handler FedEx are the REIT's largest tenants.

	Annual Growth	12/05	12/06	12/07	12/08	12/09
Sales ($ mil.)	(1.6%)	676.1	729.9	669.7	715.0	633.8
Net income ($ mil.)	—	257.8	223.9	314.3	(49.3)	(28.0)
Market value ($ mil.)	(15.1%)	8,268.9	9,856.4	9,679.9	3,938.5	4,296.7
Employees	14.0%	309	416	513	645	521

⊞ AMBAC FINANCIAL GROUP, INC.

NYSE: ABK

1 State Street Plaza
New York, NY 10004
Phone: 212-668-0340
Fax: 212-509-9190
Web: www.ambac.com

CEO: David W. Wallis
CFO: David Trick
HR: —
FYE: December 31
Type: Public

Ambac Financial Group used to give an A+ to school bonds, until its own ratings fell to C's. Ambac Assurance, the holding company's primary subsidiary, sold financial guarantee insurance and other credit enhancement products for municipal bonds in the US market. However, the company has halted all new business and has placed its remaining business in "run-off" — meaning it is only taking in premium payments and paying out claims as it is able. In better days it also insured infrastructure and utility deals internationally. Its Ambac Financial Services unit offered interest rate swaps, credit swaps, and investment management primarily to states and municipal authorities tied to their bond financing.

	Annual Growth	12/05	12/06	12/07	12/08	12/09
Assets ($ mil.)	(1.1%)	19,725.1	20,267.8	23,565.0	17,256.4	18,886.4
Net income ($ mil.)	—	751.0	875.9	(3,248.2)	(5,609.2)	(14.6)
Market value ($ mil.)	(67.8%)	22,222.6	25,686.1	7,431.6	374.9	239.4
Employees	(4.6%)	354	359	367	328	293

⊞ An in-depth profile of this company is available to Hoover's Online members at hoovers.com.

AMBASSADORS GROUP, INC.

NASDAQ (GS): EPAX

Dwight D. Eisenhower Bldg., 1956 Ambassador Way
Spokane, WA 99224
Phone: 509-568-7000
Fax: —
Web: www.ambassadorsgroup.com

CEO: Jeffrey D. (Jeff) Thomas
CFO: Kristi Gravelle
HR: —
FYE: December 31
Type: Public

Ambassadors Group provides students and professionals with opportunities to meet their counterparts overseas. It organizes trips under contracts with the People to People organization, which was founded by President Eisenhower to promote world peace. Ambassadors Group markets trips using the People to People name and makes travel arrangements for participants, which include student athletes and leaders as well as professionals. It also offers international adventure travel services to students through its World Adventures Unlimited subsidiary. Outside the travel industry, the firm operates BookRags.com, a research website with more than 8 million pages of educational content for students and teachers.

	Annual Growth	12/05	12/06	12/07	12/08	12/09
Sales ($ mil.)	10.4%	66.4	89.0	114.5	97.9	98.6
Net income ($ mil.)	(2.4%)	22.4	26.7	31.0	18.5	20.3
Market value ($ mil.)	(12.8%)	436.6	578.9	349.2	175.5	252.9
Employees	1.8%	234	273	276	275	251

AMBASSADORS INTERNATIONAL, INC.

NASDAQ (GM): AMIE

1071 Camelback St.
Newport Beach, CA 92660
Phone: 949-759-5900
Fax: 949-759-5901
Web: www.ambassadors.com

CEO: Hans Birkholz
CFO: Mark Detillion
HR: —
FYE: December 31
Type: Public

Ambassadors International represents itself around the world in the small ship cruise business. Its primary Windstar Cruises unit operates three luxury yachts that offer guests a more intimate cruise experience, carrying just 150 to 300 passengers. Windstar sails to almost 50 countries, including Europe, the Mediterranean, the Americas, and the Caribbean. In 2008 Ambassadors International was forced to shut down its seven-vessel Majestic America Line, which proved unprofitable. The company also shed noncore assets in April and May 2009, including its marina design and travel and events businesses, in order to focus on its Windstar Cruises line.

	Annual Growth	12/05	12/06	12/07	12/08	12/09
Sales ($ mil.)	22.9%	26.9	144.4	287.0	274.6	61.3
Net income ($ mil.)	—	3.1	5.6	(26.9)	(36.0)	(51.6)
Market value ($ mil.)	(55.8%)	411.0	1,209.7	386.6	17.2	15.7
Employees	(22.0%)	157	765	1,038	518	58

AMBIENT CORPORATION

OTC: ABTG

7 Wells Ave.
Newton, MA 02459
Phone: 617-332-0004
Fax: 617-332-7260
Web: www.ambientcorp.com

CEO: John J. Joyce
CFO: John J. Joyce
HR: —
FYE: December 31
Type: Public

Ambient wants to put real power behind communications. The company develops technology that allows power lines to serve as high-speed data communications networks. Ambient's products — including nodes, couplers, and network management software — utilize Broadband over Power Line (BPL) and other technologies to create advanced power grids (also known as smart grids) with two-way communication capabilities. Its systems are designed to be used by utility companies for such applications as demand management, direct load control, meter reading, and real-time pricing. Ambient has partnerships with utilities such as Con Ed and Duke Energy to develop its technology.

	Annual Growth	12/05	12/06	12/07	12/08	12/09
Sales ($ mil.)	82.1%	0.2	2.3	2.3	12.6	2.2
Net income ($ mil.)	—	(11.2)	(12.7)	(15.8)	(11.3)	(14.2)
Market value ($ mil.)	10.2%	160.4	135.0	46.0	28.6	236.6
Employees	8.3%	32	34	28	38	44

AMC ENTERTAINMENT INC.

920 Main St.
Kansas City, MO 64105
Phone: 816-221-4000
Fax: 816-480-4617
Web: www.amctheatres.com

CEO: Gerardo I. (Gerry) Lopez
CFO: Craig R. Ramsey
HR: Keith Wiedenkeller
FYE: March 31
Type: Private

AMC Entertainment shines when the lights go down. The #2 movie theater chain in the US (behind Regal Entertainment), the company owns about 380 theaters with 5,300 screens, most of which are in megaplexes (units with more than 14 screens and stadium seating). The majority of its theaters can be found throughout the US and Canada; about a dozen theaters are in China (Hong Kong), France, and the UK. The firm is part owner (more than 25%) of MovieTickets.com, along with Hollywood Media and rivals Cineplex and National Amusements, among others. The company bought rival Loews Cineplex in 2006, significantly boosting its holdings. AMC is controlled by J.P. Morgan Partners and Apollo Management.

	Annual Growth	3/05	3/06	3/07	3/08	3/09
Sales ($ mil.)	7.5%	1,698.7	1,686.9	2,461.6	2,333.0	2,265.5
Net income ($ mil.)	—	(80.3)	(216.2)	116.9	43.4	(81.2)
Employees	(6.7%)	22,200	21,400	22,900	20,200	16,800

AMC, INC.

240 Peachtree St., Ste. 2200
Atlanta, GA 30303
Phone: 404-220-3000
Fax: 404-220-3030
Web: www.americasmart.com

CEO: John C. Portman Jr.
CFO: Henry G. (Hank) Almquist Jr.
HR: Bob Brush
FYE: August 31
Type: Private

AMC isn't a theater, but it likes to put on a show. AMC owns and manages the AmericasMart Atlanta trade show center, one of the largest such facilities in the world. The firm also organizes and runs about 20 wholesale markets every year and a handful of regular markets — including an apparel market and a gift products market. AmericasMart Atlanta consists of three buildings that house permanent showroom space, exhibit halls, convention space, and meeting rooms. AmericasMart Atlanta is focused on bringing retailers and wholesalers together. It was established in 1957 by architect John Portman.

	Annual Growth	8/04	8/05	8/06	8/07	8/08
Est. sales ($ mil.)	—	—	—	—	—	12.4
Employees	—	—	—	—	—	240

AMCOL INTERNATIONAL CORPORATION

NYSE: ACO

2870 Forbs Ave.
Hoffman Estates, IL 60192
Phone: 847-851-1500
Fax: —
Web: www.amcol.com

CEO: Lawrence E. (Larry) Washow
CFO: Donald W. Pearson
HR: —
FYE: December 31
Type: Public

AMCOL International is nothing if not diverse, with operations in minerals, environmental services, oilfield services, and transportation. Its minerals segment is a global supplier of bentonite products used in cat litter, laundry detergent, metal casting, paper manufacturing, and as a plastic additive. Its environmental segment provides building materials and construction services to concrete waterproofing, drilling, flood control, and site remediation projects. AMCOL's oilfield services unit offers water treatment and well testing to the oil and gas industry. The company's transportation business provides longhaul trucking and freight brokerage services to AMCOL units and third parties in the US and Canada.

	Annual Growth	12/05	12/06	12/07	12/08	12/09
Sales ($ mil.)	7.0%	535.9	611.6	744.3	883.6	703.2
Net income ($ mil.)	(3.9%)	41.0	50.2	56.7	25.3	34.9
Market value ($ mil.)	8.5%	635.2	858.7	1,115.3	648.5	879.8
Employees	(38.8%)	15,742	1,759	2,017	2,388	2,211

AMCON DISTRIBUTING COMPANY

NYSE Amex: DIT

7405 Irvington Rd.
Omaha, NE 68122
Phone: 402-331-3727
Fax: 402-331-4834
Web: www.amcon.com

CEO: Christopher H. Atayan
CFO: Andrew C. Plummer
HR: —
FYE: September 30
Type: Public

AMCON Distributing enjoys a healthy meal, but it's not without its vices. It's a wholesale distributor of consumer products, including cigarettes, and a retailer of health and natural foods. AMCON serves about 4,200 convenience stores, supermarkets, drug stores, tobacco shops, and institutional customers in the Great Plains and Rocky Mountain regions. It also distributes candy, beverages, groceries, paper products, and health and beauty aids. AMCON also operates about 15 health food stores under the Chamberlin's Market & Cafe and Akin's Natural Foods banners in five states.

	Annual Growth	9/05	9/06	9/07	9/08	9/09
Sales ($ mil.)	1.8%	845.9	839.5	853.6	860.5	908.0
Net income ($ mil.)	—	(12.7)	(1.1)	4.4	5.3	13.0
Market value ($ mil.)	29.9%	12.3	7.6	15.8	14.1	35.1
Employees	(4.7%)	972	901	874	845	801

AMCOR PET PACKAGING

935 Technology Dr., Ste. 100
Ann Arbor, MI 48108
Phone: 734-428-9741
Fax: 734-302-2298
Web: www.amcor.com/businesses/pet

CEO: William J. (Bill) Long
CFO: Larry Weber
HR: —
FYE: June 30
Type: Business segment

Plastic bottles don't grow on trees but they do produce some green, if you're Amcor PET, that is. The company is #1 in the Americas for manufacturing polyethylene terephthalate (PET) containers. Customers include those in the food industry (dressings, sauces and salsas, fruit and nut spreads) and beverage producers (soft drinks, water, juices, dairy, and beer). Amcor PET supplies non-food applications, too, from household cleaners to liquid soap and lotion, hair care, pharmaceutical, automotive, and agro-chemical goods. Practicing another kind of green, it recycles a hefty 100 million pounds of PET a year. A business unit of Amcor Limited, Amcor PET's 60-plus manufacturing facilities dot a dozen countries.

AMCOR SUNCLIPSE NORTH AMERICA

6600 Valley View St.
Buena Park, CA 90620
Phone: 714-562-6000
Fax: 714-562-6059
Web: www.amcor.com/businesses/sunclipse

CEO: Eric Bloom
CFO: Eric Petty
HR: Thomas Sarnecki
FYE: December 30
Type: Subsidiary

Amcor Sunclipse North America, a subsidiary of Australian packaging manufacturing giant Amcor, aims to cast a bright light on the corrugated products industry in North America. The company manufactures corrugated products, packing material, janitorial products, shipping supplies, promotional products, custom-built corrugated packaging, and industrial packaging products. It distributes these products through its Kent H. Landsberg Company division, while KHL Engineered Packaging distributes and warehouses packaging equipment. With its headquarters and manufacturing facilities based in California, Amcor Sunclipse operates over 35 distribution and redistribution centers throughout the US, Mexico, and Europe.

	Annual Growth	6/04	6/05	6/06	6/07	*12/08
Sales ($ mil.)	(6.3%)	—	928.0	943.0	1,061.6	763.5
Employees	4.2%	—	2,000	2,097	2,173	—

*Fiscal year change

AMEC GEOMATRIX CONSULTANTS, INC.

2101 Webster St., 12th Fl.
Oakland, CA 94612
Phone: 510-663-4100
Fax: 510-663-4141
Web: www.amecgeomatrix.com

CEO: Anthony D. (Tony) Daus
CFO: Martin (Marty) Mullins
HR: Nicole Silverman
FYE: December 31
Type: Subsidiary

Neo of *The Matrix* was the chosen one, while AMEC Geomatrix Consultants hopes to be chosen to provide engineering, environmental, and geological consulting services. Its environmental-related services include support for air quality compliance, licensing and regulatory assistance, site assessment, and remediation. The firm also provides assessments of seismic activity and earthquake-related engineering services, cartography and other geographic information systems (GIS) design, decision analysis consulting, and natural resources optimization. AMEC Geomatrix, a unit of AMEC Earth & Environmental, conducts projects worldwide and has 19 offices located throughout the US, and one in Canada.

AMEDISYS, INC.

NASDAQ (GS): AMED

5959 S. Sherwood Forest Blvd.
Baton Rouge, LA 70816
Phone: 225-292-2031
Fax: 225-292-8163
Web: www.amedisys.com

CEO: William F. (Bill) Borne
CFO: Dale E. Redman
HR: Cindy L. Phillips
FYE: December 31
Type: Public

Because the last thing you want to do when you're ailing is drive to a doctor's office, Amedisys has decided to bring health care to you. Through some 520 home health care agencies located across the US, the company provides skilled nursing and home health aide services to primarily geriatric patients covered by Medicare. Its range of services includes disease-specific programs that help patients recovering from stroke, for instance, or assist those coping with emphysema or diabetes. In addition to its home health services, Amedisys owns or manages about 65 hospice agencies that offer palliative care to terminally ill patients.

	Annual Growth	12/05	12/06	12/07	12/08	12/09
Sales ($ mil.)	41.1%	381.6	541.1	697.9	1,187.4	1,513.5
Net income ($ mil.)	45.7%	30.1	38.3	65.1	86.7	135.8
Market value ($ mil.)	11.3%	904.8	938.8	1,385.7	1,180.7	1,388.0
Employees	28.1%	6,206	6,892	8,900	14,800	16,700

AMEGY CORPORATION

4400 Post Oak Pkwy.
Houston, TX 77027
Phone: 713-235-8800
Fax: 713-439-5949
Web: www.amegybank.com

CEO: Scott J. McLean
CFO: Randall E. Meyer
HR: —
FYE: December 31
Type: Subsidiary

Amegy knows banking from A to Z. Amegy Corporation, the parent of Amegy Bank of Texas (also known as the A Bank), is a subsidiary of Zions Bancorporation. The bank has more than 85 branches, primarily in Houston but also in Dallas and San Antonio (through its 2007 acquisition of Intercontinental Bank Shares). Specializing in serving small businesses, it offers standard services, such as deposit accounts, commercial and industrial loans, construction and land development loans, and trust services. The bank provides brokerage, insurance, and wealth management services through Amegy Investments. Subsidiary Amegy Mortgage originates and services commercial, residential, and construction mortgages.

	Annual Growth	12/04	12/05	12/06	12/07	12/08
Est. sales ($ mil.)	—	—	—	—	—	612.0
Employees	—	—	—	—	—	1,534

An in-depth profile of this company is available to Hoover's Online members at hoovers.com.

AMEN PROPERTIES, INC.

NASDAQ (CM): AMEN

303 W. Wall St., Ste. 2300
Midland, TX 79701
Phone: 972-664-1610
Fax: —
Web: amenproperties.com

CEO: Jon M. Morgan
CFO: Kris Oliver
HR: —
FYE: December 31
Type: Public

AMEN Properties is hoping that the answer to its prayers are power and energy, and a little property thrown in for good measure. The company's Priority Power subsidiary provides energy management and consulting services. This unit has current or previous business activities in Texas and 21 other states, and serves more than 1,200 clients (including a large number of oil and gas companies.) These activities include electricity load aggregation, natural gas and electricity procurement, energy risk management, and energy consulting. AMEN Properties also invests in commercial real estate in secondary markets and in oil and gas royalties.

AMERALIA, INC.

Pink Sheets: AALA

9233 Park Meadows Dr., Ste. 431
Lone Tree, CO 80124
Phone: 720-876-2373
Fax: 970-878-5866
Web: www.naturalsoda.com

CEO: Bill H. Gunn
CFO: Robert C. J. van Mourik
HR: —
FYE: June 30
Type: Public

AmerAlia is sold on soda. Through subsidiary Natural Soda, Inc., AmerAlia owns sodium bicarbonate leases in the region of Colorado's Piceance Creek Basin. AmerAlia can produce about 110,000 tons of various grades of sodium bicarbonate per year. Sodium bicarbonate (baking soda) is used in animal feed, food, and pharmaceuticals. Byproducts such as soda ash and caustic soda are used to make glass, detergents, and chemicals. Investment group Sentient USA Resources Fund owns about three-quarters of AmerAlia. The company's operations are handled through 18%-owned subsidiary Natural Soda Holdings, which itself owns Natural Soda, Inc. outright.

	Annual Growth	6/05	6/06	6/07	6/08	6/09
Sales ($ mil.)	(17.6%)	14.1	15.3	17.0	17.9	6.5
Net income ($ mil.)	—	(6.7)	(7.8)	(8.0)	(46.4)	(5.8)
Market value ($ mil.)	(2.4%)	36.5	19.9	26.5	56.3	33.1
Employees	2.7%	35	39	39	39	39

AMERAMEX INTERNATIONAL INC.

Pink Sheets: AMMX

3930 Esplanade
Chico, CA 95973
Phone: 530-895-8955
Fax: 530-895-8959
Web: www.ammx.net

CEO: Lee Hamre
CFO: Steve Champagne
HR: —
FYE: December 31
Type: Public

Let AmeraMex take care of the heavy stuff. The company sells, leases, services, and maintains heavy equipment to businesses such as heavy construction, surface mining, infrastructure, logging, shipping, and transportation. AmeraMex has four business units: Hamre Equipment, Hamre Heavy Haul Industry, Hamre Parts and Service, and John's Radiator. Its inventory includes front-end loaders, excavators, container handlers, and trucks and trailers; manufacturers represented include Taylor Machine Works, Terex Heavy Equipment, and Barko Hydraulics. The firm is active in the Americas, Europe, the Middle East, and Asia. AmeraMex also provides heavy hauling services throughout the US.

AMERCO

NASDAQ (GS): UHAL

1325 Airmotive Way, Ste. 100
Reno, NV 89502
Phone: 775-688-6300
Fax: 775-688-6338
Web: www.amerco.com

CEO: Edward J. (Joe) Shoen
CFO: Jason A. Berg
HR: —
FYE: March 31
Type: Public

U-Haul, u-work, u-strain, u-hurt . . . u-sure you don't want to spend the extra money for movers? If not, there's AMERCO, whose principal subsidiary, U-Haul International, rents its orange-and-white trucks, trailers, and vehicle tow devices and sells packing supplies to do-it-yourself movers through more than 14,400 independent dealers and 1,400 company-owned centers in the US and Canada. In addition, U-Haul is a leading operator of self-storage facilities, maintaining about 1,100 storage locations in North America. Established in 1945, AMERCO is 55%-owned by the founding Schoen family. It is led by chairman and president Edward "Joe" Shoen. The firm has been facing mounting losses due to the economic downturn.

	Annual Growth	3/05	3/06	3/07	3/08	3/09
Sales ($ mil.)	(0.2%)	2,008.1	2,106.6	2,085.6	2,049.2	1,992.3
Net income ($ mil.)	(37.8%)	89.4	121.2	90.6	67.8	13.4
Market value ($ mil.)	(7.8%)	907.8	1,940.6	1,372.3	1,119.4	657.4
Employees	(0.8%)	18,300	17,500	18,000	18,500	17,700

AMEREN CORPORATION

NYSE: AEE

1901 Chouteau Ave.
St. Louis, MO 63103
Phone: 314-621-3222
Fax: 314-554-3801
Web: www.ameren.com

CEO: Thomas R. Voss
CFO: Martin J. Lyons Jr.
HR: Mark C. Lindgren
FYE: December 31
Type: Public

Ameren provides the power that makes much of the American Midwest run. The holding company distributes electricity to 2.4 million customers and natural gas to almost 1 million customers in Missouri and Illinois through utility subsidiaries. Ameren has a generating capacity of more than 16,500 MW (primarily coal-fired), most of which is controlled by utility AmerenUE and non-regulated subsidiary AmerenEnergy Resources Generating Company. Ameren also operates a nuclear power facility, three hydroelectric plants, and several turbine combustion facilities.

	Annual Growth	12/05	12/06	12/07	12/08	12/09
Sales ($ mil.)	1.1%	6,780.0	6,880.0	7,546.0	7,839.0	7,090.0
Net income ($ mil.)	(0.6%)	628.0	547.0	618.0	605.0	612.0
Market value ($ mil.)	(14.1%)	12,209.8	12,803.1	12,917.5	7,925.4	6,660.1
Employees	1.7%	9,136	8,988	9,069	9,524	9,780

AMERIANA BANCORP

NASDAQ (GM): ASBI

2118 Bundy Ave.
New Castle, IN 47362
Phone: 765-529-2230
Fax: 765-529-2232
Web: www.ameriana.com

CEO: Jerome J. (Jerry) Gassen
CFO: John J. Letter
HR: —
FYE: December 31
Type: Public

Ameriana Bancorp may sound merry, but it takes business seriously. It's the parent of Ameriana Bank, which has about a dozen offices in central Indiana. The bank offers standard deposit products, including checking, savings, and money market accounts; CDs; and IRAs. It focuses on real estate lending: Residential mortgages account for about half of its loan portfolio, and commercial real estate loans represent about 30%. The company sells auto, home, life, health, and business coverage through its Ameriana Insurance Agency subsidiary. Another unit, Ameriana Investment Management, provides brokerage and investment services through an agreement with LPL Financial.

	Annual Growth	12/05	12/06	12/07	12/08	12/09
Assets ($ mil.)	(0.4%)	449.4	437.2	426.8	463.5	441.6
Net income ($ mil.)	—	2.1	(1.0)	1.2	0.7	(0.3)
Market value ($ mil.)	(32.7%)	38.7	39.1	25.4	16.7	8.0
Employees	0.0%	171	177	171	171	—

AMERICA FIRST CREDIT UNION

1344 W. 4675 South	
Riverdale, UT 84405	CEO: Rick Craig
	CFO: —
Phone: 801-627-0900	HR: —
Fax: 801-778-8079	FYE: December 31
Web: www.americafirst.com	Type: Not-for-profit

If saving your money makes you feel like doing a little flag-waving, could there be a more appropriate place for it than America First Credit Union? Founded in 1939, the institution offers deposits, lending, investments, and other financial services to both business and consumer customers through more than 80 branches in Utah and Nevada. With more than 475,000 members, America First ranks among the nation's top 10 credit unions by membership. It ranks among the 15 largest credit unions by assets. America First acquired local rival Intermountain Credit Union in 2008. It is also growing by opening new branches.

	Annual Growth	12/04	12/05	12/06	12/07	12/08
Sales ($ mil.)	19.6%	184.6	221.1	279.9	347.0	377.4
Employees	—	—	—	—	1,500	—

AMERICA FIRST TAX EXEMPT INVESTORS, L.P.

NASDAQ (GM): ATAX

1004 Farnam St.	
Omaha, NE 68102	CEO: Mark A. Hiatt
	CFO: Michael J. Draper
Phone: 402-444-1630	HR: —
Fax: 402-930-3047	FYE: December 31
Web: www.ataxz.com	Type: Public

Shout it from the rooftops of its properties: America First Tax Exempt Investors is indeed, for the most part, tax exempt. The company invests in federally tax-exempt mortgage revenue bonds, which are issued by state and local governments to help fund construction of, and provide financing for, multi-family housing complexes; ultimately, the bonds are designed to provide affordable mortgages to low- to middle-income homebuyers. Currently, America First Tax Exempt Investors' portfolio consists of more than 15 tax-exempt bonds that fund about 20 multifamily properties. The firm is managed by America First Real Estate Group and is part of Burlington Capital Group.

	Annual Growth	12/05	12/06	12/07	12/08	12/09
Sales ($ mil.)	3.0%	18.6	15.9	20.3	18.1	20.9
Net income ($ mil.)	5.0%	19.6	12.8	0.9	(1.0)	23.8
Market value ($ mil.)	(5.3%)	162.1	174.5	140.7	107.9	130.6
Employees	—	—	—	—	—	—

AMERICA SERVICE GROUP INC.

NASDAQ (GS): ASGR

105 Westpark Dr., Ste. 200	
Brentwood, TN 37027	CEO: Richard (Rich) Hallworth
	CFO: Michael W. Taylor
Phone: 615-373-3100	HR: T. Scott Hoffman
Fax: 888-729-0069	FYE: December 31
Web: www.asgr.com	Type: Public

Talk about capturing your clients: America Service Group's subsidiaries provide managed health care services to prisoners in state, county, and local correctional facilities throughout the US. Through subsidiaries Prison Health Services and Correctional Health Services, the company contracts with government agencies to provide physical and mental health screenings and treatment, as well as dental care and medication administration. America Service Group also oversees off-site services, including outpatient testing and care, emergency room care, surgery, and hospitalization.

	Annual Growth	12/05	12/06	12/07	12/08	12/09
Sales ($ mil.)	1.9%	562.7	569.4	489.1	497.7	606.2
Net income ($ mil.)	(6.9%)	4.4	(3.4)	2.8	3.8	3.3
Market value ($ mil.)	0.0%	142.5	143.5	65.9	96.1	142.6
Employees	(2.4%)	4,230	5,030	4,100	4,812	3,840

AMERICALL GROUP, INC.

1230 E. Diehl Rd., Ste. 300	
Naperville, IL 60563	CEO: George A. Kestler
	CFO: —
Phone: 630-955-9100	HR: —
Fax: 630-955-9955	FYE: December 31
Web: www.teleperformance.com/americall	Type: Subsidiary

Americall would have no problem fulfilling Blondie's request to "Call Me." The company, a unit of French call-center behemoth Teleperformance, specializes in outbound teleservices for companies in the financial services and insurance industries. Other customers include membership organizations and telecommunications companies. Americall handles functions such as customer acquisition, customer care, product recall and warranty administration, and technical support from about half a dozen facilities in the US and Latin America. The company was founded by CEO George Kestler in 1984 and acquired by Teleperformance in 1998.

AMERICAN AGIP COMPANY, INC.

485 Madison Ave.	
New York, NY 10022	CEO: Bruno Bertuccioli
	CFO: Carlos Titanti
Phone: 646-264-2100	HR: Pasqua Ratti
Fax: 646-264-2222	FYE: December 31
Web: www.americanagip.com	Type: Subsidiary

You might say that American Agip is as slick as a whistle. Formed in 1987, the subsidiary of Italian energy heavyweight Eni operates three major petrochemical businesses: the manufacturing and marketing of lubricants; the marketing and trading of MTBE and methanol; and the trading of refined petroleum products. American Agip supplies bulk and package customers throughout the eastern US, and across Canada. It has a manufacturing center in Cabot, Pennsylvania (where it has more than 1 million gallons of lubricant storage), and distribution centers located in New Jersey, New York, Ohio, Pennsylvania, and West Virginia as well as in Quebec, Canada.

	Annual Growth	12/04	12/05	12/06	12/07	12/08
Est. sales ($ mil.)	—	—	—	—	—	1,367.5
Employees	—	—	—	—	—	116

AMERICAN AIR LIQUIDE HOLDINGS, INC.

2700 Post Oak Blvd., Ste. 1800	
Houston, TX 77056	CEO: Michael J. (Mike) Graff
	CFO: Scott Krapf
Phone: 713-624-8000	HR: —
Fax: 713-624-8085	FYE: December 31
Web: www.us.airliquide.com	Type: Subsidiary

Break out the Tums, because things are awfully gassy over at American Air Liquide. The company supplies industrial gases (oxygen, nitrogen, CO_2, argon, etc.) to companies in the automotive, chemicals, food and beverage, and health care industries. The US distribution arm of industrial gas provider Air Liquide, the company can, depending on its customers' needs, ship its product in cylinders or by pipelines, or it can manufacture onsite. It operates 200 locations throughout the US, including 100 manufacturing facilities. American Air Liquide also fulfills semiconductor companies' gas and liquid chemical requirements from their own fabrication plants.

An in-depth profile of this company is available to Hoover's Online members at hoovers.com.

111

AMERICAN AIRLINES FEDERAL CREDIT UNION

4151 Amon Carter Blvd.
Fort Worth, TX 76155
Phone: 817-963-6000
Fax: 817-963-6108
Web: www.aacreditunion.org

CEO: Angela (Angie) Owens
CFO: Eli Vazquez
HR: —
FYE: December 31
Type: Not-for-profit

American Airlines Federal Credit Union won't hassle you about the position of your tray table. The company, which operates branches in or near airports in about 20 cities in the US and Puerto Rico, provides standard financial services such as checking and savings accounts and credit cards to more than 200,000 members. It also sells investments and insurance. Its lending program consists of home mortgages and vehicle loans, education loans, and other personal loans. Also known as AA Credit Union, American Airlines Federal Credit Union was founded in 1936 by employees of American Airlines (now part of AMR Corporation) at Chicago's Midway Airport.

AMERICAN AMMUNITION, INC.

Pink Sheets: AAMU

3545 NW 71st St.
Miami, FL 33147
Phone: 305-835-7400
Fax: 305-694-0037
Web: www.a-merc.com

CEO: Andres F. Fernandez
CFO: Andres F. Fernandez
HR: —
FYE: December 31
Type: Public

Apple pie and ammo. American Ammunition makes small arms ammunition for commercial, law enforcement, and military use. The company, which markets itself as a low-cost ammo supplier, is a contractor for the US Department of Defense and sells its products to both domestic and international governmental agencies. The majority of components used in its assembly of finished pieces are made in-house. American Ammunition plans to boost production capacity over the next several years. Unlike most ammunition manufacturers, American Ammunition skips the distributor and sells directly to retailers through its proprietary system. The unique arrangement is part of what allows the company to sell its products at a discount.

AMERICAN APPAREL, INC.

NYSE Amex: APP

747 Warehouse St.
Los Angeles, CA 90021
Phone: 213-488-0226
Fax: 213-488-0334
Web: www.americanapparel.net

CEO: Dov Charney
CFO: Adrian Kowalewski
HR: Alejandra Flores
FYE: December 31
Type: Public

American Apparel wants you to be hip and comfortable inside and out. It designs and makes logo-free T-shirts, tank tops, yoga pants, and other items for men, women, and children — and does it all from its California-based factory, rather than exporting labor overseas. The company's brands include Classic Girl, Standard American, Classic Baby, and Sustainable Edition, among others. American Apparel boasts more than 280 retail stores located in about 20 countries. Riding the casual loungewear trend, the company is known for its no-sweat factory and the fair treatment of its workers, including up to $19 an hour pay for manufacturers. Sometimes-controversial Dov Charney founded American Apparel in 1997.

	Annual Growth	12/05	12/06	12/07	12/08	12/09
Sales ($ mil.)	20.2%	—	—	387.0	545.0	558.8
Net income ($ mil.)	(73.4%)	—	—	15.5	14.1	1.1
Market value ($ mil.)	(54.5%)	—	—	1,070.1	142.0	221.2
Employees	21.3%	—	—	6,800	9,700	10,000

AMERICAN AUTOMOBILE ASSOCIATION

1000 AAA Dr.
Heathrow, FL 32746
Phone: 407-444-7000
Fax: 407-444-7380
Web: www.aaa.com

CEO: Robert L. Darbelnet
CFO: John Schaffer
HR: —
FYE: December 31
Type: Not-for-profit

This isn't your great-grandfather's American Automobile Association (AAA). The not-for-profit organization is best known for providing emergency roadside assistance to its members. AAA is extending its reach into other areas, however, such as offering a variety of financial and travel-arrangement services (foreign currency exchange and travelers checks), as well. The organization offers its members credit cards, insurance, and vehicle financing. AAA operates travel agencies and publishes maps and travel guides, to boot. AAA and its affiliated 70-odd auto clubs maintain about 1,100 facilities to serve more than 50 million members that span the US and Canada. AAA was founded in 1902.

AMERICAN AXLE & MANUFACTURING HOLDINGS, INC.

NYSE: AXL

1 Dauch Dr.
Detroit, MI 48211
Phone: 313-758-2000
Fax: 313-758-4257
Web: www.aam.com

CEO: Richard F. (Rick) Dauch
CFO: Michael K. Simonte
HR: John E. Jerge
FYE: December 31
Type: Public

American Axle & Manufacturing (AAM) is GM's right-hand man for driveline systems and forged products. AAM manufactures axles, driveshafts, and chassis components, mainly for light trucks and SUVs, but also for cars and crossover vehicles. Axles and driveshafts account for about three-quarters of AAM's sales; chassis components, forged products, and other components make up the rest. The Tier 1 supplier gets more than three-quarters of its business from GM; other customers include PACCAR, Chrysler, Harley-Davidson, VW, and Ford. The company also sells to other Tier 1 suppliers such as Hino Motors and Jatco Ltd. Almost two-thirds of AAM's products are sold in North America.

	Annual Growth	12/05	12/06	12/07	12/08	12/09
Sales ($ mil.)	(18.1%)	3,387.3	3,191.7	3,248.2	2,109.2	1,521.6
Net income ($ mil.)	—	56.0	(222.5)	37.0	(1,224.3)	(253.1)
Market value ($ mil.)	(18.7%)	1,309.5	1,356.6	1,330.2	206.5	572.9
Employees	(12.3%)	11,000	10,000	9,800	7,250	6,500

AMERICAN BANK HOLDINGS, INC.

OTC: ABKH

4800 Montgomery Ln., 10th Fl.
Bethesda, MD 20814
Phone: 301-572-3740
Fax: 301-572-1601
Web: www.americanfsb.com

CEO: James E. Plack
CFO: John M. Wright
HR: —
FYE: December 31
Type: Public

American Bank Holdings owns American Bank, which has about five branches in Maryland and Washington, DC, plus another in Columbus, Ohio. The bank offers traditional deposit services such as checking, savings, and money market accounts and certificates of deposit. Its loan portfolio consists largely of one- to four-family residential mortgages and loans for construction and land development. The bank also offers commercial mortgages, business loans, auto loans, and lease financing, and a lower number of unsecured consumer loans. American Bank bought Columbus, Ohio-based Grange Bank from Grange Mutual Casualty Company in 2007. It is now buying four Baltimore-area branches from BCSB Bancorp.

AMERICAN BANK INCORPORATED

OTC: AMBK

4029 W. Tilghman St.
Allentown, PA 18104
Phone: 610-366-1800
Fax: 610-289-3326
Web: www.pcbanker.com

CEO: Mark W. Jaindl
CFO: Harry C. Birkhimer
HR: —
FYE: December 31
Type: Public

American Bank Incorporated is the holding company for American Bank, which operates a single branch in Allentown, Pennsylvania. It serves customers throughout the US via its pcbanker.com Web site. The bank's products and services include checking and savings accounts, money market accounts, CDs, credit cards, and discount brokerage. It primarily originates real estate loans; commercial mortgages account for more than 40% of the company's portfolio, while residential mortgages represent approximately one third. The Jaindl family, including company president and CEO Mark, owns a majority of American Bank Incorporated.

	Annual Growth	12/05	12/06	12/07	12/08	12/09
Assets ($ mil.)	—	—	—	—	—	504.1
Net Income ($ mil.)	—	—	—	—	—	3.9
Employees	—	—	—	—	—	48

AMERICAN BAR ASSOCIATION

321 N. Clark St.
Chicago, IL 60610
Phone: 312-988-5000
Fax: 312-988-5177
Web: www.abanet.org

CEO: Stephen N. Zack
CFO: Alice E. Richmond
HR: –
FYE: August 31
Type: Association

The American Bar Association (ABA) doesn't have anything to do with alcohol, except maybe defending drunken drivers. The group seeks to promote improvements in the American justice system and develop guidelines for the advancement of the legal profession and education. It provides law school accreditation, continuing education, legal information, and other services to assist legal professionals. Its roster of more than 400,000 members includes judges, court administrators, law professors, and nonpracticing lawyers. All lawyers in good standing with any US state or territory bar are eligible for membership. The ABA cannot discipline lawyers, nor can it enforce its rules; it can only develop guidelines.

AMERICAN BEVERAGE CORPORATION

1 Daily Way
Verona, PA 15147
Phone: 412-828-9020
Fax: 412-828-8876
Web: www.ambev.com

CEO: Kevin McGahren-Clemens
CFO: —
HR: —
FYE: December 31
Type: Subsidiary

American Beverage Corporation (ABC) produces bottled cocktail mixes, fruit drinks and bottled water. The company is made up of two divisions: Daily's (fruit drinks and mixers) and Twin Mountain (bottled water). Its fruit-drink brand names include Hugs, Too Tarts, and Liquid Lizard and its water brands include Glacial Ice and Twin Mountain (fruit drinks and water account for 70% of ABC's sales). The company also produces Daily's cocktail mixers (30% of sales). Its beverage products are distributed throughout the US and Canada, as well as in the Caribbean. American Beverage is a subsidiary of Dutch food giant Koninklijke Wessanen.

	Annual Growth	12/04	12/05	12/06	12/07	12/08
Est. sales ($ mil.)	—	—	—	—	—	114.3
Employees	—	—	—	—	—	550

AMERICAN BILTRITE, INC.

NYSE Amex: ABL

57 River St.
Wellesley Hills, MA 02481
Phone: 781-237-6655
Fax: 781-237-6880
Web: www.americanbiltriteinc.com

CEO: Roger S. Marcus
CFO: Howard N. Feist III
HR: Bonnie Posnak
FYE: December 31
Type: Public

American Biltrite has its hand in several different pots, some of which are sticky. Its tape division manufactures adhesive-coated, pressure-sensitive tapes and films used to protect materials during handling and storage, as well as for applications in the heating, ventilation, and air conditioning, automotive, and electrical industries. The company also designs and distributes wholesale jewelry and accessories to specialty and department stores through its K&M subsidiary, while its AB Canada subsidiary makes floor tile and rubber products. Its Congoleum unit, which makes resilient sheet and tile flooring, filed for Chapter 11 bankruptcy protection in 2003 amidst a large number of asbestos-related lawsuits.

	Annual Growth	12/05	12/06	12/07	12/08	12/09
Sales ($ mil.)	(8.8%)	445.2	435.5	420.7	375.1	307.9
Net income ($ mil.)	—	(17.6)	0.7	(2.0)	(29.0)	(12.2)
Market value ($ mil.)	(36.2%)	37.3	31.6	17.2	6.2	6.2
Employees	(9.6%)	1,650	1,590	1,500	1,300	1,100

AMERICAN BIO MEDICA CORPORATION

Pink Sheets: ABMC

122 Smith Rd.
Kinderhook, NY 12106
Phone: 518-758-8158
Fax: 518-758-8171
Web: www.americanbiomedica.com

CEO: Stan Cipkowski
CFO: Stefan Parker
HR: —
FYE: December 31
Type: Public

There's a thin line between employment and unemployment, and that line might just be on one of American Bio Medica's drug-testing kits. The company's Rapid Drug Screen products indicate within minutes the presence in a urine sample of such illegal substances as marijuana, cocaine, amphetamines, and opiates. Used by employers, law enforcement agencies, hospitals, schools, and other institutions, the tests offer up to 10-panel options (each panel tests for different substances). The company's Rapid One is a line of single-drug specific tests; its Rapid Tec and Rapid TOX products detect multiple drug classes on one panel. American Bio Medica also offers saliva-based tests for law enforcement customers.

	Annual Growth	12/05	12/06	12/07	12/08	12/09
Sales ($ mil.)	(7.1%)	13.0	13.8	13.9	12.7	9.7
Net income ($ mil.)	—	(0.4)	0.2	(1.0)	(0.9)	(0.9)
Market value ($ mil.)	(44.0%)	24.1	19.6	21.3	5.2	2.4
Employees	(4.4%)	115	131	124	99	96

AMERICAN BRIDGE COMPANY

1000 American Bridge Way
Coraopolis, PA 15108
Phone: 412-631-1000
Fax: 412-631-2000
Web: www.americanbridge.net

CEO: Robert H. (Bob) Luffy
CFO: Pamela A. Bena
HR: Tonilynn Parks
FYE: December 31
Type: Private

American Bridge Company spans the nation's modern industrial age. The firm provides general contracting, engineering, and subcontracting services to transportation, infrastructure, military, and industrial markets in North and South America. It manufactures, erects, and rehabilitates all manner of bridges, including cable-supported, movable, steel truss, and steel and concrete arch structures. American Bridge also specializes in near-shore marine facilities, security infrastructure, military and government buildings, and sports arenas and stadia. It manufactures structural steel and precast concrete bridge components and specialized equipment for bridge construction, as well.

An in-depth profile of this company is available to Hoover's Online members at hoovers.com.

113

AMERICAN BUILDERS & CONTRACTORS SUPPLY CO., INC.

1 ABC Pkwy.	CEO: David A. Luck
Beloit, WI 53511	CFO: Kendra A. Story
Phone: 608-362-7777	HR: Kim Hendricks
Fax: 608-362-2717	FYE: December 31
Web: www.abc-supply.com	Type: Private

American Builders & Contractors Supply Co. (better known as ABC Supply) has put roofs over millions of heads. A leading supplier of roofing, siding, windows, gutters, doors, and other exterior building products, ABC Supply operates about 350 outlets in 45 states and the District of Columbia. The company carries its own brand of products under the Amcraft name, as well as offering products from outside vendors. ABC Supply markets its products to builders and professional contractors. The family-owned business was founded in 1982 by the late Ken Hendricks, the son of a roofer. In May 2010 ABC Supply agreed to acquire New Jersey-based rival Bradco Supply.

	Annual Growth	12/04	12/05	12/06	12/07	12/08
Sales ($ mil.)	10.1%	2,042.0	2,597.0	2,990.0	2,630.0	3,000.0
Employees	8.9%	4,128	5,144	5,431	5,243	5,800

AMERICAN BUREAU OF SHIPPING INC.

16855 Northchase Dr.	CEO: Robert D. Somerville
Houston, TX 77060	CFO: Jeff Weiner
Phone: 281-877-5800	HR: —
Fax: 281-877-5803	FYE: December 31
Web: www.eagle.org	Type: Not-for-profit

One of the world's largest ship classification societies, American Bureau of Shipping (ABS) offers inspection and analysis services to verify that vessels are mechanically and structurally fit. The not-for-profit company's surveyors examine ships in major ports throughout the world, assessing whether the vessels comply with ABS rules for design, construction, and maintenance. Additionally, its engineers consult with shipbuilders on proposed designs and repairs. The not-for-profit company operates from more than 200 offices in about 70 countries. For-profit subsidiaries ABS Group offers risk management consulting services, while ABS Nautical Systems provides fleet management software. ABS was founded in 1862.

AMERICAN BUSINESS BANK

OTC: AMBZ

523 W. 6th St., Ste. 900	CEO: Donald P. (Don) Johnson
Los Angeles, CA 90014	CFO: Wesley E. (Wes) Schaefer
Phone: 213-430-4000	HR: Renee Moore
Fax: 213-627-2784	FYE: December 31
Web: www.americanbusinessbank.com	Type: Public

What's a middle-market, closely held, owner-managed business gotta do to get *FORTUNE* 500 treatment from a bank? American Business Bank caters to private companies in Southern California with annual sales between $5 million and $200 million, with an emphasis on wholesalers, manufacturers, service businesses, not-for-profit organizations, and professionals. It has offices in Irvine, Los Angeles, Ontario, Torrance, and Woodland Hills. The bank's commercial lending services include commercial real estate loans (more than half of its portfolio), asset-based lending, equipment finance, construction loans, and revolving lines of credit. Its deposit products consist of checking, savings, and money market accounts, and CDs.

AMERICAN CAMPUS COMMUNITIES, INC.

NYSE: ACC

805 Las Cimas Pkwy., Ste. 400	CEO: William C. Bayless Jr.
Austin, TX 78746	CFO: Jonathan A. Graf
Phone: 512-732-1000	HR: —
Fax: 512-732-2450	FYE: December 31
Web: www.studenthousing.com	Type: Public

American Campus Communities (ACC) actually does most of its business off campus. The self-managed real estate investment trust (REIT) owns and operates student housing properties in more than 20 states. Its holdings are located at or near colleges and universities. It leases the ground for on-campus properties from the schools, which in turn receive half of the net cash flow from these properties. Additionally, ACC provides leasing and management services for other student housing owners. In all, the REIT manages about 130 properties at or near 85 colleges and universities containing more than 85,000 beds. It also works with schools to develop and renovate student housing.

	Annual Growth	12/05	12/06	12/07	12/08	12/09
Sales ($ mil.)	37.2%	87.5	119.0	147.1	235.4	309.6
Net income ($ mil.)	—	9.7	22.6	(1.7)	(13.1)	(12.5)
Market value ($ mil.)	3.2%	1,297.4	1,489.4	1,404.7	1,071.4	1,470.1
Employees	27.4%	828	897	1,084	2,301	2,183

⊞ AMERICAN CANCER SOCIETY, INC.

250 Williams St., Ste. 600	CEO: John R. Seffrin
Atlanta, GA 30303	CFO: Catherine E. Mickle
Phone: 404-320-3333	HR: Laura Reeves
Fax: 404-982-3677	FYE: August 31
Web: www.cancer.org	Type: Not-for-profit

The American Cancer Society (ACS) seeks to end cancer suffering. Dedicated to the elimination of cancer, the not-for-profit organization is staffed by professionals and more than 2 million volunteers at some 3,400 local units across the country. ACS is the largest source of private cancer research funds in the US. Recipients of the society's funding include more than 40 Nobel Prize laureates. In addition to research, the ACS supports detection, treatment, and education programs. The organization encourages prevention efforts with programs such as the Great American Smokeout. Patient services include moral support, transportation to and from treatment, and camps for children who have cancer.

AMERICAN CAPITAL AGENCY CORP.

NASDAQ (GM): AGNC

2 Bethesda Metro Center, 14th Fl.	CEO: Malon Wilkus
Bethesda, MD 20814	CFO: John R. Erickson
Phone: 301-968-9300	HR: —
Fax: —	FYE: December 31
Web: www.agnc.com	Type: Public

American Capital Agency is taking on the rocky real estate market. The real estate investment trust (REIT) was created in 2008 to invest in securities backed by single-family residential mortgages and collateralized mortgage obligations guaranteed by government agencies Fannie Mae, Freddie Mac, and Ginnie Mae. The company is externally managed and advised by American Capital Agency Management, a subsidiary of US publicly traded alternative asset manager American Capital, which spun off American Capital Agency in 2008, but retained about a 33% stake in the REIT.

	Annual Growth	12/05	12/06	12/07	12/08	12/09
Sales ($ mil.)	163.0%	—	—	—	66.0	173.6
Net income ($ mil.)	235.0%	—	—	—	35.4	118.6
Market value ($ mil.)	24.3%	—	—	—	571.6	710.2
Employees	—	—	—	—		

AMERICAN CAPITAL, LTD.

NASDAQ (GS): ACAS

2 Bethesda Metro Center, 14th Fl.
Bethesda, MD 20814
Phone: 301-951-6122
Fax: 301-654-6714
Web: www.american-capital.com

CEO: Malon Wilkus
CFO: John R. Erickson
HR: Lionel Ferguson
FYE: December 31
Type: Public

Whether you make musical instruments or mints, salon appliances or safes, this company has a strategy for you. Founded in 1986, American Capital invests in middle-market companies both directly and through its global asset management business. It typically provides up to $100 million per transaction to companies for management and employee buyouts and private equity buyouts. The firm also directly provides capital to companies. Other investments include financial products such as commercial mortgage-backed securities. American Capital's portfolio consists of stakes in more than 185 companies and has a focus on manufacturing, services, and distribution.

	Annual Growth	12/05	12/06	12/07	12/08	12/09
Sales ($ mil.)	5.9%	554.5	860.0	1,240.0	1,051.0	697.0
Net income ($ mil.)	—	364.9	895.0	700.0	(3,115.0)	(910.0)
Market value ($ mil.)	(45.3%)	9,232.8	11,795.3	8,404.1	826.1	828.7
Employees	(3.8%)	308	484	580	384	264

AMERICAN CARESOURCE HOLDINGS, INC.

NASDAQ (CM): ANCI

5429 LBJ Freeway, Ste. 850
Dallas, TX 75240
Phone: 972-308-6830
Fax: 972-980-2560
Web: www.anci-care.com

CEO: David S. Boone
CFO: Matthew D. Thompson
HR: —
FYE: December 31
Type: Public

American CareSource mends the connection between medical plan sponsors and supplemental health care providers. Operating through its Ancillary Care Services subsidiary, the company negotiates contracts with more than 2,500 providers of supplemental health care (i.e., rehabilitation, hospice, laboratory, infusion, and other services); in turn, the company offers insurance companies and other health benefit administrators access to a vast network of reduced-cost supplemental care services. American CareSource's clients include preferred provider organizations (PPOs), health maintenance organizations (HMOs), third-party administrators, and self-insured employers. The company's roots go back to the mid-1990s.

	Annual Growth	12/05	12/06	12/07	12/08	12/09
Sales ($ mil.)	98.5%	4.4	11.4	23.5	58.3	68.3
Net income ($ mil.)	—	(2.4)	(1.3)	(0.8)	3.6	2.3
Market value ($ mil.)	(18.6%)	89.7	30.3	52.5	115.6	39.3
Employees	16.5%	38	33	38	59	70

AMERICAN CAST IRON PIPE COMPANY

1501 31st Ave. North
Birmingham, AL 35207
Phone: 205-325-7701
Fax: 205-325-8014
Web: www.acipco.com

CEO: Van L. Richey
CFO: J. M. Cook
HR: Leann Barr
FYE: December 31
Type: Private

American Cast Iron Pipe Co. (ACIPCO) operates one of the largest ductile iron pipe casting plants in the world. Its divisions — including American Centrifugal, American Ductile Iron Pipe, American Flow Control, and American Steel Pipe — make ductile iron pipe and fittings, cast steel tubes, electric resistance welded steel pipes, fire hydrants and fire truck pumps, and valves for water treatment and energy production. Other ACIPCO units make molded rubber products for the water utility industry and spiral-welded steel pipe. John Joseph Eagan founded ACIPCO in 1905, and in 1922 placed all of the company's stock into a trust for employees.

AMERICAN CENTURY COMPANIES, INC.

4500 Main St.
Kansas City, MO 64111
Phone: 816-531-5575
Fax: 816-340-7962
Web: www.americancentury.com

CEO: Jonathan S. Thomas
CFO: Barry Fink
HR: —
FYE: December 31
Type: Private

American Century Companies is actually closer to the half-century mark, but who's counting? The company, through its American Century Investments subsidiary, oversees mutual funds covering a range of styles including fixed income, value, quantitative, US growth, and international growth. It even has series of funds that support cancer research. The company's brokerage services offer investors access to additional mutual funds from other firms. American Century manages some $85 billion of client assets in accounts for individuals, corporations, charitable organizations, and retirement plans. It has offices in Missouri, California, and New York, as well as international offices in London and Hong Kong.

	Annual Growth	12/04	12/05	12/06	12/07	12/08
Est. sales ($ mil.)	—	—	—	—	—	249.6
Employees	—	—	—	—	—	1,837

AMERICAN CHEMICAL SOCIETY

1155 16th St., NW
Washington, DC 20036
Phone: 202-872-4600
Fax: 202-872-4615
Web: www.acs.org

CEO: Madeleine Jacobs
CFO: Brian A. Bernstein
HR: —
FYE: December 31
Type: Not-for-profit

This group has a lot of chemistry. With more than 154,000 members, the American Chemical Society (ACS) is the world's largest scientific society. It provides information, career development, and educational resources to member chemists, chemical engineers, and technicians. ACS also publishes dozens of magazines, journals, and books, and its Chemical Abstracts Service provides access to an online database of more than 25 million literature and research summaries from around the world. ACS also serves as an advocate for its members on public policy issues. The ACS Member Insurance Program provides insurance plans to members. The not-for-profit organization was founded in 1876 and chartered by Congress in 1937.

AMERICAN CITY BUSINESS JOURNALS, INC.

120 W. Morehead St., Ste. 400
Charlotte, NC 28202
Phone: 704-973-1000
Fax: 704-973-1001
Web: www.acbj.com

CEO: Whitney Shaw
CFO: Kirk Shaw
HR: —
FYE: December 31
Type: Subsidiary

Both big and small cities can turn to this company for coverage of business news. American City Business Journals (ACBJ) is a leading newspaper publisher that serves more than 500,000 subscribers with local business news through more than 40 publications. Its bizjournals subsidiary also publishes news and information online for more than 3.5 million registered users. In addition, ACBJ owns *The Sporting News*, one of the top sports magazines in the US, and Hemmings Motor News, a publisher of collectible-car books and magazines. Its Street & Smith's Sports Group publishes several sports publications including *SportsBusiness Journal*. ACBJ is a unit of newspaper and magazine publisher Advance Publications.

An in-depth profile of this company is available to Hoover's Online members at hoovers.com.

115

AMERICAN CIVIL CONSTRUCTORS HOLDINGS, INC.

225 Union Blvd., Ste. 500
Lakewood, CO 80228
Phone: 303-989-5508
Fax: 303-986-0746
Web: www.acconstructors.com

CEO: Jeffrey D. (Jeff) Rudolph
CFO: —
HR: —
FYE: December 31
Type: Holding company

American Civil Constructors (ACC) provides heavy and light civil construction services, including new work and reconstruction and rehabilitation of bridges, tunnels, and highways. It also works on right-of-way reclamation projects, design/build landscape projects, drainage and public works landscaping, and sports fields and golf courses. As part of its growth and expansion strategy the company actively seeks firms to acquire. ACC operates through a dozen offices in California, Colorado, Texas, and Washington.

AMERICAN CIVIL LIBERTIES UNION

125 Broad St., 18th Fl.
New York, NY 10004
Phone: 212-549-2500
Fax: 212-549-2646
Web: www.aclu.org

CEO: Anthony D. Romero
CFO: Alma Montclair
HR: —
FYE: March 31
Type: Not-for-profit

The philosopher Socrates once said, "I am that gadfly which God has given the state." While the American Civil Liberties Union (ACLU) might have a quarrel with the "God" part, the group has at times proved a stinging critic in its efforts to defend individual rights. It acts as a legal and legislative advocate in matters related to civil liberties and the Bill of Rights. The ACLU has participated in such cases as the 1925 Scopes trial (challenged a ban on teaching evolution), *Brown v. Board of Education* (school desegregation), *Roe v. Wade* (abortion rights), and *Romer v. Evans* (gay and lesbian rights). The group, which has more than 500,000 members, has offices throughout the US. It was founded in 1920.

	Annual Growth	3/04	3/05	3/06	3/07	3/08
Est. sales ($ mil.)	—	—	—	—	—	67.6
Employees	—	—	—	—	—	170

AMERICAN COMMERCE SOLUTIONS, INC.

OTC: AACS

1400 Chamber Dr.
Bartow, FL 33830
Phone: 863-533-0326
Fax: 863-533-0327
Web: www.aacssymbol.com

CEO: Daniel L. (Dan) Hefner
CFO: Frank D. Puissegur
HR: —
FYE: February 28
Type: Public

Holding company American Commerce Solutions (ACS), through its International Machine and Welding subsidiary, provides specialized machining and repair services for heavy equipment used in the agricultural, construction, forestry, mining, and scrap industries. Its Chariot Manufacturing Company subsidiary (which includes Chariot Trailers) manufactures open and enclosed trailers to carry motorcycles. ACS also sells aftermarket repair parts. The company also has a strategic relationship with American Fiber Green Products. The Mosaic Company generates about 36% of sales.

	Annual Growth	2/06	2/07	2/08	2/09	2/10
Sales ($ mil.)	0.0%	2.3	2.4	2.9	2.6	2.3
Net income ($ mil.)	—	(0.9)	(1.5)	(1.0)	(1.2)	0.7
Market value ($ mil.)	(48.5%)	4.8	3.7	2.3	0.6	0.3
Employees	(12.9%)	33	26	33	23	19

AMERICAN COMMERCIAL LINES INC.

NASDAQ (GS): ACLI

1701 E. Market St.
Jeffersonville, IN 47130
Phone: 812-288-0100
Fax: 812-288-1766
Web: www.aclines.com

CEO: Michael P. (Mike) Ryan
CFO: Thomas R. Pilholski
HR: Richard W. (Rich) Spriggle
FYE: December 31
Type: Public

One of the mightiest on the mighty Mississippi, barge operator American Commercial Lines (ACL) navigates the inland waterways of the US. ACL is a leading barge transporter of dry bulk commodities including alumina, cement, fertilizers, salt, coal, grain, and steel. It also transports liquid bulk cargo such as chemicals, ethanol, and petroleum products. ACL's fleet consists of about 1,765 covered dry cargo barges, 384 open dry cargo barges, and 361 tank barges, powered by 125 towboats. In addition to transportation, its Jeff-boat subsidiary designs and manufactures inland and ocean service vessels for ACL and other customers, while its Elliott Bay Design Group (EBDG) provides marine engineering.

	Annual Growth	12/05	12/06	12/07	12/08	12/09
Sales ($ mil.)	3.4%	741.4	942.6	1,050.4	1,196.8	846.0
Net income ($ mil.)	—	11.8	92.3	44.4	48.0	(12.1)
Market value ($ mil.)	(25.9%)	776.6	1,677.9	831.9	251.0	234.7
Employees	(1.1%)	2,689	2,795	3,000	3,431	2,572

AMERICAN COMMUNITY MUTUAL INSURANCE COMPANY

39201 Seven Mile Rd.
Livonia, MI 48152
Phone: 734-591-9000
Fax: 734-591-4628
Web: www.american-community.com

CEO: Michael E. Tobin
CFO: Steve Clarren
HR: Leslie J. Gola
FYE: December 31
Type: Mutual company

American Community Mutual Insurance would like to maintain the health and well-being of America's communities. American Community provides group and individual health care plans and life insurance plans in over a dozen states throughout the Midwest and Southwest. The company's offerings include PPO, short-term health, dental, vision, and prescription plans. American Community also offers health savings accounts. Focusing largely on the small to midsized employer group market, the company insures more than 165,000 individuals. The company distributes its products through a force of 14,000 independent agents. American Community was founded in 1938; it was the first health care insurance provider in Michigan.

	Annual Growth	12/04	12/05	12/06	12/07	12/08
Est. sales ($ mil.)	—	—	—	—	—	343.2
Employees	—	—	—	—	—	475

AMERICAN CRYSTAL SUGAR COMPANY

101 N. 3rd St.
Moorhead, MN 56560
Phone: 218-236-4400
Fax: 218-236-4422
Web: www.crystalsugar.com

CEO: David Berg
CFO: Thomas S. Astrup
HR: —
FYE: August 31
Type: Cooperative

Call it saccharine, but for American Crystal Sugar, business is all about sharing. This sugar-beet cooperative is owned by some 2,800 growers in the Red River Valley of North Dakota and Minnesota who farm more than one-half million owned and contracted acres of cropland. American Crystal, formed in 1899 and converted into a co-op in 1973, divides the 35-mile-wide valley into five districts, each served by a processing plant. The plants produce sugar, molasses, and beet pulp. American Crystal's products are sold internationally to industrial users and to retail and wholesale customers under the Crystal name, as well as under private labels through marketing co-ops United Sugars and Midwest Agri-Commodities.

	Annual Growth	8/05	8/06	8/07	8/08	8/09
Sales ($ mil.)	5.6%	965.5	1,005.7	1,222.2	1,232.8	1,200.2
Net income ($ mil.)	9.5%	373.3	445.1	601.4	542.7	536.2
Employees	0.6%	1,337	1,306	1,380	1,361	1,369

AMERICAN DAIRY QUEEN CORPORATION

7505 Metro Blvd.
Minneapolis, MN 55439
Phone: 952-830-0200
Fax: 952-830-0227
Web: www.dairyqueen.com

CEO: John Gainor
CFO: James S. Simpson
HR: Angela Rud
FYE: December 31
Type: Subsidiary

This company is a royal figure among ice cream fans. American Dairy Queen is a leading franchisor of quick service restaurants specializing in frozen treats, with about 5,000 Dairy Queen outlets located throughout the US. Along with ice cream, its menu also includes burgers, hot dogs, chicken, salads and sweet eats, including DQ cakes, pies, sundaes, cones, and Blizzard treats. The Dairy Queen chain was founded in 1938. American Dairy Queen is the domestic franchising arm of International Dairy Queen (IDQ), which also franchises DQ Orange Julius outlets and Karmelkorn popcorn stands. IDQ is owned by Warren Buffet's Berkshire Hathaway.

	Annual Growth	12/04	12/05	12/06	12/07	12/08
Est. sales ($ mil.)	—	—	—	—	—	91.5
Employees	—	—	—	—	—	2,000

AMERICAN DENTAL ASSOCIATION

211 E. Chicago Ave.
Chicago, IL 60611
Phone: 312-440-2500
Fax: 312-440-7494
Web: www.ada.org

CEO: John S. Findley
CFO: Edward Leone Jr.
HR: —
FYE: December 31
Type: Association

Four out of five dentists recommend the ADA to their peers who join organizations. The American Dental Association is the oldest and largest dental association in the world representing more than 155,000 dentists (nearly four out of five). The ADA provides information on oral health, promotes dental science, and conducts research, development, and testing on dental products and materials. If products are up to the organization's standards, they are allowed to carry the ADA Seal of Acceptance. In 2006 the ADA launched the Professional Product Review (PPR) for products used by dental professionals. The ADA was founded in 1859 by 26 representatives from dental societies around the country.

	Annual Growth	12/04	12/05	12/06	12/07	12/08
Est. sales ($ mil.)	—	—	—	—	—	121.6
Employees	—	—	—	—	—	475

AMERICAN DENTAL PARTNERS, INC.

NASDAQ (GS): ADPI

401 Edgewater Place, Ste. 430
Wakefield, MA 01880
Phone: 781-224-0880
Fax: 781-224-4216
Web: www.amdpi.com

CEO: Gregory A. Serrao
CFO: Breht T. Feigh
HR: —
FYE: December 31
Type: Public

Helping dentists focus on drilling (and not billing) is the mission of American Dental Partners. The company provides management and support services for the growing group practice segment of the dental care industry. Through long-term service agreements, the company manages about 25 general and specialty dental practice groups operating some 250 dental facilities in 18 states, mainly in the eastern and midwestern US. Its services include planning and budgeting, facilities development and management, scheduling, training, recruiting, economic analysis, financial reporting, and quality assurance.

	Annual Growth	12/05	12/06	12/07	12/08	12/09
Sales ($ mil.)	8.6%	196.9	217.9	278.8	291.1	274.3
Net income ($ mil.)	(7.0%)	10.3	11.1	(7.7)	30.1	7.7
Market value ($ mil.)	(8.1%)	284.4	297.1	157.8	109.2	202.7
Employees	4.1%	2,197	2,347	3,418	2,531	2,585

AMERICAN DERRINGER CORPORATION

127 N. Lacy Dr.
Waco, TX 76715
Phone: 254-799-9111
Fax: 254-799-7935
Web: www.amderringer.com

CEO: Elizabeth Saunders
CFO: Elizabeth Saunders
HR: Elizabeth Saunders
FYE: December 31
Type: Private

American Derringer owner Elizabeth Saunders is a real pistol. She stars in her own ads clad in a bustier while brandishing her signature handgun and the company's best-seller, the Lady Derringer. The tiny pistol of Wild West fame fits a petite palm with its faux ivory grip engraved with the image of a Victorian lady. American Derringer peddles a variety of pistols and accessories, such as holsters, perfume, scarves, and ties. The gun manufacturer targets women in need of a shooting iron and collectors looking for an item with a history. Company founder Robert Saunders hired Elizabeth for his sales staff. They married, and when he died in 1993, she took over the company.

	Annual Growth	12/04	12/05	12/06	12/07	12/08
Est. sales ($ mil.)	—	—	—	—	—	0.5
Employees	—	—	—	—	—	8

AMERICAN DIABETES ASSOCIATION

1701 N. Beauregard St.
Alexandria, VA 22311
Phone: 703-549-1500
Fax: 703-739-9346
Web: www.diabetes.org

CEO: Laurence W. (Larry) Hausner
CFO: Debbie Johnson
HR: Don Laing
FYE: June 30
Type: Not-for-profit

The American Diabetes Association (ADA) lives for the day when it has no customers, but for now seeks to serve the more than 20 million children and adults in the US who have the disease. It is a not-for-profit research, information, and advocacy organization that is working to prevent and cure diabetes as well as to improve the lives of people affected by diabetes. The ADA has operations in all 50 states and Washington, DC. America's Walk for Diabetes is the group's main fund-raiser; others include the Tour de Cure (cycling), School Walk for Diabetes, and Kiss-A-Pig, to honor the pig for its role in discovering the effectiveness of insulin in controlling diabetes. The ADA was founded in 1940.

	Annual Growth	6/04	6/05	6/06	6/07	6/08
Est. sales ($ mil.)	—	—	—	—	—	233.8
Employees	—	—	—	—	—	838

AMERICAN EAGLE OUTFITTERS, INC.

NYSE: AEO

77 Hot Metal St.
Pittsburgh, PA 15203
Phone: 412-432-3300
Fax: 412-432-3955
Web: www.ae.com

CEO: James V. (Jim) O'Donnell
CFO: Joan H. Hilson
HR: Thomas A. (Tom) DiDonato
FYE: January 31
Type: Public

It was once a purveyor of outdoor gear, but American Eagle Outfitters now feathers its nest with polos and khakis. The mall-based retailer sells casual apparel and accessories (shirts, jeans, shorts, sweaters, skirts, footwear, belts, bags) aimed at men and women ages 15-25. The chain operates about 1,100 stores in all 50 US states, Puerto Rico, Canada, and now in the Middle East. Virtually all of the company's products bear its private-label brand names: American Eagle Outfitters, aerie, 77kids, and (for now) MARTIN + OSA. Direct sales come from the company's website and its *AE* magazine, a lifestyle publication that doubles as a catalog.

	Annual Growth	1/06	1/07	1/08	1/09	1/10
Sales ($ mil.)	6.7%	2,309.4	2,794.4	3,055.4	2,988.9	2,990.5
Net income ($ mil.)	(12.9%)	294.2	387.4	400.0	179.1	169.0
Market value ($ mil.)	(3.1%)	3,760.0	6,768.9	4,803.8	1,883.5	3,321.7
Employees	14.4%	23,000	27,600	38,700	37,500	39,400

An in-depth profile of this company is available to Hoover's Online members at hoovers.com.

117

THE AMERICAN EDUCATION CORPORATION

Pink Sheets: AECC

7506 N. Broadway Extension, Ste. 505
Oklahoma City, OK 73116
Phone: 405-840-6031
Fax: 405-848-3960
Web: www.amered.com

CEO: Jeffrey E. Butler
CFO: Neil R. Johnson
HR: Grant Aguirre
FYE: December 31
Type: Public

The American Education Corporation (AEC) has edification aspirations for the nation's teens and their younger siblings. The educational software maker's primary offering is its A+nyWhere Learning System software line, which includes titles providing instruction in reading and writing, as well as math, science, history, geography, and language arts for K-12 students. AEC's system includes a learning management application that helps teachers monitor student performance. Some 10,000 schools have used the company's software, which AEC also sells to adult literacy centers, junior and community colleges, and correctional facilities.

AMERICAN ELECTRIC POWER COMPANY, INC.

NYSE: AEP

1 Riverside Plaza
Columbus, OH 43215
Phone: 614-716-1000
Fax: 614-716-1823
Web: www.aep.com

CEO: Michael G. (Mike) Morris
CFO: Brian X. Tierney
HR: —
FYE: December 31
Type: Public

American Electric Power (AEP) takes its slice of the US power pie out of Middle America. The holding company is one of the largest power generators and distributors in the US. AEP owns the nation's largest electricity transmission system, a network of almost 39,000 miles. Its electric utilities serve 5.2 million customers in 11 states and have about 39,000 MW of largely coal-fired generating capacity. AEP is a top wholesale energy company; it markets and trades electricity, natural gas, and other commodities and has stakes in independent power plants. Other operations include natural gas transportation, storage, and processing, and barge transportation services.

	Annual Growth	12/05	12/06	12/07	12/08	12/09
Sales ($ mil.)	2.7%	12,111.0	12,622.0	13,380.0	14,440.0	13,489.0
Net income ($ mil.)	6.7%	1,056.0	1,002.0	1,168.0	1,380.0	1,370.0
Market value ($ mil.)	(1.6%)	17,761.4	20,390.4	22,296.4	15,936.9	16,660.0
Employees	2.5%	19,630	20,442	20,861	21,912	21,673

AMERICAN ELECTRIC TECHNOLOGIES, INC.

NASDAQ (CM): AETI

6410 Long Dr.
Houston, TX 77087
Phone: 713-644-8182
Fax: 713-644-7805
Web: www.aeti.com

CEO: Charles M. Dauber
CFO: John H. Untereker
HR: Rachel Acree
FYE: December 31
Type: Public

American Electric Technologies (AETI) tames wild and woolly wiring. The company makes power-delivery distribution systems that control the flow of electricity. Its systems are sold primarily to oil and gas industry customers including Exxon Mobil, Chevron, and Transocean. It also serves municipal power companies and industrial users Honeywell and HP. AETI's American Access makes zone-cabling cabinets that streamline distribution of telephone lines, data networking, security systems, and other cable and wire. The company's Omega Metals subsidiary fabricates precision sheet metal and provides assembling and packaging, while its Technical Products and Services division makes low- and medium-voltage switchgears.

	Annual Growth	12/05	12/06	12/07	12/08	12/09
Sales ($ mil.)	57.9%	8.4	8.4	55.7	65.4	52.2
Net income ($ mil.)	—	(0.2)	0.0	0.6	1.7	0.7
Market value ($ mil.)	(29.4%)	70.5	35.2	31.0	14.3	17.5
Employees	33.7%	100	100	569	401	320

AMERICAN ENTERPRISE DEVELOPMENT

Pink Sheets: AEND

2544 Tarpley Rd., Ste. 104
Carrollton, TX 75006
Phone: 972-266-0225
Fax: 972-418-8558
Web: www.havocenergy.com

CEO: Carey K. Williams
CFO: Luther (Bud) Reynolds
HR: —
FYE: December 31
Type: Public

American Enterprise Development Corporation knows there's value in creating havoc. After completing a reverse merger with HAVOC Distribution, the company does business through HAVOC Energy Drink, a developer and marketer of energy drinks. The company has affiliations with universities and collegiate conferences, professional sports franchises, and corporate alliances. It has licensing agreements with professional sports teams such as the Dallas Stars and the Florida Panthers, as well as collegiate sports conferences, including the Gulf South Conference and the Horizon League. Among its corporate alliances is the Golf Club at McKinney in McKinney, Texas.

AMERICAN ENTERPRISE MUTUAL HOLDING COMPANY

601 6th Ave.
Des Moines, IA 50309
Phone: 515-245-2000
Fax: 515-247-2435
Web: www.americanrepublic.com

CEO: Michael E. Abbott
CFO: Sarah Jane Roy
HR: —
FYE: December 31
Type: Holding company

Like any good parent, American Enterprise Mutual Holding (AEMHC) prefers to focus on the activities of its family. The company is parent to American Republic Insurance Company (ARIC) and World Insurance Company. While ARIC offers major medical, long-term care, life, and related insurance products, its sister company World Insurance sticks to just medical and dental coverage. Both companies sell to individual customers through some 30,000 career and independent agents across the US. AEMHC was created from the 2004 merger of American Republic Mutual Holding with World Mutual Holding.

AMERICAN EQUIPMENT COMPANY, INC.

2106 Anderson Rd.
Greenville, SC 29611
Phone: 864-295-7800
Fax: 864-295-7843
Web: www.ameco.com

CEO: Gary C. Bernardez
CFO: Bill Shalkham
HR: Jane Davis
FYE: December 31
Type: Subsidiary

With American Equipment Company (AMECO), the fleet is always in. The industrial fleet outsourcer supplies construction equipment (backhoes, forklifts, compressors, cranes, lifts, trucks) and other supplies for mining, construction, government, and industrial markets. It also provides a selection of construction-site services, such as equipment maintenance, mobile-office installation, and site clean-up. It serves customers primarily in the oil and gas, mining, energy, and infrastructure industries. Founded in 1947 as part of Daniel Construction and incorporated as AMECO in 1971, the company is a subsidiary and fleet management and construction support unit of Fluor, a construction and engineering giant.

	Annual Growth	12/04	12/05	12/06	12/07	12/08
Est. sales ($ mil.)	—	—	—	—	—	823.2
Employees	—	—	—	—	—	1,230

AMERICAN EQUITY INVESTMENT LIFE HOLDING

NYSE: AEL

5000 Westown Pkwy., Ste. 440
West Des Moines, IA 50266
Phone: 515-221-0002
Fax: 515-221-9947
Web: www.american-equity.com

CEO: Wendy L. Carlson
CFO: John M. Matovina
HR: —
FYE: December 31
Type: Public

Seeking to save? American Equity Investment Life Holding Company issues and administers fixed rate and index annuities through subsidiaries American Equity Investment Life Insurance and American Equity Investment Life Insurance Company of New York. Licensed in 50 states and the District of Columbia, the company sells its products through more than 52,000 independent agents and 70 national marketing associations. American Equity Investment Life targets individuals between the ages of 45 to 75. The company also offers a variety of whole, term, and universal life insurance products.

	Annual Growth	12/05	12/06	12/07	12/08	12/09
Assets ($ mil.)	11.0%	14,042.8	14,990.1	16,394.4	17,087.8	21,312.0
Net income ($ mil.)	12.3%	43.0	75.5	29.0	20.8	68.5
Market value ($ mil.)	(13.1%)	763.2	762.1	484.8	409.4	435.1
Employees	7.5%	270	280	290	330	360

AMERICAN EUROCOPTER LLC

2701 Forum Dr.
Grand Prairie, TX 75052
Phone: 972-641-0000
Fax: 972-641-3550
Web: www.eurocopterusa.com

CEO: Marc Paganini
CFO: Romain Trapp
HR: Audrey Elliott
FYE: December 31
Type: Subsidiary

You've heard of *An American In Paris*? Well, how about a Eurocopter in America? American Eurocopter is the US-based arm of European helicopter giant Eurocopter, itself a subsidiary of aerospace conglomerate EADS. American Eurocopter's primary offerings include Eurocopter helicopter repair and overhaul services, spares and parts support, technical publications, and maintenance training services. It also provides manufacturing, completion, and final assembly for A-Star AS350 helicopters and provides customization services for Eurocopter EC120, EC135, EC145, and EC155 helicopter models.

AMERICAN EXPRESS CENTURION BANK

6985 Union Park Center, Ste. 235
Midvale, UT 84047
Phone: 801-945-3000
Fax: —
Web: www.americanexpress.com

CEO: Kenneth I. (Ken) Chenault
CFO: —
HR: —
FYE: December 31
Type: Subsidiary

When in Rome, do as the Romans do; when using your American Express card, do what American Express Centurion Bank allows you to do. A subsidiary of credit card and travel giant American Express, the company issues and services its parent company's revolving credit cards, including the Blue, Blue Cash, and Blue Sky cards. (Revolving cards carry no annual fees, but levy finance charges on revolving balances.) The bank also issues consumer charge cards, raising funds for all of its lending activities by selling short- and medium-term debt and securitized assets. It offers CDs to retail and institutional customers as well. The company mainly markets its cards via direct mail, the Internet, and television.

	Annual Growth	12/04	12/05	12/06	12/07	12/08
Est. sales ($ mil.)	—	—	—	—	—	259.6
Employees	—	—	—	—	—	120

AMERICAN EXPRESS COMPANY

NYSE: AXP

World Financial Center, 200 Vesey St.
New York, NY 10285
Phone: 212-640-2000
Fax: —
Web: www.americanexpress.com

CEO: Kenneth I. (Ken) Chenault
CFO: Daniel T. (Dan) Henry
HR: L. Kevin Cox
FYE: December 31
Type: Public

American Express makes money even if you do leave home without it. The company is one of the world's largest travel agencies, but it is better known for its charge cards and revolving credit cards. And yes, the company still issues traveler's checks and publishes such magazines as *Food & Wine* and *Travel + Leisure* through its American Express Publishing unit. Its travel agency operations have thousands of locations worldwide, and its Travelers Cheque Group is the world's largest issuer of traveler's checks. But the company's charge and credit cards are its bread and butter; American Express has some 88 million cards in circulation worldwide.

	Annual Growth	12/05	12/06	12/07	12/08	12/09
Assets ($ mil.)	2.2%	113,960.0	127,853.0	149,830.0	126,074.0	124,088.0
Net income ($ mil.)	(13.1%)	3,734.0	3,707.0	4,012.0	2,699.0	2,130.0
Market value ($ mil.)	(5.8%)	61,816.9	72,880.5	62,489.6	22,283.4	48,675.1
Employees	(3.0%)	65,800	65,400	67,700	66,000	58,300

AMERICAN FAMILY MUTUAL INSURANCE COMPANY

6000 American Pkwy.
Madison, WI 53783
Phone: 608-249-2111
Fax: 608-243-4921
Web: www.amfam.com

CEO: David R. Anderson
CFO: Daniel R. Schultz
HR: Daniel J. Kelly
FYE: December 31
Type: Mutual company

Even confirmed bachelors can get insured through American Family Insurance. The company specializes in property/casualty insurance, but also offers life and health coverage, as well as investment and retirement-planning products. The company operates in about 20 states, primarily in the midwestern and western US. It is among the largest US mutual companies that concentrate on auto insurance (State Farm is the biggest). American Family Insurance also provides coverage for homeowners and farmers, as well as restaurants, contractors, and other businesses. Through the company's consumer finance division, agents can also offer their customers home equity and personal lines of credit.

	Annual Growth	12/05	12/06	12/07	12/08	12/09
Sales ($ mil.)	(1.7%)	6,820.6	6,789.4	6,867.9	6,742.6	6,360.1
Net income ($ mil.)	(21.4%)	671.5	24.4	82.4	(297.9)	256.9
Employees	(1.2%)	8,135	8,237	8,482	8,071	7,745

AMERICAN FARMERS & RANCHERS MUTUAL INSURANCE COMPANY

800 N. Harvey
Oklahoma City, OK 73102
Phone: 405-218-5400
Fax: 405-218-5587
Web: www.americanfarmersandranchers.com

CEO: Terry Detrick
CFO: Bobby Green
HR: —
FYE: December 31
Type: Mutual company

American Farmers & Ranchers Mutual Insurance wanted to become more inclusive, hence its change from the former company name, Oklahoma Farmers Union Mutual Insurance. The company offers personal property/casualty and life insurance coverage including homeowners, farm liability, and automobile in the southern and western US. It also sells commercial insurance tailored for small businesses. Despite the name change, the company still primarily serves customers in Oklahoma. Some 200 agencies throughout the state sell American Farmers & Ranchers Mutual's products. The insurance company was founded in 1905.

	Annual Growth	12/04	12/05	12/06	12/07	12/08
Est. sales ($ mil.)	—	—	—	—	—	92.7
Employees	—	—	—	—	—	240

AMERICAN FIBER GREEN PRODUCTS INC.

Pink Sheets: AFBG

4209 Raleigh St.
Tampa, FL 33619
Phone: 813-247-2770
Fax: 813-677-7168
Web: americanfibergreenproducts.com

CEO: Daniel L. (Dan) Hefner
CFO: Michael A. Freid
HR: —
FYE: December 31
Type: Public

The recycled fiberglass molding to be made by American Fiber Green Products will come in more colors than green. American Fiber Green Products announced plans in 2008 to build the first fiberglass recycling plant in the US. Its subsidiaries, including American Leisure Products and Chariot Manufacturing, will incorporate the recycled resin products into their manufacturing process to build such products as picnic tables, park benches, trailers, boats, and vehicle bodies for replicas of vintage cars. American Fiber Green Products is working on other uses to circumvent fiberglass away from landfills. Company president and CEO Dan Hefner also holds those positions for American Commerce Solutions.

AMERICAN FIDELITY ASSURANCE COMPANY

2000 N. Classen Blvd.
Oklahoma City, OK 73106
Phone: 405-523-2000
Fax: 405-523-5421
Web: www.afadvantage.com

CEO: William M. (Bill) Cameron
CFO: Robert (Bob) Brearton
HR: Jeanette M. Rice
FYE: December 31
Type: Private

American Fidelity Assurance (AFA) provides voluntary supplemental life and health insurance products and related services to more than 1 million customers across the US and in about 30 countries. The company's insurance plans include cancer, disability, life, long term care, and hospitalization insurance. The company also provides tax deferred annuity and flexible spending programs. It has tailored units to serve primary and secondary education employees and trade association members. Products and services are sold via worksite marketing by the company's salaried sales force and a network of insurance brokers. AFA is a subsidiary of American Fidelity Corporation, which is owned by the founding Cameron family.

	Annual Growth	12/04	12/05	12/06	12/07	12/08
Est. sales ($ mil.)	—	—	—	—	—	360.6
Employees	—	—	—	—	—	1,250

AMERICAN FINANCIAL GROUP, INC.

NYSE: AFG

1 E. 4th St.
Cincinnati, OH 45202
Phone: 513-579-2121
Fax: 513-412-0200
Web: www.afginc.com

CEO: S. Craig Lindner
CFO: Keith A. Jensen
HR: —
FYE: December 31
Type: Public

American Financial Group (AFG) insures American businessmen in pursuit of the great American Dream. Through the Great American Insurance Group of companies and its flagship Great American Insurance Company, AFG offers commercial property/casualty insurance focused on specialties such as workers' compensation, professional liability, ocean and inland marine, and multiperil crop insurance. The company also provides surety coverage for contractors and risk management services. For individuals and employers AFG provides supplemental medical insurance products, and a wide range of annuities sold through its Great American Financial Resources (GAFRI) subsidiary.

	Annual Growth	12/05	12/06	12/07	12/08	12/09
Assets ($ mil.)	5.0%	22,816.0	25,101.1	25,807.5	26,427.5	27,683.3
Net income ($ mil.)	26.6%	206.6	453.4	383.2	195.8	530.7
Market value ($ mil.)	(0.6%)	2,840.3	3,993.5	3,211.7	2,544.4	2,774.6
Employees	3.1%	6,100	5,200	500	600	6,900

AMERICAN FOODS GROUP, LLC

2209 Jefferson St., Ste. 301
Alexandria, MN 56308
Phone: 320-759-5900
Fax: 320-159-5910
Web: www.americanfoodsgroup.com

CEO: Thomas J. (Tom) Rosen
CFO: Robert Hovde
HR: —
FYE: December 31
Type: Private

American Foods Group is a *bona fide* Green Bay packer. With facilities in that Wisconsin city, as well as in Ohio, Nebraska, South Dakota, and Minnesota, the company slaughters cattle and produces branded and private-label beef products for the US retail grocery and foodservice industries, as well as for school lunch programs. Its products include fresh, frozen, and cooked meats as well as smoked and fresh sausage. The company's meat products are exported to 40 countries overseas. American Foods also has a canned pet food and pet treat business, Performance Pet Products (Performance Pet and Canine Cattle). The company is associated with agricultural holding company Rosen's Diversified Inc. (RDI).

AMERICAN FURNITURE MANUFACTURING, INC.

604 Pontotoc County Industrial Park Rd.
Ecru, MS 38841
Phone: 662-489-2633
Fax: 662-488-9558
Web: www.americanfurn.net/comersus/store/comersus_listCategories.asp

CEO: Michael (Mike) Thomas
CFO: Blair Taylor
HR: —
FYE: December 31
Type: Private

American Furniture Manufacturing (AFM) does most of its business at home. The company makes low-cost upholstered home furnishings, including sofas, chairs, and recliners, as well as accent tables. Its products are distributed to independent furniture stores in the US. AFM can ship most furniture within 48 hours, and delivery is handled by its American Furniture Trucking division, which maintains a fleet of trucks. The furniture maker sources wood and fabrics from the Asia/Pacific region, which has also helped to keep costs down. AFM is owned by investment firm Compass Diversified Holdings.

	Annual Growth	12/04	12/05	12/06	12/07	12/08
Est. sales ($ mil.)	—	—	—	—	—	42.7
Employees	—	—	—	—	—	800

AMERICAN FURNITURE WAREHOUSE CO., INC.

8820 American Way
Englewood, CO 80112
Phone: 303-799-9044
Fax: 720-873-8600
Web: www.afwonline.com

CEO: Jacob (Jake) Jabs
CFO: Bob Schwartz
HR: —
FYE: March 31
Type: Private

Tony the Tiger hawking home furnishings might give some marketers pause, but the combination seems to work for American Furniture Warehouse. The company sells furniture and electronics at discounted prices through a dozen retail locations in Colorado and via its Web site, which also features bridal and gift registries. American Furniture's television commercials often spotlight white-haired president and CEO Jake Jabs (who has become a well-known personality in the state as well as in the home furnishings industry) accompanied by baby exotic animals, mostly tigers. Jabs bought the company in 1975.

	Annual Growth	3/04	3/05	3/06	3/07	3/08
Est. sales ($ mil.)	—	—	—	—	—	330.5
Employees	—	—	—	—	—	1,650

AMERICAN FURUKAWA, INC.

47677 Galleon Drive
Plymouth, MI 48170
Phone: 734-446-2200
Fax: 734-446-2260
Web: www.americanfurukawa.com

CEO: Yukimasa Shiga
CFO: Yukimasa Shiga
HR: —
FYE: March 31
Type: Subsidiary

American Furukawa, Inc. (formerly named Furukawa Electric North America or FENA) is a subsidiary of Japan-based parent, the Furukawa Electric Co. In April 2009 American Furukawa, Inc. (AFI) was established to merge Furukawa Electric North America, Automotive Products Division, Inc. (FENA APD), and Furukawa America Inc. (FAI) to supply products for automotive, electronics, medical, and industrial applications in North America. Products include heat sinks and thermal solutions, memory disks for hard drives, wire harnesses, insulated wire, copper products, and magnet wire, to name a few. AFI's headquarters are now in Plymouth, Michigan.

AMERICAN GIRL BRANDS, LLC

8400 Fairway Place
Middleton, WI 53562
Phone: 608-836-4848
Fax: 608-836-1999
Web: www.americangirl.com

CEO: Ellen L. Brothers
CFO: Bill McAleer
HR: Ray Greger
FYE: December 31
Type: Subsidiary

Pleasant Rowland introduced American Girl dolls in 1986 as a historically-themed alternative to Barbie and the Cabbage Patch Kids. Since 1998 her firm has been owned by the maker of both rival dolls, #1 toy maker Mattel. American Girl (formerly Pleasant Company) makes the American Girls Collection of 18-inch, high-dollar dolls, including Addy (an escaped slave) and Rebecca Rubin (a young Jewish immigrant). It also publishes *American Girl* magazine and American Girl books (more than 127 million copies sold) and sells room décor, clothing, and accessories, including items that match the dolls. Items are sold through catalogs, its Web site, at American Girl Place stores, and an outlet store in Wisconsin.

	Annual Growth	12/04	12/05	12/06	12/07	12/08
Est. sales ($ mil.)	—	—	—	—	—	116.2
Employees	—	—	—	—	—	1,400

AMERICAN GOLF CORPORATION

2951 28th St.
Santa Monica, CA 90405
Phone: 310-664-4000
Fax: 310-664-4386
Web: www.americangolf.com

CEO: Paul Major
CFO: Mike Moecker
HR: Joe Stegman
FYE: December 31
Type: Private

You might say this company knows to stay out of the rough. American Golf Corporation (AGC) is one of the largest golf course management firms in the world with more than 110 public, private, and resort properties in more than 25 states. Its portfolio of courses includes such country clubs as The Golf Club at Mansion Ridge (Monroe, New York), Oakhurst Country Club (Clayton, California), and Palm Valley Country Club (Palm Desert, California). The company also runs the American Golf Foundation, which helps promote the game through charity and education. AGC is owned by investment firms Goldman Sachs and Starwood Capital.

AMERICAN GREETINGS CORPORATION

NYSE: AM

1 American Rd.
Cleveland, OH 44144
Phone: 216-252-7300
Fax: 216-252-6778
Web: corporate.americangreetings.com

CEO: Zev Weiss
CFO: Stephen J. Smith
HR: Brian T. McGrath
FYE: February 28
Type: Public

American Greetings has been building its sturdy house of cards for more than a century. The #2 US maker of greeting cards (behind Hallmark), the company makes American Greetings, Carlton Cards, and Gibson Greetings brand missives. While greeting cards make up about 70% of sales, the company also produces DesignWare party goods, Plus Mark gift wrap, and DateWorks calendars. The company's AG Interactive subsidiary distributes online greeting cards and other interactive media. American Greetings' products are sold through card and stationery stores, mass merchants, and other retail outlets worldwide. The family of chairman Morry Weiss controls about 45% of the company's voting stock.

	Annual Growth	2/06	2/07	2/08	2/09	2/10
Sales ($ mil.)	(3.5%)	1,885.7	1,744.6	1,776.5	1,690.7	1,635.9
Net income ($ mil.)	(0.8%)	84.4	42.4	83.0	(227.8)	81.6
Market value ($ mil.)	(2.4%)	829.3	924.2	743.9	147.4	753.8
Employees	(3.1%)	29,500	9,400	27,300	26,600	26,000

AMERICAN HEALTHCHOICE, INC.

Pink Sheets: AMHI

4300 Windsor Centre Trail, Ste. 100
Flower Mound, TX 75028
Phone: 817-837-8000
Fax: 817-837-8004
Web: www.americanhealthchoice.com

CEO: Joseph W. (Wes) Stucki
CFO: John C. Stuecheli
HR: —
FYE: September 30
Type: Public

American HealthChoice operates medical clinics, makes medical devices, and provides other health related services in the southeastern US. Its AHC Medical Clinics unit owns and operates eight medical clinics in Texas and Tennessee and provides support services to about 35 affiliated clinics. Through its TelmedCo unit, American HealthChoice offers telemedicine services, allowing doctors at its own and third-party clinics to get second opinions from remote specialists. A third unit, RehabCo, has developed the OmniBody Scan medical imaging system, which uses infrared technology to detect breast cancer and other conditions.

AMERICAN HEART ASSOCIATION, INC.

7272 Greenville Ave.
Dallas, TX 75231
Phone: 214-373-6300
Fax: 214-706-1191
Web: www.americanheart.org

CEO: Nancy A. Brown
CFO: Sunder Joshi
HR: —
FYE: June 30
Type: Not-for-profit

The American Heart Association (AHA) is a not-for-profit organization devoted to the fight against heart disease and stroke (both among the nation's top killers), and other cardiovascular illnesses. In addition to conducting research, the association serves as a clearinghouse for information on heart-related diseases and conditions and acts as an advocate on public policy issues related to its mission. The organization boasts a National Center in Dallas, as well as eight affiliate offices located throughout the US and in Puerto Rico. The AHA was founded in 1924 by six cardiologists, who recognized the need to widely share their heart disease education and research.

	Annual Growth	6/04	6/05	6/06	6/07	6/08
Est. sales ($ mil.)	—	—	—	—	—	641.6
Employees	—	—	—	—	—	3,500

An in-depth profile of this company is available to Hoover's Online members at hoovers.com.

121

AMERICAN HOME FOOD PRODUCTS, INC.

OTC: AHFP

500 W. 37th St.
New York, NY 10018
Phone: 212-239-1200
Fax: 212-239-1437
Web: www.artisanalcheese.com

CEO: Daniel W. Dowe
CFO: —
HR: —
FYE: May 31
Type: Public

American Home Food Products, which does business as Artisanal Cheese, aspires to be the big cheese. Formerly a building supply marketing firm, the company is now active in the marketing of private-label foods. In 2007 it acquired specialty food company Artisanal Premium Cheese for about $4.5 million. At the same time, the company sold its building material assets for approximately $1 million. Artisanal Cheese markets and sells specialty and handmade cheeses to upscale restaurants and retailers. In addition to wholesale and foodservice distribution, the company sells products in supermarkets, through catalogs, and on its website.

	Annual Growth	5/05	5/06	5/07	5/08	5/09
Sales ($ mil.)	131.1%	0.2	0.2	0.2	5.0	5.7
Net income ($ mil.)	—	(0.4)	(0.3)	(0.4)	(0.6)	(1.6)
Market value ($ mil.)	20.0%	3.3	2.9	4.8	7.1	6.9
Employees	125.8%	1	1	1	25	26

AMERICAN HOME SHIELD CORPORATION

889 Ridgelake Blvd.
Memphis, TN 38120
Phone: 901-537-8000
Fax: —
Web: www.americanhomeshield.com

CEO: Dave Crawford
CFO: —
HR: —
FYE: December 31
Type: Subsidiary

Protecting you against those pesky domestic disasters, American Home Shield (AHS), a subsidiary of The ServiceMaster Company, provides homeowners with home warranty plans. These cover the repair or replacement of electrical, plumbing, and heating and cooling systems; hot water heaters; and major home appliances. It administers more than 1.3 million contracts in 49 states and the District of Columbia. AHS's biggest sales channels are renewals (it has an approximately 60% retention rate) and contracts sold through real estate brokers; it also sells directly to consumers.

AMERICAN HOMEPATIENT, INC.

OTC: AHOM

5200 Maryland Way, Ste. 400
Brentwood, TN 37027
Phone: 615-221-8884
Fax: 615-373-9932
Web: www.ahom.com

CEO: Joseph F. Furlong III
CFO: Stephen L. Clanton
HR: Sandy Irvin
FYE: December 31
Type: Public

American HomePatient is making sure no one is home alone when it comes to health care. American HomePatient provides home health services from about 240 locations in more than 30 states. The company provides respiratory therapy and equipment, including oxygen therapy, sleep apnea systems, and nebulizers. It also offers home infusion therapy services, including feeding and intravenous drug administration. Additionally, American HomePatient rents and sells durable hospital equipment, including beds, wheelchairs, and other aids. American HomePatient has announced plans to restructure its debt by becoming a privately owned company.

	Annual Growth	12/05	12/06	12/07	12/08	12/09
Sales ($ mil.)	(7.9%)	328.4	328.1	293.0	266.9	236.3
Net income ($ mil.)	—	7.7	(2.6)	(5.5)	0.5	(12.8)
Market value ($ mil.)	(55.3%)	57.5	24.6	18.5	2.5	2.3
Employees	(5.6%)	2,955	2,576	2,586	2,398	2,348

AMERICAN HOMESTAR CORPORATION

Pink Sheets: AHMS

2450 South Shore Blvd., Ste. 300
League City, TX 77573
Phone: 281-334-9700
Fax: 281-334-9737
Web: www.americanhomestar.com

CEO: Finis F. (Buck) Teeter
CFO: Craig A. Reynolds
HR: —
FYE: June 30
Type: Public

Stormy weather in the manufactured housing market hasn't snowed American Homestar. The company produces factory-built, modular and multi-section and single-section manufactured homes that sell for about half the price of comparable site-built homes. Its modular homes range from 1,200 to 2,600 sq. ft.; its multisection homes can have as many as six bedrooms. American Homestar sells its homes through company-owned retail centers in the South and the Southeast, independent dealers, and through sales centers in manufactured housing communities. Other operations include insurance and mortgage services.

AMERICAN HONDA FINANCE CORPORATION

20800 Madronna
Torrance, CA 90503
Phone: 310-972-2200
Fax: 310-972-2244
Web: www.hondafinancialservices.com

CEO: Tetsuo Iwamura
CFO: Stephen E. Smith
HR: —
FYE: March 31
Type: Subsidiary

If you're fonda the idea of driving a Honda, you might want to call on American Honda Finance. Operating as Honda Financial Services, the company provides retail financing for Honda and Acura automobiles, motorcycles, power equipment, and parts and accessories throughout the US. The company's American Honda Service division administers service contracts, while Honda Lease Trust offers leases on new and used vehicles. Honda Financial Services also offers dealer financing and related dealer services. A subsidiary of American Honda Motor Co., the company began operating as a wholesale motorcycle finance provider in 1980.

	Annual Growth	3/04	3/05	3/06	3/07	3/08
Est. sales ($ mil.)	—	—	—	—	—	1,835.7
Employees	—	—	—	—	—	1,000

AMERICAN HONDA MOTOR CO., INC.

1919 Torrance Blvd.
Torrance, CA 90501
Phone: 800-999-1009
Fax: 310-783-3023
Web: corporate.honda.com

CEO: Tetsuo Iwamura
CFO: —
HR: —
FYE: March 31
Type: Subsidiary

American Honda Motor helps to find new homes for cars, trucks, motorcycles, engines, all-terrain vehicles, and power equipment in the US and abroad. The company is the North American sales, marketing, and distribution arm for Japan-based Honda Motor. Working in tandem with some 20 manufacturing plants, design centers, and research and development facilities in the US, the company also oversees the export of US-made Honda and Acura products. American Honda Motor came to the US in 1959 as the first Honda subsidiary to be established outside of Japan.

An in-depth profile of this company is available to Hoover's Online members at hoovers.com.

AMERICAN HOSPITAL ASSOCIATION

1 N. Franklin	CEO: Richard J. (Rich) Umbdenstock
Chicago, IL 60606	CFO: John Evans
Phone: 312-422-3000	HR: —
Fax: 312-422-4796	FYE: December 31
Web: www.aha.org	Type: Not-for-profit

The American Hospital Association (AHA) represents about 5,700 hospitals and other care providers and some 37,000 individuals from various health care fields. The AHA acts as an advocate in national health care policy development and provides services to its members, such as helping hospitals and other health care providers form networks for patient care, conducting research and development projects on the structuring and delivery of health care services, and producing educational programs and publications. The AHA Resource Center maintains an extensive collection of books and documents relating to hospitals and health care. AHA was founded in 1898.

	Annual Growth	12/04	12/05	12/06	12/07	12/08
Est. sales ($ mil.)	—	—	—	—	—	120.8
Employees	—	—	—	—	—	450

AMERICAN HOTEL REGISTER COMPANY

100 S. Milwaukee Ave.	CEO: Lawrence J. (Larry) Morse
Vernon Hills, IL 60061	CFO: —
Phone: 847-564-4000	HR: Julie Baker
Fax: 847-743-2098	FYE: December 31
Web: www.americanhotel.com	Type: Private

Intrigued by embossed soaps and other sundries enjoyed during your hotel visits? Thank American Hotel Register. The company supplies hotels of all sizes with more than 50,000 products, including toiletries, cleaning products, appliances, furniture, carpeting, drapery, linens, and embossed items. It also caters to funeral homes, health care facilities, government offices, and military institutions. American Hotel Register sells its products through its 2,000-page catalog and its Web site. The company was founded in 1865 to sell hotel guest registers. It was acquired by Thomas Leahy in the early 1900s and his descendants still own and operate the company.

AMERICAN INDEPENDENCE CORP.

NASDAQ (GM): AMIC

485 Madison Ave.	CEO: Roy T. K. Thung
New York, NY 10022	CFO: Teresa A. Herbert
Phone: 212-355-4141	HR: —
Fax: 212-644-7450	FYE: December 31
Web: www.americanindependencecorp.com	Type: Public

Since the name American Independence tells you nothing about the company, we'll help you out. What sounds like a lone, bold ideal is really a holding company which, through its subsidiaries, provides reinsurance, specializing in medical stop-loss insurance for self-insured employers. It also offers group and individual health and short-term medical insurance. Subsidiary Independence American is licensed to provide property/casualty insurance in more than 40 states and Washington, DC. American Independence is majority-owned by Independence Holding, which also owns Madison National Life Insurance and Standard Security Life Insurance.

	Annual Growth	12/05	12/06	12/07	12/08	12/09
Assets ($ mil.)	0.9%	129.7	134.8	146.1	130.6	134.4
Net income ($ mil.)	(12.7%)	5.5	1.5	1.1	1.0	3.2
Market value ($ mil.)	(20.7%)	97.7	91.9	77.0	23.2	38.7
Employees	(7.2%)	77	59	53	59	57

AMERICAN INFRASTRUCTURE, INC.

1805 Berks Rd.	CEO: A. Ross Myers
Worcester, PA 19490	CFO: William Murdock III
Phone: 610-584-6020	HR: —
Fax: 610-584-8205	FYE: December 31
Web: www.americaninfrastructure.com	Type: Private

Like any good parent, American Infrastructure provides balance and structure. Through subsidiaries Allan A. Myers and American Infrastructure-Virginia, the firm provides heavy civil construction services for projects in the Mid-Atlantic. It builds and reconstructs highways, water treatment plants, medical facilities, and shopping centers, and offers site development for homebuilders. Its Independence Construction Materials (ICM) subsidiary supplies aggregates, asphalt, and ready-mixed concrete to its construction companies. The family-run business was established in 1939 as Allan A. Myers and Son, a local hauling company in the suburbs of Philadelphia.

	Annual Growth	12/04	12/05	12/06	12/07	12/08
Est. sales ($ mil.)	—	—	—	—	—	484.9
Employees	—	—	—	—	—	2,045

▥ AMERICAN INTERNATIONAL GROUP, INC.

NYSE: AIG

70 Pine St.	CEO: Robert H. (Bob) Benmosche
New York, NY 10270	CFO: David L. Herzog
Phone: 212-770-7000	HR: Jeffrey J. Hurd
Fax: 212-509-9705	FYE: December 31
Web: www.aigcorporate.com	Type: Public

Even to this day American International Group (AIG) is one of the world's largest insurance firms. While it remains in the spotlight for staggering losses and government bailouts, the company's subsidiaries are still providing general property/casualty insurance, life insurance and retirement services, and other financial services to commercial, institutional, and individual customers in the US and more than 130 countries around the world. Some of its non-insurance activities include financing commercial aircraft leasing and port operations in the US. After $182 billion in bailouts, the US government holds more than 80% of the company, and its future and holdings remain in a state of flux.

	Annual Growth	12/05	12/06	12/07	12/08	12/09
Assets ($ mil.)	(0.2%)	853,370.0	979,414.0	1,060,505.0	860,418.0	847,585.0
Net income ($ mil.)	—	10,477.0	14,014.0	6,200.0	(99,289.0)	(12,313.0)
Market value ($ mil.)	(61.5%)	184,317.4	193,583.2	157,492.3	4,241.2	4,049.4
Employees	(0.3%)	97,000	106,000	116,000	116,000	96,000

AMERICAN INTERNATIONAL INDUSTRIES, INC.

NASDAQ (CM): AMIN

601 Cien St., Ste. 235	CEO: Daniel Dror
Kemah, TX 77565	CFO: Sherry L. Couturier
Phone: 281-334-9479	HR: —
Fax: 281-334-9508	FYE: December 31
Web: www.americanii.com	Type: Public

Nothing says Texas like oil and real estate. American International Industries (AII) covers those bases — and more — from its home in the Houston metro area. The company typically takes a controlling interest in undervalued companies; it holds investments in oil wells, real estate, and various industrial manufacturers. AII owns Delta Seaboard International (formerly Hammonds Industries), which operates technical services, fuel additives, and water treatment systems divisions. Its Northeastern Plastics subsidiary makes automotive after-market products. International Diversified Corporation (a firm connected with the brother of chairman and CEO Daniel Dror) owns 27% of the firm.

	Annual Growth	12/05	12/06	12/07	12/08	12/09
Sales ($ mil.)	0.2%	25.5	33.4	34.9	32.1	25.7
Net income ($ mil.)	—	(4.5)	1.6	(1.8)	8.4	(3.6)
Market value ($ mil.)	(26.0%)	43.5	36.5	39.9	18.9	13.0
Employees	6.8%	30	50	47	40	39

AMERICAN ITALIAN PASTA COMPANY

NASDAQ (GS): AIPC

4100 N. Mulberry Dr., Ste. 200
Kansas City, MO 64116
Phone: 816-584-5000
Fax: 816-584-5100
Web: www.aipc.com

CEO: John P. (Jack) Kelly
CFO: Paul R. Geist
HR: —
FYE: September 30
Type: Public

American Italian Pasta Company (AIPC) uses its noodle in many different ways. The company is the largest maker of dry pasta in North America, offering some 300 different pasta shapes (and 3,700 SKUs), everything from angel hair to ziti. Its consumer brands, such as Golden Grain, Heartland, and Mrs. Grass, are staples on supermarket shelves throughout the US, as well as overseas. The Kansas City, Missouri-based company's private-label customers include most major US grocers and club stores. It also serves the food ingredient sector, supplying companies with pasta products for use in food manufacturing.

	Annual Growth	9/05	9/06	9/07	9/08	9/09
Sales ($ mil.)	14.6%	364.2	367.0	398.1	569.2	628.2
Net income ($ mil.)	—	(100.2)	(30.4)	5.3	19.1	88.3
Market value ($ mil.)	27.4%	224.4	169.3	179.2	361.1	591.3
Employees	2.8%	604	620	651	665	675

AMERICAN LEARNING CORPORATION

NASDAQ (CM): ALRN

1 Jericho Plaza
Jericho, NY 11753
Phone: 516-938-8000
Fax: 516-938-0405
Web: www.interactivetherapygroup.com

CEO: Gary Gelman
CFO: Gary J. Knauer
HR: —
FYE: March 31
Type: Public

American Learning (formerly American Claims Evaluation) has undergone a transition. The company historically provided vocational rehabilitation and disability management services through its RPM Rehabilitation & Associates subsidiary; but in 2008 it sold those operations and got into the business of helping kids with developmental delays and disabilities. It acquired private New York-based Interactive Therapy Group Consultants, which provides comprehensive therapy services, including early intervention programs, preschool programs, and school staffing services, to developmentally delayed and disabled children, primarily in New York. Chairman, president, and CEO Gary Gelman owns two-thirds of the company.

	Annual Growth	3/05	3/06	3/07	3/08	3/09
Sales ($ mil.)	—	—	—	—	—	3.3
Net income ($ mil.)	—	—	—	—	—	(0.8)
Market value ($ mil.)	—	—	—	—	—	3.3
Employees	—	—	—	—	—	153

AMERICAN LEATHER

4501 Mountain Creek Pkwy.
Dallas, TX 75236
Phone: 972-296-9599
Fax: 972-296-8859
Web: www.americanleather.com

CEO: Bob Duncan
CFO: Mel Henson
HR: —
FYE: December 31
Type: Private

It may not be as American as apple pie, but American Leather hopes to make itself into a household name. The company, a manufacturer of custom-made leather and upholstered furniture, offers furnishing pieces such as sofas, sleepers, beds, recliners, chairs, and ottomans in more than a dozen styles (including traditional, transitional, and contemporary) and nearly 300 colors and textures. American Leather sells its products through independent retailers located throughout the US and has showrooms in Dallas, San Francisco, and High Point, North Carolina. It also makes exclusive styles for Crate & Barrel, Design Within Reach, and Room & Board. CEO Bob Duncan has a controlling interest in the company.

AMERICAN LEISURE CORPORATION

414 Airport Executive Park
Nanuet, NY 10954
Phone: 845-371-5670
Fax: 845-371-5680
Web: www.americanleisure.com

CEO: Steve Kass
CFO: Beth Caplan
HR: —
FYE: December 31
Type: Private

Just relax, American Leisure is on the job. The company designs, builds, and manages on-site physical fitness and recreational facilities for corporate clients, schools and universities, municipalities, and real estate developers. Services include planning, construction, installation, and management of facilities as well as marketing and ongoing staffing. The company has created private and corporate fitness centers, wellness and commercial spas, country clubs, and YMCAs for customers including Sheraton, Hilton, Starwood Hotels, Bulova, the NFL, and Avatar Holdings. American Leisure was founded in 1967 by CEO Steve Kass.

AMERICAN LOCKER GROUP INCORPORATED

Pink Sheets: ALGI

815 S. Main St.
Grapevine, TX 76051
Phone: 817-329-1600
Fax: —
Web: www.americanlocker.com

CEO: Allen E. Tilley
CFO: Paul M. Zaidins
HR: —
FYE: December 31
Type: Public

Ever carried around one of those orange plastic-capped locker keys at the theme park? That's American Locker Group. The company sells and rents coin-, key-, and electronically controlled lockers used by health clubs, amusement parks, ski resorts, bus stations, and employee locker rooms. Customers include SeaWorld, Vail Resorts, Walt Disney World, The UPS Store, and the University of Colorado. Postal mailboxes, such as those used by apartment complexes, make up about a third of sales. Besides the US, American Locker Group serves customers in Canada, Chile, Greece, India, Mexico, and the UK (less than 20% of sales in 2009). The company was founded in 1958.

	Annual Growth	12/05	12/06	12/07	12/08	12/09
Sales ($ mil.)	(21.1%)	32.3	25.1	20.2	14.1	12.5
Net income ($ mil.)	—	(8.1)	0.6	(1.9)	(2.7)	(0.4)
Market value ($ mil.)	(27.9%)	9.5	7.0	6.0	1.4	2.6
Employees	0.9%	132	147	126	117	137

AMERICAN MANAGEMENT ASSOCIATION INTERNATIONAL

1601 Broadway
New York, NY 10019
Phone: 212-586-8100
Fax: 212-903-8168
Web: www.amanet.org

CEO: Edward T. Reilly
CFO: Vivianna Guzman
HR: Manny Avramidis
FYE: December 31
Type: Not-for-profit

If you need a little bit of assistance managing your association, you might consider giving American Management Association a call. American Management Association (AMA) provides a variety of educational and management development services to businesses, government agencies, and individuals. The not-for-profit membership organization offers seminars, conferences, workshops, Webcasts, podcasts, and books in areas such as communication, leadership, project management, sales and marketing, human resources, and finance and accounting. AMA was founded in 1913 as the National Association of Corporation Schools; it became the American Management Association in 1923.

	Annual Growth	12/04	12/05	12/06	12/07	12/08
Est. sales ($ mil.)	—	—	—	—	—	54.0
Employees	—	—	—	—	—	580

AMERICAN MANAGEMENT SERVICES WEST LLC

Pier 70, 2801 Alaskan Way, Ste. 200
Seattle, WA 98121
Phone: 206-215-9700
Fax: 206-215-9777
Web: www.pinnaclerealty.com

CEO: Stan Harrelson
CFO: John L. Carrosino
HR: Jean Reynolds
FYE: December 31
Type: Private

With some help from American Management Services (operating as Pinnacle), real estate investors ensure their assets are in top form. Pinnacle provides property management and brokerage services for clients, which include financial institutions, foreign investors, government housing agencies, pension funds, and private partnerships. Its portfolio of properties — worth more than $18 billion — spans 250 cities across the US, as well as Asia and Canada. Its assets under management include about 185,000 apartment units and some 15 million sq. ft. of industrial, retail, and office space. Pinnacle also offers such services as customized financial reporting, risk management, recruitment, and technology planning.

⊞ AMERICAN MEDIA, INC.

1000 American Media Way
Boca Raton, FL 33464
Phone: 561-997-7733
Fax: —
Web: www.americanmediainc.com

CEO: David J. Pecker
CFO: Chris Polimeni
HR: Ken Slivken
FYE: March 31
Type: Private

These publications cover gossip and good health. American Media is the nation's top publisher of tabloid newspapers and magazines, including *National Enquirer* and *Star*. It also publishes women's health magazine *Shape*, as well as a number of other magazines such as *Flex*, *Men's Fitness*, and *Natural Health*. In addition to publishing, American Media offers distribution services to other publishers to get their periodicals in the racks at supermarkets throughout the US and Canada. American Media is owned by a group of investment firms including Angelo, Gordon & Co.

AMERICAN MEDICAL ALERT CORP.

NASDAQ (CM): AMAC

3265 Lawson Blvd.
Oceanside, NY 11572
Phone: 516-536-5850
Fax: 516-536-5276
Web: www.amacalert.com

CEO: Jack Rhian
CFO: Richard Rallo
HR: —
FYE: December 31
Type: Public

It's like having a guardian angel hovering above, but without the wings. American Medical Alert Corp (AMAC) provides health care communication and monitoring services. The company's Health Safety and Monitoring Services (HSMS) unit markets remote patient monitoring systems, including personal emergency response systems, health management and medication management systems, and safety monitoring systems. Its Telephony Based Communication Services (TBCS) unit provides telephone answering services and operates clinical trial recruitment call centers. Products are sold to consumers and health care facilities such as home care, hospice, pharmacy, managed care, and other health care organizations.

	Annual Growth	12/05	12/06	12/07	12/08	12/09
Sales ($ mil.)	15.2%	22.4	30.8	35.6	38.6	39.5
Net income ($ mil.)	34.0%	0.9	1.3	1.5	1.4	2.9
Market value ($ mil.)	1.7%	59.3	63.9	67.2	45.9	63.4
Employees	9.9%	389	531	580	528	567

AMERICAN MEDICAL ASSOCIATION

515 N. State St.
Chicago, IL 60610
Phone: 312-464-5000
Fax: 312-464-4184
Web: www.ama-assn.org

CEO: Michael D. Maves
CFO: Denise Hagerty
HR: Robert W. (Bob) Davis
FYE: December 31
Type: Association

The AMA knows whether there's a doctor in the house. The American Medical Association (AMA) prescribes the standards for the medical profession. The membership organization's activities include advocacy for physicians, promoting ethics standards in the medical community, and improving health care education. Policies are set by the AMA's House of Delegates, which is made up mainly of elected representatives. The AMA also publishes books and products for physicians, is a partner in the Medem online physician network, sells medical malpractice insurance, and helps doctors fight legal claims. The organization was founded in 1847 by a physician to establish a code of medical ethics. The AMA has some 236,000 members.

	Annual Growth	12/04	12/05	12/06	12/07	12/08
Sales ($ mil.)	1.1%	269.9	280.1	286.0	289.5	282.0
Net income ($ mil.)	—	—	—	25.2	50.3	(100.0)
Employees	1.8%	—	—	1,114	1,121	1,155

⊞ AMERICAN MEDICAL RESPONSE AMBULANCE SERVICE, INC.

6200 S. Syracuse Way, #200
Greenwood Village, CO 80111
Phone: 303-495-1200
Fax: 303-495-1295
Web: www.amr.net

CEO: William A. (Bill) Sanger
CFO: Timothy J. Dorn
HR: Kimberly Norman
FYE: December 31
Type: Subsidiary

Because driving yourself to the emergency room isn't always the best plan, there is American Medical Response (AMR). With thousands of vehicles in some 40 states, AMR is the largest contract provider of emergency and non-emergency ambulance services in the US. Non-emergency services include transportation for medically unstable patients and such non-medical transport services as transfers to and from health care facilities. The company provides around 4 million transports per year for customers that also include hospitals and local government agencies. AMR is a subsidiary of Emergency Medical Services, which is owned by Onex, an investment firm with holdings in health care and other industries.

AMERICAN MEDICAL SYSTEMS HOLDINGS, INC.

NASDAQ (GS): AMMD

10700 Bren Rd. West
Minnetonka, MN 55343
Phone: 952-930-6000
Fax: 952-930-6373
Web: www.americanmedicalsystems.com

CEO: Anthony P. (Tony) Bihl III
CFO: Mark A. Heggestad
HR: Janet L. Dick
FYE: December 31
Type: Public

American Medical Systems (AMS) aims to make life better for millions of patients afflicted with pelvic disorders. A leading maker of urological devices, AMS makes erectile dysfunction products such as inflatable penile implants, as well as urinary incontinence devices for men and women. Its other products treat such conditions as menorrhagia (excessive uterine bleeding), enlarged prostate, and fecal incontinence. AMS has around 60 international distributors in addition to a direct sales force of nearly 500 employees. Marketing efforts target urologists, gynecologists, colorectal surgeons, and other specialty physicians.

	Annual Growth	12/05	12/06	12/07	12/08	12/09
Sales ($ mil.)	18.6%	262.6	358.3	463.9	501.6	519.3
Net income ($ mil.)	21.2%	39.3	(49.3)	12.9	42.6	84.8
Market value ($ mil.)	2.0%	1,344.0	1,396.0	1,090.0	677.6	1,454.0
Employees	14.1%	720	1,095	1,239	1,205	1,221

⊞ An in-depth profile of this company is available to Hoover's Online members at hoovers.com.

125

AMERICAN MEDICAL TECHNOLOGIES, INC. OTC: ADLI

5655 Bear Ln.	CEO: Jeffrey (Jeff) Goodman
Corpus Christi, TX 78405	CFO: Barbara D. Woody
Phone: 361-289-1145	HR: —
Fax: 361-289-5554	FYE: December 31
Web: www.americanmedicaltech.com	Type: Public

American Medical Technologies (AMT) can get you a good deal on dental products. The company makes the Hydro Jet system, which removes tooth decay with a stream of tiny particles and water propelled by compressed air. However, as the market for the system has softened, AMT is increasingly focused on its role as a distributor or broker for products made by others. It uses its worldwide network of dealers and sales representatives to distribute the tooth-whitening products of Spectrum Dental, for instance, as well as crowns, bridges, dental head light systems, and other oral care products made by third parties.

AMERICAN MILLENNIUM CORPORATION, INC. Pink Sheets: AMCI

17301 W. Colfax Ave., Ste. 400	CEO: Bruce R. Bacon
Golden, CO 80401	CFO: David E. Welch
Phone: 303-279-2002	HR: —
Fax: 303-271-9777	FYE: July 31
Web: www.amc-wireless.com	Type: Public

American Millennium Corporation, Inc. (AMCi) can help you keep track of all your assets. The company offers hardware and software that tracks and monitors remote commercial or industrial assets, such as vehicles, oil-field equipment, and large tanks for fluids or gases. The company is a value-added reseller for the Transcore/Vistar GlobalWave and for the Globalstar Telecommunications SENS satellite communications systems. AMCi's product line includes the SatAlarm-Sentry, SatAlarm-Server, and SatAlarm-Watchdog. The company was established in 1979.

AMERICAN MUNICIPAL POWER-OHIO, INC.

2600 Airport Dr.	CEO: Marc S. Gerken
Columbus, OH 43219	CFO: Robert W. Trippe
Phone: 614-337-6222	HR: —
Fax: 614-337-6220	FYE: December 31
Web: www.amp-ohio.org	Type: Government-owned

American coal and water supplies the power for American Municipal Power-Ohio. The non-profit membership organization supplies wholesale power to 81 community-owned distribution utilities in Ohio, 27 in Pennsylvania, seven in Michigan, five in Virginia, two in West Virginia, and one in Kentucky. The power generation company, which is owned by its member municipalities, was formed in 1971. American Municipal Power-Ohio owns and operates a 213 MW coal-fired facility (Richard H. Gorsuch Generating Station), in Marietta, Ohio. The company also handles projects on behalf of the Ohio Municipal Electric Generating Agency (OMEGA) Joint Ventures program (jointly owned generation and transmission projects).

	Annual Growth	12/04	12/05	12/06	12/07	12/08
Est. sales ($ mil.)	—	—	—	—	—	596.5
Employees	—	—	—	—	—	229

AMERICAN NATIONAL BANKSHARES INC. NASDAQ (GS): AMNB

628 Main St.	CEO: Charles H. (Charlie) Majors
Danville, VA 24541	CFO: William W. Traynham
Phone: 434-792-5111	HR: Jeffrey V. Haley
Fax: 434-792-1582	FYE: December 31
Web: www.amnb.com	Type: Public

American National Bankshares wants to carry the deposits of its customers back to old Virginny and its American National Bank and Trust subsidiary. Founded in 1909, the bank operates about 20 branches and a loan office serving southern and central Virginia and north central North Carolina. It offers checking and savings accounts, CDs, IRAs, trust and investment services, and insurance. Its lending activities primarily consist of real estate loans: Commercial mortgages account for about one-third of the company's loan portfolio; residential mortgages, another quarter. The bank also originates construction, consumer, business, home equity, and land development loans.

	Annual Growth	12/05	12/06	12/07	12/08	12/09
Assets ($ mil.)	6.7%	623.5	777.7	772.3	789.2	809.0
Net income ($ mil.)	(9.2%)	10.0	11.4	11.4	8.0	6.8
Market value ($ mil.)	(1.5%)	142.4	142.8	122.3	104.1	134.1
Employees	2.0%	220	253	263	258	238

AMERICAN NATIONAL INSURANCE COMPANY NASDAQ (GS): ANAT

1 Moody Plaza	CEO: Robert L. Moody
Galveston, TX 77550	CFO: Stephen Pavlicek
Phone: 409-763-4661	HR: Carol Ann Kratz
Fax: 409-766-2912	FYE: December 31
Web: www.anico.com	Type: Public

You can't get much more American than this. Through subsidiaries, American National offers personal life insurance, as well as property and casualty insurance, annuities, supplemental health insurance, and other types of insurance throughout the US, Puerto Rico, and other territories. It also provides policies for US military personnel in Western Europe. The company's subsidiaries include Garden State Life Insurance, Standard Life and Accident Insurance, and Farm Family Holdings. The Securities Management and Research subsidiary provides investment advisory and manages mutual funds.

	Annual Growth	12/05	12/06	12/07	12/08	12/09
Assets ($ mil.)	3.6%	17,516.9	17,932.2	18,464.9	18,379.4	20,149.5
Net income ($ mil.)	(49.6%)	235.9	273.2	240.8	(154.0)	15.2
Market value ($ mil.)	0.5%	3,137.7	3,060.4	3,251.7	1,977.5	3,203.4
Employees	(7.8%)	4,439	4,439	—	2,150	3,211

🏛 THE AMERICAN NATIONAL RED CROSS

2025 E St. NW	CEO: Gail J. McGovern
Washington, DC 20006	CFO: Brian Rhoa
Phone: 202-303-4498	HR: Floyd W. Pitts
Fax: —	FYE: June 30
Web: www.redcross.org	Type: Not-for-profit

A specialist in dealing with events beyond its control, The American National Red Cross offers disaster relief, shelter, and other humanitarian services through more than 700 chapters nationwide. Although it was chartered by Congress in 1905, the American Red Cross isn't a government agency. The not-for-profit charitable organization relies on the efforts of about 1 million volunteers. Aside from helping victims of about 70,000 disasters large and small each year, the American Red Cross teaches CPR and first aid courses; provides support for US military personnel; and maintains some of the largest blood and plasma banks nationwide. The group is a member of the International Red Cross and Red Crescent Movement.

	Annual Growth	6/04	6/05	6/06	6/07	6/08
Sales ($ mil.)	0.9%	3,091.5	3,919.3	6,008.6	3,175.2	3,204.1
Net income ($ mil.)	—	34.2	445.1	539.4	38.7	(664.7)
Employees	0.0%	—	35,000	35,000	35,000	35,000

AMERICAN NATURAL ENERGY CORPORATION

TSX Venture: ANR

6100 S. Yale Ave., Ste. 300
Tulsa, OK 74136
Phone: 918-481-1440
Fax: 918-481-1473
Web: www.annrg.com

CEO: Michael K. Paulk
CFO: Steven P. Ensz
HR: —
FYE: December 31
Type: Public

American Natural Energy Corp. is not selling organic food and dietary supplements to boost metabolism, it is tapping into that other American natural energy source — hydrocarbons. Doing business as ANEC, the company is an oil and natural gas exploration and production company which focuses its operations on a property in St. Charles Parish, Louisiana. ANEC works in tandem with partner Exxon Mobil to develop this Louisiana project. In 2007 the company sold 75% of ANEC's development rights in this project to Dune Energy.

	Annual Growth	12/05	12/06	12/07	12/08	12/09
Sales ($ mil.)	(15.9%)	2.2	1.8	1.4	2.2	1.1
Net income ($ mil.)	—	(5.3)	(2.5)	(3.2)	(0.1)	24.0
Market value ($ mil.)	(17.6%)	8.7	12.8	4.7	2.0	4.0
Employees	(3.8%)	7	—	—	6	6

AMERICAN OIL & GAS, INC.

NYSE Amex: AEZ

1050 17th St., Ste. 2400
Denver, CO 80265
Phone: 303-991-0173
Fax: 303-595-0709
Web: www.americanoilandgasinc.com

CEO: Patrick D. (Pat) O'Brien
CFO: Joseph B. Feiten
HR: —
FYE: December 31
Type: Public

Deep in the heart of the North American continent lie untapped natural gas deposits, and American Oil & Gas is searching for them. The exploration and production company is focusing its efforts on the Rocky Mountains, a region with one of the largest underdeveloped natural gas fields in the US (the Bakken Shale formation). American Oil & Gas in 2009 reported that it had estimated proved reserves of about 64,420 barrels of oil, and 645.3 million cu. ft. of natural gas. The company is concentrating on developing its 68,000 net acre position in the Bakken and Three Forks plays in the Williston Basin in North Dakota.

	Annual Growth	12/05	12/06	12/07	12/08	12/09
Sales ($ mil.)	(20.3%)	4.7	3.8	2.0	2.9	1.9
Net income ($ mil.)	—	1.1	1.2	(2.7)	(23.5)	(10.3)
Market value ($ mil.)	0.9%	245.4	394.5	351.5	48.5	254.5
Employees	20.7%	8	13	15	17	17

AMERICAN PACIFIC CORPORATION

NASDAQ (GM): APFC

3883 Howard Hughes Pkwy., Ste. 700
Las Vegas, NV 89169
Phone: 702-735-2200
Fax: 702-735-4876
Web: www.apfc.com

CEO: Joseph (Joe) Carleone
CFO: Dana M. Kelley
HR: Linda G. Ferguson
FYE: September 30
Type: Public

American Pacific knows how to have a blast. The company's products launch rockets, propel missiles, deploy airbags, and suppress fires. Its largest unit also makes active pharmaceutical ingredients. American Pacific's specialty chemicals include ammonium perchlorate, a rocket fuel oxidizer; sodium azide, an airbag deployment chemical also used in pharmaceuticals; and Halotron, an ozone-friendly fire suppressant. The company also makes commercial packaged explosives, aerospace propulsion equipment for satellites, and environmental protection products.

	Annual Growth	9/05	9/06	9/07	9/08	9/09
Sales ($ mil.)	24.0%	83.3	141.9	183.9	203.1	197.1
Net income ($ mil.)	—	(11.2)	(3.9)	5.0	9.0	(6.0)
Market value ($ mil.)	6.6%	44.6	57.8	117.8	98.5	57.7
Employees	23.4%	254	485	487	530	589

AMERICAN PAD & PAPER LLC

3101 E. George Bush Hwy., Ste. 200
Richardson, TX 75082
Phone: 972-578-2000
Fax: 972-424-7493
Web: www.ampad.com

CEO: Donald Meltzer
CFO: Edward (Ed) Byrne
HR: Janine Adamski
FYE: December 31
Type: Subsidiary

Pssst! Wanna buy a pad? It's legal. American Pad & Paper (AMPAD) has been in the legal pad business for more than a century. Credited with designing the first legal pad in 1888, AMPAD manufactures and distributes more than 1,400 quality, paper-based office supply products. The offerings include subject and business notebooks, personal journals, filing products such as file folders, hanging folders, case and expanding files, all sizes of envelopes, and specialty papers for scrapbooking to small business exchanges. AMPAD's national brands and private label paper products supply North American retailers and distributors, including Staples and Wal-Mart. The company is owned by office products firm Esselte.

AMERICAN PHYSICIANS CAPITAL, INC.

NASDAQ (GS): ACAP

1301 N. Hagadorn Rd.
East Lansing, MI 48823
Phone: 517-351-1150
Fax: 517-351-7866
Web: www.apcapital.com

CEO: R. Kevin Clinton
CFO: Frank H. Freund
HR: —
FYE: December 31
Type: Public

American Physicians Capital (APCapital) helps doctors sleep more soundly at night. The company writes medical professional-liability insurance through subsidiary American Physicians Assurance Corporation. Operating principally in a handful of states in the Midwest, it concentrates on individual and small-group practices and has more than 9,000 policies in force. Other subsidiaries deal with income portfolio management, health care consulting, and physician and medical staff credential verification and review. Founded in 1975, the company was known as Mutual Insurance Corporation until 2000, when it was demutualized.

	Annual Growth	12/05	12/06	12/07	12/08	12/09
Assets ($ mil.)	(3.9%)	1,109.3	1,095.8	1,057.5	1,005.8	944.5
Net income ($ mil.)	(13.5%)	72.4	43.2	52.8	45.2	40.6
Market value ($ mil.)	7.3%	218.1	286.0	296.2	343.6	288.8
Employees	(2.7%)	162	164	167	162	145

AMERICAN PHYSICIANS SERVICE GROUP, INC.

NASDAQ (CM): AMPH

1301 S. Capital of Texas Hwy., Ste. C300
Austin, TX 78746
Phone: 512-328-0888
Fax: 512-314-4398
Web: www.amph.com

CEO: Kenneth S. (Ken) Shifrin
CFO: Mark J. Zimmerman
HR: —
FYE: December 31
Type: Public

Medical claims are nothing new; neither is the need for doctors to protect themselves against lawsuits. American Physicians Service Group is a liability insurance writer and provider for medical professionals through its wholly owned subsidiary American Physicians Insurance Company (API). It insures about 6,400 individual doctors and group practices primarily in Texas, but also in Arkansas and Oklahoma. Approximately 90% of its premiums are written through purchasing groups. The group sells its insurance products through independent agents and reinsurance brokers. About one-fifth of its premiums come from selling directly to policyholders.

	Annual Growth	12/05	12/06	12/07	12/08	12/09
Assets ($ mil.)	73.0%	33.5	36.3	282.8	283.6	299.8
Net income ($ mil.)	42.8%	5.5	3.2	21.0	19.2	22.9
Market value ($ mil.)	15.0%	90.6	109.9	137.7	147.7	158.4
Employees	(3.0%)	112	107	102	102	99

AMERICAN PLASTIC TOYS, INC.

799 Ladd Rd.	CEO: John Gessert
Walled Lake, MI 48390	CFO: James Grau
Phone: 248-624-4881	HR: Patricia Worden
Fax: 248-624-4918	FYE: December 31
Web: www.aptoys.net	Type: Private

If your child spends hours applying pretend makeup at her Enchanted Beauty Salon, or hammering away at his Build & Play Tool Bench, or digging in the sand with her Castle Pail of Toys, you can thank American Plastic Toys for the much-needed break. The company manufactures plastic toys, including doll accessories (strollers, nurseries), children's furniture, role-playing items (kitchen sets, tool benches), riding toys (trikes, wagons), seasonal toys (pail and shovel sets), and vehicles (dump trucks, airplanes). Products are sold by such retailers as Wal-Mart, Kmart, and Toys "R" Us across the US, as well as in Canada, the Caribbean, Central and South America, and Mexico. The company was founded in 1962.

	Annual Growth	12/04	12/05	12/06	12/07	12/08
Est. sales ($ mil.)	—	—	—	—	—	42.2
Employees	—	—	—	—	—	300

AMERICAN POOL ENTERPRISES, INC.

11515 Cronridge Dr., Ste. Q	CEO: Mitchell B. Friedlander
Owings Mills, MD 21117	CFO: Richard Naden
Phone: 443-471-1190	HR: —
Fax: 443-471-1189	FYE: March 31
Web: www.americanpool.com	Type: Subsidiary

American Pool Enterprises offers commercial swimming pool and recreational facility management services. The company maintains some 3,000 commercial swimming facilities and more than 7,000 residential pools. Besides its administrative staff, American Pool Enterprises employs about 5,000 lifeguards. Other services include new build construction, repair and renovation, and construction of fountains and water features. It operates through its more than 20 branches in the Eastern US, Texas, Nevada, California, and Canada. American Pool was founded in 1984 and is a subsidiary of FirstService Corporation.

AMERICAN PUBLIC EDUCATION, INC.   NASDAQ (GM): APEI

111 W. Congress St.	CEO: Wallace E. (Wally) Boston Jr.
Charles Town, WV 25414	CFO: Harry T. Wilkins
Phone: 304-724-3700	HR: Sharon van Wyk
Fax: 304-724-3780	FYE: December 31
Web: www.apus.edu	Type: Public

American Public Education promotes military intelligence. The company offers online postsecondary education to those in the military and other public servants such as police or firefighters. Its American Military University and American Public University make up the American Public University System, which offers more than 70 degree programs and nearly as many certificate programs in such disciplines as business administration, criminal justice, intelligence, technology, liberal arts, and homeland security. Enrollment in the online university consists of more than 42,000 part-time students from all 50 states and about 100 foreign countries. More than 80% of students serve in the US military or are veterans.

	Annual Growth	12/05	12/06	12/07	12/08	12/09
Sales ($ mil.)	51.6%	28.2	40.0	69.1	107.1	149.0
Net income ($ mil.)	115.9%	1.1	1.8	8.8	16.2	23.9
Market value ($ mil.)	(9.3%)	—	—	767.9	683.5	631.5
Employees	10.4%	660	798	910	1,180	980

AMERICAN RAILCAR INDUSTRIES, INC.   NASDAQ (GS): ARII

100 Clark St.	CEO: James A. (Jim) Cowan
St. Charles, MO 63301	CFO: Dale C. Davies
Phone: 636-940-6000	HR: —
Fax: 636-940-6030	FYE: December 31
Web: www.americanrailcar.com	Type: Public

American Railcar Industries (ARI) doesn't make the little engine that could, but it does make the cars that the engine pulls. A North American manufacturer of railcars and railcar components, the company also provides maintenance and fleet management services to freight shippers, railcar leasing companies, and railroads. Its two Arkansas manufacturing facilities make several types of railcars including covered hoppers for grains, cement, and other dry bulk and tank cars for liquid and gas commodities. The company also serves non-rail industries with industrial products such as steel and aluminum casting, machining, stamping, welding, and fabrication. Chairman and billionaire financier Carl Icahn owns 54% of ARI.

	Annual Growth	12/05	12/06	12/07	12/08	12/09
Sales ($ mil.)	(8.7%)	608.2	646.1	698.1	808.8	423.4
Net income ($ mil.)	1.2%	14.8	35.2	37.3	31.4	15.5
Market value ($ mil.)	(31.3%)	—	725.1	410.1	224.3	234.8
Employees	(13.9%)	2,425	2,575	2,238	2,353	1,335

AMERICAN REALTY INVESTORS, INC.   NYSE: ARL

1800 Valley View Ln., Ste. 300	CEO: Daniel J. (Danny) Moos
Dallas, TX 75234	CFO: Gene S. Bertcher
Phone: 469-522-4200	HR: —
Fax: 469-522-4299	FYE: December 31
Web: www.amrealtytrust.com	Type: Public

American Realty Investors (ARI) invests in, develops, and operates commercial properties and land in growing suburban markets. The company's portfolio includes approximately 60 apartment communities, about 20 office buildings, and about five each of industrial, retail, and hotel properties. It also owns a trade show and exhibit hall, as well as undeveloped land. ARI has properties in about 20 states, but most of its holdings are located in Texas. The company is part of a complex web of ownership that includes Prime Income Asset Management, which manages ARI and owns about 15% of it. Through various entities, Texas real estate mogul Gene Phillips and his family control around three-quarters of ARI.

	Annual Growth	12/05	12/06	12/07	12/08	12/09
Sales ($ mil.)	(2.4%)	202.6	182.3	176.9	181.9	183.7
Net income ($ mil.)	—	47.4	13.1	(2.6)	22.6	(82.7)
Market value ($ mil.)	11.2%	92.3	89.8	112.8	103.1	141.0
Employees	—	895	—	—	—	—

AMERICAN RECREATION PRODUCTS, INC.

1224 Fern Ridge Pkwy., 2nd Fl.	CEO: Dale Philippi
St. Louis, MO 63141	CFO: Casey Hofmann
Phone: 314-576-8000	HR: Kristen Busch
Fax: 314-576-8072	FYE: January 31
	Type: Private

For those who trek into the great outdoors and commune with wildlife, American Recreation Products (ARP) might be behind the items on their packing list. ARP makes and markets outdoor gear including tents, backpacks, sleeping bags, outdoor clothing, outdoor furniture, and related camping accessories. Brand names include Kelty, Royal Robbins, Sierra Designs, Slumberjack, and Wenzel. Its products are sold through sporting goods stores and outdoor specialty stores, as well as through mail order via brand Web sites. ARP is owned by the private equity firm Sun Capital Partners (SCP), which acquired its former parent company, women's apparel marketer Kellwood, in 2008. Kellwood purchased ARP in 1989.

AMERICAN REPROGRAPHICS COMPANY
NYSE: ARP

700 N. Central Ave., Ste. 550
Glendale, CA 91203
Phone: 818-500-0225
Fax: 818-500-0195
Web: www.e-arc.com

CEO: Kumarakulasingam (Suri) Suriyakumar
CFO: Jonathan R. Mather
HR: —
FYE: December 31
Type: Public

This "arc" keeps builders from being flooded with too much paper. American Reprographics Company (ARC) provides large-format document reproduction services, mainly to architectural, engineering, and construction firms. It operates about 300 facilities under a variety of local brands and offers on-site document management services at some 5,600 customer locations. In addition, the company sells reprographics equipment and supplies and licenses its proprietary PlanWell document management software to independent reprographers. Although ARC's network of facilities extends across more than 40 states and into Canada, China, Mexico, and the UK, operations in California account for about 40% of the company's sales.

	Annual Growth	12/05	12/06	12/07	12/08	12/09
Sales ($ mil.)	0.4%	494.2	591.8	688.4	701.0	501.5
Net income ($ mil.)	—	60.5	51.4	69.1	36.8	(14.9)
Market value ($ mil.)	(27.5%)	1,161.2	1,522.2	753.1	315.3	320.4
Employees	(2.0%)	3,800	4,400	5,100	4,500	3,500

⊞ AMERICAN RESIDENTIAL SERVICES L.L.C.

965 Ridge Lake Blvd., Ste. 201
Memphis, TN 38120
Phone: 901-271-9700
Fax: —
Web: www.ars.com

CEO: Donald K. (Don) Karnes
CFO: James T. (Jim) McMahon
HR: Bill Young
FYE: December 31
Type: Private

For those whose home maintenance skills don't rival Bob Vila's, there's American Residential Services (operating as ARS/Rescue Rooter). The company is an amalgamation of some 100 firms combined to create a national home improvement services company specializing in heating, ventilation, air-conditioning, plumbing, sewer and rain services, and electricity, as well as major home appliance installation, maintenance, repair, and replacement. With some 60 locations across the US, ARS/Rescue Rooter services homes as well as small commercial buildings. The company is owned by CI Capital Partners, Royal Palm Capital Partners, and its management.

AMERICAN RESTAURANT GROUP, INC.

4410 El Camino Real, Ste. 201
Los Altos, CA 94022
Phone: 650-949-6400
Fax: 650-917-9207
Web: www.blackangus.com

CEO: Meredith Taylor
CFO: Ronald (Ron) Maccarone
HR: Doug Gammon
FYE: December 31
Type: Private

As far as this company is concerned, Angus beef is as American as apple pie. American Restaurant Group owns and operates the Black Angus Steakhouse chain with about 50 locations in half a dozen western states. The upscale casual dinnerhouses offer a menu of Black Angus steaks and prime rib, along with chicken, seafood, and pasta dishes. Some locations also offer happy hour specials. In addition to dine-in seating, the chain provides drive-up take-out service at many of its units. Rancher and entrepreneur Stuart Anderson opened the first Black Angus restaurant in Seattle in 1964. The chain was acquired in 2009 by affiliates of private equity firm Versa Capital Management.

AMERICAN RICE, INC.

10700 North Fwy., Ste. 800
Houston, TX 77037
Phone: 281-272-8800
Fax: 281-272-9707
Web: www.amrice.com

CEO: Vicente Sos
CFO: Rick Arredondo
HR: Rebecca Rodriguez
FYE: August 31
Type: Subsidiary

American Rice, Inc. (ARI) knows a thing or two about its namesake foodstuff. Formed in 1969 as a marketing cooperative, American Rice is one of the largest rice millers in the US. Its US brands include Comet, Adolphus, and Blue Ribbon. Its customers are food retailers and foodservice providers. Outside the US, it sells such brands as Abu Bint, Golden Chopstick, and Golden Sail. In addition to the US, ARI sells rice in more than other 50 countries and regions, including Saudi Arabia, Haiti, Mexico, the Caribbean, and EU member countries. ARI is part of the Spanish food company Grupo SOS.

AMERICAN RIVER BANKSHARES
NASDAQ (GS): AMRB

3100 Zinfandel Dr., Ste. 450
Rancho Cordova, CA 95670
Phone: 916-851-0123
Fax: 916-641-1262
Web: www.amrb.com

CEO: David T. Taber
CFO: Mitchell A. (Mitch) Derenzo
HR: Anneliese Hein
FYE: December 31
Type: Public

American River Bankshares' family is growing. The holding company is the parent of American River Bank, which has about a dozen branches in Central California. About half of the bank's offices are operating under the North Coast Bank or Bank of Amador names. The bank serves area small to midsized businesses and individuals, offering traditional deposit products such as checking and savings accounts and CDs. It offers commercial and residential mortgages, as well as business, construction, and consumer loans, and lease financing for business equipment.

	Annual Growth	12/05	12/06	12/07	12/08	12/09
Assets ($ mil.)	(0.8%)	612.8	604.0	573.7	563.2	594.4
Net income ($ mil.)	(35.4%)	9.2	9.1	8.5	7.6	1.6
Market value ($ mil.)	(19.8%)	186.9	214.1	160.7	99.1	77.4
Employees	(0.8%)	122	129	124	122	118

AMERICAN SAFETY INSURANCE HOLDINGS, LTD.
NYSE: ASI

100 Galleria Pkwy. SE, Ste. 700
Atlanta, GA 30339
Phone: 770-916-1908
Fax: 770-916-0618
Web: www.americansafetyinsurance.com

CEO: Stephen R. Crim
CFO: Mark W. Haushill
HR: Laurie Ramondi
FYE: December 31
Type: Public

Ah, Bermuda. Beaches. Bikinis. Insurance holding companies. American Safety Insurance Holdings (ASI) was part of the first wave of insurance firms domiciling in this tax-sheltered location. Formed to offer insurance to asbestos removers and other environmental risk-remediation providers, the company has expanded into other specialty lines. American Safety Insurance now underwrites residential and commercial construction risks, as well as professional and product liability, and excess and surplus policies. The company also offers alternative risk transfer programs that rely on some measure of self-insurance or shared risk on the part of the insured. The firm sells through a network of 250 agencies in the US.

	Annual Growth	12/05	12/06	12/07	12/08	12/09
Assets ($ mil.)	13.3%	697.1	847.1	934.0	1,026.4	1,147.7
Net income ($ mil.)	13.4%	14.7	20.5	28.2	0.3	24.3
Market value ($ mil.)	(3.6%)	173.3	192.0	203.4	136.7	149.6
Employees	13.8%	114	138	178	182	191

⊞ An in-depth profile of this company is available to Hoover's Online members at hoovers.com.

129

⊞ AMERICAN SAFETY RAZOR COMPANY

240 Cedar Knolls Rd., Ste. 401
Cedar Knolls, NJ 07927
Phone: 973-753-3000
Fax: 973-326-9004
Web: www.asrco.com

CEO: J. Andrew (Andy) Bolt
CFO: —
HR: —
FYE: December 31
Type: Private

There's nothing dull about American Safety Razor (ASR). The company, which also does business as Personna American Safety Razor, is a leading maker of private-label shaving razors and blades. Its value-priced products are sold through mass merchandisers and supermarkets under retailer names as well as under ASR's roughly 30 own brands (including Matrix3, Mystique, and Personna). In addition to shaving products, ASR makes bladed hand tools (such as carpet knives and paint scrapers) and specialty industrial and medical blades. With roots going back to 1875, ASR is owned by London-based private equity firm Lion Capital.

AMERICAN SCIENCE AND ENGINEERING, INC.   NASDAQ (GS): ASEI

829 Middlesex Tpke.
Billerica, MA 01821
Phone: 978-262-8700
Fax: 978-262-8804
Web: www.as-e.com

CEO: Anthony R. Fabiano
CFO: Kenneth J. (Ken) Galaznik
HR: George M. Peterman
FYE: March 31
Type: Public

You can't hide from American Science and Engineering (AS&E). The company makes X-ray detection systems for inspection and security applications at airports, border protection sites, shipping ports, and special events. Unlike ordinary X-rays, AS&E's backscatter technology detects organic materials such as illegal drugs, plastic explosives, and plastic weapons; its Z Backscatter three-sided X-ray system is built into a delivery van for remote detection. AS&E also makes scanning equipment for detecting contraband on persons, in aircraft, vehicles, and in luggage and packages. Customers include the Department of Homeland Security. About 55% of sales are to the US government and its contractors.

	Annual Growth	3/05	3/06	3/07	3/08	3/09
Sales ($ mil.)	25.4%	88.3	163.6	153.2	166.7	218.4
Net income ($ mil.)	26.2%	11.2	29.8	24.6	17.5	28.4
Market value ($ mil.)	5.7%	402.3	840.4	473.9	491.0	502.1
Employees	7.0%	286	288	299	346	375

AMERICAN SEAFOODS GROUP LLC

Marketplace Tower, 2025 1st Ave., Ste. 900
Seattle, WA 98121
Phone: 206-374-1515
Fax: 206-374-1516
Web: www.americanseafoods.com

CEO: Bernt O. Bodal
CFO: Brad D. Bodenman
HR: Tammy French
FYE: December 31
Type: Private

With operations in the northern Pacific (i.e., in the Bering Sea and Aleutian Islands), American Seafoods Group casts a bountiful net. The company offers frozen and processed fish such as Alaska pollock, Pacific whiting, Pacific cod, sea and bay scallops, haddock, sole, and farm-raised tilapia and catfish. It operates its own fleet of ships that process and freeze the catch while at sea, as well as a fleet of transport trucks. American Seafoods' land-based operations in Massachusetts make breaded seafood products. It sells its fish under the American Pride and Frionor brand names in North America, Asia, and Europe.

	Annual Growth	12/04	12/05	12/06	12/07	12/08
Sales ($ mil.)	9.1%	—	—	—	550.0	600.0
Employees	—	—	—	—	—	—

AMERICAN SHARED HOSPITAL SERVICES   NYSE Amex: AMS

4 Embarcadero Center, Ste. 3700
San Francisco, CA 94111
Phone: 415-788-5300
Fax: 415-788-5660
Web: www.ashs.com

CEO: Ernest A. Bates
CFO: Craig K. Tagawa
HR: —
FYE: December 31
Type: Public

Business *is* brain surgery for American Shared Hospital Services (ASHS). The company owns 81% of GK Financing (GKF), which installs, finances, and services the Leksell Gamma Knife, a noninvasive surgical device that uses gamma rays to destroy brain tumors without harming surrounding tissue. Sweden-based Elekta, which makes the Gamma Knife, owns the other 19% of GKF. GKF usually leases the Gamma Knife units on a per-use basis to major urban medical centers; it has contracts for units installed in about 20 hospitals in the US; it markets the product in the US and Brazil.

	Annual Growth	12/05	12/06	12/07	12/08	12/09
Sales ($ mil.)	(2.0%)	18.2	20.4	22.6	19.1	16.8
Net income ($ mil.)	—	1.8	1.7	1.0	0.5	(0.2)
Market value ($ mil.)	(17.2%)	28.9	30.6	9.5	4.8	13.6
Employees	3.9%	12	12	12	12	14

AMERICAN SIGNATURE, INC.

4300 E. 5th Ave.
Columbus, OH 43219
Phone: 614-221-9200
Fax: —
Web: www.asfurniture.com

CEO: Jay L. Schottenstein
CFO: Edward L. (Ed) Cornell
HR: Hyman Albritton
FYE: July 31
Type: Subsidiary

You don't have to have a signature as famous as John Hancock's to leave an impression on American Signature's bottom line. The company operates about 130 stores in 20 states under the American Signature Furniture and Value City Furniture banners. Stores feature wood and upholstered home furnishing collections, as well as bedding. In addition to its retail operations, American Signature designs and manufactures its own pieces and operates its own warehouses and distribution centers. The American Signature Furniture concept was introduced by parent Schottenstein Stores in 2002, in an effort to expand the company's higher-end offerings.

AMERICAN SNUFF COMPANY, LLC

813 Ridge Lake Blvd., #100
Memphis, TN 38120
Phone: 901-761-2050
Fax: 901-767-1302
Web: www.cwdlp.com

CEO: Bryan K. Stockdale
CFO: Michael D. Flaherty
HR: Carol Novosad
FYE: January 31
Type: Subsidiary

American Snuff Company (formerly Conwood) loves a bear market when it comes to moist snuff and other smokeless tobacco products. It makes the Grizzly, Kodiak, Hawken, and Cougar brands of moist tobacco and is the second-largest maker of smokeless tobacco products in the US. American Snuff also makes loose-leaf tobacco (including Morgan's, Levi Garrett, and Taylor's Pride brands), snuff (Garrett and Dental brands), and an assortment of other smokeless tobacco (including twist, moist, and plug). It also makes Captain Black flavored little cigars. The firm renamed itself American Snuff in 2010. It was acquired by Reynolds American in 2006 for $3.5 billion. It now generates about 8% of its parent's annual revenue.

An in-depth profile of this company is available to Hoover's Online members at hoovers.com.

AMERICAN SOFTWARE, INC.　NASDAQ (GS): AMSWA

470 E. Paces Ferry Rd. NE	CEO: James C. Edenfield
Atlanta, GA 30305	CFO: Vincent C. (Vince) Klinges
Phone: 404-264-5296	HR: —
Fax: 404-264-5206	FYE: April 30
Web: www.amsoftware.com	Type: Public

American Software sells business software from sea to shining sea. The company's supply chain management and enterprise resource planning software is used by manufacturers and distributors to manage back-office operations, including global supply chain, warehouse, and transportation operations. Its Logility subsidiary makes collaborative applications that connect buyers with suppliers and help in planning transportation and logistics. American Software also provides IT staffing and consulting services. Co-founders James Edenfield (CEO) and Thomas Newberry (chairman) together control a majority of the voting power of the company.

	Annual Growth	4/05	4/06	4/07	4/08	4/09
Sales ($ mil.)	4.9%	64.5	76.6	84.4	89.0	78.0
Net income ($ mil.)	(2.4%)	3.3	5.0	8.4	6.5	3.0
Market value ($ mil.)	1.2%	134.1	186.0	222.7	155.9	140.4
Employees	(1.1%)	304	321	308	315	291

AMERICAN SOIL TECHNOLOGIES, INC.　OTC: SOYL

12224 Montague St.	CEO: Carl P. Ranno
Pacoima, CA 91331	CFO: Carl P. Ranno
Phone: 818-899-4686	HR: —
Fax: 818-899-4670	FYE: September 30
Web: www.americansoiltech.com	Type: Public

American Soil Technologies works to make sure your farmland isn't dirt poor. The company manufactures agricultural chemicals that help retain water in soil, the direct benefit of which is manifold. In addition to minimizing the frequency of irrigation, the chemicals also decrease the likelihood of erosion and reduce other damage. Its products are used by agricultural, residential, and recreational clients. Subsidiary Smart World Organics gives American Soil entrance to the organic turf and horticultural markets. Though primarily operating in the US, it also distributes internationally to the Middle East, North Africa, and China. The family of the late chairman Louie Visco controls 30% of the company.

	Annual Growth	12/04	12/05	12/06	*9/08	9/09
Sales ($ mil.)	(24.0%)	0.6	0.6	0.6	0.6	0.2
Net income ($ mil.)	—	(1.7)	(2.1)	(2.3)	(2.7)	(2.8)
Market value ($ mil.)	(54.1%)	49.0	16.7	14.3	1.7	2.2
Employees	(20.5%)	10	12	19	8	4
						*Fiscal year change

AMERICAN SPECTRUM REALTY, INC.　NYSE Amex: AQQ

2401 Fountain View, Ste. 510	CEO: William J. Carden
Houston, TX 77057	CFO: G. Anthony Eppolito
Phone: 713-706-6200	HR: —
Fax: 713-706-6201	FYE: December 31
Web: www.americanspectrum.com	Type: Public

American Spectrum Realty has narrowed the spectrum of its property portfolio. The firm invests in, expands, renovates, and manages commercial real estate, primarily multi-tenant office and industrial space. Its portfolio includes about 30 properties totaling some 2.5 million sq. ft. of leasable space. Most properties are located in Texas, but it also owns assets in the Midwest, Southern California, and Arizona. Since 2002, the company has sold more than 20 noncore properties (multifamily, retail, land parcels, and properties in the Midwest) while buying up several Houston commercial buildings. CEO William Carden controls 37% of the company; officers and directors collectively own 52%.

	Annual Growth	12/05	12/06	12/07	12/08	12/09
Sales ($ mil.)	13.2%	20.3	26.0	30.5	35.1	33.3
Net income ($ mil.)	—	(2.3)	6.5	(10.1)	(6.6)	(9.3)
Market value ($ mil.)	8.7%	23.3	34.6	32.9	36.1	32.6
Employees	78.3%	28	34	44	40	283

AMERICAN STATES WATER COMPANY　NYSE: AWR

630 E. Foothill Blvd.	CEO: Robert J. Sprowls
San Dimas, CA 91773	CFO: Eva G. Tang
Phone: 909-394-3600	HR: Diane D. Rentfrow
Fax: 909-394-1382	FYE: December 31
Web: www.aswater.com	Type: Public

American States Water holds the essence of life for Californians and Arizonans. Its main subsidiary, regulated public utility Golden State Water Company (GSWC), which was formerly known as Southern California Water Company, supplies water to more than 255,000 customers in 75 communities, primarily in Los Angeles, San Bernardino, and Orange counties. GSWC's Bear Valley Electric subsidiary distributes electricity to about 23,250 Californians. American States Water's Chaparral City Water unit serves more than 13,000 customers in Fountain Hills and Scottsdale, Arizona. In 2010, in order to pay down debt, the company decided to sell this Arizona unit to EPCOR Utilities for $35 million.

	Annual Growth	12/05	12/06	12/07	12/08	12/09
Sales ($ mil.)	11.2%	236.2	268.6	301.4	318.7	361.0
Net income ($ mil.)	2.4%	26.8	23.1	28.0	22.0	29.5
Market value ($ mil.)	3.5%	571.9	717.1	699.7	612.4	657.5
Employees	(30.3%)	513	516	529	569	121

AMERICAN SUPERCONDUCTOR　NASDAQ (GM): AMSC

68 Jackson Rd.	CEO: Gregory J. (Greg) Yurek
Devens, MA 01434	CFO: David A. (Dave) Henry
Phone: 978-842-3000	HR: —
Fax: 978-842-3024	FYE: March 31
Web: www.amsuper.com	Type: Public

American Superconductor Corporation (AMSC) gets a charge out of carrying a heavy load. The company has two units — AMSC Superconductors, which combined AMSC Wires and SuperMachines (prototype electric motors and synchronous condensers), and AMSC Power Systems. In 2007 AMSC acquired a company that previously was a customer, Windtec Consulting, to expand into the alternative energy market. The Austrian firm develops and licenses wind turbine system designs, and sells wind turbine electrical systems. Windtec became part of AMSC Power Systems. Customers in the Asia/Pacific region account for about three-quarters of sales.

	Annual Growth	3/06	3/07	3/08	3/09	3/10
Sales ($ mil.)	56.3%	52.9	52.2	112.4	182.8	316.0
Net income ($ mil.)	—	(30.9)	(34.7)	(25.4)	(16.6)	16.2
Market value ($ mil.)	26.3%	509.1	604.2	1,040.1	776.4	1,296.2
Employees	31.2%	241	263	382	519	714

AMERICAN SUZUKI MOTOR CORPORATION

3251 E. Imperial Hwy.	CEO: Kinji Saito
Brea, CA 92821	CFO: Seijiro Ando
Phone: 714-996-7040	HR: Martha Barrera
Fax: 714-524-8499	FYE: December 31
Web: www.suzuki.com	Type: Subsidiary

American Suzuki Motor Corp. (ASMC), the US subsidiary of Japan's Suzuki Motor, markets Suzuki cars, motorcycles, ATVs, and marine engines in the US. ASMC's automotive offerings include the Equator (midsize pickup truck), Forenza (sedan and wagon), Grand Vitara (SUV), Reno (five-door hatchback), SX4 (crossover and sedan), and XL7 (seven-passenger luxury SUV). The company markets Suzuki cars through a network of about 400 dealerships across the US. As sales plummeted in 2009, ASMC laid off nearly 17% of its employees, closed one of its four regional offices, and consolidated other functions.

AMERICAN SYSTEMS CORPORATION

13990 Parkeast Circle
Chantilly, VA 20151
Phone: 703-968-6300
Fax: 703-968-5151
Web: www.2asc.com

CEO: William C. Hoover
CFO: Mark Danisewicz
HR: Teresa Baskerville
FYE: December 31
Type: Private

American Systems provides government and commercial clients worldwide with IT management and consulting services, including custom engineering and application development. Its consulting division advises clients on such issues as access and identity management, data security, and process optimization. The company also provides staff augmentation and other human capital services. American Systems works with government customers to develop systems related to command and control, logistics, and national security. Its commercial-focused operations serve the energy, financial services, health care, retail, telecommunications, and travel industries. The employee-owned company was established in 1975.

	Annual Growth	12/04	12/05	12/06	12/07	12/08
Est. sales ($ mil.)	—	—	—	—	—	230.5
Employees	—	—	—	—	—	1,343

AMERICAN TIRE DISTRIBUTORS HOLDINGS, INC.

12200 Herbert Wayne Ct., Ste. 150
Huntersville, NC 28078
Phone: 704-992-2000
Fax: 704-992-1384
Web: www.americantiredistributors.com

CEO: William E. (Bill) Berry
CFO: David L. Dyckman
HR: —
FYE: December 31
Type: Private

Business for American Tire Distributors Holdings starts where the rubber meets the road. The company, through its American Tire Distributors (ATD) unit, is one of the largest independent tire wholesalers in the US. Its offerings include flagship brands Bridgestone, Continental, Goodyear, Pirelli, and Michelin, as well as budget brands and private-label tires. Tires account for some 90% of sales. ATD also markets custom wheels and tire service equipment. Its roughly 80 distribution centers serve independent tire dealers, retail chains, and auto service centers in some 40 states. After filing to go public in 2010, the company was acquired by private equity firm TPG Capital later that year.

	Annual Growth	12/05	12/06	12/07	12/08	12/09
Sales ($ mil.)	17.2%	1,150.9	1,578.0	1,877.5	1,960.8	2,171.8
Net income ($ mil.)	—	(1.6)	(4.6)	1.4	9.7	4.9
Employees	2.0%	2,127	2,100	2,400	2,900	2,300

AMERICAN TOWER CORPORATION

NYSE: AMT

116 Huntington Ave., 11th Fl.
Boston, MA 02116
Phone: 617-375-7500
Fax: 617-375-7575
Web: www.americantower.com

CEO: James D. (Jim) Taiclet Jr.
CFO: Thomas A. (Tom) Bartlett
HR: Allen Todres
FYE: December 31
Type: Public

American Tower hopes to take its business to new heights. The tower management firm operates about 26,000 broadcast and communications towers, wireless towers, and distributed antenna systems in the US, Brazil, and Mexico. The company rents space on towers and rooftop antenna systems to wireless carriers and radio and TV broadcasters, who use the infrastructure to offer their own services. American Tower also offers some tower-related services: it provides site acquisition for new tower construction, performs structural analyses for carriers to determine if a tower can support additional equipment, and offers zoning and permitting services.

	Annual Growth	12/05	12/06	12/07	12/08	12/09
Sales ($ mil.)	16.2%	944.8	1,317.4	1,456.6	1,593.5	1,724.1
Net income ($ mil.)	—	(136.1)	27.5	56.3	347.2	247.1
Market value ($ mil.)	12.4%	10,912.3	15,011.5	17,153.7	11,806.3	17,399.3
Employees	12.0%	904	995	1,124	1,198	1,420

AMERICAN TRUCKING ASSOCIATIONS

950 N. Glebe Rd., Ste. 210
Alexandria, VA 22203
Phone: 703-838-1700
Fax: 703-836-5880
Web: www.truckline.com

CEO: Bill Graves
CFO: Robert A. (Bob) Davidson
HR: —
FYE: December 31
Type: Not-for-profit

American Trucking Associations (ATA) aims to be heard over the roar of diesel engines on the interstate as the unified voice of the trucking industry. The group seeks to represent the national interests of truckers in legislation, regulation, the courts, and the media. It works closely with state trucking associations and with groups concerned with segments of the trucking business and key industry issues, such as safety. ATA produces several publications and hosts seminars, meetings, and conventions. The organization was formed in 1933 and in 1944 adopted a federation structure comprising national, state and local, and special affiliated interests. ATA has more than 37,000 members.

AMERICAN UNITED MUTUAL INSURANCE HOLDING COMPANY

1 American Sq.
Indianapolis, IN 46206
Phone: 317-285-1111
Fax: 317-285-1728
Web: www.aul.com

CEO: Dayton H. Molendorp
CFO: J. Scott Davison
HR: Mark C. Roller
FYE: December 31
Type: Mutual company

There are 50 states, but only OneAmerica. American United Mutual Insurance Holding Company is primarily a life insurer whose operating units do business under the OneAmerica Financial Partners banner. The company offers individual life insurance, disability and long-term-care coverage, and annuities. For businesses the company offers employee benefits, medical stop-loss coverage, retirement plans, and group life insurance. Its subsidiaries include American United Life Insurance, The State Life Insurance Company, OneAmerica Securities, Pioneer Mutual Life Insurance, and R.E. Moulton. The company operates in 49 states and Washington, DC.

	Annual Growth	12/04	12/05	12/06	12/07	12/08
Assets ($ mil.)	5.3%	15,028.0	17,606.7	18,491.3	19,921.0	18,493.7
Net income ($ mil.)	(8.5%)	56.3	62.1	67.7	88.1	39.5
Employees	—	1,800	—	—	—	—

AMERICAN UNIVERSITY

4400 Massachusetts Ave. NW
Washington, DC 20016
Phone: 202-885-1000
Fax: 202-885-3265
Web: www.american.edu

CEO: Cornelius M. (Neil) Kerwin
CFO: Donald L. (Don) Myers
HR: Mary Beth Muha Priest
FYE: April 30
Type: School

Fulfilling the vision of George Washington for a national university in the country's capital, American University was chartered by an Act of Congress in 1893 as a private, independent, co-educational institution under the auspices of the United Methodist Church. Today, the school offers a broad range of undergraduate and graduate degree programs to some 11,800 students from more than 150 countries. American University has schools devoted to arts and sciences, business, communications, international service, public affairs, and law. It is one of the top producers of Peace Corps volunteers serving overseas. Nine US presidents have served on American University's Board of Trustees.

	Annual Growth	4/04	4/05	4/06	4/07	4/08
Est. sales ($ mil.)	—	—	—	—	—	398.1
Employees	—	—	—	—	—	2,000

AMERICAN VANGUARD CORPORATION
NYSE: AVD

4695 MacArthur Ct.
Newport Beach, CA 92660
Phone: 949-260-1200
Fax: 949-260-1201
Web: www.american-vanguard.com

CEO: Eric G. Wintemute
CFO: David T. Johnson
HR: Teresa Chavez
FYE: December 31
Type: Public

American Vanguard Corporation (AMVAC) bugs bugs, roots out weeds, and helps people take care of their person. The company makes specialty chemicals designed to protect the health of animals, crops, and people. Products made by its AMVAC Chemical subsidiary include pesticides, plant-growth regulators, herbicides, and soil fumigants. Its GemChem subsidiary distributes the company's chemicals nationally to the cosmetic, nutritional, and pharmaceutical industries. American Vanguard also has marketing subsidiaries in the UK, Switzerland, and Mexico. Collectively, co-chairmen Herbert Kraft and Glenn Wintemute and CEO Eric Wintemute own almost a quarter of American Vanguard.

	Annual Growth	12/05	12/06	12/07	12/08	12/09
Sales ($ mil.)	2.5%	189.8	193.8	216.7	237.5	209.3
Net income ($ mil.)	—	19.0	15.4	18.7	20.0	(5.8)
Market value ($ mil.)	(17.2%)	481.8	434.6	474.2	319.8	226.9
Employees	2.4%	300	285	309	320	330

AMERICAN VANTAGE COMPANIES
Pink Sheets: AVCS

4735 S. Durango Dr., Ste. 105
Las Vegas, NV 89147
Phone: 702-227-9800
Fax: 702-227-8525

CEO: Ronald J. Tassinari
CFO: Anna M. Morrison
HR: —
FYE: December 31
Type: Public

American Vantage Companies is a holding company that operates through subsidiaries in the gaming industry and the corporate staffing business. Its majority-owned subsidiary Brownstone provides consulting and development services to clients in the casino gaming industry, as well as to those clients trying to get in. It also owns Candidates on Demand Group, a New York City-based recruiting and temporary placement company with offices in Nevada, New York, and Texas. In addition, American Vantage owns a stake in the Border Grill, a restaurant in the Mandalay Bay Hotel & Casino in Las Vegas (owned by casino gaming giant MGM MIRAGE).

AMERICAN WAGERING, INC.
OTC: BETM

675 Grier Dr.
Las Vegas, NV 89119
Phone: 702-735-5529
Fax: 702-735-0142
Web: www.americanwagering.com

CEO: Victor J. (Vic) Salerno
CFO: Victor J. (Vic) Salerno
HR: Elaine Elliot
FYE: January 31
Type: Public

This company lets you play the ponies without being there. American Wagering owns and operates Leroy's Horse and Sports Place, a chain of about 80 race and sports books located throughout Nevada. Patrons can place bets on horse races and a variety of other sporting events. The company also markets sports wagering equipment, kiosks, and software to other gaming operators through its subsidiaries AWI Manufacturing and Computerized Bookmaking Systems. In addition, American Wagering owns and operates Sturgeon's Inn & Casino in Lovelock, Nevada. CEO Victor Salerno owns about 30% of the company.

	Annual Growth	1/06	1/07	1/08	1/09	1/10
Sales ($ mil.)	3.8%	12.5	19.4	18.7	15.5	14.5
Net income ($ mil.)	25.7%	0.4	1.8	(0.8)	(1.0)	1.0
Market value ($ mil.)	(48.8%)	14.7	9.2	6.6	1.4	1.0
Employees	3.5%	198	224	365	251	227

AMERICAN WATER WORKS COMPANY, INC.
NYSE: AWK

1025 Laurel Oak Rd.
Voorhees, NJ 08043
Phone: 856-346-8200
Fax: 856-346-8440
Web: www.amwater.com

CEO: Donald L. (Don) Correll
CFO: Ellen C. Wolf
HR: Sean G. Burke
FYE: December 31
Type: Public

Water, water, everywhere — and American Water Works wants to own it. The company, once a subsidiary of German utility giant RWE, is by far the largest public water utility in the US. Through its regulated utilities and its contract services division, American Water Works serves about 15 million consumers in 32 US states, plus Ontario. The company also provides wastewater treatment in some of its service areas. Its regulated operations account for nearly 90% of sales. Nonregulated subsidiary American Water Works Service provides contract management services for water and wastewater systems. In 2008 RWE spun off American Water Works, but retained a majority stake, which has since been reduced to about 25%.

	Annual Growth	12/05	12/06	12/07	12/08	12/09
Sales ($ mil.)	3.4%	2,136.7	2,093.1	2,214.2	2,336.9	2,440.7
Net income ($ mil.)	—	(325.0)	(162.2)	(342.8)	(562.4)	(233.1)
Market value ($ mil.)	7.3%	—	—	—	3,647.8	3,915.1
Employees	3.7%	—	6,900	7,000	7,300	7,700

AMERICAN WOODMARK CORPORATION
NASDAQ (GS): AMWD

3102 Shawnee Dr.
Winchester, VA 22601
Phone: 540-665-9100
Fax: 540-665-9176
Web: www.americanwoodmark.com

CEO: Kent B. Guichard
CFO: Jonathan H. (Jon) Wolk
HR: Rick Hardy
FYE: April 30
Type: Public

American Woodmark has more cabinet selections than the prime minister of Russia. A top maker of kitchen cabinets in the US, the company manufactures and distributes about 400 lines of low- to mid-priced kitchen cabinets in oak, cherry, hickory, and maple. Brands include American Woodmark, Shenandoah Cabinetry, Potomac, and Timberlake. Targeting the remodeling and new home construction markets, American Woodmark sells its products through home centers and independent dealers and distributors; it also sells directly to builders through about 10 US service centers. Lowe's and The Home Depot account for approximately three-quarters of sales.

	Annual Growth	4/05	4/06	4/07	4/08	4/09
Sales ($ mil.)	(8.4%)	777.0	837.7	760.9	602.4	545.9
Net income ($ mil.)	—	35.6	33.2	32.6	4.3	(3.2)
Market value ($ mil.)	(10.2%)	451.0	492.4	488.9	267.3	293.2
Employees	(12.7%)	6,370	6,360	5,148	—	3,701

AMERICANWEST BANCORPORATION
NASDAQ (GS): AWBC

41 W. Riverside Ave., Ste. 400
Spokane, WA 99201
Phone: 509-467-6993
Fax: 509-465-9681
Web: www.awbank.net

CEO: Patrick J. (Pat) Rusnak
CFO: Shelly L. Krasselt
HR: —
FYE: December 31
Type: Public

If you rustle up some cash, AmericanWest will help you ride herd on it. AmericanWest Bancorporation is the holding company for AmericanWest Bank, which has more than 45 branches in eastern and central Washington and northern Idaho, and about 15 more in Utah, where it operates as Far West Bank. The banks serve consumers and small to mid-sized businesses, offering standard services such as checking and savings accounts, CDs, and ATM and debit cards. The company's loan portfolio is dominated by commercial real estate, construction, land, and business loans. The bank also originates agricultural, consumer, and residential mortgage loans.

	Annual Growth	12/05	12/06	12/07	12/08	12/09
Assets ($ mil.)	10.5%	1,109.1	1,416.5	2,120.2	1,874.6	1,655.6
Net income ($ mil.)	—	13.9	7.6	8.5	(192.4)	(71.1)
Market value ($ mil.)	(63.8%)	406.8	417.0	303.5	12.9	7.0
Employees	5.1%	436	508	703	615	531

An in-depth profile of this company is available to Hoover's Online members at hoovers.com.

AMERICA'S CAR-MART, INC.

NASDAQ (GS): CRMT

802 SE Plaza Ave., Ste. 200
Bentonville, AR 72712
Phone: 479-464-9944
Fax: 479-273-7556
Web: www.car-mart.com

CEO: William H. (Hank) Henderson
CFO: Jeffrey A. Williams
HR: —
FYE: April 30
Type: Public

No Credit? Bad Credit? No problem. America's Car-Mart targets car buyers with poor or limited credit histories. Car-Mart's subsidiaries operate 90 used-car dealerships in more than half a dozen states, primarily in smaller urban and rural markets throughout the South-Central region of the US. The dealerships focus on selling basic, affordable transportation (average selling price about $8,700). The company is expanding primarily in Alabama, Oklahoma, and Missouri. While its traditional business plan has focused on cities of 20,000 to 50,000 in population, the company has begun opening dealerships in more populous cities, including Tulsa, Oklahoma. America's Car-Mart was founded in 1981 as the Crown Group.

	Annual Growth	4/05	4/06	4/07	4/08	4/09
Sales ($ mil.)	9.9%	204.8	234.2	240.4	274.6	299.0
Net income ($ mil.)	(0.1%)	18.0	16.7	4.2	15.0	17.9
Market value ($ mil.)	(6.4%)	244.5	235.2	148.3	166.4	187.6
Employees	6.4%	715	779	800	840	915

AMERICAS POWER PARTNERS, INC.

Pink Sheets: APPN

710 N. York Rd.
Hinsdale, IL 60521
Phone: 630-288-4651
Fax: 630-325-8167
Web: www.americaspowerpartners.com

CEO: Mark A. Margason
CFO: Jerome P. Frett
HR: —
FYE: June 30
Type: Public

Generating profits through cogeneration, Americas Power Partners focuses on cogeneration technologies as it develops small-scale independent power plants (generating less than 100 MW of power) in the US and sells electricity to utilities, marketers, and industrial and commercial users. The company also provides on-site distributed generation and optimization services (whereby it improves plant operations but leaves ownership in the hands of the client). In other cases the company assumes ownership and operation of the utility, optimizing the plant's operations and selling the power back to the customer at a contracted rate. Armstrong Service is the company's major strategic partner.

AMERICAS STYRENICS LLC

24 Waterway Ave., Ste. 1200
The Woodlands, TX 77380
Phone: 888-552-6789
Fax: 281-296-5830
Web: www.amstyrenics.com

CEO: Tim Roberts
CFO: Thomas Egolf
HR: Doug Chauveaux
FYE: December 31
Type: Joint venture

Hoping to cushion its parent companies' rides through a bumpy economy, Americas Styrenics combines the styrene operations of Dow Chemical and Chevron Phillips Chemical (CP Chem). The 50-50 joint venture makes styrene monomer and a number of polystyrene resins. Its products go into the obvious (packaging and foam peanuts) and the unlikely (envelope windows and lighting applications). Americas Styrenics operates eight manufacturing plants throughout the US and in Brazil and Colombia. It is the #1 producer of polystyrene and the #2 styrene maker in the Western Hemisphere. In 2010, pessimistic about the unit's opportunities for growth, Dow put the Styron unit up for sale, including Dow's stake in Americas Styrenics.

AMERICATEL CORPORATION

7361 Calhoun Pl., Ste. 650
Rockville, MD 20855
Phone: 301-610-4300
Fax: 301-610-4301
Web: www.americatel.com

CEO: Charles (Chuck) G. Taylor
CFO: Laurie Rodriguez
HR: Johnna McCooey
FYE: December 31
Type: Subsidiary

Born of NAFTA, Americatel is a telecommunications services reseller that focuses on the needs of multinational companies operating in Latin America and the Caribbean region. The company offers residential domestic and international long-distance services throughout the continental US, targeting primarily Hispanic customers; its key voice brands are Cellular Accesso and LíneaPaís. Americatel also offers residential Internet access, prepaid calling cards, and long-distance services. Its Maryland-based subsidiary Startec Global Communications largely serves immigrants from India, as well as other Asian and Middle Eastern populations. Founded in 1993, the company is owned by investment firm Platinum Equity.

AMERICHOICE CORPORATION

8045 Leesburg Pike, 6th Fl.
Vienna, VA 22182
Phone: 703-506-3555
Fax: 703-506-3556
Web: www.americhoice.com

CEO: Rick Jelinek
CFO: Steve Swift
HR: —
FYE: December 31
Type: Subsidiary

AmeriChoice offers health care for those who don't have much choice. The company, specializing in the federal health care market, operates managed care plans for Medicaid, Medicare, and state Children's Health Insurance Program (CHIP) recipients. AmeriChoice has some 2.6 million members in more than 20 states. The company also provides managed care information technology services such as medical and dental claims processing and member databases, as well as clinical care and consulting services, to government agencies and medical practices. AmeriChoice is a subsidiary of UnitedHealth Group.

AMERICHOICE OF PENNSYLVANIA, INC.

The Wanamaker Bldg., 100 Penn Sq. East, Ste. 900
Philadelphia, PA 19107
Phone: 215-832-4500
Fax: 215-832-4644
Web: www.americhoice.com

CEO: Ernest Montiletto
CFO: Andy Bhugra
HR: —
FYE: December 31
Type: Subsidiary

AmeriChoice of Pennsylvania is one health insurance option available to the Keystone State's Medicaid beneficiaries. The company is a health maintenance organization serving members of Pennsylvania's HealthChoices program, a state program requiring Medicaid recipients and their families to enroll in managed care plans. In exchange for a fixed monthly premium per member, AmeriChoice of Pennsylvania coordinates the care for low-income families and provides services such as disease management and pharmacy benefit management. The company is a subsidiary of Americhoice, one of the nation's largest providers of public sector health care programs. Americhoice, in turn, is a subsidiary of UnitedHealth Group.

AMERICO LIFE, INC.

1055 Broadway
Kansas City, MO 64105
Phone: 816-391-2000
Fax: 816-391-2083
Web: www.americo.com

CEO: Gary L. Muller
CFO: Mark K. Fallon
HR: —
FYE: December 31
Type: Private

Americo Life sells insurance to cover American lives. The holding company sells life insurance and annuities to individuals, families, and groups, mainly through its Americo Financial Life and Annuity Insurance unit. Americo Life companies also offer insurance policies that cover funeral expenses and mortgages. Policies are distributed through 15,000 independent agents nationwide to about 850,000 policyholders. The firm is a wholly owned subsidiary of Financial Holding Corporation, which the family of chairman Michael Merriman controls. Other Financial Holding business interests include real estate ventures in the Southeast and a 50% stake in Argus Health Systems, a processor of prescription drug claims.

[H] AMERICREDIT CORP.

NYSE: ACF

801 Cherry St., Ste. 3900
Fort Worth, TX 76102
Phone: 817-302-7000
Fax: 817-302-7101
Web: www.americredit.com

CEO: Daniel E. (Dan) Berce
CFO: Chris A. Choate
HR: —
FYE: June 30
Type: Public

AmeriCredit gives credit where it's not necessarily due. The company purchases loans made by about 10,000 franchised and independent auto dealers primarily to consumers with less-than-ideal credit histories. It typically finances low-mileage, late-model used cars (about 80% of all loans), and the occasional new automobile. The company then periodically transfers its loans to securitization trusts, retains the servicing, and reinvests the proceeds in new loans. Post-credit market meltdown, the lender has nearly 1 million customers and approximately $11 billion in managed auto receivables. It operates about 15 credit centers in suburban locations close to car dealerships.

	Annual Growth	6/05	6/06	6/07	6/08	6/09
Assets ($ mil.)	2.3%	10,947.0	13,067.9	17,811.0	16,547.2	11,984.2
Net income ($ mil.)	(53.0%)	285.9	306.2	360.2	(69.3)	13.9
Market value ($ mil.)	(14.6%)	3,431.3	3,756.9	3,572.6	1,159.9	1,823.3
Employees	(4.3%)	3,653	4,025	4,831	3,832	3,064

[H] AMERIGAS PARTNERS, L.P.

NYSE: APU

460 N. Gulph Rd.
King of Prussia, PA 19406
Phone: 610-337-7000
Fax: 610-992-3259
Web: www.amerigas.com

CEO: Eugene V. N. Bissell
CFO: Jerry E. Sheridan
HR: William D. Katz
FYE: September 30
Type: Public

America has a gas with AmeriGas Partners. Purveying propane has propelled the company to its position as one of the top two US retail propane marketers (rivaling Ferrellgas for the #1 slot). It serves 1.3 million residential, commercial, industrial, agricultural, motor fuel, and wholesale customers from about 1,200 locations in 50 states. AmeriGas also sells propane-related supplies and equipment and exchanges prefilled portable tanks for empty ones. The company stores propane in Arizona, California, and Virginia and distributes its products through an interstate carrier structure that runs across the US and in Canada. Utility holding company UGI owns 44% of AmeriGas.

	Annual Growth	9/05	9/06	9/07	9/08	9/09
Sales ($ mil.)	3.6%	1,963.3	2,119.3	2,277.4	2,815.2	2,260.1
Net income ($ mil.)	38.6%	60.8	91.2	190.8	158.0	224.6
Market value ($ mil.)	2.9%	1,837.1	1,761.8	2,038.1	1,737.2	2,057.5
Employees	(0.2%)	6,000	5,900	6,200	5,900	5,950

AMERIGON INCORPORATED

NASDAQ (GM): ARGN

21680 Haggerty Rd., Ste. 101
Northville, MI 48167
Phone: 248-504-0500
Fax: 248-348-9735
Web: amerigon.com

CEO: Daniel R. Coker
CFO: Barry G. Steele
HR: —
FYE: December 31
Type: Public

Amerigon wants to put you in the hot seat — or the cool seat, depending on the season. The company's branded Climate-Control Seat (CCS), based on Amerigon's thermoelectric device (TED) technologies, allows year-round temperature control of car seats on over 40 vehicle models available in North America and Asia that are made by Ford, General Motors, and Toyota, among others. Amerigon provides the CCS under contracts with auto industry suppliers such as Lear, Bridgewater, and NHK Spring; the three customers collectively account for about two-thirds of the company's sales. Amerigon makes about half of its sales outside the US.

	Annual Growth	12/05	12/06	12/07	12/08	12/09
Sales ($ mil.)	14.3%	35.7	50.6	63.6	63.6	60.9
Net income ($ mil.)	(54.6%)	16.5	3.5	7.4	3.6	0.7
Market value ($ mil.)	8.0%	126.2	208.7	456.8	70.4	171.6
Employees	4.1%	58	59	71	78	68

AMERIGROUP CORPORATION

NYSE: AGP

4425 Corporation Ln.
Virginia Beach, VA 23462
Phone: 757-490-6900
Fax: 757-222-2330
Web: www.amerigroupcorp.com

CEO: James G. (Jim) Carlson
CFO: James W. (Jim) Truess
HR: Linda K. Whitley-Taylor
FYE: December 31
Type: Public

AMERIGROUP looks after the health of America's needy. The managed care provider targets people eligible for Medicaid, the State Children's Health Insurance Program (SCHIP), FamilyCare, and other government special needs plans. Its top Medicaid plans include a product for families receiving temporary assistance to needy families (TANF) benefits and one for aged, blind, or disabled (ABD) persons receiving supplemental income. AMERIGROUP's SCHIP programs cover uninsured kids ineligible for Medicaid. The company contracts with more than 100,000 primary care doctors and specialists, as well as 700 hospitals, to serve about 1.8 million members in about a dozen states.

	Annual Growth	12/05	12/06	12/07	12/08	12/09
Sales ($ mil.)	22.2%	2,329.9	2,835.1	3,945.5	4,516.0	5,188.1
Net income ($ mil.)	29.1%	53.7	107.1	116.4	(50.7)	149.3
Market value ($ mil.)	8.5%	1,006.2	1,855.7	1,884.6	1,526.3	1,393.9
Employees	10.3%	2,700	3,500	4,200	4,100	4,000

AMERIHEALTH MERCY HEALTH PLAN

2404 Park Dr.
Harrisburg, PA 17110
Phone: 717-651-3540
Fax: 717-651-3555
Web: www.amerihealthmercyhp.com

CEO: Michael A. Rashid
CFO: Steven H. Bohner
HR: —
FYE: December 31
Type: Joint venture

AmeriHealth Mercy Health Plan provides Medicaid health insurance plans to more than 100,000 recipients in 15 Central and Northeastern Pennsylvania counties. It provides managed care services including medical, dental, vision, prescription, and special needs. The company was founded with 300 members in 1982 as the Mercy Health Plan at Philadelphia's Misericordia Hospital. AmeriHealth Mercy Health Plan is part of the AmeriHealth Mercy family of companies, which includes the Keystone Mercy Health Plan, University Health Care, and PerformRx, and is a partnership between Mercy Health System and AmeriHealth.

	Annual Growth	12/04	12/05	12/06	12/07	12/08
Est. sales ($ mil.)	—	—	—	—	—	848.1
Employees	—	—	—	—	—	200

[H] An in-depth profile of this company is available to Hoover's Online members at hoovers.com.

135

AMERIPRIDE SERVICES INC.

10801 Wayzata Blvd.
Minnetonka, MN 55305
Phone: 952-738-4200
Fax: 952-738-4252
Web: www.ameripride.com

CEO: Bill Evans
CFO: Kay Barber
HR: Kurt Gray
FYE: December 31
Type: Private

Keeping its customers covered is AmeriPride's business. From business-casual clothing to protective apparel, AmeriPride Services offers work uniforms and apparel to US and Canadian companies in the maintenance, foodservice, health care, and technology industries. The firm rents, sells, and maintains such garments as shirts, pants, scrubs, hospital gowns, aprons, clean room coveralls, and jackets. It also supplies floor mats, mops, and a variety of towels, as well as restroom products including hand soap, room deodorizer, and paper towels. AmeriPride boasts about 150 facilities and a fleet of 2,000-plus trucks throughout North America. Founded in 1889 by George Steiner, AmeriPride is still family owned and run.

AMERIPRISE ADVISOR SERVICES, INC.

719 Griswold St., Ste. 1700
Detroit, MI 48226
Phone: 313-961-6666
Fax: 313-628-1492
Web: www.hrblock.com/investments

CEO: Joan K. Cohen
CFO: Joan K. Cohen
HR: —
FYE: April 30
Type: Subsidiary

Need advice on how to make your nest egg grow? Ameriprise Advisor Services can help. A subsidiary of Ameriprise, the company (formerly H&R Block Financial Advisors) provides securities brokerage, investment advice, cash management, banking, and lending, and retirement and college savings plans. The company also offers access to thousands of mutual funds. In recent years the unit has been trying to secure a spot among more traditional brokerage firms, and now boasts more than 950 financial advisors who manage accounts from about 135 offices nationwide. Ameriprise bought the firm for some $329 million in 2008.

AMERIPRISE FINANCIAL, INC.

NYSE: AMP

55 Ameriprise Financial Center
Minneapolis, MN 55474
Phone: 612-671-3131
Fax: 612-671-5112
Web: www.ameriprise.com

CEO: James M. (Jim) Cracchiolo
CFO: Walter S. Berman
HR: Kelli A. Hunter
FYE: December 31
Type: Public

It's no surprise that Ameriprise Financial is a leading provider of financial advice. The company offers financial planning, products, and services to nearly 3 million individual and institutional investors, primarily in the US. Through Ameriprise Financial Services and other affiliates, the company sells insurance, mutual funds, college savings plans, personal trust services, retail brokerage, and other products and services. Its Ameriprise Bank subsidiary offers deposits and loans. Ameriprise distributes its products primarily through a network of more than 12,400 financial advisors that includes direct employees, franchisees, affiliates, and its Securities America broker-dealer subsidiary.

	Annual Growth	12/05	12/06	12/07	12/08	12/09
Assets ($ mil.)	5.1%	93,121.0	104,172.0	109,230.0	95,676.0	113,774.0
Net income ($ mil.)	5.9%	574.0	631.0	814.0	(38.0)	722.0
Market value ($ mil.)	(1.4%)	10,558.0	14,034.5	14,191.6	6,015.5	9,996.7
Employees	(4.8%)	11,900	11,858	8,750	11,093	9,793

AMERIRESOURCE TECHNOLOGIES, INC.

Pink Sheets: ARIO

3440 E. Russell Rd., Ste. 217
Las Vegas, NV 89120
Phone: 702-214-4249
Fax: 702-214-4221
Web: www.ameriresourcetechnologies.com

CEO: Delmar A. Janovec
CFO: Delmar A. Janovec
HR: —
FYE: December 31
Type: Public

AmeriResource Technologies is resourceful when it comes to finding business opportunities. A holding company, AmeriResource Technologies operates through wholly owned and minority-owned subsidiaries, including RoboServer Systems, which makes software for point-of-sale systems, self-serve touch-screen kiosks, and payment processing systems; BizAuctions, a reseller of overstock retail merchandise through eBay; and ATTO Enterprises, a freight shipping cost analysis business. AmeriResource's RoboServer kiosks (made by third-party manufacturers) are often used in fast-food and full-service restaurants for inputting and processing food orders. The company was originally established in 1989 as a construction business.

AMERIS BANCORP

NASDAQ (GS): ABCB

24 2nd Ave. SE
Moultrie, GA 31768
Phone: 229-890-1111
Fax: 229-890-2235
Web: www.amerisbank.com

CEO: Edwin W. (Ed) Hortman Jr.
CFO: Dennis J. Zember Jr.
HR: —
FYE: December 31
Type: Public

Ameris Bancorp enjoys the financial climate of the Deep South. It is the holding company of Ameris Bank, which serves retail and consumer customers through some 55 branches in Alabama, Georgia, South Carolina, and northern Florida. The bank provides standard products and services, including checking and savings accounts, money market accounts, CDs, IRAs, and credit cards; it offers investment services through an agreement with Raymond James Financial. Loans secured by commercial real estate and farmland account for approximately two-thirds of the company's loan portfolio, while residential mortgages and business loans account for about 10% each.

	Annual Growth	12/05	12/06	12/07	12/08	12/09
Assets ($ mil.)	9.3%	1,697.2	2,047.5	2,112.1	2,407.1	2,424.0
Net income ($ mil.)	—	13.7	22.1	15.2	(3.9)	(41.8)
Market value ($ mil.)	(22.2%)	456.0	647.6	387.2	272.3	167.1
Employees	1.3%	585	600	620	595	615

AMERISAFE, INC.

NASDAQ (GS): AMSF

2301 Hwy. 190 West
DeRidder, LA 70634
Phone: 337-463-9052
Fax: 337-463-7298
Web: www.amerisafe.com

CEO: C. Allen Bradley Jr.
CFO: G. Janelle Frost
HR: Cynthia P. Harris
FYE: December 31
Type: Public

AMERISAFE has what it takes to insure roughnecks and truckers. AMERISAFE specializes in providing workers' compensation insurance for businesses in hazardous industries including agriculture, manufacturing, construction, logging, oil and gas, and trucking. Through its subsidiaries, American Interstate Insurance, Silver Oak Casualty, and American Interstate Insurance of Texas, the company writes coverage for more than 7,000 employers (mainly small and midsized firms). In addition, AMERISAFE offers worksite safety reviews, loss prevention, and claims management services. AMERISAFE sells its products in more than 30 states and the District of Columbia.

	Annual Growth	12/05	12/06	12/07	12/08	12/09
Assets ($ mil.)	5.8%	892.3	994.1	1,061.9	1,107.8	1,118.8
Net income ($ mil.)	67.5%	5.9	37.4	50.2	43.8	46.4
Market value ($ mil.)	15.6%	189.7	291.3	292.2	386.8	338.6
Employees	1.3%	435	451	461	468	458

AMERISERV FINANCIAL, INC.

NASDAQ (GM): ASRV

216 Franklin St.
Johnstown, PA 15907
Phone: 814-533-5300
Fax: 814-533-5427
Web: www.ameriservfinancial.com

CEO: Glenn L. Wilson
CFO: Jeffrey A. Stopko
HR: Jack W. Babich
FYE: December 31
Type: Public

AmeriServ Financial offers up a smorgasbord of banking services for Pennsylvanians. The company owns AmeriServ Financial Bank, which primarily serves the southwestern portion of the state through some 20 branches. Targeting individuals and local businesses, the bank offers standard services such as deposits, credit cards, and loans. Commercial mortgages account for more than half of its loan portfolio; other real estate loans, including residential mortgage and construction loans, make up about 30%. One of a handful of unionized banks in the US, AmeriServ also manages union pension funds through its AmeriServ Trust and Financial Services subsidiary, which provides trust and wealth management services as well.

	Annual Growth	12/05	12/06	12/07	12/08	12/09
Assets ($ mil.)	2.5%	880.2	896.0	904.9	966.9	970.0
Net income ($ mil.)	—	(9.1)	2.3	3.0	5.5	(4.9)
Market value ($ mil.)	(21.4%)	93.0	104.6	58.8	42.2	35.4
Employees	(3.0%)	428	414	385	379	379

AMERISOURCEBERGEN CORPORATION

NYSE: ABC

1300 Morris Dr.
Chesterbrook, PA 19087
Phone: 610-727-7000
Fax: 610-727-3600
Web: www.amerisourcebergen.com

CEO: R. David (Dave) Yost
CFO: Michael D. DiCandilo
HR: —
FYE: September 30
Type: Public

AmerisourceBergen is *the* source for many of North America's pharmacies and health care providers. The company serves as a go-between for drugmakers and the pharmacies, doctors' offices, hospitals, and other health care providers who dispense drugs. Operating primarily in the US and Canada, it distributes generic, branded, and over-the-counter pharmaceuticals, as well as some medical supplies and other products, using its network of more than two dozen facilities. Its specialty distribution unit focuses on sensitive and complex biopharmaceuticals, such as cancer drugs, vaccines, and plasma products. The company also has some pharmaceutical packaging operations.

	Annual Growth	9/05	9/06	9/07	9/08	9/09
Sales ($ mil.)	7.1%	54,577.3	61,203.1	66,074.3	70,189.7	71,760.0
Net income ($ mil.)	13.0%	309.0	467.7	469.2	250.6	503.4
Market value ($ mil.)	4.5%	5,297.7	6,195.5	6,403.3	5,318.4	6,322.8
Employees	(6.4%)	13,400	14,700	11,300	10,900	10,300

AMERISTAR CASINOS, INC.

NASDAQ (GS): ASCA

3773 Howard Hughes Pkwy., Ste. 490 South
Las Vegas, NV 89109
Phone: 702-567-7000
Fax: 702-369-8860
Web: www.ameristarcasinos.com

CEO: Gordon R. Kanofsky
CFO: Thomas M. (Tom) Steinbauer
HR: —
FYE: December 31
Type: Public

When you wish upon Ameristar, you can hit the jackpot on land or on boat. Ameristar Casinos owns six casino hotels and two casinos. Properties include Ameristar St. Charles and Ameristar Kansas City (both in Missouri), Ameristar Black Hawk (Colorado), and The Jackpot Properties (Nevada). Ameristar Casino Vicksburg in Mississippi is a permanently docked riverboat casino on the Mississippi River, and Ameristar Casinos' Council Bluffs (Iowa) riverboat casino sits on the Missouri River. Ameristar's casinos offer slot machines (about 85% of gaming sales), blackjack, craps, roulette, and poker. Properties also include movie theaters, shops, entertainment arenas, restaurants, bars, and private clubs.

	Annual Growth	12/05	12/06	12/07	12/08	12/09
Sales ($ mil.)	6.0%	961.4	1,000.3	1,080.5	1,267.9	1,215.4
Net income ($ mil.)	—	66.3	59.6	69.4	(130.7)	(4.7)
Market value ($ mil.)	(9.5%)	1,313.7	1,779.0	1,593.8	500.0	881.4
Employees	0.5%	7,460	7,200	9,000	7,700	7,600

AMERISURE MUTUAL INSURANCE COMPANY

26777 Halsted Rd.
Farmington Hills, MI 48331
Phone: 248-615-9000
Fax: 248-615-8548
Web: www.amerisure.com

CEO: Richard F. Russell
CFO: R. Douglas Kinnan
HR: Derick W. Adams
FYE: December 31
Type: Mutual company

This company wants to help all businesses rest Amerisured. Amerisure provides a range of commercial property & casualty products with a special focus on the manufacturing and contracting industries. Coverage includes general and employee benefits liability, workers compensation, property, auto, inland marine, and equipment insurance. Amerisure has expanded to provide coverage to the health care industry, including long-term care facilities and hospitals. The company operates out of 10 offices around the US. It uses a network of independent agents and brokers to distribute its products. Amerisure was founded as Michigan Workmen's Compensation Mutual Insurance in 1912.

	Annual Growth	12/04	12/05	12/06	12/07	12/08
Est. sales ($ mil.)	—	—	—	—	—	430.8
Employees	—	—	—	—	—	700

AMERITRANS CAPITAL CORPORATION

NASDAQ (CM): AMTC

747 3rd Ave., 4th Fl.
New York, NY 10017
Phone: 212-355-2449
Fax: 212-759-3338
Web: www.ameritranscapital.com

CEO: Michael Feinsod
CFO: Gary C. Granoff
HR: —
FYE: June 30
Type: Public

The taxi meter has been switched off at Ameritrans Capital Corporation. The company in 2008 sold its portfolio of medallion loans held by subsidiary Elk Associates Funding to Medallion Financial for $31 million. Elk Associates provides taxicab owners in Boston, Chicago, Miami, and New York City with financing to acquire medallions, or city-granted operating licenses. Medallion loans accounted for about half of Ameritrans' lending portfolio. Ameritrans will use the proceeds of that sale to pay down debt and build its portfolio of corporate loans, including commercial mortgages and mid-market commercial loans.

	Annual Growth	6/05	6/06	6/07	6/08	6/09
Assets ($ mil.)	(16.4%)	57.9	56.0	63.9	62.0	28.3
Net income ($ mil.)	—	0.1	(0.2)	0.0	(0.5)	(5.5)
Market value ($ mil.)	(27.5%)	20.0	17.2	17.7	10.2	5.5
Employees	(2.6%)	10	10	10	10	9

AMERITYRE CORPORATION

OTC: AMTY

1501 Industrial Rd.
Boulder City, NV 89005
Phone: 702-294-2689
Fax: 702-294-3873
Web: www.amerityre.com

CEO: Michael J. Kapral Jr.
CFO: Anders A. Suarez
HR: —
FYE: June 30
Type: Public

Amerityre makes polyurethane foam tires, which are unable to go flat, for the bicycle and lawn equipment industries. The company also offers composite tires, pneumatic tires, and solid tires, along with tire-filling materials. Central Purchasing accounts for one-fifth of Amerityre's sales. In 2008 the company acquired the manufacturing assets of a competitor, KIK Technology International, and KIK went out of business.

	Annual Growth	6/05	6/06	6/07	6/08	6/09
Sales ($ mil.)	17.1%	1.7	2.0	3.4	2.9	3.2
Net income ($ mil.)	—	(10.1)	(5.3)	(5.0)	(4.2)	(3.6)
Market value ($ mil.)	(56.3%)	225.9	251.3	139.1	42.6	8.2
Employees	(10.1%)	26	26	28	22	17

AMERON INTERNATIONAL CORPORATION NYSE: AMN

245 S. Los Robles Ave.
Pasadena, CA 91101
Phone: 626-683-4000
Fax: 626-683-4060
Web: www.ameron.com

CEO: James S. Marlen
CFO: Gary Wagner
HR: Terrence P. (Terry) O'Shea
FYE: November 30
Type: Public

Hardly a gearhead, Ameron is more interested in fluid transmission, not transmission fluid. The company designs, makes, and markets fiberglass-composite pipes for transmitting oil, chemicals, corrosive liquids, and other specialty materials. Ameron also makes and sells concrete and steel pipe used for water transmission and wind towers to developers, contractors, and government agencies in the western US. Additionally, the company supplies ready-mix concrete and aggregates, box culverts, and dune sand for construction projects in Hawaii; it also manufactures concrete and steel poles for lighting and traffic signals.

	Annual Growth	11/05	11/06	11/07	11/08	11/09
Sales ($ mil.)	(6.1%)	704.6	549.2	631.0	667.5	546.9
Net income ($ mil.)	0.5%	32.6	52.2	67.2	58.6	33.3
Market value ($ mil.)	6.1%	414.5	693.5	975.4	496.8	525.2
Employees	(5.4%)	3,000	2,500	2,600	2,800	2,400

AMES CONSTRUCTION, INC.

2000 Ames Dr.
Burnsville, MN 55306
Phone: 952-435-7106
Fax: 952-435-7142
Web: www.amesconstruction.com

CEO: Raymond G. Ames
CFO: Dennis D. McGill
HR: —
FYE: November 30
Type: Private

Ames Construction aims right for the heart of the heavy construction industry. The company is primarily a general contractor, providing heavy civil and industrial construction services to the transportation, mining, and power industries, primarily in the West and Midwest. The family-owned company works on highways, airports, bridges, pipelines, power plants, and other infrastructure projects. Ames also performs flood control, environmental remediation, reclamation, and landfill work. Additionally, the firm builds golf courses and undertakes other commercial and residential site development projects. It typically partners with other companies to perform the engineering and design portion of construction jobs.

AMES NATIONAL CORPORATION NASDAQ (CM): ATLO

405 5th St.
Ames, IA 50010
Phone: 515-232-6251
Fax: 515-663-3033
Web: www.amesnational.com

CEO: Thomas H. Pohlman
CFO: John P. Nelson
HR: Jennifer J. Thompson
FYE: December 31
Type: Public

This company wants you to take Ames . . . and central Iowa. Ames National Corporation is the multi-bank holding company for flagship subsidiary First National Bank, Ames, Iowa, as well as Boone Bank & Trust, Randall-Story State Bank, State Bank & Trust, and United Bank & Trust. With a total of about a dozen branches, the banks provide area individuals and businesses with standard services such as checking and savings accounts, CDs, IRAs, and credit and debit cards. Commercial and agricultural real estate loans account for about half of the company's loan portfolio, which also includes residential, construction, consumer, and business loans. The banks also offer trust and financial management services.

	Annual Growth	12/05	12/06	12/07	12/08	12/09
Assets ($ mil.)	2.8%	819.4	838.9	861.6	858.1	915.6
Net income ($ mil.)	(6.1%)	11.6	10.9	11.0	6.4	9.0
Market value ($ mil.)	(4.8%)	242.5	198.1	183.9	250.3	199.1
Employees	0.7%	182	184	95	25	187

AMES TRUE TEMPER, INC.

465 Railroad Ave.
Camp Hill, PA 17011
Phone: 717-737-1500
Fax: 717-730-2552
Web: www.ames.com

CEO: Duane Greenly
CFO: David M. (Dave) Nuti
HR: Chris Ebling
FYE: September 30
Type: Private

It could be said that Ames True Temper is at the root of all lawn and garden tool manufacturers in the US. Tracing its history to 1774, the company was founded by John Ames as a shovel maker. Today it's one of the largest suppliers of non-powered yard equipment in North America. Its product portfolio includes long-handle tools, planters, pruning and striking tools, wheelbarrows, hoses and hose reels, and snow tools. Products are marketed under the Ames, True Temper, Garant, Hound Dog, Jackson Professional, Razor-Back, and Union Tools names. They are sold in North America, Europe, and Australia via mass merchandisers, wholesalers, and distributors. Ames True Temper is controlled by affiliates of Castle Harlan.

	Annual Growth	9/04	9/05	9/06	9/07	9/08
Est. sales ($ mil.)	—	—	—	—	—	415.9
Employees	—	—	—	—	—	1,690

AMETEK, INC. NYSE: AME

37 N. Valley Rd., Bldg. 4
Paoli, PA 19301
Phone: 610-647-2121
Fax: 610-323-9337
Web: www.ametek.com

CEO: Frank S. Hermance
CFO: John J. Molinelli
HR: John J. Weaver
FYE: December 31
Type: Public

You might say that AMETEK is *instrument*al when it comes to monitoring equipment and electric motors. The company's Electronic Instruments Group makes monitoring, calibration, and display devices for the aerospace, heavy equipment, power generation, and other industrial markets. Its Electromechanical Group makes air-moving electric motors for vacuum cleaners and other floor care equipment, blowers and heat exchangers, connectors for moisture-proof applications, and specialty metals for the aerospace, mass transit, medical, and office products markets. AMETEK gets about half of its sales in the US.

	Annual Growth	12/05	12/06	12/07	12/08	12/09
Sales ($ mil.)	10.0%	1,434.5	1,819.3	2,136.9	2,531.1	2,098.4
Net income ($ mil.)	10.0%	140.6	181.9	228.0	247.0	205.8
Market value ($ mil.)	7.8%	3,016.2	3,386.3	4,981.6	3,212.9	4,066.9
Employees	0.8%	9,800	10,400	11,300	5,700	10,100

AMEXDRUG CORPORATION OTC: AXRX

8909 W. Olympic Blvd., Ste. 208
Beverly Hills, CA 90211
Phone: 310-855-0475
Fax: 888-325-2499
Web: www.amexdrug.com

CEO: Jack Amin
CFO: Jack Amin
HR: —
FYE: December 31
Type: Public

Amexdrug, through subsidiaries Allied Med and Dermagen, is a wholesale distributor of pharmaceuticals, nutritional supplements, and beauty products to pharmacies and other retailers. The company allows small pharmacies to get the lower prices that large pharmaceutical chains such as Walgreen and CVS enjoy. Its customers are primarily located in California. Part of Allied Med's growth strategy includes increasing its online traffic, so it is increasing its name recognition and branding efforts. Top executive Jack Amin and his wife own more than 90% of the company.

	Annual Growth	12/05	12/06	12/07	12/08	12/09
Sales ($ mil.)	18.3%	5.0	4.6	6.1	5.7	9.8
Net income ($ mil.)	—	0.0	0.0	0.0	0.0	0.0
Market value ($ mil.)	2.4%	16.9	17.3	10.2	8.6	18.6
Employees	23.6%	6	6	6	15	14

AMF BOWLING WORLDWIDE, INC.

7313 Bell Creek Rd.	CEO: Frederick R. (Fred) Hipp
Mechanicsville, VA 23111	CFO: Steve Satterwhite
Phone: 804-730-4000	HR: Evelyn Walter
Fax: —	FYE: June 30
Web: www.amf.com	Type: Subsidiary

If you're a fan of knocking down pins, this company is right down your alley. AMF Bowling Worldwide is a leading operator of bowling centers with more than 300 locations in about 35 states. Operated through subsidiary AMF Bowling Centers, the chain offers league and non-league bowling, along with video games, billiards, and other amusements. AMF's activity centers also offer food and beverage service and sell bowling gear. In addition to its chain of bowling centers, the company owns 50% of QubicaAMF Worldwide, a joint venture with Italian manufacturer Qubica that sells such bowling center equipment as refurbished pinsetters and scoring systems. AMF Bowling is controlled by investment firm Code Hennessy.

AMGEN INC.

NASDAQ (GS): AMGN

1 Amgen Center Dr.	CEO: Kevin W. Sharer
Thousand Oaks, CA 91320	CFO: Michael A. Kelly
Phone: 805-447-1000	HR: Brian M. McNamee
Fax: 805-447-1010	FYE: December 31
Web: www.amgen.com	Type: Public

Amgen is among the biggest of the biotech big'uns, and it's determined to get even bigger. The company uses cellular biology and medicinal chemistry to target cancers, kidney ailments, inflammatory disorders, and metabolic diseases. Anti-anemia drugs Epogen and Aranesp account for more than one-third of its sales. Enbrel, another leading drug, treats rheumatoid arthritis and is one of the best-selling drugs in this multi-billion-dollar market. The company has a healthy drug pipeline, as well as marketing alliances with Japanese brewer and drugmaker Kirin, Johnson & Johnson, and other pharmaceutical companies. Amgen sells its products primarily through wholesale distributors in North America and Europe.

	Annual Growth	12/05	12/06	12/07	12/08	12/09
Sales ($ mil.)	4.2%	12,430.0	14,268.0	14,771.0	15,003.0	14,642.0
Net income ($ mil.)	5.8%	3,674.0	2,950.0	3,166.0	4,196.0	4,605.0
Market value ($ mil.)	(8.0%)	75,543.0	65,436.8	44,486.7	55,320.9	54,190.6
Employees	1.0%	16,500	20,100	17,500	16,900	17,200

AMICA MUTUAL INSURANCE COMPANY

100 Amica Way	CEO: Robert A. DiMuccio
Lincoln, RI 02865	CFO: —
Phone: 401-334-6000	HR: Jill H. Andy
Fax: 401-334-4241	FYE: December 31
Web: www.amica.com	Type: Mutual company

Amica will amicably serve your insurance needs. The company provides a variety of personal insurance products, including auto, home, and life policies. Amica sells its policies directly to customers through some 40 offices throughout the US. The oldest mutual automobile insurance company in the US, it traces its roots back to 1907 (when fire coverage was a car owner's most important need due to the danger of exploding gas tanks). Amica, the company's current incarnation, was formed in 1973 when Automobile Mutual Insurance Company of America combined with Factory Mutual Liability Insurance Company of America.

	Annual Growth	12/04	12/05	12/06	12/07	12/08
Est. sales ($ mil.)	—	—	—	—	—	1,318.4
Employees	—	—	—	—	—	3,000

AMICAS, INC.

20 Guest St., Ste. 200	CEO: Stephen N. Kahane
Boston, MA 02135	CFO: Kevin C. Burns
Phone: 617-779-7878	HR: Denise Mitchell
Fax: 617-779-7879	FYE: December 31
Web: www.amicas.com	Type: Subsidiary

Information technology company AMICAS has a friend in radiology and cardiology professionals. Serving medical imaging centers, ambulatory care facilities, and hospitals, AMICAS offers radiology and cardiology information systems, picture archiving and communications (PACS) systems, Web-based and wireless image and report distribution tools, and billing systems, among other products. The company also offers consulting, implementation, and support services, as well as electronic data transfer services to customers using its billing and claims systems. AMICAS traces its roots back to 1996. The company was acquired by rival Merge Healthcare for about $248 million in cash.

	Annual Growth	12/05	12/06	12/07	12/08	12/09
Sales ($ mil.)	14.0%	52.8	49.4	49.9	50.4	89.1
Net income ($ mil.)	—	44.2	(1.0)	(0.9)	(30.1)	(4.0)
Employees	12.4%	246	247	253	230	393

AMICUS THERAPEUTICS, INC.

NASDAQ (GM): FOLD

6 Cedar Brook Dr.	CEO: John F. Crowley
Cranbury, NJ 08512	CFO: John M. McAdam
Phone: 609-662-2000	HR: S. Nicole Schaeffer
Fax: 609-662-2001	FYE: December 31
Web: www.amicustherapeutics.com	Type: Public

Amicus Therapeutics develops drugs that treat rare genetic diseases known as lysosomal storage disorders. Unlike other treatments which replace defective enzymes, Amicus uses small molecule pharmacological "chaperones" which bind to a patient's own defective proteins and restore their functions. Its lead drug candidate, Amigal, is aimed at aiding patients with Fabry disease. Another candidate, Plicera, is in development to treat Gaucher disease, while a third candidate, AT2220 is targeting Pompe disease. The company is also researching treatments for neurodegenerative diseases including Alzheimer's and Parkinson's.

	Annual Growth	12/05	12/06	12/07	12/08	12/09
Sales ($ mil.)	498.1%	—	—	1.8	15.0	64.4
Net income ($ mil.)	—	—	—	(41.2)	(39.4)	(6.6)
Market value ($ mil.)	(39.2%)	—	—	297.1	220.6	109.7
Employees	(8.2%)	—	—	115	115	97

AMKOR TECHNOLOGY, INC.

NASDAQ (GS): AMKR

1900 S. Price Rd.	CEO: Kenneth T. (Ken) Joyce
Chandler, AZ 85286	CFO: Joanne Solomon
Phone: 480-821-5000	HR: Dave Lawton
Fax: 480-821-8276	FYE: December 31
Web: www.amkor.com	Type: Public

Amkor Technology is more than amicable about lending a hand with microchip packaging. Amkor claims a top spot in contract packaging/assembly and testing services for semiconductor manufacturers. Packaging involves dicing semiconductor wafers into separate chips, die bonding, wire bonding, and encapsulating chips in protective plastic. Amkor's testing procedures verify current, function, timing, and voltage. The company has some 250 customers worldwide, including big semiconductor companies and electronics OEMs, such as Altera, Intel, IBM, LSI Corp., QUALCOMM, STMicroelectronics, Texas Instruments, and Toshiba. Nearly two-thirds of Amkor's sales are outside the US.

	Annual Growth	12/05	12/06	12/07	12/08	12/09
Sales ($ mil.)	0.9%	2,099.9	2,728.6	2,739.4	2,658.6	2,179.1
Net income ($ mil.)	—	(136.9)	170.1	219.9	(456.7)	156.0
Market value ($ mil.)	6.3%	1,028.9	1,716.1	1,567.2	400.5	1,315.5
Employees	(6.7%)	24,000	22,700	21,600	20,500	18,200

AML COMMUNICATIONS, INC.

OTC: AMLJ

1000 Avenida Acaso
Camarillo, CA 93012
Phone: 805-388-1345
Fax: 805-484-2191
Web: www.amlj.com

CEO: Jacob Inbar
CFO: Heera Lee
HR: —
FYE: March 31
Type: Public

AML Communications wants to pump up the volume — and its sales — with its microwave amplifiers for wireless communications. The amplifiers support defense-related radar, satellite, and surveillance systems, as well as commercial wireless applications. AML also makes higher-power microwave amplifiers for the defense market through subsidiary Microwave Power. AML's customers include defense equipment manufacturers (such as Raytheon and Boeing), systems integrators, and commercial wireless operators (AT&T Mobility and Verizon Wireless).

	Annual Growth	3/05	3/06	3/07	3/08	3/09
Sales ($ mil.)	11.5%	8.6	9.5	8.9	12.7	13.3
Net income ($ mil.)	2.7%	0.9	2.2	1.6	2.2	1.0
Market value ($ mil.)	(26.7%)	12.9	13.0	14.5	16.0	3.7
Employees	7.6%	70	71	80	95	94

AMN HEALTHCARE SERVICES, INC.

NYSE: AHS

12400 High Bluff Dr., Ste. 100
San Diego, CA 92130
Phone: 866-871-8519
Fax: 800-282-0328
Web: www.amnhealthcare.com

CEO: Susan R. Nowakowski
CFO: Bary G. Bailey
HR: Julie Fletcher
FYE: December 31
Type: Public

Understaffed hospitals say "amen" for AMN Healthcare Services. Operating as American Mobile Healthcare, Medical Express, NurseChoice, NursesRx, Preferred Healthcare Staffing, and O'Grady-Peyton International, the firm is one of the leading temporary health care staffing companies in the world. It places nurses, technicians, and therapists for 13-week stints at hospitals, clinics, and schools nationwide. With professionals recruited from Australia, Canada, South Africa, the UK, and the US, AMN provides travel reimbursement and housing for its 6,800 nurse and health care workers on assignment. The majority of temporary assignments for its 3,000 clients are at acute-care hospitals in the US.

	Annual Growth	12/05	12/06	12/07	12/08	12/09
Sales ($ mil.)	1.9%	705.8	1,081.7	1,164.0	1,217.2	759.8
Net income ($ mil.)	—	22.2	35.1	36.5	34.4	(122.2)
Market value ($ mil.)	(17.7%)	648.3	902.7	562.8	277.3	297.0
Employees	(9.7%)	1,700	2,000	2,000	2,000	1,130

AMPAC PACKAGING, LLC

12025 Tricon Rd.
Cincinnati, OH 45246
Phone: 513-671-1777
Fax: 513-671-2920
Web: www.ampaconline.com

CEO: John Q. Baumann
CFO: Jon Dill
HR: —
FYE: December 31
Type: Private

Ampac Packaging packs a lot into its products. The company manufactures flexible packaging including stand-up pouches and rollstock for food and beverages, high-end performance flexible packaging materials for pharmaceutical and health and beauty products, and bags of all styles for garments and more. Ampac also makes security products such as cash transfer and deposit bags. Offering 200-plus custom films, the company courts business from retailers, restaurants, and groceries, to convenience stores and even gaming venues. A private investor group comprising Prudential Capital, Falcon Investment Advisors, and Ampac executives has owned the company since 2000.

	Annual Growth	12/04	12/05	12/06	12/07	12/08
Est. sales ($ mil.)	—	—	—	—	—	119.2
Employees	—	—	—	—	—	922

AMPCO-PITTSBURGH CORPORATION

NYSE: AP

600 Grant St., Ste. 4600
Pittsburgh, PA 15219
Phone: 412-456-4400
Fax: 412-456-4404
Web: www.ampcopgh.com

CEO: Robert A. Paul
CFO: Marliss D. (Dee Ann) Johnson
HR: —
FYE: December 31
Type: Public

All amped up to make some financial noise, Ampco-Pittsburgh manufactures a variety of heavy metal products. Operations straddle two arenas. Its forged and cast steel rolls units, Union Electric Steel and Davy Roll Co., make hardened-steel rolls for steel and aluminum manufacturers. Its air and liquid processing segment comprises three companies: Buffalo Pumps, offering centrifugal pumps for refrigeration, marine defense, and power generation industries; Aerofin, driving finned-tube heat-exchange coils for construction and utility applications, and Buffalo Air Handling, supplying custom air-handling systems used in commercial, industrial, and institutional buildings.

	Annual Growth	12/05	12/06	12/07	12/08	12/09
Sales ($ mil.)	4.9%	247.0	301.8	346.8	394.5	299.2
Net income ($ mil.)	16.6%	15.0	16.6	39.2	12.6	27.7
Market value ($ mil.)	21.4%	148.7	343.1	390.7	222.4	323.1
Employees	(0.1%)	1,234	1,324	1,323	1,306	1,231

AMPHASTAR PHARMACEUTICALS, INC.

11570 6th St.
Rancho Cucamonga, CA 91730
Phone: 909-980-9484
Fax: 909-980-8296
Web: www.amphastar.com

CEO: Jack Y. Zhang
CFO: John Webber
HR: —
FYE: December 31
Type: Private

Amphastar Pharmaceuticals wants to help drugs help themselves. A maker of injectable and inhalant drugs and drug delivery systems, the company focuses on drugs that are difficult to manufacture or can be improved with new delivery systems. Amphastar's products include Amphadase (increases absorption and dispersion of injected drugs), Duocaine (anesthetic for eye surgery), Cortrosyn (tests for adrenal gland disorders), and prefilled disposable pipettes (single-dose dispenser for liquids, creams, and mists). The company also markets inhalants, and it offers contract manufacturing services that include labeling and packaging, cold storage, and aseptic filling.

	Annual Growth	12/04	12/05	12/06	12/07	12/08
Est. sales ($ mil.)	—	—	—	—	—	300.0
Employees	—	—	—	—	—	1,040

AMPHENOL CORPORATION

NYSE: APH

358 Hall Ave.
Wallingford, CT 06492
Phone: 203-265-8900
Fax: 203-265-8516
Web: www.amphenol.com

CEO: Richard A. (Adam) Norwitt
CFO: Diana G. Reardon
HR: Jerome F. Monteith
FYE: December 31
Type: Public

Amphenol knows it's all about connections. The company makes cable and connectors for the communications, industrial, medical, and military markets. Amphenol's interconnect products, which account for about 90% of sales, are used in computers, wired and wireless communications and networking equipment, medical instruments, office equipment, aircraft and spacecraft, and energy applications. Its Times Fiber subsidiary is a leading maker of coaxial cable for the cable TV industry and flat-ribbon cable for computer and telecommunications products. Amphenol ships products to more than 10,000 customer locations around the world, and it has a diverse customer base. Nearly two-thirds of sales are outside the US.

	Annual Growth	12/05	12/06	12/07	12/08	12/09
Sales ($ mil.)	11.8%	1,808.1	2,471.4	2,851.0	3,236.5	2,820.1
Net income ($ mil.)	11.4%	206.3	255.7	353.2	419.2	317.8
Market value ($ mil.)	20.2%	3,840.7	5,387.1	8,047.6	4,161.8	8,014.7
Employees	9.1%	22,700	25,600	32,000	30,000	32,200

AMPLIFON USA INC.

5000 Cheshire Pkwy. N.
Plymouth, MN 55446
Phone: 763-268-4000
Fax: 763-268-4254
Web: www.amplifonusa.com

CEO: Heinz Ruch
CFO: Mario Riemma
HR: Deb Gran
FYE: December 31
Type: Subsidiary

You don't have to yell! Amplifon USA manages the US holdings of hearing aid company Amplifon S.p.A. The company's brands include Miracle-Ear and Sonus. Amplifon USA controls the distribution, sales, and follow-up services for its hearing aids through some 4,000 owned or affiliated clinics throughout the US. Many of its Miracle-Ear clinics are located in Sears stores while its Amplifon Hearing Aid Centers are usually located in Wal-Mart stores. The company also supports a network of independent hearing care practices through its Elite Hearing Network and provides hearing benefit plans through its HearPO division.

AMPRO COMPUTERS, INC.

5215 Hellyer Ave., Ste. 110
San Jose, CA 95138
Phone: 408-360-0200
Fax: 408-360-0222
Web: www.ampro.com

CEO: Joanne L. Mumola Williams
CFO: —
HR: —
FYE: December 31
Type: Subsidiary

Ampro Computers may be high-tech, but it's no stranger to factory floors and other rugged environments. The company makes single-board computers and computer-on-module products, specializing in embedded applications in industrial automation. Its products are well-suited for the harsh environments of factories and other places where computer gear is expected to keep working despite the debilitating effects of dust, heat, and vibrations. Ampro supports various computer operating systems, including Linux, QNX Neutrino, VxWorks, and Windows. The company was acquired by ADLINK Technology in 2008.

AMR CORPORATION

NYSE: AMR

4333 Amon Carter Blvd.
Fort Worth, TX 76155
Phone: 817-963-1234
Fax: 817-967-4162
Web: www.aa.com

CEO: Gerard J. Arpey
CFO: Thomas W. Horton
HR: Mark Burdette
FYE: December 31
Type: Public

AMR knows America's spacious skies — and lots of others. Its main subsidiary is American Airlines, one of the largest airlines in the world. Together with sister company American Eagle and regional carriers that operate as American Connection, American Airlines serves some 250 destinations in about 40 countries in the Americas, Europe, and the Asia/Pacific region. The overall fleet exceeds 900 aircraft; American Airlines operates about 625 jets. The carrier extends its geographic reach through code-sharing arrangements. It is part of the Oneworld global marketing alliance, along with British Airways, Cathay Pacific, Iberia, Qantas, and other airlines.

	Annual Growth	12/05	12/06	12/07	12/08	12/09
Sales ($ mil.)	(1.0%)	20,712.0	22,563.0	22,935.0	23,766.0	19,917.0
Net income ($ mil.)	—	(861.0)	231.0	504.0	(2,071.0)	(1,468.0)
Market value ($ mil.)	(23.2%)	7,396.2	10,057.9	4,667.9	3,550.0	2,571.9
Employees	(2.8%)	88,400	86,600	85,500	84,100	78,900

AMREP CORPORATION

NYSE: AXR

300 Alexander Park, Ste. 204
Princeton, NJ 08540
Phone: 609-716-8200
Fax: 609-716-8255
Web: amrepcorp.com

CEO: James H. Wall
CFO: Peter M. Pizza
HR: —
FYE: April 30
Type: Public

Mailing magazines and developing land in New Mexico keep AMREP hopping. About 80% of the company's sales come from newsstand distribution and subscription and product fulfillment services it provides through its Kable Media Services and Palm Coast Data subsidiaries. The units serve about 200 publishing clients by managing subscriptions and mailing 900-plus magazine titles. Through its AMREP Southwest subsidiary, the company develops its Rio Rancho property (roughly 17,300 acres) as well as certain parts of Sandoval County outside Albuquerque, New Mexico. AMREP was founded in 1961.

	Annual Growth	4/05	4/06	4/07	4/08	4/09
Sales ($ mil.)	2.1%	134.5	148.3	204.8	172.1	145.9
Net income ($ mil.)	—	15.5	26.0	45.1	13.7	(43.5)
Market value ($ mil.)	(6.5%)	145.7	280.3	361.3	312.7	111.5
Employees	8.2%	1,365	1,295	3,300	3,300	1,870

AMSCAN HOLDINGS, INC.

80 Grasslands Rd.
Elmsford, NY 10523
Phone: 914-345-2020
Fax: 914-345-3884
Web: www.amscan.com

CEO: Gerald C. (Jerry) Rittenberg
CFO: Michael A. Correale
HR: —
FYE: December 31
Type: Private

Amscan Holdings caters to the party animal in all of us. The company makes party goods, such as balloons, invitations, piñatas, stationery, and tableware, and supplies party superstores and other retailers worldwide. It operates production and distribution facilities in Asia, Australia, Europe, and North America. Amscan also markets its products through about 900 company-owned or franchised stores in the US, Puerto Rico, and the United Arab Emirates. Shops operate under the Party City, Party America, Factory Card & Party Outlet, and Halloween USA banners, among others. Amscan is a subsidiary of AAH Holdings, which is controlled by Berkshire Partners and Weston Presidio.

	Annual Growth	12/04	12/05	12/06	12/07	12/08
Sales ($ mil.)	40.6%	399.2	417.7	1,015.1	1,247.4	1,559.7
Net income ($ mil.)	51.4%	7.7	12.3	6.4	19.3	40.5
Employees	68.6%	1,750	6,720	8,138	12,569	14,130

AMSTED INDUSTRIES INCORPORATED

2 Prudential Plaza, 180 N. Stetson St., Ste. 1800
Chicago, IL 60601
Phone: 312-645-1700
Fax: 312-819-8494
Web: www.amsted.com

CEO: W. Robert Reum
CFO: Thomas E. (Tom) Bergmann
HR: Shirley J. Whitesell
FYE: September 30
Type: Private

Wilbur and Orville Wright's first flight might never have succeeded without an assist from Amsted Industries' Diamond Chain subsidiary. A maker of bicycle and industrial roller chains, Diamond produced the propeller chain for the Wright brothers' aircraft. The company's three different segments manufacture highly engineered industrial components for locomotive and railcar makers, automotive OEMs, and construction and building suppliers. Amsted is a major force in making freight car undercarriages, too. Its main subsidiaries include ASF-Keystone, Griffin Pipe Products, and Means Industries. Employee-owned, Amsted runs nearly 50 plants worldwide. North American markets account for 85% of the company's sales.

An in-depth profile of this company is available to Hoover's Online members at hoovers.com.

141

AMSURG CORP.

NASDAQ (GS): AMSG

20 Burton Hills Blvd., Ste. 500
Nashville, TN 37215
Phone: 615-665-1283
Fax: 615-665-0755
Web: www.amsurg.com

CEO: Christopher A. Holden
CFO: Claire M. Gulmi
HR: —
FYE: December 31
Type: Public

AmSurg serves only certain cuts, but it's not a pricey steakhouse — the company operates specialty ambulatory surgery centers that focus on a narrow range of high-volume, low-risk procedures. Specialties include gastroenterology (colonoscopy and endoscopy), orthopedics (knee scopes and carpal tunnel repair), and ophthalmology (cataracts and laser eye surgery). AmSurg promotes its centers, which are each affiliated with a physicians practice group, to patients and doctors, as well as managed care organizations and employers. AmSurg owns a majority interest in more than 190 outpatient centers in 32 states and the District of Columbia. It also has three centers under development.

	Annual Growth	12/05	12/06	12/07	12/08	12/09
Sales ($ mil.)	14.3%	391.8	464.6	531.1	600.7	668.8
Net income ($ mil.)	50.7%	35.2	37.7	44.2	47.0	181.4
Market value ($ mil.)	(0.9%)	706.9	711.2	836.7	721.7	680.9
Employees	13.0%	1,705	2,000	2,150	2,460	2,780

AMTECH SYSTEMS, INC.

NASDAQ (GM): ASYS

131 S. Clark Dr.
Tempe, AZ 85281
Phone: 480-967-5146
Fax: 480-968-3763
Web: www.amtechsystems.com

CEO: Jong S. Whang
CFO: Bradley C. Anderson
HR: —
FYE: September 30
Type: Public

Amtech Systems furnishes fabs with furnaces and more. The company's Tempress Systems subsidiary makes diffusion furnaces for semiconductor and solar cell fabrication, as well as for precision thermal processing (annealing, brazing, silvering, sealing, and soldering) of electronic devices, including optical components and photovoltaic (PV) solar cells. Its P.R. Hoffman Machine Products subsidiary makes equipment used to polish items such as silicon wafers, precision optics, ceramic components, and disk media. About two-thirds of sales come from customers in the Asia/Pacific region, primarily from China and Taiwan.

	Annual Growth	9/05	9/06	9/07	9/08	9/09
Sales ($ mil.)	17.4%	27.9	40.4	46.0	80.3	53.0
Net income ($ mil.)	—	(0.3)	1.3	2.4	2.9	(1.6)
Market value ($ mil.)	(2.0%)	51.9	60.0	115.6	84.0	47.8
Employees	7.2%	144	153	165	210	190

AMTRUST FINANCIAL SERVICES, INC.

NASDAQ (GM): AFSI

59 Maiden Ln., 6th Fl.
New York, NY 10038
Phone: 212-220-7120
Fax: 212-220-7130
Web: www.amtrustgroup.com

CEO: Barry D. Zyskind
CFO: Ronald E. Pipoly Jr.
HR: —
FYE: December 31
Type: Public

Insurance holding company AmTrust Financial Services likes a mix of businesses on its plate. The company's 11 subsidiaries offer a range of specialty and commercial property/casualty insurance products for small and medium sized customers including workers' compensation products, commercial auto and general liability, and extended service and warranty coverage of consumer and commercial goods. Its subsidiaries, which operate in the US, Bermuda, Ireland, and England, underwrite insurance policies that are then distributed through brokers, agents, and claims administrators. Its customers include restaurants, retail stores, physicians' offices, auto and consumer electronics manufacturers, and nonprofit organizations.

	Annual Growth	12/05	12/06	12/07	12/08	12/09
Assets ($ mil.)	53.5%	612.9	1,185.4	2,322.8	3,143.9	3,400.4
Net income ($ mil.)	28.7%	37.6	48.9	90.1	82.9	103.2
Market value ($ mil.)	11.4%	—	507.5	817.3	688.5	701.6
Employees	36.7%	286	325	625	900	1,000

AMWAY CORP.

5101 Spaulding Plaza
Ada, MI 49355
Phone: 616-787-6000
Fax: 616-787-7102
Web: www.quixtar.com

CEO: Steve Lieberman
CFO: David Bartlett
HR: —
FYE: August 31
Type: Subsidiary

Customers who want one-stop shopping for their home and body turn to Amway Corp., which does business as Amway Global. Formerly Quixtar, the North American affiliate of Alticor's Amway International is an online retailer and direct seller of personal care products, health supplements, laundry care products, and household cleaners. It also supplies car care items, cosmetics, hair care and skin care products, fragrances, and infant care items. Top brands include eSpring, clear.now, Glister, Trim Body System, Nutrilite, and Momentum, among others. To leverage the international status of the Amway brand, the company in 2009 dropped the Quixtar moniker and adopted the Amway Global trade name.

AMWAY INTERNATIONAL, INC.

7575 Fulton St. East
Ada, MI 49355
Phone: 616-787-6000
Fax: 616-682-4000
Web: www.amway.com

CEO: Steve Van Andel
CFO: Russ Evans
HR: —
FYE: August 31
Type: Subsidiary

Selling makeup and vitamins to friends and family is a way of life at Amway International. One of the world's largest direct-sales businesses, Amway boasts more than 3 million independent consultants who sell its catalog of more than 450 personal care, home care, nutrition, and commercial products. It also markets products and services of other companies in more than 80 countries. Revival-like techniques are used to motivate its distributors (mostly part-timers) to sell products and find new recruits. Founder Richard DeVos and the Van Andel family own Amway and its parent company, Alticor. Steve Van Andel is chairman of Amway, and Doug DeVos is its president.

AMX, LLC

3000 Research Dr.
Richardson, TX 75082
Phone: 469-624-8000
Fax: 469-624-7153
Web: www.amxcorp.com

CEO: Rashid M. Skaf
CFO: Chris Apple
HR: Steve H. Byars
FYE: December 31
Type: Subsidiary

Like a football fan on Sunday, AMX knows how to work the remote control. The company designs and sells systems that control devices such as lights, audio and video equipment, and security cameras from a common remote interface. Its systems are used in corporate, educational, entertainment, industrial, and government settings. AMX also offers residential systems that control security systems, lighting, and electronic devices in the home. The firm sells its products through distributors and OEMs. It partners with a number of leading manufacturers, such as Fujitsu, Hitachi, NEC, Samsung, and Sony. Founded in 1982, AMX is a subsidiary of The Duchossois Group.

An in-depth profile of this company is available to Hoover's Online members at hoovers.com.

AMYLIN PHARMACEUTICALS, INC.
NASDAQ (GS): AMLN

9360 Towne Centre Dr.
San Diego, CA 92121
Phone: 858-552-2200
Fax: 858-552-2212
Web: www.amylin.com

CEO: Daniel M. (Dan) Bradbury
CFO: Mark G. Foletta
HR: Roger Marchetti
FYE: December 31
Type: Public

Amylin Pharmaceuticals helps diabetics gain the upper hand in their battle with the disease. The company makes and markets two injectable diabetes drugs, Byetta and Symlin, that are approved as adjunct therapies to other diabetes treatments such as metformin and insulin. Byetta is also approved as a stand-alone diabetes therapy. Development partner Eli Lilly markets Byetta worldwide and is responsible for the development of Byetta in international markets. Amylin's US-based sales force co-promotes Byetta with Eli Lilly and markets Symlin on its own. The company is working on other diabetes drugs, including a once-weekly version of Byetta, as well as treatments for obesity.

	Annual Growth	12/05	12/06	12/07	12/08	12/09
Sales ($ mil.)	52.4%	140.5	510.9	781.0	840.1	758.4
Net income ($ mil.)	—	(206.8)	(218.9)	(211.1)	(315.4)	(186.3)
Market value ($ mil.)	(22.8%)	5,733.5	5,180.6	5,314.1	1,558.3	2,038.0
Employees	6.9%	1,150	1,550	1,900	1,800	1,500

AMY'S KITCHEN, INC.

Corporate Circle, Ste. 200
Petaluma, CA 94954
Phone: 707-578-7270
Fax: —
Web: www.amyskitchen.com

CEO: Andy Berliner
CFO: Don Watts
HR: Cindy Gillespie
FYE: June 30
Type: Private

Amy's Kitchen is an answer to the prayers of vegetarians scouring the frozen-dinner and packaged-food aisles of their supermarkets. The company, which makes frozen and pre-packaged vegetarian meals and other food products using all-natural and organic ingredients, is also a popular option for non-vegetarian, health-conscious consumers. Its products include frozen entrees, pocket sandwiches, pizzas, pot pies, toaster pops, veggie burgers, canned soups, beans, and chili, along with jarred pasta sauces and salsa. Amy's distributes its specialty foods through national supermarket chains, natural food and grocery stores, warehouse and club stores, and college campuses throughout the US.

	Annual Growth	6/04	6/05	6/06	6/07	6/08
Est. sales ($ mil.)	—	—	—	—	—	187.8
Employees	—	—	—	—	—	860

ANACOMP, INC.
Pink Sheets: ANCPA

15378 Avenue of Science
San Diego, CA 92128
Phone: 858-716-3400
Fax: 858-716-3775
Web: www.anacomp.com

CEO: Howard Dratler
CFO: Jeffrey S. (Jeff) Cartwright
HR: —
FYE: September 30
Type: Public

Forget *The X-Files*, Anacomp has the e-files. The company offers information management software and services, including document scanning and indexing, digital conversion, and archiving for multiple file types. Its document management applications include docHarbor Online and CaseLogistix, which allow users to review, analyze, and produce digital files through its Web-enabled platforms. Clients have included ADP, Goldman Sachs, IBM, MetLife, and the Social Security Administration, as well as law firms and corporate counsel departments. The company, founded in 1968, takes its name from the combination of "ANAlyse" and "COMPute." In 2009 Anacomp sold its UK operations and data center support business.

ANADARKO PETROLEUM CORPORATION
NYSE: APC

1201 Lake Robbins Dr.
The Woodlands, TX 77380
Phone: 832-636-1000
Fax: 832-636-8220
Web: www.anadarko.com

CEO: James T. (Jim) Hackett
CFO: Robert G. Gwin
HR: Julia A. Struble
FYE: December 31
Type: Public

Anadarko Petroleum has ventured beyond its original area of operation — the Anadarko Basin — to explore for, develop, produce, and market oil, natural gas, natural gas liquids, and related products worldwide. The large independent company has proved reserves of 1 billion barrels of crude oil and 7.8 trillion cu. ft. of natural gas, more than 89% of which are located in the US. Other activities include coal, trona, and mineral mining. Anadarko operates a handful of gas-gathering systems in the Mid-Continent. Internationally, the company has substantial oil and gas interests in Algeria, Brazil, China, Indonesia, Mozambique, and West Africa.

	Annual Growth	12/05	12/06	12/07	12/08	12/09
Sales ($ mil.)	6.1%	7,100.0	10,187.0	15,892.0	15,723.0	9,000.0
Net income ($ mil.)	—	2,471.0	4,854.0	3,781.0	3,261.0	(103.0)
Market value ($ mil.)	7.1%	23,438.5	21,531.3	32,499.8	19,072.4	30,881.9
Employees	6.8%	3,300	5,200	4,000	4,300	4,300

ANADIGICS, INC.
NASDAQ (GM): ANAD

141 Mt. Bethel Rd.
Warren, NJ 07059
Phone: 908-668-5000
Fax: 908-668-5068
Web: www.anadigics.com

CEO: Mario A. Rivas
CFO: Thomas C. Shields
HR: Brad Yates
FYE: December 31
Type: Public

ANADIGICS makes chips that cook with GaAs. The company makes gallium arsenide (GaAs) and indium phosphide (InP) radio-frequency integrated circuits for cable television systems, wireless communications devices, and fiber-optic equipment. GaAs and InP are costlier than silicon, but their physical properties allow the compound materials to be used for chips that are smaller and faster or more energy-efficient than silicon chips. ANADIGICS' power amplifiers, switches, and other chips can be found in the cable modems, set-top boxes, wireless phones, and other gear of companies including LG Electronics (15% of sales) and Research In Motion (14%). Asian customers account for nearly three-quarters of sales.

	Annual Growth	12/05	12/06	12/07	12/08	12/09
Sales ($ mil.)	6.7%	108.3	169.9	230.6	258.2	140.5
Net income ($ mil.)	—	(31.2)	(8.9)	6.0	(41.9)	(57.1)
Market value ($ mil.)	(8.4%)	391.3	577.8	754.6	96.5	275.2
Employees	6.5%	439	508	625	657	564

ANADYS PHARMACEUTICALS, INC.
NASDAQ (GM): ANDS

3115 Merryfield Row
San Diego, CA 92121
Phone: 858-530-3600
Fax: 858-527-1540
Web: www.anadyspharma.com

CEO: Stephen T. Worland
CFO: Peter T. Slover
HR: —
FYE: December 31
Type: Public

Anadys Pharmaceuticals has hepatitis and cancer in the crosshairs. The biotechnology company is developing new therapeutic treatments for those infected with hepatitis C (HCV) and other bacterial infections, as well as for applications in oncology. Anadys is exploring compounds that either act as direct antivirals or stimulate the body's immune system responses to fight disease. Anadys Pharmaceuticals seeks out strategic alliances with other pharmaceutical firms for development and licensing arrangements. The company has licensed its drug discovery technologies to such firms as Daiichi Sankyo, Roche, and Amgen.

	Annual Growth	12/05	12/06	12/07	12/08	12/09
Sales ($ mil.)	—	—	—	—	—	0.0
Net income ($ mil.)	—	—	—	—	—	(27.3)
Market value ($ mil.)	—	—	—	—	—	78.8
Employees	—	—	—	—	—	34

ANALOG DEVICES, INC.
NYSE: ADI

1 Technology Way
Norwood, MA 02062
Phone: 781-329-4700
Fax: —
Web: www.analog.com

CEO: Jerald G. (Jerry) Fishman
CFO: David A. (Dave) Zinsner
HR: —
FYE: October 31
Type: Public

Analog Devices, Inc. (ADI) is fluent in both analog and digital. The company is a leading maker of analog (linear and mixed-signal) and digital integrated circuits (ICs), including digital signal processors (DSPs). Its linear ICs translate real-world phenomena such as pressure, temperature, and sound into digital signals. ADI's thousands of chip designs are used in industrial process controls, medical and scientific instruments, communications gear, computers, and consumer electronics devices. ADI's chips go into high-tech goods from such companies as Ericsson, Mitsubishi Electric, Philips, Siemens, and Sony. Customers outside the US account for more than three-quarters of ADI's sales.

	Annual Growth	10/05	10/06	10/07	10/08	10/09
Sales ($ mil.)	(4.2%)	2,388.8	2,573.2	2,546.1	2,582.9	2,014.9
Net income ($ mil.)	(12.1%)	414.8	549.5	496.9	786.3	247.8
Market value ($ mil.)	(7.3%)	10,363.8	9,481.8	9,970.5	6,364.9	7,637.3
Employees	(1.5%)	8,800	9,800	9,600	9,000	8,300

ANALOGIC CORPORATION
NASDAQ (GS): ALOG

8 Centennial Dr.
Peabody, MA 01960
Phone: 978-326-4000
Fax: 978-977-6810
Web: www.analogic.com

CEO: James W. (Jim) Green
CFO: Michael L. Levitz
HR: Douglas B. (Doug) Rosenfeld
FYE: July 31
Type: Public

Analogic envisions a logical use for data. The company's data acquisition, conversion, and signal processing gear converts analog signals such as pressure, temperature, and X-rays into digital computer data. Its medical image processing systems, digital signal processors, and security imaging products are used in equipment including CAT and MRI scanners, luggage inspection systems, semiconductor test equipment, and industrial weighing products. Top customers include Toshiba, L-3 Communications, Siemens, GE, and Philips. Analogic also owns a Boston-area hotel managed by Marriott. The company has facilities located in Canada, China, Denmark, and the US.

	Annual Growth	7/05	7/06	7/07	7/08	7/09
Sales ($ mil.)	2.1%	364.6	351.4	340.8	413.5	396.1
Net income ($ mil.)	(40.2%)	28.9	24.9	15.4	23.5	3.7
Market value ($ mil.)	(7.3%)	661.9	589.1	855.4	942.9	488.5
Employees	(4.2%)	1,725	1,500	1,500	1,700	1,450

ANALYSTS INTERNATIONAL CORPORATION
NASDAQ (GM): ANLY

3601 W. 76th St.
Minneapolis, MN 55435
Phone: 952-835-5900
Fax: 952-897-4555
Web: www.analysts.com

CEO: Andrew K. Borgstrom
CFO: Randy W. Strobel
HR: Julie Duwenhoegger
FYE: December 31
Type: Public

These analysts will put your technology on the couch. Analysts International provides a wide range of business consulting and IT services, including mainframe migrations, network analysis and design, custom programming, project management, and Internet/intranet development. The company's customers come from industries such as oil and gas, manufacturing, telecommunications, and retail. Its Managed Services division provides help desk, software engineering, and other outsourced technical staffing, primarily to large corporations. Analysts International gets all of its sales in North America.

	Annual Growth	12/05	12/06	12/07	12/08	12/09
Sales ($ mil.)	(18.4%)	322.3	347.0	359.7	284.2	143.2
Net income ($ mil.)	—	(17.7)	(1.1)	(16.2)	(10.1)	(15.9)
Market value ($ mil.)	(27.3%)	59.8	46.6	38.4	14.5	16.7
Employees	(24.3%)	3,095	2,397	2,093	1,700	1,015

ANAREN, INC.
NASDAQ (GM): ANEN

6635 Kirkville Rd.
East Syracuse, NY 13057
Phone: 315-432-8909
Fax: 315-432-9121
Web: www.anaren.com

CEO: Lawrence A. Sala
CFO: George A. Blanton
HR: Amy B. Tewksbury
FYE: June 30
Type: Public

Anaren is hot for wireless. The company makes microwave and radio-frequency (RF) components, assemblies, and subsystems used in signal processing devices for defense, satellite, and wireless communications applications. Its products include the Xinger line of surface mount passive microwave components, RF power amplifiers, ferrite devices, signal splitters, and backplanes that are incorporated into amplifiers, receivers, and cellular base station gear. Other products range from RF measurement devices to beamformers (used to locate fixed beams from antennas) and switch matrices (used to route RF signals). The company counts Lockheed Martin, Nokia Siemens, Northrup Grumman, and Raytheon among its customers.

	Annual Growth	6/05	6/06	6/07	6/08	6/09
Sales ($ mil.)	15.3%	94.5	105.5	129.0	131.3	166.9
Net income ($ mil.)	7.5%	7.4	12.2	15.3	9.2	9.9
Market value ($ mil.)	7.6%	194.0	301.1	259.6	155.4	259.8
Employees	15.9%	587	708	871	930	1,060

ANATOLIA MINERALS DEVELOPMENT LIMITED
Pink Sheets: ALIAF

10333 E. Dry Creek Rd., Ste. 240
Englewood, CO 80228
Phone: 303-292-1299
Fax: 303-297-0538
Web: www.anatoliaminerals.com

CEO: Edward C. (Ed) Dowling Jr.
CFO: Douglas Tobler
HR: —
FYE: December 31
Type: Public

Anatolia is exploring and developing mining properties in Turkey, with projects for gold, copper, and other minerals. The company has focused its exploratory drilling efforts on its Çöpler gold project, which is believed to contain 4 million ounces of gold. Turkish company Çalik Mining owns a 5% interest in the Çöpler mine and an option to buy another 15% by 2011; it's provided development funds to Anatolia in exchange for the stake. In 2010 Anatolia bought out its joint venture partner Rio Tinto's share of the Cevizlidere Copper-Gold Project for some C$2 million ($1.9 million).

	Annual Growth	12/05	12/06	12/07	12/08	12/09
Sales ($ mil.)	—	—	—	—	—	0.0
Net income ($ mil.)	—	—	—	—	—	(31.9)
Market value ($ mil.)	—	—	—	—	—	419.9
Employees	—	—	—	—	—	110

ANCESTRY.COM INC.
NASDAQ (GS): ACOM

360 W. 4800 North
Provo, UT 84604
Phone: 801-705-7000
Fax: 801-705-7001
Web: corporate.ancestry.com

CEO: Timothy P. (Tim) Sullivan
CFO: Howard Hochhauser
HR: —
FYE: December 31
Type: Public

Got the urge to know your roots? Ancestry.com helps people discover, research, and share family histories, and create family trees. Users can search through a variety of documents, photographs, maps, and newspapers on the company's Web site. In addition to user generated content, the site's information comes from the digitized archives of publicly available US and UK census records and other government documents, historical societies, religious institutions, and private collectors of historical content. The company also provides family history desktop software Family Tree Maker. Most of Ancestry.com's revenues come from subscription fees. The company was founded in 1983. It filed an IPO in 2009.

	Annual Growth	12/05	12/06	12/07	12/08	12/09
Sales ($ mil.)	14.3%	—	150.6	166.4	197.6	224.9
Net income ($ mil.)	38.0%	—	8.1	6.5	2.4	21.3
Market value ($ mil.)	—	—	—	—	—	595.2
Employees	7.5%	—	—	—	670	720

ANCHOR BANCORP WISCONSIN INC.

NASDAQ (GS): ABCW

25 W. Main St.	CEO: Chris M. Bauer
Madison, WI 53703	CFO: Dale C. Ringgenberg
Phone: 608-252-8700	HR: —
Fax: 608-252-8976	FYE: March 31
Web: www.anchorbank.com	Type: Public

Anchor BanCorp Wisconsin is the holding company for AnchorBank, which has about 75 branches across the Badger State. The thrift targets individuals and local businesses, offering checking and savings accounts, money market accounts, CDs, and IRAs, as well as insurance and investment products. Single-family residential mortgages account for some 20% of the bank's loan book; commercial and multifamily real estate loans make up another 40%. Other loans include construction loans, second mortgages, business loans, and student loans. AnchorBank was founded in 1919.

	Annual Growth	3/05	3/06	3/07	3/08	3/09
Assets ($ mil.)	6.8%	4,050.5	4,275.1	4,539.7	5,149.6	5,273.1
Net income ($ mil.)	—	48.3	44.7	39.0	31.1	(228.3)
Market value ($ mil.)	(53.2%)	609.5	657.2	614.7	411.3	29.3
Employees	4.9%	967	988	976	1,153	1,169

ANCHOR GLASS CONTAINER CORPORATION

401 E. Jackson St., Ste. 2800	CEO: Brian N. Bussell
Tampa, FL 33602	CFO: James (Jim) Fredlake
Phone: 813-884-0000	HR: —
Fax: —	FYE: December 31
Web: www.anchorglass.com	Type: Private

In a sea of options, Anchor Glass Container has anchored its reputation on manufacturing sustainable, safe, aesthetic glass packaging. Among the leading glass container-makers in the US, it ranks behind only two, Owens-Illinois and Saint-Gobain Containers. Anchor Glass Container serves manufacturers in beverage and food markets, including producers of beer and liquor. It produces clear and colored glass containers in a myriad of sizes via eight glassmaking plants and one for making molds. For years the company's largest customer has been beer giant Anheuser-Busch. Anchor Glass Container's lineup also holds thirst quenchers from Snapple, LiDestri Foods, and High Falls Brewing. The company is privately held.

ANCHOR HOCKING COMPANY

519 Pierce Ave.	CEO: Mark R. Eichhorn
Lancaster, OH 43130	CFO: Mark Hedstrom
Phone: 740-681-6478	HR: —
Fax: 740-681-6040	FYE: December 31
Web: www.anchorhocking.com	Type: Private

The Anchor Hocking name is nearly synonymous with glassware. The Anchor Hocking Company, in existence for more than a century, makes and markets beverageware (glasses, pitchers), cookware (pans, casserole dishes), servingware (platters, cake sets, punch bowls), storage items (canisters), and giftware (vases). It also serves as a third-party manufacturer for other companies. Anchor Hocking products are sold through US retailers, such as Wal-Mart and Target, as well as directly to foodservice and specialty markets. Private equity firm Monomoy Capital Partners, which focuses on middle market investments, bought Anchor Hocking in 2007 for $75 million.

	Annual Growth	12/04	12/05	12/06	12/07	12/08
Est. sales ($ mil.)	—	—	—	—	—	40.7
Employees	—	—	—	—	—	600

⊞ ANDERSEN CORPORATION

100 4th Ave. North	CEO: James E. (Jim) Humphrey
Bayport, MN 55003	CFO: Philip (Phil) Donaldson
Phone: 651-264-5150	HR: Mary D. Carter
Fax: 651-264-5107	FYE: December 31
Web: www.andersenwindows.com	Type: Private

Windows of opportunity open daily for Andersen, a well-known maker of wood-clad windows and patio doors in North America. Andersen offers window designs from hinged, bay, and double-hung to skylight, gliding, and picture windows. Its Renewal by Andersen subsidiary provides start-to-finish window renewal services, including in-home consultations, in more than 100 markets in the US. Subsidiary EMCO Doors makes storm and screen doors. Through independent and company-owned distributorships (including its Andersen Logistics division), Andersen sells to homeowners, architects, builders, designers, and remodelers. The company is owned by the Andersen family, the Andersen Foundation, and company employees.

	Annual Growth	12/04	12/05	12/06	12/07	12/08
Sales ($ mil.)	0.0%	2,500.0	3,000.0	3,000.0	3,000.0	2,500.0
Employees	4.1%	8,500	16,000	14,000	13,000	10,000

ANDERSON TRUCKING SERVICE, INC.

725 Opportunity Dr.	CEO: Rollie Anderson
St. Cloud, MN 56301	CFO: Scott E. Fuller
Phone: 320-255-7400	HR: Oscar D. Kleman Jr.
Fax: 320-255-7438	FYE: December 31
Web: www.ats-inc.com	Type: Private

Anderson Trucking Service (ATS) moves cargo that ranges from cranes to chairs. The company's ATS Specialized unit transports heavy equipment and other cargo requiring flatbed trailers; an offshoot concentrates on wind energy equipment. Its ATS Van Solutions unit offers dry van truckload transportation, and SunBelt Furniture Xpress transports new furniture for manufacturers. Overall, the company's trucking units operate a fleet of some 2,000 tractors and 6,500 trailers. ATS also offers logistics services, including international freight forwarding. Harold Anderson established the family-owned business in 1955.

	Annual Growth	12/04	12/05	12/06	12/07	12/08
Est. sales ($ mil.)	—	—	—	—	—	64.3
Employees	—	—	—	—	—	900

THE ANDERSONS, INC.

NASDAQ (GS): ANDE

480 W. Dussel Dr.	CEO: Michael J. Anderson
Maumee, OH 43537	CFO: Nicholas C. Conrad
Phone: 419-893-5050	HR: Arthur D. Depompei
Fax: 419-891-6670	FYE: December 31
Web: www.andersonsinc.com	Type: Public

The Andersons earns its daily bread on a mix of grains, trains, and corncobs. The agricultural company's main business (and most lucrative at 71% of 2009 sales) — the Grain & Ethanol Group — consists of the buying, conditioning, and reselling of corn, soybeans, and wheat, which it acquires from US grain farmers and stores, using a system of elevators and terminals located in the Midwest. But there's more — the company has five operating segments. In addition to the Grain & Ethanol Group, its other segments are the Plant Nutrient Group, the Retail Group, the Turf & Specialty Group, and the Rail Group. The Andersons has operations in seven US states, as well as rail-leasing interests in Canada and Mexico.

	Annual Growth	12/05	12/06	12/07	12/08	12/09
Sales ($ mil.)	23.6%	1,296.7	1,458.1	2,379.1	3,489.5	3,025.3
Net income ($ mil.)	10.1%	26.1	36.3	68.8	32.9	38.4
Market value ($ mil.)	4.6%	396.3	780.0	824.3	303.2	475.1
Employees	1.0%	2,750	2,862	2,953	3,077	2,862

⊞ An in-depth profile of this company is available to Hoover's Online members at hoovers.com.

145

ANDREA ELECTRONICS CORPORATION

OTC: ANDR

65 Orville Dr., Ste. 1
Bohemia, NY 11716
Phone: 631-719-1800
Fax: 631-719-1998
Web: www.andreaelectronics.com

CEO: Douglas J. Andrea
CFO: Corisa L. Guiffre
HR: —
FYE: December 31
Type: Public

Andrea Electronics wants to make a big noise with its Anti-Noise technology. The company's Anti-Noise products include software that increases voice clarity and reduces background noise, plus headsets that enhance audio in high-noise environments. Andrea Electronics also offers voice recognition products for voice-activated computing applications, such as word processing. The company designs its products for audio- and videoconferencing, call centers, in-vehicle communications, and personal computing. Andrea Electronics sells directly and through distributors, software publishers, ISPs, and other resellers. The company gets most of its sales in the US.

	Annual Growth	12/05	12/06	12/07	12/08	12/09
Sales ($ mil.)	2.9%	4.2	5.7	5.0	4.7	4.7
Net income ($ mil.)	—	(0.6)	0.0	(0.4)	(0.3)	(0.2)
Market value ($ mil.)	13.6%	2.3	8.6	3.5	2.5	3.8
Employees	6.1%	15	16	16	19	19

ANDRITZ INC.

35 Sherman St.
Muncy, PA 17756
Phone: 570-546-8211
Fax: 570-546-1306
Web: www.andritzsproutbauer.com

CEO: Timothy J. Ryan
CFO: Chris Keays
HR: Dennis M. Shulick
FYE: December 31
Type: Subsidiary

When it's time to break stuff into bits and move it along its way, Andritz Inc. probably makes a machine for the job. Andritz Inc., also known as Andritz Sprout, is the American arm of Austria's Andritz AG. With more than 15 locations in the US, the company is a supplier of rotary valves, hammer mills, screeners, agitators, and other specialized machinery for the pulp and paper, wet corn milling, and sewage sludge processing industries. The company also works with its customers to help with customized installations, factory automation systems, and related services. Andritz acquired Sprout-Bauer, Inc. in 1990 and still uses the Sprout-Bauer brand name.

	Annual Growth	12/04	12/05	12/06	12/07	12/08
Est. sales ($ mil.)	—	—	—	—	—	425.0
Employees	—	—	—	—	—	646

ANESIVA, INC.

Pink Sheets: ANSVQ

650 Gateway Blvd.
South San Francisco, CA 94080
Phone: 650-624-9600
Fax: 650-624-7540
Web: www.anesiva.com

CEO: Michael L. Kranda
CFO: —
HR: —
FYE: December 31
Type: Public

Anesiva wants to keep pain at bay. The biopharmaceutical firm is developing treatments for pain management with product candidates that include Adlea, an analgesic for post-surgical pain after orthopedic surgery and osteoarthritis treatment. Anesiva agreed to be purchased by Arcion Therapeutics to create a new company focused on pain drug development, with an emphasis on Arcion's existing portfolio of drug candidates in late 2009. However, the deal fell through and instead Anesiva announced it would file for bankruptcy protection in early 2010.

	Annual Growth	12/04	12/05	12/06	12/07	*12/08
Sales ($ mil.)	73.2%	—	—	0.1	0.1	0.3
Net income ($ mil.)	—	—	—	(55.6)	(59.3)	(103.2)
Market value ($ mil.)	(77.5%)	—	—	281.2	202.3	14.2
Employees	27.0%	—	—	62	100	100

*Most recent year available

ANGEION CORPORATION

NASDAQ (CM): ANGN

350 Oak Grove Pkwy.
St. Paul, MN 55127
Phone: 651-484-4874
Fax: 651-379-8227
Web: www.angeion.com

CEO: Rodney A. Young
CFO: William J. (Bill) Kullback
HR: —
FYE: October 31
Type: Public

Angeion Company knows your breath can tell more about you than just what your last meal was. The company designs and sells cardiorespiratory diagnostic systems that analyze lung function and diagnose disease. Its MedGraphics-branded systems are aimed at health care providers and life sciences researchers; they are non-invasive devices that analyze a patient's inhaled and exhaled breath and can help detect emphysema, asthma, and heart disease, among other things. Angeion sells one of its diagnostic systems to the health and fitness market under the brand name New Leaf; fitness professionals can help users design personalized training regimens based on the metabolic data gleaned from the New Leaf device.

	Annual Growth	10/05	10/06	10/07	10/08	10/09
Sales ($ mil.)	1.7%	23.8	33.7	38.6	30.0	25.5
Net income ($ mil.)	—	(0.9)	1.4	1.1	(0.7)	(1.6)
Market value ($ mil.)	12.8%	9.4	44.4	32.7	16.0	15.2
Employees	1.2%	127	155	140	125	133

ANGELICA CORPORATION

424 S. Woods Mill Rd.
Chesterfield, MO 63017
Phone: 314-854-3800
Fax: 314-854-3890
Web: www.angelica.com

CEO: Stephen M. (Steve) O'Hara
CFO: John Fry
HR: —
FYE: January 31
Type: Private

Hospitals don't have to move heaven and earth to get clean sheets — Angelica will do it for them. The firm provides laundry services and rents linens to more than 4,200 health care providers, including dentists, medical clinics, hospitals, and nursing homes. It rents and cleans scrubs, bed sheets, towels, gowns, and surgical linens. Angelica also provides mops, mats, sterile surgical packs, and on-site linen room management. The firm operates about 30 laundry service centers across the US. Angelica traces its roots back to 1878, when it was established as a uniform manufacturer. It is owned by private equity firm Trilantic Capital Partners.

	Annual Growth	1/04	1/05	1/06	1/07	1/08
Est. sales ($ mil.)	—	—	—	—	—	264.2
Employees	—	—	—	—	—	6,400

ANGELO, GORDON & CO.

245 Park Ave.
New York, NY 10167
Phone: 212-692-2000
Fax: 212-867-9328
Web: www.angelogordon.com

CEO: John M. Angelo
CFO: Joseph (Joe) Wekselblatt
HR: Linda Eichenbaum
FYE: December 31
Type: Private

For Angelo, Gordon, bucking tradition goes hand-in-hand with making money. The hedge fund firm specializes in alternative investments such as distressed assets (nonperforming loans, junk bonds, and bankrupt or otherwise troubled companies), public-private partnerships, risk and convertible arbitrage, real estate, and private equity. Its strategy also involves hedging stock and bond investments and attempting to exploit market inefficiencies. Affiliate Angelo, Gordon Advisors offers multi-manager investment portfolios. Angelo, Gordon has about $21 billion in assets under management. The company was co-founded in 1988 by CEO John Angelo and chief investment officer and COO Michael Gordon.

ANGIODYNAMICS, INC.
NASDAQ (GS): ANGO

603 Queensbury Ave.
Queensbury, NY 12804
Phone: 518-798-1215
Fax: 518-798-3625
Web: www.angiodynamics.com

CEO: Jan Keltjens
CFO: D. Joseph (Joe) Gersuk
HR: —
FYE: May 31
Type: Public

AngioDynamics gets your blood flowing, and flowing easier if need be. The company makes medical devices for the treatment of peripheral vascular disease (PVD, where arteries or veins in the arms or legs become blocked or restricted by plaque), including catheters for use in angiography and angioplasty procedures to treat PVD. Other interventional products made by AngioDynamics include laser venous systems to treat varicose veins, vascular access products for drug delivery, kidney dialysis catheters, and abscess drainage products. The company also offers tools and systems for minimally invasive oncological treatments. AngioDynamics' sales force markets products to doctors in the US and internationally.

	Annual Growth	5/05	5/06	5/07	5/08	5/09
Sales ($ mil.)	34.1%	60.3	78.5	112.2	166.5	195.1
Net income ($ mil.)	21.8%	4.5	6.9	(9.1)	10.9	9.9
Market value ($ mil.)	(11.2%)	488.9	692.4	391.9	383.0	304.1
Employees	29.8%	252	306	530	566	715

⊞ ANHEUSER-BUSCH COMPANIES, INC.

1 Busch Place
St. Louis, MO 63118
Phone: 314-577-2000
Fax: 314-577-2900
Web: www.anheuser-busch.com

CEO: Luiz F. Z. de Saint Edmond
CFO: David Almeida
HR: James G. Brickey
FYE: December 31
Type: Subsidiary

Anheuser-Busch Companies (A-B) wants to be the life of every party, whether with its beer or its majestic Clydesdales. The company is best known for brewing Budweiser (one of the world's best-selling beers by volume) and Bud Light, along with labels that include Busch and Michelob. A-B also owns a 50% stake in Mexico's GRUPO MODLEO, maker of Corona and Negra Modelo. In addition to beer, Anheuser-Busch produces distilled beverages, energy drinks, and non-alcoholic malt beverages. In 2008 Belgium brewer InBev acquired A-B for $52 billion, creating Anheuser-Busch InBev (ABInBev), the world's largest beer maker.

ANIKA THERAPEUTICS, INC.
NASDAQ (GS): ANIK

32 Wiggins Ave.
Bedford, MA 01730
Phone: 781-457-9000
Fax: 781-305-9720
Web: www.anikatherapeutics.com

CEO: Charles H. Sherwood
CFO: Kevin W. Quinlan
HR: William J. Mrachek
FYE: December 31
Type: Public

Anika Therapeutics is roosterrific. The company uses hyaluronic acid (HA), a natural polymer extracted from rooster combs and other sources, to make products that treat bone, cartilage, and soft tissue. Anika's OrthoVisc treats osteoarthritis of the knee and is available in the US and overseas. DePuy Mitek sells the product in the US. A unit of Boehringer Ingelheim sells Anika's osteoarthritis treatment for racehorses, Hyvisc. Bausch & Lomb sells two of the company's products that maintain eye shape and protect tissue during eye surgery. Other products include surgical anti-adhesives and aesthetic dermatology products.

	Annual Growth	12/05	12/06	12/07	12/08	12/09
Sales ($ mil.)	7.7%	29.8	26.8	30.8	35.8	40.1
Net income ($ mil.)	(11.0%)	5.9	4.6	6.0	3.6	3.7
Market value ($ mil.)	(10.1%)	157.6	178.8	196.1	41.0	102.8
Employees	19.6%	65	64	82	84	133

ANIMAL HEALTH INTERNATIONAL, INC.
NASDAQ (GM): AHII

7 Village Circle, Ste. 200
Westlake, TX 76262
Phone: 817-859-3000
Fax: 817-859-3099
Web: www.ahii.com

CEO: James C. Robison
CFO: William F. (Bill) Lacey
HR: Kathy C. Hassenpflug
FYE: June 30
Type: Public

If dog is man's best friend, then perhaps Animal Health International (AHI) is dog's best friend. As one of the largest distributors of veterinary products in the US, AHI operates through several subsidiaries including Walco International, Cattleman's Supply, and Kane Veterinary Supplies. Its companies sell more than 40,000 prescription and OTC pharmaceuticals, nutritional supplements, vaccines, and other products to customers in the US and Canada. Other products include capital equipment, devices and supplies, diagnostics, parasiticides, and sanitizers. Its primary customers are livestock operations (dairy farms, feedlots, poultry), retailers, and veterinarians. At AHI's helm is CEO James Robison.

	Annual Growth	6/05	6/06	6/07	6/08	6/09
Sales ($ mil.)	5.6%	535.7	571.2	629.5	716.5	666.9
Net income ($ mil.)	—	7.3	7.4	5.2	11.1	(27.1)
Market value ($ mil.)	(67.3%)	—	—	353.3	151.6	37.7
Employees	5.7%	—	811	897	1,024	957

ANIMAS CORPORATION

200 Lawrence Dr.
West Chester, PA 19380
Phone: 610-644-8990
Fax: 877-331-7300
Web: www.animascorp.com

CEO: Michael (Mike) Rechtiene
CFO: —
HR: Sandra Thompson
FYE: December 31
Type: Subsidiary

Animas wants to *pump you up* . . . with insulin. The company's computerized insulin pumps are pager-sized devices that diabetes patients "wear" and which continuously deliver rapid-acting insulin into the body. The infusion pumps, which are connected to a tube with a needle at the end that's inserted under the skin, replace the use of periodic insulin injections. Animas also sells diabetes management software and various pump accessories. It markets its products worldwide through a combination of direct sales representatives and distributors. The company is a subsidiary of Johnson & Johnson, reporting to J&J's LifeScan division.

⊞ ANIXTER INTERNATIONAL INC.
NYSE: AXE

2301 Patriot Blvd.
Glenview, IL 60026
Phone: 224-521-8000
Fax: 224-521-8100
Web: www.anixter.com

CEO: Robert J. Eck
CFO: Dennis J. Letham
HR: Rodney A. Smith
FYE: December 31
Type: Public

Pssst, need to get wired? Anixter International's got connections. The company is a distributor of communication products used to connect voice, video, data, and security systems. It sells more than 450,000 products, including electrical and electronic wire, cable, fasteners, and security system components, through a global network of sales and distribution centers. The company's 230-plus warehouses stock products from more than 7,000 suppliers. Some 70 sales centers cater to such markets as education, government, health care, manufacturing, retail, and transportation. Among its 100,000 customers, Anixter also serves contractors and integrators who install and maintain communications networks and data centers.

	Annual Growth	12/05	12/06	12/07	12/08	12/09
Sales ($ mil.)	6.7%	3,847.4	4,938.6	5,852.9	6,136.6	4,982.4
Net income ($ mil.)	—	90.0	209.3	253.5	195.7	(29.3)
Market value ($ mil.)	4.8%	1,317.4	1,828.6	2,097.0	1,014.3	1,586.1
Employees	3.5%	6,800	7,500	8,000	8,645	7,811

ANNALY CAPITAL MANAGEMENT, INC.

NYSE: NLY

1211 Avenue of the Americas, Ste. 2902
New York, NY 10036
Phone: 212-696-0100
Fax: 212-696-9809
Web: www.annaly.com

CEO: Michael A. J. Farrell
CFO: Kathryn F. Fagan
HR: —
FYE: December 31
Type: Public

Annaly cannily invests its capital. A real estate investment trust (REIT), Annaly Capital Management invests in and manages mortgage-backed securities. Among its investments are mortgage pass-through certificates, collateralized mortgage obligations, and agency callable debentures. Certificates are issued or guaranteed by third-party issuers like Freddie Mac, Fannie Mae, and Ginnie Mae. At least 75% of its assets are high-quality, mortgage-backed securities or short-term investments. All of the REIT's assets are agency certificates with implied AAA ratings backed by single-family residential mortgages. Subsidiary Fixed Income Discount Advisory Company (FIDAC) provides investment advisory services.

	Annual Growth	12/05	12/06	12/07	12/08	12/09
Sales ($ mil.)	45.6%	687.4	1,202.7	2,416.7	3,134.6	3,087.9
Net income ($ mil.)	—	(9.2)	93.8	414.4	346.2	1,961.5
Market value ($ mil.)	12.2%	6,123.0	7,785.2	10,175.1	8,882.2	9,710.6
Employees	29.4%	31	34	39	65	87

ANNAPOLIS BANCORP, INC.

NASDAQ (CM): ANNB

1000 Bestgate Rd., Ste. 400
Annapolis, MD 21401
Phone: 410-224-4455
Fax: 410-224-3132
Web: www.bankannapolis.com

CEO: Richard M. (Rick) Lerner
CFO: Edward J. Schneider
HR: —
FYE: December 31
Type: Public

You don't have to attend "Canoe U" to bank with Annapolis Bancorp. It's the holding company for BankAnnapolis, which serves individual and small business customers through about 10 branches in and around the Maryland capital. The bank offers such retail services as checking, savings, and money market accounts; IRAs; and CDs. It also provides private business banking, including cash management and credit products. Its lending activities are composed of commercial mortgages (about 30% of its total loan portfolio), one- to four-family real estate loans (more than 25%), business loans (some 20%), and to a lesser extent, construction and consumer loans.

	Annual Growth	12/05	12/06	12/07	12/08	12/09
Assets ($ mil.)	9.9%	304.9	351.9	361.9	394.9	444.3
Net income ($ mil.)	—	3.0	3.0	2.4	1.4	(1.7)
Market value ($ mil.)	(23.3%)	35.1	37.2	29.9	13.1	12.1
Employees	6.3%	79	91	90	94	101

ANNA'S LINENS

3550 Hyland Ave.
Costa Mesa, CA 92626
Phone: 714-850-0504
Fax: 714-850-9170
Web: www.annaslinens.com

CEO: Alan Gladstone
CFO: Neil T. Watanabe
HR: Linda Norton Wendt
FYE: January 31
Type: Private

Motherly devotion paid off for entrepreneur and company founder Alan Gladstone. Anna's Linens (which is named after Gladstone's mother, Anna) is a specialty retailer of discounted home furnishings, including bed linens, kitchen textiles, area rugs, window coverings, bath accessories, and housewares, featuring brand names such as Wamsutta and Grand Patrician. Founded in 1988, the company operates more than 250 locations in about 20 states as well as an e-commerce site. Chairman, president, and CEO Gladstone envisions Anna's Linens eventually growing to 1,000 storefronts nationwide.

	Annual Growth	1/04	1/05	1/06	1/07	1/08
Est. sales ($ mil.)	—	—	—	—	—	342.4
Employees	—	—	—	—	—	2,000

ANNETT HOLDINGS, INC.

6115 SW Leland Ave.
Des Moines, IA 50321
Phone: 515-287-6380
Fax: 515-287-3249
Web: www.annettholdings.com

CEO: Harrold Annett
CFO: Larry Clark
HR: Glen McCravy
FYE: September 30
Type: Private

Freight that travels on flatbed trailers might travel with TLC from TMC. Through its main subsidiary, TMC Transportation, Annett Holdings hauls freight such as steel and building materials throughout the US on flatbed trailers. The company's fleet includes some 2,900 trucks and tractors. TMC offers both regional and long-haul service and also provides logistics services, such as freight transportation arrangement, and dedicated fleet services, in which drivers and equipment are assigned to a customer long-term. Chairman and CEO Harrold Annett founded the company in 1972.

ANNIE'S, INC.

564 Gateway Dr.
Napa, CA 94558
Phone: 707-254-3700
Fax: 707-259-0219
Web: www.anniesinc.com

CEO: John Foraker
CFO: Steve Jackson
HR: Amy Barberi
FYE: March 31
Type: Private

You could say this company's food is natural and homegrown. Annie's, an organic and natural food producer, makes some 60 cereals, dressings, pasta, and snacks through its two subsidiaries — Annie's Homegrown and Annie's Naturals. Annie's Homegrown banner includes breakfast cereals (Bunny Love, Cinna Bunnies), fruit snacks (Bunny Fruit), boxed organic macaroni and cheese, and organic ready meals. Under the Annie's Naturals name, the company offers organic and natural salad dressings, condiments (marinades, sauces, mustard, ketchup), and olive oil. Owned by private investment firm Solera Capital, Annie's sells its products through US and some Canadian grocery retailers, specialty food shops, and club stores.

☐ ANNTAYLOR STORES CORPORATION

NYSE: ANN

7 Times Sq., 15th Fl.
New York, NY 10036
Phone: 212-541-3300
Fax: 212-541-3379
Web: www.anntaylor.com

CEO: Katherine L. (Kay) Krill
CFO: Michael J. (Mike) Nicholson
HR: Mark Morrison
FYE: January 31
Type: Public

At AnnTaylor, basic black is as appreciated by its customers as its classic styles. The company (named for a fictional person) is a national retailer of upscale women's clothing designed exclusively for its stores. Its AnnTaylor and AnnTaylor LOFT shops offer apparel, shoes, and accessories. Targeting fashion-conscious career women, AnnTaylor operates about 900 stores (more than 500 are LOFT outlets) in some 45 US states, the District of Columbia, and Puerto Rico. Most are located in malls or upscale retail centers. AnnTaylor LOFT stores offer their own label of mid-priced casual apparel, while AnnTaylor Factory and LOFT Outlet stores sell clearance merchandise. AnnTaylor also has its own e-commerce website.

	Annual Growth	1/06	1/07	1/08	1/09	1/10
Sales ($ mil.)	(3.1%)	2,073.1	2,342.9	2,396.5	2,194.6	1,828.5
Net income ($ mil.)	—	81.9	143.0	97.2	(333.9)	(18.2)
Market value ($ mil.)	(21.6%)	1,958.4	2,027.7	1,477.0	289.2	738.2
Employees	2.7%	16,900	17,700	18,400	18,400	18,800

ANR PIPELINE COMPANY

717 Texas Ave.	CEO: Lee G. Hobbs
Houston, TX 77002	CFO: —
Phone: 832-320-5000	HR: —
Fax: —	FYE: December 31
Web: www.anrpl.com	Type: Subsidiary

ANR Pipeline keeps natural gas in line — a pipeline that is. The company operates one of the largest interstate natural gas pipeline systems in the US. A subsidiary of TransCanada Corp., ANR controls more than 10,600 miles of pipeline and delivers more than a trillion cubic feet of natural gas per year. The company primarily serves customers in the Midwest, but through its network is capable of connecting to all major gas basins in North America. Through its ANR Storage subsidiary, the company also provides natural gas storage services and has ownership interests in more than 250 billion cu. ft. of underground natural gas storage capacity.

	Annual Growth	12/04	12/05	12/06	12/07	12/08
Est. sales ($ mil.)	—	—	—	—	—	540.0
Employees	—	—	—	—	—	1,000

ANSALDO STS USA

1000 Technology Dr.	CEO: Alan E. Calegari
Pittsburgh, PA 15219	CFO: Jack Borman
Phone: 412-688-2400	HR: Ann Michalski
Fax: 412-688-2589	FYE: December 31
Web: www.ansaldo-sts.com	Type: Subsidiary

Ansaldo STS USA (formerly Union Switch & Signal) helps the trains run on time. The company is a maker of products and systems that signal, automate, control, and manage rail-based traffic for freight, passenger, and metropolitan rail transit. Products include wayside and carborne control systems, automatic signal stop systems, ground switches, and railroad crossing gates and signals. Ansaldo STS USA also provides related services such as maintenance and distribution of rail equipment, and warehousing. The company is a subsidiary of Finmeccanica's Ansaldo STS unit, a global supplier of automation, control, and signaling systems.

ANSCHUTZ COMPANY

555 17th St., Ste. 2400	CEO: Philip F. Anschutz
Denver, CO 80202	CFO: Wayne A. Barnes
Phone: 303-298-1000	HR: —
Fax: 303-298-8881	FYE: December 31
	Type: Private

Denver multibillionaire Philip Anschutz is a man of varied interests. His holding company includes an eclectic stable of entertainment, media, and sports businesses, in addition to telecom and energy development. Through Anschutz Entertainment Group (AEG), Anschutz owns sports and entertainment centers, as well as hockey, soccer, and other pro teams in the US and Europe. It also promotes concerts and other events. Other Anschutz holdings include movie chain Regal Entertainment Group, *The San Francisco Examiner*, and the family-oriented Anschutz Film Group. Anschutz, who founded the firm in 1958, made his first fortune in the oil and gas industry. He also founded Qwest Communications.

ANSYS, INC.

NASDAQ (GS): ANSS

275 Technology Dr.	CEO: James E. (Jim) Cashman III
Canonsburg, PA 15317	CFO: Maria T. Shields
Phone: 724-746-3304	HR: Elaine Keim
Fax: 724-514-9494	FYE: December 31
Web: www.ansys.com	Type: Public

ANSYS helps designers and engineers around the world really visualize their ideas. With the company's software, developers and engineers can see a simulation of their design concept on their desktop computer before a prototype is built. The computerized models are analyzed for their response to combinations of such physical variables as stress, pressure, impact, temperature, and velocity. Ranging from small consulting firms to multinational industrial firms, the company's customers come from a broad range of industries and have included Boeing, Cummins, and Motorola. ANSYS sells its products directly and through channel partners worldwide.

	Annual Growth	12/05	12/06	12/07	12/08	12/09
Sales ($ mil.)	34.5%	158.0	263.6	385.3	478.3	516.9
Net income ($ mil.)	27.6%	43.9	14.2	82.4	111.7	116.4
Market value ($ mil.)	19.5%	1,931.9	1,968.1	3,752.5	2,524.3	3,933.5
Employees	27.8%	600	1,400	1,400	1,750	1,600

ANTARES PHARMA, INC.

NYSE Amex: AIS

250 Phillips Blvd., Ste. 290	CEO: Paul K. Wotton
Ewing, NJ 08618	CFO: Robert F. (Bob) Apple
Phone: 609-359-3020	HR: —
Fax: 609-359-3015	FYE: December 31
Web: www.antarespharma.com	Type: Public

Antares Pharma understands antagonism towards needles. The company develops needle-free systems for administering injectable drugs. Its Medi-Jector Vision system, for instance, injects a thin, high-pressure stream of liquid, eliminating the need for a needle. The Vision system is used primarily for the delivery of insulin and of human growth hormones; it is available over-the-counter and by prescription in the US and is also sold overseas. In addition to its needle-free systems, the company develops other drug delivery platforms, including topical gels, orally administered disintegrating tablets, and mini-needle injection systems.

	Annual Growth	12/05	12/06	12/07	12/08	12/09
Sales ($ mil.)	39.4%	2.2	4.3	7.9	5.7	8.3
Net income ($ mil.)	—	(8.5)	(8.1)	(8.6)	(12.7)	(10.3)
Market value ($ mil.)	(7.4%)	128.6	99.6	81.3	30.7	94.6
Employees	(5.7%)	24	30	33	24	19

ANTHEM HEALTH PLANS OF VIRGINIA, INC.

2015 Staples Mill Rd.	CEO: C. Burke King
Richmond, VA 23230	CFO: —
Phone: 804-354-7000	HR: —
Fax: 804-354-2578	FYE: December 31
Web: www.anthem.com	Type: Subsidiary

Anthem Health Plans of Virginia sings a song of health insurance to residents of the Old Dominion State. A subsidiary of WellPoint and the state's largest health insurer, the company provides PPO, HMO, and traditional indemnity health plans to individuals, groups, and government employees. Its health plan offerings include Medicare supplemental and Medicare Advantage plans, as well as HMOs (under the name HealthKeepers Plus) for Medicaid recipients. Anthem Health Plans of Virginia also sells some non-Blue insurance products including life, accident, and disability coverage. The company is a licensee of the Blue Cross and Blue Shield Association and does business as Anthem Blue Cross and Blue Shield.

An in-depth profile of this company is available to Hoover's Online members at hoovers.com.

149

ANTHERA PHARMACEUTICALS, INC.
NASDAQ (GM): ANTH

25801 Industrial Blvd., Ste. B	CEO: Paul F. Truex
Hayward, CA 94545	CFO: Christopher P. Lowe
Phone: 510-856-5600	HR: —
Fax: 510-856-5597	FYE: December 31
Web: www.anthera.com	Type: Public

Biopharmaceutical company Anthera Pharmaceuticals develops drug treatments for respiratory, cardiovascular, and immunological diseases. Its current candidates, which are in various phases of clinical development, include therapies for acute coronary syndrome (inflammation of heart muscle), lupus, and sickle cell disease. The company also has treatments for asthma and dermatitis in earlier stages of development. Since its founding in 2004, Anthera Pharmaceuticals' operations have consisted primarily of research and development activities. The company went public in early 2010 in an initial public offering (IPO) worth about $37 million.

	Annual Growth	12/05	12/06	12/07	12/08	12/09
Sales ($ mil.)	—	—	0.0	0.0	0.0	0.0
Net income ($ mil.)	—	—	(8.7)	(25.7)	(18.1)	(12.2)
Employees	(12.5%)	—	—	—	16	14

ANTIGENICS INC.
NASDAQ (GM): AGEN

162 5th Ave., Ste. 900	CEO: Garo H. Armen
New York, NY 10111	CFO: Shalini Sharp
Phone: 212-994-8200	HR: John Cerio
Fax: 212-994-8299	FYE: December 31
Web: www.antigenics.com	Type: Public

Cancer and other diseases had better beware — Antigenics is packing heat. The firm develops heat shock proteins, which are related to the immune system's response to disease. Its patient-specific vaccines work on the theory that each person's cancer has a unique signature and are derived from the tumor after it has been removed. Lead drug candidate Oncophage is the first personalized cancer vaccine to receive FDA fast track status (a designation that expedites the approval of treatments for serious diseases); it has this designation for kidney and skin cancers. Another cancer vaccine candidate in the firm's pipeline targets genital herpes.

	Annual Growth	12/05	12/06	12/07	12/08	12/09
Sales ($ mil.)	53.1%	0.6	0.7	5.6	2.7	3.3
Net income ($ mil.)	—	(74.1)	(51.9)	(36.8)	(28.7)	(30.3)
Market value ($ mil.)	(39.4%)	448.5	172.4	192.2	45.2	60.3
Employees	(25.0%)	171	100	100	80	54

ANTS SOFTWARE INC.
OTC: ANTS

71 Stevenson St., Ste. 400	CEO: Joseph M. (Joe) Kozak
San Francisco, CA 94105	CFO: David A. Buckel
Phone: 650-931-0500	HR: —
Fax: 650-931-0510	FYE: December 31
Web: www.ants.com	Type: Public

ANTs software hopes to help your data march about in perfect order, with no locking up. The company develops and markets software used to improve the performance of database-driven enterprise applications. ANTs' technology is designed to process and manipulate data with no database locking. Its primary product is its ANTs Compatibility Server, which enables customers to move software applications from one company's database product to another. ANTs markets its products to information technology departments, application developers, and database architects. The company also provides professional services such as consulting, training, support, implementation, and maintenance.

	Annual Growth	12/05	12/06	12/07	12/08	12/09
Sales ($ mil.)	84.6%	0.5	0.3	0.4	8.3	5.8
Net income ($ mil.)	—	(8.7)	(15.1)	(16.3)	(11.6)	(23.3)
Market value ($ mil.)	(25.5%)	227.4	264.6	77.6	40.3	70.0
Employees	51.0%	10	49	49	45	52

ANWORTH MORTGAGE ASSET CORPORATION
NYSE: ANH

1299 Ocean Ave., 2nd Fl.	CEO: Lloyd McAdams
Santa Monica, CA 90401	CFO: Thad M. Brown
Phone: 310-255-4493	HR: —
Fax: 310-434-0070	FYE: December 31
Web: www.anworth.com	Type: Public

What's an Anworth? Depends on the mortgage market. A self-managed real estate investment trust (REIT), Anworth Mortgage invests in mortgage-related assets, primarily mortgage-backed securities (MBS) guaranteed by the US government or federally sponsored entities like Fannie Mae and Freddie Mac. As a REIT, the company must invest at least three-quarters of its assets in real estate, government securities, cash, or cash-equivalents, and it more than complies: More than 99% of Anworth Mortgage's assets are invested in agency-backed MBS; the remainder is invested in non-agency collateralized mortgage obligations (CMOs). The company funds its investment activities mainly through short-term loans.

	Annual Growth	12/05	12/06	12/07	12/08	12/09
Sales ($ mil.)	(1.8%)	281.9	301.8	225.2	287.5	262.1
Net income ($ mil.)	45.7%	28.9	(14.2)	(156.5)	62.6	130.2
Market value ($ mil.)	(1.0%)	867.2	1,129.8	981.3	763.9	831.6
Employees	0.0%	12	12	12	12	12

🔲 A. O. SMITH CORPORATION
NYSE: AOS

11270 W. Park Place, Ste. 170	CEO: Paul W. Jones
Milwaukee, WI 53224	CFO: Terry M. Murphy
Phone: 414-359-4000	HR: Mark A. Petrarca
Fax: 414-359-4115	FYE: December 31
Web: www.aosmith.com	Type: Public

Aerosmith has a lot of fans — A. O. Smith has a lot of fan motors. The company makes the guts of buildings, i.e., residential and commercial water heaters and electric motors. Its Water segment makes residential gas and electric water heaters and commercial water-heating systems. Electrical products include pump motors for home water systems, swimming pools, and hot tubs; fan motors for furnaces and air conditioners; and hermetic motors for compressors and commercial refrigeration units. Routes to retail shelves include private-label agreements with Lowe's and Sears. Customers in the US make up close to three-quarters of A. O. Smith's sales. Members of the founding Smith family control the company.

	Annual Growth	12/05	12/06	12/07	12/08	12/09
Sales ($ mil.)	4.2%	1,689.2	2,161.3	2,312.1	2,304.9	1,991.5
Net income ($ mil.)	17.8%	46.5	76.5	88.2	81.9	89.6
Market value ($ mil.)	5.4%	1,071.2	1,146.2	1,069.6	900.9	1,324.2
Employees	(2.3%)	17,650	18,000	16,800	15,350	16,067

AOL ADVERTISING

1020 Hull St., Ivory Bldg.	CEO: Jeffrey A. (Jeff) Levick
Baltimore, MD 21230	CFO: Don Neff
Phone: 410-244-1370	HR: —
Fax: 410-244-1699	FYE: December 31
Web: advertising.aol.com	Type: Subsidiary

AOL Advertising (formerly Platform-A) offers a host of digital marketing and advertising services including display, video, mobile, contextual, and search marketing. Its sponsored listing network allows advertisers to target an ad's placement, whether it be by site, section, or page. Clients have included T-Mobile USA (advertising its G1 phone), FreeCreditReport.com, and TurboTax. Other AOL Advertising businesses include ADTECH (online ad serving), buy.at (e-commerce marketing), and Third Screen Media (mobile ad serving). Owned by AOL, the company operates from about 20 offices in the US, Europe, and Japan.

AOL INC.
NYSE: AOL

770 Broadway
New York, NY 10003
Phone: 212-652-6400
Fax: —
Web: www.corp.aol.com

CEO: Tim Armstrong
CFO: Arthur (Artie) Minson
HR: Tiane Mitchell Gordon
FYE: December 31
Type: Public

Everybody's favorite spinoff is still serving America online. Formerly a subsidiary of Time Warner, AOL was spun off to shareholders at the end of 2009. AOL operates a Web portal serving users with an array of content and entertainment, including news, sports, games, music, video, and maps (MapQuest). It also boasts interactive services such as e-mail and instant messaging. Its advertising-supported content business operates through units such as AOL Advertising (digital advertising), AOL Media (digital publishing), and AOL Ventures (new projects). In addition, the company still offers dial-up Internet access services for a monthly fee to some 5 million subscribers in the US.

APAC CUSTOMER SERVICES INC.
NASDAQ (GM): APAC

2333 Waukegan Rd., Ste. 100
Bannockburn, IL 60015
Phone: 847-374-4980
Fax: —
Web: www.apaccustomerservices.com

CEO: Michael P. (Mike) Marrow
CFO: Andrew B. Szafran
HR: Eric Tinch
FYE: December 31
Type: Public

The telephone isn't the instrument of choice for APAC Customer Services anymore. The company, formerly APAC TeleServices, provides outsourced customer-management and acquisition services using the telephone and the Internet. It operates 13 customer interaction centers (they aren't just call centers anymore) in the US and the Philippines. APAC's customer management services include customer retention, help-line information, direct mail response, and order entry services. Clients include companies in the parcel delivery, pharmaceutical, telecommunications, retail, and financial services industries.

	Annual Growth	12/05	12/06	12/07	12/08	12/09
Sales ($ mil.)	5.2%	239.8	224.3	224.7	248.8	293.2
Net income ($ mil.)	—	(22.4)	(30.5)	5.1	3.0	58.1
Market value ($ mil.)	34.3%	95.8	196.2	59.6	63.3	311.8
Employees	9.6%	8,500	7,900	9,500	10,500	12,250

AON CORPORATION
NYSE: AON

Aon Center, 200 E. Randolph St.
Chicago, IL 60601
Phone: 312-381-1000
Fax: 312-381-6032
Web: www.aon.com

CEO: Gregory C. (Greg) Case
CFO: Christa Davies
HR: Jeremy G. O. Farmer
FYE: December 31
Type: Public

Aon (the name means "oneness" in Gaelic) is one of the world's leading insurance brokerages, as well as a top reinsurance broker. The company operates in two major segments: commercial brokerage and consulting services. The company's Aon Risk Services brokerage unit provides retail property/casualty, liability, workers' compensation, and other insurance products for groups and businesses, as well as risk management services. Aon Benfield handles reinsurance brokerage and analysis services to protect insurers from losses on traditional and specialty property/casualty policies. Aon's consulting unit, Aon Consulting Worldwide, specializes in employee benefits administration.

	Annual Growth	12/05	12/06	12/07	12/08	12/09
Sales ($ mil.)	(6.3%)	9,837.0	8,954.0	7,471.0	7,631.0	7,595.0
Net income ($ mil.)	1.8%	737.0	719.0	864.0	1,462.0	792.0
Market value ($ mil.)	1.6%	9,685.6	9,521.3	12,848.6	12,307.1	10,329.5
Employees	(6.1%)	46,600	43,100	42,500	37,700	36,200

APACHE CORPORATION
NYSE: APA

2000 Post Oak Blvd., Ste. 100
Houston, TX 77056
Phone: 713-296-6000
Fax: 713-296-6496
Web: www.apachecorp.com

CEO: G. Steven (Steve) Farris
CFO: Roger B. Plank
HR: Margery M. (Margie) Harris
FYE: December 31
Type: Public

There's more than a patch of oil in Apache's portfolio. Apache is an oil and gas exploration and production company with onshore and offshore operations in North America and in Argentina, Australia, Egypt, and the UK (offshore in the North Sea). The company has estimated proved reserves of about 2.4 billion barrels of oil equivalent, mostly from five North American regions: the Gulf of Mexico, the Gulf Coast of Texas and Louisiana, the Permian Basin in West Texas, the Anadarko Basin in Oklahoma, and Canada's Western Sedimentary Basin. Of its international operations, Apache's assets in Egypt and the North Sea are the largest. Shell is Apache's largest customer, accounting for 18% of sales in 2009.

	Annual Growth	12/05	12/06	12/07	12/08	12/09
Sales ($ mil.)	3.2%	7,584.2	8,288.8	9,977.9	12,327.8	8,614.8
Net income ($ mil.)	—	2,623.7	2,552.5	2,812.4	712.0	(284.4)
Market value ($ mil.)	10.8%	23,109.6	22,431.7	36,269.8	25,136.6	34,796.0
Employees	5.3%	2,805	3,150	3,521	3,639	3,452

A.P. PHARMA, INC.
NASDAQ (GM): APPA

123 Saginaw Dr.
Redwood City, CA 94063
Phone: 650-366-2626
Fax: 650-365-6490
Web: www.appharma.com

CEO: John B. Whelan
CFO: —
HR: Sandra Squires
FYE: December 31
Type: Public

A.P. Pharma wants to hit you where it hurts. The firm develops bioerodible polymers for injectable and implantable drug delivery. Its Biochronomer technology delivers medication directly to the site where the drug is needed. A.P. Pharma's leading drug candidate, APF530, could ease chemotherapy-induced nausea and vomiting. A second candidate in clinical trials is a post-surgical pain management product that delivers pain relief right to the surgical site. A.P. Pharma is also developing therapies for inflammation and chronic pain using its Biochronomer technology. Its drug candidates combine approved therapeutics with its bioerodible polymers.

	Annual Growth	12/05	12/06	12/07	12/08	12/09
Sales ($ mil.)	80.3%	—	—	0.4	0.4	1.3
Net income ($ mil.)	—	—	—	(20.2)	(22.9)	(10.2)
Market value ($ mil.)	(10.7%)	—	—	62.4	16.6	49.8
Employees	(30.9%)	—	—	44	33	21

APARTMENT INVESTMENT AND MANAGEMENT
NYSE: AIV

4582 S. Ulster Street Pkwy., Ste. 1100
Denver, CO 80237
Phone: 303-757-8101
Fax: 303-759-3226
Web: www.aimco.com

CEO: Terry Considine
CFO: Ernest M. Freedman
HR: —
FYE: December 31
Type: Public

Apartment Investment and Management Company (AIMCO) is one of the hosts with the most — apartment units, that is. A self-managed real estate investment trust (REIT), AIMCO owns, manages, and redevelops multifamily residential properties throughout the US. It is one of the nation's largest apartment owner/managers (surpassed only by Sam Zell's Equity Residential) with some 870 properties comprising 135,000 units in its portfolio. Operating arm AIMCO Properties holds and manages most of AIMCO's assets, which include suburban communities, high-rises, and subsidized affordable housing. The REIT targets the largest multifamily markets in the US, namely coastal cities, the Sunbelt, and Chicago.

	Annual Growth	12/05	12/06	12/07	12/08	12/09
Sales ($ mil.)	(6.6%)	1,570.8	1,758.7	1,795.5	1,527.0	1,195.8
Net income ($ mil.)	—	71.0	176.8	29.9	415.5	(44.8)
Market value ($ mil.)	(19.5%)	4,424.6	6,545.2	4,057.7	1,349.5	1,860.0
Employees	(14.0%)	6,400	6,000	4,400	4,500	3,500

An in-depth profile of this company is available to Hoover's Online members at hoovers.com.

151

APCO ARGENTINA INC.

NASDAQ (CM): APAGF

One Williams Center, Mail Drop 26-4
Tulsa, OK 74172
Phone: 918-573-2164
Fax: —
Web: www.williams.com/productservices/exploration/argentina.asp

CEO: Ralph A. Hill
CFO: Landy L. Fullmer
HR: —
FYE: December 31
Type: Public

Aptly named, Apco Argentina exploits oil and gas resources in Argentina. Deregulation gave Apco Argentina's joint venture with Petrobras Energia and Petrolera Entre Lomas the right to pump oil from the Entre Lomas concession in southwestern Argentina until 2026. The exploration and production company (69%-owned by US powerhouse The Williams Companies) holds a 53% stake in the Entre Lomas joint venture. In 2007 Apco Argentina, which also holds interests in other oil and gas concessions in Argentina, reported consolidated proved reserves of 11 million barrels of oil and 24.1 billion cu. ft. of gas.

	Annual Growth	12/05	12/06	12/07	12/08	12/09
Sales ($ mil.)	14.9%	41.7	58.0	61.7	69.1	72.7
Net income ($ mil.)	(5.8%)	29.8	40.1	31.3	23.8	23.5
Market value ($ mil.)	14.4%	380.0	645.9	810.2	784.0	650.7
Employees	17.5%	11	13	17	21	21

APEX OIL COMPANY, INC.

8235 Forsyth Blvd., Ste. 400
Clayton, MO 63105
Phone: 314-889-9600
Fax: 314-854-8539
Web: www.apexoil.com

CEO: P. Anthony (Tony) Novelly
CFO: John L. Hank Jr.
HR: Julie Cook
FYE: September 30
Type: Private

Always at the top of its game, Apex Oil sells, stores, and distributes petroleum products. Its range of refined products includes asphalt, biodiesel, kerosene, fuel oil, diesel fuel, heavy oil, gasoline, and bunker fuels. The company's terminals are primarily located on the East Coast and Gulf Coast, in California, and in the Midwest. Internationally, Apex Oil has operations in the Bahamas, Monaco, and the Netherlands. The company's subsidiaries include Apex Towing, a tug boat and barge business; Petroleum Fuel and Terminal, a storage and truck rack operation; and Enjet (oil and carbon black marketing). Apex Oil is controlled by CEO Tony Novelly.

API GROUP, INC.

1100 Old Hwy. 8 NW
New Brighton, MN 55112
Phone: 651-223-4922
Fax: 651-636-0312
Web: www.apigroupinc.com

CEO: Russell (Russ) Becker
CFO: Gregory J. Keup
HR: —
FYE: December 31
Type: Private

Holding company APi Group has a piece of the action in two main sectors: industrial and specialty construction services and life safety. APi has more than 30 subsidiaries, which operate as independent companies across the US, UK, and Canada. Services provided by the company's construction subsidiaries include energy conservation; electrical, industrial, and mechanical contracting; industrial insulation; and overhead door installation. Other units install fire protection, security, and alarm systems; fabricate structural steel; and distribute building materials. The family-owned company was founded in 1926 by Reuben Anderson, father of chairman Lee Anderson.

	Annual Growth	12/04	12/05	12/06	12/07	12/08
Sales ($ mil.)	33.3%	—	—	900.0	1,000.0	1,600.0
Employees	34.2%	—	—	5,000	9,000	9,000

APL LIMITED

16220 N. Scottsdale Rd., Ste. 300
Scottsdale, AZ 85254
Phone: 602-586-4800
Fax: 303-645-7679
Web: www.apl.com

CEO: Eng Aik Meng
CFO: Cedric Foo
HR: —
FYE: December 31
Type: Subsidiary

It's full steam ahead for APL. The company is the US-based container shipping arm of Singapore's Neptune Orient Lines (NOL). APL's fleet comprises around 140 containerships, serving 140 ports worldwide. It also operates marine terminals at eight locations, including three on the US West Coast. APL's partnerships enable the company to offer intermodal transportation — movement of freight through combinations of ship, train, and truck. The liner operator coordinates its offerings with those of sister company APL Logistics, which provides supply chain management services. APL and APL Logistics are the principal operating brands of NOL and account for the vast majority of NOL's revenues.

	Annual Growth	12/04	12/05	12/06	12/07	12/08
Est. sales ($ mil.)	—	—	—	—	—	1,195.5
Employees	—	—	—	—	—	4,782

APL LOGISTICS, LTD.

16220 N. Scottsdale Rd., Ste. 300
Scottsdale, AZ 85254
Phone: 602-586-4800
Fax: 602-586-4861
Web: www.apllogistics.com

CEO: Jim McAdam
CFO: Cedric Foo
HR: —
FYE: December 31
Type: Subsidiary

APL Logistics, the logistics arm of Singapore-based marine transportation giant Neptune Orient Lines, offers a wide range of supply chain management services. These include freight forwarding (purchasing transportation capacity from carriers and reselling it to customers), warehousing and distribution (with 25 million sq. ft. globally), manufacturing support, and merchandise consolidation. The company draws customers from automotive/industrial, consumer goods, retail, and electronics/high technology. APL Logistics operates from more than 300 offices serving more than 55 countries in Africa, the Americas, Asia, Europe, and the Middle East. A sister company, APL, offers ocean container transportation services.

APM TERMINALS NORTH AMERICA, INC.

1000 APM Terminals Blvd.
Portsmouth, VA 23703
Phone: 757-686-6000
Fax: —
Web: www.apmterminals.com

CEO: Eric A. Sisco
CFO: Christian M. Laursen
HR: Tiemen G. Meester
FYE: December 31
Type: Subsidiary

A containership with cargo bound for the US might very well want to unload it at a terminal run by APM Terminals North America. The company oversees the operations of about a dozen container terminals on the Atlantic, Pacific, and Gulf coasts of the US. APM Terminals North America is present at major trade gateways such as Charleston, South Carolina; Houston; Los Angeles; Oakland, California; and Port Elizabeth, New Jersey. The company is part of APM Terminals Management, a leading terminal operator, which in turn is owned by marine transportation giant A.P. Møller – Mærsk.

APOGEE ENTERPRISES, INC.

NASDAQ (GS): APOG

7900 Xerxes Ave. South, Ste. 1800
Minneapolis, MN 55431
Phone: 952-835-1874
Fax: 952-487-7565
Web: www.apog.com

CEO: Russell Huffer
CFO: James S. Porter
HR: Warren Planitzer
FYE: February 28
Type: Public

Apogee Enterprises goes to great panes for its glass customers. The company focuses on two segments within the glass market. Operating through multiple businesses, its architectural products and services unit fabricates, installs, maintains, and renovates the glass walls and windows used in high-rises, store entrances, and other commercial and institutional buildings. Apogee's large-scale optical technologies unit, under the Tru Vue brand, makes specialized glass and acrylic primarily for the custom picture framing market. Tru Vue goods are distributed through mass merchandisers and independent distributors. Construction contractors, building owners, and architects account for over 90% of the company's sales.

	Annual Growth	2/06	2/07	2/08	2/09	2/10
Sales ($ mil.)	0.0%	696.7	778.8	881.8	925.5	696.7
Net income ($ mil.)	7.4%	23.8	31.7	48.6	51.0	31.7
Market value ($ mil.)	(4.7%)	483.5	586.7	430.4	264.8	399.6
Employees	(6.5%)	4,465	4,645	5,438	4,422	3,407

APOLLO ADVISORS, L.P.

1 Manhattanville Rd., Ste. 201
Purchase, NY 10577
Phone: 914-694-8000
Fax: 914-694-6380

CEO: Leon D. Black
CFO: —
HR: —
FYE: December 31
Type: Private

In Greek and Roman mythology, Apollo is the god of light, medicine, arts, and archery, but Apollo Advisors is even more diverse. Also known as Apollo Management, the leveraged buyout specialist invests in a wide variety of industries. Its portfolio holdings include movie theater chain AMC Entertainment, Berry Plastics, CEVA Logistics, realty franchiser Realogy, Jacuzzi Brands, specialty manufacturer RBS Global, and Hexion Specialty Chemicals. Apollo joined forces with TPG to purchase gaming company Harrah's Entertainment for nearly $28 billion in early 2008. Founded in 1990, Apollo initially earned a reputation for being a vulture investor by specializing in distressed assets.

APOLLO COMMERCIAL REAL ESTATE FINANCE, INC.

NYSE: ARI

9 W. 57th St., 43rd Fl.
New York, NY 10019
Phone: 212-515-3200
Fax: —
Web: www.apolloreit.com

CEO: Joseph F. Azrack
CFO: Stuart A. Rothstein
HR: —
FYE: December 31
Type: Public

Apollo Commercial Real Estate Finance is taking one giant leap into the mortgage universe. The company was formed in 2009 by Apollo Global Management to be a mortgage real estate investment trust (REIT). Externally managed by ACREFI Management (an indirect subsidiary of Apollo Global Management), the firm plans to use proceeds from its 2009 IPO to invest in performing, non-distressed, US commercial real estate loans; commercial mortgage-backed securities (CMBS); and other commercial real estate debt investments. Apollo Commercial Real Estate Finance expects its average investment to range between $25 million and $75 million.

	Annual Growth	12/05	12/06	12/07	12/08	12/09
Sales ($ mil.)	—	—	—	—	—	0.6
Net income ($ mil.)	—	—	—	—	—	(2.2)
Market value ($ mil.)	—	—	—	—	—	191.9
Employees	—	—	—	—	—	—

APOLLO GOLD CORPORATION

NYSE Amex: AGT

5655 S. Yosemite St., Ste. 200
Greenwood Village, CO 80111
Phone: 720-886-9656
Fax: 720-482-0957
Web: www.apollogold.com

CEO: Wade K. Dawe
CFO: Melvyn Williams
HR: —
FYE: December 31
Type: Public

Apollo Gold is not something you might find on Mount Olympus, but rather a mining company operating in Canada and the US. The company has gold, silver, lead, and zinc mine operations in Montana and Ontario; it also operates an exploration project in Chihuahua, Mexico. The company's Montana Tunnels facility accounts for the majority of the company's silver, lead, and zinc production. In the near term, Apollo is primarily focused on developing its Black Fox Project gold mine operation in Ontario. It also has begun to look for external growth, agreeing to buy Linear Gold for about $100 million in 2010. Apollo Gold said it expected to change its name when the acquisition is closed.

	Annual Growth	12/05	12/06	12/07	12/08	12/09
Sales ($ mil.)	2.1%	43.3	10.2	38.5	46.4	47.0
Net income ($ mil.)	—	(22.2)	(15.6)	2.4	1.6	(61.7)
Market value ($ mil.)	16.4%	81.1	155.5	202.8	77.7	148.7
Employees	14.1%	129	165	230	225	219

APOLLO GROUP, INC.

NASDAQ (GS): APOL

4025 S. Riverpoint Pkwy.
Phoenix, AZ 85040
Phone: 480-966-5394
Fax: —
Web: www.apollogrp.edu

CEO: Charles B. (Chas) Edelstein
CFO: Brian L. Swartz
HR: Frederick J. (Fred) Newton III
FYE: August 31
Type: Public

Apollo's creed could be that we all deserve the chance to advance. The for-profit group provides educational programs and services through a number of subsidiaries, including online stalwart University of Phoenix, which also has physical campuses in North America and Europe. The largest private university in the US, the University of Phoenix accounts for some 95% of Apollo's sales. Other schools include Western International University (graduate and undergraduate courses) and Insights Schools (online high school education for homeschooled students). Apollo has more than 440,000 degreed students, or students enrolled in degree programs ranging from the associate's to the doctoral level.

	Annual Growth	8/05	8/06	8/07	8/08	8/09
Sales ($ mil.)	15.3%	2,251.5	2,477.5	2,723.8	3,140.9	3,974.2
Net income ($ mil.)	7.7%	444.7	414.8	408.8	476.5	598.3
Market value ($ mil.)	(4.7%)	11,924.5	7,611.6	8,894.1	9,653.6	9,829.5
Employees	13.1%	32,666	36,416	36,418	44,647	53,498

APOLLO INVESTMENT CORPORATION

NASDAQ (GS): AINV

9 W. 57th St., 41st Fl.
New York, NY 10019
Phone: 212-515-3450
Fax: —
Web: www.apolloic.com

CEO: James C. Zelter
CFO: Richard L. Peteka
HR: —
FYE: March 31
Type: Public

Private equity investor Apollo Investment shines its light on the world of middle-market corporate finance. A business development company (BDC) and a closed-end investment fund, it specializes in subordinated debt and equity capital investments, providing middle-market companies ($50 million to $2 billion in annual revenues) with mezzanine or senior subordinated loans. It also makes direct equity investments. The company, which typically invests between $20 million and $250 million per transaction, has stakes in about 70 companies in the US, Canada, and western Europe, including financial services behemoth First Data, technology insurer Asurion, and human resources outsourcer Ceridian.

	Annual Growth	3/06	3/07	3/08	3/09	3/10
Sales ($ mil.)	25.0%	139.4	245.3	122.8	377.3	340.2
Net income ($ mil.)	21.6%	120.4	312.2	(33.4)	(611.9)	263.3
Market value ($ mil.)	(8.1%)	3,452.4	4,148.3	3,068.6	674.6	2,467.6
Employees	0.0%	2	2	2	—	—

An in-depth profile of this company is available to Hoover's Online members at hoovers.com.

153

APP PHARMACEUTICALS, LLC

1501 E. Woodfield Rd., Ste. 300 E.
Schaumburg, IL 60173
Phone: 847-413-2075
Fax: 800-743-7082
Web: www.appdrugs.com

CEO: John Ducker
CFO: Richard J. Tajak
HR: James Callanan
FYE: December 31
Type: Subsidiary

Your eyes are getting heavy. You're getting sleepy. No hypnotist here, just APP Pharmaceuticals, a company that develops, makes, and markets anesthetics and other injectable drugs. Specializing in generics, APP's critical care products segment includes market-leading general anesthetic Diprivan and blood thinner Heparin. Other product segments focus on injectable oncology treatments and drugs that fight ear, heart, respiratory tract, skin, and sinus infections. APP markets through a direct sales force and often sells through group purchasing organizations to customers that include hospitals, long-term care facilities, and clinics in North America. The company is a subsidiary of German medical firm Fresenius.

APPLE AMERICAN GROUP LLC

6200 Oak Tree Blvd., Ste. 250
Independence, OH 44131
Phone: 216-525-2775
Fax: 216-328-1956
Web: www.appleamerican.com

CEO: Gregory G. (Greg) Flynn
CFO: Lorin M. Cortina
HR: Jim Gamelin
FYE: December 31
Type: Private

You might say this company is into neighborhood casual dining. Apple American Group is a leading franchisee of Applebee's, with more than 200 Applebee's Neighborhood Grill & Bar locations in about 10 states. The largest casual dining chain in the US, Applebee's restaurants offer a full-service menu of beef, chicken, and seafood entrees, as well as a wide selection of appetizers. Most of Apple American's restaurants are found in the Midwest (Ohio, Indiana, Pennsylvania) and on the West Coast (California, Washington). Founded in 1998 by CEO Greg Flynn, Apple American is controlled by private equity firm Weston Presidio Service.

	Annual Growth	12/04	12/05	12/06	12/07	12/08
Est. sales ($ mil.)	—	—	—	—	—	431.1
Employees	—	—	—	—	—	5,500

⊞ APPLE INC.

NASDAQ (GS): AAPL

1 Infinite Loop
Cupertino, CA 95014
Phone: 408-996-1010
Fax: 408-974-2113
Web: www.apple.com

CEO: Steven P. (Steve) Jobs
CFO: Peter Oppenheimer
HR: —
FYE: September 30
Type: Public

Apple aims for nothing short of a revolution, whether in personal computing or digital media distribution. The company's desktop and laptop computers — all of which feature its OS X operating system — include its Mac mini, iMac, and MacBook for the consumer and education markets, and more powerful Mac Pro and MacBook Pro for high-end consumers and professionals involved in design and publishing. Apple scored a runaway hit with its digital music players (iPod) and online music store (iTunes). Other products include mobile phones (iPhone), servers (Xserve), wireless networking equipment (AirPort), and publishing and multimedia software. Apple gets more than half of its sales in the US.

	Annual Growth	9/05	9/06	9/07	9/08	9/09
Sales ($ mil.)	27.3%	13,931.0	19,315.0	24,006.0	32,479.0	36,537.0
Net income ($ mil.)	43.8%	1,335.0	1,989.0	3,496.0	4,834.0	5,704.0
Market value ($ mil.)	36.4%	48,781.8	70,047.1	139,648.2	103,423.6	168,657.1
Employees	21.6%	16,820	17,787	21,600	35,100	36,800

APPLETON COATED LLC

569 Carter Ct.
Kimberly, WI 54136
Phone: 920-968-3999
Fax: 920-968-3950
Web: www.appletoncoated.com

CEO: John Cappy
CFO: Sandy Van Ert
HR: Debbie (Deb) Six
FYE: December 31
Type: Subsidiary

Curious paper buyers may find that Appleton Coated has the ticket to Utopia. The company manufactures and markets coated free-sheet carbonless paper products under brands names including Altima, Curious, and Utopia. The company's products are used to make such goods as books, magazines, corporate annual reports, and consumer product packaging. Its Curious products include metallic, tactile, and translucent sheets. Appleton Coated primarily serves printers and paper merchants, and produces about 400,000 tons of paper per year. The company is a subsidiary of France-based paper manufacturer ArjoWiggins, which is in turn owned by Sequana Capital.

APPLETON PAPERS INC.

825 E. Wisconsin Ave.
Appleton, WI 54911
Phone: 920-734-9841
Fax: 920-991-7365
Web: www.appletonideas.com

CEO: Mark R. Richards
CFO: Thomas J. Ferree
HR: —
FYE: December 31
Type: Private

Paper is the apple of Appleton Papers' eye. The company manufactures specialty paper products through two divisions: technical papers and performance packaging. It is the world's #1 producer of carbonless paper; sold under the NCR Paper brand, carbonless paper is used in multi-part business forms (such as invoices). Appleton also makes security papers for government documents, and thermal papers used in coupons, gaming and transportation tickets, shipping labels, and medical charts. Performance packaging products include blown films and vacuum pouches used for packaging retail foods, medical goods, and industrial products. Customers in the US account for about three-quarters of sales.

	Annual Growth	12/04	12/05	12/06	12/07	12/08
Sales ($ mil.)	(0.6%)	989.5	1,046.5	1,087.4	963.2	964.6
Net income ($ mil.)	—	(25.0)	(3.0)	11.3	(6.3)	(97.4)
Employees	(10.2%)	3,406	3,238	3,144	3,001	2,210

APPLIANCE RECYCLING CENTERS OF AMERICA

NASDAQ (CM): ARCI

7400 Excelsior Blvd.
Minneapolis, MN 55426
Phone: 952-930-9000
Fax: 952-930-1800
Web: www.arcainc.com

CEO: Edward R. (Jack) Cameron
CFO: Peter P. Hausback
HR: —
FYE: December 31
Type: Public

Appliance Recycling Centers of America, Inc. (ARCA), retrieves, recycles, repairs, and resells household appliances. The company's retail business (about 75% of sales) operates about 20 ApplianceSmart Factory Outlet stores in Minnesota, Georgia, Ohio, and Texas that sell new, reconditioned, and "special-buy" appliances from manufacturers such as Electrolux, GE, and Whirlpool. Additionally, ARCA provides recycling and replacement services for electric utilities and other operators of energy efficiency programs in the US and Canada. It also collects fees for appliance disposal, and sells scrap metal and reclaimed chlorofluorocarbons from processed appliances. ARCA was founded in 1976 as a used-appliance retailer.

	Annual Growth	12/05	12/06	12/07	12/08	12/09
Sales ($ mil.)	7.8%	74.9	77.8	100.8	111.0	101.3
Net income ($ mil.)	—	(0.9)	(1.4)	2.5	0.4	(3.3)
Market value ($ mil.)	(17.2%)	26.9	11.8	49.2	16.2	12.6
Employees	6.5%	294	30	411	429	378

APPLIED DNA SCIENCES, INC.
OTC: APDN

25 Health Sciences Dr., Ste. 113
Stony Brook, NY 11790
Phone: 631-444-6862
Fax: 631-444-8848
Web: www.adnas.com

CEO: James A. Hayward
CFO: Kurt Jensen
HR: —
FYE: September 30
Type: Public

Counterfeiters needn't apply here. Applied DNA Sciences makes product authentication and anti-counterfeiting solutions. Its products are encoded with botanical DNA sequences that can distinguish counterfeits from the genuine article. The DNA markers (which hold the SigNature DNA brand) can be employed in ink, glue, holograms, microchips, and paint, and are then used to tag documents, currency, event tickets, and clothing labels. The company applies its SigNature markers to art and collectibles, fine wine, consumer products, digital recording media, pharmaceuticals, and homeland security products.

	Annual Growth	9/05	9/06	9/07	9/08	9/09
Sales ($ mil.)	—	—	0.0	0.1	0.9	0.3
Net income ($ mil.)	—	—	(2.4)	(13.3)	(6.8)	3.9
Market value ($ mil.)	8.9%	—	30.2	30.2	13.6	39.0
Employees	18.6%	—	9	10	5	15

APPLIED ENERGETICS, INC.
NASDAQ (GM): AERG

3590 E. Columbia St.
Tucson, AZ 85714
Phone: 520-628-7415
Fax: 520-622-3835
Web: www.appliedenergetics.com

CEO: James M. (Jim) Feigley
CFO: Humberto Astorga
HR: —
FYE: December 31
Type: Public

Bullets?!! We don't need no stinkin' bullets — not with the Buck Rogers technology of Applied Energetics. The company is developing Laser Guided Energy and Laser Induced Plasma Channel directed-energy weapons for sale to the US government. In plain English? Laser-guided, man-made lightning! Applied Energetics is developing more compact laser sources and field testing its technology for mobile platforms such as tanks, Humvees, and personnel carriers. Depending on the military situation, the charge can be set to stun or kill people, or to disable vehicles. Applied Energetics also develops technology for neutralizing car bombs and other explosives.

	Annual Growth	12/05	12/06	12/07	12/08	12/09
Sales ($ mil.)	(20.6%)	18.9	10.0	12.4	16.6	7.5
Net income ($ mil.)	—	(3.6)	(17.5)	(13.7)	(8.7)	(9.4)
Market value ($ mil.)	(56.9%)	913.5	370.5	258.4	28.9	31.6
Employees	(17.2%)	104	83	79	70	49

APPLIED INDUSTRIAL TECHNOLOGIES, INC.
NYSE: AIT

1 Applied Plaza
Cleveland, OH 44115
Phone: 216-426-4000
Fax: 216-426-4845
Web: www.appliedindustrial.com

CEO: David L. Pugh
CFO: Mark O. Eisele
HR: Barbara D. Emery
FYE: June 30
Type: Public

Just imagine getting lost in *that* warehouse. Applied Industrial Technologies distributes millions of industrial parts made by thousands of manufacturers. The short list includes bearings, power transmission components, hydraulic and pneumatic components, fabricated rubber products, and linear motion systems. It sells primarily through some 460 service centers peppering the US, Canada, and Mexico. Customers are concentrated in maintenance repair operations (MRO) and OEM markets. Applied also operates regional mechanical, rubber, and fluid power shops that offer a slate of services, from engineering design to conveyor belt repair, to such industrial giants as Vulcan Materials and Goodyear Engineered Products.

	Annual Growth	6/05	6/06	6/07	6/08	6/09
Sales ($ mil.)	2.9%	1,717.1	1,900.8	2,014.1	2,089.5	1,923.1
Net income ($ mil.)	(6.5%)	55.3	72.3	86.0	95.5	42.3
Market value ($ mil.)	(2.2%)	911.4	1,029.2	1,249.0	1,023.3	834.1
Employees	1.4%	4,415	4,683	4,635	4,805	4,673

APPLIED MATERIALS, INC.
NASDAQ (GS): AMAT

3050 Bowers Ave.
Santa Clara, CA 95052
Phone: 408-727-5555
Fax: 408-748-9943
Web: www.appliedmaterials.com

CEO: Michael R. (Mike) Splinter
CFO: George S. Davis
HR: Steve Yamasaki
FYE: October 31
Type: Public

Today, semiconductor manufacturing; tomorrow, the world — of alternative energy sources. Applied Materials is, by far, the world's largest maker of semiconductor production equipment. With its 2006 acquisition of Applied Films, the company moved into the market for equipment used in making solar power cells. Applied's machines vie for supremacy in many segments of the chip-making process, including deposition (layering film on wafers), etching (removing portions of chip material to allow precise construction of circuits), and semiconductor metrology and inspection equipment. About two-thirds of Applied's sales come from the Asia/Pacific region, with Taiwan leading the way.

	Annual Growth	10/05	10/06	10/07	10/08	10/09
Sales ($ mil.)	(8.0%)	6,991.8	9,167.0	9,734.9	8,129.2	5,013.6
Net income ($ mil.)	—	1,209.9	1,516.7	1,710.2	960.7	(305.3)
Market value ($ mil.)	(7.1%)	21,975.9	23,359.5	26,086.3	17,341.6	16,387.9
Employees	0.9%	12,576	14,072	15,328	15,410	13,032

APPLIED MICRO CIRCUITS CORPORATION
NASDAQ (GS): AMCC

215 Moffett Dr.
Sunnyvale, CA 94089
Phone: 408-542-8600
Fax: 405-542-8601
Web: www.amcc.com

CEO: Paramesh Gopi
CFO: Robert G. (Bob) Gargus
HR: Michael (Mike) Major
FYE: March 31
Type: Public

Applied Micro Circuits applies most of its microchip expertise to communications, but does more than a micro business in storage, as well. Customers use AppliedMicro's chips — which include controllers, host bus adapters, network processors, and switch fabrics — to control the flow of voice and data transmissions in LANs, WANs, and storage networks. Having shut down its own wafer fabrication plant (or fab), the fabless semiconductor company outsources manufacturing to IBM Microelectronics, TSMC, and UMC. Its top customers include Alcatel-Lucent, Avnet (30% of sales), Cisco, Hitachi, Hon Hai (13%), Sanmina-SCI, and Siemens. AppliedMicro gets nearly two-thirds of its sales outside North America.

	Annual Growth	3/06	3/07	3/08	3/09	3/10
Sales ($ mil.)	(5.9%)	261.8	292.9	246.1	214.2	205.6
Net income ($ mil.)	—	(148.4)	(24.2)	(115.1)	(309.3)	(7.5)
Market value ($ mil.)	(14.7%)	1,065.7	955.7	470.0	318.1	564.9
Employees	(1.7%)	602	619	583	551	562

APPLIED NANOTECH HOLDINGS, INC.
OTC: APNT

3006 Longhorn Blvd., Ste. 107
Austin, TX 78758
Phone: 512-339-5020
Fax: 512-339-5021
Web: www.appliednanotech.net

CEO: Douglas P. (Doug) Baker
CFO: Douglas P. (Doug) Baker
HR: —
FYE: December 31
Type: Public

Applied Nanotech Holdings hopes to make it big by thinking small. The company conducts research on carbon nanotubes — molecular-sized cylindrical structures that could be used in making electronic displays and other products. Applied Nanotech derives most of its revenues from contracts with agencies of the US government or by doing research on a contract basis with other entities. The company is developing nanomaterials for use in epoxies, glass fibers, and nylons. Other applications of carbon nanotube technology are in conductive inks (used in communications instrumentation, flexible electronics, printed circuit boards, and radio-frequency identification tags), sensors, and thermal management.

	Annual Growth	12/05	12/06	12/07	12/08	12/09
Sales ($ mil.)	61.7%	0.6	1.1	4.0	4.0	4.1
Net income ($ mil.)	—	(4.7)	(6.6)	(4.3)	(2.7)	(2.2)
Market value ($ mil.)	(42.8%)	231.3	150.6	116.2	25.8	24.7
Employees	(1.8%)	29	35	38	32	27

An in-depth profile of this company is available to Hoover's Online members at hoovers.com.

155

APPLIED SCIENCE PRODUCTS, INC.   Pink Sheets: APLD

924 Corridor Park Blvd.   CEO: Kenneth S. Wood
Knoxville, TN 37932   CFO: Richard S. Rosenfeld
Phone: 865-777-3776   HR: —
Fax: 865-777-3767   FYE: May 31
Web: www.flysafetech.com   Type: Public

Applied Science Products (ASP, formerly Flight Safety Technologies) has its
sights set on another atmosphere. Through its Advanced Plasma Products
unit, ASP develops products using glow discharge plasma technology, which
uses electricity to purify air at standard pressure and room temperature. Its
TriClean Pro stand-alone air purifier removes bacteria, viruses, allergens,
molds, and other contaminants in settings where air quality is an issue, such
as hospitals, schools, and nursing homes. Other products in development
include a disinfectant chamber to rid surfaces of microbial contamination,
and the PlasmaGen DNA sample preparation unit. Funding issues forced
Flight Safety to change its name and direction in 2009.

	Annual Growth	5/04	5/05	5/06	5/07	*5/08
Sales ($ mil.)	(46.3%)	3.6	3.3	3.9	1.5	0.3
Net income ($ mil.)	—	(0.4)	(1.4)	(2.3)	(2.8)	(3.3)
Market value ($ mil.)	2.6%	14.7	14.3	20.6	16.1	16.3
Employees	(8.5%)	10	10	11	12	7

*Most recent year available

⊞ APPLIED SIGNAL TECHNOLOGY, INC.   NASDAQ (GS): APSG

460 W. California Ave.   CEO: William B. Van Vleet III
Sunnyvale, CA 94086   CFO: James E. Doyle
Phone: 408-749-1888   HR: —
Fax: 408-738-1928   FYE: October 31
Web: www.appsig.com   Type: Public

Eavesdropping is no accident at Applied Signal Technology. The company
makes reconnaissance equipment — including receivers, processors, and software — used by the US government and its contractors to collect and process
electronic communications and other electronic signals. Applied Signal's
products are used to scan and filter cell phone, ship-to-shore, microwave, and
military transmissions and evaluate them for relevant information. Other
products are designed to collect and process radar signals for weapons systems. The company sells primarily to intelligence and military agencies,
though it generates a small portion of its revenues from commercial clients.

	Annual Growth	10/05	10/06	10/07	10/08	10/09
Sales ($ mil.)	6.7%	156.1	161.9	170.4	186.3	202.6
Net income ($ mil.)	12.0%	9.2	4.3	6.8	8.0	14.5
Market value ($ mil.)	4.5%	228.3	197.4	191.2	238.4	272.6
Employees	4.1%	677	647	635	672	794

APPLIED SYSTEMS, INC.

200 Applied Pkwy.   CEO: James P. (Jim) Kellner
University Park, IL 60466   CFO: Colleen E. Mikuce
Phone: 708-534-5575   HR: —
Fax: 708-534-8016   FYE: December 31
Web: www.appliedsystems.com   Type: Private

Applied Systems applies technology to automate the insurance industry —
from lone agent to large agency. The company helps independent insurance
agents become more efficient by minimizing paperwork, streamlining workflows, and improving access to information. Applied Systems' main product,
The Agency Manager (TAM) system, assists with client management, policy
pricing, electronic data interchange, policy and claims servicing, and office
administration. Its Vision system provides large carriers with automated
billing, policy and claims processing, and reports. Applied Systems is owned
by Bain Capital and James Kellner, the chairman and CEO.

APPROACH RESOURCES INC.   NASDAQ (GM): AREX

1 Ridgmar Centre, 6500 West Fwy., Ste. 800   CEO: J. Ross Craft
Fort Worth, TX 76116   CFO: Steven P. Smart
Phone: 817-989-9000   HR: —
Fax: 817-989-9001   FYE: December 31
Web: www.approachresources.com   Type: Public

Approach Resources takes a different approach to natural gas and oil exploration, development, and production. Specializing in finding and exploiting
unconventional reservoirs, the company operates primarily in West Texas'
Ozona Northeast field. It also has operations in western Kentucky and northern New Mexico. The company's unconventional designation results from a
focus on developing natural gas reserves in tight gas sands and shale areas,
necessitating a reliance on advanced completion, fracturing, and drilling techniques. In 2008 Approach Resources reported proved reserves of 193.7 billion
cu. ft. of oil equivalent, with a reserve life index of about 19 years. Yorktown
Energy Partners controls the company.

	Annual Growth	12/05	12/06	12/07	12/08	12/09
Sales ($ mil.)	(1.6%)	43.3	46.7	39.1	79.9	40.6
Net income ($ mil.)	—	12.1	21.2	2.7	23.4	(5.2)
Market value ($ mil.)	(22.5%)	—	—	270.2	153.6	162.2
Employees	24.1%	19	19	25	36	45

APPTIS, INC.

4800 Westfields Blvd.   CEO: Albert A. (Bert) Notini
Chantilly, VA 20151   CFO: Patrick Attilio
Phone: 703-279-3000   HR: —
Fax: 703-691-4911   FYE: December 31
Web: www.apptis.com   Type: Private

Apptis — 'tis an appropriate name for a company that provides many "apps"
for its customers. A provider of IT services to the government sector, Apptis
wants to expand its client base to more corporations and other nongovern-
ment enterprises. The company offers a wide range of IT services, including
network engineering, software application development, and systems integration, for agencies of the federal government and commercial clients. It also
builds custom computer systems and resells equipment from such vendors as
Cisco, Dell, and Hewlett-Packard. Clients include the FAA, the Department of
Defense, and the Veterans Health Administration. New Mountain Capital is
among the company's investors.

	Annual Growth	12/04	12/05	12/06	12/07	12/08
Est. sales ($ mil.)	—	—	—	—	—	162.2
Employees	—	—	—	—	—	700

APPTIX, INC.   Oslo: APP

13461 Sunrise Valley Dr., Ste. 300   CEO: David (Dave) Ehrhardt
Herndon, VA 20171   CFO: Chris Mack
Phone: 703-890-2800   HR: —
Fax: 703-890-2801   FYE: December 31
Web: www.apptix.com   Type: Public

Apptix is an application service provider which offers such software as
Microsoft's Exchange Server and Windows SharePoint Services applications
on a hosted basis. In addition to Microsoft, the company counts Citrix Systems, Global Relay, MX Logic, and Research In Motion among its technology
partners. Its channel partners include Bell Canada, Hewlett-Packard, IBM, and
SAVVIS Communications. Apptix was established in 1997 as the US software
and engineering division of TeleComputing, and was spun off from the Norwegian ASP in 2002.

	Annual Growth	12/04	12/05	12/06	12/07	*12/08
Sales ($ mil.)	52.1%	6.2	8.1	21.4	38.8	33.2
Net income ($ mil.)	—	(7.9)	(6.3)	(6.0)	(25.6)	(8.2)
Employees	—	—	—	—	—	206

*Most recent year available

APRIA HEALTHCARE GROUP INC.

26220 Enterprise Ct.
Lake Forest, CA 92630
Phone: 949-639-2000
Fax: 949-587-9363
Web: www.apria.com

CEO: Norman C. Payson
CFO: Chris A. Karkenny
HR: Howard Derman
FYE: December 31
Type: Private

With about 500 branches nationwide, Apria Healthcare Group is one of the country's largest home health firms. Serving some 1.2 million clients across the US, the company's staff provides supplemental oxygen, ventilators, nebulizers, and sleep monitoring equipment and medication to patients with emphysema, sleep apnea, and other respiratory conditions. Its infusion therapy nurses administer intravenous or injectable therapies — including pain drugs, chemotherapy, and parenteral nutrition — at home or in one of the company's outpatient infusion clinics. Apria also delivers home medical equipment such as walkers and hospital beds. The company is owned by the Blackstone Group.

APRIMO, INCORPORATED

900 E. 96th St., Ste. 400
Indianapolis, IN 46240
Phone: 317-803-4300
Fax: 317-803-4251
Web: www.aprimo.com

CEO: William M. (Bill) Godfrey
CFO: Umesh Singh
HR: Kim Kean
FYE: December 31
Type: Private

Aprimo understands that successful marketing is a prime concern of most businesses. The company provides software that customers use to manage marketing efforts, including applications to automate and analyze marketing campaigns. Aprimo's products are used for tasks such as planning, budgeting, and campaign analysis. The company also offers services such as consulting, maintenance, support, installation, and training. Aprimo's customers come from a wide range of industries and have included Bank of America, Sony, Home Depot, Intel, and Toyota.

APS HEALTHCARE, INC.

44 S. Broadway, Ste. 1200
White Plains, NY 10601
Phone: 800-305-3720
Fax: —
Web: www.apshealthcare.com

CEO: Gregory W. (Greg) Scott
CFO: John McDonough
HR: —
FYE: December 31
Type: Private

At APS Healthcare attitude is everything. What started out as a behavioral health services provider has morphed into a full-service health management firm aiming to reduce health care costs and improve wellness through lifestyle changes. APS provides disease and care management, wellness and prevention, clinical quality reviews, and mental health services to Medicaid agencies, state and local governments, health plans, and employers. The company also provides employee assistance and work-life programs to help workers manage their daily activities. APS, which is owned by private equity firm GTCR Goldner Rauner and led by CEO Gregory Scott, serves some 20 million members in more than 25 states and Puerto Rico.

APTARGROUP, INC.
NYSE: ATR

475 W. Terra Cotta Ave., Ste. E
Crystal Lake, IL 60014
Phone: 815-477-0424
Fax: 815-477-0481
Web: www.aptar.com

CEO: Peter H. Pfeiffer
CFO: Robert Kuhn
HR: Lawrence Lowrimore
FYE: December 31
Type: Public

AptarGroup hopes its dispensers are, well, indispensable. The company's pump dispensers are used for fragrances and cosmetics, food and pharmaceuticals, and a myriad of other personal care items. AptarGroup also makes dispensing closures for plastic-capped squeezable containers holding toiletries, and to a lesser extent, food and beverage, and household goods. The company offers aerosol valves in both continuous-spray and metered-dose options. Lines are branded under the AptarGroup subsidiaries that produce them — Emsar, Pfeiffer, Seaquist, and Valois. Customers include Revlon, Kraft, and Procter & Gamble. AptarGroup operates on five continents, selling dispensers worldwide through an in-house sales network.

	Annual Growth	12/05	12/06	12/07	12/08	12/09
Sales ($ mil.)	7.5%	1,380.0	1,601.4	1,892.2	2,071.7	1,841.6
Net income ($ mil.)	5.7%	100.0	102.9	141.7	153.5	124.6
Market value ($ mil.)	8.2%	1,771.8	2,004.0	2,777.2	2,392.3	2,426.2
Employees	4.8%	7,200	8,200	8,400	8,700	8,700

⊞ APTIUM ONCOLOGY, INC.

8201 Beverly Blvd.
Los Angeles, CA 90048
Phone: 323-966-3400
Fax: 323-966-3685
Web: www.aptiumoncology.com

CEO: Peter H. Jessup
CFO: Peter J. Rogers
HR: Daniel E. (Dan) Wilbur
FYE: December 31
Type: Subsidiary

The side effects of cancer treatment can be nearly as devastating as the disease itself, but Aptium Oncology offers treatment variations to make the best of a bad situation for patients. Aptium Oncology manages hospital-based, outpatient, and comprehensive cancer treatment centers for patients with all types of cancer. It operates a network of 24-hour cancer treatment centers in hospitals in California, Florida, New York, and New Jersey. Aptium Oncology provides consulting, management, information technology, and research coordination services. The company is a subsidiary of UK-based AstraZeneca, a top maker of cancer drugs.

AQUA AMERICA, INC.
NYSE: WTR

762 W. Lancaster Ave.
Bryn Mawr, PA 19010
Phone: 610-527-8000
Fax: 610-525-7658
Web: www.aquaamerica.com

CEO: Nicholas DeBenedictis
CFO: David P. Smeltzer
HR: —
FYE: December 31
Type: Public

Aqua America is all wet and proud of it. The utility holding company provides water and wastewater services through its operating subsidiaries to about 3 million residents in more than a dozen states, including Florida, New Jersey, New York, and Pennsylvania. The state of Pennsylvania is the company's most important market. Aqua America provides water or wastewater services to Philadelphia and in 24 other counties in Pennsylvania, which represents more than half of the company's operating revenues. It contracts with municipalities to operate their water and wastewater systems. The company has grown through more than 130 acquisitions since the early 1990s.

	Annual Growth	12/05	12/06	12/07	12/08	12/09
Sales ($ mil.)	7.8%	496.8	533.5	602.5	627.0	670.5
Net income ($ mil.)	3.4%	91.2	92.0	95.0	97.9	104.4
Market value ($ mil.)	(10.5%)	3,738.9	3,119.8	2,903.4	2,819.9	2,398.1
Employees	2.3%	1,489	1,540	1,585	1,638	1,632

⊞ An in-depth profile of this company is available to Hoover's Online members at hoovers.com.

157

AQUA LUNG AMERICA, INC.

2340 Cousteau Ct.
Vista, CA 92081
Phone: 760-597-5000
Fax: 760-597-4900
Web: www.aqualung.com

CEO: Don Rockwell
CFO: —
HR: —
FYE: December 31
Type: Business segment

Aqua Lung breathes life into water trekking. It makes scuba diving and snorkeling gear and related accessories for recreational, technical, and military customers. The company's name was established more than 60 years ago when Jacques-Yves Cousteau and Emille Gagnan created the first aqua-lung. Aqua Lung sells its products — such as regulators, masks, fins, snorkels, and wetsuits — through selected dive shops and the firm's catalog. Brands sold and distributed by the company include Aqua Flex, Aqua Lung, Apeks, Impulse, SeaQuest, and Tyke. Part of the Air Liquide business, the company and its sister company Aqua Lung International sell its products in more than 30 countries.

	Annual Growth	12/04	12/05	12/06	12/07	12/08
Est. sales ($ mil.)	—	—	—	—	—	40.8
Employees	—	—	—	—	—	400

AQUARION COMPANY

835 Main St.
Bridgeport, CT 06604
Phone: 203-445-7310
Fax: 203-330-4613
Web: www.aquarion.com

CEO: Charles V. (Chuck) Firlotte
CFO: Donald J. Morrissey
HR: —
FYE: March 31
Type: Subsidiary

Through its regulated utility subsidiaries, Aquarion distributes water to more than 203,000 homes and businesses (or about 657,000 people) in more than 50 communities in Connecticut, Massachusetts, New Hampshire, and New York. It is one of the 10 largest investor-owned utilities in the US. The company's Aquarion Services unit provides contract management of municipal water and wastewater systems, along with engineering and management consulting services and consumer water line protection plans. In 2007 UK-based Kelda Group sold control of Aquarion to Australia's Macquarie Bank for $860 million.

AQUENT

711 Boylston St.
Boston, MA 02116
Phone: 617-535-5000
Fax: 617-535-5005
Web: www.aquent.com

CEO: John H. Chuang
CFO: Nunzio Domilici
HR: —
FYE: December 31
Type: Private

Aquent can help quench the thirst of firms in need of good employees. The staffing and consulting agency places contract workers with specialized creative, technical, and Web skills such as graphic design, writing and editing, and print production. In addition to temporary services, Aquent offers permanent staffing, executive search, and creative and IT outsourcing. It also offers financial services to small businesses, as well as recruiting help to health care organizations. Aquent operates from 70 offices in more than 15 countries across Europe, North America, and the Asia/Pacific region. CEO John Chuang controls Aquent.

	Annual Growth	12/04	12/05	12/06	12/07	12/08
Sales ($ mil.)	(2.2%)	—	—	—	460.0	450.0
Employees	—	—	—	—	—	10,000

AQUILEX CORPORATION

3339 Peachtree Rd. NE
Atlanta, GA 30326
Phone: 404-869-6677
Fax: 404-869-6678
Web: www.aquilex.com

CEO: L. William (Bill) Varner Jr.
CFO: Jay W. Ferguson
HR: Juanita M. Biasini
FYE: December 31
Type: Private

Through its operating subsidiaries, Aquilex provides maintenance, repair services and technical support to heavy industry worldwide. Customers include power generation facilities and other industrial plants, including cement, chemical, petrochemical, oil and natural gas processing, pulp and paper, metal refining, and steel manufacturing operations. The company was controlled by private equity firm Harvest Partners (which bought the company from First Reserve in 2007). In 2008 Harvest Partners sold the company to Teachers' Private Capital, the private investment arm of the Ontario Teachers' Pension Plan.

ARABIAN AMERICAN DEVELOPMENT COMPANY

NASDAQ (GS): ARSD

10830 N. Central Expwy., Ste. 175
Dallas, TX 75231
Phone: 214-692-7872
Fax: 214-692-7874

CEO: Nicholas N. Carter
CFO: Connie J. Cook
HR: —
FYE: December 31
Type: Public

Arabian American Development may dream of making a fortune exploring for precious minerals in Saudi Arabia, but it generates most of its bread-and-butter income as an independent refiner in Texas. Through US subsidiary American Shield Refining, it operates a specialty petrochemical product refinery that primarily produces high-purity solvents used in the plastics and foam industries. Subsidiary Gulf State Pipe Line owns and operates three pipelines. In addition, Arabian American holds a mining lease (for copper, gold, silver, and zinc) in southwestern Saudi Arabia's Al Masane area and has mining claims in Nevada. Arabian American Development was formed in 1967.

	Annual Growth	12/05	12/06	12/07	12/08	12/09
Sales ($ mil.)	10.0%	80.4	98.5	108.6	154.6	117.6
Net income ($ mil.)	(20.6%)	16.6	7.9	7.8	(8.9)	6.6
Market value ($ mil.)	13.3%	34.2	73.9	179.4	37.5	56.3
Employees	10.2%	95	133	150	130	140

ARADIGM CORPORATION

OTC: ARDM

3929 Point Eden Way
Hayward, CA 94545
Phone: 510-265-9000
Fax: 510-265-0277
Web: www.aradigm.com

CEO: Igor Gonda
CFO: Nancy E. Pecota
HR: —
FYE: December 31
Type: Public

Aradigm helps the medicine go down for people who swoon at the sight of a needle. Aradigm develops orally inhaled drug delivery systems that treat respiratory diseases. Its lead delivery technology, AERx (an aerosol created from liquid drug formulations), is being adapted to deliver a variety of drugs to treat pulmonary diseases. Aradigm has focused its efforts on developing respiratory treatments for cystic fibrosis, bronchiectasis, inhaled anthrax, smoking cessation, pulmonary arterial hypertension, and asthma. Aradigm typically elects to reformulate already-approved drugs (such as ciprofloxacin) and combine them with its inhalation delivery technologies in order to speed up the regulatory process.

	Annual Growth	12/05	12/06	12/07	12/08	12/09
Sales ($ mil.)	(17.3%)	10.5	4.8	1.0	0.3	4.9
Net income ($ mil.)	—	(29.2)	(13.0)	(24.2)	(22.6)	(13.8)
Market value ($ mil.)	(55.5%)	373.7	92.1	155.6	25.6	14.6
Employees	(38.2%)	103	54	51	38	15

⊞ ARAMARK CORPORATION

ARAMARK Tower, 1101 Market St.
Philadelphia, PA 19107
Phone: 215-238-3000
Fax: 215-238-3333
Web: www.aramark.com

CEO: Joseph (Joe) Neubauer
CFO: L. Frederick Sutherland
HR: Lynn B. McKee
FYE: September 30
Type: Private

Keeping employees fed and clothed is one mark of this company. ARAMARK is the world's #3 contract foodservice provider (behind Compass Group and Sodexo) and the #2 uniform supplier (behind Cintas) in the US. It offers corporate dining services and operates concessions at many sports arenas and other entertainment venues, while its ARAMARK Refreshment Services unit is a leading provider of vending and beverage services. The company also provides facilities management services. Through ARAMARK Uniform and Career Apparel, the company supplies uniforms for health care, public safety, and technology workers. Founded in 1959, ARAMARK is owned by an investment group led by chairman and CEO Joseph Neubauer.

	Annual Growth	9/05	9/06	9/07	9/08	9/09
Sales ($ mil.)	(0.3%)	—	—	12,384.3	13,470.2	12,297.9
Net income ($ mil.)	—	—	—	30.9	39.5	(6.9)
Employees	1.0%	—	—	250,000	260,000	255,000

ARAMARK REFRESHMENT SERVICES, LLC

ARAMARK Tower, 1101 Market St.
Philadelphia, PA 19107
Phone: 215-238-3000
Fax: 215-238-3333
Web: www.aramarkrefreshments.com

CEO: Joseph Neubauer
CFO: David Luckner
HR: Nicole L. Johnson-Reece
FYE: September 30
Type: Subsidiary

You might say this company facilitates water cooler discussions and breakroom meetings. ARAMARK Refreshment Services is a leading supplier of vending machines and office coffee and water services with about 90 distribution facilities serving more than 100,000 locations in North America. It offers a wide variety of coffee and brewing systems, along with water dispensing equipment and other supplies. Its vending unit stocks and maintains vending machines primarily in workplaces. ARAMARK Refreshment Services is a subsidiary of foodservices provider ARAMARK.

	Annual Growth	9/04	9/05	9/06	9/07	9/08
Est. sales ($ mil.)	—	—	—	—	—	80.7
Employees	—	—	—	—	—	4,500

ARB, INC.

26000 Commercentre Dr.
Lake Forest, CA 92630
Phone: 949-598-9242
Fax: 949-454-7190
Web: www.arbinc.com

CEO: Brian L. Pratt
CFO: Alfons Theeuwes
HR: Lauren Liu
FYE: December 31
Type: Private

The nation's growing infrastructure need is ARB's gain. The pipeline and industrial construction services company has benefited from power plant construction booms in low-supply regions of the western US, particularly in California, where it maintains the majority of its offices. ARB also stays busy building underground pipelines. Other services include cable and conduit installation, structural steel fabrication and installation, water treatment plant construction, and horizontal directional drilling. Customers include companies in the manufacturing, mining, oil and gas, and utilities industries. ARB is owned by Primoris Corporation, which merged with Rhapsody Acquisition Corp. in 2008.

	Annual Growth	12/04	12/05	12/06	12/07	12/08
Est. sales ($ mil.)	—	—	—	—	—	343.6
Employees	—	—	—	—	—	1,200

ARBELLA INSURANCE GROUP

1100 Crown Colony Dr.
Quincy, MA 02169
Phone: 617-328-2800
Fax: 617-328-2970
Web: www.arbella.com

CEO: John F. Donohue
CFO: Robert P. Medwid
HR: Gayle O'Connell
FYE: December 31
Type: Private

Safe drivers, snug homes, and small businesses are beautiful to Arbella Insurance. The New England company provides consumer auto and homeowners insurance in Massachusetts and is the state's #3 auto insurer. Its primary operating unit is Arbella Mutual, which underwrites auto, homeowners, and other personal insurance products in Massachusetts. The group has expanded its offerings to other lines and states, however. It also provides business insurance products (auto fleet coverage and workers' compensation, for instance) in its home state, New Hampshire, and Rhode Island. Arbella's Covenant Insurance affiliate writes personal insurance policies in Connecticut.

	Annual Growth	12/04	12/05	12/06	12/07	12/08
Est. sales ($ mil.)	—	—	—	—	—	54.1
Employees	—	—	—	—	—	1,000

ARBINET CORPORATION

NASDAQ (GM): ARBX

120 Albany St., Tower II, Ste. 450
New Brunswick, NJ 08901
Phone: 732-509-9100
Fax: 732-509-9101
Web: www.arbinet.com

CEO: Shawn F. O'Donnell
CFO: Gary G. Brandt
HR: —
FYE: December 31
Type: Public

Arbinet helps make communications capacity a tradable commodity. The company created and operates the leading electronic marketplace for communications trading. Used by its roughly 1,000 members, primarily communications services providers, the Arbinet automated platform offers anonymous buying and selling of voice and data traffic capacity. Arbinet also offers credit risk management, billing, and commercial settlement of these transactions. Utilizing a direct sales force, the company targets customers in the Americas, Asia, Europe, and the Middle East.

	Annual Growth	12/05	12/06	12/07	12/08	12/09
Sales ($ mil.)	(10.6%)	530.5	543.0	534.0	466.8	339.5
Net income ($ mil.)	—	10.8	(0.4)	(6.9)	(14.9)	(8.7)
Market value ($ mil.)	(22.8%)	153.7	120.4	132.7	32.9	54.6
Employees	3.0%	112	137	137	121	126

⊞ ARBITRON INC.

NYSE: ARB

9705 Patuxent Woods Drive
Columbia, MD 21046
Phone: 410-312-8000
Fax: 410-312-8650
Web: www.arbitron.com

CEO: William T. (Bill) Kerr
CFO: Sean R. Creamer
HR: Mary Lou Legge
FYE: December 31
Type: Public

Arbitron watches radio listeners. The top provider of radio station audience ratings in the US, Arbitron surveys radio listeners in about 280 local markets throughout the country. Its survey reports measure not only what stations people are listening to but also demographic information about those listeners, including income, lifestyles, and shopping habits. Thousands of radio stations and advertising agencies subscribe to Arbitron's services. In addition to radio ratings data, Arbitron offers market research for cable TV, Internet, and outdoor advertising customers.

	Annual Growth	12/05	12/06	12/07	12/08	12/09
Sales ($ mil.)	5.6%	310.0	329.3	338.5	368.8	385.0
Net income ($ mil.)	(11.0%)	67.3	50.7	40.2	37.2	42.2
Market value ($ mil.)	(11.4%)	1,010.9	1,156.3	1,106.5	353.5	623.4
Employees	(5.7%)	1,742	1,908	1,620	1,616	1,379

⊞ An in-depth profile of this company is available to Hoover's Online members at hoovers.com.

159

ARBOR REALTY TRUST, INC.
NYSE: ABR

333 Earle Ovington Blvd., Ste. 900
Uniondale, NY 11553
Phone: 516-832-8002
Fax: 516-832-8045
Web: www.arborrealtytrust.com

CEO: Ivan Kaufman
CFO: Paul Elenio
HR: —
FYE: December 31
Type: Public

Investing wisely can be a real ART . . . Arbor Realty Trust, that is. The real estate investment trust (REIT) invests in real estate-related bridge (short term financing) and mezzanine loans (large and usually unsecured loans), mortgage-related securities, and interests in first mortgages and preferred and direct equity. To a lesser extent, it also invests in discounted mortgage notes and other real estate-related assets. The REIT targets lending and investment opportunities with borrowers seeking interim financing until permanent financing is attained.

	Annual Growth	12/05	12/06	12/07	12/08	12/09
Sales ($ mil.)	14.1%	130.1	178.5	308.6	207.4	220.3
Net income ($ mil.)	—	50.4	50.4	84.5	(81.2)	(212.0)
Market value ($ mil.)	(47.4%)	660.4	766.6	410.4	75.2	50.7
Employees	6.0%	23	30	29	32	29

ARBY'S RESTAURANT GROUP, INC.

1155 Perimeter Center West, 12th Fl.
Atlanta, GA 30338
Phone: 678-514-4100
Fax: —
Web: www.arbys.com

CEO: Hala G. Moddelmog
CFO: John Dasis
HR: Melissa Strait
FYE: January 1
Type: Subsidiary

Sandwich fans hungry for beef that's not in the form of a patty can turn to this company. Arby's Restaurant Group (ARG) operates the Arby's fast food chain popular for its hot roast beef sandwiches. Arby's ranks as the #3 sandwich chain behind Subway and Quiznos with more than 3,700 locations across the US and in a handful of other countries. In addition to roast beef sandwiches, its menu features chicken sandwiches, salads, and some dessert items. More than 1,100 Arby's locations are company-owned, while the rest are franchised. The chain was started in 1964 by brothers Forrest and Leroy Raffel. ARG is owned by Wendy's/Arby's Group.

	Annual Growth	12/04	12/05	12/06	12/07	12/08
Est. sales ($ mil.)	—	—	—	—	—	1,217.3
Employees	—	—	—	—	—	27,930

ARC INTERNATIONAL NORTH AMERICA INC.

Box 5001, Wade Blvd.
Millville, NJ 08332
Phone: 856-825-5620
Fax: 856-696-3442
Web: www.arc-intl.us

CEO: Susan Saideman
CFO: Ken Bell
HR: —
FYE: December 31
Type: Subsidiary

Clumsy friends aren't a friend of ARC International North America. The US subsidiary of French tableware producer ARC International, the company distributes glassware and tableware in North America to the business-to-business, foodservice, and consumer markets. Brands include Luminarc, Crystal D' Arques Paris, Pyrex, and Chef & Sommelier. (The firm's most recognized brand Mikasa was sold to Lifetime Brands in mid-2008.) Fellow New Jersey-based glass maker Durand Glass Manufacturing Company acts as a sister company (and manufacturing arm) to ARC International North America.

ARC WIRELESS SOLUTIONS, INC.
NASDAQ (CM): ARCW

10601 W. 48th Ave.
Wheat Ridge, CO 80033
Phone: 303-421-4063
Fax: 303-424-5085
Web: www.arcwireless.net

CEO: Jason T. Young
CFO: —
HR: —
FYE: December 31
Type: Public

ARC Wireless Solutions offers a boatload of wireless technology products. Its Wireless Communications Solutions division markets wireless communications equipment — including cellular base station, mobile, cellular, conformal, and flat-panel antennas — which it sells directly to wireless carriers and through third-party distributors. Subsidiary Starworks Wireless sells coaxial cable products for satellite television and other wireless applications. ARC still purchases cable through Starworks for its own use, but the company has shifted its focus to higher-margin antenna products, which account for the bulk of its annual revenue.

	Annual Growth	12/05	12/06	12/07	12/08	12/09
Sales ($ mil.)	(42.3%)	39.7	6.5	8.0	7.3	4.4
Net income ($ mil.)	—	1.3	(0.7)	(0.7)	(1.8)	(0.9)
Market value ($ mil.)	(17.4%)	15.5	14.8	15.3	9.3	7.2
Employees	(41.5%)	111	40	41	18	13

ARC WORLDWIDE

35 W. Wacker Dr.
Chicago, IL 60601
Phone: 312-220-3200
Fax: 312-220-1995
Web: www.arcww.com

CEO: William Rosen
CFO: —
HR: —
FYE: December 31
Type: Subsidiary

This firm wants to help your brand have a successful story arc. Arc Worldwide offers a variety of marketing services to such big clients as Procter & Gamble, United Airlines, and McDonald's. It develops and manages direct marketing and promotional campaigns as well as point-of-sale marketing efforts. It also offers Web site development, creative interactive development, and other multimedia marketing services. Arc operates through more than 40 offices located around the world. It is a unit of Leo Burnett, a global ad agency of French conglomerate Publicis. Arc works closely with Leo Burnett, integrating its own direct marketing capabilities with its parent agency's extensive advertising network.

ARCA BIOPHARMA, INC.
NASDAQ (GM): ABIO

8001 Arista Place, Ste. 200
Broomfield, CO 80021
Phone: 720-940-2200
Fax: 720-208-9261
Web: www.arcabiopharma.com

CEO: Michael R. Bristow
CFO: Patrick M. Wheeler
HR: —
FYE: December 31
Type: Public

ARCA biopharma want to get into your genes before it gets serious with your heart. The biopharmaceutical development company believes that genetic variations in patients help determine how well they will respond to drugs. Its lead candidate, Gencaro, is being developed to treat heart failure and other cardiovascular diseases. Pending regulatory approval, ARCA biopharma plans to market it in the US through its own sales force and outside the US through partnerships. If approved, it will be the first genetically targeted cardiovascular drug. Earlier stages of its development were undertaken at the University of Colorado.

	Annual Growth	12/05	12/06	12/07	12/08	12/09
Sales ($ mil.)	—	0.5	3.9	46.9	15.3	0.0
Net income ($ mil.)	—	(71.6)	(132.8)	(12.3)	(29.9)	(9.1)
Market value ($ mil.)	(62.3%)	1,416.8	698.8	319.7	53.3	28.5
Employees	(32.0%)	103	146	76	85	22

ARCADIA RESOURCES, INC.

NYSE Amex: KAD

9229 Delegates Row, Ste. 260
Indianapolis, IN 46240
Phone: 317-569-8234
Fax: 317-575-6195
Web: www.arcadiaresourcesinc.com

CEO: Marvin R. Richardson
CFO: Matthew R. Middendorf
HR: —
FYE: March 30
Type: Public

We all know home is where the heart is, but in the case of Arcadia Resources, it's also where the health care is. The company, which does business as Arcadia HealthCare, provides home health care and medical staffing in more than 20 states through about 70 facilities. Its home care services include nursing and personal care. It also provides temporary medical staffing services to hospitals and other health care providers. Arcadia's mail-order pharmacy segment operates nationwide and features a packaging service called DailyMed designed to help customers comply with their medication regimens. The company's biggest investor (with about 20%) is hedge fund Vicis Capital. Arcadia is led by CEO Marvin Richardson.

	Annual Growth	3/05	3/06	3/07	3/08	3/09
Sales ($ mil.)	2.6%	95.9	130.9	158.4	151.0	106.1
Net income ($ mil.)	—	(7.9)	(4.7)	(43.8)	(16.0)	(46.5)
Market value ($ mil.)	(31.4%)	346.7	558.2	352.0	152.9	76.5
Employees	(15.3%)	8,500	14,000	16,500	16,501	4,376

ARCADIS US INC.

630 Plaza Dr., Ste. 200
Highlands Ranch, CO 80129
Phone: 720-344-3500
Fax: 720-344-3535
Web: www.arcadis-us.com

CEO: Steven B. (Steve) Blake
CFO: Pete Dyke
HR: James Barrett
FYE: December 31
Type: Subsidiary

ARCADIS US is the US-based arm of Netherlands environmental and engineering services company ARCADIS. The company provides consulting, design, and project management services related to infrastructure, environment, and facilities. Services include the designing of groundwater monitoring and treatment systems, feasibility studies, construction management, and the operation and maintenance of remedial technologies. The group also offers risk evaluation and assessment services, bioremediation services, regulatory compliance support, and testing and sampling services. The US accounts for more than one-third of parent ARCADIS' sales and is its largest geographic market.

	Annual Growth	12/04	12/05	12/06	12/07	12/08
Est. sales ($ mil.)	—	—	—	—	—	916.9
Employees	—	—	—	—	—	3,875

ARCELORMITTAL USA INC.

3210 Watling St.
East Chicago, IN 46312
Phone: 312-899-3400
Fax: —
Web: www.arcelormittal.com

CEO: Michael G. (Mike) Rippey
CFO: John L. Brett
HR: —
FYE: December 31
Type: Subsidiary

ArcelorMittal USA ranks as the nation's top steel producer, ahead of U.S. Steel and Nucor, and maintains about 20 facilities (including integrated plants, electric arc furnace plants, and finishing facilities), mostly in the Midwest. Its primary market is the automotive industry, but it also serves makers of appliances, industrial machinery, and packaging products. In addition to long carbon and flat carbon steel products, ArcelorMittal USA also makes tinplate and wire rod. Parent company ArcelorMittal is far and away the world's largest steel producer; ArcelorMittal USA is its representative in the US.

	Annual Growth	12/04	12/05	12/06	12/07	12/08
Est. sales ($ mil.)	—	—	—	—	—	12,899.0
Employees	—	—	—	—	—	20,500

ARCH CAPITAL GROUP LTD.

NASDAQ (GS): ACGL

Wessex House, 4th Fl., 45 Reid St.
Hamilton, HM 12, Bermuda
Phone: 441-278-9250
Fax: 441-278-9255
Web: www.archcapgroup.com

CEO: Constantine P. Iordanou
CFO: John C. R. Hele
HR: —
FYE: December 31
Type: Public

No sharply raised eyebrows or dry witticisms here — Arch Capital Group is just not "arch" in that way. Instead the company offers property/casualty insurance and reinsurance through subsidiaries in Bermuda, Canada, Europe, and the US. Its insurance subsidiaries offer marine and aviation, professional liability, health care liability, and other specialty lines. The company's US subsidiary Arch Insurance Group specializes in excess and surplus lines coverage. The company's Arch Re reinsurance subsidiaries focus on property/casualty coverage, including catastrophe and some specialty lines. The company distributes its products through both wholesale and retail brokers.

	Annual Growth	12/05	12/06	12/07	12/08	12/09
Assets ($ mil.)	7.6%	11,488.4	14,312.5	15,624.3	14,616.5	15,375.8
Net income ($ mil.)	36.0%	256.5	692.6	832.1	291.0	876.9
Market value ($ mil.)	6.9%	2,863.9	3,536.5	3,679.9	3,666.8	3,742.6
Employees	3.4%	980	1,100	1,215	1,200	1,120

ARCH CHEMICALS, INC.

NYSE: ARJ

501 Merritt 7
Norwalk, CT 06851
Phone: 203-229-2900
Fax: 203-229-3652
Web: www.archchemicals.com

CEO: Michael E. Campbell
CFO: Steven C. (Steve) Guiliano
HR: Hayes Anderson
FYE: December 31
Type: Public

Arch Chemicals and its line of pool-cleaning products may make it safe to go back in the water. But the company is after bigger fish. Arch calls itself "The Biocides Company" to emphasize its line of products designed to destroy and control the growth of harmful microbes in several areas. In addition to products for the pool, Arch sells chemicals for hair and skin care, wood treatment, preservation and protection applications for paints and building products, and health and hygiene applications. The company operates two business segments: biocides products and performance products. It operates globally and is especially strong in Europe. However, the US accounts for almost half of its sales.

	Annual Growth	12/05	12/06	12/07	12/08	12/09
Sales ($ mil.)	1.6%	1,305.1	1,434.7	1,487.6	1,492.1	1,391.9
Net income ($ mil.)	3.5%	41.0	14.2	35.3	37.0	47.1
Market value ($ mil.)	0.8%	750.9	836.5	922.9	654.7	775.5
Employees	0.4%	3,025	3,000	2,670	2,900	3,076

⊞ ARCH COAL, INC.

NYSE: ACI

1 CityPlace Dr., Ste. 300
St. Louis, MO 63141
Phone: 314-994-2700
Fax: 314-994-2878
Web: www.archcoal.com

CEO: Steven F. Leer
CFO: John T. Drexler
HR: Sheila B. Feldman
FYE: December 31
Type: Public

What powers your power company? Perhaps Arch Coal. About half of the electricity generated in the US comes from coal, and Arch Coal is one of the country's largest coal producers, behind industry leader Peabody Energy. Arch Coal produces about 126 million tons of coal a year from about 20 mines in the western US and Central Appalachia; the company has proved and probable reserves of 2.8 billion tons. Steam coal — low-ash coal used by electric utilities to produce steam in boilers — accounts for the vast majority of the company's sales. To store and ship its Appalachian coal, the company operates the Arch Coal Terminal near the Ohio River.

	Annual Growth	12/05	12/06	12/07	12/08	12/09
Sales ($ mil.)	0.7%	2,508.8	2,500.4	2,413.6	2,983.8	2,576.1
Net income ($ mil.)	2.6%	38.1	260.9	174.9	354.3	42.2
Market value ($ mil.)	(13.5%)	6,458.4	4,879.1	7,300.0	2,646.7	3,615.1
Employees	5.6%	3,700	4,050	4,030	4,300	4,601

An in-depth profile of this company is available to Hoover's Online members at hoovers.com.

161

ARCH INSURANCE GROUP INC.

1 Liberty Plaza, 53rd Fl.
New York, NY 10006
Phone: 212-651-6500
Fax: 212-651-6499
Web: www.archinsurance.com

CEO: Mark D. Lyons
CFO: Fred S. Eichler
HR: Dennis R. Brand
FYE: December 31
Type: Subsidiary

From astronauts to energy magnets, Arch Insurance Group offers specialty property/casualty insurance for just about any business in the US and Canada. Operating through its subsidiaries (Arch Insurance Company, Arch Specialty Insurance, and Arch Excess & Surplus Insurance), the company provides specialty lines on a surplus or admitted basis, including directors and officers, construction, aviation, and professional liability. Arch Insurance Group, a subsidiary of Bermuda-based insurer and reinsurer Arch Capital Group, also offers traditional property/casualty lines for businesses in niche industries such as hospitality, commercial real estate, and aerospace.

ARCHER DANIELS MIDLAND COMPANY

NYSE: ADM

4666 Faries Pkwy.
Decatur, IL 62525
Phone: 217-424-5200
Fax: 217-424-6196
Web: www.admworld.com

CEO: Patricia A. (Pat) Woertz
CFO: Steven R. Mills
HR: Michael (Mike) D'Ambrose
FYE: June 30
Type: Public

Archer Daniels Midland (ADM) knows how to grind and squeeze a fortune out of humble plants. It is one of the world's largest processors of oilseeds, corn, and wheat. Its main offerings include soybean and other oilseed products. From corn, it produces syrups, sweeteners, citric and lactic acids, and ethanol, among other products. ADM also produces wheat flour for bakeries and pasta makers; cocoa and chocolate products for confectioners; animal-feed ingredients for farmers, and malt for brewers. It operates one of the world's largest crop origination and transportation networks, through which it connects crops and their markets across the globe.

	Annual Growth	6/05	6/06	6/07	6/08	6/09
Sales ($ mil.)	17.8%	35,943.8	36,596.1	44,018.0	69,816.0	69,207.0
Net income ($ mil.)	13.1%	1,044.4	1,312.1	2,162.0	1,802.0	1,707.0
Market value ($ mil.)	5.8%	13,748.4	26,545.1	21,278.5	21,702.9	17,214.4
Employees	2.4%	25,641	26,800	27,300	27,600	28,200

ARCHIPELAGO LEARNING, INC.

NASDAQ (CM): ARCL

3400 Carlisle St., Ste. 345
Dallas, TX 75204
Phone: 800-419-3191
Fax: 877-592-1357
Web: www.archipelagolearning.com

CEO: Tim McEwen
CFO: James B. Walburg
HR: —
FYE: December 31
Type: Public

Archipelago Learning is a subscription-based online education company that provides instruction, assessment, and productivity tools to improve student and teacher performance. Its flagship product, *Study Island* (also the company's largest revenue generator), is used by thousands of elementary and secondary schools in the US to improve student performance on standardized tests. The company provides school Web site portals and teacher productivity tools as well as adult education study and exam prep services. It expanded into the UK online education market with the purchase of EducationCity in 2010. Founded in 2000, it went public in 2009. Providence Equity Partners owns half of the company's stock.

	Annual Growth	12/05	12/06	12/07	12/08	12/09
Sales ($ mil.)	61.8%	—	10.1	18.3	32.1	42.8
Net income ($ mil.)	21.9%	—	3.7	2.9	0.3	6.7
Market value ($ mil.)	—	—	—	—	—	519.7
Employees	7.3%	—	—	—	206	221

ARCHON CORPORATION

OTC: ARHN

4336 Losee Rd., Ste. 5
North Las Vegas, NV 89030
Phone: 702-732-9120
Fax: 702-658-4331

CEO: Paul W. Lowden
CFO: Grant L. Siler
HR: —
FYE: September 30
Type: Public

Archon is banking on gamblers to follow the trail of the Pioneer. Formerly Santa Fe Gaming, the embattled company owns and operates one casino, the Pioneer Hotel & Gambling Hall, in Laughlin, Nevada. The Pioneer features some 400 guest rooms and gaming operations that consist of approximately 730 slot machines, six blackjack tables, one craps table, one roulette wheel, and five other gaming tables. The hotel includes two restaurants and bars, a special events area, banquet rooms, and a swimming pool and spa. Gaming accounts for more than half of revenues. Chairman and CEO Paul Lowden owns about 75% of the company.

	Annual Growth	9/05	9/06	9/07	9/08	9/09
Sales ($ mil.)	(7.5%)	43.7	45.2	45.2	43.2	32.0
Net income ($ mil.)	—	(4.9)	(3.4)	0.6	58.8	(1.5)
Market value ($ mil.)	(21.6%)	227.2	198.0	284.3	186.9	85.8
Employees	(2.7%)	513	512	556	471	459

ARCHON GROUP, L.P.

6011 Connection Dr.
Irving, TX 75039
Phone: 972-368-2200
Fax: 972-368-2290
Web: www.archongroup.com

CEO: James L. (Jim) Lozier Jr.
CFO: Richard Frapart
HR: Michael Blewitt
FYE: November 30
Type: Subsidiary

Archon Group keeps it real . . . real *estate*, that is. The group provides commercial real estate portfolio management and support services including accounting, information technology, and legal consultation for office, industrial, multifamily, hospitality, and retail properties. Archon Group also provides mortgage lending, origination, mezzanine and specialty financing, and other services through a number of subsidiaries. Altogether, Archon manages a portfolio worth some $54 billion in North America, Europe, and Asia. The group was established in 1996 by Goldman Sachs; its primary client is Whitehall Street Real Estate Funds, also part of the Goldman Sachs family.

	Annual Growth	11/04	11/05	11/06	11/07	11/08
Est. sales ($ mil.)	—	—	—	—	—	320.8
Employees	—	—	—	—	—	614

ARCHSTONE

9200 E. Panorama Circle, Ste. 400
Englewood, CO 80112
Phone: 303-708-5959
Fax: 303-708-5999
Web: www.archstoneapartments.com

CEO: R. Scot Sellers
CFO: Gerald R. (Gerry) Morgan
HR: —
FYE: December 31
Type: Private

Archstone has traditionally been the cornerstone of the apartment investment business. The company owns more than 440 communities (some 83,000 units) in areas such as Washington, DC (about 40% of its portfolio), Los Angeles, San Francisco, New York, Seattle, and Boston, as well as Europe. Archstone boasts modern properties with units that rent from $500 to more than $5,000 a month. Development and investment advice is offered through its Archstone Real Estate Advisory Services arm. The company was acquired by a Tishman Speyer and Lehman Brothers' real estate partnership in 2007. However, Lehman filed for bankruptcy a year later.

ARCHWAY MARKETING SERVICES, INC.

19850 S. Diamond Lake Rd.	CEO: A. Clayton (Clay) Perfall
Rogers, MN 55374	CFO: Brian Burke
Phone: 763-428-3300	HR: —
Fax: 763-428-3302	FYE: December 31
Web: www.archway.com	Type: Private

Archway Marketing Services provides marketing, information management, and customer service for clients primarily residing in the business-to-business sector. It offers such marketing services as program management for rebates, sweepstakes, and other promotions; fulfillment and distribution; merchandising; and customer relationship management through 10 facilities in the US, Canada, and Mexico. It also helps clients hit by the slumping economy by providing cost-saving ideas, integrating marketing programs, and consolidating a number of outsourced services as they relate to marketing and merchandising. Archway Marketing Services traces its roots to 1952 when it began offering mailing services in Minnesota.

ARCO ALUMINUM, INC.

9960 Corporate Campus Dr., Ste. 3000	CEO: Patrick Franc
Louisville, KY 40223	CFO: David Sourwine
Phone: 502-566-5700	HR: —
Fax: 502-566-5740	FYE: December 31
Web: www.arcoaluminum.com	Type: Subsidiary

Through its Logan Aluminum unit, ARCO Aluminum manufactures aluminum sheet used mainly by the beverage and automotive industries. Logan Aluminum's offerings include automotive sheet, building products, distributor sheet, food and beverage can stock, and rigid container sheet. Logan's mill in Kentucky is one of the largest aluminum sheet manufacturing facilities in North America. Logan Aluminum is a joint venture of ARCO Aluminum and Novelis. ARCO Aluminum is owned by oil giant BP, which acquired the company as part of its purchase of Atlantic Richfield Company (known as ARCO) in 2000.

ARCSIGHT, INC.

NASDAQ (GM): ARST

5 Results Way	CEO: Thomas (Tom) Reilly
Cupertino, CA 95014	CFO: Stewart Grierson
Phone: 408-864-2600	HR: Gail Boddy
Fax: 408-342-1615	FYE: April 30
Web: www.arcsight.com	Type: Public

ArcSight keeps a watchful eye on business risk. The company provides security and compliance management products used to identify, prioritize, and respond to corporate policy violations and cyber attacks. Its software and appliances handle such functions as compliance automation, event collection and management, identity monitoring, and log management. The company also provides consulting, implementation, maintenance, support, and training services. ArcSight markets to the aerospace and defense, energy and utilities, financial services, food production, health care, insurance, media, retail, technology, and telecom sectors.

	Annual Growth	4/05	4/06	4/07	4/08	4/09
Sales ($ mil.)	42.7%	32.8	39.4	69.8	101.5	136.2
Net income ($ mil.)	—	(2.8)	(16.7)	(0.3)	(2.0)	9.9
Market value ($ mil.)	96.4%	—	—	—	261.2	513.0
Employees	9.1%	—	308	287	335	400

⊞ ARCTIC CAT INC.

NASDAQ (GS): ACAT

601 Brooks Ave. South	CEO: Christopher A. Twomey
Thief River Falls, MN 56701	CFO: Timothy C. Delmore
Phone: 218-681-8558	HR: Terry J. Blount
Fax: 218-681-3162	FYE: March 31
Web: www.arctic-cat.com	Type: Public

Prowling over hard ground or snow, Arctic Cat gives drivers a *purrfect* ride. The company manufactures and markets 19 types of all-terrain vehicles (ATVs) and over 50 snowmobile models. Its four-wheel model ATVs and snowmobiles are marketed under the Arctic Cat name, for both recreational and utility use. Arctic Cat also supplies replacement parts and parts to upgrade its products' function and comfort, as well as Cat-branded protective clothing and riding gear to foster its drivers' experience and loyalty. The company produces and outsources parts to other vehicle OEMs, too. Products are sold through a network of independent dealers throughout North America and through representatives of dealers worldwide.

	Annual Growth	3/05	3/06	3/07	3/08	3/09
Sales ($ mil.)	(4.9%)	689.1	732.8	782.4	621.6	563.6
Net income ($ mil.)	—	28.3	23.7	22.1	(3.3)	(9.5)
Market value ($ mil.)	(38.7%)	493.2	438.6	355.3	132.9	69.8
Employees	(2.5%)	1,631	1,802	1,840	1,630	1,475

ARCTIC SLOPE REGIONAL CORPORATION

3900 C St., Ste. 801	CEO: Roberta (Bobbi) Quintavell
Anchorage, AK 99503	CFO: —
Phone: 907-339-6000	HR: —
Fax: 907-339-6028	FYE: December 31
Web: www.asrc.com	Type: Private

The Inupiat people have survived the Arctic for centuries, and now they're surviving in the business world. The Inupiat-owned Arctic Slope Regional Corporation (ASRC) was set up to manage 5 million acres on Alaska's North Slope after the Alaska Native Claims Settlement Act in 1971 cleared the way for oil development in the area. ASRC gets more than two-thirds of sales from its energy services subsidiary (ASRC Energy Services) and its petroleum refining and marketing unit (Petro Star). Other operations include construction, engineering, and governmental services.

	Annual Growth	12/04	12/05	12/06	12/07	12/08
Sales ($ mil.)	17.6%	1,200.6	1,566.5	1,700.5	1,777.5	2,300.0
Employees	8.5%	6,500	6,000	6,000	6,000	9,000

ARDEA BIOSCIENCES, INC.

NASDAQ (GM): RDEA

4939 Directors Place	CEO: Barry D. Quart
San Diego, CA 92121	CFO: John W. Beck
Phone: 858-652-6500	HR: —
Fax: 858-625-0760	FYE: December 31
Web: www.ardeabiosciences.com	Type: Public

Ardea Biosciences is on a quest to cure the incurable. The biotechnology company discovers and develops therapies for the treatment of ailments such as HIV, cancer, gout, and inflammatory diseases. The company, which focuses on the development of small molecule therapies (named as such because the molecular compounds weigh less than 1,000 Daltons), has drug candidates in clinical and preclinical stages of development. In addition to internal programs, the company is pursuing new therapies through partnerships and licensing efforts. Formerly known as IntraBiotics Pharmaceuticals, Ardea changed its name in 2006 following the acquisition of several development programs from Valeant Pharmaceuticals.

	Annual Growth	12/05	12/06	12/07	12/08	12/09
Sales ($ mil.)	171.8%	—	—	3.1	0.3	22.9
Net income ($ mil.)	—	—	—	(25.1)	(55.0)	(30.9)
Market value ($ mil.)	(4.3%)	—	—	348.5	272.7	318.9
Employees	(7.8%)	—	—	73	81	62

⊞ ARDEN GROUP, INC.

NASDAQ (GM): ARDNA

2020 S. Central Ave.	CEO: Bernard Briskin
Compton, CA 90220	CFO: Laura J. Neumann
Phone: 310-638-2842	HR: Brenda McDaniel
Fax: 310-631-0950	FYE: December 31
Web: www.gelsons.com	Type: Public

Glitz meets groceries at Arden Group's 18 supermarkets in Southern California (primarily in the Los Angeles area). Through its wholly owned subsidiary Arden-Mayfair, the company operates 17 Gelson's Markets (18,000-40,000 sq. ft.) and one Mayfair supermarket. Gelson's stores carry traditional grocery items, as well as imported foods and unusual deli selections. Most also feature coffee bars, fresh pizza, and bakeries. While some house in-store banks and pharmacies, most are too small to accommodate additional services. The company's Mayfair Markets store (about 25,000 sq. ft.) offers a more limited selection of goods. Arden Group also owns a shopping center in Calabasas, California.

	Annual Growth	12/05	12/06	12/07	12/08	12/09
Sales ($ mil.)	(2.2%)	470.4	482.7	485.9	479.1	431.2
Net income ($ mil.)	2.1%	19.9	23.2	29.2	24.7	21.6
Market value ($ mil.)	1.2%	287.6	391.4	489.0	398.3	302.3
Employees	(3.2%)	2,430	2,368	2,329	2,291	2,134

ARDENT HEALTH SERVICES LLC

1 Burton Hills Blvd., Ste. 250	CEO: David T. Vandewater
Nashville, TN 37215	CFO: Kerry Gillespie
Phone: 615-296-3000	HR: Neil Hemphill
Fax: 615-296-6351	FYE: December 31
Web: www.ardenthealth.com	Type: Private

Ardent Health Services is passionate about healing the body. The company operates seven acute care hospitals and a number of specialty care facilities in the southern US. Its facilities are located in New Mexico, where the company operates as the Lovelace Health System, and in Oklahoma, where it operates the Hillcrest Medical Center and other hospitals and clinics. Ardent Health Services' facilities also include physician group practices and medical pathology laboratories. In addition, it operates the Lovelace Health Plan, which serves some 220,000 members in New Mexico. Welsh, Carson, Anderson & Stowe owns a controlling stake in Ardent Health Services.

	Annual Growth	12/04	12/05	12/06	12/07	12/08
Sales ($ mil.)	2.9%	1,607.0	1,731.0	1,670.0	1,650.0	1,800.0
Employees	(16.5%)	15,900	8,800	9,942	8,500	7,745

ARENA PHARMACEUTICALS, INC.

NASDAQ (GM): ARNA

6166 Nancy Ridge Dr.	CEO: Jack Lief
San Diego, CA 92121	CFO: Robert E. Hoffman
Phone: 858-453-7200	HR: —
Fax: 858-453-7210	FYE: December 31
Web: www.arenapharm.com	Type: Public

Arena Pharmaceuticals is working to put weight loss in the spotlight. The company is focused on developing biopharmaceutical treatments for cardiovascular, central nervous system, inflammatory, and metabolic diseases. More specifically, it targets G protein-coupled receptors which mediate cell-to-cell communications. Its lead drug candidate lorcaserin could help assist in weight loss and maintenance in obese patients and patients with type 2 diabetes. From its manufacturing facility in Switzerland, Arena earns a portion of its revenues as a contract manufacturer for another pharmaceutical company. The rest of its revenues come from R&D partnerships, including one with Ortho-McNeil Pharmaceutical.

	Annual Growth	12/05	12/06	12/07	12/08	12/09
Sales ($ mil.)	(18.2%)	23.2	30.6	19.3	9.8	10.4
Net income ($ mil.)	—	(67.9)	(86.2)	(143.2)	(237.6)	(153.2)
Market value ($ mil.)	(29.3%)	1,438.4	1,306.8	792.6	422.1	359.4
Employees	2.6%	323	371	491	499	358

ARENA RESOURCES, INC.

NYSE: ARD

6555 S. Lewis	CEO: Phillip (Phil) Terry
Tulsa, OK 74136	CFO: William Randall (Randy) Broaddrick
Phone: 918-747-6060	HR: —
Fax: 918-747-7620	FYE: December 31
Web: www.arenaresourcesinc.com	Type: Public

Independent energy company Arena Resources battles with the big boys in the arena of oil and gas exploration and production. The company operates in Kansas, New Mexico, Oklahoma, and Texas, and in 2009 it reported proved reserves of 69.5 million barrels of oil equivalent. Its assets in Oklahoma and Texas account for the bulk of the company's proved reserves. About 30% of its reserves depend upon secondary recovery techniques to make productive. Arena Resources had an average daily production of 7,254 barrels of oil equivalent in 2009. In 2010 the company agreed to be acquired by rival SandRidge Energy in a $6.2 billion deal that would boost that company's holdings in low-risk reservoirs in the Permian Basin.

	Annual Growth	12/05	12/06	12/07	12/08	12/09
Sales ($ mil.)	48.7%	25.8	59.8	100.1	208.9	126.2
Net income ($ mil.)	45.3%	9.5	23.3	34.4	83.6	42.3
Market value ($ mil.)	33.0%	544.5	842.7	1,645.9	1,108.4	1,701.5
Employees	52.8%	22	52	86	71	120

AREVA T&D

1 International Plaza, Ste. 210	CEO: Philippe Guillemot
Philadelphia, PA 19113	CFO: Karim Vissandjee
Phone: 888-273-8283	HR: Laurent Mareschal
Fax: 610-362-2005	FYE: December 31
Web: www.areva-td.com	Type: Subsidiary

AREVA T&D is the US-based Transmission and Distribution division of parent company AREVA SA. It provides industrial equipment and services for electric power production, transmission, and distribution. The company handles disconnectors, instrument transformers, energy management systems, static power supplies, and gas-insulated switchgear for use in mining/metal, chemistry, mass transportation, manufacturing, fuel fabrication, reactors, and used fuel recycling. It also provides management, consulting, diagnostics, repair, customer support, retrofits and refurbishments, training, and turnkey construction. AREVA has agreed to sell its T&D division to ALSTOM and Schneider Electric for €2.29 billion.

ARGAN, INC.

NYSE Amex: AGX

1 Church St., Ste. 201	CEO: Rainer H. Bosselmann
Rockville, MD 20850	CFO: Arthur F. Trudel Jr.
Phone: 301-315-0027	HR: —
Fax: 301-315-0064	FYE: January 31
Web: www.arganinc.com	Type: Public

Argan makes sure its customers stay all juiced up. Its Gemma Power Systems division designs and builds power plants including traditional and alternate fuel plants. Argan's Southern Maryland Cable (SMC) unit provides inside premise wiring and also performs splicing and underground and aerial telecom infrastructure construction services to carriers, government entities, service providers, and electric utilities. SMC's three largest customers are Southern Maryland Electrical Cooperative, Verizon, and now HP Enterprise Services. The holding company's Vitarich Laboratories subsidiary makes and distributes private-label dietary supplements and other nutraceuticals and personal health-care products.

	Annual Growth	1/06	1/07	1/08	1/09	1/10
Sales ($ mil.)	69.0%	28.5	68.9	206.8	220.9	232.3
Net income ($ mil.)	—	(9.5)	(0.1)	(3.2)	10.0	7.0
Market value ($ mil.)	56.8%	31.9	84.2	154.1	152.7	192.9
Employees	46.8%	204	525	424	524	947

ARGO GROUP INTERNATIONAL HOLDINGS, LTD.

NASDAQ (GS): AGII

10101 Reunion Place, Ste. 500	CEO: Mark E. Watson III
San Antonio, TX 78216	CFO: Jay S. Bullock
Phone: 210-321-8400	HR: Kevin D. Silva
Fax: 210-377-2637	FYE: December 31
Web: www.argolimited.com	Type: Public

Based under the tax-sheltered sun of Bermuda, Argo Group International Holdings (formerly PXRE Group) provides specialty property/casualty insurance and reinsurance products in the US and Europe. Argo Group operates seven subsidiaries which focus on three well-defined markets: excess and surplus (the riskier stuff no one else likes to insure), industry-specific insurance (catering to such niches as mining, day-care centers, dry cleaners, and grocers), and international catastrophe reinsurance through its Peleus Re subsidiary. The company markets and distributes its products through independent agents and brokers.

	Annual Growth	12/05	12/06	12/07	12/08	12/09
Assets ($ mil.)	34.4%	2,116.0	1,401.3	5,123.5	6,381.5	6,896.8
Net income ($ mil.)	—	(697.6)	28.5	77.5	62.9	117.5
Market value ($ mil.)	(31.1%)	4,024.1	1,431.4	1,308.1	1,053.2	904.8
Employees	118.9%	58	45	1,181	1,359	1,331

ARGON ST, INC.

NASDAQ (GS): STST

12701 Fair Lakes Circle, Ste. 800	CEO: Terry L. Collins
Fairfax, VA 22033	CFO: Aaron N. Daniels
Phone: 703-322-0881	HR: Abbey Flowers
Fax: 703-322-0885	FYE: September 30
Web: www.argonst.com	Type: Public

Argon ST makes electronic intelligence, sensors, communications, and imaging systems and networks. It engineers, develops, deploys, and services electronic intelligence systems that intercept, interpret, and track microwave signals from hostile radar and weapons; systems that intercept and locate the source of communications signals and radar; acoustic systems used to detect undersea threats; secure communications and networking systems; and imaging systems used to survey geographic areas of interest. The US Navy accounts for almost half of the company's sales; the US Army and other US government entities provide about one-third of revenues. The company operates from a dozen locations in the US.

	Annual Growth	9/05	9/06	9/07	9/08	9/09
Sales ($ mil.)	7.7%	271.8	258.8	282.2	340.9	366.1
Net income ($ mil.)	2.1%	21.8	19.4	14.7	20.3	23.7
Market value ($ mil.)	(10.2%)	642.5	524.9	433.6	514.4	417.2
Employees	13.7%	637	840	970	990	1,063

ARGONNE NATIONAL LABORATORY

9700 S. Cass Ave.	CEO: Eric D. Isaacs
Argonne, IL 60439	CFO: Michael Besançon
Phone: 630-252-2000	HR: Jerome L. (Jerry) Gaston
Fax: 630-252-5274	FYE: September 30
Web: www.anl.gov	Type: Government-owned

Argonne National Laboratory boasts some of the top minds in science. One of the largest scientific research centers in the US, Argonne's 1,000 scientists and engineers perform basic and applied research in such areas as computer science, energy, environmental management, and national security. It is known for its high-energy physics, nuclear energy, and waste remediation projects. Three of its former scientists have won the Nobel Prize. Argonne grew out of work being performed at the University of Chicago for the famous Manhattan Project during WWII and became the first national laboratory to be chartered in 1946. Argonne is funded by the US Department of Energy and operated by the University of Chicago.

ARGO-TECH CORPORATION

23555 Euclid Ave.	CEO: Bradley J. Morton
Cleveland, OH 44117	CFO: —
Phone: 216-692-6000	HR: —
Fax: 216-692-5293	FYE: October 31
Web: www.argo-tech.com	Type: Subsidiary

Argo-Tech makes *Fantasy Island's* "De plane Boss, de plane!" a reality; the company keeps commercial and military aircraft aloft with its high-performance fuel-flow devices. It builds main engine fuel pumps and systems, airframe fuel pumps, and various ground fuel distribution products. Through its Carter Ground Fueling division, Argo-Tech also makes ground refueling equipment. Customers have included the US Army and Air Force; engine and airframe makers such as Airbus, Boeing, GE Aircraft Engines, and Lockheed Martin; and aerospace distributor Upsilon International. In 2007 investment concerns Greenbriar Equity Group and Vestar Capital Partners sold AT Holdings Corp., the parent of Argo-Tech, to Eaton.

ARI NETWORK SERVICES, INC.

OTC: ARIS

11425 W. Lake Park Dr., Ste. 900	CEO: Roy W. Olivier
Milwaukee, WI 53224	CFO: Brian E. Dearing
Phone: 414-973-4300	HR: —
Fax: 414-973-4618	FYE: July 31
Web: www.arinet.com	Type: Public

The sum of all parts results in ARI Network Services. The company provides software and technical support services for creating electronic parts catalogs in various industries including construction, farm, and marine equipment. More than 24,000 dealers and distributors in some 85 countries use ARI's catalogs. Its PartSmart application allows companies to collect, organize, and maintain product information for their suppliers and dealers, who can access and search the database using ARI's PartSmart tools suite. In addition, the company's e-commerce and communication applications process orders, product registrations, and warranty claims.

	Annual Growth	7/05	7/06	7/07	7/08	7/09
Sales ($ mil.)	6.5%	13.7	14.0	15.4	16.9	17.6
Net income ($ mil.)	(38.5%)	2.8	3.2	0.1	1.4	0.4
Market value ($ mil.)	(26.9%)	21.8	17.5	12.3	10.5	6.2
Employees	13.6%	89	91	103	102	148

ARIAD PHARMACEUTICALS, INC.

NASDAQ (GM): ARIA

26 Landsdowne St.	CEO: Harvey J. Berger
Cambridge, MA 02139	CFO: Edward M. (Ed) Fitzgerald
Phone: 617-494-0400	HR: Virginia Dean
Fax: 617-494-8144	FYE: December 31
Web: www.ariad.com	Type: Public

ARIAD Pharmaceuticals is exploring the myriad possibilities for new cancer treatments. The firm has three lead drug candidates: Ridaforolimus, AP24534, and AP26113, each being studied for the treatment of cancer. ARIAD was co-developing ridaforolimus (formerly known as deforolimus) through a partnership with Merck, but in 2010 it sold Merck the exclusive rights to develop, manufacture, and market the drug for oncology in a deal worth up to half a billion dollars, including milestone payments. Of ARIAD's other compounds, AP24534, is being investigated as a possible treatment for chronic myeloid leukemia and other malignancies. AP26113 is in preclinical studies for lung cancer and lymphoma.

	Annual Growth	12/05	12/06	12/07	12/08	12/09
Sales ($ mil.)	62.2%	1.2	0.9	3.6	7.1	8.3
Net income ($ mil.)	—	(55.5)	(61.9)	(58.5)	(71.1)	(80.0)
Market value ($ mil.)	(21.0%)	647.5	568.9	470.4	94.1	252.4
Employees	8.4%	108	103	116	150	149

⊞ An in-depth profile of this company is available to Hoover's Online members at hoovers.com.

ARIBA, INC.

NASDAQ (GS): ARBA

807 11th Ave.
Sunnyvale, CA 94089
Phone: 650-390-1000
Fax: 650-390-1100
Web: www.ariba.com

CEO: Robert M. (Bob) Calderoni
CFO: Ahmed Rubaie
HR: —
FYE: September 30
Type: Public

Ariba helps ensure that your supplies arrive in a timely fashion. The company provides spend management software and consulting services used by manufacturers, retailers, and distributors to connect with suppliers and to manage procurement. Its applications automate buying, help target preferred suppliers, and manage enterprise sourcing. Companies use the applications to procure such services as equipment repair, temporary workers, and travel. Ariba has partnered with more than 180,000 suppliers to make their wares available through its supplier network. Ariba gets the majority of its revenues in North America.

	Annual Growth	9/05	9/06	9/07	9/08	9/09
Sales ($ mil.)	1.2%	323.0	296.0	301.7	328.1	339.0
Net income ($ mil.)	—	(349.6)	(47.8)	(15.0)	(41.1)	8.2
Market value ($ mil.)	19.4%	512.3	673.2	969.0	1,270.1	1,042.7
Employees	2.0%	1,506	1,676	1,669	1,740	1,632

ARICENT INC.

700 Hansen Way
Palo Alto, CA 94304
Phone: 650-391-1088
Fax: 650-391-1089
Web: www.aricent.com

CEO: Sudip Nandy
CFO: David Freedman
HR: —
FYE: March 31
Type: Private

Your call will always go through if left to Aricent. The company, formerly known as Flextronics Software Systems (FSS), offers software and services used to manage wireline, wireless, and Internet protocol networks, as well as to develop mobile devices and applications. Its offerings include General Packet Radio Service and Universal Mobile Telephone System protocol stacks, technology that underpins a wide range of communications. The company also provides outsourcing services for product development, engineering, and testing. In 2006 Flextronics sold a majority stake in the company to KKR for about $900 million. The company was then renamed Aricent. KKR and its affiliates own 79% of Aricent.

	Annual Growth	3/04	3/05	3/06	3/07	3/08
Est. sales ($ mil.)	—	—	—	—	—	420.0
Employees	—	—	—	—	—	8,000

ARIENS COMPANY

655 W. Ryan St.
Brillion, WI 54110
Phone: 920-756-2141
Fax: 920-756-2407
Web: www.arienscorp.com

CEO: Daniel T. Ariens
CFO: Stewart Witkov
HR: Regina Kramer
FYE: June 30
Type: Private

Ariens is a manufacturer for all seasons. The company makes a line of consumer lawn and garden equipment, from mowers to tillers, under multiple brands including the Ariens name, and snow removal equipment under Sno-Thro brand. Semi-famous "Lawnmower Boy" Ryan Tripp used an Ariens mower to mow the grounds of 50 state capitols and the White House — all for charity. The company's Stens Corp division offers aftermarket replacement parts for power equipment through catalog sales and dealers in more than 30 countries. Ariens also produces Gravely-brand commercial grounds-maintenance equipment, and the Locke and National brands for intricate golf course maintenance. The family of founder Henry Ariens owns Ariens.

ARINC INCORPORATED

2551 Riva Rd.
Annapolis, MD 21401
Phone: 410-266-4000
Fax: 410-266-2020
Web: www.arinc.com

CEO: John M. Belcher
CFO: Stephen L. (Steve) Waechter
HR: Robert E. Manigold Jr.
FYE: December 31
Type: Subsidiary

ARINC is a high flyer in communications and systems integration. Commercial aviation, US defense, and government customers rely on ARINC's communications products, IT know-how, and engineering expertise to make their operations run smoothly. ARINC's broad range of products and services cover airport security, air traffic management, aircraft and satellite testing, modeling and simulation, network design, passenger and baggage processing, voice and data communications, and weather reporting. The company operates from more than 50 offices in the US, and it does business in about 100 other countries from facilities in Europe, Latin America, and Asia. ARINC is owned by private investment firm The Carlyle Group.

ARISE VIRTUAL SOLUTIONS INC.

3450 Lakeside Dr., Ste. 620
Miramar, FL 33027
Phone: 954-392-2600
Fax: 954-392-9640
Web: www.arise.com

CEO: Angela Selden
CFO: Scott Etheridge
HR: —
FYE: December 31
Type: Private

Arise Virtual Solutions provides outsourced call center services from a virtual call center. Customer support calls, e-mail, and Web chats are routed to its nearly 10,000 remote customer service agents who work from their homes. It also handles sales and technical support issues. Arise Virtual Solutions provides the underlying technology as well as training and administration of its virtual workforce; clients have included Home Depot, Carnival Cruise Lines, and Verizon. The company has operations in the US, UK, and Ireland with plans for global expansion. The "virtual call center" was founded in 1997 as Willow CSN Incorporated and changed its name in 2007.

	Annual Growth	12/04	12/05	12/06	12/07	12/08
Est. sales ($ mil.)	—	—	—	—	—	7.7
Employees	—	—	—	—	—	57

ARISTOCRAT TECHNOLOGIES, INC.

7230 Amigo St.
Las Vegas, NV 89119
Phone: 702-270-1000
Fax: 702-270-1001
Web: www.aristocrat.com.au/company/about/Pages/Americas.aspx

CEO: Nick Khin
CFO: Ron Dufficy
HR: Connie Moore
FYE: December 31
Type: Subsidiary

Aristocrat Technologies helps casino managers tell if the house is ahead. The company is the North America, Latin America, and Caribbean operations of Australian gaming machine manufacturer Aristocrat Leisure. It designs, manufactures, and markets casino management tools and software to monitor gaming machine use and control payouts. The information systems can also monitor table games and offer additional tools for marketing and accounting. In addition, the company makes a variety of gaming machines, including reel slot machines, video gaming systems, and progressive payout machines. Aristocrat Technologies has sales and support centers in Argentina and the US (Minnesota, Mississippi, New Jersey, and Nevada).

	Annual Growth	12/04	12/05	12/06	12/07	12/08
Est. sales ($ mil.)	—	—	—	—	—	450.4
Employees	—	—	—	—	—	800

THE ARISTOTLE CORPORATION

96 Cummings Point Rd.
Stamford, CT 06902
Phone: 203-358-8000
Fax: 203-358-0179
Web: www.aristotlecorp.net

CEO: Steven B. Lapin
CFO: Dean T. Johnson
HR: —
FYE: December 31
Type: Private

Students can learn a thing or two from The Aristotle Corporation — from geometry and sewing to CPR and beekeeping. The company makes educational materials for grades K-12 that cover more than a dozen subject areas, including arts and crafts, math, nutrition, science, and vocational agriculture. It also produces medical teaching aids (such as CPR mannequins and simulation kits), ranch and farm supplies, lab sampling bags and equipment, and senior care products. Aristotle sells more than 65,000 items bearing brands such as Life/Form, Simulaids, Whirl-Pak, and Triarco, primarily through catalogs and also via an independent dealer network in 60 countries. The firm was acquired by Geneve Corporation in late 2009.

	Annual Growth	12/04	12/05	12/06	12/07	12/08
Sales ($ mil.)	5.0%	175.1	188.8	203.0	211.6	212.8
Net income ($ mil.)	(16.4%)	17.6	17.9	23.8	23.5	8.6
Employees	3.0%	800	850	850	900	900

ARIZONA CHEMICAL LTD.

4600 Touchton Rd. East, Bldg. 100, Ste. 1500
Jacksonville, FL 32246
Phone: 904-928-8700
Fax: 904-928-8779
Web: www.arizonachemical.com

CEO: Cornelis K. (Kees) Verhaar
CFO: Frederic Jung
HR: David (Dave) Cowfer
FYE: December 31
Type: Private

Arizona Chemical is always pining for more business. The company is among the world's largest fractionators (separators) of crude tall oil (from the Swedish word *talloja*, or pine oil). It manufactures such pine tree-based chemicals as fatty acids, rosin esters, and terpenes. These chemicals are used to manufacture a wide variety of products, including adhesives, household cleaners, hydraulic fluids, inks, paints, personal care products, and plastics. Arizona Chemical filed for an IPO in 2010. The company is majority owned by private equity group Rhône Capital, which is expected to still control a majority stake after completion of the offering.

	Annual Growth	12/05	12/06	12/07	12/08	12/09
Sales ($ mil.)	2.6%	692.0	769.0	723.8	1,002.0	767.5
Net income ($ mil.)	—	—	—	(27.3)	(26.6)	12.1
Employees	(9.5%)	1,600	1,400	1,400	1,000	1,075

ARIZONA PUBLIC SERVICE COMPANY

400 N. 5th St.
Phoenix, AZ 85072
Phone: 602-250-1000
Fax: 602-250-3007
Web: www.aps.com

CEO: Donald E. (Don) Brandt
CFO: James R. (Jim) Hatfield
HR: Lori S. Sundberg
FYE: December 31
Type: Subsidiary

Arizona Public Service is a grand provider of energy in the Grand Canyon state. Arizona Public Service, a subsidiary of Pinnacle West Capital, distributes power to more than 1.1 million customers in 11 of 15 Arizona counties, making it the largest electric utility in the state. It operates 5,870 miles of transmission lines and more than 28,000 miles of distribution lines; it also generates 6,160 MW of capacity at mainly fossil-fueled and nuclear power plants. Arizona Public Service's marketing and trading division sells excess energy from the utility's power plants, as well as power generated by Pinnacle West Energy, to wholesale customers in the western US.

	Annual Growth	12/04	12/05	12/06	12/07	12/08
Est. sales ($ mil.)	—	—	—	—	—	3,133.5
Employees	—	—	—	—	—	6,900

ARIZONA STATE UNIVERSITY

300 E. University Dr., Ste. 410
Tempe, AZ 85281
Phone: 480-965-8972
Fax: 480-965-0865
Web: www.asu.edu

CEO: Michael M. Crow
CFO: Morgan R. Olsen
HR: Matthew McElrath
FYE: June 30
Type: School

Sun lovers and knowledge seekers can turn to Arizona State University (ASU) for a well-rounded college education. The research university offers a wide variety of bachelor's, master's, and doctoral degree programs, with more than 250 majors in areas including nursing, journalism, and engineering. It has an enrollment of more than 67,000 undergraduate, graduate, and professional students on its four campuses in metropolitan Phoenix; most students attend the Tempe campus. The university boasts some 3,000 faculty members; it has an endowment of $750 million. ASU was founded in 1885 as a teachers college.

	Annual Growth	6/04	6/05	6/06	6/07	6/08
Est. sales ($ mil.)	—	—	—	—	—	1,400.0
Employees	—	—	—	—	—	8,000

ARK RESTAURANTS CORP.

NASDAQ (GM): ARKR

85 5th Ave., 14th Fl.
New York, NY 10003
Phone: 212-206-8800
Fax: 212-206-8814
Web: www.arkrestaurants.com

CEO: Michael Weinstein
CFO: Robert J. Stewart
HR: Marilyn Guy
FYE: September 30
Type: Public

You might say this company floats the boat of fine dining fans. Ark Restaurants owns and manages about 20 chic eateries in New York City, Las Vegas, and Washington, DC, including the Bryant Park Grill, Center Café, and V-Bar. It also operates multiple locations under the names America, Gonzalez y Gonzalez, and Sequoia. In addition, Ark Restaurants manages food courts, banquet facilities, and room services at several casino resorts, including the New York-New York Hotel & Casino (owned by MGM MIRAGE), the Venetian Casino Resort (Las Vegas Sands), and the Foxwoods Resorts Casino (Mashantucket Pequot Tribal Nation). Founder and CEO Michael Weinstein owns about 30% of the company.

	Annual Growth	9/05	9/06	9/07	9/08	9/09
Sales ($ mil.)	(0.1%)	115.6	116.0	124.2	122.9	115.0
Net income ($ mil.)	(19.3%)	6.6	5.2	13.0	7.0	2.8
Market value ($ mil.)	(13.8%)	109.0	92.4	128.5	56.0	60.2
Employees	(1.7%)	1,990	2,117	2,151	1,929	1,856

ARKANSAS BEST CORPORATION

NASDAQ (GS): ABFS

3801 Old Greenwood Rd.
Fort Smith, AR 72903
Phone: 479-785-6000
Fax: 479-785-6004
Web: www.arkbest.com

CEO: Judy R. McReynolds
CFO: Michael Newcity
HR: —
FYE: December 31
Type: Public

Arkansas Best puts its best efforts on the road to provide freight transportation services in its home state and the rest of North America. Specializing in long-haul, less-than-truckload (LTL) shipments of general commodities (no hazardous waste or dangerous explosives), subsidiary ABF Freight System accounts for over 90% of the company's sales. (LTL carriers combine freight from multiple shippers into a single truckload.) ABF Freight System operates a fleet of about 2,500 tractors and 17,000 trailers from about 280 terminals in the US, Canada, and Puerto Rico; it offers service into Mexico via alliances. Freight carried by the company includes chemicals, food, textiles, apparel, appliances, and furniture.

	Annual Growth	12/05	12/06	12/07	12/08	12/09
Sales ($ mil.)	(5.7%)	1,860.3	1,860.5	1,836.9	1,833.1	1,472.9
Net income ($ mil.)	—	104.6	84.1	56.8	29.2	(127.9)
Market value ($ mil.)	(9.4%)	1,105.3	911.0	555.2	761.9	744.7
Employees	(4.3%)	12,327	12,665	11,895	10,968	10,347

An in-depth profile of this company is available to Hoover's Online members at hoovers.com.

ARKANSAS STATE UNIVERSITY

2105 E. Aggie Rd.
State University, AR 72467
Phone: 870-972-2100
Fax: 870-972-3972
Web: www.astate.edu

CEO: Leslie (Les) Wyatt
CFO: Ed Kremers
HR: Lori Roach
FYE: June 30
Type: School

Arkansas State University (ASU) provides graduate and undergraduate academic programs to approximately 12,000 students. The university has 10 colleges that offer some 170 academic programs; it also has specialty units including the Arkansas Biosciences Institute, Independent Department of Military Science, and Arkansas Heritage SITES. In additional to its flagship campus in Jonesboro, the ASU system offers courses at regional campuses and technical sites and in partnership with community colleges. Founded in 1909, ASU offered its first doctoral degree (in educational leadership) in 1992. It has since added environmental science, heritage studies, and molecular biosciences doctoral programs.

	Annual Growth	6/04	6/05	6/06	6/07	6/08
Est. sales ($ mil.)	—	—	—	—	—	102.6
Employees	—	—	—	—	—	1,600

ARKEMA INC.

2000 Market St.
Philadelphia, PA 19103
Phone: 215-419-7000
Fax: 215-419-5394
Web: www.arkema-inc.com

CEO: Bernard Roche
CFO: Patricia McCarthy
HR: Christopher (Chris) Giangrasso
FYE: December 31
Type: Subsidiary

Arkema's into vinyl, but not in a weird way. The North American branch of France-based parent Arkema, it manufactures many vinyl products, such as PVC, chlorochemicals, and assorted vinyl compounds. Its other products include industrial chemicals and plastics (acrylics, hydrogen peroxide, and fluorochemicals) and performance products (additives, agrochemicals, organic peroxides, and technical polymers). Arkema operates about 20 manufacturing facilities in North America and accounts for about a quarter of its parent's total sales. The company was created in 2004 when TOTAL broke up its former chemicals subsidiary, ATOFINA, into two units: Arkema and TOTAL Petrochemicals.

ARLINGTON ASSET INVESTMENT CORPORATION

NYSE: AI

1001 19th St. North
Arlington, VA 22209
Phone: 703-312-9500
Fax: 703-312-9501
Web: www.arlingtonasset.com

CEO: Eric F. Billings
CFO: Kurt R. Harrington
HR: —
FYE: December 31
Type: Public

Arlington Asset Investment (formerly Friedman, Billings, Ramsey) is a holding company that, through its subsidiaries, invests mostly in residential mortgage-backed securities (MBS). Prior to 2009, the company operated as a real estate investment trust, but it dropped that status in order to gain more flexibility to acquire assets and retain earnings. About one-fourth of its MBS holdings are through agencies such as Freddie Mac and Fannie Mae, with the rest being private-label funds. Arlington also manages merchant bank holdings, including interest in equity securities, mezzanine debt, and senior loans. The company changed its name in 2009 to Arlington Asset Investment Corporation.

	Annual Growth	12/05	12/06	12/07	12/08	12/09
Sales ($ mil.)	(34.9%)	995.3	1,007.9	690.6	359.9	178.3
Net income ($ mil.)	—	(170.9)	(67.3)	(660.3)	(417.5)	105.1
Market value ($ mil.)	(47.3%)	1,566.6	1,266.0	496.9	26.9	120.5
Employees	(74.7%)	2,449	3,019	1,025	579	10

ARMANINO FOODS OF DISTINCTION, INC.

Pink Sheets: AMNF

30588 San Antonio St.
Hayward, CA 94544
Phone: 510-441-9300
Fax: 510-441-0101
Web: www.armaninofoods.com

CEO: Edmond J. Pera
CFO: Edmond J. Pera
HR: Rita Rupp
FYE: December 31
Type: Public

You're too skinny! Eat! Armanino Foods of Distinction makes upscale frozen and refrigerated Italian-style food. Its flagship product is pesto, of which it makes six different varieties. The company also makes frozen filled pastas and frozen meatballs. Its customers include other US food manufacturers, restaurants, and other foodservice vendors, as well as club stores and major retail food chains. The company is headquartered in Hayward, California, where it also has pesto and pasta production facilities; its meat processing takes place in Stockton, California. It has branch offices in San Francisco, Sacramento, Los Angeles, Las Vegas, Boston, and Sioux City, Iowa.

ARMSTRONG WORLD INDUSTRIES, INC.

NYSE: AWI

2500 Columbia Ave.
Lancaster, PA 17603
Phone: 717-397-0611
Fax: 717-396-6133
Web: www.armstrong.com

CEO: Thomas B. (Tom) Mangas
CFO: Thomas B. (Tom) Mangas
HR: —
FYE: December 31
Type: Public

Armstrong World Industries (AWI) won't mind if you walk all over it. Or its products, to be more exact. AWI makes ceramic, hardwood, laminate, linoleum, and vinyl sheet flooring under such brands as Armstrong, Bruce, and Robbins; this floor products units brings in more than half of total sales. Meanwhile, its building products unit produces ceilings and suspension systems, and its cabinet products arm makes hardwood, kitchen, and bathroom cabinets. They are sold to contractors, distributors, home centers, wholesalers, and other retailers for residential and commercial use. AWI operates more than 35 plants in nine countries. North America represents its largest market in terms of sales, followed by Europe and Asia.

	Annual Growth	12/05	12/06	12/07	12/08	12/09
Sales ($ mil.)	(6.0%)	3,558.4	817.3	3,549.7	3,393.0	2,780.0
Net income ($ mil.)	(8.6%)	111.1	2.2	145.3	81.0	77.7
Market value ($ mil.)	(2.8%)	—	2,438.9	2,307.7	1,243.9	2,239.8
Employees	(7.7%)	14,900	14,500	12,900	12,200	10,800

🔳 ARMY AND AIR FORCE EXCHANGE SERVICE

3911 S. Walton Walker Blvd.
Dallas, TX 75236
Phone: 214-312-2011
Fax: 214-312-3000
Web: www.aafes.com

CEO: Maj. Gen. Keith L. Thurgood
CFO: —
HR: —
FYE: January 31
Type: Government agency

Be all that you can be and buy all that you can buy at the PX (Post Exchange). The Army and Air Force Exchange Service (AAFES) runs more than 3,100 facilities — including PXs and BXs (Base Exchanges) — at US Army and Air Force bases in more than 30 countries (including Iraq), all 50 US states, and five US territories. Its presence ranges from tents to shopping centers, including 175 retail stores, 1,300 fast-food outlets (brands like Burger King and Taco Bell), movie theaters, beauty shops, and gas stations. AAFES serves active-duty military personnel, reservists, retirees, and their family members. Although it's a government agency under the DOD, it receives less than 5% of its funding from the department.

	Annual Growth	1/04	1/05	1/06	1/07	1/08
Sales ($ mil.)	2.4%	7,905.3	8,351.7	8,667.3	8,921.4	8,704.5
Net income ($ mil.)	(2.3%)	485.0	474.1	378.4	427.5	441.8
Employees	(2.0%)	47,323	48,000	45,000	45,000	43,658

ARNOLD & PORTER LLP

555 12th St., NW	CEO: Thomas H. Milch
Washington, DC 20004	CFO: —
Phone: 202-942-5000	HR: Janet R. Robin
Fax: 202-942-5999	FYE: December 31
Web: www.arnoldporter.com	Type: Partnership

A tourist might go to Washington, DC, to see the Smithsonian's museums, but an executive's agenda might include a visit to Arnold & Porter. The law firm's wide-ranging practice areas center on business transactions and public policy; its specialties include antitrust, bankruptcy and corporate restructuring, white collar criminal defense, international trade, intellectual property, and litigation. The firm is also known for its strong pro bono work. Arnold & Porter has more than 675 lawyers at seven offices in the US and two in Europe. The firm was established in 1946 as Arnold, Fortas & Porter; Abe Fortas, later a Supreme Court justice, was a founding partner.

ARNOLD WORLDWIDE LLC

101 Huntington Ave.	CEO: Andrew Benett
Boston, MA 02199	CFO: —
Phone: 617-587-8000	HR: Melissa Morgante
Fax: 617-587-8004	FYE: December 31
Web: www.arnoldworldwide.com	Type: Business segment

A partnership with this Arnold will get your brand promoted, not terminated. Arnold Worldwide is a full-service advertising agency that offers creative ad development, campaign planning, and brand management services. Its vast advertising agency network spans offices in Canada, Italy, the Czech Republic, Portugal, Spain, the UK, and the US. In 2008 it launched an office in London. The agency's primary three East Coast offices in the US have served such brands as Titleist, McDonald's, Levi's, and Volvo. Arnold Worldwide is a unit of Paris-based advertising conglomerate Havas.

AROTECH CORPORATION

NASDAQ (GM): ARTX

1229 Oak Valley Dr.	CEO: Robert S. Ehrlich
Ann Arbor, MI 48108	CFO: Thomas J. Paup
Phone: 800-281-0356	HR: —
Fax: 734-761-5368	FYE: December 31
Web: www.arotech.com	Type: Public

It's no longer all about batteries for Arotech. The company has broadened its horizons to use-of-force simulators and vehicle armor, in addition to its line of zinc-air batteries and fuel cells. Arotech's FAAC and IES Interactive Training subsidiaries provide simulators, related software, and training for law enforcement and military entities. Arotech's majority-owned MDT Protective Industries and MDT Armor units make lightweight ceramic armor and ballistic glass for military and passenger vehicles; Armour of America produces shielding for aircraft and for people. Arotech still churns out Lithium-Ion primary and rechargeable batteries and charging systems, mainly for the military and homeland security markets.

	Annual Growth	12/05	12/06	12/07	12/08	12/09
Sales ($ mil.)	10.5%	50.0	43.1	57.7	68.9	74.5
Net income ($ mil.)	—	(24.0)	(15.6)	(3.1)	(3.8)	(3.1)
Market value ($ mil.)	(24.3%)	74.9	44.1	30.5	5.9	24.6
Employees	14.1%	277	342	407	450	470

ARQULE, INC.

NASDAQ (GM): ARQL

19 Presidential Way	CEO: Paolo Pucci
Woburn, MA 01801	CFO: Robert Weiskopf
Phone: 781-994-0300	HR: Anthony S. (Tony) Messina
Fax: 781-376-6019	FYE: December 31
Web: www.arqule.com	Type: Public

ArQule has decided to major in molecular biology. The biotechnology firm had been providing chemistry services to help drugmakers discover new potential drug compounds. However, it has switched from being a helper to becoming a doer. Now ArQule is developing its own portfolio of oncology drugs, with a handful of anti-cancer compounds undergoing clinical trials. It is testing its most advanced candidate, ARQ 197, as a treatment for a variety of tumor types; and it is working with partner Roche on a handful of other anti-cancer compounds that reactivate the cellular functions that kill cancer cells.

	Annual Growth	12/05	12/06	12/07	12/08	12/09
Sales ($ mil.)	(16.9%)	52.9	6.6	9.2	14.1	25.2
Net income ($ mil.)	—	(7.5)	(31.4)	(53.4)	(50.9)	(36.1)
Market value ($ mil.)	(11.9%)	274.1	265.1	259.8	189.0	165.3
Employees	(18.0%)	246	98	113	107	111

ARRAY BIOPHARMA INC.

NASDAQ (GM): ARRY

3200 Walnut St.	CEO: Robert E. (Bob) Conway
Boulder, CO 80301	CFO: R. Michael Carruthers
Phone: 303-381-6600	HR: —
Fax: 303-386-1390	FYE: June 30
Web: www.arraybiopharma.com	Type: Public

Array BioPharma wants to offer sufferers of cancer, inflammatory, and metabolic diseases a multitude of treatment options. The development-stage company has seven wholly owned programs in its development pipeline. Candidates include therapies for solid tumors (ARRY-543), arthritis (ARRY-162), breast cancer (ARRY-380), and type 2 diabetes (ARRY-403). Array also out-licenses some drug programs to AstraZeneca and Genentech; ARRY-886, developed with AstraZeneca, is in clinical trials for melanoma. Array's agreement with Genentech includes five candidates in various stages of development for the treatment of cancer. The company also has R&D agreements with Amgen, InterMune, Celgene, and others.

	Annual Growth	6/05	6/06	6/07	6/08	6/09
Sales ($ mil.)	(13.9%)	45.5	45.0	37.0	28.8	25.0
Net income ($ mil.)	—	(23.2)	(39.6)	(55.4)	(96.3)	(127.8)
Market value ($ mil.)	(16.0%)	334.6	456.7	619.7	249.6	166.8
Employees	7.2%	269	276	311	386	355

ARRHYTHMIA RESEARCH TECHNOLOGY, INC.

NYSE Amex: HRT

25 Sawyer Passway	CEO: James E. Rouse
Fitchburg, MA 01420	CFO: David A. Garrison
Phone: 978-345-5000	HR: —
Fax: 978-342-0168	FYE: December 31
Web: www.arthrt.com	Type: Public

It's all about heart for Arrhythmia Research Technology (ART). The company offers signal-averaging electrocardiographic (SAECG) software that collects data and analyzes electrical impulses of the heart in an effort to detect potentially lethal heart arrhythmias. The company plans to sell the products through licensing agreements with equipment makers. Until it finds a marketing partner, however, ART is relying on sales from its Micron Products subsidiary, which makes snaps and sensors used in the manufacture and operation of disposable electrodes for electrocardiographic (ECG) equipment. Micron Products has acquired assets of several companies that enhance its metal and plastics molding capabilities.

	Annual Growth	12/05	12/06	12/07	12/08	12/09
Sales ($ mil.)	13.1%	12.9	19.3	19.5	22.5	21.1
Net income ($ mil.)	(29.3%)	1.6	2.2	1.3	0.4	0.4
Market value ($ mil.)	(20.8%)	23.5	65.1	18.4	5.4	9.2
Employees	5.5%	75	100	94	85	93

An in-depth profile of this company is available to Hoover's Online members at hoovers.com.

169

⊞ ARRIS GROUP, INC.

NASDAQ (GS): ARRS

3871 Lakefield Dr.
Suwanee, GA 30024
Phone: 678-473-2000
Fax: 678-473-8470
Web: www.arrisi.com

CEO: Robert J. (Bob) Stanzione
CFO: David B. (Dave) Potts
HR: —
FYE: December 31
Type: Public

ARRIS Group brings the idea of broadband home. The company makes communications equipment and components used to enable voice and data transmission in high-speed networks and to build television broadcast networks. ARRIS' products include cable network headend gear, Internet protocol switching systems, modems, and other consumer premises products. The company also sells such related hardware as cable, connectors, and other supplies used for mounting and installation. ARRIS primarily markets to large cable network operators. Its top customers, Comcast and Time Warner Cable, together account for about half of the company's sales. Outside of North America, the company's key markets are the Asia/Pacific region, Europe, and Latin America.

	Annual Growth	12/05	12/06	12/07	12/08	12/09
Sales ($ mil.)	13.0%	680.4	891.6	992.2	1,144.6	1,107.8
Net income ($ mil.)	15.2%	51.5	142.3	98.3	(123.1)	90.8
Market value ($ mil.)	4.8%	1,200.9	1,586.4	1,265.6	1,008.2	1,449.5
Employees	26.7%	732	781	1,992	1,838	1,884

⊞ ARROW ELECTRONICS, INC.

NYSE: ARW

50 Marcus Dr.
Melville, NY 11747
Phone: 631-847-2000
Fax: 631-847-2222
Web: www.arrow.com

CEO: Michael J. (Mike) Long
CFO: Paul J. Reilly
HR: John P. McMahon
FYE: December 31
Type: Public

Arrow Electronics knows its target market. The company is one of the world's largest distributors of electronic components and computer products, alongside rival Avnet. Arrow sells semiconductors, passive components, interconnect products, and computer peripherals from about 900 suppliers to more than 125,000 OEMs, contract manufacturers, and commercial customers worldwide. Arrow also provides value-added services, such as materials planning, design and engineering, inventory management, and contract manufacturing. The company operates from more than 300 locations in some 50 countries, and gets more than half of its sales from outside the US.

	Annual Growth	12/05	12/06	12/07	12/08	12/09
Sales ($ mil.)	7.1%	11,164.2	13,577.1	15,985.0	16,761.0	14,684.1
Net income ($ mil.)	(16.5%)	253.6	388.3	407.8	(613.7)	123.5
Market value ($ mil.)	(1.9%)	3,857.5	3,799.7	4,730.6	2,269.0	3,566.0
Employees	(0.2%)	11,400	12,000	12,600	12,700	11,300

ARROW FINANCIAL CORPORATION

NASDAQ (GS): AROW

250 Glen St.
Glens Falls, NY 12801
Phone: 518-745-1000
Fax: 518-761-0843
Web: www.arrowfinancial.com

CEO: Thomas L. Hoy
CFO: Terry R. Goodemote
HR: —
FYE: December 31
Type: Public

Arrow Financial has more than one shaft in its quiver. It's the holding company for two banks: Glens Falls National Bank and Trust Company and Saratoga National Bank and Trust Company, which together operate more than 30 branches in five counties in eastern upstate New York. Targeting individuals and area businesses, the banks offer standard deposit products like checking, savings, and money market accounts; CDs; and IRAs. They also provide retirement, trust, and estate planning services and employee benefit plan administration. Residential mortgages make up the largest segment of Arrow Financial's loan portfolio (more than 40%); indirect and installment loans to individuals account for about 30%.

	Annual Growth	12/05	12/06	12/07	12/08	12/09
Assets ($ mil.)	4.9%	1,519.6	1,520.2	1,584.8	1,665.1	1,841.6
Net income ($ mil.)	4.0%	18.6	16.9	17.3	20.4	21.8
Market value ($ mil.)	1.1%	262.1	255.7	228.5	267.3	273.8
Employees	3.0%	420	438	448	477	473

ARROW FINANCIAL SERVICES LLC

5996 W. Touhy Ave.
Niles, IL 60714
Phone: 847-557-1100
Fax: 847-647-9526
Web: www.arrow-financial.com

CEO: Jack Lavin
CFO: Michael Valentino
HR: Paul Kottmer
FYE: December 31
Type: Subsidiary

Sallie Mae giveth what Arrow Financial Services taketh back, with interest. The collection services company, which is majority owned by student loan provider SLM (Sallie Mae), performs contingency collection services on past-due consumer accounts, working on behalf of its parent as well as credit card issuers; telecommunications providers; utility companies; and auto, education, and other consumer lenders. The company also purchases and services performing and nonperforming consumer debt. It has call centers in Illinois and Wisconsin, as well as other operations in New York and Texas. Sallie Mae acquired a majority stake in Arrow Financial in 2004.

	Annual Growth	12/04	12/05	12/06	12/07	12/08
Est. sales ($ mil.)	—	—	—	—	—	175.0
Employees	—	—	—	—	—	1,300

ARROW RESOURCES DEVELOPMENT, INC.

OTC: ARWD

152 W. 57th St.
New York, NY 10019
Phone: 212-262-2300
Fax: —
Web: www.arrowrd.com

CEO: Peter John Frugone
CFO: —
HR: —
FYE: December 31
Type: Public

Arrow Resources Development may have found its bullseye. After stints in wireless equipment, merchant banking, and real estate, the company is targeting natural resources. Arrow provides corporate, marketing, sales, and other services for regional companies that exploit timber, oil, and other natural resources in Indonesia. Working to restore areas that have been illegally deforested, the company combines tree farms (primarily eucalyptus, for the paper products industries) with farming operations (mostly corn), while using organic fertilizers and renewable energy sources and focusing on environmental and wildlife issues. Indonesian financier Hans Karundeng's Arrow Pacific Resources Group owns 53% of the firm.

	Annual Growth	12/05	12/06	12/07	12/08	12/09
Sales ($ mil.)	—	—	—	—	0.1	0.0
Net income ($ mil.)	—	—	—	—	(5.4)	(6.5)
Market value ($ mil.)	(68.7%)	—	—	—	61.1	19.1
Employees	—	—	—	—	—	—

ARROWHEAD RESEARCH CORPORATION

NASDAQ (GM): ARWR

201 S. Lake Ave., Ste. 703
Pasadena, CA 91101
Phone: 626-304-3400
Fax: 626-304-3401
Web: www.arrowheadresearch.com

CEO: Christopher (Chris) Anzalone
CFO: Kenneth (Ken) Myszkowski
HR: —
FYE: September 30
Type: Public

Arrowhead Research is a development-stage holding company with several subsidiaries focused on developing and commercializing nanotechnologies. Its Agonn Systems unit is developing nanotechnology-based storage devices used for hybrid electric vehicles, while Unidym focuses on the commercialization of carbon nanotube-based (sphere-like molecules that can transfer electricity, heat, and other forms of energy) properties. In addition, Calando Pharmaceuticals develops and commercializes therapeutics. Arrowhead has also funded nanoscience research at universities (including the California Institute of Technology and Duke University) in exchange for the right to commercialize the resulting intellectual property.

	Annual Growth	9/05	9/06	9/07	9/08	9/09
Sales ($ mil.)	58.6%	0.6	0.6	1.2	1.3	3.8
Net income ($ mil.)	—	(6.6)	(19.0)	(29.9)	(27.1)	(19.3)
Market value ($ mil.)	(31.3%)	191.1	318.9	322.8	66.5	42.5
Employees	(11.1%)	32	40	58	68	20

ARROW-MAGNOLIA INTERNATIONAL, INC.

2646 Rodney Ln.
Dallas, TX 75229
Phone: 972-247-7111
Fax: 972-484-2896
Web: www.arrowmagnolia.com

CEO: David J. Tippeconnic
CFO: James Barry
HR: —
FYE: December 31
Type: Private

Whether it flies, bulldozes, or hauls golfers, Arrow-Magnolia International has something that cleans it. The company makes about 400 chemical cleaners that it sells under its own brands; it also distributes nonchemical janitorial supplies. Its products include chemicals used in construction (concrete and rust removers), government engineering (street and equipment cleaners), aviation (carbon and dirt removers), and golf course maintenance. Arrow-Magnolia makes more than half of its products in-house and sells them through independent representatives and a dozen distributors. An investment group led by Tanya Tippeconnic-Shaw has owned Arrow-Magnolia since 2005.

	Annual Growth	12/04	12/05	12/06	12/07	12/08
Est. sales ($ mil.)	—	—	—	—	—	10.8
Employees	—	—	—	—	—	56

ARROWPOINT CAPITAL CORPORATION

Whitehall Corporate Center, Bldg. 3, 3600 Arco Corporate Dr.
Charlotte, NC 28273
Phone: 704-522-2000
Fax: —
Web: www.arrowpointcapitalcorp.com

CEO: John Tighe
CFO: Sean Beatty
HR: Bob Dixon
FYE: December 31
Type: Private

Even though its former parent company no longer wanted it, Arrowpoint Capital (formerly Royal & SunAlliance USA) has the will to live on and sell insurance. The company was a subsidiary of UK-based insurer Royal & Sun Alliance, but suffered from relentless trimmings when its business was deemed to be noncore. The business was eventually acquired by a group of its management and outside directors. Renamed Arrowpoint Capital, it operates through its Royal Indemnity, Royal Surplus Lines Insurance, and Security Insurance Company of Hartford subsidiaries. The company continues to offer individual and commercial property/casualty coverage under the Royal Care brand.

ART TECHNOLOGY GROUP, INC.

NASDAQ (GM): ARTG

1 Main St.
Cambridge, MA 02142
Phone: 617-386-1000
Fax: 617-386-1111
Web: www.atg.com

CEO: Robert D. (Bob) Burke
CFO: Julia M.B. Bradley
HR: Patricia (Pat) O'Neill
FYE: December 31
Type: Public

Art Technology Group (ATG) knows there's a fine art to managing customers. The company's offerings include e-commerce software and related IT services for online retail, travel, media, insurance, and financial services companies. Used by merchandising and marketing professionals, its software tracks and analyzes online customer behavior and enables users to manage e-commerce Web sites. ATG also makes various customer-facing applications, including "Click to Chat" and "Click to Call" Web page links that allow online customers to contact customer service agents. Its IT services include consulting, custom application development, and support. Clients include Amazon, J. Crew, Target, and Walgreens.

	Annual Growth	12/05	12/06	12/07	12/08	12/09
Sales ($ mil.)	18.6%	90.6	103.2	137.1	164.6	179.4
Net income ($ mil.)	30.5%	5.8	9.7	(4.2)	3.8	16.8
Market value ($ mil.)	23.2%	307.7	365.8	678.3	303.0	708.1
Employees	15.2%	309	378	442	502	545

ART VAN FURNITURE, INC.

6500 14 Mile Rd.
Warren, MI 48092
Phone: 586-939-0800
Fax: 586-939-3055
Web: www.artvan.com

CEO: Kim Yost
CFO: Michael Bolton
HR: Michael (Mike) Zambricki
FYE: September 30
Type: Private

Family-owned Art Van Furniture ought to be family friendly. The firm — Michigan's #1 furniture seller — offers medium-priced home furniture in more than 30 Michigan stores. The chain has undergone a renovation, adding more upscale furniture (it sells Sealy, Simmons, and Broyhill brands) and perks such as children's play areas. The company is known for its aggressive sales and service. (Employees have been known to greet patrons carside with umbrellas on rainy days.) Chairman Art Van Elslander, who has 10 children (some active in the business), founded the firm with an East Detroit store in 1959. The company celebrated its 50th anniversary in 2009.

ARTESIAN RESOURCES CORPORATION

NASDAQ (GM): ARTNA

664 Churchmans Rd.
Newark, DE 19702
Phone: 302-453-6900
Fax: 302-453-6957
Web: www.artesianwater.com

CEO: Dian C. Taylor
CFO: David B. Spacht
HR: Patti Cumpston
FYE: December 31
Type: Public

All's well that ends in wells for Artesian Resources. Operating primarily through regulated utility Artesian Water, the company provides water in all three Delaware counties (New Castle, Kent, and Sussex). Its 75,800 customer accounts represent about 250,000 Delaware residents, about 29% of the state's population; residential customers account for 94% of the utility's water sales. Artesian pumps about 17.9 million gallons of water daily from its wells, then sends it to customers through more than 1,100 miles of mains and some 5,230 hydrants. The company operates a wastewater facility in New Castle County.

	Annual Growth	12/05	12/06	12/07	12/08	12/09
Sales ($ mil.)	7.7%	45.3	48.6	52.5	56.2	60.9
Net income ($ mil.)	9.9%	5.0	6.1	6.3	6.4	7.3
Market value ($ mil.)	(1.9%)	148.4	147.8	142.1	119.5	137.7
Employees	5.6%	189	204	209	245	235

ARTHROCARE CORPORATION

Pink Sheets: ARTC

7500 Rialto Blvd., Bldg. 2, Ste. 100
Austin, TX 78735
Phone: 512-391-3900
Fax: 512-391-3901
Web: www.arthrocare.com

CEO: David F. Fitzgerald
CFO: Todd Newton
HR: —
FYE: December 31
Type: Public

With the wave of a wand, ArthroCare makes tissue disappear. The company's proprietary Coblation technology uses radio frequency energy to remove soft tissue from the body. With its minimally invasive surgery systems, specialized wands focus the energy and minimize damage to nearby healthy tissue, simultaneously sealing small bleeding vessels. First used in arthroscopic procedures to repair joints, the electrosurgery system line now includes equipment used in a wide range of minimally invasive surgeries. The company also makes ligament-repair, spinal-stabilization, and wound-care products. ArthroCare makes it products in Costa Rica and sells them in the US, Europe, and Japan.

	Annual Growth	12/05	12/06	12/07	12/08	12/09
Sales ($ mil.)	11.5%	214.3	263.0	319.2	314.2	331.6
Net income ($ mil.)	—	23.5	31.7	43.2	(34.7)	(5.8)
Market value ($ mil.)	(13.4%)	1,135.9	1,076.1	1,295.2	128.6	638.9
Employees	0.7%	1,324	881	413	1,140	1,363

An in-depth profile of this company is available to Hoover's Online members at hoovers.com.

171

ARTHUR D. LITTLE

125 High St., High St. Tower, 28th Fl.
Boston, MA 02210
Phone: 617-532-9550
Fax: 617-261-6630
Web: www.adl.com

CEO: Michael R. Träm
CFO: —
HR: Marie Jerusalem
FYE: December 31
Type: Subsidiary

There's nothing small about ideas from ADL. Management consulting company Arthur D. Little (ADL) offers advice in areas such as corporate finance, environmental risk, information management, operations, strategy and organization, and technology and innovation. The firm operates from about 30 offices in some 20 countries. Clients come from a variety of industries, including manufacturing, health care, and energy. Today's ADL is a successor to industry pioneer Arthur D. Little Inc., which filed for bankruptcy in 2002 and auctioned off its operations. That year French technology consulting company Altran Technologies bought the rights to the Arthur D. Little name and the core management consulting business.

ARTHUR J. GALLAGHER & CO.

NYSE: AJG

The Gallagher Centre, 2 Pierce Place
Itasca, IL 60143
Phone: 630-773-3800
Fax: 630-285-4000
Web: www.ajg.com

CEO: J. Patrick Gallagher Jr.
CFO: Douglas K. (Doug) Howell
HR: Susan E. McGrath
FYE: December 31
Type: Public

Arthur J. Gallagher knows all about risky business. The company provides insurance brokerage and risk management services through a network of subsidiaries and agencies. It places traditional and niche property/casualty lines in addition to offering retirement solutions and managing employee benefits programs. Risk management services include claims management, loss control consulting, and workers' compensation investigations. Gallagher UK places insurance with the Lloyd's of London exchange. The global company has sales and service operations in about 15 nations and, through correspondent brokers and consultants, does business in more than 100 countries.

	Annual Growth	12/05	12/06	12/07	12/08	12/09
Sales ($ mil.)	3.9%	1,483.9	1,534.0	1,623.3	1,611.2	1,729.3
Net income ($ mil.)	42.9%	30.8	128.5	138.8	77.3	128.6
Market value ($ mil.)	(7.6%)	3,199.2	3,061.4	2,506.1	2,684.3	2,332.0
Employees	5.1%	8,100	8,750	9,300	9,900	9,900

ARTIFICIAL LIFE, INC.

OTC: ALIF

520 Broadway, Ste. 350
Santa Monica, CA 90401
Phone: 310-496-4288
Fax: —
Web: www.artificial-life.com

CEO: Eberhard Schoneburg
CFO: Eberhard Schoneburg
HR: Nettie So
FYE: December 31
Type: Public

Artificial Life isn't into clones, unless they play video games on their cell phones. The company provides entertainment products, games, and technologies for telecommunications devices, mobile phones, and the Internet. Artificial Life also designs and sells software for creating interactive agents, or bots, that clients can use to automate and simplify complex Internet activities, such as electronic commerce, direct marketing, and sales response. The company's mobile games are distributed by botme.com to more than 200 countries. Titles include *America's Next Top Model*, *V-girl* and *V-boy* (your virtual girlfriend or boyfriend), *Tokio Hotel*, and *Shooter*.

	Annual Growth	12/05	12/06	12/07	12/08	12/09
Sales ($ mil.)	209.4%	0.3	0.9	5.8	22.5	27.5
Net income ($ mil.)	—	(1.7)	(2.9)	1.0	10.6	7.6
Market value ($ mil.)	9.5%	40.0	102.4	121.2	55.4	57.6
Employees	15.1%	37	42	55	68	65

ARTIO GLOBAL INVESTORS INC.

NYSE: ART

330 Madison Ave.
New York, NY 10017
Phone: 212-297-3600
Fax: —
Web: www.artioglobal.com

CEO: Richard Pell
CFO: Francis Harte
HR: —
FYE: December 31
Type: Public

Specializing in international equity strategies, Artio Global Investors (formerly Julius Baer Americas) is the holding company for Artio Global Management. It provides investment management services to intermediary clients, as well as institutional clients such as corporations, financial institutions, pension funds, hospitals, universities, and endowments. Its products include separate accounts, commingled funds, offshore funds, and sub-advised accounts. The company also manages about 10 mutual funds, which it offers to retail investors as well as to institutional ones. Artio Global has more than $50 billion under management. Swiss private bank Julius Baer spun off Artio Global Investors in 2009.

	Annual Growth	12/05	12/06	12/07	12/08	12/09
Assets ($ mil.)	12.8%	121.2	244.7	355.4	319.5	196.0
Net income ($ mil.)	—	26.1	44.8	68.0	61.2	(364.2)
Market value ($ mil.)	—	—	—	—	—	5,375.6
Employees	3.3%	—	183	188	198	202

ARTISTDIRECT, INC.

OTC: ARTDE

1601 Cloverfield Blvd., Ste. 400 South
Santa Monica, CA 90404
Phone: 310-956-3300
Fax: 310-956-3301
Web: www.artistdirect.com

CEO: Dimitri S. Villard
CFO: René Rousselet
HR: —
FYE: December 31
Type: Public

Are you an artist fearful of pirates? Head for ARTISTdirect. The company's Peer Media Technologies subsidiary analyzes digital content distribution and peer-to-peer networks, and helps aid in the prevention of illegal music downloading and sharing. The company additionally operates the ARTISTdirect Network, a collection of Web sites featuring music-related content, including music news and information and an online database covering more than 100,000 artists. The ARTISTdirect Network is classified under the company's media segment, which earns money through online advertising and marketing fees. ARTISTdirect's e-commerce operations offer a selection of music recordings and other music-related merchandise.

	Annual Growth	12/04	12/05	12/06	12/07	*12/08
Sales ($ mil.)	24.1%	5.1	14.0	24.1	24.2	12.1
Net income ($ mil.)	—	(3.3)	20.1	(4.9)	11.5	(48.0)
Market value ($ mil.)	(62.8%)	14.6	185.1	131.8	21.3	0.3
Employees	45.9%	15	65	74	80	68

*Most recent year available

ART'S-WAY MANUFACTURING CO., INC.

NASDAQ (CM): ARTW

5556 Hwy. 9
Armstrong, IA 50514
Phone: 712-864-3131
Fax: 712-864-3154
Web: www.artsway-mfg.com

CEO: Carrie L. Majeski
CFO: Carrie L. Majeski
HR: —
FYE: November 30
Type: Public

Sinatra did it his way, but farmers have been doing it Art's way since 1956. Art's-Way Manufacturing makes an assortment of machinery under its own label and its customers' private labels. Art's-Way equipment includes custom animal-feed processing machines, high-bulk mixing wagons, mowers and stalk shredders, and equipment for harvesting sugar beets and potatoes. Its private-label OEM customers include CNH Global, for whom Art's-Way makes and supplies hay blowers. Equipment dealers throughout the US sell Art's-Way products. Steel truck bodies are also manufactured under the Cherokee Truck Bodies name. Art's-Way owns subsidiaries Art's-Way Vessels and Art's-Way Scientific.

	Annual Growth	11/05	11/06	11/07	11/08	11/09
Sales ($ mil.)	15.9%	14.6	19.9	25.5	32.0	26.3
Net income ($ mil.)	(5.4%)	1.0	0.9	2.2	1.8	0.8
Market value ($ mil.)	12.3%	9.7	12.7	47.1	16.3	15.4
Employees	(0.7%)	116	102	107	129	113

An in-depth profile of this company is available to Hoover's Online members at hoovers.com.

ARUBA NETWORKS, INC.

NASDAQ (GM): ARUN

1344 Crossman Ave.
Sunnyvale, CA 94089
Phone: 408-227-4500
Fax: 408-227-4550
Web: www.arubanetworks.com

CEO: Dominic P. Orr
CFO: Steffan Tomlinson
HR: Aaron Bean
FYE: July 31
Type: Public

Aruba Networks wants to turn your business into a wireless paradise. The company designs equipment used to build wireless LANs. Its products include controllers, access points, and concentrators, as well as operating system and management software. Aruba also provides professional and support services. The company targets the corporate, education, and government sectors, selling directly and through distributors, resellers, and OEMs. Its customers include California State University, NTT DATA, and the US Air Force. Aruba outsources the manufacturing of its products to Flextronics. The company gets about two-thirds of its sales in the US.

	Annual Growth	7/05	7/06	7/07	7/08	7/09
Sales ($ mil.)	100.2%	12.4	72.5	127.5	178.3	199.3
Net income ($ mil.)	—	(32.6)	(12.1)	(24.4)	(17.1)	(23.4)
Market value ($ mil.)	(33.5%)	—	—	1,793.9	520.8	793.3
Employees	33.6%	171	282	441	541	545

ARVEST BANK GROUP

125 W. Central, Ste. 218
Bentonville, AR 72712
Phone: 479-750-1400
Fax: 479-273-7477
Web: www.arvest.com

CEO: Jim C. Walton
CFO: Karla Payne
HR: Laura Andress
FYE: December 31
Type: Private

Arvest Bank Group operates more than 200 locations in Arkansas, Kansas, Missouri, and Oklahoma. It provides traditional deposit and loan products, as well as trust, asset management, and brokerage services. The group maintains a decentralized structure of about 15 individually chartered banks; local managers and directors control lending decisions and deposit rates in many communities. Arvest has grown to be the biggest bank in Arkansas largely via acquisitions; it expanded into Kansas when it bought Caney Valley Bancshares in 2007. Descendants of Wal-Mart founder Sam Walton (including bank CEO Jim Walton, a son of Sam and one of the richest men in America) own Arvest Bank Group.

ARVIN SANGO, INC.

2905 Wilson Ave.
Madison, IN 47250
Phone: 812-265-2888
Fax: 812-273-8339
Web: www.arvinsango.com

CEO: Tom Hashiguchi
CFO: Dan Baughman
HR: —
FYE: December 31
Type: Joint venture

Arvin Sango is the intersection where ArvinMeritor, SANGO Co., Ltd., and Toyota all collide. A joint venture created by ArvinMeritor and SANGO, the company supplies automotive components, almost exclusively for Toyota Motor North America's assembly plants. Arvin Sango's products include exhaust system assemblies, body panels, door impact beams, instrument panel reinforcements, tubular manifolds, and underfloor converters. Its facilities, which neighbor Toyota's plants, utilize Pokayok, a defect protection technology, and just-in-time (JIT) and continuous improvement manufacturing processes. The company is held equally by EMCON Technologies (part of Faurecia's emissions control business group) and Sango.

ARVINMERITOR, INC.

NYSE: ARM

2135 W. Maple Rd.
Troy, MI 48084
Phone: 248-435-1000
Fax: 248-435-1393
Web: www.arvinmeritor.com

CEO: Charles G. (Chip) McClure Jr.
CFO: Jeffrey A. (Jay) Craig
HR: Bill Fisher
FYE: September 30
Type: Public

Whether it's building axles or drum brakes for big rigs or buses, this company's products are meritorious. ArvinMeritor makes products such as axles, brakes, drivelines, suspension systems, and aftermarket transmissions for commercial truck, trailer, off-highway, construction, military, bus, and specialty vehicle manufacturers. It also makes door and roof systems for light vehicle makers. ArvinMeritor began divesting its light vehicle businesses in 2009 in order to focus on the more profitable commercial vehicle and industrial market segments. The global company gets about 60% of sales from outside the US.

	Annual Growth	9/05	9/06	9/07	9/08	9/09
Sales ($ mil.)	(17.6%)	8,903.0	9,195.0	6,449.0	7,167.0	4,108.0
Net income ($ mil.)	—	12.0	(175.0)	(219.0)	(101.0)	(1,212.0)
Market value ($ mil.)	(17.3%)	1,572.9	1,339.6	1,582.3	1,226.7	735.6
Employees	(17.9%)	29,000	27,500	18,000	19,800	13,200

ARYX THERAPEUTICS, INC.

NASDAQ (GM): ARYX

6300 Dumbarton Cir.
Fremont, CA 94555
Phone: 510-585-2200
Fax: 510-585-2202
Web: www.aryx.com

CEO: Paul Goddard
CFO: John Varian
HR: David Nagler
FYE: December 31
Type: Public

Retro is big these days, including in the drugmaking world. ARYx Therapeutics is developing drugs using its "RetroMetabolic Drug Design" technology, which takes old drugs and makes them better and safer. In particular, the technology improves the way certain drugs are metabolized in the liver, thus reducing unwanted side effects. ARYx's lead drug candidate, ATI-7505, uses the same active ingredient as Johnson & Johnson's gastrointestinal drug Propulsid; it was developing the rights for the drug with Procter & Gamble, but P&G pulled out of the deal in 2008. ARYx is also developing "retrometabolized" drugs using the common anticoagulant warfarin and amiodarone, a drug used to treat atrial fibrillation.

	Annual Growth	12/05	12/06	12/07	12/08	12/09
Sales ($ mil.)	—	—	4.7	4.2	19.7	0.0
Net income ($ mil.)	—	—	(27.3)	(27.6)	(31.2)	(33.2)
Market value ($ mil.)	(35.6%)	—	—	259.3	97.0	107.4
Employees	(7.2%)	—	70	68	75	56

AS AMERICA, INC.

1 Centennial Ave.
Piscataway, NJ 08855
Phone: 800-442-1902
Fax: —
Web: www.americanstandard-us.com

CEO: Donald C. Devine
CFO: —
HR: —
FYE: December 31
Type: Private

The flush heard around the world might be the one made by AS America. Doing business as American Standard Brands, the company is a leading manufacturer of bath and kitchen products, holding the top spot for toilets and the #2 position for bathroom fixtures in the US. It is also a leader in those categories in Canada, Mexico, and the Dominican Republic. Among other products it offers are faucets, sinks, bathtubs, bathroom furniture, and accessories. They are aimed at both the residential and commercial markets (products are found in homes, as well as airports, hotels, and stadiums) and are sold through a network of dealers, wholesale distributors, online retailers, and stores such as The Home Depot.

ASA INTERNATIONAL LTD.

Pink Sheets: ASAL

10 Speen St.
Framingham, MA 01701
Phone: 508-626-2727
Fax: 508-626-0645
Web: www.asaint.com

CEO: Alfred C. Angelone
CFO: Terrence C. McCarthy
HR: —
FYE: December 31
Type: Public

ASA International treads a path through a variety of industries. Through its operating divisions, the company provides software, systems, and services to tire dealers and retreaders, systems integrators, law firms, and manufacturing and distribution companies. ASA Tire Systems builds network systems for the tire and automotive aftermarket industries and operates online marketplace eTireLink. Khameleon Software provides e-business management tools for systems integrators. ASA's Rainmaker Software division develops accounting and practice management applications for law firms, and Verticent offers enterprise software for manufacturers and distributors.

ASAHI/AMERICA, INC.

35 Green St.
Malden, MA 02148
Phone: 781-321-5409
Fax: 781-321-4421
Web: www.asahi-america.com

CEO: Hidetoshi Hashimoto
CFO: Steven Harrington
HR: Barbara Johnson
FYE: March 31
Type: Subsidiary

Asahi/America has made it its mission in life to keep track of the ebb and flow. A subsidiary of Japan-based Asahi Organic Chemicals Industry, Asahi/America makes and distributes corrosion-resistant products for fluid and gas flow, such as thermoplastic valves, tubing and piping systems, filtration equipment, flow meters, and components used in mining, pulp and paper, chemical/petrochemical, water treatment, aquarium, and semiconductor manufacturing applications. Asahi/America's revenues come from the distribution of valves made by its parent company, pipe made by Asahi partner Austrian firm Alois-Gruber, and from the sale of its own products (flow meters, actuators, valve controls, filtration equipment).

⊞ ASARCO LLC

5285 E. Williams Cir., Ste. 2000
Tucson, AZ 85711
Phone: 520-798-7500
Fax: 520-798-7780
Web: www.asarco.com

CEO: Manuel E. Ramos
CFO: Oscar Gonzalez Barron
HR: Raul Blanco
FYE: December 31
Type: Subsidiary

A subsidiary of diversified mining firm Grupo México, ASARCO operates mining and copper smelting activities primarily in the southwestern US. Each year its mines produce around 400 million pounds of copper, as well as silver and gold as byproducts of the copper production. It also produces copper rod and billet. Those mines and smelting facilities are located in Arizona and Texas. The company exited Chapter 11 bankruptcy protection in late 2009 after four years. Its emergence came about through Grupo México's plan to retain control of the company. UK miner Vedanta had used its Indian subsidiary Sterlite Industries to try to buy ASARCO for $1.7 billion.

ASBURY AUTOMOTIVE GROUP, INC.

NYSE: ABG

2905 Premiere Pkwy., Ste. 300
Duluth, GA 30097
Phone: 770-418-8200
Fax: —
Web: www.asburyauto.com

CEO: Charles R. Oglesby
CFO: Craig T. Monaghan
HR: Kenneth E. Jackson
FYE: December 31
Type: Public

Asbury Automotive Group has made a living out of being large. The company oversees about 80 dealerships, which operate 110 auto franchises, in about 10 states, including California, Florida, and Texas. Its dealerships sell some three dozen US and foreign brands of new and used vehicles. Asbury dealerships also offer parts, service, and collision repair, as well as financing and insurance. In 2009 the company closed one Chrysler and two General Motors dealerships following the automakers' bankruptcy filings.

	Annual Growth	12/05	12/06	12/07	12/08	12/09
Sales ($ mil.)	(9.9%)	5,540.7	5,748.3	5,713.0	4,619.5	3,650.6
Net income ($ mil.)	(31.6%)	61.1	60.7	51.0	(338.0)	13.4
Market value ($ mil.)	(8.5%)	538.7	771.1	492.6	149.6	377.4
Employees	(6.9%)	8,800	8,300	8,300	7,300	6,600

ASCENDANT SOLUTIONS, INC.

Pink Sheets: ASDS

16250 Dallas Pkwy., Ste. 111
Dallas, TX 75248
Phone: 972-250-0945
Fax: 972-250-0934
Web: www.ascendantsolutions.com

CEO: David E. Bowe
CFO: Mark S. Heil
HR: —
FYE: December 31
Type: Public

Ascendant Solutions holds stakes in companies involved in health care, retailing, real estate, and other sectors. It seeks out opportunities among corporate divestitures, distressed or bankrupt firms, and entrepreneurs looking to sell their companies. Its investments include Dallas-based specialty pharmacy Dougherty's and CRESA Partners, which provides tenant representation and lease management services. Ascendant Solutions also owns stakes in Ampco Safety Tools and Dallas-area mixed-use real estate development firm Frisco Square. In 2008 Ascendant Solutions sold its stake in the Medicine Man chain of pharmacies to a subsidiary of Medicine Shoppe.

ASCENDENT TELECOMMUNICATIONS INC.

2000 Bridge Pkwy., Ste. 100
Redwood City, CA 94065
Phone: 818-325-2820
Fax: 650-620-4101
Web: www.ascendenttelecom.com

CEO: Deborah G. (Debbie) Miller
CFO: —
HR: —
FYE: December 31
Type: Subsidiary

Ascendent wants to scale the heights of communications convergence. The company, which does business as Ascendent Systems, develops and sells the Voice Mobility suite of applications that bridge the technical and functional gaps between mobile devices and traditional office desk phones. The platform links the range of voice technologies used by business callers — VoIP, Wi-Fi, cellular, and traditional PBX enterprise phone systems — and extends a common set of calling, conferencing, and messaging features to all devices. Clients have included Sprint Nextel and Verizon Wireless. Ascendent is a subsidiary of RIM, maker of the popular BlackBerry business and consumer wireless communications devices.

	Annual Growth	12/04	12/05	12/06	12/07	12/08
Est. sales ($ mil.)	—	—	—	—	—	0.2
Employees	—	—	—	—	—	3

⊞ ASCENSION HEALTH

4600 Edmundson Rd.
St. Louis, MO 63134
Phone: 314-733-8000
Fax: 314-733-8013
Web: www.ascensionhealth.org

CEO: Anthony R. (Tony) Tersigni
CFO: Anthony J. (Tony) Speranzo
HR: Phyllis Bruemer
FYE: June 30
Type: Not-for-profit

Ascension Health has ascended to the pinnacle of not-for-profit health care. As the largest Catholic hospital system in the US, and thus one of the top providers of charity care in the nation, the organization's health care network consists of some 70 general hospitals, along with a dozen long-term care, acute care, rehabilitation, and psychiatric hospitals. Ascension Health also operates nursing homes, community clinics, and other health care providers. Its network of medical facilities spans about 20 states and the District of Columbia. Ascension Health was created in 1999 from a union of the Daughters of Charity National Health System and the Sisters of St. Joseph Health System.

	Annual Growth	6/04	6/05	6/06	6/07	6/08
Sales ($ mil.)	7.6%	10,046.4	10,861.0	11,263.0	12,322.0	13,489.0
Employees	0.2%	106,000	107,000	106,000	106,000	107,000

⊞ ASCENT MEDIA CORPORATION   NASDAQ (GM): ASCMA

520 Broadway, 5th Fl.
Santa Monica, CA 90401
Phone: 310-434-7000
Fax: 310-434-7001
Web: www.ascentmediacorporation.com

CEO: William R. (Bill) Fitzgerald
CFO: George C. Platisa
HR: Sandy Roth
FYE: December 31
Type: Public

While Ascent Media may be no *American Beauty*, it has won its fair share of Oscars. An international provider of content production, management, and distribution services for the television and film industries, the company has brought home the gold about 15 times, winning Academy Awards for best sound and technical achievement. The company also offers commercial services. Clients include movie studios, independent producers, television broadcast networks, cable channels, and advertising agencies. In 2008 former parent Discovery Holding, controlled by Liberty Media chairman John Malone, spun off Ascent Media as a publicly traded company. Liberty Media now controls about 30% of Ascent Media.

	Annual Growth	12/05	12/06	12/07	12/08	12/09
Sales ($ mil.)	(12.3%)	—	—	589.4	600.6	453.7
Net income ($ mil.)	—	—	—	(132.3)	(64.6)	(52.9)
Market value ($ mil.)	16.9%	—	—	—	309.9	362.3
Employees	(6.5%)	—	—	—	3,100	2,900

ASCENT SOLAR TECHNOLOGIES, INC.   NASDAQ (CM): ASTI

12300 Grant St.
Thornton, CO 80241
Phone: 720-872-5000
Fax: 720-872-5077
Web: www.ascentsolar.com

CEO: Farhad Moghadam
CFO: Gary Gatchell
HR: —
FYE: December 31
Type: Public

As long as that sun keeps ascending in the eastern skies every day, there will be ventures trying to tap its enormous energy resources. Ascent Solar Technologies is a development-stage company working on photovoltaic modules for use in satellites and spacecraft. The firm aspires to make such gear smaller, lighter, and more flexible than existing solar cells for use in space by utilizing a thin-film absorbing layer on top of a polyimide substrate. The thin-film layer on top of the high-temperature plastic is made up of copper, indium, gallium, and selenium, which is why the technology is called CIGS. Norsk Hydro has a 35% stake in the company.

	Annual Growth	12/05	12/06	12/07	12/08	12/09
Sales ($ mil.)	22.5%	—	—	1.0	1.5	1.5
Net income ($ mil.)	—	—	—	(6.5)	(13.2)	(20.9)
Market value ($ mil.)	(53.8%)	—	—	663.8	100.4	141.5
Employees	77.3%	—	—	35	58	110

ASHFORD HOSPITALITY TRUST, INC.   NYSE: AHT

14185 Dallas Pkwy., Ste. 1100
Dallas, TX 75254
Phone: 972-490-9600
Fax: 972-980-2705
Web: www.ahtreit.com

CEO: Montgomery J. (Monty) Bennett
CFO: David J. Kimichik
HR: Donald J. (Don) Denzin
FYE: December 31
Type: Public

Ashford Hospitality is in with the inn crowd. A self-administered real estate investment trust (REIT), Ashford owns and has interests in more than 100 upscale hotels scattered across some two dozen states and Washington, DC; most operate under the Hilton, Hyatt, Marriott, and Sheraton nameplates. About 40 of Ashford's properties are managed by firms owned by company chairman Archie Bennett and his son, CEO Monty Bennett, with the rest overseen by other third-party management companies. In addition to making direct investments in hotels, the REIT also originates loans secured by hotel properties.

	Annual Growth	12/05	12/06	12/07	12/08	12/09
Sales ($ mil.)	28.8%	332.7	483.4	1,131.9	1,262.5	916.6
Net income ($ mil.)	—	9.4	37.8	30.2	129.2	(288.7)
Market value ($ mil.)	(18.4%)	552.2	655.3	378.5	60.5	244.2
Employees	13.1%	41	43	66	66	67

⊞ ASHLAND INC.   NYSE: ASH

50 E. RiverCenter Blvd.
Covington, KY 41011
Phone: 859-815-3333
Fax: 859-815-5053
Web: www.ashland.com

CEO: James J. (Jim) O'Brien Jr.
CFO: Lamar M. Chambers
HR: Susan B. Esler
FYE: September 30
Type: Public

Ashland's five business units are built on chemicals and cars. Ashland Distribution, which represents almost half of its business, buys chemicals and plastics and then blends and repackages them for distribution in Europe and North America. Ashland Performance Materials makes specialty resins, polymers, and adhesives. Ashland's Water Technologies unit provides chemical and non-chemical products for commercial, industrial, and municipal water treatment facilities. Consumer Markets, led by subsidiary Valvoline, runs an oil-change chain and markets Valvoline motor oil and Zerex antifreeze. Ashland Aqualon Functional Ingredients makes additives for the coatings, food, personal care, and pharmaceutical industries.

	Annual Growth	9/05	9/06	9/07	9/08	9/09
Sales ($ mil.)	(4.8%)	9,860.0	7,277.0	7,834.0	8,381.0	8,106.0
Net income ($ mil.)	(56.6%)	2,004.0	407.0	230.0	167.0	71.0
Market value ($ mil.)	(6.0%)	4,336.5	5,006.9	4,726.6	2,295.4	3,392.9
Employees	(8.4%)	20,900	11,700	11,700	11,900	14,700

ASHLEY FURNITURE INDUSTRIES, INC.

1 Ashley Way
Arcadia, WI 54612
Phone: 608-323-3377
Fax: 608-323-6008
Web: www.ashleyfurniture.com

CEO: Todd Wanek
CFO: Gino Mangione
HR: Jim Dotta
FYE: December 31
Type: Private

Not to be confused with Laura Ashley, this Ashley is more interested in peddling leather and wood than toile and chenille. Ashley Furniture Industries, one of the nation's largest furniture manufacturers, makes and imports upholstered furniture, as well as leather and hardwood pieces. The company licenses its name to more than 350 Ashley Furniture HomeStores located in the US, as well as Canada, Mexico, and Japan. These stores are independently owned and sell only Ashley Furniture-branded products. Founded by Carlyle Weinberger in 1945, Ashley Furniture is owned by father-and-son duos Ron and Todd Wanek and Chuck and Ben Vogel.

	Annual Growth	12/04	12/05	12/06	12/07	12/08
Est. sales ($ mil.)	10.7%	2,000.0	2,550.0	3,120.0	3,430.0	3,000.0
Employees	6.2%	11,000	13,400	14,600	17,000	14,000

ASI COMPUTER TECHNOLOGIES, INC.

48289 Fremont Blvd.
Fremont, CA 94538
Phone: 510-226-8000
Fax: 510-226-8858
Web: www.asipartner.com

CEO: Marcel Liang
CFO: Bill Chen
HR: Crystal Yuan
FYE: December 31
Type: Private

ASI Computer Technologies is a wholesale distributor of computer software, hardware, and accessories. It offers more than 8,000 products, including PCs, modems, monitors, networking equipment, and storage devices. ASI sells to more than 20,000 resellers throughout North America. The company's vendor partners include such companies as AMD, Intel, Microsoft, Samsung, and Western Digital. Its services include custom systems integration and contract assembly. The company also markets a line of computers and configures custom computer systems under its own Nspire brand. ASI was established in 1987 by Christine Liang, the company's president, who owns ASI.

	Annual Growth	12/04	12/05	12/06	12/07	12/08
Sales ($ mil.)	5.2%	1,060.0	1,110.0	1,110.0	1,300.0	1,300.0
Employees	12.5%	500	600	850	800	800

ASI TECHNOLOGY CORPORATION

OTC: ASIT

980 American Pacific Dr., Ste. 111
Henderson, NV 89014
Phone: 702-734-1888
Fax: 702-737-6900
Web: www.asiplasma.com

CEO: Jerry E. Polis
CFO: Eric M. Polis
HR: —
FYE: September 30
Type: Public

Despite the corporate name, ASI Technology specializes in loaning money for real estate development and for general corporate purposes. The widespread credit crisis has the company lending to less-than-creditworthy borrowers. In 2007 ASI started branching out into specialty finance, making loans to affiliates of Concordia Homes of Nevada, a residential builder in the Las Vegas area, and obtaining a mortgage banking license from the State of Nevada for its ASI Capital subsidiary. ASI Technology also is developing products based on plasma technologies, such as room-temperature ("cold") plasma decontamination and sterilization instruments.

	Annual Growth	9/05	9/06	9/07	9/08	9/09
Assets ($ mil.)	—	—	—	—	—	3.1
Net income ($ mil.)	—	—	—	—	—	(0.2)
Market value ($ mil.)	—	—	—	—	—	4.3
Employees	—	—	—	—	—	3

ASICS AMERICA CORPORATION

29 Parker, Ste. 100
Irvine, CA 92618
Phone: 949-453-8888
Fax: 949-453-0292
Web: www.asicsamerica.com

CEO: Nobuo Oda
CFO: —
HR: Eileen Schaaf
FYE: March 31
Type: Subsidiary

With ASICS America you don't have to *earn* your stripes, you just have to *purchase* them. ASICS America is the North American arm of Japanese athletic footwear, apparel, and accessories maker ASICS Corporation. Its shoe collection — featuring a trademarked stripe design — includes footwear for basketball, cheerleading, court and training, running, track and field, volleyball, walking, and wrestling. Its Budokan label represents one of its "sportstyle" products that targets a hip crowd. ASICS products, which were introduced in the US in 1977, are sold at regional and national retailers throughout the country, as well as through online vendors. In October 2009, ASICS opened its first freestanding store in the US.

☐ ASK.COM

555 12th St., Ste. 500
Oakland, CA 94607
Phone: 510-985-7400
Fax: 510-985-7412
Web: www.iacsearchandmedia.com

CEO: Scott B. Garell
CFO: Dominic Butera
HR: Angela Loeffler
FYE: December 31
Type: Subsidiary

Ask and you shall receive, especially when it comes to the Internet. Ask.com (formerly Ask Jeeves) operates a search engine that encourages users to pose their queries in the form of a question. In addition to its US site, the company operates sites for six European countries, as well as a Japanese site, through its Ask-Global operations. The business generates most revenue through ads, but also syndicates its search technology and offers paid search services. (Most of the paid listings displayed on its site are supplied by Google.) Ask.com is part of IAC/InterActiveCorp (IAC), which in 2008 split into five companies. As a result, Ask.com remains part of IAC, an entity now solely devoted to Internet properties.

ASPCA

424 E. 92nd St.
New York, NY 10128
Phone: 212-876-7700
Fax: —
Web: www.aspca.org

CEO: Edwin J. (Ed) Sayres
CFO: Linda Rosenblatt
HR: Lee J. Murray
FYE: December 31
Type: Not-for-profit

This group watches out for Fidos, Fluffies, and other furry friends all across the country. The ASPCA (American Society for the Prevention of Cruelty to Animals) is a not-for-profit organization dedicated to promoting the humane treatment of non-humans. The organization engages in education, public awareness, and government advocacy effort, and it supports the work of independent humane societies throughout the US. It provides medical services and animal placement from facilities in New York City. About two-thirds of the ASPCA's revenue comes from contributions, grants, and dues from more than 1 million members and donors. The organization was established in 1866 by Henry Bergh.

	Annual Growth	12/04	12/05	12/06	12/07	12/08
Est. sales ($ mil.)	—	—	—	—	—	70.0
Employees	—	—	—	—	—	350

ASPECT SOFTWARE, INC.

300 Apollo Dr.
Chelmsford, MA 01824
Phone: 978-250-7900
Fax: 978-244-7410
Web: www.aspect.com

CEO: James D. (Jim) Foy
CFO: Michael J. (Mike) Provenzano III
HR: —
FYE: December 31
Type: Private

Aspect Software isn't afraid of changing its look, especially if it leads to improved communications. The company provides call center software and equipment for handling customer service requests, optimizing workforces, and offering customer self-service functionality. Clients use its products to answer customer requests, log complaints, monitor workflows, and route communications. The company's systems integrate e-mail, fax, phone, wireless, and Web functions into a common channel through which customers can request and receive assistance. Aspect was formed when Aspect Communications and Concerto Software combined in a deal valued at about $1 billion.

ASPEN EXPLORATION CORPORATION

OTC: ASPN

2050 S. Oneida St., Ste. 208
Denver, CO 80224
Phone: 303-639-9860
Fax: 303-639-9863
Web: www.aspenexploration.com

CEO: R. V. Bailey
CFO: Kevan B. Hensman
HR: —
FYE: June 30
Type: Public

Aspen Exploration's original aspiration was to explore for and produce oil and gas in northern California and in Wyoming. In 2008 Aspen Exploration announced that because of high expenses and rising debt it was pursuing strategic alternatives in order to increase liquidity. Resolved on selling the company, in 2008 the company's leaders sold the exploration and production's oil and gas assets in the Sacramento Valley to Venoco for $14.3 million. In 2009 Aspen Exploration sold its remaining oil and gas interests (in the Poplar Field of Montana) for $1.2 million.

	Annual Growth	6/05	6/06	6/07	6/08	6/09
Sales ($ mil.)	—	4.1	5.9	4.4	5.4	0.0
Net income ($ mil.)	—	1.5	3.0	0.9	0.8	(2.1)
Market value ($ mil.)	(28.3%)	24.7	34.5	26.9	20.3	6.5
Employees	(9.6%)	3	3	3	3	2

ASPEN INSURANCE HOLDINGS LIMITED

NYSE: AHL

600 Atlantic Ave., Ste. 2100
Boston, MA 02210
Phone: 617-531-5100
Fax: 617-532-7314
Web: www.aspen.bm

CEO: Christopher (Chris) O'Kane
CFO: Richard Houghton
HR: Christopher J. (Chris) Woodman
FYE: December 31
Type: Public

Based in tax-sheltered Bermuda, Aspen Insurance Holdings is your guide down the slippery slopes of insurance. Through subsidiaries that include Aspen Re, Aspen Bermuda, and Aspen Specialty, the company provides property/casualty insurance, specialty insurance, and reinsurance to customers around the world. Its property/casualty reinsurance lines are offered in global markets, as are its specialty insurance products, which include marine, energy and liability, aviation, and specialty reinsurance. Aspen offers commercial property/casualty insurance primarily in the US and UK domestic markets.

	Annual Growth	12/05	12/06	12/07	12/08	12/09
Assets ($ mil.)	6.0%	6,537.8	6,640.1	7,201.3	7,288.8	8,257.2
Net income ($ mil.)	—	(177.8)	378.1	489.0	103.8	473.9
Market value ($ mil.)	1.8%	1,830.1	2,038.1	2,229.8	1,874.9	1,967.7
Employees	14.3%	360	444	490	550	614

ASPEN MARKETING SERVICES, INC.

1240 North Ave.
West Chicago, IL 60185
Phone: 630-293-9600
Fax: 630-293-7584
Web: www.aspenms.com

CEO: Patrick J. O'Rahilly
CFO: Don Danner
HR: Cathy Horn
FYE: December 31
Type: Private

As the largest privately held marketing firm in the US, Aspen Marketing Services provides integrated marketing services to clients such as Georgia-Pacific, General Motors, Omaha Steaks, and the American Cancer Society. The company blends strategic planning, public relations, and brand promotion, as well as event and direct marketing, to provide clients in a wide range of industries unified marketing for greater results. Its digital marketing capabilities utilize Web design, e-mail marketing, database processing, and online loyalty marketing services. Aspen was founded in 1986 and operates about 10 offices spanning the US. The company's growth has been attributed to a steady stream of acquisitions.

ASPEN PUBLISHERS, INC.

76 Ninth Ave, 7th Fl.
New York, NY 10011
Phone: 212-771-0600
Fax: 212-771-0885
Web: www.aspenpublishers.com

CEO: Stacey Caywood
CFO: Susan Yules
HR: —
FYE: December 31
Type: Subsidiary

Aspen Publishers provides mountains of legal research information to lawyers, business professionals, and law students. The company publishes manuals, books, periodicals, CDs, and online content, and specializes in legal, tax and business, health, and educational information. Aspen covers both US and international topics. Specific practice areas include administrative law, government contracts, intellectual property, and mergers and acquisitions. Among the company's titles are *Lawyer's Desk Book* and *Securities Act Handbook*. The company is a subsidiary of Wolters Kluwer Law & Business, itself a unit of European professional publisher Wolters Kluwer.

⊞ ASPEN TECHNOLOGY, INC.

NASDAQ (GS): AZPN

200 Wheeler Rd.
Burlington, MA 01803
Phone: 781-221-6400
Fax: 781-221-6410
Web: www.aspentec.com

CEO: Mark E. Fusco
CFO: Mark P. Sullivan
HR: Joanna Nikka
FYE: June 30
Type: Public

Aspen Technology (AspenTech) helps its customers scale mountains of supply chain and engineering challenges. The company provides supply chain management, plant operations, and engineering software for companies in the oil and gas, petrochemicals, and pharmaceuticals industries. Its software combines supplier collaboration, inventory management, and production planning functions to help manage the supply chain from start to finish. The company's engineering software offerings include collaborative engineering applications for manufacturing plant design and simulation. AspenTech sells directly and through systems integrators such as Accenture, Intergraph, Microsoft, and Schlumberger.

	Annual Growth	6/05	6/06	6/07	6/08	6/09
Sales ($ mil.)	3.7%	269.6	293.3	341.0	311.6	311.6
Net income ($ mil.)	—	(69.4)	18.3	45.5	24.9	52.9
Market value ($ mil.)	13.2%	479.3	1,209.2	1,290.3	1,225.8	786.2
Employees	(0.2%)	1,319	1,292	1,291	1,320	1,311

ASPENBIO PHARMA, INC.

NASDAQ (CM): APPY

1585 S. Perry St.
Castle Rock, CO 80104
Phone: 303-794-2000
Fax: 303-798-8332
Web: www.aspenbioinc.com

CEO: Stephen T. (Steve) Lundy
CFO: Jeffrey G. (Jeff) McGonegal
HR: —
FYE: December 31
Type: Public

Is Bessie "in the family way"? AspenBio Pharma wants to assist you in settling this all-important question. The company has animal reproductive drugs for cows and horses in development stages. Its product candidates include fertility enhancers, timed ovulation, and the reduction of pregnancy loss in cows. AspenBio Pharma doesn't just make products for animals. The company is also developing what it hopes will be the first blood test to diagnose appendicitis. It also makes purified proteins used in human diagnostics, as well as human hormones.

	Annual Growth	12/05	12/06	12/07	12/08	12/09
Sales ($ mil.)	(13.7%)	0.9	1.1	0.8	0.8	0.5
Net income ($ mil.)	—	(2.1)	(3.1)	(6.2)	(9.6)	(15.5)
Market value ($ mil.)	14.9%	40.1	118.2	349.5	247.3	69.7
Employees	37.7%	10	13	22	23	36

ASPLUNDH TREE EXPERT CO.

708 Blair Mill Rd.
Willow Grove, PA 19090
Phone: 215-784-4200
Fax: 215-784-4493
Web: www.asplundh.com

CEO: Christopher B. Asplundh
CFO: Joseph P. Dwyer
HR: Joseph (Joe) Lee
FYE: December 31
Type: Private

How much wood would a woodchuck chuck, if a woodchuck could chuck wood? A lot, if the woodchuck were named Asplundh. One of the world's leading tree-trimming businesses, Asplundh clears tree limbs from power lines for utilities and municipalities throughout the US and in Canada, Australia, and New Zealand. Asplundh also offers utility-related services such as line construction, meter reading, and pole maintenance; in addition, the company has branched out into fields such as billboard maintenance, traffic signal and highway lighting construction, and vegetation control for railroads and pipelines. The Asplundh family owns and manages the company, which was founded in 1928.

	Annual Growth	12/04	12/05	12/06	12/07	12/08
Sales ($ mil.)	5.5%	2,080.0	2,366.0	2,400.0	2,370.0	2,580.0
Employees	(0.9%)	28,638	24,000	28,831	28,606	27,589

ASPYRA, INC.

Pink Sheets: APYI

26115-A Mureau Rd.
Calabasas, CA 91302
Phone: 818-880-6700
Fax: 818-880-4398
Web: www.aspyra.com

CEO: Ademola (Ade) Lawal
CFO: Marina Varela
HR: —
FYE: December 31
Type: Public

Aspyra aspires to keep folks around the globe healthy. The company, a provider of clinical and diagnostic information solutions for the health care industry, specializes in enterprise-wide systems for hospitals, multi-specialty clinics, clinical laboratories, imaging departments and centers, orthopedic environments, and pharmacies. CEO Rodney Schutt resigned in 2009 after about a year in the job, quitting the company's board as well. COO Ademola Lawal was promoted to CEO to succeed Schutt. Aspyra was formed from the 2005 merger of Creative Computer Applications (CCA), a provider of clinical information systems, and StorCOMM, a provider of clinical image management systems.

	Annual Growth	12/04	12/05	12/06	12/07	*12/08
Sales ($ mil.)	37.2%	2.4	7.2	12.7	10.3	8.5
Net income ($ mil.)	—	(0.3)	(2.5)	(3.6)	(4.2)	(5.2)
Market value ($ mil.)	(53.1%)	60.5	43.9	31.3	30.1	2.9
Employees	1.1%	68	105	101	70	71

*Most recent year available

ASSA ABLOY DOOR GROUP, LLC

1502 12th St. NW
Mason City, IA 50401
Phone: 641-423-1334
Fax: 641-424-8305
Web: www.curries.com

CEO: Larry Denbrock
CFO: —
HR: Mark Evers
FYE: December 31
Type: Business segment

ASSA ABLOY Door Group doesn't keep things under lock and key like its lock maker parent ASSA ABLOY. The subsidiary makes, sells, and distributes metal doors and frames for commercial, industrial, and institutional construction. Products include steel doors and frames, as well as hardware, such as bolts, hinges, locks, and exit devices. US subsidiaries include Ceco Door Products and Curries; in Canada the company operates through Fleming Steel Doors & Frames. ASSA ABLOY Door Group began as a joint venture between Sweden's ASSA ABLOY and SPX Corporation in 2001. In 2003 ASSA ABLOY acquired SPX's interest for $80 million and rebranded the enterprise.

ASSA, INC.

110 Sargent Dr.
New Haven, CT 06511
Phone: 203-603-5959
Fax: 203-603-5953
Web: www.assalock.com

CEO: Thanasis Molokotos
CFO: Jeffrey Mereschuk
HR: —
FYE: December 31
Type: Subsidiary

ASSA, Inc., has a secure future. The company, a subsidiary of Swedish lock maker group ASSA ABLOY, makes a range of high-security products for institutional and residential uses. It manufactures cylinder locks, padlocks, deadbolts, and high-security auxiliary locks. The company's newly developed CLIQ lock system combines mechanical and electronic elements. ASSA is one of the largest suppliers of high-security lock cylinders to the institutional/government market in North America. Customers of ASSA have included Boeing, the Baltimore Ravens' stadium, and the US Supreme Court.

	Annual Growth	12/04	12/05	12/06	12/07	12/08
Est. sales ($ mil.)	—	—	—	—	—	950.0
Employees	—	—	—	—	—	7,524

ASSET ACCEPTANCE CAPITAL CORP.

NASDAQ (GS): AACC

28405 Van Dyke Ave.
Warren, MI 48093
Phone: 586-939-9600
Fax: 586-446-7837
Web: www.assetacceptance.com

CEO: Rion B. Needs
CFO: Reid E. Simpson
HR: Deanna S. Hatmaker
FYE: December 31
Type: Public

Asset Acceptance Capital tries to help creditors accept the things they cannot change and to have the courage to pay off the debt they can. The company buys portfolios of written-off consumer debt (credit cards, consumer loans, utilities) at a deep discount, then attempts to collect on them. About half of the value of its portfolio is made up of Visa, MasterCard, and Discover card receivables. Asset Acceptance Capital focuses on debt in the primary, secondary, and tertiary markets, which means between one and three collection agencies have already had a go at them; these portfolios are often the cheapest to acquire but are the hardest to collect on. Tertiary accounts make up about half of its portfolio.

	Annual Growth	12/05	12/06	12/07	12/08	12/09
Sales ($ mil.)	(9.1%)	252.7	254.9	248.0	234.2	172.5
Net income ($ mil.)	—	51.3	45.5	20.4	15.7	(16.4)
Market value ($ mil.)	(25.9%)	687.4	514.8	318.6	156.4	207.5
Employees	(2.9%)	1,980	1,708	1,639	1,651	1,758

🏠 ASSISTED LIVING CONCEPTS, INC.

NYSE: ALC

W140 N8981 Lilly Rd.
Menomonee Falls, WI 53051
Phone: 262-257-8888
Fax: —
Web: www.alcco.com

CEO: Laurie A. Bebo
CFO: John Buono
HR: —
FYE: December 31
Type: Public

Assisted Living Concepts (ALC) helps its residents live large. The company runs about 220 assisted living centers in some 20 states in the US. Its facilities have a total of over 9,000 dwelling units that provide full-time housing for aging adults. ALC's communities enable residents to maintain fairly independent lifestyles but provide assistance with activities such as eating, bathing, medication management, and laundry. The facilities also offer social activities, arts and crafts, and the like. The Jodrey family, of which chairman David Hennigar is a member, controls 53% of the company's voting shares through Scotia Investments.

	Annual Growth	12/05	12/06	12/07	12/08	12/09
Sales ($ mil.)	2.8%	204.9	231.1	229.3	234.1	228.7
Net income ($ mil.)	—	12.3	9.0	17.2	14.3	(0.2)
Market value ($ mil.)	(18.9%)	—	572.5	434.1	240.2	305.3
Employees	(1.2%)	4,300	4,600	4,400	4,650	4,100

ASSOCIATED BANC-CORP

NASDAQ (GS): ASBC

1200 Hansen Rd.
Green Bay, WI 54304
Phone: 920-491-7000
Fax: 920-491-7090
Web: www.associatedbank.com

CEO: Philip B. (Phil) Flynn
CFO: Joseph B. (Joe) Selner
HR: Judith M. Docter
FYE: December 31
Type: Public

A lot of Midwesterners are associated with Associated Banc-Corp, the holding company for Associated Bank. The bank operates approximately 300 branches in communities in Illinois, Minnesota, and Wisconsin. Catering to consumers and local businesses, it offers deposit accounts, loans, mortgage banking, credit and debit cards, and leasing. The bank's wealth management division offers investments, trust services, brokerage, insurance, and employee group benefits plans. Commercial loans, including agricultural, construction, and real estate loans, make up more than 60% of bank's loan portfolio, which also includes residential mortgages, consumer loans, and home equity loans.

	Annual Growth	12/05	12/06	12/07	12/08	12/09
Assets ($ mil.)	0.9%	22,100.1	20,861.4	21,592.1	24,192.1	22,874.1
Net income ($ mil.)	—	320.2	316.6	285.8	168.5	(131.9)
Market value ($ mil.)	(23.7%)	5,628.5	6,031.4	4,684.4	3,619.2	1,903.8
Employees	(1.8%)	5,146	5,101	5,110	5,140	4,784

ASSOCIATED ESTATES REALTY CORPORATION

NYSE: AEC

1 AEC Pkwy.
Richmond Heights, OH 44143
Phone: 216-261-5000
Fax: 216-289-9600
Web: www.associatedestates.com

CEO: Jeffrey I. Friedman
CFO: Lou Fatica
HR: Daniel E. Gold
FYE: December 31
Type: Public

A self-administered real estate investment trust (REIT), Associated Estates Realty acquires, develops, and operates multifamily apartment properties in nearly 10 states. Ohio and Michigan, where more than half its assets are located, represent its largest markets. The REIT's portfolio consists of about 50 apartment communities (containing more than 12,000 units) that it either wholly owns or manages for third parties through subsidiary MIG Realty Advisors. Associated Estates' portfolio also includes properties under development and land; another subsidiary, Merit Enterprises, performs general contracting and construction management services.

	Annual Growth	12/05	12/06	12/07	12/08	12/09
Sales ($ mil.)	(3.5%)	150.4	145.8	151.4	134.9	130.4
Net income ($ mil.)	(35.4%)	36.2	27.0	10.2	34.6	6.3
Market value ($ mil.)	5.7%	202.0	307.1	211.0	204.0	251.9
Employees	(16.1%)	728	650	448	380	360

ASSOCIATED FOOD STORES, INC.

1850 W. 2100 South
Salt Lake City, UT 84119
Phone: 801-978-8697
Fax: 801-974-0484
Web: www.afstores.com

CEO: Richard A. (Rich) Parkinson
CFO: Robert (Bob) Obray
HR: —
FYE: March 31
Type: Cooperative

This business makes sure there's plenty of grub for the Wild West. Associated Food Stores is a leading regional cooperative wholesale distributor that supplies groceries and other products to more than 500 independent supermarkets in about eight Western states. It also offers support services for its member-owners, including market research, real estate analysis, store design, technology procurement, and training. In addition, Associated Food Stores owns a stake in Western Family Foods, a grocery wholesalers' partnership that produces Western Family private-label goods. The co-op was formed in 1940 by Donald Lloyd, then president of the Utah Retail Grocers Association, and 34 other retailers.

	Annual Growth	3/04	3/05	3/06	3/07	3/08
Est. sales ($ mil.)	—	—	—	—	—	1,632.1
Employees	—	—	—	—	—	2,000

ASSOCIATED GROCERS OF NEW ENGLAND, INC.

11 Cooperative Way
Pembroke, NH 03275
Phone: 603-223-6710
Fax: —
Web: www.agne.com

CEO: Michael C. (Mike) Bourgoine
CFO: Steven N. (Steve) Murphy
HR: Hope Kelly
FYE: March 31
Type: Cooperative

Associated Grocers of New England (AGNE) is a leading wholesale grocery distributor serving about 500 independent grocers and convenience stores in half a dozen New England states. It supplies customers with bakery goods, fresh produce, and meat, as well as general grocery items and other merchandise. AGNE also offers such retail support services as advertising, marketing, and merchandising. In addition, it operates a small number of stores under the banners Harvest Market and Vista Foods. The cooperative was formed as New Hampshire Wholesale Grocers in 1946.

	Annual Growth	3/04	3/05	3/06	3/07	3/08
Est. sales ($ mil.)	—	—	—	—	—	315.8
Employees	—	—	—	—	—	600

ASSOCIATED MATERIALS, LLC

3773 State Rd.
Cuyahoga Falls, OH 44223
Phone: 330-929-1811
Fax: 330-922-2354
Web: www.associatedmaterials.com

CEO: Thomas N. (Tom) Chieffe
CFO: Stephen E. Graham
HR: John F. Haumesser
FYE: December 31
Type: Private

Vinyl has never gone out of style at Associated Materials (AM). The company makes and distributes vinyl siding and windows, as well as aluminum and steel siding, aluminum trim coil, and accessories. Products are marketed under the brand names of Alside, Gentek, and Revere. They are sold through about 125 supply centers and 250 independent distributors in the US and Canada. (AM generates about 70% of its sales through its supply stores.) Its top customers include contractors, remodelers, and architects. The retailer also makes UltraGuard-branded vinyl fencing and railing. AM is indirectly owned by AMH Holdings, which is controlled by Investcorp and Harvest Partners.

	Annual Growth	12/04	12/05	12/06	12/07	12/08
Sales ($ mil.)	0.9%	1,094.0	1,173.6	1,250.1	1,204.1	1,134.0
Net income ($ mil.)	—	(10.9)	22.4	33.3	39.7	21.2
Employees	(2.8%)	3,137	3,872	5,009	3,625	2,800

⊞ ASSOCIATED MILK PRODUCERS INC.

315 N. Broadway
New Ulm, MN 56073
Phone: 507-354-8295
Fax: 507-359-8651
Web: www.ampi.com

CEO: Ed Welch
CFO: —
HR: Geoff Davies
FYE: December 31
Type: Cooperative

Associated Milk Producers Inc. (AMPI) might wear a cheesy grin, but it churns up solid sales. The dairy cooperative transforms some 6 billion pounds of milk into butter, cheese, fluid milk, and other dairy products each and every year. A regional co-op with some 3,600 member/farmers from Iowa, Minnesota, Nebraska, North and South Dakota, and Wisconsin, AMPI operates 15 manufacturing plants. In addition to its State Brand and Cass-Clay brand, Associated Milk Producers also makes private-label products for food retailers, fast-food restaurants (including McDonald's), and other foodservice operators. It also makes dairy ingredients for food manufacturers.

⊞ An in-depth profile of this company is available to Hoover's Online members at hoovers.com.

179

THE ASSOCIATED PRESS

450 W. 33rd St.	CEO: Thomas (Tom) Curley
New York, NY 10001	CFO: —
Phone: 212-621-1500	HR: —
Fax: 212-621-5447	FYE: December 31
Web: www.ap.org	Type: Cooperative

This just in: The Associated Press (AP) is reporting tonight and every night wherever news is breaking. AP is one of the world's largest news gathering organizations, with about 240 news bureaus in nearly 100 countries. It provides news, photos, graphics, and audiovisual services that reach people daily through print, radio, television, and the Web. In addition to traditional news services, it operates international television news service APTN (AP Television News), photo archives, and an interactive news service (AP Digital). It also offers advertising management and distribution services. The not-for-profit cooperative is owned by 1,500 US daily newspaper members.

	Annual Growth	12/04	12/05	12/06	12/07	12/08
Est. sales ($ mil.)	—	—	—	—	—	747.7
Employees	—	—	—	—	—	3,533

ASSOCIATED WHOLESALE GROCERS, INC.

5000 Kansas Ave.	CEO: Jerry Garland
Kansas City, KS 66106	CFO: Robert C. (Bob) Walker
Phone: 913-288-1000	HR: Frank Tricamo
Fax: 913-288-1587	FYE: December 31
Web: www.awginc.com	Type: Cooperative

Associated Wholesale Grocers (AWG) knows its customers can't live on bread and milk alone. The second-largest retailer-owned cooperative in the US (behind Wakefern Food Corporation), AWG supplies more than 2,500 member-stores in about 25 states with a wide array of grocery items from its eight distribution facilities. In addition to its wholesale operation, AWG offers a variety of business services to its members, including marketing and merchandising programs, insurance, and store design. It also operates about 10 grocery store brands, including Country Mart and Homeland, and it owns a small number of supermarkets. AWG was founded by a group of independent grocers in 1924.

	Annual Growth	12/04	12/05	12/06	12/07	12/08
Sales ($ mil.)	10.8%	4,570.0	5,000.0	5,000.0	5,700.0	6,900.0
Employees	—	—	—	—	—	—

ASSOCIATED WHOLESALERS, INC.

Route 422	CEO: J. Christopher (Chris) Michael
Robesonia, PA 19551	CFO: Thomas C. Teeter
Phone: 610-693-3161	HR: Audrey Schein
Fax: 610-693-3171	FYE: July 31
Web: www.awiweb.com	Type: Cooperative

Grocery stores can profit from an association with this business. Associated Wholesalers is a retailer-owned cooperative that supplies an array of food and non-food products to independent grocers and convenience stores along the eastern seaboard. From distribution centers in Pennsylvania and New Jersey, it offers broadline grocery products, bakery goods, meat and dairy items, fresh produce, and frozen foods, as well as a full line of general merchandise products. The company's White Rose Foods unit serves supermarkets and grocers in the New York City area, New Jersey, and throughout New England. Associated Wholesalers also operates about 15 supermarkets, mostly under the Shurfine Markets banner.

	Annual Growth	7/04	7/05	7/06	7/07	7/08
Est. sales ($ mil.)	—	—	—	—	—	1,100.0
Employees	—	—	—	—	—	2,100

ASSURANCEAMERICA CORPORATION   OTC: ASAM

5500 Interstate N. Pkwy., Ste. 600	CEO: Guy W. Millner
Atlanta, GA 30328	CFO: John M. Mongelli
Phone: 770-952-0200	HR: —
Fax: 770-952-0258	FYE: December 31
Web: www.assuranceamerica.com	Type: Public

AssuranceAmerica will assure you that they meant to leave out the space between its names. Through its three operating subsidiaries the company writes and markets nonstandard (high-risk) auto insurance to customers in the Southeast. Its AssuranceAmerica Insurance subsidiary writes the policies, while its Managing General Agency markets the products and provides services through a network of 1,800 independent agencies. Its TrustWay Insurance Agencies operates retail agencies in Florida, Alabama, and Georgia, which sell nonstandard auto insurance underwritten by AssuranceAmerica and other unaffiliated carriers. Chairman and CEO Guy Millner controls nearly half of the company.

	Annual Growth	12/05	12/06	12/07	12/08	12/09
Assets ($ mil.)	19.6%	69.0	95.7	125.3	131.5	141.1
Net income ($ mil.)	(31.3%)	1.8	4.3	0.3	(3.2)	0.4
Market value ($ mil.)	(20.9%)	57.0	54.4	41.3	19.6	22.3
Employees	4.4%	221	268	282	257	263

ASSURANT, INC.   NYSE: AIZ

1 Chase Manhattan Plaza, 41st Fl.	CEO: Robert B. (Rob) Pollock
New York, NY 10005	CFO: Michael J. (Mike) Peninger
Phone: 212-859-7000	HR: Sylvia R. Wagner
Fax: 212-859-7010	FYE: December 31
Web: www.assurant.com	Type: Public

From credit cards to trailer parks, Assurant provides a range of specialty insurance products. Through Assurant Solutions and Assurant Specialty Property, the company offers such products as credit protection insurance, manufactured home coverage, creditor-placed homeowners insurance, pre-need funeral policies, and extended warranties for electronics, appliances, and vehicles. Individuals and small employer groups can choose from several types of health coverage offered by Assurant Health, while group life, dental, and disability products are available through the Assurant Employee Benefits segment. Assurant's products are distributed through sales offices and independent agents across the US and abroad.

	Annual Growth	12/05	12/06	12/07	12/08	12/09
Assets ($ mil.)	0.5%	25,365.5	25,165.1	26,750.3	24,514.6	25,841.8
Net income ($ mil.)	(2.6%)	479.4	715.9	653.7	447.8	430.6
Market value ($ mil.)	(9.3%)	4,863.3	6,178.4	7,481.2	3,354.8	3,296.6
Employees	5.7%	12,000	13,400	14,000	15,000	15,000

ASSURED GUARANTY LTD.   NYSE: AGO

30 Woodbourne Ave., 5th Fl.	CEO: Dominic J. Frederico
Hamilton, HM 08, Bermuda	CFO: Robert B. Mills
Phone: 441-279-5700	HR: —
Fax: 441-279-5701	FYE: December 31
Web: www.assuredguaranty.com	Type: Public

Assured Guaranty brings additional certainty to the not-too-risky world of public finance. The Bermuda-based holding company provides financial guaranty insurance and reinsurance, as well as mortgage guaranty coverage, through its operating subsidiaries. Products include guaranties for municipal finance, structured finance, and corporate bonds. Subsidiary Assured Guaranty Corp. is licensed in 49 US states, plus the District of Columbia and Puerto Rico; Assured Guaranty (UK) writes insurance in the UK and other European markets. The company provides financial guaranty reinsurance through Assured Guaranty Re.

	Annual Growth	12/05	12/06	12/07	12/08	12/09
Assets ($ mil.)	57.8%	2,676.5	2,935.3	3,800.4	4,555.7	16,593.4
Net income ($ mil.)	(15.2%)	188.4	159.7	(303.3)	68.9	97.2
Market value ($ mil.)	(3.8%)	4,680.9	4,904.0	4,892.9	2,101.7	4,011.7
Employees	29.1%	126	135	147	160	350

ASTA FUNDING, INC.

NASDAQ (GS): ASFI

210 Sylvan Ave.
Englewood Cliffs, NJ 07632
Phone: 201-567-5648
Fax: 201-569-4595
Web: www.astafunding.com

CEO: Gary Stern
CFO: Robert J. Michel
HR: —
FYE: September 30
Type: Public

Say *Hasta luego* to unpaid receivables. Asta Funding buys, sells, services, and collects unpaid credit card debts and consumer loans. The company buys delinquent accounts at a discount directly from the credit grantors, as well as indirectly through auctions and brokers. It buys credit card charge-offs from Visa, MasterCard, private-label issuers, and banks, in addition to telecom and other industry charge-offs. The company then collects on its debt balances either internally or through an outsourced agency. Asta Funding also invests in semi-performing and non-delinquent receivables. Subsidiary VATIV Recovery Solutions, acquired in 2006, services bankrupt and deceased accounts.

	Annual Growth	9/05	9/06	9/07	9/08	9/09
Sales ($ mil.)	0.3%	69.5	102.0	140.8	115.6	70.4
Net income ($ mil.)	—	31.0	45.8	52.3	8.8	(90.7)
Market value ($ mil.)	(29.4%)	443.2	547.3	559.4	102.3	110.4
Employees	(5.4%)	131	166	172	158	105

ASTEA INTERNATIONAL INC.

NASDAQ (CM): ATEA

240 Gibraltar Rd.
Horsham, PA 19044
Phone: 215-682-2500
Fax: 215-682-2515
Web: www.astea.com

CEO: Zack B. Bergreen
CFO: Frederic (Rick) Etskovitz
HR: Jan Schubert
FYE: December 31
Type: Public

Astea International aspires to serve a wide field of customers. The company's customer relationship management (CRM) software is used to automate sales and service processes, manage contracts and warranties, and distribute information to employees, customers, and suppliers. Astea's customers (primarily professional services firms or organizations that sell and service equipment) come from a variety of industries, including health care, medical devices, controls and instrumentation, information technology, facilities management, and telecommunications. The company also offers services such as consulting, implementation, and maintenance. Founder and CEO Zack Bergreen owns about 45% of Astea.

	Annual Growth	12/05	12/06	12/07	12/08	12/09
Sales ($ mil.)	(3.1%)	22.8	20.3	30.4	23.9	20.1
Net income ($ mil.)	—	1.8	(5.0)	2.8	(3.1)	(0.9)
Market value ($ mil.)	(30.3%)	50.4	24.0	20.1	7.3	11.9
Employees	(5.1%)	195	193	185	158	158

ASTEC INDUSTRIES, INC.

NASDAQ (GS): ASTE

1725 Shepherd Rd.
Chattanooga, TN 37421
Phone: 423-899-5898
Fax: 423-899-4456
Web: www.astecindustries.com

CEO: J. Don Brock
CFO: Fred McKamy Hall
HR: —
FYE: December 31
Type: Public

"On the Road Again" isn't just a Willie Nelson song to Astec Industries, it's a way of life. The company, and its 14 manufacturing subsidiaries, makes equipment for every phase of road building, utility, and other construction projects. Its products include aggregate crushers, pavers, and portable hot-mix asphalt plants. Its auger-boring, impact-crusher, trenching, directional-drilling, and heat-transfer equipment is used in the construction, demolition, mining, recycling, and oil and gas industries. Founded in 1972, Astec also sells replacement parts. Customers are both government and private clients, including asphalt road paving contractors, utility and pipeline contractors, and mine and quarry operators.

	Annual Growth	12/05	12/06	12/07	12/08	12/09
Sales ($ mil.)	4.6%	616.1	710.6	869.0	973.7	738.1
Net income ($ mil.)	(42.4%)	28.1	39.6	56.8	63.1	3.1
Market value ($ mil.)	(4.7%)	738.2	793.3	840.5	708.1	608.9
Employees	6.2%	826	875	991	1,135	1,051

ASTELLAS PHARMA US, INC.

3 Pkwy. North
Deerfield, IL 60015
Phone: 847-317-8800
Fax: —
Web: www.astellas.us

CEO: Seigo Kashii
CFO: Steve Knowles
HR: Collette Taylor
FYE: March 31
Type: Subsidiary

Astellas Pharma US pilots pharma efforts that are outta this world. The company conducts research, development, and marketing efforts focused on the following therapeutic areas: cardiology, dermatology, immunology, infectious diseases, neurology, and urology. The company's primary products include transplant rejection therapy Prograf, overactive bladder treatment VESIcare, and vascular dilator Andenoscan, as well as antifungals Mycamine and AmBisome and enlarged prostate treatment Flomax. Astellas Pharma US, which is a subsidiary of Japan-based pharmaceutical firm Astellas Pharma, uses a direct sales force to market its products to consumers and health professionals in the US market.

ASTELLAS VENTURE MANAGEMENT LLC

2882 Sand Hill Rd., Ste. 121
Menlo Park, CA 94025
Phone: 650-926-0731
Fax: 650-926-0740
Web: www.astellasventure.com

CEO: Yoshitaka Yoneyama
CFO: Kazumasa Saito
HR: —
FYE: March 31
Type: Subsidiary

If you want your company to grow big, you've got to shoot for the stars. Astellas Venture Management invests in seed-stage and emerging biotech companies, including drug discovery and development companies. The firm manages four venture funds and its portfolio includes more than 20 companies. Astellas Venture Management is the venture capital arm of Astellas Pharma, formed from the 2005 merger of Yamanouchi Pharmaceutical and Fujisawa Pharmaceutical. It provides its portfolio companies not only with cash, but also access to the scientific expertise, production facilities, and marketing clout of its parent firm.

ASTENJOHNSON INC.

4399 Corporate Rd.
Charleston, SC 29405
Phone: 843-747-7800
Fax: 843-747-3856
Web: www.astenjohnson.com

CEO: Dan Cappell
CFO: —
HR: —
FYE: December 31
Type: Private

Formed through the 1999 merger of two venerable paper machine clothing makers with European origins, AstenJohnson makes specialty textiles (paper machine clothing, specialty fabrics, and filaments) for the printing and papermaking industries. The company also produces monofilaments used in making paper machine clothing, and specialty fabrics for pulp mills and manufacturers in non-paper industries. It also makes specialty drainage equipment for paper machines. AstenJohnson operates about a dozen manufacturing plants in Asia, Europe, and North America, and sells its products to end users worldwide.

ASTORIA FINANCIAL CORPORATION

NYSE: AF

1 Astoria Federal Plaza
Lake Success, NY 11042
Phone: 516-327-3000
Fax: 516-327-7461
Web: www.astoriafederal.com

CEO: George L. Engelke Jr.
CFO: Frank E. Fusco
HR: Arnold K. Greenberg
FYE: December 31
Type: Public

Astoria Financial is the holding company for Astoria Federal Savings and Loan, one of the largest thrifts in the US. The bank has more than 80 branches in and around New York City (Brooklyn, Queens, Nassau, Suffolk, and Westchester counties), as well as a network of third-party mortgage brokers spanning more than a dozen states and Washington, DC. It offers standard deposit products such as CDs and checking, savings, and retirement accounts. With these funds, Astoria Federal primarily writes loans and invests in mortgage-backed securities. Subsidiary AF Insurance Agency sells life and property/casualty coverage to Astoria Federal customers.

	Annual Growth	12/05	12/06	12/07	12/08	12/09
Assets ($ mil.)	(2.5%)	22,380.3	21,554.5	21,719.4	21,982.1	20,252.2
Net income ($ mil.)	(41.3%)	233.8	174.9	124.8	75.3	27.7
Market value ($ mil.)	(19.4%)	2,878.1	2,952.5	2,278.0	1,613.3	1,216.8
Employees	(1.0%)	1,770	1,626	1,735	1,685	1,699

ASTRA TECH INC.

890 Winter St., Ste. 310
Waltham, MA 02451
Phone: 781-890-6800
Fax: 781-890-6808
Web: www.astratechusa.com

CEO: Scott A. Root
CFO: Jim Bailey
HR: Steven Cyr
FYE: December 31
Type: Subsidiary

Astra Tech makes products for two very different, yet equally important, parts of the body. The company manufactures medical devices for the fields of dentistry and urology. Its Astra Tech Dental Implants are titanium screws used to secure crowns, bridges, and dentures. Astra Tech also makes a line of catheters and catheter systems; its LoFric product is a hydrophilic urinary catheter for the intermittent emptying of the bladder. The company acquired Atlantis Components in 2007 to gain its dental abutment technology. Astra Tech's Swedish parent Astra Tech AB is a direct subsidiary of drug maker AstraZeneca.

	Annual Growth	12/04	12/05	12/06	12/07	12/08
Est. sales ($ mil.)	—	—	—	—	—	50.0
Employees	—	—	—	—	—	300

ASTRAZENECA PHARMACEUTICALS LP

1800 Concord Pike
Wilmington, DE 19850
Phone: 302-886-3000
Fax: 302-886-2972
Web: www.astrazeneca-us.com

CEO: Rich Fante
CFO: Graham Baker
HR: Marta Brito Pérez
FYE: December 31
Type: Subsidiary

Whether you've got heartburn or high cholesterol from your addiction to chili cheese dogs, AstraZeneca Pharmaceuticals (which does business as AstraZeneca US) can help. The company, a subsidiary of global drugmaker AstraZeneca, is one of the largest pharma companies in the US. Its sales represent about 5% of all the drugs sold in the US and about 40% of its parent company's revenues. AstraZeneca US' treatments focus on several therapeutic areas: cardiovascular and metabolic, gastrointestinal, neuroscience, oncology, respiratory, and infection. Its best-known products include Nexium (acid reflux), Seroquel (antipsychotic), Crestor (high cholesterol), Pulmicort (asthma), and Arimidex (breast cancer treatment).

	Annual Growth	12/04	12/05	12/06	12/07	12/08
Est. sales ($ mil.)	—	—	—	—	—	13.4
Employees	—	—	—	—	—	11,000

ASTRO-MED, INC.

NASDAQ (GM): ALOT

600 E. Greenwich Ave.
West Warwick, RI 02893
Phone: 401-828-4000
Fax: 401-822-2430
Web: www.astro-medinc.com

CEO: Albert W. Ondis
CFO: Joseph P. O'Connell
HR: Marcia Ryter
FYE: January 31
Type: Public

Astro-Med holds a high-tech trident. The company operates three divisions: QuickLabel Systems, Test & Measurement, and Grass-Telefactor. Astro-Med's QuickLabel Systems division makes digital color label printers, bar code printers, automatic labelers, and printer consumables. Its Test & Measurement division makes products that record and monitor data for customers in the aerospace, automotive, power, and telecommunications industries. The company's Grass-Telefactor Group makes EEG equipment, instruments for monitoring such conditions as epilepsy and sleep disorders, and biomedical research supplies. The company generates 30% of its sales outside the US.

	Annual Growth	1/06	1/07	1/08	1/09	1/10
Sales ($ mil.)	1.9%	59.3	65.5	72.4	71.8	64.0
Net income ($ mil.)	1.9%	2.6	6.1	4.3	3.0	2.8
Market value ($ mil.)	(3.1%)	60.1	76.0	70.7	51.0	52.9
Employees	3.2%	375	400	396	400	425

ASTRONAUTICS CORPORATION OF AMERICA

4115 N. Teutonia Ave.
Milwaukee, WI 53209
Phone: 414-449-4000
Fax: 414-447-8231
Web: www.astronautics.com

CEO: Ronald E. Zelazo
CFO: Steven Givant
HR: —
FYE: May 31
Type: Private

Sometimes it's hard to know which way is up, but Astronautics gives good directions. The company makes, maintains, and repairs electronic components and systems that enable pilots of planes, ships, autos, or spacecraft to orient them in time and space. Its lineup runs from integrated avionics, navigation, and network server systems to electronic flight bags and instruments, mission and display processors, and inertial navigation systems. Over 150,000 aircraft rely on the hardware, including ones used by the US Department of Defense, NASA-Langley, Boeing, UPS, and Continental. Founded by Nathaniel Zelazo and his sister Norma Paige, the privately held company is led by Nathaniel's son Dr. Ronald Zelazo.

	Annual Growth	5/04	5/05	5/06	5/07	5/08
Est. sales ($ mil.)	—	—	—	—	—	235.7
Employees	—	—	—	—	—	1,850

⊞ ASTRONICS CORPORATION

NASDAQ (GM): ATRO

130 Commerce Way
East Aurora, NY 14052
Phone: 716-805-1599
Fax: 716-805-1286
Web: www.astronics.com

CEO: Peter J. Gundermann
CFO: David C. Burney
HR: Jill Draper
FYE: December 31
Type: Public

Is it a UFO? Is it a shooting star? No, it's Astronics! Astronics Corporation makes external and internal lighting systems, as well as power generation and distribution technology, for commercial, general aviation, and military defense aircraft. Products include cabin emergency lighting systems (escape path markers and exit locators), cockpit lighting systems (avionics keyboards, ambient light sensors, annunciator panels, and electronic dimmers), and formation lighting systems (external lights). Astronics operates three wholly owned subsidiaries including Astronics Advanced Electronic Systems Corp. (AES), Astronics Luminescent Systems Inc. (LSI), and Astronics DME Corporation (DME).

	Annual Growth	12/05	12/06	12/07	12/08	12/09
Sales ($ mil.)	26.2%	75.4	110.8	158.2	173.7	191.2
Net income ($ mil.)	—	2.7	5.7	15.4	8.4	(3.8)
Market value ($ mil.)	(5.6%)	116.1	185.1	459.2	96.2	92.4
Employees	10.3%	700	787	967	989	1,035

ASTROTECH CORPORATION

NASDAQ (CM): ASTC

907 Gemini St.
Houston, TX 77058
Phone: 713-558-5000
Fax: 713-558-5960
Web: www.spacehab.com

CEO: Thomas B. Pickens III
CFO: John Porter
HR: Sandra Stanford
FYE: June 30
Type: Public

This company's businesses are out of this world. The Flight Services unit of Astrotech Corp. (formerly SPACEHAB) makes modules used in the living, cargo, and lab space aboard the Space Shuttle and in other space vehicles. Astrotech Engineering Services provides astronaut training, crew support services, and hardware design for space missions. Back on Earth, the company also provides satellite launch preparation services. Its Space Media unit focuses on space education and commerce, such as the creation of exhibits. NASA contracts and subcontracts account for about 45% of Astrotech's sales.

	Annual Growth	6/05	6/06	6/07	6/08	6/09
Sales ($ mil.)	(14.3%)	59.4	50.7	52.8	25.5	32.0
Net income ($ mil.)	(2.5%)	5.2	(12.4)	(16.3)	(36.0)	4.7
Market value ($ mil.)	(49.7%)	340.4	224.4	121.7	10.9	21.9
Employees	(24.4%)	233	231	176	66	76

ASURION CORPORATION

648 Grassmere Park Dr., Ste. 300
Nashville, TN 37211
Phone: 615-837-3000
Fax: 615-837-3001
Web: www.asurion.com

CEO: Kevin M. Taweel
CFO: Mark S. Gunning
HR: Vijay Velamoor
FYE: December 31
Type: Private

Dead battery? Would that be the battery on your car or cell phone? Either way, Asurion assures that you won't be stranded. A global leader in wireless and technology insurance, Asurion replaces defunct cell phones and other tech equipment, but also provides specialty services such as roadside assistance to stranded motorists via their wireless phones. The firm serves about 80 million end users through partnerships with wireless carriers including Cricket, T-Mobile, and AT&T Mobility. In 2008 Asurion merged with extended service plan provider, N.E.W. Customer Service Companies. Both companies continue to operate independently.

⊞ A.T. CROSS COMPANY

NASDAQ (GM): ATX

1 Albion Rd.
Lincoln, RI 02865
Phone: 401-333-1200
Fax: 401-334-2861
Web: www.cross.com

CEO: David G. (Dave) Whalen
CFO: Kevin F. Mahoney
HR: Tina C. Benik
FYE: December 31
Type: Public

Other than a diploma, what marks a high school graduation better than the gift of a Cross pen? Known for its tasteful writing instruments since 1846, A.T. Cross makes ball-point and fountain pens, as well as mechanical pencils. Its writing instruments are made from high-quality metals (gold, silver) and finishes (onyx, wood). The firm also makes desk sets, reading glasses, watches, and accessories (wallets, cufflinks). Products are sold throughout the US in retail stores as well as internationally via its Web site. Cross also has optical outlets under the Costa Del Mar Sunglasses and Native Eyewear banners. Director Galal Doss owns about 30% of the firm while chairman Russell Boss and his family own about 15%.

	Annual Growth	12/05	12/06	12/07	12/08	12/09
Sales ($ mil.)	2.4%	129.1	139.3	151.9	160.1	141.8
Net income ($ mil.)	47.6%	0.4	3.3	6.7	0.5	1.9
Market value ($ mil.)	6.6%	56.0	105.1	138.0	38.4	72.3
Employees	6.3%	704	900	900	800	900

A.T. KEARNEY, INC.

222 W. Adams St.
Chicago, IL 60606
Phone: 312-648-0111
Fax: 312-223-6200
Web: www.atkearney.com

CEO: Paul A. Laudicina
CFO: Dan A. DeCanniere
HR: Peter (Pete) Pesce
FYE: December 31
Type: Private

With roots going back to the founding of McKinsey & Company in 1926, A.T. Kearney has established a place for itself in the management consulting pantheon. Today's A.T. Kearney operates from offices in about 35 countries around the world. It offers consulting in a variety of areas, including growth strategies, IT strategies, and supply chain management. Clients have come from a wide range of industries, including automotive, financial services, health care, and utilities. A.T. Kearney is owned by its management team. The consulting firm took its current name in 1946 from that of Andrew T. Kearney, one of McKinsey's first partners.

AT&T CENTER

One AT&T Center Parkway
San Antonio, TX 78219
Phone: 210-444-5000
Fax: 210-444-5100
Web: www.attcenter.com

CEO: John Sparks
CFO: —
HR: Debbie Clark
FYE: December 31
Type: Government-owned

Spurs aren't the only things that jingle at the AT&T Center (formerly SBC Center). The arena is San Antonio's $175 million entertainment arena home for the NBA's San Antonio Spurs, the WNBA's San Antonio Silver Stars, minor league hockey's San Antonio Rampage, and the San Antonio Stock Show & Rodeo. Concerts from rock to country to hip hop also fill the center along with shows like *Sesame Street Live*, performances by stand-up comedians, and other entertainment events. AT&T Center hosts private events for 10 to 20,000 people and offers about 55 suites, as well as food and beverage service. The 750,000-sq.-ft. facility, which opened in 2002, is owned by Bexar County.

	Annual Growth	12/04	12/05	12/06	12/07	12/08
Est. sales ($ mil.)	—	—	—	—	—	12.4
Employees	—	—	—	—	—	240

AT&T FOUNDATION

208 S. Akard, Ste. 100
Dallas, TX 75202
Phone: 800-591-9663
Fax: 241-746-2239
Web: www.att.com/gen/corporate-citizenship?pid=7736

CEO: Laura Sanford
CFO: Tom Giltner
HR: —
FYE: December 31
Type: Not-for-profit

If you said the AT&T Foundation was phoning it in, would it be offended or complimented? One of several not-for-profit arms of AT&T Inc., the foundation provides funding for programs in education, civic and community service, arts and culture, and employee involvement. While it has supported thousands of organizations worldwide, the foundation promotes projects in areas where AT&T has a significant market presence; it focuses on advancing information technology capabilities. Recent recipients include universities, performing arts institutions, minority scholarship funds, and community technology centers. Established in 1983, the foundation and AT&T have contributed about $2 billion to communities and charities.

⊞ An in-depth profile of this company is available to Hoover's Online members at hoovers.com.

AT&T INC.   NYSE: T

208 S. Akard St.   CEO: Randall L. Stephenson
Dallas, TX 75202   CFO: Richard G. (Rick) Lindner
Phone: 210-821-4105   HR: William A. (Bill) Blase Jr.
Fax: —   FYE: December 31
Web: www.att.com   Type: Public

Through its subsidiaries, affiliates, and operating companies, holding company AT&T is the industry-leading provider of wireline voice communications services in the US. Customers in 22 states use AT&T-branded telephone, Internet, and computer telephone services; it also sells digital TV under the U-verse brand. Key markets include California, Illinois, and Texas. The company's corporate, government, and public sector clients use its range of conferencing, managed network, and wholesale communications services. Subsidiary AT&T Mobility is the nation's second-largest wireless carrier by both sales and subscriptions (after Verizon Wireless). It provides mobile voice and data services to about 85 million subscribers.

	Annual Growth	12/05	12/06	12/07	12/08	12/09
Sales ($ mil.)	29.4%	43,862.0	63,055.0	118,928.0	124,028.0	123,018.0
Net income ($ mil.)	27.2%	4,786.0	7,356.0	11,951.0	12,867.0	12,535.0
Market value ($ mil.)	3.4%	144,711.4	211,246.8	245,578.0	168,406.5	165,629.3
Employees	10.6%	189,000	302,000	310,000	301,000	282,720

AT&T MOBILITY LLC

Glenridge Highlands Two, 5565 Glenridge Connector   CEO: Ralph de la Vega
Atlanta, GA 30342   CFO: Peter A. (Pete) Ritcher
Phone: 404-236-6000   HR: Rickford D. (Rick) Bradley
Fax: 404-236-6005   FYE: December 31
Web: www.wireless.att.com   Type: Subsidiary

The second-largest wireless voice and data carrier in the US by subscribers (after Verizon), AT&T Mobility serves about 85 million mobile users via a nationwide network that spans all major metropolitan areas. The company, which accounts for about 40% of parent AT&T's business, provides a full range of wireless voice, messaging, and data services to consumer and enterprise customers. AT&T Mobility's services for businesses, government agencies, and educational institutions include e-mail, wireless Internet access, and private wireless networking. The company provides international network coverage for its subscribers in about 190 countries through partnerships with other carriers.

ATARI, INC.   Euronext Paris: ATA

417 5th Ave., 7th Fl.   CEO: David P. Gardner
New York, NY 10016   CFO: Philip (Phil) Veneziano
Phone: 212-726-6500   HR: —
Fax: 212-726-6533   FYE: March 31
Web: corporate.atari.com   Type: Public

Atari (formerly Infogrames Entertainment) has gone old school by bringing back the Atari name. Its game titles are played on major game consoles by Sony, Nintendo, and Microsoft, as well as on PCs. Hit titles include *Deer Hunter, Driver,* and *Enter the Matrix,* in addition to other games in children's, action, adventure, racing, and strategy genres. Atari produces titles from its own studios, as well as through outside studios and licensing deals. The company had operated its US subsidiary Atari as a separate company but absorbed it and took it private in 2008. In 2009 the company adopted the Atari name for its operations worldwide and shifted its headquarters to the US.

	Annual Growth	3/05	3/06	3/07	3/08	3/09
Sales ($ mil.)	(30.0%)	748.1	443.5	407.6	459.0	180.1
Net income ($ mil.)	—	(43.5)	(181.8)	(137.6)	(98.7)	(299.6)
Market value ($ mil.)	(57.9%)	2,590.0	1,133.7	363.8	2.9	81.2
Employees	(11.6%)	—	982	—	596	679

ATC GROUP SERVICES INC.

600 W. Cummings Park, Ste. 5500   CEO: Robert (Bobby) Toups
Woburn, MA 01801   CFO: Paul J. Grillo
Phone: 781-937-3320   HR: —
Fax: 781-933-5295   FYE: February 28
Web: www.atcassociates.com   Type: Private

ATC Group Services helps clients design and execute large-scale projects that can have a variety of construction, environmental, health, safety, and technical concerns. The firm, which does business as ATC Associates, often can coordinate services to save money. (ATC stands for Assess, Test, and Consult). Companies in the petroleum, health care, construction, retail, and government sectors have used ATC Associates to plan the removal of mold and asbestos, the treatment of sewage, and the proper testing of construction and construction materials. The company operates from some 68 offices in 36 states in the US.

	Annual Growth	2/04	2/05	2/06	2/07	2/08
Est. sales ($ mil.)	—	—	—	—	—	126.0
Employees	—	—	—	—	—	1,650

ATC TECHNOLOGY CORPORATION   NASDAQ (GS): ATAC

1400 Opus Place, Ste. 600   CEO: Todd R. Peters
Downers Grove, IL 60515   CFO: John M. Pinkerton
Phone: 630-271-8100   HR: John J. Machota
Fax: 630-271-9999   FYE: December 31
Web: www.goatc.com   Type: Public

ATC Technology is driving its business home. The company, formerly known as Aftermarket Technology Corp., provides logistics (supply chain management services), such as packaging and distribution, order fulfillment, and warehousing services to customers in the wireless, electronics, broadband and cable, and auto electronics industries. Its drivetrain (automotive aftermarket) business remanufactures automatic transmissions and drivetrain products for principal customers, including Chrysler, Ford, and Honda. ATC also sells to independent auto repair shops and parts retailers. North America accounts for approximately 96% of total net sales.

	Annual Growth	12/05	12/06	12/07	12/08	12/09
Sales ($ mil.)	2.3%	442.0	498.0	530.7	530.6	485.0
Net income ($ mil.)	(21.6%)	31.0	8.0	39.6	(25.2)	11.7
Market value ($ mil.)	5.2%	390.5	427.5	547.6	293.9	479.1
Employees	0.0%	3,300	4,000	3,900	3,500	3,300

ATHENAHEALTH, INC.   NASDAQ (GM): ATHN

311 Arsenal St.   CEO: Jonathan S. Bush
Watertown, MA 02472   CFO: Timothy M. (Tim) Adams
Phone: 617-402-1000   HR: —
Fax: 617-402-1099   FYE: December 31
Web: www.athenahealth.com   Type: Public

athenahealth knows that managing physician practices can result in a splitting headache, especially when patients are late paying bills. The company provides health care organizations with Web-based software and services (athenaCollector) that streamline practice management, workflow routing, revenue management, patient information management, billing and collection, and other health care management tasks. athenahealth also offers a clinical cycle management service (athenaClinicals) that automates and manages medical record-related functions for physician practices.

	Annual Growth	12/05	12/06	12/07	12/08	12/09
Sales ($ mil.)	37.0%	53.5	75.8	100.8	139.6	188.5
Net income ($ mil.)	—	(11.4)	(8.9)	(3.5)	28.9	9.3
Market value ($ mil.)	12.1%	—	—	1,191.5	1,245.1	1,497.3
Employees	16.4%	564	564	380	824	1,035

An in-depth profile of this company is available to Hoover's Online members at hoovers.com.

ATHENIX CORP.

108 T.W. Alexander Dr.
Research Triangle Park, NC 27709
Phone: 919-328-4100
Fax: 919-328-4101
Web: www.athenixcorp.com

CEO: Mike Koziel
CFO: Mark W. Hahn
HR: —
FYE: December 31
Type: Subsidiary

Saying a type of corn is transgenic doesn't mean that it likes to dress up as a soybean, but Athenix can explain all that later. The company develops enhanced plants, microbes, enzymes, and processes. It produces genes and proteins with traits such as insect and nematode resistance and herbicide tolerance, as well as developing transgenic plants for increased crop production. Athenix sells its genes, proteins, transgenic organisms, and other biological goodies to scientists involved in other life-sciences sectors, including those who develop agricultural and specialty chemicals, feed and seed, and energy production. The company was acquired by Bayer CropScience in 2009.

	Annual Growth	12/04	12/05	12/06	12/07	12/08
Est. sales ($ mil.)	—	—	—	—	—	4.5
Employees	—	—	—	—	—	50

ATHENS GROUP, INC.

5608 Parkcrest Dr., Ste. 200
Austin, TX 78731
Phone: 512-345-0600
Fax: 512-345-4088
Web: www.athensgroup.com

CEO: Mike Haney
CFO: Rick Kitslaar
HR: —
FYE: December 31
Type: Private

Athens Group helps the business of offshore drilling flow a little more smoothly. The company provides consulting services, including risk mitigation and problem remediation, to operators of offshore drilling rigs. Areas of specialty include quality assurance, trouble shooting, project management, and commissioning planning (which involves identifying control functions that need to be tested). It works with clients during the rig design and construction stages, as well as providing ongoing operational support. Clients have included ConocoPhillips, ExxonMobil, Saipem, and Shell. The employee-owned company was founded in 1998.

	Annual Growth	12/04	12/05	12/06	12/07	12/08
Est. sales ($ mil.)	—	—	—	—	—	4.0
Employees	—	—	—	—	—	40

ATHEROGENICS, INC.

OTC: AGIXQ

8995 Westside Pkwy.
Alpharetta, GA 30004
Phone: 678-336-2500
Fax: 678-336-2501
Web: www.atherogenics.com

CEO: Charles A. Deignan
CFO: Charles A. Deignan
HR: —
FYE: December 31
Type: Public

Drug company AtheroGenics develops drug candidates for the treatment of chronic inflammatory diseases, including diabetes and coronary heart disease. Its lead candidate, AGI-1067, is an oral drug intended to improve blood sugar levels. Development of the therapeutic compound is ongoing despite disappointing results from a major AGI-1067 clinical trial, which led to the termination of a licensing agreement with AstraZeneca and an organizational restructuring that cut AtheroGenics' workforce in half in 2007. The company's alliance with Astellas Pharma on a second anti-inflammatory candidate, organ transplant drug AGI-1096, also ended. In 2008 the company filed for Chapter 11 bankruptcy protection.

ATHEROS COMMUNICATIONS, INC.

NASDAQ (GS): ATHR

5480 Great America Pkwy.
Santa Clara, CA 95054
Phone: 408-773-5200
Fax: 408-773-9940
Web: www.atheros.com

CEO: Craig H. Barratt
CFO: Jack R. Lazar
HR: —
FYE: December 31
Type: Public

Atheros Communications builds high-speed connections right through the ether. Its radio-frequency transceiver chipsets combine features such as a radio, power amplifier, low-noise amplifier, and a media access control (MAC) processor onto just two or three chips, eliminating the need for bulkier components in wireless networking equipment. The company's customers include Apple, Dell, Fujitsu, Hewlett-Packard, Hon Hai Precision Industry (17% of sales), Microsoft, Nintendo (13%), Sony, and Toshiba. The fabless semiconductor company was started by faculty members from Stanford and Berkeley. Most of Atheros' sales are to customers in Asia, principally in Taiwan and China.

	Annual Growth	12/05	12/06	12/07	12/08	12/09
Sales ($ mil.)	31.1%	183.5	301.7	417.0	472.4	542.5
Net income ($ mil.)	29.1%	16.7	18.7	40.0	18.9	46.4
Market value ($ mil.)	27.4%	909.0	1,490.8	2,135.5	1,000.6	2,394.2
Employees	41.3%	327	660	878	1,079	1,302

ATHERSYS, INC.

NASDAQ (CM): ATHX

3201 Carnegie Ave.
Cleveland, OH 44115
Phone: 216-431-9900
Fax: 216-361-9495
Web: www.athersys.com

CEO: Gil Van Bokkelen
CFO: Laura K. Campbell
HR: —
FYE: December 31
Type: Public

Biotechnology is all the RAGE at Athersys. The development-stage company uses its Random Activation of Gene Expression (RAGE) technology to scan the human genome, identify proteins with specific biological functions, and link those protein functions with gene structures (functional genomics). It is also developing therapies for oncology and vascular applications based on its MultiStem technology, which uses stem cells from adult bone marrow. The firm plans to leverage its technologies by partnering with other biotechs and drugmakers, but it also aims to develop its own proprietary drugs. It counts Bristol-Myers Squibb and Angiotech Pharmaceuticals among its partners.

	Annual Growth	12/05	12/06	12/07	12/08	12/09
Sales ($ mil.)	(18.4%)	—	—	3.3	3.1	2.2
Net income ($ mil.)	—	—	—	(18.9)	(18.0)	(15.4)
Market value ($ mil.)	(8.3%)	—	—	92.9	8.5	78.2
Employees	9.2%	—	—	31	35	37

ATLANTA BREAD COMPANY INTERNATIONAL, INC.

1955 Lake Park Dr., Ste. 400
Smyrna, GA 30080
Phone: 770-432-0933
Fax: 770-444-1991
Web: www.atlantabread.com

CEO: Jerry Couvaras
CFO: Jeff Wiggins
HR: —
FYE: December 31
Type: Private

You might say this café company kneads to succeed. Atlanta Bread Company International operates and franchises more than 100 bakery cafés in about two dozen states. The chain serves sandwiches made with a variety of freshly baked breads, including ciabatta, foccacia, pumpernickel, and sourdough. Its menu also includes soups and salads. Customers can also purchase bread by the loaf, along with freshly made bagels, cookies, muffins, and pastries. Nearly all the Atlanta Bread Bakery Cafés are operated by franchisees. Brothers Bob and Rick Auffenberg opened the first Atlanta Bread café in 1993. South African-born brothers Jerry and Basil Couvaras bought into the venture and began franchising in 1995.

	Annual Growth	12/04	12/05	12/06	12/07	12/08
Est. sales ($ mil.)	—	—	—	—	—	79.6
Employees	—	—	—	—	—	135

ATLANTIC AMERICAN CORPORATION

NASDAQ (GM): AAME

4370 Peachtree Rd. NE	CEO: Hilton H. Howell Jr.
Atlanta, GA 30319	CFO: John G. Sample Jr.
Phone: 404-266-5500	HR: Barbara B. Snyder
Fax: 404-266-5702	FYE: December 31
Web: www.atlam.com	Type: Public

Atlantic American can get you a peach of an insurance deal. Through its sub-sidiaries, the company sells a mix of property/casualty, health, and life insurance in the southern US. Its Bankers Fidelity Life Insurance subsidiary provides life and supplemental health insurance. Medicare supplement products account for more than 80% of the division's premiums. Its American Southern subsidiary offer personal and commercial automobile and property coverage. It also pro-vides general commercial liability insurance. Its products are targeted at large motor pools and fleets owned by local governments. Chairman Mack Robinson and his family hold about 70% of the company's stock.

	Annual Growth	12/05	12/06	12/07	12/08	12/09
Assets ($ mil.)	(13.1%)	460.4	458.6	458.3	266.6	262.1
Net income ($ mil.)	—	(4.4)	7.6	7.3	(3.9)	(1.2)
Market value ($ mil.)	(17.0%)	60.2	66.0	31.2	16.5	28.5
Employees	(17.9%)	275	253	146	125	125

ATLANTIC BANCGROUP, INC.

NASDAQ (CM): ATBC

1315 S. 3rd St.	CEO: Barry W. Chandler
Jacksonville Beach, FL 32250	CFO: David L. Young
Phone: 904-247-9494	HR: —
Fax: 904-247-9402	FYE: December 31
Web: www.oceansidebank.com	Type: Public

Even in Florida you can't always bank on sunshine, so Atlantic BancGroup can help you save for a rainy day. Atlantic BancGroup is the holding company for Oceanside Bank, a community bank with about five branches in and around Jacksonville. The locally operated institution targets individuals and small to midsized businesses, offering deposit products such as checking and savings accounts, IRAs, and CDs. Loans include real estate mortgages, commercial loans, and consumer loans. More than 90% of Oceanside Bank's loan portfo-lio is secured by real estate mortgages. Jacksonville Bancorp is acquiring Atlantic BancGroup.

	Annual Growth	12/05	12/06	12/07	12/08	12/09
Assets ($ mil.)	8.6%	213.9	243.5	261.4	268.0	297.4
Net income ($ mil.)	—	1.5	1.9	1.4	(1.9)	(7.2)
Market value ($ mil.)	(42.7%)	36.2	41.6	21.7	7.2	3.9
Employees	0.0%	47	51	56	51	47

ATLANTIC COAST FEDERAL CORPORATION

NASDAQ (GM): ACFC

505 Haines Ave.	CEO: Robert J. Larison Jr.
Waycross, GA 31501	CFO: Thomas B. Wagers Sr.
Phone: 912-283-4711	HR: Robert J. Larison Jr.
Fax: 912-284-2284	FYE: December 31
Web: www.acfederal.net	Type: Public

Not happy simply coasting, Atlantic Coast Federal Corporation works hard as the holding company for Atlantic Coast Bank (formerly Atlantic Coast Fed-eral), a savings bank with more than a dozen branches in southeastern Geor-gia and the Jacksonville, Florida, metro area. Funds from deposits are used to make loans. The lending portfolio is dominated by mortgage loans (more than 50%); it also includes other real estate and construction loans, as well as con-sumer and business loans. Atlantic Coast Bank was established in 1939 as a credit union that served Atlantic Coast Line Railroad employees.

	Annual Growth	12/05	12/06	12/07	12/08	12/09
Assets ($ mil.)	5.0%	743.8	842.8	931.0	996.1	905.6
Net income ($ mil.)	—	4.7	5.2	1.1	(2.8)	(29.3)
Market value ($ mil.)	(42.8%)	188.6	244.6	159.4	52.3	20.3
Employees	0.8%	160	177	183	185	165

ATLANTIC EXPRESS TRANSPORTATION CORP.

7 North St.	CEO: Domenic Gatto
Staten Island, NY 10302	CFO: Nathan Schlenker
Phone: 718-442-7000	HR: —
Fax: 718-442-7672	FYE: June 30
Web: www.atlanticexpress.com	Type: Private

Driving with thousands of schoolchildren in the back seat, or rows of seats, doesn't bother Atlantic Express Transportation. The company serves about 100 school districts throughout the US with a fleet of some 5,600 vehicles. School bus services account for about 90% of the company's sales. In addition, Atlantic Express provides paratransit services (transportation of people with disabilities) in New York City and offers charter, express, and fixed-route bus services, mainly as a contractor for New York's Metropolitan Transportation Authority. Investment firm Greenwich Street Capital owns a controlling stake in Atlantic Express, which was founded in 1964.

	Annual Growth	6/04	6/05	6/06	6/07	6/08
Sales ($ mil.)	4.5%	363.5	363.7	414.1	428.8	433.5
Net income ($ mil.)	—	56.8	(42.4)	(30.0)	(17.1)	(34.4)
Employees	(3.1%)	—	—	8,100	7,600	7,600

ATLANTIC HEALTH SYSTEM, INC.

325 Columbia Tpke., 2nd Fl.	CEO: Joseph A. (Joe) Trunfio
Florham Park, NJ 07932	CFO: Kevin Shanley
Phone: 973-660-3100	HR: Andrew L. Kovach
Fax: 973-660-9065	FYE: December 31
Web: www.atlantichealth.org	Type: Not-for-profit

Got a gash in the Garden State? Head to the Atlantic. Atlantic Health, that is. Atlantic Health System (AHS) operates two acute care hospitals providing general medical and surgical services to residents of northern New Jersey. Its Morristown Memorial Hospital has nearly 700 beds, serves as a regional trauma center, and provides specialty care in a number of areas, including cancer (through the Carol G. Simon Cancer Center); pediatric care (through Goryeb Children's Hospital); and cardiac care (through Gagnon Heart Hospi-tal). A second facility, Overlook Hospital, has about 500 beds and houses the Atlantic Neuroscience Institute with the first Comprehensive Stroke Center in the state.

ATLANTIC METHANOL PRODUCTION COMPANY LLC

12600 Northborough Dr., Ste. 150	CEO: Paul Moschell
Houston, TX 77067	CFO: Jim O'Casek
Phone: 281-872-8324	HR: Doris Anderson
Fax: 281-872-1084	FYE: December 31
Web: www.atlanticmethanol.com	Type: Joint venture

Atlantic Methanol Production Company must like to think proverbially, because "Waste not, want not" seems to be its motto. The company tries not to waste the natural gas that is a by-product of its parent companies' produc-tion processes. Atlantic Methanol was founded in 1997 as a vehicle to make use of natural gas being expent each day off the coast of Equitorial Guinea. It began production four years later. It produces about 1 million tons of methanol annually. Noble Energy and Marathon Oil each own 45%, with the state-controlled SONAGAS owning the remaining 10%.

	Annual Growth	12/04	12/05	12/06	12/07	12/08
Est. sales ($ mil.)	—	—	—	—	—	389.8
Employees	—	—	—	—	—	342

ATLANTIC SOUTHERN FINANCIAL GROUP, INC.

NASDAQ (GM): ASFN

1701 Bass Rd.
Macon, GA 31210
Phone: 478-476-2170
Fax: —
Web: www.atlanticsouthernbank.com

CEO: Mark A. Stevens
CFO: Carol W. Soto
HR: —
FYE: December 31
Type: Public

Georgia-based Atlantic Southern Financial Group would probably not mind if money trees grew alongside the state's peach trees. Serving central and southeastern Georgia and northern Florida, Atlantic Southern Financial is the holding company for Atlantic Southern Bank, a community bank that offers deposit services such as checking and savings accounts, as well as loan services, to consumers and small to midsized businesses. Its primary lending services include real estate loans for construction and land development (about 40%), as well as commercial real estate loans (30%). To a lesser extent, Atlantic Southern provides consumer and residential real estate loans. The bank operates more than a dozen branches.

	Annual Growth	12/05	12/06	12/07	12/08	12/09
Assets ($ mil.)	25.0%	388.7	671.1	852.5	991.7	948.4
Net income ($ mil.)	—	3.9	6.0	7.7	(0.6)	(59.2)
Market value ($ mil.)	(52.3%)	102.1	141.1	80.0	23.0	5.3
Employees	25.2%	66	121	167	178	162

ATLANTIC TELE-NETWORK, INC.

NASDAQ (GM): ATNI

10 Derby Sq.
Salem, MA 01970
Phone: 978-619-1300
Fax: 978-744-3951
Web: www.atni.com

CEO: Michael T. Prior
CFO: Justin D. Benincasa
HR: —
FYE: December 31
Type: Public

Atlantic Tele-Network (ATN) makes connections from the rain forests of Guyana to the maple groves of Vermont. ATN owns 80% of mobile phone carrier Guyana Telephone & Telegraph (GT&T), which has about 150,000 fixed access telephone lines and has about 290,000 cellular subscribers. In the US, ATN provides wholesale wireless voice and data roaming services to local and national communications carriers through subsidiary Commnet. The company provides voice and broadband Internet communcations services in New England, particularly in the state of Vermont, through its SoVerNet subsidiary. SoVerNet subsidiary ION offers fiber optic transport services in New York State on a wholesale basis.

	Annual Growth	12/05	12/06	12/07	12/08	12/09
Sales ($ mil.)	24.0%	102.3	155.4	186.7	207.3	241.7
Net income ($ mil.)	27.1%	13.6	23.5	37.9	34.8	35.5
Market value ($ mil.)	34.6%	256.1	447.8	516.3	405.8	839.8
Employees	1.0%	853	852	823	864	889

ATLANTIC TOOL & DIE CO., INC.

19963 Progress Dr.
Strongsville, OH 44149
Phone: 440-238-6931
Fax: 440-238-2210

CEO: Frank Mehwald
CFO: —
HR: —
FYE: December 31
Type: Private

Atlantic Tool & Die found a company to die for when it hooked up with Honda in the late 1980s. The metal stamping company serves major automakers, including Honda of America Manufacturing in Marysville, Ohio. Founded in 1937, Atlantic Tool & Die manufactures metal stampings and assemblies from its five facilities in Alabama, Ohio, and Texas. The company established its main facility in Strongsville, Ohio in 1967. Atlantic Tool & Die supplies automotive parts and tools worldwide on the just-in-time delivery system. Under the leadership of Frank Mehwald, the company has grown from a small-time die maker into a major parts supplier.

	Annual Growth	12/04	12/05	12/06	12/07	12/08
Est. sales ($ mil.)	—	—	—	—	—	87.0
Employees	—	—	—	—	—	476

☐ ATLAS AIR WORLDWIDE HOLDINGS, INC.

NASDAQ (GS): AAWW

2000 Westchester Ave.
Purchase, NY 10577
Phone: 914-701-8000
Fax: 914-701-8001
Web: www.atlasair.com

CEO: William J. (Bill) Flynn
CFO: Spencer Schwartz
HR: —
FYE: December 31
Type: Public

Atlas carried the weight of the world; Atlas Air Worldwide Holdings (AAWW) carries the freight of the world. The company leases cargo planes to customers, mainly airlines, under long-term ACMI (aircraft, crew, maintenance, and insurance) contracts. The segment accounts for nearly half of AAWW's revenue. Top ACMI client, Emirates, brings in about 10% of total revenue. In addition, subsidiaries Atlas Air and Polar Air Cargo provide charter services to the US military, referred to as AMC, and to charter brokers, freight forwarders, and airlines. Combined, the carriers maintain a fleet of about 20 Boeing 747 freighters. AAWW also offers dry leasing (aircraft and engines only) via its Titan division.

	Annual Growth	12/05	12/06	12/07	12/08	12/09
Sales ($ mil.)	(10.0%)	1,617.9	1,476.3	1,562.7	1,607.5	1,061.5
Net income ($ mil.)	1.3%	73.9	59.8	132.4	63.7	77.8
Market value ($ mil.)	(4.6%)	1,162.2	1,149.3	1,400.3	488.1	962.0
Employees	(10.4%)	2,077	1,840	1,725	1,428	1,337

ATLAS COPCO USA HOLDINGS INC.

34 Maple Ave.
Pine Brook, NJ 07058
Phone: 973-439-3400
Fax: 973-439-9455
Web: www.atlascopco.com

CEO: Mark Cohen
CFO: —
HR: —
FYE: May 31
Type: Subsidiary

When you hear the phrase *Swedish American* you probably don't think construction and mining equipment, but maybe you should. Atlas Copco USA Holdings operates throughout the US, Canada, and Mexico, as an arm of Swedish manufacturing giant Atlas Copco AG. The US-based business manufactures compressors and generators, construction and mining equipment, and power tools. Its line of power tools feature air assembly tools, grinders, drills, air motors, hoists and trolleys, and related services. Demolition equipment, rock drills, blast hole drilling rigs, and exploration drilling tools are included in the list of mining and construction products. Atlas Copco USA represents nearly 20% of its parent company's sales.

	Annual Growth	5/04	5/05	5/06	5/07	5/08
Est. sales ($ mil.)	—	—	—	—	—	565.4
Employees	—	—	—	—	—	3,060

ATLAS ENERGY, INC.

NASDAQ (GS): ATLS

1550 Coraopolis Heights Rd., 2nd Fl.
Moon Township, PA 15108
Phone: 412-262-2830
Fax: 412-262-7430
Web: www.atlasamerica.com

CEO: Edward E. Cohen
CFO: Matthew A. Jones
HR: —
FYE: December 31
Type: Public

Atlas Energy's production map can be found on the page titled Appalachia. The energy company (formerly Atlas America) is engaged in the development, production, and transportation of natural gas (and some oil) primarily in Appalachia. The company has proved reserves of about 1 trillion cu. ft. of natural gas equivalent. It also operates nearly 9,500 miles of interstate natural gas gathering systems in Arkansas, New York, Ohio, Oklahoma, Pennsylvania, and Texas. In 2009, in a move to consolidate its operations, Atlas Energy Resources merged with Atlas America, and Atlas America changed its name to Atlas Energy, Inc.

	Annual Growth	9/05	*12/06	12/07	12/08	12/09
Sales ($ mil.)	35.2%	474.5	749.3	1,361.0	2,213.4	1,587.6
Net income ($ mil.)	—	32.9	12.2	35.3	(6.2)	(0.1)
Market value ($ mil.)	20.1%	1,133.7	1,774.3	3,090.2	1,163.1	2,360.7
Employees	26.5%	340	517	801	978	872
						*Fiscal year change

ATLAS MINING COMPANY

Pink Sheets: ALMI

1221 Yellowstone
Osburn, ID 83849
Phone: 208-556-1181
Fax: 208-556-6741
Web: www.atlasmining.com

CEO: Andre Zeitoun
CFO: Christopher T. Carney
HR: —
FYE: December 31
Type: Public

Atlas Mining is developing the Dragon Mine in Utah, which contains a deposit of halloysite clay, a substance used as an intermediate ingredient in chemicals manufacturing as well as to make bone china, fine china, and porcelain. Until the end of 2008 subsidiary Atlas Fausett Contracting (AFC) had also provided contract mining services for mine operators, exploration companies, and the construction and natural resource industries. It shut down those operations at the end of that year amid the economic downturn and in order to concentrate on the Dragon Mine property.

	Annual Growth	12/05	12/06	12/07	12/08	12/09
Sales ($ mil.)	—	0.6	3.8	7.7	0.0	0.0
Net income ($ mil.)	—	(3.8)	(2.0)	(1.7)	(5.4)	(6.8)
Market value ($ mil.)	(12.1%)	65.1	98.6	53.7	10.1	38.9
Employees	(3.8%)	14	58	64	19	12

ATLAS PIPELINE HOLDINGS, L.P.

NYSE: AHD

311 Rouser Rd.
Moon Township, PA 15108
Phone: 412-262-2830
Fax: 412-262-2820
Web: www.atlaspipelineholdings.com

CEO: Eugene N. (Gene) Dubay
CFO: Eric T. Kalamaras
HR: —
FYE: December 31
Type: Public

Atlas may have carried the world on his shoulders, but the Atlas group of companies is more into sharing the heavy load across a number of related companies. Atlas Pipeline Holdings helps out its ultimate parent Atlas America by managing midstream energy services provider Atlas Pipeline Partners (through Atlas Pipeline Partners GP, LLC), which is engaged in the transmission, gathering, and processing of natural gas in Appalachia and the Mid-Continent regions. Atlas Pipeline Partners operates 9,100 miles of natural gas gathering systems in eastern Ohio, southern Oklahoma, western New York, western Pennsylvania, and northern Texas. In 2008 Atlas America owned 83% of Atlas Pipeline Holdings.

	Annual Growth	12/05	12/06	12/07	12/08	12/09
Sales ($ mil.)	24.9%	371.5	465.1	842.9	1,414.2	903.8
Net income ($ mil.)	47.4%	12.3	18.5	(15.6)	(73.7)	58.0
Market value ($ mil.)	(34.3%)	—	661.8	751.6	104.7	187.8
Employees	10.2%	210	188	373	549	310

ATLAS PIPELINE PARTNERS, L.P.

NYSE: APL

1550 Coraopolis Heights Rd.
Moon Township, PA 15108
Phone: 412-262-2830
Fax: 412-262-2820
Web: www.atlaspipelinepartners.com

CEO: Eugene N. (Gene) Dubay
CFO: Eric T. Kalamaras
HR: —
FYE: December 31
Type: Public

Atlas Pipeline Partners shoulders the burden of getting natural gas from wellheads to major gas utilities such as Peoples Natural Gas, National Fuel Gas, and East Ohio Gas. Atlas Pipeline operates about 9,100 miles of natural gas gathering systems in Arkansas, southeastern Missouri, eastern Ohio, southern Oklahoma, western New York, western Pennsylvania, and northern Texas. It also operates eight gas processing plants, and one treatment plant. The company was formed to buy the gas gathering systems of its former owners Atlas America and Resource Energy. Atlas America subsidiary Atlas Pipeline Holdings L.P. controls the general partner of Atlas Pipeline.

	Annual Growth	12/05	12/06	12/07	12/08	12/09
Sales ($ mil.)	24.9%	371.5	464.7	668.8	1,414.2	904.2
Net income ($ mil.)	24.9%	25.8	33.7	(144.3)	(581.9)	62.7
Market value ($ mil.)	(29.9%)	2,160.4	2,554.2	2,280.1	319.3	522.0
Employees	10.2%	210	188	373	549	310

ATLAS ROOFING CORPORATION

2000 RiverEdge Pkwy., Ste. 800
Atlanta, GA 30328
Phone: 770-952-1442
Fax: 770-952-3170
Web: www.atlasroofing.com

CEO: Kenneth Farrish
CFO: Jeffery L. Fricks
HR: Sara L. Dunham
FYE: December 31
Type: Private

This Atlas may not be able to hold up the sky, but it can certainly protect you from its elements. Atlas Roofing manufactures residential and commercial roofing and insulation products that include polyiso and polystyrene sheathing and insulation, foam insulation, roll roofing, and shingles. It is a pioneer in manufacturing foam insulation products free of environmentally harmful blowing agents. Its Falcon Foam division specializes in earth-friendly HCFC-free (hydrochlorofluorocarbon-free) insulation products. Atlas also offers field services for drainage assessments. Founded in 1981, Atlas Roofing operates 15 manufacturing facilities across North America and distributes its products throughout the world.

ATLAS WORLD GROUP, INC.

1212 St. George Rd.
Evansville, IN 47711
Phone: 812-424-2222
Fax: 812-421-7125
Web: www.atlasworldgroup.com

CEO: Glen E. Dunkerson
CFO: Richard J. (Rick) Olson
HR: —
FYE: December 31
Type: Private

Willing to carry the weight of a moving world, Atlas World Group is the holding company for Atlas Van Lines, one of the largest moving companies in the US. Atlas Van Lines transports household goods domestically and between the US and Canada; it also offers specialized transportation of items such as trade show exhibits, fine art, and electronics. Other Atlas World Group companies provide international corporate relocation and freight forwarding services. Its Atlas Canada unit moves household goods in that country while American Red Ball International specializes in military relocations and serves van lines outside Atlas' network. Atlas World Group was formed in 1994 and is owned by its agents.

	Annual Growth	12/04	12/05	12/06	12/07	12/08
Est. sales ($ mil.)	—	—	—	—	—	908.4
Employees	—	—	—	—	—	450

⊞ ATMEL CORPORATION

NASDAQ (GS): ATML

2325 Orchard Pkwy.
San Jose, CA 95131
Phone: 408-441-0311
Fax: 408-436-4314
Web: www.atmel.com

CEO: Steven A. (Steve) Laub
CFO: Stephen M. Cumming
HR: —
FYE: December 31
Type: Public

Atmel's product lines include nonvolatile memory devices, such as flash memory and ROMs, as well as programmable logic chips, microcontroller units (MCUs) for an array of devices, application-specific integrated circuits (ASICs), and touchscreen products. Atmel's chips are favored in consumer electronics, communications, industrial, military, and networking products, including base stations and wireless handsets, along with avionics systems, networking switches and routers, digital still cameras, smart credit cards, and television set-top boxes. Top customers include Alcatel-Lucent, Cisco, and Siemens. Most of the company's sales come from customers outside the US.

	Annual Growth	12/05	12/06	12/07	12/08	12/09
Sales ($ mil.)	(7.7%)	1,675.7	1,670.9	1,639.2	1,566.8	1,217.3
Net income ($ mil.)	—	(32.9)	14.6	47.9	(27.2)	(109.5)
Market value ($ mil.)	10.5%	1,423.6	2,787.2	1,990.2	1,442.0	2,123.8
Employees	(8.8%)	8,080	7,992	7,400	6,400	5,600

ATMI, INC.

NASDAQ (GS): ATMI

7 Commerce Dr.
Danbury, CT 06810
Phone: 203-794-1100
Fax: 203-792-8040
Web: www.atmi.com

CEO: Douglas A. (Doug) Neugold
CFO: Timothy C. (Tim) Carlson
HR: Thomas J. McGowan
FYE: December 31
Type: Public

ATMI's original name — Advanced Technology Materials, Inc. — is a pretty good summary of its business. The company furnishes chip makers with ultra-pure materials and related packaging and delivery systems used during semiconductor production (about 90% of sales). ATMI also serves manufacturers of flat-panel displays (produced much like semiconductors, with glass substrates). As part of its move into the life sciences market, the company in 2008 acquired LevTech, a provider of disposable mixing systems to the biotechnology and pharmaceutical industries. Customers in the Asia/Pacific region account for around two-thirds of sales, while the US provides approximately one-fifth of sales.

	Annual Growth	12/05	12/06	12/07	12/08	12/09
Sales ($ mil.)	(2.5%)	281.8	325.9	364.1	339.1	254.7
Net income ($ mil.)	—	30.7	40.0	40.5	33.3	(6.7)
Market value ($ mil.)	(9.7%)	880.8	961.4	1,015.5	485.9	586.3
Employees	(0.6%)	711	806	809	761	693

ATMOS ENERGY CORPORATION

NYSE: ATO

3 Lincoln Centre, Ste. 1800, 5430 LBJ Fwy.
Dallas, TX 75240
Phone: 972-934-9227
Fax: 972-855-3040
Web: www.atmosenergy.com

CEO: Robert W. (Bob) Best
CFO: Fred E. Meisenheimer
HR: Michael E. (Mike) Haefner
FYE: September 30
Type: Public

Atmos Energy, the largest gas-only utility company in the US, is interested in more than atmospherics; it is focused on delivery. Through its utility units, which operate under the Atmos Energy brand, the holding company distributes natural gas to more than 3 million residential, commercial, and industrial customers in more than 1,600 communities in 12 midwestern and southern states. Nonregulated subsidiary Atmos Energy Marketing sells natural gas and offers energy management services to more than 1,000 utility and industrial customers in 22 states. The company also has power generation and gas transportation and storage operations.

	Annual Growth	9/05	9/06	9/07	9/08	9/09
Sales ($ mil.)	(0.0%)	4,973.3	6,152.4	5,898.4	7,221.3	4,969.1
Net income ($ mil.)	8.9%	135.8	147.7	168.5	180.3	191.0
Market value ($ mil.)	(0.1%)	2,628.8	2,656.7	2,635.3	2,477.1	2,622.3
Employees	1.9%	4,543	4,402	4,653	4,750	4,891

ATOS ORIGIN, INC.

5599 San Felipe St., Ste. 300
Houston, TX 77056
Phone: 713-513-3000
Fax: 713-403-7204
Web: www.na.atosorigin.com

CEO: Paul Stewart
CFO: Jerry Anderson
HR: Sabrina Shumsky
FYE: December 31
Type: Subsidiary

Atos Origin Inc., a US division of Paris-based Atos Origin, provides information technology services to large businesses in the consumer products, retail, automotive, financial services, oil and gas, and telecommunications industries. The company, which does business as Atos Origin North America, also serves utilities service providers and major events like the Olympic Games. Enterprise clients have included the North American units of automaker Nissan and electronics manufacturer Philips. Atos Origin offers consulting and systems integration services, as well as ongoing managed IT services including recurring and multi-year outsourcing and maintenance contracts to oversee corporate communications networks.

ATP OIL & GAS CORPORATION

NASDAQ (GS): ATPG

4600 Post Oak Place, Ste. 200
Houston, TX 77027
Phone: 713-622-3311
Fax: 713-622-5101
Web: www.atpog.com

CEO: T. Paul Bulmahn
CFO: Albert L. Reese Jr.
HR: —
FYE: December 31
Type: Public

ATP Oil & Gas looks for its revenues where others have shelved their operations. The company's strategy is to exploit continental shelf assets that are being sold by larger oil companies searching for higher returns in deeper waters. It explores and develops natural gas and oil properties primarily on the outer continental shelf of the Gulf of Mexico (where it has interests in about 80 offshore blocks, 40 platforms, and 130 wells) and in the Southern Gas Basin of the UK's North Sea. In 2008 ATP Oil & Gas reported proved reserves of 713.6 billion cu. ft. of natural gas equivalent; natural gas makes up the bulk of the reserves.

	Annual Growth	12/05	12/06	12/07	12/08	12/09
Sales ($ mil.)	20.8%	146.7	419.8	607.9	618.0	312.2
Net income ($ mil.)	—	(2.7)	6.9	48.6	121.7	(49.0)
Market value ($ mil.)	(16.2%)	1,894.3	2,025.3	2,586.8	299.4	935.6
Employees	7.0%	48	59	64	63	63

ATRIA SENIOR LIVING GROUP, INC.

401 S. 4th St., Ste. 1900
Louisville, KY 40202
Phone: 502-779-4700
Fax: 502-779-4701
Web: www.atriaseniorliving.com

CEO: John A. Moore
CFO: Mark Jessee
HR: Anne Pinter
FYE: December 31
Type: Private

Atria Senior Living Group keeps the elderly close to its heart. The company operates retirement and assisted-living centers for the elderly who may need assistance with routine daily tasks, but who don't need comprehensive skilled nursing. Its services range from independent living units in private apartment settings to more specialized care facilities for residents suffering from Alzheimer's disease or who require respite care. Atria Senior Living Group owns or manages more than 120 senior living communities in more than 25 states throughout the country. The company serves a middle-to-high income assisted living demographic, primarily in suburban markets.

ATRICURE, INC.

NASDAQ (GM): ATRC

6033 Schumacher Park Dr.
West Chester, OH 45069
Phone: 513-755-4100
Fax: 513-755-4108
Web: www.atricure.com

CEO: David J. (Dave) Drachman
CFO: Julie A. Piton
HR: —
FYE: December 31
Type: Public

If your heart thumps to the beat of a different drummer, AtriCure wants to clamp down on that activity. The medical device maker has developed a system used in the treatment of atrial fibrillation (AF), a common type of heart arrhythmia. Its primary product, the Isolator bipolar ablation system, allows surgeons to manipulate clamps designed for both open-heart and minimally invasive procedures. Although the FDA has cleared Isolator for the ablation of cardiac tissue, none of AtriCure's products have received approval specifically for the treatment of AF. Nevertheless, cardiothoracic surgeons have adopted the system to create lesions in the tissue to block electrical impulses that cause quivering in the heart.

	Annual Growth	12/05	12/06	12/07	12/08	12/09
Sales ($ mil.)	15.1%	31.0	38.2	48.3	55.3	54.5
Net income ($ mil.)	—	(12.7)	(13.7)	(11.3)	(10.2)	(16.5)
Market value ($ mil.)	(13.2%)	164.7	138.4	202.7	34.3	93.4
Employees	5.7%	160	176	200	200	200

ATRINSIC, INC.

NASDAQ (GM): ATRN

469 7th Ave., 10th Fl.
New York, NY 10018
Phone: 212-273-1141
Fax: —
Web: www.atrinsic.com

CEO: Jeffrey A. Schwartz
CFO: Thomas Plotts
HR: —
FYE: December 31
Type: Public

Connecting online with music fans and gamers is an intrinsic part of Atrinsic. Formerly New Motion, the company is an online marketing and advertising firm that helps companies reach audiences through search marketing, e-mail advertising, and traditional display ads. Atrinsic also serves as marketing partner for a network of online content sites including GameFiesta, SmartCredit, and music downloading service Kazaa (owned by Brilliant Digital Entertainment). In addition, the company operates its own subscription content sites (GatorArcade, RingTone.com) and e-commerce site ShopIt.com.

	Annual Growth	12/05	12/06	12/07	12/08	12/09
Sales ($ mil.)	85.0%	5.9	18.7	37.0	113.9	69.1
Net income ($ mil.)	—	0.4	0.7	(4.1)	(115.8)	(29.5)
Market value ($ mil.)	(78.2%)	—	1,313.8	292.0	24.0	13.6
Employees	55.9%	—	38	75	206	144

ATRION CORPORATION

NASDAQ (GM): ATRI

1 Allentown Pkwy.
Allen, TX 75002
Phone: 972-390-9800
Fax: 972-396-7581
Web: www.atrioncorp.com

CEO: Emile A. Battat
CFO: Jeffery Strickland
HR: —
FYE: December 31
Type: Public

Atrion is only a little bit gassy. The company owns a 22-mile pipeline that transports gaseous oxygen in Alabama, but its primary focus is on the health care market. Subsidiary Quest Medical makes cardiovascular and intravenous fluid delivery products; its MPS2 Myocardial Protection System manages fluid delivery to the heart during open-heart surgery. Another subsidiary, Halkey-Roberts, makes medical tubing clamps and fluid and gas valves for health care equipment, marine and airplane safety devices, toys, and other inflatable products. Its Atrion Medical Products subsidiary makes ophthalmic, diagnostic, and cardiovascular equipment, including balloon catheter inflation devices and needle storage kits.

	Annual Growth	12/05	12/06	12/07	12/08	12/09
Sales ($ mil.)	8.7%	72.1	81.0	88.5	95.9	100.6
Net income ($ mil.)	16.9%	9.0	10.8	14.0	15.7	16.8
Market value ($ mil.)	22.4%	140.3	157.1	252.7	196.3	315.3
Employees	(1.5%)	493	486	492	485	465

ATRIUM COMPANIES, INC.

3890 W. Northwest Hwy., Ste. 500
Dallas, TX 75220
Phone: 214-630-5757
Fax: 214-630-5001
Web: home.atrium.com

CEO: Gregory T. (Greg) Faherty
CFO: Wayne Terry
HR: D. D. (Gus) Agostinelli
FYE: December 31
Type: Private

The way to Atrium's heart? Right through that sliding door. Atrium Companies makes and distributes vinyl and aluminium windows and patio doors for residential use. The company's brand names include Atrium, HR Windows, Champion Window, Superior Windows, and Darby Doors. It also makes the SafeHarbor brand of hurricane-resistant windows, doors, and shutters. Products are sold to the wholesale and retail markets. Atrium also offers installation and repair services. The group operates more than 50 manufacturing facilities and distribution centers throughout North America. Atrium was founded in 1948 and is majority-owned by investment firm Kenner & Company. Atrium had a brief stint in Chapter 11 bankruptcy in 2010.

	Annual Growth	12/04	12/05	12/06	12/07	12/08
Sales ($ mil.)	(6.9%)	800.0	800.0	840.0	700.0	600.0
Employees	(10.7%)	6,300	7,000	6,000	5,100	4,000

ATS CORPORATION

NYSE Amex: ATSC

7925 Jones Branch Dr.
McLean, VA 22102
Phone: 571-766-2400
Fax: 571-766-2401
Web: www.atsva.com

CEO: Edward H. (Ed) Bersoff
CFO: Pamela A. Little
HR: —
FYE: October 31
Type: Public

ATS Corporation knows that the key to technological success lies in the right mix of services. The company provides a variety of IT services to the federal government, including consulting, systems integration, network design, and support. Its Appix subsidiary is an IT consulting services provider to the mortgage lending and other financial services industries. The company also develops software used for managing public safety operations (Pyramid), homeland security responses (HLS-RAM), and law enforcement activities (Voyager). The US government and government-sponsored enterprises account for about three-quarters of sales.

	Annual Growth	12/05	12/06	12/07	12/08	12/09
Sales ($ mil.)	5.4%	—	—	106.9	131.5	118.7
Net income ($ mil.)	—	—	—	(6.6)	(49.8)	3.1
Market value ($ mil.)	(17.0%)	—	—	80.7	23.5	55.6
Employees	(10.8%)	—	—	769	547	612

ATS MEDICAL, INC.

NASDAQ (GM): ATSI

3905 Annapolis Ln., Ste. 105
Minneapolis, MN 55447
Phone: 763-553-7736
Fax: 763-557-2244
Web: www.atsmedical.com

CEO: Michael D. Dale
CFO: Michael (Mike) Kramer
HR: Barbara (Barb) Searle
FYE: December 31
Type: Public

ATS Medical keeps its products close to the heart. The company's main product is its ATS Open Pivot mechanical heart valve, which has been implanted in more than 140,000 patients worldwide. The valve was designed to lower the risk of blood clotting, reduce noise levels, and make the implantation procedure easier. ATS Medical also develops and markets tissue heart valves, cryosurgery (cold therapy) devices for cardiac procedures, and other cardiac surgery supplies. The company markets its products through a direct sales force in the US and some key international markets and through distributors elsewhere. ATS Medical has agreed to be acquired by Medtronic.

	Annual Growth	12/05	12/06	12/07	12/08	12/09
Sales ($ mil.)	21.6%	34.6	40.4	49.6	65.8	75.7
Net income ($ mil.)	—	(16.6)	(27.7)	(23.0)	(19.3)	(6.3)
Market value ($ mil.)	4.0%	216.3	162.2	173.2	217.8	253.1
Employees	9.0%	227	254	245	301	321

ATSI COMMUNICATIONS, INC.

OTC: ATSX

3201 Cherry Ridge, Bldg. C, Ste. 300
San Antonio, TX 78230
Phone: 210-614-7240
Fax: 210-614-7264
Web: www.atsi.net

CEO: Arthur L. (Art) Smith
CFO: Antonio Estrada Jr.
HR: Kathleen Keller
FYE: July 31
Type: Public

ATSI Communications helps international telecommunications carriers use the Internet to their advantage. Through its Digerati Networks subsidiary, the company provides telecommunications companies with Voice-over-IP (VoIP) call termination services in Latin America (with a particular focus on Mexico), Asia, and the Middle East. Such customers typically lack transmission facilities, require additional capacity, or lack regulatory licenses to terminate traffic in selected areas. ATSI also provides VoIP gateway services, including data, fax, and voice transmission.

	Annual Growth	7/05	7/06	7/07	7/08	7/09
Sales ($ mil.)	35.0%	6.0	14.7	31.7	42.0	19.9
Net income ($ mil.)	—	10.3	0.9	(0.3)	0.1	(1.5)
Market value ($ mil.)	(27.0%)	8.2	9.6	10.5	10.0	2.3
Employees	21.8%	5	8	9	12	11

An in-depth profile of this company is available to Hoover's Online members at hoovers.com.

ATTACHMATE CORPORATION

1500 Dexter Ave. North
Seattle, WA 98109
Phone: 206-217-7100
Fax: 206-217-7515
Web: www.attachmate.com

CEO: Jeff Hawn
CFO: Charles W. Sansbury
HR: —
FYE: December 31
Type: Private

Attachmate believes in the power of connection. The company provides software used to manage access to enterprise applications and databases, including information stored on mainframes and other legacy systems. Its products include terminal emulation and host connectivity applications, desktop management software, development toolkits, and connectivity hardware. The company also offers applications for systems and security management (a business line fueled by its acquisition of NetIQ) as well as application integration software. Attachmate is owned by an investment group led by Golden Gate Capital, Francisco Partners, and Thoma Cressey Equity Partners.

ATWOOD OCEANICS, INC.

NYSE: ATW

15835 Park Ten Place Dr.
Houston, TX 77084
Phone: 281-749-7800
Fax: 281-492-7871
Web: www.atwd.com

CEO: Robert J. (Rob) Saltiel
CFO: James M. (Jim) Holland
HR: —
FYE: September 30
Type: Public

Atwood Oceanics is at work in oceans all over the world. An offshore oil and gas drilling contractor, the firm owns nine drilling rigs, including four semisubmersible rigs, three jack-ups, one submersible, and one semisubmersible tender assist vessel (which places drilling equipment on permanent platforms). Its rigs operate in the Gulf of Mexico, offshore Southeast Asia, offshore Africa, offshore India, offshore Australia, and in the Mediterranean. In fiscal 2009 some 97% of Atwood Oceanics' sales came from its international operations; the company had contracts with 13 different customers.

	Annual Growth	9/05	9/06	9/07	9/08	9/09
Sales ($ mil.)	35.1%	176.2	276.6	403.0	526.6	586.5
Net income ($ mil.)	76.2%	26.0	86.1	139.0	215.4	250.7
Market value ($ mil.)	13.8%	1,356.3	1,448.6	2,466.3	2,345.1	2,272.3
Employees	(2.4%)	1,100	1,100	900	1,200	1,000

ATX GROUP, INC.

8550 Freeport Pkwy.
Irving, TX 75063
Phone: 972-753-6200
Fax: 972-753-6226
Web: www.atxg.com

CEO: Steven A. (Steve) Millstein
CFO: —
HR: Gwen Daniels
FYE: December 31
Type: Private

ATX Group takes its business in every direction. The company provides telematics services to automobile manufacturers primarily in the US and Europe, including BMW, Daimler (Maybach and Mercedes-Benz lines), PSA Group Peugeot, and Rolls-Royce. Drivers of telematics-enabled vehicles can utilize ATX's collision notification, emergency assistance, navigation, roadside diagnostics, stolen vehicle tracking, and traffic information services. In addition to managing a telematics service network and response centers, ATX provides dealer support, remote activation services, and maintenance. A division of Cross Country Automotive Services, the company operates from offices in Texas and Germany.

AUBURN NATIONAL BANCORPORATION, INC.

NASDAQ (CM): AUBN

100 N. Gay St.
Auburn, AL 36830
Phone: 334-821-9200
Fax: 334-887-2772
Web: www.auburnbank.com

CEO: E. L. Spencer Jr.
CFO: David A. Hedges
HR: Laura Carrington
FYE: December 31
Type: Public

War Eagle! Auburn National Bancorporation is the holding company for AuburnBank, which operates about 10 branches and a handful of loan offices in and around its headquarters in the eastern Alabama home of Auburn University. Formed in 1907, AuburnBank offers traditional retail banking services such as checking and savings accounts and CDs. Commercial real estate loans make up slightly more than half of the bank's loan portfolio, which also includes business loans and leases, residential mortgages, and consumer installment loans. CEO E. L. Spencer owns nearly 20% of Auburn National; vice chairman Emil Wright owns more than 10%.

	Annual Growth	12/05	12/06	12/07	12/08	12/09
Assets ($ mil.)	6.2%	608.2	635.1	688.7	746.0	773.4
Net income ($ mil.)	(22.0%)	6.5	6.6	6.9	6.6	2.4
Market value ($ mil.)	(2.9%)	80.7	105.3	80.0	73.2	71.7
Employees	3.7%	133	137	147	148	154

AUBURN UNIVERSITY

202 Martin Hall
Auburn, AL 36849
Phone: 334-844-4000
Fax: 334-844-3585
Web: www.auburn.edu

CEO: Jay Gogue
CFO: Donald L. Large Jr.
HR: Lynne Hammond
FYE: September 30
Type: School

Most of us bleed red, but students and alumni of this university bleed auburn. One of the largest schools in the South, Auburn University has an enrollment of more than 24,000 students and offers bachelor's, master's, and doctoral degrees in more than 125 different fields of study through about a dozen colleges and schools. It also has a branch campus in Montgomery, Alabama. Auburn was founded by the Alabama Conference of the Methodist Episcopal Church in 1856 as the East Alabama Male College. It became a state institution in 1872 and adopted its current name in 1960.

	Annual Growth	9/04	9/05	9/06	9/07	9/08
Est. sales ($ mil.)	—	—	—	—	—	486.2
Employees	—	—	—	—	—	6,000

AUDIBLE, INC.

1 Washington Park
Newark, NJ 07102
Phone: 973-820-0400
Fax: 973-820-0505
Web: www.audible.com

CEO: Donald R. Katz
CFO: William H. (Bill) Mitchell
HR: —
FYE: December 31
Type: Subsidiary

Audible has a story to tell. It sells downloadable audio versions of books, as well as radio broadcasts, speeches, and other spoken word performances, via its Audible Web site. Some 50,000 titles are available. Users can buy individual titles or subscribe to AudibleListener to download content. Users can listen to programs on their computer, or via an MP3 player or PDA. Subscribers to a recurring title (newspaper, magazine, radio program) can have it automatically delivered to their PC, or wirelessly to their handheld device. Audible also offers a CD burning feature for listening on CD players, and has international versions of its site for the UK, France, and Germany. Amazon.com bought the company in 2008.

	Annual Growth	12/04	12/05	12/06	12/07	12/08
Est. sales ($ mil.)	—	—	—	—	—	38.2
Employees	—	—	—	—	—	180

An in-depth profile of this company is available to Hoover's Online members at hoovers.com.

AUDIO VISUAL SERVICES GROUP, INC.

111 W. Ocean Blvd., Ste. 1110
Long Beach, CA 90802
Phone: 562-366-0620
Fax: 562-366-0628
Web: www.psav.com

CEO: Digby J. Davies
CFO: J. Michael (Mike) McIlwain
HR: Kate Daly
FYE: September 30
Type: Cooperative

This company puts a little show biz into business. Audio Visual Services Group, doing business as PSAV Presentation Services (PSAV), rents and sells audiovisual equipment and provides staging services and related technology support for live events and meetings. It offers onsite lighting, sound, and projection equipment, as well as video recording and broadcasting equipment and services. PSAV additionally provides staging and exhibit displays, as well as planning and consulting services. The company serves meeting planners, producers, associations, and corporations in the US, Canada, Mexico, and Europe through more than 800 US and international locations.

AUGUSTA SPORTSWEAR GROUP

425 Park West Dr.
Grovetown, GA 30813
Phone: 706-860-4633
Fax: 706-868-5672
Web: www.augustasportswear.com

CEO: Jon Letzler
CFO: Pat Harris
HR: Mike Holliman
FYE: February 28
Type: Private

Because naked athletes aren't likely to be supported, people turn to Augusta Sportswear Group. The company makes non-branded athletic apparel, such as tops, warm-ups, jackets, and headwear, as well as team uniforms. It also markets bags, aprons, and other accessories. The firm's brands include Augusta Sportswear, Holloway Sportswear, High Five Sportswear, and Jones & Mitchell. Among its customers are uniform suppliers, athletics teams and leagues, decorators, distributors, and sporting goods stores. Augusta Sportswear Group was founded in 1977. It was acquired in 2008 by investment firm Quad-C Management and members of the sportswear maker's management team.

AUDIO-TECHNICA U.S., INC.

1221 Commerce Dr.
Stow, OH 44224
Phone: 330-686-2600
Fax: 330-688-3752
Web: www.audio-technica.com

CEO: Philip (Phil) Cajka
CFO: Bruce Vanzo
HR: —
FYE: March 31
Type: Subsidiary

Audio-Technica U.S. wants its customers to get wired, or wireless if that's the preferred method. The company distributes sound equipment to consumers and professional users primarily in North America. Audio-Technica's products include wired and wireless microphones, headphones, audio mixers, and related accessories, such as microphone mounts, windscreens, and cables. It also makes turntables, cartridges, and styli. Formed in 1972, Audio-Technica U.S. is a subsidiary of Japan's Audio-Technica Corporation. The company's microphones have been used for such high-profile events as the GRAMMY Awards, the Rock & Roll Hall of Fame's induction ceremonies, and the US presidential debates.

	Annual Growth	3/04	3/05	3/06	3/07	3/08
Est. sales ($ mil.)	—	—	—	—	—	70.0
Employees	—	—	—	—	—	120

AUNTIE ANNE'S, INC.

48-50 W. Chestnut St., Ste. 200
Lancaster, PA 17603
Phone: 717-435-1435
Fax: 717-435-1436
Web: www.auntieannes.com

CEO: Samuel R. (Sam) Beiler
CFO: Jim Moss
HR: Dawn N. Moslander
FYE: December 31
Type: Private

You don't have to be twisted to enjoy one of these pretzels. Auntie Anne's is a leading franchisor of snack outlets, with about 1,000 pretzel stores located in some 45 states and 20 other countries. The stores offer a variety of pretzel flavors, including original, cinnamon sugar, garlic, almond, and sesame, as well as the popular pretzel-wrapped hot dog. They are primarily found in high-traffic areas, such as malls, airports, train stations, and stadiums. Anne Beiler started the company in 1988 to help fund a faith-based family assistance foundation. Sam Beiler, a cousin, bought the company in 2005.

	Annual Growth	12/04	12/05	12/06	12/07	12/08
Sales ($ mil.)	7.9%	—	—	—	309.0	333.4
Employees	0.0%	—	—	—	200	200

AUDIOVOX CORPORATION

NASDAQ (GM): VOXX

180 Marcus Blvd.
Hauppauge, NY 11788
Phone: 631-231-7750
Fax: 631-434-3995
Web: www.audiovox.com

CEO: Patrick M. (Pat) Lavelle
CFO: Charles M. Stoehr
HR: Liz O'Connell
FYE: February 28
Type: Public

Audiovox answers the call for electronics. The company sells primarily consumer electronics for communications, mobile, and home use and acts as an original equipment manufacturer (OEM) for car makers. Products include automotive security devices, digital picture frames, HD TV antennae, stereo and speaker systems, portable DVD players, two-way radios, and universal remotes. Its goods are marketed under such brand names as Acoustic Research, Advent, Audiovox, Code-Alarm, Energizer, Jensen, Mac Audio, and Terk, among others. Audiovox's distribution network is composed of major retailers, distributors, car dealers, and other OEMs. Founded by its chairman John Shalam in 1960, Audiovox went public in 1987.

	Annual Growth	11/04	11/05	*2/07	2/08	2/09
Sales ($ mil.)	1.6%	567.1	539.7	456.7	591.4	603.1
Net income ($ mil.)	—	77.2	(9.6)	2.9	8.5	(71.0)
Market value ($ mil.)	(34.2%)	342.1	316.5	345.5	206.0	64.1
Employees	1.0%	770	750	840	1,000	800
					*Fiscal year change	

AURA SYSTEMS, INC.

OTC: AUSI

2330 Utah Ave.
El Segundo, CA 90245
Phone: 310-643-5300
Fax: 310-643-7457
Web: www.aurasystems.com

CEO: Melvin Gagerman
CFO: Melvin Gagerman
HR: —
FYE: February 28
Type: Public

Aura Systems is charging ahead with its AuraGen electric generator, which can produce 8,500 watts of power from an idling car engine. Companies in the telecommunications, utilities, and oil and gas industries use the AuraGen to generate mobile power; the military version of the AuraGen is marketed as the VIPER. RV maker Country Coach announced plans in 2004 to install the AuraGen on its Prevost model. Aura Systems also is entitled to royalties from Daewoo Electronics for use of electro-optical technology found in projection TVs. The company gets about 80% of its sales in the US.

	Annual Growth	2/05	2/06	2/07	2/08	2/09
Sales ($ mil.)	(1.0%)	2.5	1.8	1.6	2.8	2.4
Net income ($ mil.)	—	(28.3)	6.9	(6.2)	(9.0)	(9.8)
Employees	6.9%	46	29	47	59	60

AURORA BANK FSB

Brandywine Bldg., 1000 West St., Ste. 200
Wilmington, DE 19801
Phone: 302-654-6179
Fax: 302-428-3673
Web: www.aurorabankfsb.com

CEO: William E. (Bill) Lighten
CFO: —
HR: —
FYE: November 30
Type: Subsidiary

Aurora Bank (formerly Lehman Brothers Bank) offers retail banking services such as checking accounts, money market and retirement accounts, certificates of deposit, credit cards, fixed- and adjustable-rate home mortgages, and mortgage refinancing to customers nationwide on the Web and from two branches in New Jersey and Delaware. It also provides financing to mortgage brokers and owns mortgage lender Aurora Loan Services. Parent company Lehman Brothers filed for bankruptcy protection in September 2008, but Aurora Bank was not part of the filing.

AURORA CASKET COMPANY, INC.

10944 Marsh Rd.
Aurora, IN 47001
Phone: 812-926-1111
Fax: 800-457-1112
Web: www.auroracasket.com

CEO: William E. (Bill) Barrott III
CFO: Tom Heintz
HR: Kirk Flory
FYE: December 31
Type: Private

Aurora Casket Company won't meet you at the Pearly Gates, but it will get you there in style. The largest privately owned casket and cremation urn manufacturer nationwide, it sells its products directly to licensed funeral homes through 60 US service centers. Though known for its stainless-steel line, Aurora Caskets makes caskets in a variety of woods and metals. Its cremation offerings extend beyond urns to include memorial markers, tablets, and plaques. It also provides online information on funeral planning and grief support and offers consulting, software, and Web site design services to funeral homes. Founded in 1890 by John Backman with 30 employees, Aurora Casket is owned and managed by his descendants.

AURORA LOAN SERVICES LLC

10350 Park Meadows Dr.
Littleton, CO 80124
Phone: 720-945-3000
Fax: 720-945-3084
Web: www.alservices.com

CEO: Craig Wildrick
CFO: —
HR: Mary Bowman
FYE: November 30
Type: Subsidiary

The ancient Romans worshiped Aurora, goddess of the dawn. Today, homebuyers might worship Aurora Loan Services, a company that represents, for some, the dawn of the American Dream. Aurora Loan Services originates prime and nonprime residential mortgage loans through its direct lending channel. It services the loans as well and is one of the top residential loan servicers in the US. Parent company Lehman Brothers filed for bankruptcy in 2008, but, as a subsidiary of that firm's Aurora Bank (formerly Lehman Brothers Bank) division, Aurora Loan Services was not included in the filing.

AURORA OIL & GAS CORPORATION

4110 Copper Ridge Dr., Ste. 100
Traverse City, MI 49684
Phone: 231-941-0073
Fax: 231-933-0757
Web: www.auroraogc.com

Pink Sheets: AOGS

CEO: Sanford Edlein
CFO: Barbara E. Lawson
HR: –
FYE: December 31
Type: Public

The drilling of oil and gas wells has an aura of profitability for independent Aurora Oil & Gas (formerly Cadence Resources), which has exploration and production projects primarily in Indiana, Kentucky, and Michigan. The company focuses on developing unconventional gas reservoirs such as black shales, coal seams, and tight sands, including the black shales of Michigan and Indiana. It has more than 1.2 million gross acres of undeveloped land. Aurora Oil & Gas has estimated net proved reserves of more than 166 billion cu. ft. of natural gas equivalent. Saddled by heavy debt, the company filed for Chapter 11 bankruptcy protection in 2009.

	Annual Growth	9/05	*12/05	12/06	12/07	†12/08
Sales ($ mil.)	85.8%	2.5	7.4	23.1	28.5	29.8
Net income ($ mil.)	—	(4.8)	(0.5)	(1.9)	(4.4)	(107.4)
Market value ($ mil.)	(62.1%)	346.0	468.9	331.5	160.1	7.1
Employees	18.5%	32	47	90	68	63

*Fiscal year change †Most recent year available

AUSTIN COCA-COLA BOTTLING COMPANY

9600 Burnet Rd.
Austin, TX 78758
Phone: 512-836-7272
Fax: 512-832-2515

CEO: Terri Gann
CFO: —
HR: —
FYE: December 31
Type: Subsidiary

The Austin Coca-Cola Bottling Company is a regional bottling unit of Coca-Cola Enterprises, the world's largest Coke bottler. The company bottles and distributes Coca-Cola products, including soft drinks, juices, and bottled water. Austin Coca-Cola Bottling also has an exclusive agreement with the Austin Independent School District to supply Coke beverage products to the district's schools.

AUSTIN INDUSTRIES, INC.

3535 Travis St., Ste. 300
Dallas, TX 75204
Phone: 214-443-5500
Fax: —
Web: www.austin-ind.com

CEO: Ronald J. (Ron) Gafford
CFO: JT Fisher
HR: James (Jim) Schranz
FYE: December 31
Type: Private

Belying its name, Austin Industries is actually based in Dallas. The company provides civil, commercial, and industrial construction services in the southern half of the US. Its oldest subsidiary, Austin Bridge & Road, provides road, bridge, and parking lot construction across Texas. (It built the longest bridge in Texas, the Queen Isabella Causeway.) Subsidiary Austin Commercial builds office buildings, technology sites, hospitals, and other commercial projects. The group's Austin Industrial arm provides construction, maintenance, and electrical services for the chemical, refining, power, and manufacturing industries. The employee-owned company was founded in 1918.

	Annual Growth	12/04	12/05	12/06	12/07	12/08
Sales ($ mil.)	12.9%	1,230.0	1,359.0	1,310.0	1,700.0	2,000.0
Employees	3.1%	5,300	6,000	6,000	5,600	6,000

AUSTRALIAN-CANADIAN OIL ROYALTIES LTD.
OTC: AUCAF

1301 Ave. M	CEO: Andre Sakhai
Cisco, TX 76437	CFO: Mahnaz (Michelle) Nourmand
Phone: 254-442-2638	HR: —
Fax: 254-442-3843	FYE: December 31
Web: www.aussieoil.com	Type: Public

Its British Commonwealth perspective recognizes royalties, and more. Australian-Canadian Oil Royalties explores for and produces oil and natural gas from properties located in Australia. Originally formed as a trust, the company did not operate or control any of its properties until 2005, when Australian-Canadian Oil Royalties decided to become an oil and gas explorer as well. The company's principal assets are 15.8 million gross acres of royalty interest in Australia's Cooper-Eromanga and Gippsland Basins. It also has minor oil and gas assets in the US (in Kentucky). Director Robert Kamon controls about 22% of Australian-Canadian Oil Royalties; president Ely Sakhai owns about 19%.

	Annual Growth	12/05	12/06	12/07	12/08	12/09
Sales ($ mil.)	—	0.0	0.0	0.1	0.1	0.1
Net income ($ mil.)	—	(0.6)	(0.6)	(0.3)	(0.3)	(0.2)
Market value ($ mil.)	(17.5%)	5.3	5.8	9.4	2.5	2.4
Employees	(12.0%)	5	3	3	3	3

AUTHENTEC, INC.
NASDAQ (GM): AUTH

100 Rialto Rd., Ste. 400	CEO: F. Scott Moody
Melbourne, FL 32901	CFO: Gary Larsen
Phone: 321-308-1300	HR: —
Fax: 321-308-1430	FYE: December 31
Web: www.authentec.com	Type: Public

AuthenTec is good at fingering out who's using your electronic gear. The company designs biometric fingerprint sensor chips, a high-tech way to authenticate identity and to allow only authorized users to utilize the equipment. Electronics makers incorporate AuthenTec's TruePrint devices into a variety of goods, such as automotive subsystems, PCs, and wireless devices, with customers including Fujitsu (about 13% of sales), Fujitsu Siemens, Hewlett-Packard, Lenovo, Samsung, and Toshiba. The technology was originally developed within Harris Semiconductor, and AuthenTec was spun out of Harris Corporation. The company gets most of sales from the Asia/Pacific region.

	Annual Growth	12/05	12/06	12/07	12/08	12/09
Sales ($ mil.)	15.4%	19.2	33.2	52.3	63.9	34.1
Net income ($ mil.)	—	(6.6)	(9.8)	(10.9)	0.0	(17.4)
Market value ($ mil.)	(61.0%)	—	—	434.5	49.9	66.1
Employees	6.2%	99	97	115	130	126

⊞ AUTHENTIDATE HOLDING CORP.
NASDAQ (CM): ADAT

300 Connell Dr., 5th Fl.	CEO: O'Connell (Ben) Benjamin
Berkeley Heights, NJ 07922	CFO: William A. (Bill) Marshall
Phone: 908-787-1700	HR: —
Fax: 908-673-9920	FYE: June 30
Web: authentidate.com	Type: Public

AuthentiDate Holding puts its stamp on time-sensitive documents. The company provides secure workflow management services, such as electronic signing, identity management, and content authentication. In 2007 AuthentiDate sold its document management and systems integration businesses to a group of former officers; the sale enabled the company to better focus on its health care, e-billing, and other security application development. AuthentiDate's Web-based authentication services are utilized for managing digital documents, while its Inscrybe platform provides electronic signing, document exchange, and content authentication services for enterprises and health care providers.

	Annual Growth	6/05	6/06	6/07	6/08	6/09
Sales ($ mil.)	(20.9%)	17.6	16.6	5.0	6.1	6.9
Net income ($ mil.)	—	(19.2)	(17.8)	(15.1)	(15.8)	(9.4)
Market value ($ mil.)	(18.5%)	104.5	101.9	59.2	15.8	46.1
Employees	(14.7%)	123	141	74	70	65

AUTHORIA, INC.

300 5th Ave.	CEO: Joseph G. (Joe) Licata Jr.
Waltham, MA 02451	CFO: Stephen J. (Steve) Lifshatz
Phone: 781-530-2000	HR: Stephen Bruce
Fax: 781-530-2001	FYE: December 31
Web: www.authoria.com	Type: Private

Authoria has an authoritative view when it comes to human resources. The company provides human capital management software (also known as talent management software) that combines communications, compensation and performance management, succession planning, recruiting, and benefits plan administration applications. Its customers include Aetna, Bank of America, Carlson, Pepsi, Pfizer, Royal Caribbean Cruises, and Sears. Founded in 1997, the company was acquired in 2008 by Bedford Funding for about $63 million. As part of the deal, Bedford announced it was investing an additional $8 million in expanding Authoria's marketing and sales efforts.

AUTOALLIANCE INTERNATIONAL, INC.

1 International Dr.	CEO: Phil Spender
Flat Rock, MI 48134	CFO: Don Gellinas
Phone: 734-782-7800	HR: Rex Johnson
Fax: 734-783-8216	FYE: December 31
	Type: Joint venture

Two heads are better than one at AutoAlliance International. A joint venture between Ford Motor and Mazda, the company is a contract manufacturer of the Mazda6 and Ford Mustang. AutoAlliance's history traces back to 1984 when Mazda built a plant in Michigan to make the Mazda MX-6 and called the new company Mazda Motor Manufacturing (USA) Corporation (MMUC). In 1992 MMUC teamed up with Ford and the name of the company took its present form. In addition to its current model lineup, AutoAlliance International produces the Mazda 626 and Mustang GT500.

	Annual Growth	12/04	12/05	12/06	12/07	12/08
Est. sales ($ mil.)	—	—	—	—	—	418.9
Employees	—	—	—	—	—	3,200

⊞ AUTOBYTEL INC.
NASDAQ (GM): ABTL

18872 MacArthur Blvd.	CEO: Jeffrey H. Coats
Irvine, CA 92612	CFO: Curtis E. DeWalt
Phone: 949-225-4500	HR: —
Fax: 949-225-4557	FYE: December 31
Web: www.autobytel.com	Type: Public

Autobytel puts cars on the information superhighway. Using the Autobytel's network of websites, a potential car buyer can complete an online request form for the desired new or used car. The form is forwarded to local auto dealers and manufacturers, who contact the shopper within 24 hours. Autobytel generates most of its revenue through lead referral fees it charges dealers and manufacturers (car buyers pay no fees). However, the company also operates advertising-driven websites such as Autoweb.com (Internet car buying), CarSmart.com (vehicle data), AutoSite.com (resource for entry-level buyers), Car.com (consumer auto portal), CarTV.com (multimedia content), and MyRide.com (flagship auto site for consumers).

	Annual Growth	12/05	12/06	12/07	12/08	12/09
Sales ($ mil.)	(19.4%)	125.3	111.1	84.4	71.2	52.9
Net income ($ mil.)	—	(6.3)	(31.5)	(5.4)	(79.9)	(2.4)
Market value ($ mil.)	(32.9%)	223.1	158.1	124.2	20.3	45.2
Employees	(27.1%)	426	364	269	115	120

🏢 AUTOCAM CORPORATION

4436 Broadmoor SE
Kentwood, MI 49512
Phone: 616-698-0707
Fax: 616-698-6876
Web: www.autocam.com

CEO: John C. Kennedy
CFO: Warren A. Veltman
HR: Jim Wojczynski
FYE: December 31
Type: Private

Members of both the UAW and the AMA use Autocam's products. The company makes precision components for the automotive and medical device industries. Autocam makes parts used in automotive air bags, brake systems, electric motors, fuel systems, and power steering systems. The company's medical components are used in the manufacture of stents, joint implants, DNA testing equipment, and ophthalmic and surgical devices. Autocam also offers machined components for power tools. Investment firm Aurora Capital Group sold Autocam in 2004 to investors including GS Capital, Roger Penske, and Autocam president and CEO John Kennedy.

	Annual Growth	12/04	12/05	12/06	12/07	12/08
Est. sales ($ mil.)	—	—	—	—	—	132.5
Employees	—	—	—	—	—	2,300

🏢 AUTODESK, INC.

NASDAQ (GS): ADSK

111 McInnis Pkwy.
San Rafael, CA 94903
Phone: 415-507-5000
Fax: 415-507-5100
Web: usa.autodesk.com

CEO: Carl Bass
CFO: Mark J. Hawkins
HR: Jan Becker
FYE: January 31
Type: Public

Autodesk has creative designs on moving past the desks of architects. The company is a provider of computer-aided design (CAD) software. Its flagship AutoCAD product is used primarily by architects and engineers to design, draft, and model products and buildings. Autodesk's other products include geographic information systems (GIS) packages for mapping and precision drawing software for drafting. The company also develops multimedia tools for digital content creation, including applications for animation, film editing, and creating special effects. In addition, Autodesk offers professional consulting and training services.

	Annual Growth	1/06	1/07	1/08	1/09	1/10
Sales ($ mil.)	3.0%	1,523.2	1,839.8	2,171.9	2,315.2	1,713.7
Net income ($ mil.)	(35.2%)	328.9	289.7	356.2	183.6	58.0
Market value ($ mil.)	(12.5%)	9,313.9	10,032.1	9,442.4	3,799.9	5,458.9
Employees	9.0%	4,813	5,169	7,300	7,800	6,800

AUTO-GRAPHICS, INC.

3201 Temple Ave., Ste. 100
Pomona, CA 91768
Phone: 909-595-7004
Fax: 909-595-3506
Web: www4.auto-graphics.com

CEO: Paul R. Cope
CFO: —
HR: —
FYE: December 31
Type: Subsidiary

Auto-Graphics makes software that puts library catalogs at your fingertips. The company's AGent library management system is a modular tool that allows users to search multiple databases, including full-text repositories, the Web, and local catalogs, through a single search interface. AGent is offered through licenses or as a hosted service to more than 10,000 libraries in North America. The company (originally founded in 1950) is a subsidiary of Agent Information Software, which was created in 2009 to serve as a parent company of Auto-Graphics and other potential business ventures.

AUTOGRILL GROUP, INC.

6905 Rockledge Dr.
Bethesda, MD 20817
Phone: 240-694-4100
Fax: 240-694-4790
Web: www.hmshost.com

CEO: Elie W. Maalouf
CFO: Mark Ratych
HR: Chuck Powers
FYE: December 31
Type: Subsidiary

Autogrill Group knows some travelers hunger for more than just transportation. Operating as HMSHost, the company is a leading contract foodservices operator focused on the travel market with restaurant operations in more than 100 airports in North America, Europe, and parts of the Asia/Pacific. Its eateries operate under such licensed brands as Burger King, Chili's Too (owned by Brinker International), and Starbucks, as well as proprietary names Fresh Attractions Deli and Flatbreadz. HMSHost also has service operations at more than 80 highway rest areas; it runs newsstands and other retail locations in addition to restaurants. HMSHost is a unit of Italian contract foodservices giant Autogrill.

AUTOINFO, INC.

OTC: AUTO

6413 Congress Ave., Ste. 260
Boca Raton, FL 33487
Phone: 561-988-9456
Fax: 561-994-8033
Web: www.suntecktransport.com

CEO: Harry M. Wachtel
CFO: William I. (Bill) Wunderlich
HR: —
FYE: December 31
Type: Public

Once an automobile financing company, AutoInfo is still focused on transportation — but of goods, not people. Through its subsidiary Sunteck Transport, the company acts as a freight broker, arranging the transportation of freight for customers in the US and Canada through alliances with both truckload and less-than-truckload carriers, along with air, rail, and ocean transportation providers. Separately, Sunteck Transport acts as a contract carrier, generating business through a network of sales agents and contracting with truck owner-operators to haul customers' freight. Sunteck Transport doesn't own any transportation equipment of its own.

	Annual Growth	12/05	12/06	12/07	12/08	12/09
Sales ($ mil.)	28.2%	68.0	84.1	110.3	180.2	183.9
Net income ($ mil.)	(21.0%)	3.6	3.6	1.6	2.2	1.4
Market value ($ mil.)	(8.9%)	19.4	34.5	22.8	11.4	13.4
Employees	15.4%	35	45	52	52	62

AUTOLIV ASP, INC.

1320 Pacific Dr.
Auburn Hills, MI 48326
Phone: 248-475-9000
Fax: —
Web: www.autoliv.com

CEO: Michael Ward
CFO: Dave Braegger
HR: Kris Bessinger
FYE: December 31
Type: Subsidiary

Autoliv ASP, Inc., the North American subsidiary of Sweden-based Autoliv Inc., designs and manufactures automobile safety restraint systems. The subsidiary manufactures airbag inflators (the highest-cost item in making an airbag module), seatbelts, cushions, steering wheels, electronics, seat subsystems, and other automotive products. It also provides testing of automotive safety products for vehicle manufacturers. In addition to providing engineering design of products, the company is involved in research and development of driver and passenger airbag inflators, side impact airbag inflators, and inflatable curtain airbags. Autoliv ASP, with about a dozen locations across the US, was founded in 1996.

	Annual Growth	12/04	12/05	12/06	12/07	12/08
Est. sales ($ mil.)	—	—	—	—	—	1,635.4
Employees	—	—	—	—	—	7,250

🏢 An in-depth profile of this company is available to Hoover's Online members at hoovers.com.

195

AUTOMATIC DATA PROCESSING, INC.

NASDAQ (GS): ADP

1 ADP Blvd.
Roseland, NJ 07068
Phone: 973-974-5000
Fax: 973-974-3334
Web: www.adp.com

CEO: Gary C. Butler
CFO: Christopher R. (Chris) Reidy
HR: Benito Cachinero
FYE: June 30
Type: Public

The original outsourcer, Automatic Data Processing (ADP) has still got it. ADP is one of the largest payroll and tax filing processors in the world, serving about 570,000 clients. Employer services account for the majority of the company's sales; ADP also provides inventory and other computing and data services to some 25,000 auto, motorcycle, truck, and recreational vehicle dealers. Other offerings include accounting, auto collision estimates for insurers, employment background checks, desktop applications support, and business development training services. ADP also provides outsourcing services to Broadridge Financial Solutions, its former brokerage services division it spun off in 2007.

	Annual Growth	6/05	6/06	6/07	6/08	6/09
Sales ($ mil.)	1.1%	8,499.7	8,881.5	7,800.0	8,776.5	8,867.1
Net income ($ mil.)	6.0%	1,055.4	1,554.0	1,138.7	1,235.7	1,332.6
Market value ($ mil.)	(1.5%)	18,962.3	20,489.4	24,379.8	21,075.2	17,825.9
Employees	0.6%	44,000	46,000	46,000	47,000	45,000

AUTOMOBILE CLUB OF SOUTHERN CALIFORNIA

2601 S. Figueroa St.
Los Angeles, CA 90007
Phone: 213-741-3686
Fax: 213-741-4890
Web: www.aaa-calif.com

CEO: Thomas V. McKernan
CFO: John F. Boyle
HR: James (Jim) Philipp
FYE: December 31
Type: Not-for-profit

Ready to ride to the rescue for cars that have gone south in SoCal is the Automobile Club of Southern California. The largest member of the American Automobile Association (AAA) federation of motor clubs, the Auto Club of Southern California is a not-for-profit that serves about 6 million members from 70-plus offices in about a dozen counties. The club provides 24-hour roadside assistance, travel planning, auto pricing, buying, and maintenance services, as well as a host of insurance plans. In addition, members can renew vehicle registrations, plates, and stickers at club offices. The club also publishes *Westways* magazine, which offers travel tips and discounts. Ten auto enthusiasts founded the club in 1900.

	Annual Growth	12/04	12/05	12/06	12/07	12/08
Est. sales ($ mil.)	—	—	—	—	—	544.5
Employees	—	—	—	—	—	8,051

AUTOMOTIVE FINANCE CORPORATION

13085 Hamilton Crossing Blvd., Ste. 300
Carmel, IN 46032
Phone: 317-815-9645
Fax: 317-815-1477
Web: www.afcdealer.com

CEO: Donald S. (Don) Gottwald
CFO: Jim Money
HR: —
FYE: December 31
Type: Subsidiary

Automotive Finance Corp. (AFC) is where auto dealers go to make a deal. The firm finances floor planning, or inventory purchases, for independent used car dealers that buy vehicles from sister company ADESA Auctions, as well as independent auctions, auctions affiliated with other networks, and non-auction purchases. Through more than 80 North American offices (about half of which are located at ADESA sites) AFC provides short-term (30- to 60-day) loans; it sells most of its finance receivables to subsidiary, AFC Funding Corp., which then sells them to a bank conduit facility. Proceeds from the revolving sale of receivables are used to fund new loans. AFC is a subsidiary of KAR Auction Services.

AUTONATION, INC.

NYSE: AN

200 SW 1st Ave.
Fort Lauderdale, FL 33301
Phone: 954-769-6000
Fax: 954-769-6537
Web: corp.autonation.com

CEO: Michael J. (Mike) Jackson
CFO: Michael J. (Mike) Short
HR: Julie Staub
FYE: December 31
Type: Public

AutoNation wants to instill patriotic fervor in the fickle car-buying public. The brainchild of entrepreneur and ex-chairman Wayne Huizenga (Waste Management, Blockbuster Video), AutoNation is the #1 car dealer in the US (ahead of Penske Automotive Group and Group 1 Automotive). The firm owns about 250 new-vehicle franchises (down from 300 in 2008) in 15 states, and it conducts online sales through AutoNation.com and individual dealer websites. AutoNation operates under different brands in local markets (including Mike Shad in Jacksonville, Florida, and Go in Colorado). In addition to auto sales, AutoNation provides maintenance and repair services, sells auto parts, and finances and insures vehicles.

	Annual Growth	12/05	12/06	12/07	12/08	12/09
Sales ($ mil.)	(13.5%)	19,253.4	18,988.6	17,691.5	14,131.9	10,757.8
Net income ($ mil.)	(20.5%)	496.5	316.9	278.7	(1,243.1)	198.0
Market value ($ mil.)	(3.1%)	3,655.2	3,586.2	2,634.2	1,661.9	3,221.2
Employees	(9.6%)	27,000	26,000	25,000	20,000	18,000

AUTO-OWNERS INSURANCE GROUP

6101 Anacapri Blvd.
Lansing, MI 48917
Phone: 517-323-1200
Fax: 517-323-8796
Web: www.auto-owners.com

CEO: Ron H. Simon
CFO: —
HR: —
FYE: December 31
Type: Private

There's more to Auto-Owners Insurance Group than the name implies. In addition to auto coverage, the company provides a range of personal property/casualty and life insurance products including disability and annuities. Auto-Owners Insurance operates through its aptly named subsidiaries (including Auto-Owners Life Insurance, Home-Owners Insurance, and Property-Owners Insurance Company). Its Southern-Owners Insurance subsidiary offers property/casualty insurance in Florida. Auto-Owners Insurance also sells commercial auto, liability, and workers' compensation policies. Established in 1916, the company operates in 25 states nationwide and is represented by some 35,000 independent agents in about 6,000 agencies.

	Annual Growth	12/04	12/05	12/06	12/07	12/08
Sales ($ mil.)	1.2%	4,714.0	5,001.1	5,074.3	4,802.0	4,950.5
Net income ($ mil.)	1.9%	190.6	623.1	634.3	466.8	205.5
Employees	1.0%	3,270	3,300	3,400	3,400	3,400

AUTOTRADER.COM, L.L.C.

5775 Peachtree Dunwoody Rd., Ste. A-200
Atlanta, GA 30342
Phone: 404-843-5000
Fax: 404-568-3060
Web: www.autotrader.com

CEO: Victor A. (Chip) Perry III
CFO: —
HR: —
FYE: December 31
Type: Subsidiary

AutoTrader.com gives the Internet its very own Motor Mile. The company operates the largest used vehicle website, with more than 3 million vehicle listings from both private owners and dealers. It draws an average of about 15 million visitors a month to browse through its extensive site, which also features related content, such as vehicle reviews, warranty information, insurance, and financing. In addition to used cars and trucks, the site offers listings for motorcycles and classic cars for collectors (at AutoTrader Classics), as well as some new cars. AutoTrader.com generates revenue from its paid listings and from other advertising. Launched in 1998, AutoTrader.com is owned by Cox Enterprises.

	Annual Growth	12/04	12/05	12/06	12/07	12/08
Est. sales ($ mil.)	—	—	—	—	—	516.5
Employees	—	—	—	—	—	2,167

AUTOZONE, INC.
NYSE: AZO

123 S. Front St.
Memphis, TN 38103
Phone: 901-495-6500
Fax: 901-495-8300
Web: www.autozone.com

CEO: William C. (Bill) Rhodes III
CFO: William T. (Bill) Giles
HR: Ann A. Morgan
FYE: August 31
Type: Public

Imagine that you are in your garage making some weekend car repairs. The wheel cylinders are leaking . . . the brake shoe adjuster nut is rusted solid . . . you're about to enter . . . the AutoZone. With some 4,230 stores in the US and Puerto Rico, AutoZone is the nation's #1 auto parts chain. It also operates more than 185 stores in Mexico. AutoZone stores sell hard parts (alternators, engines, batteries), maintenance items (oil, antifreeze), accessories (car stereos, floor mats), and non-automotive merchandise under brand names as well as under private labels, including Duralast and Valucraft. AutoZone's commercial sales program distributes parts and other products to garages, dealerships, and other businesses.

	Annual Growth	8/05	8/06	8/07	8/08	8/09
Sales ($ mil.)	4.5%	5,710.9	5,948.4	6,169.8	6,522.7	6,816.8
Net income ($ mil.)	3.6%	571.0	569.3	595.7	641.6	657.0
Market value ($ mil.)	11.7%	4,607.8	4,403.0	5,914.1	6,691.3	7,179.9
Employees	3.6%	52,000	53,000	55,000	57,000	60,000

AUXILIO, INC.
OTC: AUXO

27401 Los Altos, Ste. 100
Mission Viejo, CA 92691
Phone: 949-614-0700
Fax: 949-614-0701
Web: www.auxilioinc.com

CEO: Joseph J. (Joe) Flynn
CFO: Paul T. Anthony
HR: —
FYE: December 31
Type: Public

Hospitals count on Auxilio to streamline their printing processes; you can print, copy, scan, and fax that. The company is a managed print services provider, meaning it does not sell printing equipment and related supplies. Rather, it is vendor neutral and procures different makes and models of equipment depending on the needs of its US health care industry clients, which include California Pacific Medical Center, Saddleback Memorial Medical Center, and St. Joseph Health System. Often working with IT departments, Auxilio's consultants assess clients' print environments and assist them with plans to minimize costs on supplies that will maximize their productivity and also reduce unnecessary paper waste.

	Annual Growth	12/05	12/06	12/07	12/08	12/09
Sales ($ mil.)	38.9%	4.3	10.2	19.6	21.0	16.0
Net income ($ mil.)	—	(3.4)	(3.9)	(0.1)	(0.1)	0.0
Market value ($ mil.)	(15.8%)	28.9	8.3	30.8	10.6	14.5
Employees	10.5%	51	60	70	80	76

AUXILIUM PHARMACEUTICALS, INC.
NASDAQ (GM): AUXL

40 Valley Stream Pkwy.
Malvern, PA 19355
Phone: 484-321-5900
Fax: 484-321-5999
Web: www.auxilium.com

CEO: Armando Anido
CFO: James E. (Jim) Fickenscher
HR: Jennifer Evans-Stacey
FYE: December 31
Type: Public

Auxilium Pharmaceuticals is supplementing men's manliness. The company develops treatments for urological and sexual health. Auxilium's lone marketed product is Testim, a topical testosterone gel used to treat hypogonadism (low or decreased testosterone production). To increase Testim's market penetration, Auxilium has entered into partnerships to disseminate its product abroad. Paladin Labs sells Testim in Canada, while Ferring International markets it in Europe. DPT Laboratories does the manufacturing. In addition to Testim, Auxilium is also researching treatments for unusual soft tissue conditions and pain.

	Annual Growth	12/05	12/06	12/07	12/08	12/09
Sales ($ mil.)	39.9%	42.8	68.5	95.7	125.4	164.0
Net income ($ mil.)	—	(38.3)	(45.9)	(40.7)	(46.3)	(53.5)
Market value ($ mil.)	52.8%	260.9	696.9	1,422.8	1,349.2	1,422.3
Employees	32.7%	174	278	300	340	540

AVALON CORRECTIONAL SERVICES, INC.
Pink Sheets: CITY

13401 Railway Dr.
Oklahoma City, OK 73114
Phone: 405-752-8802
Fax: 405-752-8852
Web: www.avaloncorrections.com

CEO: Donald E. Smith
CFO: Michael C. Bradley
HR: —
FYE: December 31
Type: Public

Avalon Correctional Services benefits from its captive market. The company manages about 10 community corrections facilities in four states: Colorado, Oklahoma, Texas, and Wyoming. Its facilities have a total capacity of some 2,600 beds. Avalon Correctional Services provides a variety of programs for offenders, who usually are within a few months of freedom. The company's services include drug abuse treatment, work release programs, family and individual counseling, and educational and vocational training. The company was founded in 1985 by CEO Donald E. Smith.

AVALON HOLDINGS CORPORATION
NYSE Amex: AWX

1 American Way
Warren, OH 44484
Phone: 330-856-8800
Fax: 330-856-8480
Web: www.avalonholdings.com

CEO: Steven M. Berry
CFO: Timothy C. Coxson
HR: —
FYE: December 31
Type: Public

The magical promise of this Avalon is waste management services and golf courses. Through its American Waste Management Services subsidiary, Avalon Holdings helps customers manage and dispose of wastes. Services include hazardous and nonhazardous waste brokerage and management services and captive landfill management services — management of landfills used exclusively by their owners. The company also operates two golf courses near its headquarters. The golf operations include the management of dining and banquet facilities and a travel agency. Chairman Ronald Klingle controls a 67% voting stake in Avalon Holdings.

	Annual Growth	12/05	12/06	12/07	12/08	12/09
Sales ($ mil.)	1.9%	34.2	39.3	45.4	49.0	36.9
Net income ($ mil.)	—	0.4	1.3	1.5	0.7	(0.8)
Market value ($ mil.)	(18.2%)	17.8	27.4	20.5	5.6	8.0
Employees	12.6%	143	152	167	217	230

AVALON OIL & GAS, INC.
OTC: AOGN

310 4th Ave. South
Minneapolis, MN 55415
Phone: 612-359-9020
Fax: 612-359-9017
Web: www.avalonoilinc.com

CEO: Kent A. Rodriguez
CFO: Kent A. Rodriguez
HR: —
FYE: March 31
Type: Public

Avalon Oil & Gas is looking for that legendary prize — making consistent profits in the oil business. The company focuses on acquiring mature oil and gas wells in Kansas, Louisiana, Oklahoma, and Texas and in 2009 it reported proved reserves of about 45,650 barrels of oil equivalent. In addition to its oil and gas assets, Avalon Oil & Gas' technology segment (through majority-owned Oiltek) provides explorers with oil production enhancing technologies. To develop this segment the company has a strategic partnership with UK technology group UTEK. CEO Kent Rodriguez owns 46% of Avalon Oil & Gas.

	Annual Growth	3/05	3/06	3/07	3/08	3/09
Sales ($ mil.)	—	—	—	0.0	0.2	0.3
Net income ($ mil.)	—	—	—	(3.4)	(3.2)	(2.1)
Market value ($ mil.)	(85.6%)	—	—	110.5	14.5	2.3
Employees	0.0%	—	—	2	2	2

An in-depth profile of this company is available to Hoover's Online members at hoovers.com.

197

AVALONBAY COMMUNITIES, INC.   NYSE: AVB

2900 Eisenhower Ave., Ste. 300
Alexandria, VA 22314
Phone: 703-329-6300
Fax: 703-329-1459
Web: www.avalonbay.com

CEO: Bryce Blair
CFO: Thomas J. (Tom) Sargeant
HR: Charlene Rothkopf
FYE: December 31
Type: Public

AvalonBay Communities likes to go where the living is easy but the rules are strict. AvalonBay develops, acquires, refurbishes, leases, and manages apartment complexes. The real estate investment trust (REIT) focuses on upscale areas where low supplies of apartment-zoned land drives up demand and rent prices. AvalonBay owns about 170 apartment complexes containing more than 50,000 apartments in 10 states and Washington, DC. Most are branded under the Avalon name. Key markets include Boston and San Jose, California. Apartments are typically newer and upscale and offer such amenities as swimming pools, tennis courts, and patios; most are garden-style, but about three dozen are mid- or high-rise communities.

	Annual Growth	12/05	12/06	12/07	12/08	12/09
Sales ($ mil.)	6.2%	670.7	737.3	812.7	854.2	851.6
Net income ($ mil.)	(16.8%)	322.4	278.4	358.2	411.5	154.3
Market value ($ mil.)	(2.1%)	7,406.4	10,792.2	7,812.2	5,027.2	6,813.9
Employees	3.3%	1,647	1,767	1,989	1,830	1,877

AVANADE INC.

818 Stewart St., Ste. 400
Seattle, WA 98101
Phone: 206-239-5600
Fax: 206-239-5605
Web: www.avanade.com

CEO: Adam Warby
CFO: Steve Stone
HR: Simone Reynolds
FYE: September 30
Type: Subsidiary

Avanade tries to give its customers a fresh view into their own operations. A subsidiary of information technology services provider Accenture, the company provides IT consulting services centered primarily around Microsoft products. With customers and offices worldwide, Avanade helps large corporations with the design, implementation, and support of software systems related to communications, operations management, resource planning, and customer relationship management (CRM). A large portion of Avanade's business comes from subcontracting services provided to its parent company and minority shareholder Microsoft. The company's other clients have included European electricity company Vattenfall and EMI Music.

AVANIR PHARMACEUTICALS   NASDAQ (GM): AVNR

101 Enterprise, Ste. 300
Aliso Viejo, CA 92656
Phone: 949-389-6700
Fax: 949-643-6800
Web: www.avanir.com

CEO: Keith A. Katkin
CFO: Christine G. Ocampo
HR: Michael McFadden
FYE: September 30
Type: Public

Baseball players and AVANIR Pharmaceuticals know: A sacrifice is sometimes the only way to get ahead. The drug development firm in 2007 opted to sacrifice its marketed schizophrenia drug, FazaClo, in order to advance lead candidate Zenvia in clinical trials. It sold FazaClo, which it had bought just the year before; it is using the proceeds to continue developing Zenvia as a treatment for pseudobulbar affect — the involuntary crying or laughing experienced by some people with such neurological disorders as Lou Gehrig's disease and multiple sclerosis. Zenvia is also in late-stage trials for diabetic neuropathic pain.

	Annual Growth	9/05	9/06	9/07	9/08	9/09
Sales ($ mil.)	(29.2%)	16.7	15.2	9.2	7.0	4.2
Net income ($ mil.)	—	(30.6)	(58.9)	(20.9)	(17.5)	(22.0)
Market value ($ mil.)	(36.0%)	1,049.8	586.1	181.8	49.3	176.7
Employees	(28.4%)	76	150	25	20	20

AVANTAIR INC.   OTC: AAIR

4311 General Howard Dr.
Clearwater, FL 33762
Phone: 727-539-0071
Fax: 727-539-7007
Web: www.avantair.com

CEO: Steven F. (Steve) Santo
CFO: Richard A. Pytak Jr.
HR: —
FYE: June 30
Type: Public

As an alternative to a seat on a commercial jet, Avantair offers a share of a private jet. The company sells fractional ownership interests in Piaggio Avanti P.180 jet aircraft. More expensive than commercial flights, but cheaper than owning a plane, fractional ownership of the fuel-efficient light jets enables travelers to schedule their own flights, generally from smaller airports. Ownership can be purchased in increments beginning with a 1/16th share of a jet, which covers 50 hours of flight time per year. The company's fleet includes about 50 Avanti aircraft. Avantair, which operates from facilities in California, Florida, and New Jersey, offers service throughout the US, Canada, Mexico, and the Bahamas.

	Annual Growth	6/05	6/06	6/07	6/08	6/09
Sales ($ mil.)	33.8%	—	—	76.4	115.6	136.8
Net income ($ mil.)	—	—	—	(21.7)	(18.9)	(4.5)
Market value ($ mil.)	(52.7%)	—	—	135.6	51.1	30.3
Employees	24.3%	—	—	288	403	445

AVATAR HOLDINGS INC.   NASDAQ (GS): AVTR

201 Alhambra Cir.
Coral Gables, FL 33134
Phone: 305-442-7000
Fax: 305-448-9927
Web: www.avatarhomes.com

CEO: Gerald D. Kelfer
CFO: Randy L. Kotler
HR: —
FYE: December 31
Type: Public

Avatar aspires to be the embodiment of retirement living. The company develops residential communities and builds homes in the popular retirement destinations of central Florida and Arizona. Its master planned communities are often surrounded by woods, or are on the waterfront and offer amenities such as golf courses, restaurants, and fitness centers. The company owns nearly 17,000 acres of developed and developable land as well as wetlands and other open space. Avatar also operates a title insurance agency and manages the day-to-day operations of its communities' amenities. The company's development activities have been minimal as it weathers the economic downturn.

	Annual Growth	12/05	12/06	12/07	12/08	12/09
Sales ($ mil.)	(38.6%)	516.8	835.1	291.4	112.0	73.5
Net income ($ mil.)	—	63.1	174.7	21.4	(107.2)	(29.0)
Market value ($ mil.)	(25.4%)	623.6	918.1	474.9	301.1	193.2
Employees	(20.6%)	585	483	321	245	233

AVATAR SYSTEMS, INC.   OTC: AVSYE

2801 Network Blvd., Ste. 210
Frisco, TX 75034
Phone: 972-720-1800
Fax: 972-720-1900
Web: www.avatarsystems.net

CEO: Robert C. (Chuck) Shreve Jr.
CFO: Robert C. (Chuck) Shreve Jr.
HR: Cindy Skelton
FYE: December 31
Type: Public

Avatar Systems hopes to help you drill down to a more profitable bottom line. The company provides enterprise resource planning software for companies engaged in the petroleum exploration and production industries. The company's products and services are used to automate and integrate data and workflows across businesses, share information with external partners and suppliers, manage accounting and inventory, and handle payroll and billing. Avatar's professional services include consulting, implementation, integration, support, and maintenance.

AVATECH SOLUTIONS, INC.
OTC: AVSO

10715 Red Run Blvd., Ste. 101
Owings Mills, MD 21117
Phone: 410-581-8080
Fax: 410-581-8088
Web: www.avatechsolutions.com

CEO: George M. Davis
CFO: Lawrence (Larry) Rychlak
HR: —
FYE: June 30
Type: Public

Avatech Solutions wants to help make the design process automatic. The company resells and services third-party CAD/CAM software. One of the world's largest integrators of Autodesk software, it generates about 90% of its revenues from AutoCAD and other Autodesk packages. Avatech targets customers involved in architectural, mechanical, surveying, and civil engineering. The company's services include application development, document management, support, and training. Avatech Solutions was formed in 1997 with the merger of four Autodesk resellers.

	Annual Growth	6/05	6/06	6/07	6/08	6/09
Sales ($ mil.)	0.9%	34.1	39.6	50.5	49.6	35.4
Net income ($ mil.)	—	1.9	2.2	(0.6)	3.1	(0.3)
Market value ($ mil.)	(2.8%)	9.4	36.8	19.7	15.1	8.4
Employees	(1.1%)	158	237	231	204	151

AVAX TECHNOLOGIES, INC.
OTC: AVXT

2000 Hamilton St., Ste. 204
Philadelphia, PA 19130
Phone: 215-241-9760
Fax: 215-241-9684
Web: www.avax-tech.com

CEO: François R. Martelet
CFO: Richard P. (Rich) Rainey
HR: —
FYE: December 31
Type: Public

AVAX Technologies wants to turn cancer cells into cancer fighters. The company is developing vaccines created by extracting a patient's own cancer cells and chemically treating them to induce an immune system response. The technology used to create the vaccines (called AC Vaccine) is licensed from Thomas Jefferson University. AVAX's lead vaccine candidate M-Vax is intended as a post-surgical treatment for late-stage melanoma, but the company is also developing vaccine candidates to fight ovarian cancer (O-Vax) and non-small cell lung cancer (L-Vax). The company also offers contract manufacturing services to other biotech and pharmaceutical companies.

AVAYA INC.

211 Mount Airy Rd.
Basking Ridge, NJ 07920
Phone: 908-953-6000
Fax: 908-953-7609
Web: www.avaya.com

CEO: Kevin J. Kennedy
CFO: Anthony J. (Tony) Massetti
HR: Roger C. Gaston
FYE: September 30
Type: Private

Avaya helps to tie the corporate world together. The company's communication equipment and software integrates voice and data services for customers including large corporations, government agencies, and small businesses. Avaya's office phone systems incorporate Internet protocol (IP) and Session Initiation protocol (SIP) telephony, messaging, Web access, and interactive voice response. The company offers a wide array of consulting, integration, and managed services through its Avaya Global Services unit. It sells directly and through distributors, resellers, systems integrators, and telecommunications service providers. Avaya was acquired by Silver Lake Partners and TPG Capital for $8.2 billion in 2007.

AVENTINE RENEWABLE ENERGY HOLDINGS, INC.
NYSE: AVR

120 N. Parkway
Pekin, IL 61554
Phone: 309-347-9200
Fax: 309-346-0742
Web: www.aventinerei.com

CEO: Thomas L. Manuel
CFO: John W. Castle
HR: Ray Godbout
FYE: December 31
Type: Public

Aventine Renewable Energy Holdings is a leading US producer and marketer of ethanol, a grain alcohol mainly used as a fuel additive in gasoline to reduce vehicle emissions and enhance engine performance. It produces about 190 million gallons of ethanol at facilities in Illinois and Nebraska, and through purchase and resale operations and marketing alliances with other producers, the company distributes approximately 750 million additional gallons. Major customers include BP, ConocoPhillips, Chevron, Royal Dutch Shell, Marathon Oil, and Valero. In 2010 Aventine emerged from Chapter 11 bankruptcy protection.

	Annual Growth	12/05	12/06	12/07	12/08	12/09
Sales ($ mil.)	(10.7%)	935.5	1,592.4	1,571.6	2,248.3	594.6
Net income ($ mil.)	—	32.2	54.9	33.8	(47.1)	(46.3)
Market value ($ mil.)	(75.0%)	—	158.3	85.8	4.4	2.5
Employees	1.0%	290	321	331	346	302

AVENUE GROUP, INC.
OTC: AVNU

405 Lexington Ave., 26th Floor
New York, NY 10174
Phone: 888-612-4188
Fax: 347-952-3683
Web: www.avenuegroupinc.com

CEO: Levi Mochkin
CFO: —
HR: —
FYE: December 31
Type: Public

Avenue Group, once solely located in the world of cyberspace, is now traveling along the down and dirty pathways of the oil and gas industry. Chairman and CEO Levi Mochkin formed the company in 1999 to invest in Internet, e-commerce, and related IT ventures, but the company is now focusing on the oil and gas sector though the formation of its Avenue Energy subsidiary. It explores for oil and gas in the Appalachian Basin through its Avenue Appalachia 2006-LP unit. Subsidiary Avenue Energy Israel LTD, is the license holder of the Heletz-Kokhav field. The most prolific oil field in Israel, Heletz-Kokhav has produced more than 17.2 million barrels of oil equivalent. Mochkin owns 28% of Avenue Group.

	Annual Growth	12/04	12/05	12/06	12/07	*12/08
Sales ($ mil.)	0.0%	0.1	0.0	0.1	0.0	0.1
Net income ($ mil.)	—	(12.5)	(6.0)	(0.5)	(1.5)	(3.6)
Market value ($ mil.)	(21.5%)	12.8	12.8	4.9	3.9	4.9
Employees	(8.1%)	7	5	5	4	5

*Most recent year available

AVEO PHARMACEUTICALS, INC.
NASDAQ (GM): AVEO

75 Sidney St.
Cambridge, MA 02139
Phone: 617-299-5000
Fax: 617-995-4995
Web: aveopharma.com

CEO: Tuan Ha-Ngoc
CFO: David B. Johnston
HR: —
FYE: December 31
Type: Public

AVEO Pharmaceuticals' models don't pout, strut, or even turn heads — unless you're a cancer drug researcher. The biotech firm develops cancer models to uncover how genes mutate into tumors and how tumors progress through additional mutations. AVEO then builds genetic profiles of such tumors and applies them to antibody (protein) drug candidates in preclinical and clinical development to help predict actual human responses. In addition to its own pipeline of potential drugs, AVEO has partnered with other pharmaceutical developers to apply its Human Response Platform to their drug candidates. The company filed an IPO in late 2009 and began trading the following March.

	Annual Growth	12/05	12/06	12/07	12/08	12/09
Sales ($ mil.)	38.4%	—	7.8	11.0	19.7	20.7
Net income ($ mil.)	—	—	(24.9)	(25.0)	(32.5)	(44.1)
Employees	(0.7%)	—	—	—	134	133

An in-depth profile of this company is available to Hoover's Online members at hoovers.com.

199

AVERITT EXPRESS, INC.

1415 Neal St.
Cookeville, TN 38501
Phone: 931-526-3306
Fax: 931-520-5603
Web: www.averittexpress.com

CEO: Gary D. Sasser
CFO: George Johnson
HR: —
FYE: December 31
Type: Private

Averitt Express provides less-than-truckload (LTL) freight transportation service. (LTL carriers combine freight from multiple shippers into a single trailer.) The company operates a fleet of about 4,000 tractors and 11,250 trailers from a network of some 80 terminals. Averitt Express directly serves the southern US and Mexico, and it provides service elsewhere in North America through partnerships with other carriers such as Lakeville Motor Express and DATS. The company also offers truckload and expedited freight transportation, along with logistics, warehousing, and international freight forwarding. Customers have included Home Depot, Shoe Carnival, and V.F. Corporation.

	Annual Growth	12/04	12/05	12/06	12/07	12/08
Est. sales ($ mil.)	—	—	—	—	—	966.9
Employees	—	—	—	—	—	8,208

⊞ AVERY DENNISON CORPORATION

NYSE: AVY

150 N. Orange Grove Blvd.
Pasadena, CA 91103
Phone: 626-304-2000
Fax: 626-304-2192
Web: www.averydennison.com

CEO: Dean A. Scarborough
CFO: Mitchell R. Butier
HR: Anne Hill
FYE: December 31
Type: Public

Avery Dennison is easy to label: It's a global leader in the making of adhesive labels used on packaging, mailers, and other items. Pressure-sensitive adhesives and materials account for more than half of the company's sales. Under the Avery Dennison and Fasson brands, the company makes papers, films, and foils coated with adhesive and sold in rolls to printers. The company also makes school and office products (Avery, Marks-A-Lot, HI-LITER) such as notebooks, three-ring binders, markers, fasteners, business forms, tickets, tags, and imprinting equipment. Perhaps its most widely used products are the self-adhesive stamps used by the US Postal Service since 1974.

	Annual Growth	12/05	12/06	12/07	12/08	12/09
Sales ($ mil.)	2.1%	5,473.5	5,575.9	6,307.8	6,710.4	5,952.7
Net income ($ mil.)	—	226.4	367.2	303.5	266.1	(746.7)
Market value ($ mil.)	(9.9%)	6,104.1	7,502.2	5,868.8	3,614.7	4,030.0
Employees	12.1%	22,600	22,700	37,300	36,000	35,700

AVERY WEIGH-TRONIX, LLC

1000 Armstrong Dr.
Fairmont, MN 56031
Phone: 507-238-4461
Fax: 507-238-8258
Web: www.wtxweb.com

CEO: Andy Caffyn
CFO: Ross Hunwardsen
HR: Len Bakken
FYE: December 31
Type: Subsidiary

Avery Weigh-Tronix puts the whole weight of its being into its work. The company makes a full slate of industrial and retail weighing systems, from bench scales to conveyor scales, counting scales, floor scales, truck scales, and weigh bars. It also produces accessories, such as printers, remote displays, signal processors, and wireless transceivers. Although several of Avery Weigh-Tronix's predecessor companies, such as Avery and Salter, date back to the 18th century, Avery Weigh-Tronix was formed in the 21st century through the merger of Weigh-Tronix and Avery Berkel. The company operates worldwide, garnering about 60% of sales outside North America. In 2008 Illinois Tool Works (ITW) acquired Avery Weigh-Tronix.

	Annual Growth	12/04	12/05	12/06	12/07	12/08
Est. sales ($ mil.)	—	—	—	—	—	471.4
Employees	—	—	—	—	—	5,500

AVI BIOPHARMA, INC.

NASDAQ (GM): AVII

1 SW Columbia St., Ste. 1105
Portland, OR 97258
Phone: 503-227-0554
Fax: 503-227-0751
Web: www.avibio.com

CEO: J. David Boyle II
CFO: J. David Boyle II
HR: —
FYE: December 31
Type: Public

AVI BioPharma has a sixth sense about antisense. A developer of biopharmaceutical compounds, AVI's investigational therapies are based on its NeuGene antisense drug technology, which can halt disease processes at the genetic level. BioPharma is developing antisense drugs used in the treatment of a wide range of diseases, including hepatitis C, Dengue Fever, cancer, and genetic diseases. Its lead candidate, Resten-NG, is undergoing clinical testing as a treatment for restenosis, or narrowing of the arteries. Additionally, Cook Group is using the drug to develop drug-eluting stents that prop open clogged arteries.

	Annual Growth	12/05	12/06	12/07	12/08	12/09
Sales ($ mil.)	38.4%	4.8	0.1	11.0	21.3	17.6
Net income ($ mil.)	—	(16.7)	(31.1)	(27.2)	(24.0)	(25.2)
Market value ($ mil.)	(19.3%)	380.8	351.0	155.6	72.6	161.1
Employees	(15.4%)	123	117	125	83	63

AVIALL, INC.

2750 Regent Blvd.
Dallas Fort Worth Airport, TX 75261
Phone: 972-586-1000
Fax: 972-586-1361
Web: www.aviall.com

CEO: Dan P. Komnenovich
CFO: Colin M. Cohen
HR: Curt Brusto
FYE: December 31
Type: Subsidiary

When it comes to aviation, Aviall has the right parts. The Boeing subsidiary is one of the top global distributors of commercial and aftermarket aircraft components. It straddles two operating units: Aviall Services markets and distributes aviation parts and supplies for some 230 OEMs to commercial airlines, military and government agencies, and general aviation operators. The unit also offers upkeep and repair of batteries to brakes, hose assembly, and paint-mixing. Aviall's Inventory Locator Service provides online inventory, and IT and logistics help for aerospace, marine, and defense markets. Customers are served from centers in North America, Europe, Dubai, India, Australia, and the Asia/Pacific region.

	Annual Growth	12/04	12/05	12/06	12/07	12/08
Est. sales ($ mil.)	—	—	—	—	—	1,300.0
Employees	—	—	—	—	—	1,200

AVIAT NETWORKS, INC.

NASDAQ (GM): AVNW

637 Davis Dr.
Morrisville, NC 27560
Phone: 919-767-3230
Fax: 919-767-3233
Web: www.aviatnetworks.com

CEO: Harald J. Braun
CFO: Thomas L. Cronan III
HR: Stephen J. (Steve) Gilmore
FYE: June 30
Type: Public

Aviat Networks (formerly known as Harris Stratex Networks) makes data fly. The company designs and manufactures wireless network transmission equipment used to link and manage both fixed and wireless voice and data networks. Customers include mobile network operators, public safety agencies, private network operators, and utility and transportation companies in more than 150 countries worldwide; Aviat gets more than two-thirds of its sales outside the US. Sold under the Eclipse and Constellation brands, among others, the company's core products are microwave radios that enable network access and interconnection. Aviat also sells a range of software applications used to monitor and manage network performance.

	Annual Growth	3/05	3/06	*6/07	6/08	6/09
Sales ($ mil.)	39.4%	180.3	230.9	507.9	718.4	679.9
Net income ($ mil.)	—	(45.9)	(2.3)	(17.9)	(11.9)	(355.0)
Market value ($ mil.)	37.0%	109.8	367.0	1,072.4	566.4	386.7
Employees	61.6%	223	224	1,440	1,410	1,521

*Fiscal year change

AVID TECHNOLOGY, INC.   NASDAQ (GS): AVID

1 Park West	CEO: Gary G. Greenfield
Tewksbury, MA 01876	CFO: Kenneth A. (Ken) Sexton
Phone: 978-640-6789	HR: Ed Raine
Fax: 978-640-3366	FYE: December 31
Web: www.avid.com	Type: Public

Media professionals are keen on Avid Technology. The company provides digital editing and professional audio systems for the film, music, and television industries. Its products, including Composer, Symphony, and Avid Xpress, are used by music and film studios, postproduction facilities, radio broadcasters, and TV stations, including the BBC, CBS, and NBC. Its Digidesign unit markets the ProTools line of sound editing systems. Avid also makes newsroom automation systems and digital storage systems. The company provides video editing products for the consumer market through its Pinnacle Systems division. Its M-Audio brand makes digital audio recording and performance software, instruments, and accessories.

	Annual Growth	12/05	12/06	12/07	12/08	12/09
Sales ($ mil.)	(5.1%)	775.4	910.6	929.6	844.9	629.0
Net income ($ mil.)	—	34.0	(42.9)	(8.0)	(198.2)	(68.4)
Market value ($ mil.)	(30.5%)	2,082.7	1,417.1	1,077.9	414.9	485.3
Employees	(3.5%)	2,613	2,792	2,731	2,350	—

AVIS BUDGET GROUP, INC.   NYSE: CAR

6 Sylvan Way	CEO: Ronald L. (Ron) Nelson
Parsippany, NJ 07054	CFO: David B. Wyshner
Phone: 973-496-3500	HR: Mark J. Servodidio
Fax: 888-304-2315	FYE: December 31
Web: www.avisbudgetgroup.com	Type: Public

Whether you're a business traveler on an expense account or you're on a family vacation and you're counting every penny, Avis Budget Group has a car rental brand for you. The company's Avis Rent A Car unit, which targets corporate and leisure travelers at the high end of the market, has 2,200 locations in the Americas and the Asia/Pacific region. Budget Rent A Car, marketed to those who watch costs closely, rents cars from 2,700 locations in the same regions and trucks from 2,550 dealers in the US. Avis Budget Group, formerly known as Cendant, changed its name in 2006 after spinning off its hotel operations (Wyndham Worldwide) and its real estate division (Realogy) and selling its travel unit (Travelport).

	Annual Growth	12/05	12/06	12/07	12/08	12/09
Sales ($ mil.)	(27.2%)	18,236.0	5,689.0	5,986.0	5,984.0	5,131.0
Net income ($ mil.)	—	1,349.0	(1,930.0)	(916.0)	(1,124.0)	(47.0)
Market value ($ mil.)	(13.1%)	2,356.8	2,226.8	1,334.6	71.9	1,347.0
Employees	(28.1%)	84,800	30,000	30,000	26,000	22,700

AVIS RENT A CAR SYSTEM, LLC

6 Sylvan Way	CEO: Ronald L. (Ron) Nelson
Parsippany, NJ 07054	CFO: David B. Wyshner
Phone: 973-496-3500	HR: Mark J. Servodidio
Fax: 888-304-2315	FYE: December 31
Web: www.avis.com	Type: Subsidiary

A major player in the car rental industry, Avis Rent A Car System maintains more than 2,260 locations, primarily in the US and Canada but also in Australia, New Zealand, Latin America, and the Caribbean. The company owns about 1,300 of its locations; franchisees operate the rest. A separate company with rights to the Avis name, UK-based Avis Europe, operates in Europe, Africa, the Middle East, and parts of Asia. Together with sister company Budget Rent A Car System, Avis Rent A Car System has a fleet of more than 380,000 rental cars. The premium Avis fleet averages about 217,500 vehicles. The company is a subsidiary of Avis Budget Group, the remaining unit of the former Cendant conglomerate.

AVISTA CORPORATION   NYSE: AVA

1411 E. Mission Ave.	CEO: Scott L. Morris
Spokane, WA 99202	CFO: Mark T. Thies
Phone: 509-489-0500	HR: Karen S. Feltes
Fax: 509-495-8725	FYE: December 31
Web: www.avistacorp.com	Type: Public

It is no shock that Avista is a leading utility serving the northwestern US. The firm's regulated utility unit has a generation capacity of more than 2,380 MW of electricity, which is distributed to 355,000 customers in Idaho and Washington. It also supplies natural gas to about 314,000 customers in Idaho, Oregon, and Washington. The company operates eight hydroelectric projects and owns coal, natural gas, and wood waste plants. Avista has no natural gas reserves and purchases its supply from the wholesale market. The company also operates Advantage IQ, which manages energy expenses for its multi-site companies across the US.

	Annual Growth	12/05	12/06	12/07	12/08	12/09
Sales ($ mil.)	2.7%	1,359.6	1,506.3	1,417.8	1,676.8	1,512.6
Net income ($ mil.)	17.8%	45.2	73.1	38.5	73.6	87.1
Market value ($ mil.)	5.1%	972.3	1,389.6	1,182.6	1,064.0	1,185.3
Employees	14.1%	1,435	1,995	2,117	2,127	2,435

AVISTAR COMMUNICATIONS CORPORATION   Pink Sheets: AVSR

1875 S. Grant St., 10th Fl.	CEO: Robert F. (Bob) Kirk
San Mateo, CA 94402	CFO: Elias MurrayMetzger
Phone: 650-525-3300	HR: —
Fax: 650-525-1360	FYE: December 31
Web: www.avistar.com	Type: Public

If geography prevents you from concluding business with a firm handshake, Avistar Communications is ready to furnish the next-best thing. The company provides communication software and hardware used to equip communications networks with video capabilities. Its systems enable videoconferencing, content creation, video broadcasting, and data sharing between users over telephony networks and the Internet. Avistar markets its products primarily to corporations in the financial services industry, including UBS Investment Bank, Deutsche Bank, and JPMorgan Chase. Chairman Gerald Burnett owns about 43% of the company.

	Annual Growth	12/05	12/06	12/07	12/08	12/09
Sales ($ mil.)	6.3%	6.9	13.2	12.0	8.8	8.8
Net income ($ mil.)	—	(5.2)	(8.1)	(2.9)	(6.4)	(4.0)
Market value ($ mil.)	(26.6%)	60.1	69.1	14.0	34.3	17.4
Employees	(10.7%)	77	88	74	50	49

AVIZA TECHNOLOGY, INC.   Pink Sheets: AVZAQ

440 Kings Village Rd.	CEO: Patrick C. O'Connor
Scotts Valley, CA 95066	CFO: —
Phone: 831-438-2100	HR: Ted Washington
Fax: 831-439-6223	FYE: September 30
Web: www.avizatechnology.com	Type: Public

Here's an updated advisory on Aviza Technology: The company has sold the majority of its semiconductor manufacturing business. Aviza made atomic layer deposition (ALD), chemical vapor deposition (CVD), and physical vapor deposition (PVD) gear. These machines deposit semiconductor materials in precise layers onto microchip wafers. It also made equipment used to etch circuit patterns on wafers and specialized furnaces used in microchip production. Aviza filed for Chapter 11 bankruptcy protection in 2009; later that year it sold the majority of its assets and certain of its subsidiaries to Surface Technology Systems plc (STS), a subsidiary of Sumitomo Precision Products (SPP), for about $60 million.

	Annual Growth	12/04	*9/05	9/06	9/07	†9/08
Sales ($ mil.)	37.9%	36.8	171.2	160.9	231.4	133.2
Net income ($ mil.)	—	(13.7)	(16.0)	(14.7)	0.4	(47.4)
Market value ($ mil.)	(67.6%)	—	—	83.1	75.4	8.7
Employees	5.6%	—	417	675	670	491

*Fiscal year change   †Most recent year available

AVMED HEALTH PLANS

4300 NW 89th Blvd.
Gainesville, FL 32606
Phone: 352-372-8400
Fax: 352-337-8521
Web: www.avmed.com

CEO: Michael P. Gallagher
CFO: Randall L. Stuart
HR: Kay Ayers
FYE: December 31
Type: Not-for-profit

AvMed Health Plans is flying high in the Florida HMO world. The not-for-profit company is one of the state's leading health plan providers, serving more than 300,000 members. AvMed designs policies for small to large employer groups throughout Florida. It also provides Medicare Advantage plans for retirees, as well as other individual health plans, in Miami-Dade and Broward counties in South Florida. Founded in 1969 as a health care system for pilots in the Miami area, AvMed (short for "aviation medicine") has a broad product offering, introducing HMO, PPO, point-of-service (POS), and high-deductible plans with health savings accounts.

	Annual Growth	12/04	12/05	12/06	12/07	12/08
Est. sales ($ mil.)	—	—	—	—	—	980.0
Employees	—	—	—	—	—	850

AVNET, INC.

NYSE: AVT

2211 S. 47th St.
Phoenix, AZ 85034
Phone: 480-643-2000
Fax: 480-643-7370
Web: www.avnet.com

CEO: Roy A. Vallee
CFO: Raymond (Ray) Sadowski
HR: MaryAnn G. Miller
FYE: June 30
Type: Public

If you're after an electronic component, Avnet probably has it. The company is one of the world's largest distributors of electronic components and computer products, alongside rival Arrow Electronics. Avnet's suppliers include 300-plus component and systems makers; the company distributes these suppliers' products to some 100,000 manufacturers and resellers. Avnet Electronics Marketing offers semiconductors and other components. Avnet Technology Solutions provides computer products and services to resellers, large end-users, systems integrators, and software vendors. The company distributes products in more than 70 countries; customers located in the Americas account for nearly half of sales.

	Annual Growth	6/05	6/06	6/07	6/08	6/09
Sales ($ mil.)	10.0%	11,066.8	14,253.6	15,681.1	17,952.7	16,229.9
Net income ($ mil.)	—	168.2	204.5	393.1	499.1	(1,122.5)
Market value ($ mil.)	(1.7%)	3,420.6	3,039.5	6,018.4	4,141.8	3,192.9
Employees	7.1%	9,800	10,900	11,700	12,800	12,900

AVOCENT CORPORATION

4991 Corporate Dr.
Huntsville, AL 35805
Phone: 256-430-4000
Fax: 256-430-4030
Web: www.avocent.com

CEO: Michael J. (Mike) Borman
CFO: Edward H. (Teddy) Blankenship
HR: Julie Yarbrough
FYE: December 31
Type: Subsidiary

Avocent tries to give network administrators what they really need — the ability to be in multiple places at once. The company makes analog and digital KVM (keyboard, video, mouse) switching systems used to manage multiple servers. Its LongView extension products let computer users locate their mouse, monitor, keyboard, and other peripherals up to 500 feet away from their CPU. The company also provides systems management software through its LANDesk division. Avocent's key clients have included manufacturers such as Dell, Hewlett-Packard, and IBM, as well as IT product distributors such as Ingram Micro and Tech Data. Emerson Electric bought the company in late 2009 for about $1.2 billion in cash.

	Annual Growth	12/04	12/05	12/06	12/07	12/08
Sales ($ mil.)	15.8%	365.3	369.9	519.2	600.9	657.1
Net income ($ mil.)	9.1%	18.0	48.3	45.5	45.9	25.5
Employees	16.4%	599	560	997	1,797	1,099

AVON PRODUCTS, INC.

NYSE: AVP

1345 Avenue of the Americas
New York, NY 10105
Phone: 212-282-5000
Fax: 212-282-6049
Web: www.avoncompany.com

CEO: Andrea Jung
CFO: Charles W. (Chuck) Cramb
HR: Lucien Alziari
FYE: December 31
Type: Public

"Avon calling" — calling for a younger crowd, overseas reps, and improved global operational efficiencies. Avon Products, the world's largest direct seller of cosmetics and beauty-related items, is busy building a global brand and enticing younger customers to buy its products. Direct selling remains the firm's *modus operandi*, but sales also come from catalogs and a website. Its products include cosmetics, fragrances, toiletries, jewelry, apparel, home furnishings, and more. Avon boasts about 6.2 million independent representatives. With sales operations and distribution in more than 100 countries and territories, the firm continues to morph its operations on a multiyear turn-around plan launched in 2009.

	Annual Growth	12/05	12/06	12/07	12/08	12/09
Sales ($ mil.)	6.2%	8,149.6	8,677.3	9,938.7	10,690.1	10,382.8
Net income ($ mil.)	(7.3%)	847.6	477.6	530.7	875.3	625.8
Market value ($ mil.)	2.5%	12,230.9	14,154.5	16,934.8	10,294.5	13,494.7
Employees	(4.4%)	49,000	40,300	42,000	42,000	41,000

AVSTAR AVIATION GROUP, INC.

Pink Sheets: AAVG

9801 Westheimer, Ste. 302
Houston, TX 77042
Phone: 713-706-6350
Fax: 713-706-6351
Web: avstargroup.com

CEO: Russell Ivy
CFO: Robert Wilson
HR: —
FYE: December 31
Type: Public

AvStar Aviation Group is making the switch from searching for oil and gas to investing in the aviation sector. Once known as Pangea Petroleum, the company formerly specialized in oil and natural gas exploration and production in the US Gulf Coast region. In 2009, however, Pangea Petroleum was acquired by AvStar Aviation Services, which redirected the company's focus as a service provider to the general aviation industry. Now known as AvStar Aviation Group, the company plans to acquire fixed base operations (FBOs) at airports. Its San Diego Airmotive subsidiary provides maintenance, repair, and overhaul services for aircraft.

	Annual Growth	12/05	12/06	12/07	12/08	12/09
Sales ($ mil.)	62.7%	0.1	0.0	0.1	0.0	0.7
Net income ($ mil.)	—	(0.5)	(1.0)	(0.4)	(0.3)	(1.0)
Market value ($ mil.)	(65.5%)	92.7	128.8	31.9	—	1.3
Employees	49.5%	2	2	2	8	10

AVX CORPORATION

NYSE: AVX

801 17th Ave. South
Myrtle Beach, SC 29577
Phone: 843-448-9411
Fax: 843-916-7751
Web: www.avx.com

CEO: John S. Gilbertson
CFO: Kurt P. Cummings
HR: —
FYE: March 31
Type: Public

AVX proves that tiny parts can add up to big business. The company's Passive Components segment makes passive electronic components for automotive braking systems, copiers, hearing aids, locomotives, and wireless phones. The KED Resale segment specializes in products made by Kyocera Electronic Devices, such as ceramic and tantalum capacitors that store, filter, and regulate electrical energy in electronic devices. The Connectors segment makes electronic connectors for automotive and medical electronics applications. Customers include Motorola, Nokia, and Robert Bosch. Nearly half of the company's sales are made in Asia.

	Annual Growth	3/06	3/07	3/08	3/09	3/10
Sales ($ mil.)	(0.5%)	1,333.2	1,498.5	1,619.3	1,389.6	1,305.0
Net income ($ mil.)	15.0%	81.8	153.9	149.5	80.8	142.9
Market value ($ mil.)	(5.4%)	3,011.3	2,586.0	2,179.4	1,544.8	2,415.8
Employees	(3.3%)	12,100	13,000	14,000	9,900	10,600

AWARE, INC.

NASDAQ (GM): AWRE

40 Middlesex Tpke.	CEO: Edmund C. Reiter
Bedford, MA 01730	CFO: Richard P. (Rick) Moberg
Phone: 781-276-4000	HR: —
Fax: 781-276-4001	FYE: December 31
Web: www.aware.com	Type: Public

Aware takes an intellectual approach to the DSL market. The company, which sells hardware and software used to make asymmetric DSL equipment, derives some of its revenue from contract design services and licensing fees for its ADSL semiconductor intellectual property designs. Aware's products help telephone companies upgrade their systems without replacing transmission lines; they also help reduce download time for Internet users. Aware additionally develops compression software for video, image, and data transmission. The company sells to the likes of Daphimo, Infineon Technologies, and Spirent Communications. Aware gets more than three-quarters of its sales in the US.

	Annual Growth	12/05	12/06	12/07	12/08	12/09
Sales ($ mil.)	8.8%	15.7	24.1	26.4	30.5	22.0
Net income ($ mil.)	—	(2.5)	1.0	0.2	1.8	1.0
Market value ($ mil.)	(10.9%)	88.7	106.4	83.7	37.3	55.8
Employees	(7.5%)	112	117	126	122	82

AXA ADVISORS, LLC

1290 Avenue of the Americas, 8th Fl.	CEO: Christine Nigro
New York, NY 10104	CFO: —
Phone: 212-554-1234	HR: —
Fax: 212-314-2837	FYE: December 31
Web: www.axaonline.com	Type: Subsidiary

Have financial planning questions? Ask AXA Advisors. The company is the broker-dealer subsidiary of AXA Financial and part of French financial services powerhouse AXA. AXA Advisors offers retirement planning, education funding, and estate transfer services to consumers through a network of more than 6,000 advisors. The firm also sells life insurance (through AXA Equitable Life Insurance Company), annuities, and mutual funds, and provides online trading services. To corporations, the company provides employee benefit and 401(k) plans. AXA Advisors has offices throughout the US, as well as Puerto Rico and the Virgin Islands.

AXA EQUITABLE LIFE INSURANCE COMPANY

1290 Avenue of the Americas	CEO: Christopher M. (Kip) Condron
New York, NY 10104	CFO: Richard S. Dziadzio
Phone: 212-554-1234	HR: Jennifer L. Blevins
Fax: 212-314-3954	FYE: December 31
Web: www.axa-equitable.com	Type: Subsidiary

This company definitely has what it takes to be equitable. AXA Equitable Life Insurance is the US life insurance and annuities underwriting arm of its globe-spanning ultimate parent, AXA. The company, together with subsidiary AXA Life and Annuity, has more than 2.3 million life insurance policies in force, and is licensed throughout the US and Puerto Rico. Policies are sold through affiliates AXA Advisors and AXA Network, as well as by independent brokers and financial institutions via wholesale brokerage unit AXA Distributors. AXA Equitable, a subsidiary of AXA Financial, has about $540 billion under management, and offers investment products and services through its majority stake in Alliance Bernstein.

	Annual Growth	12/04	12/05	12/06	12/07	12/08
Est. sales ($ mil.)	—	—	—	—	—	18,581.3
Employees	—	—	—	—	—	5,770

AXA FINANCIAL, INC.

1290 Avenue of the Americas	CEO: Christopher M. (Kip) Condron
New York, NY 10104	CFO: Richard S. Dziadzio
Phone: 212-554-1234	HR: Jennifer L. Blevins
Fax: 212-314-4480	FYE: December 31
Web: www.axa-financial.com	Type: Subsidiary

A US-based subsidiary of French insurance giant AXA, AXA Financial provides financial advisory and insurance services through AXA Equitable, AXA Advisors, AXA Distributors, and the MONY Companies. The units offer life insurance, annuities, mutual funds, separate accounts, and other investment products to individuals, small businesses and professional organizations. Its investment management business is anchored by majority-owned affiliate AllianceBernstein and serves institutional and retail clients, including high-net-worth individuals. AXA Financial and its subsidiaries have approximately $580 billion in assets under management, most of it at AllianceBernstein.

	Annual Growth	12/04	12/05	12/06	12/07	12/08
Est. sales ($ mil.)	—	—	—	—	—	20,140.5
Employees	—	—	—	—	—	11,350

AXA ROSENBERG GROUP LLC

4 Orinda Way, Bldg. E	CEO: Stéphane Prunet
Orinda, CA 94563	CFO: —
Phone: 925-254-6464	HR: —
Fax: 925-253-0141	FYE: December 31
Web: www.axarosenberg.com	Type: Subsidiary

No need for rose-colored glasses; AXA Rosenberg Group prefers a more analytical approach to equity investing. The unit of insurance giant AXA manages investment portfolios for some 300 institutional clients such as corporations, pension funds, endowments, foundations, and government entities. It also acts as a manager or subadvisor for several mutual funds with holdings in global equities; such funds are available to retail customers as well. AXA Rosenberg operates nearly 10 offices in financial centers around the globe and has more than $40 billion of assets under management. Established in 1985, the company became part of AXA in 1999.

AXCELIS TECHNOLOGIES, INC.

NASDAQ (GM): ACLS

108 Cherry Hill Dr.	CEO: Mary G. Puma
Beverly, MA 01915	CFO: Stephen G. (Steve) Bassett
Phone: 978-787-4000	HR: Lynnette C. Fallon
Fax: 978-787-3000	FYE: December 31
Web: www.axcelis.com	Type: Public

Ion implantation devices are axial to Axcelis Technologies' business. Semiconductor makers use these implanters to insert ions into silicon wafers to change their conductive properties. Axcelis' other offerings include systems for dry strip, photostabilization, and rapid thermal processing of wafers. Axcelis and Sumitomo Heavy Industries (SHI) were equal owners of SEN Corporation, which Axcelis licensed to manufacture and sell certain implant products in Japan. SHI purchased Axcelis' 50% share in SEN in 2009, with the two companies sharing cross licenses for patents and technical information. Axcelis gets nearly two-thirds of its sales in the US.

	Annual Growth	12/05	12/06	12/07	12/08	12/09
Sales ($ mil.)	(22.7%)	372.5	461.7	404.8	250.2	133.0
Net income ($ mil.)	—	(3.9)	40.8	(11.4)	(196.7)	(77.5)
Market value ($ mil.)	(26.3%)	496.9	607.3	479.1	53.1	146.9
Employees	(14.5%)	1,615	1,755	1,638	1,162	864

An in-depth profile of this company is available to Hoover's Online members at hoovers.com.

203

AXCESS INTERNATIONAL INC.
OTC: AXSI

3208 Commander Dr.
Carrollton, TX 75006
Phone: 972-407-6080
Fax: 972-407-9085
Web: www.axcessinc.com

CEO: Allan Griebenow
CFO: Allan L. Frank
HR: —
FYE: December 31
Type: Public

Axcess International can watch the door and mind the store. The company's ActiveTag radio-frequency identification (RFID) system is for tracking people, vehicles, inventory, and equipment. Axcess International's Onlinesupervisor system integrates RFID data and digital video to a standard Web browser. The company has also developed a micro-wireless technology platform called Dot, a small, low-cost battery-powered wireless computer for the automatic identification, locating, tracking, protecting, and monitoring of personnel, physical assets, and vehicles. Customers include security systems integrators and distributors in the US.

	Annual Growth	12/05	12/06	12/07	12/08	12/09
Sales ($ mil.)	44.5%	1.1	1.5	3.4	1.5	4.8
Net income ($ mil.)	—	(3.3)	(3.4)	(4.9)	(4.8)	(1.1)
Market value ($ mil.)	(16.4%)	27.6	39.4	43.1	8.4	13.5
Employees	(6.5%)	17	17	19	18	13

AXESSTEL, INC.
OTC: AXST

6815 Flanders Dr., Ste. 210
San Diego, CA 92121
Phone: 858-625-2100
Fax: 858-625-2110
Web: www.axesstel.com

CEO: H. Clark Hickock
CFO: Patrick C. Gray
HR: —
FYE: December 31
Type: Public

Axesstel can soup up that old phone on your desk. The company designs and manufactures fixed wireless voice and broadband data systems that link stationary office phones to the communications network via cellular connections. Axesstel's products include fixed wireless telephones, transmission terminals, and wireless modems. The company mostly sells its products to telecommunications companies in developing countries that then resell the products to consumers. Principal clients include India's Bharat Sanchar Nigam Limited and the Latin American operations of Telefónica Móviles and Telecommunications Movilnet.

	Annual Growth	12/05	12/06	12/07	12/08	12/09
Sales ($ mil.)	(14.4%)	94.7	95.5	82.4	109.6	50.8
Net income ($ mil.)	—	(10.2)	(6.6)	(9.0)	1.4	(10.1)
Market value ($ mil.)	(41.8%)	26.5	45.7	6.8	8.2	3.0
Employees	(31.0%)	97	87	63	71	22

AXION INTERNATIONAL HOLDINGS, INC.
OTC: AXIH

665 Martinsville Rd.
Basking Ridge, NJ 07060
Phone: 908-542-0888
Fax: —
Web: www.axionintl.com

CEO: James Kerstein
CFO: Gary R. Anthony
HR: —
FYE: September 30
Type: Public

Axion International Holdings surveyed the landscape and decided to shift into a new line of business. Formerly operating as Analytical Surveys, the company completed a reverse merger with Axion in 2008 and adopted that company's name and line of business. Axion is a licensee of technology regarding the manufacture of plastic composites used for structural applications such as railroad crossties, bridge infrastructure, marine pilings. and bulk headings. While the company is initially targeting the railroad industry, it has yet to generate any significant revenues.

	Annual Growth	9/05	9/06	9/07	9/08	9/09
Sales ($ mil.)	(30.8%)	6.1	4.3	0.6	6.5	1.4
Net income ($ mil.)	—	(3.3)	(0.3)	(4.5)	(2,271.3)	(5.8)
Market value ($ mil.)	(14.2%)	115.5	59.4	8.5	22.9	62.6
Employees	(44.1%)	82	9	4	6	8

AXIS CAPITAL HOLDINGS LIMITED
NYSE: AXS

92 Pitts Bay Rd.
Pembroke, HM 08, Bermuda
Phone: 441-496-2600
Fax: 441-405-2640
Web: www.axis.bm

CEO: John R. Charman
CFO: David B. Greenfield
HR: Brian W. Goshen
FYE: December 31
Type: Public

AXIS Capital is going where fewer and fewer insurance companies dare to go. Comprised of Axis Insurance and Axis Re, the company offers specialty insurance and treaty reinsurance. Its specialty coverage includes terrorism, aviation and marine war, and political risk; commercial property; professional liability; and onshore and offshore energy. AXIS Capital's reinsurance products, which allow for risk-sharing among insurance companies, include catastrophe, property, liability, credit, auto, and engineering lines. The company sells its products through such brokers as Marsh, Aon, and Willis Group.

	Annual Growth	12/05	12/06	12/07	12/08	12/09
Assets ($ mil.)	6.4%	11,926.0	13,665.3	14,675.3	14,282.8	15,306.5
Net income ($ mil.)	53.3%	90.1	925.8	1,055.2	387.4	497.9
Market value ($ mil.)	(2.4%)	3,964.3	4,229.2	4,939.0	3,690.6	3,600.6
Employees	18.9%	441	570	730	801	882

AXM PHARMA, INC.
Pink Sheets: AXMP

20955 Pathfinder Rd., Ste. 100
Diamond Bar, CA 91765
Phone: 909-843-6338
Fax: 909-843-6350
Web: www.axmpharma.com

CEO: Wang Wei Shi
CFO: —
HR: —
FYE: December 31
Type: Public

AXM Pharma puts its weight into selling pharmaceutical products in Asia. The company makes and sells prescription and OTC products through its AXM Pharma Shenyang subsidiary. It has more than 40 licenses to products but so far has only commercialized about a dozen of them, including LiveComf for dermatitis; Bodyward, an alternative to penicillin for infections; and Asarone, an anti-inflammatory for respiratory ailments. AXM Pharma also makes vitamins and supplements. AXM Pharma sells its products through direct marketing and independent distributors primarily in China, as well as other Asian countries such as Hong Kong, Singapore, and Taiwan. Chairman Wang Wei Shi owns nearly 30% of the company.

AXS-ONE INC.
OTC: AXSO

301 Rte. 17 North
Rutherford, NJ 07070
Phone: 201-935-3400
Fax: 201-935-7678
Web: www.axsone.com

CEO: William P. (Bill) Lyons
CFO: Joseph P. (Joe) Dwyer
HR: —
FYE: December 31
Type: Public

AXS-One's first priority is to help customers get right down to business. The company offers Web-based applications that are used to manage and integrate a variety of back-office functions. Clients use AXS-One's software to manage tasks including data processing, asset management, and the delivery of Web-based content, as well as budgeting, forecasting, and revenue lifecycle management. The company also offers services such as consulting, training, and support. Customers come from fields such as manufacturing, telecommunications, and financial services. Data management software developer Unify acquired AXS-One in 2009 in an all-stock, $10 million transaction.

	Annual Growth	12/04	12/05	12/06	12/07	*12/08
Sales ($ mil.)	(23.1%)	38.4	32.8	10.3	11.9	13.4
Net income ($ mil.)	—	(5.2)	(9.0)	5.5	(14.9)	(10.1)
Market value ($ mil.)	(60.9%)	105.7	72.0	31.3	16.5	2.5
Employees	(6.1%)	104	209	135	118	81

*Most recent year available

AXSYS TECHNOLOGIES, INC.

175 Capital Blvd., Ste. 103
Rocky Hill, CT 06067
Phone: 860-257-0200
Fax: 860-594-5750
Web: www.axsys.com

CEO: Stephen W. Bershad
CFO: David A. Almeida
HR: Lynn Kerley
FYE: December 31
Type: Subsidiary

Precision products are precisely Axsys Technologies' line of work. The company makes electro-optical systems used in fighter planes, tanks, and other military and commercial applications. Offerings include precision metal optical, infrared optical, and motion control devices. It also makes multi-axis stabilized cameras. US military and aerospace demand contributes to most of the company's business; BAE Systems represents nearly 25% of sales. Customers also draw from the television production and broadcasting, law enforcement, maritime, and space industries. Axsys Technologies joined the General Dynamics Advanced Information Systems' portfolio of intelligence, surveillance, and reconnaissance operations in 2009.

	Annual Growth	12/04	12/05	12/06	12/07	12/08
Sales ($ mil.)	24.1%	103.5	133.5	156.3	171.6	245.5
Net income ($ mil.)	31.4%	8.7	7.3	10.3	16.8	25.9
Employees	11.3%	645	749	765	822	991

AXT, INC.

NASDAQ (GM): AXTI

4281 Technology Dr.
Fremont, CA 94538
Phone: 510-683-5900
Fax: 510-353-0668
Web: www.axt.com

CEO: Morris S. Young
CFO: Raymond A. Low
HR: —
FYE: December 31
Type: Public

For applications in which plain silicon would get the ax, AXT offers fancier fare. AXT makes semiconductor substrates from compounds such as gallium arsenide (GaAs) and indium phosphide (InP), and from single elements such as germanium. Manufacturers use AXT's substrates to make high-performance semiconductors for products — including fiber-optic devices, satellite solar cells, and wireless handsets — for which standard silicon microchips are not adequate. AXT's customers include Avago, Freescale, Kopin, Oclaro, and Samsung Electronics. Most of its employees are in China. Nearly two-thirds of sales are to customers in the Asia/Pacific region.

	Annual Growth	12/05	12/06	12/07	12/08	12/09
Sales ($ mil.)	20.2%	26.5	44.4	58.2	73.1	55.4
Net income ($ mil.)	—	(12.2)	0.9	5.3	(0.7)	(1.9)
Market value ($ mil.)	11.0%	66.3	146.3	192.2	41.8	100.7
Employees	6.7%	842	1,022	1,057	1,120	1,091

AZ3, INC.

2761 Fruitland Ave.
Vernon, CA 90058
Phone: 323-589-2224
Fax: 323-277-5461
Web: www.bcbg.com

CEO: Max Azria
CFO: Brian Fleming
HR: —
FYE: December 31
Type: Private

Its dba name may come from Parisian slang (*bon chic, bon genre*, meaning "good style, good attitude"), but fashion firm AZ3 (better known as BCBG Max Azria) is rooted in America. French designer Max Azria started BCBG in Los Angeles, making his name with the novel baby-doll dress, and now sells his women's and men's collections in more than 520 company-owned stores in the US (with 180 there), Canada, France, and Japan. AZ3 also sells its clothing and accessories worldwide through specialty stores and in-store shops in major department stores (Saks Fifth Avenue, Macy's, Harvey Nichols, Mitsukoshi, Takashimaya). Azria owns the company, which purchased the bankrupt G+G Retail in February 2006 for $45 million.

AZURE DYNAMICS CORPORATION

Toronto: AZD

14925 W. Eleven Mile Rd.
Oak Park, MI 48237
Phone: 248-298-2403
Fax: 248-298-2410
Web: www.azuredynamics.com

CEO: Scott T. Harrison
CFO: Ryan Carr
HR: Ryan Carr
FYE: December 31
Type: Public

Azure Dynamics (AZD) has a blue-sky vision for how to make heavy vehicles run in an ecologically friendly way. The development-stage company designs energy management systems for use in commercial vehicles. AZD's hybrid electric vehicle (HEV) control systems include both vehicle management software and controllers used with a variety of drive components. Customers and partners include Canada Post, the US Postal Service, London Taxis, and Purolator Courier. As part of efforts to build a US battery supply base and infrastructure support for hybrid electric vehicles, in early 2009 AZD signed a five-year agreement with lithium-ion suppliers Johnson Controls-SAFT (a joint venture).

	Annual Growth	12/05	12/06	12/07	12/08	12/09
Sales ($ mil.)	22.5%	4.0	4.9	2.9	6.3	9.0
Net income ($ mil.)	—	(18.8)	(20.1)	(30.8)	(31.8)	(26.5)
Market value ($ mil.)	(33.8%)	555.4	410.0	234.2	19.8	106.7
Employees	2.2%	109	112	112	148	119

AZZ INCORPORATED

NYSE: AZZ

3100 W. Seventh St., 1 Museum Place, Ste. 500
Fort Worth, TX 76107
Phone: 817-810-0095
Fax: 817-336-5354
Web: www.azzincorporated.com

CEO: David H. Dingus
CFO: Dana L. Perry
HR: Francis D. Quinn
FYE: February 28
Type: Public

When companies need to power up or get that "zinc-ing" feeling, they give AZZ incorporated a buzz. AZZ has two business segments: electrical and industrial products, and galvanizing services. Through subsidiaries, AZZ makes electrical power distribution systems, industrial lighting, switchgear, motor control centers, bus duct systems, and tubular goods. Industrial, petrochemical, and power-generation and power-transmission industries use the company's products. To protect steel from environmental corrosion, galvanizing services dip steel products into baths of molten zinc. The process is vital for steel fabricators who serve highway construction, electrical utility, transportation, and water-treatment industries.

	Annual Growth	2/06	2/07	2/08	2/09	2/10
Sales ($ mil.)	17.5%	187.2	260.3	320.2	412.4	357.0
Net income ($ mil.)	48.3%	7.8	21.7	27.7	42.2	37.7
Market value ($ mil.)	28.9%	141.5	251.5	440.0	251.4	390.2
Employees	10.7%	1,019	1,301	1,422	1,722	1,530

B. BRAUN MEDICAL INC.

824 12th Ave.
Bethlehem, PA 18018
Phone: 610-691-5400
Fax: 610-691-6249
Web: www.bbraunusa.com

CEO: Caroll H. Neubauer
CFO: Bruce A. Heugel
HR: —
FYE: December 31
Type: Subsidiary

B. Braun Medical is the US arm of German medical supply firm B. Braun Melsungen. The company's products and services include a wide range of IV systems and accessories, pharmaceutical devices, dialysis machines, critical care products, and vascular access and interventional product lines, as well as outsourced pharmacy services and continuing education programs. B. Braun's customers include hospitals, outpatient surgery centers, and home care services. Its network of CAPS (Central Admixture Pharmacy Services) compounding pharmacies provides IV admixtures and solutions to hospitals, clinics, and home care providers throughout the US.

BAB, INC.

OTC: BABB

500 Lake Cook Rd., Ste. 475	CEO: Michael W. Evans
Deerfield, IL 60015	CFO: Jeffrey M. Gorden
Phone: 847-948-7520	HR: Jeffrey M. Gorden
Fax: 847-405-8140	FYE: November 30
Web: www.babcorp.com	Type: Public

Bagels, muffins, and coffee are fueling this company. BAB operates a chain of about 120 franchised coffee and baked goods outlets under the brand names Big Apple Bagels and My Favorite Muffin. The stores offer several varieties of bagels and spreads, muffins, sandwiches, soups, salads, and gourmet coffee. The company also markets a proprietary java brand, Brewster's Coffee. BAB has coffee shops in more than 25 states, as well as in the United Arab Emirates. An investment group controlled by CEO Michael Evans and VP Michael Murtaugh owns nearly 40% of the company.

	Annual Growth	11/05	11/06	11/07	11/08	11/09
Sales ($ mil.)	(11.0%)	5.1	3.9	4.0	3.8	3.2
Net income ($ mil.)	—	0.7	0.7	1.2	0.6	(2.3)
Market value ($ mil.)	(19.7%)	8.7	7.3	7.1	4.8	3.6
Employees	(14.1%)	44	33	33	28	24

THE BABCOCK & WILCOX COMPANY

800 Main St., 4th Fl.	CEO: Brandon C. Bethards
Lynchburg, VA 24504	CFO: David S. Black
Phone: 434-522-6800	HR: Van Athanas
Fax: —	FYE: December 31
Web: www.babcock.com	Type: Subsidiary

New York's first subway was powered by The Babcock & Wilcox Company (B&W), but don't blame the company if your train was running late this morning. B&W designs, supplies, and services power generation systems and equipment, from boilers to nuclear steam generators. The company provides about 25% of the world's boiler-powered electricity, and it has made nearly half of the process recovery boilers used in paper mills in the US. B&W also owns specialty nuclear fuels company Nuclear Fuel Services (NFS), which has a production plant in Tennessee. B&W owner, McDermott International has announced plans to spin off B&W in 2010.

BABCOCK & WILCOX NUCLEAR POWER GENERATION GROUP, INC.

2016 Mt. Athos Rd.	CEO: Richard E. Reimels
Lynchburg, VA 24504	CFO: —
Phone: 434-522-6000	HR: —
Fax: 434-522-5922	FYE: December 31
Web: www.babcock.com	Type: Subsidiary

Babcock & Wilcox Nuclear Power Generation Group (B&W NPG, formerly BWX Technologies) is an affiliate of McDermott International's Babcock & Wilcox Company (B&W), and specializes in the management of nuclear materials, facilities, and technologies. It is part of B&W's Power Generation division which represents 75% of company revenues. Core activities include the fabrication of nuclear power generation components using applied mechanics, robotics engineering, and integrated CAD/CAM computer systems. The Canadian division of B&W NPG has provided nuclear services and more than 200 nuclear steam generators to clients around the world.

BABCOCK EAGLETON, INC.

2900 North Loop West, Ste. 1000	CEO: Duain Cagle
Houston, TX 77092	CFO: Mark Meis
Phone: 713-871-8787	HR: Karen Van Wicklen
Fax: 713-871-1914	FYE: March 31
Web: www.eagletoninc.com	Type: Subsidiary

A subsidiary of Babcock International Group, Babcock Eagleton provides engineering and contracting services, primarily to the pipeline industry. Founded in 1965, Babcock Eagleton offers project services such as conceptual studies, route selection, right-of-way acquisition, surveying and mapping, and procurement. It also offers construction management and field inspection. The group, which works on small to multimillion-dollar projects, designs pipelines and related facilities (such as process plants and compressor and pump stations) and provides full turnkey responsibility. It delivers projects on either a full lump-sum turnkey basis or reimbursable basis.

	Annual Growth	3/04	3/05	3/06	3/07	3/08
Est. sales ($ mil.)	—	—	—	—	—	20.0
Employees	—	—	—	—	—	110

BABYCENTER, L.L.C.

163 Freelon St.	CEO: Tina Sharkey
San Francisco, CA 94107	CFO: Jeffrey Ash
Phone: 415-537-0900	HR: —
Fax: 415-537-0909	FYE: December 31
Web: www.babycenter.com	Type: Subsidiary

If the parenting information you're getting from other sources is a bit too infantile, turn to BabyCenter. The company operates websites for parents of infants and young children. Its BabyCenter.com, Baby.com, and Pregnancy.com sites contain content for parents of offspring from pre-conception through age eight. The sites also include the BabyCenter Community feature for interactive communication, advice, and support. BabyCenter additionally has several international sites, and a retail partnership with Diapers.com to sell clothing and baby products online. Johnson & Johnson owns BabyCenter, which was founded in 1997 by Matt Glickman and Mark Selcow. The company was acquired by Johnson & Johnson in 2001.

BACARDI U.S.A., INC.

2701 Le Jeune Rd.	CEO: John P. Esposito
Coral Gables, FL 33134	CFO: Michael Misiorski
Phone: 305-573-8511	HR: —
Fax: 305-573-0756	FYE: March 31
Web: www.bacardi.com	Type: Subsidiary

Bacardi U.S.A. is truly a story of liquid assets — in more than one way. The company is the US import, sales, and marketing arm of privately owned Bacardi Limited, one of the leading wine and spirits producers in the world. Bacardi U.S.A. markets Bacardi rums (the #1 rum in the world) and Martini & Rossi wines and spirits, including vermouth. It also sells other liquid assets such as Dewar's Blended Scotch Whisky, Bombay Gin, Bénédictine liqueur, Cazdores Blue Agave Tequila, and Grey Goose Vodka. The company changed its name from Bacardi-Martini U.S.A. to Bacardi U.S.A. in 1999.

	Annual Growth	3/04	3/05	3/06	3/07	3/08
Est. sales ($ mil.)	—	—	—	—	—	154.8
Employees	—	—	—	—	—	475

BACCHUS VASCULAR, INC.

3110 Coronado Dr.
Santa Clara, CA 95054
Phone: 408-980-8300
Fax: 408-980-8383
Web: www.bacchusvascular.com

CEO: Scott Cramer
CFO: Mike Gandy
HR: —
FYE: December 31
Type: Subsidiary

Bacchus Vascular lets the good times keep flowing. The company makes the Trellis infusion system, which treats deep vein thrombosis and other clotting disorders. Where typical medication treatments used alone are effective in preventing further clots, they do not always remove clots. The Trellis system is designed to permanently dissolve blood clots in one quickly administered catheter-based procedure. Currently, the system is designed to treat only deep vein thrombosis, but the company is looking into how it can be used to treat other vascular disorders. The company is also focused on making its system an industry standard. Bacchus Vascular was acquired by health care equipment maker Covidien in 2009.

	Annual Growth	12/04	12/05	12/06	12/07	12/08
Est. sales ($ mil.)	—	—	—	—	—	0.1
Employees	—	—	—	—	—	27

BACK BAY RESTAURANT GROUP, INC.

284 Newbury St.
Boston, MA 02115
Phone: 617-536-2800
Fax: 617-236-4175
Web: www.backbayrestaurantgroup.com

CEO: Charles F. Sarkis Sr.
CFO: Robert J. (Bobby) Ciampa
HR: —
FYE: December 31
Type: Private

You might say this company offers its patrons a taste of New England. Back Bay Restaurant Group is a leading regional dining operator with more than 30 locations encompassing more than a dozen different restaurant concepts. Its Papa Razzi trattorias offer Italian cuisine, while Joe's American Bar & Grill serves up steak, burgers, and more in a saloon setting. Back Bay Restaurants also operates upscale steakhouse Abe & Louie's, Atlantic Fish Company, and the Coach Grill, along with a small number of Charley's pubs. Most of the company's restaurants are found in Massachusetts and a few other New England states. CEO and majority owner Charles Sarkis opened his first restaurant in 1963 and formed Back Bay in 1983.

BACK YARD BURGERS, INC.

St. Cloud Corner, 500 Church St., Ste. 200
Nashville, TN 37219
Phone: 615-620-2300
Fax: 615-620-2301
Web: www.backyardburgers.com

CEO: C. Stephen (Steve) Lynn
CFO: Steve Neuroth
HR: —
FYE: December 31
Type: Private

Back Yard Burgers offers diners the chance to eat a charbroiled burger without having to slave over hot coals. The company operates and franchises about 135 quick service restaurants in Tennessee, Mississippi, and more than 15 other states in the Southeast and Midwest. The eateries are known for their made-to-order charbroiled hamburgers made from 100% Black Angus beef. Back Yard Burgers' menu also includes chicken sandwiches, chili, milkshakes, salads, and cobbler. Most of the company's restaurants offer both dine-in and drive-through service. Founded by Lattimore Michael in 1987, the company is controlled by an investment group led by CEO Steve Lynn.

BAD BOY WORLDWIDE ENTERTAINMENT GROUP

1710 Broadway
New York, NY 10019
Phone: 212-381-1540
Fax: 212-381-1599
Web: www.badboyonline.com

CEO: Sean (Diddy) Combs
CFO: —
HR: —
FYE: December 31
Type: Private

From music to fashion to food, Bad Boy Worldwide Entertainment Group sells attitude and image. The company oversees the business interests of its founder, owner, and CEO Sean "Diddy" Combs, a music impresario, fashion designer, and business mogul. Combs' core business is Bad Boy Records, founded in 1994 with Craig Mack and the late Notorious B.I.G., which produces such artists as Yung Joc, Danity Kane, and Cassie, as well as the music of Diddy himself. The label is 50% owned by Warner Music Group (WMG). Combs also markets branded clothing through Sean John Clothing and operates two upscale restaurants called Justin's (named after Combs' oldest son) in New York City and Atlanta.

	Annual Growth	12/04	12/05	12/06	12/07	12/08
Sales ($ mil.)	(40.0%)	—	—	—	500.0	300.0
Employees	—	—	—	—	—	600

BADGER METER, INC.

NYSE: BMI

4545 W. Brown Deer Rd.
Milwaukee, WI 53223
Phone: 414-355-0400
Fax: 414-371-5956
Web: www.badgermeter.com

CEO: Richard A. Meeusen
CFO: Richard E. Johnson
HR: —
FYE: December 31
Type: Public

Badger Meter does not measure the frequency of the appearance of a certain nocturnal carnivorous mammal. Instead, it provides water utilities and industrial customers with instruments that measure and control the flow of liquids. Badger, which was established in 1905, makes meters, valves, flow tubes, and other measurement devices for original equipment manufacturers, water and wastewater utilities, and companies in the pharmaceutical, chemical, concrete, and food and beverage industries. Its utility meters come with manual or automatic reading technology systems. Badger also makes a handheld device that dispenses and monitors oil and other fluids for the automotive market.

	Annual Growth	12/05	12/06	12/07	12/08	12/09
Sales ($ mil.)	3.7%	216.7	229.8	234.8	279.6	250.3
Net income ($ mil.)	26.6%	13.3	7.5	16.5	25.1	34.2
Market value ($ mil.)	19.4%	294.0	415.0	673.5	434.8	596.6
Employees	2.4%	1,052	1,113	1,132	1,224	1,157

BAE SYSTEMS, INC.

1601 Research Blvd.
Rockville, MD 20850
Phone: 301-838-6000
Fax: 301-838-6925
Web: www.baesystems.com

CEO: Linda P. Hudson
CFO: Bradley W. (Brad) Jacobs
HR: Curtis L. (Curt) Gray
FYE: December 31
Type: Subsidiary

BAE Systems takes care of business in North America for parent BAE SYSTEMS plc — the largest foreign player in the US defense market. Operations include the design, manufacture, and maintenance of military aircraft controls, combat vehicles, radar, surveillance systems, navigation systems, missile and satellite electronics, weapons, and other defense systems. BAE Systems also provides IT, systems engineering, and ship repair services. It is a top supplier to the US Department of Defense (DoD), and has a special security agreement with the Pentagon that ensures control of sensitive technology. The company has operations in 38 states and in Germany, Israel, Mexico, Sweden, Switzerland, South Africa, and the UK.

	Annual Growth	12/04	12/05	12/06	12/07	12/08
Est. sales ($ mil.)	—	—	—	—	—	17,000.0
Employees	—	—	—	—	—	50,000

An in-depth profile of this company is available to Hoover's Online members at hoovers.com.

207

BAE SYSTEMS LAND & ARMAMENTS L.P.

1525 Wilson Blvd., Ste. 700	CEO: Robert T. (Bob) Murphy
Arlington, VA 22209	CFO: Gary Slack
Phone: 703-312-6100	HR: Debbie Sallis
Fax: 703-312-6111	FYE: December 31
Web: www.baesystems.com	Type: Subsidiary

Need to storm a beach? Land & Armaments, a BAE Systems subsidiary, operates through four business units. Its US Combat Systems (USCS) provides gun and launching systems, advanced munitions, and armored vehicles such as the Bradley Combat System and Hercules Recovery Vehicle. Global Combat Systems (GCS) and Global Tactical Systems (GTS) produce all sizes of tactical vehicles for high threat areas. The Security & Survivability division manufactures armor systems and products for vehicle and soldier protection, including combat vehicle armor for tactical vehicles such as the HUMVEE and MRAP, aircraft armor, helmets, body armor, and parachutes. Land & Armaments has 55 locations around the world.

	Annual Growth	12/04	12/05	12/06	12/07	12/08
Est. sales ($ mil.)	—	—	—	—	—	513.0
Employees	—	—	—	—	—	5,130

BAE SYSTEMS TECHNOLOGY SOLUTIONS & SERVICES INC.

1601 Research Blvd.	CEO: John Baran
Rockville, MD 20850	CFO: Carroll Marcus Jr.
Phone: 301-738-4000	HR: Mary E. Vohringer
Fax: 301-738-4643	FYE: December 31
Web: www.baesystems.com	Type: Subsidiary

BAE Systems Technology Solutions & Services, a subsidiary of BAE Systems, Inc. (formerly BAE Systems North America), is part of the Support Solutions division of its parent company's Electronics, Intelligence & Support business. BAE Technology Solutions & Services is focused on providing management and operational support to the US Department of Defense (DoD) and other US federal agencies. Operations include ordnance program management; systems engineering, design, and test services; software development; program management support; technical services; and integrated logistical support. Services are provided in three main areas: Ordnance, Systems Engineering, and Integrated Technical Solutions.

	Annual Growth	12/04	12/05	12/06	12/07	12/08
Est. sales ($ mil.)	—	—	—	—	—	579.8
Employees	—	—	—	—	—	6,770

BAER'S FURNITURE CO INC

1589 NW 12th Ave.	CEO: Robert M. (Bobby) Baer
Pompano Beach, FL 33069	CFO: Ira Baer
Phone: 954-946-8001	HR: Sue Scovin
Fax: 954-946-8006	FYE: December 31
Web: www.baersfurniture.com	Type: Private

Having assembled a furniture portfolio full of big-name brands, Baer's Furniture counts the likes of Lexington Home Brands and Bernhardt as family. Family-owned Baer's Furniture operates about 15 retail furniture showrooms throughout Florida. The company offers furnishings (living room, dining room, bedroom, and office furniture), bedding, rugs, and accessories made by popular manufacturers that are designed to fit the budgets of shoppers who have a little cash tucked away. The chain was founded in 1945 by Melvin and Lucile Baer in South Bend, Indiana. Their sons Robert, now the company's CEO, and Allan, company president, moved the business to Florida in 1968.

BAIN & COMPANY, INC.

131 Dartmouth St.	CEO: Steve Ellis
Boston, MA 02116	CFO: —
Phone: 617-572-2000	HR: Deanne Sisco
Fax: 617-572-2427	FYE: December 31
Web: www.bain.com	Type: Private

Bain aims to be ready when corporate titans need a little direction. One of the world's leading management consulting firms, Bain & Company offers a wide array of services aimed at increasing efficiency and streamlining business processes. The firm also consults on strategic business issues, such as potential mergers and acquisitions and private equity investments; services include due-diligence preparation. In addition, Bain consultants address topics such as information technology, marketing, and performance improvement. With more than 3,500 consultants, the firm operates from more than 35 offices in about two dozen countries. It was founded in 1973 by Boston Consulting Group alumnus Bill Bain.

BAIN CAPITAL, LLC

111 Huntington Ave.	CEO: Joshua (Josh) Bekenstein
Boston, MA 02199	CFO: —
Phone: 617-516-2000	HR: —
Fax: 617-516-2010	FYE: December 31
Web: www.baincapital.com	Type: Private

If you want to make a big deal out of it, chances are Bain Capital will be there. The private equity and venture capital firm invests in companies in the retail and consumer products, information technology, communications, health care, and manufacturing industries. Its holdings include stakes in Domino's Pizza, pharmaceutical group Warner Chilcott, Toys "R" Us, sportswear distributor Broder Bros., and SunGard Data Systems. The firm has made private equity investments in more than 240 companies since its 1984 founding. Bain Capital joined Thomas H. Lee Partners in a nearly $24 billion offer for broadcasting giant Clear Channel in 2008, and was part of a group that bought HCA for about $33 billion in 2006.

BAKBONE SOFTWARE INCORPORATED

OTC: BKBO

9540 Towne Centre Dr., Ste. 100	CEO: Steven R. (Steve) Martin
San Diego, CA 92121	CFO: Steven R. (Steve) Martin
Phone: 858-450-9009	HR: —
Fax: 858-450-9929	FYE: March 31
Web: www.bakbone.com	Type: Public

BakBone Software bends over backwards to back up bytes. The company provides storage management software that is used to backup, protect, and recover enterprise data. The company's NetVault backup and restore applications are available with various plug-in modules that work with software from vendors including Microsoft, Oracle, SAP, and Sybase. BakBone also offers a variety of professional services including consulting, training, maintenance, and support. Its customers come from a wide variety of fields such as publishing, financial services, and health care.

BAKEMARK USA LLC

7351 Crider Ave.
Pico Rivera, CA 90660
Phone: 562-949-1054
Fax: 562-949-1257
Web: www.bakemarkusa.com

CEO: William (Bill) Day
CFO: —
HR: —
FYE: December 31
Type: Subsidiary

BakeMark helps bakers reach their mark. The company offers bakery ingredients such as cake and cookie mixes, pie and pastry fillings, and specialty prebaked products along with paper goods. Its brand names include BakeMark (mixes, bases, fillings, icings, glazes, flavors), Produits Marguerite (nut pastes, mousses, custards for French pastries), Trigal Dorado (mixes, margarines, fillings, frozen toppings for Mexican pastries), and Westco (fillings, bases, icings, glazes). The company's customers include retail, wholesale, and in-store bakeries, as well as bakery chains throughout the US. BakeMark USA is a subsidiary of Netherlands-based ingredient maker CSM, the world's largest bakery supplier.

BAKER & HOSTETLER LLP

3200 National City Center, 1900 E. 9th St.
Cleveland, OH 44114
Phone: 216-621-0200
Fax: 216-696-0740
Web: www.bakerlaw.com

CEO: R. Steven (Steve) Kestner
CFO: Kevin L. Cash
HR: Michelle Gray Merrill
FYE: December 31
Type: Partnership

Like Major League Baseball, a longtime client, law firm Baker & Hostetler has players from coast to coast. The firm's more than 600 lawyers practice from about 10 offices in the US, from New York to Los Angeles. In addition, Baker & Hostetler maintains affiliations with firms in Brazil and Mexico. Besides baseball and other sports and entertainment enterprises, the firm's roster of clients has included leading companies in the automotive, energy, health care, hospitality, and media industries. Among Baker & Hostetler's major practice groups are teams devoted to intellectual property, business, employment and labor, and tax and litigation. The firm was founded in 1916.

	Annual Growth	12/04	12/05	12/06	12/07	12/08
Sales ($ mil.)	1.3%	—	—	—	315.0	319.0
Employees	—	—	—	—	—	—

BAKER & MCKENZIE, LLP

1 Prudential Plaza, 130 E. Randolph Dr., Ste. 2500
Chicago, IL 60601
Phone: 312-861-8800
Fax: 312-861-8823
Web: www.bakernet.com

CEO: John J. Conroy Jr.
CFO: Robert S. Spencer
HR: Vicki Kelley
FYE: June 30
Type: Private

Baker & McKenzie believes big is good and bigger is better. One of the world's largest law firms, it has about 3,900 attorneys practicing from some 70 offices — from Bangkok to Berlin to Buenos Aires — in almost 40 countries. It offers expertise in a wide range of practice areas, including antitrust, intellectual property, international trade, mergers and acquisitions, project finance, and tax law. Baker & McKenzie's client list includes big companies from numerous industries, including banking and finance, construction, and technology, as well as smaller enterprises.

	Annual Growth	6/05	6/06	6/07	6/08	6/09
Sales ($ mil.)	11.8%	1,352.0	1,522.0	1,829.0	2,190.0	2,110.0
Employees	3.4%	8,500	9,503	9,600	9,700	9,700

BAKER & TAYLOR, INC.

2550 W. Tyvola Rd., Ste. 300
Charlotte, NC 28217
Phone: 704-998-3100
Fax: 704-998-3316
Web: www.btol.com

CEO: Thomas I. (Tom) Morgan
CFO: Jeff Leonard
HR: —
FYE: June 30
Type: Private

If you've strolled through a library recently, you likely saw a lot of Baker & Taylor (B&T) without knowing it. The #1 supplier of paper and digital books to libraries, B&T primarily serves two types of markets. Its core business distributes books, videos, and music, and provides value-added services to thousands of school, public, and specialty libraries worldwide. The firm's retail unit supplies storefront and Internet book and music retailers, as well as independent booksellers, with a million book titles and about 385,000 DVD and CD titles. On the Internet (where it formerly operated as Informata.com), B&T offers B2B e-commerce fulfillment services. B&T is owned by investment firm Castle Harlan.

BAKER BOTTS L.L.P.

1 Shell Plaza, 910 Louisiana St.
Houston, TX 77002
Phone: 713-229-1234
Fax: 713-229-1522
Web: www.bakerbotts.com

CEO: Walter J. (Walt) Smith
CFO: Lydia Companion
HR: Roger Walter
FYE: December 31
Type: Partnership

Baker Botts is a Lone Star legal legend. The law firm's history stretches back to 1840, when founding partner Peter Gray was admitted to the bar of the Republic of Texas. The firm became Baker & Botts after Walter Browne Botts and James Addison Baker (great-grandfather of former US Secretary of State and current partner James A. Baker III) joined the partnership. The firm has some 800 lawyers in about a dozen offices worldwide. Over the years Baker Botts has represented numerous clients from the energy industry, including Exxon Mobil and Halliburton. The firm practices in such areas as corporate, intellectual property, and tax law.

	Annual Growth	12/04	12/05	12/06	12/07	12/08
Sales ($ mil.)	9.9%	420.2	365.0	502.5	577.5	613.5
Employees	—	1,601	—	—	—	—

BAKER BOYER BANCORP

OTC: BBBK

7 W. Main St.
Walla Walla, WA 99362
Phone: 509-525-2000
Fax: 509-525-1034
Web: www.bakerboyer.com

CEO: Megan Clubb
CFO: —
HR: —
FYE: December 31
Type: Public

For Baker Boyer Bancorp, it *is* personal. The holding company for Baker Boyer National Bank takes pride in the personal touch it applies to its services, which include standard deposit products, loans, financial planning, and insurance services. One- to four-family residential mortgages account for the largest portion of the bank's loan portfolio. Through Baker Boyer Wealth Management Services, the company offers investments, private banking, brokerage, and trust services. Baker Boyer National Bank serves individual and business customers through about 10 branches in southern Washington and northern Oregon. Founded in 1869, the family-owned company is the oldest bank in Washington State.

	Annual Growth	12/06	12/07	12/08	12/09	12/10
Assets ($ mil.)	—	—	—	—	—	426.6
Net income ($ mil.)	—	—	—	—	—	4.4
Employees	—	—	—	—	—	170

BAKER COMMODITIES, INC.

4020 Bandini Blvd.
Los Angeles, CA 90023
Phone: 323-268-2801
Fax: 323-268-5166
Web: www.bakercommodities.com

CEO: James Andreoli
CFO: Robert Alves
HR: Martha Morales
FYE: December 31
Type: Private

This Baker is somewhere between a butcher and a candlestick maker. Baker Commodities is a rendering company that takes unused animal byproducts from meat processing plants, supermarkets, restaurants, and butcher shops and produces animal fats and oils, poultry and bone meal, and tallow. These products then can be used to make candles, cosmetics, paints, plastics, organic detergents, livestock feed, pet food, and biodiesel. It is one of the nation's largest rendering companies, with 21 plants in about a dozen US states, including four in California, four in New York, and one in Hawaii.

BAKER CONCRETE CONSTRUCTION, INC.

900 N. Garver Rd.
Monroe, OH 45050
Phone: 513-539-4000
Fax: 513-539-4380
Web: www.bakerconcrete.com

CEO: Daniel L. (Dan) Baker
CFO: Tom Bell
HR: Mike Schneider
FYE: March 31
Type: Private

Baker Concrete Construction really likes to pour it on. The company installs concrete slabs for heavy construction projects — from airports, arenas, and industrial plants to hospitals, hotels, and highways. Its work includes the installation of industrial floors, concrete paving, and site concrete. Baker, founded in 1968, also specializes in highrise concrete construction and offers architectural and design/build services and repair and restoration. Baker Concrete Construction operates throughout the US, with offices in Arizona, Colorado, Florida, Ohio, and Texas. Clients have included General Motors, Samsung, Target, and the Ohio Department of Transportation. President and founder Daniel Baker owns the company.

	Annual Growth	3/04	3/05	3/06	3/07	3/08
Est. sales ($ mil.)	—	—	—	—	—	341.4
Employees	—	—	—	—	—	4,000

BAKER HUGHES INCORPORATED

NYSE: BHI

2929 Allen Pkwy., Ste. 2100
Houston, TX 77019
Phone: 713-439-8600
Fax: 713-439-8699
Web: www.bakerhughes.com

CEO: Chad C. Deaton
CFO: Peter A. Ragauss
HR: Didier Charreton
FYE: December 31
Type: Public

Baker Hughes cooks up a baker's dozen of products and services for the global petroleum market. Through its Drilling and Evaluation segment, Baker Hughes makes products and services used to drill oil and natural gas wells. Through its Completion and Production segment, the company provides equipment and services used from the completion phase through the productive life of oil and natural gas wells. The company tests potential well sites and drills and operates the wells; it also makes bits and drilling fluids and submersible pumps, and provides equipment and well services. In a major industry consolidation, in 2010 Baker Hughes acquired oil field services titan BJ Services for $5.5 billion.

	Annual Growth	12/05	12/06	12/07	12/08	12/09
Sales ($ mil.)	7.7%	7,185.5	9,027.4	10,428.2	11,864.0	9,664.0
Net income ($ mil.)	(16.8%)	879.3	2,419.0	1,513.9	1,635.0	421.0
Market value ($ mil.)	(9.7%)	26,077.4	32,032.6	34,795.6	13,759.5	17,367.8
Employees	4.3%	29,100	34,600	35,800	39,800	34,400

BAKER PETROLITE CORPORATION

12645 W. Airport Blvd.
Sugar Land, TX 77478
Phone: 281-276-5400
Fax: 281-275-7392
Web: www.bakerhughes.com/bakerpetrolite

CEO: Chad C. Deaton
CFO: —
HR: —
FYE: December 31
Type: Subsidiary

You can't just dig a hole and expect the oil to come right out. Baker Petrolite's products — petrochemicals and additives — play a big part in getting all that oil out of the ground. A business unit of oilfield equipment maker Baker Hughes, Baker Petrolite manufactures specialty chemicals for oil and natural gas production — fluid stimulants for oil drillers, as well as hydrate, corrosion, paraffin, and scale inhibitors. (The range of inhibitors are designed to reduce drag in pipelines.) It also makes additives for refineries, herbicides for farmers, and polymers for everyone from candle makers to the toner and ink industries.

	Annual Growth	12/04	12/05	12/06	12/07	12/08
Est. sales ($ mil.)	—	—	—	—	—	844.0
Employees	—	—	—	—	—	2,550

BAKERS FOOTWEAR GROUP, INC.

NASDAQ (GM): BKRS

2815 Scott Ave.
St. Louis, MO 63103
Phone: 314-621-0699
Fax: 314-621-0708
Web: www.bakersshoes.com

CEO: Peter A. Edison
CFO: Charles R. Daniel III
HR: Vicky Williams
FYE: January 31
Type: Public

Mall rats in need of new shoes might step into Bakers Footwear. The mall-based vendor of women's shoes and accessories runs about 240 stores in about three dozen states, with some 20 stores doing business under the Wild Pair banner. Wild Pair shops offer edgier fashion footwear to tempt women ages 17 to 29. Bakers Footwear sells dress, casual, and sport shoes, as well as boots, sandals, and accessories, targeting women ages 16 to 35. Private labels account for more than 70% of company sales. National brands on sale in Bakers' stores include Ed Hardy, Jessica Simpson, BCB Girls, and Baby Phat, among others. The company also operates an online shoe store and catalog.

	Annual Growth	1/06	1/07	1/08	1/09	1/10
Sales ($ mil.)	(1.2%)	194.8	204.8	186.3	183.7	185.4
Net income ($ mil.)	—	6.6	(1.5)	(17.7)	(15.0)	(9.1)
Market value ($ mil.)	(52.2%)	155.7	87.1	20.2	3.0	8.1
Employees	1.4%	2,250	2,450	4,520	2,403	2,380

BALBOA INSURANCE GROUP, INC.

3349 Michelson, Ste. 200
Irvine, CA 92612
Phone: 949-222-8000
Fax: 949-222-8777
Web: www.balboainsurance.com

CEO: Mark A. McElroy
CFO: Kenneth Mertzel
HR: —
FYE: December 31
Type: Subsidiary

When life gets rocky, Balboa is there to insure you. Balboa Insurance Group provides commercial and personal life, liability, and property insurance through subsidiaries including Balboa Insurance Company, Meritplan Insurance Company, Newport E&S Insurance Company, Newport Insurance Company, Balboa Life Insurance Company, and Balboa Life Insurance Company of New York. The company specializes in insurance programs for such customers as financial institutions and mortgage lenders. Products include credit life, homeowners insurance, lender-placed property hazard insurance, and home warranties. It is a subsidiary of Bank of America.

	Annual Growth	12/04	12/05	12/06	12/07	12/08
Est. sales ($ mil.)	—	—	—	—	—	1,517.6
Employees	—	—	—	—	—	2,100

⊞ BALCHEM CORPORATION

NASDAQ (GS): BCPC

52 Sunrise Park Rd.
New Hampton, NY 10958
Phone: 845-326-5600
Fax: 845-326-5742
Web: www.balchem.com

CEO: Dino A. Rossi
CFO: Francis J. (Frank) Fitzpatrick
HR: —
FYE: December 31
Type: Public

Believe Balchem when they say they have it covered. The company has developed a technology that covers or encapsulates ingredients used in food and animal health products; the encapsulation improves nutritional value and shelf life and allows for controlled time release. Balchem also distributes specialty gases such as ethylene oxide (used to sterilize medical instruments), propylene oxide (used to reduce bacteria in spice treating and chemical processing), and methyl chloride. The company's unencapsulated-feed-ingredients segment supplies the nutrient choline chloride to poultry and swine farmers. Reashure, an encapsulated choline product, increases milk production in dairy cows.

	Annual Growth	12/05	12/06	12/07	12/08	12/09
Sales ($ mil.)	(28.5%)	839.1	100.9	176.2	232.1	219.4
Net income ($ mil.)	24.9%	11.0	12.3	16.1	19.0	26.8
Market value ($ mil.)	26.1%	249.0	321.8	420.6	468.2	629.8
Employees	13.9%	200	230	320	332	337

⊞ BALDOR ELECTRIC COMPANY

NYSE: BEZ

5711 R. S. Boreham, Jr. St.
Fort Smith, AR 72901
Phone: 479-646-4711
Fax: 479-648-5792
Web: www.baldor.com

CEO: John A. McFarland
CFO: George E. Moschner
HR: Jason W. Green
FYE: December 31
Type: Public

Electricity drives Baldor Electric's sales — and its products. The company manufactures industrial AC and DC electric motors, controls, and speed drives that power products ranging from material handling conveyors to fluid handling pumps. Other products include industrial grinders, buffers, polishing lathes, and generators. Baldor Electric sells to OEMs primarily in the agricultural and semiconductor equipment industries and to independent distributors for resale as replacement parts. The company has some 75 sales offices and warehouses in North America and abroad. It maintains manufacturing plants in Canada, China, Mexico, the UK, and the US. Baldor Electric gets most of its sales in the US.

	Annual Growth	12/05	12/06	12/07	12/08	12/09
Sales ($ mil.)	20.6%	721.6	811.3	1,824.9	1,954.7	1,524.1
Net income ($ mil.)	8.6%	43.0	48.1	94.1	99.4	59.8
Market value ($ mil.)	2.3%	1,200.9	1,564.7	1,576.0	835.7	1,315.2
Employees	17.2%	3,841	3,950	8,083	7,891	7,250

BALDUCCI'S

10411 Motor City Dr., Ste. 500
Bethesda, MD 20817
Phone: 240-403-2440
Fax: 240-403-2520
Web: www.balduccis.com

CEO: Pascal Jubault
CFO: —
HR: —
FYE: January 31
Type: Private

Balducci's has the right ingredients to attract hungry gourmands. The chain operates half a dozen upscale specialty food stores under the Balducci's name in Connecticut, Maryland, New York, and Virginia. The markets offer such fare as fresh pasta, Wagyu beef, and imported cheeses. It also stocks prepared meals and beer and wine. Louis "Pop" Balducci opened the first Balducci's in Brooklyn in 1915 and expanded to Greenwich Village in Manhattan in 1946. In 2009 the private equity firm Irving Place Capital (formerly Bear Stearns Merchant Banking) sold six Balducci's stores to an investor group led by Jim Demme, senior advisor to the New York City-based investment firm Angelo, Gordon & Co.

BALDWIN & LYONS, INC.

NASDAQ (GM): BWINB

1099 N. Meridian St.
Indianapolis, IN 46204
Phone: 317-636-9800
Fax: 317-632-9444
Web: www.baldwinandlyons.com

CEO: Gary W. Miller
CFO: G. Patrick (Pat) Corydon
HR: Hugh Cameron
FYE: December 31
Type: Public

Baldwin & Lyons insures truckers and the bad car drivers who terrorize them. The company's Protective Insurance subsidiary, licensed throughout the US and Canada, writes property and casualty insurance for large trucking fleets with substantial self-insurance and for medium-sized trucking companies with small deductibles. Baldwin & Lyons' Sagamore Insurance unit specializes in providing insurance to high-risk private auto drivers through a network of independent agents in some 30 states. Sagamore also sells physical-damage insurance and liability insurance for small trucking fleets.

	Annual Growth	12/05	12/06	12/07	12/08	12/09
Assets ($ mil.)	(0.3%)	860.4	853.7	842.8	777.7	851.3
Net income ($ mil.)	7.0%	34.2	38.2	55.1	(7.7)	44.8
Market value ($ mil.)	0.3%	359.5	377.9	406.3	269.1	364.3
Employees	1.5%	276	279	284	312	293

⊞ BALDWIN PIANO INC.

309 Plus Park Blvd.
Nashville, TN 37217
Phone: 615-871-4500
Fax: 615-889-5509
Web: www.baldwinpiano.com

CEO: Henry E. Juszkiewicz
CFO: —
HR: —
FYE: December 31
Type: Subsidiary

The keys to success for Baldwin alternate in color — black and white. One of the top piano manufacturers in the US, Baldwin Piano is best known for making concert and upright pianos under the Baldwin, Howard, Hamilton, Chickering, and Wurlitzer names. The company also makes ConcertMaster computerized player pianos. Its custom models feature hand-painted designs, including gold-leaf scrollwork and pinstripes, marble finishes, and exotic leopard spots and zebra stripes. Gibson Guitar, which has been working to breathe new life into Baldwin, bought the ailing piano maker from GE Capital in 2001. Dwight Hamilton Baldwin established the company as Baldwin Piano & Organ in 1862.

⊞ BALDWIN TECHNOLOGY COMPANY, INC.

NYSE Amex: BLD

2 Trap Falls Rd., Ste. 402
Shelton, CT 06484
Phone: 203-402-1000
Fax: 203-402-5500
Web: www.baldwintech.com

CEO: Karl S. Puehringer
CFO: John P. Jordan
HR: —
FYE: June 30
Type: Public

Baldwin Technology has pressing business. The company specializes in process automation technology for the printing and publishing industries. It manufactures printing press equipment and control systems for press cleaning, ink control, drying, water-regulating fountains, as well as for controlling paper flow. Baldwin's products are marketed to printing press manufacturers, which bolt the products onto their own systems for sale to printers. The company also sells directly to printers wanting to upgrade their presses. Offset (lithographic) printing applications represent its largest market. Baldwin positions the lineup as a premium technology through subsidiaries in 11 countries.

	Annual Growth	6/05	6/06	6/07	6/08	6/09
Sales ($ mil.)	0.5%	173.2	179.4	201.5	236.3	176.6
Net income ($ mil.)	—	5.0	6.3	6.6	6.4	(11.8)
Market value ($ mil.)	(24.6%)	48.2	83.9	93.7	36.7	15.5
Employees	0.3%	534	551	717	699	540

⊞ An in-depth profile of this company is available to Hoover's Online members at hoovers.com.

BALFOUR BEATTY CONSTRUCTION LLC

3100 McKinnon St., 10th Fl.
Dallas, TX 75201
Phone: 214-451-1000
Fax: —
Web: www.balfourbeattyus.com

CEO: Robert C. Van Cleave
CFO: Mark W. Layman
HR: J. David Preston
FYE: March 31
Type: Subsidiary

Balfour Beatty Construction is deep in the heart of Texas — and other locales as well. The company provides start-to-finish project management, pre-construction, and related services for commercial construction projects. Offerings include site evaluation and analysis, general contracting, cost consulting, process equipment installation, turnkey medical facility development, capital equipment planning, and closeout services. The company works on a range of facilities including hotels, office buildings, civic centers, airports, hospitals, schools, public buildings, and retail locations. UK firm Balfour Beatty PLC acquired the company, then named Centex Construction, from Centex Corporation in 2007.

BALFOUR BEATTY, INC.

999 Peachtree St. NE, Ste. 900
Atlanta, GA 30309
Phone: 404-875-0356
Fax: 404-875-0508
Web: www.balfourbeatty.com

CEO: James J. (Jim) Moynihan
CFO: Ray Bond
HR: —
FYE: December 31
Type: Subsidiary

For Balfour Beatty, Inc., building is best. The US arm of UK-based Balfour Beatty plc provides engineering and construction services. The group operates through civil and specialist engineering firm Balfour Beatty Infrastructure, rail construction and engineering firm Balfour Beatty Rail, and engineering and architectural project manager Heery International. Projects have ranged from work on one of the largest design/build transportation projects in the US (Texas SH 130) to designing for The Centennial Olympic Stadium (now the Atlanta Braves' Turner Field). The group has become active in the transportation, bridges, mass transit and rail, highways, and water supply markets.

	Annual Growth	12/04	12/05	12/06	12/07	12/08
Est. sales ($ mil.)	—	—	—	—	—	0.9
Employees	—	—	—	—	—	10

BALFOUR BEATTY INFRASTRUCTURE, INC.

999 Peachtree St. NE, Ste. 200
Atlanta, GA 30309
Phone: 404-875-0356
Fax: 404-607-7319
Web: www.bbinfrastructureinc.com

CEO: James J. (Jim) Moynihan
CFO: Mark Birch
HR: David L. Confer
FYE: December 31
Type: Subsidiary

Balfour Beatty Infrastructure is the North American heavy construction and civil engineering arm of UK-based Balfour Beatty plc. The contractor has expertise in transportation and water infrastructure projects ranging in size from about $3 million to $400 million. It specializes in constructing bridges, highways, tunnels, rail lines, and water treatment plants. The firm's primary clients are public agencies, including municipalities and state departments of transportation. In addition to taking on stand-alone projects, it is involved in multiple joint ventures, including one of the largest public works projects in the US, the design and construction of the $1.5 billion Texas State Highway 130 toll road.

	Annual Growth	12/04	12/05	12/06	12/07	12/08
Est. sales ($ mil.)	—	—	—	—	—	478.1
Employees	—	—	—	—	—	1,100

BALFOUR BEATTY RAIL, INC.

999 Peachtree St. NE, Ste. 200
Atlanta, FL 30309
Phone: 404-875-0356
Fax: 404-607-0319
Web: www.bbri.com

CEO: Joseph (Joe) Reed
CFO: —
HR: —
FYE: December 31
Type: Subsidiary

As far as engineering marvels go, Balfour Beatty Rail knows that few things beat working on the railroad. The company designs and builds railroads from light-rail to heavy-rail transit systems across the US. It tackles construction of large, complex rail infrastructure systems for regional and short line railroads, transit authorities, ports, and industrial markets. Balfour Beatty Rail also offers construction and rehabilitation services as well as project estimation and management, heavy excavation, grading, and equipment rental, repair, and maintenance of train control signal and communication systems. Formerly Marta Track Constructors, Balfour Beatty Rail is part of UK-headquartered Balfour Beatty plc.

	Annual Growth	12/04	12/05	12/06	12/07	12/08
Est. sales ($ mil.)	—	—	—	—	—	77.9
Employees	—	—	—	—	—	681

BALL AEROSPACE & TECHNOLOGIES CORP.

1600 Commerce St.
Boulder, CO 80301
Phone: 303-939-4000
Fax: 303-939-6104
Web: www.ballaerospace.com

CEO: David L. (Dave) Taylor
CFO: William Unger
HR: James P. (Jim) Stevens
FYE: December 31
Type: Subsidiary

Ball Aerospace & Technologies runs the gamut from A to V — antennas to video systems — with stops in between for GPS equipment, high-tech subsystems, and systems integration. A subsidiary of Ball Corporation, the company develops satellites and spacecraft, instruments and sensors, antennas and microwave systems, and aerospace components for the military and commercial sectors, as well as provides engineering services and testing. Ball cameras/video equipment include night-vision systems and high-resolution satellite cameras for NASA vehicles, weather satellites, and the military. Ball's other offerings include cryogenic systems, fast-steering mirrors, and satellite accessory control systems.

BALL CORPORATION

NYSE: BLL

10 Longs Peak Dr.
Broomfield, CO 80021
Phone: 303-469-3131
Fax: 303-460-2127
Web: www.ball.com

CEO: R. David Hoover
CFO: Scott C. Morrison
HR: —
FYE: December 31
Type: Public

The well-rounded Ball Corporation pitches packaging to companies producing food, beverage, and household products. Food and beverage packaging includes aluminum and steel cans, and polyethylene terephthalate (PET) plastic bottles. A large part of Ball's packaging revenue derives from long-term contracts with SABMiller and bottlers of Pepsi-Cola and Coca-Cola brands, in North America, Europe, China, Brazil, and Argentina. Ball Aerospace & Technologies manufactures an array of systems, from remote sensing satellites to telescopes, surveillance, and antenna and video devices. Agencies such as the US Department of Defense and NASA, or their prime contractors, represent more than 90% of this segment's sales.

	Annual Growth	12/05	12/06	12/07	12/08	12/09
Sales ($ mil.)	6.3%	5,751.2	6,621.5	7,389.7	7,561.5	7,345.3
Net income ($ mil.)	10.4%	261.5	329.6	281.3	319.5	387.9
Market value ($ mil.)	6.8%	3,667.4	4,025.6	4,154.9	3,840.0	4,773.5
Employees	2.6%	13,100	15,500	15,500	14,500	14,500

BALL HORTICULTURAL COMPANY

622 Town Rd.
West Chicago, IL 60185
Phone: 630-231-3600
Fax: 630-231-3605
Web: www.ballhort.com

CEO: Anna C. Ball
CFO: Todd Billings
HR: Mike Williams
FYE: June 30
Type: Private

Flower power still reigns at Ball Horticultural. One of the nation's largest sellers of commercial seed for flowers and ornamental crops, Ball Horticultural develops, produces, and distributes seeds, young plants, and cuttings to professional growers, landscapers, wholesalers, and retailers. It operates in more than 20 countries through subsidiaries and joint ventures, including PanAmerican Seed and Ball Seed. The firm sells through its own sales force and online. It also publishes *FloraCulture International, Green Profit,* and *GrowerTalks* magazines. Founded in 1905 by George Ball, Ball Horticultural remains family owned. The Ball clan also owns W. Atlee Burpee, a major seed seller to home gardeners.

BALL STATE UNIVERSITY

2000 W. University Ave.
Muncie, IN 47306
Phone: 765-289-1241
Fax: 765-285-1461
Web: www.bsu.edu

CEO: Jo Ann M. Gora
CFO: —
HR: Thomas Morrison
FYE: June 30
Type: School

Students at this university are on the ball. Ball State University (BSU) has an enrollment of about 20,000 undergraduate and graduate students. It offers about 170 undergraduate majors, more than 75 master's degree programs, and about a dozen each of certificate, preprofessional, and doctoral degree programs. Begun as a private teacher's college in 1899, Ball St. became a university in 1965. It still has a Teachers College, as well as colleges of applied sciences and technology; architecture and planning; business; communication, information, and media; fine arts; and sciences and humanities. Notable alumni include late night talk show host David Letterman and *Garfield* comic strip creator Jim Davis.

	Annual Growth	6/04	6/05	6/06	6/07	6/08
Est. sales ($ mil.)	—	—	—	—	—	224.1
Employees	—	—	—	—	—	6,426

🏢 BALLANTYNE OF OMAHA, INC.

NYSE Amex: BTN

4350 McKinley St.
Omaha, NE 68112
Phone: 402-453-4444
Fax: 402-453-7238
Web: www.ballantyne-omaha.com

CEO: John P. Wilmers
CFO: Kevin S. Herrmann
HR: —
FYE: December 31
Type: Public

Ballantyne of Omaha projects a lot of images. The company is an international supplier of motion picture theater equipment used by major theater chains such as AMC Entertainment and Regal Entertainment. Primary offerings include its Strong brand of film and digital projectors and accessories. Ballantyne of Omaha's Strong Entertainment lighting division manufactures lighting systems. Its spotlights and searchlights have been used by movie and TV producers, hotels, sporting arenas, and amusement parks, including Walt Disney World and Universal Studios.

	Annual Growth	12/05	12/06	12/07	12/08	12/09
Sales ($ mil.)	7.5%	53.9	49.7	51.5	54.8	72.1
Net income ($ mil.)	(16.4%)	4.3	1.6	0.2	(2.7)	2.1
Market value ($ mil.)	(6.5%)	69.4	75.0	83.0	17.4	52.9
Employees	(2.1%)	197	197	187	173	181

BALLISTIC RECOVERY SYSTEMS

Pink Sheets: BRSI

380 Airport Rd.
South St. Paul, MN 55075
Phone: 651-457-7491
Fax: 651-457-8651
Web: www.brsaerospace.com

CEO: Larry E. Williams
CFO: —
HR: —
FYE: September 30
Type: Public

Ballistic Recovery Systems (doing business as BRS Aerospace) lets you down easy with its rocket-deployed emergency recovery parachute system, which has been credited with saving over 200 lives. BRS is unique in its fabrication of whole-aircraft canopies designed to bring recreational, general and light sport aircraft, including the Cessna 172/182 and Cirrus SR20/SR22, safely to the ground. BRS is partnered with CIMSA Ingenieria de Sistemas (Spain) to expand its share in civil and military markets worldwide. Wholly owned subsidiary Advanced Tactical Fabrication (ATF) produces personal safety equipment, such as high-visibility apparel, components, trims, and emergency lighting systems under the Head Lites brand.

BALLSTON SPA BANCORP INC.

OTC: BSPA

87 Front St.
Ballston Spa, NY 12020
Phone: 518-885-6781
Fax: 518-885-6711
Web: www.bsnb.com

CEO: Christopher R. Dowd
CFO: Timothy E. Blow
HR: Lesley S. Dorsey
FYE: December 31
Type: Public

Ballston Spa Bancorp is the holding company for Ballston Spa National Bank, which serves Saratoga County in New York from about 10 branches. It offers traditional deposit products including checking and savings accounts, IRAs, and CDs. The bank also offers investment products, wealth and estate planning, insurance, and trust services. Residential mortgages account for about two-thirds of the company's loan portfolio; the company also writes commercial mortgages, consumer loans, and business loans. Ballston Spa National Bank was established in 1838.

🏢 BALLY TECHNOLOGIES, INC.

NYSE: BYI

6601 S. Bermuda Rd.
Las Vegas, NV 89119
Phone: 702-584-7700
Fax: 702-584-7710
Web: www.ballytech.com

CEO: Richard M. (Dick) Haddrill
CFO: Robert C. Caller
HR: —
FYE: June 30
Type: Public

This company helps keep the casinos buzzing. Bally Technologies is a leading manufacturer and supplier of casino gaming machines and information systems. Its Bally Gaming Equipment and Systems division makes both video and mechanical-reel slot machines used in gambling casinos in the US and abroad. The company also makes enterprise computer systems used by casinos to monitor their gaming operations by tracking machine activity and payouts. Its systems can also track player activity for rewards programs. In addition, Bally Technologies develops systems for linking slot machines together so that players can gamble for progressively increasing jackpots.

	Annual Growth	6/05	6/06	6/07	6/08	6/09
Sales ($ mil.)	16.2%	484.0	547.1	682.3	899.7	883.4
Net income ($ mil.)	—	(25.0)	(46.1)	22.3	107.2	126.3
Market value ($ mil.)	20.9%	774.2	909.5	1,459.0	1,866.6	1,652.3
Employees	15.4%	1,640	2,020	2,262	2,814	2,907

BALLY TOTAL FITNESS HOLDING CORPORATION

8700 W. Bryn Mawr Ave.	CEO: Michael (Mike) Sheehan
Chicago, IL 60631	CFO: Steven D. (Steve) Barnhart
Phone: 773-380-3000	HR: —
Fax: —	FYE: December 31
Web: www.ballyfitness.com	Type: Private

Bally Total Fitness Holding is trying to work it out. The fitness center operator has about 270 facilities in the US that are used by more than 3 million active members. Its members have access to pools, aerobics classes, running tracks, and racquet courts, as well as personal trainers and sports medicine services. Bally Total Fitness also offers many online services to its members, including electronic payment and account management, as well as online fitness newsletter *The Skinny*. The company has had its share of time in bankruptcy court, having filed Chapter 11 twice in nearly as many years. It most recently emerged from bankruptcy in 2009.

BALTIC TRADING LIMITED   NYSE: BALT

299 Park Ave., 20th Fl.	CEO: John C. Wobensmith
New York, NY 10171	CFO: John C. Wobensmith
Phone: 646-443-8550	HR: —
Fax: —	FYE: December 31
	Type: Public

Baltic Trading swims against the current in international shipping. While most cargo carriers look for long-term contracts to fill their holds, Baltic Trading operates in the spot market, immediate charters that are usually single voyages. The company was formed in 2009 by parent Genco Shipping & Trading to serve the dry bulk industry. Its initial fleet of six drybulk vessels (two Capesize and four Supramax) will have an aggregate carrying capacity of 566,000 deadweight tons (DWT). Genco providing strategic and administrative services, and establishing a link to companies like Cargill, COSCO, and Louis Dreyfus. Baltic Trading completed an IPO in 2010, with Genco investing $75 million for majority control.

BALTIMORE GAS AND ELECTRIC COMPANY

100 Constellation Way	CEO: Kenneth W. (Ken) DeFontes Jr.
Baltimore, MD 21202	CFO: Kevin W. Hadlock
Phone: 410-470-2800	HR: David Vosvick
Fax: —	FYE: December 31
Web: www.bge.com	Type: Subsidiary

Baltimore Gas and Electric (BGE) provides electricity and natural gas services without having to pull anyone's finger. The company not only provides services in Baltimore, but to all or parts of 10 surrounding central Maryland counties as well in a service area of 2,300 square miles. The company's regulated power transmission and distribution system consists of 24,500 circuit miles of distribution lines, and 1,300 circuit miles of transmission lines, and serves more than 1.2 million customers; its gas system serves 648,900 homes and businesses in an 800-square-mile service area. BGE is a subsidiary of Constellation Energy Group.

	Annual Growth	12/04	12/05	12/06	12/07	12/08
Est. sales ($ mil.)	—	—	—	—	—	3,703.7
Employees	—	—	—	—	—	10,200

BANANA REPUBLIC, LLC

2 Folsom St.	CEO: Jack Calhoun
San Francisco, CA 94105	CFO: Sabrina Simmons
Phone: 650-952-4400	HR: —
Fax: 415-427-2553	FYE: January 31
Web: www.bananarepublic.com	Type: Subsidiary

Banana Republic has grown from a two-store wannabe safari outfitter to an empire in its own right, though no pith hats or fake palm trees can be found now at its stores. Instead, the well-known retailer of men's and women's midscale (not high-dollar, but far from discount) casual and tailored apparel has a sprawling territory of some 600 stores in North American, Europe, and Asia, and a website, through which it distributes its well-put-together look. A division of ailing retail giant Gap Inc. since 1983, at one point it was dangerously close to cannibalizing its parent's customers. In contrast to Gap, however, the company buys up historic landmarks and refurbishes them (as opposed to paving paradise).

BANC OF AMERICA INVESTMENT SERVICES, INC.

Gateway Village, Bldg. 900, 900 W. Trade St.	CEO: Timothy P. (Tim) Maloney
Charlotte, NC 28255	CFO: John G. Romano
Phone: 800-926-1111	HR: —
Fax: —	FYE: December 31
Web: www.baisidirect.com	Type: Subsidiary

One of the top bank-owned brokerages in the US, Banc of America Investment Services (BAI) is the primary retail brokerage unit of banking powerhouse Bank of America. The unit offers online brokerage services for do-it-yourself investors; customers with a balance of more than $25,000 get up to 30 free trades per month. BAI provides access to stocks, bonds, options, mutual funds, exchange-traded funds (ETFs), as well as investment research, retirement accounts, and college savings plans. It offers full-service financial advisory services to clients with investable assets in excess of $100,000. BAI is a part of Bank of America's Premier Banking and Investments division.

BANC OF AMERICA MERCHANT SERVICES, LLC

1231 Durrett Ln.	CEO: Thomas R. (Tom) Bell Jr.
Louisville, KY 40213	CFO: —
Phone: 502-315-2000	HR: —
Fax: 502-315-3535	FYE: December 31
Web: corp.bankofamerica.com/public/merchant	Type: Joint venture

The next time you swipe your card and it clears, you might thank Banc of America Merchant Services. A 2009 joint venture between Bank of America and First Data, it is one of the largest processors of electronic payments in the US. The firm handles more than 7 billion check and credit, debit, stored value, payroll, and electronic benefits transfer card transactions annually. Its clients are small businesses and large corporations including retailers, restaurants, hotels, supermarkets, utilities, gas stations, convenience stores, and government entities. First Data owns 48.5% of Banc of America Merchant Services, while Bank of America owns 46.5%. Third-party investor Rockmount Investments holds the rest.

BANC OF AMERICA SECURITIES LLC

9 W. 57th St.
New York, NY 10019
Phone: 212-583-8000
Fax: 415-627-2010
Web: www.bofasecurities.com

CEO: Brian T. Moynihan
CFO: —
HR: —
FYE: December 31
Type: Subsidiary

Banc of America Securities makes its marc as the investment banking arm of Bank of America. Operating as Bank of America Merrill Lynch, the firm offers trading and brokerage services; securities underwriting; debt and equity research; and advice on public offerings, leveraged buyouts, and M&A deals. It has several offices in Australasia, Europe, and North America. The firm's client list includes corporations (including many *FORTUNE* 500 firms), institutional investors, and government entities. In a notorious deal that caused widespread ripple effects, Bank of America acquired troubled investment bank Merrill Lynch for some $50 billion in early 2009.

BANCFIRST CORPORATION

NASDAQ (GS): BANF

101 N. Broadway, Ste. 200
Oklahoma City, OK 73102
Phone: 405-270-1086
Fax: 405-270-1089
Web: www.bancfirst.com

CEO: David E. Rainbolt
CFO: Joe T. Shockley Jr.
HR: J. Michael Rogers
FYE: December 31
Type: Public

This Oklahoma bank wants to be more than OK. It wants to be *super*. BancFirst Corporation is the holding company for BancFirst, a super-community bank that emphasizes decentralized management and centralized support. BancFirst operates more than 100 locations in some 45 Oklahoma communities. It targets small to midsized businesses and individuals, offering a full range of traditional deposit products, including checking, savings, NOW, and money market accounts, as well as CDs and IRAs. Real estate lending (including residential and commercial property loans) makes up about a third of the bank's loan portfolio, which also includes business loans (some 20%), and consumer and agriculture loans.

	Annual Growth	12/05	12/06	12/07	12/08	12/09
Assets ($ mil.)	8.2%	3,223.0	3,418.6	3,743.0	3,867.2	4,416.1
Net income ($ mil.)	(6.6%)	42.8	49.4	53.1	44.4	32.6
Market value ($ mil.)	(1.6%)	606.2	828.7	657.6	812.2	568.4
Employees	0.5%	1,400	1,400	1,443	1,457	1,428

BANCINSURANCE CORPORATION

OTC: BCIS

250 E. Broad St., 10th Fl.
Columbus, OH 43215
Phone: 614-220-5200
Fax: 614-228-5552
Web: www.bancins.com

CEO: John S. Sokol
CFO: Matthew C. Nolan
HR: —
FYE: December 31
Type: Public

Holding company Bancinsurance Corporation underwrites niche insurance products through its subsidiary Ohio Indemnity Company. Operating throughout most of the US, it provides coverage to protect automobile lenders and dealers by insuring collateralized personal property against damage and theft. It also bonds employers that elect not to pay unemployment taxes. Subsidiary Ultimate Services Agency offers property/casualty insurance to lenders in the Northeast. Chairman and CEO John Sokol and his family own half of the firm, which his father founded.

	Annual Growth	12/05	12/06	12/07	12/08	12/09
Assets ($ mil.)	5.8%	128.3	122.3	154.3	150.4	160.8
Net income ($ mil.)	(5.1%)	6.3	5.5	3.0	1.4	5.1
Market value ($ mil.)	7.2%	23.4	31.5	27.1	19.0	30.9
Employees	(16.8%)	69	34	34	—	33

BANCO POPULAR NORTH AMERICA

9600 W. Bryn Mawr Ave.
Rosemont, IL 60018
Phone: 847-994-5400
Fax: 847-994-6969
Web: www.bancopopular.com

CEO: Richard L. Carrión
CFO: Jorge A. Junquera
HR: —
FYE: December 31
Type: Subsidiary

A subsidiary of Puerto Rican bank Popular, Banco Popular North America (BPNA) provides checking and savings accounts, CDs, credit cards, mortgages, loans, insurance, and investment products to consumer and business clients. Commercial real estate loans, business loans, and residential mortgages make up most of the lending activities of the company, which is one of the nation's leading SBA lenders. BPNA operates more than 100 branches in California, Florida, Illinois, New York, and New Jersey. (It exited Texas in early 2008.) Faced with losses, the company sold its Popular Equipment Financing leasing portfolio and stripped down the offerings of its online unit E-LOAN in 2009.

	Annual Growth	12/04	12/05	12/06	12/07	12/08
Est. sales ($ mil.)	—	—	—	—	—	3,822.5
Employees	—	—	—	—	—	1,716

THE BANCORP, INC.

NASDAQ (GM): TBBK

405 Silverside Rd.
Wilmington, DE 19809
Phone: 302-385-5000
Fax: 302-385-5194
Web: www.thebancorp.com

CEO: Betsy Z. Cohen
CFO: Paul Frenkiel
HR: —
FYE: December 31
Type: Public

The Bancorp is — what else? — the holding company for The Bancorp Bank, which provides financial services in the virtual world. On its home turf of the Philadelphia-Wilmington metropolitan area, The Bancorp Bank offers deposit, lending, and similar services, targeting the wealthy individuals and small to midsized businesses it believes are underserved by larger banks in the market. Nationally, The Bancorp provides private-label online banking services for affinity groups, issues prepaid debit cards, processes merchant credit card transactions, and acts as a custodian for health savings accounts (HSAs). It also operates fleet leasing businesses Jefferson Leasing and Mears Motor Leasing.

	Annual Growth	12/05	12/06	12/07	12/08	12/09
Assets ($ mil.)	22.2%	917.5	1,334.8	1,568.4	1,792.4	2,043.5
Net income ($ mil.)	(13.7%)	7.4	12.5	14.3	(42.4)	4.1
Market value ($ mil.)	(20.3%)	445.1	775.0	352.4	98.2	179.6
Employees	25.1%	150	181	306	306	367

BANCORP RHODE ISLAND, INC.

NASDAQ (GS): BARI

1 Turks Head Place
Providence, RI 02903
Phone: 401-456-5000
Fax: 401-456-5059
Web: www.bankri.com

CEO: Merrill W. Sherman
CFO: Linda H. Simmons
HR: —
FYE: December 31
Type: Public

Bancorp Rhode Island is the holding company for Bank Rhode Island, which serves individuals and small businesses through about 15 branches in the state's Providence, Kent, and Washington counties. The community bank provides traditional banking products and services including checking and savings accounts, mortgages and other loans, cash management services, and investment services. Bank Rhode Island was formed in 1996 as the result of the acquisition of branches divested in the merger between FleetBoston and Shawmut Financial, which are now part of Bank of America.

	Annual Growth	12/05	12/06	12/07	12/08	12/09
Assets ($ mil.)	2.5%	1,442.3	1,479.1	1,477.1	1,529.0	1,589.9
Net income ($ mil.)	(13.0%)	9.6	7.7	9.0	9.1	5.5
Market value ($ mil.)	(6.3%)	155.5	202.0	159.5	99.0	119.9
Employees	(3.7%)	309	270	268	271	266

BANCORPSOUTH, INC.

NYSE: BXS

1 Mississippi Plaza, 201 S. Spring St.
Tupelo, MS 38804
Phone: 662-680-2000
Fax: 662-678-7299
Web: www.bancorpsouth.com

CEO: Aubrey B. Patterson Jr.
CFO: William L. (Bill) Prater
HR: —
FYE: December 31
Type: Public

Elvis Presley may be the Boy from Tupelo, but BancorpSouth is the Bank from Tupelo. It's the holding company for BancorpSouth Bank, which operates more than 300 branches in eight southern and midwestern states. The bank offers checking and savings accounts, loans, credit cards, and commercial banking services. BancorpSouth also sells insurance and provides brokerage, investment advisory, and asset management services throughout most of its market area. Real estate loans, including consumer and commercial mortgages and home equity, construction, and agricultural loans, comprise approximately three-quarters of its loan portfolio.

	Annual Growth	12/05	12/06	12/07	12/08	12/09
Assets ($ mil.)	2.8%	11,768.7	12,040.5	13,189.8	13,480.2	13,167.9
Net income ($ mil.)	(8.0%)	115.2	125.2	137.9	120.4	82.7
Market value ($ mil.)	1.5%	1,842.3	2,238.8	1,970.9	1,950.0	1,958.4
Employees	2.6%	4,008	4,100	4,400	4,500	4,450

BANCTEC, INC.

2701 E. Grauwyler Rd.
Irving, TX 75061
Phone: 972-821-4000
Fax: 972-821-4823
Web: www.banctec.com

CEO: J. Coley Clark
CFO: Jeffrey D. (Jeff) Cushman
HR: —
FYE: December 31
Type: Private

BancTec keeps tabs on all sorts of financial transactions. The company offers electronic processing systems, business process outsourcing, software, hardware, and services for government agencies, banks, utility and telecommunications companies, and other organizations that do high-volume financial transactions. BancTec's systems and software capture and process checks, bills, and other documents; products include digital archiving systems, workflow software, and scanners. BancTec's services include cost estimates and contingency planning. Founded in 1972, BancTec is owned by investment firm Welsh, Carson, Anderson & Stowe, which took BancTec private in 1999.

	Annual Growth	12/05	12/06	12/07	12/08	12/09
Sales ($ mil.)	(5.7%)	344.9	379.5	390.2	271.9	272.6
Net income ($ mil.)	—	(7.3)	(0.8)	(6.1)	(40.5)	(8.0)
Employees	(8.5%)	2,750	2,670	2,526	1,949	1,924

BANCTRUST FINANCIAL GROUP, INC.

NASDAQ (GS): BTFG

100 St. Joseph St.
Mobile, AL 36602
Phone: 251-431-7800
Fax: 251-431-7851
Web: www.banctrustfinancialgroupinc.com

CEO: W. Bibb Lamar Jr.
CFO: F. Michael Johnson
HR: J. Dianne Hollingsworth
FYE: December 31
Type: Public

BancTrust Financial makes its sweet home in Alabama, but also spends a little time in the Florida panhandle. It is the holding company for two banks that operate as BankTrust throughout southern Alabama and neighboring parts of Florida. Through more than 50 branch offices, the banks offer such deposit products as CDs and checking, savings, and retirement accounts. The company's lending activities include mortgages (more than 40% of its loan portfolio), construction loans (nearly 30%), and commercial, agricultural, and consumer loans. Subsidiaries offer insurance, trust, and investment services. BancTrust Financial bought fellow Alabama bank holding company The Peoples BancTrust Company in 2007.

	Annual Growth	12/05	12/06	12/07	12/08	12/09
Assets ($ mil.)	10.5%	1,305.5	1,353.4	2,240.1	2,088.2	1,946.7
Net income ($ mil.)	—	15.1	13.3	6.2	1.3	(121.3)
Market value ($ mil.)	(38.5%)	355.5	451.3	214.0	261.0	50.8
Employees	9.3%	396	419	686	621	565

BANCWEST CORPORATION

180 Montgomery St.
San Francisco, CA 94104
Phone: 415-765-4800
Fax: —
Web: www.bancwestcorp.com

CEO: J. Michael Shepherd
CFO: Thibault Fulconis
HR: —
FYE: December 31
Type: Subsidiary

BancWest knows which direction it's heading. The subsidiary of French banking group BNP Paribas is the holding company for Bank of the West and First Hawaiian Bank. On the US mainland, Bank of the West (founded in 1874) has about 700 branches in nearly 20 states west of the Mississippi River. Founded in 1858, First Hawaiian has more than 60 branches in Hawaii, Guam, and Saipan. The banks' services include residential and commercial real estate lending, commercial banking (with expertise in niche lending such as agricultural loans, church loans, and loans to RV and boat dealers), consumer finance, credit cards, insurance, investments, private banking, and wealth management. BNP Paribas acquired BancWest in 2001.

BANDAI AMERICA INCORPORATED

5551 Katella Ave.
Cypress, CA 90630
Phone: 714-816-9500
Fax: 714-816-6710
Web: www.bandai.com

CEO: Masaaki (Mark) Tsuji
CFO: Paul Hausback
HR: —
FYE: March 31
Type: Subsidiary

Confused as to who Sword Strike Gundam and Astro Boy are? Bandai America, the North American marketing arm of Japanese toy maker Namco Bandai, can help clear up any action figure confusion you may have. Licensed toy and video game product lines include Power Rangers, Ben 10, Dragon Ball Z, Girlz Connect, and Tamagotchi Connection. The company also makes a number of original products to supplement its licensed toys and games. Bandai America's operations consist of candy and toy distribution, Japanese animation home-video distribution (through Bandai Entertainment), video game production, and the development of wireless technology and content that works with existing mobile phones.

B&G FOODS, INC.

NYSE: BGF

4 Gatehall Dr., Ste. 110
Parsippany, NJ 07054
Phone: 973-401-6500
Fax: 973-364-1037
Web: www.bgfoods.com

CEO: David L. Wenner
CFO: Robert C. Cantwell
HR: Cynthia Wojcik
FYE: December 31
Type: Public

Peter Piper can pick more than peppers or pickles from B&G Foods. There's jalapeños, beans, sandwich spreads, and an array of other products sold regionally and nationally through B&G's network of subsidiaries. B&G brands its pickles, peppers, and hot sauces under the B&G and Trappey labels. Other key brands include Ac'cent meat flavoring, Emeril's seasonings (under license), Ortega Mexican products, Grandma's and Brer Rabbit molasses, and Underwood meat spreads. Products are sold at grocery retailers, mass merchandisers, warehouse clubs, wholesalers, drug store chains, dollar stores, and foodservice companies throughout the US.

	Annual Growth	12/05	12/06	12/07	12/08	12/09
Sales ($ mil.)	7.2%	379.3	411.3	471.3	486.9	501.0
Net income ($ mil.)	21.4%	8.0	11.6	17.8	9.7	17.4
Employees	(0.4%)	744	721	749	721	731

BANGOR HYDRO-ELECTRIC COMPANY

21 Telcom Dr.
Bangor, ME 04401
Phone: 207-945-5621
Fax: 207-973-2813
Web: www.bhe.com

CEO: Robert (Bob) Hanf
CFO: Peter Dawes
HR: Robert Lysaght
FYE: December 31
Type: Subsidiary

Bangor Hydro-Electric (BHE) has dropped its hydro, but the company still has plenty of electricity. As part of the restructuring of the electric utility industry in the state of Maine, BHE has shed its generating facilities, including its hydroelectric projects, to focus on distribution and transmission. The regulated utility serves 117,000 customers in six counties in southeastern Maine. The company is also a member of the New England Power Pool. Bangor Hydro-Electric is a subsidiary of Canada's Emera, the parent company of electric utility Nova Scotia Power.

	Annual Growth	12/04	12/05	12/06	12/07	12/08
Est. sales ($ mil.)	—	—	—	—	—	119.0
Employees	—	—	—	—	—	250

THE BANK HOLDINGS

Pink Sheets: TBHS

9990 Double R Blvd.
Reno, NV 89521
Phone: 775-853-8600
Fax: 775-853-2068
Web: www.thebankholdings.com

CEO: Harold G. (Hal) Giomi
CFO: Jack B. Buchold
HR: —
FYE: December 31
Type: Public

You can probably guess what The Bank Holdings does. Where they do it is out west. As the holding company for Nevada Security Bank, it operates branches in northern Nevada, and in California under the Silverado Bank brand. The bank offers typical deposit products, such as checking and savings accounts, as well as CDs and IRAs. Real estate loans make up nearly 80% of the bank's loan portfolio, which also includes mortgages, construction/industrial, consumer, and business loans. The Bank Holdings moved into California in 2004 after it acquired CNA Trust Corporation of Costa Mesa. The company grew again in 2006 with the purchase of Northern Nevada Bank. The company also owns exchange companies.

	Annual Growth	12/05	12/06	12/07	12/08	12/09
Assets ($ mil.)	6.6%	384.6	651.5	626.6	556.0	496.8
Net income ($ mil.)	—	1.4	2.1	1.7	(37.4)	(45.5)
Market value ($ mil.)	(67.5%)	104.0	104.8	52.1	4.3	1.2
Employees	7.2%	59	121	124	99	78

BANK LEUMI USA

579 5th Ave.
New York, NY 10017
Phone: 917-542-2343
Fax: 917-542-2254
Web: www.leumiusa.com

CEO: Uzi Rosen
CFO: —
HR: John P. McGann
FYE: December 31
Type: Subsidiary

Bank Leumi USA is a subsidiary of Bank Leumi le-Israel, one of Israel's leading banks. It provides commercial and international banking services to large and midsized corporations, specializing in import and export lending, as well as lending to businesses in such industries as textiles and apparel, real estate, diamonds, technology, and entertainment. The bank, which also acts as an intermediary for American firms and individuals with investments in Israel, has more than a dozen offices in California, Florida, Illinois, New York, and the Cayman Islands. Some of Bank Leumi USA's other services for individuals include private banking and wealth management.

BANK MUTUAL CORPORATION

NASDAQ (GS): BKMU

4949 W. Brown Deer Rd.
Milwaukee, WI 53223
Phone: 414-354-1500
Fax: 414-354-5450
Web: www.bankmutualcorp.com

CEO: Michael T. Crowley Jr.
CFO: Michael W. (Mike) Dosland
HR: Diane Selfworth
FYE: December 31
Type: Public

Bank Mutual Corporation is the holding company for Bank Mutual, which offers consumer and business banking through around 80 branches in Wisconsin and one in Minnesota. Deposit products include CDs and checking, money market, and savings accounts. The company mainly uses funds gathered to originate a variety of loans and to invest in mortgage-backed securities. Residential mortgages and consumer loans dominate the bank's loan portfolio (representing about 50% and 20% respectively), which also includes commercial real estate, construction, and business loans. Bank subsidiary BancMutual Financial and Insurance Services offers mutual funds, annuities, insurance, and brokerage and wealth management services.

	Annual Growth	12/05	12/06	12/07	12/08	12/09
Assets ($ mil.)	0.6%	3,431.4	3,451.4	3,488.0	3,489.7	3,512.1
Net income ($ mil.)	(16.4%)	28.0	20.6	17.1	17.2	13.7
Market value ($ mil.)	(10.1%)	482.1	550.8	480.7	524.8	315.2
Employees	0.7%	792	781	657	769	815

BANK OF AMERICA CORPORATION

NYSE: BAC

100 N. Tryon St.
Charlotte, NC 28255
Phone: 704-386-5681
Fax: 704-386-6699
Web: www.bankofamerica.com

CEO: Brian T. Moynihan
CFO: Charles H. (Chuck) Noski
HR: Andrea B. Smith
FYE: December 31
Type: Public

Welcome to the machine. One of the largest banks in the US by assets (along with Citigroup and JPMorgan Chase), Bank of America also boasts one of the country's most extensive branch networks with more than 6,200 locations covering some 40 states from coast to coast. Its core services include consumer and small business banking, credit cards, and asset management. In early 2009 Bank of America paid some $50 billion in stock for Merrill Lynch, which had been crippled by the global credit crisis. The acquisition of the once-mighty investment bank known as "The Bull," which has an extensive retail brokerage network, beefs up Bank of America's wealth management, investment banking, and international business.

	Annual Growth	12/05	12/06	12/07	12/08	12/09
Assets ($ mil.)	14.5%	1,291,803.0	1,459,737.0	1,715,746.0	1,817,943.0	2,223,299.0
Net income ($ mil.)	(21.4%)	16,465.0	21,133.0	14,982.0	4,008.0	6,276.0
Market value ($ mil.)	(24.4%)	463,020.5	535,659.0	413,959.3	141,263.9	151,096.2
Employees	12.6%	176,638	203,425	210,000	243,000	284,000

BANK OF COMMERCE HOLDINGS

NASDAQ (GM): BOCH

1951 Churn Creek Rd.
Redding, CA 96002
Phone: 530-224-3333
Fax: 530-224-3337
Web: www.bankofcommerceholdings.com

CEO: Patrick J. (Pat) Moty
CFO: Samuel D. Jimenez
HR: Becky Looper
FYE: December 31
Type: Public

Bank of Commerce Holdings provides traditional banking services through subsidiary Redding Bank of Commerce and its Roseville Bank of Commerce and Sutter Bank of Commerce divisions. It targets small to midsized businesses and medium- to high-net-worth individuals in the northern California communities of Redding, Roseville, and Yuba City. Through more than five branches, the banks offer checking and savings accounts, CDs, IRAs, and money market accounts. Commercial mortgages and business and industrial loans account for more than two-thirds of the company's loan portfolio.

	Annual Growth	12/05	12/06	12/07	12/08	12/09
Assets ($ mil.)	12.3%	511.6	583.4	618.3	774.2	813.4
Net income ($ mil.)	(1.2%)	6.3	6.6	6.1	2.2	6.0
Market value ($ mil.)	(15.0%)	171.6	203.7	148.7	71.9	89.6
Employees	20.0%	125	115	114	120	259

BANK OF GRANITE CORPORATION
NASDAQ (GS): GRAN

23 N. Main St.	CEO: R. Scott Anderson
Granite Falls, NC 28630	CFO: Jerry A. Felts
Phone: 828-496-2027	HR: Karen Warlick
Fax: 828-496-2077	FYE: December 31
Web: www.bankofgranite.com	Type: Public

This company doesn't take its customers for granite. Bank of Granite Corporation is the holding company for a community bank of the same name that serves individuals and small businesses in about 10 west-central North Carolina counties. From 20 branches, Bank of Granite offers traditional demand and time deposit products mostly for individuals and small businesses. Before the economic downturn, mortgages made up more than half of Bank of Granite's loan portfolio. However, the slowdown deeply affected customers' ability to repay their loans and in 2009 Bank of Granite stopped originating mortgage loans altogether.

	Annual Growth	12/05	12/06	12/07	12/08	12/09
Assets ($ mil.)	(1.1%)	1,106.7	1,199.8	1,219.1	1,147.0	1,060.1
Net income ($ mil.)	—	15.0	18.0	(15.3)	(36.3)	(25.6)
Market value ($ mil.)	(56.9%)	229.1	293.2	163.4	37.9	7.9
Employees	(12.0%)	333	337	358	335	200

⊞ BANK OF HAWAII CORPORATION
NYSE: BOH

130 Merchant St.	CEO: Allan R. (Al) Landon
Honolulu, HI 96813	CFO: Kent T. Lucien
Phone: 888-643-3888	HR: Jean Hamakawa
Fax: 808-537-8440	FYE: December 31
Web: www.boh.com	Type: Public

Bank of Hawaii knows there's no place like home. It is the holding company for Bank of Hawaii (familiarly known as Bankoh), which has more than 70 branches in its home state, plus an additional dozen in American Samoa, Guam, Palau, and Saipan. The bank operates through four business segments: retail banking for consumers and small businesses in Hawaii; commercial banking, including property/casualty insurance, for middle-market and large corporations in Hawaii (this segment also includes the bank's activities beyond the state); investment services, including trust, asset management, and private banking; and treasury, which performs corporate asset and liability management services.

	Annual Growth	12/05	12/06	12/07	12/08	12/09
Assets ($ mil.)	5.1%	10,187.0	10,571.8	10,472.9	10,763.5	12,414.8
Net income ($ mil.)	(5.6%)	181.6	180.4	183.7	192.2	144.0
Market value ($ mil.)	(2.2%)	2,476.1	2,591.9	2,456.9	2,170.0	2,260.8
Employees	(2.0%)	2,600	2,600	2,600	2,600	2,400

THE BANK OF KENTUCKY FINANCIAL
NASDAQ (GM): BKYF

111 Lookout Farm Dr.	CEO: Robert W. (Bob) Zapp
Crestview Hills, KY 41017	CFO: Martin J. Gerrety
Phone: 859-371-2340	HR: —
Fax: 859-578-2487	FYE: December 31
Web: www.bankofky.com	Type: Public

The Bank of Kentucky Financial Corporation is the holding company for The Bank of Kentucky, which provides a variety of personal and commercial banking services from more than 25 branches in northern portions of the Bluegrass State. It attracts deposits by offering checking and savings accounts, CDs, and IRAs. Commercial real estate loans make up about 40% of the bank's loan portfolio, while residential mortgage loans account for more than 20%. The bank also offers business and consumer loans, as well as credit cards, investments, and trust services.

	Annual Growth	12/05	12/06	12/07	12/08	12/09
Assets ($ mil.)	13.1%	957.3	1,051.6	1,232.7	1,255.4	1,565.0
Net income ($ mil.)	(3.4%)	10.1	10.5	11.1	11.3	8.8
Market value ($ mil.)	(7.8%)	147.3	148.8	141.7	123.3	106.4
Employees	4.1%	300	314	332	331	352

BANK OF MARIN BANCORP
NASDAQ (CM): BMRC

504 Redwood Blvd., Ste. 100	CEO: Russell A. (Russ) Colombo
Novato, CA 94947	CFO: Christina J. Cook
Phone: 415-763-4520	HR: —
Fax: —	FYE: December 31
Web: www.bankofmarin.com	Type: Public

Bank of Marin Bancorp was formed in 2007 to be the holding company for community-oriented Bank of Marin, which operates a loan production office in San Francisco and about a dozen branches in the posh California counties of Marin and Sonoma in the hills north of the city. Targeting area residents and small to midsized businesses, the bank offers such standard retail products as checking and savings accounts, CDs, credit cards, and loans. Commercial mortgages account for the largest portion of the company's loan portfolio, followed by business, construction, and home equity loans. Bank of Marin also provides private banking, trust services, investment management, financial planning, and philanthropic advice.

	Annual Growth	12/05	12/06	12/07	12/08	12/09
Assets ($ mil.)	7.5%	840.4	876.6	933.9	1,049.6	1,121.7
Net income ($ mil.)	2.3%	11.7	11.9	12.3	12.1	12.8
Market value ($ mil.)	0.2%	170.0	189.4	153.6	126.0	171.0
Employees	1.8%	185	194	190	197	199

⊞ THE BANK OF NEW YORK MELLON CORPORATION
NYSE: BK

1 Wall St., 10th Fl.	CEO: Robert P. (Bob) Kelly
New York, NY 10286	CFO: Thomas P. (Todd) Gibbons
Phone: 212-495-1784	HR: William A. (Woody) Kerr
Fax: 212-809-9528	FYE: December 31
Web: www.bnymellon.com	Type: Public

Big Apple, meet Iron City. The Bank of New York cemented its status as one of the world's largest securities servicing firms with the 2007 acquisition of Pittsburgh-based Mellon Financial. The merger also fits in with the company's other areas of focus, including asset management and corporate trust and treasury services. It was The Bank of New York's third attempt to acquire Mellon. Now known as The Bank of New York Mellon (BNY Mellon), the firm has about $20 trillion in assets under custody and some $1 trillion of assets under management. Its Pershing subsidiary is a leading securities clearing firm. BNY Mellon has a presence in about 35 countries.

	Annual Growth	12/05	12/06	12/07	12/08	12/09
Assets ($ mil.)	20.1%	102,074.0	103,370.0	197,656.0	237,512.0	212,224.0
Net income ($ mil.)	—	1,571.0	3,011.0	2,219.0	1,445.0	(1,083.0)
Market value ($ mil.)	(3.2%)	38,632.2	47,753.5	59,143.0	34,362.6	33,925.9
Employees	15.8%	23,451	22,961	42,100	42,900	42,200

BANK OF SOUTH CAROLINA CORPORATION
NASDAQ (CM): BKSC

256 Meeting St.	CEO: Hugh C. Lane Jr.
Charleston, SC 29401	CFO: Sheryl G. (Sherry) Sharry
Phone: 843-724-1500	HR: —
Fax: 843-724-1513	FYE: December 31
Web: www.banksc.com	Type: Public

What, were you expecting something different? The Bank of South Carolina Corporation is the holding company for The Bank of South Carolina, which was founded in 1987. It operates four branches in and around Charleston. Targeting individuals and small to midsized business customers, the bank offers such standard retail services as checking and savings accounts, credit cards, and money market and NOW accounts. Real estate loans make up more than 70% of the The Bank of South Carolina's loan portfolio, which also includes commercial loans (around 20%) and to a lesser extent, personal loans. President and CEO Hugh Lane and his family control about 12% of the company.

	Annual Growth	12/05	12/06	12/07	12/08	12/09
Assets ($ mil.)	4.6%	222.5	243.5	225.2	243.7	265.9
Net income ($ mil.)	(12.2%)	3.2	3.9	3.8	2.9	1.9
Market value ($ mil.)	(10.1%)	61.0	63.0	56.8	50.0	39.9
Employees	2.6%	65	69	70	68	72

An in-depth profile of this company is available to Hoover's Online members at hoovers.com. ⊞

BANK OF THE CAROLINAS CORPORATION

NASDAQ (GM): BCAR

135 Boxwood Village Dr.
Mocksville, NC 27028
Phone: 336-751-5755
Fax: 336-751-4222
Web: www.bankofthecarolinas.com

CEO: Robert E. Marziano
CFO: Robert E. Marziano
HR: —
FYE: December 31
Type: Public

It would be more accurate to call it Bank of the North Carolina. Bank of the Carolinas Corporation was formed in 2006 to be the holding company for Bank of the Carolinas, which provides traditional deposit and lending services to individuals and businesses through about 10 branches in central North Carolina. Deposit services include checking, savings, and money market accounts; IRAs; and CDs. Commercial real estate loans account for the largest portion of the company's loan portfolio; the bank's lending activities also include business, construction, and consumer loans, residential mortgages, and home equity lines of credit.

	Annual Growth	12/05	12/06	12/07	12/08	12/09
Assets ($ mil.)	11.8%	390.2	454.6	506.0	562.0	610.4
Net income ($ mil.)	—	2.3	3.5	2.0	(3.6)	(3.1)
Market value ($ mil.)	(27.8%)	63.5	57.5	40.8	16.6	17.3
Employees	41.4%	30	101	113	114	120

BANK OF THE JAMES FINANCIAL GROUP, INC.

OTC: BOJF

828 Main St.
Lynchburg, VA 24504
Phone: 434-846-2000
Fax: 434-846-4450
Web: www.bankofthejames.com

CEO: Robert R. Chapman III
CFO: J. Todd Scruggs
HR: —
FYE: December 31
Type: Public

Bank of the James Financial Group is the holding company for Bank of the James, a financial institution serving central Virginia from about 10 branch locations. Catering to individuals and small businesses, the bank offers standard retail products and services including checking and savings accounts, CDs, and IRAs. Funds from deposits are mainly used to originate residential mortgages, which make up about half of the bank's loan portfolio, and commercial and consumer loans. Subsidiary BOTJ Investment Group offers bank customers brokerage services, annuities, and related investment products through a third-party broker-dealer.

	Annual Growth	12/05	12/06	12/07	12/08	12/09
Assets ($ mil.)	22.3%	195.9	232.7	270.1	328.6	437.7
Net income ($ mil.)	—	1.8	1.8	2.1	0.2	(0.6)
Market value ($ mil.)	(11.9%)	36.9	44.8	36.4	22.9	22.2
Employees	7.5%	90	107	108	120	120

BANK OF THE OZARKS, INC.

NASDAQ (GS): OZRK

12615 Chenal Pkwy.
Little Rock, AR 72231
Phone: 501-978-2265
Fax: 501-978-2350
Web: www.bankozarks.com

CEO: George G. Gleason
CFO: Paul Moore
HR: Diane Hilburn
FYE: December 31
Type: Public

Bank of the Ozarks is the holding company for the bank of the same name, which has around 80 branches in Arkansas, northern Texas, and northern Georgia. It also operates a loan production office in Charlotte, North Carolina. Serving individuals and small to midsized businesses, the bank offers traditional deposit and loan services, in addition to trust services, retirement and financial planning, and investment management. It has more than $800 million of assets under management or administration. Commercial real estate and construction and land development loans make up the largest portion of Bank of the Ozarks' loan portfolio, followed by residential mortgage, business, and agricultural loans.

	Annual Growth	12/05	12/06	12/07	12/08	12/09
Assets ($ mil.)	6.7%	2,134.9	2,529.4	2,710.9	3,233.3	2,770.8
Net income ($ mil.)	(0.8%)	31.5	31.7	31.7	34.7	30.5
Market value ($ mil.)	(5.6%)	624.6	559.6	443.5	501.7	495.4
Employees	3.0%	629	699	689	705	707

BANKATLANTIC BANCORP, INC.

NYSE: BBX

2100 W. Cypress Creek Rd.
Fort Lauderdale, FL 33309
Phone: 954-940-5000
Fax: 954-940-5250
Web: www.bankatlanticbancorp.com

CEO: Alan B. Levan
CFO: Valerie C. Toalson
HR: Susan D. McGregor
FYE: December 31
Type: Public

BankAtlantic Bancorp has an ocean of ideas about what to do with your money. The company owns BankAtlantic, which operates more than 100 branches in Florida, with a focus on the Miami and Tampa metropolitan areas. Residential real estate loans make up more than 45% of BankAtlantic's loan portfolio; commercial real estate loans add nearly 20% more. The bank also makes a variety of business and personal loans. Holding company BFC Financial, headed by BankAtlantic Bancorp chairman Alan Levan and vice chairman John Abdo, controls the company; BFC Financial also controls Woodbridge Holdings (formerly Levitt Corporation) and, indirectly, Bluegreen.

	Annual Growth	12/05	12/06	12/07	12/08	12/09
Assets ($ mil.)	(7.1%)	6,471.4	6,495.7	6,378.8	5,814.6	4,815.6
Net income ($ mil.)	—	59.2	15.4	(22.2)	(202.6)	(185.8)
Market value ($ mil.)	(63.1%)	3,564.1	3,515.7	1,043.8	295.3	66.2
Employees	(13.4%)	2,921	2,819	2,569	1,847	1,644

BANKFINANCIAL CORPORATION

NASDAQ (GM): BFIN

15W060 N. Frontage Rd.
Burr Ridge, IL 60527
Phone: 630-242-7700
Fax: 708-675-6699
Web: www.bankfinancial.com

CEO: F. Morgan Gasior
CFO: Paul A. Cloutier
HR: Patricia M. Smith Lawler
FYE: December 31
Type: Public

If you need a BankNow to handle all your BankBusiness, try BankFinancial. The holding company's subsidiary BankFinancial, F.S.B. provides banking and financial services to individuals and businesses through about 20 branches in the northeastern Illinois counties of Cook, DuPage, Lake, and Will. It offers such products as savings, money market, demand, and NOW accounts, as well as loans. Nonresidential real estate loans account for more than 25% of the bank's loan portfolio; one- to four-family residential mortgages account for more than 20%. The bank also offers business, construction, and consumer loans.

	Annual Growth	12/05	12/06	12/07	12/08	12/09
Assets ($ mil.)	(0.7%)	1,614.4	1,613.1	1,480.5	1,554.7	1,566.9
Net income ($ mil.)	—	11.1	10.0	7.2	(19.4)	(0.7)
Market value ($ mil.)	(9.4%)	314.4	381.4	338.8	218.2	212.0
Employees	(2.0%)	418	452	393	403	385

BANKRATE, INC.

11760 U.S. Hwy. 1, Ste. 200
North Palm Beach, FL 33408
Phone: 561-630-2400
Fax: 561-625-4540
Web: www.bankrate.com

CEO: Thomas R. Evans
CFO: Edward J. (Ed) DiMaria
HR: —
FYE: December 31
Type: Private

Bankrate knows there's life after budget-cutting. The firm's Bankrate.com provides personal finance information on more than 300 products including mortgages, credit cards, money market accounts, certificates of deposit, and home equity loans. Its Interest.com publishes financial rates and information connecting consumers with lenders, and its FastFind sells consumer leads to lenders for mortgages, home-equity loans, auto financing, and online education. Other sites include Mortgagecalc.com and Mortgagemath.com, while print publication *Mortgage Guide* offers information from local mortgage companies and financial institutions. Private equity firm Apax Partners owns Bankrate.

	Annual Growth	12/04	12/05	12/06	12/07	12/08
Sales ($ mil.)	—	0.0	0.9	3.0	6.7	1.6
Net income ($ mil.)	10.0%	13.4	9.7	10.0	20.1	19.6
Employees	26.0%	113	159	163	277	285

An in-depth profile of this company is available to Hoover's Online members at hoovers.com.

219

BANNER CORPORATION

NASDAQ (GS): BANR

10 S. First Ave.
Walla Walla, WA 99362
Phone: 509-527-3636
Fax: 509-526-8898
Web: www.banrbank.com

CEO: D. Michael Jones
CFO: Lloyd W. Baker
HR: Debi Sapp
FYE: December 31
Type: Public

Flagging bank accounts? See Banner Corporation. Banner is the holding company for Banner Bank, which serves the Pacific Northwest through some 80 branches and about a dozen loan production offices in nearly 30 Washington, Oregon, and Idaho counties. The company offers traditional retail banking products, as well as business, consumer, and agriculture loans. Construction and land loans make up about one-third of the company's loan portfolio; commercial real estate loans account for around a quarter. Bank subsidiary Community Financial writes residential mortgage and construction loans. Banner is also parent to Islanders Bank, which operates three branches in Washington's San Juan Islands.

	Annual Growth	12/05	12/06	12/07	12/08	12/09
Assets ($ mil.)	11.6%	3,040.6	3,495.6	4,492.7	4,584.4	4,722.2
Net income ($ mil.)	—	12.4	32.2	36.9	(128.0)	(35.8)
Market value ($ mil.)	(45.9%)	734.4	1,043.8	676.3	221.5	63.1
Employees	7.5%	821	924	1,178	1,140	1,098

BANNER HEALTH

1441 N. 12th St.
Phoenix, AZ 85006
Phone: 602-495-4000
Fax: —
Web: www.bannerhealth.com

CEO: Peter S. Fine
CFO: Dennis Dahlen
HR: Sandra Herr
FYE: December 31
Type: Not-for-profit

Hoist this Banner high! Banner Health is one of the largest secular not-for-profit health systems in the US. The organization operates more than 20 hospitals (with nearly 4,000 beds). It also operates clinics, nursing homes, clinical laboratories, ambulatory surgery centers, home health agencies, and other health care-related organizations, including physician practices and a captive insurance company. Banner Health also participates in medical research in areas such as Alzheimer's disease and spinal cord injuries through its Banner Research division. The company provides services in seven states in the western US; its largest concentration of facilities is in Arizona.

	Annual Growth	12/04	12/05	12/06	12/07	12/08
Est. sales ($ mil.)	—	—	—	—	—	3,970.8
Employees	—	—	—	—	—	25,000

BANNER LIFE INSURANCE COMPANY

1701 Research Blvd.
Rockville, MD 20850
Phone: 301-279-4800
Fax: 301-294-6960
Web: www.bannerlife.com

CEO: David S. Lenaburg
CFO: Gene Gilbertson
HR: —
FYE: December 31
Type: Subsidiary

Is it a banner day every day at Banner Life? Legal & General subsidiary Banner Life Insurance offers various life insurance products, including term life and fixed universal life, sold through independent brokers in 49 states and in the District of Columbia. The company has been in business for more than 50 years, having started out as Government Employees Life Insurance Company (GELICO). Legal & General bought the company in 1981 and changed its name to Banner Life two years later. Banner Life and its sister company, William Penn Life Insurance Company of New York, are the primary operations of Legal & General America.

BANNER PHARMACAPS INC.

4100 Mendenhall Oaks Pkwy., Ste. 301
High Point, NC 27265
Phone: 336-812-3442
Fax: 336-812-7030
Web: www.banpharm.com

CEO: Roger E. Gordon
CFO: Robert Gretton
HR: Charles L. Cain
FYE: December 31
Type: Subsidiary

Skip the spoonful of sugar, Banner Pharmacaps uses gelatin-based capsules to help the medicine go down. The company makes softgel capsules used for everything from prescription pharmaceuticals to vitamin supplements. Banner also makes consumer health products and some prescription drugs, including a bipolar disorder treatment called Stavzor. Banner, a subsidiary of VION N.V., offers its products in a range of colors and configurations, including non-animal-based, controlled release, and chewable softgels. The company cooks up its various formulations in research labs around the world, and works closely with pharmaceutical makers to design softgels that enable precise delivery of drug doses in the human body.

BANYAN CORPORATION

OTC: BNYN

1925 Century Park East, Ste. 500
Los Angeles, CA 90067
Phone: 800-808-0899
Fax: 403-287-8804
Web: www.chiropracticusa.net

CEO: Michael J. Gelmon
CFO: Cory H. Gelmon
HR: —
FYE: December 31
Type: Public

Banyan Corporation banishes bad backs. Banyan is developing a national chain of franchised chiropractic clinics under the Chiropractic USA brand. The company provides consulting, corporate identity and marketing materials, operating formats, and other related support services to its franchising chiropractors. Banyan also offers diagnostic testing services to doctors and chiropractors through subsidiary Premier Medical Group. Its diagnostic tests help detect nervous system disorders. Another division, Virtual Medical Systems, markets the VT3000 electro-diagnostic nerve testing machine.

BAPTIST HEALTH SOUTH FLORIDA, INC.

6855 Red Rd.
Coral Gables, FL 33143
Phone: 786-662-7000
Fax: 786-662-7334
Web: www.baptisthealth.net

CEO: Brian E. Keeley
CFO: Ralph E. Lawson
HR: Ricardo Forbes
FYE: September 30
Type: Not-for-profit

Baptist Health South Florida is a not-for-profit health care organization composed of five acute-care hospitals in the Miami area, as well as a children's hospital and numerous outpatient centers. Its flagship facility, Baptist Hospital, has more than 680 beds and provides a comprehensive range of medical and surgical services. The systems also includes South Miami Hospital, with 460 beds, as well as several smaller inpatient facilities in surrounding communities. In all, Baptist Health South Florida hospitals contain around 1,600 beds. In addition to its inpatient services, the organization provides outpatient care, including ambulatory surgery, urgent care, diagnostic imaging, and home health services.

	Annual Growth	9/04	9/05	9/06	9/07	9/08
Est. sales ($ mil.)	—	—	—	—	—	1,517.6
Employees	—	—	—	—	—	9,374

BAR HARBOR BANKSHARES

NYSE Amex: BHB

82 Main St.
Bar Harbor, ME 04609
Phone: 207-288-3314
Fax: 207-288-2626
Web: www.bhbt.com

CEO: Joseph M. Murphy
CFO: Gerald Shencavitz
HR: Elizabeth B. McMillan
FYE: December 31
Type: Public

Bar Harbor Bankshares is a *Maine*-stay for communities in the Pine Tree State's Hancock, Knox, and Washington counties. Through about a dozen branches, subsidiary Bar Harbor Bank & Trust offers such deposit products as checking, savings, and money market accounts; NOW accounts; IRAs; and CDs. Real estate mortgages make up some 80% of the bank's loan portfolio, which also includes consumer, commercial, and agricultural loans. About 10% of the bank's lending is focused on the tourist industry associated with nearby Acadia National Park. Bar Harbor Trust Services, a subsidiary of the bank, offers trust and estate planning services.

	Annual Growth	12/05	12/06	12/07	12/08	12/09
Assets ($ mil.)	9.4%	747.9	824.9	889.5	972.3	1,072.4
Net income ($ mil.)	12.9%	6.4	6.9	7.2	7.7	10.4
Market value ($ mil.)	1.1%	99.4	119.9	118.6	97.2	103.7
Employees	1.7%	154	159	154	139	165

BARAN TELECOM INC.

2355 Industrial Park Blvd.
Cumming, GA 30041
Phone: 678-513-1501
Fax: 678-513-1501
Web: www.barantelecom.com

CEO: Saar Bracha
CFO: Ron Raviv
HR: —
FYE: December 31
Type: Subsidiary

Baran Telecom provides network infrastructure development services to the global wireless telecommunications industry. The company specializes in planning, design, deployment, and maintenance of mobile phone and other wireless and broadband networks. It has undertaken projects at more than 50,000 communication facilities in all states of the US and in more than 35 countries in Europe, Africa, and Asia. Baran Telecom primarily serves mobile phone operators and other telecom carriers, tower operators, and equipment vendors. Clients have included Ericsson, Nokia, Orange, and Vodafone. It is a subsidiary of Israel's engineering, construction, and technology giant Baran Group.

BARBARA'S BAKERY INC.

3900 Cypress Dr.
Petaluma, CA 94954
Phone: 707-765-2273
Fax: 707-765-2927
Web: www.barbarasbakery.com

CEO: Charles R. (Chuck) Marble
CFO: —
HR: —
FYE: December 31
Type: Subsidiary

A company for mom facing her breakfast-ready brood, Barbara's Bakery whips out batches of cookies, crackers, breakfast cereals, and salty snacks with no preservatives, white sugar, or other artificial ingredients. The company's products (from Puffins cereal to Snakimals animal crackers) are primarily sold through natural food retailers in Canada and the US. Barbara's Bakery is owned by UK cereal maker Weetabix and oversees the US distribution, sales, and marketing of its parent's Alpen and Weetabix brands. The company was founded in 1971 by 17-year-old Barbara Jaffe.

BARCLAYS BANK DELAWARE

100 S. West St.
Wilmington, DE 19801
Phone: 302-622-8990
Fax: 302-888-0405
Web: www.barclaycardus.com

CEO: Lloyd M. Wirshba
CFO: Barney C. Briggs
HR: Kathleen (Kathy) Kreusch Cobb
FYE: December 31
Type: Subsidiary

Buying something today can earn you points for a vacation or another purchase tomorrow. With co-branded credit cards from Barclays Bank Delaware (also known as Barclaycard US) customers rack up points that can be redeemed for air travel, hotel stays, and other perks. The company, a division of Barclays, issues Visa and MasterCard credit cards, in addition to co-branded credit cards through partnerships with more than 60 companies and institutions, including Best Western, US Airways, Carnival Cruise Lines, L.L. Bean, and Harvard University. The company was founded as Juniper Financial in 2000. It became a part of Barclays in 2004.

BARE ESCENTUALS, INC.

71 Stevenson St., 22nd Fl.
San Francisco, CA 94105
Phone: 415-489-5000
Fax: 877-963-3329
Web: www.bareescentuals.com

CEO: Myles B. McCormick
CFO: —
HR: —
FYE: December 31
Type: Subsidiary

When it comes to keeping its customers looking naturally pretty, Bare Escentuals has a mineral interest. The company, which rolled out its bareMinerals makeup brand in 1976 along with its first retail shop, develops, markets, and sells natural cosmetics, skin care, and body care items. Brand names include bareMinerals, Buxom, md formulations, RareMinerals, and its namesake line. Bare Escentuals sells its products in the US through about 120 company-owned shops, 870 beauty product retailers, and 1,470 spas and salons. It also boasts distributors in Canada, Japan, and the UK, among other European countries. Japanese cosmetics company Shiseido acquired Bare Escentuals for $1.7 billion in March 2010.

	Annual Growth	12/05	12/06	12/07	12/08	12/09
Sales ($ mil.)	21.1%	259.3	394.5	511.0	556.2	557.5
Net income ($ mil.)	42.3%	23.9	50.2	88.1	98.0	98.1
Employees	45.3%	576	863	1,571	2,779	2,568

BARLOWORLD INDUSTRIAL DISTRIBUTION

11301-C Granite St.
Charlotte, NC 28273
Phone: 704-587-1003
Fax: 704-587-9269
Web: www.handling.barloworld.com

CEO: Peter John Blackbeard
CFO: Eugene Smith
HR: Scott Simmons
FYE: September 30
Type: Business segment

Barloworld Industrial Distribution forks over lots of business. The company, a division of UK-based Barloworld Limited, rents and leases new and used forklifts, lift trucks, and other warehouse and material handling equipment, as well as Ditch Witch brand trenchers and plows, from its Barloworld Truck Center locations. Barloworld Industrial stocks parts for Caterpillar, Clark, Hyster, and Nissan container-handling machinery. The company leases new and sells used Freightliner heavy trucks and trailers in the US. Other services include fleet management, training, and maintenance. The business operates in Belgium, the Netherlands, the UK, and throughout the southeastern US.

	Annual Growth	9/04	9/05	9/06	9/07	9/08
Est. sales ($ mil.)	—	—	—	—	—	249.5
Employees	—	—	—	—	—	1,011

An in-depth profile of this company is available to Hoover's Online members at hoovers.com.

221

BARNARD COLLEGE

3009 Broadway
New York, NY 10027
Phone: 212-854-5262
Fax: 212-854-6220
Web: www.barnard.edu

CEO: Debora L. Spar
CFO: —
HR: Lori McFarland
FYE: December 31
Type: School

Barnard College is an all-female, liberal arts college in New York City. The school is affiliated with the Columbia University system, but has its own campus, faculty, administration, trustees, operating budget, and endowment. The school offers degree programs in about 50 fields in the humanities, social sciences, arts, and natural sciences. Founded in 1889, the college enrolls some 2,400 undergraduates from 48 states and 39 countries. Barnard was named after Frederick A.P. Barnard, the 10th president of Columbia College, who argued unsuccessfully for the admission of women to Columbia University.

	Annual Growth	12/04	12/05	12/06	12/07	12/08
Est. sales ($ mil.)	—	—	—	—	—	103.0
Employees	—	—	—	—	—	650

BARNES & NOBLE, INC.

NYSE: BKS

122 5th Ave.
New York, NY 10011
Phone: 212-633-3300
Fax: 212-675-0413
Web: www.barnesandnobleinc.com

CEO: William J. Lynch Jr.
CFO: Joseph J. Lombardi
HR: Michelle Smith
FYE: January 31
Type: Public

Barnes & Noble does business — big business — by the book. As the #1 bookseller in the US, it operates about 720 Barnes & Noble superstores (selling books, music, movies, and gifts) throughout all 50 US states and the District of Columbia. The stores are typically 10,000 to 60,000 sq. ft. in size and stock between 60,000 and 200,000 book titles. Many of its locations contain Starbucks cafes, as well as music departments that carry more than 30,000 titles. In cyberspace, the firm conducts sales through subsidiary Barnesandnoble.com (BN.com), which accounts for about 10% of revenue. Its e-bookstore features more than 1 million titles. In 2009 Barnes & Noble introduced the Nook digital-book reader.

	Annual Growth	1/05	1/06	1/07	1/08	1/09
Sales ($ mil.)	1.2%	4,873.6	5,103.0	5,261.3	5,410.8	5,121.8
Net income ($ mil.)	(14.7%)	143.4	146.7	150.5	135.8	75.9
Market value ($ mil.)	(15.8%)	1,882.2	2,441.6	2,240.7	1,953.0	945.1
Employees	(3.1%)	42,000	39,000	39,000	40,000	37,000

BARNES GROUP INC.

NYSE: B

123 Main St.
Bristol, CT 06011
Phone: 860-583-7070
Fax: 860-589-3507
Web: www.barnesgroupinc.com

CEO: Gregory F. Milzcik
CFO: Christopher J. (Chris) Stephens Jr.
HR: Dawn N. Edwards
FYE: December 31
Type: Public

Barnes Group keeps a positive spring in its step by making springs and managing the supply of things. The aerospace and industrial components manufacturer produces a range of engineered springs for electronics and machinery, as well as fabricated components and assemblies for turbine engines and airframes. It is North America's #1 maker of precision mechanical springs and nitrogen gas products. The group's second business offers logistical support and repair services covering aerospace spare parts for commercial and military aviation. Customers are OEMs of aircraft engines, consumer electronics, farm equipment, home appliances, and medical devices, located primarily in the US. GE is Barnes' largest customer.

	Annual Growth	12/05	12/06	12/07	12/08	12/09
Sales ($ mil.)	(1.6%)	1,102.2	1,259.7	1,439.5	1,362.1	1,034.2
Net income ($ mil.)	(10.5%)	60.9	73.8	101.3	87.0	39.0
Market value ($ mil.)	0.6%	907.9	1,196.8	1,837.3	797.9	929.9
Employees	(6.2%)	6,205	6,666	6,523	5,643	4,800

BARNEYS NEW YORK, INC.

575 5th Ave., 11th Fl.
New York, NY 10017
Phone: 212-339-7300
Fax: 212-450-8489
Web: www.barneys.com

CEO: Michael Celestino
CFO: Vince Phelan
HR: Marc H. Perlowitz
FYE: December 31
Type: Subsidiary

Barneys New York is no purple dinosaur, even if it did have a brush with extinction. The luxury department store chain sells designer apparel for men, women, and children; shoes; accessories; and home furnishings. The chain operates some 40 locations including about 10 full-size Barneys New York flagship stores in New York City, Beverly Hills, Boston, Chicago, and other major cities; some 20 smaller Barneys Co-Op shops; and about a dozen outlet stores. Barney Pressman founded the firm in 1923. Former owner Jones Apparel Group, which acquired Barneys in 2004 for about $400 million, sold the company in 2007 for $945 million to an affiliate of Istithmar PJSC, an investment firm owned by the Dubai government.

BARNWELL INDUSTRIES, INC.

NYSE Amex: BRN

1100 Alakea St., Ste. 2900
Honolulu, HI 96813
Phone: 808-531-8400
Fax: 808-531-7181
Web: www.brninc.com

CEO: Morton H. Kinzler
CFO: Russell M. Gifford
HR: —
FYE: September 30
Type: Public

Barnwell Industries has more than a barnful of assets, which range from oil and gas production, contract well drilling, and Hawaiian land and housing investments. Barnwell Industries explores for and produces oil and natural gas primarily in Alberta. In 2009 it reported proved reserves of 1.3 million barrels of oil and 20.6 billion cu. ft. of gas. Subsidiary Water Resources International drills water and geothermal wells and installs and repairs water pump systems in Hawaii. The company also owns a 78% interest in Kaupulehu Developments, which owns leasehold rights to more than 1,000 acres in Hawaii, and is engaged in other real estate activities.

	Annual Growth	9/05	9/06	9/07	9/08	9/09
Sales ($ mil.)	(7.6%)	44.2	58.0	47.4	65.6	32.2
Net income ($ mil.)	—	6.0	14.6	3.5	11.7	(24.4)
Market value ($ mil.)	(32.8%)	176.5	161.4	137.7	78.3	36.0
Employees	(3.4%)	54	55	68	53	47

BARRACUDA NETWORKS, INC.

3175 Winchester Blvd.
Campbell, CA 95008
Phone: 408-342-5400
Fax: 408-342-1061
Web: www.barracudanetworks.com

CEO: Dean Drako
CFO: David Faugno
HR: —
FYE: December 31
Type: Private

Barracuda Networks hunts down network threats. The company provides firewalls that protect enterprises from e-mail spam, viruses, and spyware. Other products include appliances for e-mail archiving, Web filtering, and load balancing. Barracuda serves businesses of all sizes in industries such as consumer goods, financial services, manufacturing, retail, technology, and utilities. The company also provides professional services, such as support, consulting, and implementation. Barracuda's more than 100,000 customers include Coca-Cola, FedEx, IBM, and Toshiba. Barracuda Networks was founded in 2002 by Dean Drako, its president and CEO. The company's outside investors are Francisco Partners and Sequoia Capital.

BARRETT BUSINESS SERVICES, INC.

NASDAQ (GS): BBSI

8100 NE Parkway Dr., Ste. 200
Vancouver, WA 98662
Phone: 360-828-0700
Fax: 360-828-0701
Web: www.barrettbusiness.com

CEO: William W. (Bill) Sherertz
CFO: James D. Miller
HR: —
FYE: December 31
Type: Public

Barrett Business Services likes to put people to work. The company offers both temporary and long-term staffing to some 2,300 small and midsized businesses. Its staffing services focus on light industrial, clerical, and technical businesses. Barrett also does business as a professional employment organization (PEO), providing outsourced human resource services, such as payroll management, benefits administration, risk management, recruiting, and placement for about 1,300 clients. Established in 1965, Barrett operates through about 45 branch offices across 10 US states. Each year about 90% of its PEO revenue comes from customers residing in the states of California and Oregon.

	Annual Growth	12/05	12/06	12/07	12/08	12/09
Sales ($ mil.)	0.5%	231.4	259.2	289.2	280.5	236.5
Net income ($ mil.)	—	12.5	16.3	16.8	6.3	(4.8)
Market value ($ mil.)	(16.3%)	261.4	245.0	188.4	114.0	128.6
Employees	6.1%	27,400	25,300	43,065	33,555	34,725

BARRETT PAVING MATERIALS, INC.

3 Becker Farm Rd.
Roseland, NJ 07068
Phone: 973-533-1001
Fax: 973-533-1020
Web: www.barrettpaving.com

CEO: Robert Doucet
CFO: —
HR: —
FYE: December 31
Type: Subsidiary

The folks at Barrett Paving Materials want the road-to-road construction to begin with them. The company, which works primarily in the Mid-Atlantic and Midwest, manufactures asphalt, ready-mix concrete, and other paving materials. It also works as a road construction and paving contractor. Barrett Paving Materials produces its own raw materials through stone quarries and sand and gravel facilities. Its projects have included highways, parking lots, airport runways, race tracks, and driveways. Barrett Paving Materials is owned by French construction firm Colas. The company has offices in Michigan, New Jersey, New York, Ohio, and Pennsylvania.

	Annual Growth	12/04	12/05	12/06	12/07	12/08
Est. sales ($ mil.)	—	—	—	—	—	317.4
Employees	—	—	—	—	—	250

BARRICK GOLDSTRIKE MINES INC.

Goldstrike Property
Carlin, NV 89822
Phone: 801-990-3900
Fax: —
Web: www.barrick.com

CEO: Gregory A. Lang
CFO: —
HR: —
FYE: December 31
Type: Subsidiary

Barrick Goldstrike Mines is the mother lode for Barrick Gold. The company operates two producing ore mines (the open pit Betze-Post and the underground Meikle and Rodeo) on the property, located on the prolific Carlin Trend in Nevada. Goldstrike produces more than 1.5 million ounces of gold annually and has reserves of about 13 million ounces. It's the largest gold-producing operation for Canadian mining company Barrick Gold, the largest gold miner in the world. There are two processing plants located on the property that separate the gold from the recovered ore. Barrick is actively exploring other areas of the Goldstrike property for development.

BARRY-WEHMILLER COMPANIES, INC.

8020 Forsyth Blvd.
St. Louis, MO 63105
Phone: 314-862-8000
Fax: 314-862-8858
Web: www.barry-wehmiller.com

CEO: Robert H. (Bob) Chapman
CFO: James W. (Jim) Lawson
HR: Donn Boyer
FYE: December 31
Type: Private

With Barry-Wehmiller, you get the whole package. The company manufactures and supplies packaging, corrugating, paper converting, filling, and labeling automation equipment primarily for the food and beverage industry. The company conducts business around the world through 10 divisions including Accraply (labeling machinery), Barry-Wehmiller Company (bottle washers and pasteurizers), HayssenSandiacre (packaging systems), PneumaticScaleAngelus (bottle fillers and cappers), FleetwoodGoldcoWyard (conveyor systems), and Central Bottling International (industrial manufacturing equipment). Other Barry-Wehmiller units offer IT, engineering, and design consulting services.

	Annual Growth	12/04	12/05	12/06	12/07	12/08
Sales ($ mil.)	(8.3%)	—	—	—	1,200.0	1,100.0
Employees	4.0%	—	—	—	5,000	5,200

BAR-S FOODS CO.

3838 N. Central Ave., Ste. 1900
Phoenix, AZ 85012
Phone: 602-264-7272
Fax: 602-285-5252
Web: www.bar-s.com

CEO: Timothy T. (Tim) Day
CFO: James S. (Jim) Kuykendall
HR: Martin (Marty) Thompson
FYE: September 30
Type: Private

Bar-S Foods hopes to raise the bar in the processed meat industry. The company manufactures hot dogs, corn dogs, bacon, lunch meats, hams, turkey breasts, and processed deli meats under brands including Bar-S, Extra Lean, Old World Premium, Jumbo Jumbos, President's Pride, and Chuck Wagon. Its more than 100 meat products are sold to deli, retail grocery, warehouse club, and military and other institutional customers throughout the US; Bar-S also exports its meat products. Heaquartered in Phoenix, the company operates three production facilities and a distribution center, all in Oklahoma. Bar-S was founded in 1981, following the acquistion of the assets of Cudahy Company.

	Annual Growth	9/04	9/05	9/06	9/07	9/08
Est. sales ($ mil.)	—	—	—	—	—	480.6
Employees	—	—	—	—	—	1,500

BARTLETT AND COMPANY

4900 Main St., Ste. 1200
Kansas City, MO 64112
Phone: 816-753-6300
Fax: 816-753-0062
Web: www.bartlettandco.com

CEO: James B. (Jim) Hebenstreit
CFO: Arnold F. (Arnie) Wheeler
HR: Bill Webster
FYE: December 31
Type: Private

When the cows come home, Bartlett and Company will be ready. The company's primary business is grain merchandising, but it also runs cattle feedlots, mills flour, and sells feed and fertilizer. Bartlett operates grain storage facilities, terminal elevators, and country elevators in the midwestern US, including locations in Kansas, Iowa, Missouri, and Nebraska. Bartlett also operates flour mills and feed stores in the Midwest and along the East Coast; its cattle operations are based in Texas. The Bartlett and Company Grain Charitable Foundation makes financial gifts to local causes. Founded in 1907 as Bartlett Agri Enterprises, the company is still owned by the founding Bartlett family.

	Annual Growth	12/04	12/05	12/06	12/07	12/08
Sales ($ mil.)	36.2%	—	—	1,100.0	1,510.0	2,040.0
Employees	(3.4%)	—	—	750	700	700

An in-depth profile of this company is available to Hoover's Online members at hoovers.com.

223

BARTON MALOW COMPANY

26500 American Dr.
Southfield, MI 48034
Phone: 248-436-5000
Fax: 248-436-5001
Web: www.bmco.com

CEO: Ben C. Maibach III
CFO: Lori R. Howlett
HR: Jim Nahrgang
FYE: March 31
Type: Private

Barton Malow scores by building end zones and home plates. The construction management and general contracting firm, which has built its share of sporting facilities, also makes points for its schools, hospitals, offices, and plants. The company offers design/build services ranging from the pre-planning stage to completion throughout the US and Mexico. Projects have included the Detroit Institute of Arts and Cultural Center and the Baltimore Orioles stadium. Barton Malow provides architecture and engineering services, and its Barton Malow Rigging unit installs process equipment and machinery. Carl Osborn Barton founded the employee-owned firm as C.O. Barton Company in 1924.

BARUCH COLLEGE

1 Bernard Baruch Way, 55 Lexington Ave.
New York, NY 10010
Phone: 646-312-1000
Fax: 212-802-5903
Web: www.baruch.cuny.edu

CEO: Kathleen M. Waldron
CFO: Johanna D'Aleo
HR: Aurea (Abby) Santana
FYE: June 30
Type: School

Part of the City University of New York, Baruch College has an enrollment of some 16,000 students. The institution offers undergraduate and graduate study programs through its three schools: the Zicklin School of Business; the Mildred and George Weissman School of Arts and Sciences; and the School of Public Affairs. It also offers non-degree and certificate programs. The college's roots go back to 1847 when the Free Academy, the first free public higher education institution in the US, was founded in New York City, home to nearly 90% of its students. The school was renamed in 1953 in honor of financier and statesman Bernard Baruch. The college became part of the City University system in 1968.

BASF BUILDING SYSTEMS

889 Valley Park Dr.
Shakopee, MN 55379
Phone: 952-496-6000
Fax: 952-496-6062
Web: www.buildingsystems.basf.com

CEO: Doug MacRae
CFO: —
HR: —
FYE: December 31
Type: Business segment

What, other than gravity, keeps your floor from floating up into the heavens? It might be the products manufactured by BASF Building Systems, a business unit within BASF's Construction Chemicals division. The division makes adhesives and sealants that bond wood and rubberized flooring to various substrates; its products are also used by the automotive industry to bond metal, plastics, and laminates. BASF Building Systems also manufactures sealants, water repellents, grouting, and concrete and masonry repair products. In 2006 BASF, the world's largest chemicals maker, bought Degussa's Construction Chemicals unit for about $3 billion.

🖳 BASF CATALYSTS LLC

25 Middlesex/Essex Tpke.
Iselin, NJ 08830
Phone: 732-205-5000
Fax: 732-321-1161
Web: www.catalysts.basf.com

CEO: Kurt W. Bock
CFO: Fried-Walter Münstermann
HR: —
FYE: December 31
Type: Subsidiary

BASF Catalysts converts base materials into wealth — but no alchemy is involved. The company makes chemical catalysts and adsorbents, used in manufacturing pharmaceutical, steel, and packaging products as well as other chemicals. BASF Catalysts' environmental technologies segment makes catalysts used in emission-control systems, such as catalytic converters for automobiles. It also provides precious and base metals as raw materials for manufacturers through its material services segment. The company is a global leader in many of its markets, #1 in both emission-control catalysts and chemical catalysts, and among the world's top three makers of refinery catalysts.

	Annual Growth	12/04	12/05	12/06	12/07	12/08
Est. sales ($ mil.)	—	—	—	—	—	1,017.3
Employees	—	—	—	—	—	6,284

BASF CORPORATION

100 Campus Dr.
Florham Park, NJ 07932
Phone: 973-245-6000
Fax: 973-245-6714
Web: www.basf.us

CEO: Kurt W. Bock
CFO: Fried-Walter Münstermann
HR: Andre D. Becker
FYE: December 31
Type: Subsidiary

If you're a North American chemical company, BASF might strike you as a four-letter word. BASF Corporation — the North American subsidiary of the world's largest chemicals company, BASF SE — makes nearly every chemical under the sun. The company operates five core segments: chemicals (inorganics, petrochemicals, and intermediate products), plastics (engineering plastics, foams, and polyurethanes), performance products (acrylics, paper chemicals, personal care products, and pharmaceutical ingredients), functional solutions (catalysts, industrial coatings, and construction chemicals), and agricultural chemicals (herbicides, insecticides). The company is responsible for about a fifth of BASF's total sales.

BASHAS' INC.

22402 S. Basha Rd.
Chandler, AZ 85248
Phone: 480-895-9350
Fax: 480-895-5371
Web: www.bashas.com

CEO: Edward N. (Eddie) Basha Jr.
CFO: James (Jim) Buhr
HR: —
FYE: December 31
Type: Private

Bashas' is working up a sweat standing its ground in the Southwest. The regional grocery chain operates about 130 stores (down from more than 160 in 2008) located primarily in Arizona, as well as a few stores in California and New Mexico. Its holdings include Bashas' traditional supermarkets, AJ's Fine Foods (gourmet-style supermarkets), and about a dozen Food City supermarkets (which cater to Hispanics in southern Arizona). It also operates a handful of Dine Markets in the Navajo Nation ("dine" means "the people" in Navajo). Founded in 1932, family-owned Bashas' filed for Chapter 11 bankruptcy protection in July 2009 and has been shuttering stores. Rival Albertsons has launched a hostile bid for the grocery chain.

BASIC AMERICAN FOODS, INC.

2121 North California Blvd., Ste. 400
Walnut Creek, CA 94596
Phone: 925-472-4000
Fax: 925-472-4360
Web: www.baf.com

CEO: Loren Kimura
CFO: John Argent
HR: Sandy Makamura
FYE: December 31
Type: Private

Basic American Foods caters to your basic meat-and-potatoes type of guy. The company makes dehydrated potato products (varieties include au gratin, hash brown, mashed, and scalloped) for the foodservice industry under such brands as Potato Pearls, Nature's Own, and Naturally Potatoes. It also produces refried and black beans (under the Santiago label) and Quick-Start chili mixes. Basic American Foods has processing and sales facilities in the US and international marketing offices in Mexico City and Hong Kong. The company's customers include foodservice distributors and operators, industrial food manufacturers, and wholesale club and retail food operations.

BASIC EARTH SCIENCE SYSTEMS, INC.   OTC: BSIC

1801 Broadway, Ste. 620
Denver, CO 80202
Phone: 303-296-3076
Fax: 303-773-8099
Web: www.basicearth.net

CEO: Ray Singleton
CFO: Joseph B. Young
HR: —
FYE: March 31
Type: Public

You don't have to be an earth scientist to know that Basic Earth Science Systems gets down to the basics — oil and gas. It is involved in exploration, production, operation, and development activities, exploiting crude oil and natural gas assets in Colorado's Denver-Julesburg Basin, the Williston Basin of Montana and North Dakota, and along the Gulf Coast. In 2009 the company reported it had drilled 48 net wells and had proved reserves of 638,000 barrels of oil and 936 million cu. ft. of gas. Most of Basic Earth Science Systems' productive wells are in Montana, North Dakota, and Texas.

	Annual Growth	3/05	3/06	3/07	3/08	3/09
Sales ($ mil.)	16.7%	4.9	6.6	7.2	7.4	9.1
Net income ($ mil.)	(24.0%)	1.8	2.8	2.5	1.8	0.6
Market value ($ mil.)	(18.2%)	25.6	39.3	27.8	18.8	11.4
Employees	5.1%	9	8	59	10	11

BASIC ENERGY SERVICES, INC.   NYSE: BAS

500 W. Illinios, Ste. 800
Midland, TX 79701
Phone: 432-620-5500
Fax: 432-620-5501
Web: www.basicenergyservices.com

CEO: Kenneth V. (Ken) Huseman
CFO: Alan Krenek
HR: James E. Tyner
FYE: December 31
Type: Public

Oil and gas producers turn to Basic Energy Services for the fundamentals. The company provides well site services with its fleet of well-servicing rigs (at more than 410, the third-largest in the US behind Key Energy Services and Nabors Industries), 820 fluid service trucks, and related equipment. These services include acidizing, cementing, fluid handling, fracturing, well construction, well maintenance, and workover. Basic Energy Services serves about 2,000 producers operating in Louisiana, New Mexico, Oklahoma, and Texas. It also has a contract drilling operation. Investment firm DLJ Merchant Banking Partners III, L.P., owns 44.4% of the company.

	Annual Growth	12/05	12/06	12/07	12/08	12/09
Sales ($ mil.)	3.4%	459.8	730.1	877.2	1,004.9	526.6
Net income ($ mil.)	—	44.8	98.8	87.7	68.2	(253.5)
Market value ($ mil.)	(18.3%)	823.4	1,017.4	906.0	538.2	367.3
Employees	3.7%	3,280	4,000	4,500	5,000	3,800

BASIN ELECTRIC POWER COOPERATIVE

1717 E. Interstate Ave.
Bismarck, ND 58503
Phone: 701-223-0441
Fax: 701-224-5346
Web: www.basinelectric.com

CEO: Ronald R. (Ron) Harper
CFO: Clifton T. Hudgins
HR: —
FYE: December 31
Type: Cooperative

Ranges at home on the range depend on Basin Electric Power Cooperative, as do other electric-powered items in nine states from Montana to Iowa to New Mexico. The regional, consumer-owned power generation and transmission co-op generates about 3,650 MW of capacity (mostly coal-fired) for 136 rural electric member systems, which serve about 2.8 million people. Basin Electric's subsidiaries include Dakota Gasification (produces natural gas from coal), Dakota Coal (markets lignite and limestone), Basin Telecommunications (Internet access), and Basin Cooperative Services (property management).

	Annual Growth	12/04	12/05	12/06	12/07	12/08
Est. sales ($ mil.)	—	—	—	—	—	817.6
Employees	—	—	—	—	—	1,212

BASS PRO, INC.

2500 E. Kearney
Springfield, MO 65898
Phone: 417-873-5000
Fax: 417-873-4672
Web: www.basspro.com

CEO: John L. (Johnny) Morris
CFO: —
HR: Mike Roland
FYE: December 31
Type: Private

Bass Pro Shops (BPS) knows how to reel in shoppers. The company operates about 60 Outdoor World stores in the US and Canada that sell boats, firearms, equipment, and apparel for most outdoor activities. Stores feature archery ranges, fish tanks, bowling lanes, billiards tables, and dining areas. BPS also catches shoppers at home with its catalogs, online store, and TV and radio programs. The first Outdoor World store (in Missouri) has been one of the state's biggest tourist attractions since it opened in 1981. The company owns Tracker Marine (boat manufacturing) and American Rod & Gun (sporting goods wholesale) and runs an 850-acre resort in the Ozark Mountains. Founder John Morris owns BPS.

	Annual Growth	12/04	12/05	12/06	12/07	12/08
Est. sales ($ mil.)	13.5%	2,050.0	1,915.0	2,660.0	2,650.0	3,400.0
Employees	9.1%	11,300	12,500	13,000	14,000	16,000

⊞ BASSETT FURNITURE INDUSTRIES   NASDAQ (GS): BSET

3525 Fairystone Park Hwy.
Bassett, VA 24055
Phone: 276-629-6000
Fax: 276-629-6333
Web: www.bassettfurniture.com

CEO: Robert H. (Rob) Spilman Jr.
CFO: J. Michael Daniel
HR: Eddie White
FYE: November 30
Type: Public

Bassett Furniture Industries, Incorporated, works to get a leg up on the competition. The company, founded in 1902, makes wooden and upholstered furniture for home use, featuring bedroom and dining suites, sofas, chairs, love seats, and home office furniture. Bassett sells its products primarily through more than 100 Bassett Furniture Direct stores (about 70 of which are licensed) and Bassett Home Furnishings locations. Bassett boasts nearly 40 company-owned stores located mostly in the southern and northeastern US. Dogged by disappointing sales, the company has spent the past several years reducing its number of manufacturing, warehouse, and showroom facilities and paring down its workforce from 4,200 to 1,300 employees.

	Annual Growth	11/05	11/06	11/07	11/08	11/09
Sales ($ mil.)	(8.7%)	335.2	328.2	295.4	288.3	232.7
Net income ($ mil.)	—	7.6	5.4	(9.9)	(40.4)	(22.7)
Market value ($ mil.)	(32.7%)	206.7	202.9	102.0	48.7	42.3
Employees	(14.3%)	2,200	1,800	1,443	1,329	1,189

BATES COLLEGE

2 Andrews Rd.
Lewiston, ME 04240
Phone: 207-786-6255
Fax: 207-786-6025
Web: www.bates.edu

CEO: Elaine Tuttle Hansen
CFO: Terry J. Beckmann
HR: —
FYE: June 30
Type: School

Bates College is a selective, private, co-educational liberal arts college granting bachelor of arts and bachelor of science degrees. The more than 1,750 students can choose from 24 majors, the most popular of which include history, environmental studies, political science, English, biology, economics, and psychology. Students enjoy a 10-to-1 student-to-faculty ratio. Bates's endowment is an estimated $150 million. With tuition and fees hitting $51,000, most students receive financial aid. Bates College was founded in 1855 by Maine abolitionists.

	Annual Growth	6/04	6/05	6/06	6/07	6/08
Est. sales ($ mil.)	—	—	—	—	—	84.5
Employees	—	—	—	—	—	720

BATESVILLE CASKET COMPANY, INC.

1 Batesville Blvd.
Batesville, IN 47006
Phone: 812-934-7500
Fax: 812-934-7598
Web: www.batesville.com

CEO: Joseph A. (Joe) Raver
CFO: —
HR: Philip C. Waddell
FYE: September 30
Type: Subsidiary

A pine box it is not. Batesville Casket, founded in 1884, is a leading maker of bronze, copper, stainless steel, steel, and hardwood caskets. It also makes urns and other memorial products for the cremation market. The firm's direct sales force sells Batesville caskets to licensed funeral homes in the US, as well as in Australia, Mexico, Canada, Puerto Rico, South Africa, and the UK. It supplies about half of the US market. Batesville makes most of its caskets in the US, but boasts additional manufacturing plants in Mexico. It also offers display furniture for funerals. Batesville Casket is owned by Hillenbrand, created when Hillenbrand Industries spun off its funeral services unit in 2008.

BATH & BODY WORKS, LLC

7 Limited Pkwy.
Reynoldsburg, OH 43068
Phone: 614-856-6000
Fax: 614-856-6013
Web: www.bathandbodyworks.com

CEO: Diane L. Neal
CFO: Andrew Meslow
HR: —
FYE: January 31
Type: Subsidiary

Women turn to Bath & Body Works (BBW) to help wash away the daily stresses of life. A subsidiary of Limited Brands, BBW operates more than 1,650 stores throughout North America and an online store. The company sells natural body, hair care, and personal care products and fragrances under its own BBW brand, as well as the C.O. Bigelow and White Brand Candle brands. Customers in need of rejuvenation can also find a line of aromatherapy and at-home spa treatments, and in some stores, extra indulgences such as massages and pedicures. The BBW brand has had an image makeover, from country-inspired to a modern-day apothecary of beauty. BBW accounts for about 40% of Limited Brands' sales.

	Annual Growth	1/05	1/06	1/07	1/08	1/09
Sales ($ mil.)	—	—	—	—	—	2,374.0
Employees	—	—	—	—	—	—

[H] BATTELLE MEMORIAL INSTITUTE

505 King Ave.
Columbus, OH 43201
Phone: 614-424-6424
Fax: 614-424-5263
Web: www.battelle.org

CEO: Jeffrey (Jeff) Wadsworth
CFO: I. Martin Inglis
HR: —
FYE: September 30
Type: Not-for-profit

When you use a copier, hit a golf ball, or listen to a CD, you're using technologies developed by Battelle Memorial Institute. The not-for-profit is one of the world's largest research enterprises, with more than 20,400 scientists, engineers, and staff serving 1,100 corporate and government clients. Research areas include national security, energy, and health and life sciences. Battelle owns facilities in the US, Asia, and Europe and manages four Department of Energy-sponsored labs: Brookhaven National Laboratory, Oak Ridge National Laboratory, Idaho National Laboratory, and Pacific Northwest National Laboratory. The institute was established by the family of steel industry pioneer Gordon Battelle in 1929.

BAUER HOCKEY, INC.

150 Ocean Rd.
Greenland, NH 03840
Phone: 603-430-2111
Fax: 603-430-3010
Web: www.bauer.com

CEO: Kevin Davis
CFO: —
HR: —
FYE: May 31
Type: Private

Bauer Hockey outfits the biggest players who showcase their talents on ice. Previously a subsidiary of NIKE, the firm makes ice and roller hockey equipment, including sticks, custom-made sticks, skates, helmets, protective gear, and apparel under the NIKE, Mission, ITECH, and Bauer brand names. Bauer sells its products worldwide in more than 9,000 stores in some 35 countries. It's among the most widely used brands in the National Hockey League and other leagues. After more than a dozen years together, NIKE sold the firm (then named Bauer Nike Hockey U.S.A.) in 2008 for about $200 million to a group of investors that included Canadian entrepreneur W. Graeme Roustan and Kohlberg & Company.

	Annual Growth	5/04	5/05	5/06	5/07	5/08
Est. sales ($ mil.)	—	—	—	—	—	215.7
Employees	—	—	—	—	—	950

BAUER PUBLISHING USA

270 Sylvan Ave.
Englewood Cliffs, NJ 07632
Phone: 201-569-6699
Fax: 201-510-3297
Web: www.bauerpublishing.com

CEO: Hubert Boehle
CFO: Richard (Rich) Teehan
HR: —
FYE: December 31
Type: Subsidiary

Feeling out of touch? Turn to Bauer Publishing USA, publisher of celebrity and style magazines *In Touch Weekly* and *Life & Style Weekly*, women's magazines *First* and *Woman's World*, soap magazine *Soaps in Depth*, and teen magazines *TWIST*, *M*, and *J-14*. Bauer Publishing USA uses a European approach to publishing, which includes a focus on newsstand, not subscription, sales. The company is owned by German parent company Bauer Verlagsgruppe (also known as The Bauer Publishing Group). The Bauer Publishing Group operates in the UK through Bauer Publishing USA sister companies H. Bauer Publishing and Bauer Consumer Media.

	Annual Growth	12/04	12/05	12/06	12/07	12/08
Est. sales ($ mil.)	—	—	—	—	—	33.4
Employees	—	—	—	—	—	300

BAUSCH & LOMB INCORPORATED

1 Bausch & Lomb Place
Rochester, NY 14604
Phone: 585-338-6000
Fax: 585-338-6007
Web: www.bausch.com

CEO: Brent Saunders
CFO: Brian J. Harris
HR: Michelle Graham
FYE: December 31
Type: Private

Eyes are the windows to profit for Bausch & Lomb. The eye care company is best known as a leading maker of contact lenses and lens care solutions (including the PureVision and ReNu brands). In addition to its lens products, Bausch & Lomb makes prescription ophthalmic drugs Lotemax, Alrex, and Zylet, along with over-the-counter vitamins and drops through its pharmaceuticals division. Its surgical unit makes equipment for cataract, refractive (LASIK laser vision correction), and other ophthalmic surgeries. Bausch & Lomb markets its products in more than 100 countries worldwide. The company, which does business as Bausch + Lomb, is owned by private equity firm Warburg Pincus.

	Annual Growth	12/04	12/05	12/06	12/07	12/08
Sales ($ mil.)	0.0%	—	—	—	2,500.0	2,500.0
Employees	(80.8%)	—	—	—	13,000	2,500

BAXTER INTERNATIONAL INC.

NYSE: BAX

1 Baxter Pkwy.
Deerfield, IL 60015
Phone: 847-948-2000
Fax: 847-948-2016
Web: www.baxter.com

CEO: Robert L. Parkinson Jr.
CFO: Robert J. Hombach
HR: Jeanne K. Mason
FYE: December 31
Type: Public

Why choose between making drugs and making medical equipment? Baxter International does it all. The company makes a wide variety of medical products across its three divisions, including drugs and vaccines, dialysis equipment, and IV supplies. Its BioScience segment makes protein and plasma therapies to treat hemophilia and immune disorders, as well as vaccines and biological sealants used to close surgical wounds. Baxter is a leading maker of intravenous (IV) supplies and systems via its Medication Delivery segment; the segment also makes infusion pumps and inhaled anesthetics. Baxter's Renal division makes dialyzers and other products for the treatment of end-stage renal disease (ESRD).

	Annual Growth	12/05	12/06	12/07	12/08	12/09
Sales ($ mil.)	6.3%	9,849.0	10,378.0	11,263.0	12,348.0	12,562.0
Net income ($ mil.)	23.2%	956.0	1,396.0	1,707.0	2,014.0	2,205.0
Market value ($ mil.)	11.7%	22,456.5	27,669.4	34,624.1	31,963.9	34,999.9
Employees	1.4%	47,000	48,000	46,000	48,500	49,700

BAY NATIONAL CORPORATION

NASDAQ (GM): BAYN

2328 W. Joppa Rd.
Lutherville, MD 21093
Phone: 410-494-2580
Fax: 410-494-2589
Web: www.baynational.com

CEO: Hugh W. Mohler
CFO: David E. Borowy
HR: —
FYE: December 31
Type: Public

Bay National Corporation is staying afloat in the banking waters. It is the holding company for Bay National Bank, which operates two branches in Lutherville and Salisbury, Maryland. Targeting small to midsized businesses, as well as professionals and high-net-worth individuals, the bank offers traditional banking products including checking and savings accounts, CDs, and loans. Commercial and industrial loans represent roughly half of the company's loan portfolio; commercial mortgages account for another quarter. After posting losses in 2009 and being ordered by regulators to raise capital levels, the company agreed to sell its core deposits and its Salisbury branch location to Maryland's Hebron Savings Bank.

	Annual Growth	12/05	12/06	12/07	12/08	12/09
Assets ($ mil.)	8.4%	210.0	254.8	256.5	270.6	290.3
Net income ($ mil.)	—	2.7	2.4	0.9	(5.1)	(16.1)
Market value ($ mil.)	(49.9%)	41.1	37.6	21.0	5.2	2.6
Employees	(9.2%)	56	57	72	47	38

BAY STATE GAS COMPANY

300 Friberg Pkwy.
Westborough, MA 01581
Phone: 508-836-7000
Fax: 508-836-7070
Web: www.baystategas.com

CEO: Stephen H. (Steve) Bryant
CFO: —
HR: —
FYE: December 31
Type: Subsidiary

New England is really pretty, and luckily for gas utility Bay State Gas, it can also be pretty chilly. Bay State Gas distributes natural gas to about 300,000 customers in 60 communities throughout Massachusetts. Bay State Gas also provides energy products and services, including heating system installation and maintenance and water heater and conversion burner rentals. In response to Massachusetts' deregulation measures, the company is participating in a customer choice program. Bay State Gas is a wholly owned subsidiary of energy power player NiSource.

BAYCARE HEALTH SYSTEM, INC.

16255 Bay Vista Dr.
Clearwater, FL 33760
Phone: 727-820-8200
Fax: —
Web: www.baycare.org

CEO: Stephen R. (Steve) Mason
CFO: Tommy Inzia
HR: Craig Brethauer
FYE: December 31
Type: Not-for-profit

BayCare Health System takes care of folks lounging (or limping) on the bay in the Sunshine State. Established in 1997, the health system operates 10 hospitals (about 2,700 beds) that serve residents of Tampa Bay and surrounding areas in Florida. Its member hospitals (eight full-service acute-care facilities and two specialty units) are grouped together into the Morton Plant Mease Health Care, St. Anthony's Health Care, and St. Joseph's-Baptist Health Care systems. The system offers a wide variety of specialty services ranging from orthopedics to cancer care to women's services. The health system also operates area ambulatory and outpatient clinics, and it provides visiting nurse home health care services.

	Annual Growth	12/04	12/05	12/06	12/07	12/08
Sales ($ mil.)	12.3%	—	—	169.1	213.5	213.1
Net income ($ mil.)	—	—	—	7.7	6.7	(3.0)
Employees	31.2%	—	—	1,286	1,375	2,213

BAYER CORPORATION

100 Bayer Rd.
Pittsburgh, PA 15205
Phone: 412-777-2000
Fax: 412-777-3883
Web: www.bayerus.com

CEO: Gregory S. (Greg) Babe
CFO: Willy Scherf
HR: Claus Fey
FYE: December 31
Type: Subsidiary

For when you can't "bayer" the pain, Bayer Corporation makes your medicine. The US subsidiary of pharmaceuticals and materials giant Bayer AG (or Bayer Group), the company operates through three divisions and an internal services company. Bayer Corporation handles Bayer Group's US operations in three segments: Bayer HealthCare (pharmaceuticals, animal health, and over-the-counter medicines), MaterialScience (plastics, coatings, and polyurethanes), and Bayer CropScience (herbicides, fungicides, and insecticides). The internal services unit, Bayer Corporate and Business Services, handles administrative, technology, human resources, legal, and procurement functions for the Bayer Group's US operations.

BAYER HEALTHCARE PHARMACEUTICALS INC.

6 W. Belt
Wayne, NJ 07470
Phone: 973-694-4100
Fax: 973-487-2003
Web: pharma.bayer.com

CEO: Reinhart Franzen
CFO: —
HR: —
FYE: December 31
Type: Subsidiary

Take a pinch of Bayer, add a dash of Schering, put it in the oven of the US pharmaceuticals market, and you've got the recipe for Bayer HealthCare Pharmaceuticals. The company develops and markets prescription medicines for sale in the US. It also markets products of sister company Bayer Schering Pharma. Bayer HealthCare Pharmaceuticals is focused on specialty therapeutics in the areas of diagnostic imaging, hematology, neurology, cancer, and women's health. Its products target serious chronic diseases such as multiple sclerosis (Betaseron), as well as general health ailments such as infections (Avelox and Cipro). Bayer HealthCare Pharmaceuticals handles the US pharmaceutical operations of Bayer HealthCare.

BAYLOR HEALTH CARE SYSTEM

3500 Gaston Ave.
Dallas, TX 75246
Phone: 214-820-0111
Fax: 214-820-7499
Web: www.bhcs.com

CEO: Joel T. Allison
CFO: Frederick Savelsbergh
HR: Keith Holtz
FYE: June 30
Type: Not-for-profit

It's not a veterinary health system, but they do treat injured Bears from time to time. The Baylor Health Care System (BHCS) offers a bundle of services. Founded in 1981, it was governed by Baylor University until establishing autonomy in 1997. The not-for-profit medical network serves seven counties in the Dallas-Fort Worth metroplex through more than a dozen hospitals and medical centers, including the Baylor University Medical Center complex, one of the state's major teaching and referral facilities. Other system members include rehabilitation facilities and primary care, senior health, and family health centers. The system also provides home health care and specialized pediatric services.

BAYHILL CAPITAL CORPORATION

OTC: BYHL

10757 S. River Front Pkwy., Ste. 125
South Jordan, UT 84095
Phone: 801-705-5128
Fax: 801-705-9372
Web: www.bayhillcapital.com

CEO: Robert K. Bench
CFO: Gary L. Cook
HR: —
FYE: June 30
Type: Public

BayHill Capital (formerly Cognigen Networks) hopes to rev up its commissions. Through its subsidiary Commission River, the company primarily earns commissions from online sales of domestic and international long-distance calling cards — as well as Internet access, wireless phone, and other telecom services — using independent sales agents and affinity group marketing programs. In 2008 the company changed its name from Cognigen to BayHill Capital Corporation. The following year the company agreed to be acquired by wireless broadband ISP Yonder Media, but the terms of the agreement were not met and the deal expired.

	Annual Growth	6/05	6/06	6/07	6/08	6/09
Sales ($ mil.)	(28.8%)	11.7	10.1	5.6	4.1	3.0
Net income ($ mil.)	—	1.8	(1.3)	(0.7)	(2.4)	(0.5)
Market value ($ mil.)	(54.5%)	82.0	18.4	14.2	4.2	3.5
Employees	(11.4%)	13	12	4	12	8

BAYLOR UNIVERSITY

1 Bear Place #97096
Waco, TX 76798
Phone: 254-710-1011
Fax: 254-710-1490
Web: www.baylor.edu

CEO: David E. Garland
CFO: Reagan M. Ramsower
HR: —
FYE: May 31
Type: School

Don't mess with Texas, and don't mess around at Baylor University. The world's largest Baptist institution of higher learning requires its more than 14,000 students to follow a strict code of conduct. The university has approximately 150 undergraduate degree programs, as well as about 75 master's and more than 20 doctoral programs. The private, co-educational university also offers degrees from its law school (juris doctor) and theological seminary (master of divinity and doctor of ministry). Founded in 1845, the college is affiliated with the Baptist General Convention of Texas.

BAYLAKE CORP.

OTC: BYLK

217 N. 4th Ave.
Sturgeon Bay, WI 54235
Phone: 920-743-5551
Fax: 920-746-3984
Web: www.baylake.com

CEO: Robert J. (Rob) Cera
CFO: Kevin L. LaLuzerne
HR: Sharon A. Haines
FYE: December 31
Type: Public

In need of a loan? Just row, row, row your boat all the way to Baylake Corp. The institution is the holding company for Baylake Bank, which provides financial services from more than 25 offices in northeastern Wisconsin. Serving individuals and local businesses, the bank provides standard products and services including checking and savings accounts, IRAs, CDs, credit cards, mortgages, and personal and business loans. It also offers trust, financial planning, asset management, and brokerage services. Additionally, Baylake Bank owns an insurance agency and holds a 49.8% stake in United Financial Services, which performs electronic banking and data processing services for other banks (and Baylake, too).

	Annual Growth	12/05	12/06	12/07	12/08	12/09
Assets ($ mil.)	(1.0%)	1,089.4	1,111.7	1,106.6	1,062.9	1,044.5
Net income ($ mil.)	(16.6%)	8.9	7.4	0.2	(9.8)	4.3
Market value ($ mil.)	(35.6%)	128.6	127.4	81.9	39.6	22.2
Employees	(0.9%)	317	327	327	315	306

BAYOU CITY EXPLORATION, INC.

OTC: BYCX

632 Adams St., Ste. 700
Bowling Green, KY 42101
Phone: 800-798-3389
Fax: —
Web: www.bcexploration.com

CEO: Robert D. Burr
CFO: Stephen C. Larkin
HR: —
FYE: December 31
Type: Public

An affiliate of the Blue Ridge Group, Bayou City Exploration is engaged in oil and gas exploration primarily in Texas and Louisiana. It conducts its activities through partnerships and the acquisition of direct stakes in oil and gas properties, and in exploratory and development wells. In 2008 the company reported proved reserves of about 1.1 billion cu. ft. of natural gas equivalent. The Blue Ridge Group owns 14% of Bayou City Exploration. Shifting its exploration focus from Appalachia to the Gulf Coast, in 2005 Blue Ridge Energy, the exploration and production unit of Blue Ridge Group, renamed itself Bayou City Exploration. To raise cash, in 2010 the company sold its stakes in two wells in Texas.

	Annual Growth	12/05	12/06	12/07	12/08	12/09
Sales ($ mil.)	13.6%	0.6	0.3	0.5	0.3	1.0
Net income ($ mil.)	—	(1.8)	(3.9)	(1.5)	(0.2)	0.8
Market value ($ mil.)	(56.0%)	53.3	24.3	5.9	0.3	2.0
Employees	(29.3%)	8	5	—		2

BAYSTATE HEALTH, INC.

759 Chestnut St.
Springfield, MA 01199
Phone: 413-794-0000
Fax: 413-794-8274
Web: baystatehealth.com

CEO: Mark R. Tolosky
CFO: Keith C. McLean-Shinaman
HR: Paula C. Squires
FYE: September 30
Type: Not-for-profit

Patients in need of medical care can dock at this bay. Not-for-profit Baystate Health is the largest health care services provider in western Massachusetts. The system operates four acute-care hospitals with a total of more than 750 beds, and a specialized children's hospital with nearly 60 bassinettes. Baystate Health offers ancillary medical services, including cancer care, respiratory care, infusion therapy, visiting nurse, and hospice services. The system holds a majority of Health New England, a for-profit HMO with more than 100,000 members in western Massachusetts. Baystate Health is the only Level 1 Trauma Center and teaching hospital in the region.

	Annual Growth	9/04	9/05	9/06	9/07	9/08
Est. sales ($ mil.)	—	—	—	—	—	1,286.3
Employees	—	—	—	—	—	5,000

[H] BB&T CORPORATION

NYSE: BBT

200 W. 2nd St.
Winston-Salem, NC 27101
Phone: 336-733-2000
Fax: 336-733-2470
Web: www.bbt.com

CEO: Kelly S. King
CFO: Daryl N. Bible
HR: Henry M. Skinner
FYE: December 31
Type: Public

Big, Bold & Temerarious? That might be an apt description of BB&T, the banking company that covers the Southeast like kudzu. The company serves consumers, small to midsized businesses, and government entities through more than 1,800 branches. Its flagship subsidiary, Branch Banking and Trust (also known as BB&T), is one of North Carolina's oldest banks and a leading originator of residential mortgages in the Southeast. In addition to deposit accounts and loans, the company offers insurance, mutual funds, discount brokerage, wealth management, and financial planning services. Business services include leasing, factoring, and investment banking (through Scott & Stringfellow).

	Annual Growth	12/05	12/06	12/07	12/08	12/09
Assets ($ mil.)	11.0%	109,169.8	121,351.0	132,618.0	152,015.0	165,764.0
Net income ($ mil.)	(15.3%)	1,653.8	1,528.0	1,734.0	1,519.0	853.0
Market value ($ mil.)	(11.8%)	29,006.0	30,404.0	21,226.8	19,005.1	17,558.6
Employees	4.0%	27,700	29,300	29,400	29,600	32,400

BBDO WORLDWIDE

1285 Avenue of the Americas
New York, NY 10019
Phone: 212-459-5000
Fax: 212-459-6645
Web: www.bbdo.com

CEO: Andrew Robertson
CFO: James A. (Jim) Cannon
HR: —
FYE: December 31
Type: Subsidiary

This alphabet soup of advertising hopes to spell success for its clients. As the flagship agency of media conglomerate Omnicom Group, BBDO Worldwide offers creative development services for some of the world's top brands using television, print, and other media. BBDO Worldwide also provides campaign planning and management services, as well as other brand promotion services. The firm's Atmosphere BBDO unit offers interactive marketing services in North America. BBDO's clients have included Chrysler, FedEx, and PepsiCo. The company operates through some 290 offices in about 80 countries, featuring outposts such as Abbott Mead Vickers and Proximity London.

BBJ ENVIRONMENTAL TECHNOLOGIES, INC.

Pink Sheets: BBJE

5910-A Breckenridge Pkwy.
Tampa, FL 33610
Phone: 813-622-8550
Fax: 813-623-4032
Web: www.bbjenviro.com

CEO: Jean Caillet
CFO: Robert G. Baker
HR: —
FYE: December 31
Type: Public

BBJ Environmental Technologies' prospects are moldy. Through its BBJ Environmental Solutions subsidiary, the company manufactures chemicals that control and remove mold. Mold colonies, left unchecked, produce spores and mycotoxins which can cause allergic reactions in about 20% of the US population. The company's mission is to improve public health and safety through the control of this kind of microbial contamination in heating, ventilating, air-conditioning and refrigeration systems. BBJ Environmental Solutions has developed specific indoor air solutions for commercial buildings (such as hospitals, schools, and offices, and manufacturing operations), mold remediation contractors, and homeowners.

BCB BANCORP, INC.

NASDAQ (GM): BCBP

104-110 Ave. C
Bayonne, NJ 07002
Phone: 201-823-0700
Fax: 201-339-0403
Web: bayonnecommunitybank.com

CEO: Donald Mindiak
CFO: Donald Mindiak
HR: —
FYE: December 31
Type: Public

BCB Bancorp be the holding company for BCB Community Bank, a relative newcomer on the scene that opened its doors in late 2000. The independent bank serves Hudson County and the surrounding area from about five offices in Bayonne and Hoboken, New Jersey. The bank offers traditional deposit products and services, including savings accounts, money market accounts, CDs, and IRAs. Funds from deposits are used to originate mortgages and loans, primarily commercial real estate and multi-family property loans (which together account for more than half of the bank's loan portfolio). BCB Bancorp is acquiring rival New Jersey bank holding company Pamrapo Bancorp.

	Annual Growth	12/05	12/06	12/07	12/08	12/09
Assets ($ mil.)	7.9%	466.2	510.8	563.5	578.6	631.5
Net income ($ mil.)	(5.8%)	4.7	5.6	4.4	3.5	3.7
Market value ($ mil.)	(12.8%)	72.8	78.2	72.5	48.5	42.0
Employees	9.6%	63	99	104	93	91

BCSB BANCORP, INC.

NASDAQ (GM): BCSB

4111 E. Joppa Rd., Ste. 300
Baltimore, MD 21236
Phone: 410-256-5000
Fax: 410-256-0261
Web: www.baltcosavings.com

CEO: Joseph J. Bouffard
CFO: Anthony R. (Tony) Cole
HR: —
FYE: September 30
Type: Public

BCSB Bancorp is the holding company for Baltimore County Savings Bank, which has about 20 branches in the Baltimore metropolitan area. Serving individuals and local businesses, the community-oriented bank offers such standard retail products as deposit accounts, CDs, and IRAs, and checking, savings, and money market accounts. It uses funds from deposits to originate real estate loans, primarily residential mortgages as well as commercial mortgages, construction loans, and consumer loans. To narrow its focus on northeastern Maryland, particularly the IH-95 corridor, the bank is selling four branches to American Bank.

	Annual Growth	9/05	9/06	9/07	9/08	9/09
Assets ($ mil.)	(8.5%)	812.7	785.9	642.4	567.1	569.4
Net income ($ mil.)	—	0.6	(7.4)	(2.9)	0.9	(2.0)
Market value ($ mil.)	(24.3%)	81.2	74.5	48.9	32.6	26.7
Employees	(0.3%)	173	173	155	154	171

[H] An in-depth profile of this company is available to Hoover's Online members at hoovers.com.

229

BDO SEIDMAN, LLP

130 E. Randolph, Ste. 2800, 1 Prudential Plaza
Chicago, IL 60601
Phone: 312-240-1236
Fax: 312-240-3311
Web: www.bdo.com

CEO: Jack Weisbaum
CFO: —
HR: —
FYE: June 30
Type: Partnership

BDO knows accounting. BDO Seidman is the US member of BDO International, one of the largest accounting firms outside of the Big Four (Deloitte Touche Tohmatsu, Ernst & Young, KPMG, and PricewaterhouseCoopers). BDO Seidman, which goes by the BDO brand name, has nearly 40 locations and offers midsized companies a broad range of accounting and consulting services such as auditing, tax planning, litigation consulting, and appraisals and valuations. More than 400 additional offices are operated by independent US firms that are members of the BDO Seidman Alliance. The international BDO network includes more than 1,130 offices around the globe. BDO was founded in 1910.

	Annual Growth	6/05	6/06	6/07	6/08	6/09
Sales ($ mil.)	—	—	—	—	—	659.0
Employees	—	—	—	—	—	3,020

BDP INTERNATIONAL, INC.

510 Walnut St.
Philadelphia, PA 19106
Phone: 215-629-8900
Fax: 215-629-8940
Web: www.bdpinternational.com

CEO: Richard J. Bolte Jr.
CFO: Frank P. Osusky
HR: Doug Waitzman
FYE: December 31
Type: Private

Be it by air, ground, or ocean, BDP International is in the business of moving raw materials and finished products around the globe. The company provides logistics services such as customs brokerage, freight forwarding, and warehousing and distribution for customers in a variety of industries, including chemicals and retail. It serves more than 4,000 customers worldwide, including Dow Chemical, Cargill, and Johnson & Johnson. BDP International and its subsidiaries have about 25 offices in the US; internationally, it operates through subsidiaries, joint ventures, and agents in some 120 countries. President and CEO Richard Bolte Jr. and his family own the company, which was founded by his father in 1966.

⊞ BE AEROSPACE, INC.

NASDAQ (GS): BEAV

1400 Corporate Center Way
Wellington, FL 33414
Phone: 561-791-5000
Fax: 561-791-7900
Web: www.beaerospace.com

CEO: Amin J. Khoury
CFO: Thomas P. McCaffrey
HR: R. J. Landry
FYE: December 31
Type: Public

BE Aerospace (B/E) ensures that travelers truly enjoy air travel. A leading maker of cabin components for commercial, business jets, and military aircraft, B/E's offerings include aircraft seats, coffeemakers, refrigeration equipment, galley structures, and emergency oxygen systems. In addition to its three business segments — Consumables Management, Commercial Aircraft, and Business Jet — B/E also provides maintenance and repair services for cabin interior products, converts passenger aircraft into freighters, and distributes aerospace fasteners. B/E aftermarket operations and military demand represent approximately 50% of its revenues. B/E sells its products to most major airlines and aviation OEMs.

	Annual Growth	12/05	12/06	12/07	12/08	12/09
Sales ($ mil.)	23.1%	844.1	1,128.2	1,677.7	2,110.0	1,937.7
Net income ($ mil.)	13.8%	84.6	85.6	147.3	(99.4)	142.0
Market value ($ mil.)	1.7%	2,248.6	2,624.8	5,407.0	786.0	2,402.0
Employees	8.4%	3,980	5,058	6,298	6,485	5,500

BEACON FEDERAL BANCORP, INC.

NASDAQ (GM): BFED

5000 Brittonfield Pkwy.
East Syracuse, NY 13057
Phone: 315-433-0111
Fax: —
Web: www.beaconfederal.com

CEO: Ross J. Prossner
CFO: Lisa M. Jones
HR: —
FYE: December 31
Type: Public

Beacon Federal Bancorp was created in 2007 as the holding company for Beacon Federal, a thrift serving selected markets in Massachussetts, New York, Tennessee, and Texas. The company operates about a half-dozen branches that offer standard retail products and loans, primarily residential mortgages, consumer loans, and home equity loans. Subsidiary Beacon Comprehensive Services provides investment products and tax preparation services. Beacon Federal was founded in 1953 as a credit union serving employees of air conditioner manufacturer Carrier Corporation.

	Annual Growth	12/05	12/06	12/07	12/08	12/09
Assets ($ mil.)	20.0%	515.1	607.7	878.0	1,021.3	1,066.9
Net income ($ mil.)	(6.1%)	4.5	2.3	2.4	(3.0)	3.5
Market value ($ mil.)	(3.0%)	—	—	65.3	53.6	61.4
Employees	6.5%	—	116	121	134	140

BEACON INDUSTRIAL GROUP, INC.

4404-A Chesapeake Dr.
Charlotte, NC 28216
Phone: 704-398-7747
Fax: 704-398-7820
Web: www.beaconindustrial.com

CEO: Tom Gilboy
CFO: Deanna Dycus
HR: —
FYE: December 31
Type: Private

Beacon Industrial Group's companies shed a shining light on a murky world of grime and pollution so that manufacturing clients can operate more efficiently in cleaner environments. Group companies manufacture air, gas, and liquid filtration systems; develop dust collection technology and equipment; and make air pollution control systems and wet scrubbers. Applications include power generation, textile manufacturing, chemicals, and waste handling. Operating subsidiaries include Pneumafil Group, LCI Corporation, Menardi, and MikroPul. The group operates in North America, Europe, and Australia.

	Annual Growth	12/04	12/05	12/06	12/07	12/08
Est. sales ($ mil.)	—	—	—	—	—	108.2
Employees	—	—	—	—	—	1,200

BEACON POWER CORPORATION

NASDAQ (CM): BCON

65 Middlesex Rd.
Tyngsboro, MA 01879
Phone: 978-694-9121
Fax: 978-694-9127
Web: www.beaconpower.com

CEO: F. William (Bill) Capp
CFO: James M. Spiezio
HR: —
FYE: December 31
Type: Public

Beacon Power is a beacon of hope for companies seeking backup power. The development-stage company's flywheel energy storage systems provide uninterruptible electric power for communications networks, computers, industrial manufacturing, and other power generation applications. Beacon Power's flywheel systems draw electrical energy from a power source, such as an electric power grid or a fuel cell, and then store it. The power can then be delivered as needed when a primary energy source either fails or is disrupted. Beacon Power also makes photovoltaic power conversion systems (solar inverters).

	Annual Growth	12/05	12/06	12/07	12/08	12/09
Sales ($ mil.)	(9.6%)	1.5	1.0	1.4	0.1	1.0
Net income ($ mil.)	—	(9.3)	(12.2)	(12.9)	(23.6)	(19.1)
Market value ($ mil.)	(27.7%)	330.7	180.9	277.7	96.8	90.4
Employees	23.6%	30	49	47	65	70

BEACON ROOFING SUPPLY, INC.

NASDAQ (GS): BECN

1 Lakeland Park Dr.
Peabody, MA 01960
Phone: 978-535-7668
Fax: 978-535-7358
Web: www.beaconroofingsupply.net

CEO: Robert R. (Bob) Buck
CFO: David R. (Dave) Grace
HR: David Pasternak
FYE: September 30
Type: Public

Not all products from Beacon Roofing Supply (BRS) are over your head. One of North America's largest roofing materials distributors, the company operates about 170 branches in more than 35 states and three Canadian provinces. BRS distributes some 10,000 stock keeping units (SKUs) to more than 40,000 customers. Along with roofing products, Beacon distributes related materials, such as siding, windows, and waterproofing systems. The company's customers include contractors, home builders, building owners, and other resellers. BRS was formed in 1997 when investment firm Code Hennessy & Simmons acquired a controlling interest in Beacon Sales, a commercial roofer founded in 1928.

	Annual Growth	9/05	9/06	9/07	9/08	9/09
Sales ($ mil.)	19.5%	850.9	1,500.6	1,645.8	1,784.5	1,734.0
Net income ($ mil.)	12.3%	32.9	49.3	25.3	40.3	52.4
Market value ($ mil.)	(7.4%)	992.1	921.9	465.5	711.5	727.9
Employees	1.2%	2,157	2,641	2,708	2,464	2,258

BEALL'S INC.

1806 38th Ave. East
Bradenton, FL 34208
Phone: 941-747-2355
Fax: 941-746-1171
Web: www.beallsinc.com

CEO: Stephen M. Knopik
CFO: Dan Love
HR: Dan Doyle
FYE: August 31
Type: Private

Residents of the Sun Belt have been known to leave their homes with Beall's on. The retail holding company operates through subsidiaries Beall's Department Stores, Beall's Outlet, and Burkes Outlet Stores in a dozen states. It has more than 560 stores (about 200 are in Florida) located throughout states in the southern and western US, including Arizona, California, Georgia, and Louisiana. Products range from off-price clothing and footwear for men and women to cosmetics, gifts, and housewares. Each chain has its own online shopping destination. The family-owned company was founded in 1915 by the grandfather of Chairman Bob Beall (pronounced "bell").

BEAM GLOBAL SPIRITS & WINE, INC.

510 Lake Cook Rd.
Deerfield, IL 60015
Phone: 847-948-8888
Fax: 847-948-8610
Web: www.beamglobal.com

CEO: Matthew J. (Matt) Shattock
CFO: Robert (Bob) Probst
HR: Florence Pramberger
FYE: December 31
Type: Subsidiary

At Beam Global Spirits & Wine, the spotlight is on the world. Headquartered in the US, it offers libations with global origins: Canadian Club Whiskey from our neighbor country just to the north; Courvoisier Cognac from France; Kummerling Liqueur from Germany; VOX Vodka from the Netherlands; Laphroaig Scotch from Scotland; and Sauza Tequila with roots dating back to the Spanish conquistadors in Mexico. The company's Jim Beam is the #1 selling branded bourbon in the world; its DeKuyper, from the Netherlands, is the #1 cordial brand in the US. These and Beam's other premium branded beverages are bound to show up for Christmas parties at Fortune Brands, of which Beam Global Spirits & Wine is a subsidiary.

BE&K BUILDING GROUP, LLC

5605 Carnegie Blvd., Ste. 200
Charlotte, NC 28209
Phone: 704-551-2700
Fax: 704-551-2799
Web: www.bekbuildinggroup.com

CEO: Luther P. Cochrane
CFO: Trilby Carriker
HR: —
FYE: March 31
Type: Subsidiary

A busy bee in commercial construction, BE&K Building Group is a top US contractor. The company, which is part of Houston-based construction giant KBR, provides design-build services, construction management, general contracting, and other construction services. It specializes in mixed-use projects, educational facilities, entertainment venues, food and beverage plants, hospitals, hotels, laboratories, and manufacturing facilities. BE&K Building Group operates mostly in the Southeast, but also works on projects in other parts of the country. KBR bought BE&K for some $550 million in 2008.

BEARINGPOINT, INC.

100 Crescent Ct., Ste. 700
Dallas, TX 75201
Phone: 703-747-3000
Fax: —
Web: www.bearingpoint.com

CEO: John DeGroote
CFO: David Johnston
HR: —
FYE: December 31
Type: Private

Management consulting and systems integration firm BearingPoint wanted to help its clients navigate their way to success across the uncharted seas of modern business and technology, but the company lost its own way. BearingPoint filed for Chapter 11 bankruptcy protection in February 2009. Racked with a heavy debt load, it launched a fire sale to shed its remaining divisions and business segments. The BearingPoint brand is still being used by the company's former Europe, Middle East, and Africa practice, which it sold to its European management team in August 2009. In its heyday, BearingPoint operated in some 60 countries, providing services to businesses, government agencies, and other enterprises.

	Annual Growth	12/04	12/05	12/06	12/07	12/08
Sales ($ mil.)	(1.4%)	3,375.8	3,388.9	3,444.0	3,455.6	3,197.0
Net income ($ mil.)	—	(546.2)	(721.6)	(213.4)	(362.7)	(32.1)
Employees	(2.5%)	16,800	17,400	17,500	17,100	15,200

BEASLEY BROADCAST GROUP, INC.

NASDAQ (GM): BBGI

3033 Riviera Dr., Ste. 200
Naples, FL 34103
Phone: 239-263-5000
Fax: 239-263-8191
Web: www.beasleybroadcasting.com

CEO: George G. Beasley
CFO: B. Caroline Beasley
HR: Patricia (Pat) Russell
FYE: December 31
Type: Public

Beasley Broadcast Group is a leading radio broadcaster with more than 40 stations operating in about a dozen markets in six states, primarily Florida, Georgia, and North Carolina. The company's stations broadcast a variety of formats, including news, sports, and talk radio, as well as several music formats. Most of its stations operate as part of a cluster within a specific market, allowing the company to combine certain business functions between those stations and achieve greater operating efficiencies. Chairman and CEO George Beasley controls about 80% of the company.

	Annual Growth	12/05	12/06	12/07	12/08	12/09
Sales ($ mil.)	(6.1%)	124.3	125.2	133.9	121.4	96.7
Net income ($ mil.)	(24.9%)	10.7	10.1	4.8	(30.5)	3.4
Market value ($ mil.)	(28.3%)	306.8	217.3	118.1	40.9	81.1
Employees	(1.5%)	662	748	772	654	622

An in-depth profile of this company is available to Hoover's Online members at hoovers.com.

231

BEAULIEU GROUP, L.L.C.

1502 Coronet Dr.	CEO: Ralph Boe
Dalton, GA 30720	CFO: Del Land
Phone: 706-876-2900	HR: Bernadette Martin
Fax: 706-695-6237	FYE: December 31
Web: www.beaulieu-usa.com	Type: Private

Doing business as Beaulieu of America, the closely held Beaulieu Group rolls out a line of berber, commercial, and indoor/outdoor (nonwoven, turf) carpet. Chances are you have had Beaulieu underfoot; the company is the third-largest carpet manufacturer in the world. Through its dealers, carpets are distributed to home improvement chains, including The Home Depot and Lowe's Companies, and commercial contractors. The company's facilities operate in North America and Australia. Consumer brands include Beaulieu, Coronet, and Hollytex. The company markets commercial products under the Bolyu (high-end), Cambridge (value), and Aqua (hospitality) labels. The Beaulieu Group is controlled by the Bouckaert family.

⊞ BEAUTICONTROL, INC.

2121 Midway Rd.	CEO: Albert Bosch
Carrollton, TX 75006	CFO: Tim Kulhanek
Phone: 972-458-0601	HR: —
Fax: 972-341-3071	FYE: December 31
Web: www.beauticontrol.com	Type: Subsidiary

BeautiControl has a firm grip on the business of aesthetics and enjoys calling Texas home, alongside direct-selling rival Mary Kay. A subsidiary of household products maker Tupperware Brands Corporation, BeautiControl sells its beauty care items to its 1.1 million independent sales consultants, who in turn sell to consumers in 23 markets worldwide. Consultants provide computer-assisted, head-to-toe makeup advice through in-home demos. Its products include skin and nail care, fragrances, cosmetics, toiletries, nutritional and weight-management food supplements, and in-home spa retreats. Tupperware purchased BeautiControl in 2000 in a bid to expand its direct-selling reach to beauty and personal care products.

BEAUTY SYSTEMS GROUP LLC

3001 Colorado Blvd.	CEO: John R. Golliher
Denton, TX 76210	CFO: —
Phone: 940-898-7500	HR: —
Fax: 940-383-8143	FYE: September 30
Web: www.sallybeautyholdings.com/holdings/bsg.asp	Type: Subsidiary

Sally Beauty Holdings' Beauty Systems Group (BSG) distributes hair care products, nail polish, makeup, and other personal care items through its sales force of more than 1,000 consultants both directly to salons and from about 990 CosmoProf shops, open only to the beauty trade. Customers primarily include salons, spas, licensed beauticians, and nail technicians. Its 9,800 products include brands such as Paul Mitchell, Wella, and more. BSG covers all 50 US states, Puerto Rico, and parts of Canada, Mexico, and Europe. It has grown through acquisitions. Alberto-Culver spun off Sally Beauty Company in 2006 in a $3 billion deal that created Sally Beauty Holdings.

⊞ BEAZER HOMES USA, INC.

NYSE: BZH

1000 Abernathy Rd., Ste. 1200	CEO: Ian J. McCarthy
Atlanta, GA 30328	CFO: Allan P. Merrill
Phone: 770-829-3700	HR: Fred Fratto
Fax: 770-481-2808	FYE: September 30
Web: www.beazer.com	Type: Public

Beazer Homes USA builds for the middle-class buyer who's ready to make the move into the white-picket-fence scene. Building homes with an average price of about $230,900, the company courts the entry-level, move-up, and active adult markets. Beazer Homes USA focuses on high-growth regions in the Southeast, Mid-Atlantic, and West; it closed on some 4,300 homes in 2009 (down from more than 18,000 homes closed in 2006). It also provides title insurance services in some markets. Company design centers offer homebuyers limited customization for such features as appliances, cabinetry, flooring, fixtures, and wall coverings. Like most large homebuilders, Beazer subcontracts to build its homes.

	Annual Growth	9/05	9/06	9/07	9/08	9/09
Sales ($ mil.)	(33.0%)	4,995.4	5,462.0	3,490.8	2,074.3	1,005.2
Net income ($ mil.)	—	262.5	388.8	(411.1)	(951.9)	(189.4)
Market value ($ mil.)	(44.4%)	3,648.6	2,427.9	513.1	371.9	347.6
Employees	(33.4%)	4,578	4,234	2,619	1,444	901

BEBE STORES, INC.

NASDAQ (GS): BEBE

400 Valley Dr.	CEO: Manny Mashouf
Brisbane, CA 94005	CFO: Walter J. Parks
Phone: 415-715-3900	HR: —
Fax: 415-715-3939	FYE: June 30
Web: www.bebe.com	Type: Public

Retailer bebe stores offers apparel in two main sizes: slim and none. bebe (pronounced "beebee") designs and sells contemporary women's clothing and accessories under the bebe, PH8 (formerly BEBE SPORT), and 2b bebe banners through some 300 stores in the US, Canada, and Puerto Rico; abroad through licensees; and online. The company targets hip, "body-conscious" (some say skinny) 18- to 34-year-olds. bebe also licenses its name for items such as eyewear and swimwear. The majority of bebe's products are designed in-house and produced by contract manufacturers. Chairman and CEO Manny Mashouf, who founded bebe in 1976, controls the company.

	Annual Growth	6/05	6/06	6/07	6/08	6/09
Sales ($ mil.)	4.3%	509.5	579.1	670.9	687.6	603.0
Net income ($ mil.)	(34.0%)	66.3	73.8	77.3	63.1	12.6
Market value ($ mil.)	(28.6%)	2,278.8	1,327.5	1,377.4	827.3	592.3
Employees	4.0%	3,400	3,975	4,297	4,433	3,973

⊞ BECHTEL GROUP, INC.

50 Beale St.	CEO: Riley P. Bechtel
San Francisco, CA 94105	CFO: Peter Dawson
Phone: 415-768-1234	HR: John MacDonald
Fax: 415-768-9038	FYE: December 31
Web: www.bechtel.com	Type: Private

Whether the job is raising an entire city or razing a nuclear power plant, you can bet the Bechtel Group will be there to bid on the business. The engineering, construction, and project management firm was named the US's #1 contractor (ahead of Fluor) by *Engineering News-Record* for 11 consecutive years. It operates worldwide and has participated in such historic projects as the construction of Hoover Dam and the cleanup of the Chernobyl nuclear plant. Bechtel's Oil, Gas & Chemical business unit and Bechtel National, its government contracts group, are its leading revenue producers. The group is in its fourth generation of leadership by the Bechtel family, with chairman and CEO Riley Bechtel at the helm.

	Annual Growth	12/04	12/05	12/06	12/07	12/08
Sales ($ mil.)	15.9%	17,378.0	18,100.0	20,500.0	27,000.0	31,400.0
Employees	2.4%	40,000	40,000	40,000	42,500	44,000

BECHTEL NATIONAL, INC.

5275 Westview Dr.	CEO: David Walker
Frederick, MD 21703	CFO: Maureen Mendez
Phone: 301-228-6000	HR: —
Fax: 301-228-2200	FYE: December 31
Web: www.bechtel.com/government-services.html	Type: Subsidiary

Bechtel National, the government services arm of engineering giant Bechtel Group, helps the US destroy stockpiles of chemical weapons and treat contaminated wastes. It has worked toward developing a national repository for nuclear waste in Nevada and it also helped the US defense program by managing the awarding of certain subcontracts in Iraq. Bechtel and the University of California manage and operate two to institutions for nuclear and scientific research labs — Los Alamos National Laboratory in New Mexico and Lawrence Livermore National Laboratory in California. Among the other governmental agencies it works with are NASA, the EPA, and the US Agency for International Development (USAID).

THE BECK GROUP

1807 Ross Ave., Ste. 500	CEO: Henry C. (Peter) Beck III
Dallas, TX 75201	CFO: Mark Collins
Phone: 214-303-6200	HR: —
Fax: 214-303-6300	FYE: December 31
Web: www.beckgroup.com	Type: Private

At the beck and call of commercial developers, The Beck Group has built everything from racetracks to runways, retail centers, hotels, and hospitals. The firm provides design/build, general contracting, and construction management services in the US and Mexico. Focusing on commercial and institutional building, Beck offers services such as project management and outsourcing of facilities construction. The firm has recently begun emphasizing sustainable — or green — elements, having completed several projects meeting LEED (Leadership in Energy & Environmental Design) standards. The company also provides real estate development services. The Beck Group, founded in 1912 by Henry Beck, is owned by the group's managing directors.

🔲 BECKMAN COULTER, INC.   NYSE: BEC

250 S. Kraemer Blvd.	CEO: Scott Garrett
Brea, CA 92822	CFO: Charles P. (Charlie) Slacik
Phone: 714-993-5321	HR: J. Robert Hurley
Fax: 714-773-8111	FYE: December 31
Web: www.beckmancoulter.com	Type: Public

Like the nerdiest kid in school, Beckman Coulter never saw a test it didn't love. The company makes more than 600 diagnostic testing systems and supplies, from simple blood tests to complicated genetic diagnostic tools. Its wares are used by hospital and other clinical laboratories to suss out diseases and monitor their progression. Its clinical products include immunoassay, clinical chemistry, and hematology systems, as well as products in the growing field of molecular diagnostics. In addition to its systems for diagnosing patients, Beckman Coulter makes products used by life sciences researchers, including those at academic research centers and drug companies, to understand diseases and develop new therapies.

	Annual Growth	12/05	12/06	12/07	12/08	12/09
Sales ($ mil.)	7.5%	2,443.8	2,528.5	2,761.3	3,098.9	3,260.6
Net income ($ mil.)	(0.6%)	150.6	186.9	211.3	194.0	147.1
Market value ($ mil.)	3.6%	3,988.8	4,192.1	5,103.5	3,080.3	4,587.5
Employees	3.2%	10,416	10,340	10,500	11,000	11,800

🔲 BECTON, DICKINSON AND COMPANY   NYSE: BDX

1 Becton Dr.	CEO: Edward J. (Ed) Ludwig
Franklin Lakes, NJ 07417	CFO: David V. Elkins
Phone: 201-847-6800	HR: Donna M. Boles
Fax: 201-847-6475	FYE: September 30
Web: www.bd.com	Type: Public

Don't worry; you'll only feel a slight prick if Becton, Dickinson (BD) is at work. The company's BD Medical segment is one of the top manufacturers of syringes and other injection and infusion devices. BD Medical also makes IV catheters and syringes, prefillable drug delivery systems, self-injection devices for diabetes patients, and surgical instruments (scalpels and anesthesia trays, for instance). The BD Diagnostics segment offers tools for collecting specimens and the equipment and reagents to detect diseases in them. Finally, Becton Dickinson caters to researchers through its BD Biosciences unit, which makes reagents, antibodies, cell imaging systems, and labware used in basic and clinical research.

	Annual Growth	9/05	9/06	9/07	9/08	9/09
Sales ($ mil.)	7.2%	5,414.7	5,834.8	6,359.7	7,155.9	7,160.9
Net income ($ mil.)	14.3%	722.3	752.3	890.0	1,127.0	1,231.6
Market value ($ mil.)	7.4%	12,233.6	16,489.5	19,144.8	18,727.2	16,274.9
Employees	3.3%	25,571	26,990	28,018	28,300	29,116

🔲 BED BATH & BEYOND INC.   NASDAQ (GS): BBBY

650 Liberty Ave.	CEO: Steven H. (Steve) Temares
Union, NJ 07083	CFO: Eugene A. (Gene) Castagna
Phone: 908-688-0888	HR: Concetta Van Dyke
Fax: 908-688-6483	FYE: February 28
Web: www.bedbathandbeyond.com	Type: Public

Bed Bath & Beyond (BBB) has everything you need to play "house" for real. It's the #1 domestics retailer superstore in the US, with about 965 BBB stores throughout the US, Puerto Rico, and Canada. The stores' floor-to-ceiling shelves stock better-quality (brand-name and private-label) goods in two main categories: domestics (bed linens, bathroom and kitchen items) and home furnishings (cookware and cutlery, small household appliances, picture frames, and more). BBB relies exclusively on circulars, mailings, and word-of-mouth for advertising. The company also operates three smaller specialty chains: some 60 Christmas Tree Shops; 45 Harmon discount health and beauty shops; and 30 buybuy Baby locations.

	Annual Growth	2/06	2/07	2/08	2/09	2/10
Sales ($ mil.)	7.7%	5,809.6	6,617.4	7,048.9	7,208.3	7,828.8
Net income ($ mil.)	1.2%	572.8	594.2	562.8	425.1	600.0
Market value ($ mil.)	3.7%	9,487.9	10,501.5	7,460.8	5,607.4	10,954.3
Employees	5.6%	33,000	35,000	39,000	37,000	41,000

BEECH-NUT NUTRITION CORPORATION

13 British American Blvd.	CEO: Christoph Rudolf
Latham, NY 12110	CFO: Tim Kennedy
Phone: 518-595-6600	HR: Amy McGrath
Fax: —	FYE: June 30
Web: www.beechnut.com	Type: Private

Peas and applesauce — Beech-Nut Nutrition puts them in jars for baby's lunch or baby's finger-painting. As the #2 US baby-food maker (trailing Nestlé's #1 Gerber), Beech-Nut Nutrition hopes baby will open up ever wider for the airplane. In addition to jars of pureed fruits, vegetables, meats, and meals, the company makes cereals, juices and water for the youngest palates. It offers more than 125 baby and toddler food products. The company's Good Morning and Good Evening line of baby food was created as a result of research showing the benefits of time-of-day feeding. Beech-Nut is owned by Swiss branded-food manufacturer Hero.

🔲 An in-depth profile of this company is available to Hoover's Online members at hoovers.com.

233

BEHR PROCESS CORPORATION

3400 W. Segerstrom Ave.
Santa Ana, CA 92704
Phone: 714-545-7101
Fax: 714-241-1002
Web: www.behr.com

CEO: Jeffrey D. Filley
CFO: —
HR: Richard Moss
FYE: December 31
Type: Subsidiary

Brown bears, black bears, snow-white polar bears — BEHR Process Corporation manufactures all the colors in the bear rainbow. The company produces coatings such as paints, stains, and varnishes that are sold primarily through The Home Depot; its best-selling line is exclusive to the home-improvement warehouse giant. The company was founded in 1947 out of Otho Behr's garage as a marketer of linseed oil. It grew into a stain and varnish manufacturer and, by the mid-1980s, began to make architectural paints. BEHR also owns Masterchem Industries, which makes the primer KILZ. Home-improvement materials company Masco owns BEHR.

BEIERSDORF, INC.

187 Danbury Rd., Ste. 7
Wilton, CT 06897
Phone: 203-563-5800
Fax: 203-563-5893
Web: www.bdfusa.com

CEO: Iain Holding
CFO: Raymond Englebrecht
HR: —
FYE: December 31
Type: Subsidiary

Beiersdorf loves the skin you're in and wants to improve it one product at a time. A subsidiary of Beiersdorf AG, the company makes and markets skin care brands NIVEA, Aquaphor, and Eucerin. Beiersdorf's products are sold in some 100 countries. NIVEA, developed and named in 1911 from the Latin word "nivius," meaning "snow-white," marked the foundation of Beiersdorf's portfolio of brands. In addition to body care, NIVEA's product lineup now extends to lip care, anti-aging creams, and men's products (DNAge). It discovered Eucerit, the industry's first water-in-oil emulsifier, at the turn of the century. Beiersdorf products are available worldwide through grocery stores and mass merchant retailers, such as Target.

	Annual Growth	12/04	12/05	12/06	12/07	12/08
Est. sales ($ mil.)	—	—	—	—	—	62.0
Employees	—	—	—	—	—	525

BEKAERT CORPORATION

3200 W. Market St., Ste. 303
Akron, OH 44333
Phone: 330-867-3325
Fax: 330-867-3424
Web: www.bekaert.com/na

CEO: Bert De Graeve
CFO: David Best
HR: Bart Wille
FYE: December 31
Type: Subsidiary

Bekaert Corporation goes right down to the wire on a daily basis. The company, a division of Belgium-based NV Bekaert SA, manufactures a variety of wire, as well as wire and film coatings. For automobiles, Bekaert makes products such as control cables, spring wire, and clips. The company also makes high carbon, low carbon, and stainless steel wire for industrial applications. Other Bekaert products include telecom and power cables, agricultural fencing material, and sawing cable. The company's solar and safety window films can be used on commercial and residential buildings as well as automobiles.

BEL BRANDS USA

25 NW Point Blvd., Ste. 1000
Elk Grove Village, IL 60007
Phone: 847-879-1900
Fax: —
Web: www.kaukaunacheese.com

CEO: Lance Chambers
CFO: Didier Aziza
HR: —
FYE: December 31
Type: Subsidiary

Bel Brands USA spreads its products far and wide but never too thinly. The company makes branded cheese products for consumers throughout the US, from Kaukauna aged cheddar spreads to The Laughing Cow processed wedges. Other brands include WisPride, Merkts, and Owls Nest spreadable cheeses, as well as Mini Babybel natural cheese snacks, Price's pimento spreads, and Connoisseur gourmet spreads. The company's cheeses are available in cups, tubs, balls, and logs. These products are distributed to US grocery stores and retail chains, such as Kroger and Wal-Mart. Bel Brands USA is a subsidiary of Paris-based Fromageries Bel.

BEL FUSE INC.

206 Van Vorst St.
Jersey City, NJ 07302
Phone: 201-432-0463
Fax: 201-432-9542
Web: www.belfuse.com

NASDAQ (GS): BELFB

CEO: Daniel (Dan) Bernstein
CFO: Colin Dunn
HR: Miriam Martinez
FYE: December 31
Type: Public

Bel Fuse manufactures electronic components for networking, telecommunications, high-speed data transmission, and automotive and consumer electronics. Its magnetic products include discrete components, power transformers, and MagJack connector modules. It also offers power conversion modules for a variety of applications. Bel Fuse's miniature, micro, and surface-mounted fuses create supplementary circuit protection for televisions, VCRs, computers, and telephones. The company also makes passive jacks, plugs, and cable assemblies. Asian customers account for about two-thirds of Bel Fuse's sales.

	Annual Growth	12/05	12/06	12/07	12/08	12/09
Sales ($ mil.)	(4.1%)	215.9	254.9	259.1	258.4	182.8
Net income ($ mil.)	—	20.2	25.2	26.3	(14.9)	(8.3)
Market value ($ mil.)	(9.3%)	370.1	404.9	340.7	246.7	250.1
Employees	9.6%	1,851	1,956	1,948	2,135	2,674

BELCAN CORPORATION

10200 Anderson Way
Cincinnati, OH 45242
Phone: 513-891-0972
Fax: 513-985-7276
Web: www.belcan.com

CEO: Ralph G. Anderson
CFO: Michael J. Wirth
HR: —
FYE: December 31
Type: Private

From engineering to information technology to multimedia, Belcan can take care of the technical stuff. The company's engineering division provides such services as product design, testing, procurement, and computer modeling. Its IT and media division produces videos and interactive presentations and provides desktop publishing and e-learning services. Belcan's automation and design/build team engineers and installs complete factory automation systems. The firm also offers technical and general staffing services. With nearly 60 offices in the US and around the world, Belcan reaches clients in the aerospace, energy, health care, and manufacturing industries. The company was founded in 1958 by CEO Ralph Anderson.

	Annual Growth	12/04	12/05	12/06	12/07	12/08
Est. sales ($ mil.)	—	—	—	—	—	514.1
Employees	—	—	—	—	—	6,700

BELDEN & BLAKE CORPORATION

1001 Fannin St., Ste. 800
Houston, TX 77002
Phone: 713-659-3500
Fax: —

CEO: John B. Walker
CFO: James M. Vanderhider
HR: Sue Bowden
FYE: December 31
Type: Private

It may sound like a law firm, but Belden & Blake is in fact an energy company that obeys the laws of supply and demand in the oil and gas market. It acquires properties, explores for and develops oil and gas reserves, and gathers and markets natural gas in the Appalachian and Michigan basins. In 2008 Belden & Blake reported interests in 4,550 gross wells and leases on about 562,100 net acres, and it owned and operated 1,660 miles of gas gathering lines. The company had estimated proved reserves of 223 billion cu. ft. of gas equivalent. Belden & Blake is controlled by Capital C Energy Operations, itself controlled by EnerVest Ltd.

	Annual Growth	12/04	12/05	12/06	12/07	12/08
Sales ($ mil.)	11.7%	101.8	154.8	159.1	125.7	158.4
Net income ($ mil.)	—	12.7	17.2	52.2	(35.3)	(28.9)
Employees	—	180	134	0	0	0

BELDEN INC.

NYSE: BDC

7733 Forsyth Blvd., Ste. 800
St. Louis, MO 63105
Phone: 314-854-8000
Fax: 314-854-8001
Web: www.beldencdt.com

CEO: John S. Stroup
CFO: Gray G. Benoist
HR: Cathy Odom Staples
FYE: December 31
Type: Public

Can you hear me, now? If you didn't, Belden can help. The company designs, makes, and markets thousands of signal transmission products to hook up entertainment, residential, industrial, and security markets. Its lineup includes flat and optical fiber cables, coaxial and multi-conductor cables, connectivity and active components. Connecting access points to area networks, Belden cable is the wire in wireless. It produces connectors, patch panels, and interconnect hardware for end-to-end structured cabling solutions and industrial and data networking uses, largely outside of the US. Distributors are core customers — Anixter accounts for more than 15% of sales; Belden also sells to OEMs and systems integrators.

	Annual Growth	12/05	12/06	12/07	12/08	12/09
Sales ($ mil.)	1.1%	1,352.1	1,495.8	2,032.8	2,005.9	1,415.3
Net income ($ mil.)	—	47.6	65.9	137.1	(361.0)	(24.9)
Market value ($ mil.)	(2.7%)	1,142.2	1,827.6	2,080.6	976.2	1,024.9
Employees	0.4%	6,100	5,400	9,500	7,500	6,200

BELFOR USA GROUP, INC.

185 Oakland Ave., Ste. 300
Birmingham, MI 48009
Phone: 248-594-1144
Fax: 248-594-3190
Web: www.us.belfor.com

CEO: Sheldon Yellen
CFO: Joe Ciolino
HR: —
FYE: December 31
Type: Subsidiary

BELFOR USA will not just clean up the mess but will even help restore things to the way they were when disaster strikes. BELFOR provides restoration services to businesses and residences through more than 60 offices in North America. Services include reconstruction, drying, contents restoration, emergency power, mold remediation, semiconductor services, and recovery of data, electronics, and books. Additionally, BELFOR USA provides consulting and pre-planning services in an attempt to minimize problems customers can potentially encounter. Customers may pre-register with the company in order to save time and money. BELFOR USA is primarily owned by a group of its managing directors.

	Annual Growth	12/04	12/05	12/06	12/07	12/08
Est. sales ($ mil.)	—	—	—	—	—	651.5
Employees	—	—	—	—	—	1,500

BELK, INC.

2801 W. Tyvola Rd.
Charlotte, NC 28217
Phone: 704-357-1000
Fax: 704-357-1876
Web: www.belk.com

CEO: Thomas M. (Tim) Belk Jr.
CFO: Brian T. Marley
HR: —
FYE: January 31
Type: Private

Belk is busy bulking up. Already the nation's largest privately owned department store chain, Belk now operates more than 300 stores in some 15 states, following its 2006 purchase of the Parisian chain from Saks. Previously, Belk acquired Saks' McRae's and Proffitt's divisions. Belk stores are located primarily in the Southeast and Mid-Atlantic (the Carolinas, Florida, and Georgia) states and offer mid-priced brand-name and private-label apparel, shoes, jewelry, cosmetics, gifts, and home furnishings. Its stores usually anchor malls or shopping centers in small to midsized markets and target 35-to-54-year-old middle- and upper-income women. The Belk family runs the show and owns most of the company.

BELKIN INTERNATIONAL, INC.

12045 E. Waterfront Dr.
Playa Vista, CA 90094
Phone: 310-898-1100
Fax: 310-898-1111
Web: www.belkin.com

CEO: Mark Reynoso
CFO: Ross Crane
HR: Andrea Kane
FYE: December 31
Type: Private

Got a gadget? There's a good chance it's attached to an accessory from Belkin. The company makes a variety of connectivity and power products. A leading manufacturer of Universal Serial Bus (USB) devices, such as networking hubs, Belkin also provides media player accessories, surge protectors, uninterruptible power supplies, and computer cables. Other products include networking upgrade cards for notebook computers, LAN cabling and networking hardware, and home theater networking gear. The company, which was founded in 1983, sells its products worldwide, primarily through resellers and distributors. Founder and chairman Chet Pipkin owns Belkin International.

BELL HELICOPTER TEXTRON INC.

600 E. Hurst Blvd.
Hurst, TX 76053
Phone: 817-280-2011
Fax: 817-280-2321
Web: www.bellhelicopter.com

CEO: John L. Garrison Jr.
CFO: Tony Viotto
HR: Martha May
FYE: December 31
Type: Subsidiary

Referred to as Bell Helicopter, a Textron segment, this company is a rising power. Bell makes commercial and military helicopters and tiltrotor aircraft. Its commercial helicopters seat up to 15 passengers and include models designed for transport, emergency medical services, and search and rescue efforts. Military models include the venerable H-1 "Huey," with its utility model, as well as its UH-1Y attack model; the AH-1Z Super Cobra reconnaissance/attack helicopter; the Eagle Eye UAS (unmanned aircraft system); and the V-22 Osprey tiltrotor (with Boeing). Bell makes tiltrotor aircraft through joint venture Bell/Agusta Aerospace. The company also provides training, and repair/maintenance/overhaul services.

	Annual Growth	12/04	12/05	12/06	12/07	12/08
Sales ($ mil.)	9.8%	—	—	2,347.0	2,581.0	2,827.0
Net income ($ mil.)	60.4%	—	—	108.0	144.0	278.0
Employees	—	—	—	—	—	—

An in-depth profile of this company is available to Hoover's Online members at hoovers.com.

235

BELL INDUSTRIES, INC.

Pink Sheets: BLLI

8888 Keystone Crossing, Ste. 1700
Indianapolis, IN 46240
Phone: 317-704-6000
Fax: 317-575-9401
Web: www.bellind.com

CEO: Clinton J. Coleman
CFO: —
HR: Kathleen Gilmore
FYE: December 31
Type: Public

Bell Industries is nothing if not diverse. The holding company operates through two separate business units that specialize in technology consulting and recreational vehicle products. Its Bell Techlogix unit (formerly Technology Solutions Group) offers IT systems integration services, including network assessment and design, project management, software procurement, technical and customer support, and training throughout the US, primarily in the East and Midwest. It is one of Apple's largest service providers in North America. Bell's Recreational Products Group is a wholesale distributor of more than 50,000 aftermarket parts for motorcycles, boats, snowmobiles, and recreational vehicles.

	Annual Growth	12/05	12/06	12/07	12/08	12/09
Sales ($ mil.)	(6.4%)	130.9	120.3	119.9	101.9	100.6
Net income ($ mil.)	—	(0.8)	(2.9)	(15.2)	(4.9)	(1.9)
Market value ($ mil.)	(62.3%)	22.6	32.9	7.8	0.1	0.5
Employees	(7.8%)	850	1,150	936	600	615

BELL MICROPRODUCTS INC.

NASDAQ (GM): BELM

1941 Ringwood Ave.
San Jose, CA 95131
Phone: 408-451-9400
Fax: 408-451-1600
Web: www.bellmicro.com

CEO: W. Donald (Don) Bell
CFO: William E. (Bill) Meyer
HR: Richard J. (Dick) Jacquet
FYE: December 31
Type: Public

Bell Microproducts aims to be ahead of the curve in its industry. The company distributes network storage, semiconductor, and other computer products, primarily to computer makers and resellers. It sells more than 140 product lines, including offerings from AMD, EMC, IBM, NEC, Quantum, Seagate, Sony, and Toshiba. Specializing in data storage products, Bell Micro offers services such as subsystems integration and kitting (providing materials in kit form, ready for assembly). The company markets its own data storage devices under the Galaxy and Rorke brands while reselling and supporting storage products from Brocade Communications, Hewlett-Packard, and Hitachi. In 2010 Avnet agreed to buy Bell Micro.

	Annual Growth	12/05	12/06	12/07	12/08	12/09
Sales ($ mil.)	(15.6%)	—	—	—	3,579.5	3,021.2
Net income ($ mil.)	—	—	—	—	(74.8)	7.5
Market value ($ mil.)	491.7%	—	—	—	19.5	115.5
Employees	(3.2%)	—	—	—	1,973	1,910

BELL-CARTER FOODS, INC.

3742 Mount Diablo Blvd.
Lafayette, CA 94549
Phone: 925-284-5933
Fax: 925-284-2377
Web: www.bellcarter.com

CEO: Ken Wienholz
CFO: John Toth
HR: —
FYE: July 31
Type: Private

If olives ring your bell, turn to Bell-Carter Foods. The California company is a top manufacturer of canned and jarred black and green olives and olive spreads. Its products, which are sold under the Lindsay and Bell's labels, also include capers, cocktail onions, and pimentos. The company's products can be found in grocery stores and other food retailers throughout the US, including Walgreen, Sam's Club, and Costco, as well as in selected Canadian stores. Bell-Carter also serves foodservice customers and has import and export operations.

	Annual Growth	7/04	7/05	7/06	7/07	7/08
Est. sales ($ mil.)	—	—	—	—	—	200.0
Employees	—	—	—	—	—	450

BELO CORP.

NYSE: BLC

400 S. Record St.
Dallas, TX 75202
Phone: 214-977-6606
Fax: 214-977-6603
Web: www.belo.com

CEO: Dunia A. Shive
CFO: Carey P. Hendrickson
HR: —
FYE: December 31
Type: Public

You might say this company has a starring role in the lives of small-screen fans. Belo Corp. is a leading TV broadcaster with about 20 local television stations serving markets in 10 states, mostly in Texas and Washington. Its portfolio includes affiliate stations of all four major broadcast networks, as well as a few independent stations and affiliates of mini-networks The CW and MyNetworkTV. Belo also operates a small number of local and regional cable news outlets, including NWCN (NorthWest Cable News in Seattle) and TXCN (Texas Cable News). Chairman Robert Decherd and his family control about 60% of Belo's voting stock.

	Annual Growth	12/05	12/06	12/07	12/08	12/09
Sales ($ mil.)	(21.1%)	1,521.2	1,588.3	1,515.6	733.5	590.3
Net income ($ mil.)	—	127.7	130.5	(262.8)	(333.3)	(109.1)
Market value ($ mil.)	(24.9%)	1,762.1	1,511.9	1,435.3	160.6	560.0
Employees	(23.9%)	7,800	7,100	7,100	2,916	2,610

BELRON US INC.

2400 Farmers Dr., 5th Fl.
Columbus, OH 43235
Phone: 614-210-9000
Fax: 614-210-9451
Web: www.belronus.com

CEO: Thomas M. (Tom) Feeney
CFO: Douglas A. (Doug) Herron
HR: —
FYE: March 31
Type: Subsidiary

Belron US (operating as Safelite Group) has the answer to what blew into your windshield. The company, an operating segment of global auto glass repair giant Belron, is one of the largest auto glass repair providers in the US. It fixes and replaces windshields through a network of facilities in all 50 states, operating under the names of Safelite AutoGlass, AutoGlass Specialists, and Elite Auto Glass, among others. In addition, Belron US makes its own replacement windshields and distributes materials and tools to other auto glass repair companies. Founded in 1947 as Safelite AutoGlass, the company was acquired by D'Ieteren, Belron's parent, for about $330 million in 2007.

BELSHAW BROS., INC.

814 44th St. NW, Ste. 103
Auburn, WA 98001
Phone: 206-322-5474
Fax: 206-322-5425
Web: www.belshaw.com

CEO: Roger Faw
CFO: —
HR: —
FYE: December 31
Type: Subsidiary

The Belshaw brothers had a glazed look in their eyes when they began selling "sanitary doughnut machines" in 1923. The company manufactures a branded line of foodservice equipment designed for producing baked-goods. A 14-foot model fries up 7,400 same-size donuts an hour! Along with fryers, glazers, proofers, and ovens, Belshaw Bros. also makes specialized equipment for preparing pancakes. Both retail and wholesale producers are catered to, including institutional and commercial restaurants, concession stands, chain bakeries, and even military bases and ships. Formerly part of the Aga Rangemaster Group, Belshaw Bros. was acquired by Italian conglomerate Ali SpA in 2007.

THE BELT RAILWAY COMPANY OF CHICAGO

6900 S. Central Ave.
Bedford Park, IL 60638
Phone: 708-496-4000
Fax: 708-496-2608
Web: www.beltrailway.com

CEO: Patrick J. O'Brien
CFO: Dennis A. Warford
HR: Timothy E. Coffey
FYE: December 31
Type: Joint venture

Belt Railway of Chicago is a railroad's railroad. Freight trains converge on its Clearing Yards facility to have their cars separated and moved from one rail line to another in order to reach their destinations. To accomplish these tasks, the company operates 28 miles of mainline track and 300 miles of switching lines. Belt Railway of Chicago is owned by six of the largest North American railroads: Burlington Northern Santa Fe, Canadian National, Canadian Pacific, CSX, Norfolk Southern, and Union Pacific. Customers include not only the company's owners but also other railroads that serve the Chicago area, which is one of North America's primary rail hubs. Belt Railway of Chicago began operations in 1882.

BELTONE

2601 Patriot Blvd.
Glenview, IL 60026
Phone: 847-832-3300
Fax: —
Web: www.beltone.com

CEO: Todd Murray
CFO: —
HR: —
FYE: December 31
Type: Subsidiary

Beltone helps reopen the world of sound to people who are hearing impaired. The company provides a variety of hearing instruments and related products, including customized hearing instruments that fit in the ear canal as well as behind the ear. Beltone also offers hearing aids with digitally programmable technology, which adjusts the hearing instrument for individual needs. The company operates retail centers in North America where customers can have their hearing screened and be fitted with an instrument. Founded in 1940, the company sells its products in more than 40 countries around the globe. Beltone is part of GN ReSound.

BEMIS COMPANY, INC.

NYSE: BMS

1 Neenah Center, 4th Fl.
Neenah, WI 54957
Phone: 920-727-4100
Fax: 920-527-7600
Web: www.bemis.com

CEO: Henry J. Theisen
CFO: Scott Ullem
HR: Timothy S. Fliss
FYE: December 31
Type: Public

Thanks to companies like Bemis, delectables such as potato chips and snack cakes have a longer shelf life than most marriages. Bemis makes a broad line of flexible packaging materials, including polymer films, barrier laminates, and paper-bag packaging, nearly 60% of which are used by the food industry to bundle all manner of edibles. In addition to bags, Bemis produces pressure-sensitive products, ranging from label paper and graphic films to thin-film adhesives. Bemis' core customer, the food industry, represents 85% of sales; the company also sells to the agricultural, chemical, medical, personal care, and printing industries. With 84 facilities in 13 countries, the US accounts for some two-thirds of sales.

	Annual Growth	12/05	12/06	12/07	12/08	12/09
Sales ($ mil.)	0.3%	3,473.9	3,639.4	3,649.3	3,779.4	3,514.6
Net income ($ mil.)	(2.4%)	162.5	176.3	181.6	166.2	147.2
Market value ($ mil.)	1.6%	3,039.6	3,706.0	2,986.2	2,582.6	3,233.8
Employees	6.4%	15,900	15,700	15,678	15,400	20,400

BEMIS MANUFACTURING COMPANY

300 Mill St.
Sheboygan Falls, WI 53085
Phone: 920-467-4621
Fax: 920-467-8573
Web: www.bemismfg.com

CEO: Richard (Dick) Bemis
CFO: —
HR: —
FYE: December 31
Type: Private

Staying focused on the water closet keeps Bemis Manufacturing flushed with success. One of the world's largest manufacturers of toilet seats, the company offers a lineup in dozens of styles and colors. But far from taking a seat, the company makes molded and extruded disposable-plastic products for the health care industry as well as industrial caps, gauges, and reservoirs through its plastic fluid management division, Kelch Manufacturing. Bemis also provides a breadth of contract manufacturing services for auto, large appliance, office furniture, and more. The company's brand names include Carrara, Church, Mayfair, and PlastExport. Bemis operates throughout Asia, North America, Latin America, and Europe.

	Annual Growth	12/04	12/05	12/06	12/07	12/08
Est. sales ($ mil.)	—	—	—	—	—	135.7
Employees	—	—	—	—	—	1,800

⊞ BEN & JERRY'S HOMEMADE INC.

30 Community Dr.
South Burlington, VT 05403
Phone: 802-846-1500
Fax: 802-846-1610
Web: www.benjerry.com

CEO: Jostein Solheim
CFO: Michael Graning
HR: Jane Bowman
FYE: December 31
Type: Subsidiary

Not yet ready for a scoop of Dulce Delish? Don't worry, Ben & Jerry's is still Ben & Jerry's Homemade: a top maker of super premium ice cream (along with rival Nestlé's Häagen-Dazs). The quirky company was bought by consumer products giant Unilever in 2000, but it still marches to the beat of its own ice cream scoops on its drums of ice cream. The company sells its colorfully named ice cream, ice-cream novelties, and frozen yogurt ("FroYo") under such monikers as Chunky Monkey, Phish Food, and Cherry Garcia. It also franchises some 750 Ben & Jerry's SCOOP SHOPS worldwide. Ben & Jerry's donates a minimum of $1.1 million of pretax profits to philanthropic causes yearly.

BEN E. KEITH COMPANY

601 E. 7th St.
Fort Worth, TX 76102
Phone: 817-877-5700
Fax: 817-338-1701
Web: www.benekeith.com

CEO: Robert Hallam
CFO: Mel Cockrell
HR: Elliott Stephenson
FYE: June 30
Type: Private

Ben E. Keith is your bud if you like eating out and drinking brew. A leading food and beverage distributor, the company supplies its 22,000 customers with a bevy of food and non-food products from its six distribution centers. Its customers include restaurants, hotels, schools, and other institutional foodservice operators in 11 southern states. Ben E. Keith is also one of the largest Anheuser-Busch distributors, delivering beer to retail beverage outlets in 61 Texas counties. The company operates more than a dozen food and beer distribution facilities in Arkansas, Colorado, Kansas, Louisiana, Mississippi, Missouri, New Mexico, Oklahoma, Tennessee, and Texas.

⊞ An in-depth profile of this company is available to Hoover's Online members at hoovers.com.

237

BEN VENUE LABORATORIES, INC.

300 Northfield Rd.	CEO: Thomas Murphy
Bedford, OH 44146	CFO: Thomas Murphy
Phone: 440-232-3320	HR: —
Fax: 440-439-6398	FYE: December 31
Web: www.benvenue.com	Type: Subsidiary

Ben Venue Laboratories prides itself on having products that are clean, clear, and cold. A subsidiary of German drug firm Boehringer Ingelheim, the company provides contract manufacturing services, including product and process development and regulatory compliance services. The company specializes in manufacturing liquid and lyophilized (freeze-dried) pharmaceuticals. Ben Venue's Bedford Laboratories division provides contract manufacturing of generic injectable pharmaceuticals. Customers include multinational drugmakers, small biotech development firms, and government agencies.

BENDIX COMMERCIAL VEHICLE SYSTEMS LLC

901 Cleveland St.	CEO: Joseph J. (Joe) McAleese
Elyria, OH 44035	CFO: Arnfred Kulenkampff
Phone: 440-329-9000	HR: Diane Shields
Fax: 440-329-9557	FYE: December 31
Web: www.bendix.com	Type: Subsidiary

If you slow down on the interstate and notice an 18-wheeler in your rearview mirror, you may be more grateful for Bendix Commercial Vehicle Systems (Bendix CVS) than you realize. The company develops and makes systems for braking, stability, and traction, along with related components for heavy- and medium-duty trucks, trailers, tractors, buses, and other commercial vehicles. Additional products include night vision systems, adaptive cruise control, warning devices, and fan clutches. Customers include Blue Bird, Caterpillar, Mack Trucks, Peterbilt, and PACCAR. Bendix operates plants in Canada, Mexico, and the US. The company is a unit of German brake manufacturing giant Knorr-Bremse AG.

	Annual Growth	12/04	12/05	12/06	12/07	12/08
Est. sales ($ mil.)	—	—	—	—	—	269.6
Employees	—	—	—	—	—	2,110

⊞ BENCHMARK ELECTRONICS, INC.　　　　　NYSE: BHE

3000 Technology Dr.	CEO: Cary T. Fu
Angleton, TX 77515	CFO: Donald F. Adam
Phone: 979-849-6550	HR: Gail Combs
Fax: 979-848-5270	FYE: December 31
Web: www.bench.com	Type: Public

Benchmark Electronics is setting a benchmark for electronics manufacturing services (EMS). The company, which provides contract manufacturing services to electronics makers, produces complex printed circuit boards and related electronics systems and subsystems. Its customers include manufacturers of computers, industrial control equipment, medical devices, telecommunications systems, and test and measurement instruments. Benchmark also offers design, direct order fulfillment, distribution, engineering, materials management, and testing services. The company gets about three-quarters of its revenues in the US.

	Annual Growth	12/05	12/06	12/07	12/08	12/09
Sales ($ mil.)	(1.9%)	2,257.2	2,907.3	2,915.9	2,590.2	2,089.3
Net income ($ mil.)	(9.6%)	80.6	111.7	93.3	(135.6)	53.9
Market value ($ mil.)	(4.2%)	1,413.4	1,535.7	1,117.7	805.0	1,192.1
Employees	2.4%	8,972	9,548	10,920	10,522	9,849

BENEFICIAL MUTUAL BANCORP, INC.　　　NASDAQ (GS): BNCL

510 Walnut St., 19th Fl.	CEO: Gerard P. Cuddy
Philadelphia, PA 19106	CFO: Thomas D. Cestare
Phone: 215-864-6000	HR: —
Fax: 215-864-6177	FYE: December 31
Web: www.thebeneficial.com	Type: Public

You would expect something beneficial from the city of brotherly love. Beneficial Mutual Bancorp is the holding company for Beneficial Bank, which serves the greater Philadelphia area and southern New Jersey through about 70 branches. Founded in 1853 as Beneficial Mutual Savings Bank, the bank provides traditional deposit products such as checking, savings, and money market accounts; IRAs; and CDs. Commercial real estate loans account for approximately a third of the company's loan portfolio; residential mortgages are more than 20%. Home equity, business, and consumer loans help round out its lending activities.

	Annual Growth	12/05	12/06	12/07	12/08	12/09
Assets ($ mil.)	18.2%	2,392.4	2,300.2	3,557.8	4,002.1	4,673.7
Net income ($ mil.)	6.7%	13.2	11.6	(1.5)	16.5	17.1
Market value ($ mil.)	0.6%	—	—	795.6	920.9	805.4
Employees	13.7%	577	577	912	970	965

BENCO DENTAL SUPPLY COMPANY

295 CenterPoint Blvd.	CEO: Charles Cohen
Pittston, PA 18640	CFO: —
Phone: 570-825-7781	HR: George Rable
Fax: 570-825-7642	FYE: December 31
Web: www.benco.com	Type: Private

Benco Dental Supply is a one-stop shop for the tooth doc. Benco distributes dental and dentistry supplies through more than 40 regional showrooms in some 35 states for about 25,000 customers. Its BencoNET division develops and distributes custom computers and proprietary programming and networking systems specially for dentists. Other services include dental office design, business practice consulting, and inventory management, as well the Painless online ordering systems. Established in 1930, the company has a 300-strong sales force and distribution centers in Florida, Indiana, Pennsylvania, and Texas. The company is controlled by the founding Cohen family; its name is derived from originator Benjamin Cohen.

	Annual Growth	12/04	12/05	12/06	12/07	12/08
Est. sales ($ mil.)	—	—	—	—	—	389.2
Employees	—	—	—	—	—	1,120

BENEFIT COSMETICS LLC

685 Market St., 7th Fl.	CEO: Jean-André Rougeot
San Francisco, CA 94105	CFO: —
Phone: 415-781-8153	HR: —
Fax: 415-781-3930	FYE: December 31
Web: www.benefitcosmetics.com	Type: Subsidiary

Give them the benefit of the doubt. BeneFit Cosmetics will make you look lovely, and it's for a good cause. The company's products have a madcap glamour-girl sensibility, with clever names and pin-up lasses on nearly every package. BeneFit sells its lines and offers facial services through more than 2,000 counters (called "Beauty Bars") in department stores and beauty specialty shops worldwide. It also has about a dozen dedicated boutiques. BeneFit Cosmetics, whose celebrity-endorsed Benetint product brought the fledgling company into the mainstream, was founded in 1976 in San Francisco by sisters Jean Ann and Jane Ann Ford as The Face Place. Glamour leviathan LVMH holds a 70% stake.

BENIHANA INC.

NASDAQ (GS): BNHN

8685 NW 53rd Terrace
Miami, FL 33166
Phone: 305-593-0770
Fax: 305-592-6371
Web: www.benihana.com

CEO: Richard C. (Rich) Stockinger
CFO: Gene R. Baldwin
HR: Laurie Casey
FYE: March 31
Type: Public

The main course at Benihana comes with an appetizer of culinary entertainment. The company's flagship chain of teppanyaki-style Asian restaurants offers a dining experience that is part theater as wisecracking, fast-chopping chefs prepare the meals on a grill that is part of the table. Benihana owns and operates more than 60 Benihana and Benihana Grill locations in more than 20 states, and it has more than 20 franchised restaurants in a dozen other countries. In addition, the company operates more than 30 other restaurants doing business under the names Haru and RA Sushi. Benihana of Tokyo, a company controlled by the family of founder Rocky Aoki, owns nearly 30% of Benihana.

	Annual Growth	3/05	3/06	3/07	3/08	3/09
Sales ($ mil.)	8.8%	218.3	245.6	272.6	296.9	305.6
Net income ($ mil.)	—	7.8	14.6	14.5	12.8	(5.1)
Market value ($ mil.)	(28.9%)	152.0	314.4	290.0	172.9	38.9
Employees	10.5%	4,226	4,600	5,000	5,700	—

BENJAMIN MOORE & CO.

101 Paragon Dr.
Montvale, NJ 07645
Phone: 201-573-9600
Fax: 201-573-0046
Web: www.benjaminmoore.com

CEO: Denis S. Abrams
CFO: —
HR: Liz Edwards
FYE: December 31
Type: Subsidiary

Not only can you paint the town red with Benjamin Moore paints, you can stain and finish it as well. In addition to ready-mixed colors — sold under such brands as Benjamin Moore Paints, Moorcraft, and Benwood — the company can match almost any shade with roughly 3,300 colors. Benjamin Moore also makes industrial coatings and coatings for manufacturers of furniture and roof decking. The company sells its paints through a dealer network of about 4,000 independent paint and decorating stores, most of which are in North America. Benjamin Moore became a subsidiary of Warren Buffett's Berkshire Hathaway in 2000.

BENNINGTON COLLEGE

1 College Dr.
Bennington, VT 05201
Phone: 802-442-5401
Fax: 802-440-4350
Web: www.bennington.edu

CEO: Elizabeth Coleman
CFO: William Morgan
HR: Heather Faley
FYE: June 30
Type: School

Bennington College offers bachelor's and master's degrees in areas such as the humanities, social sciences, mathematics, and visual and performing arts. The liberal arts college enrolls some 725 students, about 20% of which are graduate students. It has a student-faculty ratio of 8 to 1. Tuition and fees for undergraduates is more than $41,000 per year. Bennington College was founded in 1932.

	Annual Growth	6/04	6/05	6/06	6/07	6/08
Est. sales ($ mil.)	—	—	—	—	—	44.6
Employees	—	—	—	—	—	265

BENTELER AUTOMOTIVE CORPORATION

1780 Pond Run
Auburn Hills, MI 48326
Phone: 248-377-9999
Fax: 248-364-7102
Web: www.benteler.de/english/automotive

CEO: Pat D'Eramo
CFO: Ulf M. Kranz
HR: Ulrike Hildebrand
FYE: December 31
Type: Subsidiary

Benteler Automotive is the US automotive parts manufacturing outpost of Germany's Benteler Group. Benteler Automotive, the major revenue generating segment the Benteler Group, manufactures auto parts, including chassis components (such as crossmembers and suspension modules), structural safety components (bumper and door beams, pillar reinforcements, roof and side rails), exhaust manifolds and complete exhaust systems, and fuel components. The company also offers engineering services. The Benteler Group's global automotive operations include about 70 locations in 22 countries. Benteler Automotive got its start in 1935 after its first order of exhaust pipes for the Ford Eifel.

	Annual Growth	12/04	12/05	12/06	12/07	12/08
Est. sales ($ mil.)	—	—	—	—	—	233.1
Employees	—	—	—	—	—	2,500

BENTLEY MOTORS, INC.

3 Copley Place, Ste. 3701
Boston, MA 02116
Phone: 617-488-8500
Fax: 617-488-8550
Web: www.bentleymotors.com

CEO: Christophe Georges
CFO: —
HR: —
FYE: December 31
Type: Subsidiary

What do entertainers and blue-blooded aristocrats have in common? They both have a passion for expensive luxury automobiles. And cars don't get much more extravagant than Bentley. Bentley Motors, Inc. is the US marketing and sales division of Volkswagen's Bentley Motors Limited subsidiary. The extremely expensive and luxurious Bentley models include the Arnage, Continental GT, and Continental Flying Spur, as well as the Mulsanne, the company's new flagship sedan, which debuts in the fall of 2010 (starting price is $285,000). The company prides itself on craftsmanship and the fact that it takes some 150 hours to hand-build a single Continental GT and 400 for the Arnage. Bentley was founded in 1919.

BENTLEY SYSTEMS, INCORPORATED

685 Stockton Dr.
Exton, PA 19341
Phone: 610-458-5000
Fax: —
Web: www.bentley.com

CEO: Gregory S. (Greg) Bentley
CFO: David Hollister
HR: David G. Nation
FYE: December 31
Type: Private

Bentley Systems moves ideas from inception to groundbreaking to ribbon cutting. Engineers use the company's computer-aided design software to design and build such large-scale projects as airports, transit and utilities systems, manufacturing plants, and buildings. Available on both a perpetual license and subscription basis, Bentley's software lets architects, engineers, builders, and property owners collaborate over the Web to develop and maintain their projects. The company also provides content management applications, as well as consulting, systems integration, and training services. Key industries for the company include the architecture, engineering, and construction fields.

	Annual Growth	12/04	12/05	12/06	12/07	12/08
Est. sales ($ mil.)	—	—	—	—	—	450.4
Employees	—	—	—	—	—	2,774

An in-depth profile of this company is available to Hoover's Online members at hoovers.com.

239

BEREA COLLEGE

101 Chestnut St.
Berea, KY 40404
Phone: 859-985-3000
Fax: —
Web: www.berea.edu

CEO: Larry D. Shinn
CFO: Jeff Amburgey
HR: Gail W. Wolford
FYE: June 30
Type: School

Founded in 1855 by abolitionist John G. Fee, Berea College was the first inter-racial and coeducational school in the South. The Christian school provides a private, tuition-free, liberal arts education to about 1,500 students each year, most of whom come from Kentucky and the Appalachian region. In lieu of tuition, Berea has a work program that requires its students to work in on-campus jobs for at least 10 hours each week in their choice of some 130 different departments. Berea offers about 30 majors leading to bachelor of arts and bachelor of science degrees, and each student is required to attend seven convocations (guest lectures, concerts, or other cultural events) each term.

	Annual Growth	6/04	6/05	6/06	6/07	6/08
Est. sales ($ mil.)	—	—	—	—	—	72.6
Employees	—	—	—	—	—	550

BERETTA USA, CORP.

17601 Beretta Dr.
Accokeek, MD 20607
Phone: 301-283-2191
Fax: 301-283-0435
Web: www.berettausa.com

CEO: Ugo Gussalli Beretta
CFO: Steve Biondi
HR: Paola Bonifonti
FYE: December 31
Type: Subsidiary

Beretta USA is right on target. It's the North American manufacturing and marketing arm of the oldest gunsmith company in the world. Its products include handguns, rifles, and shotguns, as well as knives, accessories, and sporting apparel. Beretta USA sells to law enforcement agencies through exclusive distributors and peddles its products at its high-end galleries in Dallas and New York City. The gun maker also provides weapons to the US military. The manufacturer also offers hand-finished firearms, specialty books, gift items, and custom-made hunting apparel. Berretta USA, established in 1977, showcases its guns in a TV show broadcast on cable channel Versus called *The World of Beretta*.

	Annual Growth	12/04	12/05	12/06	12/07	12/08
Est. sales ($ mil.)	—	—	—	—	—	72.7
Employees	—	—	—	—	—	325

BERGDORF GOODMAN, INC.

754 5th Ave.
New York, NY 10019
Phone: 212-753-7300
Fax: 212-872-8677
Web: www.bergdorfgoodman.com

CEO: James J. (Jim) Gold
CFO: David Percha
HR: John Marazio
FYE: July 31
Type: Subsidiary

Ladies who lunch love to shop at Bergdorf Goodman, a Fifth Avenue purveyor of luxury women's apparel, handbags, jewelry, makeup, perfume, shoes, and tableware, as well as men's accessories, by designer labels such as Chloe, Giorgio Armani, and Marc Jacobs. Owned by the upscale department store operator Neiman Marcus, Bergdorf Goodman operates two stores across from each other on 58th Street in Manhattan, that ring up about 12% of Neiman's total revenue. The smaller store is devoted exclusively to men. The elite retailer also operates a catalog and a Web site. The deep recession in the US and consequent downturn in demand for luxury goods has hurt sales at both Bergdorf Goodman and its parent, Neiman Marcus.

BERKLEE COLLEGE OF MUSIC

1140 Boylston St.
Boston, MA 02215
Phone: 617-266-1400
Fax: 617-747-2047
Web: www.berklee.edu

CEO: Roger H. Brown
CFO: David R. Hornfischer
HR: Myra Hindus
FYE: May 31
Type: School

If you get accepted to this school, you've no doubt hit a high note in your musical career. Berklee College of Music, the largest independent music college in the world, offers bachelor's degrees in a dozen majors including film scoring, jazz composition, music education, music production and engineering, performance, and songwriting. Located in Boston, the school has some 4,000 students and 522 faculty members. Notable alumni include Branford Marsalis, Quincy Jones, Melissa Etheridge, and Steely Dan vocalist Donald Fagen. Pianist Lawrence Berk founded the college in 1945. The school was named after his son, Lee Berk, who served as Berklee president from 1979 to 2004.

	Annual Growth	5/04	5/05	5/06	5/07	5/08
Est. sales ($ mil.)	—	—	—	—	—	127.7
Employees	—	—	—	—	—	600

BERKLINE BENCHCRAFT HOLDINGS, LLC

1 Berkline Dr.
Morristown, TN 37813
Phone: 423-585-1500
Fax: 423-585-4420
Web: www.berkline.com

CEO: Robert (Rob) Burch
CFO: Ben Wart
HR: Glendora Coleman
FYE: December 31
Type: Private

Berkline BenchCraft Holdings would be tickled for you to kick back, slip off your tired loafers, and recline in one of its upholstered chairs. The company makes and markets mid-priced upholstered furniture for home use under the Berkline, BenchCraft, and Natural Elements brands. Berkline makes specialty motion upholstery and reclining chairs, while BenchCraft primarily crafts stationary fabric and leather pieces. The company also makes island-styled furnishings under the Natural Elements label. With operations in Tennessee, Mississippi, and Montreal, the company sells through independent, regional, and national furniture retailers. It is majority owned by Sun Capital Partners.

BERKSHIRE BANCORP INC.

NASDAQ (GM): BERK

160 Broadway
New York, NY 10038
Phone: 212-791-5362
Fax: 212-791-5367
Web: www.berkbank.com

CEO: Steven Rosenberg
CFO: Steven Rosenberg
HR: —
FYE: December 31
Type: Public

This company may not win a Tony Award, but it is on Broadway. Headquartered on this famous Manhattan street, Berkshire Bancorp is the holding company for The Berkshire Bank, which operates about a dozen branches mostly in New York, but also in New Jersey. The bank's products and services include individual and business checking and savings accounts, money market accounts, and CDs. Lending activities consist mostly of non-residential mortgages (about half of the company's total loan portfolio) and one- to four-family real estate loans (more than 30%). Through subsidiaries, the bank offers title insurance and property investment services.

	Annual Growth	12/04	12/05	12/06	12/07	*12/08
Assets ($ mil.)	(0.8%)	972.6	977.5	948.7	1,120.5	943.7
Net income ($ mil.)	—	7.5	5.5	4.9	5.4	(79.9)
Market value ($ mil.)	(30.8%)	144.6	120.3	116.7	112.9	33.2
Employees	3.8%	100	107	106	106	116

*Most recent year available

BERKSHIRE HATHAWAY INC.

NYSE: BRK

3555 Farnam St., Ste. 1440	CEO: Warren E. Buffett
Omaha, NE 68131	CFO: Marc D. Hamburg
Phone: 402-346-1400	HR: —
Fax: 402-346-3375	FYE: December 31
Web: www.berkshirehathaway.com	Type: Public

Berkshire Hathaway is where Warren Buffett, the world's third-richest man (behind Mexican billionaire Carlos Slim and good buddy Bill Gates), spreads his risk by investing in a variety of industries, from insurance and utilities to apparel and food, and building materials to jewelry and furniture retailers. Its core insurance subsidiaries include National Indemnity, GEICO Corporation, and reinsurance giant General Re. The company's other largest holdings include Marmon Holdings, McLane Company, MidAmerican Energy Holdings, and Shaw Industries. Known as the Oracle of Omaha, Buffett holds about a quarter of Berkshire Hathaway, which owns more than 70 firms and has stakes in more than a dozen others.

	Annual Growth	12/05	12/06	12/07	12/08	12/09
Sales ($ mil.)	8.3%	81,663.0	98,539.0	118,245.0	107,786.0	112,493.0
Net income ($ mil.)	(1.4%)	8,528.0	11,015.0	13,213.0	4,994.0	8,055.0
Market value ($ mil.)	2.9%	145,397.5	180,458.9	232,321.0	158,490.2	162,756.0
Employees	7.6%	192,000	217,000	233,000	246,000	257,000

BERKSHIRE HILLS BANCORP, INC.

NASDAQ (GS): BHLB

24 North St.	CEO: Michael P. Daly
Pittsfield, MA 01201	CFO: Kevin P. Riley
Phone: 413-443-5601	HR: Linda A. Johnston
Fax: 413-443-3587	FYE: December 31
Web: www.berkshirebank.com	Type: Public

Berkshire Hills Bancorp is the holding company for Berkshire Bank, which serves individuals and small businesses through about 40 branches in western Massachusetts, eastern New York, and southern Vermont. Established in 1846, the bank provides an array of deposit products such as savings, checking, and money market accounts; CDs; and IRAs. It also offers credit cards, insurance, investments, private banking, and wealth management services. Berkshire Hills Bancorp also owns Berkshire Bank Municipal Bank, which collects deposits from municipalities and other government entities in New York.

	Annual Growth	12/05	12/06	12/07	12/08	12/09
Assets ($ mil.)	7.3%	2,035.6	2,149.6	2,513.4	2,666.7	2,700.4
Net income ($ mil.)	—	8.2	11.3	13.5	22.2	(16.1)
Market value ($ mil.)	(11.4%)	470.1	469.5	364.8	433.0	290.2
Employees	11.7%	399	522	560	610	622

BERKSHIRE INCOME REALTY, INC.

NYSE Amex: BIR

1 Beacon St., Ste. 1500	CEO: David C. Quade
Boston, MA 02108	CFO: David C. Quade
Phone: 617-523-7722	HR: —
Fax: 617-646-2375	FYE: December 31
Web: www.berkshireincomerealty.com	Type: Public

If you enjoy attractive landscaping and swimming pools, but can't stand the upkeep and maintenance, Berkshire Income Realty might have just the spot for you. The real estate investment trust (REIT) invests and operates apartment communities. It owns more than 25 properties in major cities in Texas, Georgia, Florida, California, Oregon, North Carolina, and Pennsylvania, as well as the Washington, DC, metropolitan area. The company (which is controlled by chairman Donald Krupp and his family) often acquires neglected properties and then rehabilitates them. Affiliate Berkshire Property Advisors provides day-to-day management and business operations services to the company.

	Annual Growth	12/05	12/06	12/07	12/08	12/09
Sales ($ mil.)	—	—	—	—	—	79.5
Net income ($ mil.)	—	—	—	—	—	2.9
Employees	—	—	—	—	—	4

BERLIN CAMERON UNITED

100 Avenue of the Americas	CEO: Ewen Cameron
New York, NY 10013	CFO: Kerry Ernst
Phone: 212-824-2000	HR: —
Fax: 212-268-8454	FYE: December 31
Web: www.bc-p.com	Type: Subsidiary

You might say this company is united behind the idea of making great ads. Berlin Cameron is a leading creative advertising agency in the US, offering ad development services for television, print, and interactive media, as well as services for campaign planning and management. The firm has worked for such clients as Nextel, Pfizer, and *The Wall Street Journal*. Founded in 1997, Berlin Cameron is the flagship agency of The United Network, one of the advertising networks of UK-based marketing services conglomerate WPP Group. Other units and agencies within the micro-network include Cole & Weber (based in Seattle), BTS (Oslo, Norway), and 1861 (Milan, Italy).

BERLITZ LANGUAGES, INC.

400 Alexander Park	CEO: Yukako Uchinaga
Princeton, NJ 08540	CFO: —
Phone: 609-514-3400	HR: —
Fax: 609-514-3405	FYE: March 31
Web: www.berlitz.com	Type: Subsidiary

Do you speak Dansk, Deutsch, Español, Magyar, or Português? If not, Berlitz can teach you. Berlitz International owns or franchises some 470 language centers in 70 nations around the world. Founded to teach languages through a conversational approach to pleasure travelers, the company has broadened its scope to include services for professional and corporate clients. In addition to its small-group and one-on-one language courses, the company offers cultural-awareness training as well as study-abroad and online programs for all ages. Its Berlitz-branded books and audio products are published by Langenscheidt. Berlitz was founded in 1878 and acquired by Japanese education group Benesse Corporation in 2001.

BERNARD CHAUS, INC.

OTC: CHBD

530 7th Ave.	CEO: Josephine Chaus
New York, NY 10018	CFO: David Stiffman
Phone: 212-354-1280	HR: —
Fax: 201-863-6307	FYE: June 30
Web: www.bernardchaus.com	Type: Public

Bernard Chaus' clothes are made for the days when a woman "has nothing to wear." The firm designs and sells upscale women's career and casual sportswear, primarily under the Josephine Chaus, Chaus, and Cynthia Steffe trademarks. Its jackets, skirts, pants, blouses, sweaters, dresses, and accessories are coordinated by style, color, and fabric. Bernard Chaus' clothing is sold in about 4,000 US department and specialty stores and is manufactured mostly in Asia. The company also manufactures private-label apparel and holds an exclusive license to make and sell the Kenneth Cole New York clothing lines. Chairwoman and CEO Josephine Chaus, widow of founder Bernard Chaus, owns about 45% of the company.

	Annual Growth	6/05	6/06	6/07	6/08	6/09
Sales ($ mil.)	(6.0%)	143.3	136.8	146.8	118.0	112.1
Net income ($ mil.)	—	(1.2)	(4.9)	0.5	(7.7)	(9.6)
Market value ($ mil.)	(39.2%)	39.7	34.5	29.6	11.2	5.4
Employees	(18.9%)	286	223	228	189	124

An in-depth profile of this company is available to Hoover's Online members at hoovers.com.

241

THE BERRY COMPANY LLC

3170 Kettering Blvd.
Dayton, OH 45439
Phone: 937-296-2121
Fax: 937-296-2011
Web: www.theberrycompany.com

CEO: Scott A. Pomeroy
CFO: Richard Jenkins
HR: Richard L. (Rick) Shaum Jr.
FYE: December 31
Type: Subsidiary

This company is juiced up about the Yellow Pages. The Berry Company is a leading provider of Yellow Pages publishing and advertising services. It publishes nearly 900 print directories for telephone companies, generally in small and medium-sized markets. It also provides local search solutions, including websites and search engine marketing and optimization services. Through a deal with AT&T, The Berry Company is an authorized reseller of YellowPages.com online advertising (YellowPages.com is a subsidiary of AT&T). A subsidiary of Local Insight Regatta Holdings, the company expanded in 2009 when Local Insight Regatta merged its Local Insight Yellow Pages subsidiary with The Berry Company.

BERRY PETROLEUM COMPANY

NYSE: BRY

1999 Broadway, Ste. 3700
Denver, CO 80202
Phone: 303-999-4400
Fax: —
Web: www.bry.com

CEO: Robert F. Heinemann
CFO: David D. Wolf
HR: Walter B. Ayers
FYE: December 31
Type: Public

It may be small fruit in the giant petroleum industry, but Berry Petroleum delivers the juice. The company buys properties with heavy crude oil reserves for exploitation and sale to refining companies. Berry Petroleum's core properties are in California (Kern, Los Angeles, and Ventura counties), Colorado, and Utah. In 2009 it reported proved reserves of 235.3 million barrels of oil equivalent. The company squeezes the most from its Californian heavy oil assets by using thermal recovery: Steam is injected into heavy crude oil reserves to reduce oil viscosity and allow it to flow to the surface. Berry Petroleum also owns three gas-fired cogeneration facilities.

	Annual Growth	12/05	12/06	12/07	12/08	12/09
Sales ($ mil.)	9.0%	406.7	486.3	583.5	801.5	574.7
Net income ($ mil.)	(16.7%)	112.4	107.9	129.9	133.5	54.0
Market value ($ mil.)	0.5%	1,513.8	1,641.4	2,352.7	400.1	1,542.9
Employees	3.8%	209	243	263	303	243

BERRY PLASTICS CORPORATION

101 Oakley St.
Evansville, IN 47710
Phone: 812-424-2904
Fax: 812-424-0128
Web: www.berryplastics.com

CEO: Ira G. Boots
CFO: James M. (Jim) Kratochvil
HR: —
FYE: September 30
Type: Private

Berry Plastics makes bunches and bunches of plastic products. The company is a leading maker of injection-molded plastic products. Its lineup includes drink cups, bottles, closures, tubes and prescription containers, stretch films, plastic sheeting, tapes, and housewares. Customers include the health care, personal care, food and beverage, agricultural, industrial, construction, aerospace, and automotive industries. The company operates more than 60 manufacturing facilities and has extensive distribution capabilities. Apollo Management and Graham Partners acquired Berry Plastics in 2006; Apollo owns approximately 75% of the company.

	Annual Growth	12/04	12/05	12/06	*9/07	9/08
Sales ($ mil.)	44.1%	814.2	1,169.7	1,431.8	3,055.0	3,513.1
Net income ($ mil.)	—	22.9	19.8	(75.2)	(116.2)	(101.1)
Employees	32.0%	4,550	6,800	6,600	12,700	13,800

*Fiscal year change

BERTUCCI'S CORPORATION

155 Otis St.
Northborough, MA 01532
Phone: 508-351-2500
Fax: 508-393-8046
Web: www.bertuccis.com

CEO: David G. Lloyd
CFO: Brian P. Connell
HR: Bryan Schwanke
FYE: December 31
Type: Private

New Englanders in need of a taste of Italy can turn to Bertucci's. The company owns and operates more than 90 casual-dining establishments operating under the Bertucci's Italian Restaurant banner. The restaurants, located in about 10 states primarily in the Northeast, feature a wide array of Tuscan-style dishes, including pasta, chicken, and seafood dishes, as well as appetizers and desserts. Bertucci's also offers a variety of premium brick oven pizzas available with a number of different topping combinations. Chairman Benjamin Jacobson controls the company through his Jacobson Partners holding company. The first Bertucci's opened in 1981.

BERWIND CORPORATION

3000 Centre Sq. West, 1500 Market St.
Philadelphia, PA 19102
Phone: 215-563-2800
Fax: 215-575-2314
Web: www.berwind.com

CEO: Michael B. McClelland
CFO: Van Billet
HR: —
FYE: December 31
Type: Holding company

Founded in 1886 to mine Appalachian coal, Berwind began leasing its mining operations in 1962 to fund investments in new ventures. Berwind Corporation gives autonomy to the management teams of its portfolio companies while adding investment fuel to their financial fires. The company's portfolio includes Elmer's Products, maker of Elmer's Glue, Krazy Glue, and other products; specialty chemicals companies CRC and Colorcon; and promotional products firm National Pen. Berwind Property Group (or BPG Properties) owns more than 30 million sq. ft. of residential, multifamily, student, retail, hotel, and industrial properties. The Berwind family owns Berwind Corporation.

THE BESSEMER GROUP, INCORPORATED

630 5th Ave.
New York, NY 10111
Phone: 212-708-9100
Fax: 212-265-5826
Web: www.bessemer.com

CEO: John A. Hilton Jr.
CFO: John G. MacDonald
HR: Evelyn Santana-Buonsante
FYE: December 31
Type: Private

Forget the cold, hard steel and think cold, hard cash. The Bessemer Group manages more than $50 billion in assets for wealthy individuals and families with more than $10 million to invest. Main subsidiary Bessemer Trust administers portfolios with holdings in domestic and international equities and bonds, as well as such alternative assets as hedge funds, real estate, and private equity funds of funds. The group also provides trust, custody, tax and estate planning, strategic philanthropy, and financial advisory services. The group has some 15 US offices in addition to locations in London and the Cayman Islands.

	Annual Growth	12/05	12/06	12/07	12/08	12/09
Assets ($ mil.)	7.6%	1,268.7	1,091.1	1,450.7	1,793.1	1,701.0
Net income ($ mil.)	1.0%	21.5	43.6	67.0	28.2	22.4
Employees	—	—	—	—	—	—

BEST BRANDS CORP.

111 Cheshire Ln., Ste. 100	CEO: G. Scott Humphrey
Minnetonka, MN 55305	CFO: Jody Anderson
Phone: 952-404-7500	HR: —
Fax: 952-404-7501	FYE: December 31
Web: www.bestbrandscorp.com	Type: Subsidiary

Best Brands believes it can be the best in the baking industry. The company makes an oven full of fillings, frozen doughs and batters, icings, and baked goods, such as cakes, cookies, muffins, croissants, puff pastry, and baking ingredients. It owns Multifoods Bakery Products, which produces muffins and baking mixes, and Telco Food Products, a maker of retail-ready brownies and bundt and loaf cakes. It has customers in the food retail, foodservice, and wholesale food and baking industries across North America and has seven production plants and three distribution sites. The company was acquired by Dutch baking-ingredient giant CSM in early 2010.

BESTWAY, INC.

Pink Sheets: BSWY

12400 Coit Rd., Ste. 950	CEO: David A. Kraemer
Dallas, TX 75251	CFO: Beth A. Durrett
Phone: 214-630-6655	HR: —
Fax: 214-630-8404	FYE: July 31
Web: www.bestwayrto.com	Type: Public

Where there's a will for a big-screen TV or a posh new sofa, rent-to-own chain Bestway finds a way for customers who are unable to pay cash or get credit. Bestway operates about 75 stores in seven Southern states. The stores offer weekly and monthly rates on brand-name furniture, electronics, appliances, computers, and accessories. Customers may return products and cancel rental agreements at any time or renew at the end of each rental period. Lease agreements also include purchase options. In 2006 the company acquired seven rent-to-own stores from Rent World. Director James O'Donnell and business partner Mark Masur own more than 50% of Bestway.

BEST BUY CO., INC.

NYSE: BBY

7601 Penn Ave. South	CEO: Brian J. Dunn
Richfield, MN 55423	CFO: James L. (Jim) Muehlbauer
Phone: 612-291-1000	HR: Carol A. Surface
Fax: 612-292-4001	FYE: February 28
Web: www.bestbuyinc.com	Type: Public

The biggest consumer electronics outlet in the US is also the best — Best Buy, that is. The company operates more than 1,400 stores throughout the US and Canada, and another 2,600 stores in Europe, China, and now Turkey, mostly under the Best Buy, Best Buy Mobile, and The Car Phone Warehouse banners. The stores sell a wide variety of electronic gadgets, movies, music, computers, and appliances. In addition to selling products, Best Buy offers installation and maintenance services, technical support, and subscriptions for cell phone and Internet services. As the dominant consumer electronics chain in the US, following the demise of rival Circuit City, Best Buy is looking abroad for growth.

	Annual Growth	2/06	2/07	2/08	2/09	2/10
Sales ($ mil.)	12.7%	30,848.0	35,934.0	40,023.0	45,015.0	49,694.0
Net income ($ mil.)	3.7%	1,140.0	1,377.0	1,407.0	1,003.0	1,317.0
Market value ($ mil.)	(9.3%)	22,723.5	19,609.9	18,145.9	12,159.2	15,399.3
Employees	8.9%	128,000	140,000	150,000	155,000	180,000

BEST WESTERN INTERNATIONAL, INC.

6201 N. 24th Pkwy.	CEO: David T. Kong
Phoenix, AZ 85016	CFO: Mark Straszynski
Phone: 602-957-4200	HR: Barbara Bras
Fax: 602-957-5641	FYE: November 30
Web: www.bestwestern.com	Type: Association

Western hospitality has really spread. Begun in 1946 by hotelier M. K. Guertin and named for its California origins, Best Western has more than 4,000 independently owned and operated hotels (including 2,200-plus in the US, Canada, and the Caribbean), making it the world's largest hotel brand (by number of rooms). Hotels sport its flag in about 80 countries and territories; Australia and the UK have the most outside the US. The company has about 100 Best Western Premier branded hotels in Asia and Europe, which offer a higher level of amenities and services. Best Western is organized as a not-for-profit membership association, with most of its sales coming from monthly fees and annual dues.

BETAWAVE CORPORATION

OTC: GOFH

706 Mission St., 10th Fl.	CEO: Tabreez Verjee
San Francisco, CA 94103	CFO: Lennox L. Vernon
Phone: 415-738-8706	HR: —
Fax: —	FYE: December 31
Web: www.betawave.com	Type: Public

If you decide to "Go Fish" on this company's website, there's no telling what you might find. Betawave Corporation operates The GoFish Network, a group of websites aimed at six-to-17 year-olds. The company earns money through advertising. Betawave was founded in 2003 by former CEO Michael Downing and Pierce Ledbetter, CEO of LEDIC Management Group; the firm evolved from a music sharing program called Musicbank that Downing and Ledbetter created in 2001. After receiving funding from Global Asset Capital, the company went public through a reverse merger with GoFish Technologies in 2006. It terminated plans to acquire the youth-oriented website Bolt for $30 million in 2007.

	Annual Growth	12/05	12/06	12/07	12/08	12/09
Sales ($ mil.)	—	—	0.0	2.1	7.7	7.7
Net income ($ mil.)	—	—	(5.3)	(16.4)	(17.0)	(15.5)
Market value ($ mil.)	(67.1%)	—	114.6	6.9	6.4	4.1
Employees	11.1%	—	27	34	46	37

COUNCIL OF BETTER BUSINESS BUREAUS, INC.

4200 Wilson Blvd., Ste. 800	CEO: Stephen A. (Steve) Cox
Arlington, VA 22203	CFO: Joseph E. Dillion
Phone: 703-276-0100	HR: Anaise Schroeder
Fax: 703-525-8277	FYE: December 31
Web: www.bbb.org	Type: Not-for-profit

The Council of Better Business Bureaus (BBB) helps North American consumers and businesses know who's on the up-and-up. The not-for-profit organization comprises independent BBBs and branches in about 125 locations throughout North America, as well as some 240 national companies that have shown a commitment to business ethics. More than 300,000 companies that have demonstrated a similar commitment belong to local BBBs. The companies can promote their adherence to BBB standards; in return, they are subject to "reliability reports" that consist of any complaints clients or partners have had about them. BBBs work to resolve disputes between consumers and businesses and review companies' advertising.

	Annual Growth	12/04	12/05	12/06	12/07	12/08
Est. sales ($ mil.)	—	—	—	—	—	17.8
Employees	—	—	—	—	—	119

An in-depth profile of this company is available to Hoover's Online members at hoovers.com.

243

THE BETTY FORD CENTER

39000 Bob Hope Dr.
Rancho Mirage, CA 92270
Phone: 760-773-4100
Fax: 760-773-4141
Web: www.bettyfordcenter.org

CEO: John T. Schwarzlose
CFO: Jim Onorato
HR: Charlene Montgomery
FYE: June 30
Type: Not-for-profit

The health care center with a lengthy list of euphemisms for its name, The Betty Ford Center provides a variety of drug and alcohol rehabilitation services for all members of a family system affected by addiction. Services include a children's program, outpatient and inpatient support, a 90-day treatment program, a clinical diagnostic evaluation, and a program for licensed professionals. The not-for-profit organization also offers professional education programs for helping professionals. Its primary facility is in California on the grounds of the Eisenhower Medical Center; the children's center is in Texas. Betty Ford, the wife of the late President Gerald Ford, started the center in 1982.

BEVERAGE-AIR CORPORATION

700 Buffington Rd.
Spartanburg, SC 29303
Phone: 864-582-8111
Fax: 864-582-5083
Web: www.beverage-air.com

CEO: Philippo Berti
CFO: —
HR: Kathleen Nawrocki
FYE: December 31
Type: Subsidiary

If you like a cold beer or a hot pizza, raise your mug to Beverage-Air. The company manufactures commercial foodservice and beverage equipment under such brands as Breeze and Maxi Marketeer. The company makes refrigerated display cases, coolers, freezers, beer dispensing equipment, and pizza and food preparation units. Beverage-Air operates plants in South Carolina and Pennsylvania. It sells its products around the world, with sales offices throughout the US, in Asia, Central and South America, and in the Middle East. Founded in 1944, the company was acquired by Italy's Ali in 2008. The deal joined Beverage-Air with more than 65 other brands under the global food service company.

BEVERAGE DISTRIBUTORS COMPANY, LLC

14200 E. Moncrieff Place, Ste. E
Aurora, CO 80011
Phone: 303-371-3421
Fax: 303-371-3975

CEO: Robert (Bob) Catalani
CFO: Justin Voights
HR: Linda Hollman
FYE: March 31
Type: Subsidiary

Beverage Distributors Company delivers relief from dry throats. The company is a wholesale supplier of wine, beer, and spirits through its Summit Beverage and Pinnacle Distributing selling divisions. In addition to alcoholic refreshments, Beverage Distributors also supplies soda, water, mixes, and juices. It carries libations from producers that include Pyramid Breweries, Mondavi, Diageo North America, Vincor, and Anheuser-Busch InBev. Beverage Distributors operates throughout Colorado. In 2000 it became part of a 50-50 joint venture between the founding Obernauer family and the Charmer Sunbelt Group.

	Annual Growth	3/04	3/05	3/06	3/07	3/08
Est. sales ($ mil.)	—	—	—	—	—	129.9
Employees	—	—	—	—	—	400

BFC FINANCIAL CORPORATION

Pink Sheets: BFCF

2100 W. Cypress Creek Rd.
Fort Lauderdale, FL 33309
Phone: 954-940-4900
Fax: 954-940-4910
Web: www.bfcfinancial.com

CEO: Alan B. Levan
CFO: John K. Grelle
HR: —
FYE: December 31
Type: Public

Holding company BFC Financial controls Florida-based bank BankAtlantic Bancorp and investment firm Woodbridge Holdings, formerly Levitt Corporation, which has holdings in a real estate developer in Florida and other companies. (Famous for constructing Levittown, New York — widely regarded as the first planned community in the US — Levitt filed for Chapter 11 bankruptcy protection in 2007 and reemerged the following year as Woodbridge.) BFC maintains voting control in BankAtlantic Bancorp through its ownership of the company's common stock and Class B stock. BFC also owns a minority stake in Asian-themed restaurant chain Benihana.

	Annual Growth	12/05	12/06	12/07	12/08	12/09
Sales ($ mil.)	(15.4%)	1,294.9	1,105.5	966.6	502.5	662.0
Net income ($ mil.)	—	12.8	(2.2)	(32.9)	(68.0)	(96.7)
Market value ($ mil.)	(40.8%)	399.5	493.7	113.1	39.2	49.0
Employees	15.9%	2,978	3,559	1,704	1,847	5,368

BGC PARTNERS, INC.

NASDAQ (GS): BGCP

499 Park Ave.
New York, NY 10022
Phone: 212-938-5000
Fax: 212-829-4866
Web: www.bgcpartners.com

CEO: Howard W. Lutnick
CFO: Graham Sadler
HR: —
FYE: December 31
Type: Public

BGC Partners (formerly eSpeed) specializes in electronic, integrated voice, and hybrid trading, clearing, and settlement services for banks, investment firms, and brokerages. Its software and services help institutional traders make real-time transactions in US treasuries, foreign government securities, Eurobonds, corporate and municipal bonds, futures, options, and other instruments. Active in the Americas, Europe, and Asia, the company also provides information and analytics products. BGC Partners is closely allied with former parent Cantor Fitzgerald. (It's named after Cantor founder B. Gerald Cantor.) In 2008 Cantor merged its brokerage affiliates eSpeed and BGC Partners into a single entity.

	Annual Growth	12/05	12/06	12/07	12/08	12/09
Sales ($ mil.)	66.0%	152.9	164.3	159.2	1,228.9	1,162.3
Net income ($ mil.)	77.8%	2.0	4.4	(32.5)	(29.7)	20.0
Market value ($ mil.)	(12.0%)	639.7	724.4	937.6	229.0	383.3
Employees	60.5%	380	400	427	2,277	2,524

BIDZ.COM, INC.

NASDAQ (CM): BIDZ

3562 Eastham Dr.
Culver City, CA 90232
Phone: 310-280-7373
Fax: 310-280-7375
Web: www.bidz.com

CEO: David Zinberg
CFO: Lawrence Y. Kong
HR: —
FYE: December 31
Type: Public

Bidz.com combines the markdowns of a dollar store, the format of an auction house, and the convenience of the Internet to bring sparkling deals to shoppers. The company buys closeout merchandise and sells it using a live-auction format, with no reserve prices and $1 opening bids, even on items that might retail for more than $20,000. It mostly sells jewelry, including gold, platinum, and silver items set with diamonds, and other precious and semi-precious stones, but visitors will also find deals on electronics and collectibles such as art and antiques, coins, and sports cards. In 2008 the company introduced foreign language versions of its auction site and launched Buyz.com, a fixed-price e-commerce site.

	Annual Growth	12/05	12/06	12/07	12/08	12/09
Sales ($ mil.)	5.1%	90.6	131.8	187.1	207.4	110.4
Net income ($ mil.)	(1.0%)	2.6	5.4	18.1	14.4	2.5
Market value ($ mil.)	(52.8%)	—	—	195.9	100.4	43.7
Employees	0.3%	170	198	240	165	172

BIG 5 SPORTING GOODS CORPORATION

NASDAQ (GS): BGFV

2525 E. El Segundo Blvd.
El Segundo, CA 90245
Phone: 310-536-0611
Fax: 310-297-7585
Web: www.big5sportinggoods.com

CEO: Steven G. Miller
CFO: Barry D. Emerson
HR: Jeffrey L. (Jeff) Fraley
FYE: December 31
Type: Public

Big 5 Sporting Goods has outgrown its name. The company, which started out with five army surplus shops in California in 1955, is a leading sporting goods retailer with about 385 stores in a dozen mostly Western states, including California, Washington, and Arizona. The company sells brand-name (adidas, Coleman, Easton) and private-label equipment, apparel, and footwear for indoor and outdoor activities such as camping, hunting, fishing, tennis, golf, and snowboarding. Big 5 has stuck with a neighborhood-store format (averaging approximately 11,000 square feet) instead of opening massive superstores. Big 5 Sporting Goods is run by its chairman and CEO Steven Miller, the son of company co-founder Robert Miller.

	Annual Growth	12/05	12/06	12/07	12/08	12/09
Sales ($ mil.)	2.4%	814.0	876.8	898.3	864.7	895.5
Net income ($ mil.)	(5.6%)	27.5	30.8	28.1	13.9	21.8
Market value ($ mil.)	(5.9%)	476.7	531.8	314.0	113.5	374.3
Employees	3.5%	7,500	8,100	9,500	8,900	8,600

BIG BOY RESTAURANTS INTERNATIONAL, LLC

1 Big Boy Dr.
Warren, MI 48091
Phone: 586-759-6000
Fax: 586-757-4737
Web: www.bigboy.com

CEO: Keith E. Sirois
CFO: —
HR: Debra Murphy
FYE: December 31
Type: Private

This restaurant chain has been feeding boys big and small for more than 70 years. Big Boy Restaurants International operates and franchises more than 150 of its signature family-dining spots in Michigan and more than half a dozen other states. Known for their hamburgers (and the iconic Big Boy figure holding a plate-sized sandwich), the restaurants also offer a full menu of breakfast options along with such home-style dinner favorites as meat loaf, pork chops, and chicken fried steak. More than 20 locations are company-owned, while the rest are franchised. The company also has some 300 licensed Big Boy units operating in Japan. Founded by Bob Wian in 1936, the Big Boy chain is owned by chairman Robert Liggett.

	Annual Growth	12/04	12/05	12/06	12/07	12/08
Est. sales ($ mil.)	—	—	—	—	—	57.8
Employees	—	—	—	—	—	1,500

⊞ BIG LOTS, INC.

NYSE: BIG

300 Phillipi Rd.
Columbus, OH 43228
Phone: 614-278-6800
Fax: 614-278-6676
Web: www.biglots.com

CEO: Steven S. (Steve) Fishman
CFO: Joe R. Cooper
HR: Jo L. Roney
FYE: January 31
Type: Public

Big Lots believes that a product's shelf life depends solely on which shelf it's on. The company is the nation's #1 broadline closeout retailer, with some 1,360 Big Lots stores (down from a high of 1,500 in at the start of 2005) in 47 states. (More than one-third of its stores are located in California, Florida, Ohio, and Texas.) It sells a variety of brand-name products that have been overproduced, returned, discontinued, or result from liquidations, typically at 20% to 40% below discounters' prices, as well as private-label items and furniture. Its wholesale division, Big Lots Wholesale, sells its discounted merchandise to a variety of retailers, manufacturers, distributors, and other wholesalers.

	Annual Growth	1/06	1/07	1/08	1/09	1/10
Sales ($ mil.)	1.6%	4,429.9	4,743.0	4,656.3	4,645.3	4,726.8
Net income ($ mil.)	—	(10.1)	124.0	158.5	151.5	200.4
Market value ($ mil.)	20.7%	1,075.0	2,084.9	1,395.9	1,081.5	2,284.3
Employees	(5.2%)	43,985	38,738	38,153	37,000	35,600

BIG M INC.

12 Vreeland Ave.
Totowa, NJ 07512
Phone: 973-890-0021
Fax: 973-890-5994
Web: www.mandee.com

CEO: Alan Mandelbaum
CFO: Robert Edmond
HR: Michael Bush
FYE: January 31
Type: Private

Annie says savings start with Big M. The company operates about 40 Annie Sez off-price women's apparel shops, 10 Afaze accessory shops, and 120 Mandee shops (mostly in New Jersey and New York) that target young women and teens. Its stores are also located in Connecticut, Delaware, Florida, Illinois, Maryland, Michigan, and Pennsylvania. Mandee shops account for nearly two-thirds of the company's sales, with Annie Sez stores contributing about 30%. Mandee also sells through its e-commerce site and offers store credit cards. The family-owned and -operated company was founded in Brooklyn in 1948 by the Mandelbaum brothers (Leon, Max, and Bernard) and today is run by their descendants.

BIG TEN NETWORK, LLC

600 W. Chicago Ave., Ste. 875
Chicago, IL 60654
Phone: 312-665-0700
Fax: 312-665-0740
Web: www.bigtennetwork.com

CEO: Mark Silverman
CFO: —
HR: —
FYE: June 30
Type: Joint venture

Buckeyes, Wolverines, Gophers, Badgers, Nittany Lions, Illini, Hoosiers, Hawkeyes, Spartans, Wildcats, and Boilermakers all stop bickering and get along under the Big Ten Network banner. The official TV network of the Big Ten Conference produces 400 live events and about 600 hours of original programming each year. Broadcasts are primarily football and other NCAA sports along with sports news and analysis. It also airs campus activities and academic programs. A joint venture between FOX Sports Net and the Big Ten conference, Big Ten Network programs are broadcast on Comcast, DIRECTV, DISH Network, and about 230 other cable operators. It also distributes some content through AT&T and Verizon.

	Annual Growth	6/04	6/05	6/06	6/07	6/08
Est. sales ($ mil.)	—	—	—	—	—	1.4
Employees	—	—	—	—	—	25

BIG Y FOODS, INC.

2145 Roosevelt Ave.
Springfield, MA 01102
Phone: 413-784-0600
Fax: —
Web: www.bigy.com

CEO: Donald H. D'Amour
CFO: William (Bill) White
HR: Jack Henry
FYE: June 30
Type: Private

Why call it Big Y? Big Y Foods began as a 900-sq.-ft. grocery at a Y intersection in Chicopee, Massachusetts. It now operates about 55 supermarkets throughout Massachusetts and Connecticut. Most of its stores are Big Y World Class Markets, offering specialty areas such as bakeries and floral shops, as well as banking. The rest consist of Big Y Supermarkets and a single gourmet food and liquor store called Table & Vine in Springfield, Massachusetts. Some Big Y stores provide child care, dry cleaning, photo processing, and even propane sales, and their delis and food courts offer to-go foods. Big Y is owned and run by the D'Amour family and is one of New England's largest independent supermarket chains.

⊞ An in-depth profile of this company is available to Hoover's Online members at hoovers.com.

245

BIGBAND NETWORKS, INC.

NASDAQ (GM): BBND

475 Broadway St.
Redwood City, CA 94063
Phone: 650-995-5000
Fax: 650-995-0060
Web: www.bigbandnet.com

CEO: Amir Bassan-Eskenazi
CFO: Ravi Narula
HR: —
FYE: December 31
Type: Public

BigBand Networks helps communications service providers keep the broadband beat. Customers use its routing and switching systems to offer advanced video services. BigBand's hardware and software products support digital broadcast television, HDTV, video-on-demand (VOD), and interactive television. The company's systems also help customers manage service quality and insert tailored advertising based on geography and demographics. BigBand counts Comcast, Cox Communications, Time Warner Cable, and Verizon Communications among its customers. BigBand generates about 90% of its revenues in the US.

	Annual Growth	12/05	12/06	12/07	12/08	12/09
Sales ($ mil.)	9.2%	98.0	176.6	176.5	185.3	139.5
Net income ($ mil.)	—	(24.9)	8.9	(25.4)	9.8	(6.7)
Market value ($ mil.)	(18.2%)	—	—	347.6	373.3	232.6
Employees	(1.2%)	507	562	518	485	484

BIGLARI HOLDINGS INC.

NYSE: BH

36 S. Pennsylvania St., Ste. 500
Indianapolis, IN 46204
Phone: 317-633-4100
Fax: 317-633-4105
Web: www.steaknshake.com

CEO: Sardar Biglari
CFO: Duane E. Geiger
HR: —
FYE: September 30
Type: Public

Beef and ice cream is an unbeatable combination for this restaurant company. Formerly The Steak n Shake Company, Biglari Holdings is a multi-concept dining operator with two chains operating under the names Steak n Shake and WesterN SizzliN. Its flagship concept encompasses more than 480 company-owned and franchised family dining spots in more than 20 states, mostly in the Midwest and Southeast. The diners, open 24-hours a day, are popular for their Steakburger sandwiches and milkshakes, as well as breakfast items and other dishes. About 400 of the units are company-owned, while the rest are franchised. WesterN SizzliN, meanwhile, oversees more than 100 franchised steak buffet restaurants in about 20 states.

	Annual Growth	9/05	9/06	9/07	9/08	9/09
Sales ($ mil.)	0.8%	606.9	638.8	654.1	610.1	627.0
Net income ($ mil.)	(33.2%)	30.2	28.0	11.8	(23.0)	6.0
Market value ($ mil.)	(10.3%)	520.4	484.3	430.4	248.9	337.5
Employees	(1.8%)	21,500	23,000	22,000	20,000	20,000

BILCARE, INC.

300 Kimberton Rd.
Phoenixville, PA 19460
Phone: 610-935-4300
Fax: 610-935-4301
Web: www.bilcaregcs.com

CEO: Vincent Santa Maria
CFO: Jerry Decker
HR: Kathleen Roesing
FYE: December 31
Type: Subsidiary

Bilcare, Inc., formerly ProClinical Pharmaceutical Services, is in favor of pharma. The company, which also operates as Bilcare Global Clinical Services, is the American arm of parent company Bilcare Ltd. Its aim is to help pharmaceutical companies prepare for and conduct clinical trials. Bilcare's offerings include a wide range of analytical research, formulation development, manufacturing, and packaging and labeling of clinical supplies. Logistics services include the storage, distribution, reconciliation, and destruction of clinical trial supplies and investigational medicines. Its services encompass all levels of pharmaceutical drug trials.

BILL & MELINDA GATES FOUNDATION

1551 Eastlake Ave. East
Seattle, WA 98102
Phone: 206-709-3100
Fax: 206-709-3180
Web: www.gatesfoundation.org

CEO: Jeffrey S. (Jeff) Raikes
CFO: Richard C. Henriques Jr.
HR: Franci Phelan
FYE: December 31
Type: Foundation

You don't have to be one of the world's richest men or know one to make a difference with your charitable gifts — but it helps. Established by the chairman of Microsoft Corporation and his wife, the Bill & Melinda Gates Foundation works in developing countries to improve health and reduce poverty, and in the US to support education and libraries nationwide and children and families in the Pacific Northwest. With an endowment of about $33.5 billion, the foundation is the largest in the US. Investor Warren Buffett plans to give the Bill & Melinda Gates Foundation about $30 billion worth of Berkshire Hathaway stock in installments, the first of which was received in 2006.

	Annual Growth	12/04	12/05	12/06	12/07	12/08
Sales ($ mil.)	—	3,343.5	1,864.0	5,703.6	8,082.4	(5,836.2)
Net income ($ mil.)	—	—	—	—	—	(9,809.3)
Employees	34.2%	234	270	457	626	760

BILL BARRETT CORPORATION

NYSE: BBG

1099 18th St., Ste. 2300
Denver, CO 80202
Phone: 303-293-9100
Fax: 303-291-0420
Web: www.billbarrettcorp.com

CEO: Fredrick J. (Fred) Barrett
CFO: Bob Howard
HR: —
FYE: December 31
Type: Public

Bill Barrett Corp. (named after a veteran oil industry wildcatter) is hoping for a Rocky Mountain high as it digs down deep for oil and gas. The company focuses its exploration and development activities in the Wind River, Uinta, Piceance, Powder River, Big Horn, and Paradox Basins and the Montana Overthrusts. Bill Barrett holds about 1.2 million net undeveloped leasehold acres. Some 90% of the company's properties are unconventional resources, such as coal bed methane and shale gas. In 2008 the oil and gas firm had working interests in 950 drilling locations and had estimated net proved reserves of 818.3 billion cu. ft. of natural gas equivalent. It also directly operates 97% of its net production.

	Annual Growth	12/05	12/06	12/07	12/08	12/09
Sales ($ mil.)	20.0%	288.8	375.3	390.3	617.9	598.2
Net income ($ mil.)	20.5%	23.8	62.0	26.8	107.6	50.2
Market value ($ mil.)	(5.3%)	1,773.4	1,249.8	1,923.1	970.5	1,428.9
Employees	8.4%	190	216	252	274	262

BILLING SERVICES GROUP, LLC

7411 John Smith Dr., Ste. 200
San Antonio, TX 78229
Phone: 210-949-7000
Fax: 210-692-7101
Web: www.bsgclearing.com

CEO: Gregory M. (Greg) Carter
CFO: Norman M. Phipps
HR: —
FYE: December 31
Type: Subsidiary

The idea behind Billing Services Group (doing business as BSG Clearing Solutions) is simple: Leave the bills to someone else. The company provides outsourced bill processing and settlement to telecommunications companies around the world. Its technology platform tracks direct long-distance calls, as well as operator-assisted and calling-card calls, and enables authentication, invoicing, collection, and settlement. Originally a subsidiary of U.S. Long Distance, the company (then Billing Concepts) was spun off as a public company in 1996. ABRY Partners took the company private in 2003 and merged it with ACI Billing Services the next year to form parent Billing Services Group, which is domiciled in Bermuda.

	Annual Growth	12/04	12/05	12/06	12/07	12/08
Est. sales ($ mil.)	—	—	—	—	—	12.0
Employees	—	—	—	—	—	109

BI-LO, LLC

208 BI-LO Blvd.
Greenville, SC 29607
Phone: 864-213-2500
Fax: 864-234-6999
Web: www.bi-lo.com

CEO: Michael D. (Mike) Byars
CFO: Brian P. Carney
HR: Ken Peterson
FYE: December 31
Type: Private

To buy low, try BI-LO. It operates about 210 supermarkets in the Carolinas, Georgia, and Tennessee. Many of BI-LO's stores house pharmacies and some boast in-store WI-FI cafes. Brands include national names, as well as BI-LO's own brands: Southern Hearth Bakery items, Full Circle natural and organic foods, Top Care health and beauty aids, and Paws Premium pet foods. Founded in 1964 by Frank Outlaw, the chain is owned by Dallas-based investment firm Lone Star Funds, which acquired BI-LO and its sister chain Bruno's Supermarkets in 2005. Falling sales, increased competition, and reluctant lenders led BI-LO to file for Chapter 11 bankruptcy protection in 2009. It reorganized and emerged from bankruptcy in 2010.

	Annual Growth	12/04	12/05	12/06	12/07	12/08
Sales ($ mil.)	(14.1%)	—	4,263.5	4,749.5	2,620.0	2,700.0
Employees	(13.0%)	—	23,500	23,000	17,000	15,500

THE BILTMORE COMPANY

1 North Pack Sq.
Asheville, NC 28801
Phone: 828-225-1333
Fax: —
Web: www.biltmore.com

CEO: William A. V. (Bill) Cecil Jr.
CFO: Steve Watson
HR: Ann Ashley
FYE: December 31
Type: Private

The Biltmore Company doesn't need to build more. It oversees the Biltmore Estate, which includes the 250-room home (the largest privately owned in the US), as well as a hotel, a winery, restaurants and retail shops, and licensing rights for a line of home decor products. (Guests don't stay at the Biltmore House, but at the Inn on Biltmore Estate.) Some one million visitors tour the home and grounds each year. The house sits on 8,000 acres of land and encompasses four acres of floor space. It has 35 bedrooms, some 40 bathrooms, 65 fireplaces, and three kitchens. The Biltmore is family-owned by descendants of the Vanderbilts and is one of the few National Historic Landmarks that is entirely privately funded.

	Annual Growth	12/04	12/05	12/06	12/07	12/08
Est. sales ($ mil.)	—	—	—	—	—	77.6
Employees	—	—	—	—	—	380

BI-MART CORPORATION

220 S. Seneca Rd.
Eugene, OR 97402
Phone: 541-344-0681
Fax: 541-342-4241
Web: www.bimart.com

CEO: Marty W. Smith
CFO: David (Dave) Zientara
HR: Dennis Down
FYE: December 31
Type: Private

Bi-Mart wants you to join the club. The company operates a chain of about 70 general merchandise membership stores in the Pacific Northwest. Just $5 buys a lifetime membership to the deep-discount chain, which has enrolled more than 1 million members to date. Stores offer automotive departments, clothing and shoes, food and alcohol, housewares, full-service pharmacies, and photo departments, with a focus on national brands. A pioneer in membership-based retail, Bi-Mart was started in 1955 by a group of investors in Yakima, Washington. The firm was bought by CEO Marty Smith and other senior managers from Rite Aid Corporation in 1997. Today, the company is employee-owned.

	Annual Growth	12/04	12/05	12/06	12/07	12/08
Est. sales ($ mil.)	—	—	—	—	—	720.0
Employees	—	—	—	—	—	3,000

BIMBO BAKERIES USA

255 Business Center Dr.
Horsham, PA 19044
Phone: 215-672-8010
Fax: —
Web: www.bimbobakeriesusa.com

CEO: Gary J. Prince
CFO: —
HR: Maria Wong
FYE: December 31
Type: Subsidiary

No snickering about the name — Bimbo Bakeries USA (BBU) is serious about making breads, cakes, and cookies. The US subsidiary of Mexico's baking giant, Grupo Bimbo ("bimbo" is a shortened version of the Spanish word "bambino" — or "small child"), BBU operates bakeries. In addition to bread, the company also manufactures tortillas, bagels, snack cakes, muffins, and pizza crust, as well as sweet and salty snacks. It makes and distributes products under the Bimbo, Boboli, Mrs Baird's, Oroweat, Old Country, Weber, Francisco, Tia Rosa, and Marinela brands.

BIMINI CAPITAL MANAGEMENT, INC.

Pink Sheets: BMNM

3305 Flamingo Dr.
Vero Beach, FL 32963
Phone: 772-231-1400
Fax: 772-231-8896
Web: www.biminireit.com

CEO: Robert E. Cauley
CFO: G. Hunter Haas IV
HR: —
FYE: December 31
Type: Public

Bimini Capital Management (formerly Opteum) invests in residential mortgage-backed securities and related securities issued by the likes of Fannie Mae, Freddie Mac, and Ginnie Mae. The real estate investment trust (REIT) manages a portfolio worth more than $100 million, mainly consisting of mortgage-related securities backed by adjustable-rate mortgages. Bimini Capital also invests in fixed-rate mortgage-backed securities and inverse interest-only securities. The company sold its residential mortgage origination business, which consisted of about 25 offices in five states, to Prospect Mortgage in 2007. It also ceased conduit and wholesale lending.

	Annual Growth	12/05	12/06	12/07	12/08	12/09
Sales ($ mil.)	(29.5%)	41.3	21.0	(26.1)	(0.2)	10.2
Net income ($ mil.)	17.1%	24.3	(49.5)	(247.7)	(56.4)	45.7
Market value ($ mil.)	(59.6%)	914.0	767.6	25.2	3.9	24.2
Employees	(76.4%)	1,066	901	—	14	—

BINGHAM MCCUTCHEN LLP

1 Federal St.
Boston, MA 02110
Phone: 617-951-8000
Fax: 617-951-8736
Web: www.bingham.com

CEO: Jay S. Zimmerman
CFO: Richard Calcasola
HR: Lynn Carroll
FYE: December 31
Type: Partnership

Big and getting bigger, Bingham McCutchen has about 1,100 lawyers overall. Bingham has grown over the years by absorbing other law firms — more than half a dozen since 1997. It maintains about 15 offices in the US, Europe, and the Asia/Pacific region, with concentrations in California and New England. Bingham's wide range of practice areas is divided into major groups such as corporate, finance, litigation, and securities. Along with its law practices, the firm offers consulting services through subsidiaries such as Bingham Consulting Group and Bingham Strategic Advisors. Clients have included Guantanamo Bay detainees and ESPN reporter Erin Andrews. The firm was founded in 1891.

BIOANALYTICAL SYSTEMS, INC.

NASDAQ (GM): BASI

2701 Kent Ave.
West Lafayette, IN 47906
Phone: 765-463-4527
Fax: 765-497-1102
Web: www.bioanalytical.com

CEO: Anthony S. Chilton
CFO: Michael R. Cox
HR: Lina L. Reeves-Kerner
FYE: September 30
Type: Public

Analyze this! Bioanalytical Systems, Inc. (BASi) provides contract research and development services for the pharmaceutical, medical device, and biotechnology industries. In addition to providing support functions for pre-clinical research and clinical drug trials, the firm's research services include product purity tests, safety evaluations, characterization analysis of compounds, in vivo (in the body) testing to measure how drugs are metabolized in living systems, and pathological laboratory testing. BASi also sells analytical instruments and other products, including bioanalytical separation instrumentation, patient monitoring and diagnostic equipment, and miniaturized in-vivo sampling devices.

	Annual Growth	9/05	9/06	9/07	9/08	9/09
Sales ($ mil.)	(6.9%)	42.4	43.0	45.2	41.7	31.8
Net income ($ mil.)	—	(0.1)	(2.6)	0.9	(1.5)	(5.5)
Market value ($ mil.)	(34.1%)	26.7	25.9	34.2	22.6	5.0
Employees	(7.2%)	370	330	306	281	274

BIOCLINICA, INC.

NASDAQ (GM): BIOC

826 Newtown-Yardley Rd.
Newtown, PA 18940
Phone: 267-757-3000
Fax: 267-757-3010
Web: www.bioclinica.com

CEO: Mark L. Weinstein
CFO: Ted I. Kaminer
HR: Carmella Miller
FYE: December 31
Type: Public

BioClinica (formerly Bio-Imaging Technologies) helps drug developers keep track of their X-rays, MRIs, and other forms of medical imaging collected during clinical drug and medical device trials. The company provides medical imaging support services including image processing and analysis, digitizing, archival services, and database maintenance. Its proprietary software systems, including Bio/ImageBase, let clients and regulatory officials electronically review images and related data. The company's eClinical Services division provides electronic data capture for large drug developers. BioClinica serves clients primarily in the US and Europe; its European operations are based in the Netherlands.

	Annual Growth	12/05	12/06	12/07	12/08	12/09
Sales ($ mil.)	24.3%	30.5	40.5	47.9	69.1	72.7
Net income ($ mil.)	—	(2.5)	1.0	2.3	2.8	3.0
Market value ($ mil.)	7.0%	48.9	122.1	122.5	55.4	64.1
Employees	16.1%	264	283	337	474	479

BIOCRYST PHARMACEUTICALS, INC.

NASDAQ (GM): BCRX

2190 Parkway Lake Dr.
Birmingham, AL 35244
Phone: 205-444-4600
Fax: 205-444-4640
Web: www.biocryst.com

CEO: Jon P. Stonehouse
CFO: Stuart Grant
HR: Robert Stoner
FYE: December 31
Type: Public

BioCryst Pharmaceuticals is tackling the bad enzymes that spread disease. The firm creates small molecule compounds that inhibit enzymes associated with viral diseases, autoimmune conditions, and cancer. BioCryst's lead product candidate, fodosine HCl, may treat T-cell cancers, including T-cell lymphomas and leukemias, by preventing T-cells from wildly multiplying and harming the body. With funding from the Department of Health and Human Services, it is developing peramavir, a potential treatment for various strains of influenza. A third clinical-stage candidate may treat autoimmune conditions.

	Annual Growth	12/05	12/06	12/07	12/08	12/09
Sales ($ mil.)	339.5%	0.2	6.2	71.2	56.6	74.6
Net income ($ mil.)	—	(26.1)	(43.6)	(29.1)	(24.7)	(13.5)
Market value ($ mil.)	(21.2%)	737.7	509.1	272.2	60.3	284.5
Employees	11.0%	52	85	106	80	79

BIODEL INC.

NASDAQ (GM): BIOD

100 Saw Mill Rd.
Danbury, CT 06810
Phone: 203-796-5000
Fax: 203-796-5001
Web: www.biodel.com

CEO: Errol B. De Souza
CFO: Gerard J. (Gerry) Michel
HR: —
FYE: September 30
Type: Public

Biodel delves into the development of viable treatments for diabetes. The company uses its VIAdel biological technology to reformulate and administer existing peptide hormones (such as insulin) for the treatment of diabetes and its complications including hyper- and hypoglycemia, cardiovascular problems, and weight control. Its two lead product candidates are VIAject, an injectable insulin formulation designed to be rapidly absorbed into the bloodstream, and VIAtab tablets, which are administered sublingually (under the tongue). Both candidates are in clinical trials; VIAject is closest to commercialization. Biodel has three other diabetes-related candidates in its pipeline at varying stages of development.

	Annual Growth	9/05	9/06	9/07	9/08	9/09
Sales ($ mil.)	—	—	—	—	—	0.0
Net income ($ mil.)	—	—	—	—	—	(43.3)
Market value ($ mil.)	—	—	—	—	—	128.3
Employees	—	—	—	—	—	54

BIODELIVERY SCIENCES INTERNATIONAL, INC.

NASDAQ (CM): BDSI

801 Corporate Center Drive, Ste. 210
Raleigh, NC 27607
Phone: 919-582-9050
Fax: 919-582-9051
Web: www.bdsinternational.com

CEO: Mark A. Sirgo
CFO: James A. (Jim) McNulty
HR: —
FYE: December 31
Type: Public

BioDelivery Sciences International isn't inventing new drugs, but it is looking for better ways to administer them. The development-stage firm takes already approved drugs that are normally delivered intravenously and reformulates them into buccal (absorbed by the inner cheek) and oral treatments. Drugs delivered via its BEMA and Bioral systems are being studied to treat acute pain and fungal infections, respectively. BioDelivery Sciences is awaiting FDA approval of its BEMA Fentanyl candidate, which consists of a dissolving disc that delivers the cancer pain drug buccally. Swedish partner Meda AB has commercial rights to this product in the US, Canada, Europe, and Mexico.

	Annual Growth	12/05	12/06	12/07	12/08	12/09
Sales ($ mil.)	197.7%	0.8	2.8	0.2	0.3	62.8
Net income ($ mil.)	—	(10.1)	(19.9)	(25.2)	(17.2)	33.0
Market value ($ mil.)	12.2%	59.6	76.6	70.4	69.7	94.4
Employees	6.9%	13	16	22	22	17

BIOFORM MEDICAL, INC.

1875 S. Grant St., Ste. 110
San Mateo, CA 94402
Phone: 650-286-4000
Fax: 650-286-4090
Web: www.bioformmedical.com

CEO: Steven L. (Steve) Basta
CFO: Frederick Lwee
HR: —
FYE: June 30
Type: Subsidiary

While some believe that wrinkles are a sign of wisdom and experience, BioForm Medical caters to a different clientele. The company's Radiesse is an injectable dermal filler used mainly for cosmetic reasons to temporarily mask wrinkles brought on by aging or loss of fat; other uses include plumping up folds in the vocal chords of patients who have impairments due to stroke. Radiesse is sold directly to physicians in the US and Europe and through distributors elsewhere. BioForm's other injectable product, Coaptite, is used to treat abnormalities of the urinary tract in women; it is sold in the US through a partnership with distributor Boston Scientific. The company was acquired by Germany's Merz in 2010.

	Annual Growth	6/05	6/06	6/07	6/08	6/09
Sales ($ mil.)	42.3%	16.2	22.6	47.4	67.5	66.5
Net income ($ mil.)	—	(10.7)	(11.4)	(13.6)	(29.5)	(21.1)
Employees	7.3%	—	251	292	340	310

BIOFUEL ENERGY CORP.

NASDAQ (GM): BIOF

1600 Broadway, Ste. 2200
Denver, CO 80202
Phone: 303-640-6500
Fax: 303-592-8117
Web: www.bfenergy.com

CEO: Scott H. Pearce
CFO: Kelly G. Maguire
HR: —
FYE: December 31
Type: Public

BioFuel Energy has climbed aboard the ethanol bandwagon. Construction on the company's first two plants was completed in 2008 and production soon commenced. It produces 230 million gallons annually. The company is partnering with agribusiness giant Cargill, which gives it reliable corn supplies, an established logistics/transportation network, and marketing expertise. BioFuel Energy went public in 2007, using the proceeds to repay outstanding debts, as well as to fund construction of its ethanol facilities. Greenlight Capital still owns about one-third of the company.

	Annual Growth	12/05	12/06	12/07	12/08	12/09
Sales ($ mil.)	131.0%	—	—	—	179.9	415.5
Net income ($ mil.)	—	—	—	—	(40.9)	(13.6)
Market value ($ mil.)	674.3%	—	—	—	8.9	69.0
Employees	(0.7%)	—	—	—	151	150

BIOGEN IDEC INC.

NASDAQ (GS): BIIB

14 Cambridge Center
Cambridge, MA 02142
Phone: 617-679-2000
Fax: 617-679-2617
Web: www.biogenidec.com

CEO: William D. Young
CFO: Paul J. Clancy
HR: Craig E. Schneier
FYE: December 31
Type: Public

With its pipeline full of biotech drugs, Biogen Idec aims to meet the unmet needs of patients. The biotech giant is focused on developing treatments in the areas of oncology, immunology, and neurology. Its product roster includes best-selling Avonex, the most popular drug for the treatment of relapsing multiple sclerosis; Rituxan, a monoclonal antibody developed with Genentech that treats non-Hodgkin's lymphoma, rheumatoid arthritis, and multiple sclerosis; Crohn's disease drug Tysabri; and Fumaderm, a psoriasis drug marketed in Germany. Biogen Idec serves customers in more than 90 countries.

	Annual Growth	12/05	12/06	12/07	12/08	12/09
Sales ($ mil.)	15.9%	2,422.5	2,692.7	3,171.6	4,097.5	4,377.3
Net income ($ mil.)	56.7%	160.7	213.7	638.2	783.2	970.1
Market value ($ mil.)	4.3%	12,089.7	13,133.6	15,197.5	12,717.1	14,284.4
Employees	9.2%	3,340	3,750	4,300	4,700	4,750

BIOHEART, INC.

OTC: BHRT

13794 NW 4th St., Ste. 212
Sunrise, FL 33325
Phone: 954-835-1500
Fax: 954-845-9976
Web: www.bioheartinc.com

CEO: Karl E. Groth
CFO: Peggy A. Farley
HR: Catherine Sulawske-Guck
FYE: December 31
Type: Public

Broken hearts are no fun, but damaged hearts are worse, and Bioheart aims to help. The biotech company is focused on the discovery, development, and commercialization of therapies treating heart damage. Because the heart does not have cells to naturally repair itself, Bioheart is exploring the use of cells derived from the patient's own thigh muscle to improve cardiac function after a heart has been damaged by a heart attack. Its lead candidate, MyoCell, uses precursor muscle cells called myoblasts to strengthen scar tissue with living muscle tissue. The company is also developing a number of proprietary techniques and processes used to obtain and inject MyoCell.

	Annual Growth	12/05	12/06	12/07	12/08	12/09
Sales ($ mil.)	41.4%	0.1	0.1	0.3	0.2	0.4
Net income ($ mil.)	—	(7.3)	(13.2)	(18.1)	(14.2)	(3.8)
Market value ($ mil.)	(25.3%)	—	—	—	25.7	19.2
Employees	8.4%	22	27	28	28	—

BIOJECT MEDICAL TECHNOLOGIES INC.

OTC: BJCT

20245 SW 95th Ave.
Tualatin, OR 97062
Phone: 503-692-8001
Fax: 503-692-6698
Web: www.bioject.com

CEO: Ralph Makar
CFO: Christine M. Farrell
HR: —
FYE: December 31
Type: Public

Bioject Medical Technologies wants to give the medical community a shot in the arm. Its Biojector 2000 jet injection system delivers injectable medication without a needle (and thus without needle-associated risks) by using a fine, high-pressure stream that goes through the skin; the injector is powered by CO_2 disposable cartridges or tanks. The accompanying vial adapter device allows the Biojector system to be filled without a needle. The company also markets Vitajet, a spring-powered, needle-free self-injection device that has been cleared for administering injections of insulin and Merck Serono's human growth hormones. Investment firm Signet Healthcare Partners and affiliates own one-third of Bioject.

	Annual Growth	12/05	12/06	12/07	12/08	12/09
Sales ($ mil.)	(14.1%)	12.3	10.8	8.3	6.5	6.7
Net income ($ mil.)	—	(6.6)	(7.0)	(4.0)	(3.0)	(1.1)
Market value ($ mil.)	(43.7%)	22.9	16.9	9.8	1.2	2.3
Employees	(21.4%)	84	82	36	33	32

BIO-KEY INTERNATIONAL, INC.

OTC: BKYI

3349 Hwy. 138, Bldg. D, Ste. B
Wall, NJ 07719
Phone: 732-359-1100
Fax: 732-359-1101
Web: www.bio-key.com

CEO: Michael W. (Mike) DePasquale
CFO: Ceci Welch
HR: —
FYE: December 31
Type: Public

BIO-key International has its finger securely on the pulse of biometrics. The company develops biometric security software and technology designed to secure access to enterprise applications and mobile devices. Its products incorporate biometric technology to scan and analyze fingerprints in order to grant or deny user access to wireless and enterprise data. BIO-key licenses its technology to original equipment manufacturers, systems integrators, and application developers. End users of its technology include corporations, government agencies, and other organizations concerned about the theft or misuse of sensitive data.

	Annual Growth	12/05	12/06	12/07	12/08	12/09
Sales ($ mil.)	(35.9%)	14.2	15.2	10.0	12.9	2.4
Net income ($ mil.)	85.1%	0.4	(11.1)	(1.1)	0.1	4.7
Market value ($ mil.)	(23.4%)	53.6	25.6	8.5	3.7	18.4
Employees	(36.1%)	90	90	57	42	15

BIOLARGO, INC.

OTC: BLGO

2603 Main St., Ste. 1155
Irvine, CA 92614
Phone: 949-235-8062
Fax: 949-625-9819
Web: www.biolargolifetechnologies.com

CEO: Dennis Calvert
CFO: Charles K. Dargan II
HR: —
FYE: December 31
Type: Public

After morphing identities several times over the past few years, BioLargo (formerly NuWay Medical) hopes that it has found its way. The company went from car dealership and casino ownership to being a medical device maker and application service provider (ASP). It believes it has found its future in designing sanitizing chemicals for specialty packaging (such as pads, protective liners, and surgical drapes) used for shipping blood, biohazardous materials, meat and poultry, and other items requiring sanitary containment. Consultant Kenneth Code controls 56% of BioLargo.

	Annual Growth	12/05	12/06	12/07	12/08	12/09
Sales ($ mil.)	0.0%	—	—	0.1	0.0	0.1
Net income ($ mil.)	—	—	—	(5.3)	(7.1)	(15.6)
Market value ($ mil.)	(14.6%)	—	—	41.8	17.8	30.5
Employees	0.0%	—	—	3	3	3

BIOLASE TECHNOLOGY, INC.

NASDAQ (GM): BLTI

4 Cromwell
Irvine, CA 92618
Phone: 949-361-1200
Fax: 949-273-6677
Web: www.biolase.com

CEO: David M. (Dave) Mulder
CFO: Brett L. Scott
HR: Jodie Saundersen
FYE: December 31
Type: Public

BioLase Technology is causing dentists to drop the knife and pick up the laser. The company makes laser-based systems for use primarily in dental applications. BioLase's surgical cutting system, Waterlase, uses laser pulses to turn water droplets into high-speed particles that can cut both hard and soft tissues and bones in the mouth. Waterlase is used in procedures traditionally performed with dental drills and scalpels. The company's DioLase system is used to perform soft tissue and cosmetic procedures, including its LaserSmile teeth whitening procedure. BioLase markets its products in the US through distributor Henry Schein, as well as through international representatives in more than 50 countries.

	Annual Growth	12/05	12/06	12/07	12/08	12/09
Sales ($ mil.)	(8.6%)	62.0	69.7	66.9	64.6	43.3
Net income ($ mil.)	—	(17.5)	(4.7)	(7.3)	(9.1)	(3.0)
Market value ($ mil.)	(30.1%)	194.9	213.4	57.6	36.3	46.6
Employees	(7.8%)	209	199	216	180	151

BIOLIFE SOLUTIONS, INC.

OTC: BLFS

3303 Monte Villa Pkwy., Ste. 310
Bothell, WA 98021
Phone: 425-402-1400
Fax: 425-402-1433
Web: www.biolifesolutions.com

CEO: Michael (Mike) Rice
CFO: —
HR: —
FYE: December 31
Type: Public

BioLife Solutions makes sure your tissues and organs don't get freezer burn. The company has designed liquid media technologies for frozen (cryogenic) storage and cold (hypothermic) storage of biological products including cells, tissues, and organs. Its HypoThermosol and CryoStor products minimize the damage done to these biological products during refrigeration and freezing, making them viable for transplant or experimentation for longer periods. The company sells its products directly to academic institutions, companies, and laboratories conducting clinical research.

	Annual Growth	12/05	12/06	12/07	12/08	12/09
Sales ($ mil.)	27.8%	0.6	0.6	1.0	1.3	1.6
Net income ($ mil.)	—	(0.6)	(1.1)	(2.9)	(2.8)	(2.8)
Market value ($ mil.)	(1.1%)	8.0	4.5	4.2	2.1	7.7
Employees	0.0%	10	10	7	10	10

BIOMARIN PHARMACEUTICAL INC.

NASDAQ (GM): BMRN

105 Digital Dr.
Novato, CA 94949
Phone: 415-506-6700
Fax: 415-382-7889
Web: www.biomarinpharm.com

CEO: Jean-Jacques (J.J.) Bienaimé
CFO: Jeffrey H. (Jeff) Cooper
HR: Mark Wood
FYE: December 31
Type: Public

BioMarin Pharmaceuticals works to raise orphan drugs up right. The company has developed three FDA-approved drugs that qualify for orphan drug status, a financial incentive that encourages companies to create drugs for rare diseases by giving the compounds a period of market exclusivity. BioMarin's Aldurazyme (co-developed with Genzyme) treats the life-threatening inherited condition MPS I, caused by a rare enzyme deficiency. Its drug Naglazyme is approved in the US and Europe to treat another rare genetic disease called MPS VI. BioMarin's drug Kuvan is the only drug approved to treat phenylketonuria (PKU), an enzyme deficiency which prevents patients from metabolizing certain proteins.

	Annual Growth	12/05	12/06	12/07	12/08	12/09
Sales ($ mil.)	88.5%	25.7	84.2	121.6	296.5	324.7
Net income ($ mil.)	—	(74.3)	(28.5)	(15.8)	30.8	(0.5)
Market value ($ mil.)	14.9%	1,095.5	1,665.7	3,597.6	1,809.0	1,911.6
Employees	23.1%	314	410	525	649	720

BIOMED REALTY TRUST, INC.

NYSE: BMR

17140 Bernardo Center Dr., Ste. 222
San Diego, CA 92128
Phone: 858-485-9840
Fax: 858-485-9843
Web: www.biomedrealty.com

CEO: Alan D. Gold
CFO: Greg N. Lubushkin
HR: —
FYE: December 31
Type: Public

BioMed Realty knows its niche. A self-administered real estate investment trust (REIT), the company acquires, develops, leases, and manages research laboratories and offices for biotechnology companies, pharmaceutical firms, research institutions, and other life science tenants. BioMed owns more than 70 properties in about a dozen states; the properties contain around 120 buildings and total approximately 11 million sq. ft. of rentable space. The REIT's preferred markets include research and development hubs such as Boston, New York, San Diego, San Francisco, and Seattle.

	Annual Growth	12/05	12/06	12/07	12/08	12/09
Sales ($ mil.)	26.7%	140.3	222.6	266.2	281.3	361.2
Net income ($ mil.)	37.2%	17.0	35.0	72.5	64.9	60.2
Market value ($ mil.)	(10.3%)	2,770.2	3,247.0	2,630.6	1,330.6	1,791.6
Employees	27.5%	50	87	113	126	132

BIOMEDICAL TECHNOLOGY SOLUTIONS

OTC: BMTL

9800 Mount Pyramid Ct., Ste. 250
Englewood, CO 80112
Phone: 303-653-0100
Fax: 303-653-0120
Web: www.bmtscorp.com

CEO: Donald G. (Don) Cox Jr.
CFO: David A. Kempf
HR: —
FYE: December 31
Type: Public

BioMedical Technology Solutions Holdings, Inc. (formerly CET Services) takes the hazard out of hazardous medical waste. Its flagship product is the Demolizer, a desktop device that uses dry heat to sterilize medical waste and to destroy sharps (needles, lancets, scalpel blades, etc.). In 2008 CET Services, which managed residential real estate redevelopment projects, including demolition, environmental remediation, and construction services, acquired BioMedical Technology Solutions (BMTS) in a reverse merger and assumed that company's name. Prior to embarking on its property development activities, CET Services was a provider of environmental consulting and engineering services for water and wastewater projects.

	Annual Growth	12/04	12/05	12/06	12/07	*12/08
Sales ($ mil.)	(26.0%)	4.0	3.2	3.0	2.1	1.2
Net income ($ mil.)	—	(0.3)	(0.4)	(0.3)	(1.3)	(1.2)
Market value ($ mil.)	(28.1%)	52.7	44.1	30.2	5.2	14.1
Employees	33.7%	5	4	3	1	16

*Most recent year available

BIOMERICA, INC.

OTC: BMRA

1533 Monrovia Ave.
Newport Beach, CA 92663
Phone: 949-645-2111
Fax: 949-722-6674
Web: www.biomerica.com

CEO: Zackary S. Irani
CFO: Janet Moore
HR: —
FYE: May 31
Type: Public

God bless Biomerica. The firm makes diagnostic tests for use worldwide in hospitals and other clinical laboratories, as well as in doctors' offices and homes. Its clinical laboratory products are immunoassay tests for conditions such as food allergies, diabetes, infectious diseases, and hyperthyroidism. Its point-of-care product portfolio, which includes products that produce rapid results, provides tests for prostate cancer, pregnancy, cat allergies, and drugs of abuse. Biomerica has manufacturing facilities in the US and in Mexico. It once owned a minority interest in Lancer Orthodontics, a maker of orthodontic products such as arch wires, lingual attachments, and buccal tubes, but it sold its stake in 2008.

	Annual Growth	5/04	5/05	5/06	5/07	*5/08
Sales ($ mil.)	(14.6%)	9.2	9.3	7.2	5.7	4.9
Net income ($ mil.)	—	(0.2)	0.2	0.2	0.5	1.7
Market value ($ mil.)	17.5%	3.7	2.9	2.7	5.3	7.0
Employees	(19.3%)	57	62	27	30	—

*Most recent year available

BIOMET, INC.

56 E. Bell Dr.	CEO: Jeffrey R. Binder
Warsaw, IN 46582	CFO: Daniel P. (Dan) Florin
Phone: 574-267-6639	HR: Peggy Taylor
Fax: 574-267-8137	FYE: May 31
Web: www.biomet.com	Type: Private

When the leg bone and the knee bone don't connect so well anymore, Biomet may have a solution. Orthopedic specialists use the medical devices made by Biomet, whose wares include reconstructive products (hips, knees, and shoulders), dental implants, bone cement systems, orthopedic support devices, and operating-room supplies. Through its EBI subsidiary, the firm also sells fixation devices (bone screws and pins), electrical bone-growth stimulators, and bone grafting materials. Subsidiary Biomet Microfixation markets implants and bone substitute material for craniomaxillofacial (head and face) surgeries. Biomet is controlled by LVB Acquisition, which is owned by a group of private equity firms.

	Annual Growth	5/05	5/06	5/07	5/08	5/09
Sales ($ mil.)	17.3%	—	—	—	2,134.5	2,504.1
Net income ($ mil.)	—	—	—	—	(964.2)	(749.2)
Employees	(50.9%)	—	—	—	7,220	3,548

BIOMIMETIC THERAPEUTICS, INC.

NASDAQ (GM): BMTI

389-A Nichol Mill Ln.	CEO: Samuel E. Lynch
Franklin, TN 37067	CFO: Lawrence E. (Larry) Bullock
Phone: 615-844-1280	HR: —
Fax: 615-844-1281	FYE: December 31
Web: www.biomimetics.com	Type: Public

BioMimetic Therapeutics' GEM might not sparkle, but it does attract cells that promote tissue and bone growth when it is applied to damaged tissue or a bone fracture. The company's product candidates are based on the GEM (Growth-factor Enhanced Matrix) technology, a combination drug and medical device platform that includes a human tissue growth factor with a synthetic bone matrix. BioMimetic Therapeutics is working to develop the GEM technology as a treatment for various fractures, where its bone matrix can be used to repair, reinforce, or fuse broken bones, as well as repair tendons, ligaments, and cartilage. The company is focused on orthopedic, spine, and sports injuries.

	Annual Growth	12/05	12/06	12/07	12/08	12/09
Sales ($ mil.)	(22.8%)	4.5	4.1	7.0	3.1	1.6
Net income ($ mil.)	—	(11.7)	(17.1)	(24.6)	(8.0)	(21.2)
Market value ($ mil.)	(3.3%)	—	291.8	384.3	204.0	263.9
Employees	21.4%	41	61	87	88	89

BION ENVIRONMENTAL TECHNOLOGIES, INC.

OTC: BNET

1774 Summitview Way	CEO: Mark A. Smith
Crestone, CO 81131	CFO: Mark A. Smith
Phone: 303-843-6191	HR: —
Fax: —	FYE: June 30
Web: www.biontech.com	Type: Public

A "moo moo" here and an "oink oink" there are music to the ears of Bion Environmental Technologies. The company provides waste stream remediation for animal operations, primarily for large dairy and hog farms. To reduce pollution caused by animal waste, Bion Environmental uses organic nutrients, bacteria, and other microbes to treat the waste before disposal. The treatment creates organic soil and fertilizer products, which the company markets for use on athletic fields, gardens, and golf courses. The company is working closely with government bodies and universities in Pennsylvania to address the major problem of animal waste run-off from farms into the Chesapeake Bay.

	Annual Growth	6/05	6/06	6/07	6/08	6/09
Sales ($ mil.)	—	—	—	—	—	0.0
Net income ($ mil.)	—	—	—	—	—	(1.3)
Market value ($ mil.)	—	—	—	—	—	11.4
Employees	—	—	—	—	—	9

BIONOVO, INC.

NASDAQ (CM): BNVI

5858 Horton St., Ste. 400	CEO: Isaac Cohen
Emeryville, CA 94608	CFO: Thomas C. (Tom) Chesterman
Phone: 510-601-2000	HR: —
Fax: 510-601-5050	FYE: December 31
Web: bionovo.com	Type: Public

Women's health and cancer are top concerns for drug discovery company Bionovo. Using botanically derived pharmaceutical ingredients and traditional Chinese herbs, Bionovo is formulating and testing oral and topical drug candidates — including its most advanced, Menerba — designed to help reduce menopause symptoms (hot flashes, night sweats, and vaginal dryness) and kill breast cancer cells. It has therapeutic agents in both clinical and preclinical stages. Bionovo was founded by CEO Isaac Cohen and president Mary Tagliaferri, who collectively own about a quarter of the company's stock.

	Annual Growth	12/05	12/06	12/07	12/08	12/09
Sales ($ mil.)	—	0.0	0.0	0.6	0.2	0.3
Net income ($ mil.)	—	(3.6)	(5.6)	(12.9)	(16.7)	(16.4)
Market value ($ mil.)	(14.7%)	96.9	160.4	184.0	20.4	51.2
Employees	55.2%	10	20	35	49	58

BIOPHAN TECHNOLOGIES, INC.

OTC: BIPH

15 Schoen Place	CEO: John F. Lanzafame
Pittsford, NY 14534	CFO: Margaret V. Russell
Phone: 585-267-4800	HR: —
Fax: 585-267-4819	FYE: February 28
Web: www.biophan.com	Type: Public

Biophan Technologies appreciates high visibility and smooth circulation. The company develops blood circulation support systems and technologies to help make medical devices compatible with MRI (magnetic resonance imaging) equipment. Its majority-owned Myotech unit is developing a system to restore and sustain blood flow in patients with acute heart failure. The system is based on a device that even a general surgeon can fit directly on a patient's heart to restart its pumping. Biophan's other technologies improve the visibility of coronary stents and vena cava filters in MRIs.

	Annual Growth	2/05	2/06	2/07	2/08	2/09
Sales ($ mil.)	(11.2%)	—	1.0	1.0	11.7	0.7
Net income ($ mil.)	—	—	(14.3)	(17.7)	(5.2)	(17.1)
Market value ($ mil.)	(81.7%)	—	390.9	98.0	13.6	2.4
Employees	(32.7%)	—	23	22	11	7

BIO-RAD LABORATORIES, INC.

NYSE: BIO

1000 Alfred Nobel Dr.	CEO: Norman Schwartz
Hercules, CA 94547	CFO: Christine A. Tsingos
Phone: 510-724-7000	HR: Colleen Corey
Fax: 510-741-5815	FYE: December 31
Web: www.bio-rad.com	Type: Public

Bio-Rad Laboratories makes a most excellent array of research laboratory and medical testing equipment. The company manufactures and supplies more than 8,000 products through two segments. Its life science unit offers instruments, apparatus, reagents, and software used in lab settings to study life processes, potential drugs, and food pathogens. Its clinical diagnostics segment makes products used in blood, fluid, and tissue testing to detect diseases such as diabetes. Bio-Rad has a sales force that sells directly to such end users as clinical labs, pharmaceutical companies, hospitals, government agencies, and universities. More than two-thirds of its sales are made outside the US.

	Annual Growth	12/05	12/06	12/07	12/08	12/09
Sales ($ mil.)	10.9%	1,181.0	1,273.9	1,461.1	1,764.4	1,784.2
Net income ($ mil.)	15.4%	81.6	103.3	93.0	89.5	144.6
Market value ($ mil.)	10.2%	1,805.8	2,277.1	2,859.4	2,078.2	2,661.8
Employees	6.1%	5,200	5,400	6,400	6,600	6,600

An in-depth profile of this company is available to Hoover's Online members at hoovers.com.

251

BIO-REFERENCE LABORATORIES, INC.

NASDAQ (GS): BRLI

481 Edward H. Ross Dr.
Elmwood Park, NJ 07407
Phone: 201-791-2600
Fax: 201-791-1941
Web: www.bioreference.com

CEO: Marc D. Grodman
CFO: Sam Singer Sr.
HR: —
FYE: October 31
Type: Public

Bio-Reference Laboratories has tested positive as the lab of choice for many in the Northeast. Primarily serving the greater New York Metropolitan Area, the company offers routine clinical tests, including Pap smears, pregnancy tests, cholesterol checks, and blood cell counts. Through its GenPath business unit, it also performs more sophisticated "esoteric" testing such as cancer pathology and molecular diagnostics. It gets most of its orders (more than 4 million per year) from doctors' offices, collecting specimens at draw stations scattered throughout its primary service area in the New York area. Bio-Reference Laboratories also provides services in Connecticut, Delaware, Maryland, New Jersey, and Pennsylvania.

	Annual Growth	10/05	10/06	10/07	10/08	10/09
Sales ($ mil.)	22.0%	163.9	193.1	250.4	301.1	362.7
Net income ($ mil.)	30.3%	7.6	11.3	14.0	15.6	21.9
Market value ($ mil.)	14.3%	263.1	327.8	445.1	341.2	448.5
Employees	14.2%	1,276	1,551	1,648	1,907	2,174

BIOSANTE PHARMACEUTICALS, INC.

NASDAQ (GM): BPAX

111 Barclay Blvd.
Lincolnshire, IL 60069
Phone: 847-478-0500
Fax: 847-478-9152
Web: www.biosantepharma.com

CEO: Stephen M. Simes
CFO: Phillip B. Donenberg
HR: —
FYE: December 31
Type: Public

BioSante Pharmaceuticals wants to be the patron saint of hormonal ups and downs. The firm is developing topical hormone therapy gels to deliver supplemental estrogen, progestogen, and testosterone. Lead product Elestrin has received its FDA approval to treat menopausal symptoms in women. The company's other product candidates still in development include gels that treat female sexual dysfunction (LibiGel) and testosterone deficiency in men (Bio-T-Gel), as well as vaccine therapies. BioSante has licensed to Solvay Pharmaceuticals its Bio-E/P-Gel, a combination of estrogen and progestogen to help menopausal women.

	Annual Growth	12/05	12/06	12/07	12/08	12/09
Sales ($ mil.)	44.3%	0.3	14.4	0.5	3.8	1.3
Net income ($ mil.)	—	(9.7)	2.8	(7.6)	(17.4)	(47.5)
Market value ($ mil.)	(20.6%)	233.8	177.4	242.1	64.1	92.9
Employees	15.6%	14	8	11	23	25

BIOSCRIP, INC.

NASDAQ (GM): BIOS

100 Clearbrook Rd.
Elmsford, NY 10523
Phone: 914-460-1600
Fax: 914-460-1660
Web: www.bioscrip.com

CEO: Richard H. Friedman
CFO: Stanley G. Rosenbaum
HR: Lisa Nadler
FYE: December 31
Type: Public

By land, by mail, or at the pharmacy counter, BioScrip gets medications to the people who need them. The company distributes biotech and other high-cost drugs (including injectable and intravenous drugs) to patients with chronic and life-threatening diseases such as HIV, multiple sclerosis, and cancer. It distributes the medicines through its own community pharmacies, home delivery services, and a specialty mail order pharmacy. Additionally, BioScrip offers pharmacy benefit management (PBM) services for such customers as managed care organizations, government agencies, and self-funded employer groups.

	Annual Growth	12/05	12/06	12/07	12/08	12/09
Sales ($ mil.)	5.5%	1,073.2	1,152.5	1,197.7	1,401.9	1,329.5
Net income ($ mil.)	—	(23.8)	(38.3)	3.3	(74.0)	54.1
Market value ($ mil.)	2.6%	404.1	185.4	414.2	119.0	448.0
Employees	8.3%	974	867	904	1,158	1,342

BIOSENSE WEBSTER, INC.

3333 Diamond Canyon Rd.
Diamond Bar, CA 91765
Phone: 909-839-8500
Fax: 909-468-2905
Web: www.biosensewebster.com

CEO: Shlomi Nachman
CFO: —
HR: —
FYE: December 31
Type: Subsidiary

Biosense Webster makes products that explore, and in some cases alter, the terrain of the human heart. Its catheters and imaging systems are used by electrophysiologists and interventional cardiologists worldwide to find and treat heart arrhythmias (irregular heart rhythms). Its CARTO XP EP Navigation System uses 3-D imaging technology to map the heart's electrical activity and lets doctors navigate the heart using the company's diagnostic catheters. Biosense Webster also makes therapeutic ablation catheters and systems that destroy faulty electric pathways in the heart that cause arrhythmias. Biosense Webster is a member of parent Johnson & Johnson's medical devices and diagnostics division.

	Annual Growth	12/04	12/05	12/06	12/07	12/08
Est. sales ($ mil.)	—	—	—	—	—	200.0
Employees	—	—	—	—	—	525

BIOSITE INCORPORATED

9975 Summers Ridge Rd.
San Diego, CA 92121
Phone: 858-805-2000
Fax: 858-455-4815
Web: www.biosite.com

CEO: Kim D. Blickenstaff
CFO: Christopher J. (Chris) Twomey
HR: —
FYE: December 31
Type: Private

Biosite makes truth serum for specimen cups. The company's diagnostic products include its Triage Drugs of Abuse Panel and Triage TOX Drug Screen, which are used in hospital settings to test for commonly abused drugs. Its other diagnostic products include tests to detect intestinal parasites, diagnose congestive heart failure, and measure the biomarkers associated with stroke. The Biosite Discovery program is a collaborative research effort to identify protein markers for a variety of ailments. Medical diagnostics firm Inverness Medical Innovations acquired Biosite in 2007.

BIO-SOLUTIONS MANUFACTURING, INC.

OTC: BSOM

4440 Arville St., Ste. 6
Las Vegas, NV 89103
Phone: 702-222-9532
Fax: 702-222-9126
Web: www.todaysalternativeenergy.net

CEO: David S. Bennett
CFO: —
HR: —
FYE: October 31
Type: Public

Clogged drains? Nothing at all! Backed up pipes? P'shaw! Diesel tank empty? No problem for the guys at Bio-Solutions Manufacturing (BSM). The company has two divisions: the Cleaning Division and the Bio Diesel Division. The Cleaning Division's products make use of microbes and enzymes that can be used to treat sites contaminated by such pollutants as hydrocarbons, grease, hydrogen sulfide, and ammonia. In addition, Bio-Solutions' microorganisms can clean up oil spills and contaminated groundwater by literally eating the contaminants. The Bio Diesel Division turns many of the waste products the company collects into biodiesel fuel. BSM distributes its products through subsidiary Bio-Solutions Franchise.

	Annual Growth	10/05	10/06	10/07	10/08	10/09
Sales ($ mil.)	—	—	—	—	—	0.0
Net income ($ mil.)	—	—	—	—	—	(0.9)
Market value ($ mil.)	—	—	—	—	—	7.5
Employees	—	—	—	—	—	2

BIOSOUND ESAOTE, INC.

8000 Castleway Dr.
Indianapolis, IN 46250
Phone: 317-849-1793
Fax: 317-813-6600
Web: www.biosound.com

CEO: Claudio Bertolini
CFO: Thomas B. Feick
HR: —
FYE: December 31
Type: Subsidiary

Biosound Esaote manufactures electronic diagnostic imaging equipment for the medical industry and specializes in portable ultrasound equipment. The company's ultrasound equipment is used for abdominal, cardiac, obstetric, and vascular imaging, as well as other applications. Biosound Esaote's products are sold to mobile and stationary health clinics, doctors offices, imaging centers, and hospitals, primarily under the MyLab brand. The company is a subsidiary of Italian ultrasound and magnetic resonance imaging (MRI) equipment maker Esaote.

BIOSPECIFICS TECHNOLOGIES CORP.　OTC: BSTC

35 Wilbur St.
Lynbrook, NY 11563
Phone: 516-593-7000
Fax: 516-593-7039
Web: www.biospecifics.com

CEO: Thomas L. Wegman
CFO: Thomas L. Wegman
HR: —
FYE: December 31
Type: Public

BioSpecifics Technologies previously made the active pharmaceutical ingredient collagenase for a topical ointment used to treat severe burns and skin ulcers; the Ross Products unit of Abbott Laboratories was its primary customer. However, because of steadily declining demand for the ointment, BioSpecifics sold the business in 2006 to DFB Biotech. It is instead developing an injectable collagenase as a treatment for a number of conditions, including skin-thickening disorders Dupuytren's disease and Peyronie's disease. The company is working with Auxilium Pharmaceuticals on these indications. The family of founder Edwin Wegman owns about 20% of BioSpecifics; Wegman died in 2007.

	Annual Growth	12/05	12/06	12/07	12/08	12/09
Sales ($ mil.)	(12.7%)	5.5	1.9	1.5	8.4	3.2
Net income ($ mil.)	—	(1.3)	1.2	(4.5)	3.7	(2.0)
Market value ($ mil.)	144.6%	5.1	23.9	62.8	133.4	184.2
Employees	0.0%	5	6	4	5	5

BIOSPHERE MEDICAL, INC.　NASDAQ (GM): BSMD

1050 Hingham St.
Rockland, MA 02370
Phone: 781-681-7900
Fax: 781-792-2745
Web: www.biospheremed.com

CEO: Richard J. (Rick) Faleschini
CFO: Martin J. (Marty) Joyce
HR: —
FYE: December 31
Type: Public

BioSphere Medical's products are extremely well-rounded. The firm makes bioengineered polymer beads called microspheres for use in embolotherapy, a process in which materials are injected into a blood vessel to cut blood flow to tumors and other vascular abnormalities, such as uterine fibroids. Interventional radiologists inject the company's Embosphere Microspheres (approved in the US, Europe, and other international markets) in a minimally invasive, catheter-based procedure. BioSphere Medical has also developed microspheres to treat liver cancer; its cancer-fighting HepaSphere Microspheres are approved in the European Union. BioSphere has agreed to be acquired by Merit Medical Systems for roughly $96 million.

	Annual Growth	12/05	12/06	12/07	12/08	12/09
Sales ($ mil.)	14.1%	18.5	22.9	26.9	29.3	31.4
Net income ($ mil.)	—	(2.8)	(2.3)	(1.9)	(5.5)	(2.7)
Market value ($ mil.)	(23.7%)	151.8	124.6	96.1	36.2	51.3
Employees	6.3%	69	83	80	84	88

BIOTEL, INC.　OTC: BTEL

1285 Corporate Center Dr., Ste. 150
Eagan, MN 55121
Phone: 651-286-8620
Fax: 952-882-6550
Web: www.biotelinc.com

CEO: B. Steven (Steve) Springrose
CFO: Judy E. Naus
HR: —
FYE: June 30
Type: Public

Biotel can tell you how your body is doing by reading your vital signs. Through its subsidiaries, Biotel manufactures and distributes medical devices and patient monitoring systems along with the custom-built software needed to operate such medical equipment. Subsidiary Braemar is a leading maker of portable heart monitoring devices such as Holter recorders and also makes liposuction and ultrasound components. Most of the company's products are made for and marketed through other medical device makers. Biotel also provides data management services for clinical trials through its Agility Centralized Research unit. Former CEO Charles Moyer and his wife Donna Horschmann Moyer hold about 20% of the company's shares.

	Annual Growth	6/05	6/06	6/07	6/08	6/09
Sales ($ mil.)	5.4%	10.2	10.2	11.2	11.5	12.6
Net income ($ mil.)	22.5%	0.4	0.5	0.5	0.7	0.9
Market value ($ mil.)	24.0%	5.6	5.3	9.4	8.3	13.2
Employees	0.0%	51	52	53	—	51

BIOTIME, INC.　NYSE Amex: BTIM

1301 Harbor Bay Pkwy.
Alameda, CA 94502
Phone: 510-521-3390
Fax: 510-521-3389
Web: www.biotimeinc.com

CEO: Michael D. West
CFO: Steven A. Seinberg
HR: —
FYE: December 31
Type: Public

After a long day in surgery, it's BioTime. Actually, BioTime is more useful *during* a long day of surgery, with its water-based solutions to prevent massive blood loss after traumatic injury, preserve organs for transplant, and replace blood during such procedures as cardiac bypass. BioTime's Hextend product has received FDA approval to maintain blood volume during surgery. The firm is also developing PentaLyte, a version of the blood volume replacement product that metabolizes more quickly, and HetaCool, intended to replace blood volume in cryosurgery and preserve donated organs. Hospira distributes Hextend in the US and Canada, and CJ markets the drug in South Korea.

	Annual Growth	12/05	12/06	12/07	12/08	12/09
Sales ($ mil.)	20.5%	0.9	1.2	1.0	1.5	1.9
Net income ($ mil.)	—	(2.1)	(1.9)	(1.4)	(3.8)	(5.1)
Market value ($ mil.)	92.2%	10.5	9.0	13.9	60.2	143.8
Employees	18.9%	10	10	10	12	20

BIRDS EYE FOODS, INC.

90 Linden Oaks
Rochester, NY 14625
Phone: 585-383-1850
Fax: 585-385-2857
Web: www.birdseyefoods.com

CEO: Neil Harrison
CFO: Linda K. Nelson
HR: —
FYE: June 30
Type: Business segment

Whether from a bird's eye or with eyes on the bottom line, the view is excellent at Birds Eye Foods. Its namesake frozen vegetables hold the #1 position in the US's frozen vegetable sector, generating some $1 billion in retail sales in 2009; it holds the #2 position in the bagged meal category. Lucky for kids, Birds Eye offers more than vegetables. It also makes specialty foods, such as an array of salty snacks, as well as canned pie fillings and chili, and salad dressings. In addition to retail food outlets, the company supplies foodservice and industrial-market customers throughout the nation. The company became part of Pinnacle Foods at the close of 2009.

An in-depth profile of this company is available to Hoover's Online members at hoovers.com.

BIRDSONG CORPORATION

612 Madison Ave.
Suffolk, VA 23434
Phone: 757-539-3456
Fax: 757-539-7360

CEO: George Y. Birdsong
CFO: Stephen L. Huber
HR: —
FYE: June 30
Type: Private

If it had to pick a mascot, Birdsong would probably pick Woodstock from the Peanuts gang. The company's primary operating division, Birdsong Peanuts, is a top US peanut processor. The unit shells raw peanuts (purchased from peanut farmers) and markets them to customers throughout the world. Birdsong Peanuts operates plants in Texas, North Carolina, and Georgia, and it serves food manufacturers including Planters, Smuckers, and Nestlé's candy division. Birdsong was formed in 1974 to consolidate the assets of the Birdsong family, which owns the company.

BIRNER DENTAL MANAGEMENT SERVICES, INC. NASDAQ (CM): BDMS

3801 E. Florida Ave., Ste. 508
Denver, CO 80210
Phone: 303-691-0680
Fax: 303-691-0889
Web: www.bdms-perfectteeth.com

CEO: Frederic W. J. Birner
CFO: Dennis N. Genty
HR: Carl Budke
FYE: December 31
Type: Public

Birner Dental Management Services hopes to leave its customers smiling. The company acquires, develops, and manages dental practice networks, freeing dentists of their administrative duties by providing management services such as billing, accounting, and marketing. Birner Dental manages about 60 offices under the Perfect Teeth brand name; more than 40 of the practices are located in Colorado, and the rest are in Arizona and New Mexico. Some locations offer special services such as orthodontics, oral surgery, and periodontics. Brothers and co-founders Frederic (chairman and CEO) and Mark Birner (president) together own more than one-quarter of the company.

	Annual Growth	12/05	12/06	12/07	12/08	12/09
Sales ($ mil.)	12.9%	36.7	39.4	40.8	34.5	59.6
Net income ($ mil.)	(3.6%)	2.2	2.3	2.4	1.8	1.9
Market value ($ mil.)	(4.6%)	37.6	34.9	39.8	21.0	31.1
Employees	1.6%	531	566	565	546	565

BISSELL HOMECARE, INC.

2345 Walker St. NW
Grand Rapids, MI 49544
Phone: 616-453-4451
Fax: 616-453-1383
Web: www.bissell.com

CEO: Mark J. Bissell
CFO: —
HR: —
FYE: December 31
Type: Private

BISSELL's in the business of seeing spots and taking care of dust bunnies. A pioneer in the carpet-cleaning industry, BISSELL Homecare makes a full line of vacuum cleaners, sweepers, steam cleaners, deep cleaners, and cleaning chemicals for home use. Its models include the Powersteamer, Little Green, and Spotlifter machines. The firm sells its products worldwide under the BISSELL and Woolite brand names through mass merchandisers (Best Buy, Target, Wal-Mart), home centers (Lowe's, Home Depot), and hardware stores (Ace Hardware). Its products are sold online at BISSELL.com, as well. Founded in 1876 by Melville and Anna Bissell, the company is still owned and operated by the Bissell family.

BITSTREAM INC. NASDAQ (CM): BITS

245 1st St., 17th Fl.
Cambridge, MA 02142
Phone: 617-497-6222
Fax: 617-868-0784
Web: www.bitstream.com

CEO: Anna M. Chagnon
CFO: James P. (Jim) Dore
HR: —
FYE: December 31
Type: Public

Bitstream counts on its fonts to keep business flowing. The company develops software that creates and manages typefaces. It has a library of more than 1,000 fonts and develops technology for delivering typographic capabilities to hardware, software, and Web applications. Bitstream also develops browser software for mobile handsets. Its products include the BOLT and Thunder-Hawk browsers, as well as text distribution applications (TrueDoc). Subsidiary Pageflex offers publishing software that designs and creates custom business documents based on customer profiles. Bitstream's MyFonts.com subsidiary offers a website for locating, testing, and purchasing more than 60,000 different fonts.

	Annual Growth	12/05	12/06	12/07	12/08	12/09
Sales ($ mil.)	8.2%	15.7	20.2	23.6	24.0	21.5
Net income ($ mil.)	(2.6%)	1.0	3.2	4.0	2.4	0.9
Market value ($ mil.)	19.2%	37.6	87.1	64.2	45.9	75.9
Employees	11.8%	62	67	72	96	97

B.J. VINES, INC.

498 7th Ave., 21st Fl.
New York, NY 10018
Phone: 212-244-0843
Fax: 212-244-0855
Web: www.betseyjohnson.com

CEO: Betsey Johnson
CFO: John Freidman
HR: —
FYE: December 31
Type: Private

B.J. Vines, aka Betsey Johnson, is a perennial favorite among women who are funky and consider themselves eclectic, and after more than 30 years in the business, the eccentric designer and her company namesake are still going strong. Betsey Johnson clothes, shoes, fragrance, makeup, lingerie, legwear, and accessories are distributed through about 50 specialty stores of the same name and department stores worldwide. B.J. Vines has expanded its product offerings and operations through about a dozen licensing agreements. Having owned a majority of the firm, Johnson sold a controlling stake to Boston-based private equity firm Castanea Partners in August 2007.

BJC HEALTHCARE

4444 Forest Park Ave.
St. Louis, MO 63108
Phone: 314-286-2000
Fax: 314-286-2060
Web: www.bjc.org

CEO: Steven H. Lipstein
CFO: Kevin V. Roberts
HR: Carlos Perea
FYE: December 31
Type: Not-for-profit

If it's health care you are looking for in the Gateway City, chances are BJC HealthCare is where you'll find it. The system operates more than a dozen hospitals — including Barnes-Jewish Hospital, Boone Hospital Center, and Christian Hospital — and some 100 primary care and specialty care facilities in and around St. Louis. BJC HealthCare's facilities combined have more than 3,200 beds. Specialized services include hospice and home health care, behavioral health, and long-term care at a handful of nursing facilities. The company's BarnesCare and OccuMed subsidiaries offer occupational health care and workers' compensation services. The system is led by long-time health care administrator CEO Steven Lipstein.

	Annual Growth	12/04	12/05	12/06	12/07	12/08
Est. sales ($ mil.)	—	—	—	—	—	3,218.4
Employees	—	—	—	—	—	25,525

BJ'S RESTAURANTS, INC.

NASDAQ (GS): BJRI

7755 Center Ave., Ste. 300
Huntington Beach, CA 92647
Phone: 714-500-2400
Fax: —
Web: www.bjsbrewhouse.com

CEO: Gerald W. (Jerry) Deitchle
CFO: Gregory S. (Greg) Levin
HR: Matthew J. Kimble
FYE: December 31
Type: Public

The Windy City inspires the food and drink at BJ's. BJ's Restaurants owns and operates more than 80 restaurants in California and a dozen other mostly Western states under the names BJ's Restaurant & Brewhouse, BJ's Restaurant & Brewery, and BJ's Pizza & Grill. The casual-dining eateries offer Chicago-style pizza, salads, sandwiches, pasta, and the company's own handcrafted beers. Its dozen Restaurant & Brewery locations, which feature an onsite microbrewery, help supply beer to the rest of the chain. Holding company The Jacmar Companies owns more than 15% of BJ's.

	Annual Growth	12/05	12/06	12/07	12/08	12/09
Sales ($ mil.)	24.4%	178.2	238.9	316.1	374.1	426.7
Net income ($ mil.)	11.5%	8.4	9.8	11.7	10.3	13.0
Market value ($ mil.)	(4.7%)	617.5	546.0	439.3	290.9	508.7
Employees	19.7%	5,424	6,546	8,610	9,200	11,130

BJ'S WHOLESALE CLUB, INC.

NYSE: BJ

1 Mercer Rd.
Natick, MA 01760
Phone: 508-651-7400
Fax: 508-651-6114
Web: www.bjs.com

CEO: Laura J. Sen
CFO: Frank D. Forward
HR: Annette M. Zola
FYE: January 31
Type: Public

"Exclusive membership" has never been as common as it is at BJ's Wholesale Club. The firm is the nation's #3 membership warehouse club (behind leaders Costco and SAM'S CLUB) and #1 in New England, with more than nine million members and some 185 locations in 15 states, mostly along the Eastern Seaboard. Food, including canned, fresh, and frozen items, accounts for about two-thirds of sales at BJ's. The remainder comes from general merchandise, including apparel, housewares, office equipment, small appliances, and gas. BJ's also offers auto and home insurance, travel and other services through its Web site. Unlike its major rivals, BJ's targets individual retail customers rather than small businesses.

	Annual Growth	1/06	1/07	1/08	1/09	1/10
Sales ($ mil.)	6.4%	7,949.9	8,480.3	9,005.0	10,027.4	10,187.0
Net income ($ mil.)	0.7%	128.5	72.0	122.9	134.6	132.1
Market value ($ mil.)	1.3%	1,730.1	1,644.0	1,743.6	1,543.9	1,819.0
Employees	3.7%	20,300	21,200	20,800	22,000	23,500

BKD, LLP

910 E. St. Louis St., Ste. 400, P.O. Box 1900
Springfield, MO 65806
Phone: 417-831-7283
Fax: 417-831-4763
Web: www.bkd.com

CEO: Neal D. Spencer
CFO: Brad Buehler
HR: —
FYE: May 31
Type: Partnership

BKD, among the largest US accounting firms, has more than 30 offices throughout the heartland states, offering individuals and businesses a variety of accounting, auditing, consulting, risk management, valuation, and related services. Subsidiaries include BKD Corporate Finance, which offers mergers and acquisitions and IPO advice, financing, and employee stock option plans. BKD Wealth Advisors provides investment management and estate planning, while BKD Insurance handles insurance consulting. BKD serves international clients through its affiliation with Praxity, an association of independent accounting practices in some 70 countries; it is the largest US member of the London-based association.

	Annual Growth	5/04	5/05	5/06	5/07	5/08
Sales ($ mil.)	18.8%	—	—	287.0	353.9	405.0
Employees	11.8%	—	—	1,600	1,900	2,000

BKF CAPITAL GROUP, INC.

Pink Sheets: BKFG

1 North Federal Highway, Ste. 201
Boca Raton, FL 33432
Phone: 561-362-4199
Fax: —
Web: www.bkfcapital.com

CEO: Steven N. Bronson
CFO: —
HR: —
FYE: December 31
Type: Public

Wanted: business opportunity for former investment firm. Contact BKF Capital Group. BKF is evaluating strategic alternatives (either a merger or liquidation). The company has no operations and only a small revenue stream (more like a trickle) from its days as an asset manager and broker dealer; it is no longer a registered investment advisor and has also surrendered its broker license. The company's primary subsidiary is BKF Asset Management, but as the company itself points out, it has no operations either. BKF Capital's search for a new *raison d'etre* was put on hold when it was named in a class action shareholder lawsuit, but the suit was dropped in 2007 and the search resumed.

	Annual Growth	12/05	12/06	12/07	12/08	12/09
Sales ($ mil.)	(71.6%)	123.2	24.5	3.6	2.8	0.8
Net income ($ mil.)	—	(15.9)	(47.0)	(5.7)	(1.3)	(0.2)
Market value ($ mil.)	(52.9%)	151.1	26.7	17.7	6.4	7.4
Employees	(68.3%)	99	3	2	1	1

BLACK & VEATCH CORPORATION

11401 Lamar Ave.
Overland Park, KS 66211
Phone: 913-458-2000
Fax: 913-458-2934
Web: www.bv.com

CEO: Leonard C. (Len) Rodman
CFO: Karen L. Daniel
HR: Shirley Gaufin
FYE: December 31
Type: Private

Black & Veatch (BV) provides the ABCs of construction, engineering, and consulting. The international group is one of the largest private companies in the US. It specializes in infrastructure development for the energy, water, environmental, federal, and telecommunications markets. BV engages in all phases of building projects, from design and engineering to financing and construction. The company offers environmental consulting, operations and maintenance, security design and consulting, management consulting, and IT services. The employee-owned firm has worked on coal, nuclear, and combustion turbine plants; drinking water and coastal water operations; and wireless and broadband installation.

	Annual Growth	12/04	12/05	12/06	12/07	12/08
Sales ($ mil.)	23.0%	1,400.0	1,573.0	2,200.0	3,200.0	3,200.0
Employees	9.0%	6,800	7,500	8,600	9,600	9,600

BLACK BEAUTY COAL COMPANY

7100 Eagle Crest Blvd.
Evansville, IN 47715
Phone: 812-434-8500
Fax: 812-428-0712

CEO: Charles A. (Chuck) Burggraf
CFO: Jim Marchino
HR: Gene Koch
FYE: December 31
Type: Subsidiary

Little girls who love horses won't necessarily love this Black Beauty. A subsidiary of Peabody Energy, Black Beauty Coal Company operates about half a dozen coal properties in Indiana and in Illinois. The company primarily supplies power companies in the Midwestern US. Black Beauty holds a 75% stake in the United Minerals Company and operates the properties owned by fellow Peabody subsidiary Coulterville Coal. Peabody made Black Beauty a wholly owned subsidiary in 2003. Black Beauty produces somewhere around 25 million tons of compliance, medium sulfur, and high sulfur stem coal annually.

An in-depth profile of this company is available to Hoover's Online members at hoovers.com.

BLACK BOX CORPORATION
NASDAQ (GS): BBOX

1000 Park Dr.
Lawrence, PA 15055
Phone: 724-746-5500
Fax: 724-746-0746
Web: www.blackbox.com

CEO: R. Terry Blakemore
CFO: Michael (Mike) McAndrew
HR: —
FYE: March 31
Type: Public

Black Box establishes a lot of connections. The company distributes and supports voice and data networking infrastructure. Its offerings include modems, routers, switches, and testing equipment, as well as cabinets, cables, and training materials. Black Box primarily distributes third-party equipment, some of which carries the Black Box brand, but it also manufactures select products. In addition, the company maintains technical support hotlines and provides services such as on-site design, installation, and maintenance. Black Box sells its products to corporations, schools, and government agencies worldwide, but the majority of its revenue is generated in North America.

	Annual Growth	3/06	3/07	3/08	3/09	3/10
Sales ($ mil.)	7.4%	721.3	1,016.3	1,016.7	999.5	961.4
Net income ($ mil.)	(2.0%)	37.4	35.6	39.2	45.3	34.5
Market value ($ mil.)	(10.6%)	843.2	641.3	541.4	414.3	539.8
Employees	7.1%	3,300	5,000	5,000	4,542	4,348

BLACK HILLS CORPORATION
NYSE: BKH

625 9th St.
Rapid City, SD 57701
Phone: 605-721-1700
Fax: 605-721-2599
Web: www.blackhillscorp.com

CEO: David R. Emery
CFO: Anthony S. Cleberg
HR: Robert A. (Bob) Myers
FYE: December 31
Type: Public

Black Hills is alive with the sound of energy. Its Black Hills Power utility unit distributes electricity to 69,000 customers in Montana, South Dakota, and Wyoming, while its Cheyenne Light Fuel & Power unit serves 39,800 electric customers and 33,300 natural gas customers in the greater Cheyenne area. Its Black Hills Energy unit serves 524,000 natural gas customers in Colorado, Iowa, Kansas, and Nebraska, and 93,300 electricity customers in Colorado. Black Hills' power plants produce more than 1,000 MW a year. The company's wholesale segment is engaged in energy marketing, coal mining, power generation, and oil and gas production (185.4 billion cu. ft. of natural gas reserves in 2008).

	Annual Growth	12/05	12/06	12/07	12/08	12/09
Sales ($ mil.)	(2.3%)	1,391.6	656.9	695.9	1,005.8	1,269.6
Net income ($ mil.)	25.0%	33.4	81.0	98.8	105.1	81.6
Market value ($ mil.)	(6.3%)	1,355.9	1,447.1	1,727.6	1,056.2	1,043.2
Employees	28.2%	803	819	998	2,122	2,171

BLACKBAUD, INC.
NASDAQ (GS): BLKB

2000 Daniel Island Dr.
Charleston, SC 29492
Phone: 843-216-6200
Fax: 843-216-6100
Web: www.blackbaud.com

CEO: Marc E. Chardon
CFO: Timothy V. (Tim) Williams
HR: John J. Mistretta
FYE: December 31
Type: Public

Blackbaud's customers aren't in it for the cash, but that doesn't mean they can't use some financial help. Blackbaud provides financial, fundraising, and administrative software for not-for-profit organizations and educational institutions. Software offerings include The Raiser's Edge for fundraising management, The Financial Edge for accounting, and The Education Edge for managing school admissions, registration, and billing. Blackbaud has about 22,000 customers in 55 countries, including colleges, environmental groups, health and human services providers, churches, and animal welfare groups. The company gets most of its sales in North America.

	Annual Growth	12/05	12/06	12/07	12/08	12/09
Sales ($ mil.)	16.8%	166.3	192.0	257.0	302.5	309.3
Net income ($ mil.)	(3.9%)	33.3	30.5	31.7	29.9	28.4
Market value ($ mil.)	8.5%	765.4	1,165.1	1,256.5	604.9	1,058.9
Employees	17.9%	1,014	1,165	1,655	1,977	1,956

BLACKBOARD INC.
NASDAQ (GS): BBBB

1899 L St. NW, 11th Fl.
Washington, DC 20036
Phone: 202-463-4860
Fax: 202-463-4863
Web: www.blackboard.com

CEO: Michael L. Chasen
CFO: John Kinzer
HR: —
FYE: December 31
Type: Public

Chalk up Blackboard's success to the Internet. Blackboard develops software that enables schools to create Internet-based learning programs and communities. The company's software connects teachers, students, parents, and administrators via the Web, enabling Internet-based assignments, class websites, and online collaboration with classmates. The software also assists instructors with course administration and includes a content management system for creating and managing digital course content. Blackboard's software includes transaction, community, and payment management tools that enable students to use their college IDs for meal plans, event access, and tuition payments.

	Annual Growth	12/05	12/06	12/07	12/08	12/09
Sales ($ mil.)	29.1%	135.7	183.1	239.4	312.1	377.0
Net income ($ mil.)	(34.1%)	41.9	(10.7)	12.9	2.8	7.9
Market value ($ mil.)	11.9%	989.3	1,025.5	1,374.1	895.5	1,549.6
Employees	21.2%	549	765	890	1,087	1,183

BLACKMAN PLUMBING SUPPLY CO., INC.

120 Hicksville Rd.
Bethpage, NY 11714
Phone: 516-579-2000
Fax: 516-579-2012
Web: www.blackman.com

CEO: Robert Mannheimer
CFO: Steve Grillo
HR: Sue Cook
FYE: December 31
Type: Private

Blackman Plumbing has everything for the kitchen — and bathroom — sinks. The company emphasizes personal appointments at its dozen or so designer showrooms located in Manhattan, Queens, and throughout Long Island, New York. Blackman stores feature kitchen and bathroom products, including cabinets, countertops, faucets, hardware, showers, sinks, and toilets from manufacturers such as Delta Faucet, Grohe, and Moen. The company also stocks heating, industrial, and HVAC equipment and products for building and remodeling professionals. Founded in 1921 by Sam Blackman, the company is owned by president Richard Blackman.

BLACKROCK, INC.
NYSE: BLK

40 E. 52nd St.
New York, NY 10022
Phone: 212-810-5300
Fax: 212-810-8760
Web: www.blackrock.com

CEO: Laurence D. (Larry) Fink
CFO: Ann Marie Petach
HR: —
FYE: December 31
Type: Public

Now this is the kind of coal you want in your stocking. BlackRock is one of the world's largest money managers. The firm, with some $3 trillion under management, specializes in fixed-income products and money market instruments for mostly institutional clients worldwide, including pension plans, insurance companies, mutual funds, endowments, foundations, and charities. It also provides risk management services, manages hedge funds, and oversees the operations of publicly traded real estate investment trust Anthracite Capital. CEO Laurence Fink, who has overseen a string of major acquisitions in recent years, engineered a blockbuster merger with Barclays Global Investors in 2009.

	Annual Growth	12/05	12/06	12/07	12/08	12/09
Assets ($ mil.)	213.3%	1,848.0	20,469.5	22,561.5	19,924.0	177,994.0
Net income ($ mil.)	39.1%	233.9	322.6	995.3	786.0	875.0
Market value ($ mil.)	21.0%	6,977.9	9,770.8	13,945.4	8,629.1	14,936.0
Employees	41.5%	2,151	5,113	5,500	5,341	8,629

THE BLACKSTONE GROUP L.P.

NYSE: BX

345 Park Ave., 31st Fl.
New York, NY 10154
Phone: 212-583-5000
Fax: 212-583-5712
Web: www.blackstone.com

CEO: Stephen A. Schwarzman
CFO: Laurence A. Tosi
HR: Laura Waitz
FYE: December 31
Type: Public

The Blackstone Group knows how to make a scene. Founded in 1985 by industry veterans Peter Peterson and Stephen Schwarzman, the once-reclusive company underwent one of the largest IPOs in the history of mankind in 2007. The massive private equity firm owns stakes in more than 40 companies, manages hedge funds and other funds, and provides mergers and acquisitions and restructuring advice to corporate clients. Blackstone closed its latest private equity fund — worth more than $21 billion — after going public. The firm made one of the largest private equity transactions ever when it acquired Equity Office Properties Trust for some $39 billion in 2007. Blackstone has some $90 billion in assets under management.

	Annual Growth	12/05	12/06	12/07	12/08	12/09
Sales ($ mil.)	(25.1%)	5,639.3	1,120.3	3,050.1	(349.4)	1,773.7
Net income ($ mil.)	—	1,330.7	2,266.2	1,623.2	(1,163.0)	(715.3)
Market value ($ mil.)	(23.0%)	—	—	7,684.9	2,267.6	4,556.1
Employees	14.6%	750	770	1,020	1,340	1,295

BLACKWELL'S BOOK SERVICES

6024 Jean Rd., Bld. G
Lake Oswego, OR 97035
Phone: 503-684-1140
Fax: 503-639-2481
Web: www.blackwell.com

CEO: Andrew Hutchings
CFO: Theresa Evans-Ybarra
HR: Caron Strutz
FYE: August 31
Type: Business segment

Blackwell's Book Services wants you to be more than well-read; it wants you to actively respect the publishing industry and all that is entailed therein. Blackwell's Book Services supplies books and bibliographic products to public, academic, and research libraries around the world. The company's services include physical processing (catalog cards, spine labels, binding), library vendor system interfaces, table of contents enrichment, database maintenance, and collection development and acquisition. The company boasts operations in the UK and the US, but its products are distributed worldwide. Blackwell's Book Services is part of UK-based book retailer Blackwell UK.

BLAIR CORPORATION

220 Hickory St.
Warren, PA 16366
Phone: 814-723-3600
Fax: 814-726-6376
Web: www.blair.com

CEO: Shelley S. Nandkeolyar
CFO: Michael R. (Mike) DelPrince
HR: Daniel R. (Dan) Blair
FYE: December 31
Type: Private

Before you get engrossed in that new issue of *Modern Maturity*, Blair hopes you'll give some attention to its latest mailing. Through its Web site, catalogs, and letter-style pitches, Blair sells men's and women's clothing (most of its sales) to middle-aged and elderly low- to middle-income customers. It also sells home products, such as bath items, bedspreads, collectibles, drapes, kitchenware, and rugs. Most of its merchandise is made to its specifications by independent suppliers. Established in 1910, Blair operates a retail store and a factory outlet in Pennsylvania. Apparel marketer Orchard Brands (formerly Appleseed's Topco), owned by Golden Gate Capital, acquired Blair in May 2007.

BLANDIN PAPER COMPANY

115 SW 1st St.
Grand Rapids, MN 55744
Phone: 218-327-6200
Fax: 218-327-6212

CEO: J. Kevin Lyden
CFO: —
HR: Dale Reed
FYE: December 31
Type: Subsidiary

If you have ever read a magazine or a catalog, then chances are you've touched Blandin Paper. Blandin produces lightweight, coated publication-grade paper for use in magazines, brochures, and direct-mail advertising. It has scored such high-profile deals as supplying the paper for *Sky*, the inflight magazine of Delta Air Lines. Finland-based forestry company UPM-Kymmene bought Blandin in 1997 from the Canadian subsidiary of New Zealand-based Fletcher Challenge Group in order to establish a presence in North America. Blandin's magazine papers production contributes to UPM-Kymmene's largest product segment. The paper business group as a whole accounts for more than 72% of the parent company's sales.

BLARNEY CASTLE OIL AND PROPANE CO.

12218 West St.
Bear Lake, MI 49614
Phone: 231-864-3111
Fax: 231-864-2302
Web: www.blarneycastleoil.com

CEO: D.E. McCarthy
CFO: —
HR: Bill Voeris
FYE: December 31
Type: Private

While kissing the Blarney stone has a reputation for reliably making people loquacious, Blarney Castle Oil and Propane has a reputation for reliably supplying its customers with fuels. The family-owned company transports petroleum products to customers through about 10 office locations in Michigan. Its products include agricultural and commercial fuels (diesel and gasoline), commercial and industrial lubricants and coolants, home heating oil, fuel oil, and propane. Blarney Castle Oil and Propane also operates 90 convenience stores under the EZ Mart brand name.

	Annual Growth	12/04	12/05	12/06	12/07	12/08
Est. sales ($ mil.)	—	—	—	—	—	334.3
Employees	—	—	—	—	—	700

BLAST ENERGY SERVICES, INC.

OTC: BESV

14550 Torrey Chase Blvd., Ste. 330
Houston, TX 77014
Phone: 281-453-2888
Fax: 281-453-2899
Web: www.blastenergyservices.com

CEO: Michael L. Peterson
CFO: John MacDonald
HR: —
FYE: December 31
Type: Public

Despite some financial struggles, Blast Energy Services (formerly Verdisys) is having a blast helping its customers keep pumping out oil from mature fields. Using specially fabricated mobile drilling rigs, the company provides a range of oil and gas services, including lateral drilling and well production enhancement. It also provides satellite telecommunications services to oil and gas companies operating throughout North America. The company, which revamped its management organization following an investigation of its accounting practices, filed for Chapter 11 bankrutcy protection in 2007. It emerged from Chapter 11 in 2008.

	Annual Growth	12/05	12/06	12/07	12/08	12/09
Sales ($ mil.)	(29.3%)	1.2	3.2	0.4	0.4	0.3
Net income ($ mil.)	—	(2.9)	(38.1)	(9.9)	7.0	(1.7)
Market value ($ mil.)	(47.3%)	48.3	22.6	10.5	5.0	3.7
Employees	(13.1%)	7	42	7	6	4

An in-depth profile of this company is available to Hoover's Online members at hoovers.com.

257

BLAST RADIUS INC.

285 Madison Ave., 12th Fl.
New York, NY 10017
Phone: 212-925-4900
Fax: 212-925-5247
Web: www.blastradius.com

CEO: Gurval Caer
CFO: Don Miller
HR: Minda Sherman
FYE: December 31
Type: Subsidiary

Blast Radius wants to help companies leave a crater-sized impression on their customers. The firm provides strategic and marketing consulting services aimed at creating memorable experiences for customers. Its services focus on discovering and meeting customer needs and developing profitable business models for the Internet commerce world. Other services include market research and analysis, as well as marketing consulting services such as brand strategy development. The company has industry practices in retail and consumer goods, media and entertainment, travel and transportation, financial services, and automotive. Founded in 1996, it was acquired by media conglomerate WPP in October 2007.

	Annual Growth	12/04	12/05	12/06	12/07	12/08
Est. sales ($ mil.)	—	—	—	—	—	37.4
Employees	—	—	—	—	—	350

BLISTEX INC.

1800 Swift Dr.
Oak Brook, IL 60523
Phone: 630-571-2870
Fax: 630-571-3437
Web: www.blistex.com

CEO: David C. Arch
CFO: Phillip (Phil) Hoolehan
HR: Dawn Naydenoff
FYE: June 30
Type: Private

As one of the largest lip-care product makers in the US, Blistex would like to gloss over its competition. The company is best known for its Blistex lip-care products, but it also has been delving into other niches of the personal care industry. Blistex has extended its reach and added new products to its existing brands by acquiring new product lines — such as Stridex acne treatments, Kank-A for mouth pain, Foille first aid spray, and Ivarest for poison ivy itch — all in an effort to grow its business. Blistex sells its products mostly through supermarkets (Kroger) and drug and beauty stores (Ulta) worldwide. The Arch family has owned and operated Blistex since founding it in 1947.

BLIZZARD ENTERTAINMENT, INC.

P.O. Box 18979
Irvine, CA 92623
Phone: 949-955-1380
Fax: 949-737-2000
Web: www.blizzard.com

CEO: Michael (Mike) Morhaime
CFO: —
HR: Leonard Grossi Jr.
FYE: December 31
Type: Subsidiary

Blizzard Entertainment hopes to continue to produce a flurry of hit games. A unit of Activision Blizzard, the company develops and publishes video game software, including the popular *Warcraft*, *Starcraft*, and *Diablo* series available for play on PCs and console systems. Blizzard offers its Battle.net online gaming service that enables millions of players around the world to simultaneously play its games. The company has also leveraged its popular games into related products such as action figures, board games, novels, and comic books. Blizzard's parent company, Vivendi Games, was merged with Activision to form Activision Blizzard in 2008.

⊞ BLOCKBUSTER INC.

NYSE: BBI

1201 Elm St.
Dallas, TX 75270
Phone: 214-854-3000
Fax: 214-854-3677
Web: www.blockbuster.com

CEO: James W. (Jim) Keyes
CFO: Thomas M. Casey
HR: —
FYE: December 31
Type: Public

When it comes to renting movies, this company's goal is to remain a Block-buster. Blockbuster is the world's largest video rental chain, with more than 6,500 company-owned or franchised stores in some 17 countries (about 62% are in the US). The chain rents more than 1 billion videos, DVDs, and video games through its Blockbuster Video outlets each year. Customers also can make rentals, purchases, and watch instant downloads through its website Blockbuster Online, which competes with the likes of Netflix and Redbox. The firm is shuttering hundreds of stores and has plans to divest its foreign operations (about a third of revenues) to focus on its North American business as it navigates toward a digital future.

	Annual Growth	12/05	12/06	12/07	12/08	12/09
Sales ($ mil.)	(8.8%)	5,864.4	5,523.5	5,542.4	5,287.9	4,062.4
Net income ($ mil.)	—	(588.1)	54.7	(73.8)	(374.1)	(558.2)
Market value ($ mil.)	(35.0%)	817.0	1,152.5	849.7	274.5	146.0
Employees	(9.8%)	72,600	67,300	59,643	58,561	48,000

BLONDER TONGUE LABORATORIES, INC.

NYSE Amex: BDR

1 Jake Brown Rd.
Old Bridge, NJ 08857
Phone: 732-679-4000
Fax: 732-679-4353
Web: www.blondertongue.com

CEO: James A. Luksch
CFO: Eric S. Skolnik
HR: —
FYE: December 31
Type: Public

Blonder Tongue Laboratories isn't involved in genetic research; the company makes equipment for acquiring and distributing cable TV signals. Its headend system wares include satellite receivers, antennas, and other signal processing devices. Blonder also makes products that distribute signals to TV sets, control subscriber access to programming, and convert microwave signals. It offers a line of concentrators and multiplexers designed for deploying telephony service. Blonder sells to distributors, cable operators, TV broadcasters, and systems integrators that build and operate cable systems for hotels and other multi-unit buildings. Blonder Tongue was founded in 1950 by Isaac Blonder and Ben Tongue.

	Annual Growth	12/05	12/06	12/07	12/08	12/09
Sales ($ mil.)	(5.6%)	36.5	35.8	33.2	35.3	29.0
Net income ($ mil.)	—	(5.5)	(0.6)	(0.6)	(0.4)	0.1
Market value ($ mil.)	(12.6%)	12.1	10.5	10.5	6.3	7.1
Employees	(9.7%)	271	250	232	232	180

BLOOD SYSTEMS, INC.

6210 E. Oak St.
Scottsdale, AZ 85257
Phone: 480-946-4201
Fax: 480-675-5767
Web: www.bloodsystems.org

CEO: J. Daniel (Dan) Connor
CFO: Susan L. Barnes
HR: —
FYE: December 31
Type: Not-for-profit

Blood Systems is a not-for-profit health care service company that operates a network of blood bank facilities. The company collects blood and provides blood products and services to more than 500 hospitals in about 20 states through its United Blood Services and Blood Centers of the Pacific subsidiaries. Blood Systems also provides blood donor testing services through its Blood Systems Laboratories facilities. Its BioCARE division distributes plasma derivative products, and the Quality Source unit provides safety consulting services. The company, which was founded in 1943 as the Salt River Valley Blood Bank, is governed by a voluntary board of directors consisting of community and medical industry leaders.

	Annual Growth	12/04	12/05	12/06	12/07	12/08
Est. sales ($ mil.)	—	—	—	—	—	619.3
Employees	—	—	—	—	—	3,900

BLOOMBERG L.P.

731 Lexington Ave.
New York, NY 10022
Phone: 212-318-2000
Fax: —
Web: www.bloomberg.com

CEO: Daniel L. (Dan) Doctoroff
CFO: —
HR: —
FYE: December 31
Type: Private

What do you do when you've conquered Wall Street? You become mayor of the city that the famous financial district calls home. After leading his financial news and information company to success, Michael Bloomberg left to run the Big Apple. His namesake company remains a leader in the market for business media. Its core product, the Bloomberg Professional, is a service terminal that provides real-time financial news, market data, and analysis. The company also has a syndicated news service, publishes magazines (including *Bloomberg BusinessWeek*), and disseminates business information via Bloomberg Television, radio, and the Web. Michael Bloomberg founded the company in 1981; he owns a majority of the firm.

	Annual Growth	12/04	12/05	12/06	12/07	12/08
Sales ($ mil.)	14.9%	3,500.0	4,100.0	4,700.0	5,400.0	6,100.0
Employees	7.0%	8,000	8,200	9,500	10,800	10,500

BLOOMINGDALE'S, INC.

1000 3rd Ave.
New York, NY 10022
Phone: 212-705-2000
Fax: —
Web: www.bloomingdales.com

CEO: Michael (Mike) Gould
CFO: Bruce Berman
HR: William Baer
FYE: January 31
Type: Subsidiary

Popular culture goes on sale every day at Bloomingdale's. The company runs about 40 upscale stores in a dozen states, including California, Florida, Illinois, and New York. The company's flagship store at 59th and Lexington is a Manhattan institution and tourist attraction in its own right. A smaller Manhattan store opened in SoHo in 2004. In 2010 Bloomies opened its first store outside the US: a 200,000-sq.-ft. outlet in Dubai. Founded in 1872 by brothers Lyman and Joseph Bloomingdale, the store rode the popularity of the hoop skirt to sales success and practically invented the department store concept at the start of the 20th Century. Bloomingdale's is a division of Macy's, Inc.

	Annual Growth	1/04	1/05	1/06	1/07	1/08
Est. sales ($ mil.)	—	—	—	—	—	685.8
Employees	—	—	—	—	—	10,500

BLOUNT INTERNATIONAL, INC.

NYSE: BLT

4909 SE International Way
Portland, OR 97222
Phone: 503-653-4573
Fax: 503-653-4612
Web: www.blount.com

CEO: Joshua L. Collins
CFO: Calvin E. Jenness
HR: Dale C. Johnson Jr.
FYE: December 31
Type: Public

Blount International has its work cut out for it. The outdoor products manufacturer produces cutting chain, guide bars, sprockets, and accessories for chainsaws, concrete-cutting equipment, and lawnmower blades. Blount's lineup is sold under brands Oregon, Carlton, Tiger, and Windsor to chainsaw and yard care equipment OEMs, distributors, and retailers in more than 100 countries. End users include professional loggers, construction workers, and even, homeowners. Subsidiary Gear Products makes hydraulic pump drives and winches, and rotational bearings, for heavy equipment OEMs. The company has manufacturing operations in the US, Canada, Brazil, and China. About two-thirds of its sales are made outside of the US.

	Annual Growth	12/05	12/06	12/07	12/08	12/09
Sales ($ mil.)	(9.7%)	756.6	651.1	515.5	597.0	502.4
Net income ($ mil.)	(31.8%)	106.6	42.5	42.9	38.6	23.0
Market value ($ mil.)	(10.8%)	762.0	643.9	588.8	453.5	483.1
Employees	(5.0%)	3,800	3,400	3,200	3,600	3,100

BLUE BIRD CORPORATION

402 Blue Bird Blvd.
Fort Valley, GA 31030
Phone: 478-825-2021
Fax: 478-822-2457
Web: www.blue-bird.com

CEO: Greg Bennett
CFO: —
HR: Herb Clark
FYE: December 31
Type: Private

Blue Bird is from the "old school" of bus manufacturers. The US's largest school bus maker, Blue Bird also produces commercial and specialty/activity buses. Blue Bird's line of school buses vary in size, engine location, and fuel used. A network of independent distributors sells the company's buses to school districts, churches, businesses, government agencies, and not-for-profit organizations. Blue Bird specialty division makes security buses, shell buses that are finished out by customers, and buses for export. The company also provides financing services through its Blue Bird Financial Services affiliate. In 2006 Blue Bird was acquired by Traxis Group, a subsidiary of Cerberus Capital Management L.P.

BLUE COAT SYSTEMS, INC.

NASDAQ (GM): BCSI

420 N. Mary Ave.
Sunnyvale, CA 94085
Phone: 408-220-2200
Fax: 408-220-2250
Web: www.bluecoat.com

CEO: Brian M. NeSmith
CFO: Brian M. NeSmith
HR: —
FYE: April 30
Type: Public

Blue Coat Systems protects and serves corporate networks. Its proxy appliances protect networks from viruses and other security threats and improve network performance. The company's appliances provide Web content filtering, antivirus protection, spyware prevention, user authentication, and the ability to limit or block peer-to-peer applications such as instant messaging. They can also be configured to provide WAN acceleration, speeding the delivery of business applications with Blue Coat's bandwidth management, protocol optimization, compression, and caching technologies. More than half of its revenues come from customers outside the Americas.

	Annual Growth	4/06	4/07	4/08	4/09	4/10
Sales ($ mil.)	36.8%	141.7	177.7	305.4	444.7	496.1
Net income ($ mil.)	96.1%	2.9	(7.2)	32.6	(8.5)	42.9
Market value ($ mil.)	31.5%	463.8	747.2	899.8	565.2	1,386.6
Employees	21.9%	572	708	1,033	1,434	1,261

BLUE CROSS AND BLUE SHIELD ASSOCIATION

225 N. Michigan Ave.
Chicago, IL 60601
Phone: 312-297-6000
Fax: 312-297-6609
Web: www.bcbs.com

CEO: Scott P. Serota
CFO: Robert J. (Bob) Kolodgy
HR: William J. (Bill) Colbourne
FYE: December 31
Type: Association

These Blue insurers prefer to sing a happy tune. Health plan providers affiliated with the Blue Cross and Blue Shield Association (BCBSA) — known as "the Blues" — serve more than 100 million members nationwide. The association is a federation of about 40 independent health insurance companies who license the Blue Cross and Blue Shield brand names. Member companies own the rights to sell Blue-branded health plans within defined regions. BCBSA coordinates some national programs such as BlueCard, which allows members of one franchisee to have coverage in other service areas, and the Federal Employee Program (FEP), which covers more than half of federal government employees, retirees, and their families.

	Annual Growth	12/04	12/05	12/06	12/07	12/08
Est. sales ($ mil.)	—	—	—	—	—	320.5
Employees	—	—	—	—	—	880

An in-depth profile of this company is available to Hoover's Online members at hoovers.com.

259

BLUE CROSS BLUE SHIELD OF GEORGIA INC

3350 Peachtree Rd., NE	CEO: Monye Connolly
Atlanta, GA 30326	CFO: Jacqueline Williams
Phone: 404-842-8000	HR: Darlene Andrews
Fax: 404-842-8100	FYE: December 31
Web: www.bcbsga.com	Type: Subsidiary

Blue Cross Blue Shield of Georgia (BCBSGA) provides health insurance and related services for more than 3.3 million members in Georgia. The company offers a variety of insurance plans, including HMO, PPO, indemnity, and point-of-service (POS) programs, to groups and individuals throughout the state. BCBSGA also provides disease management services and supplemental insurance products such as dental, vision, life, and disability coverage, as well as Medicare plans. BCBSGA, an independent licensee of Blue Cross and Blue Shield Association, is a subsidiary of WellPoint.

BLUE CROSS BLUE SHIELD OF MICHIGAN

600 E. Lafayette Blvd.	CEO: Daniel J. Loepp
Detroit, MI 48226	CFO: Mark R. Bartlett
Phone: 313-225-9000	HR: Darrell E. Middleton
Fax: 313-225-6764	FYE: December 31
Web: www.bcbsm.com	Type: Not-for-profit

Blue Cross Blue Shield of Michigan is that state's leading health benefits organization, serving millions of members residing in the state or employed by companies headquartered there. The not-for-profit company's insurance offerings include traditional indemnity, PPO, and POS plans, in addition to its Blue Care Network HMO plans. It also provides consumer-directed Flexible Blue plans paired with health savings accounts, as well as options for individual buyers and Medicare beneficiaries. The organization is an independent licensee of the Blue Cross and Blue Shield Association.

	Annual Growth	12/04	12/05	12/06	12/07	12/08
Sales ($ mil.)	7.3%	8,044.2	8,150.6	8,686.5	9,849.0	10,679.8
Net income ($ mil.)	—	411.0	294.9	243.0	177.3	(144.9)
Employees	(0.3%)	—	—	7,047	8,945	7,000

BLUE CROSS OF CALIFORNIA

One WellPoint Way	CEO: Leslie A. Margolin
Thousand Oaks, CA 91362	CFO: —
Phone: 805-557-6655	HR: —
Fax: 805-557-6872	FYE: December 31
Web: www.anthem.com/ca	Type: Subsidiary

Blue Cross of California, which does business as Anthem Blue Cross, provides health insurance and related services to more than 8 million residents of the Golden State. Along with its Anthem Blue Cross Life and Health Insurance affiliate, it offers HMO, PPO, and point-of-service health plans for individuals, employer groups, and public entities. It also sells Medicare supplemental and Medicare Advantage plans to seniors and manages the health care of participants in state-funded programs, such as Medi-Cal (Medicaid) and Healthy Families. Blue Cross of California is a licensee of the Blue Cross and Blue Shield Association and a subsidiary of WellPoint.

BLUE DIAMOND GROWERS

1802 C St.	CEO: Douglas D. Youngdahl
Sacramento, CA 95814	CFO: Robert S. Donovan
Phone: 916-442-0771	HR: Sheryl Guzman
Fax: 916-446-8461	FYE: August 31
Web: bluediamond.com	Type: Cooperative

Blue Diamond Growers is one nutty business. Some 3,000 California almond growers belong to the cooperative, which is a top global player in the tree nut market. The co-op sells almonds and almond products, hazelnuts, macadamia, pistachio, and other nuts to food and candy makers, the foodservice industry, and food retailers. Blue Diamond Growers has developed products such as Almond Breeze, an almond-based, lactose-free milk substitute; Nut Thins crackers; and special cuts and flavored varieties of the nuts. Blue Diamond, formed in 1910, sells its products throughout the US and in more than 90 other countries. It operates processing plants, receiving stations, and retail nut stores in California and Oregon.

	Annual Growth	8/04	8/05	8/06	8/07	8/08
Est. sales ($ mil.)	—	—	—	—	—	711.2
Employees	—	—	—	—	—	1,100

BLUE DOLPHIN ENERGY COMPANY

NASDAQ (CM): BDCO

801 Travis, Ste. 2100	CEO: Ivar Siem
Houston, TX 77002	CFO: —
Phone: 713-227-7660	HR: —
Fax: 713-227-7626	FYE: December 31
Web: www.blue-dolphin.com	Type: Public

Blue Dolphin Energy is trying to stay afloat in the waters of the Gulf of Mexico. The company's primary asset is its 40-mile-long Blue Dolphin Pipeline System, which includes an offshore platform for separation, metering, and compression; the onshore Buccaneer oil pipeline; onshore facilities including 85,000 barrels of surface tankage, separation and dehydration facilities; 360 acres of land; and a barge-loading terminal. On the exploration and production side, Blue Dolphin Energy owns interests in three producing blocks in the High Island area in the Gulf of Mexico and has two exploratory prospects for sale. In 2008 the company reported proved reserves of 162.8 cu. ft. of natural gas equivalent.

	Annual Growth	12/05	12/06	12/07	12/08	12/09
Sales ($ mil.)	(18.4%)	4.5	4.3	3.0	3.0	2.0
Net income ($ mil.)	—	0.5	0.9	(1.6)	(2.0)	(4.1)
Market value ($ mil.)	(37.7%)	25.8	36.7	18.6	4.2	3.9
Employees	(2.9%)	9	9	10	8	8

BLUE NILE, INC.

NASDAQ (GS): NILE

705 5th Ave. South, Ste. 900	CEO: Diane Irvine
Seattle, WA 98104	CFO: Marc D. Stolzman
Phone: 206-336-6700	HR: —
Fax: 206-336-6750	FYE: December 31
Web: www.bluenile.com	Type: Public

Blue Nile helps tech-savvy Marc Antonys bejewel their Cleopatras. The company, which offers luxury-grade jewelry online at bluenile.com, sells loose diamonds, settings, engagement rings, and other jewelry made of gold, platinum, and silver set with diamonds, pearls, emeralds, rubies, and sapphires. It is the leader in online jewelry sales, offering more than 1,000 styles of jewelry, watches, and accessories. Blue Nile also operates Canadian and UK Web sites. Executive chairman Mark Vadon, a discouraged engagement-ring shopper, and Ben Elowitz, formerly of Fatbrain.com, founded the site in 1999 as RockShop.com and, briefly, Internet Diamonds Inc., before adopting the Blue Nile brand name later that year.

	Annual Growth	12/05	12/06	12/07	12/08	12/09
Sales ($ mil.)	10.4%	203.2	251.6	319.3	295.3	302.1
Net income ($ mil.)	(0.8%)	13.2	13.1	17.5	11.6	12.8
Market value ($ mil.)	12.0%	584.7	535.1	987.2	355.2	918.6
Employees	6.7%	146	161	198	177	189

BLUE NOTE LABEL GROUP

150 5th Ave.
New York, NY 10011
Phone: 212-786-8600
Fax: 212-786-8613
Web: www.bluenote.com

CEO: Bruce Lundvall
CFO: —
HR: —
FYE: March 31
Type: Subsidiary

Many jazz enthusiasts would be blue without this venerable label. The legendary Blue Note Label Group is one of the seminal US jazz labels, with a catalog that includes such greats as Art Blakey, John Coltrane, Miles Davis, and Thelonious Monk. The company continues to release re-issues from such masters as Cannonball Adderley, Stan Kenton, and Jimmy Smith while promoting new artists including Terence Blanchard, Norah Jones, and Amos Lee. Blue Note was founded in 1939 by German immigrants Alfred Lion and Francis Wolff, who arrived in the US shortly before the Nazis banned jazz in their home country. The label now operates as part of the jazz division of UK-based EMI Group.

BLUE TEE CORP.

250 Park Ave. South
New York, NY 10003
Phone: 212-598-0880
Fax: 212-598-0896
Web: www.bluetee.com

CEO: William M. Kelly
CFO: David P. Alldian
HR: Annette Marino D'Arienzo
FYE: December 31
Type: Private

Blue Tee has stayed out of the rough through diversification. The company, operating through its many subsidiaries, distributes steel and scrap metal and manufactures a variety of industrial equipment. Blue Tee's Brown-Strauss Steel subsidiary is a leading distributor of structural steel products (beams, pipe, tubing) in the western US. Other operations include AZCON (scrap metal sales and rail cars and parts), GEFCO (portable drilling rigs), Standard Alloys (pump parts), and Steco (dump-truck trailers). Union Tractor provides replacement parts for construction and transportation equipment in western Canada. Blue Tee is owned by its employees.

	Annual Growth	12/04	12/05	12/06	12/07	12/08
Sales ($ mil.)	20.3%	740.7	698.8	852.4	1,103.0	1,549.3
Employees	(16.7%)	—	—	—	1,050	875

BLUE VALLEY BAN CORP.

OTC: BVBC

11935 Riley
Overland Park, KS 66225
Phone: 913-338-1000
Fax: 913-338-2801
Web: www.bankbv.com

CEO: Robert D. (Bob) Regnier
CFO: Mark A. Fortino
HR: Jill Krizek
FYE: December 31
Type: Public

Protect your green at Blue Valley Ban Corp, the holding company of Bank of Blue Valley. Founded in 1989, the bank targets closely-held small to midsized businesses and their owners, plus professionals and residents in Johnson County, Kansas. Through about a half dozen branches located within the Kansas City metropolitan area, the bank provides traditional deposit products, cash management services, investment brokerage, and trust services. Its lending activities are focused on construction loans, which account for about 30% of its portfolio, as well as business and commercial real estate loans, which each account for about a quarter.

	Annual Growth	12/05	12/06	12/07	12/08	12/09
Assets ($ mil.)	2.9%	689.6	692.2	736.2	815.7	774.0
Net income ($ mil.)	—	4.6	6.9	4.5	(10.3)	(14.6)
Market value ($ mil.)	(23.5%)	84.7	96.0	87.6	42.4	28.9
Employees	(6.6%)	265	224	214	197	202

BLUEBOOK INTERNATIONAL

Pink Sheets: BBKH

21098 Bake Pkwy., Ste. 100
Lake Forest, CA 92630
Phone: 949-470-9534
Fax: 949-470-9563
Web: www.bluebook.net

CEO: Mark Josipovich
CFO: Mark Josipovich
HR: –
FYE: December 31
Type: Public

The Bluebook International Holding Company is a provider of estimating software for the insurance industry, focusing on estimates for residential repair and replacement costs for homes. Daniel and Dorothy Josipovich founded the company in 1964; today their sons and daughter run the company. Bluebook International started with publishing a guide to rebuilding costs, called the Bluebook of Cleaning, Reconstruction, and Repair Costs; it later moved into software employing the data from the books, available in desktop and pocket-sized editions. The Josipovich family holds about 80% of the company.

BLUECROSS BLUESHIELD OF TENNESSEE, INC.

1 Cameron Hill Cir.
Chattanooga, TN 37402
Phone: 423-535-5600
Fax: 423-535-6255
Web: www.bcbst.com

CEO: Vicky Gregg
CFO: John Giblin
HR: Ron Harr
FYE: December 31
Type: Not-for-profit

BlueCross BlueShield of Tennessee (BCBST) is the oldest and largest not-for-profit managed care provider in the state of Tennessee. Serving around 3 million people through group and individual policies, the company offers HMO, PPO, and high-deductible health plans. Founded in 1945, BCBST also provides Medicare plans to 2 million customers, and its Group Insurance Services unit brokers vision, dental, life, and disability plans. Its provider network includes some 20,000 physicians, 150 hospitals, and 2,000 pharmacies. The company is a member of the Blue Cross and Blue Shield Association.

BLUEFLY, INC.

NASDAQ (CM): BFLY

42 W. 39th St., 9th Fl.
New York, NY 10018
Phone: 212-944-8000
Fax: 212-354-3400
Web: www.bluefly.com

CEO: Melissa Payner-Gregor
CFO: Kara B. Jenny
HR: —
FYE: December 31
Type: Public

Bargain e-tailer Bluefly aims to fly anywhere but further into the red. The company is an online retailer of designer brand apparel and home accessories for men, women, and teens at prices it claims are 30%–75% cheaper than retail. The Bluefly.com Web site carries more than 50,000 styles from more than 350 brands, including Prada and Calvin Klein. Former chairman Ken Seiff founded the company in 1991 as Pivot Rules to sell golf apparel to young golfers. It discontinued its golf sportswear line and sold its Pivot Rules trademarks to make the transition to an off-price e-tailer. The Bluefly.com site was launched in 1998. Financier George Soros owns about 39% of Bluefly's shares.

	Annual Growth	12/05	12/06	12/07	12/08	12/09
Sales ($ mil.)	8.4%	58.8	77.1	91.5	95.8	81.2
Net income ($ mil.)	—	(3.8)	(12.2)	(15.8)	(11.3)	(4.4)
Market value ($ mil.)	(31.4%)	275.6	314.9	184.5	17.8	61.0
Employees	(0.6%)	85	96	105	88	83

An in-depth profile of this company is available to Hoover's Online members at hoovers.com.

261

BLUEGATE CORPORATION
OTC: BGAT

701 N. Post Oak Rd., Ste. 600
Houston, TX 77024
Phone: 713-686-1100
Fax: 713-682-7402
Web: www.bluegate.com

CEO: Stephen Sperco
CFO: Charles E. (Charlie) Leibold
HR: —
FYE: December 31
Type: Public

Bluegate holds the keys to the gates of medical information. The company provides information technology (IT) services to the health care industry. It specializes in medical-grade network and managed services that meet HIPAA compliance regulations. It serves hospitals, medical practices, and other centralized health care providers. The company operates a leading Medical Grade Network dedicated to health care-related security and privacy concerns; Bluegate markets it as the only such network in the US. Memorial Hermann Health Net Providers, a subsidiary of the Memorial Hermann Healthcare System, is a client; Bluegate also provides services to the Texas-based Renaissance Healthcare Systems.

	Annual Growth	12/05	12/06	12/07	12/08	12/09
Sales ($ mil.)	(36.8%)	2.5	3.7	5.8	4.4	0.4
Net income ($ mil.)	—	(4.2)	(9.2)	(5.1)	(1.8)	(0.3)
Market value ($ mil.)	(74.4%)	18.2	24.7	4.4	0.3	0.1
Employees	(17.9%)	33	35	37	29	15

BLUEGREEN CORPORATION
NYSE: BXG

4960 Conference Way North, Ste. 100
Boca Raton, FL 33431
Phone: 561-912-8000
Fax: 561-912-8100
Web: www.bluegreenonline.com

CEO: John M. Maloney Jr.
CFO: Anthony M. Puleo
HR: Susan J. Saturday
FYE: December 31
Type: Public

If blue-green makes you think of think sunny breezes and tropical waters, then Bluegreen has a time-share for you. Through its Bluegreen Vacation Club, members use points to stay in one of the company's nearly 30 Bluegreen Resorts, or at some 20 other affiliated resorts in such popular vacation spots as Florida; the Carolina coast; the Smoky Mountains; Hershey, Pennsylvania; and Branson, Missouri. The Bluegreen Vacation Club has more than 160,000 members. Through its Bluegreen Communities, the company develops upscale residential subdivisions and golf communities in Texas, Georgia, and North Carolina. The company provides financing for land and time-share purchases.

	Annual Growth	12/05	12/06	12/07	12/08	12/09
Sales ($ mil.)	(14.5%)	684.2	673.4	691.5	602.0	366.0
Net income ($ mil.)	(46.2%)	46.6	34.3	31.9	(0.5)	3.9
Market value ($ mil.)	(37.4%)	514.3	417.6	234.0	101.9	78.8
Employees	(6.6%)	4,789	5,342	5,971	3,369	3,651

BLUEKNIGHT ENERGY PARTNERS, L.P.
Pink Sheets: BKEP

Two Warren Place, 6120 S. Yale Ave., Ste. 500
Tulsa, OK 74136
Phone: 918-524-5500
Fax: 918-524-5805
Web: www.bkep.com

CEO: J. Michael Cockrell
CFO: Alex G. Stallings
HR: —
FYE: December 31
Type: Public

Blueknight Energy Partners (formerly SemGroup Energy Partners) provides gathering, transporting, terminalling, and storage of crude oil in Oklahoma, Kansas, and Texas. The company operates two pipeline systems (1,150 miles of pipeline) delivering crude oil to refineries, and provides storage services with a capacity of about 8.2 million barrels. Blueknight Energy Partners has about 7.4 million barrels of asphalt and residual fuel storage in 46 terminals located in 23 states. Not coincidentally, Blueknight Energy Partners' primary customer is former parent and midstream asset consolidator SemGroup L.P.

	Annual Growth	12/05	12/06	12/07	12/08	12/09
Sales ($ mil.)	66.5%	20.4	28.8	74.6	192.2	156.8
Net income ($ mil.)	—	(27.0)	(35.9)	(12.9)	17.8	(16.5)
Market value ($ mil.)	(43.4%)	—	—	988.8	86.4	317.3
Employees	—	—	0	2,200	400	400

BLUELINX HOLDINGS INC.
NYSE: BXC

4300 Wildwood Pkwy.
Atlanta, GA 30339
Phone: 770-953-7000
Fax: 770-221-8902
Web: bluelinxco.com

CEO: George R. Judd
CFO: Douglas (Doug) Goforth
HR: Dean Adelman
FYE: December 31
Type: Public

You won't find many building products missing from BlueLinx. Through 70-plus warehouses, the company distributes more than 10,000 building products to some 11,500 customers. Structural products, including plywood, oriented strand board, and lumber, account for nearly half of BlueLinx's revenues. The company also offers specialty products, such as roofing, insulation, molding, and engineered wood products. BlueLinx serves building material dealers, home improvement retailers, manufactured housing builders, and industrial users of building products. Founded in 1954 as a division of Georgia-Pacific, the company has been been owned by private equity firm Cerberus Capital Management since 2004.

	Annual Growth	12/05	12/06	12/07	12/08	12/09
Sales ($ mil.)	(26.4%)	5,622.1	4,899.4	3,833.9	2,779.7	1,646.1
Net income ($ mil.)	—	44.6	15.8	(27.9)	(31.7)	(61.5)
Market value ($ mil.)	(29.6%)	367.6	339.8	128.4	61.8	90.5
Employees	(14.8%)	3,600	3,300	2,800	2,100	1,900

BLUESCOPE CONSTRUCTION, INC.

1540 Genessee St.
Kansas City, MO 64102
Phone: 816-245-6000
Fax: 816-245-6099
Web: www.bucon.com

CEO: Dan Kumm
CFO: Kerry Domke
HR: Richard Van Auken
FYE: June 30
Type: Subsidiary

Steel fabrication and construction is within the scope of BlueScope Construction (BSC). The company is the US-based construction subsidiary of Australian steel maker BlueScope Steel. BSC receives its steel materials directly from 10 BlueScope mills in the US. As a design/build general contractor, BSC plans, develops, and builds pre-engineered shells for large structures. Company divisions handle government projects and offer concrete services. BSC usually builds commercial and industrial facilities such as distribution centers, airplane hangars, arenas, manufacturing plants, offices, and warehouses. Customers have included Toys "R" Us, Best Buy, and FedEx Ground.

⊞ BLUESTEM BRANDS, INC.

6509 Flying Cloud
Eden Prairie, MN 55344
Phone: 952-656-3700
Fax: 952-656-4112
Web: www.bluestembrands.com

CEO: Brian Smith
CFO: Karen Miller
HR: —
FYE: January 31
Type: Subsidiary

You might say this company lets your fingers do the shopping. Bluestem Brands (formerly Fingerhut Direct Marketing) offers a broad line of private-label and brand-name merchandise, including apparel, appliances, electronics, furniture, health and beauty products, jewelry, kitchenware, luggage, sporting goods, tools, and toys through its Fingerhut and Gettington.com home shopping businesses. The company also offers credit in partnership with CIT Bank. Founded in 1948 as Fingerhut Companies by William Fingerhut, the company underwent several name and ownership changes before adopting the Bluestem Brands name in 2010. The firm is controlled by Bain Capital and Battery Ventures.

BLUM CAPITAL PARTNERS, L.P.

909 Montgomery St.
San Francisco, CA 94133
Phone: 415-434-1111
Fax: 415-434-3130
Web: www.blumcapital.com

CEO: N. Colin Lind
CFO: Marc T. Schölvinck
HR: Judith van Es
FYE: December 31
Type: Private

Investment firm Blum Capital Partners targets small and middle-market US firms, providing capital for such transactions as share repurchases, acquisitions and divestitures, and privatizations. The partnership invests in a relatively small number of public or private companies (usually around five per year), but typically takes a substantial position either by acquiring a strategic block of the company's shares or through a negotiated transaction. Blum Capital often takes an active role in management. It oversees investments for wealthy families, corporations, and university and philanthropic endowment funds, as well as its own account. Chairman Richard Blum founded the company in 1975.

	Annual Growth	12/04	12/05	12/06	12/07	12/08
Est. sales ($ mil.)	—	—	—	—	—	7.8
Employees	—	—	—	—	—	48

BLYTH, INC.

NYSE: BTH

1 E. Weaver St.
Greenwich, CT 06831
Phone: 203-661-1926
Fax: 203-661-1969
Web: www.blyth.com

CEO: Robert B. Goergen Sr.
CFO: Robert H. Barghaus
HR: Jane F. Casey
FYE: January 31
Type: Public

Blyth prefers to light up the party with one of its wicked products. As the largest candle maker in the US, Blyth sells its scented and unscented candles under the Colonial Candle, PartyLite, Ambria Table Lighting, and Seasons of Cannon Falls names, among others. Its portfolio also extends beyond the candle business with Sterno butane products and lighting, Two Sisters Gourmet sauces and condiments, and ViSalus nutritional supplements, as well as a variety of catalog and online businesses that market household goods and gifts. Blyth's products are sold through home parties and retailers worldwide. It also supplies institutional customers, such as restaurants and hotels. The company was founded in 1977.

	Annual Growth	1/06	1/07	1/08	1/09	1/10
Sales ($ mil.)	(11.7%)	1,573.1	1,220.6	1,164.9	1,050.8	958.1
Net income ($ mil.)	(8.2%)	24.9	(103.2)	11.1	(15.5)	17.7
Market value ($ mil.)	(24.6%)	763.4	731.4	764.8	120.0	247.1
Employees	(19.6%)	5,500	4,000	3,200	2,600	2,300

BMC SOFTWARE, INC.

NASDAQ (GS): BMC

2101 CityWest Blvd.
Houston, TX 77042
Phone: 713-918-8800
Fax: 713-918-8000
Web: www.bmc.com

CEO: Robert E. (Bob) Beauchamp
CFO: Stephen B. (Steve) Solcher
HR: —
FYE: March 31
Type: Public

BMC doesn't stand for Business Mismanagement Cure, but it could. BMC Software is a leading provider of enterprise management software used for a variety of functions, including recovery and storage management, business process scheduling and integration, service management, and application and database performance management. BMC provides tools designed to manage enterprise servers, speed up and monitor databases, eliminate unplanned outages, and recover system assets. It also provides professional services such as consulting and systems integration. BMC sells directly and through channel partners worldwide.

	Annual Growth	3/06	3/07	3/08	3/09	3/10
Sales ($ mil.)	6.3%	1,498.4	1,580.4	1,731.6	1,871.9	1,911.2
Net income ($ mil.)	41.3%	102.0	215.9	313.6	238.1	406.1
Market value ($ mil.)	15.1%	3,931.8	5,589.1	5,903.1	5,990.3	6,897.9
Employees	(0.4%)	6,200	6,000	5,800	5,800	6,100

BMP SUNSTONE CORPORATION

NASDAQ (GM): BJGP

600 W. Germantown Pike, Ste. 400
Plymouth Meeting, PA 19462
Phone: 610-940-1675
Fax: 610-940-1676
Web: www.beijingmedpharm.com

CEO: Xiaoying (David) Gao
CFO: Fred M. Powell
HR: —
FYE: December 31
Type: Public

BMP Sunstone wants to bridge the pharmaceutical divide between the east and west. Through its Chinese-based subsidiaries, BMP offers services to western pharmaceutical and over-the-counter (OTC) drug companies that want to sell their products in China. Services include sales, marketing, pre-market entry analysis, clinical trial management, product registration, and distribution (BMP's largest business segment). The company has agreements with several pharmaceutical companies, including exclusive rights to market and distribute a handful of products. BMP also sells a line of OTC health products targeted to children and women.

	Annual Growth	12/05	12/06	12/07	12/08	12/09
Sales ($ mil.)	143.2%	4.2	24.3	31.0	114.9	146.9
Net income ($ mil.)	—	(5.7)	(6.8)	(11.6)	(3.4)	(1.9)
Market value ($ mil.)	10.1%	163.1	273.9	462.8	234.7	239.8
Employees	96.7%	80	185	1,163	1,273	1,198

BMW MANUFACTURING CORPORATION

1400 Hwy. 101 S.
Greer, SC 29651
Phone: 864-989-6000
Fax: —
Web: www.bmwusfactory.com

CEO: Josef Kerscher
CFO: Sean Noonan
HR: Kathleen Wall
FYE: December 31
Type: Subsidiary

BMW Manufacturing Corporation serves up German engineering with a little Southern hospitality on the side. The company builds the M Roadster and Coupe, the X5 SUV and xDrive35d (diesel), and the X6 SUV Coupe and ActiveHybrid. The 2.5-million-sq.-ft. factory, BMW's first full manufacturing facility outside Germany and the only US BMW plant, delivers its cars throughout the US and worldwide. One of the greenest car manufacturing facilities anywhere, BMW Manufacturing uses water-based (rather than solvent) paints and powers the plant with recycled landfill methane gas. The plant, built in 1994, averages a daily output of approximately 600 vehicles.

BMW OF NORTH AMERICA, LLC

300 Chestnut Ridge Rd.
Woodcliff Lake, NJ 07677
Phone: 201-307-4000
Fax: 201-307-0880
Web: www.bmwgroupna.com

CEO: Jim O'Donnell
CFO: Stefan Sengewald
HR: —
FYE: December 31
Type: Subsidiary

A subsidiary of BMW, BMW of North America provides marketing, sales, and financial services through almost 900 dealerships and motorcycle retailers. The company imports and manufactures BMW brands, such as the 1, 3, 5, 6, 7 Series; the X5, X6, and 24M models; and the MINI and Rolls-Royce brands. Styles include coupes, convertibles, sedans, roadsters, sports activity, and luxury vehicles. Divisions include BMW Manufacturing (South Carolina), industrial-design firm DesignworksUSA, a parts distribution center, a technology office, a technical training center, and other operations in the US. Charged to oversee the group's largest single market — the US — BMW of North America was established in 1975.

An in-depth profile of this company is available to Hoover's Online members at hoovers.com.

263

BNC BANCORP

NASDAQ (CM): BNCN

831 Julian Ave.
Thomasville, NC 27360
Phone: 336-476-9200
Fax: 336-476-5818
Web: www.bankofnc.com

CEO: W. Swope Montgomery Jr.
CFO: David B. Spencer
HR: —
FYE: December 31
Type: Public

BNC Bancorp knows the ABCs of the financial world. The firm is the holding company for Bank of North Carolina, which has about 20 locations in both North and South Carolina. The bank offers community-oriented services to local business and retail customers, providing checking, savings, and money market accounts, credit cards, and CDs. Its loan portfolio is mainly composed of residential and commercial mortgages and construction loans. Bank of North Carolina also offers insurance, retirement planning, and other investment products and services. In 2010 BNC Bancorp acquired the failed Beach First National Bank in an FDIC-assisted transaction, expanding Bank of North Carolina's branch network into South Carolina.

	Annual Growth	12/05	12/06	12/07	12/08	12/09
Assets ($ mil.)	28.8%	594.5	951.7	1,130.1	1,572.9	1,634.2
Net income ($ mil.)	9.6%	4.5	6.2	7.4	4.0	6.5
Market value ($ mil.)	(18.1%)	123.8	136.4	124.2	55.1	55.7
Employees	16.5%	142	193	223	222	262

BNCCORP, INC.

Pink Sheets: BNCC

322 E. Main Ave.
Bismarck, ND 58501
Phone: 701-250-3040
Fax: 701-222-3653
Web: www.bnccorp.com

CEO: Gregory K. Cleveland
CFO: Timothy J. Franz
HR: —
FYE: December 31
Type: Public

BNCCORP is the holding company for BNC National Bank, which has about 20 branches in Arizona, North Dakota, and Minnesota. Serving individuals and small and midsized businesses, the bank offers deposit accounts, credit cards, and wealth management services. It also has residential mortgage banking operations in Iowa, Kansas, and Missouri. Real estate loans account for nearly half of the company's portfolio; commercial, industrial, construction, agricultural, and consumer loans make up most of the remainder. BNCCORP sold its insurance agency subsidiary BNC Insurance Services to Hub International in 2007 for more than $37 million.

BNS HOLDING, INC.

Pink Sheets: BNSSA

61 E. Main St., Ste. B
Los Gatos, CA 95031
Phone: 401-848-6300
Fax: —
Web: www.bnsholding.com

CEO: Kenneth N. Kermes
CFO: Terry Gibson
HR: —
FYE: October 31
Type: Public

BNS has a new bag. Without any business operations for two years, the company acquired 80% of bus manufacturer Collins Industries in late 2006. Formerly Brown & Sharpe Manufacturing, BNS changed its name in 2001 when debt and a history of losses prompted it to sell its metrology instrument business (substantially all of its sales) to Hexagon AB. Included in the sale were BNS' Measuring Systems Group (coordinate measuring machines), its Precision Measuring Instruments Division (mechanical and electronic measuring tools), its Xygent subsidiary (metrology software), and the Brown & Sharpe brand name. BNS has also sold its remaining UK real estate. Steel Partners owns about 42% of the firm.

BOARDWALK PIPELINE PARTNERS, LP

NYSE: BWP

9 Greenway Plaza, Ste. 2800
Houston, TX 77046
Phone: 713-479-8000
Fax: —
Web: www.boardwalkpipelines.com

CEO: Rolf A. Gafvert
CFO: Jamie L. Buskill
HR: —
FYE: December 31
Type: Public

Boardwalk Pipeline Partners is in the business of interstate transportation, gathering, and storage of natural gas, and it operates three subsidiaries — Texas Gas Transmission, Gulf South Pipeline Company, and Gulf Crossing Pipeline Company — with a combined 14,200 miles of pipeline in 11 states. Texas Gas operates in Arkansas, Illinois, Indiana, Kentucky, Louisiana, Mississippi, Ohio, Tennessee, and Texas. Gulf South operates in Alabama, Florida, Louisiana, Mississippi, and Texas. Customers include local gas distribution companies, local governments, other interstate and intrastate pipeline companies, industrial users, and electric power generators. Boardwalk Pipeline Partners is owned by Loews Corporation.

	Annual Growth	12/05	12/06	12/07	12/08	12/09
Sales ($ mil.)	12.9%	560.5	607.6	643.3	784.8	909.2
Net income ($ mil.)	12.7%	100.9	197.6	220.7	294.0	162.7
Market value ($ mil.)	13.7%	3,462.7	5,935.6	5,989.5	3,424.2	5,783.4
Employees	0.2%	1,100	1,150	1,084	1,128	1,110

BOAR'S HEAD PROVISIONS CO., INC.

1819 Main St., Ste. 800
Sarasota, FL 34236
Phone: 941-955-0994
Fax: —
Web: www.boarshead.com

CEO: Robert S. Martin
CFO: —
HR: Scott Habermehl
FYE: August 31
Type: Private

Boar's Head Provisions is more of a ham than a bore. Under the Boar's Head brand name, the company manufactures and distributes specialty deli meats, cheeses, and soups to restaurants, grocers, and delicatessens throughout the US. Its products are distributed in distinctive black and red refrigerated trucks owned by its sister company, Frank Brunckhorst Company. Boar's Head has operations in Arkansas, Florida, Michigan, New Jersey, New York, and Virginia. The company was founded in 1905 by Frank Brunckhorst, who delivered his foods by horse-drawn wagon to small delicatessens and mom-and-pop stores in New York City. It is still owned and operated by his descendants.

BOART LONGYEAR LIMITED

Australian: BLY

2640 W. 1700 St. South
Salt Lake City, UT 84104
Phone: 801-972-6430
Fax: 801-977-3374
Web: www.boartlongyear.com

CEO: Craig P. Kipp
CFO: Joseph D. (Joe) Ragan III
HR: Brad Baker
FYE: December 31
Type: Public

Boart Longyear is the company to call if you need to dig yourself out of a big hole — literally. The company manufactures drilling machinery and provides services to mining, energy, and infrastructure companies worldwide. Although the majority of Boart Longyear's business is geared toward mining activities, the company also caters to industrial businesses that utilize its hardmetal and diamond technologies. The company, which was founded in 1936 to develop new ways to make use of Anglo American's excess boart (low-grade natural diamond), now operates worldwide.

	Annual Growth	12/05	12/06	12/07	12/08	12/09
Sales ($ mil.)	(21.4%)	—	—	1,583.5	1,850.3	978.2
Net income ($ mil.)	—	—	—	80.6	156.2	(14.8)
Market value ($ mil.)	(56.3%)	—	—	7,656.7	513.7	1,461.8
Employees	—	—	—	7,800	—	—

BOB EVANS FARMS, INC.

NASDAQ (GS): BOBE

3776 S. High St.
Columbus, OH 43207
Phone: 614-491-2225
Fax: 614-492-4949
Web: www.bobevans.com

CEO: Steven A. (Steve) Davis
CFO: Tod P. Spornhauer
HR: Joseph R. (Joe) Eulberg
FYE: April 30
Type: Public

This company might suggest that breakfast sausage is the most important meal of the day. Bob Evans Farms operates a chain of 570 family-style restaurants in about 20 states that are best known for their breakfast menu of bacon, eggs, hotcakes, and sausage products. The company also has three production facilities where it makes its own sausage and bacon products that are sold under the Bob Evans and Owens brands at supermarkets and other grocery retailers. In addition, subsidiary SWH Corporation operates Mimi's Café, a chain of more than 140 full-service restaurants offering American-style dishes served with a New Orleans twist.

	Annual Growth	4/05	4/06	4/07	4/08	4/09
Sales ($ mil.)	4.6%	1,460.2	1,584.8	1,654.5	1,737.0	1,750.5
Net income ($ mil.)	—	37.0	54.8	60.5	64.9	(5.1)
Market value ($ mil.)	4.4%	621.8	879.6	1,118.6	855.5	739.1
Employees	(3.0%)	52,558	50,810	51,092	49,149	46,495

BOBCAT COMPANY

250 E. Beaton Dr.
West Fargo, ND 58078
Phone: 701-241-8700
Fax: —
Web: www.bobcat.com

CEO: Scott R. Nelson
CFO: —
HR: —
FYE: December 31
Type: Subsidiary

What a cute little bulldozer you've got there! Bobcat Company specializes in compact construction and utility equipment. Its products include mini-track and skid-steer loaders, loader backhoes, excavators, and attachments for all of them. Its brand lines include the M-Series (mini), CT-Series (compact tractor), Toolcat (utility), and VersaHandler (telescopic tool). Based in North Dakota, the company operates manufacturing facilities in the US, the Czech Republic, and France. There are more than 900 Bobcat dealers in 75 countries. In 2007 Ingersoll-Rand sold Bobcat, along with its utility equipment and attachments businesses, to Korea's Doosan Infracore and Doosan Engine for almost $5 billion.

BOB'S DISCOUNT FURNITURE, LLC.

428 Tolland Tpke.
Manchester, CT 06040
Phone: 860-645-3208
Fax: 860-645-4056
Web: www.mybobs.com

CEO: Edmond J. (Ted) English
CFO: Bill Ballou
HR: —
FYE: December 31
Type: Private

Bob's Discount Furniture operates about 35 furniture stores (featuring mini-golf courses and complimentary refreshments) in Connecticut, Massachusetts, New Hampshire, and four other eastern states. Bob's also offers several in-store "outlets" where customers can buy discounted furniture that has been discontinued, returned, or slightly damaged. Following a 1976 motorcycle accident, company founder and president Bob Kaufman (who's something of a celebrity in the Northeast, thanks to his quirky television commercials) spent months recuperating in a waterbed. Fully recovered and inspired by his experience, Kaufman partnered with cousin Gene Rosenberg and opened up the first Bob's Discount Furniture shop in 1991.

	Annual Growth	12/04	12/05	12/06	12/07	12/08
Est. sales ($ mil.)	—	—	—	—	—	460.0
Employees	—	—	—	—	—	1,800

BOB'S STORES CORP.

160 Corporate Ct.
Meriden, CT 06450
Phone: 203-235-5775
Fax: 203-634-0129
Web: www.bobstores.com

CEO: Kelly Toussaint
CFO: Tom Glynn
HR: Allison Baldwin
FYE: January 31
Type: Private

Bob's Stores sells name-brand clothing, including casual and sports apparel, and footwear at discount prices for men, women, and children. The company operates about 35 locations in six northeastern states (primarily Connecticut and Massachusetts) that target moderate to upper-middle income shoppers. Bob's Stores average about 45,000 square feet. The company was established in 1954 by Bob Lapidus. In 2008 private equity firms Versa Capital Management and Crystal Capital purchased Bob's Stores from off-price giant TJX Companies, which had acquired the retailer out of bankruptcy five years earlier.

BOCA FOODS COMPANY

910 Mayer Ave.
Madison, WI 53704
Phone: 608-285-3311
Fax: 608-285-6741
Web: www.bocafoods.com

CEO: Michael Hsu
CFO: —
HR: —
FYE: December 31
Type: Subsidiary

Boca Foods is saving cows, one burger at a time. The company, a subsidiary of Kraft Foods, makes frozen low-fat meatless products, including burgers, breakfast links, ground crumbles, and breaded *faux* chicken nuggets and patties. It also offers entrees such as "meat" lasagna and chili. The products, which are soy-based (using organic and non-organic soy protein), provide the consumer with the needed protein normally found in meat. The company's products are mainly sold through US grocery retailers, but Boca has begun to offer its products to restaurants as well. Kraft acquired Boca Foods from private investment firm Austin Ventures in 2000.

BODDIE-NOELL ENTERPRISES, INC.

1021 Noell Ln.
Rocky Mount, NC 27804
Phone: 252-937-2800
Fax: 252-937-2978
Web: www.bneinc.com

CEO: William L. (Bill) Boddie
CFO: Craig Worthy
HR: Robert Crumley
FYE: December 31
Type: Private

Boddie-Noell Enterprises (BNE) is a hearty competitor in the fast-food business. The company is one of the largest franchise operators of Hardee's, a fast-food chain owned by CKE Restaurants, with about 340 locations in four southeastern states. BNE also operates 10 Moe's Southwest Grill quick-Mex units franchised from FOCUS Brands. In addition, the company has three of its own restaurant concepts, Texas Steakhouse & Saloon, Café Carolina & Bakery, and The Highway Diner. BNE is also involved in real estate development through BNE Land & Development. The family-owned company was started in 1962 by Carleton Noell and his nephews Nick and Mayo Boddie.

	Annual Growth	12/04	12/05	12/06	12/07	12/08
Est. sales ($ mil.)	—	—	—	—	—	397.8
Employees	—	—	—	—	—	13,000

An in-depth profile of this company is available to Hoover's Online members at hoovers.com.

265

BODYCOTE THERMAL PROCESSING, INC.

12700 Park Central Dr., Ste. 700
Dallas, TX 75251
Phone: 214-904-2420
Fax: 214-904-2424
Web: htna.bodycote.com

CEO: Martyn A. Wilton
CFO: David Starkie
HR: Alan Madden
FYE: December 31
Type: Subsidiary

Bodycote Thermal Processing knows how to turn up the heat. The company, a subsidiary of UK-based Bodycote International plc, heat-treats metal components to improve their mechanical properties, durability, and wear resistance. Bodycote Thermal Processing processes aircraft and auto parts, sporting goods (golf clubs), and oil field, mining, and agricultural equipment. Its heat-treating processes include hardening, tempering, and annealing. The company doesn't sell parts, but its customers are primarily parts suppliers to manufacturers in the commercial aerospace, automotive, defense, and consumer products industries. It operates over 50 facilities throughout the US and Canada, with major operations in Texas and California.

BOEHRINGER INGELHEIM CORPORATION

900 Ridgebury Rd.
Ridgefield, CT 06877
Phone: 203-798-9988
Fax: 203-791-6234
Web: us.boehringer-ingelheim.com

CEO: J. Martin Carroll
CFO: —
HR: —
FYE: December 31
Type: Subsidiary

As the US headquarters of German drugmaker Boehringer Ingelheim, Boehringer Ingelheim Corporation oversees about half a dozen stateside subsidiaries that produce and sell drugs (both prescription and over-the-counter), animal health products, and chemicals for the US market. It sells its prescription and OTC products through its largest unit, Boehringer Ingelheim Pharmaceuticals. Additionally, the firm's Roxane Laboratories makes generic drugs, and its Ben Venue Laboratories is a contract pharmaceutical manufacturer and provides drug development services to other pharmaceutical companies.

BOEHRINGER INGELHEIM PHARMACEUTICALS, INC.

900 Ridgebury Rd.
Ridgefield, CT 06877
Phone: 203-798-9988
Fax: 203-791-6234
Web: us.boehringer-ingelheim.com

CEO: J. Martin Carroll
CFO: Stefan Rinn
HR: David Nurnberger
FYE: December 31
Type: Subsidiary

Boehringer Ingelheim Pharmaceuticals brings a little German drugmaking know-how to the USA. The firm is the pharmaceuticals unit of Boehringer Ingelheim Corporation, which is the US headquarters of Germany's Boehringer Ingelheim. It sells a range of prescription and over-the-counter drugs in the US market, including respiratory treatments Spiriva and Atrovent; high blood pressure medication Micardis; enlarged prostate treatment Flomax; Parkinson's disease drug Mirapex; and HIV/AIDS products Aptivus and Viramune. It is also an R&D center for Boehringer Ingelheim, specializing in immunology, inflammatory conditions, and cardiovascular disease.

🔲 THE BOEING COMPANY

NYSE: BA

100 N. Riverside Plaza
Chicago, IL 60606
Phone: 312-544-2000
Fax: 312-544-2082
Web: www.boeing.com

CEO: W. James (Jim) McNerney Jr.
CFO: James A. Bell
HR: Gary Moore
FYE: December 31
Type: Public

The world's largest aerospace company, Boeing is the #2 maker of large commercial jets (behind rival Airbus) and the #2 defense contractor behind Lockheed Martin. Boeing's business units include Commercial Airplanes and Boeing Defense, Space & Security (BDS; composed of Military Aircraft, Network & Space Systems, and Global Services & Support). The company also provides financing and leasing services to both commercial and military/aerospace customers through its Boeing Capital Corporation. Boeing makes about 60% of its sales in the Americas. The US DoD generates about 80% of BDS revenues; NASA and international defense agencies, as well as satellite markets, are also customers.

	Annual Growth	12/05	12/06	12/07	12/08	12/09
Sales ($ mil.)	5.6%	54,845.0	61,530.0	66,387.0	60,909.0	68,281.0
Net income ($ mil.)	(15.3%)	2,555.0	2,215.0	4,074.0	2,672.0	1,312.0
Market value ($ mil.)	(6.3%)	53,314.7	67,432.8	66,385.3	32,388.1	41,086.6
Employees	0.7%	153,000	154,000	159,300	162,200	157,100

BOEING SATELLITE SYSTEMS INTERNATIONAL, INC.

2260 E. Imperial Hwy.
El Segundo, CA 90245
Phone: 310-662-9000
Fax: —
Web: www.boeing.com/satellite

CEO: Craig R. Cooning
CFO: John Sebek
HR: Diane Shapiro
FYE: December 31
Type: Subsidiary

Boeing Satellite Systems International is happiest when its products are far, far away. The company is a contracting unit for commercial spacecraft within Boeing's Space & Intelligence Systems division. It manufactures communications, meteorological, military, and research satellites. Boeing Satellite Systems International built the world's first geosynchronous communications satellite (Syncom); since its inception in 1961, the company estimates that it has manufactured almost 40% of all the communications satellites in commercial service today. Typical satellite applications include weather forecasting, radar mapping, telecommunications, satellite television, and national security.

	Annual Growth	12/04	12/05	12/06	12/07	12/08
Est. sales ($ mil.)	—	—	—	—	—	640.8
Employees	—	—	—	—	—	7,500

BOFI HOLDING, INC.

NASDAQ (GM): BOFI

12777 High Bluff Dr., Ste. 100
San Diego, CA 92130
Phone: 858-350-6200
Fax: 858-350-0443
Web: www.bofiholding.com

CEO: Gregory Garrabrants
CFO: Andrew J. Micheletti
HR: —
FYE: June 30
Type: Public

BofI Holding owns Bank of Internet USA, a savings bank that operates online in all 50 states. The bank offers checking, savings, and money market accounts, CDs, and ATM and check cards. Multifamily real estate loans account for nearly two-thirds of the company's loan portfolio, although the bank only offers them in selected states; it also acquires them on the secondary market. Offered nationwide, single-family residential mortgages make up nearly 30% of its loan portfolio. Bank of Internet USA also issues home equity, automobile, and recreational vehicle loans. Officers and directors own more than 30% of BofI Holding's stock.

	Annual Growth	6/05	6/06	6/07	6/08	6/09
Assets ($ mil.)	20.9%	609.5	737.8	947.2	1,194.2	1,302.2
Net income ($ mil.)	22.4%	2.9	3.3	3.3	4.2	6.5
Market value ($ mil.)	(9.4%)	90.9	80.3	72.8	74.3	61.2
Employees	21.7%	26	26	40	44	57

BOGEN COMMUNICATIONS INTERNATIONAL, INC.

Pink Sheets: BOGN

50 Spring St.
Ramsey, NJ 07446
Phone: 201-934-8500
Fax: 201-934-9832
Web: www.bogen.com

CEO: Jonathan G. Guss
CFO: Maureen A. Flotard
HR: Jill Glatman
FYE: December 31
Type: Public

Bogen Communications knows how the soothing sounds of smooth jazz can make time fly while holding on the telephone. Through subsidiaries Bogen Communications and Speech Design, the company makes telecommunications peripherals and sound equipment. Bogen Communications sells telecom equipment, including music-on-hold devices, unified messaging systems, call distributors, and voice mail systems. Speech Design sells call processing and PBX products, primarily in Germany. Bogen also makes audio amplifiers and speaker systems. Schools, restaurants, and stores use the company's line of intercom and paging systems for public address and background music. Executives and directors together own a majority of Bogen.

BÖHLER-UDDEHOLM CORPORATION

2505 Milennium Dr.
Elgin, IL 60124
Phone: 800-638-2520
Fax: 630-883-3101
Web: www.bucorp.com

CEO: Theresa Brisko
CFO: —
HR: —
FYE: December 31
Type: Subsidiary

Böhler-Uddeholm Corporation makes tooling materials for the North American industrial community. The company's main product is high-performance tool steel, which includes cold work steels, hot work steels, and plastics molding steels. The company's Steel Stores are warehouses that sell custom-cut steel to US tool and die customers. The company is the North American unit of Austrian specialty steel manufacturer BÖHLER-UDDEHOLM.

⊞ BOISE CASCADE HOLDINGS, L.L.C.

1111 W. Jefferson St., Ste. 900
Boise, ID 83702
Phone: 208-384-6161
Fax: —
Web: www.bc.com

CEO: Thomas E. Carlile
CFO: Wayne M. Rancourt
HR: John Sahlberg
FYE: December 31
Type: Private

Boise Cascade Holdings (BCH) manufactures and distributes lumber, plywood, particleboard, and engineered products such as wood I-joists and laminated lumber. It also operates about 30 wholesale building material distribution centers throughout the US that sell a broad line of building materials, including those made by the company. To better focus on its core wood products and building materials distribution businesses, the firm sold its paper, packaging, and newsprint businesses in 2008. Formerly part of Boise Cascade Corporation (now OfficeMax), BCH is controlled by private investment firm Madison Dearborn Partners through Forest Products Holdings.

	Annual Growth	12/04	12/05	12/06	12/07	12/08
Sales ($ mil.)	(15.1%)	5,734.8	5,907.0	5,779.9	5,413.5	2,977.5
Net income ($ mil.)	—	94.2	121.0	71.6	127.7	(288.0)
Employees	(18.6%)	10,494	10,155	10,191	10,042	4,600

BOISE INC.

NYSE: BZ

1111 W. Jefferson St., Ste. 200
Boise, ID 83799
Phone: 208-384-7000
Fax: 208-384-7332
Web: www.boiseinc.com

CEO: Alexander Toeldte
CFO: Robert McNutt
HR: —
FYE: December 31
Type: Public

Boise Inc. may have built its business on paper, but this company is no house of cards. Boise Inc. manufactures paper and packaging products including corrugated containers, containerboard, label and release paper, flexible packaging paper, multipurpose office paper, and newsprint. The company operates five paper mills, five corrugated products plants, a corrugated sheet plant, and two distribution facilities. Boise Inc.'s customers include retail paper merchants, commercial and financial printers, manufacturers of forms and envelopes, and clients in the packaging industry. The company was formed in 2008 when Aldabra 2 Acquisition Corp. purchased the paper and packaging assets of Boise Cascade.

	Annual Growth	12/05	12/06	12/07	12/08	12/09
Sales ($ mil.)	1,279.2%	—	—	10.4	2,070.6	1,978.2
Net income ($ mil.)	428.8%	—	—	5.5	(45.5)	153.8
Market value ($ mil.)	(26.0%)	—	—	821.9	36.4	450.1
Employees	(5.7%)	—	—	—	4,350	4,100

BOISE STATE UNIVERSITY

1910 University Dr.
Boise, ID 83725
Phone: 208-426-1000
Fax: 208-426-2449
Web: www.boisestate.edu

CEO: Robert W. (Bob) Kustra
CFO: Stacy Pearson
HR: Jane Buser
FYE: June 30
Type: School

It's gotta be noisy at Boise. Boise State University (BSU) has an enrollment of approximately 20,000 students and a faculty and a staff of more than 2,400. The university offers nearly 200 undergraduate, graduate, and technical fields of study through seven colleges: Arts and Sciences, Business and Economics, Education, Engineering, Health Sciences, Social Sciences and Public Affairs, and Graduate Studies. In addition to its main campus in Boise, Idaho, it operates a satellite campus in Nampa (Boise State West), which offers academic, non-credit, and applied technology courses. BSU also has three centers elsewhere in the state, as well as online learning programs.

	Annual Growth	6/04	6/05	6/06	6/07	6/08
Est. sales ($ mil.)	—	—	—	—	—	166.6
Employees	—	—	—	—	—	1,879

BOJANGLES' HOLDINGS INC.

9432 Southern Pines Blvd.
Charlotte, NC 28273
Phone: 704-527-2675
Fax: 704-523-6803
Web: www.bojangles.com

CEO: Randy Kibler
CFO: John Jordan
HR: Vickie Smith
FYE: December 31
Type: Subsidiary

This Bojangles doesn't dance in worn-out shoes, but it will cook some chicken for you. Bojangles' Holdings operates and franchises more than 440 quick-service eateries in North Carolina and about a dozen other states. Operating under the name Bojangles' Famous Chicken & Biscuits, the restaurants specialize in Cajun-style chicken and biscuits. The menu also includes chicken sandwiches and Buffalo-style chicken wings, along with breakfast items. The chain includes more than 150 company-owned locations; the rest are operated by franchisees. Founded in 1977 by former KFC president Richard Thomas and partner Jack Fulk, Bojangles' is owned by an investor group led by Falfurrias Capital Partners.

	Annual Growth	12/04	12/05	12/06	12/07	12/08
Est. sales ($ mil.)	—	—	—	—	—	97.6
Employees	—	—	—	—	—	4,500

⊞ An in-depth profile of this company is available to Hoover's Online members at hoovers.com.

267

BOK FINANCIAL CORPORATION

NASDAQ (GS): BOKF

Bank of Oklahoma Tower
Tulsa, OK 74192
Phone: 918-588-6000
Fax: 918-588-6853
Web: www.bokf.com

CEO: Stanley A. (Stan) Lybarger
CFO: Steven E. Nell
HR: —
FYE: December 31
Type: Public

Will your money BOK? Multibank holding company BOK Financial tries to make sure it is. With seven principal banking subsidiaries in eight midwestern and southwestern states, BOK offers a range of financial services to consumers and regional businesses. The banks provide deposits, loans, and credit cards, as well as brokerage, investment management, and trust services through a network of about 200 branches in Arizona, Arkansas, Colorado, Kansas, Missouri, New Mexico, Oklahoma, and Texas. Commercial loans, primarily to the energy, services, health care, and wholesale and retail industries, make up a majority of BOK's loan portfolio. Commercial real estate, residential mortgage, car, and consumer loans round out its lending.

	Annual Growth	12/05	12/06	12/07	12/08	12/09
Assets ($ mil.)	9.7%	16,252.9	18,059.6	20,839.9	22,734.6	23,516.8
Net income ($ mil.)	(0.1%)	201.5	213.0	217.7	153.2	200.6
Market value ($ mil.)	1.1%	3,091.2	3,741.0	3,517.8	2,748.9	3,233.4
Employees	3.3%	3,825	3,958	4,110	4,300	4,355

THE BOLDT COMPANY

2525 N. Roemer Rd.
Appleton, WI 54911
Phone: 920-739-6321
Fax: 920-739-4409
Web: www.theboldtcompany.com

CEO: Thomas J. Boldt
CFO: Dale Von Behren
HR: Jeff Johnson
FYE: December 31
Type: Holding company

The Boldt Company is a fourth-generation, family-run construction firm operating through three divisions: Boldt Consulting Services, Oscar J. Boldt Construction, and Boldt Technical Services. The group offers strategic planning, program and design management, and maintenance services. It has worked on sports facilities, schools and universities, and power facilities. The group's Boldt Consulting Services unit provides planning services for the health care, senior living, higher education, and commercial sectors. Founded by Martin Boldt in Appleton, Wisconsin, in 1889, the company has grown to be one of the state's largest general contractors.

	Annual Growth	12/04	12/05	12/06	12/07	12/08
Est. sales ($ mil.)	—	—	—	—	—	651.8
Employees	—	—	—	—	—	1,500

BOLT TECHNOLOGY CORPORATION

NASDAQ (GS): BOLT

4 Duke Place
Norwalk, CT 06854
Phone: 203-853-0700
Fax: 203-854-9601
Web: www.bolt-technology.com

CEO: Raymond M. Soto
CFO: Joseph Espeso
HR: Jolsen Stetso
FYE: June 30
Type: Public

Bolt Technology's action is technology, the kind used to map out oil and gas discoveries. The company's product suite consists of the key components needed by seismic exploration vessels to acquire seismic data: an energy source (air guns); synchronization (controllers); and communication (cables) linking the guns and the controllers. Its marine air guns help produce 3-D seismic maps for oil and gas exploration by firing high-pressure air into the water, producing elastic waves that penetrate deep into the earth. These waves are then used to create a "map" of the subsurface geography. The company's major customers include CCG-Veritas and Schlumberger. Bolt Technology was established in 1962.

	Annual Growth	6/05	6/06	6/07	6/08	6/09
Sales ($ mil.)	27.0%	18.8	32.6	50.5	61.6	48.9
Net income ($ mil.)	57.6%	1.7	4.8	10.6	14.6	10.5
Market value ($ mil.)	27.4%	37.1	70.0	255.3	196.2	97.7
Employees	12.8%	86	100	113	132	139

BOMBARDIER FLEXJET

3400 Waterview Pkwy., Ste. 400
Richardson, TX 75080
Phone: 972-720-2400
Fax: —
Web: www.flexjet.com

CEO: Frederick W. Reid
CFO: —
HR: —
FYE: January 31
Type: Business segment

Bombardier's Flexjet division (known as Flexjet) offers fractional jet ownership services, in which customers acquire partial ownership of aircraft operated by the company. With ownership comes a specified number of flying hours — think of the arrangement as an airborne timeshare. (A one-sixteenth share of an airplane equates to 50 hours of flight time per year.) Through its Flexjet 25 program, customers can also buy flight time in 25-hour blocks without taking an ownership interest in a plane. Flexjet's fleet of around 100 aircraft includes Learjet and Challenger business jets manufactured by the company's parent, Montreal-based Bombardier. Flexjet was established in 1995 as a JV with American Airlines.

BOMBARDIER SKYJET

3400 Waterview Pkwy., Ste. 400
Dallas, TX 75080
Phone: 888-275-9538
Fax: 469-791-4470
Web: www.skyjet.com

CEO: Chris Milligan
CFO: Amy van Doren
HR: —
FYE: January 31
Type: Subsidiary

Bombardier Skyjet, a division of Bombardier Aerospace, provides on-demand private jet charter and jet card programs for frequent travelers of the jet-set variety, particularly corporate executives. The company maintains a website for customers to book flights and access accounts. Established in 1997, Bombardier Skyjet serves more than 5,000 airports, primarily in the US and Europe. Customers can fly across more than 60 countries worldwide.

BON SECOURS HEALTH SYSTEM, INC.

1505 Marriottsville Rd.
Marriottsville, MD 21104
Phone: 410-442-5511
Fax: 410-442-1082
Web: www.bshsi.com

CEO: Richard J. (Rich) Statuto
CFO: Katherine A. (Kathy) Arbuckle
HR: Frances Sequeira
FYE: August 31
Type: Not-for-profit

Bon Secours Health System provides succor to the sick and injured. The Roman Catholic health care organization, sponsored by the Bon Secours Ministries, is home to about 20 hospitals with some 4,400 licensed acute care beds. First founded in 1919, the organization's facilities are in seven states in the eastern US, from New York to Florida. In addition to its acute care hospitals, the not-for-profit health care system operates numerous nursing homes and assisted-living facilities, as well as outpatient centers, hospices, and home health care agencies. Its Global Ministry Initiative provides outreach for health care and social services in developing countries, particularly Haiti, Peru, and South Africa.

	Annual Growth	8/04	8/05	8/06	8/07	8/08
Est. sales ($ mil.)	—	—	—	—	—	2,436.5
Employees	—	—	—	—	—	19,000

BONHAMS & BUTTERFIELDS

220 San Bruno Ave.	CEO: Malcolm Barber
San Francisco, CA 94103	CFO: Brenda Greene
Phone: 415-861-7500	HR: Kevin Smith
Fax: 415-861-8951	FYE: December 31
Web: www.butterfields.com	Type: Subsidiary

In the market for antique armor, classic timepieces, or fine art and wines? Look no further than auction house Bonhams & Butterfields. Staging more than 50 live auctions a year in its San Francisco and Los Angeles salerooms, the company specializes in appraisal and disposition of fine art, antiques, books, jewelry, and collectibles. It features a range of 19th century pictures and fine jewelry. The auction house also provides consignment-management and insurance services. Tracing its auction roots back to 1865 when it was founded by former sheriff William Butterfield, Bonhams & Butterfields is the US subsidiary of British auctioneering giant Bonhams.

BONNEVILLE POWER ADMINISTRATION

905 NE 11th Ave.	CEO: Stephen J. (Steve) Wright
Portland, OR 97208	CFO: David J. (Dave) Armstrong
Phone: 503-230-3000	HR: Roy Fox
Fax: 503-230-5884	FYE: September 30
Web: www.bpa.gov	Type: Government-owned

Bonneville Power Administration (BPA) keeps the lights on in the Pacific Northwest. The US Department of Energy power marketing agency operates more than 15,000-mile high-voltage transmission grid that delivers about 35% of the electrical power consumed in the region. The electricity that BPA wholesales is generated primarily by 31 federal hydroelectric plants and one private nuclear facility. BPA also purchases power from other hydroelectric, gas-fired, and wind and solar generation facilities in North America. Founded in 1937, BPA sells power to more than 140 primary customers, mainly public and investor-owned utilities in the Pacific Northwest.

	Annual Growth	9/04	9/05	9/06	9/07	9/08
Sales ($ mil.)	(1.0%)	3,197.9	3,268.1	3,419.4	3,268.6	3,067.2
Employees	(1.9%)	3,153	3,028	2,923	2,896	2,925

BONTEX, INC.

Pink Sheets: BOTX

One Bontex Dr.	CEO: James C. Kostelni
Buena Vista, VA 24416	CFO: —
Phone: 540-261-2181	HR: Brenda Clark
Fax: 540-261-3784	FYE: June 30
Web: www.bontex.com	Type: Public

C'est bon! Bontex makes coated and uncoated fiberboard products for myriad applications, including footwear, headwear, luggage, and, even automotive panels. In addition to a variety of cushion insoles for footwear, Bontex supplies a polyurethane material with moisture wicking ability for sock linings and insoles. Its fiberboard products, sold under various brands (such as BONTEX), are made from recycled and primary cellulose fibers and touted as environmentally friendly. Through its subsidiaries, Bontex sells most of its lineup directly to customers worldwide. It is family owned, held largely by the Kostelnis and former director Patricia Surmonte Tischio, daughter of the company's founder, Hugo Surmonte.

THE BON-TON STORES, INC.

NASDAQ (GS): BONT

2801 E. Market St.	CEO: Byron L. (Bud) Bergren
York, PA 17402	CFO: Keith E. Plowman
Phone: 717-757-7660	HR: Denise M. Domian
Fax: 717-751-3108	FYE: January 31
Web: www.bonton.com	Type: Public

Fashion hounds lost in the wilds from Maine to Montana can take refuge in The Bon-Ton Stores. The company operates more than 275 department stores under eight nameplates, including the Bon-Ton, Elder-Beerman, and Carson Pirie Scott banners, in some two dozen states. The stores sell branded (Calvin Klein, Estée Lauder, Liz Claiborne, Nautica, and Waterford) and private-label women's, children's, and men's clothing; accessories; cosmetics; and home furnishings. Bon-Ton acquired the 142-store Northern Department Store Group (NDSG) from Saks in 2006, doubling its store count. The Bon-Ton Stores was founded in 1898 by the Grumbacher family, and today is controlled by its chairman Tim Grumbacher.

	Annual Growth	1/06	1/07	1/08	1/09	1/10
Sales ($ mil.)	23.4%	1,307.6	3,455.8	3,467.7	3,225.4	3,034.9
Net income ($ mil.)	—	26.0	46.9	11.6	(169.9)	(4.1)
Market value ($ mil.)	(19.7%)	390.4	676.3	143.6	25.3	162.1
Employees	(4.7%)	33,500	33,000	32,700	29,100	27,600

BOOKS-A-MILLION, INC.

NASDAQ (GS): BAMM

402 Industrial Ln.	CEO: Clyde B. Anderson
Birmingham, AL 35211	CFO: Brian W. White
Phone: 205-942-3737	HR: Chad Tice
Fax: 205-942-6601	FYE: January 31
Web: www.bamm.com	Type: Public

Books-A-Million is made for readers who aren't millionaires. The #3 US book chain (after Barnes & Noble and Borders) has about 220 stores in some 20 southeastern states and the District of Columbia. Most of its outlets are superstores operating under the Books-A-Million and Books & Co. names and offer discounted books, magazines, music, DVDs, and general merchandise. Most locations also feature Joe Muggs cafes, which serve coffee and pastries. In addition to it superstores, Books-A-Million runs about 20 smaller-sized Bookland and Books-A-Million stores. Other operations include book wholesalers American Wholesale Book and Book$mart. Chairman Clyde Anderson and his family own about 51% of the firm.

	Annual Growth	1/06	1/07	1/08	1/09	1/10
Sales ($ mil.)	0.2%	503.8	520.4	535.1	513.3	508.7
Net income ($ mil.)	1.3%	13.1	18.9	16.5	10.6	13.8
Market value ($ mil.)	(13.6%)	180.1	300.4	167.8	36.8	100.2
Employees	2.4%	5,000	5,000	5,300	5,300	5,500

BOOKSPAN

501 Franklin Ave.	CEO: Deborah I. (Debi) Fine
Garden City, NY 11530	CFO: —
Phone: 516-490-4561	HR: —
Fax: 516-490-4714	FYE: December 31
Web: www.booksonline.com	Type: Private

Spanning the globe to bring you . . . books. Bookspan is a direct marketer of books, operating book clubs under such familiar names as the Book-of-the-Month Club, Doubleday Book Club, and The Literary Guild. The company operates about 20 clubs that offer bestsellers and feature titles from specific genres, including history, military, mystery, and science fiction. Book selections are chosen by editors in various areas. The company was created through a partnership between Bertelsmann and Time Warner, which sold its stake to Bertelsmann in 2007. Bertelsmann sold Bookspan, Columbia House, and its other direct marketing operations in the US to Phoenix-based private investment firm Najafi Cos. in 2008.

An in-depth profile of this company is available to Hoover's Online members at hoovers.com.

269

BOON EDAM, INC.

402 McKinney Pkwy.
Lillington, NC 27546
Phone: 910-814-3800
Fax: 910-814-3899
Web: www.boonedam.us/inc

CEO: Tom Devine
CFO: Dan Camp
HR: —
FYE: December 31
Type: Subsidiary

Boon Edam Inc.'s door is always open to you — and, paradoxically, always closed, too. The company is the main US subsidiary of Netherlands-based Boon Edam B.V., one of the world's leading makers of entrance technology products such as revolving doors and security doors. The company markets aluminum, wood, brass, bronze, and stainless steel doors. It also manufactures turnstiles and barriers. The parent company markets its doors in more than 40 countries worldwide and operates factories in China, the Netherlands, and the US. Founded in 1873, Boon Edam B.V. produced its first revolving door in 1903. The US subsidiary took on its current form in 2005 when Boon Edam Inc. acquired Tomsed Corp.

	Annual Growth	12/04	12/05	12/06	12/07	12/08
Est. sales ($ mil.)	—	—	—	—	—	10.8
Employees	—	—	—	—	—	80

BOOST MOBILE, LLC

9060 Irvine Center Dr.
Irvine, CA 92618
Phone: 949-748-3200
Fax: 949-748-3272
Web: www.boostmobile.com

CEO: Matt Carter
CFO: Cary Baker
HR: Sarah Reeves
FYE: December 31
Type: Subsidiary

Boost Mobile is hoping to get a rise out of the young and the restless mobile phone market. A subsidiary of Sprint Nextel, the unit sells the parent company's mobile services on a prepaid basis across the US, marketing simplified payment plans primarily to the youth market. Boost Mobile, which has more than 3 million subscribers, also offers prepaid calling cards sold under the Re-Boost brand. Because Boost Mobile tailors the marketing message for its products and services to a younger demographic, the company's mobile data services and entertainment offerings are a central part of its product package. These services include text messaging, wireless Internet access, and games.

	Annual Growth	12/04	12/05	12/06	12/07	12/08
Est. sales ($ mil.)	—	—	—	—	—	0.9
Employees	—	—	—	—	—	10

BOOTS & COOTS INTERNATIONAL WELL CONTROL
NYSE Amex: WEL

7908 N. Sam Houston Pkwy. West, Ste. 500
Houston, TX 77064
Phone: 281-931-8884
Fax: 281-931-8392
Web: www.bncg.com

CEO: Jerry L. Winchester
CFO: Cary D. Baetz
HR: John (Kelly) Hebert
FYE: December 31
Type: Public

Boots & Coots International Well Control, Inc., scoots to the rescue of oil companies faced with oil and gas well blowouts and fires. Besides being in the "hellfighting" business, the company contains oil and hazardous material spills, restores affected sites, and provides snubbing, hydraulic workover, and noncritical services such as troubleshooting and contingency planning. It also has a wide range of pressure control tools which it rents out to customers. Boots & Coots offers its suite of integrated pressure control and related services to oil and gas exploration and production companies worldwide. In 2010 the company agreed to be acquired by Halliburton.

	Annual Growth	12/05	12/06	12/07	12/08	12/09
Sales ($ mil.)	60.4%	29.5	97.0	105.3	209.2	195.1
Net income ($ mil.)	21.0%	2.8	11.2	7.9	21.8	6.0
Market value ($ mil.)	12.2%	85.1	183.3	133.4	95.8	135.0
Employees	17.3%	355	399	526	697	672

BOOZ ALLEN HAMILTON INC.

8283 Greensboro Dr.
McLean, VA 22102
Phone: 703-902-5000
Fax: 703-902-3333
Web: www.boozallen.com

CEO: Ralph W. Shrader
CFO: Samuel R. (Sam) Strickland
HR: Horacio Rozanski
FYE: March 31
Type: Private

For more than 95 years, consultants at Booz Allen Hamilton have been helping US government agencies operate more efficiently at home and abroad. The firm provides a wide range of management consulting and technology integration services; its specialties include information technology, operations, organization and change, program management, strategy, training programs, and systems engineering. Booz Allen has worked for such agencies as the Department of Defense, the Federal Aviation Administration, and the Internal Revenue Service. Investment firm The Carlyle Group owns a majority interest in the consulting firm, which traces its roots to 1914.

	Annual Growth	3/06	3/07	3/08	3/09	3/10
Sales ($ mil.)	7.8%	3,700.0	4,100.0	3,147.0	3,680.0	5,000.0
Employees	6.2%	17,300	19,000	20,000	20,000	22,000

BOOZ & COMPANY

101 Park Ave., 18th Fl.
New York, NY 10178
Phone: 212-697-1900
Fax: 212-551-6732
Web: www.booz.com

CEO: Shumeet Banerji
CFO: Douglas G. (Doug) Swenson
HR: —
FYE: March 31
Type: Private

Created from the commercial consulting arm of venerable Booz Allen Hamilton, Booz & Company was spun off in 2008 as part of a transaction in which Booz Allen sold a controlling stake in its US government consulting unit to The Carlyle Group. Booz & Company emerged as an independent firm, owned by its officers. The firm's consultants work with businesses, governments, and other organizations from more than 55 offices around the world. Booz & Company's specialties include corporate finance, IT, mergers and acquisitions, and organization. The commercial consulting business has counted the New York Stock Exchange, Deutsche Post, and publishing giant Wolters Kluwer among its clients.

	Annual Growth	3/04	3/05	3/06	3/07	3/08
Est. sales ($ mil.)	—	—	—	—	—	1,100.0
Employees	—	—	—	—	—	3,300

THE BOPPY COMPANY

560 Golden Ridge Rd., Ste. 150
Golden, CO 80401
Phone: 720-746-3820
Fax: 720-746-3838
Web: www.boppy.com

CEO: Nancy Bartley
CFO: Caroline Portis
HR: —
FYE: December 31
Type: Subsidiary

The Boppy Company has a baby's and mom's best interests in mind. It makes a line of comfort products designed to support both a baby's head and his or her mother's back or growing belly. In addition to the original Boppy, an infant support pillow, it makes the Boppy Pregnancy Wedge, Boppy Total Body Pillow, Boppy Changing Pad Set, and Boppy Noggin Nest, and other products that offer both support and play. To target medical professionals and support staff, Boppy has developed products for hospital use, such as the Boppy Disposable Slipcover. Boppy products are sold in specialty stores and big box retailers, such as Target. In May 2008 Artsana, an Italian firm, bought Boppy.

BORAL USA

200 Mansell Ct. East, Ste. 310	CEO: Mike Kane
Roswell, GA 30076	CFO: —
Phone: 770-645-4500	HR: Robin J. Town
Fax: 770-645-2888	FYE: June 30
Web: www.boral.com.au/boral_companies/Boral_USA.asp	Type: Business segment

Boral USA operates some of the largest brick and clay tile manufacturing businesses in the US. The company's operations include Boral Bricks, clay roof tile maker US Tile, concrete roof tile maker MonierLifetile (a 50/50 joint venture with France-based Lafarge), fly ash (cement substitute) marketer Boral Material Technologies Inc (BMTI), and construction materials (concrete/sand deposits and quarries). The company's Boral Brick business manufactures about 1.5 billion bricks annually through more than 20 brick plants in the southeastern and southwestern US, making it a leading domestic brick maker. Boral USA is a division of Australian building and construction materials supplier Boral Limited.

	Annual Growth	6/04	6/05	6/06	6/07	6/08
Est. sales ($ mil.)	—	—	—	—	—	128.6
Employees	—	—	—	—	—	1,900

BORDER STATES INDUSTRIES, INC.

105 25th St. North	CEO: Tammy Miller
Fargo, ND 58108	CFO: Brian J. Becker
Phone: 701-293-5834	HR: Sherri Sandvig
Fax: 701-237-9811	FYE: March 31
Web: www.borderstateselectric.com	Type: Private

If you're running for this Border, you probably have current needs. Border States Industries (also known as Border States Electric Supply, or BSE) distributes electrical and electronic products for such industries as automation, communications, construction, plumbing, and utilities. The company has a distribution partnership with OSRAM SYLVANIA. Border States carries data networking equipment in its product catalog. The company operates about 57 branches serving customers in over 10 states, primarily along the northern and southern borders of the nation. It also has a location in Juárez, Mexico. The employee-owned company was established in 1952.

	Annual Growth	3/04	3/05	3/06	3/07	3/08
Est. sales ($ mil.)	—	—	—	—	—	885.0
Employees	—	—	—	—	—	1,300

⊞ BORDERS GROUP, INC.   NYSE: BGP

100 Phoenix Dr.	CEO: Bennett S. LeBow
Ann Arbor, MI 48108	CFO: Mark R. Bierley
Phone: 734-477-1100	HR: —
Fax: 734-477-1285	FYE: January 31
Web: www.bordersgroupinc.com	Type: Public

If you want John Updike or Janet Jackson to go with your java, Borders is for you. The #2 bookstore operator in the US (after Barnes & Noble), Borders Group runs more than 500 Borders superstores in about 45 states and Puerto Rico, as well as about 175 small-format shops under the Waldenbooks, Borders Express, and Borders Outlet banners. Its bookstores offer up to 170,000 book, music, and movie titles and regularly host live literary events and musician showcases to attract customers. The chain also peddles products via its website. In addition, Borders markets gifts and stationery through its Paperchase unit, which operates about 85 stores across the UK and has more than 330 counters in Borders superstores.

	Annual Growth	1/06	1/07	1/08	1/09	1/10
Sales ($ mil.)	(8.8%)	4,079.2	4,113.5	3,820.9	3,275.4	2,823.9
Net income ($ mil.)	—	101.0	(151.3)	(157.4)	(186.7)	(109.4)
Market value ($ mil.)	(56.8%)	1,488.3	1,268.3	682.5	26.6	52.0
Employees	(12.7%)	35,500	33,600	29,500	25,600	20,600

⊞ BORGWARNER INC.   NYSE: BWA

3850 Hamlin Rd.	CEO: Timothy M. (Tim) Manganello
Auburn Hills, MI 48326	CFO: Robin J. Adams
Phone: 248-754-9200	HR: —
Fax: 248-754-9397	FYE: December 31
Web: www.bwauto.com	Type: Public

If suburbanites need four-wheel-drive vehicles to turbocharge their urban drive, that's OK with BorgWarner, a leading maker of engine and drivetrain products for the world's major automotive manufacturers. Products include turbochargers, air pumps, timing chain systems, four-wheel-drive and all-wheel-drive transfer cases (primarily for light trucks and SUVs), and transmission components. Its largest customers include Volkswagen, Ford, and Daimler. BorgWarner operates about 60 manufacturing and technical facilities worldwide. The company gets around 70% of sales from outside the US; more than half of sales comes from its European operations.

	Annual Growth	12/05	12/06	12/07	12/08	12/09
Sales ($ mil.)	(2.0%)	4,293.8	4,585.4	5,328.6	5,263.9	3,961.8
Net income ($ mil.)	(42.1%)	239.6	211.6	288.5	(35.6)	27.0
Market value ($ mil.)	2.3%	3,568.8	3,474.0	5,698.9	2,562.8	3,910.7
Employees	(7.9%)	17,400	17,400	17,700	13,800	12,500

BOSCH REXROTH CORPORATION

5150 Prairie Stone Pkwy.	CEO: Berend Bracht
Hoffman Estates, IL 60192	CFO: Steve Roberts
Phone: 847-645-3600	HR: —
Fax: 847-645-6201	FYE: December 31
Web: www.boschrexroth-us.com	Type: Subsidiary

No driver's ed. instructor, Bosch Rexroth is a pro in drive, motion, and control. The company engineers a slew of automated technologies designed to increase productivity and trim waste. Its operations straddle electric drives (servo drives and controls), hydraulic systems (industrial and mobile), bushings and shafts, and pneumatic valves and actuators. The resulting lineup is used in a wide range of equipment, from automobiles to construction tools (backhoes, cranes, and excavators), material handling (conveyors to linear motion systems), and semiconductor manufacturing. Operating as the US arm of Germany-based Bosch Rexroth AG, Bosch Rexroth caters to a myriad of industries and federal agencies.

	Annual Growth	12/04	12/05	12/06	12/07	12/08
Est. sales ($ mil.)	—	—	—	—	—	198.9
Employees	—	—	—	—	—	1,996

BOSCH SECURITY SYSTEMS, INC.

130 Perinton Pkwy.	CEO: Christopher P. Gerace
Fairport, NY 14450	CFO: —
Phone: 585-223-4060	HR: —
Fax: 585-223-9180	FYE: December 31
Web: www.boschsecurity.com	Type: Subsidiary

Bosch Security Systems has a sixth sense for finding business. The company makes electronic detection and communications equipment for firms that provide security and fire protection systems and services. Its products include smoke detectors, motion detectors, closed-circuit TV systems, access control systems, and control panels. Related communications equipment sends alarm signals over telephone lines, wireless networks, and WANs. Bosch also makes personal safety systems that, when activated, transmit the user's identity and location to a monitoring station. The company has sales offices and distribution centers worldwide. Bosch Security Systems is a subsidiary of German manufacturing giant Robert Bosch.

⊞ An in-depth profile of this company is available to Hoover's Online members at hoovers.com.

271

BOSCOV'S DEPARTMENT STORE, LLC

4500 Perkiomen Ave.	CEO: Albert R. (Al) Boscov
Reading, PA 19606	CFO: Toni Miller
Phone: 610-779-2000	HR: Ed Elko
Fax: 610-370-3495	FYE: January 31
Web: www.boscovs.com	Type: Private

Outlet mall capital Reading, Pennsylvania, has conceived more than bargain shopping. It's given us Boscov's Department Store, which operates about 40 stores (down from 50 in 2007) that anchor malls mainly in Pennsylvania and four other mid-Atlantic states. The stores sell men's, women's, and children's apparel, shoes, and accessories, as well as jewelry, cosmetics, housewares, appliances, and sporting goods. It also operates an online store. After expanding too rapidly amid a worsening outlook for department stores, Boscov's filed for Chapter 11 bankruptcy protection in 2008 and was later purchased by a group led by its chairman and CEO Albert Boscov. Boscov's was founded by Solomon Boscov in 1911.

▣ BOSE CORPORATION

The Mountain	CEO: Amar G. Bose
Framingham, MA 01701	CFO: Daniel A. Grady
Phone: 508-879-7330	HR: John C. Ferrie
Fax: —	FYE: March 31
Web: www.bose.com	Type: Private

Bose has been making noise in the audio products business for some time. The firm is one of the world's leading manufacturers of speakers for the home entertainment, automotive, and pro audio markets. It makes a variety of consumer models for stereo systems and home theaters, including its compact Wave radio system. For sound professionals, Bose offers loudspeakers and amplifiers, as well as products designed for musicians. Bose sells its products at more than 100 factory and showcase stores and through affiliated retailers. The company is using its expertise to branch out into other markets. Founder Amar Bose, a former professor of electrical engineering at Massachusetts Institute of Technology, owns the company.

BOSS HOLDINGS, INC.　　　　OTC: BSHI

221 W. 1st St.	CEO: G. Louis Graziadio III
Kewanee, IL 61443	CFO: Steven G. Pont
Phone: 309-852-2131	HR: Beverley Williams
Fax: 309-852-0848	FYE: December 31
Web: www.bossgloves.com	Type: Public

Boss Holdings would rather take orders (for its gloves, boots, and rainwear) than give them. Subsidiary Boss Manufacturing Company (BMC) imports and markets gloves and protective wear sold through mass merchandisers, hardware stores, and other retailers in the US and Canada. It also sells its products directly to commercial users in industries such as agriculture and automotive. The company's Boss Pet Products markets pet supplies (collars, chains, shampoos, toys) to US retailers. The company also sells latex balloons through Galaxy Balloons and hands-free flashlights through its Boss Head-Lite unit. Boss Holdings was founded in 1893 as a manufacturer of work gloves. The company's gloves and protective gear account for about 70% of sales.

	Annual Growth	12/05	12/06	12/07	12/08	12/09
Sales ($ mil.)	(2.5%)	54.2	53.7	55.2	55.7	49.0
Net income ($ mil.)	26.6%	0.7	3.9	1.4	0.5	1.8
Market value ($ mil.)	(7.4%)	16.9	13.0	19.0	11.3	12.4
Employees	(3.6%)	235	210	241	223	203

▣ BOSTON ACOUSTICS, INC.

300 Jubilee Dr.	CEO: Steve Chilinski
Peabody, MA 01960	CFO: Debra A. Ricker
Phone: 978-538-5000	HR: —
Fax: 978-538-5199	FYE: March 31
Web: www.bostonacoustics.com	Type: Subsidiary

Play "Dark Side of the Moon" on a set of Boston Acoustics' speakers and you'll see the light. The company designs and makes moderately priced and high-end loudspeaker systems for the home and auto markets. It also makes home entertainment systems, amplifiers, and ancillary speaker equipment, including selectors and volume controls. Boston Acoustics mostly tunes out mass retailers, selling its products through a select group of specialty dealers. Its products are manufactured by third parties in the Asia/Pacific region, Europe, and North America. Former chairman Andrew Kotsatos and ex-CEO Frank Reed founded the company in 1979. D&M Holdings acquired Boston Acoustics in 2005.

▣ THE BOSTON BEER COMPANY, INC.　　　NYSE: SAM

1 Design Center, Ste. 850	CEO: Martin F. Roper
Boston, MA 02110	CFO: William F. Urich
Phone: 617-368-5000	HR: Amy Waryas
Fax: 617-368-5500	FYE: December 31
Web: www.bostonbeer.com	Type: Public

A half-pint compared to megabrewers like the world's #1 beer maker Anheuser-Bush InBev, The Boston Beer Company holds a distinction all its own — it is the US's largest microbrewer. The company produces some 30 seasonal and year-round varieties of craft-brewed beers at its Cincinnati and Boston breweries. Annually, it sells more than 2 million barrels of lager (such as its flagship Samuel Adams Boston Lager), ales (other Samuel Adams brands), HardCore brand cider, and Twisted Tea malt beverages. The company distributes its brews primarily in the US, but they are also sold in Canada, Mexico, the Caribbean, Europe, Israel, and the Pacific Rim.

	Annual Growth	12/05	12/06	12/07	12/08	12/09
Sales ($ mil.)	14.9%	238.3	285.4	341.6	398.4	415.1
Net income ($ mil.)	18.8%	15.6	18.2	22.5	8.1	31.1
Market value ($ mil.)	16.8%	350.2	504.0	527.4	397.8	652.8
Employees	18.9%	390	433	500	775	780

BOSTON COLLEGE

140 Commonwealth Ave.	CEO: William P. Leahy
Chestnut Hill, MA 02467	CFO: Peter C. McKenzie
Phone: 617-552-8000	HR: Leo V. Sullivan
Fax: 617-552-3959	FYE: May 31
Web: www.bc.edu	Type: School

Students at Boston College (BC) get both academic excellence and the Red Sox. Located six miles from downtown Boston, the university currently enrolls about 14,000 full- and part-time students (about a third of whom are graduate students) from every US state and 84 countries. Chartered in 1863, BC offers degrees in more than 50 fields of study through its seven schools and colleges on four campuses. The university also has about two dozen research centers, including the Small Business Development Center, the Institute for Scientific Research, and the Center for International Higher Education. BC is one of the oldest Jesuit Catholic universities in the nation and has the largest Jesuit community in the world.

	Annual Growth	5/04	5/05	5/06	5/07	5/08
Est. sales ($ mil.)	—	—	—	—	—	600.7
Employees	—	—	—	—	—	3,000

THE BOSTON CONSULTING GROUP INC.

1 Exchange Place, 31st Fl.
Boston, MA 02109
Phone: 617-973-1200
Fax: 617-973-1339
Web: www.bcg.com

CEO: Hans-Paul Bürkner
CFO: Debbie Simpson
HR: —
FYE: December 31
Type: Private

Global corporations are willing to give much more than a penny for the thoughts of Boston Consulting Group (BCG). One of the world's top-ranked consulting practices, BCG operates from about 65 offices in more than 35 countries in the Americas, Europe, and the Asia/Pacific region. The firm's 4,300 consultants offer a wide array of services, mainly to large corporate clients. BCG's practice areas include branding and marketing, corporate finance, globalization, and information technology. Founded in 1963 by industry pioneer Bruce Henderson, the firm is owned by its employees.

	Annual Growth	12/04	12/05	12/06	12/07	12/08
Est. sales ($ mil.)	17.0%	—	1,500.0	1,800.0	2,332.0	2,400.0
Employees	2.9%	—	5,500	6,270	6,000	6,000

BOSTON FINANCIAL DATA SERVICES, INC.

2 Heritage Dr.
Quincy, MA 02171
Phone: 617-483-5000
Fax: 617-483-2562
Web: www.bostonfinancial.com

CEO: Terry L. Metzger
CFO: Jay Shuman
HR: —
FYE: December 31
Type: Joint venture

Boston Financial Data Services is not your ordinary bean counter. Established in 1973 as a 50-50 joint venture between State Street and DST Systems, the company performs shareholder accounting, transaction settlement, and recordkeeping services to approximately 120 US mutual fund companies. Other clients include insurance companies, banks, 401(k) retirement plans, and education savings plans. The company also provides outsourced services such as mail and cash processing, tax reporting, regulatory compliance, telephone servicing and support, and participant correspondence.

	Annual Growth	12/04	12/05	12/06	12/07	12/08
Est. sales ($ mil.)	—	—	—	—	—	200.2
Employees	—	—	—	—	—	2,037

BOSTON MARKET CORPORATION

14103 Denver West Pkwy.
Golden, CO 80401
Phone: 303-278-9500
Fax: 303-216-5678
Web: www.bostonmarket.com

CEO: F. Lane Cardwell Jr.
CFO: Gregory S. (Greg) Uhing
HR: Anne Mitchell
FYE: December 31
Type: Private

This company takes home-style cooking far beyond the borders of the commonwealth. A leader in quick-casual dining, Boston Market owns and operates more than 500 restaurants in more than 25 states. The chain's menu features grilled and rotisserie chicken, ham, meat loaf, and turkey, as well as such side dishes as mashed potatoes, macaroni and cheese, and stuffing. Boston Market's locations feature a cafeteria-style serving line and dine-in seating, as well as drive-through and carry-out service. In addition to its restaurants, Boston Market sells retail frozen food items through a licensing deal with H. J. Heinz. The company, founded in 1985 as Boston Chicken, is owned by investment firm Sun Capital Partners.

BOSTON PRIVATE FINANCIAL HOLDINGS, INC.

NASDAQ (GS): BPFH

10 Post Office Sq.
Boston, MA 02109
Phone: 617-912-1900
Fax: 617-912-4550
Web: www.bostonprivate.com

CEO: Timothy L. (Tim) Vaill
CFO: David J. Kaye
HR: Constance I. Katsaros
FYE: December 31
Type: Public

Boston Private — isn't that David Kelley's old TV series? Not exactly. The holding company owns several private banks and investment management companies that primarily serve wealthy and institutional clients on both US coasts. Offerings include deposit accounts, loans, trust services, and financial advice. Boston Private Bank & Trust operates about 10 branches in Massachusetts. In California, the company runs Borel Private Bank & Trust and First Private Bank & Trust. In 2007 it acquired Washington-based Charter Bank (now Charter Private Bank) for about $80 million. Boston Private sold Gibraltar Private Bank & Trust, which serves southern Florida and New York City, to private investors in 2009.

	Annual Growth	12/05	12/06	12/07	12/08	12/09
Assets ($ mil.)	4.2%	5,134.1	5,763.5	6,818.1	7,266.3	6,049.3
Net income ($ mil.)	(33.8%)	46.3	54.4	4.2	(388.8)	8.9
Market value ($ mil.)	(34.0%)	2,106.3	1,953.2	1,875.0	473.6	399.5
Employees	(0.9%)	892	1,031	1,166	1,220	859

BOSTON PROPERTIES, INC.

NYSE: BXP

800 Boylston St., The Prudential Center
Boston, MA 02199
Phone: 617-236-3300
Fax: 617-536-5087
Web: www.bostonproperties.com

CEO: Mortimer B. (Mort) Zuckerman
CFO: Michael E. LaBelle
HR: —
FYE: December 31
Type: Public

Boston Properties knows more than beans about real estate. The firm invests in, develops, and manages primarily Class A office buildings. In addition to Boston, the self-administered real estate investment trust (REIT) focuses on the markets in Midtown Manhattan, San Francisco, and Washington, DC. Boston Properties' portfolio includes about 150 buildings, including development and redevelopment projects. In 2008 the REIT acquired 60% ownership of the iconic GM Building, previously owned by Macklowe Properties, for $2.8 billion, a record price for a US office building. Chairman and CEO Mort Zuckerman, the media czar of *U.S. News & World Report* and New York's *Daily News*, owns a 7% stake in Boston Properties.

	Annual Growth	12/05	12/06	12/07	12/08	12/09
Sales ($ mil.)	1.4%	1,437.6	1,477.6	1,482.3	1,488.4	1,522.2
Net income ($ mil.)	(15.0%)	442.5	873.6	1,324.7	125.2	231.0
Market value ($ mil.)	(2.5%)	10,305.4	15,553.3	12,763.2	7,646.0	9,323.9
Employees	1.0%	673	650	660	700	700

BOSTON RED SOX BASEBALL CLUB LIMITED PARTNERSHIP

4 Yawkey Way
Boston, MA 02215
Phone: 617-267-9440
Fax: 617-375-0944
Web: boston.redsox.mlb.com

CEO: Larry Lucchino
CFO: Steve Fitch
HR: Craig Shipley
FYE: December 31
Type: Private

You might say this team is now a curse on the other clubs in Major League Baseball. Boston Red Sox Baseball Club operates one of the oldest and most storied franchises in the major leagues. Founded as a charter member of the American League in 1901, the team owns seven World Series titles but at one time suffered through an 86-year championship drought popularly attributed to "The Curse of the Bambino." Boston broke The Curse in 2004 and then won its seventh championship three years later. Red Sox fans root for their home team at venerable Fenway Park, the oldest pro baseball stadium in the country. Businessman John Henry leads a group that has owned the Red Sox franchise since 2002.

	Annual Growth	12/04	12/05	12/06	12/07	12/08
Sales ($ mil.)	5.2%	220.0	206.0	234.0	263.0	269.0
Employees	—	—	—	—	—	—

An in-depth profile of this company is available to Hoover's Online members at hoovers.com.

273

BOSTON SCIENTIFIC CORPORATION
NYSE: BSX

1 Boston Scientific Place	CEO: J. Raymond (Ray) Elliott
Natick, MA 01760	CFO: Jeffrey D. (Jeff) Capello
Phone: 508-650-8000	HR: Andrew N. (Andy) Milani II
Fax: 508-650-8910	FYE: December 31
Web: www.bostonscientific.com	Type: Public

Boston Scientific knows that nothing is simple in matters of the heart. It makes medical supplies and devices used to diagnose and treat conditions in a variety of medical fields, with an emphasis on cardiology and cardiac rhythm management. It also makes devices used for gynecology and urology (endo-surgery group) and pain management (neuromodulation). Its 13,000-plus products, made in a dozen factories worldwide, include defibrillators, catheters, coronary and urethral stents, pacemakers, biopsy forceps and needles, and urethral slings. Boston Scientific markets its wares in more than 40 countries worldwide, primarily through its own direct sales staff.

	Annual Growth	12/05	12/06	12/07	12/08	12/09
Sales ($ mil.)	6.8%	6,283.0	7,821.0	8,357.0	8,050.0	8,188.0
Net income ($ mil.)	—	628.0	(3,577.0)	(495.0)	(2,036.0)	(1,025.0)
Market value ($ mil.)	(22.1%)	37,134.8	26,050.4	17,634.8	11,736.3	13,646.9
Employees	7.0%	19,800	28,600	27,500	24,800	26,000

BOSTWICK LABORATORIES, INC.

4355 Innslake Dr.	CEO: David G. Bostwick
Glen Allen, VA 23060	CFO: Gary Levine
Phone: 804-967-9225	HR: Carolyn Bell
Fax: 804-288-6568	FYE: December 31
Web: www.bostwicklaboratories.com	Type: Private

Nobody wants to hear that it's cancer, but Bostwick Laboratories at least tries to get the news to you quick — within 24 hours on average. The pathology lab focuses on diagnosing cancer; it began by analyzing prostate biopsies and urine tests but is expanding into other specialized areas. The company's Bostwick Scientific division provides clinical trial support to pharmaceutical and biotechnology firms. It has half a dozen labs in the US and one in the UK offering services in the diagnosis, treatment, prevention, and management of cancer. CEO Dr. David Bostwick, a former professor of pathology and urology at the Mayo Clinic, formed Bostwick Laboratories in 1999.

BOTTOMLINE TECHNOLOGIES (DE), INC.
NASDAQ (GM): EPAY

325 Corporate Dr.	CEO: Robert A. (Rob) Eberle
Portsmouth, NH 03801	CFO: Kevin M. Donovan
Phone: 603-436-0700	HR: —
Fax: 603-436-0300	FYE: June 30
Web: www.bottomline.com	Type: Public

Bottomline Technologies helps you track both the bottom dollar and the bill. The company provides financial resource management software that lets financial institutions and other corporations convert from paper-based billing systems to systems that enable electronic funds transfer, banking, and bill presentment and payment. Bottomline's Purchase-to-Pay software enables corporations to electronically present bills and accept payments from external parties, while its PayBase and WebSeries products allow customers to manage and track internal billing and payment processes.

	Annual Growth	6/05	6/06	6/07	6/08	6/09
Sales ($ mil.)	9.4%	96.5	101.7	118.3	131.2	138.0
Net income ($ mil.)	—	5.9	(1.8)	(7.0)	(5.3)	(12.3)
Market value ($ mil.)	(11.9%)	408.6	222.2	337.1	265.6	245.9
Employees	9.2%	475	481	555	679	676

BOURNS, INC.

1200 Columbia Ave.	CEO: Gordon Bourns
Riverside, CA 92507	CFO: William P. McKenna
Phone: 951-781-5690	HR: —
Fax: 951-781-5273	FYE: December 31
Web: www.bourns.com	Type: Private

Bourns shows great potential in potentiometers, which are included in a broad range of electronic components the company provides, such as power protection devices, sensors, resistors, switches, encoders, panel controls, dials, and chip resistor arrays. The company offers automotive technologies to enhance its sensors, component miniaturization (microelectronic modules), and reference designs (product design kits). The company serves the automotive, computing, consumer electronics, medical, test and measurement, office machines, and telecommunications markets. Headquartered in the US, Bourns has sales and distributor locations in both hemispheres. It is owned by the Bourns family.

BOVIE MEDICAL CORPORATION
NYSE Amex: BVX

734 Walt Whitman Rd.	CEO: Andrew Makrides
Melville, NY 11747	CFO: Gary D. Pickett
Phone: 631-421-5452	HR: Vera MacElroy
Fax: 631-421-5821	FYE: December 31
Web: www.boviemedical.com	Type: Public

Surgeons don't think about Bovie during surgery, but Bovie constantly thinks about them. Bovie Medical makes and markets electrosurgical devices and power generators primarily used for outpatient surgical procedures under its Bovie and Aaron brands and for private-label clients. Its top-selling products include generators used in physicians' offices, electrodes, and other devices for cutting and cauterizing tissue in dermatology, urology, gynecology, or cosmetic procedures. Bovie also makes battery-operated cauteries (to stop bleeding), physician pen lights, other medical lighting equipment, and a nerve locator simulator used mainly to locate motor nerves in hand and facial reconstruction procedures.

	Annual Growth	12/05	12/06	12/07	12/08	12/09
Sales ($ mil.)	7.5%	20.2	26.7	28.8	28.1	27.0
Net income ($ mil.)	10.7%	0.4	2.7	2.4	1.8	0.6
Market value ($ mil.)	27.2%	52.7	160.2	113.2	110.4	138.1
Employees	3.9%	140	161	162	174	163

BOWDOIN COLLEGE

5007 College Station	CEO: Barry Mills
Brunswick, ME 04011	CFO: S. Catherine Longley
Phone: 207-725-3000	HR: Tamara Spoerri
Fax: 207-725-3101	FYE: June 30
Web: www.bowdoin.edu	Type: School

The classes at Bowdoin College might be challenging, but pronouncing the school's name correctly is nearly impossible. Bowdoin (bow, as in bowtie + din with a short "i") is an undergraduate, liberal arts school that serves more than 1,700 students. The college offers degrees in about 40 fields of study, including English, psychology, history, mathematics, and biology. Bowdoin also includes a Coastal Studies Center, some eight miles from campus on Orr's Island. Notable alumni include writers Nathanial Hawthorne and Henry Wadsworth Longfellow, as well as former Senate majority leader George Mitchell. Established in 1794, Bowdoin is Maine's oldest college.

	Annual Growth	6/04	6/05	6/06	6/07	6/08
Est. sales ($ mil.)	—	—	—	—	—	0.6
Employees	—	—	—	—	—	8

BOWL AMERICA INCORPORATED

NYSE Amex: BWL

6446 Edsall Rd.
Alexandria, VA 22312
Phone: 703-941-6300
Fax: 703-256-2430
Web: www.bowlamericainc.com

CEO: Leslie H. (Les) Goldberg
CFO: Cheryl A. Dragoo
HR: —
FYE: June 30
Type: Public

This company is looking to make a strike in the recreation business. Bowl America owns and operates about 20 bowling centers in four markets, including the Baltimore-Washington, DC, area; Jacksonville and Orlando, Florida; and Richmond, Virginia. The bowling centers offer a total of more than 750 lanes for both league and non-league bowling, as well as Cosmic Bowling (with glow-in-the-dark balls and laser light shows) for younger patrons. The centers also feature game rooms, food and beverage services, and other amenities. President Leslie Goldberg and his sister Merle Fabian together own more than 50% of Bowl America.

	Annual Growth	6/05	6/06	6/07	6/08	6/09
Sales ($ mil.)	0.9%	28.6	30.3	32.0	30.1	29.7
Net income ($ mil.)	(5.0%)	3.8	3.6	4.2	3.5	3.1
Market value ($ mil.)	(3.3%)	71.8	74.8	87.7	71.7	62.7
Employees	(1.8%)	700	750	750	—	650

BOWLIN TRAVEL CENTERS, INC.

OTC: BWTL

150 Louisiana NE
Albuquerque, NM 87108
Phone: 505-266-5985
Fax: 505-266-7821
Web: www.bowlintc.com

CEO: Michael L. Bowlin
CFO: Nina J. Pratz
HR: Johnny Riley
FYE: January 31
Type: Public

Dotting the desert with gas pumps and gifts, Bowlin Travel Centers (BTC) operates about 10 full-service, southwestern-themed travel centers along interstates I-10 and I-40 in arid Arizona and New Mexico. Its travel centers offer snacks, souvenirs provided by Native American tribes or imported from Mexico, gas (Citgo and ExxonMobil brands), and restaurants (Dairy Queen at five locations). It also sells gasoline wholesale. BTC was spun off by Bowlin Outdoor Advertising & Travel Centers immediately before the former parent company was acquired by Louisiana-based Lamar Advertising in 2001. Chairman, president, and CEO Michael Bowlin and his family own about 61% of BTC.

	Annual Growth	1/04	1/05	1/06	1/07	*1/08
Sales ($ mil.)	7.0%	21.5	23.6	27.7	27.8	28.2
Net income ($ mil.)	—	0.5	0.4	0.7	0.4	(0.1)
Employees	1.9%	129	146	165	154	139

*Most recent year available

⊞ BOWNE & CO., INC.

NYSE: BNE

55 Water St.
New York, NY 10041
Phone: 212-924-5500
Fax: 212-229-3400
Web: www.bowne.com

CEO: David J. Shea
CFO: John J. Walker
HR: Susan W. Cummiskey
FYE: December 31
Type: Public

Savvy investors see the work of Bowne & Co. every day. The firm specializes in printing financial documents, such as prospectuses, annual and interim reports, and other paperwork required by the SEC. Bowne (rhymes with "down") also handles electronic filings via the SEC's EDGAR system and provides electronic distribution and high-volume mailing services. Documents associated with transactions, such as equity and debt issuances and mergers and acquisitions, generate a significant share of sales. Turmoil in the financial world led Bowne to reorganize, cut jobs, and diversify into areas not tied directly to the capital markets, such as marketing communications for the financial services and health care industries.

	Annual Growth	12/05	12/06	12/07	12/08	12/09
Sales ($ mil.)	(0.7%)	694.1	832.2	850.6	766.6	675.8
Net income ($ mil.)	—	(0.6)	(1.8)	27.1	(23.2)	(16.6)
Market value ($ mil.)	(17.3%)	573.6	616.2	680.3	227.3	267.9
Employees	(2.5%)	3,100	3,200	3,600	3,200	2,800

BOY SCOUTS OF AMERICA

1325 W. Walnut Hill Ln.
Irving, TX 75015
Phone: 972-580-2000
Fax: 972-580-7870
Web: www.scouting.org

CEO: Robert J. (Bob) Mazzuca
CFO: Jim Terry
HR: James S. Turley
FYE: December 31
Type: Not-for-profit

Scouts enter dens as Tigers and eventually take flight as Eagles. Boy Scouts of America (BSA), one of the nation's largest youth organizations, has about 3 million youth members and more than 1 million adult leaders in its ranks. BSA offers educational and character-building programs emphasizing leadership, citizenship, personal development, and physical fitness. In addition to traditional scouting programs (Tiger, Cub, Webelos, and Boy Scouts, ranging up to Eagle rank), it offers the Venturing program for boys and girls ages 14-20. BSA generates revenue through membership and council fees, supply and magazine sales, and contributions. The organization was founded by Chicago publisher William Boyce in 1910.

	Annual Growth	12/04	12/05	12/06	12/07	12/08
Sales ($ mil.)	(13.6%)	269.7	180.6	194.5	175.0	150.5
Net income ($ mil.)	—	—	25.8	64.6	32.2	(19.9)
Employees	0.0%	500	500	500	500	—

⊞ BOYD GAMING CORPORATION

NYSE: BYD

3883 Howard Hughes Pkwy., 9th Fl.
Las Vegas, NV 89169
Phone: 702-792-7200
Fax: 702-792-7313
Web: www.boydgaming.com

CEO: Keith E. Smith
CFO: Josh Hirsberg
HR: Robert Gerst
FYE: December 31
Type: Public

A key ingredient for Boyd Gaming's success is — or was — stardust. One of the country's leading casino operators, Boyd demolished the iconic Stardust Resort and Casino on the Las Vegas Strip to make way for the Echelon Place; the development is currently on hiatus. Boyd has some 15 properties, which include locations in Florida, Indiana, Illinois, Louisiana, Mississippi, and Nevada; together they have some 21,000 slot machines and 450 table games. Boyd also owns 50% of Atlantic City's Borgata Hotel Casino. The company's significant $1.3 billion purchase of Coast Casinos in 2004 created the fifth-largest gaming company in the US. Chairman William S. Boyd and his family own more than 35% of Boyd Gaming.

	Annual Growth	12/05	12/06	12/07	12/08	12/09
Sales ($ mil.)	(7.3%)	2,223.0	2,192.6	1,997.1	1,781.0	1,641.0
Net income ($ mil.)	(59.8%)	161.0	116.8	303.0	(223.0)	4.2
Market value ($ mil.)	(35.3%)	4,105.9	3,903.5	2,935.1	407.5	721.1
Employees	(9.9%)	23,400	18,300	16,900	16,000	15,400

THE BOYDS COLLECTION, LTD.

Pink Sheets: BYDC

350 South St.
McSherrystown, PA 17344
Phone: 717-633-9898
Fax: 717-633-5511
Web: www.boydsstuff.com

CEO: Robert Coccoluto
CFO: Joseph E. Macharsky
HR: Ruth Karabeievschy
FYE: December 31
Type: Public

In the forest of collectibles, The Boyds Collection bears are watching. It sells resin, porcelain, and plush renditions of bears and other animals, including its Bearstones figurines and its J.B. Bean & Associates line of fully jointed bears and other animals. It also sells other collectibles and home décor items, such as stationery and picture frames. Boyds has boasted licensed products via deals with NASCAR and Coca-Cola. Products are designed to appeal to older women (although it has added items for men). Its products are sold primarily in US gift shops and department stores, as well as through catalogs and trade shows. In 2008 Boyds granted Enesco a license to design, make, and market some of its products.

⊞ An in-depth profile of this company is available to Hoover's Online members at hoovers.com.

275

BOYS & GIRLS CLUBS OF AMERICA

1275 Peachtree St. NE
Atlanta, GA 30309
Phone: 404-487-5700
Fax: 404-487-5705
Web: www.bgca.org

CEO: Roxanne Spillett
CFO: Gary C. Wendt
HR: —
FYE: December 31
Type: Not-for-profit

There's no secret handshake — or specific gender — required to get into this club, only the desire to have fun. The Boys & Girls Clubs of America (BGCA) runs after-school programs throughout the US in an effort to give children and teenagers a safe and supervised environment. Operating through local affiliates, BGCA has more than 4,300 locations serving about 5 million youth. Members engage in sports, recreation, and fitness activities, as well as in programs centered on character development, leadership, and life skills. BGCA alumni include President Bill Clinton, Bill Cosby, Jackie Joyner-Kersee, Martin Sheen, Michael Jordan, and Queen Latifah. Founded in 1906, the organization traces its roots to 1860.

	Annual Growth	12/04	12/05	12/06	12/07	12/08
Est. sales ($ mil.)	—	—	—	—	—	126.3
Employees	—	—	—	—	—	360

BOZZUTO'S INC.

275 School House Rd.
Cheshire, CT 06410
Phone: 203-272-3511
Fax: 203-250-2954
Web: www.bozzutos.com

CEO: Michael A. Bozzuto
CFO: Robert H. (Bob) Wood
HR: Lilly Branco
FYE: September 30
Type: Private

Bozzuto's is a leading wholesale grocery distribution company that supplies food and non-food products to independent supermarkets belonging to the IGA network in New Jersey, New York, Pennsylvania, and in New England. The company distributes a full line of grocery items, including meat products, produce, and frozen food, as well as household goods and other general merchandise. It carries goods sold under both the IGA and Hy-Top labels, in addition to national brands. Bozzuto's also owns about half a dozen supermarkets in Connecticut and Massachusetts operating under the Adams Super Food Stores banner. The company, founded in 1945, is owned and operated by the Bozzuto family.

BP LUBRICANTS USA, INC.

1500 Valley Rd.
Wayne, NJ 07470
Phone: 973-633-2200
Fax: 973-633-0879
Web: www.castrolusa.com

CEO: Paul Waterman
CFO: Dave Duggan
HR: —
FYE: December 31
Type: Subsidiary

BP Lubricants USA (formerly Castrol Consumer North America) spends as much time on top of a hood as it does under them. The company, the Castrol brand sponsor of a variety of drag racing, funny car, and Formula 1 race car drivers, is a distributor of Castrol synthetic lubricants to automotive service providers and retailers in North America. It also provides specialty lubricants, including degreasers, lubes, and transmission fluids, for boating, motorcycling, racing, and snowmobile customers. BP Lubricants USA is a regional unit of Castrol, the UK-based lubricants firm owned by global oil giant BP.

BP NGL

150 W. Warrenville Rd.
Naperville, IL 60563
Phone: 630-836-5000
Fax: 630-836-6535
Web: www.ngl.com

CEO: H. Lamar McKay
CFO: —
HR: —
FYE: December 31
Type: Business segment

BP NGL is just marketing what comes natural. A regional unit of oil giant BP's BP Gas Power and NGL division, BP NGL is one of North America's leading natural gas producers, with extraction, fractionation, storage, transportation, and gas processing plants throughout the US and Canada. BP NGL markets more than 670,000 barrels of natural gas liquids per day. The company explores for and holds large reserves of gas in western Canada. It also operates gas gathering systems and gas plants, markets and trades gas and natural gas liquids, and is entering the petrochemicals industry. The company is expanding its exploration activities in northern and eastern Canada.

BP PRUDHOE BAY ROYALTY TRUST

NYSE: BPT

101 Barclay St.
New York, NY 10286
Phone: 212-815-6908
Fax: 212-815-2293

CEO: Remo J. Reale
CFO: Remo J. Reale
HR: —
FYE: December 31
Type: Public

BP Prudhoe Bay Royalty Trust may not literally be on top of the world, but it's close: It makes its money from assets at the top end of Alaska (the North Slope). The trust was set up in 1989 by The Standard Oil Company and BP Exploration (both part of BP), along with The Bank of New York to passively administer overriding royalty interests. It distributes royalties on 16.4% of the first 90,000 barrels of the average actual daily net production per quarter from BP's working interest in the Prudhoe Bay Field, one of the largest oil-producing areas in North America. BP Prudhoe Bay Royalty Trust owns net interests in proved remaining reserves of 55 million barrels of crude oil and condensate at the site.

	Annual Growth	12/05	12/06	12/07	12/08	12/09
Sales ($ mil.)	1.0%	153.0	184.9	177.3	252.3	159.5
Net income ($ mil.)	1.0%	151.9	183.9	175.7	250.5	158.0
Market value ($ mil.)	5.6%	1,425.2	1,647.4	1,716.3	1,569.5	1,771.9
Employees	—	0	0	0	0	0

BP SOLAR INTERNATIONAL INC.

630 Solarex Ct.
Frederick, MD 21703
Phone: 301-698-4200
Fax: —
Web: www.bpsolar.com

CEO: Reyad Fezzani
CFO: —
HR: —
FYE: December 31
Type: Subsidiary

BP Solar International displays a certain star power as it seeks to transform the sun's energy into electricity. A subsidiary of UK oil giant BP, the company designs, manufactures, supplies, and installs photovoltaic (PV) solar cells and modules that provide power for homes, remote villages and industrial facilities, commercial businesses, and local government. Its plants are in the US, India, and China. BP Solar also offers an array of services, from cost estimation to logistic management, remote monitoring, and training. Customers include Ericsson, FedEx Freight, NEC, and Telstra. BP Solar sells through a network of distributors, resellers, and dealers, and its home solar power systems at Home Depot stores.

BPO MANAGEMENT SERVICES, INC.   Pink Sheets: HAXS

1290 N. Hancock St., Ste. 202   CEO: Patrick A. Dolan
Anaheim, CA 92807   CFO: Ronald K. (Ron) Herbert
Phone: 714-974-2670   HR: —
Fax: 714-974-4771   FYE: December 31
Web: www.bpoms.com   Type: Public

BPO Management Services (formerly netGuru) isn't coy about what it does. The company offers business process outsourcing (BPO) engineering services such as custom application development, systems integration, network design, and support, training, and data migration. The company's clients have included Agilent, Ericsson, McGraw-Hill, and Tetra Tech. In late 2008 the company merged with Healthaxis; the combined entity retained the BPO Management Services name. Chairman and CEO Patrick Dolan and president James Cortens own 34% and 23% of company shares, respectively.

BRADFORD WHITE CORPORATION

725 Talamore Dr.   CEO: A. Robert (Bob) Carnevale
Ambler, PA 19002   CFO: Robert Hunter
Phone: 215-641-9400   HR: Herbert Foster
Fax: 215-641-1612   FYE: December 31
Web: www.bradfordwhite.com   Type: Private

Bradford White Corporation helps folks get in — and stay in — hot water. The company manufactures water heaters for residential, commercial, and hydronic space heating applications. It makes oil-fired products, gas power burners, and indirect-fired units. Through subsidiaries Bradford White-Canada and LAARS Heating Systems, it also manufactures products such as pool heaters, oil burners, and air handlers. The company wholesales its products through a network of plumbing and heating professionals. Subsidiary Niles Steel Tank produces custom steel tanks for companies in the automotive, petrol-chemical, pharmaceutical, and refrigeration industries. Bradford White Corporation was founded in 1881.

BPZ RESOURCES, INC.   NYSE Amex: BPZ

580 Westlake Park Blvd., Ste. 525   CEO: Manuel Pablo Zúñiga-Pflücker
Houston, TX 77079   CFO: Edward G. (Ed) Caminos
Phone: 281-556-6200   HR: —
Fax: 281-556-6377   FYE: December 31
Web: www.bpzenergy.com   Type: Public

BPZ Resources is committed to exploring for oil and gas resources in South America. The company once provided information technology services, including security and access services, application integration, and software development but has been focusing on oil and gas exploration and production in recent years. It operates through its BPZ Energy subsidiary and that unit's BPZ Energy International Holdings subsidiary. BPZ Resources owns 2.4 million acres, in four blocks, of oil and gas properties in northwest Peru. It also holds acreage in Ecuador. In 2008 the company reported proved reserves of 17.2 million barrels of oil equivalent.

	Annual Growth	12/05	12/06	12/07	12/08	12/09
Sales ($ mil.)	—	—	—	—	—	52.5
Employees	—	—	—	—	—	175

BRADLEY CENTER SPORTS & ENTERTAINMENT CORPORATION

1001 N. 4th St.   CEO: Stephen A. (Steve) Costello
Milwaukee, WI 53203   CFO: —
Phone: 414-227-0400   HR: —
Fax: 414-227-0497   FYE: June 30
Web: www.bradleycenter.com   Type: Government-owned

Bradley Center Sports & Entertainment is all about the Bucks. And the Admirals and Eagles. The not-for-profit company owns and operates Milwaukee's Bradley Center, home to the NBA's Milwaukee Bucks, the Milwaukee Admirals minor league hockey team, and Marquette University's Golden Eagles men's basketball team. The arena hosts about 150 events a year, which have included WWE Smackdown!, Sesame Street Live!, and the Harlem Globetrotters. Opened in 1988, the Bradley Center was built without tax dollars, using a $70 million gift from Jane Bradley Pettit in honor of her father, Harry Bradley, co-founder of the Allen-Bradley Company (now part of Rockwell Automation).

	Annual Growth	6/04	6/05	6/06	6/07	6/08
Est. sales ($ mil.)	—	—	—	—	—	13.8
Employees	—	—	—	—	—	560

BRADCO SUPPLY CORP.

34 Englehard Ave.   CEO: Larry J. Stoddard
Avenel, NJ 07001   CFO: Joe Stacy
Phone: 732-382-3400   HR: Gary Schneid
Fax: 732-382-6577   FYE: December 31
Web: www.bradcosupply.com   Type: Private

Bradco Supply offers building contractors everything they need to put a roof over their clients' heads. The company distributes roofing, siding, windows, and other building materials through about 130 locations in 30 states under several names, including Admiral Building Products, Bak-A-Lum, FlexMaster, and H. Verby. It is one of the nation's largest distributors of roofing materials for commercial use. Bradco also exports its construction materials to the Caribbean, Europe, Latin America, and the Middle East. Founded in 1966, the company was acquired in 2008 by private equity firm Advent International. In May 2010 Wisconsin-based rival ABC Supply agreed to take over Bradco.

	Annual Growth	12/04	12/05	12/06	12/07	12/08
Sales ($ mil.)	4.5%	1,340.0	1,760.0	1,920.0	1,700.0	1,600.0
Employees	(11.4%)	3,250	3,200	3,100	2,600	2,000

⊞ BRADY CORPORATION   NYSE: BRC

6555 W. Good Hope Rd.   CEO: Frank M. Jaehnert
Milwaukee, WI 53223   CFO: Thomas J. (Tom) Felmer
Phone: 414-358-6600   HR: Patrick S. Ference
Fax: 800-292-2289   FYE: July 31
Web: www.bradycorp.com   Type: Public

It's the story, of a firm named Brady. Brady Corporation makes more than 50,000 industrial identification and specialty coated material products. These include industrial and facility ID products such as printable labels, wire markers, and informational signs; safety and regulatory compliance offerings, including lockout/tagout products, safety signs, and traffic control products; and other products such as specialty tapes, photo ID card systems, software, and die-cut tapes. Through Accidental Health & Safety and its Trafalgar First Aid unit, it supplies safety and first aid products in Australia. Trusts controlled by direct descendants of founder William H. Brady own almost all of the company's voting shares.

	Annual Growth	7/05	7/06	7/07	7/08	7/09
Sales ($ mil.)	10.3%	816.4	1,018.4	1,362.6	1,523.0	1,208.7
Net income ($ mil.)	(3.8%)	81.9	104.2	109.4	132.2	70.1
Market value ($ mil.)	(3.7%)	1,792.2	1,769.1	1,833.6	1,921.6	1,541.2
Employees	10.9%	4,500	8,000	8,600	7,800	6,800

BRAKEBUSH BROTHERS, INC.

N4993 6th Dr.
Westfield, WI 53964
Phone: 608-296-2121
Fax: 608-296-3192
Web: www.brakebush.com

CEO: William C. Brakebush
CFO: Thomas Ludwig
HR: Jeff Pratsch
FYE: December 31
Type: Private

It should be pointed out that chickens don't start out with fingers, but Brakebush Brothers produces plenty of 'em. The company manufactures processed value-added chicken products (wings, nuggets, patties, fingers, and strips) for sale through retail grocery and foodservice operators. Its subsidiary, Squawkers, is a branded, restaurant-concept family of products marketed to the foodservice industry; Brakebush Transportation distributes the company's products to destinations in the 48 contiguous US states. Brakebush Brothers, a family-owned company, was founded by William and Otto Brakebush in 1925.

BRAND ENERGY, INC.

1325 Cobb International Dr., Ste. A-1
Kennesaw, GA 30152
Phone: 678-285-1400
Fax: 770-514-0285
Web: www.beis.com

CEO: Paul T. Wood
CFO: Anthony A. (Tony) Rabb
HR: George R. Fleck
FYE: December 31
Type: Private

Unlike Superman, Brand Energy (formerly Brand Energy & Infrastructure) cannot leap tall buildings in a single bound, but it can provide a safe way to scale a tall building. The company provides specialty services to the North American downstream energy infrastructure industry, including work access (front-end application design and project management for scaffolding systems), painting and coatings, abrasive blasting, insulation, refractory, corrosion protection, and fireproofing. Customers include global energy companies such as BP, Royal Dutch/Shell, and ExxonMobil. The company operates more than 200 service centers, half of which are located on its customers' sites.

BRAND MATTER LLC

1400 Broadway, 32nd Fl.
New York, NY 10018
Phone: 212-515-5300
Fax: 212-398-1678
Web: www.brand-matter.com

CEO: James Salter
CFO: Charlie Bang
HR: Charlie Bang
FYE: December 31
Type: Private

Brand Matter uses its gray matter to manage and market consumer brands. The brand management and licensing company owns the Ellen Tracy clothing brand, which is targeted toward professional women. (Ellen Tracy struggled under several owners in recent years until it was purchased by Brand Matter from Liz Claiborne in early 2008.) Brand Matter licenses the Caribbean Joe Island Supply Co. lifestyle brand of beach-inspired apparel and accessories, such as sunglasses and luggage. It also advises companies that own brands, including The Bombay Company and Linens n Things, that were once part of now-defunct retail chains. Brand Matter is owned by private equity firms Windsong Brands and Hilco Consumer Capital.

BRAND PHARM

79 Madison Ave., 3rd F.
New York, NY 10016
Phone: 212-684-0909
Fax: —
Web: brandpharmusa.com

CEO: Kathy Magnuson
CFO: —
HR: —
FYE: December 31
Type: Subsidiary

Brand Pharm provides marketing services for pharmaceutical manufacturers and other companies that sell health care products. Its subsidiaries handle medical marketing and professional selling services such as advertising, public relations, door-to-door doctor's office sales, sales force training, and telemarketing. Clients have included Abbott Labs, Bristol-Myers Squibb, Pfizer, and Procter & Gamble. The firm operates within the Publicis Healthcare Communications Group, which is a unit of Paris-based advertising services conglomerate Publicis.

	Annual Growth	12/04	12/05	12/06	12/07	12/08
Est. sales ($ mil.)	—	—	—	—	—	1.0
Employees	—	—	—	—	—	220

BRANDEIS UNIVERSITY

415 South St.
Waltham, MA 02453
Phone: 781-736-2000
Fax: 781-736-8699
Web: www.brandeis.edu

CEO: Jehuda Reinharz
CFO: Maureen Murphy
HR: Scot Bemis
FYE: June 30
Type: School

Brandeis University offers more than 40 undergraduate majors and more than 30 master's and doctoral degree programs. Located just west of Boston, it comprises the College of Arts and Sciences, the Graduate School of Arts and Sciences, the International Business School, the Heller School for Social Policy and Management, the Lown School for Near Eastern and Judaic Studies, and the Rabb School of Continuing Studies. The university has an enrollment of more than 5,000 students; the student/faculty ratio is 9-to-1. A nonsectarian Jewish community-sponsored institution, Brandeis University was founded in 1948 and is named after the late Justice Louis Brandeis of the US Supreme Court.

	Annual Growth	6/04	6/05	6/06	6/07	6/08
Est. sales ($ mil.)	—	—	—	—	—	217.5
Employees	—	—	—	—	—	1,200

BRANDPARTNERS GROUP, INC.

OTC: BPTR

10 Main St.
Rochester, NH 03839
Phone: 603-335-1400
Fax: 603-332-7429
Web: www.bptr.com

CEO: James F. (Jim) Brooks
CFO: James F. (Jim) Brooks
HR: —
FYE: December 31
Type: Public

From conception to construction, BrandPartners Group will help you build a better brand. Through subsidiaries BrandPartners and BrandPartners Europe, the company offers architectural design and construction services, as well as advertising, marketing, and other branding and operations consulting, primarily to the retail banking industry. Another subsidiary, Grafico Incorporated, provides advertising and marketing services, mainly to the sub-prime retail financial services sector, and the company's Building Partners unit provides general contracting services. Originally established in 1984, BrandPartners Group has offices in the US and the UK.

	Annual Growth	12/04	12/05	12/06	12/07	*12/08
Sales ($ mil.)	(8.0%)	50.6	52.0	52.5	43.8	36.3
Net income ($ mil.)	—	14.2	1.9	(2.3)	(12.3)	(2.3)
Market value ($ mil.)	(54.7%)	41.8	19.8	4.6	3.2	1.8
Employees	(5.2%)	145	144	152	123	117

*Most recent year available

BRANDYWINE REALTY TRUST
NYSE: BDN

555 E. Lancaster Ave., Ste. 100
Radnor, PA 19087
Phone: 610-325-5600
Fax: 610-325-5622
Web: www.brandywinerealty.com

CEO: Gerard H. (Jerry) Sweeney
CFO: Howard M. Sipzner
HR: Beth R. Glassman
FYE: December 31
Type: Public

If the thought of making it big in real estate intoxicates you, look into Brandywine. A real estate investment trust (REIT), Brandywine buys, leases, sells, and manages commercial properties. It owns some 214 office properties, 22 industrial properties, a mixed-use property, some eight properties under development or redevelopment, and almost 500 acres of undeveloped land. Its portfolio totals roughly 26 million sq. ft. of rentable space, mainly located in the Mid-Atlantic region, as well as California and Texas. Brandywine also manages properties and offers such services as construction and redevelopment to other property owners.

	Annual Growth	12/05	12/06	12/07	12/08	12/09
Sales ($ mil.)	10.4%	391.5	662.8	684.0	608.1	582.2
Net income ($ mil.)	(34.0%)	42.8	10.5	56.5	43.5	8.1
Market value ($ mil.)	(20.1%)	3,667.0	4,368.6	2,355.7	1,013.0	1,497.8
Employees	7.6%	300	599	562	482	402

BRANT INDUSTRIES, INC.

80 Field Point Rd.
Greenwich, CT 06830
Phone: 203-661-3344
Fax: 203-661-3349
Web: www.whitebirchpaper.com

CEO: Peter M. Brant
CFO: Edward D. Sherrick
HR: Daniel Boucher
FYE: December 31
Type: Private

Brant Industries does its part to keep newspaper delivery boys busy. Doing business as White Birch Paper, the company produces approximately 1.3 million tons of newsprint and directory paper a year. Brant touts operations at four wholly owned pulp and paper mills, three in Canada and one in the US, from which it ships its lineup to markets in North America, and to some extent overseas. The company also manufactures uncoated specialty paper and paperboard, with up to 50% recycled content. Vertically integrated, Brant runs a saw mill, churning out lumber and wood chips, and owns some 30,000 acres of forestland. Led by CEO Peter Brant, and COO Christopher Brant, the company is family-owned and -operated.

BRASFIELD & GORRIE, LLC

3021 7th Ave. South
Birmingham, AL 35233
Phone: 205-328-4000
Fax: 205-251-1304
Web: www.brasfieldgorrie.com

CEO: M. Miller Gorrie
CFO: Randall J. Freeman
HR: Charles Mason
FYE: December 31
Type: Private

If the South will rise again, Brasfield & Gorrie should have something to do with it. One of the leading construction companies in the Southeast, Brasfield & Gorrie builds high rises and hotels, bridges and churches, hospitals and malls. Other projects include industrial plants, water and wastewater treatment facilities and schools. Commercial and industrial construction together account for most of its revenues; the company is a leading health care facilities contractor. Brasfield & Gorrie provides general contracting, design/build, and construction management services. Founded in 1922 by Thomas C. Brasfield, the company was sold to owner Miller Gorrie (chairman and CEO) in 1964.

	Annual Growth	12/04	12/05	12/06	12/07	12/08
Sales ($ mil.)	14.2%	1,260.0	1,645.0	1,980.0	2,006.2	2,139.5
Employees	9.0%	2,267	2,743	2,939	3,000	3,200

THE BRAVO GROUP

285 Madison Ave., 12th Fl.
New York, NY 10017
Phone: 212-780-5800
Fax: 212-780-0936
Web: www.thinkbravo.com

CEO: Eddie Gonzalez
CFO: Jesús Portillo
HR: Laura Quesada
FYE: December 31
Type: Subsidiary

Companies looking to market themselves to the Hispanic community can applaud the efforts of this firm. The Bravo Group, a top multicultural advertising agency, specializes in campaigns targeting Spanish speakers in the US. The Bravo Group offers creative development, brand promotion, and other marketing services through five offices around the country. It also oversees the operations of Kang & Lee, an ad agency focusing on Asian-American consumers. The agency operates as part of Young & Rubicam Brands, a division of UK-based communications services giant WPP Group, and is not related to public relations firm Bravo Group.

BRAZAURO RESOURCES CORPORATION
TSX Venture: BZO

16360 Park Ten Place, Ste. 217
Houston, TX 77084
Phone: 281-579-3400
Fax: 281-579-9799
Web: www.brazauroresources.com

CEO: Mark E. Jones III
CFO: Brian C. Irwin
HR: —
FYE: January 31
Type: Public

Brazauro Resources is hunting for buried treasure in Brazil. The company focuses on acquiring, exploring, and developing properties primarily for gold. Brazauro Resources currently holds stakes in property in the Tapajos gold district in northern Brazil. The company shifted its focus to Brazilian gold after results from its diamond mining business in Arkansas proved to be disappointing. Founded in 1986, Brazauro Resources plans to acquire more mineral properties in the Tapajos area, as well as in other regions around the globe.

	Annual Growth	1/05	1/06	1/07	1/08	1/09
Sales ($ mil.)	(20.6%)	0.0	0.2	0.2	0.3	0.1
Net income ($ mil.)	—	(3.0)	(7.2)	(4.4)	(4.5)	(2.7)
Market value ($ mil.)	(26.1%)	92.8	115.1	57.7	44.5	27.7
Employees	66.4%	3	38	24	26	23

BRE PROPERTIES, INC.
NYSE: BRE

525 Market St., 4th Fl.
San Francisco, CA 94105
Phone: 415-445-6530
Fax: 415-445-6505
Web: www.breproperties.com

CEO: Constance B. Moore
CFO: John A. Schissel
HR: —
FYE: December 31
Type: Public

The huddled masses that yearn to breathe free of high housing costs turn to BRE Properties. The real estate investment trust (REIT) acquires, develops, and manages multifamily properties in the western US. It owns about 70 apartment communities with some 21,000 units in Arizona, California, and Washington. Most properties offer an array of amenities, including clubhouses, exercise facilities, business centers, and swimming pools. The REIT also has several properties under development and owns stakes in about a dozen more. BRE Properties has eliminated its holdings in Colorado and Nevada to focus on markets in California, where high housing costs and a stable occupancy rate make for an attractive environment.

	Annual Growth	12/05	12/06	12/07	12/08	12/09
Sales ($ mil.)	3.4%	306.1	357.9	353.1	363.7	349.5
Net income ($ mil.)	(5.6%)	80.9	120.2	128.1	140.8	64.3
Market value ($ mil.)	(7.7%)	2,900.9	4,147.3	2,585.2	1,784.7	2,110.0
Employees	(2.8%)	824	836	814	793	737

BREEZE-EASTERN CORPORATION

NYSE Amex: BZC

700 Liberty Ave.
Union, NJ 07083
Phone: 908-686-4000
Fax: 908-686-9292
Web: breeze-eastern.com

CEO: Donald Michael Harlan Jr.
CFO: Mark D. Mishler
HR: —
FYE: March 31
Type: Public

Products made by Breeze-Eastern, formerly TransTechnology, don't lift aircraft into the sky, but they do lift people and cargo onto aircraft. The company makes helicopter rescue hoists, cargo winches, cargo tie-downs, external hook systems, and weapons handling systems. Its external cargo hook systems for helicopters range in capacity from 1,000 pounds to 36,000 pounds. The company's weapons-handling products include hoists to lift weapons onto carrier-based aircraft and to manipulate weapons on ground-based fighting vehicles. US government (primarily military) contracts account for more than 50% of Breeze-Eastern's sales.

	Annual Growth	3/05	3/06	3/07	3/08	3/09
Sales ($ mil.)	4.6%	62.9	64.4	73.3	76.0	75.4
Net income ($ mil.)	—	(2.8)	1.3	4.0	9.4	5.8
Market value ($ mil.)	(4.7%)	75.2	87.0	95.9	102.5	62.0
Employees	2.7%	172	198	206	192	191

BREG, INC.

2611 Commerce Way, Ste. C
Vista, CA 92081
Phone: 760-599-3000
Fax: 800-329-2734
Web: www.breg.com

CEO: Brad Lee
CFO: Bill Hopson
HR: Nancy Rogala
FYE: December 31
Type: Subsidiary

BREG is in the business of broken bones — and sprained ankles and wounded ACLs and all kinds of other injuries to the bones, joints, and ligaments that afflict athletes and non-athletes alike. A maker of orthopedic braces and other devices, BREG's product line includes soft goods, functional braces, and post-operative immobilizers for joints and body parts from shoulder to foot. The sports medicine company also makes devices for rehabilitation and pain management, such as home physical therapy kits and cold therapy products. BREG is a subsidiary of Orthofix International and accounts for more than 15% of its parent's sales.

	Annual Growth	12/04	12/05	12/06	12/07	12/08
Est. sales ($ mil.)	—	—	—	—	—	16.3
Employees	—	—	—	—	—	170

BREITBURN ENERGY PARTNERS L.P.

NASDAQ (GM): BBEP

515 S. Flower St., Ste. 4800
Los Angeles, CA 90071
Phone: 213-225-5900
Fax: 213-225-5916
Web: www.breitburn.com

CEO: Halbert S. (Hal) Washburn
CFO: James G. Jackson
HR: —
FYE: December 31
Type: Public

Oil and gas futures burn brightly for BreitBurn Energy Partners, one of California's largest independent exploration and production companies. With assets in Antrim Shale (Michigan), the Los Angeles Basin, the Wind River and Big Horn Basins (both in Wyoming), the Sunniland Trend (Florida), the New Albany Shale (Indiana and Kentucky), and the Permian Basin (West Texas), in 2008 the company reported estimated proved reserves of 103.6 million barrels of oil equivalent (78% of which were located in Michigan). In 2008 Canada's Provident Energy Trust sold its 96% stake in BreitBurn Energy Partners to Metalmark Capital, Greenhill Capital Partners, and BreitBurn managers for $305 million.

	Annual Growth	12/05	12/06	12/07	12/08	12/09
Sales ($ mil.)	15.7%	114.4	18.5	184.4	802.4	204.9
Net income ($ mil.)	—	39.0	1.9	(60.4)	378.2	(107.3)
Market value ($ mil.)	(24.0%)	—	1,284.4	1,540.2	375.7	564.4
Employees	26.2%	146	150	335	395	370

BRENDAN TECHNOLOGIES, INC.

OTC: BDTE

2236 Rutherford Rd., Ste. 107
Carlsbad, CA 92008
Phone: 760-929-7500
Fax: —
Web: www.brendan.com

CEO: John R. Dunn
CFO: Lowell W. Giffhorn
HR: —
FYE: June 30
Type: Public

Omni U.S.A. has shifted gears. In January 2006 the company sold its power transmission and jack manufacturing units and acquired software company Brendan Technologies, changing its name in the process. Brendan's StatLIA software is used to manage immunoassay testing in agricultural, biopharmaceutical, clinical, research, and veterinary laboratories. Applications include automating of immunoassay testing, data management, quality assurance, and regulatory compliance. Its products can be installed across single or multiple workstations and include the ability to upload worklists and download results to spreadsheets, databases, and laboratory information management systems.

BRENNTAG NORTH AMERICA, INC.

5083 Pottsville Pike
Reading, PA 19605
Phone: 610-926-6100
Fax: 610-926-0420
Web: www.brenntagnorthamerica.com

CEO: William A. (Bill) Fidler
CFO: H. Edward Boyadjian
HR: —
FYE: December 31
Type: Subsidiary

If you live in the US and need a chemical fix, Brenntag North America can hook you up. One of the largest chemical distributors in North America, the company offers hundreds of industrial and specialty chemicals — from acetic acid to zinc oxide — and provides custom blending and packaging of chemicals in dry, liquid, or gaseous states. Customers include manufacturers in such industries as chemicals, pharmaceuticals, paints, electronics, pulp and paper, cosmetics, food and beverages, textiles, and water treatment. European private equity group BC Partners owns Brenntag, and thus Brenntag North America.

BRESLER & REINER, INC.

Pink Sheets: BRER

11200 Rockville Pike, Ste. 502
Rockville, MD 20852
Phone: 301-945-4300
Fax: 301-945-4301
Web: www.breslerandreiner.com

CEO: Darryl M. Edelstein
CFO: —
HR: —
FYE: December 31
Type: Public

Bresler & Reiner are like the bosom buddies of property development primarily in the Mid-Atlantic region. The firm acquires and develops commercial, residential, and hospitality properties in such markets as Philadelphia, Baltimore, and Washington, DC, as well as further south in Houston. It owns or holds ownership interests in nearly 50 commercial office and flex warehouse buildings, totaling nearly 4 million sq. ft. of space, plus five apartment communities, one hotel, and land slated for development. The Bresler and Reiner families collectively own more than 70% of the company.

	Annual Growth	12/04	12/05	12/06	12/07	*12/08
Sales ($ mil.)	4.5%	78.3	122.9	103.3	103.9	93.2
Net income ($ mil.)	—	4.4	(2.2)	16.3	(13.2)	(21.4)
Market value ($ mil.)	(18.9%)	164.3	180.7	194.7	156.1	71.2
Employees	15.8%	15	22	28	27	27

*Most recent year available

THE BRICKMAN GROUP, LTD.

18227D Flower Hill Way	CEO: Scott W. Brickman
Gaithersburg, MD 20879	CFO: Tony Skarupa
Phone: 301-987-9200	HR: —
Fax: 240-683-2030	FYE: December 31
Web: www.brickmangroup.com	Type: Private

The Brickman Group offers landscape design and maintenance services for college campuses, municipal properties, sports facilities, and retail establishments. It provides sports turf services such as field design and consulting, irrigation, mowing, and field maintenance for MLB and the Olympic Games. Serving thousands of clients, the company has also taken on such special projects as repairing New Orleans City Park's irrigation system after Hurricane Katrina. Founded in 1939 by Theodore Brickman, the group has more than 150 branch offices in about 25 US states. Private equity firm Leonard Green & Partners owns a majority shareholding of the company.

	Annual Growth	12/04	12/05	12/06	12/07	12/08
Est. sales ($ mil.)	—	—	—	—	—	332.2
Employees	—	—	—	—	—	6,600

BRIDGE BANCORP, INC.

NASDAQ (GS): BDGE

2200 Montauk Hwy.	CEO: Kevin M. O'Connor
Bridgehampton, NY 11932	CFO: Howard H. Nolan
Phone: 631-537-1000	HR: Deborah McGrory
Fax: 631-537-1835	FYE: December 31
Web: www.bridgenb.com	Type: Public

Bridge Bancorp wants you to cross over to its subsidiary The Bridgehampton National Bank, which operates more than a dozen locations in eastern Long Island, New York. Founded in 1910, the bank offers traditional deposit services to area individuals, small businesses, and municipalities, including checking, savings, and money market accounts, and CDs. Deposits are invested primarily in mortgages, which account for some 80% of the bank's loan portfolio. Title insurance services are available through bank subsidiary Bridge Abstract; wealth management services include financial planning, estate administration, and trustee services.

	Annual Growth	12/05	12/06	12/07	12/08	12/09
Assets ($ mil.)	13.9%	533.4	573.6	607.4	839.1	897.3
Net income ($ mil.)	(2.2%)	9.6	8.2	8.3	8.8	8.8
Market value ($ mil.)	(0.7%)	155.4	151.0	152.9	116.4	151.3
Employees	12.9%	120	123	157	175	195

BRIDGE CAPITAL HOLDINGS

NASDAQ (GM): BBNK

55 Almaden Blvd.	CEO: Daniel P. (Dan) Myers
San Jose, CA 95113	CFO: Thomas A. (Tom) Sa
Phone: 408-423-8500	HR: —
Fax: 408-423-8520	FYE: December 31
Web: www.bridgebank.com	Type: Public

Bridge Capital Holdings helps its business clients get from here to there. It is the holding company of Bridge Bank, which serves small, midsized, and emerging technology businesses in California's Silicon Valley. The bank has regional branches in Palo Alto and San Jose; it also has Small Business Administration (SBA) loan production offices in Redwood City, San Francisco, San Ramon, and Sacramento. Additional SBA offices are located in Southern California; Dallas, Texas; and Reston, Virginia. Bridge Bank converted to a holding company structure in 2004.

	Annual Growth	12/05	12/06	12/07	12/08	12/09
Assets ($ mil.)	12.0%	536.5	722.0	774.8	947.6	844.1
Net income ($ mil.)	(29.6%)	5.7	8.6	10.9	(7.3)	1.4
Market value ($ mil.)	(20.9%)	200.2	221.2	232.5	43.3	78.5
Employees	18.4%	103	134	170	171	—

BRIDGELINE DIGITAL, INC.

NASDAQ (CM): BLIN

10 6th Rd.	CEO: Thomas L. Massie
Woburn, MA 01801	CFO: Ronald M. Levenson
Phone: 781-376-5555	HR: Peter (Pip) Winslow
Fax: 781-376-5033	FYE: September 30
Web: www.bridgelinedigital.com	Type: Public

Bridgeline Digital believes the key to business optimization lies in the Web. The company develops Web service applications, including content and relationship management, e-commerce, and analytics tools. It also offers e-commerce, usability engineering, e-training, search engine optimization, and rich media development services. Bridgeline targets financial services providers, government agencies, foundations and non-profit organizations, and companies involved in technology and life sciences. Its customers have included Depository Trust & Clearing, John Hancock, Nomura Securities, and Pfizer.

	Annual Growth	9/05	9/06	9/07	9/08	9/09
Sales ($ mil.)	42.5%	5.8	8.2	11.2	21.3	23.9
Net income ($ mil.)	—	(0.5)	(1.4)	(1.9)	(10.3)	0.8
Market value ($ mil.)	(45.5%)	—	—	45.2	14.3	13.4
Employees	13.5%	85	80	138	204	141

BRIDGEPOINT EDUCATION, INC.

NYSE: BPI

13500 Evening Creek Dr. North, Ste. 600	CEO: Andrew S. Clark
San Diego, CA 92128	CFO: Daniel J. (Dan) Devine
Phone: 858-668-2586	HR: Charlene Dackerman
Fax: 858-408-2903	FYE: December 31
Web: www.bridgepointeducation.com	Type: Public

Bridgepoint Education invites students from all walks of life to cross on over to the higher-education side. The for-profit company offers graduate and undergraduate programs online and at its traditional campuses: Ashford University in Iowa and University of the Rockies in Colorado. Academic disciplines include education, business, psychology, and health and social sciences. Most of the company's campus-based revenues are derived from federal financial aid. About 99% of Bridgepoint Education's 65,000-plus students are enrolled exclusively online. Hoping to take advantage of the growing market for online and nontraditional schools, the company went public in 2009.

	Annual Growth	12/05	12/06	12/07	12/08	12/09
Sales ($ mil.)	174.5%	8.0	28.6	85.7	218.3	454.3
Net income ($ mil.)	—	(8.0)	(5.2)	3.3	26.4	47.1
Market value ($ mil.)	—	—	—	—	—	820.0
Employees	(5.6%)	—	—	2,800	1,200	2,495

BRIDGESTONE AMERICAS, INC.

535 Marriott Dr.	CEO: Gary A. Garfield
Nashville, TN 37214	CFO: Tim Walsh
Phone: 615-937-1000	HR: Linda Baskin
Fax: 615-937-3621	FYE: December 31
Web: www.bridgestone-firestone.com	Type: Subsidiary

The marks that Bridgestone Americas (BSAM) leaves on this world have everything to do with tires, and more. A Bridgestone Corp. subsidiary, the company is best known for its Bridgestone, Firestone, and Dayton branded tires for cars, trucks, motorcycles, tractors, as well as earthmoving equipment and aircraft. BSAM operates through a family of companies; in addition to consumer and commercial tire making and marketing across the Americas, it drives more than 2,000 vehicle service and tire outlets in the US (including Firestone Complete Auto Care, and Fleet Care). BSAM puts its mark on a range of construction products, too, along with natural rubber, industrial fibers and textiles, and Airide vehicle air springs.

An in-depth profile of this company is available to Hoover's Online members at hoovers.com.

281

BRIDGESTONE BANDAG, LLC

2905 N. Hwy. 61
Muscatine, IA 52761
Phone: 563-262-1400
Fax: 563-262-1069
Web: www.bandag.com

CEO: Saul A. Solomon
CFO: Jeffrey C. Pattison
HR: —
FYE: December 31
Type: Subsidiary

It might be a tired cliché to say that Bridgestone Bandag is on a roll, but the company does deal in tires. Bridgestone Bandag makes precured tread rubber, as well as equipment and supplies for retreading tires for trucks, buses, cars, and industrial and off-road vehicles. The company also sells new and retreaded tires to commercial and industrial customers. The company's integrated dealer network includes more than 1,600 North American sales and service locations. Subsidiary Speedco is a lube service chain for heavy-duty trucks. Bandag is owned by Bridgestone Americas.

BRIDGESTONE GOLF, INC.

15320 Industrial Park Blvd., NE
Covington, GA 30014
Phone: 770-787-7400
Fax: 770-787-4915
Web: www.bridgestonegolf.com

CEO: Shig Nakayama
CFO: —
HR: —
FYE: December 31
Type: Subsidiary

Players fell in love with Bridgestone Golf's Lady, and now they're pretty fond of the Laddie, too. The company sells golf balls, including the Laddie and Lady lines, as well as golf clubs and accessories under the Precept and Bridgestone names. Touring pros Fred Couples, Matt Kuchar, Shigeki Maruyama, Nick Price, and Lee Trevino have played with Bridgestone Golf's gear, which is made at the company's Georgia plant and sold around the world. The Distance iQ ball, originally designed for women golfers, earned a place in men's bags when it was discovered the ball could be hit great distances by players with slower swings. Bridgestone Golf is a wholly owned subsidiary of Bridgestone Sports Co., Ltd.

	Annual Growth	12/04	12/05	12/06	12/07	12/08
Est. sales ($ mil.)	—	—	—	—	—	85.5
Employees	—	—	—	—	—	225

BRIDGESTONE RETAIL OPERATIONS

333 E. Lake St.
Bloomingdale, IL 60108
Phone: 630-259-9000
Fax: 630-259-9158
Web: www.bfmastercare.com

CEO: Larry J. Magee
CFO: Terry Reedy
HR: Ron Tepner
FYE: December 31
Type: Subsidiary

You'll find plenty of rolling stock at these stores. Through its network of more than 2,200 company-owned service centers in the US and Canada, Bridgestone Retail Operations (BSRO) offers a variety of automotive repair services, including drivetrain, engine, heating and cooling, steering, and suspension maintenance, as well as tire sales. The company is the North American retail division of Japan-based tire giant Bridgestone. It serves both consumers and commercial clients under banners such as Commercial & Farm, Expert Tire, Firestone Complete Auto Care, GCR Truck Tire, Morgan Tire, and Tires Plus. BSRO, which was named BFS Retail & Commercial until January 2009, also maintains its own credit card operation.

BRIDGFORD FOODS CORPORATION

NASDAQ (GM): BRID

1308 N. Patt St.
Anaheim, CA 92801
Phone: 714-526-5533
Fax: 714-526-4360
Web: www.bridgford.com

CEO: John V. Simmons
CFO: Raymond F. Lancy
HR: Brenda Potts
FYE: October 31
Type: Public

Bridgford Foods is comfortable with comfort food and eschews fat-free fads to pile on what it knows customers want: gooey sticky buns, and dried sausage (it's one of the nation's largest sellers of jerky and other meat snacks). Refrigerated and snack foods account for 55% of its 2009 sales; the remainder comes from frozen foods. Bridgford Foods' 410 bread, roll, frozen hand-held and fresh prepared sandwiches, deli meats, and meat snack products are marketed to food retailers, restaurants, and foodservice operators across the US and Canada. About one-fifth of Bridgford's products are manufactured or processed by third parties.

	Annual Growth	10/05	10/06	10/07	10/08	10/09
Sales ($ mil.)	(1.6%)	130.8	134.3	125.1	121.0	122.7
Net income ($ mil.)	—	(0.9)	1.2	(0.3)	(12.4)	6.8
Market value ($ mil.)	2.9%	69.4	57.6	66.0	39.8	77.9
Employees	(5.6%)	739	684	660	613	586

BRIGGS & STRATTON CORPORATION

NYSE: BGG

12301 W. Wirth St.
Wauwatosa, WI 53222
Phone: 414-259-5333
Fax: 414-259-5773
Web: www.briggsandstratton.com

CEO: Todd J. Teske
CFO: David J. Rodgers
HR: Jeffrey G. Mahloch
FYE: June 30
Type: Public

It's no BS, Briggs & Stratton knows outdoor housework. For power equipment, the company is #1 among manufacturers of air-cooled gas engines. Lawn and garden OEMs Husqvarna Outdoor Products, MTD, and Deere are key engine customers; generator, pressure washer, and pump makers are less so. Replacement engines and parts are made for aftermarkets, too. Engines are sold worldwide direct through sales and service arms. Subsidiary Briggs & Stratton Power Products also produces generators, pressure washers, mowers, and other outdoor tools, retailed through Lowe's, Home Depot, and Sears, as well as independent dealers. Briggs & Stratton engine and power product facilities dot the US, Europe, Australia, and China.

	Annual Growth	6/05	6/06	6/07	6/08	6/09
Sales ($ mil.)	(5.8%)	2,654.9	2,542.2	2,157.2	2,151.4	2,092.2
Net income ($ mil.)	(27.7%)	116.8	102.3	0.1	22.6	32.0
Market value ($ mil.)	(21.2%)	1,733.1	1,557.4	1,579.9	634.8	667.8
Employees	14.0%	4,058	3,874	3,693	7,145	6,847

BRIGGS & STRATTON POWER PRODUCTS GROUP, LLC

900 North Pkwy.
Jefferson, WI 53549
Phone: 920-674-3750
Fax: —
Web: www.briggsandstratton.com/engine_power

CEO: Harold L. Redman
CFO: —
HR: —
FYE: June 30
Type: Subsidiary

Briggs & Stratton Power Products Group (BSPPG), the outdoor power equipment manufacturing division of Briggs & Stratton, sells pressure washers, pumps, portable generators, outboard motors, and other related products. BSPPG's chief product lines are portable and home standby generators and pressure washers, which the company sells through multiple distribution channels, including home centers, warehouse clubs, independent dealers, and mass merchants. Customers include Lowe's, Sam's Club, Sears, The Home Depot, Tractor Supply Company, True Value, and W.W. Grainger. The Power Products Group accounts for more than a third of its parent company's sales.

BRIGHAM EXPLORATION COMPANY
NASDAQ (GS): BEXP

6300 Bridge Point Pkwy., Building 2, Ste. 500
Austin, TX 78730
Phone: 512-427-3300
Fax: 512-427-3400
Web: www.bexp3d.com

CEO: Ben M. (Bud) Brigham
CFO: Eugene B. Shepherd Jr.
HR: —
FYE: December 31
Type: Public

Still a young company, Brigham Exploration was one of the first small independent exploration and production firms to use 3-D seismic imaging. The company continues to rely on 3-D and other advanced technologies for onshore exploration. It explores mainly in the Anadarko Basin, the onshore Texas/Lousiana Gulf Coast, the Rockies, and West Texas. Since its founding by CEO Ben Brigham in 1990, Brigham Exploration has drilled more than 880 gross wells. In 2009 the company was working on 356 gross and 107 net productive wells. That year Brigham Exploration reported proved reserves of 27.7 million barrels of oil equivalent.

	Annual Growth	12/05	12/06	12/07	12/08	12/09
Sales ($ mil.)	(7.7%)	97.0	106.3	120.6	125.2	70.3
Net income ($ mil.)	—	27.4	19.8	10.2	(162.2)	(123.0)
Market value ($ mil.)	3.4%	1,380.4	850.8	875.3	372.5	1,577.1
Employees	3.0%	64	69	67	73	72

BRIGHAM YOUNG UNIVERSITY

1 University Hill
Provo, UT 84602
Phone: 801-422-4636
Fax: 801-422-0272
Web: www.byu.edu

CEO: Cecil O. Samuelson
CFO: Brian K. Evans
HR: Anna W. King
FYE: December 31
Type: School

Mormons looking for an education don't have to look far — they can go to Brigham Young University (BYU), where they can get schooling based on the values of The Church of Jesus Christ of Latter-Day Saints (also known as Mormons). Through about a dozen colleges, the Mormon-owned university offers bachelor's degrees in some 185 academic programs, master's in nearly 65, doctorates in another 25, and a juris doctorate. Its enrollment includes about 33,000 students, with more than 98% identifying themselves as Mormon; the student/teacher ratio is 20-to-1. BYU was founded in 1875 by Brigham Young, who led some 3,500 church members fleeing religious persecution to found their own settlement in Salt Lake City.

	Annual Growth	12/04	12/05	12/06	12/07	12/08
Est. sales ($ mil.)	—	—	—	—	—	202.6
Employees	—	—	—	—	—	3,767

BRIGHT HORIZONS FAMILY SOLUTIONS LLC

200 Talcott Ave. South
Watertown, MA 02472
Phone: 617-673-8000
Fax: 617-673-8001
Web: www.brighthorizons.com

CEO: David H. Lissy
CFO: Elizabeth J. Boland
HR: Danroy T. (Dan) Henry
FYE: December 31
Type: Private

With Bright Horizons Family Solutions, kids learn while parents earn. The firm operates more than 600 workplace child care centers throughout the US and in Canada, Ireland, and the UK. Bright Horizons offers day care, emergency back-up for when regular care arrangements fall through, before-and after-school care, and vacation care, as well as summer camps, elementary schools, and college admissions counseling services. Most of its centers are accredited by the National Association for the Education of Young Children, which generally uses more stringent standards than those required by states. Bright Horizons is owned by an affiliate of Bain Capital.

BRIGHT HOUSE NETWORKS, LLC

2251 Lucien Way
Maitland, FL 32751
Phone: 407-215-5524
Fax: —
Web: www.mybrighthouse.com

CEO: Steven A. Miron
CFO: Bill Futera
HR: —
FYE: December 31
Type: Joint venture

Bright House Networks lights up living rooms — more than 2 million of them, in fact. The company offers digital cable television, video-on-demand (VOD), digital phone service, and broadband Internet connections to both residential and business customers in select metropolitan markets in Alabama, California, Florida, Indiana, and Michigan. Its Florida systems offer about 300 cable channels. Bright House Networks also owns and operates two 24-hour local news TV stations: Central Florida News 13 in the Orlando area and Bay News 9 for the Tampa Bay area. Bright House Networks is owned by the Advance/Newhouse Partnership (part of Advance Publications) and Time Warner Cable.

BRIGHTPOINT, INC.
NASDAQ (GS): CELL

7635 Interactive Way, Ste. 200
Indianapolis, IN 46278
Phone: 317-707-2355
Fax: 317-707-2512
Web: www.brightpoint.com

CEO: Robert J. Laikin
CFO: Anthony W. (Tony) Boor
HR: Annette Cyr
FYE: December 31
Type: Public

Brightpoint makes money moving mobiles. The company is a top global distributor of mobile phones and other wireless products, acting as a middleman between manufacturers and wireless service providers. It ships the equipment to companies that sell mobile phones and accessories, including wireless carriers, dealers, and retailers; customers include Vodafone, Best Buy, and Sprint Nextel. Brightpoint also offers a range of services that includes warehousing, product fulfillment, purchasing, contract manufacturing, call center outsourcing, customized packaging, activation, and Web marketing. The company gets more than half of its sales in the region of Europe, the Middle East, and Africa.

	Annual Growth	12/05	12/06	12/07	12/08	12/09
Sales ($ mil.)	10.5%	2,140.2	2,425.4	4,300.3	4,640.5	3,185.3
Net income ($ mil.)	26.5%	10.4	35.6	47.4	(342.1)	26.6
Market value ($ mil.)	(16.9%)	1,085.3	947.5	1,082.0	306.4	517.8
Employees	12.6%	1,683	2,112	3,269	3,032	2,705

BRIGHTSTAR CORP.

9725 NW 117th Ave., Ste. 300
Miami, FL 33178
Phone: 305-421-6000
Fax: —
Web: www.brightstarcorp.com

CEO: R. Marcelo Claure
CFO: Dennis Strand
HR: Michael (Mike) Cost
FYE: December 31
Type: Private

Brightstar shines in the constellation of telecommunications distributors. The company distributes wireless communications products, including cell phones and accessories, wireless data equipment, and prepaid wireless products. The company offers inventory management, logistics, fulfillment, customized packaging, and assembly services, as well as supply chain and reverse logistics services. It distributes cell phones made by the likes of Motorola, Kyocera, Samsung, LG, and Sony Ericsson. With operations in more than 40 countries, the company serves network operators, retailers, and resellers in the Americas, Europe, Asia, and the Asia/Pacific region. Brightstar was founded in 1997 by CEO Marcelo Claure.

	Annual Growth	12/04	12/05	12/06	12/07	12/08
Sales ($ mil.)	16.6%	—	2,252.0	3,590.0	4,400.0	3,570.0
Employees	13.4%	—	1,441	1,684	3,500	2,101

An in-depth profile of this company is available to Hoover's Online members at hoovers.com.

283

BRILLIANT DIGITAL ENTERTAINMENT, INC.

Pink Sheets: BDLN

14011 Ventura Blvd., Ste. 501
Sherman Oaks, CA 91423
Phone: 818-386-2180
Fax: 818-386-2179
Web: www.brilliantdigital.com

CEO: Kevin G. Bermeister
CFO: Kevin G. Bermeister
HR: —
FYE: December 31
Type: Public

Not sure how brilliant digital entertainment gets to your PC? Brilliant Digital Entertainment operates a peer-to-peer network through its Altnet subsidiary that distributes digital content such as music, video, games, software, and other digital files to PC users through a subscription-based download service. Brilliant Digital also has agreements with distribution partners such as Sharman Networks, operator of the Kazaa Media Desktop, where Brilliant Digital provides technology and services to clients (owners and licensees of content, including music labels, video and film companies, software publishers, and game developers) so they can distribute content through their own website.

BRILLSTEIN ENTERTAINMENT PARTNERS, LLC

9150 Wilshire Blvd., Ste. 350
Beverly Hills, CA 90212
Phone: 310-275-6135
Fax: 310-275-6180

CEO: Jon Liebman
CFO: Naren G. Ramanuj
HR: —
FYE: December 31
Type: Private

Brillstein Entertainment Partners (formerly Brillstein-Grey Entertainment) has its eyes on the talent. The agency is a powerful Hollywood management firm with a roster of some 200 clients, including such stars as Brad Pitt, Jennifer Aniston, Adam Sandler, and Lorne Michaels. It also produces TV shows and films that showcase the talents of its clients. Producer Bernie Brillstein founded the agency in 1969 and later partnered with his protégé, Brad Grey. Following Grey's departure, the company changed its name to Brillstein Entertainment Partners in 2007.

BRINKER INTERNATIONAL, INC.

NYSE: EAT

6820 LBJ Fwy., Ste. 200
Dallas, TX 75240
Phone: 972-980-9917
Fax: 972-770-9593
Web: www.brinker.com

CEO: Douglas H. (Doug) Brooks
CFO: Charles M. (Chuck) Sonsteby
HR: Valerie L. Davisson
FYE: June 30
Type: Public

More than a few Chili's heat up this restaurant business. Brinker International is the world's #3 casual-dining operator in terms of revenue (behind Darden Restaurants and OSI Restaurant Partners), with more than 1,650 locations in about 30 countries. Its flagship Chili's Grill & Bar chain boasts about 1,500 outlets and trails only Applebee's as the largest full-service restaurant chain. Specializing in southwestern-style dishes, Chili's menu features fajitas, margarita grilled chicken, and its popular baby back ribs. Brinker also operates On The Border Mexican Grill & Cantina, a Mexican-themed chain with 160 locations, and Maggiano's Little Italy. More than 650 of the eateries are operated by franchisees.

	Annual Growth	6/05	6/06	6/07	6/08	6/09
Sales ($ mil.)	(1.9%)	3,912.9	4,151.3	4,376.9	4,235.2	3,620.6
Net income ($ mil.)	(16.1%)	160.2	212.4	230.0	51.7	79.2
Market value ($ mil.)	(10.6%)	2,738.9	2,482.4	3,002.5	1,938.8	1,746.9
Employees	(8.2%)	108,500	110,800	113,900	100,400	77,100

THE BRINK'S COMPANY

NYSE: BCO

1801 Bayberry Ct.
Richmond, VA 23226
Phone: 804-289-9600
Fax: 804-289-9770
Web: www.brinkscompany.com

CEO: Michael T. Dan
CFO: Joseph W. (Joe) Dziedzic
HR: —
FYE: December 31
Type: Public

Teetering on the brink of a security disaster? The Brink's Company can help. It is the largest and oldest operator, and logistics supplier of armored cars used in transporting cash for banks and retailers (85% of sales). Brink's also provides various other security-related services — such as ATM management, secure long-distance transportation of valuables, and guarding services, including airport security — which government-agencies avail themselves of. The company serves customers in more than 50 countries. Its operations include more than 800 facilities and some 15,500 vehicles. Globally known, the company garners more than 70% of its revenues outside of North America.

	Annual Growth	12/05	12/06	12/07	12/08	12/09
Sales ($ mil.)	5.3%	2,549.0	2,837.6	3,219.0	3,163.5	3,135.0
Net income ($ mil.)	11.9%	147.8	587.2	137.3	183.3	231.9
Market value ($ mil.)	(2.0%)	1,265.5	1,688.3	1,577.9	1,287.5	1,165.8
Employees	6.7%	45,800	48,700	53,900	56,900	59,400

BRISTOL FARMS

915 E. 230th St
Carson, CA 90745
Phone: 310-233-4700
Fax: 310-233-4701
Web: www.bristolfarms.com

CEO: Kevin Davis
CFO: —
HR: Yolie Pepin
FYE: December 31
Type: Subsidiary

Bristol Farms operates about 15 upscale specialty supermarkets in California's Los Angeles, Orange, and Ventura counties, as well as one store in San Francisco. Smaller than traditional supermarkets (stores average about 14,000 sq. ft.), more than two-thirds of the company's sales come from fresh products. The chain also sells wine and spirits. Once owned by Los Angeles-based investment firm Oaktree Capital Management, Bristol Farms was sold to grocery giant Albertsons in 2004, but continued to operate independently. Ownership of the specialty foods retailer changed again in mid-2006 following grocery wholesaler and retailer SUPERVALU's acquisition of more than 1,100 stores from ailing Albertsons.

BRISTOL-MYERS SQUIBB COMPANY

NYSE: BMY

345 Park Ave.
New York, NY 10154
Phone: 212-546-4000
Fax: 212-546-4020
Web: www.bms.com

CEO: Lamberto Andreotti
CFO: Charles Bancroft
HR: Anthony McBride
FYE: December 31
Type: Public

Pharmaceutical giant Bristol-Myers Squibb (BMS) makes big bucks on matters of the heart. The company's blockbuster cardiovascular lineup includes heart disease drug Plavix and Avapro for hypertension. BMS also makes antipsychotic medication Abilify and HIV treatments Reyataz and Sustiva. Most of the company's sales come from products in the therapeutic areas of cardiovascular, immunoscience, metabolics, neuroscience, oncology, and virology. BMS, which has about 20 manufacturing plants worldwide and about 10 R&D centers in five countries, sells its products globally; the US accounts for more than half of sales.

	Annual Growth	12/05	12/06	12/07	12/08	12/09
Sales ($ mil.)	(0.5%)	19,207.0	17,914.0	19,348.0	20,597.0	18,808.0
Net income ($ mil.)	37.4%	3,000.0	1,585.0	2,165.0	5,247.0	10,681.0
Market value ($ mil.)	2.4%	39,518.1	45,261.8	45,605.8	39,982.4	43,421.8
Employees	(10.2%)	43,000	43,000	42,000	35,000	28,000

An in-depth profile of this company is available to Hoover's Online members at hoovers.com.

BRISTOW GROUP INC.

NYSE: BRS

2000 W. Sam Houston Pkwy. South, Ste. 1700	CEO: William E. (Bill) Chiles
Houston, TX 77042	CFO: William E. (Bill) Chiles
Phone: 713-267-7600	HR: Hilary Ware
Fax: 713-267-7620	FYE: March 31
Web: www.bristowgroup.com	Type: Public

Bristow Group takes its customers for a ride. The company offers helicopter transportation services for offshore petroleum workers and equipment. Through its Air Logistics and Bristow Helicopters units and several affiliates, Bristow Group serves oil and gas exploration and production companies in the world's major offshore oil production zones. Its main operating areas are the North Sea and the Gulf of Mexico. About 30% of the company's sales come from Shell Oil, Chevron and each company's related entities. Bristow Group operates a fleet of about 380 aircraft, which consists primarily of helicopters but also includes some fixed-wing aircraft. Affiliates operate another 120 or so aircraft.

	Annual Growth	3/06	3/07	3/08	3/09	3/10
Sales ($ mil.)	11.0%	768.9	897.9	1,012.8	1,133.8	1,167.8
Net income ($ mil.)	18.4%	57.8	67.5	104.0	124.3	113.5
Market value ($ mil.)	5.1%	1,110.6	1,310.0	1,928.9	770.2	1,356.0
Employees	(5.1%)	4,200	4,159	3,644	3,569	3,410

BRITTON & KOONTZ CAPITAL CORPORATION

NASDAQ (CM): BKBK

500 Main St.	CEO: W. Page Ogden
Natchez, MS 39120	CFO: William M. Salters
Phone: 601-445-5576	HR: —
Fax: 601-445-2488	FYE: December 31
Web: www.bkbank.com	Type: Public

You'll find this bank along the banks of the Mississippi. Britton & Koontz Capital is the holding company for Britton & Koontz Bank, which has about a half-dozen branches in Natchez and Vicksburg, Mississippi, and Baton Rouge, Louisiana, where the company plans to expand. Targeting individual and local business customers, the bank offers such standard deposit products as checking, savings, and money market accounts; CDs; and trust services. A majority of the bank's loan portfolio consists of real estate loans, however, Britton & Koontz Capital also makes agricultural, business, and consumer loans. Brothers William and Audley Britton, along with George Koontz, established the bank in 1836.

	Annual Growth	12/05	12/06	12/07	12/08	12/09
Assets ($ mil.)	0.2%	389.3	369.3	368.3	413.1	393.1
Net income ($ mil.)	(15.9%)	3.2	3.6	3.0	3.5	1.6
Market value ($ mil.)	(14.1%)	45.1	42.2	33.7	25.6	24.6
Employees	2.3%	103	108	113	116	113

BROADCAST INTERNATIONAL, INC.

OTC: BCST

7050 Union Park Ave., Ste. 600	CEO: Rodney M. (Rod) Tiede
Salt Lake City, UT 84047	CFO: James E. (Jim) Solomon
Phone: 801-562-2252	HR: —
Fax: 801-562-1773	FYE: December 31
Web: www.brin.com	Type: Public

Broadcast International (BI) provides communication network integration services for large retailers and other geographically dispersed businesses. The company utilizes satellite, Internet video streaming, and Wi-Fi technologies to connect businesses with employees and customers. Clients use its networks to deliver training programs and make product announcements. BI primarily uses third-party equipment, but it also supplies some proprietary technologies. BI also offers hosting of video streaming, as well as audio and video production services. Its customers have included Caterpillar, Safeway, and Chevron.

	Annual Growth	12/05	12/06	12/07	12/08	12/09
Sales ($ mil.)	(9.6%)	5.4	13.9	4.3	3.4	3.6
Net income ($ mil.)	—	(5.6)	(15.6)	(26.3)	(12.5)	(13.4)
Market value ($ mil.)	(14.9%)	92.3	48.0	151.8	90.3	48.4
Employees	2.7%	44	35	43	38	49

BROADCAST MUSIC, INC.

320 W. 57th St.	CEO: Del R. Bryant
New York, NY 10019	CFO: Bruce A. Esworthy
Phone: 212-586-2000	HR: Robert Boone
Fax: 212-245-8986	FYE: June 30
Web: www.bmi.com	Type: Not-for-profit

If you are a composer or musician, Broadcast Music, Inc. (BMI) is here to see that your royalties are paid. The not-for-profit organization collects licensing fees from a host of outlets and venues (such as radio stations, TV programs, websites, restaurants, and nightclubs) and distributes them to the more than 375,000 songwriters, composers, and music publishers it represents. Its catalog of compositions includes more than 6.5 million works by a diverse range of artists including Carrie Underwood, the Foo Fighters, Shakira, Herbie Hancock, and Kanye West. BMI was founded in 1939.

	Annual Growth	6/04	6/05	6/06	6/07	6/08
Sales ($ mil.)	7.6%	673.0	728.0	779.0	839.0	901.0
Employees	—	700	—	—	—	—

BROADCASTER, INC.

OTC: BCAS

9201 Oakdale Ave., Ste. 200	CEO: Martin R. Wade III
Chatsworth, CA 91311	CFO: Blair Mills
Phone: 818-206-9274	HR: —
Fax: 818-206-9371	FYE: June 30
Web: www.broadcaster.com	Type: Public

Broadcaster has something to say about game developing and mobile phone value added services. The company operates through two businesses. Broadcaster's LampLighter Studios, acquired in 2008, provides graphic art for online games, cell phone games, video games, and commercial video projects. Its Eyecandy Media subsidiary, also acquired that year, offers video technology and value added services for mobile phones in China. In 2007 Broadcaster discontinued its Social Media Network, an Internet entertainment network that allowed users to upload and view videos, publish and access live Web cam feeds, and chat with other users.

BROADCOM CORPORATION

NASDAQ (GS): BRCM

5300 California Ave.	CEO: Scott A. McGregor
Irvine, CA 92617	CFO: Eric K. Brandt
Phone: 949-926-5000	HR: Terri L. Timberman
Fax: 949-926-6589	FYE: December 31
Web: www.broadcom.com	Type: Public

Broadcom harbors broad ambitions for its semiconductors' impact on broadband communications: it wants them to drive every part of the high-speed wired and wireless networks of the future. The core applications for its integrated circuits (ICs) are digital set-top boxes, cable modems, servers, and networking gear for homes and offices. Broadcom also makes semiconductors for carrier access, DSL, and wireless communications equipment, including mobile phones. Customers include 3Com, Apple, Cisco, Dell, Hewlett-Packard, IBM, LG, Motorola, Nokia, and Samsung Electronics (about 10% of sales). The Asia/Pacific region contributes around 90% of Broadcom's sales.

	Annual Growth	12/05	12/06	12/07	12/08	12/09
Sales ($ mil.)	13.9%	2,670.8	3,667.8	3,776.4	4,658.1	4,490.3
Net income ($ mil.)	(36.9%)	411.7	379.0	213.3	214.8	65.3
Market value ($ mil.)	0.0%	15,603.3	16,038.7	12,975.9	8,423.9	15,621.7
Employees	14.6%	4,287	5,233	6,347	7,402	7,407

An in-depth profile of this company is available to Hoover's Online members at hoovers.com.

285

BROADLANE, INC.

13727 Noel Rd., Ste. 1400
Dallas, TX 75240
Phone: 972-813-7500
Fax: 972-813-8400
Web: www.broadlane.com

CEO: Patrick T. Ryan
CFO: Laurie Jackson
HR: Kathleen (Kathy) Ayres
FYE: May 31
Type: Private

Broadlane directs traffic between hospitals and medical equipment makers. The company is a group purchasing organization (GPO) that negotiates contracts on behalf of its customers, using the combined purchasing power of its client base to get good deals on medical and surgical supplies, capital equipment, drugs, information technology systems, and even labor. Its proprietary OnRamp and BroadLink online portals allow clients to order supplies, view contracts, track pending transactions, and obtain reports. Broadlane serves thousands of hospitals, physician practices, and other health care facilities. Private equity firm TowerBrook Capital Partners owns a majority interest in Broadlane.

BROADRIDGE FINANCIAL SOLUTIONS, INC.   NYSE: BR

1981 Marcus Ave.
Lake Success, NY 11042
Phone: 516-472-5400
Fax: —
Web: www.broadridge.com

CEO: Richard J. Daly
CFO: Dan Sheldon
HR: Maryjo T. Charbonnier
FYE: June 30
Type: Public

Broadridge Financial Solutions does business by proxy. The New York company provides technology-based outsourcing to companies in the financial services industry (especially banks and broker-dealers) around the world and specializes in three specific areas of service: investor communications, securities processing, and clearing and outsourcing. Its investors communications division, which accounts for some 70% of Broadridge's sales provides, among other services, the processing and distribution of proxy materials and voting instruction forms (VIFs) to investors through its proprietary ProxyEdge. The company operates out of about 40 offices in 10 countries including the US, Canada, Germany, and Japan.

	Annual Growth	6/05	6/06	6/07	6/08	6/09
Sales ($ mil.)	5.8%	1,717.1	1,933.3	2,137.9	2,207.5	2,149.3
Net income ($ mil.)	7.8%	165.4	166.7	197.1	192.2	223.3
Market value ($ mil.)	(6.9%)	—	—	2,603.9	2,866.7	2,258.0
Employees	7.3%	—	4,100	4,241	4,850	5,060

BROADSOFT, INC.

220 Perry Pkwy.
Gaithersburg, MD 20877
Phone: 301-977-9440
Fax: —
Web: www.broadsoft.com

CEO: Michael (Mike) Tessler
CFO: James A. (Jim) Tholen
HR: —
FYE: December 31
Type: Private

BroadSoft hopes to remove some of hard work from the process of supplying voice and data services. The company designs software that fixed-line, mobile, and cable service providers use to provide voice and data services over IP-based networks. Customers use its BroadWorks software to offer their own clients services such as video calling, hosted multimedia communications, PBX exchanges, and collaboration tools. The company was founded in 1998 and has received funding from investors including Bessemer Venture Partners, Charles River Ventures, and Grotech Partners. BroadSoft filed for an IPO in March 2010.

BROADVIEW INSTITUTE, INC.   OTC: BVII

8089 Globe Dr.
Woodbury, MN 55125
Phone: 651-332-8000
Fax: 651-332-8001
Web: www.broadviewmedia.com

CEO: Jeffrey D. Myhre
CFO: Kenneth J. (Ken) McCarthy
HR: —
FYE: March 31
Type: Public

Broadview Institute isn't narrow-minded about education. The company owns and operates C Square Educational Enterprises, dba Utah Career College or UCC, which offers career vocational training programs in the Salt Lake City area to about 1,000 students. Its degree programs span four growing industries: business and accounting, health sciences (including veterinary studies), information technology, and legal science. Classes are offered at three campuses in Utah and through online and accelerated programs. Chairman Terry Myhre owns about 65% of Broadview. Additionally, Myhre has controlling interest in two other post-secondary career colleges, Globe University and Minnesota School of Business.

	Annual Growth	3/05	3/06	3/07	3/08	3/09
Sales ($ mil.)	39.2%	3.3	9.9	9.2	10.3	12.4
Net income ($ mil.)	—	(0.8)	(0.5)	0.2	2.3	0.3
Market value ($ mil.)	(29.7%)	33.0	18.9	14.0	16.9	8.1
Employees	68.2%	25	127	124	154	200

BROADVIEW NETWORKS HOLDINGS, INC.

800 Westchester Ave., Ste. N501
Rye Brook, NY 10573
Phone: 914-922-7000
Fax: —
Web: www.broadviewnet.com

CEO: Michael K. Robinson
CFO: Corey Rinker
HR: —
FYE: December 31
Type: Private

Broadview Networks seeks to expand its customers' horizons. The company provides such telecommunications services as local and long-distance voice, broadband Internet access, and Web hosting. It caters primarily to small and midsized businesses, serving 10 states in the northeastern and mid-Atlantic US; Broadview serves such major metropolitan markets as Baltimore, Boston, New York, Philadelphia, and Washington, DC. The company's enterprise data services include hosted business networks, as well as hosted computer telephony services (sold under the OfficeSuite brand), which are offered nationwide. MCG Capital is the majority shareholder of Broadview Networks.

	Annual Growth	12/04	12/05	12/06	12/07	12/08
Est. sales ($ mil.)	—	—	—	—	—	500.7
Employees	—	—	—	—	—	1,290

⊞ BROADVISION, INC.   NASDAQ (GM): BVSN

1600 Seaport Blvd., Ste. 550
Redwood City, CA 94063
Phone: 650-331-1000
Fax: 650-364-3425
Web: www.broadvision.com

CEO: Pehong Chen
CFO: Shin-Yuan Tzou
HR: —
FYE: December 31
Type: Public

BroadVision gives companies a peek into the world of customer self-service. The company provides software applications that enable businesses to offer their customers personalized self-service via the Internet. BroadVision's software suite includes applications for integrating business processes with self-service operations; managing the sales process, including lead generation, execution, and customer service; connecting customers to personalized online views of content; and managing content from creation through distribution. Founder and CEO Pehong Chen owns 37% of BroadVision.

	Annual Growth	12/05	12/06	12/07	12/08	12/09
Sales ($ mil.)	(15.3%)	60.1	52.0	50.0	35.9	31.0
Net income ($ mil.)	—	(39.0)	15.0	17.3	(15.0)	3.7
Market value ($ mil.)	2.6%	54.5	86.8	199.3	49.4	60.4
Employees	4.3%	181	159	195	219	214

BROADWAY FINANCIAL CORPORATION

NASDAQ (CM): BYFC

4800 Wilshire Blvd.
Los Angeles, CA 90010
Phone: 323-634-1700
Fax: 323-634-1717
Web: www.broadwayfederalbank.com

CEO: Paul C. Hudson
CFO: Sam Sarpong
HR: Kim Johnson
FYE: December 31
Type: Public

This company won't quit 'til it's a star! Broadway Financial is the holding company for Broadway Federal Bank, a savings and loan that serves the low- and moderate-income minority neighborhoods of central and south central Los Angeles and nearby Inglewood. Through about a half-dozen branches and loan offices, the bank primarily originates multifamily (about 40% of its loan portfolio) and commercial real estate loans (another 40%). These loans are secured primarily by multifamily dwellings and properties used for business and religious purposes. Deposit products include CDs and savings, checking, money market, and NOW accounts.

	Annual Growth	12/04	12/05	12/06	12/07	*12/08
Assets ($ mil.)	10.2%	276.5	292.3	301.0	356.8	407.9
Net income ($ mil.)	7.8%	1.7	1.7	1.7	1.5	2.3
Market value ($ mil.)	(25.5%)	21.8	19.1	18.3	15.1	6.7
Employees	7.2%	69	56	72	84	91

*Most recent year available

BROAN-NUTONE LLC

926 W. State St.
Hartford, WI 53027
Phone: 262-673-4340
Fax: 262-673-8638
Web: www.broan-nutone.com

CEO: David L. (Dave) Pringle
CFO: John M. Pendergast
HR: Joe Podawiltz
FYE: December 31
Type: Subsidiary

Customers are big fans of Broan-NuTone products. Henry Broan started the company in 1932 with the Motordor kitchen fan; today Broan-NuTone is a leading maker of residential ventilation products. Offerings include ventilation and ceiling fans, heaters, range hoods, indoor air quality products and trash compactors. Central vacuums, intercom systems, medicine cabinets, ironing centers, speakers, and doorbells are marketed under the NuTone name. The company's products are sold through Lowe's and The Home Depot, as well as distributors. It also makes private label products for GE, Sears, Whirlpool, and others. The company's parent, Nortek, filed Chapter 11 bankruptcy in 2009, but exited that same year.

BROCADE COMMUNICATIONS SYSTEMS, INC.

NASDAQ (GS): BRCD

1745 Technology Dr.
San Jose, CA 95110
Phone: 408-333-8000
Fax: 408-333-8101
Web: www.brocade.com

CEO: Michael (Mike) Klayko
CFO: Richard Deranleau
HR: —
FYE: October 31
Type: Public

Brocade Communications Systems maintains silky smooth computer network operations. A leading supplier of data center networking products, Brocade makes Fibre Channel switches and related software for connecting corporate storage systems and servers. Its products are used in storage area networks (SANs), which pool storage resources across enterprises for easier management and more efficient utilization of assets. The company's SilkWorm switches automatically reroute data upon path failure and reconfigure the SAN when new devices are added. Brocade sells its products primarily through equipment manufacturers, including EMC, Hewlett-Packard, and IBM, which together generate nearly half of the company's revenues.

	Annual Growth	10/05	10/06	10/07	10/08	10/09
Sales ($ mil.)	35.8%	574.1	750.6	1,236.9	1,466.9	1,952.9
Net income ($ mil.)	—	43.1	67.6	76.9	167.1	(76.6)
Market value ($ mil.)	23.3%	1,652.4	3,602.3	4,224.2	1,674.6	3,820.0
Employees	36.9%	1,160	1,440	2,368	2,834	4,070

BRODER BROS., CO.

6 Neshaminy Interplex, 6th Fl.
Trevose, PA 19053
Phone: 215-291-6140
Fax: 800-521-1251
Web: www.broderbros.com

CEO: Thomas (Tom) Myers
CFO: Martin J. (Marty) Matthews
HR: —
FYE: December 31
Type: Private

Selling clothes had been in the genes of sportswear distributor Broder Bros. for years. Begun as a haberdashery in 1919, it evolved from making hats and gloves into a leading distributor of imprintable sportswear distributing more than products under 35 retail brands, including adidas Golf, Champion, and Dickies, and private labels and operates under the Broder, Alpha, and NES divisions. Its private labels include Devon & Jones, Desert Wash, Harvard Square, and others. Customers, mostly small US retailers, order merchandise through seasonal catalogs or online. Private investment firm Bain Capital has held a majority interest of the company since May 2000, when the Broder family sold the firm.

	Annual Growth	12/04	12/05	12/06	12/07	12/08
Sales ($ mil.)	1.4%	877.4	978.4	959.3	929.1	926.1
Net income ($ mil.)	—	(1.5)	—	(7.7)	(124.1)	(68.9)
Employees	(3.0%)	1,498	1,571	1,799	1,743	1,326

THE BROE COMPANIES, INC.

252 Clayton St., 4th Fl.
Denver, CO 80206
Phone: 303-393-0033
Fax: 303-393-0041
Web: www.broe.com

CEO: Patrick D. (Pat) Broe
CFO: Thomas Mandula
HR: —
FYE: December 31
Type: Private

Million-dollar investments don't phase this Broe. The secretive Broe Companies invests in a variety of industries in the US and Canada, largely funded by profits made in real estate investments. It focuses primarily on hard asset-based investment opportunities, as well as distressed businesses. Broe's brotherhood of companies include a short-line railroad owner (OmniTRAX), a pain management medical device manufacturer (McKinley Medical), and a Kentucky coal company (Century Coal). Denver property investor Pat Broe controls the company, which he founded in 1972.

BROMLEY COMMUNICATIONS

401 E. Houston St.
San Antonio, TX 78205
Phone: 210-244-2000
Fax: 210-244-2442
Web: www.bromleyville.com

CEO: Ernest W. Bromley
CFO: Ray Ives
HR: —
FYE: December 31
Type: Subsidiary

Marketers looking to put a multicultural spin on their brand can turn to this company. Bromley Communications is the #1 advertising agency offering communications services targeting the Hispanic population in the US. The firm provides creative ad development and strategic planning services, as well as media buying and allied marketing and promotional services. It also offers public relations services through a partnership with PR firm Manning, Selvage & Lee. Bromley has served such clients as Burger King, Procter & Gamble, and Western Union. Founded as Sosa, Bromley & Aguilar Associates in 1981, the agency is part of Publicis Worldwide's regional operating unit, Publicis USA.

An in-depth profile of this company is available to Hoover's Online members at hoovers.com.

BRONCO DRILLING COMPANY, INC.
NASDAQ (CM): BRNC

16217 N. May Ave.
Edmond, OK 73013
Phone: 405-242-4444
Fax: 405-285-0478
Web: broncodrill.com

CEO: D. Frank Harrison
CFO: Matthew S. (Matt) Porter
HR: —
FYE: December 31
Type: Public

Bronco Drilling is game to compete in that wild ride called oil and gas drilling, where the chances of getting bucked off are as likely as the chance of making a buck. The contract land driller owns a fleet of 56 land drilling rigs, of which 45 are in use. Many of its rigs, ranging from 500 to 2,000 horsepower, can drill to depths between 15,000 and 25,000 feet. Bronco Drilling offers both contract drilling services and well servicing services (such as downhole equipment removal and obstruction removal). The company, which operates rigs in Colorado, Louisiana, North Dakota, Oklahoma, Pennsylvania, Texas, and Mexico, has 63 trucks to transport its rigs.

	Annual Growth	12/05	12/06	12/07	12/08	12/09
Sales ($ mil.)	9.1%	77.9	285.8	299.0	284.3	110.5
Net income ($ mil.)	—	5.1	59.8	37.6	(8.2)	(57.6)
Market value ($ mil.)	(31.5%)	654.3	488.8	422.3	183.7	144.2
Employees	(17.6%)	1,400	2,050	1,551	1,059	646

BRONCO WINE COMPANY

6342 Bystrum Rd.
Ceres, CA 95307
Phone: 209-538-3131
Fax: 209-538-4634

CEO: Fred T. Franzia
CFO: Daniel J. (Dan) Leonard
HR: Patty Glennon
FYE: December 31
Type: Private

Bronco Wine has been known to buck the system. One of the nation's top wine producers, the vintner makes some 60 labels, including Charles Shaw, Forest Glen, and Coastal Ridge. Operating a 40,000-acre vineyard, the California bulk wine producer is the fourth-largest wine seller in the US. It produces some 20 million cases of wine every year. Bronco Wine created a stir in the wine industry and continues to do so by selling its Charles Shaw brand for $1.99 at Trader Joe's Company locations. (The wine, dubbed "drinkable" by many, quickly gained the nickname Two-Buck Chuck.) Other Bronco labels include Carmenet, Crane Lake, and Ridge.

BRONX-LEBANON HOSPITAL CENTER

1650 Grand Concourse
Bronx, NY 10457
Phone: 718-590-1800
Fax: 718-299-5447
Web: www.bronxcare.org

CEO: Miguel A. Fuentes Jr.
CFO: Victor DeMarco
HR: Selena Griffin-Mahon
FYE: December 31
Type: Not-for-profit

Bronx-Lebanon Hospital Center sees to the health of patients in the central and south Bronx, no doubt while rooting for the Yankees a few blocks away. The health care provider has about 960 beds on its two campuses, as well as psychiatric and nursing home facilities. Hospital specialty units include chest pain, orthopedic, cancer, and women's health centers. In addition, Bronx-Lebanon manages a network of about 70 owned and affiliated medical practices; the network — branded as BronxCare — includes primary care doctors and specialty clinics, as well as rehabilitation facilities. The hospital is also a primary teaching hospital for the Albert Einstein College of Medicine.

	Annual Growth	12/04	12/05	12/06	12/07	12/08
Est. sales ($ mil.)	—	—	—	—	—	634.2
Employees	—	—	—	—	—	4,000

BROOKDALE SENIOR LIVING, INC.
NYSE: BKD

111 Westwood Place, Ste. 200
Brentwood, TN 37027
Phone: 615-221-2250
Fax: 615-221-2289
Web: www.brookdaleliving.com

CEO: William E. (Bill) Sheriff
CFO: Mark W. Ohlendorf
HR: Glenn Maul
FYE: December 31
Type: Public

Brookdale Senior Living's communities aim to make folks feel at home. The company operates assisted and independent living centers and retirement communities for middle- and upper-income elderly clients. Brookdale Senior Living has about 570 facilities in 35 states comprising roughly 53,600 studio, one-bedroom, and two-bedroom units. The company provides meal service, 24-hour emergency response, housekeeping, concierge services, transportation, and recreational activities. It also operates skilled nursing facilities designed for the treatment of Alzheimer's patients and others who require ongoing care. Chairman Wesley Edens owns more than half of the company through Fortress Investment Group.

	Annual Growth	12/05	12/06	12/07	12/08	12/09
Sales ($ mil.)	26.5%	790.6	1,309.9	1,839.3	1,928.1	2,023.1
Net income ($ mil.)	—	(67.4)	(108.1)	(162.0)	(373.2)	(66.3)
Market value ($ mil.)	(11.6%)	3,558.4	5,729.7	3,391.2	666.1	2,171.3
Employees	10.5%	15,760	32,000	32,700	31,200	23,500

BROOKFIELD GLOBAL RELOCATION SERVICES

900 S. Frontage Rd., Ste. 200
Woodridge, IL 60517
Phone: 800-589-7858
Fax: 630-910-1299
Web: www.brookfieldgrs.com

CEO: Richard E. (Rick) Schwartz
CFO: —
HR: —
FYE: December 31
Type: Subsidiary

It's a small world after all — unless, of course, you have to move halfway around it. Brookfield Global Relocation Services takes the headache out of corporate relocation. It provides relocation and assignment management services such as home sale assistance, area orientation, payroll and tax coordination, student relocation assistance, property management, and language training. It also conducts regional and global relocation benchmarking studies for the financial, aerospace, chemical, oil, high-tech, consumer products, and pharmaceutical industries. Once a part of the GMAC Home Services division of Ally Financial (formerly GMAC), the company was sold to Brookfield Asset Management in late 2008.

BROOKFIELD HOMES CORPORATION
NYSE: BHS

8500 Executive Park Ave., Ste. 300
Fairfax, VA 22031
Phone: 703-270-1700
Fax: —
Web: www.brookfieldhomes.com

CEO: Ian G. Cockwell
CFO: Craig J. Laurie
HR: —
FYE: December 31
Type: Public

Brookfield Homes builds you up as the master of your own domain. A spinoff of Brookfield Properties, the land developer and homebuilder designs and constructs single- and multifamily homes for move-up and luxury buyers. Its homes average about $550,000 and are located in master-planned communities in Los Angeles, Riverside, San Diego, Sacramento, and San Francisco Bay Area, California, as well as Washington, DC. The company entitles and develops land for its own properties and also sells lots to third-party homebuilders. Through Brookfield Asset Management Inc., chairman J. Bruce Flatt and president and CEO Ian Cockwell own around 60% of the company.

	Annual Growth	12/05	12/06	12/07	12/08	12/09
Sales ($ mil.)	(25.7%)	1,231.1	887.8	583.4	449.0	376.0
Net income ($ mil.)	—	218.7	148.4	15.6	(115.6)	(27.7)
Market value ($ mil.)	(36.7%)	1,413.5	1,067.3	449.1	122.8	227.4
Employees	(17.8%)	636	591	459	379	291

BROOKHAVEN NATIONAL LABORATORY

2 Center St.
Upton, NY 11973
Phone: 631-344-8000
Fax: 631-344-5803
Web: www.bnl.gov

CEO: Samuel Aronson
CFO: John Hauser
HR: Shirley Kendall
FYE: September 30
Type: Government-owned

Brookhaven National Laboratory is one of the leading government research centers in the US, with about 3,000 scientists and staff and more than 4,000 visiting researchers investigating such areas as the environment, high-energy physics, materials science, neuroscience, and nuclear energy. The lab has produced work leading to new medical techniques and is home to one of the world's largest particle accelerators. In addition, past work has garnered six of the prestigious Nobel Prizes. Established in 1947, Brookhaven Lab is funded by the US Department of Energy and operated by Brookhaven Science Associates, a joint venture between Battelle Memorial Institute and Stony Brook University.

BROOKLINE BANCORP, INC.

NASDAQ (GS): BRKL

160 Washington St.
Brookline, MA 02447
Phone: 617-730-3500
Fax: 617-730-3552
Web: www.brooklinebank.com

CEO: Paul A. Perrault
CFO: Paul R. Bechet
HR: —
FYE: December 31
Type: Public

Brookline Bancorp wants to be one of Boston's greatest hits. It's the holding company for Brookline Bank, a community-oriented financial institution with approximately 20 branches throughout Greater Boston. The bank offers checking, savings, NOW, and money market accounts, as well as IRAs and CDs. In 2003 it started offering indirect auto loans originated by car dealerships; they now account for the largest portion of its loan portfolio (about 30%). Commercial real estate loans account for another 20%, while one- to four-family and multifamily mortgages each account for about 15%. Brookline Bank was established in 1871.

	Annual Growth	12/05	12/06	12/07	12/08	12/09
Assets ($ mil.)	4.3%	2,214.7	2,373.0	2,418.5	2,613.0	2,615.9
Net income ($ mil.)	(3.3%)	22.0	20.8	17.7	12.9	19.2
Market value ($ mil.)	(8.6%)	836.6	777.5	599.8	628.8	585.1
Employees	4.9%	202	248	243	245	245

BROOKLYN FEDERAL BANCORP, INC.

NASDAQ (GM): BFSB

81 Court St.
Brooklyn, NY 11201
Phone: 718-855-8500
Fax: 718-858-5174
Web: www.brooklynbank.com

CEO: Richard A. Kielty
CFO: Michael Trinidad
HR: —
FYE: September 30
Type: Public

Brooklyn Federal Bancorp won't sell you a bridge, but it might loan you money to build one yourself. It's the holding company for Brooklyn Federal Savings Bank, which has been operating since 1887. As one might expect, the thrift operates in the New York City area, with two branches in Brooklyn and two on Long Island. It provides traditional deposit and loan services for area individuals and businesses and focuses on real estate lending: Commercial mortgages make up more than 40% of the company's loan portfolio, which also includes one- to four-family home mortgages (more than 30%), multifamily residential loans (about 15%), and construction loans.

	Annual Growth	9/05	9/06	9/07	9/08	9/09
Assets ($ mil.)	11.2%	340.9	408.0	390.4	483.8	521.4
Net income ($ mil.)	(23.5%)	3.8	4.6	3.8	5.6	1.3
Market value ($ mil.)	1.1%	150.7	166.3	177.2	190.6	157.3
Employees	15.2%	59	91	94	103	104

BROOKMOUNT EXPLORATIONS INC.

OTC: BMXI

1465 Slater Rd.
Ferndale, WA 98248
Phone: 206-497-2138
Fax: —
Web: www.brookmount.com

CEO: Peter Flueck
CFO: —
HR: —
FYE: November 30
Type: Public

Brookmount Explorations hopes it has the Midas touch. Formed in 1999, the exploration-stage mining company is engaged in the exploration of precious metal resource properties located Peru and Canada. Its primary project is the Mercedes 100 gold/silver/lead/zinc property in Peru. The company is also on the lookout for potential acquisitions in Canada and elsewhere in South America. President Peter Flueck controls approximately 40% of Brookmount Explorations, having joined the company when he sold his ownership interests in the Mercedes property to Brookmount in 2005.

	Annual Growth	11/05	11/06	11/07	11/08	11/09
Sales ($ mil.)	—	—	—	—	0.0	0.0
Net income ($ mil.)	—	—	—	—	(0.3)	(0.4)
Market value ($ mil.)	14.3%	—	—	—	2.9	3.3
Employees	—	—	—	—	—	—

BROOKS AUTOMATION, INC.

NASDAQ (GS): BRKS

15 Elizabeth Dr.
Chelmsford, MA 01824
Phone: 978-262-2400
Fax: 978-262-2500
Web: www.brooks.com

CEO: Robert J. (Bob) Lepofsky
CFO: Martin S. Headley
HR: William T. (Bill) Montone
FYE: September 30
Type: Public

Brooks Automation supplies a steady stream of production tools and factory automation products for the semiconductor industry. It makes tool automation products, such as vacuum robots and cluster assemblies used by semiconductor manufacturers. Brooks' wafer handling systems include vacuum cassette elevator loadlocks, transfer robots, and thermal conditioning modules and aligners. It also makes vacuum equipment for makers of flat-panel displays and data storage devices. Brooks serves top customers, such as Applied Materials and Lam Research, through three segments: Critical Solutions, Systems Solutions, and Global Customer Operations. The company realizes about 53% of its sales from customers in North America.

	Annual Growth	9/05	9/06	9/07	9/08	9/09
Sales ($ mil.)	(17.1%)	463.7	692.9	743.3	526.4	218.7
Net income ($ mil.)	—	(10.1)	25.9	151.5	(235.9)	(227.9)
Market value ($ mil.)	(12.7%)	866.4	848.2	925.5	543.3	502.4
Employees	(7.4%)	1,800	2,400	2,200	1,866	1,323

BROOKS BROTHERS INC.

346 Madison Ave.
New York, NY 10017
Phone: 212-682-8800
Fax: 212-309-7273
Web: www.brooksbrothers.com

CEO: Claudio Del Vecchio
CFO: Brian Baumann
HR: —
FYE: March 31
Type: Subsidiary

Known for its classic — some would say staid — styling, Brooks Brothers has been getting men dressed for nearly two centuries. Brooks Brothers is one of America's oldest retailers, specializing in men's suits and outerwear (Abe Lincoln was wearing a Brooks Brothers suit and overcoat when he was assassinated); the company also sells women's apparel. Brooks Brothers operates about 180 upscale retail stores and outlet locations in the US. Through partnerships, Brooks Brothers has 100-plus stores in about 15 countries including Chile, China, Italy, and Japan. The UK's Marks and Spencer sold the chain in 2001 for $225 million to Retail Brand Alliance, which is trying to return Brooks Brothers to its glory days.

An in-depth profile of this company is available to Hoover's Online members at hoovers.com.

289

BROOKSHIRE BROTHERS, LTD.

1201 Ellen Trout Dr.
Lufkin, TX 75904
Phone: 936-634-8155
Fax: —
Web: www.brookshirebrothers.com

CEO: Jerry Johnson
CFO: —
HR: Emily Watts
FYE: April 30
Type: Private

From its roots in East Texas, Brookshire Brothers operates more than 100 supermarkets and convenience stores from Louisiana to Central Texas. The regional grocery company primarily operates under the Brookshire Brothers banner, but some of its supermarkets operate under the B&B Foods name. Nearly all of the stores feature outlets selling Conoco gasoline (the company is one of Conoco's largest distributors). Brookshire Brothers is not affiliated with Brookshire Grocery of Tyler, Texas. The companies share a common ancestry dating back to 1921, but a split between the founding brothers in the late 1930s resulted in separate grocery chains. Formerly family-owned, the grocery chain is now 100% employee owned.

BROOKSHIRE GROCERY COMPANY

1600 W. South West Loop 323
Tyler, TX 75701
Phone: 903-534-3000
Fax: 903-534-2206
Web: www.brookshires.com

CEO: Rick Rayford
CFO: Tim King
HR: —
FYE: September 30
Type: Private

By selling staples, specialties, and Southern hospitality, Brookshire Grocery Co. has grown into a chain of about 155 Brookshire's, Super 1 Food, and Olé Foods supermarkets in Texas, Arkansas, Louisiana, and Mississippi. The company also owns three distribution centers, a dairy, and BGC Manufacturing, its private label manufacturing unit. Brookshire's stores average about 40,000 sq. ft., while its warehouse-style Super 1 Foods stores average 80,000 sq. ft. More than 110 of Brookshire Grocery's stores have pharmacy departments. Originally part of the Brookshire Brothers grocery chain (dating back to 1921), the company split from it in 1939. The Brookshire family is still among the company's owners.

⊞ BROOKSTONE, INC.

1 Innovation Way
Merrimack, NH 03054
Phone: 603-880-9500
Fax: 603-577-8005
Web: www.brookstone.com

CEO: Ronald D. (Ron) Boire
CFO: Philip W. Roizin
HR: Carol A. Lambert
FYE: December 31
Type: Private

Need a putting green for the office? How about an alarm clock set to respond to your spoken commands? Then Brookstone is the place for you. It sells gifts, gadgets, and other doodads targeted primarily to men through more than 300 stores in more than 40 states, Washington, DC, and Puerto Rico. The company's functional yet unique product categories include audio and technology, health and fitness, home and office, and travel. Brookstone also sells its wares online and through its name-brand catalog. Because gifts contribute to most of its sales, the company operates temporary kiosks during the busy Father's Day and December holiday seasons. The company is owned by Osim International.

	Annual Growth	1/05	*12/05	12/06	12/07	12/08
Sales ($ mil.)	(0.1%)	498.9	440.6	511.9	562.8	496.7
Net income ($ mil.)	—	21.4	(3.6)	1.6	6.4	(148.3)
Employees	5.1%	3,016	—	3,278	3,504	—

*Fiscal year change

BROTHER INTERNATIONAL CORPORATION

100 Somerset Corporate Blvd.
Bridgewater, NJ 08807
Phone: 908-704-1700
Fax: 908-704-8235
Web: www.brother-usa.com

CEO: Tadashi Ishiguro
CFO: Anthony (Tony) Melfi
HR: —
FYE: March 31
Type: Subsidiary

Brother International is a part of one big global family. Headquartered in New Jersey and serving the Americas, Brother International, a subsidiary of Japan-based Brother Industries, makes and sells fax machines, printers, sewing machines, laminators, typewriters, garment printers, stamp-making systems, and the P-touch labeling system. The Brother subsidiary operates facilities in California, Georgia, Illinois, Massachusetts, and Tennessee. Brother International also has its own subsidiaries in Ohio and in Argentina, Brazil, Canada, Chile, and Mexico. Brother International was formed in 1954.

	Annual Growth	3/04	3/05	3/06	3/07	3/08
Est. sales ($ mil.)	—	—	—	—	—	1,445.2
Employees	—	—	—	—	—	1,500

BROWN & BROWN, INC.

NYSE: BRO

220 S. Ridgewood Ave.
Daytona Beach, FL 32114
Phone: 386-252-9601
Fax: 386-239-5729
Web: www.brown-n-brown.com

CEO: J. Powell Brown
CFO: Cory T. Walker
HR: Linda S. Downs
FYE: December 31
Type: Public

Brown & Brown (B&B) can help you with property & casualty. The independent insurance agency and brokerage firm provides property/casualty, life, and health insurance, and risk management services through its retail division, mainly to commercial clients. Its National Programs division designs customized programs for niche clients, such as dentists, lawyers, optometrists, and towing operators. Subsidiary Axiom Re provides reinsurance as part of the wholesale brokerage division, which also distributes excess and surplus commercial insurance through independent agents. B&B's services segment provides self-insured and third-party administrator services. The company has some 170 offices in about 40 states.

	Annual Growth	12/05	12/06	12/07	12/08	12/09
Sales ($ mil.)	5.3%	785.8	878.0	959.7	977.6	967.9
Net income ($ mil.)	0.4%	150.6	172.4	191.0	166.1	153.3
Market value ($ mil.)	(12.4%)	4,340.6	4,009.5	3,340.0	2,970.5	2,554.1
Employees	3.5%	4,540	4,733	5,047	5,398	5,206

BROWN AND CALDWELL

201 N. Civic Dr.
Walnut Creek, CA 94596
Phone: 925-937-9010
Fax: 925-937-9026
Web: www.brownandcaldwell.com

CEO: Craig A. Goehring
CFO: Angela Ferrif
HR: Susy Pepper
FYE: September 30
Type: Private

Brown and Caldwell is headed straight to the gutter — to clean it up. The employee-owned firm provides environmental consulting and engineering services to industrial, governmental, and utility clients. Brown and Caldwell designs and builds water, wastewater, and solid waste systems for clients in the paper and pulp, food processing, and chemical manufacturing industries. It offers watershed and stormwater management services, as well as pipeline engineering and repair services. The company provides soil and groundwater remediation, underground storage-tank management, risk assessment, and customized data management systems. It operates from 45 offices spread throughout the US.

An in-depth profile of this company is available to Hoover's Online members at hoovers.com. ⊞

BROWN BROTHERS HARRIMAN & CO.

140 Broadway
New York, NY 10005
Phone: 212-483-1818
Fax: —
Web: www.bbh.com

CEO: Douglas A. (Digger) Donahue Jr.
CFO: Charles H. Schreiber
HR: —
FYE: December 31
Type: Private

Brown Brothers Harriman is one of the oldest, largest, and most prestigious private banks in the US. The company organizes its activities into three segments: Investor Services, Investment and Wealth Management, and Banking and Advisory. It possesses expertise in securities lending, global custody, foreign exchange, and asset administration. Additional services include commercial banking, mutual fund management, securities research, mergers and acquisition advice, and trade execution services. The company serves asset managers, financial institutions, corporations, not-for-profit organizations, entrepreneur-owned businesses, and well-off individuals and families around the world.

BROWN JORDAN INTERNATIONAL, INC.

475 W. Town Place, Ste. 201
St. Augustine, FL 32092
Phone: 904-495-0717
Fax: —
Web: www.bji.com

CEO: Gene J. Moriarty
CFO: Vincent A. Tortorici Jr.
HR: —
FYE: December 31
Type: Private

Brown Jordan International (BJI) prefers that its customers take a seat — inside or out. The firm makes indoor and outdoor chairs, tables, sofas, and love seats for home and commercial use. Its brands include Brown Jordan, Casual Living, Charter, La-Z-Boy (under license), Lodging by Liberty, Wabash, Winston, and Stuart Clark (for commercial customers). Residential products are sold by mass merchants (Home Depot and SAM'S CLUB); commercial lines are sold to hotels, restaurants, health care facilities, and schools. BJI also sells Southern Wood-brand ready-to-assemble furniture via mass retailers and catalogs. Hedge funds TCW Group, Stonehill, and Litespeed Capital own a controlling interest in the company.

BROWN PRINTING COMPANY

2300 Brown Ave.
Waseca, MN 56093
Phone: 507-835-2410
Fax: 507-835-0420
Web: www.bpc.com

CEO: Volker Petersen
CFO: Mike Amundson
HR: —
FYE: June 30
Type: Subsidiary

Brown doesn't mind getting its hands dirty — with four-color or black and white — with plenty of printer ink. Founded by Wayne "Bumps" Brown in 1949, Brown Printing Company is one of the largest publication printers in the US. The company prints magazines (more than 700 of them), catalogs, and inserts for some 400 customers, such as catalog retailer Hanover Direct and marketing company Valassis. Brown also provides direct-mail production and distribution through its Alliance List Services division, while its Specialty Printing segment concentrates on digital print services. The company is a unit of large European magazine publisher Gruner + Jahr (G+J).

BROWN SHOE COMPANY, INC.

NYSE: BWS

8300 Maryland Ave.
St. Louis, MO 63105
Phone: 314-854-4000
Fax: 314-854-4274
Web: www.brownshoe.com

CEO: Ronald A. (Ron) Fromm
CFO: Mark E. Hood
HR: Douglas W. (Doug) Koch
FYE: January 31
Type: Public

There's no business like the retail and wholesale shoe business for Brown Shoe Company. Brown Shoe operates more than 1,100 Famous Footwear stores in the US and Guam, about 240 Naturalizer stores in the US and Canada, and a dozen F.X. LaSalle stores around Montreal, as well as shops in China. Besides its venerable Buster Brown line, its brands include Aerosoles, Connie, LifeStride, and Nickels; it also sells Dr. Scholl's and Disney licensed footwear. The company distributes footwear worldwide through more than 2,000 retailers, including independent, chain (DSW), and department stores (Sears). Brown Shoe is opening new stores, closing underperforming ones, and updating styles to appeal to younger bipeds.

	Annual Growth	1/06	1/07	1/08	1/09	1/10
Sales ($ mil.)	(0.6%)	2,292.1	2,470.9	2,359.9	2,276.4	2,242.0
Net income ($ mil.)	(30.6%)	41.0	65.7	60.4	(133.2)	9.5
Market value ($ mil.)	(11.5%)	868.8	1,573.3	746.4	203.6	531.9
Employees	(1.4%)	12,800	12,700	13,100	12,400	12,100

BROWN UNIVERSITY

1 Prospect St.
Providence, RI 02912
Phone: 401-863-1000
Fax: 401-863-7737
Web: www.brown.edu

CEO: Ruth J. Simmons
CFO: Elizabeth C. Huidekoper
HR: Karen Davis
FYE: June 30
Type: School

Ivy isn't always green — particularly when it's Brown. Founded as the College of Rhode Island in 1764 and renamed Brown University for benefactor Nicholas Brown in 1804, the Ivy League school is one of the oldest universities in the US. About 8,000 undergraduate, graduate, and medical students have nearly 100 programs of study at their disposal, taught by more than 650 faculty members. Ruth Simmons was sworn in as president of the university in 2001, the first African-American to hold such a position at an Ivy League school. Brown University is expanding beyond its College Hill location. In 2006 it announced the purchase of seven buildings in Providence's Jewelry District for future expansion.

	Annual Growth	6/04	6/05	6/06	6/07	6/08
Est. sales ($ mil.)	—	—	—	—	—	597.3
Employees	—	—	—	—	—	5,100

BROWN-FORMAN CORPORATION

NYSE: BFB

850 Dixie Hwy.
Louisville, KY 40210
Phone: 502-585-1100
Fax: 502-774-7876
Web: www.brown-forman.com

CEO: Paul C. Varga
CFO: Donald C. Berg
HR: Ralph de Chabert
FYE: April 30
Type: Public

Don't blame Brown-Forman (B-F) employees if the company Christmas party gets out of control; they have lots to drink on hand. The company's portfolio of some 30 mid-priced to super-premium brands includes such well-known spirits as Jack Daniel's, Canadian Mist, Finlandia, and Southern Comfort. Its wine labels include Fetzer and Korbel. Jack Daniel's is the company's leading brand and is the largest selling American whiskey in the world (by volume). Offering some 30 brands of wines and spirits, the company's beverages are available in 135 countries throughout the world. The founding Brown family, including former chairman Owsley Brown II, controls the company.

	Annual Growth	4/05	4/06	4/07	4/08	4/09
Sales ($ mil.)	8.4%	2,312.0	1,976.0	2,218.0	2,582.0	3,192.0
Net income ($ mil.)	9.0%	308.0	320.0	389.0	440.0	435.0
Market value ($ mil.)	1.2%	6,521.7	8,754.4	7,512.3	7,992.9	6,830.2
Employees	(9.5%)	6,100	3,750	4,400	4,466	4,100

An in-depth profile of this company is available to Hoover's Online members at hoovers.com.

291

BROWNING ARMS COMPANY

1 Browning Place
Morgan, UT 84050
Phone: 801-876-2711
Fax: 801-876-3331
Web: www.browning.com

CEO: Charles Guevremont
CFO: Kraig Walker
HR: Arlys Johanson
FYE: December 31
Type: Subsidiary

Browning Arms Company has drawn a bead on the firearms market for more than 125 years. The company traces its roots to the late 19th Century, when John Moses Browning established his firearms factory in Utah. Mr. Browning, who earned many patents for his gunsmithing inventions, developed designs that were manufactured by Winchester, Colt, and Fabrique Nationale. The arms firm, which also has operated as the J. M. & M. S. Browning Company and as Browning Industries, has built a business making rifles, shotguns, pistols, and accessories, along with archery and fishing equipment, knives, flashlights, outdoor apparel, footwear, and security safes.

	Annual Growth	12/04	12/05	12/06	12/07	12/08
Est. sales ($ mil.)	—	—	—	—	—	0.2
Employees	—	—	—	—	—	150

BRT REALTY TRUST

NYSE: BRT

60 Cutter Mill Rd., Ste. 303
Great Neck, NY 11021
Phone: 516-466-3100
Fax: 516-466-3132
Web: www.brtrealty.com

CEO: Jeffrey A. Gould
CFO: George E. Zweier
HR: —
FYE: September 30
Type: Public

BRT Realty is a real estate investment trust (REIT) that originates and holds senior and junior mortgage loans for income-producing commercial property. Most are high-yield short-term mortgages or bridge loans secured by shopping centers, office buildings, hotels and apartments that are being converted into condominiums, and other multifamily residential properties. The REIT also invests in real estate joint ventures and in stock of other real estate companies. BRT Realty's loan portfolio consists of approximately 40 mortgages on properties in about a dozen states, mainly New York, New Jersey, and Florida. Chairman Fredric Gould and his family control about a quarter of BRT Realty.

	Annual Growth	9/05	9/06	9/07	9/08	9/09
Sales ($ mil.)	(13.2%)	25.7	37.5	42.9	23.1	14.6
Net income ($ mil.)	—	16.2	20.1	35.1	(0.3)	(47.8)
Market value ($ mil.)	(29.7%)	329.8	400.5	244.7	121.2	80.4
Employees	—	6	—	—	—	—

BRUCE FOODS CORPORATION

Hwy. 182 West
New Iberia, LA 70561
Phone: 337-365-8101
Fax: 337-364-3742
Web: www.brucefoods.com

CEO: Joseph S. Brown III
CFO: —
HR: Brenda Warfield
FYE: December 31
Type: Private

Hot sauce and candied yams — aaiiieeee! Bruce Foods was Cajun long before Cajun was, well, hot. The company's Original Louisiana Hot Sauce is a top-selling US hot sauce (along with rival McIlhenny's Tabasco brand hot-pepper sauce.) Louisiana-brand hot peppers — for brave souls — are available, too. The company makes less lethal offerings, including Tex-Mex products and traditional Southern favorites — canned yams and sweet potato pancake, muffin, bread-pudding, and biscuit mixes. Cajun King seasonings, Casa Fiesta Mexican foods, Cajun Injector marinades, and Mexene chili seasonings round out the company's menu.

BRUEGGER'S ENTERPRISES, INC.

159 Bank St.
Burlington, VT 05402
Phone: 802-660-4020
Fax: 802-652-9293
Web: www.brueggers.com

CEO: James J. (Jim) Greco
CFO: Robert D. (Bob) Parette
HR: Matt Riley
FYE: December 31
Type: Private

Bagels are the focus of this dough-making enterprise. Bruegger's Enterprises operates and franchises the second-largest chain of bagel outlets in the US (behind Einstein Noah Restaurant Group's Einstein Bros. Bagels chain), with about 300 locations in some 20 states. The eateries feature fresh, New York-style bagels that are kettle boiled and available in a variety of flavors, along with several kinds of cream cheese. Bruegger's offers soups, salads, and sandwiches, as well as premium coffee. In addition to its flagship chain, the company has about 140 Timothy's coffee shops in Canada. Founded by partners Nord Brue and Mike Dressell in 1983, Bruegger's is controlled by private equity firm Sun Capital Partners.

BRUKER CORPORATION

NASDAQ (GM): BRKR

40 Manning Rd.
Billerica, MA 01821
Phone: 978-663-3660
Fax: 978-667-5993
Web: www.bruker-biosciences.com

CEO: Frank H. Laukien
CFO: Brian P. Monahan
HR: —
FYE: December 31
Type: Public

Bruker (formerly Bruker BioSciences) is the parent company of a handful of operating subsidiaries working in the life sciences research field. The company sells X-ray analysis products from the Bruker AXS portfolio and Bruker Daltonics' life science tools based on mass spectrometry for customers such as pharmaceutical companies, biotechs, academic institutions, and government agencies. Bruker Optics develops tools based on molecular spectroscopy, and Bruker BioSpin makes research equipment using magnetic resonance technology. Advanced Supercon makes the superconducting wires used in magnetic resonance imaging (MRI) and other magnet applications, and superconducting devices used in motors and generators.

	Annual Growth	12/05	12/06	12/07	12/08	12/09
Sales ($ mil.)	39.1%	297.6	435.8	547.6	1,107.1	1,114.5
Net income ($ mil.)	117.9%	3.6	18.5	31.5	64.9	81.2
Market value ($ mil.)	25.5%	800.4	1,236.8	2,190.3	665.3	1,986.1
Employees	15.3%	2,549	3,542	2,212	4,400	4,500

BRUNSWICK BANCORP

OTC: BRBW

439 Livingston Ave.
New Brunswick, NJ 08901
Phone: 732-247-5800
Fax: 732-247-5996
Web: www.brunswickbank.com

CEO: Roman T. Gumina
CFO: Thomas A. Fornale
HR: —
FYE: December 31
Type: Public

Brunswick Bancorp is the holding company for Brunswick Bank and Trust, which serves central New Jersey's Monmouth and Middlesex counties through six branches. The bank attracts customers by offering standard deposit products such as checking and savings accounts in addition to investment options like CDs, IRAs, and 401(k) plans. It mainly originates commercial real estate loans (more than half of its loan portfolio). To a lesser extent, the bank also writes construction, land development, consumer, farm, and residential mortgage loans. In 2007 Brunswick Bancorp voluntarily delisted its stock from the NYSE Amex to save regulatory costs.

⊞ BRUNSWICK CORPORATION   NYSE: BC

1 N. Field Ct.	CEO: Dustan E. (Dusty) McCoy
Lake Forest, IL 60045	CFO: Peter B. Hamilton
Phone: 847-735-4700	HR: B. Russell (Russ) Lockridge
Fax: 847-735-4765	FYE: December 31
Web: www.brunswick.com	Type: Public

Brunswick's business is everyone else's free time. A global manufacturer of marine, recreation, and fitness products, its primary business is marine engines, including outboard, inboard, and sterndrive engines, propellers, and engine control systems. The company also makes and markets pleasure boats, from fiberglass boats to sports fishing convertibles, offshore fishing boats, and pontoons. Its fitness business pushes treadmills, total body cross trainers, stair climbers, and stationary bicycles under brands Life Fitness, ParaBody, and Hammer Strength. Brunswick's bowling and billiards activities produce game equipment and operate more than 100 fun centers, featuring bowling, billiards, and dining.

	Annual Growth	12/05	12/06	12/07	12/08	12/09
Sales ($ mil.)	(17.3%)	5,923.8	5,665.0	5,671.2	4,708.7	2,776.1
Net income ($ mil.)	—	385.4	133.9	111.6	(788.1)	(586.2)
Market value ($ mil.)	(25.2%)	3,599.5	2,824.0	1,509.4	372.7	1,125.2
Employees	(14.1%)	27,500	28,000	29,920	19,760	15,003

BRUSH ENGINEERED MATERIALS INC.   NYSE: BW

6070 Parkland Blvd.	CEO: Richard J. (Dick) Hipple
Mayfield Heights, OH 44124	CFO: John D. Grampa
Phone: 216-486-4200	HR: —
Fax: 216-383-4091	FYE: December 31
Web: www.beminc.com	Type: Public

Brush Engineered Materials, through Brush Wellman and other subsidiaries, makes precious and specialty metal products for the medical, communications, and high-tech industries. It also is a supplier of beryllium, alloys such as copper beryllium, and beryllia ceramics. Its Metal Systems Group supplies beryllium products and alloys and accounts for not quite half of its sales. Beryllium's properties — high thermal conductivity, strength, hardness, and resistance to corrosion and wear — give it a wide variety of uses in the computer, telecommunications, medical, and electronics industries. The company also produces special materials such as high-temperature braze materials and precious metal preforms.

	Annual Growth	12/05	12/06	12/07	12/08	12/09
Sales ($ mil.)	7.2%	541.3	763.1	955.7	909.7	715.2
Net income ($ mil.)	—	17.8	49.6	53.3	18.4	(12.4)
Market value ($ mil.)	3.9%	322.4	684.8	750.7	257.9	375.9
Employees	2.8%	1,970	2,185	2,201	2,235	2,196

BRYAN CAVE LLP

1 Metropolitan Sq., 211 N. Broadway, Ste. 3600	CEO: Don G. Lents
St. Louis, MO 63102	CFO: Michael D. Stolte
Phone: 314-259-2000	HR: Lori A. Johnson
Fax: 314-259-2020	FYE: December 31
Web: www.bryancave.com	Type: Partnership

With offices in regions ranging from the Midwest to the Middle East, law firm Bryan Cave is able to represent its clients' interests worldwide. The firm focuses on corporate transactions and litigation; specialties include agribusiness, entertainment, environmental, health care, intellectual property, real estate, and tax law. It has more than 1,000 lawyers in about 20 offices in the US, Europe, the Middle East, and the Asia/Pacific region. Two affiliates — Bryan Cave International Trade and Bryan Cave Strategies — offer consulting services. Bryan Cave was founded in St. Louis in 1873.

	Annual Growth	12/04	12/05	12/06	12/07	12/08
Sales ($ mil.)	7.1%	—	—	—	469.0	502.5
Employees	—	—	—	—	—	—

BRYCE CORPORATION

4505 Old Lamar Ave.	CEO: Thomas J. Bryce
Memphis, TN 38118	CFO: Ramon A. Marus Jr.
Phone: 901-369-4400	HR: —
Fax: 901-369-4419	FYE: December 31
Web: www.brycecorp.com	Type: Private

Sweet! Bryce Corporation builds a brace of plastic-film packaging products for markets including snack food and candy. It has a wrap on consumer products as well as graphic arts, household, label, and photographic solutions. The company, a pro in film conversion and flexible packaging, makes films, sleeves, printing plates, and converting technologies. Bryce offers flexographic printing in up to 10 colors, a range of laminations such as solvent adhesives, multilayer barrier extrusions, and tandem laminations, and barrier, coextrusion, emulsion, and wax coatings. Its line extends to bags, pouches, and custom items. Chairman and CEO Thomas J. Bryce preserves the family's stake in the company, founded in 1969.

	Annual Growth	12/04	12/05	12/06	12/07	12/08
Est. sales ($ mil.)	—	—	—	—	—	300.0
Employees	—	—	—	—	—	800

BRYN MAWR BANK CORPORATION   NASDAQ (GM): BMTC

801 Lancaster Ave.	CEO: Frederick C. (Ted) Peters II
Bryn Mawr, PA 19010	CFO: J. Duncan Smith
Phone: 610-525-1700	HR: —
Fax: 610-526-2450	FYE: December 31
Web: www.bmtc.com	Type: Public

Bryn Mawr Bank Corporation stands atop a "big hill" in Pennsylvania. The corporation is the holding company for Bryn Mawr Trust, which operates more than 15 offices (about half are limited-service branches located in retirement communities) in Pennsylvania's Chester, Delaware, and Montgomery counties, including Philadelphia's tony Main Line suburbs. In addition to such traditional services as checking and savings accounts, CDs, mortgages, and business and consumer loans, the bank also provides insurance products, equipment leasing, investment management, retirement planning, tax planning and preparation, and trust services. Bryn Mawr Bank Corporation has nearly $3 billion of assets under management.

	Annual Growth	12/05	12/06	12/07	12/08	12/09
Assets ($ mil.)	14.2%	727.2	826.7	1,002.1	1,151.3	1,238.8
Net income ($ mil.)	(2.5%)	11.4	12.7	13.6	9.3	10.3
Market value ($ mil.)	(8.6%)	194.8	212.6	206.2	180.7	135.7
Employees	2.4%	255	265	274	266	280

BRYN MAWR COLLEGE

101 N. Merion Ave.	CEO: Jane Dammen McAuliffe
Bryn Mawr, PA 19010	CFO: John Griffith
Phone: 610-526-5000	HR: Joseph (Joe) Bucci
Fax: 610-526-7471	FYE: May 31
Web: www.brynmawr.edu	Type: School

These Mawrters aren't sacrificing *anything*, especially when it comes to their education. Bryn Mawr is a college for women, often referred to as Mawrters, who hail from all over the world. Its undergraduate programs, including biology, English, math, political science, and psychology, enroll more than 1,300. Bryn Mawr also offers degrees through its co-educational Graduate School of Arts and Sciences and Graduate School of Social Work and Social Research, which enrolls some 425 students. The college pools resources with Haverford to offer arts courses. Founded in 1885, Bryn Mawr is one of the oldest women's colleges in the United States, and was the first to offer women an education through the Ph.D. level.

	Annual Growth	5/04	5/05	5/06	5/07	5/08
Est. sales ($ mil.)	—	—	—	—	—	103.3
Employees	—	—	—	—	—	777

⊞ An in-depth profile of this company is available to Hoover's Online members at hoovers.com.

293

BSD MEDICAL CORPORATION

NASDAQ (GM): BSDM

2188 W. 2200 South
Salt Lake City, UT 84119
Phone: 801-972-5555
Fax: 801-972-5930
Web: www.bsdmc.com

CEO: Harold R. Wolcott
CFO: Dennis P. Gauger
HR: —
FYE: August 31
Type: Public

BSD Medical has developed equipment to provide hyperthermia treatment, specifically for treating cancer (including melanoma, breast cancer, brain cancer, and cervical cancer) in tandem with chemotherapy and radiation therapy or as a stand-alone treatment. BSD Medical was the first to develop an approvable hyperthermia system, which uses focused radio frequencies and microwaves to heat cancer cells until they die. The company's devices are designed to target superficial tumors, as well as tumors located deep within a patient's body. Its products are sold to clinics, hospitals, and other cancer-treatment institutions through its sales force and external distributors.

	Annual Growth	8/05	8/06	8/07	8/08	8/09
Sales ($ mil.)	15.0%	2.0	2.9	2.8	5.1	3.5
Net income ($ mil.)	—	3.3	9.2	(3.3)	(2.4)	(11.4)
Market value ($ mil.)	(24.6%)	153.0	109.8	161.3	184.6	49.4
Employees	10.4%	33	39	45	47	49

BSH HOME APPLIANCES CORPORATION

5551 McFadden Ave.
Huntington Beach, CA 92649
Phone: 714-901-6600
Fax: 714-901-5980
Web: www.bsh-group.us

CEO: Michael Traub
CFO: Thorsten Rosenberg
HR: Victor Poglinco
FYE: December 31
Type: Subsidiary

BSH can help make a HSH — a home sweet home, that is. BSH Home Appliances is a subsidiary of German manufacturer BSH Bosch und Siemens Hausgeräte. The company makes and distributes a variety of home appliances under the Gaggenau, Siemens, Bosch, and Thermador brands, including dishwashers, ovens, cooktops, ranges, washing machines, and dryers. Its products are manufactured at plants in North Carolina and Tennessee. BSH serves the US and Canadian markets, selling products directly to new homebuilders as well as through retailers such as Home Depot, Lowe's, and Sears. The subsidiary began operations in 1997.

BSQUARE CORPORATION

NASDAQ (GM): BSQR

110 110th Ave. NE, Ste. 200
Bellevue, WA 98004
Phone: 425-519-5900
Fax: 425-519-5999
Web: www.bsquare.com

CEO: Brian T. Crowley
CFO: Scott C. Mahan
HR: —
FYE: December 31
Type: Public

Bsquare is hip to intelligent computing devices (ICDs) and smart devices, including Internet appliances, handheld computers, TV set-top boxes, and gaming consoles. With Bsquare's engineering and development services and software, equipment makers can integrate Microsoft's Windows operating systems into their products. Its consumer software enables handheld PCs to perform such tasks as faxing and printing. Bsquare also resells products from assorted vendors, including Adobe Systems and Microsoft, which provides the majority of the company's revenues.

	Annual Growth	12/05	12/06	12/07	12/08	12/09
Sales ($ mil.)	10.7%	42.9	49.8	59.4	65.8	64.4
Net income ($ mil.)	—	(1.3)	(0.5)	2.8	2.0	(2.7)
Market value ($ mil.)	(6.3%)	33.0	29.0	69.1	24.1	25.5
Employees	15.4%	155	170	175	232	275

BT ALLIANCE

2160 E. Grand Ave.
El Segundo, CA 90245
Phone: 310-335-2600
Fax: 310-335-4507
Web: www.bt-alliance.com

CEO: José A. Collazo
CFO: Akbar H. Firdosy
HR: Robert A. Passaretti
FYE: March 31
Type: Subsidiary

"Global" is more than a buzzword for BT Alliance. The company, a subsidiary of BT Global Services, works with partners to provide a wide range of managed data network communications services for multinational corporations. BT Alliance offers local service support in more than 50 countries and its network can be reached within more than 170 countries. BT Alliance has served such clients as Allergan, Bayer, and Hitachi. Cross-border services include frame relay, virtual private networks (VPNs), dedicated Internet access, and remote network access.

BT CONFERENCING

150 Newport Avenue Extension, Ste. 400
North Quincy, MA 02171
Phone: 866-266-8777
Fax: 617-845-1058
Web: www.btconferencing.com

CEO: Aaron McCormack
CFO: Rachel O'Leary
HR: Kirsty Adams
FYE: December 31
Type: Subsidiary

BT Conferencing tries to connect people wherever they may be. The company (a subsidiary of UK-based BT Group) is a reseller and integrator of video, audio, and Web conferencing systems worldwide. Businesses, schools, and government agencies use hardware, software, and services supplied by BT Conferencing to enable meetings and training sessions between participants in far-flung locations. The company offers products supplied by such vendors as Microsoft, Polycom, TANDBERG, and Sony. It also provides online conferencing and scheduling services and offers consulting, installation, project management, and equipment support. Clients have included global food products giant Nestlé.

BT MANAGED SECURITY SOLUTIONS GROUP

1600 Memorex Dr., Ste. 200
Santa Clara, CA 95050
Phone: 408-330-2860
Fax: 408-330-2865
Web: bt.counterpane.com

CEO: Jeff Schmidt
CFO: —
HR: —
FYE: December 31
Type: Business segment

BT Managed Security Solutions Group tries to keep computer and communications networks safe. A unit of UK-based telecommunications company BT Group, it provides a variety of managed network security monitoring services to clients in such industries as financial services, health care, manufacturing, and retail industries; it also serves government agencies. Services include vulnerability scanning, security assessment, consulting, network device management, and denial of service attack prevention. BT Managed Security Solutions Group also provides data security services for corporate clients related to regulatory requirements for internal business practices.

BTMU CAPITAL CORPORATION

111 Huntington Ave.	CEO: Richard F. (Dick) Quinn
Boston, MA 02199	CFO: Paul F. Nolan
Phone: 617-573-9000	HR: Robert P. Conlon
Fax: 617-345-5153	FYE: March 31
Web: www.btmucapital.com	Type: Subsidiary

The U makes all the difference. BTMU Capital Corporation, formerly BTM Capital, offers financial services including investment banking, financing and equipment leasing, and asset management. The company operates in the US, as well as in Europe where it has two subsidiaries: London's BTMU Capital (formerly New Boston Partners), a leasing company serving the UK market, and Ireland's Engine Lease Finance, a spare engine financing and leasing company serving the airline industry. Other industries the firm serves include rail, shipping, trucking, containers, oil and gas, and utilities. BTMU Capital is a subsidiary of Mitsubishi UFJ Financial Group, one of the world's largest financial institutions.

BTU INTERNATIONAL, INC.
NASDAQ (GM): BTUI

23 Esquire Rd.	CEO: Paul J. van der Wansem
North Billerica, MA 01862	CFO: Peter J. Tallian
Phone: 978-667-4111	HR: —
Fax: 978-667-9068	FYE: December 31
Web: www.btu.com	Type: Public

Things are heating up at BTU International. BTU makes, sells, and services thermal processing equipment and controls for the manufacture of printed circuit boards and for semiconductor packaging. The company supplies systems for solder reflow (for printed circuit boards), as well as technical ceramic sintering, electrical component brazing, and the deposition of film coatings. BTU equipment is also used to make photovoltaic solar cells and solid oxide fuel cells, and for sintering nuclear fuel. The company sells its products to manufacturers of computers, printed circuit board assemblies, and consumer electronics products throughout the world. BTU gets more than half of its sales from the Asia/Pacific region.

	Annual Growth	12/05	12/06	12/07	12/08	12/09
Sales ($ mil.)	(9.2%)	66.4	78.3	63.7	72.3	45.1
Net income ($ mil.)	—	4.6	9.2	1.9	(1.1)	(14.6)
Market value ($ mil.)	(15.8%)	116.8	90.8	123.4	37.1	58.8
Employees	3.1%	311	348	351	381	352

BUCKEYE GP HOLDINGS L.P.
NYSE: BGH

Five TEK Park, 9999 Hamilton Blvd.	CEO: Forrest E. Wylie
Breinigsville, PA 18031	CFO: Keith E. St. Clair
Phone: 610-904-4000	HR: Wayne St. Claire
Fax: 484-232-4543	FYE: December 31
Web: www.buckeyegp.com	Type: Public

With the price of crude oil burgeoning, Buckeye GP Holdings L.P. sees no reason to buck the trend of making money from petroleum products. The company owns Buckeye GP LLC, the general partner of Buckeye Partners, L.P. The holding company makes all of its money from its general partner interests in Buckeye Partners, which is engaged in the transportation, terminalling, and storage of refined petroleum products across the US. In 2010 Buckeye GP Holdings agreed to be acquired by Buckeye Partners in a deal that promised to increase the liquidity of Buckeye Partners and lower that company's cost of equity capital. When the deal is done former Buckeye GP Holdings unit holders will own 28% of Buckeye Partners.

	Annual Growth	12/05	12/06	12/07	12/08	12/09
Sales ($ mil.)	44.3%	408.4	461.8	519.3	1,896.7	1,770.4
Net income ($ mil.)	63.2%	7.0	8.7	22.9	26.5	49.6
Market value ($ mil.)	20.5%	—	454.9	783.0	355.5	795.4
Employees	1.4%	801	867	—	1,000	846

BUCKEYE PARTNERS, L.P.
NYSE: BPL

5 TEK Park, 9999 Hamilton Blvd.	CEO: Forrest E. Wylie
Breinigsville, PA 18031	CFO: Keith E. St. Clair
Phone: 610-904-4000	HR: Wayne St. Claire
Fax: 484-232-4543	FYE: December 31
Web: www.buckeye.com	Type: Public

Buckeye Partners serves the Buckeye State and then some. Its main subsidiary, Buckeye Pipe Line, stretches 2,643 miles from Massachusetts to Illinois. Other pipelines include Laurel Pipe Line (Pennsylvania), Everglades Pipe Line (Florida), and Wood River Pipe Lines (Illinois, Indiana, Missouri, and Ohio). It owns a major natural gas storage facility in northern California (33 billion cu. ft. capacity); and markets refined petroleum products in a number of the geographic areas served by its pipeline and terminal operations. In a move to lower the company's cost of equity capital and increase its liquidity, in 2010 Buckeye Partners agreed to acquire Buckeye GP Holdings, the parent of its general partner.

	Annual Growth	12/05	12/06	12/07	12/08	12/09
Sales ($ mil.)	44.3%	408.4	461.8	519.3	1,896.7	1,770.4
Net income ($ mil.)	10.1%	100.0	110.2	155.4	184.4	146.9
Market value ($ mil.)	6.6%	2,174.4	2,393.8	2,544.7	1,660.9	2,804.2
Employees	1.4%	801	867	—	1,000	846

BUCKEYE TECHNOLOGIES INC.
NYSE: BKI

1001 Tillman St.	CEO: John B. Crowe
Memphis, TN 38112	CFO: Steven G. Dean
Phone: 901-320-8100	HR: Terrence M. Reed
Fax: 901-320-8836	FYE: June 30
Web: www.bkitech.com	Type: Public

Buckeye Technologies isn't a course taught at Ohio State. The company produces absorbent products, chemical cellulose products (natural fiber derived from wood and cotton), and customized paper. Buckeye's absorbent products, made from cellulose, fluff pulp, nonwovens, and other fibers, are used in diapers, napkins, tablecovers, baby and household wipes, mops, and feminine hygiene items. Buckeye's chemical cellulose is used in coat linings, cosmetics, food casings, concrete, tire/hose reinforcement, food thickeners, pharmaceuticals, plastics, and rayon filament. Its customized paper is used in automotive air and oil filters, currency, letterhead, and stationery. Procter & Gamble is Buckeye's largest customer.

	Annual Growth	6/05	6/06	6/07	6/08	6/09
Sales ($ mil.)	1.4%	712.8	728.5	769.3	825.5	754.5
Net income ($ mil.)	—	20.2	2.0	30.1	47.1	(65.4)
Market value ($ mil.)	(13.4%)	312.8	299.8	607.1	332.0	176.2
Employees	(3.9%)	1,700	1,600	1,550	1,500	1,450

THE BUCKLE, INC.
NYSE: BKE

2407 W. 24th St.	CEO: Dennis H. Nelson
Kearney, NE 68845	CFO: Karen B. Rhoads
Phone: 308-236-8491	HR: —
Fax: 308-236-4493	FYE: January 31
Web: www.buckle.com	Type: Public

The Buckle has done away with the notion that midwestern kids wear only overalls. With about 390 mostly mall-based stores in 40 states, The Buckle sells fashion-conscious 12- to 24-year-olds the clothes they've just got to have. The company retails a variety of clothing items, including mid- to higher-priced casual apparel (pants, tops, and outerwear), shoes, and accessories. Its products portfolio boasts such brands as Lucky Brand Dungarees, Hurley, Roxy, Silver, Billabong, Fossil, and Ed Hardy. The Buckle operates under the names Buckle and The Buckle; it also has an online store. Born and raised in Nebraska, it has expanded into the South and West.

	Annual Growth	1/06	1/07	1/08	1/09	1/10
Sales ($ mil.)	15.7%	501.1	530.1	619.9	792.0	898.3
Net income ($ mil.)	25.1%	51.9	55.7	75.2	104.4	127.3
Market value ($ mil.)	18.0%	731.0	1,044.5	1,293.7	986.8	1,415.6
Employees	3.5%	6,100	6,100	6,700	8,225	7,000

An in-depth profile of this company is available to Hoover's Online members at hoovers.com.

295

BUCKMAN LABORATORIES INTERNATIONAL, INC.

1256 N. McLean Blvd.
Memphis, TN 38108
Phone: 901-278-0330
Fax: 901-276-5343
Web: www.buckman.com

CEO: Steven B. (Steve) Buckman
CFO: Michael Huthwaite
HR: —
FYE: December 31
Type: Private

Buckman Laboratories International defends the world against tiny invaders. The global specialty chemicals manufacturer originated as a producer of chemicals that control the growth of microorganisms such as mold and fungi. Today the company's more than 1,000 products are key to aqueous industrial processes used in manufacturing and treating pulp and paper, leather, paint, coatings, plastics, and wood. They include chemical intermediates, coagulants, corrosion inhibitors, defoamers, dispersants, flocculants, microbicides, polymers, and scale inhibitors. The family of founder Stanley Buckman owns the company through Bulab Holdings.

	Annual Growth	12/04	12/05	12/06	12/07	12/08
Est. sales ($ mil.)	—	—	—	—	—	264.0
Employees	—	—	—	—	—	350

BUCYRUS INTERNATIONAL, INC.

NASDAQ (GS): BUCY

1100 Milwaukee Ave.
South Milwaukee, WI 53172
Phone: 414-768-4000
Fax: 414-768-4474
Web: www.bucyrus.com

CEO: Timothy W. Sullivan
CFO: Craig R. Mackus
HR: —
FYE: December 31
Type: Public

Bucyrus International caters to those who *mine* their own business. The company designs and manufactures surface and subservice extraction equipment, aftermarket replacement parts, as well as services its equpment. Its mining products include walking draglines, electric mining shovels, blast-hole drills, conveyors, and hydraulic roof supports, used for unearthing coal, gold, iron ore, oil sands, and other raw materials. Traded under the Bucyrus name, products reach a worldwide customer base, from large to small companies, and quasi-governmental agencies operating largely in South America and Australia, Canada, China, India, South Africa, and the US. International demand accounts for more than 70% of sales.

	Annual Growth	12/05	12/06	12/07	12/08	12/09
Sales ($ mil.)	46.5%	575.0	738.0	1,613.4	2,505.8	2,651.8
Net income ($ mil.)	55.4%	53.6	70.3	136.1	233.3	312.7
Market value ($ mil.)	33.8%	1,422.9	2,096.3	4,025.4	1,500.2	4,566.1
Employees	35.7%	2,125	2,400	6,050	7,200	7,200

🔲 BUDGET RENT A CAR SYSTEM, INC.

6 Sylvan Way
Parsippany, NJ 07054
Phone: 973-496-3500
Fax: 888-304-2315
Web: www.budget.com

CEO: Ronald L. (Ron) Nelson
CFO: David B. Wyshner
HR: Mark J. Servodidio
FYE: December 31
Type: Subsidiary

When your car rental budget won't allow for the fanciest car on the lot, Budget Rent A Car System might very well have a set of wheels for you. Budget rents cars through a network of about 1,850 locations, some 825 of which are company-owned, in the Americas and the Asia/Pacific region. The Budget car rental brand is pitched mainly to leisure travelers and the cost-conscious. Together with sister company Avis Rent A Car System, the company operates a fleet of more than 400,000 rental cars. Affiliate Budget Truck Rental rents some 29,700 trucks from about 2,500 franchised and company-owned locations in the US. Founded in 1958, Budget Rent A Car System is a unit of Avis Budget Group, formerly Cendant.

BUFFALO ROCK COMPANY

111 Oxmoor Rd.
Birmingham, AL 35209
Phone: 205-942-3435
Fax: 205-942-8239
Web: buffalorock.com

CEO: James C. (Jimmy) Lee III
CFO: Roger Barker
HR: —
FYE: December 31
Type: Private

You might say this company has a solid place in the soft drink market. Buffalo Rock is a leading bottling and distribution company that supplies soft drinks and other beverages from PepsiCo, including such brands as AquaFina, Mountain Dew, Pepsi, and Tropicana. The company also bottles beverages from Dr Pepper Snapple Group and Kraft Foods, as well as its own brands Buffalo Rock Ginger Ale and Dr. Wham. In addition to beverages, Buffalo Rock distributes food products and other supplies to customers in the foodservice industry, and it operates a food-vending distribution business. The family-owned company has more than a dozen distribution facilities serving customers in Alabama, Florida, and Georgia.

BUFFALO WILD WINGS, INC.

NASDAQ (GS): BWLD

5500 Wayzata Blvd., Ste. 1600
Minneapolis, MN 55416
Phone: 952-593-9943
Fax: 952-593-9787
Web: www.buffalowildwings.com

CEO: Sally J. Smith
CFO: Mary J. Twinem
HR: Judith A. (Judy) Shoulak
FYE: December 31
Type: Public

Hot sauce fuels the flight of this restaurateur. Buffalo Wild Wings (BWW) operates a chain of more than 650 Buffalo Wild Wings Grill & Bar quick-casual dining spots in about 40 states that specialize in serving Buffalo-style chicken wings. The eateries, found mostly in Midwestern and Southeastern states, offer more than a dozen dipping sauces to go with the spicy wings, as well as a complement of other items such as chicken tenders and legs. BWW's menu also features appetizers, burgers, tacos, salads, and desserts, along with beer, wine, and other beverages. The company owns and operates about 230 of the restaurants, while the rest are operated by franchisees.

	Annual Growth	12/05	12/06	12/07	12/08	12/09
Sales ($ mil.)	26.6%	209.7	278.2	329.7	422.4	538.9
Net income ($ mil.)	36.3%	8.9	16.3	19.7	24.4	30.7
Market value ($ mil.)	24.8%	301.5	482.9	421.6	465.7	731.1
Employees	23.0%	6,125	7,482	9,564	12,000	14,000

BUFFET PARTNERS, L.P.

2701 E. Plano Pkwy., Ste. 200
Plano, TX 75074
Phone: 214-291-2900
Fax: 214-291-2467
Web: www.furrs.net

CEO: Greg Buchanan
CFO: David Siebert
HR: Ken Reichart
FYE: December 31
Type: Private

All-you-can-eat is the only way to dine with this company. Buffet Partners operates about 50 cafeteria-style buffet restaurants under the names Furr's Family Dining and Furr's Fresh Buffet. The family eateries, found in Texas and half a dozen surrounding states, serve standard American fare for lunch and dinner, including chicken-fried steak, liver and onions, roast beef, and seafood. The Furr's dining chain was started in 1946 by brothers Roy and Key Furr. Buffet Partners was formed by private equity group Cardinal Investment to purchase the chain in 2003.

BUFFETS HOLDINGS, INC.

1020 Discovery Rd., Ste. 100
Eagan, MN 55121
Phone: 651-994-8608
Fax: 651-365-2356
Web: www.buffet.com

CEO: R. Michael (Mike) Andrews Jr.
CFO: A. Keith Wall
HR: Kristine Jordahl
FYE: June 30
Type: Private

You might say that customers literally line up to dine at these restaurants. Buffets Holdings is the largest operator of buffet-style eateries in the US with more than 530 locations in almost 40 states. Operating under such names as HomeTown Buffet, Old Country Buffet, and Ryan's Grill Buffet, the dining spots generally offer self-service buffets featuring entrees, sides, and desserts for an all-inclusive price. The company also operates 10 lodge-themed Tahoe Joe's Famous Steakhouse locations that offer a menu of steaks and seafood. In addition to its company-owned locations, Buffets Holdings has more than a dozen franchised buffet restaurants. A group of lenders, including Credit Suisse, control the company.

BUILD-A-BEAR WORKSHOP, INC.

NYSE: BBW

1954 Innerbelt Business Center Dr.
St. Louis, MO 63114
Phone: 314-423-8000
Fax: 314-423-8188
Web: www.buildabear.com

CEO: Maxine K. Clark
CFO: Tina Klocke
HR: Darlene Elder
FYE: December 31
Type: Public

The Build-A-Bear Workshop covers the "bear" necessities and much more. Located mainly in malls, the company's stores allow kids to design their own teddy bears and other stuffed animals complete with clothing (formal wear to western wear), shoes (including Skechers), and a barrage of accessories (eyewear, cell phones, and the like). Customers can build bears online, too. It offers an in-store Build-A-Party and an interactive online community, as well as online games and e-cards. Build-A-Bear, founded by CEO Maxine Clark in 1997, boasts about 345 stores in the US, Puerto Rico, Canada, the UK, Ireland, and France, and franchises others in Europe, Asia, Australia, and Africa.

	Annual Growth	12/05	12/06	12/07	12/08	12/09
Sales ($ mil.)	2.2%	361.8	437.1	474.4	467.9	394.4
Net income ($ mil.)	—	27.3	29.5	22.5	4.6	(12.5)
Market value ($ mil.)	(36.3%)	607.1	573.9	285.7	99.5	100.2
Employees	(1.0%)	6,350	6,900	6,900	6,000	6,100

BUILDERS FIRSTSOURCE, INC.

NASDAQ (GS): BLDR

2001 Bryan St., Ste. 1600
Dallas, TX 75201
Phone: 214-880-3500
Fax: 214-880-3599
Web: www.buildersfirstsource.com

CEO: Floyd F. Sherman
CFO: M. Chad Crow
HR: Bobby Quinten
FYE: December 31
Type: Public

If you're a new home builder, Builders FirstSource wants you to look no further. The company sells hardware and doors, windows, lumber, and other structural building products to professional homebuilders. Customers include Centex, D.R. Horton, and Hovnanian Enterprises. Builders FirstSource has grown through acquisitions to operate about 70 distribution centers and 70 manufacturing plants in nearly 15 states. The company was founded in 1998 as BSL Holdings by a management team headed by former CEO John Roach and private investment firm JLL Partners. Affiliates of JLL and private equity firm Warburg Pincus own about 50% of Builders FirstSource's stock.

	Annual Growth	12/05	12/06	12/07	12/08	12/09
Sales ($ mil.)	(26.6%)	2,337.8	2,239.5	1,592.5	1,034.5	677.9
Net income ($ mil.)	—	48.6	68.9	(23.8)	(139.5)	(61.9)
Market value ($ mil.)	(34.9%)	2,066.3	1,724.0	698.1	147.9	371.3
Employees	(20.0%)	6,600	5,900	4,900	3,300	2,700

BUILDING MATERIALS CORPORATION OF AMERICA

1361 Alps Rd.
Wayne, NJ 07470
Phone: 973-628-3000
Fax: 973-628-3865
Web: www.gaf.com

CEO: Robert B. (Bob) Tafaro
CFO: John F. Rebele
HR: Jan E. Jerger-Stevens
FYE: December 31
Type: Subsidiary

Building Materials Corporation of America (BMCA), doing business as GAF Materials, wants to keep your roof looking spiffy. BMCA, which deals primarily in shingles and roofing systems, also makes flashing, vents, decorative stone for fireplaces, decking, and wrought iron balusters. Its GAF-Elk products include Timberline- and Sovereign-brand residential shingles and GAF CompositeRoof for commercial roofing. Customers include contractors, distributors, property owners, and retail outlets like The Home Depot. Founded in 1886, BMCA is a subsidiary of G-I Holdings, which was controlled by the late Samuel Heyman. G-I Holdings has operated under bankruptcy protection since 2001, due to asbestos liability claims.

	Annual Growth	12/04	12/05	12/06	12/07	12/08
Est. sales ($ mil.)	—	—	—	—	—	2,748.9
Employees	—	—	—	—	—	3,700

BUILDING MATERIALS HOLDING CORPORATION

720 Park Blvd., Ste. 200
Boise, ID 83712
Phone: 208-331-4300
Fax: —
Web: www.bmcselect.com

CEO: Paul S. Street
CFO: Daniel (Danny) McQuary
HR: —
FYE: December 31
Type: Private

Building Materials Holding Corporation goes with the pros. The company (which does business as BMC Select) provides a variety of residential building products and construction services to builders and contractors. It provides services such as wood framing, concrete services, and plumbing. The company also sells building components such as millwork, trusses, and wall panels. It also offers installation and framing services. BMC Select serves more than 15 markets in about a dozen states, primarily in the western and southern US. Despite earlier attempts to restructure the business, the company filed for Chapter 11 bankruptcy in 2009 and emerged in early 2010.

	Annual Growth	12/04	12/05	12/06	12/07	12/08
Sales ($ mil.)	(10.8%)	2,091.0	2,912.2	3,245.2	2,285.0	1,324.7
Net income ($ mil.)	—	53.9	129.5	102.1	(312.7)	(214.8)
Employees	(9.1%)	12,000	21,000	17,000	18,000	8,200

BULL MOOSE TUBE COMPANY

1819 Clarkson Rd., Ste. 100
Chesterfield, MO 63017
Phone: 636-537-2600
Fax: 636-537-5848
Web: www.bullmoosetube.com

CEO: Jack Meyer
CFO: Steve Birk
HR: Vernon Bozarth
FYE: December 31
Type: Subsidiary

Although inspiration for its name came from the General Bullmoose character in Al Capps' Li'l Abner comic strip, Bull Moose Tube is quite serious about its role in the tubular market. A subsidiary of UK-based steel maker Caparo Group since 1988, the company manufactures mechanical and structural tubes and sprinkler pipe. Offering one of the largest size ranges in the industry, it makes as-welded mechanical tubes, hollow structural sections, V50 pipe, and sprinkler pipe, used in building structures, handrails, telescopes, and vehicle underbodies. Bull Moose Tube's growth caught investor notice in 2007 when SPP Capital Group offered $100 million for the company. The deal was later pulled due to market conditions.

BULOVA CORPORATION

1 Bulova Ave.
Woodside, NY 11377
Phone: 718-204-3300
Fax: 718-204-3546
Web: www.bulova.com

CEO: Dennis W. Perry
CFO: Al Perez
HR: Glenn M. Parker
FYE: December 31
Type: Subsidiary

Bulova is working to keep perfect time in the watch industry. It sells watches, clocks, and timepiece parts under brands such as Accutron and Wittnauer (luxury), Bulova (mid-priced), and Caravelle (lower-priced), as well as licensed Harley-Davidson and Frank Lloyd Wright styles. The firm also sells miniature collectible clocks, mostly under the Bulova name, and has expanded its licensing efforts to include items such as eyewear. Bulova peddles its products primarily through department and jewelry stores, mostly in the US. It has offices in Canada, Mexico, Switzerland, and the Far East. The Tisch brothers' holding company, Loews, bought Bulova in 1979 and sold it in 2008 to rival Citizen.

BULOVA TECHNOLOGIES GROUP, INC.

Pink Sheets: BLVT

19337 US Hwy. 19 N., Ste. 525
Clearwater, FL 33764
Phone: 727-536-6666
Fax: —
Web: www.bulovatechgroup.com

CEO: Stephen L. Gurba
CFO: Stephen C. Steckel
HR: —
FYE: June 30
Type: Public

Bulova Technologies Group believes defense, manufacturing, and technology is a recipe for business success. The company operates in three primary segments: defense, contract manufacturing, and technologies. Its defense operations provide the US Department of Defense with explosive simulators, ammunition, and pyrotechnic devices, as well as providing systems integration services. Bulova's contract manufacturing division assembles printed circuit boards and cable assemblies, while its technology lab develops and licenses applications for the defense, energy, and health care markets. Bulova completed a reverse merger with 3Si Holdings in late 2009 in order to become a publicly traded company.

BUMBLE BEE FOODS, LLC

9655 Granite Ridge Dr., Ste. 100
San Diego, CA 92123
Phone: 858-715-4000
Fax: 858-560-6045
Web: www.bumblebee.com

CEO: Christopher D. (Chris) Lischewski
CFO: Kent McNeil
HR: —
FYE: December 31
Type: Private

Nope, Bumble Bee Foods doesn't make honey. But they do make a honey of a product line, which includes canned tuna, crab, salmon, shrimp, clams, sardines, and other specialty canned and pouched seafoods. The company's brand names include Bumble Bee, of course, along with Beach Cliff, Brunswick, Snow's, and King Oscar. When combined with its Canadian operations, Clover Leaf Seafoods, Bumble Bee claims it outranks its arch rival StarKist as the largest canned seafood company in North America by sales. Bumble Bee has canning operations in California and Puerto Rico. Its customers include retail food stores and foodservice providers in the US and Canada. The company is owned by Connors Bros. Income Fund.

	Annual Growth	12/04	12/05	12/06	12/07	12/08
Sales ($ mil.)	12.5%	—	—	—	800.0	900.0
Employees	—	—	—	—	3,000	—

BUNGE LIMITED

NYSE: BG

50 Main St.
White Plains, NY 10606
Phone: 914-684-2800
Fax: 914-684-3497
Web: www.bunge.com

CEO: Alberto Weisser
CFO: Jacqualyn A. Fouse
HR: Vicente C. Teixeira
FYE: December 31
Type: Public

Bunge Limited grinds it out. The company is a leading global soy and other oilseed processor, a leading South American fertilizer maker and provider, and, through subsidiary Bunge North America, a major US food and food ingredient processor. Its joint venture with DuPont (Solae), of which Bunge owns 28%, makes soy-based food ingredients. Bunge also processes canola seed, sunflower seed, wheat, and corn. Its fertilizer operations take place mainly through its interest in Brazil-based Fosfertil. The operation involves all stages of production, from the mining of phosphate-based raw materials to the selling of blended fertilizers. However, Bunge has agreed to sell its Brazilian fertilizer nutrients business.

	Annual Growth	12/05	12/06	12/07	12/08	12/09
Sales ($ mil.)	14.6%	24,275.0	26,274.0	37,842.0	52,574.0	41,926.0
Net income ($ mil.)	(16.7%)	530.0	521.0	778.0	1,064.0	255.0
Market value ($ mil.)	3.0%	8,160.6	10,452.7	16,781.1	7,462.9	9,201.4
Employees	2.5%	23,495	22,524	23,889	24,787	25,945

BUNGE NORTH AMERICA, INC.

11720 Borman Dr.
St. Louis, MO 63146
Phone: 314-292-2000
Fax: 314-292-2110
Web: www.bungenorthamerica.com

CEO: Soren W. Schroder
CFO: Todd A. Bastean
HR: Geralyn F. (Geri) Hayes
FYE: December 31
Type: Subsidiary

Bunge North America is the world's main squeeze. Its milling division, which operates five mills, is the largest corn dry miller in the world. In addition to corn, the company also deals in soybeans, canola, wheat, and sorghum. Its grain division, with some 80 elevators, stores the oilseed crops; its processing division operates oilseed processing plants throughout the US and Canada; its crusher/refiner facility in Iowa is the one of the largest oil-extraction lines in the US. Bunge's oil division blends and sells the oil to food manufacturers, foodservice operators, and retail food outlets throughout the North American continent.

BUNZL DISTRIBUTION USA, INC.

701 Emerson Rd., Ste. 500
St. Louis, MO 63141
Phone: 314-997-5959
Fax: 314-997-1405
Web: www.bunzldistribution.com

CEO: Patrick L. Larmon
CFO: Jane Jennewein
HR: —
FYE: December 31
Type: Subsidiary

Products provided by Bunzl Distribution USA can keep your deli from getting smelly. The company supplies plastic packaging and disposable paper products used as food containers to grocery stores, convenience stores, and other food service businesses. In addition, Bunzl Distribution USA distributes a variety of cleaning supplies and safety equipment to both food and nonfood retailers in the US, Canada, Mexico, and the Caribbean. Overall, it handles more than 250,000 products, obtained from numerous manufacturers, from a network of more than 90 facilities. Clients have included Office Depot and Hormel Foods. The company is the North American arm of Bunzl plc, a leading UK-based wholesale distribution company.

THE BUREAU OF NATIONAL AFFAIRS, INC.

1801 S. Bell St.	CEO: Paul N. Wojcik
Arlington, VA 22202	CFO: Robert P. Ambrosini
Phone: 703-341-3000	HR: —
Fax: 800-253-0332	FYE: December 31
Web: www.bna.com	Type: Private

The Bureau of National Affairs (BNA) is a leading provider of legal and regulatory information. The company publishes advisory and research reports, books, newsletters, and other publications covering economic, health care, labor, public policy, and tax issues for professionals in business and government. It has a staff of 600 reporters, editors, and legal experts who gather information from around the country. BNA delivers its information online and through print and electronic products, some available through subscription services such as LexisNexis and Thomson Reuter's Westlaw. Founded in 1929, BNA was incorporated as an employee-owned company in 1946. It is the country's oldest fully employee-owned company.

	Annual Growth	12/04	12/05	12/06	12/07	12/08
Sales ($ mil.)	2.3%	321.3	329.0	344.9	352.2	352.2
Net income ($ mil.)	8.6%	22.6	24.1	19.5	88.0	31.4
Employees	(0.8%)	1,802	1,729	1,728	1,719	1,745

⊞ BURGER KING HOLDINGS, INC.   NYSE: BKC

5505 Blue Lagoon Dr.	CEO: John W. Chidsey
Miami, FL 33126	CFO: Ben K. Wells
Phone: 305-378-3000	HR: Peter C. (Pete) Smith
Fax: —	FYE: June 30
Web: www.burgerking.com	Type: Public

This king rules one whopper of a fast-food empire. Burger King Holdings operates the world's #2 hamburger chain based on locations (behind McDonald's) with more than 12,000 restaurants in the US and more than 70 other countries. In addition to its popular Whopper sandwich, the chain offers a selection of burgers, chicken sandwiches, salads, and breakfast items, along with beverages, desserts, and sides. Many of the eateries are stand-alone locations offering dine-in seating and drive-through services; the chain also includes units in high-traffic locations such as airports and shopping malls. More than 1,400 of the fast food restaurants are company-owned, while the rest are owned and operated by franchisees.

	Annual Growth	6/05	6/06	6/07	6/08	6/09
Sales ($ mil.)	6.9%	1,940.0	2,048.0	2,234.0	2,455.0	2,537.4
Net income ($ mil.)	43.6%	47.0	27.0	148.0	190.0	200.1
Market value ($ mil.)	3.1%	—	2,137.1	3,574.1	3,635.1	2,343.4
Employees	8.1%	30,300	37,000	39,000	41,000	41,320

BURKE & HERBERT BANK & TRUST COMPANY   OTC: BHRB

100 S. Fairfax St.	CEO: E. Hunt Burke
Alexandria, VA 22314	CFO: Kathy J. Younger
Phone: 703-549-6600	HR: —
Fax: 703-548-5759	FYE: June 30
Web: www.burkeandherbertbank.com	Type: Public

Founded in 1852, Burke & Herbert Bank & Trust is one of the oldest banks in Virginia. Placing an emphasis on personal service, it operates about 20 branches in the northern part of the state, including part of the Washington, DC, metropolitan area. The bank offers standard products such as checking and savings accounts, money market accounts, CDs, IRAs, and debit cards. It is primarily a real estate lender, with residential and commercial mortgages making up almost all of its loan portfolio. Construction, business, and consumer loans round out the bank's lending activities. Burke & Herbert Bank & Trust also offers trust and financial planning services.

BURLEN CORP.

1904 McCormick Dr.	CEO: Bert Klein
Tifton, GA 31794	CFO: Lisa Young
Phone: 229-382-4100	HR: David Hightower
Fax: 229-382-2629	FYE: December 31
	Type: Subsidiary

Burlen knows its business from the bottom up. The company makes ladies' private-label lingerie and underwear. Burlen's collections, manufactured primarily in the Far East and the Caribbean, are sold through mass merchandisers and specialty retailers nationwide. Wal-Mart, which has done business with Burlen since the 1960s, is its largest customer. The company was acquired by Israeli-based Delta Galil, a global apparel firm, in 2004 as a way to further increase its lingerie sales in the mass marketplace and improve its branding in the US.

⊞ BURLINGTON COAT FACTORY WAREHOUSE CORPORATION

1830 Rte. 130 N.	CEO: Thomas A. (Tom) Kingsbury
Burlington, NJ 08016	CFO: Todd Weyhrich
Phone: 609-387-7800	HR: Joyce Manning
Fax: 609-387-7071	FYE: May 31
Web: www.burlingtoncoatfactory.com	Type: Private

Burlington Coat Factory Warehouse has two *de facto* mottos: "not affiliated with Burlington Industries" (thanks to a 1981 trademark-infringement lawsuit settlement) and "We sell more than coats." The company operates about 435 no-frills retail stores offering off-price current, brand-name clothing. Although it is one of the nation's largest coat sellers, the stores also sells children's apparel, bath items, furniture, gifts, jewelry, linens, and shoes. The business operates under the names Burlington Coat Factory (98% of sales), Cohoes Fashions, MJM Designer Shoes, and Super Baby Depot in some 45 states and Puerto Rico. Founded in 1972, Burlington is owned by affiliates of buyout firm Bain Capital.

	Annual Growth	5/04	5/05	5/06	5/07	5/08
Sales ($ mil.)	4.4%	2,878.3	3,199.8	3,439.0	3,441.6	3,424.0
Net income ($ mil.)	—	67.6	106.0	67.0	(47.2)	(49.0)
Employees	2.6%	24,000	25,000	26,500	28,005	26,580

BNSF RAILWAY COMPANY

2650 Lou Menk Dr.	CEO: Matthew K. (Matt) Rose
Fort Worth, TX 76131	CFO: Thomas N. (Tom) Hund
Phone: 800-795-2673	HR: John J. Fleps
Fax: —	FYE: December 31
Web: www.bnsf.com	Type: Subsidiary

The primary subsidiary of Burlington Northern Santa Fe Corporation, BNSF Railway provides freight transportation services over a network of 32,000 miles of track in the western US and Canada. The BNSF system consists of 23,000 route miles owned by BNSF and 9,000 route miles of trackage rights, which allow BNSF Railway to use tracks owned by other railroads. Freight carried by BNSF Railway includes agricultural, consumer, and industrial products, along with coal. Consumer products, which make up the largest share of the railroad's freight traffic, consist mainly of containerized freight that comes to BNSF Railway from marine shipping lines.

	Annual Growth	12/04	12/05	12/06	12/07	12/08
Est. sales ($ mil.)	—	—	—	—	—	17,787.0
Employees	—	—	—	—	—	40,000

BURLINGTON NORTHERN SANTA FE CORPORATION

2650 Lou Menk Dr.	CEO: Matthew K. (Matt) Rose
Fort Worth, TX 76131	CFO: Thomas N. (Tom) Hund
Phone: 817-352-1000	HR: Linda T. Longo-Kazanova
Fax: 817-352-7171	FYE: December 31
Web: www.bnsf.com	Type: Subsidiary

Over the years the number of major US railroads has dwindled, but Burlington Northern Santa Fe (BNSF) thrives as one of the survivors. Through its primary subsidiary, BNSF Railway, the company is one of the largest railroad operators in the US along with rival Union Pacific. BNSF makes tracks through 28 states in the West, Midwest, and Sun Belt regions of the US and in two Canadian provinces. The company operates its trains over a system of about 32,000 route miles. Along with its rail operations, BNSF generates revenue from its BNSF Logistics unit, a provider of transportation management services. Already owning 23% of BNSF, Warren Buffett's Berkshire Hathaway bought the remaining 77% stake in February 2010.

	Annual Growth	12/05	12/06	12/07	12/08	12/09
Sales ($ mil.)	1.9%	12,987.0	14,985.0	15,802.0	18,018.0	14,016.0
Net income ($ mil.)	3.0%	1,531.0	1,887.0	1,829.0	2,115.0	1,721.0
Employees	(3.3%)	40,000	41,000	40,000	40,000	35,000

BURNES HOME ACCENTS, LLC

21 Cypress Blvd., Ste. 1010	CEO: Jean-René Gougelet
Round Rock, TX 78729	CFO: Andrea Thomason
Phone: 512-257-6500	HR: —
Fax: 512-257-6530	FYE: December 31
Web: www.burnesgroup.com	Type: Private

Burnes is behind the walls of frames featuring family and friends. Burnes Home Accents manufactures decorative picture frames, photo albums, scrapbooks, and home accessories and sells them through distributors. The decor and crafts company also makes photo album refills and had a hand in creating the Level-Line, which helps customers hang its items. Its products are available through large retailers, such as Wal-Mart, Michaels, Rite Aid, and Target. Brand names include Burnes of Boston, Carr Connoisseur, and RareWoods, among others. Burnes Home Accents is owned by Anderson Press, an Atlanta publisher of coin-collecting guides, and boasts two showrooms: one each in Georgia and Texas.

BURNS & MCDONNELL, INC.

9400 Ward Pkwy.	CEO: Greg M. Graves
Kansas City, MO 64114	CFO: Mark Taylor
Phone: 816-333-9400	HR: Melissa Wood
Fax: 816-822-3412	FYE: September 30
Web: www.burnsmcd.com	Type: Private

It may sound like a law firm, but Burns & McDonnell provides construction services, not legal advice. A top design/build firm in the US, the company provides engineering, architectural, construction, environmental remediation, and consulting services. It is one of the leading constructors of electric transmission and distribution infrastructure, airports, and fossil fuel and chemical plants. Burns & McDonnell also serves the government, manufacturing, health care, telecommunications, transportation, and water and wastewater sectors, among others. Burns & McDonnell has about 20 offices throughout the US.

THE BURTON CORPORATION

80 Industrial Pkwy.	CEO: Jake Burton
Burlington, VT 05401	CFO: Mike Abbott
Phone: 802-862-4500	HR: —
Fax: 802-660-3250	FYE: January 31
Web: www.burton.com	Type: Private

The Burton Corporation surfs the slopes with its premium snowboards and equipment. The company, which does business as Burton Snowboards, is the world's leading snowboard manufacturer. It also makes snowboarding apparel, eyewear, boots, bindings, and packs under its namesake Burton, AK, Anon, and RED brands. The company maintains a network of about 10 retail shops and factory outlets in the US, Austria, and Japan. It also markets gear through sporting goods stores and online retailers, such as Altrec.com and Snow & Rock Sports. Taking to the beach, Burton operates surfboard maker Channel Island Surfboards, whose goods are available at its store in Santa Barbara, California, and in surf shops on the West Coast.

BURT'S BEES, INC.

633 Davis Dr., Ste. 600	CEO: John Replogle
Morrisville, NC 27560	CFO: Doug Haensel
Phone: 919-998-5200	HR: Beth Ritter
Fax: 919-998-5201	FYE: December 31
Web: www.burtsbees.com	Type: Subsidiary

Burt's Bees wants to mind its own beeswax, but sting the competition. The company makes and markets lip balm, bath oils, soaps, and about 150 other personal care products made from beeswax, nut oils, and other natural ingredients. Its products are sold through some 30,000 health food and grocery stores located in the US, Canada, the UK, Ireland, Hong Kong, and Taiwan, as well as through its website. Burt's Bees was founded in Maine in 1984 when Roxanne Quimby met reclusive beekeeper Burt Shavitz and they began making candles and lip balm from his beeswax. Cleaning products giant Clorox acquired the company for $925 million in cash in late 2007.

	Annual Growth	12/04	12/05	12/06	12/07	12/08
Est. sales ($ mil.)	—	—	—	—	—	62.6
Employees	—	—	—	—	—	530

BUSH BROTHERS & COMPANY

1016 E. Weisgarber Rd.	CEO: Tom Ferriter
Knoxville, TN 37909	CFO: Al Williams
Phone: 865-588-7685	HR: —
Fax: 865-450-4100	FYE: March 31
Web: www.bushbeans.com	Type: Private

Bush Brothers & Company's success is proof that well-spent ad money makes a difference — even when you're up against the bean "big boys" (think Campbell's baked beans, or Heinz, Van Camp's, or B&M). Not deterred, however, Bush Brothers cans one of the leading US brands of baked beans, Bush's Best, which is made from a family recipe and first sold in 1969. The company also cans variety beans (black, garbanzos, pintos, refried), chili, greens, and hominy, all of which are sold in retail food outlets and to foodservice operators across the US. Company spokesbrother Jay Bush and his "talking" dog, Duke, are the stars of the company's popular TV commercials (which the man-and-his-dog duo started doing in 1995).

	Annual Growth	3/04	3/05	3/06	3/07	3/08
Est. sales ($ mil.)	—	—	—	—	—	135.4
Employees	—	—	—	—	—	650

BUSH INDUSTRIES, INC.

1 Mason Dr.	CEO: James L. (Jim) Sherbert Jr.
Jamestown, NY 14702	CFO: A. James Garde
Phone: 716-665-2000	HR: Dennis Roberts
Fax: 716-665-2510	FYE: December 31
Web: www.bushindustries.com	Type: Private

Bush Industries is jockeying for a permanent seat in the ready-to-assemble (RTA) furniture industry. A leading maker of RTA furniture for homes and offices through its Bush Furniture North America and Europe divisions, Bush's products are sold worldwide through about 10,000 retail outlets, including furniture and department stores, electronics and office product retailers, and mass merchandisers. It boasts three brands: Bush Business Furniture, Bush Furniture, and Röhr. Founded by the Bush family in 1959, the manufacturer is now owned by a group led by DDJ Capital Management LLC and JPMorgan Chase Bank. Like many furniture makers, Bush Industries has focused on consolidating its manufacturing operations.

BUSHNELL OUTDOOR PRODUCTS

9200 Cody St.	CEO: Blake Lipham
Overland Park, KS 66214	CFO: Blake Lipham
Phone: 913-752-3400	HR: —
Fax: 913-752-6112	FYE: December 31
Web: www.bushnellperformanceoptics.com	Type: Private

Bushnell Outdoor Products is one highly focused firm. It makes binoculars, telescopes, laser-guided rangefinders, night vision items, riflescopes, holographic gun sights, and other high-end optical equipment. It also sells Bollé ski goggles and sunglasses, H20Optix water sports sunglasses, and Serengeti all-purpose sunglasses. It owns the rights to the Tasco brand and has licensing agreements with Bausch & Lomb and Browning Firearms. Founded by Dave Bushnell in 1947, it has offices in Australia, Canada, France, Germany, Hong Kong, the Netherlands, and the US. Bushnell Outdoor Products is owned by the private equity firm MidOcean Partners.

BUTH-NA-BODHAIGE INC.

5036 1 World Way	CEO: Phil Kowalczyk
Wake Forest, NC 27587	CFO: Kim Mattoon
Phone: 919-554-4900	HR: Donna McClellan
Fax: 919-554-4361	FYE: February 28
Web: www.thebodyshop.com	Type: Subsidiary

Ask your Celtic friends why they smell terrific, and they're liable to answer "Buth-Na-Bodhaige." Buth-Na-Bodhaige (Gaelic for The Body Shop) does business as The Body Shop USA and oversees its UK parent company's US operations. It sells natural skin and hair care products through 300-plus company-owned and franchised US stores. It also sells its products online. Buth-Na-Bodhaige, which bought out former joint venture partner Bellamy Retail Group, became part of L'Oréal when The Body Shop International was acquired in 2006. The company faces stiff competition from Intimate Brands' copycat chain, Bath & Body Works.

	Annual Growth	2/04	2/05	2/06	2/07	2/08
Est. sales ($ mil.)	—	—	—	—	—	206.0
Employees	—	—	—	—	—	2,000

BUTLER AMERICA, LLC

2 Trap Falls Rd., Ste. 204	CEO: Christine (Tina) Ciocca
Sheldon, CT 06484	CFO: Rob Olsen
Phone: 203-926-2700	HR: —
Fax: —	FYE: December 31
Web: www.butler.com	Type: Private

This butler has several arms to serve you. Butler America provides engineering and information technology services, including communications network installation and IT support, primarily to the aerospace, defense, and telecommunications industries. It also serves the energy and financial services markets. Butler's engineering services include drafting, product design, and stress analysis; network services include equipment installation and network design technology services include software development and staffing. The company also offers fleet maintenance services for company's that operate large numbers of vehicles, and it provides technical staffing services.

BUTLER MANUFACTURING

1540 Genessee St.	CEO: Ted Wolfe
Kansas City, MO 64102	CFO: —
Phone: 816-968-3000	HR: —
Fax: 816-968-3279	FYE: December 31
Web: www.butlermfg.com	Type: Subsidiary

Need an eight-story building fast? Not a problem for Butler Manufacturing, maker of pre-engineered buildings, structural systems, and roof and wall systems for nonresidential construction. A subsidiary of Australia-based BlueScope Steel, Butler produces pre-engineered and custom-designed steel structures used in a range of projects, from offices to schools to shopping centers. Through its BUCON and Butler Heavy Structures units, the company provides general contracting services for large-scale projects. Butler also offers real estate development services. It distributes its products throughout North America.

BUTLER NATIONAL CORPORATION

OTC: BUKS

19920 W. 161st St.	CEO: Clark D. Stewart
Olathe, KS 66062	CFO: Angela D. Shinabargar
Phone: 913-780-9595	HR: —
Fax: 913-780-5088	FYE: April 30
Web: butlernational.com	Type: Public

This Butler is at the service of aircraft operators. Butler National's Avcon subsidiary (over half of sales) provides aircraft modification services, including the conversion of passenger planes to freighters. The company works mainly on Learjet models; it also modifies Beechcraft, Cessna, and Dassault Falcon aircraft. It adds aerial photography capability to aircraft and offers stability enhancements. The company's avionics unit makes airborne electronic switching components. Other Butler National businesses provide remote water and wastewater monitoring (SCADA Systems) and architectural services (BCS Design), as well as gaming management services to Indian tribes (Butler National Service Corporation; BNSC).

	Annual Growth	4/05	4/06	4/07	4/08	4/09
Sales ($ mil.)	(6.2%)	23.4	15.3	14.7	17.6	18.1
Net income ($ mil.)	(24.0%)	2.4	0.4	0.6	1.3	0.8
Market value ($ mil.)	(24.6%)	38.1	22.4	26.3	21.3	12.3
Employees	1.6%	94	82	88	89	100

An in-depth profile of this company is available to Hoover's Online members at hoovers.com.

301

BUTTERBALL, LLC

1 Butterball Ln., Greenfield North Business Park
Garner, NC 27529
Phone: 919-255-7900
Fax: 919-255-7971
Web: www.butterballcorp.com

CEO: B. Keith Shoemaker
CFO: Edward W. (Ed) Kascuta
HR: Gary R. Lenaghan
FYE: April 30
Type: Subsidiary

Come Thanksgiving when you bow your head to give thanks, remember to thank Butterball, LLC. The company is a vertically integrated turkey processor (meaning it does it all, from egg to table). Butterball produces fresh and frozen turkey products (including many of the T-Day birds that grace America's tables) for the retail grocery and foodservice industries throughout the US and about 20 other countries. It boasts the world's largest turkey-processing plant (675,000 sq. ft.), located in Mt. Olive, North Carolina. It also operates breeder, growing, and research farms; diagnostic labs; feed mills; and hatcheries. Butterball is a joint venture between Smithfield Foods (which owns 49%) and Maxwell Farms (51%).

	Annual Growth	4/04	4/05	4/06	4/07	4/08
Est. sales ($ mil.)	—	—	—	—	—	1,406.5
Employees	—	—	—	—	—	500

BUY.COM INC.

85 Enterprise, Ste. 100
Aliso Viejo, CA 92656
Phone: 949-389-2000
Fax: —
Web: www.buy.com

CEO: Neel Grover
CFO: Jennie Neil
HR: Kim Camp
FYE: December 31
Type: Private

Buy what.com you ask? E-tailer Buy.com sells books, cell phones and services, computer hardware and software, electronics, DVDs, jewelry, music, toys, and more. Founded in 1997, Buy.com initially made a splash by selling products below cost. It has since raised its prices but maintains an edge by offering to match any qualified competitor's price. In all, the company offers more than 2 million products to more than 14 million customers. Buy.com also lets third-party retailers, such as Sixth Avenue Electronics and Baby Age, sell their products through its website. The e-tailer ships to customers in Europe, North America, and the Pacific Rim. In 2010 Buy.com agreed to be acquired by Japan's Rakuten.

BUZZI UNICEM USA INC.

100 Brodhead Rd.
Bethlehem, PA 18017
Phone: 610-866-4400
Fax: 610-866-9430
Web: www.buzziunicemusa.com

CEO: David A. (Dave) Nepereny
CFO: Pietro Buzzi
HR: Thomas Marnell
FYE: December 31
Type: Subsidiary

Buzzi Unicem USA produces portland cement, masonry cement, and ready-mixed concrete. The company, a subsidiary of Italy-based BUZZI UNICEM SpA, operates nine cement plants (including one grinding plant) with a total annual capacity of nearly nine million tons. Buzzi Unicem USA mostly serves the Midwest and northeastern portions of the US. It operates 30 distribution terminals and has a fleet of river barges. Customers include ready-mix and pre-stressed concrete makers and highway builders. Buzzi Unicem USA was formed in 2004, after the merger of RC Cement and Dyckerhoff's Lone Star Industries.

⊞ BWAY HOLDING COMPANY

NYSE: BWY

8607 Roberts Dr., Ste. 250
Atlanta, GA 30350
Phone: 770-645-4800
Fax: 770-645-4810
Web: www.bwaycorp.com

CEO: Kenneth M. (Ken) Roessler
CFO: Michael B. Clauer
HR: —
FYE: September 30
Type: Public

Trouble containing yourself? BWAY Holding may be of some help. The company operates through BWAY Corp. to manufacture and distribute metal containers, from aerosol to paint cans, steel pails, and specialty boxes. It also makes rigid plastic pails, bottles, drums, and other blow-molded containers. BWAY's line packs up industrial and consumer goods, including ammunition, deck sealants, personal care items, and foods. Core subsidiaries are BWAY Packaging (metal containers), ICL Industrial Containers (steel and plastic pails), and NAMPAC Packaging (plastic containers). In March 2010 the company agreed to be acquired by Madison Dearborn Partners (MDP) for approximately $915 million and the assumption of debt.

	Annual Growth	9/05	9/06	9/07	9/08	9/09
Sales ($ mil.)	(0.4%)	—	918.5	959.0	1,019.0	904.4
Net income ($ mil.)	41.9%	—	5.8	(3.1)	11.9	23.5
Market value ($ mil.)	28.8%	—	—	249.9	262.9	414.9
Employees	(2.4%)	—	2,980	2,970	2,700	2,700

⊞ CA, INC.

NASDAQ (GS): CA

1 CA Plaza
Islandia, NY 11749
Phone: 800-225-5224
Fax: 631-342-6800
Web: www.ca.com

CEO: William E. (Bill) McCracken
CFO: Nancy E. Cooper
HR: Andrew (Andy) Goodman
FYE: March 31
Type: Public

CA wants to put your information technology under new management. One of the world's largest software companies, CA provides tools for managing networks, databases, applications, storage, security, and other systems. Its applications work across both mainframes and distributed computing environments, including cloud computing products. The company also offers consulting, implementation, and training services. It markets worldwide to businesses, government agencies, and schools. CA has actively used acquisitions to expand its product lines and grow its customer base.

	Annual Growth	3/06	3/07	3/08	3/09	3/10
Sales ($ mil.)	3.5%	3,796.0	3,943.0	4,277.0	4,271.0	4,353.0
Net income ($ mil.)	48.4%	159.0	118.0	500.0	694.0	771.0
Market value ($ mil.)	(3.6%)	13,982.2	13,314.2	11,561.9	9,049.1	12,060.4
Employees	(3.6%)	16,000	14,500	13,700	13,200	13,800

CABELA'S INCORPORATED

NYSE: CAB

1 Cabela Dr.
Sidney, NE 69160
Phone: 308-254-5505
Fax: 308-254-4800
Web: www.cabelas.com

CEO: Thomas L. (Tommy) Millner
CFO: Ralph W. Castner
HR: —
FYE: December 31
Type: Public

Cabela's is a hunter's and fisherman's Disneyland. The seller of outdoor sporting goods operates about 30 stores in 20 US states and a single location in Canada. Located mainly in the Midwest, the stores are as big as 245,000 sq. ft. and include such features as waterfalls, mountain replicas, aquariums, in-store shooting galleries, and banquet and meeting facilities. Cabela's sells footwear, clothing, and gear for fishing, hunting, camping, and other outdoor activities. Cabela's also mails more than 130 million catalogs each year, sells magazines and merchandise online, and has an outdoors show on television. Cabela's was founded in 1961 by chairman Dick Cabela and his younger brother, Jim.

	Annual Growth	12/05	12/06	12/07	12/08	12/09
Sales ($ mil.)	10.0%	1,799.7	2,063.5	2,349.6	2,552.7	2,632.2
Net income ($ mil.)	(9.1%)	72.6	85.8	87.9	76.4	49.6
Market value ($ mil.)	(3.7%)	1,123.6	1,633.3	1,020.1	394.6	965.2
Employees	7.9%	9,800	11,700	15,000	14,700	13,300

CABLE NEWS NETWORK, INC.

1 CNN Center
Atlanta, GA 30348
Phone: 404-827-1700
Fax: 404-827-1099
Web: www.cnn.com

CEO: Jim Walton
CFO: —
HR: —
FYE: December 31
Type: Subsidiary

Whether it's reporting on the news or just talking about it, this network does both all day long. Cable News Network (CNN) operates one of the top 24-hour news channels, reaching more than 100 million US homes. In addition to its flagship channel, the company offers HLN (formerly CNN Headline News), and it has an international division that keeps viewers informed in about 200 other countries. CNN has about 45 news bureaus around the world, including more than a dozen in the US. Away from the television, CNN operates a top-ranked news website and it offers syndicated news services. Founded in 1980 by cable broadcasting pioneer Ted Turner, CNN operates as part of Time Warner's Turner Broadcasting division.

	Annual Growth	12/04	12/05	12/06	12/07	12/08
Est. sales ($ mil.)	—	—	—	—	—	251.1
Employees	—	—	—	—	—	2,200

CABLE ONE, INC.

1314 N. 3rd St.
Phoenix, AZ 85004
Phone: 602-364-6000
Fax: 602-364-6010
Web: www.cableone.net

CEO: Thomas O. (Tom) Might
CFO: Patrick A. (Pat) Dolohanty
HR: Janiece St. Cyr
FYE: December 31
Type: Subsidiary

Its parent company may feed award-winning journalism to Beltway insiders, but Cable ONE gives small-town folk CNN *and* The Cartoon Network. A subsidiary of The Washington Post Company, the company provides cable television service primarily to small, non-urban communities in 19 states throughout the midwestern, southern, and western US. Its core service areas are the Gulf Coast region and western Idaho. More than 700,000 subscribers receive cable television service from Cable ONE and about half of those are also signed up for broadband Internet access sold under the CableONE.net brand. The company also offers voice-over-Internet-protocol (VoIP) computer telephony and digital video services.

	Annual Growth	12/04	12/05	12/06	12/07	12/08
Est. sales ($ mil.)	—	—	—	—	—	719.1
Employees	—	—	—	—	—	1,700

CABLEVISION SYSTEMS CORPORATION

NYSE: CVC

1111 Stewart Ave.
Bethpage, NY 11714
Phone: 516-803-2300
Fax: 516-803-3134
Web: www.cablevision.com

CEO: James L. Dolan
CFO: Michael P. Huseby
HR: Carolyn Dursi
FYE: December 31
Type: Public

There's no business like show business for Cablevision. Through its main operating subsidiary CSC Holdings, the company provides basic cable television to about 3 million customers in the New York City area. Another nearly 3 million viewers subscribe to its iO digital video service. Through subsidiary Lightpath, Cablevision serves about 2 million commerical broadband Internet users and another nearly 2 million VoIP telephony subscribers. Cablevision owns nationwide and regional cable programming networks through Rainbow Media. The family of founder and chairman Charles Dolan controls 70% of the company.

	Annual Growth	12/05	12/06	12/07	12/08	12/09
Sales ($ mil.)	10.7%	5,175.9	5,927.5	6,484.5	7,230.1	7,773.3
Net income ($ mil.)	31.9%	94.3	(125.6)	218.9	(227.6)	285.3
Market value ($ mil.)	2.4%	5,923.9	7,188.5	6,183.9	4,250.5	6,517.1
Employees	8.1%	20,425	22,075	22,935	20,105	27,940

CABO WABO LLC

1 Beach St., Ste. 300
San Francisco, CA 94133
Phone: 415-315-8000
Fax: —
Web: www.cabowabo.com

CEO: Sammy Hagar
CFO: Toni Chang
HR: —
FYE: —
Type: Subsidiary

You shouldn't drive 55 — or any other speed for that matter — after partaking of the fruit of Cabo Wabo's efforts. A holding company formed by rock star Sammy Hagar, the company oversees the marketing and distribution for his 110-proof Cabo Wabo tequila as well as the operations of his Cabo Wabo Cantina. Cabo Wabo's premium line of tequila ages for up to three years in oak barrels before ever seeing the bottom of a shot glass. The bar and restaurant, located in Cabo San Lucas, Mexico, offers Tex-Mex and Baja Mexican cuisine, as well as Cabo Wabo tequila, of course. The company also merchandises Cabo Wabo apparel and accessories. It's majority-owned by Davide Campari-Milano, which bought an 80% stake in 2008.

CABOT CORPORATION

NYSE: CBT

2 Seaport Ln., Ste. 1300
Boston, MA 02210
Phone: 617-345-0100
Fax: 617-342-6103
Web: www.cabot-corp.com

CEO: Patrick M. Prevost
CFO: Eduardo E. Cordeiro
HR: Robby D. Sisco
FYE: September 30
Type: Public

Even if it lost money, Cabot still would be in the black. The company is the world's #1 producer of carbon black, a reinforcing and pigmenting agent used in tires, inks, cables, and coatings. It has about 25% of the world market for the product. Cabot also holds its own as a maker of fumed metal oxides such as fumed silica and fumed alumina, which are used as anti-caking, thickening, and reinforcing agents in adhesives and coatings. Other products include tantalum (used to make capacitors in electronics) and specialty fluids for gas and oil drilling. It operates in about 20 countries worldwide, with combined sales to China and Japan adding up to about a quarter of Cabot's total.

	Annual Growth	9/05	9/06	9/07	9/08	9/09
Sales ($ mil.)	1.4%	2,125.0	2,543.0	2,616.0	3,191.0	2,243.0
Net income ($ mil.)	—	(48.0)	90.0	129.0	86.0	(77.0)
Market value ($ mil.)	(8.5%)	2,157.7	2,431.6	2,322.5	2,077.3	1,510.6
Employees	(2.7%)	4,400	4,300	4,300	4,300	3,950

CABOT MICROELECTRONICS CORPORATION

NASDAQ (GS): CCMP

870 N. Commons Dr.
Aurora, IL 60504
Phone: 630-375-6631
Fax: —
Web: www.cabotcmp.com

CEO: William P. (Bill) Noglows
CFO: William S. (Bill) Johnson
HR: Lisa Polezoes
FYE: September 30
Type: Public

Cabot Microelectronics sits atop a mountain of slurry. The company is the world's top maker of slurries used in chemical mechanical planarization (CMP). CMP is a wafer polishing process that enables semiconductor manufacturers to produce smaller, faster, and more complex devices. Cabot Microelectronics' CMP slurries consist of liquids containing abrasives and chemicals that aid in the CMP process. The company also makes polishing pads for CMP, as well as slurries used to polish the substrates and magnetic heads of hard-disk drives. The company's largest customers include TSMC and Intel. More than three-quarters of sales come from the Asia/Pacific region.

	Annual Growth	9/05	9/06	9/07	9/08	9/09
Sales ($ mil.)	1.9%	270.5	320.8	338.2	375.1	291.4
Net income ($ mil.)	(23.4%)	32.5	32.9	33.8	38.3	11.2
Market value ($ mil.)	4.4%	694.4	680.6	1,010.3	758.2	823.9
Employees	7.9%	650	742	742	818	882

An in-depth profile of this company is available to Hoover's Online members at hoovers.com.

CABOT OIL & GAS CORPORATION NYSE: COG

1200 Enclave Pkwy.
Houston, TX 77077
Phone: 281-589-4600
Fax: 281-589-4828
Web: www.cabotog.com

CEO: Dan O. Dinges
CFO: Scott C. Schroeder
HR: Abraham D. Garza
FYE: December 31
Type: Public

Like a cog on a gear in a well-oiled machine, Cabot Oil & Gas (ticker symbol: COG) has engaged in the oil industry very efficiently. Cabot explores for and produces natural gas and oil, and it sells gas to industrial customers, local utilities, and gas marketers. It has estimated proved reserves of 1.9 trillion cu. ft. of natural gas equivalent. Major areas of operation include Appalachia, the Anadarko Basin (Kansas, Oklahoma, and Texas), the Rocky Mountains (Wyoming), and the Texas and Louisiana Gulf Coast. The company also has reserves. In 2008 it was operating almost 4,700 net wells and had more than 183,630 net acres of undeveloped assets.

	Annual Growth	12/05	12/06	12/07	12/08	12/09
Sales ($ mil.)	6.5%	682.8	762.0	732.2	945.8	879.3
Net income ($ mil.)	(0.0%)	148.4	321.2	167.4	211.3	148.3
Market value ($ mil.)	17.9%	2,343.2	3,151.1	4,194.8	2,701.7	4,529.4
Employees	12.5%	354	374	404	560	567

CACHÉ, INC. NASDAQ (GS): CACH

1440 Broadway
New York, NY 10018
Phone: 212-575-3200
Fax: 212-944-2842
Web: www.cache.com

CEO: Thomas E. Reinckens
CFO: Margaret J. Feeney
HR: Margarita Croasdaile
FYE: December 31
Type: Public

Caché sells fashions that bring cachet to the soirée. The upscale women's apparel retailer owns and operates about 295 specialty stores in shopping malls in 40-plus US states, Puerto Rico, and the US Virgin Islands under the Caché and Caché Luxe banners, as well as an online shopping site. Sportswear, including casual wear, collections, and separates, accounts for about 60% of apparel sales. It closed all of its Lillie Rubin shops in 2006 and launched a new format — Caché Luxe. The firm buys its merchandise primarily from domestic suppliers, but it has begun to source more overseas. Caché acquired New York-based Adrienne Victoria Designs (its largest supplier) in July 2007.

	Annual Growth	12/05	12/06	12/07	12/08	12/09
Sales ($ mil.)	(4.7%)	266.3	279.0	274.5	265.7	219.8
Net income ($ mil.)	—	13.4	8.3	6.5	(7.1)	(8.7)
Market value ($ mil.)	(28.3%)	220.9	321.8	119.1	25.8	58.3
Employees	(4.5%)	2,700	2,860	2,860	2,526	2,250

CACI INTERNATIONAL INC NYSE: CACI

1100 N. Glebe Rd.
Arlington, VA 22201
Phone: 703-841-7800
Fax: 703-841-7882
Web: www.caci.com

CEO: Paul M. Cofoni
CFO: Thomas A. (Tom) Mutryn
HR: H. Robert (Bob) Boehm
FYE: June 30
Type: Public

CACI International doesn't need a lot of clients — just a few with deep pockets. As one of the largest government IT contractors, CACI derives most of its revenues from the US government. More than three-quarters of its sales come from the US Department of Defense (DOD). The company provides a wide range of technology services, including systems integration, network management, knowledge management, and engineering and simulation. Based in the UK, the company's European subsidiary, CACI Limited, accounts for all of its international sales and almost all of its commercial revenue.

	Annual Growth	6/05	6/06	6/07	6/08	6/09
Sales ($ mil.)	13.9%	1,623.1	1,755.3	1,938.0	2,420.5	2,730.2
Net income ($ mil.)	2.9%	85.3	84.8	78.5	83.3	95.5
Market value ($ mil.)	(9.3%)	1,909.7	1,814.2	1,477.0	1,383.9	1,291.4
Employees	6.6%	9,600	10,400	10,400	12,000	12,400

CADBURY ADAMS USA LLC

389 Interpace Pkwy.
Parsippany, NJ 07054
Phone: 973-909-2000
Fax: —
Web: www.usa.cadbury.com

CEO: James R. (Jim) Chambers
CFO: Andrew R. J. Bonfield
HR: —
FYE: December 31
Type: Subsidiary

Cadbury Adams USA has it all wrapped up — in thin little rectangles wrapped in foil. The US division of UK candy giant Cadbury makes candy, chewing gum, and mints. Its brands include Bubblicious, Certs, Chiclets, Dentyne, HALLS, Sour Patch, Swedish Fish, and Trident. The company also makes the retro gum brands Beeman's, Blackjack, and Clove, which it reintroduces every few years in order to cash in on nostalgia buffs and baby boomers. Cadbury Adams USA was formed after then Cadbury Schweppes bought the Adams chewing gum brands from Pfizer for $4.2 billion in 2003 and integrated it into its already existing US operations. (Cadbury Schweppes spun off its beverage operations to focus solely on candy in 2008.)

CADENCE DESIGN SYSTEMS, INC. NASDAQ (GS): CDNS

2655 Seely Ave., Bldg. 5
San Jose, CA 95134
Phone: 408-943-1234
Fax: 408-428-5001
Web: www.cadence.com

CEO: Lip-Bu Tan
CFO: Kevin S. Palatnik
HR: Tina Jones
FYE: December 31
Type: Public

Cadence Design Systems helps engineers pick up the development tempo. A leader in the electronic design automation (EDA) market, Cadence sells and leases software and hardware products for designing integrated circuits (ICs), printed circuit boards (PCBs), and other electronic systems. Electronics companies use Cadence's products to build components used in wireless devices, networking equipment, and other applications. The company also provides maintenance and support and offers design and methodology consulting services. Cadence gets more than half of its revenues outside the US.

	Annual Growth	12/05	12/06	12/07	12/08	12/09
Sales ($ mil.)	(10.5%)	1,329.2	1,483.9	1,615.0	1,038.6	852.6
Net income ($ mil.)	—	49.3	142.2	296.3	(1,854.0)	(149.9)
Market value ($ mil.)	(22.9%)	4,573.3	4,840.8	4,597.6	989.3	1,619.0
Employees	(3.1%)	5,000	5,200	5,300	4,900	4,400

CADENCE FINANCIAL CORPORATION NASDAQ (GS): CADE

301 E. Main St.
Starkville, MS 39759
Phone: 662-323-1341
Fax: 662-338-5031
Web: www.cadencebanking.com

CEO: Lewis F. Mallory Jr.
CFO: Richard T. Haston
HR: —
FYE: December 31
Type: Public

Cadence Financial is the holding company for Cadence Bank, which operates about 20 branches in the Golden Triangle area of northern Mississippi, plus nearly 20 additional locations in Alabama, Florida, Georgia, and Tennessee. The community bank offers standard deposit products such as checking and savings accounts, in addition to trust and investment services. It primarily originates real estate mortgages (more than half of its loan portfolio), but also makes financial, agricultural, business, construction, and consumer installment loans. The company's Galloway-Chandler-McKinney Insurance Agency subsidiary sells property/casualty insurance, title and life insurance, annuities, and commercial coverage.

	Annual Growth	12/05	12/06	12/07	12/08	12/09
Assets ($ mil.)	6.3%	1,446.1	1,899.9	1,984.2	1,979.3	1,844.5
Net income ($ mil.)	—	13.8	14.2	9.8	(3.4)	(109.9)
Market value ($ mil.)	(47.9%)	283.4	258.1	173.8	55.5	20.8
Employees	0.5%	419	488	473	484	428

CADENCE PHARMACEUTICALS, INC.

NASDAQ (GM): CADX

12481 High Bluff Dr., Ste. 200
San Diego, CA 92130
Phone: 858-436-1400
Fax: 858-436-1401
Web: www.cadencepharm.com

CEO: Theodore R. Schroeder
CFO: William R. (Bill) LaRue
HR: Diane K. Sheehan
FYE: December 31
Type: Public

Cadence Pharmaceuticals follows the rhythm of hospitals' medical needs. The biopharmaceutical company develops drug candidates primarily for use in a hospital setting. The company licenses rights to compounds and develops them for sale in untapped markets or for new indications. Cadence's late-stage candidates include Acetavance (injectable acetaminophen), which is marketed in Europe by the Bristol-Myers Squibb Company under the name Perfalgan, for treating acute pain and fever. The company also is developing Omigard, a topical antimicrobial gel used to prevent and treat infections in surgical wounds, burns, and medical device-related wounds such as from catheters.

	Annual Growth	12/05	12/06	12/07	12/08	12/09
Sales ($ mil.)	—	—	—	—	—	0.0
Net income ($ mil.)	—	—	—	—	—	(45.5)
Market value ($ mil.)	—	—	—	—	—	488.5
Employees	—	—	—	—	—	90

CADIZ INC.

NASDAQ (GM): CDZI

550 S. Hope St., Ste. 2850
Los Angeles, CA 90071
Phone: 213-271-1600
Fax: 213-271-1614
Web: www.cadizinc.com

CEO: Keith Brackpool
CFO: Timothy J. Shaheen
HR: —
FYE: December 31
Type: Public

Cadiz hopes to strike gold with water. The company owns some 45,000 acres of land and groundwater resources in eastern San Bernardino County near the Colorado River Aqueduct and in the eastern Mojave Desert. Cadiz is betting on its groundwater storage and distribution project as water supplies become increasingly scarce in Southern California. After the Metropolitan Water District of Southern California cancelled its agreement with Cadiz in 2002, the company has resumed the project with San Bernardino County. Cadiz is also looking into commercial and residential development of its land. It has some agricultural assets that are leased as lemon groves and grape vineyards.

	Annual Growth	12/05	12/06	12/07	12/08	12/09
Sales ($ mil.)	(9.6%)	1.2	0.6	0.4	1.0	0.8
Net income ($ mil.)	—	(23.0)	(13.8)	(13.6)	(15.9)	(14.4)
Market value ($ mil.)	(13.6%)	294.1	313.9	287.2	171.1	163.7
Employees	3.0%	8	9	9	10	9

CADUS CORPORATION

OTC: KDUS

767 5th Ave., 47th Fl.
New York, NY 10153
Phone: 212-702-4351
Fax: 212-750-5815

CEO: David Blitz
CFO: David Blitz
HR: —
FYE: December 31
Type: Public

Cadus had hoped to make some dough from yeast but now is barely more than a hollow crust. Previously, the company's drug discovery technologies used genetically engineered yeast cells, but the firm sold its discovery programs to OSI Pharmaceuticals years ago, and halted all research efforts. It dropped "Pharmaceutical" from its name to signal its interest in working outside the biotech industry. Its subsidiary Cadus Technologies still holds some assets related to its yeast cell technology and is seeking interested parties to license the intellectual properties. Investor Carl Icahn, a director and former chairman of the company, owns almost 40% of Cadus, and effectively controls the company.

	Annual Growth	12/05	12/06	12/07	12/08	12/09
Sales ($ mil.)	0.0%	0.1	0.1	0.1	0.1	0.1
Net income ($ mil.)	—	0.0	0.4	(0.3)	(1.3)	(0.3)
Market value ($ mil.)	(2.8%)	21.0	21.0	24.7	17.7	18.8
Employees	—	—	—	—	—	—

CADWALADER, WICKERSHAM & TAFT LLP

1 World Financial Center
New York, NY 10281
Phone: 212-504-6000
Fax: 212-504-6666
Web: www.cadwalader.com

CEO: Robert O. Link Jr.
CFO: Mitchel E. Sekler
HR: Jeremiah A. DeBerry
FYE: December 31
Type: Partnership

Founded during the presidency of George Washington, Cadwalader, Wickersham & Taft is one of the oldest law firms in the US. Since 1792 the firm has grown to include about 500 lawyers and to encompass offices not only in the US, but also in Europe and the Asia/Pacific region. Among the areas of practice for which the firm is regularly recognized are capital markets, financial restructuring, and mergers and acquisitions. Banks and other financial institutions have been prominently represented on Cadwalader's client list; in addition, the firm undertakes work for other large businesses and for government entities, health care organizations, nonprofits, and individuals.

CAE USA, INC.

4908 Tampa West Blvd.
Tampa, FL 33634
Phone: 813-885-7481
Fax: 813-887-1439
Web: www.cae.com

CEO: John Lenyo
CFO: John Atkinson
HR: Darren Ugles
FYE: March 31
Type: Subsidiary

Is it real, or is it CAE USA? A subsidiary of Canadian company CAE Inc., CAE USA makes flight simulators and trainers for military and civilian planes and helicopters. Products include flight and weapons simulators and tactical air defense trainers. Its systems reproduce instruments, controls, and mission operator stations, and offer computerized visual simulations with realistic, high-resolution images. CAE USA has more than 25 US training sites and aviation services. Customers include Airbus, FedEx Corporation, Lockheed Martin, the US Navy and US Air Force, and the UK's Royal Air Force. Formerly known as Reflectone (and owned by BAE), the company was acquired by CAE Inc. in 2001.

	Annual Growth	3/04	3/05	3/06	3/07	3/08
Est. sales ($ mil.)	—	—	—	—	—	64.6
Employees	—	—	—	—	—	800

CAFE ENTERPRISES, INC.

4324 Wade Hampton Blvd.
Taylors, SC 29687
Phone: 864-322-1331
Fax: 864-322-1332
Web: www.fatzcafe.com

CEO: Steve Bruce
CFO: —
HR: Steve Corson
FYE: December 31
Type: Private

You might say this company runs a plus-size restaurant chain. Cafe Enterprises owns and operates more than 40 Fatz Cafe casual-dining establishments in South Carolina, North Carolina, Georgia, Tennessee, and Virginia. The restaurants, known for their down-home atmosphere, offer standard American fare such as burgers, chicken, and steaks. The chain also serves seafood, pasta, and a selection of appetizers. Entrepreneur Jimmy Rogers opened the first Fatz Cafe in 1988. A management group led by CEO Steve Bruce and backed by such private equity firms as GE Capital Solutions, Madison Capital Funding, and Milestone Partners, owns Cafe Enterprises.

CAFE RIO, INC.

2825 E. Cottonwood Pkwy., Ste. 360
Salt Lake City, UT 84121
Phone: 801-930-6000
Fax: 801-930-6090
Web: www.caferio.com

CEO: Robert T. (Bob) Nilsen
CFO: Robert J. (Bob) Baker
HR: Tera Sunder
FYE: December 31
Type: Private

If you're feeling kind of full of Mexican food, maybe you can blame it on Rio. Cafe Rio operates more than 20 Café Rio Mexican Grill full-service restaurant locations mostly in Utah, including several in the Salt Lake City area. The chain offers traditional Tex-Mex fare, such as burritos, enchiladas, and tacos, as well as a rotating selection of daily specials. In addition to dining, the restaurants offer to-go service for those who want to enjoy their meals at home. Steve and Patricia Stanley started the business in 1997. Former Burger King president Bob Nilsen purchased Cafe Rio in 2004 with backing from private equity firm Saunders Karp & Megrue (which later merged with Apax Partners).

CAJUN OPERATING COMPANY

980 Hammond Dr. NE, Ste. 1100
Atlanta, GA 30328
Phone: 770-350-3800
Fax: 770-512-3920
Web: www.churchs.com

CEO: Mel Deane
CFO: Louis J. (Dusty) Profumo
HR: Bonita (Bunny) Williams
FYE: December 31
Type: Private

This company has several places fried-chicken worshipers can flock to. Cajun Operating Company owns and operates Church's Chicken, the #3 quick-service chicken chain behind KFC (owned by YUM! Brands) and Popeyes (AFC Enterprises), with more than 1,700 locations in more than 20 countries. The restaurants specialize in fried chicken available with such side items as biscuits, fried okra, fries, and mashed potatoes. More than 250 of the locations are company-owned, while the rest are franchised. Church's Chicken was started in 1952 by retired chicken incubator salesman George Church as Church's Fried Chicken to Go. The company is owned by investment firm Friedman Fleischer & Lowe.

	Annual Growth	12/04	12/05	12/06	12/07	12/08
Est. sales ($ mil.)	—	—	—	—	—	290.6
Employees	—	—	—	—	—	4,950

CAGLE'S, INC.

NYSE Amex: CGL

1385 Collier Rd., NW
Atlanta, GA 30318
Phone: 404-355-2820
Fax: 404-350-9605
Web: www.cagles.net

CEO: J. Douglas (Doug) Cagle
CFO: Mark M. Ham IV
HR: Lavon Waite
FYE: March 31
Type: Public

The people at Cagle's may be outnumbered, but nonetheless, the chickens never have a chance. The poultry company slaughters and processes some 2 million birds each week. Vertically integrated, it also has breeding, hatching, and feed milling operations (the birds are then raised by about 60 contract grower-farmers in Georgia and Tennessee). The company specializes in value-added meat — most of its birds wind up deboned, quick-frozen, marinated, breaded, or otherwise processed to make cooking easier for its retail and foodservice customers. Cagle's has operations in Alabama and Georgia. The founding Cagle family manages the company and owns approximately 65% of its stock.

	Annual Growth	3/05	3/06	3/07	3/08	3/09
Sales ($ mil.)	4.4%	246.3	237.3	233.9	283.6	292.6
Net income ($ mil.)	—	11.5	(0.6)	0.6	(0.8)	(11.5)
Market value ($ mil.)	(34.0%)	42.5	32.2	34.3	28.4	8.1
Employees	(1.4%)	1,975	1,909	1,850	1,794	1,865

CAKEWALK, INC.

268 Summer St.
Boston, MA 02210
Phone: 617-423-9004
Fax: 617-423-9007
Web: www.cakewalk.com

CEO: Greg Hendershott
CFO: Greg Hendershott
HR: —
FYE: December 31
Type: Subsidiary

Cakewalk wants to make it much, much easier to produce a pleasing — and musical — sound on your computer. The company develops and markets sound and music software used for tasks such as producing audio for CDs, film, TV, video games, and the Internet. Its SONAR line is its flagship digital audio workstation; other products include Projects, Rapture, and Music Creator. Customers include audio professionals, musicians, software developers, and home users. Cakewalk was founded in 1987 by CEO Greg Hendershott. Electronic instrument maker Roland, a longtime Cakewalk partner and investor, brought its ownership up to 60% in 2008 when it added 45% to its previous stake.

	Annual Growth	12/04	12/05	12/06	12/07	12/08
Est. sales ($ mil.)	—	—	—	—	—	9.2
Employees	—	—	—	—	—	55

CAI INTERNATIONAL, INC.

NYSE: CAP

1 Embarcadero Ctr., Ste. 2101
San Francisco, CA 94111
Phone: 415-788-0100
Fax: 415-788-3430
Web: www.capps.com

CEO: Masaaki (John) Nishibori
CFO: Victor M. Garcia
HR: —
FYE: December 31
Type: Public

Is it bigger than a breadbox? CAI International can pack it. Formerly Container Applications International, the company leases large steel boxes to ship freight by plane, train, or truck around the world. Over 30% of its container fleet is owned by CAI and the balance, owned by container investors, is managed by CAI. The leasing segment offers 200-plus shipping companies short-term (less than one year), and long-term (five-year) leases. Its finance leases give lessees the option to purchase the container. Management services provide container investors with the muscle to lease, re-lease, and dispose of their portfolio of containers. Management services also contract for container repair, relocation, and storage.

	Annual Growth	12/05	12/06	12/07	12/08	12/09
Sales ($ mil.)	1.5%	61.6	18.6	64.9	83.1	65.3
Net income ($ mil.)	8.0%	10.0	5.2	19.2	(27.0)	13.6
Market value ($ mil.)	(7.4%)	—	—	188.5	56.8	161.8
Employees	8.5%	—	65	75	89	83

CAL DIVE INTERNATIONAL, INC.

NYSE: DVR

2500 CityWest Blvd., Ste. 2200
Houston, TX 77042
Phone: 713-361-2600
Fax: 713-361-2690
Web: www.caldive.com

CEO: Quinn J. Hébert
CFO: Bruce P. Koch
HR: Rebecca G. Gottsegen
FYE: December 31
Type: Public

Cal Dive International may or may not be California dreaming, but its waking hours are spent beneath the waters of the world's oceans. The subsea contractor operates a fleet of 24 surface and saturation diving support vessels, six shallow water pipelay vessels, one dedicated pipebury barge, one combination pipelay/derrick barge, and two derrick barges. It installs and maintains offshore platforms, pipelines, and production systems on the Outer Continental Shelf of the Gulf of Mexico, as well as in offshore markets in the Middle East, Southeast Asia, and Trinidad. Cal Dive also provides shallow water diving services and performs salvage operations on abandoned fields.

	Annual Growth	12/05	12/06	12/07	12/08	12/09
Sales ($ mil.)	38.7%	224.3	509.9	623.6	856.9	829.4
Net income ($ mil.)	19.4%	37.7	119.4	105.6	109.5	76.6
Market value ($ mil.)	(15.5%)	—	1,182.2	1,247.2	613.2	712.1
Employees	14.3%	1,200	1,300	2,000	2,000	2,050

An in-depth profile of this company is available to Hoover's Online members at hoovers.com.

CALAMOS ASSET MANAGEMENT, INC.

NASDAQ (GS): CLMS

2020 Calamos Ct.
Naperville, IL 60563
Phone: 630-245-7200
Fax: 630-245-6335
Web: www.calamos.com

CEO: John P. Calamos Sr.
CFO: Nick P. Calamos
HR: Gary J. Felsten
FYE: December 31
Type: Public

Calamos Asset Management wants to make the most of your assets. Through its subsidiaries the company provides money management and investment advice to institutional and individual investors. The firm manages about 15 mutual funds and five closed-end funds representing a range of investment strategies and risk levels; it also offers managed accounts and wealth management services. Calamos, which has approximately $24 billion in its keep — most of it invested in equities — was founded in 1977 and went public in 2004. Chairman and CEO John Calamos and his family control the company.

	Annual Growth	12/05	12/06	12/07	12/08	12/09
Assets ($ mil.)	(4.3%)	665.5	795.8	1,217.7	475.9	557.1
Net income ($ mil.)	(19.3%)	29.2	34.0	27.7	(24.5)	12.4
Market value ($ mil.)	(22.2%)	625.7	533.7	592.4	147.2	229.2
Employees	(1.2%)	331	380	430	368	316

CALAMP CORP.

NASDAQ (GS): CAMP

1401 N. Rice Ave.
Oxnard, CA 93030
Phone: 805-987-9000
Fax: 805-856-3869
Web: www.calamp.com

CEO: Richard B. (Rick) Gold
CFO: Richard K. (Rick) Vitelle
HR: —
FYE: February 28
Type: Public

CalAmp adds a little boost even to the weakest of TV programs. The former military supplier makes microwave amplification and conversion components that improve reception in satellite television, wireless cable, and wireless broadband access systems. Its products include antennas, amplifiers, and transceivers and receivers for broadband wireless transmission. The company's leading customers include DIRECTV (about 10% of sales) and DISH Network (nearly 16%), as well as EFJ, a supplier of radios for the military and public safety markets. Most of CalAmp's sales are in the US.

	Annual Growth	2/05	2/06	2/07	2/08	2/09
Sales ($ mil.)	(18.2%)	220.0	217.5	222.3	140.9	98.4
Net income ($ mil.)	—	8.1	14.6	(31.2)	(84.1)	(49.7)
Market value ($ mil.)	(48.7%)	199.7	278.0	245.9	75.5	13.8
Employees	(10.6%)	600	480	580	420	384

CALAVO GROWERS, INC.

NASDAQ (GM): CVGW

1141-A Cummings Rd.
Santa Paula, CA 93060
Phone: 805-525-1245
Fax: 805-921-3223
Web: www.calavo.com

CEO: Lecil E. (Lee) Cole
CFO: Arthur J. (Art) Bruno
HR: Patricia (Pat) Vorhies
FYE: October 31
Type: Public

The avocado growers of Calavo Growers might not be a cooperative anymore, but they're still friendly folks. Calavo (a combination of "California" and "avocado") began as a growers' marketing cooperative founded in 1924 in order to transform the exotic hobby crop, avocados, into a culinary staple. And the avocado has become, if not a staple, a regular in US supermarket shopping carts. Calavo procures and processes avocados (one-third of California's entire crop for 2009), tomatoes, and other fresh fruits grown mainly in California but also uses fruit from Chile, Peru, and Mexico. The products are then distributed to retail food outlets, foodservice operators, and produce wholesalers throughout the world.

	Annual Growth	10/05	10/06	10/07	10/08	10/09
Sales ($ mil.)	7.4%	258.8	273.9	303.0	361.5	344.8
Net income ($ mil.)	42.5%	3.3	5.8	7.3	7.7	13.6
Market value ($ mil.)	22.3%	—	142.8	335.7	148.7	261.5
Employees	10.6%	701	750	830	876	1,049

CALGON CARBON CORPORATION

NYSE: CCC

400 Calgon Carbon Dr.
Pittsburgh, PA 15205
Phone: 412-787-6700
Fax: 412-787-4511
Web: www.calgoncarbon.com

CEO: John S. Stanik
CFO: Leroy M. Ball
HR: Gail A. Gerono
FYE: December 31
Type: Public

With pure intentions, Calgon Carbon makes activated carbons and purification systems and offers purification, separation, and concentration services to the industrial process and environmental markets. The company provides activated, impregnated, and acid-washed carbons (about 130 million pounds annually) for use in applications such as food processing, wastewater treatment, and emissions control. Calgon Carbon also sells equipment that uses activated carbon and ion exchange resins for the purification of products in the chemical, food, and pharmaceutical industries. The company's consumer products include charcoal and carbon cloth.

	Annual Growth	12/05	12/06	12/07	12/08	12/09
Sales ($ mil.)	9.1%	290.8	316.1	351.1	400.3	411.9
Net income ($ mil.)	—	(7.4)	(7.8)	15.3	38.4	39.2
Market value ($ mil.)	25.0%	319.6	348.3	892.6	862.8	780.8
Employees	(0.5%)	972	847	868	943	953

CALIFORNIA BANK & TRUST

11622 El Camino Real, Ste. 200
San Diego, CA 92130
Phone: 858-793-7400
Fax: 858-793-7438
Web: www.calbanktrust.com

CEO: David E. Blackford
CFO: Dennis Uyemura
HR: —
FYE: December 31
Type: Subsidiary

A subsidiary of Zions Bancorporation, California Bank & Trust (CB&T) has some 100 branches in the Golden State. It serves business and consumer clients, offering such standard services as checking and savings accounts, CDs, IRAs, Internet banking, mortgages, personal loans, and business loans, including Small Business Administration loans. Specialized services for companies include cash management, lines of credit, and international banking. Its Remote Deposit service lets businesses deposit checks without a trip to the bank. CB&T was formed when Zions combined three California banks in 1998.

CALIFORNIA COASTAL COMMUNITIES, INC.

Pink Sheets: CALCQ

6 Executive Circle, Ste. 250
Irvine, CA 92614
Phone: 949-250-7700
Fax: 949-250-7705
Web: www.californiacoastalcommunities.com

CEO: Raymond J. Pacini
CFO: Sandra G. Sciutto
HR: Sandra G. Sciutto
FYE: December 31
Type: Public

The tide has turned for California Coastal Communities. Long wrapped up in a battle over land development rights, the company has begun development of its Brightwater project, some 215 acres (about half of that undevelopable land) situated near important wetlands in Bolsa Chica, the last undeveloped strip of coastal property in Orange County. Besides the controversial parcels, the company is also building houses in Riverside, Los Angeles, San Bernardino and Ventura counties, where it has the option to buy some 170 acres. Its operations include home builder Hearthside Homes and Signal Landmark, which is developing the Bolsa Chica land. The company filed for voluntary reorganization under Chapter 11 in 2009.

	Annual Growth	12/05	12/06	12/07	12/08	12/09
Sales ($ mil.)	(22.3%)	129.5	95.7	47.0	46.0	47.2
Net income ($ mil.)	—	28.4	5.6	(18.9)	(44.7)	(22.4)
Market value ($ mil.)	(57.3%)	431.4	235.9	64.7	5.5	14.3
Employees	(15.3%)	64	59	55	38	33

CALIFORNIA CONSERVATION CORPS

1719 24th St.	CEO: David Muraki
Sacramento, CA 95816	CFO: Pallas Bento
Phone: 916-341-3100	HR: Glenda Smith
Fax: 916-323-4989	FYE: —
Web: www.ccc.ca.gov	Type: Government-owned

The California Conservation Corps (CCC) helps fight fires, save the environment, and respond to emergencies across the state. Made up of young adults (between the ages of 18 and 25) hired on for a year of service, the corps works on a wide variety of projects sponsored by state, city, county, and federal agencies, as well as not-for-profit organizations, schools, and private industry. Services include landscaping, trail construction, tree planting, energy auditing, and fire hazard reduction. Established in 1976, CCC is modeled after the Civilian Conservation Corps formed by President Franklin Roosevelt. CCC has an annual budget of some $100 million and is the largest conservation corps in the nation.

CALIFORNIA DAIRIES INC.

2000 N. Plaza Dr.	CEO: Richard L. Cotta
Visalia, CA 93291	CFO: Joe Heffington
Phone: 559-625-2200	HR: —
Fax: 559-625-5433	FYE: April 30
Web: www.californiadairies.com	Type: Cooperative

Herding dairies together to give them greater "ag"-gregate strength has made California Dairies one of the largest dairy cooperatives in the US. California Dairies' 620 member/farmers provide the co-op with more than 18 billion pounds of milk a year. Its plants process milk into cheese, butter, and powdered milk. The co-op's subsidiaries include Challenge Dairy Products (retail, foodservice, and ingredient products) and Los Banos Foods (cheddar cheese ingredients for food manufacturing). California Dairies is also a majority owner of DairyAmerica, which markets dairy products, including some 60% of all the milk powder produced in the US. California Dairies exports its products to some 52 countries worldwide.

	Annual Growth	4/04	4/05	4/06	4/07	4/08
Sales ($ mil.)	—	—	—	—	—	3,500.0
Employees	—	—	—	—	—	755

🖳 CALIFORNIA FIRST NATIONAL BANCORP   NASDAQ (GM): CFNB

18201 Von Karman Ave., Ste. 800	CEO: Patrick E. Paddon
Irvine, CA 92612	CFO: S. Leslie Jewett
Phone: 949-255-0500	HR: —
Fax: 949-255-0501	FYE: June 30
Web: www.calfirstbancorp.com	Type: Public

California First National Bancorp (CalFirst) wants to be first on your mind when it comes to meeting your equipment leasing needs. Through subsidiaries Amplicon and California First Leasing (CalFirst Leasing), the firm leases mainly computers and software. It also leases retail point-of-sale systems, ATMs, telecommunications equipment, office furniture, and other equipment. CalFirst also operates California First National Bank (CalFirst Bank), a branchless retail bank that accepts deposits through the mail, by phone, or over the Internet. CEO Patrick Paddon owns 64% of the company.

	Annual Growth	6/05	6/06	6/07	6/08	6/09
Sales ($ mil.)	1.5%	34.5	35.9	36.1	34.0	36.6
Net income ($ mil.)	3.2%	8.2	10.7	9.9	7.0	9.3
Market value ($ mil.)	0.2%	115.4	147.5	149.2	98.2	116.6
Employees	(6.9%)	206	171	194	178	155

CALIFORNIA INSTITUTE OF TECHNOLOGY

1200 E. California Blvd.	CEO: Jean-Lou A. Chameau
Pasadena, CA 91125	CFO: Dean W. Currie
Phone: 626-395-6811	HR: —
Fax: 626-405-9842	FYE: September 30
Web: www.caltech.edu	Type: School

The California Institute of Technology (Caltech) enrolls about 2,100 students and offers programs in areas such as chemistry and chemical engineering, geological and planetary sciences, physics, math, astronomy, humanities, social sciences, and engineering. The school receives about half of its operating revenue through research grants, primarily from government agencies. Its professors and graduates have snared a total of 32 Nobel Prizes; other alumni include filmmaker Frank Capra and Apollo 17 astronaut Harrison Schmitt. Caltech operates the Jet Propulsion Laboratory, which supervises Mars exploration programs and other interplanetary missions, under contract to NASA. The school was founded in 1891.

	Annual Growth	9/04	9/05	9/06	9/07	9/08
Est. sales ($ mil.)	—	—	—	—	—	2,142.1
Employees	—	—	—	—	—	3,980

CALIFORNIA MICRO DEVICES CORPORATION

490 N. McCarthy Blvd., Ste. 100	CEO: Robert V. Dickinson
Milpitas, CA 95035	CFO: Kevin J. Berry
Phone: 408-263-3214	HR: —
Fax: 408-263-7846	FYE: December 31
Web: www.calmicro.com	Type: Subsidiary

I wish they all could be California . . . chips? California Micro Devices (CMD) specializes in integrated passive devices (IPDs), including application-specific and customized models. IPDs are integrated circuits that combine passive components, such as capacitors and resistors, with active semiconductors. CMD makes analog and mixed-signal semiconductors, such as operational amplifiers, power management devices, and telecommunications transceivers. Its products are used in electronic gear, including PCs and wireless phones. Among its top clients are Motorola, Philips, Samsung Electronics, and Sony. In 2010 ON Semiconductor acquired CMD for $108 million in cash, making CMD a wholly owned subsidiary.

	Annual Growth	3/05	3/06	3/07	3/08	3/09
Sales ($ mil.)	(7.0%)	65.9	70.2	68.0	59.2	49.3
Net income ($ mil.)	—	4.0	10.0	(0.1)	(1.4)	(15.2)
Employees	0.7%	100	94	107	108	103

CALIFORNIA PHYSICIANS' SERVICE

50 Beale St.	CEO: Bruce G. Bodaken
San Francisco, CA 94105	CFO: Heidi Fields
Phone: 415-229-5000	HR: Marianne Jackson
Fax: 415-229-5070	FYE: December 31
Web: www.blueshieldca.com	Type: Not-for-profit

California Physicians' Service, which operates as Blue Shield of California, provides health insurance products and related services to some 3.4 million members in the state of California. The not-for-profit mutual organization's health insurance products include HMO, PPO, dental, and Medicaid or Medicare supplemental plans for individuals, families, and employer groups. Accidental death and dismemberment, executive medical reimbursement, life insurance, vision, and short-term health plans are provided by the company's Blue Shield of California Life & Health Insurance subsidiary. Blue Shield of California has more than 20 locations across California. The company was established in 1939.

	Annual Growth	12/04	12/05	12/06	12/07	12/08
Sales ($ mil.)	6.8%	6,846.2	7,518.9	8,150.0	8,364.0	8,898.0
Net income ($ mil.)	(2.1%)	334.2	329.5	382.0	318.0	307.0
Employees	3.7%	—	4,300	4,500	4,500	4,800

An in-depth profile of this company is available to Hoover's Online members at hoovers.com. 🖳

CALIFORNIA PIZZA KITCHEN, INC.

NASDAQ (GS): CPKI

6053 W. Century Blvd., 11th Fl.
Los Angeles, CA 90045
Phone: 310-342-5000
Fax: 310-342-4640
Web: www.cpk.com

CEO: Larry S. Flax
CFO: Susan M. Collyns
HR: —
FYE: December 31
Type: Public

This company's cookeries are putting a West Coast twist on an old favorite. California Pizza Kitchen (CPK) operates a chain of about 250 casual-dining restaurants that specialize in gourmet pizzas featuring unique topping combinations, including duck, barbecued chicken, and grilled shrimp. The chain also serves Neapolitan pizzas from Italy, as well as American-style pies. CPK rounds out its menu with pastas, soups, salads, and desserts. The restaurants are found in more than 30 states and about 10 other countries; more than 200 of the locations are company owned. In addition to its restaurant business, the company licenses the California Pizza Kitchen brand to Nestlé for a line of frozen pizzas.

	Annual Growth	12/05	12/06	12/07	12/08	12/09
Sales ($ mil.)	8.5%	479.6	554.6	632.9	677.1	664.7
Net income ($ mil.)	(30.3%)	19.5	21.0	14.8	8.7	4.6
Market value ($ mil.)	(10.9%)	523.5	545.4	382.4	263.3	330.3
Employees	3.1%	12,900	13,900	14,800	15,100	14,600

CALIFORNIA POLYTECHNIC STATE UNIVERSITY

1 Grand Ave.
San Luis Obispo, CA 93407
Phone: 805-756-1111
Fax: 805-756-6533
Web: www.calpoly.edu

CEO: Warren J. Baker
CFO: Lawrence (Larry) Kelley
HR: Barbara Melvin
FYE: June 30
Type: School

Cal Poly students have more than one option, actually they have many. More formally known as California Polytechnic State University, the school offers more than 65 undergraduate degree programs, almost 30 master's programs, and one doctoral program. Founded in 1901, it offers courses in agriculture, architecture and environmental design, business, education, engineering, liberal arts, and science and mathematics. More than 19,000 students attend the university, which also is one of the largest land-holding schools in the California State University System. The not-for-profit Cal Poly Corporation runs the school's non-academic businesses such as bookstores, dining halls, and even a campus market.

CALIFORNIA PUBLIC EMPLOYEES' RETIREMENT SYSTEM

Lincoln Plaza, 400 Q St.
Sacramento, CA 95811
Phone: 916-795-3829
Fax: 916-795-4001
Web: www.calpers.ca.gov

CEO: Anne Stausboll
CFO: —
HR: Kathleen Hamilton
FYE: June 30
Type: Government-owned

California's public-sector retirees already have a place in the sun; CalPERS gives them the money to enjoy it. CalPERS is the California Public Employees' Retirement System, the largest public pension system in the US. It manages retirement and health plans for nearly 2 million beneficiaries (employees, retirees, and their dependents) from more than 2,500 government agencies and school districts. Even though the system's beneficiaries are current or former employees of the Golden State, CalPERS brings its influence to bear in all 50 states and beyond.

	Annual Growth	6/04	6/05	6/06	6/07	6/08
Assets ($ mil.)	8.6%	198,633.0	235,759.0	254,762.7	303,994.5	276,658.2
Employees	8.1%	1,687	1,924	1,924	2,154	2,300

CALIFORNIA STATE AUTOMOBILE ASSOCIATION INTER-INSURANCE BUREAU

100 Van Ness Ave
San Francisco, CA 94102
Phone: 415-565-2141
Fax: —
Web: www.csaa.com

CEO: James R. Pouliot
CFO: Michael Day
HR: —
FYE: December 31
Type: Association

Why let a name limit the scope of a business? California State Automobile Association Inter-Insurance Bureau doesn't just stick to California, autos, or even just insurance. Its sister organization, California State Automobile Association (CSAA), provides automotive, travel, and financial services to some 4.3 million members in Northern California, Nevada, and Utah and is the second-largest affiliate of AAA. The Inter-Insurance Bureau arm offers auto insurance (including for motorcycles), as well as homeowners and personal umbrella insurance to AAA members. Together the organizations operate as AAA Northern California, Nevada and Utah (AAA NCNU) and have over 100 offices in the region.

	Annual Growth	12/04	12/05	12/06	12/07	12/08
Est. sales ($ mil.)	—	—	—	—	—	438.4
Employees	—	—	—	—	—	6,500

CALIFORNIA STATE LOTTERY COMMISSION

600 N. 10th St.
Sacramento, CA 95811
Phone: 916-323-7095
Fax: 916-327-0489
Web: www.calottery.com

CEO: Joan M. Borucki
CFO: Mike Ota
HR: Barbara Krabbenhoft
FYE: June 30
Type: Government-owned

There's still a gold rush going on in the Golden State, but now you only need to scratch a ticket to find your fortune. The California State Lottery Commission operates several games of chance offering big prizes while collecting money for the state's education budget. Players can choose from scratch tickets and daily numbers games, as well as the twice-weekly SuperLOTTO jackpot game. In addition, the California State Lottery produces a weekly TV show called *The Big Spin* offering more ways for contestants to win prizes. California also participates in the multi-state Mega Millions game. Created in 1985, the lottery contributes at least 34% of its proceeds to cover public education costs.

CALIFORNIA STATE UNIVERSITY SYSTEM

401 Golden Shore St.
Long Beach, CA 90802
Phone: 562-951-4000
Fax: 562-951-4956
Web: www.calstate.edu

CEO: Charles B. Reed
CFO: Richard P. West
HR: Gail E. Brooks
FYE: June 30
Type: School

California State University (CSU) turns students into teachers. The university traces its roots to the state's teaching colleges and trains the majority of California's teachers and staff. CSU is neck-and-neck with the State University of New York (SUNY) as the nation's largest university system. And it's growing. CSU's enrollment has ballooned to about 450,000. Those students are spread out among CSU's 23 campuses in cities such as Bakersfield, Los Angeles, San Francisco, and San Jose. CSU primarily awards bachelor's and master's degrees in nearly 360 subject areas, leaving most higher levels of study to the University of California (UC) system.

An in-depth profile of this company is available to Hoover's Online members at hoovers.com.

309

CALIFORNIA STEEL INDUSTRIES, INC.

14000 San Bernardino Ave.
Fontana, CA 92335
Phone: 909-350-6200
Fax: 909-350-6398
Web: www.californiasteel.com

CEO: Vicente Wright
CFO: Brett Guge
HR: —
FYE: December 31
Type: Joint venture

California Steel Industries (CSI) doesn't use forensic evidence, but its work does involve a steel slab. The company uses steel slab produced by third parties to manufacture steel products such as hot-rolled and cold-rolled steel, galvanized coils and sheets, and electric resistance weld (ERW) pipe. Its customers include aftermarket automotive manufacturers, oil and gas producers, roofing makers, tubing manufacturers, and building suppliers. CSI serves the western region of the US. The company operates slitting, shearing, coating, and single-billing services for third parties. Japan's JFE Holdings and Brazilian iron ore miner Companhia Vale do Rio Doce (Vale) each own 50% of CSI.

	Annual Growth	12/04	12/05	12/06	12/07	12/08
Sales ($ mil.)	4.7%	1,257.0	1,234.4	1,358.8	1,283.0	1,510.6
Net income ($ mil.)	(40.9%)	109.3	43.4	109.0	(0.9)	13.3
Employees	(0.9%)	944	938	931	933	911

CALIFORNIA WATER SERVICE GROUP

NYSE: CWT

1720 N. 1st St.
San Jose, CA 95112
Phone: 408-367-8200
Fax: 408-367-8430
Web: www.calwatergroup.com

CEO: Peter C. Nelson
CFO: Martin A. (Marty) Kropelnicki
HR: Paul G. Ekstrom
FYE: December 31
Type: Public

A big fish in California's water industry pond, California Water Service Group is in the swim in three other states, as well. The company's main subsidiary, regulated utility California Water Service Company (Cal Water), keeps water flowing in for 460,000 customers in California. California Water Service Group's other water utility subsidiaries include Washington Water (15,800 customers), New Mexico Water (7,600 water and wastewater customers), and Hawaii Water (3,700 customers). The company's CWS Utility Services unit contracts to provide water system operation, meter reading, and billing services. All told, California Water Service Group provides services to about 2 million people.

	Annual Growth	12/05	12/06	12/07	12/08	12/09
Sales ($ mil.)	8.8%	320.7	334.7	367.1	410.3	449.4
Net income ($ mil.)	10.5%	27.2	25.6	31.2	39.8	40.6
Market value ($ mil.)	(0.9%)	795.3	840.5	770.2	965.9	766.0
Employees	4.8%	840	869	891	929	1,013

CALIPER LIFE SCIENCES, INC.

NASDAQ (GM): CALP

68 Elm St.
Hopkinton, MA 01748
Phone: 508-435-9500
Fax: 508-435-3439
Web: www.caliperls.com

CEO: E. Kevin Hrusovsky
CFO: Peter F. McAree
HR: Paula J. Cassidy
FYE: December 31
Type: Public

Caliper Life Sciences helps biological researchers avoid teeny-tiny spills with its microscopic sample-analysis technologies. The firm's research products include the LabChip miniaturized automation system for extracting and analyzing biological samples and the Sciclone line of liquid handling systems, which measure and filter liquids robotically. The company also makes IVIS imaging systems, which allow researchers to examine molecular interactions *in vivo* (or inside an organism), as well as related software and consumables. Caliper Life Sciences also provides contract research and development services. Customers include commercial drug discovery firms, as well as government and educational organizations.

	Annual Growth	12/05	12/06	12/07	12/08	12/09
Sales ($ mil.)	10.6%	87.0	107.9	140.7	134.1	130.4
Net income ($ mil.)	—	(14.5)	(28.9)	(24.1)	(68.3)	(8.2)
Market value ($ mil.)	(18.9%)	293.9	285.9	276.4	48.5	127.0
Employees	(2.5%)	443	550	543	489	401

CALIX, INC.

NYSE: CALX

1035 N. McDowell Blvd.
Petaluma, CA 94954
Phone: 707-766-3000
Fax: 707-766-3100
Web: www.calix.com

CEO: Carl Russo
CFO: Kelyn Brannon-Ahn
HR: —
FYE: December 31
Type: Public

With Calix's access equipment, your bandwidth runneth over. Calix (Latin for "cup") markets broadband access equipment for communications service providers. Its products increase the capacity of fiber-optic and copper lines to deliver next-generation telecommunications services, such as Internet protocol television (IPTV) and VoIP, as well as high-speed DSL Internet. The company also supplies Web-based network management software that handles provisioning, testing, and troubleshooting. Calix counts CenturyLink (38% of sales) among its top customers. The company gets most of its sales in the US. Founded in 1999, Calix completed an IPO in 2010.

	Annual Growth	12/05	12/06	12/07	12/08	12/09
Sales ($ mil.)	4.6%	—	203.6	193.8	250.5	232.9
Net income ($ mil.)	—	—	(19.5)	(24.9)	(12.9)	(22.4)
Employees	1.5%	—	—	—	401	407

CALL NOW, INC.

OTC: CLNWE

1 Retama Pkwy.
Selma, TX 78154
Phone: 210-651-7145
Fax: —
Web: www.retamapark.com

CEO: Thomas R. Johnson
CFO: Thomas R. Johnson
HR: Angela C. Cooper
FYE: December 31
Type: Public

Call Now operates the Retama Park horse racing facility in Selma, Texas, through its 80%-owned subsidiary, Retama Entertainment Group. The track, which opened in 1995, offers both live and simulcast thoroughbred racing. Call Now purchased rights to operate the racetrack a year later (the actual land and facility are owned by Retama Development Corporation, which is a division of the city of Selma). Retama Park's grandstand features a dining room and sports bar. Private club facilities also are on site.

	Annual Growth	12/05	12/06	12/07	12/08	12/09
Sales ($ mil.)	(1.0%)	5.2	5.3	4.9	5.5	5.0
Net income ($ mil.)	—	0.0	0.1	(0.4)	(0.3)	(0.4)
Market value ($ mil.)	(19.7%)	14.5	30.1	34.1	2.2	6.0
Employees	16.4%	210	210	145	385	385

CALLAWAY GOLF COMPANY

NYSE: ELY

2180 Rutherford Rd.
Carlsbad, CA 92008
Phone: 760-931-1771
Fax: 760-930-5015
Web: www.callawaygolf.com

CEO: George Fellows
CFO: Bradley J. (Brad) Holiday
HR: Christopher O. (Chris) Carroll
FYE: December 31
Type: Public

Big Bertha gets Callaway Golf swinging. With its flagship driver named after a WWI cannon, Callaway makes premium-priced golf clubs that are popular with amateurs and professionals alike. The company's other drivers, as well as its fairway woods, irons, wedges, hybrids, and putters, are sold under the Top-Flite, Callaway, Ben Hogan, and Odyssey names. It also makes Top-Flite and Callaway golf balls and uPro-branded GPS range finders. At the top of the golf market, Callaway designs apparel and shoes, and licenses its name to travel gear, watches, and other golf accessories. Its products are sold through its websites and by golf pro shops, sporting goods retailers, and mass merchants in more than 100 countries.

	Annual Growth	12/05	12/06	12/07	12/08	12/09
Sales ($ mil.)	(1.2%)	998.1	1,017.9	1,124.6	1,117.2	950.8
Net income ($ mil.)	—	13.3	23.3	54.6	66.2	(15.3)
Market value ($ mil.)	(14.1%)	891.2	927.9	1,122.3	598.2	485.5
Employees	(6.4%)	3,000	3,000	3,000	2,700	2,300

CALLIDUS SOFTWARE INC.

NASDAQ (GS): CALD

160 W. Santa Clara St., Ste. 1500
San Jose, CA 95113
Phone: 408-808-6400
Fax: 408-271-2662
Web: www.callidussoftware.com

CEO: Leslie J. Stretch
CFO: Ronald J. (Ron) Fior
HR: —
FYE: December 31
Type: Public

Callidus Software takes good care of office overachievers. The company provides enterprise incentive management (EIM) software for managing compensation and commission programs, including salaries, options, bonuses, and sales commissions. Callidus Software targets CFOs and other executives, who use its applications to align employee incentive programs with corporate business and profit objectives. Products include TrueComp, a sales and channel incentive management suite; TrueResolution, an application for streamlining and automating disputes over incentive compensation; and TrueInformation, a Web-based compensation reporting and analytics tool.

	Annual Growth	12/05	12/06	12/07	12/08	12/09
Sales ($ mil.)	7.2%	61.5	76.1	101.7	107.2	81.1
Net income ($ mil.)	—	(8.6)	(8.8)	(12.5)	(13.8)	(18.0)
Market value ($ mil.)	(7.9%)	130.9	196.4	161.2	93.2	94.2
Employees	(1.4%)	300	355	382	424	284

CALLISTO PHARMACEUTICALS, INC.

OTC: CLSP

420 Lexington Ave., Ste. 1609
New York, NY 10170
Phone: 212-297-0010
Fax: 212-297-0020
Web: www.callistopharma.com

CEO: Gary S. Jacob
CFO: Bernard F. Denoyer
HR: —
FYE: December 31
Type: Public

Callisto Pharmaceuticals is working on a constellation of medical therapies. Its drug candidates include treatments for gastrointestinal diseases, inflammatory conditions, and a variety of cancers. The company is developing certain candidates through licensing and development agreements with other drug and research organizations, such as Genzyme and the M.D. Anderson Cancer Center. Callisto conducts research and development operations through its subsidiaries, Synergy Pharmaceuticals and Callisto Research Labs.

	Annual Growth	12/05	12/06	12/07	12/08	12/09
Sales ($ mil.)	—	—	—	—	—	0.0
Net income ($ mil.)	—	—	—	—	—	(15.1)
Market value ($ mil.)	—	—	—	—	—	9.5
Employees	—	—	—	—	—	9

CALLON PETROLEUM COMPANY

NYSE: CPE

200 N. Canal St.
Natchez, MS 39120
Phone: 601-442-1601
Fax: 601-446-1410
Web: www.callon.com

CEO: Fred L. Callon
CFO: Bobby F. (Bob) Weatherly
HR: —
FYE: December 31
Type: Public

Callon Petroleum can call on new technologies to find old petroleum resources, employing computer-aided techniques such as enhanced 3-D surveys to explore and develop oil and gas properties. It also focuses on acquiring properties. The firm's holdings are in federal waters in the Gulf of Mexico, and onshore in Alabama, Louisiana, and Texas. In 2008 Callon's estimated proved reserves stood at 54.8 billion cu. ft. of natural gas equivalent. Natural gas accounts for the bulk of its daily production. The company has collaborated with Murphy Oil, BP, and others in its offshore exploration activities.

	Annual Growth	12/05	12/06	12/07	12/08	12/09
Sales ($ mil.)	0.1%	141.3	182.3	170.8	141.3	142.1
Net income ($ mil.)	19.4%	26.8	40.6	15.2	(438.9)	54.4
Market value ($ mil.)	(46.0%)	507.7	432.3	473.1	74.8	43.1
Employees	(4.6%)	87	86	85	87	72

CALLOWAY'S NURSERY, INC.

Pink Sheets: CLWY

4200 Airport Fwy., Ste. 200
Fort Worth, TX 76117
Phone: 817-222-1122
Fax: 817-302-0031
Web: www.calloways.com

CEO: James C. (Jim) Estill
CFO: Daniel G. (Dan) Reynolds
HR: David S. (Sam) Weger
FYE: December 31
Type: Public

Calloway's Nursery babies its customers with green-thumb know-how — about half of its employees are certified nursery professionals. The company owns and operates about 20 nurseries under the Calloway's name in the Dallas/Fort Worth area and San Antonio and under the Cornelius Nurseries banner in Houston. The company also sells plants online. Offerings include trees, shrubs, flowers, landscaping materials, soil, fertilizer, and Christmas goods. Christmas merchandise includes trees, poinsettias, wreaths, and garlands.

CALLWAVE, INC.

NASDAQ (GM): CALL

136 W. Canon Perdido St., Ste. A
Santa Barbara, CA 93101
Phone: 805-690-4000
Fax: 805-690-4241
Web: www.callwave.com

CEO: Jeffrey M. (Jeff) Cavins
CFO: Mark Stubbs
HR: —
FYE: June 30
Type: Public

CallWave, which considered itself a lifesaver to those drowning in incoming calls, is now wading into the rising stream of messages and e-mails as well. The company is a provider of communication management software and services that use VoIP and wireless technology. Its core business has been its so-called "call bridging" services (Alert, Messenger, and Connect) that aggregate calls and faxes from multiple sources to a single phone number. Other services include call screening, call forwarding, and voicemail for landline and Web. CallWave also offers software products such as WebMessenger, which redirects calls, instant messages, and e-mail to a single device or location.

	Annual Growth	6/04	6/05	6/06	6/07	*6/08
Sales ($ mil.)	(15.3%)	38.9	45.5	36.6	25.2	20.0
Net income ($ mil.)	—	11.5	11.6	(2.0)	(7.5)	(5.7)
Market value ($ mil.)	(19.6%)	—	105.9	77.3	76.9	55.1
Employees	(14.8%)	93	103	91	113	49

*Most recent year available

⊞ CAL-MAINE FOODS, INC.

NASDAQ (GM): CALM

3320 Woodrow Wilson Ave.
Jackson, MS 39209
Phone: 601-948-6813
Fax: 601-969-0905
Web: www.calmainefoods.com

CEO: Fred R. Adams Jr.
CFO: Timothy A. Dawson
HR: Alan Holland
FYE: May 31
Type: Public

Which comes first, the chicken or the egg? At Cal-Maine Foods, it's the egg, and the company's 27 million laying hens can attest to that. It is one of the largest fresh shell egg producers in the US. Cal-Maine sells its eggs to US food retailers. It produces value-added specialty eggs (organic, Omega-3 enhanced, free range) that it sells under the Egg-Land's Best and Farmhouse labels. The company controls all aspects of the business, from hatching chicks, making feed, housing hens, and distributing eggs. Its operations include two breeding facilities, two hatcheries, five distribution centers, 19 feed mills, 37 shell-egg production operations, 26 pullet-growing facilities, and 31 processing and packing sites.

	Annual Growth	5/05	5/06	5/07	5/08	5/09
Sales ($ mil.)	25.4%	375.3	477.6	598.1	915.9	928.8
Net income ($ mil.)	—	(10.4)	(1.0)	36.7	151.9	79.5
Market value ($ mil.)	39.2%	154.6	166.8	318.1	743.3	580.6
Employees	10.7%	1,400	1,650	1,600	1,800	2,100

⊞ An in-depth profile of this company is available to Hoover's Online members at hoovers.com.

311

CALPINE CORPORATION
NYSE: CPN

717 Texas Ave., Ste. 1000
Houston, TX 77002
Phone: 713-830-2000
Fax: 713-830-2001
Web: www.calpine.com

CEO: Jack A. Fusco
CFO: Zamir Rauf
HR: Laura D. Guthrie
FYE: December 31
Type: Public

Calpine may get hot, but it also knows how to blow off some steam. The independent power producer and marketer controls more than 24,800 MW of generating capacity through interests in about 80 primarily natural gas-fired power plants in 16 US states. Its fleet also includes 15 geothermal power plants in California. Calpine, the leading geothermal power producer in North America, owns 725 MW of capacity at the largest geothermal facility in the US (the Geysers in northern California), where electricity is produced from natural steam. The company's California and Texas operations account for the great majority of its business.

	Annual Growth	12/05	12/06	12/07	12/08	12/09
Sales ($ mil.)	(10.2%)	10,112.7	6,705.8	7,970.0	9,937.0	6,564.0
Net income ($ mil.)	—	(9,939.2)	(1,765.4)	2,693.0	10.0	145.0
Market value ($ mil.)	51.1%	—	—	—	3,234.0	4,886.6
Employees	(11.0%)	3,265	2,306	2,080	2,049	2,046

CALSONICKANSEI NORTH AMERICA, INC.

1 Calsonic Way
Shelbyville, TN 37160
Phone: 931-684-4490
Fax: 931-684-2724
Web: www.calsonic.com

CEO: Kiyoto Shinohara
CFO: Kiyoto Shinohara
HR: —
FYE: March 31
Type: Subsidiary

CalsonicKansei North America's business tends to run hot and cold — which is a good thing. The Nissan-affiliated company makes car air conditioning and heating systems, exhaust systems, radiators, cooling fans, and other related automotive components. The company also offers services including engineering, testing, and development, as well as testing labs. CalsonicKansei North America is a wholly owned subsidiary of Japan's Calsonic Kansei Corporation (which itself is about 40% controlled by Nissan Motor Co.). The company began operations in 1976 at a plant in Irvine, California. Today CalsonicKansei has about 10 factories in Kentucky, Michigan, and Tennessee, as well as in Mexico.

	Annual Growth	3/04	3/05	3/06	3/07	3/08
Est. sales ($ mil.)	—	—	—	—	—	127.3
Employees	—	—	—	—	—	1,435

CALTON, INC.
OTC: CTON

2050 40th Ave., Ste. 1
Vero Beach, FL 32960
Phone: 772-794-1414
Fax: 772-794-2828
Web: www.caltoninc.com

CEO: Anthony J. Caldarone
CFO: —
HR: —
FYE: November 30
Type: Public

Calton develops residential communities and builds single-family residences through its Homes by Calton subsidiary. Active in coastal Florida's Vero Beach, the company offers some 15 floor plans for homes ranging in price from $425,000 to $775,000 and in size from 1,900 to 3,600 sq. ft. It also acts as a contractor for the construction of custom homes. The company delivers about 10 homes annually. Calton operates its own sales office within its development community. The company formed PrivilegeONE Networks subsidiary to develop a loyalty and co-branded credit card, but that segment has yet to begin actively operating.

CALUMET SPECIALTY PRODUCTS PARTNERS
NASDAQ (GS): CLMT

2780 Waterfront Parkway East Dr., Ste. 200
Indianapolis, IN 46214
Phone: 317-328-5660
Fax: 317-328-5668
Web: www.calumetlubricants.com

CEO: F. William Grube
CFO: R. Patrick Murray II
HR: −
FYE: December 31
Type: Public

It's two-faced, but there's no calumny involved at Calumet Specialty Products Partners, L.P. The specialty hydrocarbon producer operates in two business segments — specialty products and fuel products. The specialty products unit processes crude oil into lubricating oils, solvents, waxes, and other petroleum products. It sells these items primarily to industrial customers who use them in the manufacture of basic automotive, consumer, and industrial goods. The fuel products unit processes crude oil into unleaded gasoline, diesel fuel, and jet fuel. Calumet Specialty Products Partners also produces asphalt. The company is majority owned by the families of chairman Fred Fehsenfeld and CEO William Grube.

	Annual Growth	12/05	12/06	12/07	12/08	12/09
Sales ($ mil.)	9.4%	1,289.1	1,641.0	1,637.8	2,489.0	1,846.6
Net income ($ mil.)	52.1%	11.3	93.9	82.9	44.4	60.5
Market value ($ mil.)	(22.9%)	—	889.4	822.6	194.6	407.2
Employees	15.4%	350	360	640	640	620

CALVIN B. TAYLOR BANKSHARES, INC.
OTC: TYCB

24 N. Main St.
Berlin, MD 21811
Phone: 410-641-1700
Fax: —
Web: www.taylorbank.com

CEO: Raymond M. Thompson
CFO: Jennifer G. Hawkins
HR: —
FYE: December 31
Type: Public

Calvin B. Taylor Bankshares *be* the holding company for Calvin B. Taylor Banking Company (aka Taylor Bank), which has about 10 branches in southeastern Maryland and another in Delaware. The bank offers standard commercial and retail services including checking and savings accounts, money market accounts, and credit cards. It also offers discount securities brokerage through an affiliation with correspondent bank M&T Securities. Real estate loans account for some 90% of the bank's lending portfolio, including residential and commercial mortgages. The bank is named after its founder, who opened a predecessor to Calvin B. Taylor Banking Company in 1890.

	Annual Growth	12/05	12/06	12/07	12/08	12/09
Assets ($ mil.)	0.3%	389.1	367.5	369.1	372.6	393.5
Net income ($ mil.)	(6.9%)	6.8	7.4	7.3	6.1	5.1
Market value ($ mil.)	(4.0%)	113.3	107.0	117.0	108.0	96.0
Employees	(2.2%)	96	98	92	94	88

CALVIN KLEIN, INC.

205 W. 39th St.
New York, NY 10018
Phone: 866-214-6694
Fax: —
Web: www.pvh.com/calvin_klein.aspx

CEO: Paul Thomas (Tom) Murry III
CFO: John Van Glahn
HR: —
FYE: January 31
Type: Subsidiary

Mark Wahlberg's underwear and Brooke Shields' implied lack thereof made everyone aware of *Calvins*. From its men's briefs to its *haute couture*, Calvin Klein is known for simply elegant clothes for men, women, and children, as well as fragrances and accessories. It makes its flagship ready-to-wear collection of women's clothing, but gets most of its revenue from licensing its name for items such as shoes, jeans, underwear, furnishings, hosiery, watches, bedding, tabletop products, and furniture. It owns or licenses namesake stores worldwide, as well. The firm was founded in 1968 by Barry Schwartz and Calvin Klein, who were its sole owners until clothing maker Phillips-Van Heusen (PVH) bought the company.

	Annual Growth	1/04	1/05	1/06	1/07	1/08
Est. sales ($ mil.)	—	—	—	—	—	52.2
Employees	—	—	—	—	—	700

CALYPTE BIOMEDICAL CORPORATION

OTC: CBMC

16290 SW Upper Boones Ferry Rd.
Portland, OR 97224
Phone: 503-726-2227
Fax: 503-601-6299
Web: www.calypte.com

CEO: Adel Karas
CFO: Adel Karas
HR: —
FYE: December 31
Type: Public

Fear of needles need not stop you from getting tested for HIV infection. Calypte Biomedical's line of HIV testing products includes several tests that use saliva rather than blood. These rapid-detection tests (sold under the Aware brand name) don't require sophisticated laboratory equipment, and Calypte hopes that such products will appeal to markets in developing countries where the incidence of HIV is high but health care infrastructure is lacking. The company has obtained regulatory approval for its Aware Rapid HIV tests in several foreign markets, including South Africa, India, and Russia. The company has also developed an Aware HIV blood test and an over-the-counter version of its oral test.

	Annual Growth	12/05	12/06	12/07	12/08	12/09
Sales ($ mil.)	25.7%	0.4	0.5	0.6	0.7	1.0
Net income ($ mil.)	—	(8.8)	(13.8)	(8.3)	(9.2)	(3.3)
Market value ($ mil.)	(52.7%)	73.8	32.3	48.4	3.2	3.7
Employees	(19.7%)	12	9	8	2	5

CAMBREX CORPORATION

NYSE: CBM

1 Meadowlands Plaza
East Rutherford, NJ 07073
Phone: 201-804-3000
Fax: 201-804-9852
Web: www.cambrex.com

CEO: Steven M. (Steve) Klosk
CFO: Gregory P. (Greg) Sargen
HR: —
FYE: December 31
Type: Public

Cambrex focuses on health. The company develops products for the human health care market that include active pharmaceutical ingredients (APIs) and intermediates for over-the-counter and prescription drugs. It also makes intermediates used in cosmetics and food additives. Cambrex focuses on developing drug delivery technologies and the manufacture of high-potency compounds and controlled substances. It maintains manufacturing and R&D facilities in Italy, Sweden, and the US. Expanding its biocatalysis platform (which uses natural catalysts to transform organic compounds) in 2010 Cambrex acquired Germany-based IEP GmbHa, a leading industrial biocatalysis company.

	Annual Growth	12/05	12/06	12/07	12/08	12/09
Sales ($ mil.)	(15.3%)	455.1	455.5	252.5	249.2	234.6
Net income ($ mil.)	—	(110.5)	(29.9)	209.2	7.9	10.4
Market value ($ mil.)	(26.2%)	550.6	666.5	245.8	135.5	163.7
Employees	(19.6%)	2,041	1,916	844	856	854

CAMBRIDGE BANCORP

OTC: CATC

Harvard Sq., 1336 Massachusetts Ave.
Cambridge, MA 02138
Phone: 617-876-5500
Fax: 617-441-1421
Web: www.cambridgetrust.com

CEO: Joseph V. (Joe) Roller II
CFO: Albert R. (Al) Rietheimer
HR: Noreen A. Briand
FYE: December 31
Type: Public

Cambridge Bancorp is the holding company for Cambridge Trust Company, a community bank serving Cambridge, Massachusetts, and the Greater Boston area from about ten locations. It offers standard retail products and services including checking and savings accounts, CDs, IRAs, and credit cards. Residential mortgages, including home equity loans, account for more than half of the company's loan portfolio; commercial real estate loans make up approximately one-third. The company also offers commercial, industrial, and consumer loans. Cambridge Trust Company was established in 1892.

	Annual Growth	12/04	12/05	12/06	12/07	*12/08
Assets ($ mil.)	6.1%	723.2	743.1	773.0	849.6	917.2
Net income ($ mil.)	4.0%	8.2	7.7	8.7	9.2	9.6
Market value ($ mil.)	(4.8%)	118.1	102.2	106.8	111.7	97.1
Employees	(23.5%)	183	188	—	—	—

*Most recent year available

THE CAMBRIDGE GROUP

227 W. Monroe St., Ste. 3200
Chicago, IL 60606
Phone: 312-425-3600
Fax: 312-425-3601
Web: www.thecambridgegroup.com

CEO: Rick Kash
CFO: —
HR: —
FYE: December 31
Type: Subsidiary

The Cambridge Group (not to be confused with the executive search firm of the same name) provides a variety of management consulting services that help clients develop product and marketing strategies based on customer demand. The group also helps customers develop effective brands, segment their customers by profitability, and align organizational structure to their new strategies. The Cambridge Group has clients in a range of industries, including consumer goods, financial services, insurance, manufacturing, media, and telecommunications. CEO Rick Kash started the firm in 1975. In 2009, Cambridge was acquired by The Nielsen Company, the world's #1 market research firm.

	Annual Growth	12/04	12/05	12/06	12/07	12/08
Est. sales ($ mil.)	—	—	—	—	—	2.0
Employees	—	—	—	—	—	30

CAMBRIDGE HEART, INC.

OTC: CAMH

1 Oak Park Dr.
Bedford, MA 01730
Phone: 781-271-1200
Fax: 781-275-8431
Web: www.cambridgeheart.com

CEO: Ali Haghighi-Mood
CFO: Vincenzo LiCausi
HR: Janet Miller
FYE: December 31
Type: Public

It's not just a heart — it's a *Cambridge* heart. Cambridge Heart makes noninvasive tools for diagnosing cardiac arrest and ventricular arrhythmia. Its CH 2000 system conducts cardiac stress tests and measures extremely low levels of T-wave alternans, an irregularity in an electrocardiogram indicating the risk of sudden cardiac death. Another product, the Heartwave II System, allows T-wave alternans screenings to be performed with any stress test system. The company's Microvolt T-Wave Alternans technology can detect the smallest heartbeat variation, measuring from one-millionth of a volt. The company markets its products in the US through direct sales and representatives; it also has international distributors.

	Annual Growth	12/05	12/06	12/07	12/08	12/09
Sales ($ mil.)	(6.6%)	4.2	7.4	10.1	4.2	3.2
Net income ($ mil.)	—	(2.6)	(10.6)	(9.2)	(10.0)	(7.3)
Market value ($ mil.)	(43.5%)	48.4	181.8	66.5	5.0	4.9
Employees	11.1%	21	38	47	44	32

CAMBRIDGE INTEGRATED SERVICES GROUP, INC.

340 Pemberwick Rd., 2nd Fl.
Greenwich, CT 06831
Phone: 800-662-1170
Fax: —
Web: www.cambridgeintegrated.com

CEO: David Andrews
CFO: —
HR: —
FYE: December 31
Type: Private

This Cambridge educates businesses on efficient work practices and smoothes the flow of business. Cambridge Integrated Services provides business process outsourcing (BPO), also known as "back office services" and IT services. Part of its BPO services includes third-party administration (TPA) of insurance operations including risk management, insurance claims processing services, and recovery services for insurance, financial services, and health care businesses. With facilities in India, the UK, and the US, the company is one of the largest BPO providers. Cambridge Integrated Services is a subsidiary of India-based Cambridge Solutions Ltd., which is itself a subsidiary of UK-based brokerage firm Xchanging.

An in-depth profile of this company is available to Hoover's Online members at hoovers.com.

313

CAMBRIDGE SOUNDWORKS, INC.

120 Water St.
Andover, MA 01845
Phone: 978-623-4400
Fax: 978-794-2903
Web: www.cambridgesoundworks.com

CEO: Robert S. (Rob) Mainiero
CFO: —
HR: —
FYE: June 30
Type: Subsidiary

Cambridge SoundWorks wants to be speaker of the house, the car, and the computer. The company is a leading manufacturer of speaker systems for consumer use, including floor speakers and bookshelf models. It also makes home theater speaker systems, outdoor speakers, and surround sound units. In addition to its own brand, Cambridge SoundWorks markets audio and video items from such manufacturers as Samsung, Sony, and Toshiba, as well as products made by its parent company, Creative Technology. Steep discounting of consumer electronics contributed to its decision to shut down its 30-store chain to focus on online and catalog sales in 2008.

CAMCO FINANCIAL CORPORATION

NASDAQ (GM): CAFI

6901 Glenn Hwy.
Cambridge, OH 43725
Phone: 740-435-2020
Fax: 740-435-2021
Web: www.camcofinancial.com

CEO: James E. Huston
CFO: James E. Brooks
HR: James W. (Jim) Chugg
FYE: December 31
Type: Public

Camco Financial tries to give customers a financial edge through its Advantage Bank subsidiary. The company operates about 30 branches, loan offices, and Camco Title Agency offices in Ohio, northern Kentucky, and western West Virginia. The bank primarily uses funds from deposits (checking, savings, and money market accounts; CDs; and IRAs) to originate residential mortgages, which make up about 60% of its loan portfolio; the bank also issues nonresidential real estate, consumer, and construction loans. In 2008 Ohio-based First Place Financial arranged to buy Camco Financial for some $97 million in cash and stock, but the two companies called off the deal due to deteriorating market conditions.

	Annual Growth	12/05	12/06	12/07	12/08	12/09
Assets ($ mil.)	(5.8%)	1,071.2	1,048.2	1,023.3	1,000.4	842.7
Net income ($ mil.)	—	8.8	5.9	4.5	(15.3)	(11.2)
Market value ($ mil.)	(39.0%)	102.7	91.9	79.6	22.9	14.3
Employees	(2.2%)	275	320	278	276	252

CAMDEN NATIONAL CORPORATION

NASDAQ (GS): CAC

2 Elm St.
Camden, ME 04843
Phone: 207-236-8821
Fax: 207-236-6256
Web: www.camdennational.com

CEO: Gregory A. (Greg) Dufour
CFO: Deborah A. Jordan
HR: Carolyn Crosby
FYE: December 31
Type: Public

Camden National Corporation is the holding company for Camden National Bank, which was founded in 1875 and once issued its own US currency. With about 40 branches throughout Maine, the bank provides such deposit products as checking and savings accounts, CDs, and IRAs. Business loans, including commercial mortgages, make up nearly half of the company's loan portfolio; residential mortgages account for approximately a third, and consumer and municipal loans constitute almost all of the balance. In 2008 Camden National bought bank holding company Union Bankshares, which expanded its presence along coastal portions of Maine.

	Annual Growth	12/05	12/06	12/07	12/08	12/09
Assets ($ mil.)	7.8%	1,653.3	1,769.9	1,716.8	2,341.5	2,235.4
Net income ($ mil.)	1.6%	21.4	20.3	20.3	15.3	22.8
Market value ($ mil.)	(0.1%)	251.8	353.1	217.4	206.6	250.4
Employees	5.3%	320	320	315	406	394

CAMDEN PROPERTY TRUST

NYSE: CPT

3 Greenway Plaza, Ste. 1300
Houston, TX 77046
Phone: 713-354-2500
Fax: 713-354-2700
Web: www.camdenliving.com

CEO: Richard J. Campo
CFO: Dennis M. Steen
HR: Cindy Scharringhausen
FYE: December 31
Type: Public

Camden Property Trust hums along by investing in, developing, and operating luxury and middle-market apartment complexes in about a dozen states. The real estate investment trust (REIT), has a portfolio made up of both wholly owned and joint-venture holdings. About one-quarter of Camden's holdings are in Texas. Its communities include approximately 185 urban and suburban properties with more than 63,000 apartment units. Most communities carry the Camden brand name. The company (which sports a hummingbird logo) reaches top markets such as Southeast Florida, Houston, Las Vegas, and the District of Columbia.

	Annual Growth	12/05	12/06	12/07	12/08	12/09
Sales ($ mil.)	(2.2%)	711.2	737.6	635.6	568.4	649.4
Net income ($ mil.)	—	199.1	232.8	148.5	71.0	(44.2)
Market value ($ mil.)	(7.5%)	3,813.9	4,862.9	3,170.6	2,063.7	2,790.0
Employees	(3.8%)	2,042	1,920	1,900	1,800	1,750

CAMELOT ENTERTAINMENT GROUP, INC.

OTC: CMLT

8001 Irvine Center Dr., Ste. 400
Irvine, CA 92618
Phone: 949-754-3030
Fax: 949-754-4309
Web: www.camelotfilms.com

CEO: Robert P. Atwell
CFO: George Jackson
HR: —
FYE: December 31
Type: Public

Camelot Entertainment Group is participating in the quest for the holy grail of movie studios: making low-budget films that sell mountains of tickets. The company plans to produce and distribute low-budget motion pictures with a business model focusing on pre-production, digital photography, profit participation, and stock incentives for its directors and writers. Previously a development stage company, Camelot has exited that phase; it got the ball rolling in 2010 with the purchase of the assets of Liberation Entertainment. Included in the deal is Liberation's film library of 750 titles.

	Annual Growth	12/05	12/06	12/07	12/08	12/09
Sales ($ mil.)	—	—	—	—	—	0.0
Net income ($ mil.)	—	—	—	—	—	(4.3)
Market value ($ mil.)	—	—	—	—	—	2.2
Employees	—	—	—	—	—	7

CAMERON INTERNATIONAL CORPORATION

NYSE: CAM

1333 West Loop South, Ste. 1700
Houston, TX 77027
Phone: 713-513-3300
Fax: 713-513-3456
Web: www.c-a-m.com

CEO: Jack B. Moore
CFO: Charles M. Sledge
HR: Joseph H. Mongrain
FYE: December 31
Type: Public

Cameron International (formerly Cooper Cameron) knows how to work under pressure. A leading manufacturer, provider, and servicer of oil and gas industry equipment, the company makes products that control pressure at oil and gas wells, including blowout preventers, chokes, controls, wellheads, and valves. It also makes integral and separable reciprocating engines and compressors used in oil and gas and power-generation applications. Cameron International sells its products, which are used for offshore, onshore, and subsea applications, under brand names such as Ajax, Cameron, Demco, Foster, Petreco, Retsco, and Willis.

	Annual Growth	12/05	12/06	12/07	12/08	12/09
Sales ($ mil.)	20.0%	2,517.8	3,742.9	4,666.4	5,848.9	5,223.2
Net income ($ mil.)	29.1%	171.1	317.8	500.9	593.7	475.5
Market value ($ mil.)	19.2%	5,055.0	6,477.4	11,753.4	5,006.1	10,207.6
Employees	10.4%	12,200	12,400	15,400	17,100	18,100

CAMINOSOFT CORP.

Pink Sheets: CMSF

600 Hampshire Rd., Ste. 105	CEO: Stephen Crosson
Westlake Village, CA 91361	CFO: Stephen Crosson
Phone: 805-370-3100	HR: —
Fax: 805-370-3200	FYE: September 30
Web: www.caminosoft.com	Type: Public

CaminoSoft helps customers navigate the road to manageable data storage. The company markets the Managed Server HSM line of computer data storage management software. Designed for use with Novell and Microsoft-based systems, its applications automate storage and file managment. CaminoSoft sells through distributors, OEMs, resellers, and systems integrators; its target markets include architectural and engineering services, banks and financial services, government agencies, health care providers, legal services, and schools. Funds associated with RENN Capital Group collectively hold a majority stake in the company.

	Annual Growth	9/05	9/06	9/07	9/08	9/09
Sales ($ mil.)	—	2.6	1.8	2.1	1.5	0.0
Net income ($ mil.)	—	(0.8)	(1.7)	(0.7)	(0.2)	0.1
Market value ($ mil.)	(64.4%)	185.7	47.7	23.0	14.1	3.0
Employees	(30.7%)	18	11	7	6	—

CAMOZZI PNEUMATICS, INC.

2160 Redbud Blvd., Ste. 101	CEO: David (Dave) Schmidt
McKinney, TX 75069	CFO: Cathy Muller
Phone: 972-548-8885	HR: Cindy Tucker
Fax: 972-548-2110	FYE: December 31
Web: www.camozzi-usa.com	Type: Subsidiary

Other than T.S. Eliot's un-corseted woman, who else would dare give promises of pneumatic bliss? Camozzi Pneumatics would. The company manufactures and assembles directional air control valves, from automatic and manually operated valves to solenoid ones, as well as a series of air cylinders and linear actuators. Directly and through authorized representatives, the company also drives wholesale distribution of its lineup accompanied by various fittings, tubing, and filter regulator lubricator (FRL) units. Camozzi is particularly known among North American automation and mechanic industries for its super rapid push-in fittings. Established in 1986, Camozzi operates as the US subsidiary of Italy's Camozzi Group.

CAMP DRESSER & MCKEE INC.

1 Cambridge Place, 50 Hampshire St.	CEO: Richard D. Fox
Cambridge, MA 02139	CFO: —
Phone: 617-452-6000	HR: —
Fax: 617-452-8000	FYE: December 31
Web: www.cdm.com	Type: Private

Camp Dresser & McKee does not tell you what not to wear, but it has fashioned a business out of providing engineering, consulting, construction, and operations services. The company, doing business as CDM, provides services for public and private entities worldwide. Founded in 1947 by engineers Thomas Camp, Herman Dresser, and Jack McKee, CDM has expanded from its original role in water-treatment technologies to provide services in environmental management, transportation development, and facilities design. CDM specializes in environmental management, water treatment and supply, energy, wastewater treatment, and hazardous waste markets. The employee-owned company operates more than 100 offices around the world.

	Annual Growth	12/04	12/05	12/06	12/07	12/08
Est. sales ($ mil.)	—	—	—	—	—	231.9
Employees	—	—	—	—	—	4,000

THE CAMPBELL GROUP

5664 Prairie Creek Dr. SE	CEO: Edward M. (Ed) Schinnerer Jr.
Caledonia, MI 49316	CFO: Christopher (Chris) Diepenhorst
Phone: 616-541-1600	HR: Sally Williams
Fax: 800-847-3129	FYE: December 31
Web: www.campbellagency.com	Type: Private

This company isn't represented by a famous soup can, but it possesses a can-do attitude when it comes to insurance. The Campbell Group is an independent insurance brokerage that offers property/casualty, life, and health policies to individuals and businesses nationwide. Its products include automobile, homeowners, general and professional liability, surety bonds, and workers' compensation coverage. It provides specialty programs for the construction, hospitality, and grocery industries; it also offers human resources outsourcing. The group also provides financial advice to consumers and business of all sizes on estate planning, payroll issues, and retirement plans.

	Annual Growth	12/04	12/05	12/06	12/07	12/08
Est. sales ($ mil.)	—	—	—	—	—	7.1
Employees	—	—	—	—	—	90

CAMPBELL HAUSFELD

100 Production Dr.	CEO: Hilarie Meyer
Harrison, OH 45030	CFO: Dave Kohlayer
Phone: 513-367-4811	HR: —
Fax: 513-367-3176	FYE: December 31
Web: www.chpower.com	Type: Subsidiary

While elbow grease will get the job done, Campbell Hausfeld can pour on the pressure! A power-tool maker, Campbell Hausfeld manufactures as well as exports air compressors, pneumatic tools (hammers, drills and screwdrivers, and sanders), nailers and staplers, paint sprayers, pressure washers (detergents to garden hose attachments), and welders. Its tools are geared to both the professional and DIY markets worldwide. Founded in 1836, the company sells its lineup directly through its Ohio-based headquarters, or from manufacturing and distribution sites in Kentucky and Tennessee, and through such retailers as CARQUEST, Lowe's, Tractor Supply, and Wal-Mart. Campbell Hausfeld is a subsidiary of Scott Fetzer Co.

CAMPBELL MITHUN, INC.

222 S. 9th St.	CEO: Steve Wehrenberg
Minneapolis, MN 55402	CFO: Steve Arndt
Phone: 612-347-1000	HR: Debbie Fischer
Fax: 612-347-1515	FYE: December 31
Web: www.campbellmithun.com	Type: Subsidiary

This company brings a little Madison Avenue savvy to the Midwest. Campbell Mithun is one of the leading advertising agencies in the US, offering creative development and campaign services for both print and broadcast marketing efforts, especially for clients in such industries as food, health care, and consumer products. It also provides insight into youth marketing through its Boing consultancy, as well as general brand marketing services. In addition, its Compass Point Media unit offers media planning and buying for spot TV, print, and radio time. Campbell Mithun is part of global advertising and marketing services conglomerate Interpublic Group.

CAMPBELL SOUP COMPANY

NYSE: CPB

1 Campbell Place
Camden, NJ 08103
Phone: 856-342-4800
Fax: 856-342-3878
Web: www.campbellsoup.com

CEO: Douglas R. Conant
CFO: B. Craig Owens
HR: Nancy A. Reardon
FYE: July 31
Type: Public

Soup means *M'm! M'm! Money!* for Campbell Soup. The company is the world's biggest soup maker; in the US its most popular selections are chicken noodle, tomato, and cream of mushroom. Campbell also makes meal kits, Franco-American canned pasta, Pace picante sauce, V8 beverages, and Pepperidge Farm baked goods (yes, it makes the Goldfish crackers you hide in your desk at work). Its Australian division produces snack foods and that Aussie favorite, Arnott's biscuits. The company has manufacturing facilities located throughout the world. In addition to North America, its principal markets are France, Germany, Belgium, and Australia; in all, Campbell's products are sold in more than 120 countries.

	Annual Growth	7/05	7/06	7/07	7/08	7/09
Sales ($ mil.)	0.1%	7,548.0	7,343.0	7,867.0	7,998.0	7,586.0
Net income ($ mil.)	1.0%	707.0	766.0	854.0	1,165.0	736.0
Market value ($ mil.)	0.1%	10,497.2	12,481.0	12,532.0	12,378.9	10,558.5
Employees	(6.0%)	24,000	24,000	22,500	19,400	18,700

CAMPING WORLD INC.

650 Three Springs Rd.
Bowling Green, KY 42104
Phone: 270-781-2718
Fax: 270-745-7192
Web: www.campingworld.com

CEO: Marcus A. Lemonis
CFO: —
HR: —
FYE: December 31
Type: Subsidiary

Camping World thinks the world of camping, especially if it's done in an RV. The company sells RV and camping accessories and supplies through its website, catalogs, and more than 75 stores in some 30 states. (About half its stores are at or next to FreedomRoads dealerships.) Camping World's 8,000-plus products are usually not found at general merchandise retailers. It also rents and sells new and used RVs and provides repair and service, including bodywork and repair of interior appliances, through its more than 500 service bays. Other services offered by Camping World, with help from its parent, include insurance and refinancing. Founded in 1966 by David Garvin, Camping World is owned by Affinity Group.

CANACCORD GENUITY INC.

99 High St.
Boston, MA 02110
Phone: 617-371-3900
Fax: —
Web: www.canaccordgenuity.com

CEO: Paul Reynolds
CFO: Don MacFayden
HR: —
FYE: March 31
Type: Subsidiary

Canaccord Genuity (formerly Canaccord Adams) provides equities research, sales, and trading services, and investment banking services such as securities underwriting, sales, trading, M&A advice, and industry research. Formed in 1969 through the merger of Weston W. Adams & Company and Harkness & Hill, the company specializes in the technology, metals, mining, life sciences, real estate, and financial services sectors. Canaccord Genuity also acts as a market maker for small- and mid-cap stocks in the US. Canaccord Capital (now Canaccord Financial) acquired Canaccord Adams in 2006. Four years later, it acquired M&A advisory firm Genuity Capital Markets and rebranded all of its capital markets businesses.

CANAL CAPITAL CORPORATION

OTC: COWP

490 Wheeler Rd., Ste. 185
Hauppauge, NY 11788
Phone: 631-234-0140
Fax: 631-234-0215

CEO: Michael E. Schultz
CFO: Reginald Schauder
HR: —
FYE: October 31
Type: Public

Just as a canal has two different sides, Canal Capital has two different businesses. The company develops, manages, leases, and sells commercial, industrial, and retail real estate in five Midwestern states: Iowa, Minnesota, Missouri, Nebraska, and South Dakota. It develops or sells vacant land and manages properties such as offices, lumber yards, car shops, and meat-packing facilities. Capital also operates two public livestock stockyards. The company's stockyard operations (in St. Joseph, Missouri, and Sioux Falls, South Dakota) provide exchange markets for a variety of livestock and supplies. Chairman Asher Edelman owns some 44% of Canal Capital.

	Annual Growth	10/05	10/06	10/07	10/08	10/09
Sales ($ mil.)	(8.8%)	6.5	4.4	3.6	4.4	4.5
Net income ($ mil.)	—	0.7	(0.3)	(0.9)	(0.1)	0.0
Market value ($ mil.)	(33.9%)	0.5	0.4	0.2	0.1	0.1
Employees	(20.5%)	75	75	75	50	30

CANAL CORPORATION

Pink Sheets: CSKEQ

1021 E. Cary St., 22nd Fl.
Richmond, VA 23219
Phone: 804-697-1000
Fax: 804-697-1199
Web: www.canalcorporation.com

CEO: Andrew J. Kohut
CFO: Joel K. Mostrom
HR: David (Dave) Winter
FYE: December 31
Type: Public

For Canal, the total package is all about specialty paperboard and plastics. The company's paperboard goods — folding cartons, tubes, leaflets, and labels — are designed, made, and marketed to manufacturers in alcoholic beverage, cosmetics, food, household goods, health care, and tobacco industries. Paperboard products account for more than 80% of sales. Canal's plastic goods include bottles, containers, and closures for end-use markets in agriculture, specialty chemicals, and food and beverages. Canal's predominant reach is in Europe, with growing interests in North America and Asia. The company and its US subsidiaries sought relief under Chapter 11 bankruptcy protection in late 2008.

CANAM STEEL CORPORATION

4010 Clay St.
Point of Rocks, MD 21777
Phone: 301-874-5141
Fax: 301-874-5685
Web: www.canam-steeljoists.ws

CEO: Samuel (Sam) Blatchford
CFO: Mary Gordon
HR: Ronald W. (Ron) Peppe II
FYE: December 31
Type: Subsidiary

Canam Steel Corporation manufactures galvanized siding, steel joists, structural steel components, and decking. The company has steel fabrication plants in Florida, Maryland, Missouri, and Washington. Its materials have found their way into Montreal's Pierre Trudeau International Airport, New York's Citi Field, and the Cincinnati Zoo. Canam Steel is a subsidiary of the Canadian steel fabricator Canam Group.

	Annual Growth	12/04	12/05	12/06	12/07	12/08
Est. sales ($ mil.)	—	—	—	—	—	166.0
Employees	—	—	—	—	—	768

CANANDAIGUA NATIONAL CORPORATION

OTC: CNND

72 S. Main St.	CEO: George W. Hamlin IV
Canandaigua, NY 14424	CFO: Lawrence A. (Larry) Heilbronner
Phone: 585-394-4260	HR: Mary Ann M. Ridley
Fax: 585-394-4001	FYE: December 31
Web: www.cnbank.com	Type: Public

Canandaigua National can undoubtedly stake its claim as the holding company for Canandaigua National Bank and Trust, which operates more than 20 branches in the Finger Lakes region of upstate New York. In addition to traditional deposits and loans, the bank also offers online brokerage, insurance, and wealth management services, including corporate retirement plan management and individual financial planning. Its loan portfolio is composed largely of commercial mortgages (nearly 40%), other business loans, and residential mortgages (about 20% each). Canandaigua National executives and directors collectively control about one-fourth of the company.

	Annual Growth	12/05	12/06	12/07	12/08	12/09
Assets ($ mil.)	9.9%	1,071.8	1,205.9	1,256.3	1,419.0	1,566.0
Net income ($ mil.)	7.9%	11.2	11.9	12.5	13.9	15.2
Market value ($ mil.)	2.4%	141.3	152.1	164.8	97.5	155.4
Employees	6.3%	360	378	386	430	459

CANBERRA INDUSTRIES, INC.

800 Research Pkwy.	CEO: Ahmed Bennour
Meriden, CT 06450	CFO: Jean-Paul Goslin
Phone: 203-238-2351	HR: Jerome Leparoux
Fax: 203-235-1347	FYE: December 31
Web: www.canberra.com	Type: Subsidiary

The threat of dirty bombs (radiological weapons) may trigger a high alert, but it translates into business for Canberra Industries, which makes radiation detection and analysis instrumentation. A unit of nuclear power generation, and electricity transmission and distribution giant AREVA, Canberra supplies integrated nuclear gamma and alpha spectroscopy devices to the nuclear power industry, as well as the US Department of Homeland Security. The high-tech firm also helps industries engaged in fissile material production, state and Federal radioactive material repositories, and environmental agencies with its nuclear watchdog devices. Canberra mans 12 production and engineering sites in Europe and North America.

CAN-CAL RESOURCES, LTD.

OTC: CCRE

2500 Vista Mar Dr.	CEO: G. Michael Hogan
Las Vegas, NV 89128	CFO: —
Phone: 702-243-1849	HR: —
Fax: 702-243-1869	FYE: December 31
Web: www.can-cal.com	Type: Public

Can Can-Cal strike it rich? The question hasn't been answered. Can-Cal Resources is an exploration-stage mining company that owns exploration-stage precious mineral and metal properties in the southwestern US. Its focus is currently on the Pisgah and Wikieup properties in California and Arizona, respectively. It also owns the Owl Canyon in California but is holding that property in reserve for exploration at a later date.

	Annual Growth	12/05	12/06	12/07	12/08	12/09
Sales ($ mil.)	—	—	—	—	—	0.0
Net income ($ mil.)	—	—	—	—	—	(0.6)
Market value ($ mil.)	—	—	—	—	—	2.4
Employees	—	—	—	—	—	1

C&D TECHNOLOGIES, INC.

NYSE: CHP

1400 Union Meeting Rd.	CEO: Jeffrey A. (Jeff) Graves
Blue Bell, PA 19422	CFO: Ian J. Harvie
Phone: 215-619-2700	HR: Margaret Sofio
Fax: 215-619-7899	FYE: January 31
Web: www.cdtechno.com	Type: Public

"Power to the people," a popular slogan often shouted in the 1960s, also works for the folks at C&D Technologies. The company makes reserve power systems and batteries, which can be found inside corporate data centers, factories, network operations centers, and nuclear power plants. Typical customers are companies in the cable, electric utility, and telecommunications industries. Emerson is behind about 13% of sales. C&D divested certain product lines to focus on the reserve power system market. Reserve power systems monitor electrical power usage and provide a source of backup power in the case of power failures and interruptions. C&D Technologies gets around three-quarters of its sales from US customers.

	Annual Growth	1/06	1/07	1/08	1/09	1/10
Sales ($ mil.)	(9.4%)	497.4	524.6	346.1	365.5	335.7
Net income ($ mil.)	—	(60.7)	(46.1)	(18.5)	(13.9)	(25.8)
Market value ($ mil.)	(35.0%)	218.8	142.4	156.1	78.6	39.0
Employees	(15.7%)	3,065	2,900	1,400	1,350	1,550

C&D ZODIAC, INC.

5701 Bolsa Ave.	CEO: Tom McFarland
Huntington Beach, CA 92647	CFO: John Maglione
Phone: 714-934-0000	HR: —
Fax: 714-934-0088	FYE: December 31
Web: zodiac.com	Type: Subsidiary

Without companies like C&D Zodiac, air passengers would tumble around in cavernous flying tubes. The company makes the storage bins that people insist on levering trunk-sized objects into, the seats from which your invariably large and bathroom-visiting seatmates invade your space, the overhead panels that pinlight your book and keep you cool(ish), the phone-booth-sized lavatories, the oft-maligned (and now seldom-used) galleys, the ceiling panels you pray to in rough weather, and the sidewalls you lean your head against when weary. Thank goodness C&D also makes upgrade and retrofit security kits for cockpit doors. The company is a unit of France-based Zodiac.

CANDELA CORPORATION

530 Boston Post Rd.	CEO: Gerard E. Puorro
Wayland, MA 01778	CFO: Robert E. (Bob) Quinn
Phone: 508-358-7400	HR: —
Fax: 508-358-5602	FYE: June 30
Web: www.candelalaser.com	Type: Subsidiary

Medical laser maker Candela has the answer to those pesky alcohol-induced tattoos. The firm offers laser systems used for tattoo removal, treatment of dermal abnormalities (birthmarks), and other aesthetic and cosmetic procedures. Products include AlexTrivantage to remove lesions and tattoos; Vbeam for vascular lesions and leg and facial veins; and Smoothbeam, for treatment of acne and acne scarring. Candela sells to cosmetic and surgical markets through a direct sales force and distributors in the US and abroad. Rival aesthetic laser-maker Syneron Medical acquired Candela in a 2010 deal worth about $65 million.

	Annual Growth	6/05	6/06	6/07	6/08	6/09
Sales ($ mil.)	(1.5%)	123.9	149.5	148.6	148.2	116.6
Net income ($ mil.)	—	7.3	14.9	6.3	(9.1)	(29.2)
Employees	3.9%	312	334	386	144	363

An in-depth profile of this company is available to Hoover's Online members at hoovers.com.

C&F FINANCIAL CORPORATION

NASDAQ (GS): CFFI

802 Main St.
West Point, VA 23181
Phone: 804-843-7001
Fax: 804-843-3017
Web: www.cffc.com

CEO: Larry G. Dillon
CFO: Thomas F. Cherry
HR: —
FYE: December 31
Type: Public

C&F Financial Corporation is the holding company for C&F Bank (aka Citizens and Farmers Bank), which operates about 20 branches in eastern Virginia. The bank targets individuals and local businesses, offering such products and services as checking and savings accounts, CDs, credit cards, and trust services. Commercial, industrial, and agricultural loans account for the largest portion of the company's loan portfolio (about 40%), which also includes residential mortgages, consumer auto loans, and consumer and construction loans.

	Annual Growth	12/05	12/06	12/07	12/08	12/09
Assets ($ mil.)	7.2%	672.0	734.5	785.6	855.7	888.4
Net income ($ mil.)	(17.4%)	11.8	12.1	8.5	4.2	5.5
Market value ($ mil.)	(15.6%)	115.3	122.6	93.3	48.6	58.6
Employees	2.5%	461	501	512	497	509

C&H DISTRIBUTORS, LLC

770 S. 70th St.
Milwaukee, WI 53214
Phone: 414-443-1700
Fax: 800-336-1331
Web: www.chdist.com

CEO: Dave McKeon
CFO: Dan Paruzynski
HR: Karen M. Wagner
FYE: December 31
Type: Subsidiary

C&H Distributors' cup runneth over with commercial, institutional, and industrial equipment and supplies. C&H offers more than 40,000 items, ranging from packaging supplies, office equipment, and cabinets to storage bins, dock equipment, and janitorial supplies. The company, which is a subsidiary of Germany-based TAKKT AG (a division of Franz Haniel & Cie), operates throughout North America via four regional distribution centers. It distributes products in Europe and Asia through its German affiliate Kaiser + Kraft. C&H was founded by Charles Clark and Otto Henke in 1937 as electrical wiring business C&H Electric Company.

	Annual Growth	12/04	12/05	12/06	12/07	12/08
Est. sales ($ mil.)	—	—	—	—	—	158.0
Employees	—	—	—	—	—	353

C&S WHOLESALE GROCERS, INC.

7 Corporate Dr.
Keene, NH 03431
Phone: 603-354-7000
Fax: 603-354-4690
Web: www.cswg.com

CEO: Richard B. (Rick) Cohen
CFO: —
HR: Bruce Johnson
FYE: September 30
Type: Private

C&S Wholesale Grocers is at the bottom of the food chain — and likes it that way. The company is the second-largest wholesale grocery distributor in the US (behind SUPERVALU), supplying goods to some 4,600 independent supermarkets, major supermarket chains (including Safeway), mass marketers, and wholesale clubs. Serving 12 states, it distributes more than 95,000 food and non-food items from its more than 50 distribution centers. C&S Wholesale also operates dozens of grocery stores and liquor outlets through its Southern Family Markets division. Israel Cohen started the family-owned company with Abraham Siegel in 1918.

	Annual Growth	9/04	9/05	9/06	9/07	9/08
Sales ($ mil.)	8.7%	13,600.0	15,200.0	18,000.0	19,500.0	19,000.0
Employees	13.6%	12,000	18,000	20,000	17,000	20,000

CANNON DESIGN

2170 Whitehaven Rd.
Grand Island, NY 14072
Phone: 716-773-6800
Fax: 716-773-5909
Web: www.cannondesign.com

CEO: Gary R. Miller
CFO: David M. Carlino
HR: Kathleen S. Cartus
FYE: December 31
Type: Private

Cannon Design fires off blueprints for clients in several industries. The architectural design and engineering company, which was founded in 1945, provides services that include planning, exterior and interior architectural design, engineering, graphic design, and project management. The firm specializes in health care and educational facility designs as well as sports facilities, science and technology sites, and commercial facilities. Clients include Brown University, US Department of Veterans Affairs, Merrill Lynch, Citibank, and Mount Sinai Medical Center. In 2009 Cannon Design acquired Chicago-based O'Donnell Wicklund Pigozzi & Peterson (OWP/P), which specializes in educational and health care projects.

	Annual Growth	12/04	12/05	12/06	12/07	12/08
Est. sales ($ mil.)	—	—	—	—	—	12.7
Employees	—	—	—	—	—	144

⊞ CANNONDALE BICYCLE CORPORATION

16 Trowbridge Dr.
Bethel, CT 06801
Phone: 203-749-7000
Fax: 203-748-4012
Web: www.cannondale.com

CEO: Robert P. (Bob) Baird Jr.
CFO: —
HR: —
FYE: June 30
Type: Subsidiary

Cannondale's lightweight products are heavyweights in the high-performance bicycle market. The company is a leading maker of mountain, road racing, multisport, recreational, and specialty bicycles — most of them with aluminum frames. Cannondale also manufactures bicycle-related items, such as apparel, accessories, and suspension forks. The bicycle maker and marketer peddles some 80 bike models through specialty bike retailers in about 70 countries. It also co-sponsors bike-racing teams to promote its products. Cannondale boasts offices in Canada, Switzerland, Holland, Japan, and Australia. Dorel Industries, juvenile products maker and owner of Pacific Cycle, acquired Cannondale in February 2008.

CANO PETROLEUM, INC.

NYSE Amex: CFW

Burnett Plaza, 801 Cherry St., Unit 25, Ste. 3200
Fort Worth, TX 76102
Phone: 817-698-0900
Fax: 817-698-0796
Web: www.canopetro.com

CEO: S. Jeffrey (Jeff) Johnson
CFO: Benjamin (Ben) Daitch
HR: Carolyn Carroll
FYE: June 30
Type: Public

Cano Petroleum is a "can-do" independent crude oil and natural gas production company. The company (named after 16th century Spanish explorer Juan Sebastian del Cano), focuses on buying undervalued mature properties (primarily in Texas and Oklahoma) that still have development potential. Cano employs enhanced oil recovery operations, including water and chemical flooding, infill drilling, and well recompilations, to increase production on these acquired properties. In 2009 the company reported estimated proved reserves of 49.1 million barrels of oil equivalent. In late 2009 Cano agreed to be acquired by fellow oil and gas explorer Resaca Exploitation.

	Annual Growth	6/05	6/06	6/07	6/08	6/09
Sales ($ mil.)	46.6%	5.5	18.4	28.4	44.7	25.4
Net income ($ mil.)	—	(3.0)	(1.8)	(0.8)	(17.5)	(0.2)
Market value ($ mil.)	(34.3%)	232.4	258.4	273.0	361.8	43.3
Employees	48.8%	24	95	114	79	—

An in-depth profile of this company is available to Hoover's Online members at hoovers.com. ⊞

CANON U.S.A., INC.

1 Canon Plaza
Lake Success, NY 11042
Phone: 516-328-5000
Fax: 516-328-5069
Web: www.usa.canon.com

CEO: Yoroku (Joe) Adachi
CFO: Kunihiko Tedo
HR: —
FYE: December 31
Type: Subsidiary

Canon U.S.A. is the US arm of Japanese printer and peripherals giant Canon. The company, which operates offices across North, South, and Central America and the Caribbean, specializes in office and consumer imaging equipment including copiers, printers, fax machines, and scanners. Other offerings include image filing systems, calculators, cameras and lenses, video cameras, semiconductor lithography equipment, and medical equipment such as eyecare cameras and radiography systems. Canon U.S.A. was founded in 1966.

CANON VIRGINIA, INC.

12000 Canon Blvd.
Newport News, VA 23606
Phone: 757-881-6000
Fax: —
Web: www.cvi.canon.com

CEO: Yusaku Azuma
CFO: Drew Haynes
HR: Rhonda S. Bunn
FYE: December 31
Type: Subsidiary

Canon Virginia provides contract manufacturing and parts fabrication services. The company assembles new and remanufactured office equipment, including copiers, toner and toner cartridges, as well as laser printers. Its manufacturing capabilities include plastic injection molding, metal fabrication, and metal stamping. In addition to assembly, it offers painting and packaging services, as well as reverse-logistics contracts. The unit also provides return product repair services. Canon Virginia is a subsidiary of Canon U.S.A., the US arm of Japanese imaging giant Canon. Canon Virginia was founded in 1985.

CANTEL MEDICAL CORP.   NYSE: CMN

150 Clove Rd., 9th Fl.
Little Falls, NJ 07424
Phone: 973-890-7220
Fax: 973-890-7270
Web: www.cantelmedical.com

CEO: Andrew A. Krakauer
CFO: Craig A. Sheldon
HR: —
FYE: July 31
Type: Public

Cantel Medical can tell you that cleanliness is second to nothing when it comes to medical and scientific equipment. Through its subsidiaries, the firm sells infection prevention and control products to hospitals, dentists, drugmakers, researchers, and others in the US and abroad in the field of health care. Its offerings include medical device reprocessing systems and disinfectants for dialyzers and endoscopes, water purification equipment, masks and bibs used in dental offices, specialty packaging of biological and pharmaceutical products, and therapeutic filtration systems. Chairman Charles Diker owns nearly 20% of the company.

	Annual Growth	7/05	7/06	7/07	7/08	7/09
Sales ($ mil.)	7.1%	197.4	192.2	219.0	249.4	260.0
Net income ($ mil.)	0.2%	15.5	23.7	8.4	8.7	15.6
Market value ($ mil.)	(3.0%)	294.6	242.0	243.6	157.0	260.5
Employees	1.4%	828	794	843	838	874

CANTERBURY PARK HOLDING CORPORATION   NASDAQ (GM): CPHC

1100 Canterbury Rd.
Shakopee, MN 55379
Phone: 952-445-7223
Fax: 952-496-6400
Web: www.canterburypark.com

CEO: Randall D. (Randy) Sampson
CFO: David C. (Dave) Hansen
HR: Mary Fleming
FYE: December 31
Type: Public

The tails of this Canterbury are connected to horses running around a track. Canterbury Park Holding, the operator of Canterbury Park racetrack in Shakopee, Minnesota, offers live pari-mutuel horse racing from May through September. The racetrack also offers year-round betting on simulcast races from racetracks such as Churchill Downs, Hollywood Park, and Belmont Park. When horses aren't dashing down the track, the company stages other events (snowmobile races, concerts, crafts shows, private parties) at Canterbury Park. It also offers gambling for card sharks at its on-site Card Club. Chairman Curtis Sampson owns more than 20% of the company.

	Annual Growth	12/05	12/06	12/07	12/08	12/09
Sales ($ mil.)	(8.0%)	55.2	55.8	52.9	46.0	39.6
Net income ($ mil.)	(57.6%)	3.1	3.1	2.6	0.4	0.1
Market value ($ mil.)	(15.0%)	55.9	55.2	48.4	23.8	29.2
Employees	(16.9%)	1,081	690	654	549	515

CANTEX, INC.

301 Commerce St., Ste. 2700
Fort Worth, TX 76102
Phone: 817-215-7000
Fax: 817-215-7001
Web: www.cantexinc.com

CEO: Don Wirtanen
CFO: Kevin Calcote
HR: Ray Gameson
FYE: March 31
Type: Subsidiary

Cantex's fitting solutions won't answer your bra sizing problems. But its lineup will offer options for a range of building construction, electrical, communications, and utility needs. Cantex manufactures nonmetallic, polyvinyl chloride (PVC), electrical conduit, pipes, fittings, communications and utility duct, and home switch and outlet boxes. In addition to conduit and fusible pipe, used to house electrical and telephone wire, Cantex makes couplers, elbows and sweeps (for safely repairing wire direction), receptacles, and switch covers, as well as the adhesives to join pipes and connectors. Operating as a subsidiary of Sumitomo, Cantex owns 10 US manufacturing plants and three distribution centers.

	Annual Growth	3/04	3/05	3/06	3/07	3/08
Est. sales ($ mil.)	—	—	—	—	—	275.0
Employees	—	—	—	—	—	700

CANTOR FITZGERALD, L.P.

110 E. 59th St.
New York, NY 10022
Phone: 212-938-5000
Fax: 212-829-5280
Web: www.cantor.com

CEO: Howard W. Lutnick
CFO: Douglas R. Barnard
HR: —
FYE: December 31
Type: Private

One of the largest traders of government securities, Cantor Fitzgerald also deals in global equities, fixed income products and derivatives, and provides brokerage services. The financial services company with 35 offices around the world serves more than 5,000 institutional clients. It operates an electronic US Treasury futures exchange, and also offers asset management and real estate services. Other, quirkier services include Cantor Index, Cantor Entertainment, which provides financial services to the entertainment industry, and Cantor Gaming, which provides technology services to the gaming industry. CantorCO2e, is active in the environmental and alternative energy markets.

An in-depth profile of this company is available to Hoover's Online members at hoovers.com.

CAPCOM USA, INC.

800 Concar Dr., Ste. 300
San Mateo, CA 94402
Phone: 650-350-6500
Fax: —
Web: www.capcom.com

CEO: Kenzo Tsujimoto
CFO: Kazuo Kano
HR: —
FYE: March 31
Type: Subsidiary

Capcom USA takes gaming very seriously. The company, a wholly owned subsidiary of Japan-based Capcom Co., Ltd., was established as the administrative arm for Capcom's US operations in 1985. It is best known for blockbuster video game franchises (including *Breath of Fire, Megaman, Resident Evil,* and *Street Fighter*) made for Sony, Nintendo, and Microsoft game consoles, as well as personal computers. Recent releases have included *Street Fighter IV, Monster Hunter,* and *Dark Void.* Parent company Capcom was founded in 1979 as a manufacturer and distributor of electronic game machines.

CAPE BANCORP, INC.
NASDAQ (GS): CBNJ

225 N. Main St.
Cape May Court House, NJ 08210
Phone: 609-465-5600
Fax: 609-465-9040
Web: www.capesb.com

CEO: Michael D. Devlin
CFO: Guy Hackney
HR: Fred A. Houston
FYE: December 31
Type: Public

Cape Bank is a permanent fixture serving the ebb and flow of New Jersey's touristy coastal and inland towns. Serving both commercial and residential customers, the bank provides traditional deposit options such as checking and savings accounts, as well as loan services like home equity, lines of credit, and mortgages (both commercial and one- to four-family). It operates about 20 locations and serves customers in Atlantic and Cape May counties. Cape Bancorp was formed in 2007 to be the holding company for Cape Bank and went public the following year; the bank's roots go back to the 1920s.

	Annual Growth	12/05	12/06	12/07	12/08	12/09
Assets ($ mil.)	16.9%	574.5	609.8	633.8	1,090.7	1,072.8
Net income ($ mil.)	—	4.4	5.0	3.4	(42.5)	(17.9)
Market value ($ mil.)	(27.4%)	—	—	—	123.2	89.5
Employees	12.7%	132	132	135	202	213

CAPE ENVIRONMENTAL MANAGEMENT INC.

2302 Parklake Dr., Ste. 200
Atlanta, GA 30345
Phone: 770-908-7200
Fax: 770-908-7219
Web: www.capeenv.com

CEO: Fernando J. Rios
CFO: Richard Villejo
HR: John Heppner
FYE: December 31
Type: Private

Cape Environmental Management offers a number of engineering and environmental services, including facility construction and demolition, remediation, and water and wastewater utility-related services. Clients include government agencies such as the US Air Force, and the US Army Corps of Engineers, and industrial clients in the petroleum, chemical, telecommunications, and transportation sectors. Specialty areas include engineering, scientific, construction, and industrial hygiene/safety. The company operates from more than a dozen offices, located across the US. It also has two offices in Iraq. Cape Environmental Management was founded in 1965 and acquired by its executive team in 1991.

	Annual Growth	12/04	12/05	12/06	12/07	12/08
Est. sales ($ mil.)	—	—	—	—	—	92.9
Employees	—	—	—	—	—	315

CAPELLA EDUCATION COMPANY
NASDAQ (GS): CPLA

Capella Tower, 225 S. 6th St., 9th Fl.
Minneapolis, MN 55402
Phone: 612-339-8650
Fax: 612-977-5060
Web: www.capellaeducation.com

CEO: J. Kevin Gilligan
CFO: Lois M. Martin
HR: Sally B. Chial
FYE: December 31
Type: Public

At Capella Education, the line to receive your sheepskin is *online*. The fast-growing company operates Capella University, an online university that offers more than 20 undergraduate and graduate degree programs. More than 26,000 students are enrolled in the school, which employs more than 1,000 faculty members (most of which are part-time employees, typically teaching one to three courses per semester). Capella's typical student is a working adult. Nearly half are pursuing master's degrees; more than a third are doctoral candidates. Some three-quarters of the company's revenues are derived from federal student financial aid programs.

	Annual Growth	12/05	12/06	12/07	12/08	12/09
Sales ($ mil.)	22.4%	149.2	179.9	226.2	272.3	334.6
Net income ($ mil.)	42.7%	10.3	13.4	22.8	28.8	42.7
Market value ($ mil.)	45.9%	—	406.7	1,097.8	985.4	1,262.8
Employees	(6.2%)	1,649	1,787	2,207	1,140	1,277

CAPGEMINI U.S. LLC

623 5th Ave., 33rd Fl.
New York, NY 10022
Phone: 212-314-8000
Fax: 212-314-8001
Web: www.us.capgemini.com

CEO: Lanny Cohen
CFO: Thierry Delaporte
HR: Scott McMillan
FYE: December 31
Type: Subsidiary

Vive la technologie! Capgemini U.S. oversees the North American operations of Paris-based consulting giant Cap Gemini. The subsidiary offers management and IT consulting services, systems integration, technology development design, and outsourcing services through offices in a dozen US states. Its consultants serve clients in a variety of industries, including automotive, energy and utilities, financial services, high-tech, manufacturing, and transportation. The unit was formed in 2000 after Cap Gemini acquired the consulting arm of accounting giant Ernst & Young. North America represents about one-fifth of Cap Gemini's annual sales.

CAPITAL BANK CORPORATION
NASDAQ (GS): CBKN

333 Fayetteville, Ste. 700
Raleigh, NC 27601
Phone: 919-645-6400
Fax: 919-645-6435
Web: www.capitalbank-nc.com

CEO: B. Grant Yarber
CFO: Michael R. Moore
HR: Teresa White
FYE: December 31
Type: Public

Capital Bank Corporation is the holding company for Capital Bank, which capitalizes on the bustling Research Triangle area it serves. Founded in 1997, the bank has about 30 offices in central and western North Carolina. It provides a range of consumer and commercial banking services, including savings, checking, and health savings accounts, as well as CDs, IRAs, and credit cards. Commercial real estate loans, made primarily to small and midsized businesses, make up more than 60% of the bank's loan portfolio; residential mortgages are around 20%. The bank also issues business and consumer loans. It offers investments and insurance through unaffiliated third-party provider Capital Investment Group.

	Annual Growth	12/05	12/06	12/07	12/08	12/09
Assets ($ mil.)	15.9%	960.9	1,422.4	1,517.6	1,654.2	1,734.7
Net income ($ mil.)	—	6.7	12.3	7.9	(55.7)	(6.8)
Market value ($ mil.)	(29.2%)	197.7	223.2	135.9	79.1	49.8
Employees	7.3%	295	332	337	392	391

CAPITAL BLUECROSS

2500 Elmerton Ave.
Harrisburg, PA 17177
Phone: 717-541-7000
Fax: 717-541-6915
Web: www.capbluecross.com

CEO: William (Bill) Lehr Jr.
CFO: Gary D. St. Hilaire
HR: Steve Krupinski
FYE: December 31
Type: Not-for-profit

If you dwell in the Lehigh Valley, Capital BlueCross could be your direct link to health care coverage. A licensee of the Blue Cross and Blue Shield Association, the company provides health insurance products to individuals and employer groups, with a total of more than 1 million members in central and eastern Pennsylvania. It offers traditional, PPO, HMO, and POS health care plans, as well as dental and vision coverage and Medicare Advantage plans. Capital BlueCross' network includes more than 11,000 health care providers and nearly 40 hospitals. The company also provides benefits administration services to self-funded customers through for-profit subsidiary Capital Administrative Services (dba NCAS Pennsylvania).

THE CAPITAL GROUP COMPANIES, INC.

333 S. Hope St., 53rd Fl.
Los Angeles, CA 90071
Phone: 213-486-9200
Fax: 213-486-9217
Web: www.capgroup.com

CEO: Philip de Toledo
CFO: Jim Brown
HR: —
FYE: June 30
Type: Private

If mutual fund firms were described like potential romantic partners in lonely hearts ads, The Capital Group Companies might be marriage material. The mutual fund firm, founded in 1931, is quiet (it doesn't advertise or grant many interviews), stable (it prides itself on consistency and believes investment decisions should not be taken lightly), and faithful (most of its investments and its executives are long-term). Subsidiary Capital Research and Management manages The American Funds, a family of more than 30 mutual funds that ranks among the largest groups of mutual funds by assets in the US. Other Capital Group units offer mutual funds in Canada and Europe, and investment trusts in Japan.

	Annual Growth	6/04	6/05	6/06	6/07	6/08
Est. sales ($ mil.)	8.0%	5,600.0	9,246.0	11,250.0	9,900.0	7,630.0
Employees	7.5%	6,000	8,000	9,000	9,000	8,000

CAPITAL CITY BANK GROUP, INC.

NASDAQ (GS): CCBG

217 N. Monroe St.
Tallahassee, FL 32301
Phone: 850-402-7000
Fax: 850-878-9150
Web: www.ccbg.com

CEO: William G. Smith Jr.
CFO: J. Kimbrough Davis
HR: Beth H. Corum
FYE: December 31
Type: Public

Capital City Bank Group is the holding company for Capital City Bank, which serves individuals and businesses from some 70 branches in northern Florida, plus portions of Alabama and Georgia. It offers checking, savings, and money market accounts; CDs; IRAs; Internet banking; and debit and credit cards. Commercial real estate mortgages account for about a third of its loan portfolio; residential real estate loans are about a quarter. The remainder of its loan portfolio is split between business, construction, home equity, and consumer loans. Capital City also performs data processing services for other financial institutions in its market area.

	Annual Growth	12/05	12/06	12/07	12/08	12/09
Assets ($ mil.)	0.8%	2,625.5	2,597.9	2,616.3	2,488.7	2,708.3
Net income ($ mil.)	—	30.3	33.3	29.7	15.2	(3.5)
Market value ($ mil.)	(20.3%)	585.1	602.3	481.5	464.8	236.2
Employees	(0.2%)	1,013	1,056	1,097	1,042	1,006

CAPITAL ONE AUTO FINANCE, INC.

3901 N. Dallas Pkwy.
Plano, TX 75093
Phone: 800-689-1789
Fax: 888-412-7543
Web: www.capitalone.com/autoloans

CEO: Sanjiv Yajnik
CFO: —
HR: —
FYE: December 31
Type: Subsidiary

What's in your garage? Capital One hopes it's a car financed through Capital One Auto Finance. A subsidiary of Capital One Financial, the company found its niche in the e-loan market. From its history of selling loans only through direct mail and auto dealerships, the company is one of the US's largest Internet auto lenders and one of the top independent auto lenders overall. An online decision usually comes within minutes, after which the buyer receives a "blank check" for up to the approved loan amount, thus providing the negotiating power of cash to let the borrower purchase or refinance a vehicle.

CAPITAL GOLD CORPORATION

NYSE Amex: CGC

76 Beaver St., 14th Fl.
New York, NY 10005
Phone: 212-344-2785
Fax: 212-344-4537
Web: www.capitalgoldcorp.com

CEO: John Brownlie
CFO: Christopher M. Chipman
HR: —
FYE: July 31
Type: Public

Capital Gold explores for gold on its mining concessions in the state of Sonora, Mexico. The Chanate deposit produces about 60,000 ounces of gold annually, though the company is looking to expand the mine's operations. It began production in 2007, yielding both silver and gold. AngloGold Ashanti had an option to buy a 51% stake in Chanate but in 2008 chose not to do so. Capital Gold also has an exploration-stage project elsewhere in Sonora. The following year Gammon Gold entered negotiations to buy Capital Gold for about $150 million, but the two companies called it off soon after. In 2010 Capital Gold turned buyer with an agreement to acquire Nayarit Gold, which also owns a Mexican minerals property.

	Annual Growth	7/05	7/06	7/07	7/08	7/09
Sales ($ mil.)	29.3%	—	—	—	33.1	42.8
Net income ($ mil.)	62.5%	—	—	—	6.4	10.4
Market value ($ mil.)	(6.2%)	—	—	—	125.1	117.4
Employees	14.5%	—	—	—	159	182

CAPITAL ONE FINANCIAL CORPORATION

NYSE: COF

1680 Capital One Dr.
McLean, VA 22102
Phone: 703-720-1000
Fax: 703-720-2306
Web: www.capitalone.com

CEO: Richard D. (Rich) Fairbank
CFO: Gary L. Perlin
HR: Jory A. Berson
FYE: December 31
Type: Public

Capital One isn't just concerned with what's in your wallet; it's interested in your bank account as well. The company is best known as one of the largest issuers of Visa and MasterCard credit cards in the US, but it also boasts a banking network of approximately 1,000 branches, mainly in Louisiana, New Jersey, New York, and Texas; it expanded its franchise into the Washington, DC, market in 2009 by buying Chevy Chase Bank for some $475 million in cash and stock. Capital One, which serves approximately 45 million customers in the US, Canada, and the UK, also has units that offer auto financing, write home loans, sell insurance, and manage assets for institutional and high-networth clients.

	Annual Growth	12/05	12/06	12/07	12/08	12/09
Assets ($ mil.)	17.6%	88,701.4	149,739.3	150,590.4	165,913.5	169,646.4
Net income ($ mil.)	(16.4%)	1,809.1	2,414.5	1,570.3	(46.0)	883.8
Market value ($ mil.)	(18.4%)	39,444.6	35,071.0	21,575.8	14,558.9	17,503.5
Employees	7.5%	21,000	31,800	17,800	25,800	28,000

CAPITAL PROPERTIES, INC.
NYSE Amex: CPI

100 Dexter Rd.
East Providence, RI 02914
Phone: 401-435-7171
Fax: 401-435-7179

CEO: Robert H. Eder
CFO: Barbara J. Dreyer
HR: —
FYE: December 31
Type: Public

Was it providence or clear foresight that led Capital Properties to buy land in what is now Capital Center, a downtown revitalization project in Providence, Rhode Island? The company owns and leases out about a dozen parcels of land totaling some 18 acres in the project area, making it Capital Center's largest landowner. Subsidiaries of Capital Properties own and operate a petroleum storage facility in East Providence used by Global Partners, and lease land to Lamar Advertising for roadside billboards in Rhode Island and Massachusetts. Chairman and CEO Robert Eder and his wife Linda together own a majority of Capital Properties.

	Annual Growth	12/05	12/06	12/07	12/08	12/09
Sales ($ mil.)	6.5%	5.2	5.7	6.6	6.8	6.7
Net income ($ mil.)	(4.7%)	1.7	1.3	1.4	1.6	1.4
Market value ($ mil.)	(25.8%)	184.5	158.7	156.4	42.9	55.9
Employees	2.4%	10	11	2	10	11

CAPITAL SENIOR LIVING CORPORATION
NYSE: CSU

14160 Dallas Pkwy., Ste. 300
Dallas, TX 75254
Phone: 972-770-5600
Fax: 972-770-5666
Web: www.capitalsenior.com

CEO: Lawrence A. Cohen
CFO: Ralph A. Beattie
HR: Colleen Landino
FYE: December 31
Type: Public

Capital Senior Living wants to capitalize on the growing numbers of seniors in the US. The company owns or manages about 65 senior residential properties in nearly two dozen states scattered across the country. Formed in 1990 to consolidate the operations of several partnerships that previously owned its facilities, the company provides independent living, assisted living, and skilled nursing to moderate- and upper-income seniors. Capital Senior Living also operates a home health care agency that manages the health care needs of residents at one of its communities. Specialized care units for treatment of Alzheimer's patients are also available. Private pay sources comprise about 95% of the company's revenue.

	Annual Growth	12/05	12/06	12/07	12/08	12/09
Sales ($ mil.)	16.2%	105.2	159.1	189.1	193.3	192.0
Net income ($ mil.)	—	(5.4)	(2.6)	4.4	3.7	2.8
Market value ($ mil.)	(16.5%)	279.5	287.6	268.4	80.5	135.7
Employees	6.4%	2,867	3,681	3,711	3,871	3,676

CAPITAL SOUTHWEST CORPORATION
NASDAQ (GM): CSWC

12900 Preston Rd., Ste. 700
Dallas, TX 75230
Phone: 972-233-8242
Fax: 972-233-7362
Web: www.capitalsouthwest.com

CEO: Gary L. Martin
CFO: Tracy L. Morris
HR: —
FYE: March 31
Type: Public

Just don't call them a private equity company. Capital Southwest owns significant stakes in around 20 companies, many of them in Texas. The firm offers early-stage, mezzanine, and recapitalization financing, as well as funding for management buyouts to companies involved in a variety of industries. It invests anywhere from $2 million to $20 million in target companies, which do not include troubled companies, startups, oil & gas exploration companies, or other less than stable ventures. Its 12 largest holdings, including Heelys, Alamo Group, Hologic, and Palm Harbor Homes, account for more than 90% of the value of its investment portfolio.

	Annual Growth	3/06	3/07	3/08	3/09	3/10
Sales ($ mil.)	(3.7%)	98.6	119.7	(135.9)	(134.5)	84.8
Net income ($ mil.)	(6.5%)	96.2	116.9	(139.0)	(138.3)	73.5
Market value ($ mil.)	(1.2%)	357.3	575.0	462.9	285.8	340.0
Employees	6.5%	7	7	7	9	9

CAPITAL TRUST, INC.
NYSE: CT

410 Park Ave., 14th Fl.
New York, NY 10022
Phone: 212-655-0220
Fax: 212-655-0044
Web: www.capitaltrust.com

CEO: Stephen D. Plavin
CFO: Geoffrey G. Jervis
HR: —
FYE: December 31
Type: Public

Investing in mortgages? That's a capital idea. Capital Trust is a self-managed real estate investment trust (REIT) that originates, underwrites, and invests in commercial real estate assets on its own behalf and for other investors. Its portfolio includes first mortgage and bridge loans, mezzanine loans, and collateralized mortgage-backed securities. Its CT Investment Management subsidiary manages five private equity funds and a separate account for third parties. Most Capital Trust's assets are related to US properties, but the REIT does make occasional investments in international instruments. Billionaire property mogul Samuel Zell has served as the company's chairman since 1997.

	Annual Growth	12/05	12/06	12/07	12/08	12/09
Sales ($ mil.)	7.4%	104.6	182.1	277.8	207.9	139.3
Net income ($ mil.)	—	44.1	54.1	84.4	(57.5)	(576.4)
Market value ($ mil.)	(54.4%)	641.3	1,093.7	671.3	78.8	27.8
Employees	0.0%	28	29	53	33	28

CAPITALSOURCE INC.
NYSE: CSE

4445 Willard Ave., 12th Fl.
Chevy Chase, MD 20815
Phone: 301-841-2700
Fax: 301-841-2340
Web: www.capitalsource.com

CEO: James J. (Jim) Pieczynski
CFO: Donald F. (Don) Cole
HR: —
FYE: December 31
Type: Public

CapitalSource is a capital source of capital for small- and middle-market businesses. Its CapitalSource Bank subsidiary, formed in 2008, offers mortgages, operating loans, and other financial options to small and midsized companies throughout the US as well as deposit services in California. CapitalSource is in the process of selling its property portfolio of more than 140 health-care facilities to Omega Healthcare Investors in order to focus on its commercial lending and banking activities. (It sold 82 health-care properties in 2009.) The company previously divested its portfolio of Fannie Mae and Freddie Mac-backed residential mortgage-related investments and securities.

	Annual Growth	12/05	12/06	12/07	12/08	12/09
Assets ($ mil.)	15.1%	6,987.1	15,210.6	18,040.3	18,414.9	12,246.9
Net income ($ mil.)	—	164.7	278.9	176.3	(222.6)	(869.0)
Market value ($ mil.)	(35.1%)	7,226.5	8,810.5	5,674.7	1,490.5	1,280.8
Employees	6.3%	520	548	562	716	665

CAPITOL BANCORP LTD.
NYSE: CBC

Capitol Bancorp Center, 200 Washington Sq. North
Lansing, MI 48933
Phone: 517-487-6555
Fax: 517-374-2576
Web: www.capitolbancorp.com

CEO: Joseph D. Reid
CFO: Lee W. Hendrickson
HR: Michelle Hack
FYE: December 31
Type: Public

Most companies raise money and keep it in banks; Capitol Bancorp raises banks. The holding company owns a network of several community banks in about a dozen states around the country. Many of the banks have only one location and are run locally. They target area business customers and high-net-worth individuals, with offerings such as checking and savings accounts, mortgages, consumer loans, and trust and investment services. Commercial real estate loans make up about 45% of Capitol Bancorp's total loan portfolio. Home loans are offered through its Amera Mortgage subsidiary. Another unit, Capitol Wealth, provides wealth management services.

	Annual Growth	12/05	12/06	12/07	12/08	12/09
Assets ($ mil.)	10.2%	3,475.7	4,065.8	4,901.8	5,654.8	5,131.9
Net income ($ mil.)	—	35.9	42.4	21.9	(28.6)	(195.2)
Market value ($ mil.)	(52.2%)	802.2	989.9	431.1	167.1	42.0
Employees	8.1%	1,100	1,354	1,611	1,580	1,500

CAPITOL FEDERAL FINANCIAL

NASDAQ (GS): CFFN

700 S. Kansas Ave.
Topeka, KS 66603
Phone: 785-235-1341
Fax: 785-231-6264
Web: www.capfed.com

CEO: John B. Dicus
CFO: Kent G. Townsend
HR: —
FYE: September 30
Type: Public

Dorothy and Toto may not be in Kansas anymore, but Capitol Federal Financial is. The holding company owns Capitol Federal Savings Bank, a thrift that serves metropolitan areas throughout the Sunflower State, including Kansas City, Emporia, Lawrence, Manhattan, Salina, Topeka, and Wichita. It has about 40 branches serving consumers and commercial customers by offering loans, CDs, and money market, checking, and savings accounts. The thrift mainly originates one- to four-family home mortgages (about 95% of its loan portfolio), but it also writes consumer, construction, and other real estate loans.

	Annual Growth	9/05	9/06	9/07	9/08	9/09
Assets ($ mil.)	(0.0%)	8,409.7	8,199.1	7,675.9	8,055.2	8,403.7
Net income ($ mil.)	0.5%	65.1	48.1	32.3	51.0	66.3
Market value ($ mil.)	(1.0%)	2,532.0	2,631.1	2,530.5	3,280.0	2,435.8
Employees	(0.4%)	761	738	758	740	749

CAPITOL RECORDS NASHVILLE

3322 West End Ave., 11th Fl.
Nashville, TN 37203
Phone: 615-269-2000
Fax: 615-269-2059
Web: www.capitolnashville.com

CEO: Mike Dungan
CFO: Tom Becci
HR: —
FYE: March 31
Type: Business segment

Music from this company can appeal to the urban cowboy and the "Okie From Muskogee." Capitol Records Nashville operates one of the top labels in country music, sporting a roster that includes new stars such as Keith Urban, Darius Rucker, and Trace Adkins, as well as such legends as Merle Haggard and Kenny Rogers. In addition to music, the label produces and distributes comedy albums by the likes of Roy D. Mercer and Tim Wilson. Formerly the country music imprint of venerable Capitol Records, Capitol Nashville now operates alongside its sister label as a division of UK-based music giant EMI Group.

CAPLEASE, INC.

NYSE: LSE

1065 Avenue of the Americas
New York, NY 10018
Phone: 212-217-6300
Fax: 212-217-6301
Web: www.caplease.com

CEO: Paul H. McDowell
CFO: Shawn P. Seale
HR: —
FYE: December 31
Type: Public

CapLease prefers the net lease. Its tenants take care of their own utilities, taxes, insurance, and maintenance, while the real estate investment trust (REIT) can focus on money matters, such as property and loan investments. CapLease typically invests in single-tenant commercial (office, retail, industrial) properties in the metropolitan areas of Chicago, Dallas, New York City, Philadelphia, and Washington, DC. Its portfolio includes more than 60 properties in 26 states. The US government and Nestle Holdings account for about 10% apiece of the company's total revenue. Hotchkis and Wiley Capital Management, LLC owns a 10% interest in CapLease.

	Annual Growth	12/05	12/06	12/07	12/08	12/09
Sales ($ mil.)	25.0%	73.1	124.8	172.2	185.1	178.2
Net income ($ mil.)	—	5.1	7.2	(2.3)	(21.8)	(14.0)
Market value ($ mil.)	(19.7%)	602.2	663.3	481.5	98.9	250.5
Employees	(2.5%)	21	21	22	20	19

CAPMARK FINANCIAL GROUP INC.

116 Welsh Rd.
Horsham, PA 19044
Phone: 215-328-4622
Fax: —
Web: www.capmark.com

CEO: Jay N. Levine
CFO: Frederick Arnold
HR: —
FYE: December 31
Type: Private

Capmark Financial originates, invests in, and services commercial real estate including office, retail, health care, hospitality, and multifamily properties. It also provides funds and asset management and invests in real estate and commercial mortgage-related assets for institutional and high-net-worth clients. Capmark Financial filed for Chapter 11 bankruptcy protection in 2009. It sold its North American origination and servicing operations to Berkadia Commercial Mortgage, a joint enterprise formed by Berkshire Hathaway and Leucadia for some $468 million, and is selling off other assets. The company now has some $3.5 billion in assets under management, about half of what it managed previously.

	Annual Growth	12/04	12/05	12/06	12/07	12/08
Assets ($ mil.)	(11.3%)	—	—	—	23,264.4	20,638.2
Net income ($ mil.)	—	—	—	—	280.4	(1,352.8)
Employees	—	—	—	—	—	1,900

CAPRIUS, INC.

OTC: CAPI

1 University Plaza, Ste. 400
Hackensack, NJ 07601
Phone: 201-342-0900
Fax: 201-342-0991
Web: www.caprius.com

CEO: Dwight Morgan
CFO: Jonathan Joels
HR: —
FYE: September 30
Type: Public

Caprius helps doctors take out the trash. The company owns a majority interest in MCM Environmental Technologies, which provides systems for disposal of medical waste. Its SteriMed system can crush, grind, shred, and mix all types of medical waste, including metal sharps and needles, plastic tubing and IV bags, and glass items. Once this process is complete, MCM's Steri-Cid chemical process disinfects the waste, which can then be discarded as regular waste at as little as 10% of the original volume. MCM manufactures the SteriMed system in Israel; the company distributes parts and supplies from facilities in Israel. Officers and directors, led by Austin W. Marxe and David M. Greenhouse, hold about 22% of Caprius.

CAPROCK COMMUNICATIONS, INC.

4400 S. Sam Houston Pkwy. East
Houston, TX 77048
Phone: 832-668-2300
Fax: 832-668-2388
Web: www.caprock.com

CEO: Peter Shaper
CFO: Hank M. Winfield
HR: —
FYE: December 31
Type: Private

CapRock Communications provides satellite communications services where others fear to tread. The company's network enables the secure transmission of voice, data, and video primarily for customers operating in remote locations or harsh environments such as offshore drilling platforms. Clients come from such industries as construction, maritime, military, mining, and energy exploration. The company's SeaAccess Communications service provides broadband networking to ships at sea. CapRock operates a global communications network in cooperation with other satellite fleet operators. The company agreed in mid-2010 to be acquired by Harris Corporation for about $525 million.

An in-depth profile of this company is available to Hoover's Online members at hoovers.com.

323

CAPSTEAD MORTGAGE CORPORATION

NYSE: CMO

8401 N. Central Expwy., Ste. 800
Dallas, TX 75225
Phone: 214-874-2323
Fax: 214-874-2398
Web: www.capstead.com

CEO: Andrew F. Jacobs
CFO: Phillip A. Reinsch
HR: —
FYE: December 31
Type: Public

Capstead Mortgage is holding steady in a turbulent real estate market. To stay the course, the self-managed real estate investment trust (REIT) makes leveraged investments in single-family residential adjustable-rate mortgages issued and backed by government agencies such as Fannie Mae, Freddie Mac, and Ginnie Mae; it occasionally makes limited investments in credit-sensitive commercial mortgage assets, as well. The REIT typically funds its investment activities through short-term borrowings or equity offerings. Capstead Mortgage was established in 1985.

	Annual Growth	12/05	12/06	12/07	12/08	12/09
Sales ($ mil.)	24.4%	131.4	245.8	314.7	400.7	314.6
Net income ($ mil.)	22.6%	57.2	3.8	24.7	125.9	129.3
Market value ($ mil.)	23.8%	407.4	582.0	924.8	755.1	957.1
Employees	7.5%	12	15	15	17	16

CAPSTONE TURBINE CORPORATION

NASDAQ (GM): CPST

21211 Nordhoff St.
Chatsworth, CA 91311
Phone: 818-734-5300
Fax: 818-734-5320
Web: www.microturbine.com

CEO: Darren R. Jamison
CFO: Edward I. (Ed) Reich
HR: Larry N. Colson
FYE: March 31
Type: Public

Capstone Turbine's theme song could be "My Generation." The company makes the Capstone MicroTurbine, a power-generating system that produces environmentally friendly electricity and heat. The microturbines, which can operate on a stand-alone basis or connected to the utility grid, run on a variety of liquid and gaseous fuels, such as natural gas, diesel, kerosene, propane, and flare gases from landfills and sewage plants. Capstone markets its microturbines for use in cogeneration (using both electricity and heat), resource recovery (burning oil and gas production by-products), backup power supply, and remote power applications. Customers located in the US constitute over one-third of sales.

	Annual Growth	3/05	3/06	3/07	3/08	3/09
Sales ($ mil.)	26.8%	17.0	24.1	21.0	31.3	43.9
Net income ($ mil.)	—	(39.4)	(47.1)	(36.7)	(36.1)	(41.7)
Market value ($ mil.)	(17.4%)	304.8	715.8	208.5	416.9	141.6
Employees	(1.5%)	225	243	195	216	212

CAPTAIN D'S, LLC

1717 Elm Hill Pike, Ste. A-1
Nashville, TN 37210
Phone: 615-391-5461
Fax: 615-231-2309
Web: www.captainds.com

CEO: David W. Head
CFO: Michael (Mike) Payne
HR: Anthony (Tony) Sorrells
FYE: October 31
Type: Private

This Captain sails the fast food seas. Captain D's operates Captain D's Seafood Kitchen, a leading quick-service seafood chain with about 540 company-owned and franchised locations in about two dozen states. The eateries feature a menu of fried and broiled fish, shrimp, and chicken, as well as french fries, hush puppies, and corn on the cob. Captain D's also serves fish and chicken sandwiches, salads, and menu items for kids. Most of the restaurants are located in such southern states as Georgia, Tennessee, and Alabama. Ray Danner started the business as Mr. D's in 1969. Private equity firm Sun Capital Partners acquired the chain in 2010.

	Annual Growth	10/04	10/05	10/06	10/07	10/08
Est. sales ($ mil.)	—	—	—	—	—	258.0
Employees	—	—	—	—	—	6,000

CARACO PHARMACEUTICAL LABORATORIES, LTD.

NYSE Amex: CPD

1150 Elijah McCoy Dr.
Detroit, MI 48202
Phone: 313-871-8400
Fax: 313-871-8314
Web: www.caraco.com

CEO: Jitendra N. Doshi
CFO: Mukul Rathi
HR: Tammy Bitterman
FYE: March 31
Type: Public

Caraco Pharmaceutical Laboratories is cooking up cheaper versions of prescription drugs in the Motor City. The Detroit-based drug company makes generic knock-offs of a wide variety of pharmaceuticals, producing about 60 prescription products in various strengths and dosages. Its product lineup includes treatments for high blood pressure, cancer, nervous system conditions, diabetes, allergies, and pain. Indian drugmaker Sun Pharmaceutical Industries owns about 75% of the firm and licenses US marketing rights to Caraco for more than two dozen drugs. Caraco markets its products throughout the US and Puerto Rico, selling primarily to pharmaceutical wholesalers.

	Annual Growth	12/04	*3/06	3/07	3/08	3/09
Sales ($ mil.)	53.8%	60.3	82.8	117.0	350.4	337.2
Net income ($ mil.)	—	(0.2)	(10.4)	26.9	35.4	20.5
Market value ($ mil.)	(22.1%)	373.3	508.2	476.1	701.7	137.6
Employees	36.7%	191	272	718	1,108	667

*Fiscal year change

CARAUSTAR INDUSTRIES, INC.

5000 Austell Powder Springs Rd., Ste. 300
Austell, GA 30106
Phone: 770-948-3101
Fax: 770-732-3401
Web: www.caraustar.com

CEO: Michael C. (Mike) Patton
CFO: Ronald J. Domanico
HR: Barry A. Smedstad
FYE: December 31
Type: Private

Caraustar Industries thinks outside the box in order to make new ones. The company is a major manufacturer of 100% recycled paperboard and converted paperboard products. It makes products from recovered fiber, which is derived from recycled paper. Caraustar has four business segments: paperboard, recovered fiber, tube and core, and folding carton. About half of its paperboard is used by its own converting facilities; the rest is sold to independent converters, as well as the textile, paper, metal, bookbinding, printing, and furniture industries. The company's carton and packaging products are used to box a variety of consumer goods. Caraustar emerged from Chapter 11 bankruptcy in 2009 as a private company.

	Annual Growth	12/04	12/05	12/06	12/07	12/08
Sales ($ mil.)	(6.2%)	1,060.3	862.4	989.9	854.2	819.7
Net income ($ mil.)	—	(4.0)	(103.4)	47.3	(24.5)	(98.7)
Employees	(13.4%)	5,700	5,440	4,190	3,570	3,200

CARBIZ INC.

OTC: CBZFF

7115 16th St. East
Sarasota, FL 34243
Phone: 941-952-9255
Fax: 941-953-3580
Web: www.carbiz.com

CEO: Carl Ritter
CFO: Stanton Heintz
HR: Jennifer Halloran
FYE: January 31
Type: Public

CarBiz operates one-stop shops for car buyers with poor credit. The company owns and operates a chain of "buy-here pay-here" used automobile dealerships. Catering primarily to buyers with poor credit histories, such dealerships finance vehicles with their own money. CarBiz's group of auto finance credit centers includes more than 25 locations in eight states. The company in 2009 acquired about $10 million in consumer loans from Star Financial Services, a California-based indirect lender.

	Annual Growth	1/05	1/06	1/07	1/08	1/09
Sales ($ mil.)	233.5%	—	—	3.2	8.2	35.6
Net income ($ mil.)	—	—	—	(4.8)	(14.2)	(19.4)
Market value ($ mil.)	(33.3%)	—	—	18.8	22.0	8.4
Employees	108.0%	—	—	37	165	160

CARBO CERAMICS INC.

NYSE: CRR

6565 MacArthur Blvd., Ste. 1050
Irving, TX 75039
Phone: 972-401-0090
Fax: 972-401-0705
Web: www.carboceramics.com

CEO: Gary A. Kolstad
CFO: Ernesto Bautista III
HR: —
FYE: December 31
Type: Public

CARBO Ceramics' proppants (tiny alumina-based ceramic beads) are a welcome release for natural gas and oil well operators. To increase well production, operators often pump fluids down wells at high pressure to create fractures in the hydrocarbon-bearing rock formation (hydraulic fracturing). Proppants are suspended in the fluid to fill the channels and "prop" up the fissures so that natural gas and oil may flow to the surface. The company's products compete against sand-based proppants. CARBO Ceramics also operates related software, consulting services, and geotechnical monitoring businesses. Chairman William Morris owns about 14% of CARBO Ceramics.

	Annual Growth	12/05	12/06	12/07	12/08	12/09
Sales ($ mil.)	7.9%	252.7	312.1	340.4	387.8	341.9
Net income ($ mil.)	3.2%	46.6	54.3	53.9	110.3	52.8
Market value ($ mil.)	4.8%	1,307.0	864.2	860.2	821.6	1,576.4
Employees	8.7%	530	630	759	648	741

CARDENAS MARKETS, INC.

1621 E. Francis St.
Ontario, CA 91761
Phone: 909-923-7426
Fax: 909-923-5976
Web: www.cardenasmarkets.com

CEO: Jesus Cardenas Sr.
CFO: Lupe Cardenas
HR: Cecilia Solis
FYE: December 31
Type: Private

Husband and wife team Jesus and Luz Cardenas took a gamble and ended up in hog heaven. The Cardenas family got its start as hog farmers in Corona, California, but in 1979 they sold off their farm and opened their first supermarket, primarily geared toward the Hispanic population in the region. Today, Cardenas Markets operates a chain of about 25 grocery stores in Southern California that cater to Hispanic shoppers, with a wide variety of products from Mexico and Central and South America. The stores feature extensive meat and produce departments, bakeries, and tortillerias. The company's newest store — and first outside of California — opened in Las Vegas, Nevada, in 2009.

	Annual Growth	12/04	12/05	12/06	12/07	12/08
Est. sales ($ mil.)	—	—	—	—	—	13.0
Employees	—	—	—	—	—	100

CARDIAC SCIENCE CORPORATION

NASDAQ (GM): CSCX

3303 Monte Villa Pkwy.
Bothell, WA 98021
Phone: 425-402-2000
Fax: 425-402-2001
Web: www.cardiacscience.com

CEO: David L. (Dave) Marver
CFO: Michael K. (Mike) Matysik
HR: Barbara J. Thompson
FYE: December 31
Type: Public

A heart can keep no secrets from Cardiac Science Corporation. The medical device company makes cardiovascular monitoring and therapeutic equipment, including defibrillators and stress test systems that analyze the heart's performance under stress. Its monitoring systems are used for extended surveillance and include telemetry devices for evaluation of the heart during rehabilitation exercise. In addition, Cardiac Science sells accessories such as lead wires and electrodes and provides product repair and technical support services. An in-house sales force handles sales in the US, Canada, China, parts of Europe, and the UK. Distributors sell the products in about 100 other countries.

	Annual Growth	12/05	12/06	12/07	12/08	12/09
Sales ($ mil.)	10.1%	106.7	155.4	182.1	206.2	156.8
Net income ($ mil.)	—	(1.2)	0.0	8.5	(98.4)	(77.0)
Market value ($ mil.)	(29.5%)	214.0	190.8	191.3	177.4	52.7
Employees	(3.4%)	709	697	738	618	617

CARDICA, INC.

NASDAQ (GM): CRDC

900 Saginaw Dr.
Redwood City, CA 94063
Phone: 650-364-9975
Fax: 650-364-3134
Web: www.cardica.com

CEO: Bernard A. Hausen
CFO: Robert Y. Newell IV
HR: —
FYE: June 30
Type: Public

Cardica wants to help surgeons treat patients with coronary heart disease. The company makes products, including the C-Port and PAS-Port systems, that are used in coronary artery bypass surgery. The automated systems connect blood vessels that restore blood flow beyond the closed sections of coronary arteries. Its products offer a less time-consuming and simpler alternative to hand-sewn suturing. Cardica markets its C-Port and PAS-Port systems in the US via direct sales and in the EU through distributors. Century Medical is the exclusive distributor of PAS-Port systems in Japan. The company has a co-development agreement with Cook for a vascular access closure device.

	Annual Growth	6/05	6/06	6/07	6/08	6/09
Sales ($ mil.)	47.4%	2.1	2.1	3.5	7.6	9.9
Net income ($ mil.)	—	(10.9)	(12.4)	(13.6)	(18.2)	(17.2)
Market value ($ mil.)	(43.5%)	—	189.8	146.3	203.0	34.3
Employees	3.2%	37	56	68	86	42

CARDIMA, INC.

OTC: CADM

47266 Benicia St.
Fremont, CA 94538
Phone: 510-354-0300
Fax: 510-657-4476
Web: www.cardima.com

CEO: John R. (Rob) Cheney
CFO: John R. (Rob) Cheney
HR: Pat Reid-Purt
FYE: December 31
Type: Public

They may not pick up your morning radio exercise program, but Cardima's products can still get your heart pumping. Cardima's micro-catheters diagnose life-threatening heart arrhythmia by locating or "mapping" its source. The company's products then restore normal heart rhythm by destroying the arrhythmia-causing tissue with radio frequency energy, a process called ablation. Cardima markets its products to electrophysiologists and heart surgeons directly and through distributors primarily in the US; most of the rest of its sales are made in Europe. Cardima's brand names include REVELATION, PATHFINDER, and TRACER.

	Annual Growth	12/05	12/06	12/07	12/08	12/09
Sales ($ mil.)	3.7%	1.9	1.5	1.2	1.5	2.2
Net income ($ mil.)	—	(8.3)	(9.5)	(42.6)	(13.7)	(13.0)
Market value ($ mil.)	22.4%	64.8	72.0	73.4	230.4	145.4
Employees	30.4%	28	37	40	77	81

CARDINAL BANKSHARES CORPORATION

OTC: CDBK

101 Jacksonville Cir.
Floyd, VA 24091
Phone: 540-745-4191
Fax: 540-745-4133
Web: www.bankoffloyd.com

CEO: Ronald Leon Moore
CFO: J. Alan Dickerson
HR: —
FYE: December 31
Type: Public

Cardinal Bankshares may not answer to the Pope, but it does pay attention to what its shareholders have to say. It is the holding company for The Bank of Floyd, which serves southwest Virginia's Floyd County and surrounding areas from about 10 locations. The bank offers standard retail products and services, including checking and savings accounts, CDs, IRAs, and credit cards. It uses funds from deposits to write loans, primarily real estate mortgages and loans. Bank subsidiary FBC has interests in two Virginia title insurance firms and an investment services company.

	Annual Growth	12/05	12/06	12/07	12/08	12/09
Assets ($ mil.)	5.1%	196.2	207.8	209.3	221.0	239.4
Net income ($ mil.)	(27.7%)	2.2	2.5	2.3	1.6	0.6
Market value ($ mil.)	(23.8%)	32.6	30.3	27.6	18.4	11.0
Employees	(0.5%)	48	43	83	89	47

An in-depth profile of this company is available to Hoover's Online members at hoovers.com.

CARDINAL FINANCIAL CORPORATION

NASDAQ (GS): CFNL

8270 Greensboro Dr., Ste. 500
McLean, VA 22102
Phone: 703-584-3400
Fax: 703-584-3410
Web: www.cardinalbank.com

CEO: Bernard H. Clineburg
CFO: Mark A. Wendel
HR: —
FYE: December 31
Type: Public

Cardinal Financial can help you keep out of the red. The holding company owns Cardinal Bank, which operates about two dozen branches in the Washington, DC metropolitan area. Serving commercial and retail customers, it offers checking, savings, and money market accounts; IRAs; and CDs. Commercial real estate loans make up approximately 40% of Cardinal Financial's loan portfolio; residential mortgages and construction loans are about 20% each. Subsidiary Cardinal Wealth Services provides brokerage and investment services through an alliance with Raymond James Financial.

	Annual Growth	12/05	12/06	12/07	12/08	12/09
Assets ($ mil.)	8.0%	1,452.3	1,638.4	1,690.0	1,743.8	1,976.2
Net income ($ mil.)	1.0%	9.9	7.4	4.5	0.3	10.3
Market value ($ mil.)	(5.6%)	316.0	294.4	267.7	163.4	251.1
Employees	(2.4%)	406	406	364	352	368

CARDINAL HEALTH, INC.

NYSE: CAH

7000 Cardinal Place
Dublin, OH 43017
Phone: 614-757-5000
Fax: —
Web: www.cardinal.com

CEO: George S. Barrett
CFO: Jeffrey W. (Jeff) Henderson
HR: Carole S. Watkins
FYE: June 30
Type: Public

Cardinal Health seeks to deliver medicine to all points of the compass. The company is a top distributor of pharmaceuticals and other medical supplies and equipment in the US. Its pharmaceutical division provides supply chain services including prescription and over-the-counter drug distribution, while its medical division parcels out medical, laboratory, and surgical supplies. The divisions also provide logistics, consulting, and data management services. Customers include pharmacies, hospitals, doctor's offices, and other health care businesses. Cardinal Health spun off its medical equipment manufacturing and clinical technologies operations into CareFusion in 2009.

	Annual Growth	6/05	6/06	6/07	6/08	6/09
Sales ($ mil.)	7.4%	74,910.7	81,363.6	86,852.0	91,091.4	99,512.4
Net income ($ mil.)	2.3%	1,050.7	1,000.1	1,931.1	1,300.6	1,151.6
Market value ($ mil.)	(14.7%)	14,969.9	16,724.8	18,365.3	13,410.0	7,942.5
Employees	(14.3%)	55,000	55,000	43,500	47,600	29,600

CARDINGTON YUTAKA TECHNOLOGIES INC.

575 W. Main St.
Cardington, OH 43315
Phone: 419-864-8777
Fax: 419-864-7771
Web: www.yutakatech.com

CEO: Hirokazu Kawuai
CFO: —
HR: —
FYE: March 31
Type: Subsidiary

Cardington Yutaka Technologies (CYT) and its parent company, Honda Motor Co., possess a certain synergy; subsidiary CYT supplies its parent with automotive parts. Primary parts manufactured by the company include catalytic converters and torque converters. It also manufactures an assortment of other parts for manufacturers of both automobiles and all-terrain vehicles. CYT operates two manufacturing plants in the US. In addition to its plants in Ohio and South Carolina, CYT is opening a third factory in Alabama. The company's main customers are the various manufacturing plants of Honda of America Mfg., Inc.

	Annual Growth	3/04	3/05	3/06	3/07	3/08
Est. sales ($ mil.)	—	—	—	—	—	685.1
Employees	—	—	—	—	—	875

CARDIOGENESIS CORPORATION

Pink Sheets: CGCP

11 Musick
Irvine, CA 92618
Phone: 949-420-1800
Fax: 949-420-1888
Web: www.cardiogenesis.com

CEO: Paul J. McCormick
CFO: William R. Abbott
HR: —
FYE: December 31
Type: Public

Cardiogenesis will leave a hole in your heart and not feel a pang of guilt. The company's laser and fiber-optic systems are used for transmyocardial revascularization (TMR) and percutaneous myocardial channeling (PMC), procedures that use a laser to cut channels through the heart muscle into the heart chamber to help circulation in cardiac patients. Its SolarGen 2100 system, composed of fiber-optic and laser surgical tools on a powered base unit, is FDA-approved and is marketed through Cardiogenesis' sales force in the US and through international distributors. The company's PMC system is available outside the US. The company also sells catheters and other related equipment to operate its laser systems.

	Annual Growth	12/05	12/06	12/07	12/08	12/09
Sales ($ mil.)	(10.6%)	16.3	17.1	12.1	12.1	10.4
Net income ($ mil.)	—	(1.9)	(2.0)	0.6	(0.3)	(1.2)
Market value ($ mil.)	(14.0%)	19.6	14.0	17.3	7.0	10.7
Employees	(0.7%)	35	30	32	34	34

CARDIONET, INC.

NASDAQ (GM): BEAT

227 Washington St., Ste. 300
Conshohocken, PA 19428
Phone: 610-729-7000
Fax: 610-828-8048
Web: www.cardionet.com

CEO: Randy H. Thurman
CFO: Heather Getz
HR: George Hrenko
FYE: December 31
Type: Public

CardioNet wants to be as close as your next heartbeat. The company provides real-time outpatient cardiac monitoring and telemetry services for ambulatory (mobile) patients. Aiming to improve on existing monitoring technologies by providing continuous heartbeat monitoring with up to 21 days of data, the CardioNet System provides doctors with a more complete picture of heart functions when diagnosing and monitoring arrhythmias (abnormal heart rhythms). The system relies on two-way wireless communication — providing mobility for the patient and remote adjustment for physicians. CardioNet also sells traditional cardiac event and Holter monitors, which rely on digital or taped data transmissions.

	Annual Growth	12/05	12/06	12/07	12/08	12/09
Sales ($ mil.)	46.1%	30.9	33.9	73.0	120.5	140.6
Net income ($ mil.)	—	(11.5)	(7.6)	(0.4)	9.2	(20.5)
Market value ($ mil.)	(75.9%)	—	—	—	594.7	143.3
Employees	17.4%	—	509	604	756	824

CARDIOVASCULAR BIOTHERAPEUTICS, INC.

OTC: CVBT

1635 Village Center Cir., Ste. 250
Las Vegas, NV 89134
Phone: 702-839-7200
Fax: 702-304-2120
Web: www.cvbt.com

CEO: Daniel C. Montano
CFO: Mickael A. Flaa
HR: —
FYE: December 31
Type: Public

Far from being a heartbreaker, Cardiovascular BioTherapeutics works to patch 'em up. The development-stage firm is working on a therapeutic regimen to treat patients with coronary artery disease. Its lead product candidates are based on a fibroblast growth factor protein that induces angiogenesis (blood vessel growth). When injected directly into the heart near affected arteries, the protein has been shown to help repair the artery and increase blood flow to the heart. The company hopes to prove that the protein technology will also help stroke victims and diabetes patients, as well as help heal vertebral injuries and assist in bone growth.

CARDIOVASCULAR SYSTEMS, INC.
NASDAQ (GM): CSII

651 Campus Dr.
St. Paul, MN 55112
Phone: 651-259-1600
Fax: 651-259-1696
Web: www.csi360.com

CEO: David L. (Dave) Martin
CFO: Laurence L. (Larry) Betterley
HR: —
FYE: June 30
Type: Public

Cardiovascular Systems Inc. (CSI) seeks alternatives to amputations and bypass surgeries. The company has developed a minimally invasive catheter system (the Diamondback 360°) to help treat a circulatory problem called peripheral arterial disease (PAD), which occurs when plaque builds up on vessels, often resulting in complicated surgeries such as amputations. The device is also being developed for use in coronary artery disease (CAD) patients. CSI sells its products directly to physicians and hospitals in the US. The company, formerly named Replidyne, changed its name in 2009 after completing a reverse merger transaction with the predecessor Cardiovascular Systems Inc.

	Annual Growth	12/05	12/06	12/07	12/08	*6/09
Sales ($ mil.)	244.7%	0.4	16.0	58.6	0.0	56.5
Net income ($ mil.)	—	(33.7)	(29.2)	7.7	(41.1)	(9.1)
Market value ($ mil.)	(48.8%)	—	859.6	465.1	139.5	115.7
Employees	40.7%	61	85	53	3	239

*Fiscal year change

CARDIUM THERAPEUTICS, INC.
OTC: CDTP

3611 Valley Centre Dr., Ste. 525
San Diego, CA 92130
Phone: 858-436-1000
Fax: 858-436-1001
Web: www.cardiumthx.com

CEO: Christopher J. Reinhard
CFO: Dennis M. Mulroy
HR: —
FYE: December 31
Type: Public

Whether a heart goes boom-boom, pitter-patter, or is just a-flutter, Cardium Therapeutics is interested in keeping it going strong. The company's Cardium Biologics subsidiary has three growth-factor-based drug candidates aimed at treating ischemic heart disease (such as angina), and restoring heart functioning after a heart attack. Lead candidate Generx works by stimulating the growth of new blood vessels (called angiogenesis) in angina patients. In 2009 Cardium Therapeutics agreed to sell its Innercool Therapies subsidiary — which makes the Celsius Control, CoolBlue, and Rapid Blue systems that help warm or cool patients with catheters or wraps — to Royal Philips Electronics for $11 million.

	Annual Growth	12/05	12/06	12/07	12/08	12/09
Sales ($ mil.)	(20.6%)	—	0.8	1.6	2.4	0.4
Net income ($ mil.)	—	—	(18.6)	(25.3)	(24.6)	(11.7)
Market value ($ mil.)	(41.5%)	—	264.7	202.4	58.4	52.9
Employees	(37.0%)	—	56	61	43	14

CARDO MEDICAL, INC.
OTC: CDOM

9701 Wilshire Blvd., Ste. 1100
Beverly Hills, CA 90212
Phone: 310-274-2036
Fax: 310-861-5299
Web: www.cardomedical.com

CEO: Andrew A. Brooks
CFO: Derrick Romine
HR: —
FYE: December 31
Type: Public

As an early-stage orthopedic device company, Cardo Medical wants to ensure your hips and joints are in check. The company specializes in the development and distribution of reconstructive orthopedic and spinal surgery products. Its product portfolio offers replacement medical devices for hips, knees, and parts of the spinal column. Cardo Medical has filed more than 25 patent applications for technologies related to the orthopedic field. It took its current form in 2008 when a company called clickNsettle.com completed a reverse acquisition of Cardo Medical. The company's business strategy is led by CEO Dr. Andrew Brooks, an orthopedic surgeon.

CARDONE INDUSTRIES INC.

5501 Whitaker Ave.
Philadelphia, PA 19124
Phone: 215-912-3000
Fax: 215-912-3700
Web: www.cardone.com

CEO: Michael Cardone Jr.
CFO: —
HR: Frank Zgrablich
FYE: December 31
Type: Private

Old car parts get a new lease on life thanks to Cardone Industries. The company is one of the largest remanufacturers of auto parts for the aftermarket. Cardone offers seven product lines: brakes (master cylinders), drivetrain parts (constant-velocity axles), electronics (ignition distributors, mass air flow sensors), engines (intake manifolds), motors (window-lift and wiper), pumps (water and vacuum), and steering (power-steering pumps). New parts are also sold under the Cardone Select brand. Cardone touts eco-friendly benefits, including material and energy conservation, and landfill reduction. The Cardone family, led by chairman and CEO Michael Cardone Jr., controls the company, which was founded in 1970.

	Annual Growth	12/04	12/05	12/06	12/07	12/08
Est. sales ($ mil.)	—	—	—	—	—	373.3
Employees	—	—	—	—	—	4,000

CARDTRONICS, INC.
NASDAQ (GM): CATM

3250 Briarpark Dr., Ste. 400
Houston, TX 77042
Phone: 832-308-4000
Fax: 832-308-4001
Web: www.cardtronics.com

CEO: Steven A. (Steve) Rathgaber
CFO: J. Chris Brewster
HR: —
FYE: December 31
Type: Public

Cardtronics is the Godzilla of ATMs. It's big, it's bad, and it's electronically operated. Cardtronics is the #1 owner and operator of automated teller machines and related equipment in the world. It maintains more than 32,000 ATMs in the US, UK, and Mexico. More than 10,000 of those are under contracts with banks, which allow surcharge-free access to customers. The company also leases and sells machines to airports, convenience stores, supermarkets, malls, and drug stores. Merchants can take care of their own technical maintenance or have Cardtronics do it. It also provides more complex services involving transaction processing and electronic funds transfer. The company went public via an IPO in late 2007.

	Annual Growth	12/05	12/06	12/07	12/08	12/09
Sales ($ mil.)	16.4%	269.0	293.6	378.3	493.0	493.4
Net income ($ mil.)	—	(2.4)	(0.5)	(27.1)	(70.0)	5.3
Market value ($ mil.)	4.6%	—	—	422.4	53.9	462.1
Employees	13.4%	278	327	400	430	460

CARE INVESTMENT TRUST INC.
NYSE: CRE

505 Fifth Ave., 6th Fl.
New York, NY 10017
Phone: 212-771-0505
Fax: —
Web: www.carereit.com

CEO: Salvatore V. (Torey) Riso Jr.
CFO: Paul F. Hughes
HR: —
FYE: December 31
Type: Public

Care Investment Trust is interested in health and wealth. The real estate investment trust (REIT) was formed in 2007 to invest in health care-related mortgage debt and real estate, including medical office buildings, assisted living facilities, hospitals, labs, and skilled nursing centers. Its real estate portfolio consists of facilities throughout the US, including Texas, Louisiana, and Utah. Care also provides first lien, mezzanine, and construction loans. The company's external manager CIT Healthcare, a subsidiary of commercial finance giant CIT Group, feeds it mortgage business. Tiptree Financial Partners is acquiring Care Investment Trust.

	Annual Growth	12/05	12/06	12/07	12/08	12/09
Sales ($ mil.)	24.5%	—	—	12.9	22.3	20.0
Net income ($ mil.)	—	—	—	(1.6)	(30.8)	(2.8)
Market value ($ mil.)	(14.9%)	—	—	217.3	157.6	157.4
Employees	—	—	—	—	—	—

CAREADVANTAGE, INC.

OTC: CADV

485-C Rte. 1 South	CEO: Dennis J. Mouras
Iselin, NJ 08830	CFO: —
Phone: 732-362-5000	HR: —
Fax: 732-362-5005	FYE: December 31
Web: www.careadvantage.com	Type: Public

Your health care provider will be happy for you to get a checkup, and management consulting firm CareAdvantage will be happy to give your health care provider a checkup. The firm aims to help its customers — insurance plans, hospital systems, employers, and other health care providers — serve patients as efficiently as possible. Much of its business comes from Blue Cross Blue Shield organizations. CareAdvantage operates through two main units: CareAdvantage Health Systems and Contemporary HealthCare Management. The company's signature offering is its RightPath Navigator software, which helps clients analyze the health status and care usage of member populations.

	Annual Growth	12/05	12/06	12/07	12/08	12/09
Sales ($ mil.)	10.0%	2.8	4.4	4.4	3.8	4.1
Net income ($ mil.)	—	(1.6)	(0.2)	(0.1)	(0.8)	0.2
Market value ($ mil.)	(7.5%)	2.2	2.9	2.0	0.1	1.6
Employees	(4.7%)	17	17	15	13	14

CARECENTRIC, INC.

Overlook II, 2839 Paces Ferry Rd., Ste. 900	CEO: H. Darrell Young
Atlanta, GA 30339	CFO: Stephen M. Shea
Phone: 678-264-4400	HR: —
Fax: 770-384-1650	FYE: December 31
Web: www.carecentric.com	Type: Association

CareCentric helps home health care providers spend less time managing their business operations and more paying attention to patients. Formerly Simione Central Holdings, the company offers software systems that manage financial, operational, and clinical information for home health care providers, home medical equipment providers, respiratory therapy service providers, and government-managed organizations. In addition to its software offerings, CareCentric also provides outsourced billing services, business processing outsourcing, and IT services.

CAREER EDUCATION CORPORATION

NASDAQ (GS): CECO

2895 Greenspoint Pkwy., Ste. 600	CEO: Gary E. McCullough
Hoffman Estates, IL 60169	CFO: Michael J. (Mike) Graham
Phone: 847-781-3600	HR: Thomas G. (Tom) Budlong
Fax: 847-781-3610	FYE: December 31
Web: www.careered.com	Type: Public

Career Education Corporation (CEC) has made a career of handing out diplomas. The for-profit company owns and operates nearly 100 domestic and international campuses offering postsecondary education to roughly 115,000 students. CEC offers certificate and degree programs in areas including visual communication and design, culinary arts, information technology, business studies, and health education. Among the company's brand names are International Academy of Design & Technology, Le Cordon Bleu College of Culinary Arts, and Colorado Technical University. CEC schools offers non-degree certificates as well as associate, bachelor's, master's, and doctoral degrees.

	Annual Growth	12/05	12/06	12/07	12/08	12/09
Sales ($ mil.)	(2.5%)	2,034.6	1,785.6	1,674.9	1,705.4	1,836.6
Net income ($ mil.)	(23.2%)	233.9	46.6	59.6	60.1	81.2
Market value ($ mil.)	(8.8%)	2,759.0	2,027.5	2,056.9	1,467.8	1,907.2
Employees	(4.3%)	17,180	16,740	14,479	13,014	14,383

CAREERBUILDER, LLC

200 N. LaSalle St., Ste. 1100	CEO: Matthew W. (Matt) Ferguson
Chicago, IL 60601	CFO: Kevin Knapp
Phone: 773-527-3600	HR: Rosemary Haefner
Fax: 773-399-6313	FYE: December 31
Web: www.careerbuilder.com	Type: Joint venture

CareerBuilder constructs new careers by bringing employers and potential employees together through the Web. The company's CareerBuilder Network consists of its flagship site careerbuilder.com, as well as affiliated career sites including the *Los Angeles Times* and MSN Careers. CareerBuilder.com allows job seekers access to the Mega Job Search to peruse more than 1 million job openings, and more than 300,000 employers tap into its database consisting of over 30 million resumes. The company also conducts surveys and polls through the Web paneling of its vast database. Newspaper publisher Gannett owns a controlling stake in CareerBuilder, which was founded in 1995.

CAREFIRST, INC.

10455 Mill Run Circle	CEO: Chester (Chet) Burrell
Owings Mills, MD 21117	CFO: G. Mark Chaney
Phone: 410-528-7000	HR: Pamela S. Deuterman
Fax: 410-998-5351	FYE: December 31
Web: www.carefirst.com	Type: Not-for-profit

CareFirst is a not-for-profit holding company with subsidiaries that provide managed health care plans to millions of members throughout Maryland and the Washington, DC, metro area. The company's main subsidiaries are CareFirst of Maryland and Group Hospitalization and Medical Services (operating in the National Capital area, including DC and Northern Virginia). Together, the two subsidiaries do business as CareFirst BlueCross BlueShield and offer Blue-branded HMO and PPO plans to individuals and employers throughout their service areas. Other non-Blue subsidiaries provide group life insurance and third-party benefits administration. CareFirst is led by CEO Chet Burrell, a long-time health care executive.

	Annual Growth	12/04	12/05	12/06	12/07	12/08
Est. sales ($ mil.)	—	—	—	—	—	6,098.6
Employees	—	—	—	—	—	6,000

CAREFUSION CORPORATION

NYSE: CFN

3750 Torrey View Ct.	CEO: David L. (Dave) Schlotterbeck
San Diego, CA 92130	CFO: Edward J. (Ed) Borkowski
Phone: 858-617-2000	HR: Cathy Cooney
Fax: —	FYE: June 30
Web: www.carefusion.com	Type: Public

CareFusion cares about eliminating confusion and infection when it comes to hospital patients. The company's Pyxis brand automated medication dispensing units cut down on clinician error when dealing with patients in critical care settings, as well as infusion products under the Alaris brand. The company also makes AVEA respiratory ventilation devices and SensorMedics pulmonary care products. CareFusion's other primary segment focuses on products and services that help prevent the spread of hospital-acquired infections. Former parent Cardinal Health, a top US distributor of pharmaceuticals and medical supplies, spun off CareFusion into a separate, publicly traded company in 2009.

	Annual Growth	6/04	6/05	6/06	6/07	*6/08
Sales ($ mil.)	21.7%	—	—	3,051.5	3,477.8	4,518.4
Net income ($ mil.)	20.0%	—	—	460.3	502.4	662.7
Employees	—	—	—	—	—	16,000

*Most recent year available

CAREGROUP, INC.

109 Brookline Ave.
Boston, MA 02215
Phone: 617-975-5000
Fax: —
Web: www.caregroup.org

CEO: Paul F. Levy
CFO: Steve Fisher
HR: Lisa Zankman
FYE: September 30
Type: Private

Thanks to CareGroup, there's well-being in Beantown. Formed through the 1997 union of several Boston-area health care organizations, CareGroup serves Massachusetts residents through its flagship facility, the 620-bed Beth Israel Deaconess Medical Center (BIDMC), and three other hospital campuses. With about 1,000 beds total, the system provides a comprehensive range of general acute care, as well as specialty care in a number of areas including orthopedics, obstetrics, diabetes, and cardiovascular disease. In addition to hospitals, CareGroup operates a network of outpatient clinics and physician practices in the Boston area. It is also involved in biomedical research and medical education.

	Annual Growth	9/04	9/05	9/06	9/07	9/08
Est. sales ($ mil.)	—	—	—	—	—	2,075.6
Employees	—	—	—	—	—	12,000

CAREGUIDE, INC.

OTC: CGDE

4401 NW 124th Ave.
Coral Springs, FL 33065
Phone: 954-796-3714
Fax: 954-796-3703
Web: www.careguide.com

CEO: Michael J. (Mike) Condron
CFO: Thomas J. (Tom) Hannon
HR: —
FYE: December 31
Type: Public

Like a nagging parent, CareGuide is forever reminding you to take better care of yourself. The company (formerly Patient Infosystems) offers health care management products and services designed to help health plan members maintain and improve their health and to lower health care costs for its clients. Its One Care Street offering identifies patients who will likely need care and provides them with action plans and health coaching. The company also provides a 24-hour nurse helpline for its clients' members and provides disease management services for those with chronic illnesses. CareGuide customers include self-insured employers, health plans, and third-party administrators.

CARESTREAM HEALTH, INC.

150 Verona St.
Rochester, NY 14608
Phone: 585-627-1800
Fax: 800-334-9262
Web: www.carestreamhealth.com

CEO: Kevin J. Hobert
CFO: Michael C. Pomeroy
HR: —
FYE: December 31
Type: Subsidiary

Carestream Health gets the picture. The company develops and sells imaging products to help dentists, doctors, and scientists take, process, view, and store images for diagnosis and research. Its medical imaging devices include digital and computed radiography systems, as well as specialized systems for mammography and other cancer diagnostics. Carestream Health's dental products include digital and X-ray equipment. Its Molecular Imaging group makes scientific products used for capturing images at the molecular level. Carestream also offers products to industrial markets, including aircraft inspection and forensics. Carestream's products are sold worldwide; the company is owned by private investment firm Onex.

CAREY INTERNATIONAL, INC.

4530 Wisconsin Ave. NW
Washington, DC 20016
Phone: 202-895-1200
Fax: 202-895-1269
Web: www.carey.com

CEO: Gary L. Kessler
CFO: Mitchell J. (Mitch) Lahr
HR: Rae D. Fawcett
FYE: November 30
Type: Private

In about 550 cities in some 65 countries, Carey International carries passengers. Through its network of franchisees, the company provides chauffeured vehicle services, primarily to business travelers, through a network of subsidiaries, licensees, and affiliates. Transportation is available for airport pick-ups and drop-offs, conventions, special events, and leisure travel. The company's fleet consists of sedans, limousines, vans, minibuses, and buses. Carey links its centralized reservation system to terminals at travel agencies, corporate travel departments, and government offices. The company also offers online reservations. Carey was founded in 1921.

⊞ CARGILL, INCORPORATED

15407 McGinty Rd. West
Wayzata, MN 55391
Phone: 952-742-7575
Fax: 952-742-7393
Web: www.cargill.com

CEO: Gregory R. (Greg) Page
CFO: David W. (Dave) MacLennan
HR: Peter Vrijsen
FYE: May 31
Type: Private

Cargill may be private, but it's highly visible. The agribusiness giant is the US's largest private corporation and has operations in 70 countries throughout the world. The company has five main business segments — Agriculture Services (customized farm services and products); Food Ingredients and Applications (food and beverage ingredients, and meat and poultry products); Industrial, Origination and Processing (commodity origination, processing, marketing and distribution); and Risk Management and Financial (risk management and financial solutions). Its customers include food, beverage, industrial, pharmaceutical, and personal care product makers, as well as crop and livestock farmers and foodservice providers.

	Annual Growth	5/05	5/06	5/07	5/08	5/09
Sales ($ mil.)	13.2%	71,066.0	75,208.0	88,266.0	120,439.0	116,579.0
Net income ($ mil.)	12.2%	2,103.0	1,537.0	2,343.0	3,951.0	3,334.0
Employees	6.4%	124,000	149,000	158,000	160,000	159,000

CARGILL MEAT SOLUTIONS

151 N. Main St.
Wichita, KS 67202
Phone: 316-291-2500
Fax: 316-291-2590
Web: www.cargillmeatsolutions.com

CEO: Jody Horner
CFO: —
HR: Brenda Smith-Pirkle
FYE: May 31
Type: Subsidiary

Cargill Meat Solutions (CMS) is really very good at being a leading meat processor in the US. It excels at turning cows, pigs, and turkeys into meat at its plants in the US and Canada, which it then sells to countries around the world. It also produces case-ready and pre-cooked meats and meals for the grocery and foodservice industries. CMS's brands include Honeysuckle White, Sterling Silver, Angus Pride, and Tender Choice. The company also supplies fresh beef and pork to Precept Foods, a joint venture with Hormel that markets branded fresh meats. CMS is the integrated result of a string of acquisitions (Emmpak Foods, Taylor Packing, and Excel) undertaken by its parent Cargill Incorporated.

⊞ An in-depth profile of this company is available to Hoover's Online members at hoovers.com.

329

CARHARTT, INC.

5750 Mercury Dr.
Dearborn, MI 48126
Phone: 313-271-8460
Fax: 313-271-3455
Web: www.carhartt.com

CEO: Mark Valade
CFO: Linda Hubbard
HR: Jennifer Piscopink
FYE: December 31
Type: Private

Real workers don't leave home without first donning their Carhartts. The clothing manufacturer offers rugged overalls, flame-resistant work wear, outerwear, sweatshirts, sportswear, and pants favored by farmers and hardworking blue-collar types. Its clothes and footwear have shown up in such popular films as *The Perfect Storm* and *The Horse Whisperer*. Most of Carhartt's products are manufactured in about 10 US factories; the remainder are produced in Mexico and Europe. Carhartt's apparel is carried by major chains (Bass Pro Shops, Cabela's) and regional retailers in North America, Europe, and Japan. The family of founder Hamilton Carhartt owns the firm, which was founded in 1889.

CARILION CLINIC

1906 Bellevue Ave.
Roanoke, VA 24014
Phone: 540-981-7000
Fax: 540-344-5716
Web: www.carilion.com

CEO: Edward G. Murphy
CFO: Donald E. (Don) Lorton
HR: Brucie Boggs
FYE: September 30
Type: Not-for-profit

Carilion Clinic cares for the citizens of southwestern Virginia. Founded in 1899 as the Roanoke Hospital Association, the system today includes hospitals, a network of local physicians, and a research partnership with Virginia Tech. In addition to the eight hospitals it owns, Carilion co-owns one with Centra Health. The system (including affiliates) has more than 1,200 beds. Despite its already hefty size, it continues to expand its operations to include a new children's hospital within its Carilion Roanoke Memorial Hospital, as well as new heart treatment and women's health centers. Its Carilion Behavioral Health facilities include inpatient care.

	Annual Growth	9/04	9/05	9/06	9/07	9/08
Est. sales ($ mil.)	—	—	—	—	—	1,101.6
Employees	—	—	—	—	—	9,200

CARIBOU COFFEE COMPANY, INC.

NASDAQ (GM): CBOU

3900 Lakebreeze Ave. North
Minneapolis, MN 55429
Phone: 763-592-2200
Fax: 763-592-2300
Web: www.cariboucoffee.com

CEO: Michael J. (Mike) Tattersfield
CFO: Timothy J. (Tim) Hennessy
HR: Karen E. McBride-Raffel
FYE: December 31
Type: Public

This company serves hot Joe to the java herd. Caribou Coffee operates the second-largest non-franchised coffee chain in the US (based on the number of locations) behind Starbucks with more than 400 stores in about 15 states, mostly in Minnesota. The outlets, designed to resemble mountain lodges, offer fresh-brewed coffee along with specialty coffee drinks and baked goods. The stores also sell whole bean coffee and brewing supplies. Caribou Coffee has an additional 120 franchised outlets mostly in international markets. Beyond its coffee shops, the company sells roasted coffee and related supplies to grocery stores and foodservice suppliers. Bahrain-based investment group Arcapita owns 60% of Caribou Coffee.

	Annual Growth	12/05	12/06	12/07	12/08	12/09
Sales ($ mil.)	7.3%	198.0	236.2	256.8	253.9	262.5
Net income ($ mil.)	—	(4.5)	(9.1)	(30.7)	(16.3)	5.1
Market value ($ mil.)	(6.4%)	200.9	170.7	80.3	27.2	154.5
Employees	0.7%	5,745	6,698	6,616	6,013	5,917

⊞ CARLISLE COMPANIES INCORPORATED

NYSE: CSL

13925 Ballantyne Corporate Place, Ste. 400
Charlotte, NC 28277
Phone: 704-501-1100
Fax: 704-501-1190
Web: www.carlisle.com

CEO: David A. Roberts
CFO: Steven J. Ford
HR: —
FYE: December 31
Type: Public

Commercial manufacturing group Carlisle Companies is nothing if not diverse. Through dozens of subsidiaries, the company makes an array of products including roofing materials, specialty wheels and tires, truck trailers, foodservice equipment, and wire and cable assemblies for aerospace and industrial clients. Representing about half of the group's sales, the construction materials segment makes rubber roofing systems as well as rigid foam insulation, waterproofing, and protective coatings. Its next-largest segment, engineered transportation makes tires, wheels, industrial brakes, and power transmission belts. Carlisle sells its products globally, but the US accounts for around 90% of sales.

	Annual Growth	12/05	12/06	12/07	12/08	12/09
Sales ($ mil.)	1.9%	2,209.6	2,572.5	2,876.4	2,971.4	2,379.5
Net income ($ mil.)	8.0%	106.4	215.7	215.6	55.8	144.6
Market value ($ mil.)	(0.2%)	2,104.3	2,388.8	2,253.7	1,259.8	2,085.1
Employees	(2.4%)	11,000	11,000	13,000	11,000	10,000

CARIDIANBCT, INC.

10811 W. Collins Ave.
Lakewood, CO 80215
Phone: 303-232-6800
Fax: 303-231-4160
Web: www.caridianbct.com

CEO: David B. Perez
CFO: Katie MacWilliams
HR: Stacey Jo Kirkland
FYE: December 31
Type: Private

CaridianBCT (formerly Gambro BCT) knows that having blood in the bank is as good as gold, but only if it's clean and properly stored. The company develops and sells blood collection and processing systems to hospitals and blood banks. Its systems are used to separate blood into its different components, such as platelets, plasma, and leukoreduced red blood cells (or blood with the white cells removed). The company also provides apheresis systems which are used to develop blood-based therapies for the treatment of cancer and other diseases. CaridianBCT has operations in 30 countries and sells its products around the world. The company is led by CEO David Perez, formerly an executive with UroTherapies.

CARLISLE TIRE & WHEEL COMPANY

23 Windham Blvd.
Aiken, SC 29805
Phone: 803-643-2900
Fax: 803-643-2919
Web: www.carlisletire.com

CEO: Fred A. Sutter
CFO: Steven J. (Steve) Ford
HR: —
FYE: December 31
Type: Subsidiary

Biters, gliders, and handlers might not sound like synonyms for tires, but that's what goes around at Carlisle Tire & Wheel. The company, a subsidiary of Carlisle Companies, produces commercial, recreational, industrial, agricultural, and utility tires for use on ATVs, lawn and garden products, golf carts, and trailers. Carlisle Tire & Wheel also makes a variety of highway-approved trailer wheels, as well as a line of inner tubes, flaps, and valve stems. Carlisle Tire & Wheel offers an online catalog featuring its entire line of tires and accessories.

CARLO CORPORATION

45000 River Ridge Dr., Ste. 200
Clinton Township, MI 48038
Phone: 586-416-4500
Fax: 586-226-7261
Web: www.carlocompanies.com

CEO: Carlo J. Catenacci
CFO: John T. Robson
HR: —
FYE: December 31
Type: Holding company

There's nothing abstract about Carlo Corporation, the group of affiliated construction and development companies owned by the Catenacci family. The group (also known as Carlo Companies) includes transportation construction and site development firm John Carlo, Inc. Another division, National Asphalt Products, provides asphalt, aggregates, and portable crushing units in southeastern Michigan. Residential and commercial real estate development is handled by Trinity Land Development. Superior Aggregates Company, based in Canada, produces asphalt and aggregates for highway construction. Carlo Environmental Technologies specializes in underground storage tank removal, landfill construction, and wetland mitigation.

CARLSON MARKETING WORLDWIDE, INC.

1405 Xenium Lane N.
Plymouth, MN 55441
Phone: 763-212-4520
Fax: 763-212-4580
Web: www.carlsonmarketing.com

CEO: Jeffrey A. (Jeff) Balagna
CFO: Jeff Bata
HR: John Reynolds
FYE: December 31
Type: Subsidiary

Carlson Marketing Worldwide, one of the largest marketing firms in the US, provides marketing services that revolve around building relationships with employees, partners, and consumers as part of their efforts to increase sales. Its marketing services include direct marketing, sales promotion, merchandising, public relations, training, database marketing, and event marketing. Also, its Peppers & Rogers division acts as a management consulting firm. Serving such clients as British Airways, BASF, and Union Pacific, it has more than 30 offices worldwide across 20 countries. Previously a subsidiary of hotel operator Carlson Companies, Carlson Marketing was acquired by Groupe Aeroplan in December 2009.

CARLSON COMPANIES, INC.

701 Carlson Pkwy.
Minnetonka, MN 55305
Phone: 763-212-4000
Fax: 763-212-2219
Web: www.carlson.com

CEO: Hubert Joly
CFO: Trudy Rautio
HR: Jim T. Porter
FYE: December 31
Type: Private

Carlson Companies began in 1938 as the Gold Bond Stamp Company, but has evolved into a leisure services juggernaut. The company owns 55% of travel giant Carlson Wagonlit. Its Carlson Hotels Worldwide owns and operates more than 1,000 hotels in some 70 countries under brands such as Radisson, Country Inns & Suites By Carlson, and Park Plaza. In addition, its Carlson Restaurants Worldwide includes the T.G.I. Friday's and Pick Up Stix chains. Chairman Marilyn Carlson Nelson and director Barbara Carlson Gage, daughters of founder Curtis Carlson, each own half of the company.

	Annual Growth	12/04	12/05	12/06	12/07	12/08
Sales ($ mil.)	5.5%	30,700.0	34,400.0	37,100.0	39,800.0	38,075.4
Employees	(4.2%)	190,000	—	176,000	160,000	160,000

CARLSON RESTAURANTS WORLDWIDE, INC.

4201 Marsh Ln.
Carrollton, TX 75007
Phone: 972-662-5400
Fax: 972-307-2822
Web: www.fridays.com

CEO: Nicholas P. (Nick) Shepherd
CFO: Anita Phillips
HR: Anne Varano
FYE: December 31
Type: Subsidiary

Carlson Restaurants Worldwide (CRW) has a lot of Friday's for which to be thankful. The company operates and franchises more than 900 T.G.I. Friday's casual dining restaurants across the US and in about 60 other countries. The chain offers a menu of beef, chicken, and seafood dishes but the eateries are popular for their appetizers and bar-like atmosphere. CRW owns about 320 of its T.G.I. Friday's locations and franchises or licenses the rest. The company also operates more than 90 Asian-themed restaurants under the Pick Up Stix banner. The first T.G.I. Friday's was opened in 1965 in New York City. CRW is a subsidiary of travel and hospitality conglomerate Carlson Companies.

CARLSON HOTELS WORLDWIDE, INC.

701 Carlson Pkwy.
Minnetonka, MN 55305
Phone: 763-212-5000
Fax: 763-212-3400
Web: www.carlsonhotels.com

CEO: Hubert Joly
CFO: Trudy Rautio
HR: —
FYE: December 31
Type: Subsidiary

Carlson Hotels Worldwide has a little R&R on its mind. One of the world's leading hotel franchisors, Carlson operates five lodging chains with more than 1,000 properties in more than 70 countries, including the upscale Radisson Hotel brand. The Radisson chain offers upscale amenities at more than 400 locations in about 70 countries. Carlson also owns the mid-market Park Plaza Hotels & Resorts chain, as well as the Park Inn economy brand. In addition, its Country Inn & Suites chain provides extended-stay service at more than 480 locations. And with a 42% stake, Carlson is the largest shareholder in The Rezidor Hotel Group. Carlson Hotels is a division of leisure conglomerate Carlson Companies.

THE CARLYLE GROUP, L.P.

1001 Pennsylvania Ave. NW, Ste. 220 South
Washington, DC 20004
Phone: 202-729-5626
Fax: 202-347-1818
Web: www.carlyle.com

CEO: Peter H. Nachtwey
CFO: Peter H. Nachtwey
HR: Lori R. Sabet
FYE: December 31
Type: Private

The Carlyle Group, with some $85 billion under management, is one of the world's largest private investment firms. Undertakings include management-led buyouts, minority equity investments, real estate, venture capital, and leveraged finance opportunities in the energy and power, consumer and retail, and technology and business services industries. Other sectors it focuses on include financial services, health care, infrastructure, aerospace and defense, automotive, transportation, telecommunications, and media. Since its founding in 1987, The Carlyle Group has made some 900 investments; it maintains offices in some 20 countries and oversees more than 60 private equity, real estate, and leveraged buyout funds.

An in-depth profile of this company is available to Hoover's Online members at hoovers.com.

331

🔲 CARMAX, INC.
NYSE: KMX

12800 Tuckahoe Creek Parkway	CEO: Thomas J. (Tom) Folliard
Richmond, VA 23238	CFO: Keith D. Browning
Phone: 804-747-0422	HR: Michael K. (Mike) Dolan
Fax: 804-217-6819	FYE: February 28
Web: www.carmax.com	Type: Public

To the greatest extent possible, CarMax helps drivers find late-model used autos. The US's largest specialty used-car retailer buys, reconditions, and sells cars and light trucks at about 100 superstores in 25 US states, mainly in the Southeast and Midwest; CarMax also operates several new-car franchises and sells older vehicles at in-store auctions at about 50 of its superstores. CarMax sells vehicles that are generally under six years old with less than 60,000 miles. CarMax also sells older cars and trucks with higher mileage through its ValuMax program. The company's website lets customers search CarMax outlets nationwide for a particular model. Its CarMax Auto Finance unit offers financing.

	Annual Growth	2/06	2/07	2/08	2/09	2/10
Sales ($ mil.)	4.5%	6,260.0	7,465.7	8,199.6	6,974.0	7,470.2
Net income ($ mil.)	17.4%	148.1	198.6	182.0	59.2	281.7
Market value ($ mil.)	6.5%	3,505.3	5,879.4	4,096.6	2,104.1	4,504.9
Employees	2.7%	12,061	13,736	15,637	13,035	13,439

CARMEUSE LIME & STONE INC.

11 Stanwix St., 11th Fl.	CEO: Thomas A. Buck
Pittsburgh, PA 15222	CFO: Bruce Inglis
Phone: 412-995-5500	HR: Kathy Wiley
Fax: 412-995-5570	FYE: December 31
Web: www.carmeusena.com	Type: Subsidiary

If it's part of Carmeuse and produces lime and stone, why not call it Carmeuse Lime & Stone? Formerly Carmeuse North America, the company is a subsidiary of Belgium-based Carmeuse, which has been selling limestone-based products since the mid-nineteenth century. Carmeuse Lime & Stone is a top supplier of lime and limestone in North America, producing some 7 million tons annually of lime products and around 25 million tons of limestone aggregates from more than 30 plants. It makes quicklime (calcium oxide), dolomitic lime (a mixture of calcium carbonate and magnesium carbonate), and hydrated lime (calcium hydroxide). The company primarily sells its products in the eastern US and Canada.

🔲 CARMIKE CINEMAS, INC.
NASDAQ (GM): CKEC

1301 1st Ave.	CEO: S. David Passman III
Columbus, GA 31901	CFO: Richard B. Hare
Phone: 706-576-3400	HR: —
Fax: 706-576-2812	FYE: December 31
Web: www.carmike.com	Type: Public

Movies are the star at Carmike Cinemas, and the company wants to make sure the star shines brightly in your town. Among the largest theater chains in the US, Carmike owns, operates, or has stakes in about 2,300 screens at nearly 250 theaters in 35 states. Carmike's theaters are located mostly in small to midsized communities where the chain hosts the only theater in town. The company's revenues come from the sale of admission tickets and concessions. The firm also owns two Hollywood Connection family entertainment centers, which feature multiplex theaters along with skating rinks, miniature golf, and arcades.

	Annual Growth	12/05	12/06	12/07	12/08	12/09
Sales ($ mil.)	2.4%	468.9	495.5	489.3	474.4	514.7
Net income ($ mil.)	—	0.3	(19.4)	(126.9)	(41.4)	(15.4)
Market value ($ mil.)	(26.1%)	327.4	263.2	93.7	47.1	97.6
Employees	(4.3%)	7,908	7,383	6,838	7,323	6,635

🔲 CARNIVAL CORPORATION
NYSE: CCL

3655 NW 87th Ave.	CEO: Micky Arison
Miami, FL 33178	CFO: David Bernstein
Phone: 305-599-2600	HR: —
Fax: 305-406-4700	FYE: November 30
Web: www.carnivalcorp.com	Type: Public

Carnival offers a boatload of fun. The company is the world's #1 cruise operator, boasting about a dozen cruise lines and 90-plus ships with a total passenger capacity of more than 180,000. Carnival operates in North America primarily through its Princess Cruise Line, Holland America, and Seabourn luxury cruise brand, as well as its flagship Carnival Cruise Lines unit. Brands such as AIDA, P&O Cruises, and Costa Cruises offer services to passengers in Europe, and the Cunard Line runs luxury trans-Atlantic liners. Carnival operates as a dual-listed company with UK-based Carnival plc, forming a single enterprise under a unified executive team.

	Annual Growth	11/05	11/06	11/07	11/08	11/09
Sales ($ mil.)	4.4%	11,087.0	11,839.0	13,033.0	14,646.0	13,157.0
Net income ($ mil.)	(5.6%)	2,257.0	2,279.0	2,408.0	2,330.0	1,790.0
Market value ($ mil.)	(12.4%)	45,338.9	40,762.6	37,542.5	17,473.3	26,650.9
Employees	4.5%	71,200	74,700	81,200	85,900	84,800

CAROLINA BANK HOLDINGS, INC.
NASDAQ (CM): CLBH

101 N. Spring St.	CEO: Robert T. Braswell
Greensboro, NC 27401	CFO: T. Allen Liles
Phone: 336-288-1898	HR: Angela J. Nowlin
Fax: 336-286-5553	FYE: December 31
Web: www.carolinabank.com	Type: Public

Carolina Bank Holdings owns Carolina Bank, which serves individuals and small to midsized businesses through some 10 branches in northern portions of North Carolina. The community-oriented financial institution offers standard services such as checking and savings accounts, money market and individual retirement accounts, CDs, ATM and debit cards, and online banking and bill payment. Loans secured by commercial properties account for about 40% of the company's portfolio, followed by residential mortgages, construction and land development loans, commercial and industrial loans, and consumer loans.

	Annual Growth	12/05	12/06	12/07	12/08	12/09
Assets ($ mil.)	17.5%	365.2	411.6	500.1	616.6	697.1
Net income ($ mil.)	—	2.0	2.8	3.0	2.2	(0.4)
Market value ($ mil.)	(23.3%)	31.8	44.5	38.1	20.8	11.0
Employees	24.1%	59	72	89	119	140

CAROLINA TRUST BANK
NASDAQ (CM): CART

901 E. Main St.	CEO: J. Michael Cline
Lincolnton, NC 28092	CFO: Donald J. Boyer
Phone: 704-735-1104	HR: Treva J. Carey
Fax: 704-735-1258	FYE: December 31
Web: www.carolinatrust.com	Type: Public

Carolina Trust Bank serves southwestern North Carolina through about a half-dozen locations. It provides a variety of commercial and personal financial services including checking and savings accounts, IRAs, CDs, and credit cards. The bank is mainly a real estate lender, with one- to four-family residential mortgage, commercial real estate, construction, and land development loans comprising most of its portfolio. The company acquired the single-branch Carolina Commerce Bank in 2009. Carolina Trust was founded in 2000.

	Annual Growth	12/05	12/06	12/07	12/08	12/09
Assets ($ mil.)	27.2%	102.9	116.7	136.9	160.4	269.0
Net income ($ mil.)	—	1.4	1.6	1.0	(0.6)	(2.4)
Market value ($ mil.)	(22.1%)	34.3	41.7	36.7	15.6	12.7
Employees	8.9%	37	40	40	44	52

CAROLINE, INC.

104 W. 29th St., 4th Fl.
New York, NY 10001
Phone: 212-886-7500
Fax: 212-643-5563
Web: www.caroline.com

CEO: Sidney McCain
CFO: —
HR: —
FYE: March 31
Type: Subsidiary

This company gives little guys in the music business some major distribution muscle. A subsidiary of UK-based recording conglomerate EMI Group, Caroline is one of the leading distribution companies for independent music. It services hundreds of independent record labels by getting their CDs, tapes, and vinyl records into retail outlets throughout the country. In addition to its distribution business, Caroline operates its own record label, which has supported such bands as Bad Brains, Ben Folds Five, and Pussy Galore, as well as dance tracks label Astralwerks.

CARPENTER CO.

5016 Monument Ave.
Richmond, VA 23230
Phone: 804-359-0800
Fax: 804-353-0694
Web: www.carpenter.com

CEO: Stanley F. Pauley
CFO: Michael (Mike) Lowery
HR: Tom Smith
FYE: December 31
Type: Private

It's a cushy job for Carpenter Co., making polyurethane foam and chemicals and polyester fiber used as cushioning by the automotive, bedding, floor covering, packaging, and furniture industries. The company started out making foam rubber; it now also manufactures air filters, expanded polystyrene building materials, and a tire fill product used as a replacement for air in off-road construction vehicles. Carpenter also sells consumer products — which include craft fiber products, mattress pads, and pillows — through retailers. The company has facilities throughout North America and Europe. Carpenter, which was founded in 1948 by E. Rhodes Carpenter, is owned by chairman and CEO Stanley Pauley.

CARPENTER TECHNOLOGY CORPORATION   NYSE: CRS

2 Meridian Blvd.
Wyomissing, PA 19610
Phone: 610-208-2000
Fax: 610-208-3716
Web: www.cartech.com

CEO: Gregory A. Pratt
CFO: K. Douglas (Doug) Ralph
HR: T. Kathleen Hanley
FYE: June 30
Type: Public

The Tin Man never would have rusted had he been built with metal from Carpenter Technology. The company makes a variety of corrosion-resistant materials; most of its sales come from stainless steel products and alloys that provide special heat- or wear-resistance or special magnetic or conductive properties. Finished products come in billet, bar, rod, wire, and other forms. Carpenter also makes titanium products, engineered ceramic products, and tool and other specialty steels. Customers include companies in the aerospace, automotive, medical, and industrial markets. The aerospace sector, Carpenter's largest market, accounts for more than 40% of its business.

	Annual Growth	6/05	6/06	6/07	6/08	6/09
Sales ($ mil.)	0.9%	1,314.2	1,568.2	1,944.8	1,953.5	1,362.3
Net income ($ mil.)	(22.9%)	135.5	211.8	227.2	277.7	47.9
Market value ($ mil.)	(5.3%)	1,139.0	2,539.7	2,865.4	1,919.6	915.2
Employees	(5.4%)	4,003	3,990	4,152	3,400	3,200

CARQUEST CORPORATION

2635 E. Millbrook Rd.
Raleigh, NC 27604
Phone: 919-573-3000
Fax: 919-573-2501
Web: www.carquest.com

CEO: Temple Sloan III
CFO: John Gardner
HR: Scott Derrow
FYE: December 31
Type: Private

Searching for a sensor, solenoid, or switches? CARQUEST can steer you in the right direction. The replacement auto parts distribution group is owned by its member warehouse distributors (the largest is North Carolina-based General Parts). The CARQUEST group includes a network of about 40 distribution centers serving more than 3,400 distributor-owned and independent jobbers in the US, Canada, and Mexico. The company sells its own line of auto parts (made by Moog Automotive, Dana, Gabriel, and others) to the jobbers, as well as wholesalers, for eventual resale to professional repair centers, service stations, dealerships, and, to a lesser degree, do-it-yourself (DIY) customers.

CARRIAGE SERVICES, INC.   NYSE: CSV

3040 Post Oak Blvd., Ste. 300
Houston, TX 77056
Phone: 713-332-8400
Fax: 713-332-8401
Web: www.carriageservices.com

CEO: Melvin C. (Mel) Payne
CFO: Terry E. Sanford
HR: —
FYE: December 31
Type: Public

Though it buries its customers, Carriage Services hasn't come close to burying its competition. The firm is a large US death care company, but it trails far behind Service Corporation International and that firm's smaller rivals Stewart Enterprises and StoneMor Partners. Carriage Services runs about 135 funeral homes (owned and leased) and some 30 cemeteries (owned and leased) in about 25 states, but mostly in California, Massachusetts, and Texas. It removes and prepares remains, sells caskets and memorials, provides transportation services, hosts ceremonies, performs burials, and maintains cemetery grounds. Carriage Services was established in 1993. FMR and Zazove Associates each own about 15% of the company.

	Annual Growth	12/05	12/06	12/07	12/08	12/09
Sales ($ mil.)	3.5%	155.0	151.1	167.8	176.9	177.6
Net income ($ mil.)	67.0%	0.9	(1.4)	8.3	0.3	7.0
Market value ($ mil.)	(5.8%)	87.3	88.9	153.7	35.1	68.7
Employees	0.7%	1,781	1,526	1,776	1,822	1,835

CARRIER CORPORATION

1 Carrier Place
Farmington, CT 06034
Phone: 860-674-3000
Fax: 860-674-3139
Web: www.carrier.com

CEO: Geraud Darnis
CFO: —
HR: —
FYE: December 31
Type: Subsidiary

Carrier helps people keep their cool when the heat is on (and vice versa). The company is the world's largest maker of HVAC equipment and refrigeration systems for residential, commercial, industrial, and transportation needs. Through Carrier Transicold, it makes truck/trailer and container refrigeration equipment and provides transport air-conditioning systems for bus, rail, and marine customers. Carrier also provides aftermarket services and components for its products. The company is a subsidiary of diversified manufacturer United Technologies Corporation (UTC); it accounts for about a quarter of UTC's sales. Carrier operates around 60 manufacturing facilities and has dealers in more than 170 countries.

	Annual Growth	12/04	12/05	12/06	12/07	12/08
Sales ($ mil.)	2.1%	—	—	—	14,600.0	14,900.0
Employees	(4.7%)	—	—	—	43,000	41,000

CARRIZO OIL & GAS, INC.

NASDAQ (GS): CRZO

1000 Louisiana St., Ste. 1500
Houston, TX 77002
Phone: 713-328-1000
Fax: 713-328-1035
Web: www.carrizo.cc

CEO: S. P. Johnson IV
CFO: Paul F. Boling
HR: Deborah (Debbie) Soho
FYE: December 31
Type: Public

Carrizo Oil & Gas sees its future in 3-D. An independent exploration and production company that explores for oil and gas in the Barrett Shale play of North Texas, and in proven onshore fields along the Gulf Coast of Texas and Louisiana, Carrizo aggressively acquires 3-D seismic data and arranges land lease options in conjunction with conducting seismic surveys. As part of a new strategy, the company is exploiting the Marcellus Shale play (New York, Pennsylvania, West Virginia and Virginia). Carrizo has additional properties in the Rockies, Alabama, Arkansas, Kentucky, New Mexico, and in the North Sea. In 2008 the firm reported proved reserves of 432.1 billion cu. ft. of natural gas equivalent.

	Annual Growth	12/05	12/06	12/07	12/08	12/09
Sales ($ mil.)	9.9%	78.2	82.9	125.8	216.7	114.1
Net income ($ mil.)	—	10.6	18.2	15.5	(17.9)	(204.8)
Market value ($ mil.)	1.8%	854.9	1,004.4	1,895.0	557.2	917.5
Employees	22.1%	50	68	75	104	111

CARROLL SHELBY INTERNATIONAL, INC.

Pink Sheets: CSBI

19021 S. Figueroa St.
Gardena, CA 90248
Phone: 310-914-1843
Fax: 310-538-8189
Web: www.carrollshelbyinternational.com

CEO: Carroll Shelby
CFO: —
HR: —
FYE: December 31
Type: Public

The namesake for Carroll Shelby International (CSI) is one of the world's great walking brand names. From his days with the Aston Martin racing team in the 1950s to his work with Ford Motor, Carroll Shelby is an automotive living legend. CSI's Shelby American (formerly Shelby Automobiles) subsidiary builds Shelby Cobra component cars (kit cars with no engine or drivetrain), which it sells through a network of 20 dealers in North America and Europe. CSI also licenses the Shelby name for use by makers of everything from auto accessories and apparel to collectibles and golf gear. Carroll Shelby has rejoined forces with Ford to build a 550-horsepower Shelby Expedition SUV and a Shelby Mustang.

CARROLLTON BANCORP

NASDAQ (GM): CRRB

344 N. Charles St., Ste. 300
Baltimore, MD 21201
Phone: 410-536-4600
Fax: 410-625-0355
Web: www.carrolltonbank.com

CEO: Robert A. Altieri
CFO: Mark A. Semanie
HR: —
FYE: December 31
Type: Public

Carrollton Bancorp can baby-sit your money from Babe Ruth's hometown. The institution is the holding company for Carrollton Bank, a commercial bank serving Baltimore and surrounding areas from about a dozen branches. It offers standard retail services such as checking and savings accounts, money market accounts, and IRAs. Commercial real estate and residential mortgages account for about 45% and 20%, respectively, of the bank's loan portfolio. Bank subsidiary Carrollton Financial Services sells stocks, bonds, mutual funds, and annuities; Carrollton Mortgage Services originates and sells residential mortgages.

	Annual Growth	12/05	12/06	12/07	12/08	12/09
Assets ($ mil.)	4.1%	360.5	349.8	352.8	404.2	423.8
Net income ($ mil.)	—	2.5	2.6	2.1	0.8	(0.5)
Market value ($ mil.)	(24.8%)	38.5	44.1	35.8	14.9	12.3
Employees	(1.8%)	157	138	137	137	146

🔲 CARROLS RESTAURANT GROUP, INC.

NASDAQ (GM): TAST

968 James St.
Syracuse, NY 13203
Phone: 315-424-0513
Fax: 315-475-9616
Web: www.carrols.com

CEO: Alan Vituli
CFO: Paul R. Flanders
HR: —
FYE: December 31
Type: Public

This company has some fast food royalty in its blood. Carrols Restaurant Group is a leading quick-service restaurant operator and the #1 Burger King franchisee in the US, with more than 300 locations in New York, Ohio, and about 10 other states. The company also operates two of its own quick-service chains: Taco Cabana and Pollo Tropical. Taco Cabana offers Tex-Mex and Mexican dishes through more than 150 locations (mostly in Texas), while Pollo Tropical features fresh grilled chicken at more than 90 company-owned locations, primarily in Florida. In addition to its corporate-run units, Carrols has about 30 franchised Pollo Tropical restaurants mostly in Puerto Rico and Ecuador.

	Annual Growth	12/05	12/06	12/07	12/08	12/09
Sales ($ mil.)	3.7%	706.9	751.4	789.4	816.3	816.1
Net income ($ mil.)	—	(4.3)	13.4	15.1	12.8	21.8
Market value ($ mil.)	(20.7%)	—	306.6	207.1	58.4	152.8
Employees	(0.9%)	16,300	16,400	17,300	16,800	15,700

C.A.R.S. PROTECTION PLUS, INC.

4431 William Penn Hwy., Ste. 1
Murrysville, PA 15668
Phone: 724-387-2327
Fax: 724-387-2344
Web: www.carsprotectionplus.com

CEO: Michael Tedesco
CFO: —
HR: —
FYE: December 31
Type: Private

Caveat emptor! To aid in your vigilance, there's C.A.R.S. Protection Plus. The company sells limited extended warranties on used cars through registered auto dealers in more than a dozen states. It offers a variety of coverage plans ranging from three months to four years. C.A.R.S. Protection Plus was founded in 1998 and hailed as one of *Entrepreneur* magazine's top 100 fast-growing small businesses in 2003. It ran into legal trouble in 2004 when Pennsylvania's attorney general's office filed suit against the company for failing to honor warranties and for misrepresenting important terms of its warranty products.

	Annual Growth	12/04	12/05	12/06	12/07	12/08
Est. sales ($ mil.)	—	—	—	—	—	8.2
Employees	—	—	—	—	—	80

CARTER'S, INC.

NYSE: CRI

The Proscenium, 1170 Peachtree St. NE, Ste. 900
Atlanta, GA 30309
Phone: 404-745-2700
Fax: 404-892-0968
Web: www.carters.com

CEO: Michael D. (Mike) Casey
CFO: Richard F. Westenberger
HR: Jill Wilson
FYE: December 31
Type: Public

For little ones, there's nothing quite as comforting as a Carter's sleeper and snuggling up to Mom or Dad. In addition to producing babies' and children's sleepwear, Carter's (which operates through its William Carter Company unit) is a leading maker of apparel for fashionable youngsters. Its primary products include newborn layette clothing, sleepwear, and playwear. Carter's markets its apparel and accessories under the names Carter's and OshKosh B'Gosh through 340-plus department and specialty stores and in more than 445 Carter's and OshKosh stores nationwide. Wal-Mart sells its Child of Mine line, while Target offers the Just One Year and Precious Firsts brands; the two retailers generate about 15% of sales.

	Annual Growth	12/05	12/06	12/07	12/08	12/09
Sales ($ mil.)	9.1%	1,121.4	1,343.5	1,412.2	1,490.0	1,589.7
Net income ($ mil.)	25.1%	47.2	87.2	(70.6)	75.1	115.6
Market value ($ mil.)	(2.8%)	1,748.0	1,514.8	1,149.5	1,144.1	1,559.4
Employees	16.9%	4,083	6,731	7,630	6,548	7,622

CARVER BANCORP, INC.

NYSE Amex: CARV

75 W. 125th St.
New York, NY 10027
Phone: 212-876-4747
Fax: 212-426-6159
Web: www.carverbank.com

CEO: Deborah C. (Debbie) Wright
CFO: Chris A. McFadden
HR: Margaret D. Roberts
FYE: March 31
Type: Public

Carver Bancorp, one of the largest minority-led financial institutions in the US, is the holding company for Carver Federal Savings Bank, which was founded in 1948 to provide community banking services to New York City's African-American and Caribbean-American population. From about 10 branches in mostly low- to moderate-income neighborhoods in Harlem, Brooklyn, and Queens, the thrift offers deposit accounts, insurance, and investment products. Carver Federal's lending activities are focused on housing (residential mortgages and multifamily real estate loans) and non-residential real estate (churches and commercial properties.) The latter makes up about 40% of Carver's loan portfolio.

	Annual Growth	3/05	3/06	3/07	3/08	3/09
Assets ($ mil.)	6.0%	626.4	661.0	740.0	796.4	791.4
Net income ($ mil.)	—	2.6	3.8	2.6	4.0	(7.0)
Market value ($ mil.)	(34.7%)	46.3	42.2	41.3	28.7	8.4
Employees	0.9%	135	126	160	187	140

CAS MEDICAL SYSTEMS, INC.

NASDAQ (GM): CASM

44 E. Industrial Rd.
Branford, CT 06405
Phone: 203-488-6056
Fax: 203-488-9438
Web: www.casmed.com

CEO: Andrew E. Kersey
CFO: Jeffery A. Baird
HR: —
FYE: December 31
Type: Public

CAS Medical Systems (CASMED) makes blood pressure measurement devices, vital signs monitors, apnea monitors, and neonatal supplies. Major brands include the MAXNIBP blood pressure technology, the CAS 750 vital signs monitor, and the AMI and 511 cardio-respiratory monitoring system. Subsidiary Statcorp makes blood pressure cuffs, pressure infuser cuffs, and blood filter products. The company sells its products in Europe, North America, Latin America, Africa, and the Pacific Rim to hospitals and other health care professionals through specialty distributors and sales representatives.

	Annual Growth	12/05	12/06	12/07	12/08	12/09
Sales ($ mil.)	6.2%	26.9	35.2	38.2	40.6	34.2
Net income ($ mil.)	—	1.8	1.7	0.3	(0.4)	(5.8)
Market value ($ mil.)	(29.6%)	99.7	92.3	63.4	22.4	24.4
Employees	(0.2%)	143	152	165	172	142

CASCADE BANCORP

NASDAQ (CM): CACB

1100 NW Wall St.
Bend, OR 97701
Phone: 541-385-6205
Fax: 541-382-8780
Web: www.botc.com

CEO: Patricia L. Moss
CFO: Gregory D. Newton
HR: Peggy L. Biss
FYE: December 31
Type: Public

Forget the dirty dishes. Cascade Bancorp wants to provide sparkling customer service. It's the holding company for Bank of the Cascades, which operates about 35 branches in Oregon and Idaho. Targeting individuals and small to midsized businesses, the banks offer traditional retail banking services and trust and investment services. More than two-thirds of the company's loan portfolio is composed of construction, residential mortgage, and commercial real estate loans. The bank also offers business loans; consumer loans accounted for only 2% in 2007.

	Annual Growth	12/05	12/06	12/07	12/08	12/09
Assets ($ mil.)	14.7%	1,269.7	2,249.3	2,394.5	2,278.3	2,193.9
Net income ($ mil.)	—	22.4	35.7	30.0	(134.6)	(93.1)
Market value ($ mil.)	(56.2%)	518.6	874.2	392.2	190.2	19.2
Employees	9.4%	336	573	559	545	482

CASCADE CORPORATION

NYSE: CASC

2201 NE 201st Ave.
Fairview, OR 97024
Phone: 503-669-6300
Fax: 503-669-6716
Web: www.cascorp.com

CEO: Robert C. (Bob) Warren Jr.
CFO: Joseph G. Pointer
HR: Susan Chazin-Wright
FYE: January 31
Type: Public

Cascade makes light work out of heavy weights. The company's materials-handling products — attachments, forks, and accessories — are manufactured for industrial and commercial lift trucks, and occasionally construction and agricultural vehicles. Cascade offers a myriad of sizes, models, and capabilities in its line of forklift attachments, handling forks, hydraulic cylinders, as well as replacement parts. The equipment pulls, rotates, tilts, side shifts, clamps, and lifts materials as heavy as major appliances and as mountainous as industrial rolls of paper. Cascade caters to OEMs and original equipment dealers (OEDs) of lift trucks in North America and to some extent in Europe, the Asia/Pacific region, and China.

	Annual Growth	1/06	1/07	1/08	1/09	1/10
Sales ($ mil.)	(8.6%)	450.5	478.9	558.1	534.2	314.4
Net income ($ mil.)	—	42.1	45.5	60.1	1.3	(38.6)
Market value ($ mil.)	(13.2%)	555.8	584.8	561.9	249.2	315.1
Employees	(2.7%)	1,900	2,100	2,400	2,000	1,700

CASCADE FINANCIAL CORPORATION

NASDAQ (GS): CASB

2828 Colby Ave.
Everett, WA 98201
Phone: 425-339-5500
Fax: 425-259-8512
Web: www.cascadebank.com

CEO: Carol K. Nelson
CFO: Terry Stull
HR: —
FYE: December 31
Type: Public

Cascade Financial is the holding company for Cascade Bank, which operates almost 20 branches in Washington State's Puget Sound area. Founded in 1916, the bank offers such deposit products as checking, savings, and money market accounts, as well as CDs and IRAs. Funds gathered are used primarily to originate business loans (more than 40% of the company's loan portfolio), construction loans (more than 30%), commercial and residential mortgages, and consumer loans. The bank also issues Visa credit cards. It offers investment services through an agreement with Stockcross Financial Services.

	Annual Growth	12/05	12/06	12/07	12/08	12/09
Assets ($ mil.)	8.9%	1,211.8	1,345.3	1,417.6	1,637.3	1,704.6
Net income ($ mil.)	—	13.0	13.4	15.5	2.1	(23.5)
Market value ($ mil.)	(37.2%)	174.3	209.2	166.9	66.8	27.1
Employees	1.9%	206	212	211	216	222

CASCADE MICROTECH, INC.

NASDAQ (GM): CSCD

2430 NW 206th Ave.
Beaverton, OR 97006
Phone: 503-601-1000
Fax: 503-601-1002
Web: www.cascademicrotech.com

CEO: F. Paul Carlson
CFO: Jeff A. Killian
HR: —
FYE: December 31
Type: Public

In the foothills of the Cascade Range, Cascade Microtech makes test systems for microelectronics. Semiconductor makers such as Fujitsu Semiconductor, Intel, Samsung Electronics, Taiwan Semiconductor Manufacturing, and Texas Instruments use the company's probe cards, probe stations, and analytical probes to ensure the quality of their integrated circuits (ICs). Many of Cascade's customers use its tools to test their wireless, broadband, or other communications ICs at the wafer level, before the wafers are cut into individual chips. The company has a development alliance with test equipment giant Agilent Technologies. Cascade gets about two-thirds of its sales outside the US.

	Annual Growth	12/05	12/06	12/07	12/08	12/09
Sales ($ mil.)	(7.7%)	73.6	84.9	89.9	76.6	53.5
Net income ($ mil.)	—	8.3	3.6	0.9	(34.6)	(7.6)
Market value ($ mil.)	(22.4%)	180.9	187.6	145.9	27.9	65.6
Employees	1.6%	287	366	354	292	306

CASE DEALER HOLDING COMPANY LLC

1751 Bell Ave.
Sacramento, CA 95838
Phone: 916-649-0096
Fax: 916-649-3594
Web: www.casepower.com

CEO: C. Dean McLain
CFO: Mark J. Wright
HR: —
FYE: July 31
Type: Subsidiary

Getting people to doze on the job is the job of Case Dealer Holding Company (formerly Western Power & Equipment Corp.). Operating as Case Power and Equipment, the company sells, rents, and services bulldozers and other construction, industrial, and agricultural equipment. Case Power and Equipment offers equipment made by CNH Global and more than 40 other manufacturers. In late 2008 Western Power & Equipment was acquired by Case Construction Equipment, a unit of CNH, which then changed the unit's name to Case Power and Equipment. The company operates eight dealer locations in California, Nevada, Oregon, and Washington.

CASE FINANCIAL, INC.

OTC: CSEF

7720 El Camino Real, Ste. 2E
Carlsbad, CA 92009
Phone: 760-804-1449
Fax: 760-804-1566

CEO: Michael A. Schaffer
CFO: Lawrence C. Schaffer
HR: —
FYE: September 30
Type: Public

Case Financial went from the courtroom to the goldmine. The former business litigation financing business shifted its focus away from loaning money to lawyers in 2005 and now wants to invest in mine exploration. Setbacks have prevented the company from operating since 2004. However, in 2008 Case Financial announced that it would provide $4 million in funding to Canada-based Trio Gold Corp for a gold mine exploration project in Nevada.

	Annual Growth	9/05	9/06	9/07	9/08	9/09
Sales ($ mil.)	—	—	—	—	—	0.0
Net income ($ mil.)	—	—	—	—	—	(0.7)
Market value ($ mil.)	—	—	—	—	—	0.9
Employees	—	—	—	—	—	2

CASE WESTERN RESERVE UNIVERSITY

10900 Euclid Ave.
Cleveland, OH 44106
Phone: 216-368-2000
Fax: 216-368-4325
Web: www.cwru.edu

CEO: Barbara R. Snyder
CFO: John Sideras
HR: Carolyn Gregory
FYE: June 30
Type: School

Looking for a research-oriented university? Go Western, young man! Case Western Reserve University (CWRU) is a research school with an enrollment of more than 9,800 students (more than half of whom are graduate and professional students). CWRU offers undergraduate and graduate degrees from eight schools — business, engineering, law, arts and sciences, dentistry, social work, nursing, and medicine — at its campus in Cleveland. The student-to-faculty ratio is 10-to-1. The university's origins date back to 1826 in the Ohio region then known as the Western Reserve of Connecticut; its current structure was formed in 1967 with the combination of neighboring Case Institute of Technology and Western Reserve University.

	Annual Growth	6/04	6/05	6/06	6/07	6/08
Est. sales ($ mil.)	—	—	—	—	—	296.0
Employees	—	—	—	—	—	5,500

CASELLA WASTE SYSTEMS, INC.

NASDAQ (GS): CWST

25 Greens Hill Ln.
Rutland, VT 05701
Phone: 802-775-0325
Fax: 802-775-6198
Web: www.casella.com

CEO: John W. Casella
CFO: Paul J. Massaro
HR: Gerry Gormley
FYE: April 30
Type: Public

The wasteful habits of Americans are big business for Casella Waste Systems, which operates regional waste-hauling businesses, mainly in the northeastern US, that serve commercial, industrial, and residential customers. Overall, the company owns and/or operates 32 solid waste collection businesses, 37 recycling facilities, 31 transfer stations, eight ordinary and two specialized landfills, and one waste-to-energy power generation facility. In addition to its waste-related operations, Casella Waste Systems has a 50% stake in GreenFiber, a joint venture with Louisiana-Pacific that produces cellulose insulation.

	Annual Growth	4/05	4/06	4/07	4/08	4/09
Sales ($ mil.)	3.6%	482.0	525.9	547.0	579.5	554.2
Net income ($ mil.)	—	7.3	11.1	(17.9)	(7.8)	(68.0)
Market value ($ mil.)	(35.3%)	305.7	403.3	241.2	276.4	53.4
Employees	(2.1%)	2,600	2,900	2,800	2,720	2,393

CASEY'S GENERAL STORES, INC.

NASDAQ (GS): CASY

1 Convenience Blvd.
Ankeny, IA 50021
Phone: 515-965-6100
Fax: 515-965-6160
Web: www.caseys.com

CEO: Robert J. (Bob) Myers
CFO: William J. (Bill) Walljasper
HR: Julie L. Jackowski
FYE: April 30
Type: Public

Casey's General Stores makes sure that small towns in the Midwest get their fill of convenient shopping. It operates about 1,480 company-owned convenience stores, mostly in Illinois, Iowa, and Missouri, but also in Indiana, Kansas, Minnesota, Nebraska, South Dakota, and Wisconsin, all within about 500 miles of its headquarters and distribution center. Towns with 5,000 people or fewer, where rent is low, host about 60% of the chain's stores. Casey's sells beverages, gasoline, groceries, and fresh prepared foods. The company also sells tobacco products, automotive goods, and other nonfood items, such as ammunition and photo supplies. Alimentation Couche-Tard offered to buy the company in April 2010.

	Annual Growth	4/05	4/06	4/07	4/08	4/09
Sales ($ mil.)	13.6%	2,810.5	3,515.1	4,024.0	4,827.1	4,687.9
Net income ($ mil.)	23.5%	36.8	61.6	61.9	85.1	85.7
Market value ($ mil.)	12.1%	859.5	1,089.1	1,280.5	1,126.8	1,354.9
Employees	6.8%	14,440	15,692	17,136	17,983	18,780

CASH AMERICA INTERNATIONAL, INC.

NYSE: CSH

1600 W. 7th St.
Fort Worth, TX 76102
Phone: 817-335-1100
Fax: 817-570-1225
Web: www.cashamerica.com

CEO: Daniel R. (Dan) Feehan
CFO: Thomas A. Bessant Jr.
HR: —
FYE: December 31
Type: Public

If cash is king, then Cash America International is king of pawns. Ruling over a kingdom of some 500 Cash America Pawn and SuperPawn locations in 22 states, and about 175 Prenda Fácil stores in Mexico, it's one of the largest providers of secured, non-recourse loans (also known as pawn loans) in North America. Cash America offers cash advances in six states through some 250 stores operating as Cashland and Cash America Payday Advance. Check cashing, money orders, and money transfers are offered through about 130 owned and franchised Mr. Payroll stores in more than 15 states. Cash America also markets and processes stored-value debit cards issued by a third-party bank.

	Annual Growth	12/05	12/06	12/07	12/08	12/09
Assets ($ mil.)	20.7%	598.6	776.2	904.6	1,186.5	1,269.7
Net income ($ mil.)	21.1%	45.0	60.9	79.3	81.1	96.7
Market value ($ mil.)	10.8%	685.1	1,385.5	954.2	808.0	1,032.8
Employees	4.5%	4,565	5,152	5,501	5,587	5,445

CASH TECHNOLOGIES, INC.

NYSE Amex: TQ

1434 W. 11th St.
Los Angeles, CA 90015
Phone: 213-745-2000
Fax: 213-745-2005
Web: www.cashtechnologies.com

CEO: Bruce R. Korman
CFO: Edmund (Ed) King
HR: —
FYE: May 31
Type: Public

Cash Technologies got its sweet ride back. The company in 2006 sold its Tomco Auto Parts (now named TAP Holdings) subsidiary to Champion Parts and focused on payment services and stored value payment cards. Two years later, Cash Technologies bought Champion's assets when that company filed for bankruptcy protection. The company is now rebuilding the auto parts business (primarily remanufactured fuel systems) and has gained back some of the country's largest auto parts retail customers. Its Claim-Remedi subsidiary still provides health care reimbursement services. As a result of the restructuring, though, Cash Technologies terminated the operations of its CashTechCard (corporate reimbursement cards) subsidiary.

	Annual Growth	5/04	5/05	5/06	5/07	*5/08
Sales ($ mil.)	31.6%	0.1	5.7	0.1	0.3	0.3
Net income ($ mil.)	—	(4.4)	(2.6)	(5.1)	(3.4)	(8.6)
Market value ($ mil.)	(31.3%)	33.4	23.5	17.6	23.3	7.4
Employees	25.3%	13	16	172	17	32

*Most recent year available

CASIO AMERICA, INC.

570 Mount Pleasant Ave.
Dover, NJ 07801
Phone: 973-361-5400
Fax: 973-537-8926
Web: www.casio.com

CEO: Toshiharu Okimuro
CFO: —
HR: —
FYE: March 31
Type: Subsidiary

You might be (G-)shocked to learn how many products Casio America sells. As the US subsidiary of Japanese electronics giant CASIO COMPUTER, the firm markets products ranging from handheld computers and calculators to electronic keyboards and its popular G-Shock and high-end Oceanus watch lines. Established in 1957, Casio also makes and markets cell phones, digital cameras, electronic dictionaries, label printers, clocks, portable TVs, and other items. Going beyond the consumer market, Casio targets the retail, hospitality, and industrial markets (cash registers and industrial handheld PDAs). And to make sure that young consumers remember its name, the company also sells to the education market.

CASPIAN SERVICES, INC.

OTC: CSSV

257 E. 200 South, Ste. 340
Salt Lake City, UT 84111
Phone: 801-746-3700
Fax: 801-746-3701
Web: www.caspianservicesinc.com

CEO: Kerry T. Doyle
CFO: Indira Kalieva
HR: —
FYE: September 30
Type: Public

Caspian Services (formerly EMPS Corporation) provides geophysical and seismic data acquisition and interpretation services to the oil and gas industry operating in the Caspian Sea region. It also owns or leases a fleet of 15 shallow draft vessels that provide offshore marine services, including transportation, housing, and supplies for production personnel. Caspian Services' ships are chartered primarily to Agip KCO, a consortium of oil companies operating in the Caspian Sea, and CMOC/Shell joint venture. The company owns 56% of a joint venture that operates a desalinization plant and sells purified drinking water.

	Annual Growth	9/05	9/06	9/07	9/08	9/09
Sales ($ mil.)	42.5%	23.8	43.0	64.9	72.6	98.2
Net income ($ mil.)	23.4%	2.2	(1.9)	9.5	1.1	5.1
Market value ($ mil.)	(46.5%)	231.9	242.2	148.9	72.1	19.1
Employees	17.1%	447	365	560	850	840

CASS INFORMATION SYSTEMS, INC.

NASDAQ (GM): CASS

13001 Hollenberg Dr.
Bridgeton, MO 63044
Phone: 314-506-5500
Fax: 314-506-5955
Web: www.cassinfo.com

CEO: Eric H. Brunngraber
CFO: P. Stephen (Steve) Appelbaum
HR: Karen L. Lowry
FYE: December 31
Type: Public

Rolling, rolling, rolling . . . keep those payments rolling! Cass Information Systems provides freight payment and information processing services to large manufacturing, distributing, and retail firms in the US. Its offerings include freight bill payment, audit, and rating services, as well as outsourcing of utility bill processing and payments. Its telecommunications division manages telecom expenses for large companies. Cass grew out of Cass Commercial Bank (now a subsidiary), which provides banking services to private companies and churches, as well as to consumers, in the St. Louis area and Orange County, California. Other major customer bases include Massachusetts, Ohio, and South Carolina.

	Annual Growth	12/05	12/06	12/07	12/08	12/09
Sales ($ mil.)	3.4%	76.9	89.9	97.5	97.3	87.9
Net income ($ mil.)	10.2%	10.9	15.1	17.8	19.0	16.1
Market value ($ mil.)	10.9%	189.0	309.0	313.8	286.1	285.6
Employees	5.0%	716	890	964	936	870

CASTLE BRANDS INC.

NYSE Amex: ROX

570 Lexington Ave., 29th Fl.
New York, NY 10022
Phone: 646-356-0200
Fax: 646-356-0222
Web: www.castlebrandsinc.com

CEO: Richard J. (Dick) Lampen
CFO: Alfred J. Small
HR: —
FYE: March 31
Type: Public

Castle Brands hopes to earn a king's ransom selling imported distilled spirits. Among its brands are Boru Vodka (21% of sales in 2009), Sea Wynde Rum, and Knappogue Castle Whiskey. The company also owns 60% of the Celtic Crossing brand of Irish liqueur. In addition, it has marketing and distribution rights for other brands such as Gosling's Rum and Pallini liqueurs. Castle Brands mainly contracts with other firms to distill and bottle its products. Philip Frost, who is vice chairman of Teva Pharmaceutical Industries, owns almost 30% of the company; cigarette maker Vector Group has a stake of more than 10%.

	Annual Growth	3/05	3/06	3/07	3/08	3/09
Sales ($ mil.)	20.0%	12.6	21.1	25.2	27.3	26.1
Net income ($ mil.)	—	(12.5)	(13.1)	(16.6)	(27.6)	(21.7)
Market value ($ mil.)	(83.0%)	—	—	748.3	111.2	21.6
Employees	(4.4%)	49	51	62	58	41

CASTLE HARLAN, INC.

150 E. 58th St.
New York, NY 10155
Phone: 212-644-8600
Fax: 212-207-8042
Web: www.castleharlan.com

CEO: John K. Castle
CFO: Lewis A. Raibley III
HR: —
FYE: December 31
Type: Private

Castle Harlan is a private equity firm that has investments in restaurant chains, industrial and manufacturing firms, shipping and transportation support companies, and other concerns in the US and Australia. The hands-on company sniffs out established enterprises with steady earnings; it often partners with the existing management of an acquired business, places directors on its board, and eventually seeks a profitable exit. Castle Harlan owns stakes in about a dozen companies in all. Its restaurant holdings include well-known names Perkins & Marie Callender's and Morton's. The firm was co-founded in 1987 by Leonard Harlan and chairman John Castle, a former CEO of Donaldson, Lufkin & Jenrette.

	Annual Growth	12/04	12/05	12/06	12/07	12/08
Est. sales ($ mil.)	—	—	—	—	—	3,245.1
Employees	—	—	—	—	—	13,450

An in-depth profile of this company is available to Hoover's Online members at hoovers.com.

337

CASTRIP LLC

1915 Rexford Rd.
Charlotte, NC 28211
Phone: 704-972-1820
Fax: 704-972-1829
Web: www.castrip.com

CEO: Frank M. Fisher Jr.
CFO: —
HR: Peter Campbell
FYE: January 1
Type: Joint venture

Castrip understands that steel can never be too thin. The joint venture of minimill titan Nucor, BlueScope Steel, and Ishikawajima-Harima Heavy Industries offers a technology that aids steelmakers in the manufacture of flat-rolled, carbon, and stainless steel sheets at very thin gauges. The Castrip technology is based on an invention devised by Henry Bessemer in 1857. Steel produced through the Castrip process may be used in a wide variety of products, including appliances, furniture, grain bins, racking, and structural tube. Castrip was established in 2000.

	Annual Growth	1/04	1/05	1/06	1/07	1/08
Est. sales ($ mil.)	—	—	—	—	—	0.2
Employees	—	—	—	—	—	3

⊞ CASUAL MALE RETAIL GROUP, INC.

NASDAQ (GM): CMRG

555 Turnpike St.
Canton, MA 02021
Phone: 781-828-9300
Fax: 781-821-6094
Web: www.casualmalexl.com

CEO: David A. Levin
CFO: Dennis R. Hernreich
HR: Walter Sprague
FYE: January 31
Type: Public

Casual Male Retail Group sells men their Friday-wear and formalwear. The company offers private-label and name-brand casual wear, dresswear, and suits for big-and-tall men through about 500 stores in some 45 US states, as well as online and through catalogs. It also operates a single Rochester Big & Tall store in London, and recently began selling apparel online in six European countries, including Germany and France. Trade names include Casual Male XL (formerly Casual Male Big & Tall), Rochester Big & Tall Clothing, B&T Factory Direct, and Shoes XL and Living XL. Founded as Designs, Inc., in 1976, the company acquired Casual Male out of bankruptcy in 2002 and adopted the better-known name.

	Annual Growth	1/06	1/07	1/08	1/09	1/10
Sales ($ mil.)	(1.6%)	421.4	467.5	464.1	444.2	395.2
Net income ($ mil.)	(13.3%)	10.8	42.6	0.4	(109.3)	6.1
Market value ($ mil.)	(21.9%)	359.1	595.2	231.8	18.1	133.5
Employees	(2.2%)	2,770	3,092	3,079	3,015	2,529

CATALENT PHARMA SOLUTIONS, INC.

14 Schoolhouse Rd.
Somerset, NJ 08873
Phone: 732-537-6200
Fax: 732-537-6480
Web: www.catalent.com

CEO: John R. Chiminski
CFO: Matthew M. (Matt) Walsh
HR: Harry F. Weininger
FYE: June 30
Type: Private

Catalyst + talent = Catalent. At least, that's the brand Catalent Pharma Solutions is trying to convey to ensure its customers' success. The company provides contract development and manufacturing of oral (soft and hardshell capsules), topical (ointment applicators), sterile (syringes), and inhaled (nasal sprays) drug delivery products to pharmaceutical and biotechnology companies in some 100 countries. Catalent also provides packaging services, using bottles, pouches, and strips used to hold tablet, powder, and liquid medicines. Catalent operates 30 facilities worldwide. The company is owned by The Blackstone Group.

	Annual Growth	6/04	6/05	6/06	6/07	6/08
Sales ($ mil.)	6.4%	—	1,517.3	1,612.2	1,703.7	1,828.0
Net income ($ mil.)	—	—	13.9	51.0	(125.4)	(539.7)
Employees	(2.0%)	—	—	—	10,000	9,800

⊞ CATALINA MARKETING CORPORATION

200 Carillon Pkwy.
St. Petersburg, FL 33716
Phone: 727-579-5000
Fax: 727-556-2700
Web: www.catmktg.com

CEO: L. Dick Buell
CFO: Rick P. Frier
HR: —
FYE: December 31
Type: Private

To reach shoppers when they are shopping, consumer packaged-goods manufacturers call on Catalina Marketing. The company's network, installed at the cash registers of more than 23,000 supermarkets and drugstores throughout the US, prints out coupons and other marketing communications for consumers based on the products they have just purchased. A similar system, installed at more than 18,000 pharmacies, delivers health-related information to consumers based on the prescriptions they pick up. Outside the US, Catalina Marketing has installed its networks at about 7,000 retail locations in Europe and Japan. The company was established in 1983.

CATALYST HEALTH SOLUTIONS, INC.

NASDAQ (GS): CHSI

800 King Farm Blvd.
Rockville, MD 20850
Phone: 301-548-2900
Fax: 301-548-2991
Web: www.catalysthealthsolutions.com

CEO: David T. Blair
CFO: Hai V. Tran
HR: Monica Wolfe
FYE: December 31
Type: Public

Extra, extra! Read all about it: Catalyst Health Solutions (formerly HealthExtras) provides pharmacy benefit management (PBM) services to managed care organizations, self-insured employers, and third-party administrators. Its PBM business, known as Catalyst Rx, helps clients design drug benefit plans that encourage the use of preferred prescriptions bought from one of about 60,000 pharmacies (including contracted mail order pharmacies) in the company's nationwide network. It also provides customized reporting and data analysis services. The State of Maryland and Wellmark Blue Cross Blue Shield of Iowa are its largest customers.

	Annual Growth	12/05	12/06	12/07	12/08	12/09
Sales ($ mil.)	42.9%	694.5	1,271.0	1,857.7	2,543.4	2,894.4
Net income ($ mil.)	29.8%	23.0	31.6	39.3	50.4	65.2
Market value ($ mil.)	9.8%	1,122.5	1,077.7	1,166.3	1,088.9	1,630.9
Employees	35.4%	284	410	524	820	955

CATALYST PHARMACEUTICAL PARTNERS, INC.

NASDAQ (GM): CPRX

355 Alhambra Circle, Ste. 1370
Coral Gables, FL 33134
Phone: 305-529-2522
Fax: 305-529-0933
Web: www.catalystpharma.com

CEO: Patrick J. McEnany
CFO: Jack Weinstein
HR: —
FYE: December 31
Type: Public

Catalyst Pharmaceutical Partners may help certain addicts kick the habit. The development-stage company's lead candidate, CPP-109 (based on the chemical compound vigabatrin), is in clinical studies for the treatment of cocaine and methamphetamine addiction. The drug is designed to be readily absorbed into the central nervous system, preventing the perception of pleasure that results from dramatic increases in dopamine caused by cocaine and meth use. Contract manufacturer Pharmaceutics International is supplying CPP-109 for use in upcoming clinical trials and may also be contracted for future commercial supplies should the drug become approved in the US.

	Annual Growth	12/05	12/06	12/07	12/08	12/09
Sales ($ mil.)	—	—	—	—	0.0	0.0
Net income ($ mil.)	—	—	—	—	(10.6)	(7.2)
Market value ($ mil.)	(65.0%)	—	—	—	32.5	11.4
Employees	(14.3%)	—	—	—	7	6

⊞ CATERPILLAR INC.   NYSE: CAT

100 NE Adams St.	CEO: James W. (Jim) Owens
Peoria, IL 61629	CFO: Edward J. (Ed) Rapp
Phone: 309-675-1000	HR: Gregory S. (Greg) Folley
Fax: 309-675-1182	FYE: December 31
Web: www.cat.com	Type: Public

Caterpillars are remarkable creatures; Caterpillar Inc. is a remarkable company — the world's #1 maker of earthmoving machinery and a big supplier of agricultural equipment. The company makes construction, mining, and logging machinery; diesel and natural gas engines; industrial gas turbines; and electrical power generation systems. Caterpillar operates plants worldwide and sells equipment via a network of 3,500 offices in some 180 countries. It provides rental services, too, through 1,600-plus outlets, and offers financing and insurance for dealers and customers. Cat Power Ventures invests in power projects that use Caterpillar power generation equipment. Caterpillar Logistics offers supply chain services.

	Annual Growth	12/05	12/06	12/07	12/08	12/09
Sales ($ mil.)	(2.8%)	36,339.0	41,517.0	44,958.0	51,324.0	32,396.0
Net income ($ mil.)	(25.2%)	2,854.0	3,537.0	3,541.0	3,557.0	895.0
Market value ($ mil.)	(0.3%)	36,264.9	38,499.6	45,549.2	28,041.4	35,775.2
Employees	2.5%	85,116	94,593	101,333	112,887	93,813

CATHAY GENERAL BANCORP   NASDAQ (GS): CATY

777 N. Broadway	CEO: Dunson K. Cheng
Los Angeles, CA 90012	CFO: Heng W. Chen
Phone: 213-625-4700	HR: Jennifer Laforcarde
Fax: 213-625-1368	FYE: December 31
Web: www.cathaybank.com	Type: Public

Cathay General Bancorp is the holding company for Cathay Bank, which serves Chinese and Vietnamese communities from some 30 branches in California, and about 20 more in Illinois, New Jersey, New York, Massachusetts, Washington, and Texas. It also has offices in Hong Kong, Shanghai, and Taipei. Catering to small businesses and low- to middle-income consumers, the bank offers standard deposit services and loans. Commercial mortgages account for more than half of the bank's portfolio; business loans comprise more than 20%. The bank's Cathay Wealth Management unit offers online stock trading, mutual funds, and other investment products and services through an agreement with PrimeVest.

	Annual Growth	12/05	12/06	12/07	12/08	12/09
Assets ($ mil.)	16.0%	6,397.5	8,026.5	10,402.5	11,582.6	11,588.2
Net income ($ mil.)	—	104.1	117.6	125.5	50.5	(67.4)
Market value ($ mil.)	(32.3%)	2,821.7	2,709.5	2,079.8	1,864.7	592.8
Employees	2.3%	900	1,051	1,156	1,044	986

⊞ CATHOLIC HEALTH EAST

3805 W. Chester Pike, Ste. 100	CEO: Judith M. (Judy) Persichilli
Newtown Square, PA 19073	CFO: Peter L. (Pete) DeAngelis Jr.
Phone: 610-355-2000	HR: Susan Tillman-Taylor
Fax: 610-271-9600	FYE: December 31
Web: www.che.org	Type: Not-for-profit

Catholic Health East marries the physical and the spiritual in its vast network of not-for-profit health care facilities. As one of the largest religious health systems in the country, Catholic Health East carries out its mission of healing the sick through more than 30 acute-care hospitals, 25 freestanding and hospital-based long-term care facilities, about 15 assisted living homes, and numerous behavioral health and rehabilitation centers. Operating in 11 states along the East Coast from Maine to Florida, Catholic Health East is also one of the country's largest providers of home health care services. The health care organization is sponsored by nine religious congregations and Hope Ministries.

	Annual Growth	12/04	12/05	12/06	12/07	12/08
Sales ($ mil.)	(0.7%)	4,034.5	4,245.9	4,182.9	4,364.5	3,925.5
Net income ($ mil.)	—	205.1	219.2	199.2	254.8	(540.4)
Employees	5.9%	43,000	43,000	50,000	54,000	54,000

⊞ CATHOLIC HEALTH INITIATIVES

1999 Broadway, Ste. 4000	CEO: Kevin E. Lofton
Denver, CO 80202	CFO: Colleen M. Blye
Phone: 303-298-9100	HR: Herbert J. Vallier
Fax: 303-298-9690	FYE: June 30
Web: www.catholichealthinit.org	Type: Not-for-profit

For Catholic Health Initiatives (CHI), returning sick people to good health is more than a business — it's a mission. Formed in 1996 through the merger of three Catholic hospital systems, the giant not-for-profit organization is the second-largest Catholic hospital operator in the US, just behind Ascension Health. It operates more than 70 hospitals and 40 long-term care, assisted-living, and senior residential facilities in 20 states from Washington to Maryland. Its hospitals range from large urban medical centers to small critical-access hospitals in rural areas. All told, the health system has more than 14,000 acute-care beds. It is sponsored by a dozen different congregations of nuns.

	Annual Growth	6/04	6/05	6/06	6/07	6/08
Sales ($ mil.)	7.7%	6,121.1	7,091.4	8,076.8	7,731.5	8,244.6
Net income ($ mil.)	(54.8%)	770.0	460.7	687.4	902.2	32.0
Employees	7.3%	53,459	54,044	65,070	65,296	70,760

CATHOLIC HEALTHCARE PARTNERS

615 Elsinore Place	CEO: Michael D. Connelly
Cincinnati, OH 45202	CFO: James R. (Jim) Gravell Jr.
Phone: 513-639-2800	HR: John M. Starcher Jr.
Fax: 513-639-2700	FYE: December 31
Web: www.health-partners.org	Type: Not-for-profit

Catholic Healthcare Partners (CHP) performs acts of healing in the Midwest. One of the nation's largest not-for-profit health systems, CHP offers health care services primarily in Ohio but also in Indiana, Kentucky, Pennsylvania, and Tennessee through some 100 organizations. Facilities include more than 30 hospitals, over a dozen long-term care facilities, affordable housing for the elderly, and wellness centers. CHP also offers physician practices and hospice and home health care. The system is co-sponsored by the Sisters of Mercy South Central and Mid-Atlantic communities; the Sisters of the Humility of Mary of Villa Maria, Pennsylvania; the Franciscan Sisters of the Poor; and Covenant Health Systems.

	Annual Growth	12/04	12/05	12/06	12/07	12/08
Sales ($ mil.)	6.4%	3,157.9	3,360.6	3,511.1	3,715.0	4,044.7
Net income ($ mil.)	—	171.0	154.2	136.4	96.7	(548.4)
Employees	1.8%	—	35,000	34,280	36,925	36,925

⊞ CATHOLIC HEALTHCARE WEST

185 Berry St., Ste. 300	CEO: Lloyd H. Dean
San Francisco, CA 94107	CFO: Michael D. Blaszyk
Phone: 415-438-5500	HR: Ernest Urquhart
Fax: 415-438-5724	FYE: June 30
Web: www.chwhealth.org	Type: Not-for-profit

Catholic Healthcare West (CHW) has steadily grown to become the largest private, not-for-profit health care provider in the state of California. Sponsored by six congregations of nuns, CHW operates a network of more than 40 acute-care facilities located in the Golden State and, to a lesser extent, in Arizona and Nevada. Those facilities house about 8,800 acute care beds, as well as 900 skilled nursing beds. CHW provides home health and hospice services through agencies in California and Nevada. It also operates emergency and specialty clinics, imaging centers, and medical labs, as well as managed care and wellness programs. Founded in 1986, CHW is the official health care provider of the San Francisco Giants.

	Annual Growth	6/05	6/06	6/07	6/08	6/09
Sales ($ mil.)	10.5%	6,002.1	6,617.3	7,476.9	8,401.5	8,957.9
Net income ($ mil.)	—	348.2	442.9	891.3	170.0	(126.3)
Employees	10.7%	40,000	—	50,000	50,000	60,000

⊞ An in-depth profile of this company is available to Hoover's Online members at hoovers.com.

339

THE CATHOLIC UNIVERSITY OF AMERICA

620 Michigan Ave. NE
Washington, DC 20064
Phone: 202-319-5000
Fax: 202-319-6533
Web: www.cua.edu

CEO: Rev David M. O'Connell
CFO: Cathy Wood
HR: Christine Peterson
FYE: April 30
Type: School

The Catholic University of America (CUA), established in 1887 by US bishops, has an enrollment of more than 6,700 students from all 50 states and about 100 countries. With graduate and undergraduate programs in 12 colleges, CUA offers degrees in such fields as architecture and planning, arts and sciences, engineering, music, and nursing. The Catholic University of America is the only US university with ecclesiastical faculties granting canonical degrees in canon law, philosophy, and theology. Some 90% of undergraduates and 60% of graduate students are Catholic. The University's Theological College prepares men for the priesthood serving dioceses across the US.

THE CATO CORPORATION

NYSE: CTR

8100 Denmark Rd.
Charlotte, NC 28273
Phone: 704-554-8510
Fax: 704-551-7594
Web: www.catocorp.com

CEO: John P. D. Cato
CFO: John Howe
HR: Robert C. Brummer
FYE: January 31
Type: Public

The Cato Corporation caters to fashion-minded Southerners on a budget. The retailer operates about 1,270 apparel stores in 30 states (primarily in the Southeast) under the names Cato, Cato Fashions, Cato Plus, It's Fashion, and It's Fashion Metro. Its mostly private-label merchandise selection includes misses', juniors', girls', and plus-sized casualwear, career clothing, coats, shoes, and accessories geared to low- and middle-income customers, mostly females aged 18 to 50. Cato's stores are typically located in shopping centers anchored by a Wal-Mart store or another major discounter or supermarket. Founded in 1946, the company is run by John Derham Cato, the third generation of Catos in the family business.

	Annual Growth	1/06	1/07	1/08	1/09	1/10
Sales ($ mil.)	1.4%	836.4	875.9	846.4	857.7	884.0
Net income ($ mil.)	0.6%	44.8	51.5	32.3	33.6	45.8
Market value ($ mil.)	(1.3%)	638.8	667.8	484.4	391.5	605.1
Employees	(2.3%)	10,000	10,400	9,800	9,100	9,100

CAUSELOYALTY, LLC

800 Boylston St., 49th Fl.
Boston, MA 02199
Phone: 888-200-2088
Fax: 770-840-0160
Web: www.onecause.com

CEO: Stephen D. Avalone
CFO: Wai-Yan Sun
HR: —
FYE: December 31
Type: Subsidiary

CauseLoyalty manages loyalty marketing programs for schools, merchants, and non-profit organizations. Through its flagship brand OneCause, it markets a variety of loyalty programs through gift cards, catalogs, and online services that generate contributions to schools and non-profits through parent and supporter purchases. It also partners with Visa so that purchases accumulate points which turn into contributions for fundraising efforts. Founded in 1999, CauseLoyalty is a subsidiary of Rakuten, Japan's largest online retailer and leading provider of Internet-based services.

	Annual Growth	12/04	12/05	12/06	12/07	12/08
Est. sales ($ mil.)	—	—	—	—	—	0.3
Employees	—	—	—	—	—	3

CAVALIER TELEPHONE LLC

2134 W. Laburnum Ave.
Richmond, VA 23227
Phone: 804-422-4100
Fax: 804-422-4392
Web: www.cavtel.com

CEO: Danny Bottoms
CFO: Sarah Beth Murphy
HR: Jeff Snyder
FYE: December 31
Type: Private

Despite its name Cavalier Telephone takes a serious approach to residential and business telecommunications. The facilities-based competitive local-exchange carrier (CLEC) offers local and long-distance phone services in 16 states in the eastern, southeastern, and midwestern US; its fiber network spans about 17,000 miles. The company also offers broadband Internet and Voice over Internet Protocol (VoIP) telephony services. It offers digital television services through an agreement with direct broadcast satellite provider DIRECTV. Cavalier Telephone provides business data services such as private networks and broadband data connections through its Intellifiber Networks division.

CAVCO INDUSTRIES, INC.

NASDAQ (GS): CVCO

1001 N. Central Ave., 8th Fl.
Phoenix, AZ 85004
Phone: 602-256-6263
Fax: 602-256-6189
Web: www.cavco.com

CEO: Joseph H. (Joe) Stegmayer
CFO: Daniel L. Urness
HR: —
FYE: March 31
Type: Public

Cavco's constructions keep customers covered. Cavco Industries produces some 3,200 manufactured homes a year (retail prices range from $26,000 to more than $190,000) under brands including Cavco and Fleetwood. Its products include full-sized homes (about 500 sq. ft. to 3,300 sq. ft.); park model homes (less than 400 sq. ft.) for use as recreational and retirement units; camping cabins; and commercial structures for use as portable classrooms, showrooms, and offices. Cavco operates 10 factories in the West and Midwest; its homes are available from approximately 1,000 independent retailers in 35 states and seven company-owned outlets in Arizona, New Mexico, and Texas.

	Annual Growth	3/06	3/07	3/08	3/09	3/10
Sales ($ mil.)	(11.6%)	189.5	169.1	141.9	105.4	115.6
Net income ($ mil.)	—	15.0	11.5	6.3	0.5	(3.4)
Market value ($ mil.)	(8.4%)	317.9	228.6	229.2	154.4	223.3
Employees	(0.4%)	1,320	1,075	1,005	660	1,300

CAVIUM NETWORKS, INC.

NASDAQ (GM): CAVM

805 E. Middlefield Rd.
Mountain View, CA 94043
Phone: 650-623-7000
Fax: 650-625-9751
Web: www.caviumnetworks.com

CEO: Syed B. Ali
CFO: Manoj Gujral
HR: —
FYE: December 31
Type: Public

Cavium Networks can help keep networks secure without hiding them in a cave somewhere. The company designs specialized microprocessors used in secure network transmissions, based on processor technology developed by ARM and MIPS Technologies. Cavium's customers include such heavy hitters as Cisco Systems, F5 Networks, Fujitsu, Nokia, Samsung Electronics, Sumitomo, and ZTE. Manufacturing is contracted out to Fujitsu Semiconductor, Taiwan Semiconductor Manufacturing, and United Microelectronics. Distributors handle around one-third of sales. Customers in the US provide about half of Cavium's sales.

	Annual Growth	12/05	12/06	12/07	12/08	12/09
Sales ($ mil.)	51.1%	19.4	34.2	54.2	86.6	101.2
Net income ($ mil.)	—	(11.6)	(9.0)	2.2	1.5	(21.4)
Market value ($ mil.)	1.7%	—	—	1,021.2	466.2	1,057.1
Employees	24.9%	125	157	202	347	304

An in-depth profile of this company is available to Hoover's Online members at hoovers.com.

CAYWOOD-SCHOLL CAPITAL MANAGEMENT, LLC

4350 Executive Dr., Ste. 125
San Diego, CA 92121
Phone: 858-452-3811
Fax: 858-535-9068
Web: www.caywood-scholl.com

CEO: Eric K. Scholl
CFO: —
HR: —
FYE: December 31
Type: Subsidiary

The name is bond, high-yield bond. And Caywood-Scholl Capital Management knows all of the tricks of the bond trade. The firm specializes in upper-tier high-yield bonds, managing fixed income portfolios for corporate and public entities, endowments and foundations, unions, private clients, and others. Caywood-Scholl Capital Management is a part of global insurance and financial services titan Allianz's US asset management unit, Allianz Global Investors of America (formerly Allianz Dresdner Asset Management of America). Caywood-Scholl Capital Management was founded in 1986.

CB RICHARD ELLIS GROUP, INC.   NYSE: CBG

11150 Santa Monica Blvd., Ste. 1600
Los Angeles, CA 90025
Phone: 310-405-8900
Fax: —
Web: www.cbre.com

CEO: W. Brett White
CFO: Gil Borok
HR: J. Christopher (Chris) Kirk
FYE: December 31
Type: Public

CB Richard Ellis Group (CBRE) is all about location, location, location — not to mention *ubicación, l'emplacement, posizione,* and *Standort.* The world's largest commercial real estate services company and an international powerhouse, CBRE operates more than 300 offices in 30 countries. Services include property and facilities management, leasing, brokerage, valuation, asset management, financing, and research. Subsidiary Trammell Crow provides property development services for corporate and institutional clients, primarily in the US. The company manages more than 1.1 billion sq. ft. of commercial space for third-party owners and occupants.

	Annual Growth	12/05	12/06	12/07	12/08	12/09
Sales ($ mil.)	9.4%	2,910.6	4,032.0	6,034.2	5,128.8	4,165.8
Net income ($ mil.)	—	217.3	318.6	390.5	(1,012.1)	(27.6)
Market value ($ mil.)	(8.8%)	6,312.2	10,682.9	6,934.2	1,390.1	4,366.5
Employees	18.9%	14,500	24,000	29,000	30,000	29,000

CBC RESTAURANT CORP.

12700 Park Central Dr., Ste. 1300
Dallas, TX 75251
Phone: 972-619-4100
Fax: —
Web: www.cornerbakerycafe.com

CEO: Michael J. (Mike) Hislop
CFO: —
HR: Denise Clemens
FYE: December 31
Type: Holding company

The bakery does seem like a logical place to start looking for a sandwich. CBC Restaurant Corp. operates and franchises more than 100 quick-casual eateries under the name Corner Bakery Cafe. Located in a dozen metropolitan markets around the country, mostly around Chicago and Southern California, the restaurants offer a menu of sandwiches and soups, along with pasta dishes and a large variety of dessert items. The chain offers breakfast, lunch, and dinner, and most locations offer catering services. The first Corner Bakery Cafe was opened in 1991. CBC Restaurant Corp. is owned by Il Fornaio (America), an operator of upscale Italian restaurants.

CBEYOND, INC.   NASDAQ (GM): CBEY

320 Interstate North Pkwy., Ste. 500
Atlanta, GA 30339
Phone: 678-424-2400
Fax: 678-424-2500
Web: www.cbeyond.net

CEO: James F. (Jim) Geiger
CFO: J. Robert (Bob) Fugate
HR: Joan L. Tolliver
FYE: December 31
Type: Public

Cbeyond isn't looking past the millions of small businesses in the US to find customers. A telecommunications company, Cbeyond uses Voice over Internet Protocol (VoIP) technologies to provide local and long-distance services and broadband Internet access to small businesses. It offers its services over its own private IP network. The company's other offerings include mobile voice and data services, as well as file sharing and backup services. It targets businesses in large metropolitan areas, including Atlanta, Denver, Houston, Chicago, and Los Angeles. Typical customers include legal firms, physicians' offices, real estate companies, and accounting firms. Cbeyond was founded in 1991 by CEO James Geiger.

	Annual Growth	12/05	12/06	12/07	12/08	12/09
Sales ($ mil.)	27.0%	159.1	213.9	280.0	349.9	413.8
Net income ($ mil.)	—	3.7	7.8	21.5	3.7	(2.2)
Market value ($ mil.)	11.2%	314.5	934.1	1,190.7	488.0	481.0
Employees	24.1%	707	905	1,187	1,493	1,677

CBIZ, INC.   NYSE: CBZ

6050 Oak Tree Blvd. South, Ste. 500
Cleveland, OH 44131
Phone: 216-447-9000
Fax: 216-447-9007
Web: www.cbiz.com

CEO: Steven L. Gerard
CFO: Ware H. Grove
HR: Teresa E. Bur
FYE: December 31
Type: Public

CBIZ wants its customers to see the advantages of farming out some of the tasks involved in running a business. The company provides clients with outsourced business services including accounting and tax preparation, valuation, insurance and benefits administration, and IT consulting. Medical practice management, including billing services, is a CBIZ specialty. Overall, CBIZ has about 90,000 customers, mainly small and midsized businesses, but also government agencies, individuals, and not-for-profits. The company operates from more than 140 offices in about 35 states; it also does business in Canada.

	Annual Growth	12/05	12/06	12/07	12/08	12/09
Sales ($ mil.)	7.2%	559.3	601.1	643.9	704.3	739.7
Net income ($ mil.)	13.8%	18.7	24.4	34.8	32.6	31.4
Market value ($ mil.)	6.3%	375.9	435.2	612.5	540.1	480.8
Employees	4.9%	4,700	5,200	5,500	6,000	5,700

CBL & ASSOCIATES PROPERTIES, INC.   NYSE: CBL

2030 Hamilton Place Blvd., Ste. 500
Chattanooga, TN 37421
Phone: 423-855-0001
Fax: 423-490-8390
Web: www.cblproperties.com

CEO: Stephen D. Lebovitz
CFO: John N. Foy
HR: Maggie Carrington
FYE: December 31
Type: Public

CBL & Associates Properties is a self-managed real estate investment trust (REIT) that owns, develops, manages, and finances shopping malls and other retail properties, primarily in the Southeast and Midwest. It wholly owns or has interests in about 160 properties, more than half of which are regional malls and open-air shopping centers. Strip malls (typically anchored by grocery or discount stores), associated centers (retail properties located adjacent to enclosed malls, usually anchored by big-box stores), office buildings, and mortgage loans round out the firm's portfolio. Its largest tenants include The Limited, The Gap, Foot Locker, and Abercrombie & Fitch. St. Louis is CBL's largest market.

	Annual Growth	12/05	12/06	12/07	12/08	12/09
Sales ($ mil.)	4.6%	908.7	1,002.1	1,040.6	1,138.2	1,089.5
Net income ($ mil.)	—	162.5	117.5	89.1	31.6	(7.1)
Market value ($ mil.)	(29.7%)	5,454.8	5,985.0	3,301.1	897.4	1,335.1
Employees	(10.1%)	1,483	1,511	0	1,376	969

CBOE HOLDINGS, INC.

400 S. LaSalle St.
Chicago, IL 60605
Phone: 312-786-5600
Fax: 312-786-7409
Web: www.cboe.com

CEO: William J. Brodsky
CFO: Alan J. Dean
HR: Deborah Woods
FYE: December 31
Type: Private

First there was one. CBOE (or Chicago Board Options Exchange) may no longer be the *only* options exchange, but it's still the US leader in overall volume. Founded in 1973 by the Chicago Board of Trade (now part of CME Group), CBOE lists options on more than 1,900 stocks, as well as on interest rates, broad-based stock indexes (such as Standard & Poor's S&P 500 Index), and industry indexes. CBOE, which had already launched the fully electronic CBOE Futures Exchange, debuted its CBOE Stock Exchange in early 2007, going head-to-head with the New York Stock Exchange and NASDAQ. CBOE also runs The Options Institute, which trains brokers and investors in all aspects of options. CBOE plans to go public in 2010.

CBS BROADCASTING INC.

51 W. 52nd St.
New York, NY 10019
Phone: 212-975-4321
Fax: 212-975-4516
Web: www.cbs.com

CEO: David Stapf
CFO: Bruce Taub
HR: Tiffany Smith-Anoa'i
FYE: December 31
Type: Subsidiary

The forensic evidence shows this company is tops in the TV ratings. A unit of CBS Corporation, CBS Broadcasting operates the CBS Television Network, the #1 watched broadcast network in the US. Its top shows include *CSI: Crime Scene Investigation* and its two spinoffs, as well as *The Mentalist, NCIS,* and a host of prime time comedy shows. The network boasts more than 200 affiliate stations around the nation. CBS Broadcasting also oversees 50%-owned The CW Network (a joint venture with Time Warner's Warner Bros. Entertainment) and production and distribution operations including CBS Television Distribution Group. In addition, CBS owns and operates about 30 TV stations across the country.

CBS CORPORATION

NYSE: CBS

51 W. 52nd St.
New York, NY 10019
Phone: 212-975-4321
Fax: 212-975-4516
Web: www.cbscorporation.com

CEO: Leslie (Les) Moonves
CFO: Joseph R. Ianniello
HR: Anthony G. Ambrosio
FYE: December 31
Type: Public

You might say this company has a real eye for broadcasting. CBS Corporation is a leading media conglomerate with operations in television, radio, online content, and publishing. Its portfolio is anchored by CBS Broadcasting, which operates the #1 rated CBS television network, along with a group of local TV stations. CBS also produces and distributes TV programming through CBS Television Studios and CBS Television Distribution. Other operations include CBS Radio, CBS Interactive, and book publisher Simon & Schuster. In addition, the company's CBS Outdoor is a leading operator of billboards and other outdoor advertising. Chairman Sumner Redstone controls CBS Corporation through National Amusements.

	Annual Growth	12/05	12/06	12/07	12/08	12/09
Sales ($ mil.)	(2.7%)	14,536.4	14,320.2	14,072.9	13,950.4	13,014.6
Net income ($ mil.)	—	(7,089.1)	1,660.5	1,247.0	(11,673.4)	226.5
Market value ($ mil.)	(12.6%)	16,353.1	21,201.2	18,529.0	5,568.9	9,553.5
Employees	(5.6%)	32,160	23,654	23,970	25,920	25,580

CBS RADIO INC.

40 W. 57th St., 14th Fl.
New York, NY 10019
Phone: 212-649-9600
Fax: 212-315-2162
Web: www.cbsradio.com

CEO: Daniel R. (Dan) Mason
CFO: —
HR: Mark Zulli
FYE: December 31
Type: Subsidiary

This company keeps its eye on radio listeners. CBS Radio is one of the country's leading radio broadcasters with about 130 stations serving about 30 major markets over the airwaves. Its stations offer a variety of programming from news, talk, and sports to a wide range of music styles; many of the stations are affiliates of the Westwood One radio network. (CBS Radio owns nearly 10% of the radio programming syndicator.) In addition to traditional broadcasting, many CBS stations broadcast digital over-the-air signals, along with online streaming and on-demand content. CBS Radio is a subsidiary of media giant CBS Corporation.

CC SERVICES INC.

1701 Towanda Avenue
Bloomington, IL 61701
Phone: 309-821-3000
Fax: 309-821-5160
Web: www.countryfinancial.com

CEO: John D. Blackburn
CFO: David A. Magers
HR: Deanna L. Frautschi
FYE: December 31
Type: Private

Country bumpkins and city slickers alike; CC Services is out to insure its clients against life's little mishaps. Operating as COUNTRY Financial, the company provides insurance services nationwide that include life, property/casualty, farm and ranch, disability and other traditional insurance products. Its COUNTRY Trust Bank and COUNTRY Capital Management units offer retirement planning, investment advice, asset management, and mutual funds. The company offers niche coverage on farm-related products, including crop insurance and farm vehicle policies. COUNTRY Financial traces its roots back to 1925, when a group of agricultural workers created a fire and lightning insurance company.

	Annual Growth	12/04	12/05	12/06	12/07	12/08
Est. sales ($ mil.)	—	—	—	—	—	544.2
Employees	—	—	—	—	—	3,604

CCA GLOBAL PARTNERS

4301 Earth City Expwy.
St. Louis, MO 63045
Phone: 314-506-0000
Fax: 314-291-6674
Web: www.ccaglobalpartners.com

CEO: Howard Brodsky
CFO: Jim Acker
HR: —
FYE: September 30
Type: Cooperative

Business is "floor"ishing at CCA Global Partners. Formerly named Carpet Co-op, the firm operates more than 3,800 floor covering and specialty retail stores in North America and abroad. Its largest units are flooring retailers Carpet One, with more than 1,000 locations in Australia, Canada, New Zealand, and the US, and Flooring America, with about 550 stores in the US and Canada. CCA Global's other retail operations include bicycle dealer The Bike Cooperative and lighting products seller Lighting One. In addition to its retail lines, the company provides mortgage banking and business services. Howard Brodsky and Alan Greenberg founded the co-op in 1984.

	Annual Growth	9/04	9/05	9/06	9/07	9/08
Sales ($ mil.)	4.1%	8,700.0	9,393.0	10,200.0	10,200.0	10,200.0
Employees	—	—	—	—	—	—

CCA INDUSTRIES, INC.

NYSE Amex: CAW

200 Murray Hill Pkwy.
East Rutherford, NJ 07073
Phone: 201-330-1400
Fax: 201-842-6014
Web: www.ccaindustries.com

CEO: David Edell
CFO: Stephen A. (Steve) Heit
HR: Ronnie Pouch
FYE: November 30
Type: Public

CCA Industries curls its customers' hair and brightens their smiles. It markets health and beauty aids, including Plus+White, Bikini Zone, Sudden Change, Solar Sense, and Nutra Nail. It also sells dietary supplements (Mega-T), shampoos (Wash 'N Curl), perfumes (Cherry Vanilla), and other health and beauty items. CCA supplies products to more than 400 accounts, including food and drug retailers, mass merchandisers, and beauty aid wholesalers. The firm outsources its manufacturing and operates primarily in the US, with a small portion of sales generated overseas. Several of CCA's products, such as Hair-Off, Mega-T green tea, and Kids Sense, are made and marketed through licensing agreements.

	Annual Growth	11/05	11/06	11/07	11/08	11/09
Sales ($ mil.)	(2.4%)	63.7	64.1	60.9	56.7	57.7
Net income ($ mil.)	(2.7%)	3.8	5.6	5.5	1.4	3.4
Market value ($ mil.)	(15.6%)	58.3	82.2	68.7	25.7	29.6
Employees	(2.2%)	153	153	150	150	140

CCC INFORMATION SERVICES GROUP INC.

222 Merchandise Mart, Ste. 900
Chicago, IL 60654
Phone: 312-222-4636
Fax: 312-527-2298
Web: www.cccis.com

CEO: Githesh Ramamurthy
CFO: Andrew G. Balbirer
HR: Gary Newman
FYE: December 31
Type: Subsidiary

CCC Information Services Group helps smooth the dents in auto claims processing. The company offers computer software and services that help insurance agencies, independent appraisers, and collision repair shops process auto claims. CCC's offerings include its Pathways application for estimating collision and repair cost and its Valuescope claim settlement services application for estimating the worth of totaled vehicles. CCC Information Services was acquired by Investcorp for about $496 million in early 2006, joining a diverse group of businesses that Investcorp has purchased.

CCFNB BANCORP, INC.

OTC: CCFN

232 East St.
Bloomsburg, PA 17815
Phone: 570-784-4400
Fax: 570-387-4049
Web: www.firstcolumbiabank.com

CEO: Lance O. Diehl
CFO: Jeffrey T. Arnold
HR: Edwin A. (Ed) Wenner
FYE: December 31
Type: Public

CCFNB Bancorp knows the ABCs of banking. It is the holding company for First Columbia Bank & Trust, a community institution serving Pennsylvania's Columbia, Montour, Northumberland, and Luzerne counties from some 15 locations. The bank offers standard products and services as well as wealth management and trust services. It uses funds from deposits to write a variety of loans; real estate loans account for more than 80% of its loan portfolio. The bank also offers consumer and construction loans. CCFNB Bancorp owns a 50% stake in Neighborhood Group (dba Neighborhood Advisors), an insurance and financial products agency. CCFNB Bancorp merged with Columbia Financial Corporation in 2008.

	Annual Growth	12/05	12/06	12/07	12/08	12/09
Assets ($ mil.)	27.1%	231.2	241.9	245.3	568.3	602.5
Net income ($ mil.)	28.0%	2.2	2.4	2.6	3.1	5.9
Market value ($ mil.)	(1.2%)	63.7	62.9	56.0	41.9	60.8
Employees	20.3%	86	95	95	184	180

⊞ CCH INCORPORATED

2700 Lake Cook Rd.
Riverwoods, IL 60015
Phone: 847-267-7000
Fax: 773-866-3095
Web: www.cch.com

CEO: Mike Sabbatis
CFO: —
HR: —
FYE: December 31
Type: Subsidiary

Tax season must be CCH's favorite time of year. CCH, also known as Wolters Kluwer Tax and Accounting, publishes more than 700 publications in print and electronic form, primarily concerning the subjects of tax and business law. Publications are available in a variety of formats, including looseleaf reports, CD-ROMs, books, newsletters, and online. The company's flagship product is *The Standard Federal Tax Reporter*. Its Tax and Accounting unit produces software used for tax preparation, audits, and office productivity. The company was founded in 1913, the same year the US federal income tax was created. CCH is a subsidiary of Dutch publisher Wolters Kluwer.

CCS MEDICAL HOLDINGS, INC.

14255 49th St. North, Ste. 301
Clearwater, FL 33762
Phone: 727-507-2772
Fax: 727-507-2879
Web: www.ccsmed.com

CEO: John L. Miclot
CFO: Stephen M. Saft
HR: —
FYE: December 31
Type: Private

CCS Medical Holdings knows that doorstep delivery is just a convenience for many, but it's critical for patients with chronic conditions. The company provides mail-order delivery of medical supplies to treat diabetes, as well as chronic wounds, incontinence, respiratory ailments, and other illnesses. CCS distributes a variety of drugs and medical supplies including blood glucose meters, catheters, insulin pumps, nebulizers, and ostomy and wound care supplies. It is one of the largest providers of respiratory medications and diabetes testing supplies to Medicare customers. CCS is majority-owned by venture capital firm Warburg Pincus. The company emerged from Chapter 11 bankruptcy protection in 2010.

	Annual Growth	12/04	12/05	12/06	12/07	12/08
Est. sales ($ mil.)	—	—	—	—	—	432.4
Employees	—	—	—	—	—	1,434

CDC SUPPLY CHAIN

8989 N. Deerwood Dr.
Milwaukee, WI 53223
Phone: 414-362-6800
Fax: 414-362-6794
Web: www.cdcsupplychain.com

CEO: Niklas Rönnbäck
CFO: —
HR: —
FYE: December 31
Type: Subsidiary

CDC Supply Chain serves as an agent of change in supply chains. The company's supply chain execution, performance, and process management software helps clients manage inventory and fulfillment, monitor their supply chain activities, and automate a range of warehouse functions, including receiving, loading, and storage. The company targets clients in the transportation, retail, consumer packaged goods, and processed goods industries. CDC Supply Chain counts multinational companies such as AstraZeneca, Boeing, Saks, and Smucker among its customers. CDC Supply Chain is a unit of CDC Software.

⊞ An in-depth profile of this company is available to Hoover's Online members at hoovers.com.

343

CDI CORP.

NYSE: CDI

1717 Arch St., 35th Fl.
Philadelphia, PA 19103
Phone: 215-569-2200
Fax: 215-569-1300
Web: www.cdicorp.com

CEO: Roger H. Ballou
CFO: Mark A. Kerschner
HR: Cecilia J. Venglarik
FYE: December 31
Type: Public

If you want to get technical, give CDI a call. The company provides engineering and information technology (IT) staffing services to customers in such industries as aerospace, biotech, chemical, manufacturing, and pharmaceutical. Its engineering segment includes CDI Government Services, which provides naval engineering, design, and military aviation support services to the US government. Other CDI units include MRINetwork (permanent employment recruiting and temporary staffing services) and AndersElite (staffing services for the UK construction industry). In addition, the company's ITS segment offers IT staffing, testing, help desk, and consulting services.

	Annual Growth	12/05	12/06	12/07	12/08	12/09
Sales ($ mil.)	(6.0%)	1,133.6	1,265.3	1,187.3	1,118.6	885.0
Net income ($ mil.)	—	14.0	23.3	34.2	19.4	(19.9)
Market value ($ mil.)	(17.1%)	520.8	473.3	461.1	245.9	246.1
Employees	(17.3%)	18,800	1,700	1,400	10,400	8,800

⊞ CDW LLC

200 N. Milwaukee Ave.
Vernon Hills, IL 60061
Phone: 847-465-6000
Fax: 847-564-6800
Web: www.cdw.com

CEO: John A. Edwardson
CFO: Ann E. Ziegler
HR: Dennis G. Berger
FYE: December 31
Type: Private

CDW takes more orders than Beetle Bailey. The company offers about 100,000 technology products, including notebook and desktop computers, software, printers, servers, storage devices, networking tools, and accessories. Top brands include Adobe, Apple, Cisco, Hewlett-Packard, Microsoft, Sony, ViewSonic, and Xerox, among others. CDW operates a retail store at its corporate headquarters and manages an e-commerce site. It also has a Toronto-based subsidiary that markets computer products to customers across Canada. Almost all of the company's sales come from public-sector clients and private businesses. Founded in 1984, it is owned by private equity firms Madison Dearborn Partners and Providence Equity Partners.

	Annual Growth	12/04	12/05	12/06	12/07	12/08
Sales ($ mil.)	(0.4%)	—	—	—	8,100.0	8,070.0
Employees	(0.7%)	—	—	—	6,900	6,850

C-E MINERALS, INC.

901 E. 8th Ave.
King of Prussia, PA 19406
Phone: 610-768-8800
Fax: 610-337-8122
Web: www.ceminerals.com

CEO: Timothy J. McCarthy
CFO: —
HR: Carol Wilkinson
FYE: December 31
Type: Subsidiary

You can be pretty sure of the answer to the "Animal, vegetable, or mineral?" query if you're playing 20 Questions with C-E Minerals. The subsidiary of French industrial minerals company Imerys processes and distributes aluminas, alumina-silica calcines, and fused minerals used by customers in such industries as electronics, electrical equipment manufacturing, plastics, and cosmetics. C-E Minerals' products are used in refractory, metal-production, casting, abrasive, and other industrial applications. The company has operations in the US, Asia, and South America.

	Annual Growth	12/04	12/05	12/06	12/07	12/08
Est. sales ($ mil.)	—	—	—	—	—	90.3
Employees	—	—	—	—	—	928

CEC ENTERTAINMENT, INC.

NYSE: CEC

4441 W. Airport Fwy.
Irving, TX 75062
Phone: 972-258-8507
Fax: 972-258-5524
Web: www.chuckecheese.com

CEO: Michael H. (Mike) Magusiak
CFO: Christopher D. (Chris) Morris
HR: Catherine R. Olivieri
FYE: December 31
Type: Public

Don't let the mouse mascot fool you: This amusement kingdom is founded on the power of pizza. CEC Entertainment operates the Chuck E. Cheese's chain of pizza parlors with more than 540 locations throughout the US, Canada, and a half dozen other countries. The restaurants cater mostly to families with children and feature dining-room entertainment provided by robotic characters, arcade games, and other activities. (The eateries are especially popular destinations for birthday parties.) Games and merchandise account for about 50% of sales. The menu features pizzas, sandwiches, salads, and desserts. CEC Entertainment owns and operates about 500 of the pizza and fun joints, while the rest are franchised.

	Annual Growth	12/05	12/06	12/07	12/08	12/09
Sales ($ mil.)	3.0%	726.2	774.1	785.3	814.5	818.3
Net income ($ mil.)	(4.3%)	72.9	68.3	55.9	56.5	61.2
Market value ($ mil.)	(1.6%)	748.0	884.4	570.4	532.9	701.4
Employees	(3.5%)	19,408	18,395	18,500	16,800	16,800

CECIL BANCORP, INC.

OTC: CECB

127 North St.
Elkton, MD 21921
Phone: 410-398-1650
Fax: 410-392-3128
Web: www.cecilfederal.com

CEO: Mary B. Halsey
CFO: R. Lee Whitehead
HR: —
FYE: December 31
Type: Public

Cecil Bancorp is the holding company for Cecil Federal Bank, which serves northeastern Maryland's Cecil and Harford counties through about a dozen branches. Founded in 1959, Cecil Federal Bank offers standard deposit products such as checking and savings accounts, NOW and money market accounts, CDs, and retirement accounts. The bank focuses on real estate lending; commercial mortgages make up the largest portion of the bank's loan portfolio, followed by one- to four-family residential mortgages and construction loans. It offers investment and insurance services through an agreement with third-party provider Community Bankers Securities. Chairman Charles Sposato owns more than a third of Cecil Bancorp.

	Annual Growth	12/05	12/06	12/07	12/08	12/09
Assets ($ mil.)	17.5%	267.1	347.5	401.4	492.4	509.8
Net income ($ mil.)	—	2.1	2.7	3.4	1.9	(2.5)
Market value ($ mil.)	(18.4%)	29.1	34.7	33.2	24.9	12.9
Employees	3.0%	81	87	92	92	91

CECO ENVIRONMENTAL CORP.

NASDAQ (GM): CECE

3120 Forrer St.
Cincinnati, OH 45209
Phone: 513-458-2600
Fax: 513-458-2647
Web: www.cecoenviro.com

CEO: Jeff Lang
CFO: Dennis W. Blazer
HR: —
FYE: December 31
Type: Public

CECO Environmental wants to clear the air. Through its subsidiaries, CECO Environmental makes industrial ventilation and pollution control systems, including air filters to remove airborne solid and liquid pollutants. The company serves customers in the automotive, chemical, electronics, pharmaceutical, and textile industries, among others. Customers have included General Motors, Honda, and Procter & Gamble. CECO Environmental also provides custom metal fabrication services, making components for its own ventilation systems. Chairman Phillip DeZwirek and his family control CECO Environmental.

	Annual Growth	12/05	12/06	12/07	12/08	12/09
Sales ($ mil.)	14.3%	81.5	135.4	236.0	217.9	139.0
Net income ($ mil.)	—	(0.4)	3.1	6.3	5.0	(15.0)
Market value ($ mil.)	(8.9%)	82.1	128.3	157.0	34.6	56.5
Employees	10.3%	446	651	701	845	660

CEDAR FAIR, L.P.
NYSE: FUN

1 Cedar Point Dr.
Sandusky, OH 44870
Phone: 419-626-0830
Fax: 419-627-2260
Web: www.cedarfair.com

CEO: Richard L. (Dick) Kinzel
CFO: Peter J. Crage
HR: —
FYE: December 31
Type: Public

Cedar Fair wants to take you for the ride of your life. The firm owns and manages some 10 amusement parks, six outdoor water parks, one indoor water park, and five hotels. Properties include Knott's Berry Farm in California, Michigan's Adventure, and Cedar Point, located on Lake Erie in Sandusky, Ohio. Knott's Berry Farm operates year-round, while other parks are open daily from Memorial Day through Labor Day, plus additional weekends in April, May, September, and October. Cedar Fair bought Paramount Parks from CBS Corp. in 2006. Cedar Fair parks together draw some 20 million visitors.

	Annual Growth	12/05	12/06	12/07	12/08	12/09
Sales ($ mil.)	12.7%	568.7	831.4	987.0	996.2	916.1
Net income ($ mil.)	(31.5%)	160.9	87.5	(4.5)	5.7	35.4
Market value ($ mil.)	(20.5%)	1,579.0	1,539.1	1,169.0	693.2	631.2
Employees	(43.1%)	16,200	31,850	1,800	1,700	1,700

CEDAR SHOPPING CENTERS, INC.
NYSE: CDR

44 S. Bayles Ave., Ste. 304
Port Washington, NY 11050
Phone: 516-767-6492
Fax: 516-767-6497
Web: www.cedarshoppingcenters.com

CEO: Leo S. Ullman
CFO: Lawrence E. (Larry) Kreider Jr.
HR: —
FYE: December 31
Type: Public

Cedar Shopping Centers has tended its portfolio from a sapling to a full-grown evergreen. The self-managed real estate investment trust (REIT) owns, develops, and manages retail properties, mainly supermarket- or drug store-anchored strip centers in the Northeast and Mid-Atlantic. It owns about 120 properties totaling approximately 13 million sq. ft. of leasable space, as well as some 200 acres of developable land. Its portfolio spans nine states, with the heaviest concentration in Pennsylvania, Massachusetts, and Connecticut. Major tenants include Giant Foods (accounting for 10% of rental revenues), Discount Drug Mart, and CVS. The REIT usually redevelops or expands existing properties after it buys them.

	Annual Growth	12/05	12/06	12/07	12/08	12/09
Sales ($ mil.)	23.1%	79.0	127.3	154.3	175.7	181.7
Net income ($ mil.)	—	13.2	15.3	22.0	18.4	(16.8)
Market value ($ mil.)	(16.6%)	911.1	1,030.3	662.4	458.5	440.3
Employees	9.5%	71	109	91	96	102

CEDARS-SINAI MEDICAL CENTER

8700 Beverly Blvd.
Los Angeles, CA 90048
Phone: 310-423-3277
Fax: —
Web: www.csmc.edu

CEO: Thomas M. (Tom) Priselac
CFO: Edward M. Prunchunas
HR: Jeanne Flores
FYE: June 30
Type: Not-for-profit

Many a star has been born, literally, at Cedars-Sinai Medical Center. The 950-bed teaching and research hospital is located right where Los Angeles meets Beverly Hills and West Hollywood, and has tended to the medical needs of a number of celebrities since its inception in 1902. However, the center is also a major teaching hospital for UCLA's David Geffen School of Medicine and is engaged in some 600 research programs, in areas such as cancer, neuroscience, and genetics. Its Cedars-Sinai Medical Group is a multi-specialty physicians group consisting of about 90 doctors; the medical center is also affiliated with an Independent Physician Association with roughly 500 primary care and specialist doctors.

CEGEDIM DENDRITE

1207 Rte. 206 South
Bedminster, NJ 07921
Phone: 908-443-2000
Fax: —
Web: www.cegedimdendrite.com/En/Pages

CEO: Laurent Labrune
CFO: Brent J. Cosgrove
HR: —
FYE: December 31
Type: Subsidiary

Cegedim Dendrite helps salespeople conduct business, offering services and software that manage and analyze sales efforts for the pharmaceutical and consumer packaged goods industries. The company's products include applications that help salesforces access product information and physician databases, evaluate competitors, and catalog client and prospect data. It does business in more than 80 countries and serves small to large companies. Known as Dendrite International until 2007, the company changed its name after it was acquired by Cegedim for $751 million.

CELADON GROUP, INC.
NASDAQ (GS): CLDN

9503 E. 33rd St.
Indianapolis, IN 46235
Phone: 317-972-7000
Fax: 317-890-8099
Web: www.celadontrucking.com

CEO: Stephen (Steve) Russell
CFO: Paul A. Will
HR: —
FYE: June 30
Type: Public

Celadon Group provides long-haul, dry van truckload service throughout North America via subsidiaries Celadon Trucking Services, Celadon Canada, and Mexico-based Jaguar. The group maintains a fleet of about 3,100 tractors and 10,000 trailers. Celadon also offers dedicated contract carriage, in which drivers and equipment are assigned to a customer long-term, as well as freight brokerage and warehousing services. Its clients have included large shippers with strict time-delivery requirements such as Alcoa, Procter & Gamble, Philip Morris, and Wal-Mart. An e-commerce unit, TruckersB2B, serves as a purchasing cooperative for smaller trucking fleets and provides discounts on fuel, tires, and satellite systems.

	Annual Growth	6/05	6/06	6/07	6/08	6/09
Sales ($ mil.)	2.9%	436.8	480.2	502.7	565.9	490.3
Net income ($ mil.)	(32.6%)	12.6	20.5	22.3	6.5	2.6
Market value ($ mil.)	2.8%	167.2	490.6	353.7	222.4	186.8
Employees	4.2%	3,210	3,353	3,548	3,874	3,777

CELANESE CORPORATION
NYSE: CE

1601 W. LBJ Fwy.
Dallas, TX 75234
Phone: 972-443-4000
Fax: 972-443-8555
Web: www.celanese.com

CEO: David N. Weidman
CFO: Steven M. (Steve) Sterin
HR: Jacquelyn K. Wolf
FYE: December 31
Type: Public

Celanese Corporation's primary operations include the manufacture of building block chemicals like acetic acid and vinyl acetate monomers (VAM). Those chemicals are used in everything from paints and inks to agricultural products and chewing gum. Canadian subsidiary Acetex, the majority of whose sales come from Europe, is the world's largest acetyls manufacturer. Other products include acetate tow (used in cigarette filters); industrial specialties like ethylene vinyl aceta (EVA); and engineered plastics. The bulk of Celanese's sales come from the US and Germany.

	Annual Growth	12/05	12/06	12/07	12/08	12/09
Sales ($ mil.)	(4.3%)	6,070.0	6,656.0	6,444.0	6,823.0	5,082.0
Net income ($ mil.)	15.2%	277.0	406.0	426.0	282.0	488.0
Market value ($ mil.)	13.8%	2,995.6	4,054.7	6,630.4	1,947.5	5,029.2
Employees	(5.6%)	9,300	8,900	8,400	8,350	7,400

An in-depth profile of this company is available to Hoover's Online members at hoovers.com.

345

CELEBRATE EXPRESS, INC.

11220 120th Ave. NE
Kirkland, WA 98033
Phone: 425-250-1064
Fax: 425-828-6252
Web: www.celebrateexpress.com

CEO: Jalem M. Getz
CFO: —
HR: —
FYE: December 31
Type: Subsidiary

Celebrate Express provides everything for a birthday party except the birthday suit (although it does sell costumes). The e-tailer operates a trio of websites: BirthdayExpress.com; 1stWishes.com; and CostumeExpress.com, all designed to help kids party in style. Birthday Express offers more than 150 themed party packages targeting families with young children. As the name suggests, 1stWishes (launched in 2006) specializes in those all-important first birthdays. The direct retailer also sells children's costumes and accessories via Costume Express. Founded in 1994, Celebrate Express went public in 2004. The company was acquired in 2008 by the holding company Liberty Media through its BuySeasons subsidiary.

CELERA CORPORATION

NASDAQ (GS): CRA

1401 Harbor Bay Pkwy.
Alameda, CA 94502
Phone: 510-749-4200
Fax: —
Web: www.celera.com

CEO: Kathy P. Ordoñez
CFO: Ugo D. DeBlasi
HR: Paul D. Arata
FYE: December 31
Type: Public

Celera spent years unwrapping the secrets of genetics, and now it is ready to do something with all that it has learned. Celera cleared a major hurdle when it mapped the human genome, but the firm is now focused on developing diagnostics and providing clinical services. The company's Berkeley HeartLab (BHL) business provides cardiology testing and disease management services. Its products business develops and manufactures the molecular diagnostic products that it markets to detect, characterize, monitor, and select treatment for a full range of diseases and genetic mutations, including HIV and cystic fibrosis. Formerly part of Applied Biosystems, Celera split off as an independent company in 2008.

	Annual Growth	6/05	6/06	6/07	6/08	*12/09
Sales ($ mil.)	52.4%	31.0	46.2	43.4	138.7	167.1
Net income ($ mil.)	—	(77.1)	(62.7)	(19.8)	(104.1)	(32.8)
Market value ($ mil.)	(10.9%)	899.4	1,061.7	1,016.6	931.4	565.7
Employees	3.5%	480	300	290	554	551

*Fiscal year change

CELERITY SOLUTIONS, INC.

Pink Sheets: CLTY

270 Bridge St., Ste. 302
Dedham, MA 02026
Phone: 781-329-1900
Fax: 781-329-1655
Web: slingshotecity.com

CEO: Rajesh Krishnan
CFO: —
HR: —
FYE: March 31
Type: Public

Celerity Solutions (dba Slingshot Software) has a quick answer to supply chain management woes. Through its Slingshot eCity division the company sells Web-based enterprise software that manages sales and purchase orders, accounting, procurement, and customer relationship management functions, as well as supply chain planning and forecasting. Slingshot eCity targets customers in a variety of industries, including manufacturing, telecommunications, utilities, electronics, chemicals, and health care. The company also offers such services as consulting, implementation, maintenance, and support. CEO Paul Carr controls the company.

CELGENE CORPORATION

NASDAQ (GS): CELG

86 Morris Ave.
Summit, NJ 07901
Phone: 908-673-9000
Fax: 908-673-9001
Web: www.celgene.com

CEO: Sol J. Barer
CFO: David W. Gryska
HR: —
FYE: December 31
Type: Public

A terror from the past has provided hope in the present. Celgene's flagship products Thalomid and Revlimid are versions of the infamous thalidomide, the morning sickness remedy pulled from shelves in the 1960s after it was linked to birth defects. Both drugs are approved in the US and Europe as a treatment for multiple myeloma (bone marrow cancer). Revlimid also is used to treat a malignant blood disease called MDS. Celgene sells each drug under strict risk management plans that ensure they are safely administered. The firm has other drugs in development that combat inflammatory diseases and cancer. Fidelity Management and Research and Janus Capital Management combined hold about 15% of the company's shares.

	Annual Growth	12/05	12/06	12/07	12/08	12/09
Sales ($ mil.)	49.6%	536.9	898.9	1,405.8	2,254.8	2,689.9
Net income ($ mil.)	86.9%	63.7	69.0	226.4	(1,533.7)	776.7
Market value ($ mil.)	14.5%	14,931.9	26,513.4	21,296.5	25,476.5	25,660.8
Employees	31.4%	944	1,287	1,685	2,441	2,813

CELL THERAPEUTICS, INC.

NASDAQ (GM): CTIC

501 Elliott Ave. West, Ste. 400
Seattle, WA 98119
Phone: 206-282-7100
Fax: 206-284-6206
Web: www.cticseattle.com

CEO: James A. Bianco
CFO: Louis A. Bianco
HR: —
FYE: December 31
Type: Public

Cell Therapeutics (CTI) is a toxic avenger. The firm creates more effective and less toxic treatments for various forms of cancer. CTI is also developing a number of other cancer-fighting compounds, including paclitaxel poliglumex (Opaxio, formerly branded as Xyotax) for non-small cell lung and ovarian cancers, and pixantrone, another treatment for non-Hodgkin's lymphoma. The company's Systems Medicine subsidiary is working on a potential sarcoma-fighter called brostallicin. It no longer markets any commercial products and instead focuses on research and development projects.

	Annual Growth	12/05	12/06	12/07	12/08	12/09
Sales ($ mil.)	(71.9%)	16.1	0.1	0.1	11.4	0.1
Net income ($ mil.)	—	(102.5)	(135.8)	(138.1)	(180.0)	(95.4)
Market value ($ mil.)	(66.2%)	57,229.1	45,940.8	12,338.4	91.9	748.2
Employees	(16.5%)	214	197	230	194	104

CELLCO PARTNERSHIP

1 Verizon Way
Basking Ridge, NJ 07920
Phone: 908-559-2000
Fax: —
Web: www.verizonwireless.com

CEO: Lowell C. McAdam
CFO: John Townsend
HR: Martha Delehanty
FYE: December 31
Type: Joint venture

A strong alliance with a trusted partner can be the cornerstone of a great enterprise. While only time will tell how this union will fare as the telecommunications industry evolves, for now, Cellco Partnership is the #1 US wireless phone operator in terms of subscribers (ahead of rival AT&T Mobility). Serving more than 80 million consumers, business, and government customers nationwide under the Verizon Wireless brand, the joint venture is controlled by Verizon Communications (which owns 55% of the company); UK-based global communications giant Vodafone Group owns the remaining share. The company also offers mobile data services, including text messaging, multimedia content (V CAST), and Web access.

	Annual Growth	12/04	12/05	12/06	12/07	12/08
Sales ($ mil.)	15.6%	27,662.0	32,301.0	38,043.0	43,882.0	49,332.0
Net income ($ mil.)	29.7%	4,698.0	6,152.0	8,448.0	10,860.0	13,289.0
Employees	14.6%	49,800	55,700	67,000	69,000	85,800

CELLDEX THERAPEUTICS, INC.

NASDAQ (GM): CLDX

119 4th Ave.
Needham, MA 02494
Phone: 781-433-0771
Fax: 781-433-0262
Web: www.celldextherapeutics.com

CEO: Anthony S. Marucci
CFO: Avery W. (Chip) Catlin
HR: —
FYE: December 31
Type: Public

Celldex Therapeutics sees a future when a vaccine can end brain cancer and prevent the spread of cholera. It's lead candidate, CDX-110, is in late-stage clinical trials to treat malignant glioblastoma brain tumors. The biotech company has candidates in development for other types of tumors, and is developing oral vaccines to protect against maladies such as *E. coli*, cholera, and typhoid. The company developed Rotarix, an FDA-approved vaccine that combats rotavirus infection, which causes diarrhea and vomiting in infants; partner GlaxoSmithKline sells the product worldwide. The firm, formerly named AVANT Immunotherapeutics, merged with privately held biotech Celldex Therapeutics in 2008 and took on its name.

	Annual Growth	12/05	12/06	12/07	12/08	12/09
Sales ($ mil.)	48.8%	3.1	4.9	5.1	7.5	15.2
Net income ($ mil.)	—	(18.1)	(20.4)	(21.6)	(47.5)	(36.5)
Market value ($ mil.)	(32.5%)	717.0	512.0	190.7	251.7	148.4
Employees	2.3%	85	99	53	81	93

CELLU TISSUE HOLDINGS, INC.

NYSE: CLU

1855 Lockeway Dr., Ste. 501
Alpharetta, GA 30004
Phone: 678-393-2651
Fax: 678-393-2657
Web: www.cellutissue.com

CEO: Russell C. Taylor
CFO: David J. Morris
HR: W. Edwin Litton
FYE: February 28
Type: Public

Cellu Tissue Holdings manufactures large rolls of tissue from processed pulp and produces tissue products for the private-label and away-from-home industries. Most of its revenue comes from converted tissue products including paper napkins and bath tissue, but it also produces foam products such as plates and bowls. In addition to finished products, the company also sells tissue and machine glazed tissue rolls — known as hard rolls — to manufacturers of such items as diapers, feminine care products, and food wrap. The company, which is owned by Cellu Paper Holdings and backed by equity firm Weston Presidio, went public early in 2010. It was founded in 1984.

	Annual Growth	2/06	2/07	2/08	2/09	2/10
Sales ($ mil.)	11.7%	328.8	335.5	431.0	519.0	511.3
Net income ($ mil.)	—	(2.6)	(12.7)	4.0	6.6	3.8
Market value ($ mil.)	—	—	—	—	—	208.5
Employees	7.3%	—	—	—	1,160	1,245

CEL-SCI CORPORATION

NYSE Amex: CVM

8229 Boone Blvd., Ste. 802
Vienna, VA 22182
Phone: 703-506-9460
Fax: 703-506-9471
Web: www.cel-sci.com

CEO: Geert R. Kersten
CFO: Geert R. Kersten
HR: —
FYE: September 30
Type: Public

CEL-SCI hopes to make L.E.A.P.S. and bounds in preventing and treating deadly diseases. Its L.E.A.P.S. (Ligand Epitope Antigen Presentation System) technology modulates T-cells and may lead to synthetic vaccines for herpes, viral encephalitis, smallpox, and other diseases; the National Institutes of Health is testing CEL-1000 (a compound developed using L.E.A.P.S. technology) as a potential avian flu vaccine. The firm's lead drug candidate, however, is Multikine, which might make tumors more susceptible to radiation therapy and help a patient's body produce tumor-fighting antibodies. Multikine is undergoing clinical trials for the treatment of head and neck tumors.

	Annual Growth	9/05	9/06	9/07	9/08	9/09
Sales ($ mil.)	(24.0%)	0.3	0.1	0.1	0.0	0.1
Net income ($ mil.)	—	(3.0)	(7.9)	(9.6)	(7.7)	(40.9)
Market value ($ mil.)	38.3%	96.0	125.1	127.7	81.7	351.2
Employees	11.2%	19	19	26	30	29

CELSION CORPORATION

NASDAQ (GM): CLSN

10220 Old Columbia Rd., Ste. L
Columbia, MD 21046
Phone: 410-290-5390
Fax: 410-290-5394
Web: www.celsion.com

CEO: Michael H. Tardugno
CFO: —
HR: —
FYE: December 31
Type: Public

Celsion is trying to turn up the heat on cancer. The company is developing a heat-activated cancer therapy in the form of its lead drug ThermoDox. ThermoDox combines a common oncology drug, doxorubicin, with a heat-activated liposome that may help deliver and release the drug more accurately. The drug is being studied as a treatment for liver cancer and breast cancer. Celsion was previously a device maker and developed the Prolieve Thermodilatation system, an FDA-approved device used to treat benign prostatic hyperplasia (prostate enlargement). Celsion sold the product line to Boston Scientific in 2007.

	Annual Growth	12/05	12/06	12/07	12/08	12/09
Sales ($ mil.)	—	—	—	—	2.5	0.0
Net income ($ mil.)	—	—	—	—	(11.8)	(15.2)
Market value ($ mil.)	48.6%	—	—	—	26.9	40.0
Employees	11.8%	—	—	—	17	19

CELSIUS HOLDINGS, INC.

NASDAQ (CM): CELH

140 NE 4th Ave., Ste. C
Delray Beach, FL 33483
Phone: 561-276-2239
Fax: 561-276-2268
Web: www.celsius.com

CEO: Stephen C. (Steve) Haley
CFO: Geary W. Cotton
HR: –
FYE: December 31
Type: Public

Celsius Holdings wants consumers to enjoy the taste of burning calories. The company develops, markets, and distributes nutritional drinks that claim to burn calories, raise metabolism, and boost energy. Its first product, Celsius, is a canned sparkling beverage that comes in a variety of flavors and is marketed as an alternative to soda, coffee, and traditional energy drinks. Although it has undergone independent clinical studies, results have not been US FDA approved. Its products, which also include non-carbonated Celsius green tea drinks and single-serving powder mix packets that can be added to water, are manufactured by third-party co-packers. Celsius Holdings was founded in 2004 under the name Elite FX.

	Annual Growth	12/05	12/06	12/07	12/08	12/09
Sales ($ mil.)	92.0%	—	—	1.6	2.6	5.9
Net income ($ mil.)	—	—	—	(3.7)	(5.3)	(7.8)
Market value ($ mil.)	27.8%	—	—	57.0	15.5	93.1
Employees	15.5%	—	—	21	28	28

CEMEX DE PUERTO RICO, INC.

Km. 2.7 Carretera 165, Zona Industrial Amelia
Guaynabo, PR 00968
Phone: 787-783-3000
Fax: 787-781-8850
Web: www.cemexpuertorico.com

CEO: Leopoldo Navarro
CFO: —
HR: Maribel Gonzalez
FYE: December 31
Type: Subsidiary

CEMEX de Puerto Rico makes cement in Puerto Rico. Shocking, but true. Formerly Puerto Rican Cement Company (PRCC), the company operates a cement plant and about 20 ready-mix facilities, an aggregates quarry, and two land distribution centers in Puerto Rico. CEMEX de Puerto Rico serves cement customers throughout the island, but its ready-mix operations are concentrated in the eastern part of the island; it has an installed capacity of about 1.2 million tons a year. Its parent company, Mexico-based giant CEMEX, operates primarily in North America and Europe, but has customers throughout the world.

An in-depth profile of this company is available to Hoover's Online members at hoovers.com.

347

CEMEX INC.

920 Memorial City Way, Ste. 100
Houston, TX 77024
Phone: 713-650-6200
Fax: 713-653-6815
Web: www.cemexusa.com

CEO: Gilberto Perez
CFO: —
HR: Andrew M. (Andy) Miller
FYE: December 31
Type: Subsidiary

CEMEX serves up cement with a multicultural accent. The subsidiary of Mexico-based CEMEX, S.A. de C.V. is one of the largest cement companies in the US, as well as the largest ready-mix company. In addition to cement and ready-mix, CEMEX also makes and sells concrete block and aggregates. It serves customers through nearly 15 cement plants, ready-mix plants, and distribution facilities, and more than 100 aggregate quarries. The United States accounts for about 20% of the Mexican company's revenue. The parent company operates in more than 50 countries around the world.

CENGAGE LEARNING, INC.

200 First Stamford Place, Ste. 400
Stamford, CT 06902
Phone: 203-965-8600
Fax: 800-487-8488
Web: www.cengage.com

CEO: Ronald G. (Ron) Dunn
CFO: Dean D. Durbin
HR: Adrian Butler
FYE: December 31
Type: Private

Cengage Learning can engage students in a wide variety of ways. The company provides courseware, specialized content, print textbooks, homework and study tools, and e-learning services for businesses, educational institutions, government agencies, libraries, and individuals. Its offerings include online reference databases, distance learning and test preparation courses, corporate training courses, and materials for specific academic disciplines. Cengage Learning offers educational products under the Wadsworth, South-Western, Course Technology, Delmar, Gale, Prometric, and NETg names.

CENTAUR TECHNOLOGY, INC.

7600-C N. Capital of Texas Hwy., Ste. 300
Austin, TX 78731
Phone: 512-418-5700
Fax: 512-794-0717
Web: www.centtech.com

CEO: Glenn Henry
CFO: —
HR: —
FYE: December 31
Type: Subsidiary

The horsepower provided by Centaur Technology's processors is a breed apart. An independent subsidiary and design house of chipset stalwart VIA Technologies, Centaur makes low-cost microprocessors for use in mobile PCs and other portable electronics. The company designed VIA's C7-M processor, one of the world's smallest, lowest-power, and most secure x86-architecture processors. Centaur was established in Austin, Texas, in 1995 and prides itself on its employee-friendly work environment with free breakfasts and lunches and an onsite fitness facility. VIA purchased Centaur in 1999. The company has no management hierarchy, save for founder and president Glenn Henry.

CENTENE CORPORATION

NYSE: CNC

7711 Carondelet Ave., Ste. 800
St. Louis, MO 63105
Phone: 314-725-4477
Fax: 314-558-2428
Web: www.centene.com

CEO: Michael F. Neidorff
CFO: William N. Scheffel
HR: —
FYE: December 31
Type: Public

Centene provides managed care programs and related services to individuals and families enrolled in government-assisted health programs. The company operates in nearly a dozen states under the names Managed Health Services in Wisconsin and Indiana, Superior HealthPlan in Texas, and Buckeye Community Health Plan in Ohio, among others. Centene provides services to some 1.4 million low-income, elderly, and disabled people receiving Medicaid, Supplemental Security Income, and State Children's Health Insurance Program (SCHIP) benefits. Centene also offers specialty services in areas such as behavioral health, disease management, optical benefit plans, nurse triage, and pharmacy benefits management.

	Annual Growth	12/05	12/06	12/07	12/08	12/09
Sales ($ mil.)	28.5%	1,505.9	2,279.0	2,919.3	3,364.5	4,102.9
Net income ($ mil.)	11.6%	55.6	(43.6)	73.4	83.5	86.2
Market value ($ mil.)	(5.3%)	1,354.0	1,265.4	1,413.2	1,015.1	1,090.3
Employees	21.3%	1,800	2,600	3,100	3,600	3,900

CENTER BANCORP, INC.

NASDAQ (GS): CNBC

2455 Morris Ave.
Union, NJ 07083
Phone: 908-688-9500
Fax: 908-688-3043
Web: www.centerbancorp.com

CEO: Anthony C. (Tony) Weagley
CFO: Stephen J. Mauger
HR: Ruth M. Ennis
FYE: December 31
Type: Public

Center Bancorp is the holding company for Union Center National Bank, which operates about a dozen offices in northern New Jersey's Morris and Union counties. A full-service commercial bank, Union Center offers individuals and local businesses such deposit products as checking, savings, and money market accounts; CDs; and IRAs. It also offers trust services. Commercial loans account for about 50% of the bank's loan portfolio; residential mortgages account for most of the remainder. Subsidiaries offer services such as advertising, insurance (annuities, property/casualty, life, and health), wealth management, and real estate investment trust (REIT) operations.

	Annual Growth	12/05	12/06	12/07	12/08	12/09
Assets ($ mil.)	1.8%	1,114.8	1,051.4	1,017.6	1,023.3	1,196.8
Net income ($ mil.)	(11.8%)	7.6	3.9	3.9	5.8	4.6
Market value ($ mil.)	(3.9%)	152.1	219.6	161.2	119.2	130.0
Employees	(5.7%)	202	214	172	160	160

CENTER FINANCIAL CORPORATION

NASDAQ (GS): CLFC

3435 Wilshire Blvd., Ste. 700
Los Angeles, CA 90010
Phone: 213-251-2222
Fax: 213-386-6774
Web: www.centerbank.com

CEO: Jae Whan (J. W.) Yoo
CFO: Douglas J. (Doug) Goddard
HR: —
FYE: December 31
Type: Public

This company wants to be in the middle of your finances. Center Financial Corporation is the holding company for Center Bank, which caters to Korean-American businesses, professionals, and consumers. The bank has about 20 branches in California, as well as in Chicago and Seattle. Offering bilingual services, it focuses on commercial lending, including mortgages, working capital, construction loans, Small Business Administration loans, international letters of credit, and short-term trade finance for importers/exporters. In 2010 Center Bank expanded into Northern California with the acquisition of the failed Innovative Bank in an FDIC-assisted transaction.

	Annual Growth	12/05	12/06	12/07	12/08	12/09
Assets ($ mil.)	7.2%	1,661.0	1,843.3	2,080.7	2,056.6	2,192.8
Net income ($ mil.)	—	24.6	26.2	21.9	0.2	(42.5)
Market value ($ mil.)	(34.6%)	1,003.8	956.3	491.5	246.2	183.5
Employees	(4.4%)	327	344	368	316	273

CENTER OIL COMPANY

600 Mason Ridge Center Dr., 2nd Fl.	CEO: Gary R. Parker
St. Louis, MO 63141	CFO: Richard I. (Rick) Powers
Phone: 314-682-3500	HR: Richard I. (Rick) Powers
Fax: 314-682-3599	FYE: December 31
Web: www.centeroil.com	Type: Private

Center Oil's core business is peddling petroleum. The company is one of the largest private wholesale distributors of gasoline and other petroleum products to customers primarily in the eastern region of the US. Center Oil owns a dozen storage terminals capable of storing 2.8 million barrels of petroleum products. It also has access to 36 terminals in 10 states, as well as access to the Magellan, Texas Eastern, Kinder Morgan Chicago, and Kaneb pipeline systems. Its products are also distributed through a fleet of ships, barges, and trucks.

	Annual Growth	12/04	12/05	12/06	12/07	12/08
Sales ($ mil.)	—	—	—	—	—	4,900.0
Employees	—	—	—	—	—	46

CENTER PARTNERS, INC.

4401 Innovation Dr.	CEO: David Geiger
Fort Collins, CO 80525	CFO: Gordon Jones
Phone: 970-206-9000	HR: —
Fax: 970-206-8434	FYE: January 1
Web: www.centerpartners.com	Type: Subsidiary

Center Partners wants to be the nucleus of your customer care world. The company provides contact center services for inbound, outbound communications using the Internet, on the phone, and in person. The company offers expertise in creating, implementing, and managing multichannel programs covering sales and acquisition, customer care, and technical support for clients in such industries as telecommunications, utilities, health care, financial services, high technology, and insurance. Established in 1997, it is a unit of WPP Group, one of the world's largest media conglomerates.

CENTERLINE HOLDING COMPANY

OTC: CLNH

625 Madison Ave.	CEO: Robert L. (Rob) Levy
New York, NY 10022	CFO: Robert L. (Rob) Levy
Phone: 212-317-5700	HR: Katherine B. (Kelly) Schnur
Fax: 212-751-3550	FYE: December 31
Web: www.centerline.com	Type: Public

Centerline Holding sponsors funds to invest in real estate assets, including commercial mortgage-backed securities (CMBS) and collateralized debt obligations (CDOs). Centerline primarily invests in tax-exempt municipal bonds issued to finance the construction or renovation of affordable housing and other multifamily properties. Subsidiary Centerline Capital has raised some $12 billion through sponsored real estate investment funds, more than $8 billion of which has been used to finance affordable housing. Other units write and underwrite loans on behalf of Fannie Mae, Freddie Mac, and other entities. Centerline Holding has more than $14 billion in assets under management.

	Annual Growth	12/05	12/06	12/07	12/08	12/09
Assets ($ mil.)	(3.7%)	6,978.8	9,688.5	9,491.6	7,382.0	6,003.5
Net income ($ mil.)	—	59.0	41.3	(60.1)	(232.2)	(455.4)
Market value ($ mil.)	(74.1%)	1,236.9	1,253.8	445.0	8.7	5.5
Employees	(15.9%)	400	500	500	375	200

CENTERPLATE, INC.

201 E. Broad St.	CEO: Desmond (Des) Hague
Spartanburg, SC 29306	CFO: Kevin F. McNamara
Phone: 864-598-8600	HR: Nancy Robinson
Fax: 864-598-8695	FYE: December 31
Web: www.centerplate.com	Type: Private

Wherever there's a sporting event, this concessions operator likes to be front and center. Centerplate is a leading provider of catering, concessions, and facilities-management services in the US, serving stadiums, convention centers, and other venues. The company's clients include professional baseball and football stadiums, minor league parks, and college sports stadiums. It provides catering and other services at convention centers, including the Jacob K. Javits Center in Manhattan, as well as at airports, parks, performing arts centers, and ski resorts. It also handles a number of special events, such as the Kentucky Derby Festival. Centerplate is owned by investment firm Kohlberg & Co.

CENTERPOINT ENERGY HOUSTON ELECTRIC, LLC

1111 Louisiana St.	CEO: David M. McClanahan
Houston, TX 77002	CFO: Gary L. Whitlock
Phone: 713-207-1111	HR: —
Fax: —	FYE: December 31
Web: centerpointenergy.com	Type: Subsidiary

Houston, we don't have a problem. CenterPoint Energy Houston Electric's glow spreads across the fourth-largest US city and surrounding areas of the Texas Gulf Coast. The utility, formerly Reliant Energy HL&P, operates the regulated power transmission and distribution systems in the Houston metropolitan area. CenterPoint Energy Houston Electric, a subsidiary of utility holding company CenterPoint Energy, serves more than 2 million customers over its more than 47,290 miles of electric distribution lines via 230 substations; the utility's transmission assets are managed by the Electric Reliability Council of Texas (ERCOT).

	Annual Growth	12/04	12/05	12/06	12/07	12/08
Est. sales ($ mil.)	—	—	—	—	—	1,916.0
Employees	—	—	—	—	—	2,746

⊞ CENTERPOINT ENERGY, INC.

NYSE: CNP

1111 Louisiana St.	CEO: David M. McClanahan
Houston, TX 77002	CFO: Gary L. Whitlock
Phone: 713-207-1111	HR: —
Fax: 713-207-3169	FYE: December 31
Web: www.centerpointenergy.com	Type: Public

CenterPoint Energy has made a complete pivot around its core operations. The company, which had evolved from a local utility into a global power provider, has spun off most of its nonregulated operations and has returned to its roots. CenterPoint Energy's regulated utilities distribute natural gas to 3.2 million customers in six US states and electricity to 2 million customers on the Texas Gulf Coast. The company's main stomping ground is Texas, where it has regulated power distribution operations through subsidiary CenterPoint Energy Houston Electric. CenterPoint Energy also operates more than 8,000 miles of interstate gas pipeline, and it has gas gathering and storage operations.

	Annual Growth	12/05	12/06	12/07	12/08	12/09
Sales ($ mil.)	(3.9%)	9,722.0	9,319.0	9,623.0	11,322.0	8,281.0
Net income ($ mil.)	13.8%	222.0	432.0	399.0	447.0	372.0
Market value ($ mil.)	3.1%	5,068.2	6,539.3	6,756.3	4,977.5	5,722.9
Employees	(0.5%)	9,001	8,623	8,568	8,801	8,810

⊞ An in-depth profile of this company is available to Hoover's Online members at hoovers.com.

349

CENTERSTATE BANKS, INC.

NASDAQ (GM): CSFL

42745 US Hwy. 27
Davenport, FL 33837
Phone: 863-419-7750
Fax: —
Web: www.centerstatebanks.com

CEO: Ernest S. (Ernie) Pinner
CFO: James J. Antal
HR: —
FYE: December 31
Type: Public

CenterState Banks (formerly CenterState Banks of Florida) is a multibank holding company serving the Sunshine State from more than 35 branch locations. It owns CenterState Bank, CenterState Bank of Florida, CenterState Bank Central Florida, and Valrico State Bank. The banks offer standard retail products and services such as checking and savings accounts, money market accounts, and CDs. They focus on real estate lending, primarily mortgages, construction loans, and land development loans. The banks also sell mutual funds, annuities, and other investment products. Each bank is managed by its own team of executives and board members. CenterState Banks also provides correspondent banking and bond sales services.

	Annual Growth	12/05	12/06	12/07	12/08	12/09
Assets ($ mil.)	19.1%	871.5	1,077.1	1,217.4	1,333.1	1,751.3
Net income ($ mil.)	—	6.3	8.5	7.8	3.4	(6.2)
Market value ($ mil.)	(12.5%)	444.7	538.8	311.9	438.0	260.1
Employees	14.8%	275	320	371	399	478

Ⅲ CENTOCOR ORTHO BIOTECH INC.

800 Ridgeview Rd.
Horsham, PA 19044
Phone: 610-651-6000
Fax: 610-651-6100
Web: www.centocororthobiotech.com

CEO: Kim Taylor
CFO: —
HR: —
FYE: December 31
Type: Subsidiary

Centocor Ortho Biotech has ways of making your immune system behave itself. The Johnson & Johnson subsidiary makes blockbuster biotech drug Remicade, a monoclonal antibody used to treat a number of autoimmune conditions, or diseases in which the body's immune system attacks its own tissues. It is approved in the US and Europe for several indications, including Crohn's disease, ulcerative colitis, psoriasis, rheumatoid arthritis, and ankylosing spondylitis (a type of arthritis of the spine). The company also makes oncology drugs Doxil and Leustatin, and immunosuppressant Orthoclone for organ transplantation.

CENTRA HEALTH, INC.

1920 Atherholt Rd.
Lynchburg, VA 24501
Phone: 434-947-4000
Fax: 434-947-3004
Web: www.centrahealth.com

CEO: George W. Dawson
CFO: Lewis Addison
HR: Lauralyn W. Martin
FYE: December 31
Type: Not-for-profit

Centra Health is a constellation of hospitals, medical practices, outpatient facilities, and other services targeting the health care needs of residents in central Virginia. At its core are two acute care facilities in Lynchburg: 270-bed Lynchburg General, which is the region's main emergency center and specializes in orthopedic and cardiac care; and Virginia Baptist, a roughly 315-bed facility focusing on cancer treatment, women's and pediatric care, mental health, and rehabilitation. Aside from its acute care operations, Centra owns primary care physicians' practices, a home health care service, nursing homes, and numerous other physical and behavioral health businesses.

CENTRAL BANCORP, INC.

NASDAQ (GM): CEBK

399 Highland Ave.
Somerville, MA 02144
Phone: 617-628-4000
Fax: —
Web: www.centralbk.com

CEO: John D. Doherty
CFO: Paul S. Feeley
HR: Shirley M. Tracy
FYE: March 31
Type: Public

Central Bancorp is the holding company for Central Co-operative Bank. Operating as Central Bank, it serves Middlesex County in the northwestern suburbs of Boston through about 10 bank branches and loan centers. The bank's primary business is gathering deposits by offering NOW, money market, checking, and savings accounts; CDs; and retirement savings plans. It primarily uses these funds to originate commercial mortgages (more than half of all loans in the company's portfolio, up from 20% in 2001). Residential mortgages have gone down from around 70% to less than 40% since then. The bank also offers construction, home equity, business, and consumer loans, as well as credit cards.

	Annual Growth	3/05	3/06	3/07	3/08	3/09
Assets ($ mil.)	2.5%	521.1	547.3	566.1	571.2	575.8
Net income ($ mil.)	—	2.5	2.6	1.0	1.4	(6.2)
Market value ($ mil.)	(35.3%)	44.3	47.5	49.1	31.4	7.8
Employees	(3.1%)	151	153	153	142	133

CENTRAL EUROPEAN DISTRIBUTION

NASDAQ (GS): CEDC

2 Bala Plaza, Ste. 300
Bala Cynwyd, PA 19004
Phone: 610-660-7817
Fax: 610-667-3308
Web: www.cedc.com.pl

CEO: William V. Carey
CFO: Christopher (Chris) Biedermann
HR: —
FYE: December 31
Type: Public

Central European Distribution Corporation (CEDC) helped Poland toast its post-Communist economy in 1991 when co-founders William O. Carey and Jeffrey Peterson introduced Foster's lager to that country. CEDC distributes more than 700 brands of beer, spirits, and wines. With some 39,000 retail customers, its major market is Poland, but it also sells in Russia, Hungary, and to a small extent, in the US. CEDC offers spirits made by Bacardi and Diageo. Other brands include Corona, Jim Beam, and E&J Gallo wines. Also a vodka distiller, the company's flagship products include Absolwent, Zubrówka, Bols, and Royal vodkas.

	Annual Growth	12/05	12/06	12/07	12/08	12/09
Sales ($ mil.)	16.1%	828.9	944.1	1,189.8	1,647.0	1,507.1
Net income ($ mil.)	40.1%	20.3	55.5	77.1	(16.6)	78.3
Market value ($ mil.)	1.5%	1,890.5	2,098.2	4,103.2	1,391.8	2,007.1
Employees	1.8%	2,917	3,015	3,361	4,747	3,135

CENTRAL FEDERAL CORPORATION

NASDAQ (CM): CFBK

2923 Smith Rd.
Fairlawn, OH 44333
Phone: 330-666-7979
Fax: 330-666-7959

CEO: Eloise L. (Elly) Mackus
CFO: Therese A. Liutkus
HR: Michele R. Guildoo
FYE: December 31
Type: Public

Central Federal Corporation is the holding company for CFBank. Traditionally a retail-focused savings and loan, CFBank has added business banking, commercial real estate, and business lending to its foundation. It now serves not only local individuals, but also businesses through four branches in eastern Ohio and the state capital, Columbus. Its deposit products include checking, savings, NOW, and money market accounts, as well as CDs. While single-family residential mortgages made up about 60% of loans a few years ago, they represent less than 15% today. Over that same period, commercial and multifamily residential mortgages have increased to nearly 60% of its loan portfolio.

	Annual Growth	12/05	12/06	12/07	12/08	12/09
Assets ($ mil.)	12.2%	173.0	236.0	279.6	277.8	273.7
Net income ($ mil.)	—	(3.3)	0.0	0.0	0.7	(9.9)
Market value ($ mil.)	(33.9%)	32.1	30.2	15.8	12.2	6.1
Employees	10.3%	54	62	64	75	80

CENTRAL FLORIDA INVESTMENTS, INC.

5601 Windhover Dr.
Orlando, FL 32819
Phone: 407-351-3350
Fax: 407-352-8935
Web: www.westgateresorts.com

CEO: David A. Siegel
CFO: Tom Dugan
HR: —
FYE: December 31
Type: Private

Looking for a vacation home? How about a beachside resort, a mountain lodge, a gambling pad, and rustic ranch? If you are one who wants it all, a timeshare from Central Florida Investments (CFI) might be the way to go. CFI subsidiary Westgate Resorts operates about 30 timeshare resorts in more than 10 states. In addition to Westgate Resorts, CFI owns or has interests in magazines (*I Love Orlando, I Love Vacations*), real estate (Westgate Plaza Center retail space in Las Vegas), health spas (Papillon Spas), and restaurants (Westgate Smokehouse Grill). Chairman and CEO David Siegel founded the company in 1970.

CENTRAL FREIGHT LINES, INC.

5601 West Waco Dr.
Waco, TX 76710
Phone: 254-741-5370
Fax: —
Web: www.centralfreight.com

CEO: Don Orr
CFO: Vicky O'Brien
HR: Elta Russell
FYE: December 31
Type: Private

The Southwest, the Midwest, and the Northwest are all central to the business of Central Freight Lines, a leading regional less-than-truckload (LTL) carrier. (LTL carriers consolidate freight from multiple shippers into a single truckload.) The company focuses on next-day and second-day services within each of its regions. It operates a fleet of more than 1,900 tractors and about 8,500 trailers from a network of about 55 terminals. Central Freight Lines serves the rest of the US through alliances with other carriers. Trucking magnate Jerry Moyes owns the company.

⊞ CENTRAL GARDEN & PET COMPANY

1340 Treat Blvd., Ste. 600
Walnut Creek, CA 94597
Phone: 925-948-4000
Fax: 925-287-0601
Web: www.central.com

NASDAQ (GS): CENTA

CEO: William E. Brown
CFO: Stuart W. Booth
HR: Sherry Perley
FYE: September 30
Type: Public

Central Garden & Pet is happy to help with both pets and pests. The company is among the largest US manufacturers and distributors of lawn, garden, and pet supplies, providing its products to pet supplies retailers, home improvement centers, nurseries, and mass merchandisers from approximately 40 manufacturing plants and another 30 distribution centers throughout the US; it also has sales offices in the UK. Central Garden & Pet's proprietary brand lines include AMDRO fire ant bait, Four Paws animal products, Kaytee bird seed, Nylabone dog chews, Norcal pottery, Pennington grass seed and bird seed products, and TFH pet books. Chairman and CEO William Brown controls not quite 50% of the company's voting rights.

	Annual Growth	9/05	9/06	9/07	9/08	9/09
Sales ($ mil.)	4.0%	1,380.6	1,621.5	1,671.1	1,705.4	1,614.3
Net income ($ mil.)	5.2%	53.8	65.5	32.3	(267.3)	65.9
Market value ($ mil.)	10.3%	—	—	579.1	383.7	704.9
Employees	(2.7%)	4,800	4,865	4,860	4,600	4,300

CENTRAL GROCERS, INC.

2600 W. Haven Ave.
Joliet, IL 60433
Phone: 815-553-8800
Fax: 815-553-8710
Web: www.central-grocers.com

CEO: James (Jim) Denges
CFO: Tim Kubis
HR: Annalee Robish
FYE: July 31
Type: Cooperative

In a city of big stores, Central Grocers helps neighborhood markets stay afloat. The member-owned cooperative wholesale food distributor supplies food items and general merchandise to more than 400 independent retail grocery stores in Illinois, Indiana, Iowa, and Wisconsin. It distributes products under both national brands and its own Centrella brand. The co-op also operates about 30 stores under such banners as Strack & Van Til, Town & Country, Key Market, and the low-cost Ultra Foods chain. Founded in 1917, Central Grocers acquired rival distributor Certified Grocers in 2009.

	Annual Growth	7/04	7/05	7/06	7/07	7/08
Est. sales ($ mil.)	—	—	—	—	—	1,197.2
Employees	—	—	—	—	—	2,300

CENTRAL JERSEY BANCORP

NASDAQ (GM): CJBK

627 2nd Ave.
Long Branch, NJ 07740
Phone: 732-571-1300
Fax: 732-571-1037
Web: www.cjbna.com

CEO: James S. Vaccaro
CFO: Anthony Giordano III
HR: Gail Corrigan
FYE: December 31
Type: Public

Central Jersey Bancorp is the holding company for Central Jersey Bank, which operates more than a dozen branches, mostly in Monmouth County, New Jersey. Central Jersey Bank offers standard deposit products such as checking and savings accounts, CDs, and IRAs, as well as ancillary offerings like debit cards, wire transfers, and safe deposit boxes. Lending activities mainly consist of commercial real estate loans (about three-quarters of all loans). Business, consumer, industrial, home equity, and second mortgage loans round out the bank's portfolio. Another New Jersey bank, Kearny Financial is buying Central Jersey Bancorp in a $72.3 million deal.

	Annual Growth	12/05	12/06	12/07	12/08	12/09
Assets ($ mil.)	2.9%	514.6	516.3	503.5	599.4	577.7
Net income ($ mil.)	—	2.6	2.5	0.8	2.9	(26.1)
Market value ($ mil.)	(27.9%)	102.5	69.7	70.1	58.7	27.7
Employees	(3.3%)	152	147	128	140	133

CENTRAL MAINE POWER COMPANY

83 Edison Dr.
Augusta, ME 04336
Phone: 207-623-3521
Fax: 207-626-9571
Web: www.cmpco.com

CEO: Sara J. Burns
CFO: Eric N. Stinneford
HR: —
FYE: December 31
Type: Subsidiary

Central Maine Power (CMP) has electricity pumping through its veins (and transmission lines). The company, a subsidiary of utility holding firm Iberdrola USA, itself a unit of Spanish powerhouse IBERDROLA, provides regulated power services to about 590,000 residential and business customers (80% of Maine's population) in an 11,000 square mile area of southern and central Maine. CMP allows nonregulated retail electric providers to supply power to customers over its 25,000-mile transmission and distribution network via 200 substations. The utility caters to a peak demand of about 1,680 MW.

⊞ An in-depth profile of this company is available to Hoover's Online members at hoovers.com.

351

CENTRAL NATIONAL-GOTTESMAN INC.

3 Manhattanville Rd.
Purchase, NY 10577
Phone: 914-696-9000
Fax: 914-696-1066
Web: www.cng-inc.com

CEO: Kenneth L. Wallach
CFO: Steven Eigen
HR: Louise Caputo
FYE: December 31
Type: Private

All the news that's fit to print (or at least some of it) shows up on a portion of Central National-Gottesman's (CNG) products. The papermaker distributes annually 4 million tons of goods, from wood pulp to paper, paperboard, and newsprint. Markets are tapped in 75-plus countries dotting the globe. In addition to North American operations, the company's international presence is established in about 20 offices, spanning Asia, Europe, and Latin America. The CNG community includes the Lindenmeyr family of companies, paper merchants in fine paper, papers for books, magazines and catalogs, specialized papers, and packaging grades. CNG is privately held by the fourth generation of the founding Gottesman family.

	Annual Growth	12/04	12/05	12/06	12/07	12/08
Sales ($ mil.)	15.0%	2,000.0	2,300.0	2,700.0	3,000.0	3,500.0
Employees	4.5%	775	850	850	1,000	925

CENTRAL PACIFIC FINANCIAL CORP.

NYSE: CPF

220 S. King St.
Honolulu, HI 96813
Phone: 808-544-0500
Fax: 808-531-2875
Web: www.centralpacificbank.com

CEO: John C. Dean
CFO: —
HR: Karen K. Street
FYE: December 31
Type: Public

When in the Central Pacific, do as the islanders do! This might include doing business with Central Pacific Financial, the holding company for Central Pacific Bank. The bank operates some 40 branch locations throughout the Hawaiian Islands. Targeting individuals and local businesses, the bank provides such standard retail banking products as checking and savings accounts, money market accounts, and CDs. Commercial real estate loans make up about a third of the bank's loan portfolio, which also includes residential mortgages (about 25%) and business, construction, and consumer loans. The company also has real estate loan production offices in California.

	Annual Growth	12/05	12/06	12/07	12/08	12/09
Assets ($ mil.)	(1.8%)	5,239.1	5,487.2	5,680.4	5,432.4	4,869.5
Net income ($ mil.)	—	72.5	79.2	5.8	(138.4)	(313.7)
Market value ($ mil.)	(13.2%)	1,090.9	1,177.2	560.6	304.9	619.6
Employees	3.3%	904	1,008	1,085	1,065	1,030

⊞ CENTRAL PARKING CORPORATION

2401 21st Ave. South, Ste. 200
Nashville, TN 37212
Phone: 615-297-4255
Fax: 615-297-6240
Web: www.parking.com

CEO: James A. (Jim) Marcum
CFO: John I. Hill
HR: Donald N. Holmes
FYE: September 30
Type: Private

If you park your car in a central location, you might very well be doing business with Central Parking. A leading parking provider, the company oversees more than 2,500 facilities with about 1.2 million spaces, in about 40 states and Puerto Rico. Its facilities serve high-traffic locations such as airports, office buildings, and stadiums. Along with operating parking lots and garages, the company provides shuttle transportation and valet parking, plus parking meter enforcement and collection under contracts with cities. It also serves as a consultant for parking facility operators. A group of private equity firms bought Central Parking in 2007.

CENTRAL PURCHASING, LLC

3491 Mission Oaks Blvd.
Camarillo, CA 93011
Phone: 805-388-1000
Fax: 805-445-4925
Web: www.harborfreight.com

CEO: Alan Smidt
CFO: Mike Kaplan
HR: Pete Roberts
FYE: July 31
Type: Private

Central Purchasing certainly could lay claim to the expression "the right tool for the job." The company, better recognized by its trade name Harbor Freight Tools, is one of the country's largest tool and equipment catalog retailers. It offers more than 7,000 items, including hand and power tools, automotive parts and supplies, metalworking machines, pressure washers, woodworking instruments, welders, and accessories for home workshops. Top brands include Central Machinery, Chicago Electric, DeWalt, Makita, and Stanley. In addition to its catalog, the firm sells through the Internet (via its website and eBay store) and a network of more than 330 retail stores in about 45 states. It was founded in 1968.

CENTRAL REFRIGERATED SERVICE, INC.

5175 W. 2100 South
West Valley City, UT 84120
Phone: 801-924-7000
Fax: 801-924-7337
Web: www.centralref.com

CEO: Jon F. Isaacson
CFO: Bob Baer
HR: —
FYE: December 31
Type: Private

No matter the weather conditions, trucking company Central Refrigerated Service stays cool when it's on the move. The carrier provides temperature-controlled transportation and dry cargo services for major food suppliers and retailers across the US. It specializes in providing a wide array of transportation requests, from inner city and solo driver deliveries to long haul truckload transportation services. Central Refrigerated Service operates a fleet of about 1,800 tractors and 2,700 refrigerated trailers, or reefers. The company is owned by Jerry Moyes, who also owns less-than-truckload carrier Central Freight Lines and truckload carrier Swift Transportation.

	Annual Growth	12/04	12/05	12/06	12/07	12/08
Est. sales ($ mil.)	—	—	—	—	—	406.9
Employees	—	—	—	—	—	1,400

CENTRAL STEEL & WIRE COMPANY

Pink Sheets: CSTW

3000 W. 51st St.
Chicago, IL 60632
Phone: 800-621-8510
Fax: 800-232-9279
Web: www.centralsteel.com

CEO: Michael X. Cronin
CFO: Ronald Kazmar
HR: Daniel (Dan) Sopata
FYE: December 31
Type: Public

When it comes to metal, service center Central Steel & Wire Company (CS&W) can shape up and ship out. CS&W distributes ferrous and nonferrous metals in a variety of shapes and forms, including bars, coils, plates, sheets, structurals, tubing, and wire. Among the company's processing services are annealing, blanking, CNC laser cutting, galvanizing, and structural fabrication. CS&W distributes its products throughout North America from five facilities that are located primarily in the midwestern US. Central Steel & Wire was founded in 1909. Though it trades publicly, the company is majority-owned by a trust set up by a former chairman, the late James Lowenstein.

CENTRAL VALLEY COMMUNITY BANCORP
NASDAQ (CM): CVCY

7100 N. Financial Dr.
Fresno, CA 93720
Phone: 559-298-1775
Fax: 559-221-4376
Web: www.cvcb.com

CEO: Daniel J. Doyle
CFO: David A. (Dave) Kinross
HR: Barbara Gillmore
FYE: December 31
Type: Public

Central Valley Community Bancorp is the holding company for Central Valley Community Bank, which offers individuals and businesses traditional banking services through about 15 offices in California's San Joaquin Valley. Deposit products include checking, savings, and money market accounts; IRAs; and CDs. The bank offers credit card services and originates a variety of loans, including residential and commercial mortgage, Small Business Administration, and agricultural loans. Through Central Valley Community Insurance Services, it markets health and property and casualty insurance products primarily to business customers.

	Annual Growth	12/05	12/06	12/07	12/08	12/09
Assets ($ mil.)	12.2%	483.7	500.1	483.7	752.7	765.5
Net income ($ mil.)	(18.9%)	6.0	6.9	6.3	5.1	2.6
Market value ($ mil.)	(22.0%)	136.2	134.0	99.8	55.9	50.4
Employees	(6.6%)	284	162	168	207	216

CENTRAL VERMONT PUBLIC SERVICE CORPORATION
NYSE: CV

77 Grove St.
Rutland, VT 05701
Phone: 800-649-2877
Fax: 802-747-2199
Web: www.cvps.com

CEO: Robert H. (Bob) Young
CFO: Pamela J. Keefe
HR: —
FYE: December 31
Type: Public

Moonlight in Vermont may be beautiful, but it doesn't provide any power. Vermont's largest electric utility, Central Vermont Public Service (CVPS), provides power to about 159,000 customers in 163 communities across the state. It generates approximately 110 MW of nuclear, hydroelectric, and fossil-fueled capacity; it purchases most of its energy supply. CVPS owns 59% of Vermont Yankee Nuclear Power Corporation, and 47% of state transmission company Vermont Electric Power Company (VELCO). Nonregulated businesses include investments (Catamount Resources), home maintenance contracting, real estate (C.V. Realty), and energy-related services.

	Annual Growth	12/05	12/06	12/07	12/08	12/09
Sales ($ mil.)	2.4%	311.4	325.7	329.1	342.2	342.1
Net income ($ mil.)	34.6%	6.3	18.4	15.8	16.4	20.7
Market value ($ mil.)	3.7%	215.7	282.1	369.4	285.8	249.2
Employees	0.2%	529	535	552	549	534

CENTRAL VIRGINIA BANKSHARES, INC.
NASDAQ (GM): CVBK

2036 New Dorset Rd.
Powhatan, VA 23139
Phone: 804-403-2000
Fax: 804-598-5079
Web: www.centralvabank.com

CEO: Ralph L. Lyons
CFO: Charles F. Catlett III
HR: —
FYE: December 31
Type: Public

Central Virginia Bankshares is the holding company for Central Virginia Bank, which operates about 10 branches in — you guessed it — central Virginia. Targeting individuals and local business customers, the community bank offers such standard retail services as checking and savings accounts, CDs, IRAs, and credit cards. Through a partnership with Community Bankers Securities, the bank also provides non-deposit investment services. Central Virginia Bankshares' loan portfolio consists of a mix of residential and commercial mortgages, real estate construction loans, home equity loans, and business and consumer loans.

	Annual Growth	12/05	12/06	12/07	12/08	12/09
Assets ($ mil.)	4.5%	397.4	437.5	485.2	486.3	473.2
Net income ($ mil.)	—	4.9	5.2	4.0	(9.6)	(9.2)
Market value ($ mil.)	(39.3%)	65.6	64.9	45.4	12.3	8.9
Employees	(0.7%)	107	131	129	118	104

CENTRIC GROUP, L.L.C.

1260 Andes Blvd.
St. Louis, MO 63132
Phone: 314-214-2700
Fax: 314-214-2766
Web: www.centricgp.com

CEO: Jim Theiss
CFO: John T. O'Connell
HR: —
FYE: December 31
Type: Private

This company makes sure the world has enough balloons, baggage, and beverages. Centric Group is a holding company for several manufacturing and distribution businesses. Its Betallic unit manufactures latex and Mylar balloons sold through florist shops and other gift retailers. The company's TRG Group, meanwhile, manufactures luggage and other travel bags under such brands as Callaway Golf and Victorinox. In addition, Centric serves commissaries at correctional facilities with snacks, beverages, and other food and nonfood items through its Keefe Group. The company was formed in 1974 as part of Enterprise Rent-A-Car and spun off in 1999. It is controlled by the Taylor family.

	Annual Growth	12/04	12/05	12/06	12/07	12/08
Est. sales ($ mil.)	11.0%	—	600.0	700.0	750.0	820.0
Employees	14.8%	—	1,600	2,000	2,300	2,422

CENTURA HEALTH

188 Inverness Dr. West, Ste. 500
Englewood, CO 80112
Phone: 303-290-6500
Fax: 303-290-8159
Web: www.centura.org

CEO: Gary S. Campbell
CFO: Randy Safady
HR: —
FYE: June 30
Type: Not-for-profit

It's in the Centennial State and "centur" makes up a big part of its name, but it hasn't been around for 100 years. Centura Health was established in 1996 as a not-for-profit health care system serving the Denver metro area and surrounding counties. The health system boasts more than 2,500 beds, 12 acute care hospitals and nearly as many senior living and senior care facilities. The system also offers home health and hospice care. Centura Health partners with a bevy of local diagnostic imaging and ambulatory surgery centers around Colorado to provide communities there with more access to those services. The system was established by Catholic Health Initiatives and Adventist Health System.

CENTURY 21 REAL ESTATE LLC

1 Campus Dr.
Parsippany, NJ 07054
Phone: 877-221-2765
Fax: —
Web: www.century21.com

CEO: Richard W. (Rick) Davidson
CFO: —
HR: Adam Lerman
FYE: December 31
Type: Subsidiary

Home is where the money is for Century 21. A subsidiary of Realogy Corporation, Century 21 provides franchises for one of the world's largest residential real estate sales networks, with more than 8,900 offices in some 70 countries and territories worldwide. While homes are its core focus, the company also helps customers buy and sell commercial and vacation properties and provides relocation services for individuals, corporations, and members of the military. Century 21 Fine Homes & Estates offers services for seekers of luxury homes. Realogy Corporation licenses the Century 21 name, among several other major real estate brands.

An in-depth profile of this company is available to Hoover's Online members at hoovers.com.

353

CENTURY ALUMINUM COMPANY

NASDAQ (GS): CENX

2511 Garden Rd., Bldg. A, Ste. 200
Monterey, CA 93940
Phone: 831-642-9300
Fax: 831-642-9399
Web: www.centuryaluminum.com

CEO: Logan W. Kruger
CFO: Michael A. Bless
HR: —
FYE: December 31
Type: Public

When the aluminum century rolls around, it'll be ready. Century Aluminum makes primary molten and ingot aluminum at facilities in Kentucky and West Virginia, as well as in Iceland; that last facility is operated by subsidiary Nordural. Century Aluminum also owns just less than 50% of an aluminum production facility in South Carolina (Alcoa owns the rest). Four customers — aluminum producer Rio Tinto Alcan, diversified metals company BHP Billiton, commodities trader Glencore International, and wire and cable maker Southwire — account for about three-quarters of Century Aluminum's sales. Glencore is Century Aluminum's former parent, though it still has a 38% stake in the company.

	Annual Growth	12/05	12/06	12/07	12/08	12/09
Sales ($ mil.)	(5.6%)	1,132.4	1,558.6	1,798.2	1,970.8	899.3
Net income ($ mil.)	—	(116.3)	(41.0)	(101.2)	(898.3)	(206.0)
Market value ($ mil.)	(11.3%)	2,428.6	4,137.3	4,998.1	926.6	1,500.2
Employees	(7.9%)	1,750	1,850	1,900	1,370	1,260

CENTURY BANCORP, INC.

NASDAQ (GM): CNBKA

400 Mystic Ave.
Medford, MA 02155
Phone: 781-391-4000
Fax: 781-393-4071
Web: www.century-bank.com

CEO: Barry R. Sloane
CFO: William P. Hornby
HR: —
FYE: December 31
Type: Public

Century Bancorp is the holding company for Century Bank and Trust, which serves Boston and surrounding northeastern Massachusetts from about 20 branch locations. The bank offers standard deposit products, including checking, savings, and money market accounts; CDs; and IRAs. Some 45% of the bank's loan portfolio is dedicated to commercial real estate. It also writes residential mortgages (25%), construction and development loans, business loans, and home equity loans. The company provides cash management and transaction processing services to municipalities; subsidiary Century Financial Services offers investment and brokerage services. Chairman Marshall Sloane controls the company.

	Annual Growth	12/05	12/06	12/07	12/08	12/09
Assets ($ mil.)	6.9%	1,728.8	1,644.3	1,680.3	1,801.6	2,254.0
Net income ($ mil.)	10.3%	6.9	4.7	7.9	9.0	10.2
Market value ($ mil.)	(6.9%)	161.9	151.0	111.5	87.1	121.8
Employees	(1.4%)	391	373	373	380	369

CENTURY CASINOS, INC.

NASDAQ (CM): CNTY

1263 Lake Plaza Dr., Ste. A
Colorado Springs, CO 80906
Phone: 719-527-8300
Fax: 719-527-8301
Web: www.cnty.com

CEO: Erwin Haitzmann
CFO: Larry J. Hannappel
HR: —
FYE: December 31
Type: Public

In the 19th century, people rushed to Cripple Creek, Colorado, seeking their fortune in gold. Today, thanks to Century Casinos, they can do basically the same thing (but via midsized regional casinos, rather than through prospecting). The company's Womacks Casino and Hotel in Cripple Creek offers some 430 slot machines and video devices, as well as a handful of gaming tables. It also owns the Century Casino & Hotel in Central City, Colorado, and another Century Casino & Hotel in Edmonton, Canada. In addition, it operate four cruise ship casinos and is the casino concessionaire for several cruise lines run by TUI Cruises, a joint venture between German travel operator TUI and #2 cruise ship operator Royal Caribbean.

	Annual Growth	12/05	12/06	12/07	12/08	12/09
Sales ($ mil.)	7.4%	37.4	56.3	91.7	53.0	49.7
Net income ($ mil.)	27.3%	4.5	7.8	5.3	(13.5)	11.8
Market value ($ mil.)	(25.2%)	204.8	265.7	153.3	24.3	64.0
Employees	1.6%	517	1,000	1,030	950	550

CENTURY ENERGY LTD.

TSX Venture: CEY

4605 Post Oak Place Dr., Ste. 250
Houston, TX 77027
Phone: 713-658-0161
Fax: 713-222-7158
Web: www.centuryenergyltd.com

CEO: Jimmy M. McCarroll
CFO: Douglas Baker
HR: —
FYE: August 31
Type: Public

What can top Topper Resources? How about Century Energy. The junior natural resources company (formerly Topper Resources) buys interests in gas and oil exploration sites in Canada and the US. It owns the petroleum and natural gas rights to 1,100 acres in the Bakken oil formation in southern Saskatchewan. In conjunction with TriAxon Resources Ltd. (its joint venture partner with extensive experience in the Bakken Shale play) the company has succeeded in producing oil from its first exploratory Bakken well and plans to develop several others.

	Annual Growth	8/05	8/06	8/07	8/08	8/09
Sales ($ mil.)	0.0%	0.1	0.0	0.0	0.0	0.1
Net income ($ mil.)	—	(0.7)	(0.2)	(0.2)	(0.5)	(0.2)
Market value ($ mil.)	2.2%	1.8	2.8	4.1	2.3	2.0
Employees	—	—	—	—	—	—

CENTURYTEL, INC.

NYSE: CTL

100 CenturyTel Dr.
Monroe, LA 71201
Phone: 318-388-9000
Fax: 318-388-9064
Web: www.centurytel.com

CEO: Glen F. Post III
CFO: R. Stewart Ewing Jr.
HR: —
FYE: December 31
Type: Public

Bright lights and big cities are not necessarily for CenturyTel. The company (which does business as CenturyLink) mainly provides local telephone services in rural areas, as well as network access to other carriers and businesses. It also offers long-distance and Internet access. CenturyTel serves about 7 million local voice lines and provides Internet access to about 2 million subscribers in 33 US states. The company's core service areas include Alabama, Arkansas, Missouri, Washington, and Wisconsin. Additionally, it provides paid television service to residential customers through a deal with DISH Network. CenturyTel's other services include commercial printing, database management, and direct mail advertising.

	Annual Growth	12/05	12/06	12/07	12/08	12/09
Sales ($ mil.)	19.0%	2,479.3	2,447.7	2,656.2	2,599.7	4,974.2
Net income ($ mil.)	11.2%	334.5	370.0	418.4	365.7	511.3
Market value ($ mil.)	2.2%	9,961.4	13,115.7	12,454.8	8,210.1	10,877.7
Employees	30.8%	6,900	6,400	6,600	6,500	20,200

CENVEO, INC.

NYSE: CVO

1 Canterbury Green, 201 Broad St.
Stamford, CT 06901
Phone: 203-595-3000
Fax: 203-595-3070
Web: www.cenveo.com

CEO: Robert G. Burton Sr.
CFO: Mark S. Hiltwein
HR: Gina Genuario
FYE: December 31
Type: Public

Commercial printer Cenveo produces not only items that go inside envelopes, but also the envelopes themselves. The company's printing units churn out catalogs, journals, magazines, and marketing materials. Cenveo's envelopes and other packaging products are used for purposes such as billing, catalog distribution, and direct mail. The company also produces business forms and pressure-sensitive labels. Its envelopes, forms, and labels products are sold both directly to end users and through wholesalers. Cenveo operates production, fulfillment, and distribution facilities throughout the US and Canada. The company is growing rapidly as a result of an aggressive acquisition schedule.

	Annual Growth	12/05	12/06	12/07	12/08	12/09
Sales ($ mil.)	(0.5%)	1,749.4	1,511.2	2,046.7	2,098.7	1,714.6
Net income ($ mil.)	—	(135.1)	118.7	40.8	(298.0)	(30.9)
Market value ($ mil.)	(9.7%)	818.1	1,317.9	1,086.1	276.6	544.0
Employees	2.1%	8,000	6,600	10,700	9,700	8,700

CEPHALON, INC.

NASDAQ (GS): CEPH

41 Moores Rd.
Malvern, PA 19355
Phone: 610-344-0200
Fax: —
Web: www.cephalon.com

CEO: Frank Baldino Jr.
CFO: Wilco Groenhuysen
HR: —
FYE: December 31
Type: Public

Cephalon isn't asleep at the wheel. The company sells PROVIGIL, a treatment for the sleep disorder narcolepsy, in the US and select countries around the world. The company's other top sellers are cancer pain medications ACTIQ and FENTORA, epilepsy treatment GABITRIL (licensed from Abbott Labs and Novo Nordisk), cancer drug TREANDA, and narcolepsy treatment NUVIGIL. It sells seven products in the US and has more than a dozen approved drugs on the market in Europe. Cephalon's drug research and development activities focus on central nervous system disorders, cancer, pain, and inflammatory disease.

	Annual Growth	12/05	12/06	12/07	12/08	12/09
Sales ($ mil.)	16.0%	1,211.9	1,764.1	1,772.6	1,974.6	2,192.3
Net income ($ mil.)	—	(175.0)	144.8	(191.7)	222.5	342.6
Market value ($ mil.)	(0.9%)	4,867.9	5,294.2	5,395.7	5,792.8	4,693.5
Employees	1.1%	2,895	2,895	2,796	2,780	3,026

CEPHEID

NASDAQ (GM): CPHD

904 Caribbean Dr.
Sunnyvale, CA 94089
Phone: 408-541-4191
Fax: 408-541-4192
Web: www.cepheid.com

CEO: John L. Bishop
CFO: Andrew D. (Andy) Miller
HR: Laurie King
FYE: December 31
Type: Public

Cepheid sees DNA faster. The molecular diagnostics firm develops systems that automate the process of preparing and amplifying DNA in order to quickly detect diseases and harmful agents. Its two instrument platforms — SmartCycler and GeneXpert — can perform rapid molecular testing for a number of purposes, including diagnosing infectious diseases and cancer, detecting biothreats such as anthrax, and testing food and agricultural products. Cephid also makes reagents (testing chemicals) and other disposable testing components for use with its systems. The company sells its products worldwide through a combination of direct sales and distributorship deals.

	Annual Growth	12/05	12/06	12/07	12/08	12/09
Sales ($ mil.)	19.0%	85.0	87.4	129.5	169.6	170.6
Net income ($ mil.)	—	(13.6)	(26.0)	(21.4)	(21.7)	(22.5)
Market value ($ mil.)	9.2%	521.6	505.0	1,565.5	616.7	741.5
Employees	18.9%	265	307	473	547	530

CERADYNE, INC.

NASDAQ (GS): CRDN

3169 Red Hill Ave.
Costa Mesa, CA 92626
Phone: 714-549-0421
Fax: 714-549-5787
Web: www.ceradyne.com

CEO: Joel P. Moskowitz
CFO: Jerrold J. (Jerry) Pellizzon
HR: —
FYE: December 31
Type: Public

A bull in a china shop wouldn't stand a chance against Ceradyne's ceramics. The company's advanced technical ceramics products combine hardness with light weight and the ability to withstand high temperatures, resist corrosion, and insulate against electricity. Some uses of Ceradyne's materials include armor for military helicopters, missile nose cones, body armor for soldiers, diesel engine components, ceramic industrial products, and orthodontic brackets. The company sells to contractors and OEMs. The US government and government agencies represent about 40% of sales. Ceradyne operates in China, Canada, Germany, India, and the US (which accounts for two-thirds of sales).

	Annual Growth	12/05	12/06	12/07	12/08	12/09
Sales ($ mil.)	2.1%	368.3	662.9	756.8	680.2	400.6
Net income ($ mil.)	(34.7%)	46.8	128.4	144.3	106.8	8.5
Market value ($ mil.)	(18.6%)	1,114.0	1,437.0	1,193.6	516.6	488.9
Employees	2.7%	1,835	2,205	2,511	2,388	2,039

CERAGENIX PHARMACEUTICALS, INC.

OTC: CGXP

1444 Wazee St., Ste. 210
Denver, CO 80202
Phone: 720-946-6440
Fax: 303-534-1800
Web: www.ceragenix.com

CEO: Steven S. Porter
CFO: Jeffrey S. (Jeff) Sperber
HR: —
FYE: December 31
Type: Public

Ceragenix Pharmaceuticals wants to make sure nothing gets under your skin. The company is a development-stage biopharmaceutical company engaged in the development of dermatology, oncology, and infectious disease therapies. Its main product, Barrier Repair technology, which mimics the barrier against infection and dehydration provided by healthy skin, is being developed in two topical creams, EpiCeram and NeoCeram, for the treatment of atopic dermatitis (eczema), radiation dermatitis, and skin disorders of premature infants. Parent firm Osmotics Corporation owns about two-thirds of Ceragenix.

	Annual Growth	12/05	12/06	12/07	12/08	12/09
Sales ($ mil.)	—	—	—	0.0	0.8	2.1
Net income ($ mil.)	—	—	—	(6.6)	(6.3)	(8.4)
Market value ($ mil.)	(31.0%)	—	—	19.2	4.0	9.2
Employees	(15.5%)	—	—	7	7	5

CERBERUS CAPITAL MANAGEMENT, L.P.

299 Park Ave.
New York, NY 10171
Phone: 212-891-2100
Fax: 212-891-1540
Web: www.cerberuscapital.com

CEO: Stephen A. Feinberg
CFO: Jeffrey L. Lomasky
HR: —
FYE: December 31
Type: Partnership

Named after the mythical three-headed dog that guards the gates of hell, Cerberus Capital Management is a *driving* force in private equity. One of its most notable moves was its 2007 purchase of 80% of Chrysler from Daimler. Cerberus was also the lead investor of a group that acquired 51% of GMAC (now Ally Financial), the financing arm of General Motors. Additionally, the firm owns bus manufacturer Blue Bird and car parts maker Tower Automotive. Although the company has made headlines with its automotive investments (and that industry's financial woes), Cerberus hasn't been solely concerned with cars and trucks: Automobile interests actually account for less than 10% of the firm's assets under management.

CERES TERMINALS INCORPORATED

2 Tower Center Blvd.
East Brunswick, NJ 08816
Phone: 201-974-3800
Fax: 201-974-3850
Web: www.ceresglobal.com

CEO: Thomas J. Simmers
CFO: Ronald N. Rutolo
HR: —
FYE: March 31
Type: Subsidiary

Ceres Terminals is serious about providing stevedoring (ship loading and unloading) and terminal operating systems. The company focuses on container handling in the US (East and Gulf coasts and Great Lakes) and Canada (the St. Lawrence Seaway) but it also provides stevedoring for the cruise industry. The company's other services include container maintenance and repair, refrigerated container services, and drayage. (Drayage is the transportation by truck of containerized freight between railyards and trucking terminals.) Ceres Terminals operates about 20 terminals. Founded in 1958, Ceres Terminals is owned by Japan's Nippon Yusen Kabushiki Kaisha (known as NYK Line) and is part of its Harbour Division.

An in-depth profile of this company is available to Hoover's Online members at hoovers.com.

CERIDIAN CORPORATION

3311 E. Old Shakopee Rd.
Minneapolis, MN 55425
Phone: 952-853-8100
Fax: 952-853-4430
Web: www.ceridian.com

CEO: Lee A. Kennedy
CFO: Gregory J. (Greg) Macfarlane
HR: Kairus K. Tarapore
FYE: December 31
Type: Private

Problems with payroll? Trouble with taxes? Ceridian wants to help. The company provides payroll processing, tax filing, benefits administration, and other human resources services to employers mainly in the US but also in Canada and the UK. Ceridian's other business units, Comdata and Stored Value Solutions, issue and process payments for credit, debit, and stored value cards (gift cards and employee expense cards), primarily for companies in the trucking and retail industries. Investment firm Thomas H. Lee Partners and insurer Fidelity National Financial own Ceridian.

	Annual Growth	12/04	12/05	12/06	12/07	12/08
Sales ($ mil.)	(7.9%)	—	—	—	1,700.0	1,565.3
Net income ($ mil.)	—	—	—	—	—	(92.4)
Employees	(7.4%)	—	—	—	9,177	8,500

CERNER CORPORATION

NASDAQ (GS): CERN

2800 Rockcreek Pkwy.
Kansas City, MO 64117
Phone: 816-201-1024
Fax: 816-474-1742
Web: www.cerner.com

CEO: Neal L. Patterson
CFO: Marc G. Naughton
HR: Jeffrey A. (Jeff) Townsend
FYE: December 31
Type: Public

Cerner provides the IV that pumps information through a health care organization's computer network. The company's products and services combine clinical, financial, and administrative information management applications, including tools for managing electronic medical records, patient care, and health information access. Cerner's clinical and administrative information systems link emergency rooms, pharmacies, and other health care departments. The company's service offerings include data migration, implementation, maintenance, and security compliance services. Cerner gets most of its sales in the US.

	Annual Growth	12/05	12/06	12/07	12/08	12/09
Sales ($ mil.)	9.6%	1,160.8	1,378.0	1,519.9	1,676.0	1,671.9
Net income ($ mil.)	22.4%	86.3	109.9	127.1	188.7	193.5
Market value ($ mil.)	16.0%	3,736.8	3,740.5	4,636.5	3,160.9	6,777.2
Employees	2.7%	6,830	7,419	7,873	7,500	7,600

CERTAINTEED CORPORATION

750 E. Swedesford Rd.
Valley Forge, PA 19482
Phone: 610-341-7000
Fax: 610-341-7777
Web: www.certainteed.com

CEO: Peter R. Dachowski
CFO: Robert Statile
HR: —
FYE: December 31
Type: Subsidiary

There's no uncertainty about CertainTeed's business. A subsidiary of French industrial giant Compagnie de Saint-Gobain, CertainTeed makes building materials for both commercial and residential construction. Products include fiberglass insulation, asphalt roofing shingles, gypsum wallboard, fiber cement siding, foundations, fencing, pipes, PVC trim, and composite decking and railing. The company sells its products under the Bufftech, CertainTeed, Form-A-Drain, Prestige, and Wolverine brands. CertainTeed operates some 65 manufacturing plants in the US and Canada.

CERUS CORPORATION

NASDAQ (GM): CERS

2411 Stanwell Dr.
Concord, CA 94520
Phone: 925-288-6000
Fax: 925-288-6001
Web: www.cerus.com

CEO: Claes Glassell
CFO: Kevin D. Green
HR: —
FYE: December 31
Type: Public

Cerus is no religious organization, but it does preach the power of purity. The firm develops blood purification systems under the name INTERCEPT that kill bacteria, viruses, and other pathogens in donated blood to improve the safety of blood transfusions. Its INTERCEPT Blood Systems for platelets and plasma are approved for sale in some European and Middle Eastern countries, where they are marketed directly to customers through subsidiary Cerus Europe. The company is pursuing regulatory approval for its INTERCEPT plasma and platelets products to sell them in the US market, as well as in other foreign countries. Cerus also has a system for red blood cell purification in clinical development.

	Annual Growth	12/05	12/06	12/07	12/08	12/09
Sales ($ mil.)	(7.3%)	24.4	35.6	11.0	16.5	18.0
Net income ($ mil.)	—	13.1	(4.8)	(45.3)	(29.2)	(24.1)
Market value ($ mil.)	(33.5%)	394.8	228.0	253.2	27.2	77.4
Employees	(6.9%)	97	124	111	107	73

CESSNA AIRCRAFT COMPANY

1 Cessna Blvd.
Wichita, KS 67215
Phone: 316-517-6000
Fax: 316-517-5669
Web: www.cessna.com

CEO: Jack J. Pelton
CFO: Eric Salander
HR: Jim Walters
FYE: December 31
Type: Subsidiary

Blue-sky thinking is encouraged at Cessna Aircraft, one of the most famous names in small planes. A subsidiary of Textron, the company manufactures light and midsize jets, utility turboprops, and small single-engine planes. Best known for its small prop planes, Cessna also produces business jets; it makes nine variations of the popular Citation jet. Cessna's single-engine planes are typically used for personal and small-business purposes. Cessna also offers fractional ownership programs for its business jets. It has delivered more than 190,000 jets and planes during its 80-year-plus history, making it the world's leading general-aviation aircraft company. Cessna accounts for more than 30% of Textron's sales.

	Annual Growth	12/04	12/05	12/06	12/07	12/08
Est. sales ($ mil.)	—	—	—	—	—	5.7
Employees	—	—	—	—	—	11,700

CEVA, INC.

NASDAQ (GM): CEVA

2033 Gateway Place, Ste. 150
San Jose, CA 95110
Phone: 408-514-2900
Fax: 408-514-2995
Web: www.ceva-dsp.com

CEO: Gideon Wertheizer
CFO: Yaniv Arieli
HR: —
FYE: December 31
Type: Public

CEVA has a fever for semiconductor design. CEVA specializes in technology — both integrated circuit and software designs — used in cell phones, handheld computers, MP3 players, and other wireless devices. It licenses its semiconductor intellectual property (SIP) designs to such industry heavyweights as Broadcom, Fujitsu, Hitachi, National Semiconductor, Sony, and Texas Instruments. The company derives nearly 90% of its sales from technology licensing and royalties, with the remainder coming from design and consulting services, along with maintenance and support fees from licensees. CEVA's SIP is shipped in more than 300 million devices a year.

	Annual Growth	12/05	12/06	12/07	12/08	12/09
Sales ($ mil.)	2.0%	35.6	32.5	33.2	40.4	38.5
Net income ($ mil.)	—	(2.3)	(0.1)	1.3	8.6	8.3
Market value ($ mil.)	19.7%	131.3	135.7	256.2	146.9	269.8
Employees	(3.1%)	209	196	192	187	184

CEVA LOGISTICS U.S., INC.

10751 Deerwood Park Blvd., Ste. 200
Jacksonville, FL 32256
Phone: 904-928-1400
Fax: 904-928-1410
Web: www.cevalogistics.com

CEO: John Pattullo
CFO: Rubin J. McDougal
HR: Peter Dew
FYE: December 31
Type: Subsidiary

CEVA Logistics U.S. is a regional unit of CEVA Logistics, part of giant CEVA Group. CEVA Logistics US provides warehousing, freight forwarding, and contract logistics, as well as customs house brokerage and ground delivery services. With its global affiliates, the company specializes in managing the supply chains of companies in industries including automotive, consumer goods, electronics, manufacturing, and technology. CEVA Group maintains about 9.2 million square meters of warehouse space with operations in more than 100 countries. CEVA Logistics was owned by Dutch express delivery and postal services company TNT until private equity firm Apollo Management bought it in 2006 and renamed it.

CF INDUSTRIES HOLDINGS, INC.

NYSE: CF

4 Pkwy. North, Ste. 400
Deerfield, IL 60015
Phone: 847-405-2400
Fax: 847-267-1004
Web: www.cfindustries.com

CEO: Stephen R. Wilson
CFO: Anthony J. (Tony) Nocchiero
HR: Wendy S. Jablow Spertus
FYE: December 31
Type: Public

The folks at CF Industries make a lot of fertilizer, and they like to spread it around. The company is an interregional and international agricultural firm that manufactures and markets nitrogen- and phosphate-based fertilizers (including diammonium phosphate, or DAP). It operates a network of manufacturing and distribution facilities, primarily in the Midwest, through which it offers products worldwide. CF, which initially failed in repeated offers to buy fertilizer producer Terra Industries in 2009, finally made the deal in 2010 after rebuffing rivals in a bidding war. The acquisition makes CF the largest North American producer of nitrogen-based fertilizers, and #2 in the world.

	Annual Growth	12/05	12/06	12/07	12/08	12/09
Sales ($ mil.)	8.1%	1,908.4	1,949.5	2,756.7	3,921.1	2,608.4
Net income ($ mil.)	—	(36.2)	33.3	372.7	684.6	365.6
Market value ($ mil.)	56.2%	1,083.5	1,821.8	7,820.0	3,492.9	6,450.1
Employees	1.6%	1,500	1,500	1,500	1,600	1,600

CFS BANCORP, INC.

NASDAQ (GM): CITZ

707 Ridge Rd.
Munster, IN 46321
Phone: 219-836-5500
Fax: 219-836-0265
Web: www.bankcfs.com

CEO: Thomas F. Prisby
CFO: Jerry A. Weberling
HR: —
FYE: December 31
Type: Public

CFS Bancorp is the holding company for Citizens Financial Bank, a savings and loan serving residents and businesses of northwestern Indiana and northeastern Illinois, including parts of the Chicago metropolitan area, through about two dozen branches. The bank offers standard deposit products such as checking, savings, NOW, and money market accounts, as well as certificates of deposit. It uses the funds primarily to originate commercial loans (mortgages, construction and land development loans, and business loans), which account for some two-thirds of its loan portfolio. The bank also originates residential mortgages, home equity lines of credit, and other consumer loans.

	Annual Growth	12/05	12/06	12/07	12/08	12/09
Assets ($ mil.)	(3.4%)	1,242.9	1,254.4	1,150.3	1,121.9	1,081.5
Net income ($ mil.)	—	5.0	5.3	7.5	(11.3)	(0.5)
Market value ($ mil.)	(31.1%)	154.7	158.5	158.9	42.2	34.9
Employees	(2.6%)	347	360	303	322	312

CGB ENTERPRISES, INC.

1001 Hwy. 190, Ste. 200
Covington, LA 70433
Phone: 985-867-3500
Fax: 985-867-3506
Web: www.cgb.com

CEO: Kevin D. Adams
CFO: Gerard A. Brechtel
HR: Karen Hollis
FYE: March 30
Type: Joint venture

The farmer in the dell-ta relies on CGB Enterprises. Located in Louisiana, near the shores of Lake Pontchartrain and the mouth of the Mississippi River, CGB is an agricultural company that provides US farmers a range of services, including grain handling, storage, and merchandising. The company offers inland grain transportation by barge, rail, and truck and also markets and sells seeds, agricultural chemicals, and insurance. With more than 70 locations, the company has eight divisions (grain, premium grain, farm services, financial services, soybean processing, feed, fertilizer, marine, and terminals and logistics).

	Annual Growth	3/04	3/05	3/06	3/07	3/08
Est. sales ($ mil.)	—	—	—	—	—	4,402.6
Employees	—	—	—	—	—	700

CH ENERGY GROUP, INC.

NYSE: CHG

284 South Ave.
Poughkeepsie, NY 12601
Phone: 845-452-2000
Fax: 845-486-5465
Web: www.chenergygroup.com

CEO: Steven V. Lant
CFO: Christopher M. Capone
HR: Joseph J. DeVirgilio Jr.
FYE: December 31
Type: Public

From the bluestone houses of the Huguenots to the manufacturing plants of IBM, utility holding company CH Energy Group powers New York state's Hudson Valley. Utility subsidiary Central Hudson Gas & Electric provides electricity to about 300,000 electric and 74,000 natural gas customers in eight counties located in Mid-Hudson River Valley, and delivers natural gas and electricity in a 2,600-square-mile service area that runs from New York City in the south, to Albany. Subsidiary CHEC oversees CH Energy Group's nonregulated businesses in the Northeast and Mid-Atlantic, including petroleum product distribution, alternative energy projects, and energy management services.

	Annual Growth	12/05	12/06	12/07	12/08	12/09
Sales ($ mil.)	(1.1%)	972.5	993.4	1,196.8	1,332.9	931.6
Net income ($ mil.)	10.7%	45.3	43.1	42.6	36.1	68.1
Market value ($ mil.)	(1.9%)	725.8	834.9	704.3	812.6	672.4
Employees	(11.4%)	1,398	1,402	1,559	1,540	860

C.H. ROBINSON WORLDWIDE, INC.

NASDAQ (GS): CHRW

14701 Charlson Rd.
Eden Prairie, MN 55347
Phone: 952-937-8500
Fax: 952-937-6714
Web: www.chrobinson.com

CEO: John P. Wiehoff
CFO: Chad M. Lindbloom
HR: Laura Gillund
FYE: December 31
Type: Public

C.H. Robinson Worldwide (CHRW) keeps merchandise moving. A third-party logistics provider, the company arranges freight transportation using trucks, trains, ships, and airplanes belonging to other companies. It contracts with some 47,000 carriers. CHRW handles about 7.5 million shipments per year for its 35,000-plus customers, which include companies in the food and beverage, manufacturing, and retail industries. Together with overseeing freight transportation for its customers, it offers supply chain management services through some 235 offices. In addition, CHRW buys, sells, and transports fresh produce throughout the US, and its T-Chek unit provides fuel purchasing management services for motor carriers.

	Annual Growth	12/05	12/06	12/07	12/08	12/09
Sales ($ mil.)	7.4%	5,688.9	6,556.2	7,316.2	8,578.6	7,577.2
Net income ($ mil.)	15.4%	203.4	266.9	324.3	359.2	360.8
Market value ($ mil.)	12.2%	6,142.9	6,783.3	8,978.0	9,128.9	9,742.7
Employees	6.2%	5,776	6,768	7,332	7,961	7,347

An in-depth profile of this company is available to Hoover's Online members at hoovers.com.

357

CH2M HILL COMPANIES, LTD.

9191 S. Jamaica St.
Englewood, CO 80112
Phone: 303-771-0900
Fax: 720-286-9250
Web: www.ch2m.com

CEO: Lee A. McIntire
CFO: JoAnn Shea
HR: John Madia
FYE: December 31
Type: Private

Catchy, no. Descriptive, yes. CH2M HILL's name is culled from its founders (Cornell, Howland, Hayes, and Merryfield) plus HILL, from its first merger. The engineering and construction group is organized into three divisions: government, environment, and nuclear; facilities and infrastructure; and energy. Federal projects typically include nuclear and environmental cleanup and government facility operations. The firm also works for state and local governments building water and wastewater systems, airports, highways, and other transportation projects. Its energy division targets private sector companies in the chemical, energy, and life science industries. Founded in 1946, the company is owned by its employees.

	Annual Growth	12/04	12/05	12/06	12/07	12/08
Sales ($ mil.)	19.8%	2,715.4	3,152.2	4,006.9	4,376.2	5,589.9
Net income ($ mil.)	(0.2%)	32.3	81.6	38.9	66.0	32.1
Employees	14.4%	14,000	18,363	17,000	22,000	24,000

CHALLENGER, GRAY & CHRISTMAS, INC.

150 S. Wacker Dr., Ste. 2700
Chicago, IL 60606
Phone: 312-332-5790
Fax: 312-332-4843
Web: www.challengergray.com

CEO: John A. Challenger
CFO: John A. Challenger
HR: David M. Cervone
FYE: December 31
Type: Private

The oldest outplacement consulting firm in the US, Challenger, Gray & Christmas provides outplacement programs for executives, middle managers, and long-term or highly valued employees that face termination due to company closings and large volume reductions. Programs include communication strategy, employee retention, security, phasing down, public agency involvement, and community awareness. Challenger, Gray & Christmas also offers one-to-one counseling and support for employees in areas such as writing a resume, starting a business, answering ads, and retiring. The firm has offices in Canada, Japan, Mexico, and the US.

	Annual Growth	12/04	12/05	12/06	12/07	12/08
Est. sales ($ mil.)	—	—	—	—	—	2.9
Employees	—	—	—	—	—	200

CHAMPION ENTERPRISES HOLDINGS, LLC

755 W. Big Beaver, Ste. 1000
Troy, MI 48084
Phone: 248-614-8200
Fax: 248-273-4208
Web: www.championhomes.com

CEO: William C. (Bill) Griffiths
CFO: Phyllis A. Knight
HR: —
FYE: December 31
Type: Private

Champion Enterprises Holdings is a winner in the manufactured home building game. The company also is one of the largest modular homebuilders in North America. The company makes single-family ranch-style homes, as well as townhouses, duplexes, and steel-framed modular buildings for commercial use. Its homes and buildings are sold in Canada under the Moduline and SRI Homes names. Its Celedonian Building Systems arm sells pre-engineered buildings in the UK. Champion operates nearly 30 plants in North America and Europe. Back in the US, Champion's homes are sold through a network of independent and company-owned retailers. Champion Enterprises exited Chapter 11 bankruptcy in 2010.

	Annual Growth	12/04	12/05	12/06	12/07	12/08
Sales ($ mil.)	(2.6%)	1,150.2	1,272.6	1,364.6	1,273.5	1,033.2
Net income ($ mil.)	—	17.0	37.8	138.3	7.2	(199.5)
Employees	(11.9%)	6,800	7,400	7,000	6,500	4,100

CHAMPION INDUSTRIES, INC.

NASDAQ (GM): CHMP

2450 1st Ave.
Huntington, WV 25728
Phone: 304-528-2700
Fax: 304-528-2765
Web: www.champion-industries.com

CEO: Marshall T. Reynolds
CFO: Todd R. Fry
HR: —
FYE: October 31
Type: Public

This Champion hopes to win business in the printing and office supply fields. Through more than a dozen operating units, Champion Industries prints books, brochures, business cards, business forms, posters, and tags, including complex four- to six-color products. Printing accounts for more than 60% of sales. The company also sells a wide range of office products and office furniture, which it orders from manufacturers, and provides office design services. Champion Industries operates primarily in regional markets east of the Mississippi and publishes the daily newspaper in its hometown in West Virginia. Chairman and CEO Marshall Reynolds controls about 42% of the company's shares.

	Annual Growth	10/05	10/06	10/07	10/08	10/09
Sales ($ mil.)	1.2%	134.9	145.2	145.6	162.7	141.3
Net income ($ mil.)	—	1.1	5.5	6.1	6.0	(27.5)
Market value ($ mil.)	(19.1%)	42.4	69.8	62.6	32.7	18.2
Employees	1.3%	750	730	890	890	790

CHAMPION TECHNOLOGIES, INC.

3200 Southwest Freeway, Ste. 2700
Houston, TX 77027
Phone: 713-627-3303
Fax: 713-623-8083
Web: www.champ-tech.com

CEO: Thomas N. (Tom) Amonett
CFO: Chris Johnson
HR: —
FYE: December 31
Type: Subsidiary

Champion Technologies produces specialty chemicals that help companies in the oil and gas industry withstand surface equipment problems such as internal pipe corrosion and flow assurance. The company's chemicals also are used in water-oil separation. Its manufacturing facilities are located in North America and Europe, with blending facilities located throughout the world. Special Products, a division of Champion Technologies, is a supplier of base chemicals for use in oilfield cementing, drilling, refining, and stimulation. Its Champion Environmental Technologies focuses on products that combat environmental damage from underwater drilling. The company is a subsidiary of Permian Mud Service.

	Annual Growth	12/04	12/05	12/06	12/07	12/08
Est. sales ($ mil.)	—	—	—	—	—	700.0
Employees	—	—	—	—	—	2,300

CHAMPIONS BIOTECHNOLOGY, INC.

OTC: CSBR

2200 Wilson Blvd., Ste. 102-316
Arlington, VA 22201
Phone: 703-526-0400
Fax: 703-526-0825
Web: www.championsbiotechnology.com

CEO: Douglas D. (Doug) Burkett
CFO: Mark R. Schonau
HR: —
FYE: April 30
Type: Public

Champions Biotechnology is hoping to win big in the field of cancer research. In 2007 the company acquired two anticancer drugs, as well as a preclinical platform for studying them. Its Biomerk Tumorgrafts platform allows the company to implant human tumors of various cancer types into mice, allowing scientists to study the effects of investigational drugs on human cancers. The company uses the platform in its own research and also provides tumor-specific research to doctors, as well as the Tumorgraft platform to other drug developers. The company intends to develop its internal drug candidates through preclinical stages and enlist the help of larger pharmaceutical partners to continue development.

	Annual Growth	4/05	4/06	4/07	4/08	4/09
Sales ($ mil.)	164.3%	—	—	—	1.4	3.7
Net income ($ mil.)	—	—	—	—	0.0	(2.2)
Market value ($ mil.)	(21.9%)	—	—	—	45.5	35.6
Employees	175.0%	—	—	—	4	11

CHAMPLAIN CABLE CORPORATION

175 Hercules Dr.
Colchester, VT 05446
Phone: 802-654-4200
Fax: 802-654-4224
Web: www.champcable.com

CEO: Richard Hall
CFO: Tim Lizotte
HR: —
FYE: December 31
Type: Subsidiary

Champlain Cable learned how to do the twist and saw its sales rise. The subsidiary of Switzerland-based HUBER + SUHNER manufactures cable to carry power, signals and data for the industrial, automotive, and data transmission manufacturing industries. The company's products include cable that has been braided, twisted, wrapped, and jacketed for insulation. Products are designed to accommodate tight spaces, extreme temperatures, and harsh chemicals, characteristics which have led Champlain Cable to make several products tailored to the needs of the US military.

CHANGING WORLD TECHNOLOGIES, INC.

460 Hempstead Ave.
West Hempstead, NY 11552
Phone: 516-486-0100
Fax: 516-486-0460
Web: www.changingworldtech.com

CEO: Brian S. Appel
CFO: Michael J. McLaughlin
HR: —
FYE: December 31
Type: Private

Changing World Technologies (CWT) believes that all you need to change the world and take on the big oil companies is guts (preferably turkey), and the innovative technology to turn those guts into oil. The company has patented a method of breaking down carbon-based matter into petroleum products, primarily biodiesel and fertilizers. Any carbon-based matter (tires, old computers, medical waste) will work, but CWT (which operates primarily through its Renewable Environmental Solutions' unit) had an agreement with a nearby Butterball plant in Carthage, Missouri, to process its unused turkey parts. CWT withdrew its IPO registration in early 2009 and then filed for Chapter 11 bankruptcy protection soon after that.

CHANNELL COMMERCIAL CORPORATION

Pink Sheets: CHNL

26040 Ynez Rd.
Temecula, CA 92591
Phone: 951-719-2600
Fax: 951-296-2322
Web: www.channellcomm.com

CEO: William H. Channell Jr.
CFO: —
HR: Ginger Bejar
FYE: December 31
Type: Public

You can remove a letter or two, but Channell Commercial's products still won't make you smell nice. The company makes plastic and metal enclosures, copper wire connectors, fiber-optic cable management systems, and heat shrink products, primarily for broadband and telecommunications applications. Its products can be used for data, power, video, and voice transmissions, as well as Internet connectivity. Top customers are Verizon Communications, Time Warner, Cox Communications, and Comcast. Channell Commercial also supplies water tanks through its Australian subsidiary Bushman Tanks (dba Bushmans). The founding William Channell family owns a majority of the company.

CHAPARRAL ENERGY, INC.

701 Cedar Lake Blvd.
Oklahoma City, OK 73114
Phone: 405-478-8770
Fax: 405-478-1947
Web: www.chaparralenergy.com

CEO: Mark A. Fischer
CFO: Joseph O. (Joe) Evans
HR: Laura J. Martin
FYE: December 31
Type: Private

Chaparral Energy searches the scrublands of America's Mid-Continent and Permian Basin, looking for oil and natural gas. The exploration and production company also drills in North Texas, the Gulf Coast, the Ark-La-Tex region, and the Rocky Mountains. The Mid-Continent accounts for about 72% of Chaparral Energy's reserves. In 2008 the company reported estimated proved reserves of some 680.1 billion cu. ft. of natural gas equivalent. Investment firm CCMP Capital Advisors owns 37% of the company, which it acquired for $325 million in 2010 as the oil and gas company sought a capital infusion to pay down debt.

CHARLES & COLVARD, LTD.

NASDAQ (GS): CTHR

300 Perimeter Park Dr., Ste. A
Morrisville, NC 27560
Phone: 919-468-0399
Fax: 919-468-0486
Web: www.moissanite.com

CEO: Randall N. (Randy) McCullough
CFO: Timothy L. Krist
HR: —
FYE: December 31
Type: Public

Charles & Colvard hopes that it isn't just some shooting star. The company makes gemstones made from moissanite, a diamond substitute created in laboratories. Composed of silicon and carbon, moissanite (aka silicon carbide or SiC) is typically found in meteorites. Charles & Colvard makes its gemstones from SiC crystals purchased primarily from Cree, Inc., and Swedish company Norstel. Charles & Colvard markets its gemstones through two distributors (Stuller and Rio Grande) and jewelry manufacturers such as K&G Creations, Reeves Park, and Samuel Aaron International.

	Annual Growth	12/05	12/06	12/07	12/08	12/09
Sales ($ mil.)	(33.9%)	43.5	40.7	27.8	14.7	8.3
Net income ($ mil.)	—	5.9	6.1	0.0	(6.2)	(3.4)
Market value ($ mil.)	(48.2%)	308.5	152.7	42.0	3.8	22.1
Employees	(18.9%)	60	60	62	33	26

THE CHARLES MACHINE WORKS, INC.

1959 W. Fir Ave.
Perry, OK 73077
Phone: 580-336-4402
Fax: 580-572-3527
Web: www.ditchwitch.com

CEO: Tiffany Sewell-Howard
CFO: Rick Johnson
HR: Dave Lamerton
FYE: December 31
Type: Private

Ditch Witch has cast a spell over the heavy equipment industry since 1949. Captivated by its power and efficiency, The Charles Machine Works (CMW) manufactures and sells construction equipment and parts bearing the Ditch Witch name. Its lineup features trenchless machines, trenchers, mini-excavators, and plows including tractors, backhoes, and saws for home construction and underground utility projects. The company also makes electronic tools from fault locators to beacons for ground directional assistance, and trailers, both dual- and single-axle. Machine maintenance and repair services are offered, too. Founders of CMW, the Malzahn family own the company.

An in-depth profile of this company is available to Hoover's Online members at hoovers.com.

359

CHARLES RIVER LABORATORIES INTERNATIONAL, INC.   NYSE: CRL

251 Ballardvale St.
Wilmington, MA 01887
Phone: 781-222-6000
Fax: 978-658-7132
Web: www.criver.com

CEO: James C. Foster
CFO: Thomas F. Ackerman
HR: David P. Johst
FYE: December 31
Type: Public

Charles River Laboratories International counts its chickens before they're hatched. The company provides clinical and laboratory research services and related products to pharmaceutical and biotech companies, including pathogen-free, fertilized chicken eggs used in vaccine production. Its Research Models and Services (RMS) unit also produces lab rats and other animals bred specifically for use in medical testing. The company provides contract drug discovery and development services, including toxicology studies and other kinds of testing, through its Preclinical Services (PCS) segment. Customers include drug, medical device, and animal health firms, as well as educational, health care, and government institutions.

	Annual Growth	12/05	12/06	12/07	12/08	12/09
Sales ($ mil.)	1.7%	1,122.2	1,058.4	1,230.6	1,343.5	1,202.6
Net income ($ mil.)	(5.6%)	142.0	(55.8)	154.4	(521.8)	112.6
Market value ($ mil.)	(5.6%)	2,804.5	2,862.8	4,355.4	1,734.2	2,230.0
Employees	(1.2%)	8,400	8,000	8,500	9,000	8,000

◫ THE CHARLES SCHWAB CORPORATION   NYSE: SCHW

211 Main St.
San Francisco, CA 94105
Phone: 415-636-7000
Fax: 415-636-9820
Web: www.schwab.com

CEO: Walter W. (Walt) Bettinger II
CFO: Joseph R. Martinetto
HR: Jay L. Allen
FYE: December 31
Type: Public

The once-rebellious Charles Schwab is all grown up. The discount broker now offers the same traditional brokerage services it shunned some three decades ago. Schwab manages more than $1.4 trillion in assets for nearly 10 million individual and institutional clients. Traders can access its services via telephone, wireless device, the Internet, and through more than 300 offices in some 45 states, plus London and Hong Kong. Besides discount brokerage, the firm offers financial research, advice, and planning; investment management; retirement plans; and proprietary Schwab and Laudus mutual funds, in addition to mortgages, CDs, and other banking products through its Charles Schwab Bank unit.

	Annual Growth	12/05	12/06	12/07	12/08	12/09
Sales ($ mil.)	(3.8%)	5,151.0	4,988.0	5,617.0	5,393.0	4,414.0
Net income ($ mil.)	2.1%	725.0	1,227.0	2,407.0	1,212.0	787.0
Market value ($ mil.)	6.4%	17,508.8	23,082.4	30,494.1	19,299.0	22,461.8
Employees	(3.0%)	14,000	12,400	13,300	13,400	12,400

THE CHARLES STARK DRAPER LABORATORY, INC.

555 Technology Sq.
Cambridge, MA 02139
Phone: 617-258-1000
Fax: 617-258-1131
Web: www.draper.com

CEO: James D. (Jim) Shields
CFO: Elizabeth Mora
HR: —
FYE: June 30
Type: Not-for-profit

The Charles Stark Draper Laboratory guides research into space, under water, and across continents. Founded in 1932 by MIT professor Charles Stark Draper as a teaching lab, the not-for-profit corporation develops guidance, navigation, and control technologies for aircraft, submarines, missiles, and spacecraft. It works with NASA, the US Department of Defense, and commercial businesses to develop technologies and fabricate prototypes. It also solves health care problems with its work in biomedical engineering. The lab has more than 850 engineers and scientists. Originally known as the Instrument Lab, the laboratory was renamed in 1970 and became an independent institution three years later.

	Annual Growth	6/04	6/05	6/06	6/07	6/08
Est. sales ($ mil.)	—	—	—	—	—	420.0
Employees	—	—	—	—	—	1,134

CHARLOTTE PIPE & FOUNDRY COMPANY

2109 Randolph Rd.
Charlotte, NC 28207
Phone: 704-348-6450
Fax: 800-553-1605
Web: www.charlottepipe.com

CEO: Frank Dowd IV
CFO: William Hutaff
HR: Dave Magee
FYE: December 31
Type: Private

The pipe business is piping hot for Charlotte Pipe. Charlotte Pipe reportedly is the largest manufacturer of drain, waste, and vent (DWV) pipe and fittings in the US, and operates one of the largest fittings molding facilities in the world. The company's cast-iron and plastic pipes and fittings are used in commercial and residential plumbing, and, under its ChemDrain brand, for chemical waste. The company runs a foundry in the Queen City and a division in neighboring Monroe, North Carolina, that produces thermoplastic plumbing pipes and fittings. Satellite extrusion plants operate in Pennsylvania, Florida, Alabama, Texas, and Utah. Founded by W. Frank Dowd in 1901, the company is controlled by the Dowd family.

CHARLOTTE RUSSE HOLDING, INC.

4645 Morena Blvd.
San Diego, CA 92117
Phone: 858-587-1500
Fax: 858-587-0902
Web: www.charlotterusse.com

CEO: Jenny J. Ming
CFO: Frederick G. (Fred) Silny
HR: Pamela (Pam) O'Connor
FYE: September 30
Type: Private

Charlotte Russe Holding is sweet on women's clothing. The mall-based retailer operates about 500 Charlotte Russe clothing stores in some 45 US states and Puerto Rico. The stores (averaging 7,100 sq. ft.) offer value-priced established and trendy fashions for women in their twenties and teens. Most merchandise carries the company's proprietary labels (Charlotte Russe, Refuge, and blu Chic). The company shut down its struggling 64-store Rampage chain in 2006, converting several locations to Charlotte Russe stores. Charlotte Russe Holding went public in 1999. The company was taken private in 2009, when investment firm Advent International acquired Charlotte Russe.

	Annual Growth	9/04	9/05	9/06	9/07	9/08
Sales ($ mil.)	—	0.3	0.9	2.9	4.9	0.0
Net income ($ mil.)	4.4%	15.3	10.8	25.1	36.3	18.2
Employees	12.7%	6,477	7,610	8,328	8,961	10,454

THE CHARMER SUNBELT GROUP

60 E. 42nd St.
New York, NY 10165
Phone: 212-699-7000
Fax: 212-699-7099
Web: www.charmer-sunbelt.com

CEO: Charles (Charlie) Merinoff
CFO: Gene Luciano
HR: —
FYE: March 31
Type: Private

The Charmer Sunbelt Group is one of the biggest swigs in its sector. A leading US wine, beer, and spirits distributor, the company serves 13 states and The District of Columbia. Headquartered in New York City, it operates through 10 subsidiaries and eight joint ventures (JVs), including Premier Beverage (subsidiary, Florida), Bacchus Importers (subsidiary, Maryland), R & R Marketing (JV, New Jersey), and Associated Distributors (JV, Virginia). In addition to alcoholic beverages, Charmer Sunbelt also offers non-alcoholic products such as bottled water. CEO Charles (Charlie) Merinoff is the grandson of Charmer founder, Herman Merinoff.

	Annual Growth	3/04	3/05	3/06	3/07	3/08
Sales ($ mil.)	29.6%	1,700.0	2,900.0	4,100.0	4,600.0	4,800.0
Employees	23.6%	3,000	6,100	6,550	7,000	7,000

⊞ CHARMING SHOPPES, INC.
NASDAQ (GS): CHRS

450 Winks Ln.
Bensalem, PA 19020
Phone: 215-245-9100
Fax: 215-633-4640
Web: www.charmingshoppes.com

CEO: James P. (Jim) Fogarty
CFO: Eric M. Specter
HR: Frederick B. (Fred) Lamster
FYE: January 31
Type: Public

Charming Shoppes is big in women's plus-size clothing. The company runs more than 2,100 stores (and related websites) at three fashion chains that cater to the amply proportioned: about 860 Lane Bryant and Lane Bryant Outlet stores in 46 states; some 800 Fashion Bug stores that sell moderately priced apparel and accessories in girls, juniors, misses, and plus sizes; and about 460 Catherines Plus Size stores. The stores are primarily located in suburban areas and small towns across the US and court low- to middle-income women and teens who follow fashion styles rather than set them. The company's purchase of Lane Bryant from Limited Brands elevated Charming Shoppes to #1 in the plus-size market.

	Annual Growth	1/06	1/07	1/08	1/09	1/10
Sales ($ mil.)	(7.0%)	2,755.7	3,067.5	3,010.0	2,474.9	2,064.6
Net income ($ mil.)	—	99.4	108.9	(84.3)	(244.2)	(78.0)
Market value ($ mil.)	(16.8%)	1,407.8	1,520.1	747.3	125.1	673.2
Employees	(0.9%)	28,000	30,000	30,200	28,700	27,000

⊞ CHART INDUSTRIES, INC.
NASDAQ (GS): GTLS

1 Infinity Corporate Centre Dr., Ste. 300
Garfield Heights, OH 44125
Phone: 440-753-1490
Fax: 440-753-1491
Web: www.chart-ind.com

CEO: Samuel F. Thomas
CFO: Michael F. Biehl
HR: Mark H. Ludwig
FYE: December 31
Type: Public

They're just chillin' at Chart Industries. The company designs equipment for low-temperature uses, including cryogenic systems that can operate at temperatures near absolute zero. Chart's vessels are used to process, liquefy, store, and transport gases, which are marketed to petrochemical and natural gas processors, producers of industrial gas, satellite testing companies, and restaurants and convenience stores. The company also performs engineered bulk gas installations and makes specialty liquid nitrogen end-use equipment used in the hydrocarbon processing and industrial gas industries. Chart's products are sold worldwide; the US accounts for about three-quarters of sales.

	Annual Growth	12/05	12/06	12/07	12/08	12/09
Sales ($ mil.)	56.9%	97.7	537.5	666.4	744.4	591.5
Net income ($ mil.)	—	(0.5)	26.9	44.2	78.9	61.2
Market value ($ mil.)	0.6%	—	464.9	886.3	304.9	473.8
Employees	(0.4%)	2,556	2,703	2,751	2,945	2,517

⊞ CHARTER COMMUNICATIONS, INC.
Pink Sheets: CCMM

12405 Powerscourt Dr., Ste. 100
St. Louis, MO 63131
Phone: 314-965-0555
Fax: 314-965-9745
Web: www.charter.com

CEO: Michael J. (Mike) Lovett
CFO: Eloise E. Schmitz
HR: —
FYE: December 31
Type: Public

Charter Communications is a cable television system operator with about 5 million residential and commercial subscribers in 27 US states, making it one of the top cable companies, behind Comcast, Time Warner Cable, and Cox Communications. Not just a leading cable TV player, Charter offers broadband Internet to 3 million customers and computer telephony services to another 1 million users. The company also derives a portion of its revenue from the sale of local advertising on such cable networks as MTV and CNN. Charter Communications, which skirted bankruptcy for years, completed a Chapter 11 bankruptcy reorganization in 2009.

	Annual Growth	12/05	12/06	12/07	12/08	12/09
Sales ($ mil.)	6.5%	5,254.0	5,504.0	6,002.0	6,479.0	6,755.0
Net income ($ mil.)	—	(967.0)	(1,370.0)	(1,616.0)	(2,451.0)	11,366.0
Employees	(0.7%)	17,200	15,500	16,500	16,600	16,700

CHARTER FINANCIAL CORPORATION
OTC: CHFN

1233 O.G. Skinner Dr.
West Point, GA 31833
Phone: 706-645-1391
Fax: —
Web: www.charterbk.com

CEO: Robert L. Johnson
CFO: Curtis R. Kollar
HR: —
FYE: September 30
Type: Public

Charter Financial is the savings and loan holding company for CharterBank, which operates more than a dozen branches and loan production offices in western Georgia and eastern Alabama. Deposit products include consumer and commercial checking accounts, savings and money market accounts, and CDs. The bank is focused on real estate lending, with residential and commercial mortgages each accounting for more than a third of its loan portfolio. It also makes consumer, business, construction, and land development loans. The bank gives cash awards to high school customers for making straight A's. Mutual holding company First Charter MHC owns more than 80% of Charter Financial.

CHARTWELLS EDUCATIONAL DINING SERVICES

3 International Dr.
Rye Brook, NY 10573
Phone: 914-935-5300
Fax: 914-935-5550
Web: www.eatlearnlive.com

CEO: Steven M. (Steve) Sweeney
CFO: John Cautillo
HR: —
FYE: September 30
Type: Subsidiary

This company is convinced students can't learn on an empty stomach. Chartwells Educational Dining Services is a foodservice operator for schools and universities. It offers a full menu of meal planning and catering services to satisfy the tastes and nutritional requirements of students in more than 500 public school districts. The higher education division provides dining services to more than 200 colleges and universities. In addition, its FLIK Independent Schools division serves more than 115 independent private schools and academies. Chartwells is a division of Compass Group USA, the North American operating unit of UK-based contract foodservices provider Compass Group.

⊞ CHASE CORPORATION
NYSE Amex: CCF

26 Summer St.
Bridgewater, MA 02324
Phone: 508-279-1789
Fax: 508-697-6419
Web: www.chasecorp.com

CEO: Peter R. Chase
CFO: Kenneth L. (Ken) Dumas
HR: —
FYE: August 31
Type: Public

Duct tape is great, but when the task calls for higher-tech stuff, Chase has it. The company makes and sells specialty tapes, coatings, laminates, and sealants for a diversity of applications, from wire and cable to construction and electronics. Two divisions develop, manufacture, and market a protective lineup that includes insulating and conducting materials for electrical wire to anti-corrosion and waterproofing products for pipeline, bridge, highway, and electronics. Chase coating and laminating processes almost any flexible material produced on a roll — films to fabrics. A third division offers electronics manufacturing services (EMS). Chase's sales force, OEM reps, and distributors drive global sales.

	Annual Growth	8/05	8/06	8/07	8/08	8/09
Sales ($ mil.)	4.2%	91.4	108.4	127.5	132.5	107.6
Net income ($ mil.)	7.5%	4.8	6.1	10.2	12.4	6.4
Market value ($ mil.)	12.2%	63.3	73.8	152.2	152.5	100.5
Employees	2.9%	325	362	383	381	365

⊞ An in-depth profile of this company is available to Hoover's Online members at hoovers.com.

361

CHASE GENERAL CORPORATION

Pink Sheets: CSGN

1307 S. 59th St.
St. Joseph, MO 64507
Phone: 816-279-1625
Fax: 816-279-1997
Web: www.cherrymash.com

CEO: Barry M. Yantis
CFO: Barry M. Yantis
HR: Brett A. Yantis
FYE: June 30
Type: Public

They not only chase but catch the sweet life at Chase General Corporation. Its subsidiary Dye Candy Company makes and distributes candy and confections. Combining chocolate and chopped peanuts and using crushed maraschino cherries for a smooth fondant center, the company's Dye Candy division produces its flagship "Cherry Mash" candy bars. Its Seasonal Candy division makes Chase brand coconut haystacks, fudge, jelly candies, peanut brittle, and peanut clusters. Chase General's products are distributed mainly in the Midwest. Associated Wholesale Grocers accounted for 26% of the company's 2008 sales; Wal-Mart accounted for 15%.

	Annual Growth	6/05	6/06	6/07	6/08	6/09
Sales ($ mil.)	10.5%	—	2.3	2.3	2.7	3.1
Net income ($ mil.)	—	—	(0.1)	(0.2)	0.0	0.2
Employees	—	—	—	—	—	18

CHASE PAYMENTECH SOLUTIONS, LLC

14221 Dallas Pkwy., Bldg. 2
Dallas, TX 75254
Phone: 214-849-3000
Fax: 214-849-2148
Web: www.paymentech.com

CEO: Michael P. (Mike) Duffy
CFO: Kathryn (Kathy) Smith
HR: —
FYE: December 31
Type: Subsidiary

Chase Paymentech Solutions keeps the wheels of commerce churning. The company processes the merchant side of check and credit, debit, and prepaid card payments, both over the Internet and at the point of sale. Authorizing transactions in about 130 currencies globally, Chase Paymentech Solutions assembles the authorization network and recruits new merchants into the system; it also operates merchant help desks to assist point-of-sale clients. It targets such sectors as retail, hospitality, airlines, utilities, and convenience stores and gas stations. Banking behemoth JPMorgan Chase owns Chase Paymentech.

CHATHAM LODGING TRUST

NYSE: CLDT

50 Cocoanut Row, Ste. 200
Palm Beach, FL 33480
Phone: 561-802-4477
Fax: —

CEO: Jeffrey H. Fisher
CFO: —
HR: —
FYE: December 31
Type: Public

In hotels they trust. A self-advised hotel real estate investment trust (REIT), Chatham Lodging Trust was formed to acquire upscale extended-stay hotels, including Residence Inn by Marriott, Homewood Suites by Hilton, and Summerfield Suites by Hyatt; to a lesser extent, the firm will also buy select-service and full-service hotels. The REIT seeks properties being sold at a discount, particularly hotels located in the top 25 largest US metropolitan markets. Chatham Lodging, which operates through its Chatham Lodging, L.P. subsidiary, was founded in 2009. It went public the following year and has used proceeds from the offering to buy six Homewood Suites properties.

CHATTEM, INC.

1715 W. 38th St.
Chattanooga, TN 37409
Phone: 423-821-4571
Fax: 423-821-0395
Web: www.chattem.com

CEO: Alexander (Zan) Guerry III
CFO: Robert B. Long
HR: —
FYE: November 30
Type: Subsidiary

Chattem's got more brands than the Texas ranching industry. Over-the-counter drugs make a bundle of money for Chattem, which also manufactures and sells personal care products and dietary supplements. Chattem markets some two-dozen branded products, including skin care and pain treatments such as Aspercreme, Cortizone-10, Icy Hot muscle pain reliever, and Pamprin menstrual symptom reliever. The company also makes the Unisom sleep aid, medicated powder Gold Bond, Bullfrog sunscreen, and Mudd clay-based facial mask. Chattem sells its products to wholesalers and retail merchandisers. The company was acquired in 2010 by Sanofi-Aventis through a nearly $2 billion tender offer.

	Annual Growth	11/05	11/06	11/07	11/08	11/09
Sales ($ mil.)	13.5%	279.3	300.5	423.4	454.9	463.3
Net income ($ mil.)	15.1%	36.0	45.1	59.7	66.3	63.2
Employees	4.4%	449	423	474	498	533

CHECK INTO CASH, INC.

201 Keith St. SW, Ste. 80
Cleveland, TN 37311
Phone: 423-479-2400
Fax: 423-559-1099
Web: www.checkintocash.com

CEO: W. Allan Jones
CFO: Bill Lane
HR: Scott Beck
FYE: December 31
Type: Private

If you're in need of some quick cash, you might want to check into Check Into Cash. The company offers short-term payday advances and check cashing services through some 1,100 stores in more than 30 states. Loans also can be approved online. In order to receive the payday loan, customers issue a personal check to Check Into Cash to cover the amount borrowed (usually between $100 and $1,000), plus fees. The company holds the check until the customer's next payday, then cashes it. Customers must provide proof of ID and income, and have an active checking account. Check Into Cash was founded by chairman Allan Jones in 1993.

	Annual Growth	12/04	12/05	12/06	12/07	12/08
Est. sales ($ mil.)	—	—	—	—	—	31.5
Employees	—	—	—	—	—	280

CHECKERS DRIVE-IN RESTAURANTS, INC.

4300 W. Cypress St., Ste. 600
Tampa, FL 33607
Phone: 813-283-7000
Fax: 813-283-7008
Web: www.checkers.com

CEO: Enrique (Rick) Silva
CFO: Todd Lindsey
HR: Wendy Harkness
FYE: December 31
Type: Private

You might say that this company's customers are driven to eat hamburgers. Checkers Drive-In Restaurants is the #1 operator of double drive-through fast-food restaurants, with more than 800 mostly franchised locations in about 20 states. Operating under the names Checkers and Rally's Hamburgers, the restaurants offer a limited menu of burgers, fries, and hotdogs, along with beverages and shakes. The quick service eateries are typically decorated with checkered flags and racing theme exteriors and offer no inside seating or dining areas. Checkers is controlled by private equity firm Wellspring Capital.

CHECKPOINT SYSTEMS, INC.   NYSE: CKP

101 Wolf Dr.
Thorofare, NJ 08086
Phone: 856-848-1800
Fax: 856-848-0937
Web: www.checkpointsystems.com

CEO: Robert P. (Rob) van der Merwe
CFO: Raymond D. (Ray) Andrews
HR: —
FYE: December 31
Type: Public

Checkpoint Systems wants to keep shoplifters in check. The company makes electronic article surveillance systems (EAS), radio frequency identification (RFID) tags, and electronic security devices (using electromagnetic technology), such as intrusion alarms. digital video recorders, and electronic access control systems used by retailers that have included Barnes & Noble, Sears, Target, and Walgreen. Checkpoint's EAS units employ paper-thin disposable circuit tags attached to merchandise that are disarmed at checkout; if not disarmed, the tags trigger electronic sensors when the customer tries to leave. The company operates in some 30 countries worldwide; nearly two-thirds of its sales come from outside the US.

	Annual Growth	12/05	12/06	12/07	12/08	12/09
Sales ($ mil.)	1.7%	721.0	687.8	834.2	917.1	772.7
Net income ($ mil.)	(10.1%)	39.4	35.9	58.8	(29.8)	25.7
Market value ($ mil.)	(11.3%)	973.2	797.5	1,025.7	388.5	602.1
Employees	10.0%	3,955	3,213	3,930	3,878	5,785

THE CHEESECAKE FACTORY INCORPORATED   NASDAQ (GS): CAKE

26901 Malibu Hills Rd.
Calabasas Hills, CA 91301
Phone: 818-871-3000
Fax: 818-871-3001
Web: www.thecheesecakefactory.com

CEO: David Overton
CFO: W. Douglas Benn
HR: Dina R. Barmasse-Gray
FYE: December 31
Type: Public

These restaurants have some industrial strength menus for foodies. The Cheesecake Factory owns and operates about 150 casual-dining restaurants in 35 states that offer some 200 menu items ranging from sandwiches and salads to steaks and seafood. The highlight of the menu, of course, is cheesecake, which comes in about 40 varieties, including Chocolate Tuxedo Cream and Kahlua Cocoa Coffee. Each restaurant has a unique design, but all of them feature over-the-top opulence and Las Vegas-style glitz. In addition to its flagship concept, the company has more than a dozen upscale Grand Lux Cafes that offer a similar menu. The Cheesecake Factory also sells desserts to grocery stores and foodservice operators.

	Annual Growth	12/05	12/06	12/07	12/08	12/09
Sales ($ mil.)	8.0%	1,177.6	1,315.3	1,511.6	1,606.4	1,602.0
Net income ($ mil.)	(16.4%)	87.5	81.3	74.0	52.3	42.8
Market value ($ mil.)	(12.8%)	2,258.6	1,486.0	1,432.2	610.1	1,304.2
Employees	5.0%	24,700	29,400	29,400	31,000	30,000

CHEF SOLUTIONS INC.

120 W. Palatine Rd.
Wheeling, IL 60090
Phone: 847-325-7500
Fax: 847-325-7594
Web: www.chefsolutions.com

CEO: Steven B. (Steve) Silk
CFO: —
HR: —
FYE: December 31
Type: Private

Stressed-out chefs needing to find a solution for rounding out their menus can turn to this company for the latest side dishes and salads. Chef Solutions is a supplier of fresh-prepared foods to customers in the retail food and foodservice industries. The company offers fresh, refrigerated foods, such as deli-style salads, salad kits, mashed potatoes, and other side dishes, along with fresh-cut fruit, dips and salad dressings. Its Orval Kent unit makes fresh salads, dips, and other deli-style side dishes. Private equity and turnaround firm Questor Management is the majority owner of the company.

CHELSEA & SCOTT, LTD.

75 Albrecht Dr.
Lake Bluff, IL 60044
Phone: 847-615-2110
Fax: 847-615-2290
Web: www.onestepahead.com

CEO: Karen B. Scott
CFO: Susan O'Malley
HR: —
FYE: December 31
Type: Private

Chelsea & Scott wants children to grow up with its products. Through its One Step Ahead catalog and website, the company sells apparel, home furnishings, feeding and safety products, toys, and travel accessories for newborns to children under 3. It also provides educational toys and developmental products for children ages 3 to 8 through its Leaps and Bounds catalog and Web site. Chelsea & Scott offers such brands as ALEX, Infantino, Lamaze, and Manhattan Group, as well as its own One Step Ahead branded lines. The company was founded by parents Karen and Ian Scott in 1987, after discovering many of the children's products they had bought did not meet their expectations.

CHELSEA THERAPEUTICS INTERNATIONAL, LTD.   NASDAQ (CM): CHTP

3530 Toringdon Way, Ste. 200
Charlotte, NC 28277
Phone: 704-341-1516
Fax: 704-752-1479
Web: www.chelseatherapeutics.com

CEO: Simon Pedder
CFO: J. Nick Riehle
HR: —
FYE: December 31
Type: Public

When it comes to developing therapies, Chelsea Therapeutics doesn't limit itself to just one disease. The biopharmaceutical company develops treatments for various immunological disorders such as rheumatoid arthritis, inflammatory bowel disease, psoriasis, and cancer. The drugs, known as antifolates, work by blocking enzymes that aid in disease cell growth. Chelsea is also developing Droxidopa, a drug that treats neurogenic orthostatic hypotension (severe dizziness and fatigue brought on by a fall in blood pressure) through a partnership with Japanese pharmaceutical firm Dainippon Sumitomo.

	Annual Growth	12/05	12/06	12/07	12/08	12/09
Sales ($ mil.)	—	—	—	—	0.0	0.0
Net income ($ mil.)	—	—	—	—	(35.1)	(25.8)
Market value ($ mil.)	101.5%	—	—	—	53.9	108.5
Employees	5.9%	—	—	—	17	18

CHEMED CORPORATION   NYSE: CHE

2600 Chemed Center, 255 E. 5th St.
Cincinnati, OH 45202
Phone: 513-762-6900
Fax: 513-762-6919
Web: www.chemed.com

CEO: Kevin J. McNamara
CFO: David P. Williams
HR: Chauna Stewart
FYE: December 31
Type: Public

Chemed Corporation plunges right in when it comes to taking care of people. Operating through two major subsidiaries, Chemed Corporation offers care to terminally ill patients through its VITAS Healthcare subsidiary, which owns about 45 hospice programs across some 15 US states. VITAS employs doctors, nurses, and other professionals to provide at-home and inpatient services. In addition, its famous Roto-Rooter subsidiary offers plumbing and drain-cleaning services for residential and commercial customers through company-owned, contractor-operated, and franchised locations, some 600 total. A stalwart of the industry, Roto-Rooter offers services to over 90% of the US market and nearly half of Canada.

	Annual Growth	12/05	12/06	12/07	12/08	12/09
Sales ($ mil.)	6.5%	926.5	1,018.6	1,100.1	1,148.9	1,190.2
Net income ($ mil.)	19.8%	35.8	50.7	64.0	71.0	73.8
Market value ($ mil.)	(0.9%)	1,134.4	844.4	1,276.0	908.1	1,095.4
Employees	3.1%	10,881	11,621	11,783	11,884	12,308

CHEMICAL FINANCIAL CORPORATION

NASDAQ (GS): CHFC

235 E. Main St.
Midland, MI 48640
Phone: 989-839-5350
Fax: 989-839-5255
Web: www.chemicalbankmi.com

CEO: David B. Ramaker
CFO: Lori A. Gwizdala
HR: —
FYE: December 31
Type: Public

Chemical Financial has banking down to a science. It's the holding company for Chemical Bank, which provides a range of financial services to individuals and businesses in the lower peninsula of Michigan. Through about 145 branches, the bank offers standard deposit products, including checking and savings accounts, CDs, and IRAs. Commercial real estate loans, residential mortgages, and consumer loans each account for around a quarter of Chemical Financial's loan portfolio. The company also offers trust services, title insurance, and investments. Chemical Financial acquired O.A.K. Financial for some $84 million in stock in 2010, a deal that added more than a dozen bank branches in western Michigan.

	Annual Growth	12/05	12/06	12/07	12/08	12/09
Assets ($ mil.)	3.2%	3,749.3	3,789.2	3,754.3	3,874.3	4,250.7
Net income ($ mil.)	(34.1%)	52.9	46.8	39.0	19.8	10.0
Market value ($ mil.)	(7.2%)	759.2	796.0	568.7	666.5	563.7
Employees	0.9%	1,376	1,478	1,368	1,416	1,427

CHEMTURA CORPORATION

Pink Sheets: CEMJQ

199 Benson Rd.
Middlebury, CT 06749
Phone: 203-573-2000
Fax: 203-573-3711
Web: www.chemtura.com

CEO: Craig A. Rogerson
CFO: Stephen C. Forsyth
HR: Alan M. Swiech
FYE: December 31
Type: Public

Chemtura would like to be the future of chemicals-making. The company ranks among the top specialty chemical companies in the US, along with the likes of Ecolab and Hexion, and among the leading plastics additives maker globally. Aside from plastic additives, Chemtura holds niche-leading positions in petroleum additives, flame retardants, and swimming pool chemicals. Its other products include urethanes and crop protection chemicals. Just more than half of its total sales come from outside the US. In 2009 Chemtura's US operations, faced with significantly decreased sales volumes and the resultant declining liquidity, filed for Chapter 11 bankruptcy protection.

	Annual Growth	12/05	12/06	12/07	12/08	12/09
Sales ($ mil.)	(4.0%)	2,986.6	3,722.7	3,747.0	3,546.0	2,541.0
Net income ($ mil.)	—	(186.1)	(205.5)	(3.0)	(973.0)	(292.0)
Market value ($ mil.)	(44.2%)	3,085.3	2,339.5	1,894.9	340.1	298.8
Employees	(9.6%)	6,600	6,200	5,100	4,700	4,400

CHEMUNG FINANCIAL CORPORATION

OTC: CHMG

1 Chemung Canal Plaza
Elmira, NY 14901
Phone: 607-737-3711
Fax: 607-735-2035
Web: www.cctc2me.com

CEO: Ronald M. Bentley
CFO: John R. Battersby Jr.
HR: Linda M. Struble
FYE: December 31
Type: Public

"Everybody Chemung Financial Tonight" probably wouldn't make much of a pop record. The firm is parent to Chemung Canal Trust Company, which provides bank and trust services from some 20 offices in and around western New York's Chemung County. The trust company offers such deposit services as savings, checking, and money market accounts; IRAs; and CDs. It offers credit card services, and originates a variety of loans, including personal, small business, and residential mortgage loans. Other services include retirement and estate planning, and tax services. Another Chemung Financial subsidiary, CFS Group, offers mutual funds, discount brokerage, and other financial services.

	Annual Growth	12/05	12/06	12/07	12/08	12/09
Assets ($ mil.)	8.0%	718.0	738.2	788.9	838.3	975.9
Net income ($ mil.)	(5.8%)	6.6	6.6	7.3	8.4	5.2
Market value ($ mil.)	(9.8%)	108.9	113.0	98.9	70.5	72.1
Employees	3.5%	285	293	280	309	327

CHENEY BROTHERS, INC.

1 Cheney Way
Riviera Beach, FL 33404
Phone: 561-845-4700
Fax: 561-845-4701
Web: www.cheneybrothers.com

CEO: Byron C. Russell
CFO: Michael Sullivan
HR: Lisa Currier
FYE: December 31
Type: Private

Restaurants in need of supplies can get a little brotherly love from this company. Cheney Brothers is a leading wholesale distributor serving foodservice operators in Florida and other parts of the South. It supplies more than 15,000 food and nonfood items including disposable and dry goods, beverages, meats, dairy items, produce, and maintenance equipment. In addition to its distribution facilities, Cheney Brothers operates Cash & Carry locations in Ocala and Riviera Beach, Florida. The family-owned company was founded in 1925 by Joseph Cheney as a milk and egg distributor.

CHENIERE ENERGY, INC.

NYSE Amex: LNG

700 Milam St., Ste. 800
Houston, TX 77002
Phone: 713-375-5000
Fax: 713-375-6000
Web: www.cheniere.com

CEO: Charif Souki
CFO: Meg A. Gentle
HR: Ann Raden
FYE: December 31
Type: Public

Gaseous form or liquid state are both OK with Cheniere Energy, which is engaged in the development of a liquefied natural gas (LNG) receiving-terminal business. The company's vision is to build three onshore US Gulf Coast LNG receiving terminals (Sabine Pass, Corpus Christi, and Creole Trail) and develop pipelines and other infrastructure to connect these to North American natural gas markets. Cheniere Energy retains some exploration and production assets (formerly its primary business). In 2009 it had stakes in 13 active wells. The company operates along the coast of Louisiana, both onshore and in the Gulf of Mexico.

	Annual Growth	12/05	12/06	12/07	12/08	12/09
Sales ($ mil.)	178.7%	3.0	2.4	0.6	7.1	181.1
Net income ($ mil.)	—	(29.8)	(145.9)	(181.8)	(356.5)	(161.5)
Market value ($ mil.)	(49.5%)	2,131.3	1,653.2	1,869.1	163.2	138.6
Employees	10.8%	130	256	378	208	196

CHENIERE ENERGY PARTNERS, L.P.

NYSE Amex: CQP

700 Milam St., Ste. 800
Houston, TX 77002
Phone: 713-375-5000
Fax: 713-375-6000
Web: www.cheniereenergypartners.com

CEO: Charif Souki
CFO: Meg A. Gentle
HR: —
FYE: December 31
Type: Public

Cheniere Energy Partners, a subsidiary of Cheniere Energy, Inc., plans to be North America's biggest gas station — natural gas, that is. Construction began on the Sabine Pass LNG (liquefied natural gas) receiving terminal in 2005, and was completed in 2008. The terminal is the largest of its kind in North America. The terminal boasts 4 billion cu. ft. per day of regasification capacity as well as 16.9 billion cu. ft. of LNG storage capacity. All of the Sabine Pass LNG receiving terminal's capacity has already been contracted to Total Gas and Power North America (an affiliate of TOTAL S.A.), Chevron U.S.A., and Cheniere Energy Inc. subsidiary Cheniere Marketing.

	Annual Growth	12/05	12/06	12/07	12/08	12/09
Sales ($ mil.)	2,678.7%	—	—	—	15.0	416.8
Net income ($ mil.)	—	—	—	—	(78.3)	186.9
Market value ($ mil.)	248.0%	—	—	—	600.3	2,088.8
Employees	—	—	—	—	—	—

CHEP INTERNATIONAL INC.

8517 S. Park Cir.
Orlando, FL 32819
Phone: 407-370-2437
Fax: 407-355-6211
Web: www.chep.com

CEO: Jim Ritchie
CFO: —
HR: —
FYE: June 30
Type: Subsidiary

CHEP knows it's sink or swim in the pallet and plastic container pooling services business. The company, a unit of Australia-based Brambles, manages the movement of more than 300 million pallets and containers used by companies in the automotive, consumer goods, food and beverage, home improvement, petrochemical, and raw materials industries. The pallets and containers are used throughout the supply chain. The company's 345,000-plus customers have included industry leaders such as General Motors, Kraft, and Procter & Gamble. CHEP operates from a network of more than 500 service facilities in about 45 countries worldwide.

CHEROKEE INC.

NASDAQ (GS): CHKE

6835 Valjean Ave.
Van Nuys, CA 91406
Phone: 818-908-9868
Fax: 818-908-9191
Web: www.cherokeegroup.com

CEO: Robert Margolis
CFO: Russell J. Riopelle
HR: —
FYE: January 31
Type: Public

Cherokee has a license to make money from clothes and shoes. The company licenses its trademarks, which include Cherokee, Sideout, and Carole Little, to retailers and wholesalers of apparel, footwear, and accessories. The main ideas behind Cherokee's business are that large retailers can source merchandise more efficiently than individual brand owners and that licensed brands can sell better for retailers than private labels. In addition to licensing its own brands, Cherokee helps other brand owners gain licensing contracts. Target, the company's largest customer, accounts for about 40% of Cherokee's revenue; other licensees include Tesco (in Europe), Zellers (in Canada), and TJX.

	Annual Growth	1/06	1/07	1/08	1/09	1/10
Sales ($ mil.)	(6.5%)	42.7	76.6	41.6	36.2	32.6
Net income ($ mil.)	(8.9%)	18.3	34.8	16.4	14.3	12.6
Market value ($ mil.)	(20.3%)	351.1	380.9	297.8	134.7	141.5
Employees	1.4%	17	18	20	20	18

CHERRY BROS., LLC

1900 AM Dr., Ste. 203
Quakertown, PA 18951
Phone: 215-892-1900
Fax: —
Web: www.cherrydale.com

CEO: Ross Cherry
CFO: Howard Lightstone
HR: —
FYE: June 30
Type: Private

Cherry Brothers makes making money a bowl of cherries. Doing business under the name Cherrydale, the company's customers include church groups, sports leagues, and civic organizations wishing to raise funds. Cherrydale makes a full line of chocolate and non-chocolate confectionary; in addition it offers a myriad of brand-name products made by other companies, including magazines, jewelry, fashion accessories, gift wrap, home decor items, gardening products, holiday, and personal care goods, all of which are sold by Cherrydale's non-profit customers in order to make money. The company helps more than 20,000 schools and other organizations raise some $66 million every year.

	Annual Growth	6/04	6/05	6/06	6/07	6/08
Est. sales ($ mil.)	—	—	—	—	—	17.0
Employees	—	—	—	—	—	25

CHERRY LANE MUSIC PUBLISHING COMPANY, INC.

6 E. 32nd St., 11th Fl.
New York, NY 10016
Phone: 212-561-3000
Fax: 212-683-2040
Web: www.cherrylane.com

CEO: Peter W. Primont
CFO: Dan Lieblein
HR: —
FYE: December 31
Type: Subsidiary

Cherry Lane Music Publishing Company is a leading independent music publishing business, controlling the rights to a catalog of musical compositions, including songs by The Black Eyed Peas, John Denver, and Elvis Presley. It licenses the rights to those songs for use in TV, film, and advertising, and for inclusion on compilation or re-issue CDs. Through affiliated companies, the Cherry Lane Music Group produces sheet music and publishes *Music Alive!*, a magazine aimed at music teachers. The firm was founded by music producer Milton Okun in 1960. It was acquired by BMG Rights Management, a joint venture between German media conglomerate Bertelsmann and private equity firm KKR & Co., in 2010.

	Annual Growth	12/04	12/05	12/06	12/07	12/08
Est. sales ($ mil.)	—	—	—	—	—	15.8
Employees	—	—	—	—	—	80

CHESAPEAKE BIOLOGICAL LABORATORIES, INC.

1111 S. Paca St.
Baltimore, MD 21230
Phone: 410-843-5000
Fax: 410-843-4414
Web: www.cblinc.com

CEO: William Labossiere (Bill) Bees
CFO: —
HR: Mary Halpin
FYE: July 31
Type: Subsidiary

Chesapeake Biological bays about pharmaceutical prospects. Chesapeake Biological Laboratories (CBL) provides product development and commercial drug production services for pharmaceutical and biotechnology companies. It also manufactures experimental drugs for use in clinical trials. The company specializes in biopharmaceuticals, materials derived from naturally occurring biological substances. CBL's primary operations are sterilizing and filling liquid drugs and production lyophilization, the process of filling drug containers while limiting the product's exposure to room temperature. CBL is a wholly owned subsidiary of Canadian biopharma firm Cangene.

CHESAPEAKE ENERGY CORPORATION

NYSE: CHK

6100 N. Western Ave.
Oklahoma City, OK 73118
Phone: 405-848-8000
Fax: 405-843-0573
Web: www.chk.com

CEO: Aubrey K. McClendon
CFO: Marcus C. (Marc) Rowland
HR: Martha A. Burger
FYE: December 31
Type: Public

Chesapeake Energy knows the peaks and valleys of the oil and gas business, including the 2008-09 oil slump. The exploration and production company concentrates on building natural gas reserves through the acquisition and development of oil and gas assets across the US. The mid-continent region accounts for about a third of the company's estimated proved reserves of 13.5 trillion cu. ft. of natural gas equivalent, but Chesapeake also has assets along the Gulf Coast, in Appalachia, and the Ark-La-Tex region. In 2009 it owned or had stakes in 44,100 producing oil and natural gas wells that produced 2.5 billion cu. ft. of natural gas equivalent per day, 93% of which was natural gas.

	Annual Growth	12/05	12/06	12/07	12/08	12/09
Sales ($ mil.)	13.4%	4,665.3	7,325.6	7,800.0	11,629.0	7,702.0
Net income ($ mil.)	—	948.3	2,003.3	1,451.0	723.0	(5,830.0)
Market value ($ mil.)	(5.0%)	20,653.5	18,909.0	25,515.8	10,525.3	16,845.6
Employees	29.8%	2,885	4,900	6,200	7,600	8,200

An in-depth profile of this company is available to Hoover's Online members at hoovers.com.

365

CHESAPEAKE LODGING TRUST

NYSE: CHSP

710 Rte. 46 East, Ste. 206
Fairfield, NJ 07004
Phone: 201-970-2559
Fax: —
Web: www.chesapeakelodgingtrust.com

CEO: James L. Francis
CFO: Douglas W. Vicari
HR: —
FYE: December 31
Type: Public

Chesapeake Lodging Trust stays more than just a night or two at the hotels it checks into. A specialty real estate investment trust (REIT), Chesapeake Lodging is a self-managed hotel investment firm that targets upscale hotels (either existing or planned properties) located in the US near airports, convention centers, and in major business markets. The firm, which is in the process of building its portfolio, intends to lease out its hotels and will hire third-party hotel management firms to manage its properties. It intends to hold on to the majority of its investments for the long term. Chesapeake Lodging was founded in mid-2009; it filed an initial public offering (IPO) later that year.

CHESAPEAKE MIDSTREAM PARTNERS, L.P.

777 NW Grand Blvd.
Oklahoma City, OK 73118
Phone: 405-935-1500
Fax: —

CEO: J. Mike Stice
CFO: David C. Shiels
HR: —
FYE: December 31
Type: Joint venture

Like a modern day cattle driver, Chesapeake Midstream Partners (CMP) rounds up and moves along natural gas through Texas, Kansas, Oklahoma, Arkansas, and New Mexico. Formed in 2009 as a joint venture between Chesapeake Energy and private equity firm Global Infrastructure Partners (GIP), CMP offers natural gas gathering services, including channeling gas into processing plants, treating (removing unwanted substances), and transportation. It serves its parent Chesapeake and other producers that operate in the Barnett Shale and the Arkoma, Anadarko, Delaware, and Permian basins. In 2010 CMP filed to go public.

CHESAPEAKE UTILITIES CORPORATION

NYSE: CPK

909 Silver Lake Blvd.
Dover, DE 19904
Phone: 302-734-6799
Fax: 302-734-6750
Web: www.chpk.com

CEO: John R. Schimkaitis
CFO: Beth W. Cooper
HR: —
FYE: December 31
Type: Public

Chesapeake Utilities gasses up the Chesapeake Bay, and then some. The company, through its subsidiaries, serves about 34,100 retail propane customers in Delaware, Florida, Maryland, and Virginia. Another subsidiary, Xeron, sells propane at wholesale to distributors, industrial users, and resellers throughout the US. Chesapeake's natural gas distribution divisions serve 114,000 customer in the Northeast and in Florida. Another unit distributes power in Florida. Chesapeake's interstate pipeline company, Eastern Shore Natural Gas, transmits gas to its parent and other utilities. Through BravePoint, the company also offers data services, consulting, and software development.

	Annual Growth	12/05	12/06	12/07	12/08	12/09
Sales ($ mil.)	4.0%	229.6	231.2	258.3	291.4	268.8
Net income ($ mil.)	10.9%	10.5	10.5	13.2	13.6	15.9
Market value ($ mil.)	1.0%	291.3	289.9	301.2	297.7	303.1
Employees	15.7%	423	437	445	448	757

CHEVIOT FINANCIAL CORP.

NASDAQ (CM): CHEV

3723 Glenmore Ave.
Cheviot, OH 45211
Phone: 513-661-0457
Fax: 513-389-3312
Web: www.cheviotsavings.com

CEO: Thomas J. Linneman
CFO: Scott T. Smith
HR: —
FYE: December 31
Type: Public

Cheviot Financial happily puts the "buck" in "Buckeye State." It is the holding company for Cheviot Savings Bank, which operates more than five branches in Ohio's Hamilton County, in and around Cincinnati. The community-oriented savings and loan offers traditional products such as savings, checking, and money market accounts; CDs, IRAs; and credit cards. Its lending activities primarily consist of residential mortgages (about 90% of the company's loan portfolio); construction, consumer, and commercial loans round out its loan book. The bank offers investment services through an agreement with third-party provider Souders Financial Services. Cheviot Mutual Holding Company owns about 60% of Cheviot Financial.

	Annual Growth	12/05	12/06	12/07	12/08	12/09
Assets ($ mil.)	4.0%	291.8	309.8	319.1	332.0	341.9
Net income ($ mil.)	(15.9%)	2.2	1.7	0.9	1.4	1.1
Market value ($ mil.)	(10.8%)	103.6	116.8	84.3	57.2	65.5
Employees	—	—	—	—	—	—

⊞ CHEVRON CORPORATION

NYSE: CVX

6001 Bollinger Canyon Rd.
San Ramon, CA 94583
Phone: 925-842-1000
Fax: 925-842-3530
Web: www.chevron.com

CEO: John S. Watson
CFO: Patricia E. (Pat) Yarrington
HR: Joe W. Laymon
FYE: December 31
Type: Public

Having added Texaco's star (and subsequently Unocal's authority) to its stripes, Chevron can pull rank on its rivals. Among the largest US integrated oil companies, along with Exxon Mobil and ConocoPhillips, it has proved reserves of 11.3 billion barrels of oil equivalent and a daily production of 2.7 million barrels of oil equivalent, and it also owns interests in chemicals, mining, pipelines, and power production businesses. The company, which is restructuring its refinery and retail businesses to cut costs, owns or has stakes in 9,600 gas stations in the US that operate under the Chevron and Texaco brands. Outside the US it owns or has stakes in 12,400 branded gas stations, which also use the Caltex brand.

	Annual Growth	12/05	12/06	12/07	12/08	12/09
Sales ($ mil.)	(3.5%)	198,200.0	210,118.0	220,904.0	273,005.0	171,636.0
Net income ($ mil.)	(7.1%)	14,099.0	17,138.0	18,688.0	23,931.0	10,483.0
Market value ($ mil.)	7.9%	114,030.6	147,695.5	187,466.6	148,579.3	154,645.4
Employees	12.8%	59,000	62,500	65,000	67,000	95,500

CHEVRON ORONITE COMPANY LLC

6001 Bollinger Canyon Rd.
Sam Ramon, CA 94583
Phone: 713-432-2500
Fax: 713-432-3330
Web: www.chevron.com/products/oronite

CEO: Ronald (Ron) Kiskis
CFO: Rich Conway
HR: Pat Wyffels
FYE: December 31
Type: Subsidiary

Chevron Oronite Company's additives subtract the bad elements from oil and other fuels. Oronite additives disperse deposits, control corrosion, and execute oxidation, thereby reducing wear and friction in fuel-burning engines. The company is a subsidiary of Chevron and affiliated with its chemical joint venture, CP Chem. Its products are divided into components and chemicals (detergents, dispersants, polybutene), fuel additives (gasoline, diesel, and aftermarket additives), and lubricant additives (hydraulic, engine, industrial, and marine oils). Among its fuel additive products is the viscosity index improver sold under the brand name PARATONE.

	Annual Growth	12/04	12/05	12/06	12/07	12/08
Est. sales ($ mil.)	—	—	—	—	—	215.7
Employees	—	—	—	—	—	1,000

CHEVRON PHILLIPS CHEMICAL COMPANY LLC

10001 Six Pines Dr.	CEO: Greg C. Garland
The Woodlands, TX 77380	CFO: Greg G. Maxwell
Phone: 832-813-4100	HR: Chantal Veevaete
Fax: 800-231-3890	FYE: December 31
Web: www.cpchem.com	Type: Joint venture

A coin toss determined whose name would go first when Chevron and Phillips Petroleum (now ConocoPhillips) formed its 50-50 joint venture Chevron Phillips Chemical Company in 2000. Among the largest US petrochemical firms, the company produces ethylene, propylene, polyethylene, and polypropylene — sometimes used as building blocks for the company's other products such as pipe. Chevron Phillips Chemical also produces aromatics such as benzene and styrene, specialty chemicals such as acetylene black (a form of carbon black), and mining chemicals. The company has several petrochemicals joint ventures in the Middle East, including Saudi Chevron Phillips Company (50%) and Qatar Chemical Company (not quite 50%).

	Annual Growth	12/04	12/05	12/06	12/07	12/08
Sales ($ mil.)	7.2%	9,558.0	11,038.0	12,330.0	12,986.0	12,646.0
Net income ($ mil.)	(17.8%)	605.0	853.0	1,349.0	719.0	276.0
Employees	(2.4%)	5,300	5,150	5,150	5,500	4,800

CHF INDUSTRIES, INC.

8701 Red Oak Blvd., Ste. 400	CEO: Frank Foley
Charlotte, NC 28217	CFO: Camillo Farone
Phone: 704-522-5000	HR: —
Fax: —	FYE: December 31
Web: www.chfindustries.com	Type: Private

CHF Industries wants its customers to gently doze off and sleep like babies. The company is a manufacturer of fashion bedding, decorative bathroom items, window coverings, and luxury textiles for the hospitality industry. CHF's products portfolio includes brands such as DKNY, Hemingway, Green Gorilla, and Umbra, as well as private-label names from retailers such as Dillard's and Kohl's. Its DK Home division makes designer bedding and bath items in conjunction with Donna Karan International. The firm has manufacturing and distribution facilities in the US, China, Colombia, India, and Pakistan. Products are sold by mass merchandisers and in department stores throughout the US.

THE CHICAGO FAUCET COMPANY

2100 S. Clearwater Dr.	CEO: Andreas Nowak
Des Plaines, IL 60018	CFO: Bob Gilbert
Phone: 847-803-5000	HR: Cheryl Matthews
Fax: 847-803-5454	FYE: December 31
Web: www.chicagofaucets.com	Type: Subsidiary

The Chicago Faucet Company (Chicago Faucets) has something to spout off about. The company makes about 1,000 faucet components with more than 55,000 possible configurations. Six plants in the US manufacture handles, spouts, outlets, and inlets for residential, commercial, industrial, safety, and medical markets. All of the faucets are modular, interchangeable, and cast in brass. The company sells through plumbing distributors and sales representatives in the US and in most regions of the world. Geberit AG, a Switzerland-based sanitation system manufacturer, owns Chicago Faucet. The company traces its roots to 1901 when founder Albert Brown opened a small plumbing fixtures shop in Chicago.

CHICAGO GOURMET STEAKS

824 W. 38th Place	CEO: James J. (Jim) Stevens
Chicago, IL 60609	CFO: —
Phone: 773-254-2400	HR: Gail Glowacki
Fax: 773-254-4355	FYE: December 31
Web: www.chigourmetsteaks.com	Type: Private

Chicago has a loop around some of the best steer in the herd. Chicago Gourmet Steaks offers a plateful of the best cuts of beef including chateaubriand, filet mignon, and porterhouse steaks to hungry eaters. It sells its premium, flash-frozen, packed-in-ice meats through its website or by telephone or fax. The company also supplies foodservice establishments, mainly high-end restaurants. CEO James Stevens acquired the company in 1990 from the late Walter Mander, a longtime fixture in the Chicago meatpacking industry. Mander's Lincoln Meat Company, which closed that same year, was one of the last surviving slaughterhouses in the city.

	Annual Growth	12/04	12/05	12/06	12/07	12/08
Est. sales ($ mil.)	—	—	—	—	—	95.0
Employees	—	—	—	—	—	125

CHICAGO RIVET & MACHINE CO.

NYSE Amex: CVR

901 Frontenac Rd.	CEO: John A. Morrissey
Naperville, IL 60563	CFO: —
Phone: 630-357-8500	HR: —
Fax: 630-983-9314	FYE: December 31
Web: www.chicagorivet.com	Type: Public

Rosie the Riveter might have used rivets made by Chicago Rivet & Machine. The company's main business is making fasteners, including rivets, screw machine products, and cold-formed fasteners. In addition to manufacturing assembly equipment, such as automatic rivet-setting equipment and rivet-working tools, it leases rivet-setting machines. Chicago Rivet sells its products through internal and independent sales representatives to US automotive and auto parts manufacturers. Major customers include Fisher & Company (accounting for almost 20% of the company's sales) and TI Automotive (about 15% of sales).

	Annual Growth	12/05	12/06	12/07	12/08	12/09
Sales ($ mil.)	(14.4%)	39.8	40.4	37.8	28.5	21.4
Net income ($ mil.)	—	(0.4)	1.1	1.3	(0.8)	(1.3)
Market value ($ mil.)	(8.2%)	19.3	20.3	19.4	11.6	13.7
Employees	(8.5%)	297	261	252	226	208

CHICAGO TRANSIT AUTHORITY

567 W. Lake St.	CEO: Richard Rodriguez
Chicago, IL 60661	CFO: Karen Walker
Phone: 312-664-7200	HR: Gia Morris
Fax: —	FYE: December 31
Web: www.transitchicago.com	Type: Government-owned

The CTA is focused on making its ETA. Passengers on a typical weekday take about 1.8 million rides on Chicago Transit Authority buses and trains in and around Chicago and about 40 suburbs. The agency operates a fleet of 2,200 buses on more than 150 routes. The CTA rail system includes some 1,200 rail cars operating on 225 miles of track at more than 140 stations. The agency, created by the Illinois legislature, is part of the state's Regional Transportation Authority, which also oversees Metra (commuter rail system) and Pace (suburban bus system). The CTA began operations in 1947.

	Annual Growth	12/04	12/05	12/06	12/07	12/08
Est. sales ($ mil.)	—	—	—	—	—	448.4
Employees	—	—	—	—	—	12,000

An in-depth profile of this company is available to Hoover's Online members at hoovers.com.

367

⊞ CHICK-FIL-A, INC.

5200 Buffington Rd.
Atlanta, GA 30349
Phone: 404-765-8000
Fax: —
Web: www.chick-fil-a.com

CEO: S. Truett Cathy
CFO: James B. (Buck) McCabe
HR: Dee Ann Turner
FYE: December 31
Type: Private

You might say this company helps people get their fill of chicken sandwiches. Chick-fil-A operates one of the largest fast-food chains that specializes in chicken menu items, with more than 1,480 restaurants in about 40 states. The chain is popular for its breaded chicken sandwiches and waffle fries, as well as other menu items such as chicken strips and chicken nuggets. Most of its outlets are freestanding units that offer drive-through service as well as dine-in seating. The company also has a significant number of mall-based stores. The chain was started in 1946 by chairman Truett Cathy; a devout Baptist, he insists on a policy that all Chick-fil-A restaurants be closed on Sundays.

	Annual Growth	12/04	12/05	12/06	12/07	12/08
Sales ($ mil.)	14.4%	—	1,975.0	2,275.0	2,640.9	2,960.0
Employees	6.9%	—	40,924	45,000	50,000	50,000

CHICOPEE BANCORP, INC.

NASDAQ (GM): CBNK

70 Center St.
Chicopee, MA 01014
Phone: 413-594-6692
Fax: —
Web: www.chicopeesavings.com

CEO: William J. Wagner
CFO: Guida R. Sajdak
HR: Maria J. C. Aigner
FYE: December 31
Type: Public

Chicopee Bancorp is the holding company for Chicopee Savings Bank, a community bank which serves the residents and businesses of Hampden and Hampshire counties in western Massachusetts. Through a handful of branches, the bank offers deposit services such as savings and checking accounts, as well as a variety of lending services. Its loan portfolio consists of one-to-four-family residential real estate loans (its largest loan segment) and commercial real estate loans. Other lending services include multifamily, construction, home equity, commercial business, and consumer loans. Chicopee Bank was founded in 1854.

	Annual Growth	12/05	12/06	12/07	12/08	12/09
Assets ($ mil.)	8.6%	391.3	450.0	463.5	527.6	544.2
Net income ($ mil.)	—	1.4	(2.5)	1.6	0.0	(1.6)
Market value ($ mil.)	(7.3%)	—	99.8	82.6	75.9	79.6
Employees	7.8%	114	118	125	137	154

CHICO'S FAS, INC.

NYSE: CHS

11215 Metro Pkwy.
Fort Myers, FL 33966
Phone: 239-277-6200
Fax: 239-274-4018
Web: www.chicos.com

CEO: David F. Dyer
CFO: Kent A. Kleeberger
HR: Manuel O. Jessup
FYE: January 31
Type: Public

Chico's FAS wants to color-coordinate its customers with its own brands of chic clothes. Once a Mexican folk art shop, Chico's owns and operates about 1,080 specialty stores in 48 states, the District of Columbia, the US Virgin Islands, and Puerto Rico. Its stores are mostly located in enclosed malls and shopping centers under the banners Chico's, White House/Black Market (WH/BM), and Soma. The boutiques target middle-to-high-income women ages 25 to 64 with clothes made primarily from natural fabrics (cotton, linen, silk). Its casual wear includes tops, pants, shorts, skirts, and dresses, as well as jewelry and other accessories. Chico's FAS was founded in 1983 by ex-chairman Marvin Gralnick and wife Helene.

	Annual Growth	1/06	1/07	1/08	1/09	1/10
Sales ($ mil.)	5.1%	1,404.6	1,646.5	1,714.3	1,582.4	1,713.2
Net income ($ mil.)	(22.6%)	194.0	166.6	93.4	(19.1)	69.6
Market value ($ mil.)	(26.4%)	7,784.7	3,731.5	1,928.3	707.7	2,282.2
Employees	10.2%	11,000	12,500	14,300	14,460	16,200

THE CHILDREN'S HOSPITAL OF PHILADELPHIA

34th St. & Civic Center Blvd.
Philadelphia, PA 19104
Phone: 215-590-1000
Fax: —
Web: www.chop.edu

CEO: Steven M. Altschuler
CFO: —
HR: —
FYE: June 30
Type: Not-for-profit

In the City of Brotherly Love, sick little boys and little girls have a place to get better. The Children's Hospital of Philadelphia is a leading pediatric hospital with one of the largest pediatric research programs in the world. The nation's first hospital devoted exclusively to the care of children, it has about 430 beds at its primary facility and operates a pediatric health care network with owned or affiliated offices, clinics, and research facilities in Delaware, New Jersey, and Pennsylvania. The hospital is a leader in formal pediatric medical training, pediatric emergency medicine, and adolescent medicine.

	Annual Growth	6/04	6/05	6/06	6/07	6/08
Est. sales ($ mil.)	—	—	—	—	—	347.2
Employees	—	—	—	—	—	7,000

CHILDREN'S HOSPITALS AND CLINICS OF MINNESOTA

2525 Chicago Ave.
Minneapolis, MN 55404
Phone: 612-813-6100
Fax: 612-813-6699
Web: www.childrenshc.org

CEO: Alan L. Goldbloom
CFO: Jerry Massmann
HR: David A. Brumbaugh
FYE: December 31
Type: Not-for-profit

Children's Hospitals and Clinics of Minnesota is one of the largest pediatric health organizations in the US, with two full-service hospital campuses in Minneapolis and St. Paul, as well as a number of specialty clinics in the region. With more than 330 beds, Children's Hospitals and Clinics specializes in diagnosing, treating, and researching diseases that afflict babies and children, including epilepsy, diabetes, cancers, and cystic fibrosis. It also runs a Teen Age Medical Service, which provides reproductive health care, counseling, and other medical services to adolescents. The organization was founded in 1924.

THE CHILDREN'S INTERNET, INC.

OTC: CITC

2377 Gold Meadow Way, Ste. 100
Gold River, CA 95670
Phone: 916-631-1987
Fax: 916-631-1515
Web: www.childrensinternetinc.com

CEO: Richard J. Lewis III
CFO: Richard J. Lewis III
HR: —
FYE: December 31
Type: Public

The Children's Internet has a kinder, gentler Internet in mind. The company develops software to restrict access to Web-based content considered inappropriate for children. Its SafeZone technology also regulates e-mail. The company's business plan includes marketing and providing software to the Internet service called The Children's Internet. The service itself is owned by a third party called Two Dog Net. The company has an exclusive license to market The Children's Internet service worldwide, as well as Two Dog Net's wholesale dial-up Internet service.

CHILDREN'S MEDICAL CENTER OF DALLAS

1935 Medical District Dr.	CEO: Christopher J. (Chris) Durovich
Dallas, TX 75235	CFO: Ray Dziesinski
Phone: 214-456-7000	HR: James W. (Jim) Herring
Fax: 214-456-2197	FYE: December 31
Web: www.childrens.com	Type: Not-for-profit

Sick kiddos in North Texas who need specialized care don't have to travel far to find it. Children's Medical Center of Dallas treats children from birth to age 18 with various medical needs. Specialties include craniofacial deformities, cystic fibrosis, gastroenterology, and heart disease. Children's is also a major pediatric transplant center for bone marrow, heart, kidney, and liver. The hospital has nearly 500 beds and is the pediatric teaching facility for the University of Texas Southwest medical program. Children's also operates a network of some 50 outpatient clinics in and around Dallas.

	Annual Growth	12/04	12/05	12/06	12/07	12/08
Sales ($ mil.)	13.6%	447.5	514.4	579.9	639.5	744.9
Net income ($ mil.)	—	44.3	51.4	88.4	91.7	(2.7)
Employees	7.5%	—	—	4,500	4,800	5,200

THE CHILDREN'S MERCY HOSPITAL

2401 Gillham Rd.	CEO: Randall L. O'Donnell
Kansas City, MO 64108	CFO: Sandra A. J. Lawrence
Phone: 816-234-3000	HR: Dan Wright
Fax: 816-855-1989	FYE: June 30
Web: www.childrens-mercy.org	Type: Private

It's *never* a good thing to be at the children's mercy, but The Children's Mercy Hospital is a huge benefit to KC kiddos. The Children's Mercy Hospital offers pediatric health care in various specialties in and around Kansas City, Missouri. Services include home health care, endocrinology, genetics, heart surgery, neonatology, emergency medicine, and rehabilitation. Founded in 1897, the hospital has more than 300 beds. The Children's Mercy health care system also includes outpatient and outreach clinics and research facilities. It is a teaching hospital affiliated with University of Missouri-Kansas City Medical School, University of Kansas, the Stowers Institute, and Midwest Research Institute.

	Annual Growth	6/04	6/05	6/06	6/07	6/08
Est. sales ($ mil.)	—	—	—	—	—	148.6
Employees	—	—	—	—	—	3,000

THE CHILDREN'S PLACE RETAIL STORES, INC.

NASDAQ (GS): PLCE

915 Secaucus Rd.	CEO: Jane T. Elfers
Secaucus, NJ 07094	CFO: Susan J. Riley
Phone: 201-558-2400	HR: Larry McClure
Fax: 201-558-2630	FYE: January 31
Web: www.childrensplace.com	Type: Public

If The Children's Place Retail Stores had a grandma, she'd proclaim, "My, how fast you've grown!" The clothing retailer operates about 950 Children's Place stores, primarily in malls and outlet centers throughout the US and Canada. It also sells apparel online. The Children's Place outfits children from newborn to 12 years old in its own brand of value-priced apparel, shoes, and accessories, most of which is produced by manufacturers in China, Vietnam, and Africa. In 2008 the retailer exited its 200-plus-store Disney Stores retail business (30% of sales), which it obtained from The Walt Disney Company in 2004. The Children's Place Retail Stores was founded in 1988.

	Annual Growth	1/06	1/07	1/08	1/09	1/10
Sales ($ mil.)	(0.4%)	1,668.7	2,017.7	2,162.6	1,630.3	1,643.6
Net income ($ mil.)	8.5%	63.9	87.4	(59.6)	82.4	88.4
Market value ($ mil.)	(7.7%)	1,214.3	1,503.3	514.1	521.6	881.8
Employees	2.5%	21,400	25,400	23,800	23,100	23,600

CHIMERA INVESTMENT CORPORATION

NYSE: CIM

1211 Avenue of the Americas, Ste. 2902	CEO: Matthew Lambiase
New York, NY 10036	CFO: A. Alexandra Denahan
Phone: 212-696-0100	HR: —
Fax: 212-696-9809	FYE: December 31
Web: www.chimerareit.com	Type: Public

This Chimera has the body of a mortgage real estate investment trust (REIT), but its head is that of its external manager, FIDAC (Fixed Income Discount Advisory Company), a fixed-income investment management firm wholly owned by Annaly Capital Management. Formed in 2007, Chimera invests in residential mortgage loans; residential mortgage-backed securities (RMBS), such as those guaranteed by government agencies Fannie Mae and Freddie Mac; real estate-related securities; and other assets, including collateralized debt obligations, or CDOs. The REIT went public in 2007, shortly after it was formed.

	Annual Growth	12/05	12/06	12/07	12/08	12/09
Sales ($ mil.)	823.5%	—	—	3.5	105.3	298.5
Net income ($ mil.)	—	—	—	(2.9)	(119.8)	324.0
Market value ($ mil.)	(53.4%)	—	—	13,734.0	2,650.0	2,980.3
Employees	—	—	—	—	—	—

CHINA DIRECT INDUSTRIES, INC.

NASDAQ (GM): CDII

431 Fairway Dr., Ste. 200	CEO: Yuejian (James) Wang
Deerfield Beach, FL 33441	CFO: Andrew Wang
Phone: 954-363-7333	HR: —
Fax: 954-363-7320	FYE: December 31
Web: www.chinadirectinc.com	Type: Public

China Direct Industries cuts out the middleman and buys businesses directly in China. The company invests in and manages Chinese companies with revenues of less than $100 million. With a focus on raw materials, China Direct Industries owns five magnesium companies, an industrial chemical manufacturer, a metal recycling plant, a rubber recycling plant, a manufacturer of zinc concentrate, and a distributor of steel and lumber. The company also consults with Chinese companies wanting to do business with the US. China Direct Industries was founded in 1999 but only began its overseas investments and acquisitions operations in 2006.

	Annual Growth	12/04	12/05	12/06	12/07	*12/08
Sales ($ mil.)	314.0%	—	—	14.0	174.2	240.0
Net income ($ mil.)	655.0%	—	—	0.2	11.8	11.4
Market value ($ mil.)	(49.8%)	—	—	177.1	271.0	44.7
Employees	70.8%	—	—	441	1,277	1,287

*Most recent year available

CHINA LOGISTICS GROUP, INC.

OTC: CHLO

7300 E. Alondra Blvd., Ste. 108	CEO: Wei (Danny) Chen
Paramount, CA 90723	CFO: Yuan Huang
Phone: 562-408-3888	HR: —
Fax: 562-408-3887	FYE: December 31
Web: www.chinalogisticsinc.com	Type: Public

China Logistics Group offers international freight forwarding services through its 51%-owned Shandong Jiajia International Freight & Forwarding Co. The company serves clients in the shipping industry that want to import or export goods into or out of China. China Logistics also offers logistics management, warehousing, freight consolidation, inspection and customs declarations, multimodal transportation arrangement, and consulting services. Formerly known as MediaREADY, the company previously offered products and services related to the distribution of broadband digital content, including its MediaREADY 4000 Internet/DVD player.

	Annual Growth	12/05	12/06	12/07	12/08	12/09
Sales ($ mil.)	(44.4%)	—	—	—	35.6	19.8
Net income ($ mil.)	—	—	—	—	(2.1)	2.3
Market value ($ mil.)	(56.8%)	—	—	—	7.5	3.2
Employees	0.0%	—	—	—	118	118

CHINA NUVO SOLAR ENERGY, INC.
OTC: CNUV

319 Clematis St., Ste. 703
West Palm Beach, FL 33401
Phone: 561-514-9042
Fax: —
Web: www.chinanuvosolar.com

CEO: Henry Fong
CFO: Barry S. Hollander
HR: —
FYE: July 31
Type: Public

This company is taking a gamble on solar energy. Formerly game machine manufacturer Interactive Games, China Nuvo Solar Energy is a development-stage company focused on establishing a solar technology manufacturing plant in China. The company holds the rights to a patent for a new type of solar cell that it hopes will offer lower manufacturing costs than current types of silicon-based photovoltaic solar cells. Interactive Games changed its name after acquiring Nuvo Solar Energy in 2007; it is looking to spin off its former gaming business to shareholders.

	Annual Growth	7/05	7/06	7/07	7/08	7/09
Sales ($ mil.)	—	—	—	—	—	0.0
Net income ($ mil.)	—	—	—	—	—	(0.8)
Market value ($ mil.)	—	—	—	—	—	2.4
Employees	—	—	—	—	—	—

CHINDEX INTERNATIONAL, INC.
NASDAQ (GM): CHDX

4340 East West Hwy., Ste. 1100
Bethesda, MD 20814
Phone: 301-215-7777
Fax: 301-215-7719
Web: www.chindex.com

CEO: Roberta Lipson
CFO: Lawrence Pemble
HR: —
FYE: March 31
Type: Public

Chindex International is good at being a go-between. The company provides Western makers of medical equipment and supplies with access to Chinese markets. Its Medical Products division distributes capital medical equipment — such as diagnostic imaging and robotic surgery systems — and other medical products to hospitals in China and Hong Kong. A second division (Healthcare Services) operates United Family Healthcare, a growing network of private hospitals and satellite medical clinics in Shanghai and Beijing. The division's two 50-bed hospitals cater to the expatriate community and to affluent Chinese customers.

	Annual Growth	3/05	3/06	3/07	3/08	3/09
Sales ($ mil.)	14.2%	100.8	90.8	105.9	130.1	171.4
Net income ($ mil.)	—	(5.7)	(2.9)	2.7	3.7	5.0
Market value ($ mil.)	4.8%	61.3	89.9	173.3	374.6	74.0
Employees	6.2%	1,003	950	1,007	1,181	1,276

CHIPOTLE MEXICAN GRILL, INC.
NYSE: CMG

1401 Wynkoop St., Ste. 500
Denver, CO 80202
Phone: 303-595-4000
Fax: 303-595-4014
Web: www.chipotle.com

CEO: M. Steven (Steve) Ells
CFO: John R. (Jack) Hartung
HR: Robert D. (Bob) Wilner
FYE: December 31
Type: Public

You might say this company is spicing up the restaurant business. Chipotle Mexican Grill owns and operates more than 950 quick-casual eateries popular for their burritos and other Mexican food items. Customers can build a 1-1/4 pound burrito from a lineup that includes chicken, steak, barbecue or free-range pork, as well as beans, rice, guacamole, and various other veggies and salsas. The company claims that with extras, its menu offers more than 65,000 choices. Chipotle restaurants also serve tacos, chips and salsa, beer, and margaritas. Operating in more than 30 states, many of the eateries are found in and around urban retail areas.

	Annual Growth	12/05	12/06	12/07	12/08	12/09
Sales ($ mil.)	24.7%	627.7	822.9	1,085.8	1,332.0	1,518.4
Net income ($ mil.)	35.4%	37.7	41.4	70.6	78.2	126.8
Market value ($ mil.)	15.6%	—	1,793.3	4,627.1	1,950.0	2,773.7
Employees	14.4%	13,000	15,000	18,800	20,400	22,250

CHIQUITA BRANDS INTERNATIONAL, INC.
NYSE: CQB

250 E. 5th St.
Cincinnati, OH 45202
Phone: 513-784-8000
Fax: 513-784-8030
Web: www.chiquita.com

CEO: Fernando Aguirre
CFO: Michael Sims
HR: Kevin R. Holland
FYE: December 31
Type: Public

As one of the world's top banana producers, Chiquita Brands International deals in big bunches. The company grows, procures, markets, and sells bananas and other fresh fruits and vegetables under the Chiquita and other brand names. Bananas accounted for 56% of Chiquita's 2009 total sales. Its other products include whole citrus fruits, melons, grapes, apples, and tomatoes, as well as packaged fresh-cut items, juices, and processed fruit ingredients. With a 44% market share, the company's Fresh Express unit is the leading US seller of packaged ready-to-eat salads. Chiquita's products are sold in some 80 countries, mainly in North America and Europe. Lesser markets include the Middle East, Japan, and Korea.

	Annual Growth	12/05	12/06	12/07	12/08	12/09
Sales ($ mil.)	(2.9%)	3,904.4	4,499.1	4,662.8	3,609.4	3,470.4
Net income ($ mil.)	(8.9%)	131.4	(95.9)	(49.0)	(323.7)	90.5
Market value ($ mil.)	(2.6%)	898.1	716.8	825.4	663.3	809.7
Employees	(4.3%)	25,000	25,000	24,000	23,000	21,000

CHOATE CONSTRUCTION COMPANY

8200 Roberts Dr., Ste. 600
Atlanta, GA 30350
Phone: 678-892-1200
Fax: 678-892-1202
Web: www.choateco.com

CEO: William Millard Choate
CFO: David A. Page
HR: Elizabeth Douglass
FYE: December 31
Type: Private

This firm has a Choate-hold on construction activities in the Southeast. Choate Construction provides design/build, preconstruction, and management services for the construction of commercial and public facilities. It has experience in a wide range of projects including automotive showrooms, manufacturing plants, office buildings, schools, and condominiums. Completed projects include a dormitory on The University of Georgia-East campus, golf clubhouses, and a distribution warehouse for Crate & Barrel. The company has offices in Georgia, North Carolina, and South Carolina and is licensed to build throughout the US.

	Annual Growth	12/04	12/05	12/06	12/07	12/08
Est. sales ($ mil.)	—	—	—	—	—	16.3
Employees	—	—	—	—	—	350

CHOICE HOTELS INTERNATIONAL, INC.
NYSE: CHH

10750 Columbia Pike
Silver Spring, MD 20901
Phone: 301-592-5000
Fax: 301-592-6157
Web: www.choicehotels.com

CEO: Stephen P. Joyce
CFO: David L. White
HR: Anne Hendrick
FYE: December 31
Type: Public

This company offers a lot of hospitality choices. Choice Hotels is a leading hotel franchisor with more than 6,000 locations in the US and more than 40 other countries. Its flagship brands include Comfort Inn, one of the largest limited-service brands with about 2,600 properties; and Quality Inn, which serves the midscale hotel segment through more than 1,300 locations. Its Econo Lodge chain offers lodging primarily for budget-minded travelers. Other Choice Hotels brands include the full-service Clarion chain, Rodeway Inn budget hotels, and Sleep Inn. The company operates in Europe through Choice Hotels Europe. Chairman Stewart Bainum and his family control more than 50% of the company.

	Annual Growth	12/05	12/06	12/07	12/08	12/09
Sales ($ mil.)	4.3%	477.4	544.7	615.5	641.7	564.2
Net income ($ mil.)	2.9%	87.6	112.8	111.3	100.2	98.3
Market value ($ mil.)	(6.7%)	2,487.2	2,507.4	1,977.3	1,790.3	1,885.6
Employees	(2.5%)	1,728	1,860	1,816	1,789	1,560

CHOICEONE FINANCIAL SERVICES, INC.   OTC: COFS

109 E. Division St.	CEO: James A. (Jim) Bosserd
Sparta, MI 49345	CFO: Thomas L. (Tom) Lampen
Phone: 616-887-7366	HR: —
Fax: 616-887-7990	FYE: December 31
Web: www.choiceone.com	Type: Public

One choice for a place to park your money is ChoiceOne Financial Services. The institution is the holding company for ChoiceOne Bank, which has more than a dozen offices in the western part of Michigan's Lower Peninsula. The bank serves consumers and area businesses, offering checking and savings accounts, CDs, investment planning, and other services. Real estate loans, including residential and commercial mortgages, constitute more than two-thirds of the company's loan portfolio. Agricultural, consumer, and business loans help to round out the bank's lending activities. ChoiceOne Financial Services sells life, health, and disability coverage through its ChoiceOne Insurance Agencies subsidiaries.

	Annual Growth	12/05	12/06	12/07	12/08	12/09
Assets ($ mil.)	17.1%	248.1	466.6	470.2	463.6	465.9
Net income ($ mil.)	(9.1%)	2.2	2.1	3.6	1.4	1.5
Market value ($ mil.)	(16.5%)	60.5	57.9	40.9	27.1	29.4
Employees	18.2%	79	136	125	143	154

CHORDIANT SOFTWARE, INC.

20400 Stevens Creek Blvd., Ste. 400	CEO: Steven R. (Steve) Springsteel
Cupertino, CA 95014	CFO: Peter S. (Pete) Norman
Phone: 408-517-6100	HR: Jack Landers
Fax: 408-517-0270	FYE: September 30
Web: www.chordiant.com	Type: Subsidiary

Chordiant Software helps you strike a collaborative chord with customers. The company develops customer relationship management (CRM) software that links call centers, computer networks, databases, and the Internet, allowing departments and employees to share data, collaborate on projects, and retain customers while lowering their operational costs. Chordiant's other applications automate complex marketing campaigns, analyze consumer information, and provide interfaces between customers and employees. In 2010 CDC Software made an unsolicited bid to acquire the company for about $105 million; Chordiant turned down the offer. It then accepted an acquisition offer from Pegasystems valued at about $161 million.

	Annual Growth	9/05	9/06	9/07	9/08	9/09
Sales ($ mil.)	(1.9%)	83.7	97.5	124.5	113.0	77.5
Net income ($ mil.)	—	(19.5)	(16.0)	6.0	1.1	(10.8)
Employees	(5.6%)	280	325	285	272	222

CHRISTIANA CARE HEALTH SYSTEM

501 W. 14th St.	CEO: Robert J. Laskowski
Wilmington, DE 19801	CFO: Thomas Corrigan
Phone: 302-733-1900	HR: Ben Shaw
Fax: 302-428-5770	FYE: June 30
Web: www.christianacare.org	Type: Not-for-profit

Christiana Care Health System's not-for-profit health care network serves patients in Delaware and surrounding areas of Pennsylvania, Maryland, and New Jersey. Founded in 1888, the company operates Christiana Hospital and Wilmington Hospital, which together have more than 1,100 beds. The hospitals provide heart services (including cardiac surgery and coronary angioplasty), cancer treatment, women's health services, pediatrics, physical medicine and rehabilitation, general medicine, and surgery. The system also operates area physician clinics and offers home health and adult day care services. In addition, Christiana Care conducts education, training, and research programs at its facilities.

CHRISTIE DIGITAL SYSTEMS, INC.

10550 Camden Dr.	CEO: Jack Kline
Cypress, CA 90630	CFO: —
Phone: 714-236-8610	HR: —
Fax: 714-503-3375	FYE: December 31
Web: www.christiedigital.com	Type: Subsidiary

Christie Digital Systems wants to project its ideas onto the world. The company manufactures and sells film and professional projection equipment globally for venues such as movie theaters; business board, briefing, and training rooms; 3D and virtual reality simulation and education; and industrial and government environments. Christie products are used in more than 75,000 locations worldwide. The company is on the forefront of the digital cinema initiative with its rollout of DLP Cinema projectors around the world. Founded in 1929, Christie has manufacturing facilities in the US and Canada, and has additional branch offices in more than a dozen countries throughout the world. It is a subsidiary of USHIO.

CHRISTOPHER & BANKS CORPORATION   NYSE: CBK

2400 Xenium Ln. North	CEO: Lorna E. Nagler
Plymouth, MN 55441	CFO: Rodney Carter
Phone: 763-551-5000	HR: Harold E. (Kipp) Sassman
Fax: 763-551-5198	FYE: February 28
Web: www.christopherandbanks.com	Type: Public

Christopher & Banks is getting pretty big for its britches. Largely mall-based, the specialty retailer sells moderately priced private-label women's fashions. Some 815 stores nationwide operate under the Christopher & Banks and C.J. Banks banners. The Christopher & Banks and C.J. Banks brands also operate their own e-commerce sites. Sportswear accounts for about 80% of overall sales; the rest comes from sweaters and accessories. Christopher & Banks is betting big on expansion — especially in the plus-size market. Its 260-plus C.J. Banks stores offer specialty apparel in sizes 14W and up. The two chains cater to working women 40 to 60 years old with above average incomes.

	Annual Growth	2/06	2/07	2/08	2/09	2/10
Sales ($ mil.)	(1.8%)	490.5	547.3	575.8	530.7	455.4
Net income ($ mil.)	(71.5%)	30.4	33.7	17.0	(12.8)	0.2
Market value ($ mil.)	(25.0%)	785.1	664.1	386.7	139.3	248.5
Employees	6.8%	6,600	6,900	7,800	8,300	8,600

CHRISTUS HEALTH

Las Colinas Corporate Center II, 6363 N. Hwy. 161, Ste. 450	CEO: Thomas C. (Tom) Royer
Irving, TX 75038	CFO: Jay Herron
Phone: 214-492-8500	HR: Mary Lynch
Fax: 214-492-8540	FYE: June 30
Web: www.christushealth.org	Type: Not-for-profit

In CHRISTUS there is no east or west, but plenty of care nonetheless. The Catholic health care system operates more than 50 hospitals, including general hospitals and long-term acute care facilities. The majority of its operations are in Louisiana and Texas, but the not-for-profit organization also has facilities in Arkansas, Georgia, Missouri, New Mexico, and Utah, and in several states in Mexico. In addition to its acute care facilities, CHRISTUS Health runs outpatient centers, medical groups, home health and hospice agencies, and senior living facilities. Specialized services include oncology, pediatrics, rehabilitation, and women's and children's health care.

	Annual Growth	6/04	6/05	6/06	6/07	6/08
Est. sales ($ mil.)	—	—	—	—	—	3,167.5
Employees	—	—	—	—	—	25,000

CHROMALLOY GAS TURBINE CORPORATION

4430 Director Dr.
San Antonio, TX 78219
Phone: 210-333-6010
Fax: 210-359-5570
Web: www.chromalloy.com

CEO: Armand F. Lauzon Jr.
CFO: Maj. Mike Held
HR: John Bollman
FYE: December 31
Type: Subsidiary

Kodachrome gives us those nice bright colors. Chromalloy Gas Turbine gives us those nice jet engine services. Operating through two fix-it segments, Power Services and Component Services, Chromalloy Gas Turbine offers turbine airfoil maintenance and repair services, and spare parts. It taps the overhaul shops of US and international commercial aircraft as well as US Air Force bases. Pursuing land-based industrial markets, the company also caters to US and international electricity-producing turbine operators. Industrial efforts focus on non-airfoil repairs including major rotating parts, cases, frames, and combustors. Chromalloy Gas Turbine is the largest subsidiary of its diversified parent, Sequa.

CHROMCRAFT REVINGTON, INC.

NYSE Amex: CRC

1330 Win Hentschel Blvd., Ste. 250
West Lafayette, IN 47906
Phone: 765-807-2640
Fax: 765-564-3722
Web: chromcraft-revington.com

CEO: Ronald H. (Ron) Butler
CFO: Myron D. Hamas
HR: —
FYE: December 31
Type: Public

Chromcraft Revington has built a business by honing the craft of making home or office furniture. Under the Peters-Revington name, the company sells mid-priced wood furniture, such as bookcases, tables, and home office pieces. The furniture firm's casual dining and commercial furniture (such as office chairs and conference tables) are made and marketed under its namesake Chromcraft brand. Its Cochrane Furniture line includes custom casual and semi-custom dining furniture. The balance of Chromcraft's other furniture — side tables, coffee tables, and entertainment centers — is sold under the Silver Furniture name. Chromcraft Revington sells its products through US and Canadian retailers.

	Annual Growth	12/05	12/06	12/07	12/08	12/09
Sales ($ mil.)	(22.0%)	169.6	160.5	123.4	99.0	62.7
Net income ($ mil.)	—	7.2	(3.4)	(14.9)	(26.5)	(1.9)
Market value ($ mil.)	(35.4%)	80.3	52.6	29.4	2.4	14.0
Employees	(33.4%)	1,400	904	750	277	275

CHRYSLER GROUP LLC

1000 Chrysler Dr.
Auburn Hills, MI 48326
Phone: 248-576-5741
Fax: —
Web: www.chryslerllc.com

CEO: Sergio Marchionne
CFO: Richard Palmer
HR: Nancy A. Rae
FYE: December 31
Type: Private

Chrysler hopes its crisis is behind it. Having survived a brief Chapter 11 bankruptcy reorganization in 2009, the company positioned itself for an automotive resurrection by choosing a back-to-basics alliance with Fiat. The collaboration gives Chrysler access to the Italian company's small-car expertise and global markets, while still manufacturing its Chrysler brands, including Dodge, Jeep, and Ram vehicles. Chrysler's trademarked MOPAR (MOtor PARts) division, with its 30% market share, carries over 280,000 parts, options, and accessories for vehicle customization; it is expanding to incorporate Fiat parts. Chrysler's GEM (Global Electric Motor Cars) makes neighborhood electric vehicles (NEVs).

CHS INC.

NASDAQ (GS): CHSCP

5500 Cenex Dr.
Inver Grove Heights, MN 55077
Phone: 651-355-6000
Fax: —
Web: www.chsinc.com

CEO: John D. Johnson
CFO: John Schmitz
HR: Patrick (Pat) Kluempke
FYE: August 31
Type: Public

CHS goes with the grain. As one of the US's leading publicly traded, cooperative marketers of grain, oilseed and energy, it represents farmers, ranchers, and co-ops from the Great Lakes to the Pacific Northwest and from the Canadian border to Texas. CHS trades grain and sells farm supplies to members through its stores. It processes soybeans for use in food and animal feeds, and grinds wheat into flour used in pastas and bread. Through joint ventures, the company sells soybean oil and crop nutrient and protection products, and markets grain. CHS also provides insurance and financial and risk-management services, and operates petroleum refineries and sells Cenex brand fuels, lubricants, and energy products.

THE CHUBB CORPORATION

NYSE: CB

15 Mountain View Rd.
Warren, NJ 07059
Phone: 908-903-2000
Fax: 908-903-2027
Web: www.chubb.com

CEO: John D. Finnegan
CFO: Richard G. Spiro
HR: Maureen A. Brundage
FYE: December 31
Type: Public

Here's the skinny on Chubb: The insurer is best known for comprehensive homeowners insurance for the demographic that owns yachts (the company insures those, too). Chubb also offers commercial property/casualty insurance including multiple peril, property and marine, and workers' compensation. Its specialty insurance arm offers professional liability policies for executives across a spectrum of industries and also provides construction and commercial surety bonds. Chubb distributes its products through 8,500 independent agents and brokers in 120 offices across the US and in more than 25 countries. The company began in 1882 when Thomas Chubb and his son began writing marine insurance in New York City.

	Annual Growth	12/05	12/06	12/07	12/08	12/09
Assets ($ mil.)	1.2%	48,060.7	50,277.0	50,574.0	48,429.0	50,449.0
Net income ($ mil.)	4.6%	1,825.9	2,528.0	2,807.0	1,804.0	2,183.0
Market value ($ mil.)	0.2%	15,954.6	17,289.5	17,835.2	16,665.4	16,070.6
Employees	(1.4%)	10,800	10,800	10,600	10,400	10,200

CHUGACH ALASKA CORPORATION

3800 Centerpoint Dr., Ste. 601
Anchorage, AK 99503
Phone: 907-563-8866
Fax: 907-563-8402
Web: www.chugach-ak.com

CEO: Ed Herndon
CFO: Connie Baehr
HR: Renee Reynolds
FYE: December 31
Type: Private

At the heart of Chugach Alaska Corporation is a vision of indigenous people running their own businesses on their own land. Chugach Alaska was formed following the activation of the Alaska Native Claims Settlement Act (which was passed by the US Congress in 1971), to provide land management services for the 928,000-acre Chugach region of Alaska. The company derives the bulk of its sales from oil and gas production, mining, commercial timber, and tourist activities that occur in the region. Chugach Alaska's shareholders consist of Aleut, Eskimo, and Indian natives.

	Annual Growth	12/04	12/05	12/06	12/07	12/08
Est. sales ($ mil.)	—	—	—	—	—	951.9
Employees	—	—	—	—	—	5,800

CHURCH & DWIGHT CO., INC.

NYSE: CHD

469 N. Harrison St.
Princeton, NJ 08543
Phone: 609-683-5900
Fax: 609-497-7269
Web: www.churchdwight.com

CEO: James R. (Jim) Craigie
CFO: Matthew T. Farrell
HR: Jacquelin J. (Jackie) Brova
FYE: December 31
Type: Public

Whether you call it saleratus (aerated salt), sodium bicarbonate, or plain old baking soda, Church & Dwight is a top maker worldwide of the powder. Church & Dwight's ARM & HAMMER baking soda, first marketed in 1846, is used as leavening, a deodorizer, a cleaner, and a swimming pool pH stabilizer. While laundry detergent represents Church & Dwight's top consumer business by sales, the company also makes a variety of other products: bathroom cleaners, carpet deodorizer, air fresheners, toothpaste, antiperspirants, Trojan condoms, industrial-grade carbonates, cat litter, and animal nutrition. It operates in North America, as well as in Australia, Brazil, China, France, and the UK.

	Annual Growth	12/05	12/06	12/07	12/08	12/09
Sales ($ mil.)	9.8%	1,736.5	1,945.7	2,220.9	2,422.4	2,520.9
Net income ($ mil.)	18.6%	122.9	138.9	169.0	195.2	243.5
Market value ($ mil.)	16.3%	2,341.2	3,023.1	3,832.6	3,977.9	4,284.8
Employees	0.0%	3,700	3,700	3,700	3,500	3,700

CHURCHILL DOWNS INCORPORATED

NASDAQ (GS): CHDN

700 Central Ave.
Louisville, KY 40208
Phone: 502-636-4400
Fax: —
Web: www.churchilldownsincorporated.com

CEO: Robert L. (Bob) Evans
CFO: William E. (Bill) Mudd
HR: Charles G. (Chuck) Kenyon
FYE: December 31
Type: Public

You might say this company has put its money on the sport of champions to win. Churchill Downs is the leading operator of horse racing tracks in the US, with four major race courses, including its namesake track that hosts the world-famous Kentucky Derby. Its other tracks include Arlington Park (Illinois), Calder Race Course (Florida), and Fair Grounds Race Course (Louisiana). In addition to live horse racing, Churchill Downs operates a number of simulcast networks and off-track betting facilities, as well as a wagering deposit service (TwinSpires) that allows punters to place bets online. Richard Duchossois, who controls diversified holding company Duchossois Group, owns about 25% of Churchill Downs.

	Annual Growth	12/05	12/06	12/07	12/08	12/09
Sales ($ mil.)	1.8%	408.8	376.7	410.7	430.6	439.7
Net income ($ mil.)	(32.1%)	78.9	29.8	15.7	28.5	16.8
Market value ($ mil.)	0.4%	505.9	588.7	743.4	556.7	514.5
Employees	(15.5%)	2,550	1,100	1,000	1,000	1,300

CHYRON CORPORATION

NASDAQ (GM): CHYR

5 Hub Dr.
Melville, NY 11747
Phone: 631-845-2000
Fax: 631-845-3895
Web: www.chyron.com

CEO: Michael I. Wellesley-Wesley
CFO: Jerry Kieliszak
HR: —
FYE: December 31
Type: Public

Chyron wants customers to stay tuned. The company makes software and hardware for enhancing live and pre-recorded television broadcasts with special effects and animation. Chyron's Windows-based products let journalists and producers create logos, text, and other images that can be superimposed over existing images to display sports scores, stock tickers, and weather information. Chyron's clients include ABC, ESPN, FOX News, CNN, and the BBC. In addition to broadcasters, the company markets to post-production facilities, government agencies, schools, health care providers, religious institutions, and telecom service providers.

	Annual Growth	12/05	12/06	12/07	12/08	12/09
Sales ($ mil.)	0.5%	25.1	26.2	32.3	34.3	25.6
Net income ($ mil.)	—	0.7	3.1	3.7	17.8	(3.1)
Market value ($ mil.)	3.3%	29.2	56.9	86.9	23.9	33.2
Employees	3.1%	92	100	107	115	104

CIANBRO CORPORATION

1 Hunnewell Sq.
Pittsfield, ME 04967
Phone: 207-487-3311
Fax: 207-487-3861
Web: www.cianbro.com

CEO: Peter G. (Pete) Vigue
CFO: Aldo Servello
HR: Kellie Guarino
FYE: December 31
Type: Private

Brother, can you spare your pickup truck? That might have been the question posed when the four Cianchette brothers — Carl, Ken, Bud, and Chuck — pooled their savings and used Chuck's 1934 pickup truck to found Cianbro in 1949. One of the East Coast's largest civil and heavy industrial construction companies, employee-owned Cianbro specializes in modular construction, marine and piling work, transporation projects, and pulp and paper construction projects. Other areas of expertise include chemical plants, hydroelectric dams, biotech, and warehouses. Clients include L.L. Bean, International Paper, and the US government. Cianbro has locations from Maine to Maryland, along the Eastern Seaboard.

	Annual Growth	12/04	12/05	12/06	12/07	12/08
Est. sales ($ mil.)	—	—	—	—	—	429.0
Employees	—	—	—	—	—	1,496

CIB MARINE BANCSHARES, INC.

Pink Sheets: CIBH

N27 W24025 Paul Ct.
Pewaukee, WI 53072
Phone: 262-695-6010
Fax: 262-695-6014
Web: www.cibmarine.com

CEO: John P. Hickey Jr.
CFO: Edwin J. Depenbrok
HR: —
FYE: December 31
Type: Public

CIB Marine Bancshares is *semper fi* to its banking strategy. The company owns CIBM Bank, which operates in the Indianapolis, Milwaukee, and Phoenix markets. Through some 20 branches, the bank caters to individuals and small- and midsized-business customers, offering checking and savings accounts, ATM and debit cards, CDs, and IRAs. The company's loan portfolio mainly consists of commercial mortgages, business loans, and commercial real estate construction loans. CIB Marine Bancshares emerged from Chapter 11 bankruptcy protection in early 2010.

CIBA SPECIALTY CHEMICALS NORTH AMERICA

540 White Plains Rd.
Tarrytown, NY 10591
Phone: 914-785-2000
Fax: 914-785-2211
Web: www.cibasc.com/unitedstates

CEO: Eric Marohn
CFO: John Lynch
HR: Cherie Hutton
FYE: December 31
Type: Subsidiary

Ciba Specialty Chemicals North America produces chemicals for use in products ranging from automobiles to personal care items. The NAFTA regional subsidiary of Swiss chemicals maker Ciba Specialty Chemicals, the diversified company operates in the US, Canada, and Mexico and has manufacturing locations primarily in the eastern half of the US. Its main business areas of operation are plastic additives, coating effects, and water and paper treatment. Its ingredients are used in a variety of products, including inks, dyes, pigments, antimicrobials, paints, polymers, and electronic materials. Ciba's been a part of BASF since early 2009.

	Annual Growth	12/04	12/05	12/06	12/07	12/08
Est. sales ($ mil.)	—	—	—	—	—	485.1
Employees	—	—	—	—	—	3,000

An in-depth profile of this company is available to Hoover's Online members at hoovers.com.

CIBA VISION CORPORATION

11460 Johns Creek Pkwy.
Duluth, GA 30097
Phone: 678-415-3937
Fax: 678-415-3001
Web: www.cibavision.com

CEO: Andrea Saia
CFO: John McKenna
HR: Atul Khosla
FYE: December 31
Type: Subsidiary

CIBA VISION is the eye care unit of Novartis. The company researches, develops, and manufactures contact lenses and lens care products. Its contact lens brands include Air Optix, Dailies, and FreshLook (a leader in the color contact lens market), and its lens care brands include Aquify and Clear Care. With major manufacturing facilities in the US, Canada, Germany, Malaysia, and Singapore, CIBA VISION supplies contact lens wearers in more than 70 countries. Products are sold by mass merchandisers, drugstores, supermarkets, optical retail chains, and eye care professionals, as well as by online retailers. The company was established in 1980 by Ciba-Geigy, which merged with Sandoz in 1996 to form Novartis.

CICI ENTERPRISES, LP

1080 W. Bethel Rd.
Coppell, TX 75019
Phone: 972-745-4200
Fax: 972-745-4203
Web: www.cicispizza.com

CEO: Michael R. (Mike) Shumsky
CFO: Tim Alba
HR: —
FYE: December 31
Type: Private

CiCi's pleases penny pinchers and pizzaholics alike. CiCi Enterprises operates and franchises about 650 CiCi's Pizza restaurants in more than 30 states that offer several types of pizza along with salad, desserts, and pasta at an all-you-can-eat price. Concentrated in Texas, Florida, and other southern states, many of the eateries are located in shopping malls and other suburban retail areas. About 15 of the restaurants are company-owned, while the rest are franchised. CiCi Enterprises supplies its franchisees through its JMC Restaurant Distribution unit. Joe Croce opened the first CiCi's Pizza in Plano, Texas, in 1985. A group including current and former management controls the company.

CIBER, INC.

NYSE: CBR

5251 DTC Pkwy., Ste. 1400
Greenwood Village, CO 80111
Phone: 303-220-0100
Fax: 303-220-7100
Web: www.ciber.com

CEO: Peter H. Cheesbrough
CFO: Peter H. Cheesbrough
HR: David (Dave) Plisko
FYE: December 31
Type: Public

CIBER helps its customers take control of information. The company is an IT consultancy that provides enterprise systems integration through consulting practices, specializing in such software systems as Lawson, Microsoft, Oracle, and SAP, as well as custom software development. In addition, CIBER offers a number of support services, including call center and help desk operations, data hosting, and maintenance. It serves a number of federal, state, and local government agencies and commercial customers in such industries as finance, manufacturing, and telecommunications. CIBER gets about two-thirds of its sales in the US. Former CEO Bobby Stevenson founded the company with two other partners in 1974.

	Annual Growth	12/05	12/06	12/07	12/08	12/09
Sales ($ mil.)	2.1%	956.0	995.8	1,082.0	1,191.6	1,037.7
Net income ($ mil.)	(11.7%)	24.7	24.7	29.0	30.0	15.0
Market value ($ mil.)	(15.0%)	456.7	469.2	422.8	332.9	238.7
Employees	0.0%	8,000	8,300	8,400	8,300	8,000

CIENA CORPORATION

NASDAQ (GS): CIEN

1201 Winterson Rd.
Linthicum, MD 21090
Phone: 410-694-5700
Fax: 410-694-5750
Web: www.ciena.com

CEO: Gary B. Smith
CFO: James E. (Jim) Moylan Jr.
HR: Randall C. (Randy) Harris
FYE: October 31
Type: Public

Ciena doesn't limit itself to just one color of the spectrum. The company makes transport and switching equipment that increases the capacity of long-distance fiber-optic networks by transmitting multiple light signals simultaneously over the same circuit. It also sells optical transport systems for metro and enterprise wide-area networks, as well as broadband access products that enable communications companies to deliver Internet protocol (IP) services, such as VoIP, IP video, and DSL. Ciena serves telecommunications service providers, cable companies, large enterprises, and government entities. The company gets about two-thirds of its sales in the US.

	Annual Growth	10/05	10/06	10/07	10/08	10/09
Sales ($ mil.)	11.2%	427.3	564.1	779.8	902.4	652.6
Net income ($ mil.)	—	(435.7)	0.6	82.8	38.9	(581.2)
Market value ($ mil.)	(8.3%)	1,535.3	2,176.3	4,430.4	889.6	1,085.9
Employees	9.6%	1,497	1,485	1,797	2,203	2,163

CICERO, INC.

OTC: CICN

8000 Regency Pkwy., Ste. 542
Cary, NC 27518
Phone: 919-380-5000
Fax: 919-380-5121
Web: www.ciceroinc.com

CEO: John P. Broderick
CFO: John P. Broderick
HR: —
FYE: December 31
Type: Public

Cicero takes a philosophical approach to integrating your applications. The company provides application integration software used to link a variety of enterprise applications (including mainframe, client/server, and Web-based environments), primarily for financial services firms. The company also provides services, such as consulting, project management, and training. Customers include Affiliated Computer Services, IBM, and Merrill Lynch. Cicero's roster of strategic partners includes systems integrators (SAIC), as well as technology providers, such as Silent Systems, Swiss Secure, and StarNet Data Design. The company gets all of its sales in the US.

	Annual Growth	12/05	12/06	12/07	12/08	12/09
Sales ($ mil.)	33.0%	0.8	1.0	1.8	3.5	2.5
Net income ($ mil.)	—	(3.7)	(3.0)	(2.0)	(0.8)	(1.3)
Market value ($ mil.)	(55.5%)	108.3	108.3	11.8	7.1	4.2
Employees	5.7%	20	18	21	30	25

CIGNA CORPORATION

NYSE: CI

2 Liberty Place, 1601 Chestnut St.
Philadelphia, PA 19192
Phone: 215-761-1000
Fax: 215-761-5515
Web: www.cigna.com

CEO: David M. Cordani
CFO: Annmarie T. Hagan
HR: John M. Murabito
FYE: December 31
Type: Public

One of the top US health insurers, CIGNA covers nearly 12 million people with its various medical plans, which include PPO, HMO, point-of-service (POS), indemnity, and consumer-directed products. CIGNA also offers specialty health coverage in the form of dental, vision, pharmacy, and behavioral health plans, and it sells group accident, life, and disability insurance. Its customers include employers, government entities, unions, Medicare recipients, and other groups and individuals in the US and Canada. Internationally, the company sells life, accident, and health insurance in parts of Asia and the European Union, and it provides health coverage to expatriate employees of multinational companies.

	Annual Growth	12/05	12/06	12/07	12/08	12/09
Sales ($ mil.)	2.5%	16,684.0	16,547.0	17,623.0	19,101.0	18,414.0
Net income ($ mil.)	(5.3%)	1,625.0	1,155.0	1,115.0	292.0	1,305.0
Market value ($ mil.)	(1.3%)	10,301.5	12,134.0	14,865.7	4,662.0	9,758.3
Employees	(2.7%)	32,700	27,100	26,600	30,300	29,300

An in-depth profile of this company is available to Hoover's Online members at hoovers.com.

CIMAREX ENERGY CO.

NYSE: XEC

1700 Lincoln St., Ste. 1800
Denver, CO 80203
Phone: 303-295-3995
Fax: 303-295-3494
Web: www.cimarex.com

CEO: F. H. Merelli
CFO: Paul J. Korus
HR: Richard S. Dinkins
FYE: December 31
Type: Public

Cimarex Energy's energy is devoted to oil and gas exploration and production. The independent is focusing its operations on the Midcontinent, Gulf Coast, Permian Basin, and Gulf of Mexico. The company reported proved reserves in 2008 of about 1.1 trillion cu. ft. of natural gas and 45.2 million barrels of oil and natural gas liquids. Cimarex Energy participated in drilling 450 gross wells (about 280 net) during 2008. That year company-operated wells accounted for 83% of its total proved reserves and some 81% of its total production (of 22,940 barrels of oil per day).

	Annual Growth	12/05	12/06	12/07	12/08	12/09
Sales ($ mil.)	(2.5%)	1,118.6	1,267.1	1,431.2	1,970.3	1,009.8
Net income ($ mil.)	—	328.3	345.7	346.5	(901.7)	(311.9)
Market value ($ mil.)	5.3%	3,607.8	3,061.7	3,567.6	2,246.4	4,443.3
Employees	2.3%	689	734	760	831	756

CINCINNATI BELL INC.

NYSE: CBB

221 E. 4th St.
Cincinnati, OH 45202
Phone: 513-397-9900
Fax: 513-397-5092
Web: www.cincinnatibell.com

CEO: John F. (Jack) Cassidy
CFO: Gary J. Wojtaszek
HR: Brian G. Keating
FYE: December 31
Type: Public

Cincinnati Bell rings for Bengals and Bearcats, Musketeers, and even the Reds. The company provides local phone services through its Cincinnati Bell Telephone subsidiary to residential and business customers in southwestern Ohio, northern Kentucky, and eastern Indiana. It has been the incumbent local-exchange carrier (ILEC) for greater Cincinnati since the 1870s, and it operates in other areas as a competitive local-exchange carrier (CLEC), providing voice and data services through its own networks, as well as through agreements with other carriers. Cincinnati Bell also offers data center services for businesses. More than 500,000 subscribers use wireless voice and data services provided by Cincinnati Bell Wireless.

	Annual Growth	12/05	12/06	12/07	12/08	12/09
Sales ($ mil.)	2.5%	1,209.6	1,270.1	1,348.6	1,403.0	1,336.0
Net income ($ mil.)	—	(64.5)	86.3	73.2	102.6	89.6
Market value ($ mil.)	(0.4%)	706.0	919.2	955.4	388.2	693.9
Employees	2.5%	2,900	2,950	3,100	3,300	3,200

CINCINNATI CHILDREN'S HOSPITAL MEDICAL CENTER

3333 Burnet Ave.
Cincinnati, OH 45229
Phone: 513-636-4200
Fax: 513-636-2460
Web: www.cincinnatichildrens.org

CEO: Michael Fisher
CFO: Scott J. Hamlin
HR: Ronald B. McKinley
FYE: June 30
Type: Not-for-profit

Cincinnati Children's Hospital Medical Center has a special place in its heart for kids — and possibly vice versa. The pediatric health care facility offers specialty treatments for children and adolescents suffering from just about any malady, including those of the heart and liver, as well as blood diseases and cancer. Cincinnati Children's Hospital has more than 500 beds and operates nearly a dozen outpatient care centers. The not-for-profit hospital runs the only Level 1 pediatric trauma center in the region and serves as a teaching facility for the University of Cincinnati College of Medicine. Its Cincinnati Children's Research Foundation is one of the largest pediatric research institutions in the US.

CINCINNATI FINANCIAL CORPORATION

NASDAQ (GS): CINF

6200 S. Gilmore Rd.
Fairfield, OH 45014
Phone: 513-870-2000
Fax: 513-870-2911
Web: www.cinfin.com

CEO: Kenneth W. Stecher
CFO: Steven J. Johnston
HR: Greg Ziegler
FYE: December 31
Type: Public

At Skyline Chili in Cincinnati you can order your chili 3-way, 4-way, or 5-way; at Cincinnati Financial Corporation (CFC) you can order your insurance with plenty of extras as well. The company's flagship Cincinnati Insurance (operating through three subsidiaries) sells commercial property, liability, excess, surplus, auto, bond, and fire insurance; personal lines include homeowners, auto, and liability products. Cincinnati Life sells life, disability income, and annuities. The company's CFC Investment subsidiary provides commercial financing, leasing, and real estate services, and its CinFin Capital Management provides asset management services to businesses, institutions, and not-for-profits.

	Annual Growth	12/05	12/06	12/07	12/08	12/09
Assets ($ mil.)	(2.5%)	16,003.0	17,222.0	16,637.0	13,369.0	14,440.0
Net income ($ mil.)	(8.0%)	602.0	930.0	855.0	429.0	432.0
Market value ($ mil.)	(12.5%)	7,282.1	7,384.8	6,444.4	4,738.0	4,276.7
Employees	1.2%	3,983	4,048	4,087	4,179	4,170

CINEDIGM DIGITAL CINEMA CORP.

NASDAQ (GM): CIDM

55 Madison Ave., Ste. 300
Morristown, NJ 07960
Phone: 973-290-0080
Fax: 973-290-0081
Web: www.accessitx.com

CEO: A. Dale (Bud) Mayo
CFO: Adam M. Mizel
HR: —
FYE: March 31
Type: Public

Cinedigm Digital Cinema (formerly known as Access Integrated Technologies or AccessIT) hopes to help you get your digital content to the masses. The company provides software and services used for the managed storage and electronic delivery of digital content to movie theaters and other venues, as well as applications for managing theatrical releases, planning, protecting intellectual property, and theater ticketing operations. Cinedigm previously provided data center services but transitioned away from those offerings in 2007 in order to focus on its media content and services offerings.

	Annual Growth	3/05	3/06	3/07	3/08	3/09
Sales ($ mil.)	66.9%	10.7	16.8	47.1	81.0	83.0
Net income ($ mil.)	—	(6.8)	(16.8)	(26.0)	(35.7)	(37.4)
Market value ($ mil.)	(44.7%)	191.0	369.7	156.2	90.6	17.8
Employees	27.0%	93	140	348	295	242

CINEMARK HOLDINGS, INC.

NYSE: CNK

3900 Dallas Pkwy., Ste. 500
Plano, TX 75093
Phone: 972-665-1000
Fax: 972-665-1004
Web: www.cinemark.com

CEO: Alan W. Stock
CFO: Robert D. Copple
HR: —
FYE: December 31
Type: Public

Cinemark Holdings has left its mark on the cinema landscape. The third-largest movie exhibitor in the US (following Regal Entertainment and AMC) has more than 4,800 screens in some 420 theatres in the US, Canada, and Latin America. Cinemark operates its multiplex theaters in smaller cities and suburban areas of major metropolitan markets. Some larger theaters operate under the Tinseltown name; others are "discount" theaters showing no first-run films. The company prefers to build new theaters in midsized markets or in suburbs of major cities where the Cinemark theater is the only game in town.

	Annual Growth	12/05	12/06	12/07	12/08	12/09
Sales ($ mil.)	18.0%	1,020.6	1,220.6	1,682.8	1,742.3	1,976.5
Net income ($ mil.)	—	(25.4)	0.8	88.9	(48.3)	97.1
Market value ($ mil.)	(8.1%)	—	—	1,908.4	834.1	1,613.2
Employees	11.1%	13,600	13,600	12,300	18,300	20,700

CINETIC AUTOMATION CORPORATION

23400 Halsted Rd.
Farmington Hills, MI 48335
Phone: 248-477-0800
Fax: 248-615-2327
Web: www.cineticusa.com

CEO: Mike DiMichele
CFO: Jeff Ritz
HR: Gerry Makuch
FYE: December 31
Type: Subsidiary

Derived from kinetic, Cinetic Automation is known for putting a little extra energy into automating industries. The company supplies application engineering, machine tools, and automated systems for powertrain assembly. It also manufactures non-automotive automation and assembly systems, fastener tightening, washers and gantries, and testing equipment, as well as conveyors. Founded in 1965 to serve the Detroit car market, Cinetic Automation has branched into appliance, energy, and defense applications worldwide. Clients include BMW, Coca-Cola, Caterpillar, Emerson, General Motors, and Visteon. The company is a unit of Fives Cinetic, itself a subsidiary of French industrial equipment giant Fives.

	Annual Growth	12/04	12/05	12/06	12/07	12/08
Est. sales ($ mil.)	—	—	—	—	—	49.2
Employees	—	—	—	—	—	585

CINETIC SORTING CORP.

500 E. Burnett Ave.
Louisville, KY 40217
Phone: 502-636-1414
Fax: 502-636-1491
Web: www.fivesgroup.com/fivescinetic_logistics/en

CEO: Thomas (Tom) Barry
CFO: Larry Hudson
HR: Candace Bradley
FYE: December 31
Type: Subsidiary

Square pegs wouldn't have to worry about being forced into round holes if it were left up to Cinetic Sorting. The company makes automated sorting machines used by logistics and retail customers. Among the businesses that use its products are postal agencies and courier services, airports, and distribution centers (from food distributors to newspapers). Cinetic Sorting is the US regional headquarters of Fives; other operations are based in Italy and Japan. Cinetic Sorting was formed when Sandvik sold its Sorting Systems business to the Cinetic Industries (now Fives Cinetic) subsidiary of Fives.

	Annual Growth	12/04	12/05	12/06	12/07	12/08
Est. sales ($ mil.)	—	—	—	—	—	16.0
Employees	—	—	—	—	—	80

CINTAS CORPORATION

NASDAQ (GS): CTAS

6800 Cintas Blvd.
Cincinnati, OH 45262
Phone: 513-459-1200
Fax: 513-573-4130
Web: www.cintas.com

CEO: Scott D. Farmer
CFO: William C. Gale
HR: Michael A. Womack
FYE: May 31
Type: Public

If Cintas had its way, you'd never agonize over what to wear to work. The #1 uniform supplier in the US has about 800,000 clients (Delta Air Lines, DHL) and some 5 million people wear its garb each day. Cintas — which sells, leases, and rents uniforms — operates about 415 facilities across the US and Canada; it leases about half of them. Besides offering shirts, jackets, slacks, and footwear, the company provides clean room apparel and flame-resistant clothing. Other products offered by Cintas include uniform cleaning, first-aid and safety products, clean room supplies, and document handling and storage. CEO Scott Farmer owns about 10% of the firm. His father, Richard, founded the company in 1968.

	Annual Growth	5/05	5/06	5/07	5/08	5/09
Sales ($ mil.)	5.3%	3,067.3	3,403.6	3,706.9	3,937.9	3,774.7
Net income ($ mil.)	(6.8%)	300.5	327.2	334.5	335.4	226.4
Market value ($ mil.)	(12.8%)	6,171.4	6,475.6	5,864.1	4,512.7	3,560.3
Employees	0.8%	30,000	32,000	34,000	34,000	31,000

CIRCOR INTERNATIONAL, INC.

NYSE: CIR

25 Corporate Dr., Ste. 130
Burlington, MA 01803
Phone: 781-270-1200
Fax: 781-270-1299
Web: www.circor.com

CEO: A. William (Bill) Higgins
CFO: Frederic M. (Fred) Burditt
HR: Susan M. McCuaig
FYE: December 31
Type: Public

CIRCOR International is overflowing with ways to control fluids. The company makes and supplies valves, fittings, actuators, and other related fluid control products for the industrial and petrochemical markets. Its products are used in hydraulic, pneumatic, cryogenic, and steam systems. With manufacturing operations in the US, Canada, Europe, and China, the company sells its products through thousands of distributors to more than 12,000 aerospace, energy, chemical, food processing, maritime, oil and gas, pharmaceutical, semiconductor, and textile customers in more than 100 countries worldwide. CIRCOR spun off from Watts Industries (now Watts Water Technologies) in 1999.

	Annual Growth	12/05	12/06	12/07	12/08	12/09
Sales ($ mil.)	9.3%	450.5	591.7	665.7	793.8	642.6
Net income ($ mil.)	(26.7%)	20.4	29.3	37.9	(59.0)	5.9
Market value ($ mil.)	(0.5%)	437.9	627.9	791.2	469.3	429.7
Employees	2.1%	2,300	2,800	2,600	2,700	2,500

CIRCUS AND ELDORADO JOINT VENTURE

407 N. Virginia St.
Reno, NV 89501
Phone: 775-325-7401
Fax: 775-325-7330
Web: www.silverlegacyreno.com

CEO: Gary L. Carano
CFO: Stephanie D. Lepori
HR: —
FYE: December 31
Type: Joint venture

Circus and Eldorado Joint Venture knows there's gold and silver in the circuses of Reno, Nevada. The company owns and operates the Silver Legacy Resort Casino in Reno. The Silver Legacy, which features a 19th-century silver-mining theme, offers a more-than-87,000-sq.-ft. casino with about 1,500 slot machines and more than 60 table games. The casino's hotel boasts some 1,500 guest rooms and suites. The company markets the Silver Legacy to a select group of patrons, including preferred casino customers, convention groups, and specialty Internet travel groups. Circus Circus Hotel and Casino owner MGM MIRAGE and Eldorado Resorts each own 50% of the company.

CIRRUS LOGIC, INC.

NASDAQ (GS): CRUS

2901 Via Fortuna
Austin, TX 78746
Phone: 512-851-4000
Fax: 512-851-4977
Web: www.cirrus.com

CEO: Jason P. Rhode
CFO: Thurman K. Case
HR: Jo-Dee M. Benson
FYE: March 31
Type: Public

Cirrus Logic's approach to the chip business is hardly cloudy. The fabless semiconductor company, long a leader in audio chips of all kinds, develops integrated circuits (ICs) for specialized applications in consumer electronics, energy, and industrial equipment. Its more than 700 products include audio encoder/decoders (codecs), digital amplifiers, digital audio converters, energy management devices, and power amplifiers. Cirrus Logic also develops system-on-a-chip products, which unite processors, controllers, memory, and other components on a single chip. The company gets about three-quarters of its sales outside the US, primarily from customers in China and other Asian countries.

	Annual Growth	3/05	3/06	3/07	3/08	3/09
Sales ($ mil.)	(2.7%)	194.9	193.7	182.3	181.9	174.6
Net income ($ mil.)	—	(13.4)	54.1	27.9	(5.8)	3.5
Market value ($ mil.)	(4.5%)	295.9	555.2	501.5	440.0	246.2
Employees	(5.6%)	603	424	456	473	479

CIRTRAN CORPORATION

OTC: CIRC

4125 S. 6000 West
West Valley City, UT 84128
Phone: 801-963-5112
Fax: 801-963-5180
Web: www.cirtran.com

CEO: Iehab J. Hawatmeh
CFO: Iehab J. Hawatmeh
HR: —
FYE: December 31
Type: Public

CirTran provides contract electronics manufacturing services, through which it makes printed circuit boards and cables for customers in consumer electronics, networking equipment, the automotive industry, and other markets. In 2004 the company established an Asian subsidiary in Shenzhen, China, that undertakes manufacturing services for a wider variety of products, including cooking appliances, fitness equipment, and hair products. CirTran's Racore Technology subsidiary makes Ethernet adapter cards for PCs. Racore's customers include the Fire Department of New York City, Lear Siegler, Lockheed Martin, the US Air Force, and Walt Disney World. Nearly all of the company's sales are in the US.

	Annual Growth	12/05	12/06	12/07	12/08	12/09
Sales ($ mil.)	(7.1%)	13.0	8.7	12.4	13.7	9.7
Net income ($ mil.)	—	(0.5)	(2.9)	(7.2)	(3.9)	(5.8)
Market value ($ mil.)	(26.0%)	40.0	20.7	22.5	3.0	12.0
Employees	(39.2%)	110	108	120	94	15

CISCO SYSTEMS, INC.

NASDAQ (GS): CSCO

170 W. Tasman Dr., Bldg. 10
San Jose, CA 95134
Phone: 408-526-4000
Fax: 408-526-4100
Web: www.cisco.com

CEO: John T. Chambers
CFO: Frank Calderoni
HR: Brian (Skip) Schipper
FYE: July 31
Type: Public

Cisco Systems routes packets and routs competitors with equal efficiency. Dominating the market for Internet protocol-based networking equipment, the company provides routers and switches used to direct data, voice, and video traffic. Other products include remote access servers, IP telephony equipment, optical networking components, Internet conferencing systems, set-top boxes, and network service and security systems. It sells its products primarily to large enterprises and telecommunications service providers, but it also markets products designed for small businesses and consumers through its Consumer Business Group. Cisco gets about half of its sales in North America.

	Annual Growth	7/05	7/06	7/07	7/08	7/09
Sales ($ mil.)	9.9%	24,801.0	28,484.0	34,922.0	39,540.0	36,117.0
Net income ($ mil.)	1.7%	5,741.0	5,580.0	7,333.0	8,052.0	6,134.0
Market value ($ mil.)	3.5%	109,368.5	102,115.4	165,109.4	125,588.2	125,702.4
Employees	14.3%	38,413	49,926	61,535	66,129	65,550

CISION US INC.

332 S. Michigan Ave.
Chicago, IL 60604
Phone: 312-922-2400
Fax: 312-922-3126
Web: us.cision.com

CEO: Joseph (Joe) Bernardo
CFO: Michael F. (Mike) Czlonka
HR: Randy Zierfuss
FYE: December 31
Type: Subsidiary

Cision US monitors, distributes, and evaluates news and information from some 350,000 media sources for its clients in corporate communications, marketing, and public relations. The company maintains a database of media contacts, clippings, and reports for its subscribers and publishes material online and in print directories. Its CisionPoint product is an integrated software application for managing PR campaigns. The company also operates Cision Navigator, an online community for PR professionals. Cision US has nearly 25 offices throughout the US. It is a subsidiary of Sweden-based research firm Cision AB.

CIT GROUP INC.

NYSE: CIT

505 5th Ave.
New York, NY 10017
Phone: 212-771-0505
Fax: —
Web: www.cit.com

CEO: John A. Thain
CFO: —
HR: James J. (Jim) Duffy
FYE: December 31
Type: Public

If you haven't heard of CIT Group, then you're O-U-T of the proverbial loop. On the big-business landscape for about a century, CIT is a commercial bank holding company that offers lending, leasing, debt restructuring, equipment financing, and advisory services to small and midsized businesses and to more than half of the *FORTUNE* 1000 in such industries as energy, health care, communications, entertainment, aerospace, and transportation. Its real estate services include mortgage, mezzanine debt, and net lease financing. CIT has more than $60 billion in assets and serves some 1 million clients in more than 50 countries around the world. The company filed for and exited Chapter 11 bankruptcy protection in 2009.

	Annual Growth	12/04	12/05	12/06	12/07	*12/08
Assets ($ mil.)	12.0%	51,111.3	63,386.6	77,067.9	90,248.0	80,448.9
Net income ($ mil.)	—	753.6	949.1	1,046.0	(81.0)	(2,799.5)
Market value ($ mil.)	(43.9%)	18,544.8	20,957.0	22,571.8	9,725.7	1,837.5
Employees	(3.9%)	5,860	6,340	7,345	6,700	4,995

*Most recent year available

CITADEL BROADCASTING CORPORATION

7201 W. Lake Mead Blvd., Ste. 400
Las Vegas, NV 89128
Phone: 702-804-5200
Fax: 702-804-8250
Web: www.citadelbroadcasting.com

CEO: Farid Suleman
CFO: Randy L. Taylor
HR: Susan Arville
FYE: December 31
Type: Private

You might say this company has fortified its position in the radio business. Citadel Broadcasting is the #3 radio broadcaster in the US in terms of number of stations (behind Clear Channel Communications and Cumulus Media), with more than 220 stations serving more than 50 markets. Most of the company's stations operate in market clusters, sharing administration and other back-office functions. The stations offer a variety of music formats, as well as news, talk, and sports. In addition, the company's Citadel Media unit is a leading syndicator of radio news and entertainment programming serving about 4,400 affiliates. Citadel Broadcasting emerged from bankruptcy in 2010.

	Annual Growth	12/05	12/06	12/07	12/08	12/09
Sales ($ mil.)	14.6%	419.9	432.9	719.8	863.1	723.6
Net income ($ mil.)	—	69.8	(48.0)	(1,285.2)	(969.8)	(783.4)
Employees	3.9%	3,428	3,392	5,000	4,430	4,000

CITADEL INVESTMENT GROUP, L.L.C.

131 S. Dearborn St.
Chicago, IL 60603
Phone: 312-395-2100
Fax: 312-267-7100
Web: www.citadelgroup.com

CEO: Kenneth C. (Ken) Griffin
CFO: —
HR: Darcy Zulpo
FYE: December 31
Type: Private

This Citadel aspires not to turn boys into men, but to turn cash into, well, more cash. Citadel Investment Group, whose seeds were planted in supertrader Ken Griffin's Harvard dorm room in 1987, includes Citadel Asset Management, one of the world's largest hedge funds, accounting for around 8% of daily trading activity at the New York Stock Exchange and NASDAQ. Because of this high volume, the company also acts as a market maker for equity options and for some blue-chip stocks on smaller exchanges. It manages some $12 billion of assets for institutional and high-net-worth investors, as well as its own account. Citadel also provides investment banking, institutional trading, and fund administration services.

An in-depth profile of this company is available to Hoover's Online members at hoovers.com.

377

CITGO PETROLEUM CORPORATION

1293 Eldridge Pkwy.
Houston, TX 77077
Phone: 832-486-4000
Fax: 832-486-1814
Web: www.citgo.com

CEO: Alejandro Granado
CFO: Brian O'Kelly
HR: —
FYE: December 31
Type: Subsidiary

From the get-go CITGO Petroleum has been refining and marketing petroleum products, including jet fuel, diesel fuel, heating oils, and lubricants. It markets CITGO branded gasoline through about 6,500 independent retail outlets in the US, mainly east of the Rockies. CITGO Petroleum owns oil refineries in Illinois, Louisiana, and Texas. The company has refining capacity of 749,000 barrels per day and access to a total of more than 1.1 million barrels per day of refining capacity. It also has an agreement to access the St. Croix, Virgin Islands, refinery jointly owned by Venezuela's PDVSA and US-based Hess. CITGO Petroleum is the operating subsidiary of PDV America, itself a subsidiary of PDVSA.

CITIGATE CUNNINGHAM

101 2nd St., Ste. 2250
San Francisco, CA 94105
Phone: 415-618-8700
Fax: 415-618-8702
Web: www.cunningham.com

CEO: Gary Thompson
CFO: —
HR: —
FYE: December 31
Type: Subsidiary

Citigate Cunningham is a public relations firm that has served such high-tech clients as Affinnova, Nexaweb, and Sybase. The company's services include research and brand tracking as well as strategic public relations specializing in serving clients in dynamic (intensely competitive and rapidly changing) markets. It owns offices in San Francisco and Cambridge, Massachusetts. Citigate Cunningham was founded in 1985 by Andrea Cunningham and is a subsidiary of London-based marketing communications services provider Huntsworth PLC.

CITI TRENDS, INC.

NASDAQ (GS): CTRN

104 Coleman Boulevard
Savannah, GA 31408
Phone: 912-236-1561
Fax: 912-443-3663
Web: www.cititrends.com

CEO: R. David Alexander
CFO: Bruce D. Smith
HR: Ivy D. Council
FYE: January 31
Type: Public

Citi Trends hopes to transport its customers to Trend City as quickly as possible. The fast-growing urban fashion apparel and accessory chain operates about 355 stores in more than 20 US states focusing primarily on the African-American market. Its brand-name and private-label offerings — which include hip-hop jeans and oversized T-shirts; men's, women's, and children's clothing; shoes; housewares; and accessories — are sold at 30%-70% less than department and specialty stores' regular prices. Founded in 1946 as Allied Department Stores, the company changed its name to Citi Trends after it was acquired by former parent Hampshire Equity Partners.

	Annual Growth	1/06	1/07	1/08	1/09	1/10
Sales ($ mil.)	17.5%	289.8	381.9	437.5	488.2	551.9
Net income ($ mil.)	8.5%	14.2	21.4	14.2	17.4	19.7
Market value ($ mil.)	(9.3%)	683.4	585.5	203.1	141.6	462.5
Employees	13.2%	2,800	3,000	3,500	4,000	4,600

CITIGROUP GLOBAL MARKETS INC.

388 Greenwich St.
New York, NY 10013
Phone: 212-816-6000
Fax: —
Web: icg.citi.com/global_markets

CEO: Vikram S. Pandit
CFO: Cliff Verron
HR: Gary Hediger
FYE: December 31
Type: Subsidiary

Citigroup Global Markets is the brokerage and securities arm of banking behemoth Citigroup. The company provides investment banking services to corporate, institutional, government, and retail clients. It divides its business into four geographic regions: North America, Europe/Middle East/Africa, Asia, and Latin America. The group operates in Japan through Nikko Citi, Citigroup's joint venture with brokerage Nikko Cordial Corporation. As part of a major restructuring by Citigroup, Global Markets — along with its parent company's retail and private banking units — will be split from Citigroup's consumer finance business in a new company to be called Citicorp.

CITIFINANCIAL, INC.

300 St. Paul Place
Baltimore, MD 21202
Phone: 410-332-3000
Fax: 410-332-3489
Web: www.citifinancial.com

CEO: Mary McDowell
CFO: —
HR: —
FYE: December 31
Type: Subsidiary

Whether you're citified or country-fried, CitiFinancial wants to help you build that deck or fix your old clunker. A consumer lending subsidiary of Citigroup, CitiFinancial offers personal loans for debt consolidation, home improvements, vacations, and unexpected expenses such as car repairs and medical bills, through some 1,800 locations in North America. The company also writes home equity, mortgage, and refinance loans. Founded in 1912 as Commercial Credit, the company was bought by former Citigroup chairman and CEO Sandy Weill in 1986. Weill, who retired in 2006, used the acquisition as a springboard to build what eventually grew into Citigroup.

	Annual Growth	12/04	12/05	12/06	12/07	12/08
Est. sales ($ mil.)	—	—	—	—	—	1.8
Employees	—	—	—	—	—	18

CITIGROUP INC.

NYSE: C

399 Park Ave.
New York, NY 10043
Phone: 212-559-1000
Fax: —
Web: www.citigroup.com

CEO: Vikram S. Pandit
CFO: John C. Gerspach
HR: Paul D. McKinnon
FYE: December 31
Type: Public

This is the Citi. One of the largest financial services firms known to man, Citigroup (also known as Citi) has some 200 million customer accounts and does business in more than 140 countries. Citigroup offers deposits and loans (mainly through Citibank), investment banking, brokerage, wealth management, and other financial services. Reeling from $90 billion in writedowns and losses on mortgage-related securities and other investments, Citigroup has restructured itself into two primary segments — the regional consumer and institutional banking units of Citicorp and the brokerage and consumer finance units of Citi Holdings. The major reorganization hives off its money-losing assets from its banking divisions.

	Annual Growth	12/05	12/06	12/07	12/08	12/09
Assets ($ mil.)	5.6%	1,494,037.0	1,884,318.0	2,187,631.0	1,938,470.0	1,856,646.0
Net income ($ mil.)	—	24,638.0	21,538.0	3,617.0	(27,684.0)	(1,511.0)
Market value ($ mil.)	(48.9%)	1,406,393.5	1,614,179.3	853,167.7	194,455.0	95,923.4
Employees	(3.2%)	307,000	337,000	387,000	326,900	269,000

CITIZEN WATCH COMPANY OF AMERICA, INC.

1000 W. 190th St.
Torrance, CA 90502
Phone: 800-321-1023
Fax: 310-532-8171
Web: www.citizenwatch.com

CEO: Laurence R. Grunstein
CFO: —
HR: —
FYE: March 31
Type: Subsidiary

Where most people hear the ticking of the second hand, Citizen Watch Company of America also hears the ringing of the till. The company is the North American sales and marketing arm of Japan-based Citizen Watch. Citizen Watch's products include designs for sports, casual, and fashion wear for men and women. Focusing on technology, Citizen Watch boasts the slimmest LCD watch, one that uses voice recognition, and a professional dive watch with electronic depth sensor. Its Eco-Drive collection of environmentally friendly timepieces is fueled by light, rather than a battery. The company sells is products through retail jewelry and department stores. Its Japanese parent bought rival Bulova in 2008.

CITIZENS & NORTHERN CORPORATION

NASDAQ (CM): CZNC

90-92 Main St.
Wellsboro, PA 16901
Phone: 570-724-3411
Fax: 570-723-8097
Web: www.cnbankpa.com

CEO: Charles H. Updegraff Jr.
CFO: Mark A. Hughes
HR: —
FYE: December 31
Type: Public

Citizens & Northern is the holding company for Citizens & Northern Bank and First State Bank, commercial banks that serve north-central Pennsylvania and southern New York. The banks through 24 offices provide checking and savings accounts, IRAs, and CDs. The company's lending activities mainly consist of residential mortgages (nearly 60% of its loan portfolio) and commercial mortgages (more than 25%). Subsidiary Citizens & Northern Investment provides investment services; Bucktail Life Insurance provides credit, life, and property/casualty reinsurance. In 2005 Citizens & Northern acquired Canisteo Valley (holding company of First State Bank), expanding its operations into New York.

	Annual Growth	12/05	12/06	12/07	12/08	12/09
Assets ($ mil.)	3.3%	1,163.0	1,127.4	1,283.7	1,281.6	1,321.8
Net income ($ mil.)	—	13.0	12.0	10.4	10.1	(39.3)
Market value ($ mil.)	(21.5%)	304.5	264.0	213.7	239.4	115.6
Employees	(5.5%)	354	346	353	297	282

CITIZENS BANCSHARES CORPORATION

OTC: CZBS

75 Piedmont Ave. NE
Atlanta, GA 30302
Phone: 404-659-5959
Fax: 678-406-4039
Web: www.ctbconnect.com

CEO: James E. Young
CFO: Samuel J. Cox
HR: Wanda Nesbit
FYE: December 31
Type: Public

Citizens Bancshares was not founded by the proletariat, but it does share the wealth with its stockholders. One of the largest minority-owned financial institutions in the US, Citizens Bancshares is the holding company for Citizens Trust Bank, a regional commercial bank serving central Georgia and Alabama from about 10 branch offices. The bank provides traditional services such as checking and savings accounts, NOW and money market accounts, CDs, IRAs, credit cards, and investment services. Its lending portfolio includes mortgages secured by property in metropolitan Atlanta, small business loans, and consumer installment loans.

	Annual Growth	12/05	12/06	12/07	12/08	12/09
Assets ($ mil.)	4.2%	328.6	335.2	338.4	348.1	387.5
Net income ($ mil.)	(18.8%)	2.3	3.0	2.9	1.0	1.0
Market value ($ mil.)	(27.1%)	22.4	24.6	20.1	5.5	6.3
Employees	(2.3%)	147	133	126	127	134

CITIZENS COMMUNITY BANCORP, INC.

NASDAQ (GM): CZWI

2174 EastRidge Center
Eau Claire, WI 54701
Phone: 715-836-9994
Fax: —
Web: www.citizenscommunityfederal.net

CEO: Edward H. Schaefer
CFO: John D. Zettler
HR: —
FYE: September 30
Type: Public

Citizens Community Bancorp is the holding company for Citizens Community Federal, a community bank with about two dozen branches in Wisconsin, southern Minnesota, and northern Michigan. Serving consumers and businesses, the bank offers standard deposit services such as savings, checking, money market, and retirement accounts, as well as a variety of loan products. The bank focuses its lending activities on one- to four-family mortgages, which represent more than half of its loan portfolio. The bank also offers consumer loans such as auto and personal loans; it does not routinely make commercial loans. Founded in 1938, Citizens Community was a state-chartered credit union until 2001.

	Annual Growth	9/05	9/06	9/07	9/08	9/09
Assets ($ mil.)	23.7%	245.7	284.0	386.1	480.0	575.4
Net income ($ mil.)	—	1.1	0.4	0.7	1.5	(3.2)
Market value ($ mil.)	(7.7%)	33.4	50.2	48.3	37.1	24.3
Employees	23.9%	123	149	161	217	290

CITIZENS FINANCIAL CORP.

OTC: CIWV

213 3rd St.
Elkins, WV 26241
Phone: 304-636-4095
Fax: 304-636-6924
Web: www.cnbelkins.com

CEO: Robert J. (Bob) Schoonover
CFO: Nathaniel S. Bonnell
HR: Tanya Markley
FYE: December 31
Type: Public

The proletariat should not confuse Citizens Financial with Citizens Financial Corporation (in Kentucky), Citizens Financial Group (Rhode Island), or Citizens Financial Services (Pennsylvania). *This* Citizens Financial is the holding company of Citizens National Bank, which has about a half-dozen offices in central and eastern West Virginia. Citizens National Bank offers savings and checking accounts, consumer and commercial loans, trust services, and other financial services and products. Real estate loans — including mortgages, home equity loans, and construction loans — account for some 80% of the bank's lending portfolio.

	Annual Growth	12/04	12/05	12/06	12/07	*12/08
Assets ($ mil.)	7.2%	213.8	238.2	243.0	246.6	282.5
Net income ($ mil.)	(14.7%)	1.7	2.0	2.1	1.0	0.9
Market value ($ mil.)	(17.6%)	27.7	31.4	35.7	20.6	12.8
Employees	(3.8%)	98	94	91	88	84
					*Most recent year available

CITIZENS FINANCIAL GROUP

1 Citizens Plaza
Providence, RI 02903
Phone: 401-456-7000
Fax: 401-456-7819
Web: www.citizensbank.com

CEO: Ellen Alemany
CFO: John Fawcett
HR: Evelyn B. Tressitt
FYE: December 31
Type: Subsidiary

One of the largest foreign-owned banks in the country, Citizens Financial Group is the US banking arm of Royal Bank of Scotland (RBS). The parent of Citizens Bank and Charter One Bank has more than 1,600 branches — about a third of them in supermarkets — in the Northeast (Connecticut, Delaware, Massachusetts, New Hampshire, New Jersey, New York, Pennsylvania, Rhode Island, and Vermont) and the Midwest (Illinois, Michigan, Ohio); the company expanded into the latter region by buying superregional bank Charter One in 2004. It operates in five business groups: commercial markets, commercial finance, commercial real estate finance, consumer and business banking, and global transaction services.

	Annual Growth	12/04	12/05	12/06	12/07	12/08
Assets ($ mil.)	4.0%	136,666.4	155,184.3	—	159,940.0	159,925.0
Net income ($ mil.)	—	1,027.7	1,472.5	—	1,489.0	(930.0)
Employees	(2.4%)	25,000	26,000	—	—	22,700

An in-depth profile of this company is available to Hoover's Online members at hoovers.com.

379

CITIZENS FINANCIAL SERVICES, INC.

OTC: CZFS

15 S. Main St.
Mansfield, PA 16933
Phone: 570-662-2121
Fax: 570-662-3278
Web: www.firstcitizensbank.com

CEO: Randall E. (Randy) Black
CFO: Mickey L. Jones
HR: Cynthia T. (Cindy) Pazzaglia
FYE: December 31
Type: Public

Citizens Financial Services is an upstanding resident of the financial community. The holding company for First Citizens National Bank serves north-central Pennsylvania's Tioga, Potter, and Bradford counties and southern New York. Through some 15 branches, the bank offers checking, savings, time, and deposit accounts as well as real estate, commercial, industrial, residential, and consumer loans. Residential mortgage loans account for more than half of the bank's total loan portfolio. The Trust and Investment division offers investment advice and employee benefits coordination, as well as estate and retirement planning services. Insurance is offered through the First Citizen's Insurance Agency subsidiary.

	Annual Growth	12/05	12/06	12/07	12/08	12/09
Assets ($ mil.)	8.4%	529.2	572.2	591.0	668.6	729.5
Net income ($ mil.)	16.9%	5.3	5.8	6.7	6.9	9.9
Market value ($ mil.)	6.4%	57.8	62.8	56.4	55.5	74.0
Employees	2.3%	168	158	184	188	184

CITIZENS FIRST BANCORP, INC.

NASDAQ (GS): CTZN

525 Water St.
Port Huron, MI 48060
Phone: 810-987-8300
Fax: 810-987-7537
Web: www.cfsbank.com

CEO: Marshall J. Campbell
CFO: Thomas J. Young
HR: —
FYE: December 31
Type: Public

Citizens First Bancorp is the holding company for Citizens First Savings Bank, which serves the "thumb" of Michigan's Lower Peninsula through about two dozen locations. The bank attracts deposits from local individuals, businesses, and municipalities by offering such products as savings, checking, and money market accounts; certificates of deposit; and trust services. Real estate loans (including one- to four-family mortgages, commercial and multi-family mortgages, residential construction loans, and home equity loans and lines of credit) make up about three-quarters of Citizens First Bancorp's loan portfolio. Subsidiaries offer title insurance, mutual funds, and annuities.

	Annual Growth	12/04	12/05	12/06	12/07	*12/08
Assets ($ mil.)	8.9%	1,393.4	1,654.2	1,775.1	1,804.4	1,960.5
Net income ($ mil.)	—	8.2	9.0	9.1	1.9	(58.4)
Market value ($ mil.)	(45.7%)	198.9	193.8	252.8	100.9	17.3
Employees	3.4%	349	390	442	434	399

*Most recent year available

CITIZENS FIRST CORPORATION

NASDAQ (GM): CZFC

1805 Campbell Ln.
Bowling Green, KY 42104
Phone: 270-393-0700
Fax: 270-393-0716
Web: www.citizensfirstbank.com

CEO: M. Todd Kanipe
CFO: Steve Marcum
HR: Tonia Harris
FYE: December 31
Type: Public

Citizens First puts the folks of southwestern Kentucky before all else. Founded in 1975 as a small private-investment club, Citizens First is the holding company for Citizens First Bank, which serves consumers and area businesses through about a dozen locations and 20 ATMs. The company's loan portfolio includes primarily commercial and residential mortgages and business loans. The company also provides title insurance services. Through alliances with other firms, it offers its customers trust and investment services as well as insurance products. Fellow Kentucky bank Porter Bancorp withdrew its offer to acquire a controlling stake in Citizens First in late 2009.

	Annual Growth	12/05	12/06	12/07	12/08	12/09
Assets ($ mil.)	15.2%	195.5	338.8	346.4	355.1	344.2
Net income ($ mil.)	—	2.2	2.2	1.3	(5.6)	(1.6)
Market value ($ mil.)	(23.7%)	32.8	31.3	20.0	7.0	11.1
Employees	7.9%	65	119	132	107	88

CITIZENS HOLDING COMPANY

NYSE Amex: CIZN

521 Main St.
Philadelphia, MS 39350
Phone: 601-656-4692
Fax: 601-656-4183
Web: www.citizensholdingcompany.com

CEO: Greg L. McKee
CFO: Robert T. Smith
HR: —
FYE: December 31
Type: Public

Citizens Holding Company has taken the proletariat approach to banking. The firm is the holding company for The Citizens Bank of Philadelphia, Mississippi, which operates some 20 locations in the eastern part of the state. Founded in 1908, the bank targets individuals and local businesses, offering products such as checking and savings accounts, money market accounts, CDs, IRAs, and trust services. Lending activities consist mostly of real estate loans (about 70% of the loan portfolio) and commercial, industrial, and agricultural loans (more than 10%). Citizens Holding offers discount brokerage services through an agreement with First Tennessee Bank. Subsidiary Title Services offers title insurance.

	Annual Growth	12/05	12/06	12/07	12/08	12/09
Assets ($ mil.)	8.4%	607.7	621.2	680.9	766.0	840.0
Net income ($ mil.)	(2.9%)	8.0	8.4	6.9	8.3	7.1
Market value ($ mil.)	(0.2%)	108.9	108.0	88.0	101.5	108.2
Employees	3.3%	250	252	279	292	285

CITIZENS, INC.

NYSE: CIA

400 E. Anderson Ln.
Austin, TX 78752
Phone: 512-837-7100
Fax: 512-836-9785
Web: www.citizensinc.com

CEO: Harold E. Riley
CFO: Kay E. Osbourn
HR: —
FYE: December 31
Type: Public

Citizens aims to prepare its customers for two of life's certainties: living and dying. A holding company, Citizens provides ordinary life insurance in niche markets outside the US through its various operating subsidiaries. Through its CICA Life Insurance Company, it issues life insurance in US dollars to wealthy individuals in Latin America and Taiwan. On the other end of the economic and life spectrum, its Home Service segment sells life insurance to lower-income individuals in Louisiana, primarily to cover final expenses and burial costs. Chairman and CEO Harold E. Riley, who founded Citizens in 1969, is the controlling shareholder of the company.

	Annual Growth	12/05	12/06	12/07	12/08	12/09
Assets ($ mil.)	(24.0%)	661.9	711.2	787.9	832.3	220.3
Net income ($ mil.)	34.4%	5.3	6.7	14.6	(15.7)	17.3
Market value ($ mil.)	4.6%	270.8	327.9	274.8	482.0	324.5
Employees	3.2%	550	490	155	540	625

CITIZENS REPUBLIC BANCORP, INC.

NASDAQ (CM): CRBC

328 S. Saginaw St.
Flint, MI 48502
Phone: 810-766-7500
Fax: 810-342-7090
Web: www.citizensonline.com

CEO: Cathleen H. (Cathy) Nash
CFO: Lisa M. McNeely
HR: Susan P. Brockett
FYE: December 31
Type: Public

Attention, Citizens of the Republic! Citizens Republic Bancorp is the holding company for Citizens Bank, which operates nearly 220 branches primarily in Michigan, but also in Wisconsin, Ohio, and Indiana. In addition to consumer and commercial banking, Citizens Republic Bancorp also offers wealth management, brokerage services, mutual funds, annuities, and trust services. Commercial loans, including real estate, construction, and industrial loans, make up approximately 60% of the company's portfolio; consumer loans represent about 25%. Citizens sold its F&M Bank-Iowa subsidiary to Great Western Bank in 2010.

	Annual Growth	12/05	12/06	12/07	12/08	12/09
Assets ($ mil.)	11.4%	7,751.9	14,008.4	13,506.0	13,086.0	11,931.6
Net income ($ mil.)	—	80.5	63.3	100.8	(393.1)	(514.2)
Market value ($ mil.)	(60.3%)	10,944.3	10,451.3	5,722.6	1,175.3	272.1
Employees	0.0%	2,123	2,940	2,501	2,232	2,125

CITIZENS SOUTH BANKING CORPORATION

NASDAQ (GM): CSBC

519 S. New Hope Rd.
Gastonia, NC 28054
Phone: 704-868-5200
Fax: 704-868-5226
Web: www.citizenssouth.com

CEO: Kim S. Price
CFO: Gary F. Hoskins
HR: Betty B. Gaddis
FYE: December 31
Type: Public

Never mind the region, Citizens South Banking Corporation is more concerned about whether interest rates will rise again. The holding company owns Citizens South Bank, which has more than 20 branches in North Carolina and Georgia. The bank offers standard deposit products, such as checking, savings, and money market accounts; CDs; and IRAs. It also issues credit cards, provides retirement planning, and writes business and consumer loans (primarily real estate loans). Its Citizens South Financial Services subsidiary (dba Citizens South Investment Services) sells financial products. The bank moved into Georgia in 2010 when it acquired the failed Bank of Hiawassee in an FDIC-assisted deal.

	Annual Growth	12/05	12/06	12/07	12/08	12/09
Assets ($ mil.)	3.1%	701.1	743.4	779.1	817.2	791.5
Net income ($ mil.)	—	3.3	5.5	5.7	3.1	(30.0)
Market value ($ mil.)	(21.3%)	109.1	118.1	92.4	54.7	41.8
Employees	(1.1%)	160	151	160	164	153

CITRIX SYSTEMS, INC.

NASDAQ (GS): CTXS

851 W. Cypress Creek Rd.
Fort Lauderdale, FL 33309
Phone: 954-267-3000
Fax: 954-267-9319
Web: www.citrix.com

CEO: Mark B. Templeton
CFO: David J. Henshall
HR: David R. Friedman
FYE: December 31
Type: Public

Citrix Systems is taking connectivity to the next level. The company provides access infrastructure products that enable PCs, IP phones, and other devices to remotely and securely access applications across wired and wireless networks, freeing customers from facing the difficult task of installing and updating software on each piece of hardware. Its product line includes application virtualization software, VPN appliances, and password management tools, with most applications capable of being deployed in both Windows and UNIX-based computing environments. The company also offers online managed services for meetings and presentations, technical support, and remote desktop access.

	Annual Growth	12/05	12/06	12/07	12/08	12/09
Sales ($ mil.)	15.4%	908.7	1,134.3	1,391.9	1,583.4	1,614.1
Net income ($ mil.)	3.5%	166.3	183.0	214.5	178.3	191.0
Market value ($ mil.)	9.7%	5,336.5	5,024.5	7,060.3	4,378.1	7,729.0
Employees	11.0%	3,171	3,742	4,620	5,040	4,816

CITY HOLDING COMPANY

NASDAQ (GS): CHCO

25 Gatewater Rd.
Cross Lanes, WV 25313
Phone: 304-769-1100
Fax: 304-769-1111
Web: www.cityholding.com

CEO: Charles R. (Skip) Hageboeck
CFO: David L. Bumgarner
HR: Craig G. Stilwell
FYE: December 31
Type: Public

"Take Me Home, Country Roads" may be the (unofficial) state song of West Virginia, but City Holding hopes all roads lead to its City National Bank of West Virginia subsidiary, which operates some 70 branches in the Mountaineer State and in neighboring areas of southern Ohio and eastern Kentucky. Targeting individuals and regional businesses, the bank offers standard deposit products, loans, credit cards, Internet banking, and trust and investment services. City Holding also runs an insurance agency subsidiary, City Insurance Professionals.

	Annual Growth	12/05	12/06	12/07	12/08	12/09
Assets ($ mil.)	1.2%	2,502.6	2,507.8	2,482.8	2,582.4	2,622.5
Net income ($ mil.)	(4.1%)	50.3	53.2	51.0	28.1	42.6
Market value ($ mil.)	(2.6%)	567.4	645.4	534.1	548.9	509.9
Employees	1.2%	770	779	811	827	809

CITY NATIONAL CORPORATION

NYSE: CYN

City National Plaza, 555 S. Flower St.
Los Angeles, CA 90071
Phone: 310-888-6000
Fax: 310-888-6045
Web: www.cnb.com

CEO: Russell D. Goldsmith
CFO: Christopher J. (Chris) Carey
HR: Marianne Lamutt
FYE: December 31
Type: Public

For celebrity sightings, forget the Hollywood Homes Tour and camp out at City National Bank. With nearly 70 branches in Southern California, the San Francisco Bay area, Nevada, and New York City, the subsidiary of City National Corporation has been known as "Bank to the Stars" since opening in Beverly Hills, California in the 1950s. It offers a variety of services, including personal and business banking, investment management and advisory, and trust services. The bank focuses on providing customized service, tailoring its offerings to the needs of its high-powered clientele. Its target market consists of small to mid-sized businesses, entrepreneurs, professionals, and affluent individuals.

	Annual Growth	12/05	12/06	12/07	12/08	12/09
Assets ($ mil.)	9.6%	14,581.9	14,884.4	15,889.3	16,455.5	21,078.8
Net income ($ mil.)	(31.6%)	234.7	233.5	222.7	105.0	51.3
Market value ($ mil.)	(10.9%)	3,761.1	3,696.7	3,091.8	2,528.5	2,367.6
Employees	4.4%	2,539	3,000	2,914	2,989	3,017

THE CITY UNIVERSITY OF NEW YORK

535 E. 80th St.
New York, NY 10075
Phone: 212-794-5555
Fax: 212-209-5600
Web: www.cuny.edu

CEO: Matthew Goldstein
CFO: Ernesto Malave
HR: Pamela S. Silverblatt
FYE: June 30
Type: School

The City University of New York (CUNY) is the big "U" in the Big Apple. The college has more than 20 campuses in the five boroughs of New York City and is the US's largest urban university system. About 480,000 undergraduate, graduate, and continuing education students (from 205 countries) are enrolled at CUNY, which has 11 senior colleges, six community colleges, a doctoral-granting graduate school, a law school, the School of Professional Studies, and The Sophie Davis School of Biomedical Education. Its 1,750 academic programs range from specialized, career-oriented courses to traditional liberal arts curricula. CUNY employs some 6,700 full-time teaching faculty members.

	Annual Growth	6/04	6/05	6/06	6/07	6/08
Est. sales ($ mil.)	—	—	—	—	—	1.4
Employees	—	—	—	—	—	33,642

CITYBANK

Pink Sheets: CTBK

14807 Highway 99
Lynnwood, WA 98087
Phone: 425-745-5933
Fax: —
Web: www.citybankwa.com

CEO: Conrad Hanson
CFO: Chantha Bunphoath
HR: Belinda J. Faylona
FYE: December 31
Type: Public

CityBank urbanely operates about 10 branches and loan production offices in Snohomish and King counties in northwestern Washington State. Personal and business banking products include such standard fare as checking and savings accounts, money market accounts, CDs, and individual retirement accounts. Additional investment services for individuals include stocks, bonds, mutual funds, and annuities. Construction loans make up more than half of the company's loan portfolio. In 2005 the company sold its merchant and debit card processing business to NOVA Information Systems (now Elavon) and online data retrieval subsidiary Diligenz to Corporation Service Company.

	Annual Growth	12/04	12/05	12/06	12/07	*12/08
Assets ($ mil.)	18.7%	667.4	832.0	1,077.7	1,239.0	1,325.5
Net income ($ mil.)	—	19.0	22.8	37.0	41.5	(60.8)
Market value ($ mil.)	(31.8%)	379.9	373.8	564.3	353.4	82.0
Employees	(12.2%)	254	159	150	138	151

*Most recent year available

An in-depth profile of this company is available to Hoover's Online members at hoovers.com.

CITYSEARCH

8833 Sunset Blvd.
West Hollywood, CA 90069
Phone: 310-360-4500
Fax: —
Web: www.citysearch.com

CEO: Jay Herratti
CFO: John Cherry
HR: Dena Grablowsky
FYE: December 31
Type: Business segment

This online enterprise tracks down things to do all around town. Citysearch is a leading provider of local entertainment and business listings on the Internet, operating city-specific Web sites covering metropolitan areas across the US. In addition to searchable listings, the sites offer a variety of reviews and guides to help people find the best restaurants, night clubs, and other attractions that their city has to offer. Citysearch also provides local information on more than a dozen areas in Australia, Canada, and Europe. The company is part of Barry Diller's Internet conglomerate IAC/InterActiveCorp (IAC). It operates alongside other IAC Web sites such as Ask.com, Evite, and Match.com.

	Annual Growth	12/04	12/05	12/06	12/07	12/08
Est. sales ($ mil.)	—	—	—	—	—	300.0
Employees	—	—	—	—	—	29

C.J. SEGERSTROM & SONS, LLC

3315 Fairview Rd.
Costa Mesa, CA 92626
Phone: 714-546-0110
Fax: 714-546-9835

CEO: Sandra (Sandy) Segerstrom-Daniels
CFO: Mark L. Heim
HR: Nancy West
FYE: December 31
Type: Private

One of the largest real estate empires in California has been built on . . . lima beans. The C.J. Segerstrom real estate empire built its crown jewel, South Coast Plaza, in 1967 on the family's former lima bean farm in Orange County, California. The giant 2.8 million sq. ft. mall has since become one of the highest-grossing shopping centers in the US (surpassing $1 billion a year, with nearly 300 stores). The family also has interests in hotels, apartments, an industrial park, and several office buildings, including the Offices of South Coast Plaza, a 21-story high-rise. The company has long courted the tourist trade, and has invested in the local performing arts center to lure visitors.

CKE RESTAURANTS, INC.

NYSE: CKR

6307 Carpinteria Ave., Ste. A
Carpinteria, CA 93013
Phone: 805-745-7500
Fax: 714-490-3630
Web: www.ckr.com

CEO: Andrew F. Puzder
CFO: Theodore (Ted) Abajian
HR: —
FYE: January 31
Type: Public

There's really nothing junior about this company, other than the name of its flagship hamburger chain. CKE Restaurants is a leading fast-food operator with more than 3,100 company-owned and franchised eateries across the country. Its Carl's Jr. chain, known for its signature Six Dollar Burger, includes more than 1,200 locations primarily in California and other western states. CKE also owns Hardee's Food Systems, which operates and franchises more than 1,900 Hardee's locations, mostly in the Midwest and Southeast. About 900 of CKE's restaurants are corporate-owned, while the rest are franchised. The company has agreed to be taken private by investment firm Apollo Management.

	Annual Growth	1/06	1/07	1/08	1/09	1/10
Sales ($ mil.)	(1.7%)	1,518.3	1,588.4	1,534.6	1,482.7	1,418.7
Net income ($ mil.)	(29.5%)	194.6	50.2	31.1	37.0	48.2
Market value ($ mil.)	(14.5%)	865.3	1,093.1	725.4	458.9	462.2
Employees	(7.4%)	29,000	30,000	26,000	23,000	21,300

CKX, INC.

NASDAQ (GS): CKXE

650 Madison Ave.
New York, NY 10022
Phone: 212-838-3100
Fax: 212-872-1473
Web: ir.ckx.com

CEO: Michael G. Ferrel
CFO: Thomas P. Benson
HR: —
FYE: December 31
Type: Public

CKX is ready to sing "Viva Las Vegas," but any performance will be critiqued by *American Idol*'s Simon Cowell. The company controls 85% of Elvis Presley Enterprises, which manages the King's estate and licenses his likeness, songs, and name, and operates tours of Graceland. CKX also owns 19 Entertainment, the firm responsible for the *American Idol* TV show. Additionally, CKX has an 80% stake in the name, image, likeness, and intellectual property of Muhammad Ali. Entertainment impresario Robert Sillerman owns about 20% of the company. CKX is reportedly exploring a takeover offer from *Idol* creator Simon Fuller and former Barclays Capital banker Roger Jenkins that values the company at about $600 million.

	Annual Growth	12/05	12/06	12/07	12/08	12/09
Sales ($ mil.)	28.5%	120.6	210.2	266.8	288.1	328.4
Net income ($ mil.)	—	(5.9)	9.2	12.1	19.0	26.4
Market value ($ mil.)	(18.3%)	1,100.0	992.5	1,015.4	341.5	490.5
Employees	6.3%	487	564	619	629	621

CKX LANDS, INC.

NYSE Amex: CKX

751 Bayou Pines East
Lake Charles, LA 70601
Phone: 337-310-0547
Fax: —

CEO: Joseph K. Cooper
CFO: Brian R. Jones
HR: —
FYE: December 31
Type: Public

Revenues come naturally to CKX Lands. The company owns or has stakes in about 14,000 acres in Louisiana that contain oil and gas wells, mines, timber, and agricultural operations. Formed in 1930, the company does not perform any of these operations and is not involved in oil and gas exploration. Instead, it generates revenues through royalties from the natural resources produced on its land. Originally set up to receive mineral royalties spun off by a bank to its shareholders, CKX Lands' growth strategy is built around acquiring land in southwestern Louisiana. Its largest customers, Mayne and Mertz and Cox & Perkins, account for nearly 40% of sales.

	Annual Growth	12/05	12/06	12/07	12/08	12/09
Sales ($ mil.)	(10.9%)	2.7	2.7	3.3	3.3	1.7
Net income ($ mil.)	(15.9%)	1.6	1.5	2.8	2.0	0.8
Market value ($ mil.)	2.8%	20.5	25.8	22.8	26.3	22.9
Employees	0.0%	4	4	5	5	4

CLAIMSNET.COM, INC.

OTC: CLAI

14860 Montfort Dr., Ste. 250
Dallas, TX 75254
Phone: 972-458-1701
Fax: 972-458-1737
Web: www.claimsnet.com

CEO: Don Crosbie
CFO: Laura M. Bray
HR: —
FYE: December 31
Type: Public

Say good-bye to those cramped little boxes! Claimsnet.com has put the insurance claims process online. Founded in 1996, Claimsnet lets insurance companies and other health care payers log on to a Web site and file all claims information to doctors, provider organizations, and other medical and dental services providers. It collects transaction, implementation, development, license, and support fees for this service. In 2008 the company acquired Acceptius, a provider of data processing services catering to the health care industry; the deal allows Claimsnet to offer its customers conversion and claims repricing.

	Annual Growth	12/05	12/06	12/07	12/08	12/09
Sales ($ mil.)	14.1%	1.3	1.5	1.6	2.1	2.2
Net income ($ mil.)	—	(0.3)	(0.4)	(0.5)	(0.6)	(0.4)
Market value ($ mil.)	(10.9%)	6.6	6.6	5.6	5.2	4.2
Employees	5.1%	9	12	11	18	11

CLAIRE'S STORES, INC.

3 SW 129th Ave.
Pembroke Pines, FL 33027
Phone: 954-433-3900
Fax: 954-433-3999
Web: www.clairestores.com

CEO: Eugene S. (Gene) Kahn
CFO: J. Per Brodin
HR: MaryAnn Wagner
FYE: January 31
Type: Private

If the difference between men and boys is the price of their toys, for young women and girls, it may be the price of their accessories. For thrifty, fashion-conscious females ages 3 to 27, Claire's Stores is the queen of costume jewelry, handbags, and hair bows. The company operates nearly 3,000 boutiques, primarily in malls, under the Claire's and Icing banners. The chain is present in all 50 US states, Puerto Rico, the US Virgin Islands, and Canada, as well as about 10 European countries. Founded by Rowland Schaefer and later run by his daughters, Bonnie and Marla Schaefer, Claire's Stores was sold to an affiliate of the New York-based private equity firm Apollo Management for about $3 billion in 2007.

	Annual Growth	1/05	1/06	1/07	1/08	1/09
Sales ($ mil.)	(6.5%)	—	—	—	1,510.8	1,413.0
Net income ($ mil.)	—	—	—	—	(43.1)	(643.6)
Employees	(5.9%)	—	—	—	18,700	17,600

CLARCOR INC.

NYSE: CLC

840 Cresent Centre Dr., Ste. 600
Franklin, TN 37067
Phone: 615-771-3100
Fax: 615-771-5603
Web: www.clarcor.com

CEO: Norman E. (Norm) Johnson
CFO: David J. Fallon
HR: —
FYE: November 30
Type: Public

CLARCOR cleans up with filters. The company's industrial and environmental filtration unit makes air and antimicrobial filters for commercial, industrial, and residential buildings, along with filters used in industrial processes. Brands include Airguard, Facet, and Purolator. Companies in CLARCOR's engine and mobile filtration business make products under brands such as Baldwin and Clark that filter the air, oil, fuel, coolant, and hydraulic fluids used in car, truck, heavy equipment, and marine engines. CLARCOR's consumer packaging group makes custom-designed metal, plastic, and composite containers for food, drug, toiletry, and chemical products.

	Annual Growth	11/05	11/06	11/07	11/08	11/09
Sales ($ mil.)	1.0%	874.0	904.3	921.2	1,059.6	907.7
Net income ($ mil.)	(1.6%)	76.4	82.7	90.7	95.7	71.5
Market value ($ mil.)	1.8%	1,496.4	1,664.8	1,795.9	1,619.4	1,607.3
Employees	(0.4%)	5,034	5,048	5,500	5,500	4,958

CLARENDON INSURANCE GROUP

466 Lexington Ave., 19th Fl.
New York, NY 10017
Phone: 212-790-9700
Fax: 212-790-9801
Web: www.clarendon.biz

CEO: Patrick Fee
CFO: Gary Ropiecki
HR: Helga Selke-Dunn
FYE: December 31
Type: Subsidiary

Clarendon Insurance Group is still there for those who need it, but everyone else needs to go elsewhere. Clarendon Insurance Group was the US-based property and casualty subsidiary of Hannover Re. Clarendon's particular forte was specialty insurance, but all four of its property/casualty insurance companies are now in run off, meaning that they are no longer writing new business and are only servicing existing policies. In 2006 Clarendon spun off its ongoing property and casualty business as a separate entity called Praetorian Financial Group, to assume Clarendon's renewal business. Praetorian Financial was subsequently acquired by QBE Insurance Group.

CLARIAN HEALTH PARTNERS, INC.

1701 N. Senate Blvd.
Indianapolis, IN 46202
Phone: 317-962-2000
Fax: 317-962-4533
Web: www.clarian.org

CEO: Daniel F. (Dan) Evans Jr.
CFO: Marvin Pember
HR: —
FYE: December 31
Type: Not-for-profit

Sound the clarions! Clarian Health Partners has heeded the call for health care for all in the state of Indiana. As one of the largest health systems in the state, not-for-profit Clarian Health owns or is affiliated with more than 20 hospitals and health centers throughout the state, including three major hospitals — Methodist Hospital, Indiana University Hospital, and Riley Hospital for Children — that serve the downtown Indianapolis area with more than 1,300 beds. The largest, Methodist Hospital, features a Level I trauma center and the Methodist Research Institute, which conducts research and clinical trials. The system's hospitals also serve as teaching facilities for Indiana University's medical school.

	Annual Growth	12/04	12/05	12/06	12/07	12/08
Est. sales ($ mil.)	—	—	—	—	—	2,478.3
Employees	—	—	—	—	—	17,242

CLARIANT CORPORATION

4000 Monroe Rd.
Charlotte, NC 28205
Phone: 704-331-7000
Fax: 704-331-7825
Web: www.clariant-northamerica.com

CEO: Kenneth (Ken) Golder
CFO: Kenneth (Ken) Golder
HR: David Jarrett
FYE: December 31
Type: Subsidiary

Clariant Corporation is clearly into the chemicals business. The company is divided into four segments: Textile, Leather, and Paper Chemicals; Functional Chemicals; Pigments and Additives; and Masterbatches (which are color and additive concentrates). As the North American subsidiary of Swiss specialty chemicals maker Clariant Ltd, Clariant Corp. oversees operations in Canada and the US and has about 25 manufacturing facilities and service centers throughout the US and Canada. It accounts for about a quarter of its parent's total sales. Customers include the agriculture, automotive, plastics, pharmaceutical, printing, and textile industries.

CLARIENT, INC.

NASDAQ (CM): CLRT

31 Columbia
Aliso Viejo, CA 92656
Phone: 949-425-5700
Fax: 949-425-5701
Web: www.clarientinc.com

CEO: Ronald A. (Ron) Andrews Jr.
CFO: Michael R. Rodriguez
HR: —
FYE: December 31
Type: Public

Clarient can help provide clarity for cancer patients and their physicians. The firm is a specialized diagnostic services provider, offering a collection of advanced tests that detect and monitor the progression of various types of cancer. Its services aim to not only find malignancies, but also to provide information doctors use to prescribe the most effective treatments. In addition to testing materials, Clarient provides pathology lab services and delivers the test results via its PATHSiTE web portal. The primary targets for its services are community hospitals and pathology groups that outsource all or most of their specialized testing functions.

	Annual Growth	12/05	12/06	12/07	12/08	12/09
Sales ($ mil.)	46.1%	20.1	33.6	43.0	73.7	91.6
Net income ($ mil.)	—	(14.8)	(15.9)	(8.8)	(9.6)	(6.1)
Market value ($ mil.)	19.5%	111.2	147.1	175.3	139.4	226.6
Employees	26.9%	139	204	208	269	361

An in-depth profile of this company is available to Hoover's Online members at hoovers.com.

383

CLARION CORPORATION OF AMERICA

6200 Gateway Dr.
Cypress, CA 90630
Phone: 310-327-9100
Fax: 310-327-1999
Web: www.clarion.com

CEO: Tom Hayashi
CFO: —
HR: —
FYE: March 31
Type: Subsidiary

Clarion Corporation of America wants your car stereo to be loud and Clarion. The company markets and distributes electronic entertainment, communications, security, and navigation products for automobiles and boats to retailers, distributors, and carmakers such as Ford, Honda, and Nissan. The company's products include audio amplifiers, car stereos, mobile CB radios, navigation and computing systems, satellite radio systems, and subwoofers and other speakers. Established in 1967, Clarion Corporation of America is the US sales and marketing subsidiary of Japan-based electronics manufacturer Clarion Co.

	Annual Growth	3/04	3/05	3/06	3/07	3/08
Est. sales ($ mil.)	—	—	—	—	—	272.7
Employees	—	—	—	—	—	243

CLARION TECHNOLOGIES, INC.

Pink Sheets: CLAR

4595 Broadmoor SE, Ste. 300
Grand Rapids, MI 49512
Phone: 616-698-7277
Fax: 616-698-1296
Web: www.clariontechnologies.com

CEO: Steven W. (Steve) Olmstead
CFO: John Brownlow
HR: —
FYE: December 31
Type: Public

Clarion Technologies has answered the clarion call for injection-molded products. The company is a custom manufacturer of injection-molded plastic products for the automotive and consumer goods industries. Auto products include interior and exterior trim parts and door panel components. Clarion's products for the consumer goods market include parts for refrigerators and other home appliances, as well as drawer components and trim. Clarion's major customers include Electrolux Home Products, Ford, and Lear Corporation. The company has production facilities in the US (Michigan and South Carolina) and Mexico (Juarez).

CLARK CONSTRUCTION GROUP, LLC

7500 Old Georgetown Rd.
Bethesda, MD 20814
Phone: 301-272-8100
Fax: 301-272-1928
Web: www.clarkus.com

CEO: Peter C. (Pete) Forster
CFO: Timothy R. (Tim) Yost
HR: Jeff Jasnoff
FYE: December 31
Type: Subsidiary

Clark Construction Group, a major hitter on the roster of companies held by Clark Enterprises, hammers home runs with its landmark convention center and sports stadium projects. The commercial, institutional, and heavy construction group also builds office complexes, hotels, airport terminals, correctional facilities, manufacturing facilities, water treatment plants, highways and bridges, and high-rise apartments. It offers construction management, design/build, and general contracting services. Recent projects include the new McCormick Place West Hall Expansion in Chicago, the Hobby Airport expansion in Houston, Washington, DC's US Institute of Peace headquarters, and the ballpark for the Washington Nationals.

	Annual Growth	12/04	12/05	12/06	12/07	12/08
Est. sales ($ mil.)	—	—	—	—	—	3.0
Employees	—	—	—	—	—	2,500

CLARK CONSULTING

2100 Ross Ave., Ste. 2200
Dallas, TX 75201
Phone: 214-871-8717
Fax: 214-720-6050
Web: www.clarkconsulting.com

CEO: Kurt J. Laning
CFO: —
HR: Shannon Jud
FYE: December 31
Type: Subsidiary

Clark Consulting tries to make sure businesses can manage their executive and employee benefits obligations. The firm provides benefits and compensation consulting services to companies in a wide range of industries, along with banks and health care enterprises. It helps develop and implement benefit plans to cover retirement and disability, and administers executive benefit and insurance plans. Specialties include corporate-owned life insurance (COLI) and bank-owned life insurance (BOLI). Overall, Clark Consulting serves about 3,000 clients throughout the US. The firm is a subsidiary of insurance provider AEGON USA.

CLARK ENTERPRISES, INC.

7500 Old Georgetown Rd., 15th Fl.
Bethesda, MD 20814
Phone: 301-657-7100
Fax: 301-657-7263
Web: www.clarkenterprisesinc.com

CEO: A. James Clark
CFO: James J. Brinkman
HR: —
FYE: December 31
Type: Private

Like Clark Kent, this firm holds some super powers. Privately owned Clark Enterprises has holdings in real estate, private equity, venture capital, construction companies, and other investments. Its real estate holdings include some 5 million sq. ft. of office space, 15,000 residential units, and 300,000 sq. ft. of warehouse space. The company's flagship subsidiary, The Clark Construction Group, has more than $4 billion in annual revenue and is a top US contractor that performs construction management, general contracting, design, and consulting services. Other Clark units include residential builder Seawright Homes, Clark Realty Capital, and highway construction company Shirley Contracting.

	Annual Growth	12/04	12/05	12/06	12/07	12/08
Sales ($ mil.)	13.8%	2,800.0	2,844.0	3,220.0	4,220.0	4,700.0
Employees	7.4%	3,200	4,200	4,200	4,200	4,250

CLARK UNIVERSITY

950 Main St.
Worcester, MA 01610
Phone: 508-793-7711
Fax: 508-793-7724
Web: www.clarku.edu

CEO: John Bassett
CFO: Andrea Michaels
HR: Lynn Olson
FYE: May 31
Type: School

If you don't want to live in the dark, get an education at Clark! Clark University is a private, co-educational liberal arts university with an enrollment of more than 2,200 undergraduate students and roughly 900 graduate students. It offers about 30 undergraduate majors (psychology is the most popular) and about two dozen master's degree programs. The university was founded in 1887 as the first all-graduate school in the US. Clark College began educating undergraduates in 1902, and was combined into the university in 1920. Clark University has been a pioneer in the academic study of geography; it has awarded more doctorates in the discipline than any other US school.

CLARUS CORPORATION

NASDAQ (GM): BDE

2084 E. 3900 South
Salt Lake City, UT 84124
Phone: 801-278-5552
Fax: —
Web: www.claruscorp.com

CEO: Warren B. Kanders
CFO: Philip A. Baratelli
HR: —
FYE: December 31
Type: Public

Before the market downturn stormed its revenues, Clarus helped clear up cloudy supply chain processes. In its heyday the company provided procurement and sourcing software that could automate the purchase and management of such operating resources. Clarus liquidated its assets and signaled its intention to target the outdoor equipment and lifestyle markets. In May 2010 Clarus announced plans to spend about $135 million to purchase Black Diamond Equipment (equipment for rock climbers) and Gregory Mountain Products (technical backpacking and mountaineering products); the purchases were completed in June 2010. As part of the deals the company plans to change its name to Black Diamond Equipment.

	Annual Growth	12/05	12/06	12/07	12/08	12/09
Sales ($ mil.)	—	0.0	0.0	0.0	0.0	0.0
Net income ($ mil.)	—	(1.3)	(1.3)	0.1	(2.4)	(4.8)
Market value ($ mil.)	(15.5%)	145.0	122.4	102.5	73.8	73.8
Employees	7.5%	6	7	10	11	8

CLASSIFIED VENTURES, LLC

175 W. Jackson Blvd., Ste. 800
Chicago, IL 60604
Phone: 312-601-5000
Fax: 312-601-5755
Web: www.classifiedventures.com

CEO: Daniel A. (Dan) Jauernig
CFO: Richard W. (Dick) Burke Jr.
HR: Richard W. (Dick) Burke Jr.
FYE: December 31
Type: Joint venture

You don't need top secret clearance to work with Classified Ventures. It operates a network of websites offering classified advertising space primarily for real estate and automobile sales. Its sites, including Apartments.com (rental listings), Cars.com (new and used autos), and HomeGain.com (home sales), also distribute their content to a network of 170 Web sites owned and operated by newspapers and television stations around the country, as well as top portal operators such as Yahoo! and MSN. Classified Ventures is a partnership of five leading media companies: A. H. Belo, Gannett, McClatchy, Washington Post, and Tribune Company.

CLASSMATES ONLINE, INC.

333 Elliott Ave. W.
Seattle, WA 98119
Phone: 206-301-5700
Fax: —
Web: www.classmates.com

CEO: Steven B. (Steve) McArthur
CFO: Peter Wiederspan
HR: Brett Thompson
FYE: December 31
Type: Subsidiary

Maybe you didn't care much for your classmates while you were in school, but now that you've long since graduated, aren't you curious? Classmates Online hopes so. The company operates Classmates.com, a Web site that reunites classmates, friends and family, teachers, co-workers, and military personnel. Its database contains some 50 million people from schools, places of work, and the military. The Web site, which operates in the US and Canada, was founded in 1995. Classmates Online is a subsidiary of Classmates Media Corporation, which is controlled by Internet service provider United Online (UOL).

CLAYTON, DUBILIER & RICE, INC.

375 Park Ave., 18th Fl.
New York, NY 10152
Phone: 212-407-5200
Fax: 212-407-5252
Web: www.cdr-inc.com

CEO: Donald J. Gogel
CFO: —
HR: —
FYE: December 31
Type: Private

Clayton, Dubilier & Rice (CD&R) specializes in turnaround situations. The private equity firm typically acquires noncore units of large corporations and works with existing management to improve operations. Since it was formed in 1978, CD&R has raised more than $11 billion in capital (including $4 billion for its latest fund), and has invested in more than 40 businesses in the US and Europe. In 2007 the company led an investor group that bought ServiceMaster, and joined with Bain Capital and The Carlyle Group to buy the wholesale construction supply business of The Home Depot for about $8.5 billion. Each firm owns a third of the unit, known as HD Supply.

	Annual Growth	12/04	12/05	12/06	12/07	12/08
Est. sales ($ mil.)	—	—	—	—	—	1,100.3
Employees	—	—	—	—	—	15,500

CLAYTON HOLDINGS LLC

2 Corporate Dr., Ste. 800
Shelton, CT 06484
Phone: 203-926-5600
Fax: 203-926-5750
Web: www.clayton.com

CEO: Paul T. Bossidy
CFO: Peter Kushel
HR: —
FYE: December 31
Type: Private

Clayton Holdings provides technology-based services to help mortgage lenders, investors, and other financial services firms manage their operations and risk. It offers operations support, loan and portfolio analysis, and consulting for lenders and capital markets firms, and it provides transaction management, compliance, and other software. Clayton's Independent Pricing Service provides credit risk management services and risk-filtering technologies for the fixed-income securities market. The company also supplies mortgage professionals on a temporary staffing basis. Private equity firm Greenfield Partners took Clayton Holdings private for about $133 million in 2008.

CLAYTON HOMES, INC.

5000 Clayton Rd.
Maryville, TN 37802
Phone: 865-380-3000
Fax: 865-380-3742
Web: www.claytonhomes.com

CEO: Kevin T. Clayton
CFO: John J. Kalec
HR: Sharon G. Kennedy
FYE: December 31
Type: Subsidiary

If you lived in a Clayton you'd be home right now. A Berkshire Hathaway subsidiary, Clayton Homes builds one- and two-story modular and manufactured houses and other buildings that range in price from $20,000 to more than $130,000 for upscale models and range in size from around 700 to more than 3,000 sq. ft. The homes are built at about 35 plants and distributed across the US through a network of about 1,800 mostly independent, but also company-owned retailers. Clayton's homes often contain products from fellow Berkshire Hathaway companies such as Shaw flooring, Johns Manville insulation, and MiTek fasteners. Clayton Homes also offers home financing, loan-servicing, and insurance through subsidiaries.

	Annual Growth	12/04	12/05	12/06	12/07	12/08
Est. sales ($ mil.)	—	—	—	—	—	3,200.0
Employees	—	—	—	—	—	14,000

An in-depth profile of this company is available to Hoover's Online members at hoovers.com.

385

CLAYTON WILLIAMS ENERGY, INC.

NASDAQ (GM): CWEI

6 Desta Dr., Ste. 3000
Midland, TX 79705
Phone: 432-682-6324
Fax: 432-688-3247
Web: www.claytonwilliams.com

CEO: Clayton W. Williams
CFO: Mel G. Riggs
HR: LuAnn Bolding
FYE: December 31
Type: Public

Former Texas gubernatorial candidate Clayton Williams once devoted his energy to politics. Now he's devoted to the independent oil and gas firm that he founded. Clayton Williams Energy explores for oil and gas deposits primarily in Louisiana, New Mexico, and Texas and exploits those resources. In 2009 the company reported proved reserves of 33.6 million barrels of oil equivalent, located mainly in the Permian Basin and East Texas. It has stakes in 6,750 gross producing oil and gas wells and 1.1 million gross undeveloped acres. It also operates 94 miles of gas pipeline and a small natural gas processing infrastructure in Texas and Mississippi. Williams is CEO, and his family controls about 52% of the firm.

	Annual Growth	12/05	12/06	12/07	12/08	12/09
Sales ($ mil.)	(2.5%)	283.6	266.0	393.9	565.5	256.0
Net income ($ mil.)	—	0.3	17.8	6.0	140.5	(117.4)
Market value ($ mil.)	(4.3%)	507.0	441.0	378.5	551.9	425.5
Employees	15.7%	174	180	186	202	312

CLEAN DIESEL TECHNOLOGIES, INC.

NASDAQ (CM): CDTI

300 Atlantic St., Ste. 702
Stamford, CT 06901
Phone: 203-327-7050
Fax: 203-323-0461
Web: www.cdti.com

CEO: Michael L. Asmussen
CFO: John B. (Jack) Wynne Jr.
HR: —
FYE: December 31
Type: Public

Clean Diesel Technologies has developed a few cool technologies to counteract global warming. The company is starting to commercialize its chemical fuel additives and other products for reducing diesel engine emissions and improving fuel economy. These include its platinum fuel catalysts, which are marketed in Europe and the US under the Platinum Plus brand. Clean Diesel Technologies also manufactures and licenses nitrogen oxide reduction systems (under the brand name ARIS) and chemical fuel additives to help control diesel engine emissions. The company has a licensing deal with Mitsui to use the ARIS technology.

	Annual Growth	12/05	12/06	12/07	12/08	12/09
Sales ($ mil.)	10.7%	0.8	1.1	4.9	7.5	1.2
Net income ($ mil.)	—	(5.4)	(5.4)	(4.5)	(9.4)	(6.7)
Market value ($ mil.)	(26.7%)	41.1	73.9	188.9	21.3	11.8
Employees	1.9%	13	15	17	21	14

CLEAN ENERGY FUELS CORP.

NASDAQ (GM): CLNE

3020 Old Ranch Pkwy., Ste. 200
Seal Beach, CA 90740
Phone: 562-493-2804
Fax: 562-493-4532
Web: www.cleanenergyfuels.com

CEO: Andrew J. Littlefair
CFO: Richard R. Wheeler
HR: —
FYE: December 31
Type: Public

Forget cooking with gas — Clean Energy Fuels is driving with gas. Natural gas, that is. The company owns and/or supplies 184 natural gas fueling stations across the US and Canada. These enable Clean Energy's 320-plus fleet customers to tank up their more than 17,200 fleet vehicles with compressed natural gas (CNG) or liquefied natural gas (LNG). Clean Energy also helps customers buy and finance natural gas vehicles and obtain government incentives. The company buys CNG from local utilities and produces LNG at its two plants (in California and Texas) with a combined capacity of 260,000 gallons per day. Founder and billionaire oilman T. Boone Pickens and wife Madeleine own 54% of Clean Energy.

	Annual Growth	12/05	12/06	12/07	12/08	12/09
Sales ($ mil.)	13.9%	78.0	91.5	117.7	129.5	131.5
Net income ($ mil.)	—	17.3	(77.5)	(8.9)	(40.9)	(33.2)
Market value ($ mil.)	0.9%	—	—	921.5	367.6	937.9
Employees	22.4%	102	84	121	140	229

CLEAN HARBORS, INC.

NYSE: CLH

42 Longwater Dr.
Norwell, MA 02061
Phone: 781-792-5000
Fax: 781-792-5900
Web: www.cleanharbors.com

CEO: Alan S. McKim
CFO: James M. Rutledge
HR: —
FYE: December 31
Type: Public

One of North America's leading hazardous-waste management companies, Clean Harbors does more than its name suggests. Clean Harbors' technical services, which account for most of the company's sales, encompass the collection, transportation, treatment, and disposal of hazardous waste, including chemical and laboratory waste but not nuclear waste. The company's 100 service locations include nine landfills, six incineration locations, and six wastewater treatment centers. Among Clean Harbors' more than 47,000 customers are commercial and industrial companies, educational and research organizations, and health care providers. Alan McKim, the company's chairman and CEO, controls 12% of Clean Harbors.

	Annual Growth	12/05	12/06	12/07	12/08	12/09
Sales ($ mil.)	10.9%	711.2	829.8	946.9	1,030.7	1,074.2
Net income ($ mil.)	9.4%	25.6	46.7	44.2	57.5	36.7
Market value ($ mil.)	19.9%	757.1	1,272.2	1,358.7	1,667.2	1,566.6
Employees	13.2%	3,900	4,574	4,769	4,804	6,399

[H] CLEAR CHANNEL COMMUNICATIONS, INC.

200 E. Basse Rd.
San Antonio, TX 78209
Phone: 210-822-2828
Fax: 210-822-2299
Web: www.clearchannel.com

CEO: Mark P. Mays
CFO: Thomas W. (Tom) Casey
HR: Bill Feehan
FYE: December 31
Type: Private

This company leaves few open channels on the radio dial. Clear Channel Communications is the #1 radio company in the US, with about 900 stations that reach more than 110 million people. Its Premier Radio Networks produces syndicated radio content for more than 5,000 stations. Clear Channel also sells spot advertising for about 4,000 radio stations and 600 TV stations through Katz Media. In addition to radio, the company owns a 90% stake in Clear Channel Outdoor Holdings, one of the world's largest outdoor advertising companies with about 840,000 display locations worldwide. The company is owned by CC Media Holdings, an investment group led by Thomas H. Lee Partners and Bain Capital.

CLEAR CHANNEL OUTDOOR HOLDINGS, INC.

NYSE: CCO

2201 E. Camelback Rd., Ste. 500
Phoenix, AZ 85016
Phone: 602-381-5700
Fax: 602-381-5782
Web: www.clearchanneloutdoor.com

CEO: Mark P. Mays
CFO: Thomas W. (Tom) Casey
HR: Jonathan Walsh
FYE: December 31
Type: Public

In the great outdoors, billboards in clear view mean money for Clear Channel Outdoor Holdings. The company is a leading display advertising operator, with about 840,000 properties in some 50 countries. Besides billboards, the company sells advertising on buses and trains and on "street furniture" such as bus stops and information kiosks in metropolitan markets. On its 200,000 display spots in the Americas and another 640,000 internationally, the company sells advertising space in airports and malls and on the sides of high-profile buildings, and also creates displays that feature video and moving parts. Clear Channel Communications, the #1 radio broadcaster, owns about 90% of the company.

	Annual Growth	12/05	12/06	12/07	12/08	12/09
Sales ($ mil.)	0.3%	2,666.1	2,897.7	3,281.8	3,289.3	2,698.0
Net income ($ mil.)	—	61.6	153.1	246.0	(2,851.1)	(868.2)
Market value ($ mil.)	(15.2%)	7,136.1	9,933.6	9,844.7	2,188.9	3,698.0
Employees	(4.5%)	7,600	7,700	7,900	7,400	6,311

CLEARFIELD, INC.

NASDAQ (GM): CLFD

5480 Nathan Ln. North, Ste. 120
Plymouth, MN 55442
Phone: 763-476-6866
Fax: 763-475-8457
Web: www.clearfieldconnection.com

CEO: Cheri P. Beranek
CFO: Bruce G. Blackey
HR: —
FYE: September 30
Type: Public

Clearfield provides fiber optic-cable and related optical networking equipment. Products include fiber distribution panels and cable management systems, optical components (couplers, multiplexers, and splitters), and copper and fiber-optic cable assemblies. It sells directly to telecom service providers and OEMs. Formerly called APA Enterprises, the company merged its operations with those of its primary subsidiary, APA Cables & Networks (APACN), and changed its name to Clearfield in 2008. Previously the company also operated an optronics unit, but it exited that business in 2007.

	Annual Growth	3/06	3/07	*9/07	9/08	9/09
Sales ($ mil.)	12.2%	15.7	18.6	10.3	23.5	24.9
Net income ($ mil.)	—	(3.3)	(2.1)	(1.3)	1.5	3.8
Market value ($ mil.)	22.9%	23.4	14.6	12.5	13.9	53.4
Employees	(3.1%)	128	133	107	112	113

*Fiscal year change

CLEARONE COMMUNICATIONS, INC.

NASDAQ (CM): CLRO

5225 Wiley Post Way, Ste. 500
Salt Lake City, UT 84116
Phone: 801-975-7200
Fax: 801-977-0087
Web: www.clearone.com

CEO: Zeynep (Zee) Hakimoglu
CFO: Narsi Narayanan
HR: —
FYE: June 30
Type: Public

ClearOne Communications wants voices to carry, loud and clear. The company provides audio conferencing systems to small and large enterprises, educational institutions, churches, and government agencies largely in the US. It also sells related products including microphones and equipment carts. ClearOne's conferencing systems connect large venues such as auditoriums and boardrooms, as well as desktops and small conference rooms. The company markets its products worldwide, selling primarily through distributors who in turn sell to systems integrators and resellers. Former ClearOne chairman Edward Bagley owns about 20% of the company.

	Annual Growth	6/05	6/06	6/07	6/08	6/09
Sales ($ mil.)	3.1%	31.6	37.6	39.9	39.8	35.7
Net income ($ mil.)	(39.2%)	16.1	2.1	5.2	5.7	2.2
Market value ($ mil.)	(6.0%)	33.0	31.3	42.0	35.2	25.8
Employees	(4.7%)	125	127	105	103	103

CLEARPOINT BUSINESS RESOURCES, INC.

OTC: CPBR

1600 Manor Dr., Ste. 110
Chalfont, PA 18914
Phone: 215-997-7710
Fax: 215-997-7711
Web: www.clear-point.com

CEO: Michael D. (Mike) Traina
CFO: John G. (Jack) Phillips
HR: —
FYE: December 31
Type: Public

ClearPoint Business Resources aims to score points with customers by helping them obtain temporary employees. Through its iLabor online platform, the company enables customers to find temporary staff members from ClearPoint-approved third-party staffing vendors. Customers use ClearPoint's StaffPillar technology to manage human resources, including permanent as well as contract employees. ClearPoint, through third-party vendors, also offers business process outsourcing (BPO) services and project-based staffing in industries such as distribution, logistics, and transportation.

	Annual Growth	12/05	12/06	12/07	12/08	12/09
Sales ($ mil.)	(83.5%)	—	—	191.7	33.5	5.2
Net income ($ mil.)	—	—	—	(12.4)	(38.8)	(3.1)
Market value ($ mil.)	(93.1%)	—	—	69.5	1.6	0.3
Employees	(44.8%)	—	—	46	16	14

CLEARWATER PAPER CORPORATION

NYSE: CLW

601 W. Riverside, Ste. 1100
Spokane, WA 99201
Phone: 509-344-5900
Fax: —
Web: www.clearwaterpaper.com

CEO: Gordon L. Jones
CFO: Linda K. Massman
HR: Thomas H. Carter
FYE: December 31
Type: Public

No pulp fiction here — the story of Clearwater Paper is real and true. The company manufactures bleached paperboard, used by its customers to make packaging for foods, liquids, pharmaceuticals, and toiletries, along with paper plates and cups and blister packaging. Clearwater also supplies bleached softwood market pulp, which it sells to other manufacturers, and slush pulp, which it uses to make private-label tissue products for consumers. Its wood products business provides framing and finishing lumber for construction, and supplies wood chips to the company's pulp and paperboard business. Potlatch Corp. spun off Clearwater Paper in late 2008. The company makes most of its sales in the US.

	Annual Growth	12/05	12/06	12/07	12/08	12/09
Sales ($ mil.)	4.1%	—	1,106.7	1,173.3	1,255.3	1,250.1
Net income ($ mil.)	105.3%	—	21.1	25.6	9.7	182.5
Market value ($ mil.)	555.2%	—	—	—	96.3	630.9
Employees	0.2%	—	—	2,490	2,460	2,500

CLEARWIRE CORPORATION

NASDAQ (GS): CLWR

4400 Carillon Point
Kirkland, WA 98033
Phone: 425-216-7600
Fax: 425-216-7900
Web: www.clearwire.com

CEO: William T. (Bill) Morrow
CFO: Erik E. Prusch
HR: Laurent J. Bentitou
FYE: December 31
Type: Public

Clearwire operates a wireless broadband network that provides services to about 475,000 subscribers primarily in the US and Europe. The company offers such services as high-speed Internet access and computer telephony. Its service areas cover more than 50 markets located mainly along the West Coast and in Texas, Florida, North Carolina, and the Midwest. Internationally, Clearwire serves broadband users in Belgium, Ireland, Spain, Denmark (through Danske Telecom), and Mexico (through partner MVSNet). The company was founded in 2003 and is controlled by wireless pioneer Craig McCaw (founder of the one-time leading cellular service McCaw Cellular).

	Annual Growth	12/05	12/06	12/07	12/08	12/09
Sales ($ mil.)	69.2%	33.5	100.2	151.4	20.5	274.5
Net income ($ mil.)	—	(139.9)	(284.2)	(727.5)	(432.6)	(325.6)
Market value ($ mil.)	(29.8%)	—	—	12,962.9	4,661.4	6,391.6
Employees	40.3%	—	1,245	1,990	1,635	3,440

CLEARY GOTTLIEB STEEN & HAMILTON LLP

1 Liberty Plaza
New York, NY 10006
Phone: 212-225-2000
Fax: 212-225-3999
Web: www.cgsh.com

CEO: Mark A. Walker
CFO: Renée M. Lercher
HR: Georgia Emery Gray
FYE: December 31
Type: Partnership

Cleary Gottlieb Steen & Hamilton may be a big cheese in the Big Apple, but the law firm also has made a name for itself in the international arena. Cleary Gottlieb's attorneys work from about a dozen offices scattered across the globe and are known for their work in such practice areas as corporate finance, mergers and acquisitions, litigation, and intellectual property. The firm boasts about 1,100 attorneys, with almost half of those based outside the US. Representative clients have included British Airways, Deutsche Telekom, Nortel, and other international corporations. The firm was founded in 1946 by former Root Clark Buckner partners George Cleary, Leo Gottlieb, Fowler Hamilton, and Mel Steen.

An in-depth profile of this company is available to Hoover's Online members at hoovers.com.

387

CLEAVER-BROOKS, INC.

11950 W. Lake Park Dr.
Milwaukee, WI 53224
Phone: 414-359-0600
Fax: 414-438-4930
Web: www.cleaver-brooks.com

CEO: Welch P. Goggins
CFO: Jeffrey G. Beine
HR: —
FYE: March 31
Type: Private

Cleaver-Brooks (C-B) can stand a lot of heat. Through six business lines, the company makes boilers, burners, controls, and other boiler room components along with oil and gas burners. Its boiler products include complete integrated systems and specialty and custom-made boilers used in heating and manufacturing applications. Its burners and generators help refiners and manufacturers re-use exhaust heat and control emissions. C-B also offers aftermarket parts, engineering services, retrofitting, and training to its industrial, commercial, and institutional customers. About 1,500 representatives attend Boiler University so they can sell C-B products worldwide.

	Annual Growth	3/04	3/05	3/06	3/07	3/08
Est. sales ($ mil.)	—	—	—	—	—	209.7
Employees	—	—	—	—	—	1,000

CLECO CORPORATION

NYSE: CNL

2030 Donahue Ferry Rd.
Pineville, LA 71360
Phone: 318-484-7400
Fax: 318-484-7488
Web: www.cleco.com

CEO: Michael H. (Mike) Madison
CFO: Darren J. Olagues
HR: —
FYE: December 31
Type: Public

Down in the Louisiana bayous, Cleco comes alive with the click of a light switch. The holding company's utility unit, Cleco Power, generates, transmits, and distributes electricity to approximately 273,000 residential and business customers in 107 communities in Louisiana. Cleco Power has a generating capacity of about 1,360 MW from its interests in fossil-fueled power plants. It also purchases power from other utilities and energy marketers, and it sells some excess power to wholesale customers. Subsidiary Cleco Midstream Resources develops merchant power plants (with 1,355 MW of unregulated capacity) and offers energy management services.

	Annual Growth	12/05	12/06	12/07	12/08	12/09
Sales ($ mil.)	(1.9%)	920.2	1,000.7	1,030.6	1,080.2	853.8
Net income ($ mil.)	(12.7%)	182.6	74.6	151.8	102.1	106.3
Market value ($ mil.)	7.0%	1,265.3	1,531.1	1,687.1	1,385.5	1,658.6
Employees	3.0%	1,158	2,067	1,216	1,023	1,305

CLEMSON UNIVERSITY

1 Clemson University
Clemson, SC 29634
Phone: 864-656-3311
Fax: 864-656-0812
Web: www.clemson.edu

CEO: James F. Barker
CFO: Brett A. Dalton
HR: Lawrence Nichols II
FYE: December 31
Type: School

Clemson University provides South Carolina with the best of both academic worlds: a small college environment with top-tier academics and research. The state's top-ranked university, Clemson is also nationally recognized in several academic areas, and aims to be among the nation's Top 20 by 2011. Clemson was founded in 1889 with a bequest from plantation owner Thomas Green Clemson. It began accepting students in 1893, and from then until 1955 was an all-male military college. These days the land-grant school is fully coeducational and instructs lots of civilians; it offers undergraduate degrees in more than 70 areas of study and graduate degrees in 100 programs to a student body of only 17,500.

	Annual Growth	12/04	12/05	12/06	12/07	12/08
Est. sales ($ mil.)	—	—	—	—	—	436.7
Employees	—	—	—	—	—	4,961

CLEVELAND BIOLABS, INC.

NASDAQ (CM): CBLI

73 High St.
Buffalo, NY 14203
Phone: 716-849-6810
Fax: —
Web: www.cbiolabs.com

CEO: Michael Fonstein
CFO: John A. Marhofer Jr.
HR: —
FYE: December 31
Type: Public

Cleveland BioLabs' scientists are working hard to develop drugs that help healthy cells stay that way, as well as drugs that promote cell death in cancerous tumors. The company has based its research on the suppression and stimulation of the process known as apoptosis, a form of cell-death that occurs after exposure to radiation, toxic chemicals, or internal stresses. In development are two product lines: protectans (suppressing apoptosis in healthy cells after radiation exposure) and curaxins (stimulating apoptosis in some forms of cancer). Protectans have applications in reducing side effects from cancer treatment and terrorist or nuclear events, while curaxins are being developed as anticancer therapies.

	Annual Growth	12/05	12/06	12/07	12/08	12/09
Sales ($ mil.)	89.9%	1.1	1.7	2.0	4.7	14.3
Net income ($ mil.)	—	(2.4)	(7.2)	(27.0)	(14.0)	(12.8)
Market value ($ mil.)	(13.1%)	—	134.5	234.9	56.9	88.4
Employees	12.2%	24	35	48	33	38

THE CLEVELAND CLINIC FOUNDATION

9500 Euclid Ave.
Cleveland, OH 44195
Phone: 216-444-2200
Fax: —
Web: www.clevelandclinic.org

CEO: Delos M. (Toby) Cosgrove
CFO: Steven C. Glass
HR: Brian J. Bolwell
FYE: December 31
Type: Foundation

Cleveland may be home to the Rock and Roll Hall of Fame, but you don't have to have the rocking pneumonia or the boogie woogie flu to visit another Cleveland institution: The Cleveland Clinic. The heart of the Cleveland Clinic Foundation, the not-for-profit hospital has more than 1,300 beds and specializes in cardiac care, digestive disease treatment, and urological and kidney care, along with medical education and research opportunities. The clinic campus includes an international care center, a children's hospital, an outpatient center, and several research institutes. The Cleveland Clinic Foundation network also includes 10 community hospitals and additional health clinics in northeast Ohio.

	Annual Growth	12/04	12/05	12/06	12/07	12/08
Est. sales ($ mil.)	—	—	—	—	—	4,399.0
Employees	—	—	—	—	—	20,000

CLEVELAND TRACK MATERIAL, INC.

6917 Bessemer Ave.
Cleveland, OH 44127
Phone: 216-641-4000
Fax: 216-641-0882
Web: www.clevelandtrack.com

CEO: William H. Willoughby
CFO: —
HR: —
FYE: December 31
Type: Subsidiary

If you need railroad track, you can get aboard the Cleveland Track Material (CTM) train. The company manufactures railroad trackwork and components. Products include bridge joints, compromise joints, crossing diamonds, joint bars, paneled turnouts, rocker clips, slip switches, and switch points. CTM also provides maintenance services for railroads throughout North America from its locations in Cleveland and Memphis. In 2007 the company was acquired by Germany's Vossloh AG in a deal worth about $43 million. CTM became part of the German company's Switch Systems business unit.

	Annual Growth	12/04	12/05	12/06	12/07	12/08
Est. sales ($ mil.)	—	—	—	—	—	45.3
Employees	—	—	—	—	—	260

CLICKER INC.

OTC: CLKZ

2355 Main St., Ste. 120
Irvine, CA 92614
Phone: 949-486-3990
Fax: 949-486-3995
Web: www.clickerinc.com

CEO: Albert Aimers
CFO: Albert Aimers
HR: —
FYE: August 31
Type: Public

This company is much more interested in the mouse than the remote control. Clicker operates a network of Web sites focused around such topics as celebrity news, classified advertising, investing, and sports. Its online properties include the ForWant (classified ads), Sippin' It (celebrity news and gossip), SportsGulp, and Wall Street Network (investment community). Most of its sites include social networking functions to help foster interactivity and generate revenue through advertising and rewards programs. Chairman and CEO Albert Aimers owns nearly 45% of Clicker.

	Annual Growth	8/05	8/06	8/07	8/08	8/09
Sales ($ mil.)	(41.8%)	—	6.6	7.1	7.8	1.3
Net income ($ mil.)	—	—	(1.6)	(5.9)	(2.9)	(3.3)
Market value ($ mil.)	(87.5%)	—	19,167.3	2,936.3	5,301.6	37.5
Employees	(33.1%)	—	30	42	22	9

CLIF BAR & COMPANY

1610 5th St.
Berkeley, CA 94710
Phone: 510-558-7855
Fax: 510-558-7872
Web: www.clifbar.com

CEO: Gary J. Erickson
CFO: Richard (Rich) Boragno
HR: Claudia Perkins
FYE: December 31
Type: Private

Clif Bar found a toehold in a niche market and has climbed steadily up ever since. The company is a leading maker of natural energy, nutrition, and snack bars. Its high-carbohydrate CLIF and LUNA bars are aimed at sports enthusiasts and busy folk of all stripes and are distributed in bike shops, outdoor stores, and natural food markets, as well as grocery stores, convenience stores, and other retail outlets nationwide. In addition to its CLIF and LUNA bars, the company offers various iterations of its product, including MOJO, and Builder's bars, along with children's versions called ZBar and Organic Twisted Fruit. The company also sells CLIF Shots — energy drinks and gels fortified with electrolytes.

	Annual Growth	12/04	12/05	12/06	12/07	12/08
Sales ($ mil.)	—	—	—	—	—	212.0
Employees	—	—	—	—	—	230

CLIFFS NATURAL RESOURCES INC.

NYSE: CLF

200 Public Sq., Ste. 3300
Cleveland, OH 44114
Phone: 216-694-5700
Fax: 216-694-4880
Web: www.cliffsnaturalresources.com

CEO: Joseph A. Carrabba
CFO: Laurie Brlas
HR: William A. Brake Jr.
FYE: December 31
Type: Public

Cliffs Natural Resources' favorite period in history? The Iron Age, hands down. The company produces iron ore pellets, a key component of steelmaking, and owns or holds stakes in six iron ore properties that represent almost half of North America's iron ore production. Cliffs' operations, including Northshore Mining and Empire Iron, produce more than 38 million tons of iron ore pellets annually. Cliffs sells its ore primarily in North America but also in Europe and China. The company owns Australian iron properties that supply the Asia/Pacific region. It also has iron ore interests in Latin America, specifically Brazil.

	Annual Growth	12/05	12/06	12/07	12/08	12/09
Sales ($ mil.)	7.7%	1,739.5	1,921.7	2,275.2	3,609.1	2,342.0
Net income ($ mil.)	(6.9%)	272.4	280.1	270.0	515.8	204.3
Market value ($ mil.)	20.1%	2,998.8	3,280.2	6,825.8	3,468.4	6,242.1
Employees	7.2%	4,085	4,189	5,298	5,711	5,404

CLIFFSTAR CORPORATION

1 Cliffstar Ave.
Dunkirk, NY 14048
Phone: 716-366-6100
Fax: 716-363-1030
Web: www.cliffstar.com

CEO: Paul J. Harder
CFO: Dale R. Payne
HR: Tamara Bellanti
FYE: December 31
Type: Private

Cliffstar gets really jazzed up about juice. The company is one of the largest private-label juice providers in the US, offering more than 145 customized formulas for a garden full of flavors, including apple, cranberry, grape, grapefruit, lemon, orange, prune, tomato, and vegetable. It also provides enhanced fitness waters, sports drinks, and bottled teas. The company's customers include grocery chains, mass merchandisers, and foodservice providers in both Canada and the US. The Cliffstar Corporation is privately owned by members of the founding Star family, which put the company up for sale in 2009.

CLIFTON GUNDERSON LLP

10001 Innovation Dr., Ste. 201
Milwaukee, WI 53226
Phone: 414-476-1880
Fax: 414-476-7286
Web: www.cliftoncpa.com

CEO: Krista McMasters
CFO: David E. Bailey
HR: Todd C. Craft
FYE: May 31
Type: Partnership

From its Midwest roots, Clifton Gunderson has branched out to spread its All-American brand of accounting. The firm offers accounting, auditing, business valuation, management consulting, and tax services to clients in industries including agribusiness, health care, manufacturing, and others. Subsidiaries provide financial planning, technology consulting, and investment services. The firm also provides international services through an affiliation with HLB International, a member organization that represents more than 100 nations. Clifton Gunderson was founded in 1960 and has more than 45 offices across the US.

	Annual Growth	5/04	5/05	5/06	5/07	5/08
Sales ($ mil.)	—	—	—	—	—	253.0
Employees	—	—	—	—	—	2,000

CLIFTON SAVINGS BANCORP, INC.

NASDAQ (GS): CSBK

1433 Van Houten Ave.
Clifton, NJ 07015
Phone: 973-473-2200
Fax: 973-473-0451
Web: www.cliftonsavings.com

CEO: Walter Celuch
CFO: Christine R. Piano
HR: Josephine T. Scavone
FYE: March 31
Type: Public

You don't need CliffsNotes to figure out that Clifton Savings Bancorp is the holding company of Clifton Savings Bank, which operates about a dozen branches in northeastern New Jersey's Bergen and Passaic counties. Founded in 1928, the bank serves consumer and business clients, offering checking and savings accounts, IRAs, CDs, and mortgages and other loans. Its lending portfolio is dominated by real estate loans, primarily one- to four-family residential mortgages; the bank also issues multifamily and commercial real estate, construction, and consumer loans. Bank subsidiary Botany manages investments and securities. Mutual holding company Clifton MHC owns a majority of Clifton Savings Bancorp's common stock.

	Annual Growth	3/05	3/06	3/07	3/08	3/09
Assets ($ mil.)	3.3%	841.9	834.9	805.0	899.1	959.8
Net income ($ mil.)	(1.0%)	5.3	3.7	2.5	2.4	5.1
Market value ($ mil.)	(2.8%)	296.6	283.1	316.2	267.0	264.8
Employees	(1.9%)	109	98	96	95	101

An in-depth profile of this company is available to Hoover's Online members at hoovers.com.

389

CLINE DAVIS & MANN, INC.

220 E. 42nd St.
New York, NY 10017
Phone: 212-907-4300
Fax: 212-687-5411
Web: www.clinedavis.com

CEO: Ed Wise
CFO: Joe Magnemi
HR: Gloria Basem
FYE: December 31
Type: Subsidiary

As part of the Diversified Agency Services division of media conglomerate Omnicom Group, Cline Davis & Mann (CDM) provides health care marketing services. It specializes in advertising, sales-force support, and customer marketing services for such international clients as Abbot Laboratories, Boston Scientific, and Solvay Pharmaceuticals. The company also offers expertise in interactive marketing, relationship marketing, and medical education services. CDM's CultureVue unit specializes in marketing to African-American, Hispanic, and Asian-American patients.

CLINICAL DATA, INC.

NASDAQ (GM): CLDA

1 Gateway Center, Ste. 702
Newton, MA 02458
Phone: 617-527-9933
Fax: 617-965-0445
Web: www.clda.com

CEO: Andrew J. (Drew) Fromkin
CFO: C. Evan Ballantyne
HR: Lynn Ferrucci
FYE: March 31
Type: Public

Clinical Data's products and services are central to health and life. The drug development company focuses on late-stage drug candidates with an emphasis on treatments for cancer, as well as cardiovascular and psychiatric disorders. Following a series of acquisitions, divestitures, and reorganizations, Clinical Data has focused its operations around its PGxHealth division, which develops and sells genetic tests and engages in drug discovery research. It performs the bulk of its research in three labs in Virginia and Connecticut; however, the company operates globally and holds US and foreign patents. The publicly traded company is led by CEO Drew Fromkin. Chairman Randal Kirk owns nearly 45% of Clinical Data.

	Annual Growth	3/05	3/06	3/07	3/08	3/09
Sales ($ mil.)	(34.5%)	56.4	68.7	63.7	34.0	10.4
Net income ($ mil.)	—	3.4	(50.9)	(37.5)	(35.3)	(132.4)
Market value ($ mil.)	(0.3%)	290.1	362.7	366.9	491.8	286.3
Employees	(8.1%)	247	472	459	304	176

CLOAKWARE INC.

8219 Leesburg Pike, Ste. 350
Vienna, VA 22182
Phone: 703-752-4830
Fax: 703-752-2412
Web: www.cloakware.com

CEO: Graham Kill
CFO: Jeff McMullen
HR: Patricia Brander
FYE: December 31
Type: Subsidiary

Cloakware provides software and services that customers use to protect their business and digital assets. Its software is designed to help thwart piracy, subscription fraud, and the exploitation of intellectual property and confidential information. Other applications include a password manager that allows passwords to be updated and retrieved automatically as well as products for digital rights management. Cloakware primarily sells to consumer electronics and mobile device manufacturers, content distributors, defense contractors, PC makers, and software developers. The company was founded in 1997 and is part of the Irdeto group of companies, which is owned by Naspers.

	Annual Growth	12/04	12/05	12/06	12/07	12/08
Est. sales ($ mil.)	—	—	—	—	—	13.4
Employees	—	—	—	—	—	90

CLOPAY CORPORATION

8585 Duke Blvd.
Mason, OH 45040
Phone: 513-770-4800
Fax: 513-770-3984
Web: www.clopay.com

CEO: Eugene C. (Gene) Colleran
CFO: Thomas D. Gibbons
HR: Bill Brown
FYE: September 30
Type: Subsidiary

Just like Aldous Huxley and Jim Morrison, Clopay knows something about doors. The company, a subsidiary of Griffon Corporation, makes residential garage door systems. It supplies commercial doors and self-storage systems through its Clopay Building Products Company. Additionally, Clopay Plastic Products Company makes thin-gauge embossed and printed films, elastomeric films, and laminates of film and non-woven fabrics for use in disposable diapers, surgical gowns, and graphic arts applications. Clopay sells its building products under brands that include Clopay, Ideal Door, and Holmes. The company sells most of its garage doors to home remodelers, with the rest going to both new home and commercial builders.

THE CLOROX COMPANY

NYSE: CLX

1221 Broadway
Oakland, CA 94612
Phone: 510-271-7000
Fax: 510-832-1463
Web: www.thecloroxcompany.com

CEO: Donald R. (Don) Knauss
CFO: Daniel J. (Dan) Heinrich
HR: Jacqueline P. (Jackie) Kane
FYE: June 30
Type: Public

Bleach is the cornerstone of Clorox. The company's namesake household cleaning products are world leaders, but Clorox reaches far beyond bleach. While the firm makes and markets laundry and cleaning items (Formula 409, Pine-Sol, Tilex), its products portfolio also extends into dressings/sauces (Hidden Valley, KC Masterpiece), plastic wrap and containers (Glad), cat litters (Fresh Step, Scoop Away), car care products (Armor All, STP), the Brita water-filtration system (in North America), charcoal briquettes (Kingsford, Match Light), and natural personal care products (Burt's Bees).

	Annual Growth	6/05	6/06	6/07	6/08	6/09
Sales ($ mil.)	5.6%	4,388.0	4,644.0	4,847.0	5,273.0	5,450.0
Net income ($ mil.)	(16.3%)	1,096.0	444.0	501.0	461.0	537.0
Market value ($ mil.)	0.0%	7,847.7	8,587.1	8,746.2	7,351.9	7,863.2
Employees	2.2%	7,600	7,600	7,800	8,300	8,300

CLOSETMAID CORPORATION

650 SW 27th Ave.
Ocala, FL 34474
Phone: 352-401-6000
Fax: 352-867-8583
Web: www.closetmaid.com

CEO: Robert (Rob) Clements
CFO: Debbie Charles
HR: —
FYE: September 30
Type: Subsidiary

While most children are scared of monsters in the closet, ClosetMaid customers are more frightened by clutter there. The Emerson Electric subsidiary makes and markets shelving and storage products for organized consumers in the US and abroad. The company's products, sold through home improvement retailers such as Home Depot and Lowe's, are used in closets, laundry areas, kitchens, bathrooms, bedrooms, and garages. Its products are made of wood, laminate, and wire. The company also offers professional design assistance and custom installation. In addition, ClosetMaid owns Stack-A-Shelf, a Canadian manufacturer of shelving and ready-to-assemble furniture.

CLOUD PEAK ENERGY INC.

NYSE: CLD

505 S. Gillette Ave.
Gillette, WY 82718
Phone: 307-687-6000
Fax: 307-687-6015
Web: www.cloudpeakenergy.com

CEO: Colin Marshall
CFO: Michael Barrett
HR: Cary W. Martin
FYE: December 31
Type: Public

Apparently, there's also coal in them there hills. Cloud Peak Energy operates three wholly owned coal mines located in the Powder River Basin of Montana and Wyoming. Its coal is sold mainly to utilities and accounts for 6% of the electricity generated in the US. The company, formerly a subsidiary of Rio Tinto, produces about 100 million tons of coal annually and controls 1 billion tons in proved and probable reserves. It was formed in 1993 as Kennecott Coal, changed its name to Rio Tinto Energy America (RTEA) in 2006, and went public as Cloud Peak Energy two years after that. Rio Tinto retained just less than 50% ownership of Cloud Peak, post-spinoff.

	Annual Growth	12/05	12/06	12/07	12/08	12/09
Sales ($ mil.)	4.3%	1,179.6	1,424.2	1,558.7	1,239.7	1,398.2
Net income ($ mil.)	77.3%	39.8	38.0	32.8	31.1	393.5
Market value ($ mil.)	—	—	—	—	—	458.7
Employees	(21.3%)	—	—	2,469	1,502	1,529

CLOVER TECHNOLOGIES GROUP, L.L.C.

4200 Columbus St.
Ottawa, IL 61350
Phone: 815-431-8100
Fax: 815-431-8120
Web: www.clovertech.com

CEO: James (Jim) Cerkleski
CFO: Dan Ruhl
HR: Dan Ruhl
FYE: December 31
Type: Private

Clover Technologies Group has made its mark inside many a printer. The company designs, manufactures, and distributes consumable printing supplies, including toner cartridges for laser and inkjet printers, copiers, and fax machines. Its supplies work with devices made by such manufacturers as Canon, Dell, Hewlett-Packard, and Lexmark. Clover's products are sold under its Image Excellence and Dataproducts brands, as well as its customers' private label brands. The company also distributes OEM-branded imaging supplies to dealers and resellers across the nation. Clover offers toner cartridge recycling services through its Core Recycling Concepts subsidiary. The company is owned by Clover Holdings, Inc.

	Annual Growth	12/04	12/05	12/06	12/07	12/08
Est. sales ($ mil.)	—	—	—	—	—	22.6
Employees	—	—	—	—	—	1,000

CLUB CAR, INC.

4125 Washington Rd.
Augusta, GA 30917
Phone: 706-863-3000
Fax: 706-863-5808
Web: www.clubcar.com

CEO: Gary Michel
CFO: Matthew O'Donnell
HR: Kevin Erickson
FYE: December 31
Type: Subsidiary

You'll be thankful for Club Car's products on that long par five on the back nine in August. A subsidiary of industrial powerhouse Ingersoll-Rand, Club Car also manufactures utility carts used in industrial, factory, academic, rough terrain, and grounds maintenance applications, in addition to its signature line of golf carts. It offers parts and service to its customers, a growing business for the company. Club Car operates more than 600 dealer, distributor, and factory locations worldwide. The company has been making golf carts since 1958.

	Annual Growth	12/04	12/05	12/06	12/07	12/08
Est. sales ($ mil.)	—	—	—	—	—	78.4
Employees	—	—	—	—	—	1,200

CLUB JENNA, INC.

8390 E. Via De Ventura, Ste. F110 #258
Scottsdale, AZ 85258
Phone: 480-556-9595
Fax: —
Web: www.clubjenna.com

CEO: John G. (Jay) Grdina
CFO: —
HR: —
FYE: January 1
Type: Subsidiary

Membership to this club has some very adult privileges. Club Jenna is an entertainment management company formed by adult film industry megastar Jenna Jameson and her former husband Jay Grdina (an adult film actor and director). The company produces films and videos that are distributed by Vivid Entertainment Group and it licenses Jameson's name and image for other entertainment-related products. Club Jenna also runs Jameson's Web site, which offers subscription-access adult content, as well as more than 150 official sites for other adult entertainment industry stars. Club Jenna is a subsidiary of erotic entertainment pioneer Playboy.

CLUBCORP USA, INC.

3030 LBJ Fwy., Ste. 600
Dallas, TX 75234
Phone: 972-243-6191
Fax: 972-888-7558
Web: www.clubcorp.com

CEO: Eric L. Affeldt
CFO: Curt McClellan
HR: Ingrid Keiser
FYE: December 31
Type: Private

This company makes its green from the green — the golf green, that is. ClubCorp is one of the world's largest operators of golf courses and private clubs with more than 160 facilities throughout the US and in a small number of international locations. Its resorts and golf courses include such well-known venues as Firestone Country Club (Akron, Ohio), The Homestead Club (Hot Springs, Virginia), and Mission Hills Country Club (Rancho Mirage, California). ClubCorp also operates private business and sports clubs. Robert Dedman started the company in 1957. It is owned by private equity firm KSL Capital Partners.

	Annual Growth	12/04	12/05	12/06	12/07	12/08
Sales ($ mil.)	(0.6%)	944.1	1,028.1	1,020.0	897.6	921.0
Employees	(3.6%)	18,500	18,300	18,000	16,000	16,000

CMA CGM (AMERICA) LLC

5701 Lake Wright Dr.
Norfolk, VA 23502
Phone: 757-961-2100
Fax: 757-961-2151
Web: www.cma-cgm.com/USA

CEO: Frank Baragona
CFO: James Arnold
HR: —
FYE: December 31
Type: Subsidiary

The French container shipping giant CMA CGM says, "conteneur;" its US agent, CMA CGM (America), might say, "crate." It's an indispensable way of transporting cargo in today's mobile environment, and CMA CGM (America) plays an equally vital role on behalf of its principal's North American transportation business. CMA CGM (America) offers more than 20 types of services, including arranging for transportation of freight by truck, rail, ship, or intermodal (moving goods, for example, by rail with local delivery by truck) in and out of North America. The company also handles import- and export-related paperwork for its customers. CMA CGM (America) maintains some 25 offices in major trade gateways throughout the US.

An in-depth profile of this company is available to Hoover's Online members at hoovers.com.

391

CMC STEEL FABRICATORS, INC.

1 Steel Mill Dr.	CEO: Russell B. (Russ) Rinn
Seguin, TX 78155	CFO: —
Phone: 830-372-8200	HR: —
Fax: 830-379-9873	FYE: August 31
Web: www.cmcconstructionservices.com	Type: Subsidiary

It's not love for the land, but for steel and concrete that drives CMC Steel Fabricators' purpose. Doing business as CMC Construction Services, the company sells and rents construction material (forming, shoring, and tilt-up hardware) and concrete equipment to concrete installers, and to a lesser extent construction contractors. Except for a steel lineup, CMC Steel purchases its products for resale. Through its parent Commercial Metals Company, CMC Steel stocks fabricated reinforced and structural steel, used in constructing commercial buildings, hospitals, stadiums, industrial plants, and highways, as well as dams. The company distributes from 44 facilities, located predominantly in the southwestern US.

CME GROUP INC.

NASDAQ (GS): CME

20 S. Wacker Dr.	CEO: Craig S. Donohue
Chicago, IL 60606	CFO: James E. (Jamie) Parisi
Phone: 312-930-1000	HR: Hilda Harris Piell
Fax: —	FYE: December 31
Web: www.cmegroup.com	Type: Public

CME Group doesn't tell futures, but it does sell them. The company owns the Chicago Mercantile Exchange, launched in 1898 as The Chicago Butter and Egg Board, and the Chicago Board of Trade (CBOT), the futures exchange that it acquired for approximately $12 billion in 2007. CME and CBOT provide a marketplace for agricultural commodities, as well as for interest rate, equity, government paper, and foreign exchange futures. Products are traded on its CME Globex electronic trading system, on its floors via an open outcry system using elaborate hand signals, and through privately negotiated transactions. In 2010 CME bought 90% of Dow Jones & Company's index business, including the Dow Jones Industrial Average.

	Annual Growth	12/05	12/06	12/07	12/08	12/09
Sales ($ mil.)	27.9%	977.3	1,089.9	1,756.1	2,561.0	2,612.8
Net income ($ mil.)	28.1%	306.9	407.3	658.5	715.5	825.8
Market value ($ mil.)	(2.2%)	24,139.9	33,484.8	45,062.5	13,670.5	22,068.8
Employees	14.4%	1,321	1,430	1,970	2,300	2,260

CMS BANCORP, INC.

NASDAQ (CM): CMSB

123 Main St., Ste. 750	CEO: John E. Ritacco
White Plains, NY 10601	CFO: Stephen E. Dowd
Phone: 914-422-2700	HR: —
Fax: —	FYE: September 30
Web: www.cmsbk.com	Type: Public

CMS Bancorp was formed in 2007 to be the holding company for Community Mutual Savings Bank, which serves the northern suburbs of New York City. Operating through about five branches in Westchester County (one of the richest counties in the country), the bank collects deposits from area consumers and small businesses and uses the funds mainly to originate one- to four-family residential mortgages, which account for more than 85% of its loan portfolio. The bank also issues commercial mortgages, consumer and business loans, and lines of credit. Deposit products include checking, savings, and money market accounts; CDs; and IRAs. Community Mutual Savings Bank was founded in 1887.

	Annual Growth	9/05	9/06	9/07	9/08	9/09
Assets ($ mil.)	20.8%	114.3	122.5	173.5	203.9	243.2
Net income ($ mil.)	—	1.3	0.1	(0.8)	(0.9)	(0.4)
Market value ($ mil.)	(17.8%)	—	—	19.6	14.4	13.2
Employees	5.0%	—	—	40	42	—

CMS ENERGY CORPORATION

NYSE: CMS

1 Energy Plaza	CEO: John G. Russell
Jackson, MI 49201	CFO: Thomas J. (Tom) Webb
Phone: 517-788-0550	HR: John M. Butler
Fax: 517-788-1859	FYE: December 31
Web: www.cmsenergy.com	Type: Public

Michigan consumers rely on CMS Energy. The energy holding company's utility, Consumers Energy, has a generating capacity of more than 8,950 MW (primarily fossil-fueled) and distributes electricity and natural gas to 2.5 million customers (6.5 million end users) in Michigan. CMS Enterprises operates the non-utility businesses of CMS Energy, and is an operator of independent power generating plants; its independent power projects are primarily located in Michigan, but also in California and North Carolina, and have a gross capacity of 1,200 MW. Subsidiary EnerBank USA provides unsecured home improvement payment option programs for homeowners.

	Annual Growth	12/05	12/06	12/07	12/08	12/09
Sales ($ mil.)	(0.3%)	6,288.0	6,810.0	6,464.0	6,821.0	6,205.0
Net income ($ mil.)	—	(84.0)	(79.0)	(215.0)	300.0	240.0
Market value ($ mil.)	1.9%	3,335.8	3,839.3	3,995.6	2,324.3	3,600.2
Employees	(2.0%)	8,713	8,640	7,898	7,970	8,039

CNA FINANCIAL CORPORATION

NYSE: CNA

333 S. Wabash	CEO: Thomas F. (Tom) Motamed
Chicago, IL 60604	CFO: D. Craig Mense
Phone: 312-822-5000	HR: Thomas (Tom) Pontarelli
Fax: 312-822-6419	FYE: December 31
Web: www.cna.com	Type: Public

CNA Financial is the umbrella organization for a wide range of insurance providers, including Continental Casualty. The company primarily provides commercial coverage, with such standard offerings as workers' compensation, auto, general and professional liability, and other products for businesses and institutions. CNA also sells specialty insurance including professional liability for doctors, lawyers, and architects, and vehicle warranty service contracts. The company also offers commercial surety bonds, risk and health care claims management, claims administration, and information services. Its products are sold by independent agents and brokers. Holding company Loews owns about 90% of CNA.

	Annual Growth	12/05	12/06	12/07	12/08	12/09
Assets ($ mil.)	(1.5%)	58,786.0	60,283.0	56,732.0	51,688.0	55,298.0
Net income ($ mil.)	16.2%	264.0	1,108.0	851.0	(299.0)	481.0
Market value ($ mil.)	(7.5%)	8,806.8	10,849.1	9,073.2	4,423.6	6,457.8
Employees	(3.1%)	10,100	9,800	9,400	9,000	8,900

CNA SURETY CORPORATION

NYSE: SUR

333 S. Wabash Ave.	CEO: John F. Welch
Chicago, IL 60604	CFO: John F. Corcoran
Phone: 312-822-5000	HR: Barbara A. Wood
Fax: 312-755-3737	FYE: December 31
Web: www.cnasurety.com	Type: Public

If the job doesn't get done, CNA Surety pays the price. One of the largest surety companies in the US, CNA Surety offers contract and commercial surety bonds, which guarantee fulfillment of contracts. The company's Western Surety unit handles fidelity, commercial, and contract bonds and international surety and credit insurance; Surety Bonding, another subsidiary, specializes in commercial and contract bonds to small businesses. Contract surety (for construction contractors) accounts for nearly two-thirds of CNA Surety's premiums. CNA Surety sells its products in all 50 states through a network of independent agents and brokers. CNA Financial owns 62% of CNA Surety.

	Annual Growth	12/05	12/06	12/07	12/08	12/09
Assets ($ mil.)	7.9%	1,262.6	1,368.3	1,507.7	1,565.5	1,709.0
Net income ($ mil.)	32.4%	38.4	82.8	92.5	110.4	117.9
Market value ($ mil.)	0.5%	645.5	952.5	876.8	850.6	659.7
Employees	(0.3%)	747	736	739	749	739

CNB FINANCIAL CORPORATION

NASDAQ (GS): CCNE

1 S. 2nd St.
Clearfield, PA 16830
Phone: 814-765-9621
Fax: 814-765-4511
Web: www.bankcnb.com

CEO: Joseph B. Bower Jr.
CFO: Charles R. Guarino
HR: Mary Ann Conaway
FYE: December 31
Type: Public

CNB Financial is the holding company for CNB Bank (formerly County National Bank), which provides traditional deposit and loan services through more than 20 branches and two loan production offices in northwestern and central Pennsylvania. In 2005 the company opened ERIEBANK, a division of CNB Bank, in Erie, Pennsylvania. Commercial, financial, and agricultural loans make up more than 35% of CNB Financial's loan portfolio, which also includes residential mortgages (about 30%) and commercial mortgages (more than 25%). Other offerings include credit cards, investments, life insurance, wealth management, and merchant credit card processing.

	Annual Growth	12/05	12/06	12/07	12/08	12/09
Assets ($ mil.)	11.0%	764.0	780.8	856.3	1,016.5	1,161.6
Net income ($ mil.)	(1.7%)	9.1	9.6	9.1	5.2	8.5
Market value ($ mil.)	3.2%	124.1	124.7	119.2	98.4	140.7
Employees	4.6%	246	273	291	303	295

CNBC, INC.

900 Sylvan Ave.
Englewood Cliffs, NJ 07632
Phone: 201-735-2622
Fax: 201-735-3200
Web: www.cnbc.com

CEO: Mark Hoffman
CFO: Satpal Brainch
HR: Nikki Gonzalez
FYE: December 31
Type: Subsidiary

Getting to the bottom of business news is top priority for CNBC. The cable network, part of NBC Universal Cable, reaches more than 95 million homes in the US and Canada with financial news and information, as well as interviews with business leaders, industry experts, and stock analysts. After the markets close and on the weekends, CNBC offers viewers more in-depth programming such as *The Wall Street Journal Report*, as well as original shows highlighting current trends and topics. With its international divisions, including CNBC Asia, CNBC Europe, and CNBC World, CNBC reaches more than 340 million homes around the world. In addition to TV, CNBC provides news and information online through CNBC.com.

CNG FINANCIAL CORP.

7755 Montgomery Rd., Ste. 400
Cincinnati, OH 45236
Phone: 513-336-7735
Fax: —
Web: www.checkngo.com

CEO: Jared A. Davis
CFO: Roger Dean
HR: —
FYE: December 31
Type: Private

If your finances are touch-and-go, you can go to Check 'n Go. The subsidiary of CNG Financial provides customers with payday loans, which are unsecured, short-term cash advances often used to cover unplanned expenses. Borrowers can apply at any of Check 'n Go's more than 1,200 branch locations in some 30 states, or online via the company's Web site. Loan amounts range from $50 to $1,500, depending on which state the loan is originated in. As the payday loan industry faces increased scrutiny over what are perceived to be unfair lending practices, Check 'n Go has introduced new products and services such as check cashing and title loans.

CNH CAPITAL AMERICA LLC

6900 Veterans Blvd.
Burr Ridge, IL 60527
Phone: 630-887-2233
Fax: 630-887-2334
Web: www.cnhcapital.com

CEO: Steven (Steve) Bierman
CFO: Camillo Rossotto
HR: —
FYE: December 31
Type: Subsidiary

CNH Capital America reaps the benefits of its relationship to parent CNH Global, a world leader in agricultural and construction equipment manufacturing. The company provides funding to buyers and dealers of CNH Global's products in the US. CNH Capital America offers leases, installment contracts, and revolving accounts to retail, commercial, and municipal customers who purchase Case, Case IH, Kobelco, and New Holland brand machinery. The company's Equipment Alley service facilitates online purchases and sales of used agricultural equipment. CNH Capital also offers damage insurance, extended warranties, and related coverage through affiliate CNH Capital Insurance Agency.

🔲 CNO FINANCIAL GROUP, INC.

NYSE: CNO

11825 N. Pennsylvania St.
Carmel, IN 46032
Phone: 317-817-6100
Fax: 317-817-2847
Web: www.cnoinc.com

CEO: C. James (Jim) Prieur
CFO: Edward J. (Ed) Bonach
HR: Susan L. (Sue) Menzel
FYE: December 31
Type: Public

Have a modest but stable income? Graying at the temples? CNO Financial Group (formerly Conseco) finds that especially attractive and has life insurance and related products targeted towards you and 4 million other customers. Its primary units include Bankers Life & Casualty, which provides Medicare supplement, life, annuities, and long-term care insurance sold through its own agents; Colonial Penn, which offers life insurance to consumers through direct selling; and Conseco Insurance, which offers specified disease insurance, accident insurance, life insurance, and annuities through its Washington National business, as well as independent agents. CNO Financial Group operates nationwide.

	Annual Growth	12/05	12/06	12/07	12/08	12/09
Assets ($ mil.)	(1.0%)	31,557.3	32,717.3	33,514.8	28,769.7	30,343.8
Net income ($ mil.)	(28.3%)	324.9	58.5	(194.0)	(1,126.7)	85.7
Market value ($ mil.)	(31.8%)	5,814.0	5,013.6	3,151.7	1,299.8	1,254.6
Employees	(3.3%)	4,000	4,000	3,950	3,700	3,500

CNX GAS CORPORATION

NYSE: CXG

CNX Center, 1000 CONSOL Energy Dr.
Canonsburg, PA 15317
Phone: 724-485-4000
Fax: —
Web: www.cnxgas.com

CEO: J. Brett Harvey
CFO: William J. Lyons
HR: Kurt Salvatori
FYE: December 31
Type: Public

CNX Gas may sound like a product for riot control, but it is in fact a company that produces a more innocuous, but valuable, commodity. A part of CONSOL Energy, which owns 82% of the company, CNX Gas is one of the most productive coalbed methane gas (CBM) producers in the US. Through its properties in the Appalachian Basin (primarily in Pennsylvania, Tennessee, Virginia, and West Virginia), CNX Gas produces more than 94.4 billion cu. ft. of gas per year. Almost 20% of its 2009 gas production was derived in conjunction with CONSOL Energy's coal mining activity. In 2009 the company had proved reserves of 1.9 trillion cu. ft. of natural gas equivalent.

	Annual Growth	12/05	12/06	12/07	12/08	12/09
Sales ($ mil.)	2.7%	613.4	513.9	477.3	789.4	683.4
Net income ($ mil.)	12.6%	102.2	159.9	135.7	239.1	164.5
Market value ($ mil.)	5.0%	—	3,851.1	4,825.1	4,122.9	4,458.2
Employees	6.7%	134	192	281	373	174

🔲 An in-depth profile of this company is available to Hoover's Online members at hoovers.com.

393

COACH, INC.

NYSE: COH

516 W. 34th St.
New York, NY 10001
Phone: 212-594-1850
Fax: 212-594-1682
Web: www.coach.com

CEO: Lew Frankfort
CFO: Michael F. (Mike) Devine III
HR: Sarah Dunn
FYE: June 30
Type: Public

Coach is riding in style, thanks to the firm's leather items and some savvy licensing deals. The company designs and makes (mostly through third parties) high-end leather goods and accessories, including purses, wallets, and luggage. Coach, founded in 1941, also licenses its name for watches, eyewear, fragrances, scarves, and footwear. The luxury brand sells its wares through some 930 department and outlet stores (in the US and more than 20 other countries), catalogs, and its Web site. Macy's, Nordstrom, Saks, and others carry Coach items. It also runs about 520 retail and factory outlet stores in North America, Japan, and China (including Hong Kong and Macau).

	Annual Growth	6/05	6/06	6/07	6/08	6/09
Sales ($ mil.)	17.2%	1,710.4	2,111.5	2,612.5	3,180.8	3,230.5
Net income ($ mil.)	12.5%	388.7	494.3	663.7	783.1	623.4
Market value ($ mil.)	(5.4%)	10,242.4	9,122.6	14,458.9	8,811.4	8,201.2
Employees	20.5%	5,700	7,500	10,100	12,000	12,000

⊞ COACH USA, LLC

160 S. Rte. 17 North
Paramus, NJ 07652
Phone: 201-225-7500
Fax: 201-225-7590
Web: www.coachusa.com

CEO: Dale Moser
CFO: Don Carmichael
HR: —
FYE: April 30
Type: Subsidiary

Bus operator Coach USA gets a little coaching from across the Atlantic. One of the largest bus companies in the US, Coach USA is a unit of Stagecoach Group, a UK-based bus and train operator. Coach USA, through about 20 subsidiaries, operates scheduled routes (including airport transportation), charters, and sightseeing tours, primarily in the Northeast and the Midwest. The company's fleet includes about 2,400 buses, trolleys, vans, minibuses (with a 24- to 30-passenger capacity), and school buses. Coach USA's Megabus.com unit, modeled after a Stagecoach offering, provides low-fare scheduled intercity express service to about 30 destinations.

	Annual Growth	4/04	4/05	4/06	4/07	4/08
Est. sales ($ mil.)	—	—	—	—	—	783.5
Employees	—	—	—	—	—	5,000

COACHMEN INDUSTRIES, INC.

OTC: COHM

2831 Dexter Dr.
Elkhart, IN 46514
Phone: 574-266-2500
Fax: 574-266-2559
Web: www.coachmen.com

CEO: Richard M. Lavers
CFO: Colleen A. Zuhl
HR: Leslie G. (Les) Thimlar
FYE: December 31
Type: Public

Coachmen Industries makes modular housing, including single- and multi-family housing and apartments, as well as structures used in commercial or municipal applications. Doing business as All American Group, the company sells modular buildings to residential developers and to businesses, mainly in the midwestern and southeastern US, through about 530 independent builders. In late 2008 the company sold most of its recreational vehicle manufacturing business to Forest River, an RV maker owned by Berkshire Hathaway, for about $42 million in cash. All American Group retained the wheelchair-accessible bus line it produces through a joint venture with ARBOC Mobility under the Spirit of Mobility brand.

	Annual Growth	12/05	12/06	12/07	12/08	12/09
Sales ($ mil.)	(45.8%)	702.4	564.4	480.8	119.6	60.6
Net income ($ mil.)	—	(26.4)	(31.8)	(38.8)	(69.0)	(4.7)
Market value ($ mil.)	(44.1%)	191.2	178.1	96.3	29.8	18.6
Employees	(41.0%)	3,677	2,655	2,305	754	—

THE COAST DISTRIBUTION SYSTEM, INC.

NYSE Amex: CRV

350 Woodview Ave.
Morgan Hill, CA 95037
Phone: 408-782-6686
Fax: 408-782-7790
Web: www.coastdistribution.com

CEO: James (Jim) Musbach
CFO: Sandra A. Knell
HR: —
FYE: December 31
Type: Public

Be it on wheels or on the water, there's no place like home with accessories from The Coast. The Coast Distribution System wholesales accessories, replacement parts, and supplies for recreational vehicles (RVs). Tapping outdoor recreational markets with much in common, the company also distributes boating and marine accessories and parts. Its lineup includes close to 12,000 products, many of them Coast branded, from various appliances to awnings, boat covers, life jackets, and trailer hitches. Products are channeled from 17 distribution centers in the US and Canada to more than 15,000 customers, primarily RV and boat dealerships, supply stores, and service centers.

	Annual Growth	12/05	12/06	12/07	12/08	12/09
Sales ($ mil.)	(12.5%)	176.3	179.1	164.3	132.2	103.2
Net income ($ mil.)	(59.7%)	3.8	3.0	0.2	(1.8)	0.1
Market value ($ mil.)	(15.0%)	33.3	38.5	26.2	4.6	17.4
Employees	(9.8%)	400	410	405	300	265

COASTAL BANKING COMPANY, INC.

OTC: CBCO

36 Sea Island Pkwy.
Beaufort, SC 29901
Phone: 843-522-1228
Fax: 843-524-4510
Web: www.coastalbanking.com

CEO: Michael G. Sanchez
CFO: Paul R. Garrigues
HR: —
FYE: December 31
Type: Public

Hoping to provide traditional small-town banking amid rapid growth in the Southeast, a group of area banking veterans formed Coastal Banking Company in 2000. The holding company owns Lowcountry National Bank, which operates two branches in southern South Carolina and First National Bank of Nassau County which operates about five branches in northeastern Florida and in Georgia under The Georgia Bank name. The banks offer standard products and services, including loans, checking and savings accounts, NOW accounts, and CDs.

	Annual Growth	12/05	12/06	12/07	12/08	12/09
Assets ($ mil.)	6.9%	355.2	426.2	431.6	476.8	463.1
Net income ($ mil.)	—	1.5	3.4	2.6	(4.8)	(14.5)
Market value ($ mil.)	(34.1%)	48.9	57.9	34.8	15.4	9.2
Employees	15.0%	67	74	92	101	117

COATES INTERNATIONAL, LTD.

OTC: COTE

2100 Hwy. 34 & Ridgewood Rd.
Wall Township, NJ 07719
Phone: 732-449-7717
Fax: 732-449-7736
Web: www.coatesengine.com

CEO: George J. Coates
CFO: Barry C. Kaye
HR: —
FYE: December 31
Type: Public

Coates International Ltd. (CIL) may be sparking the next industrial revolution. CEO George J. Coates founded CIL to develop his many patents, the most noteworthy being the Coates Spherical Rotary Valve (CSRV). The CSRV is designed to replace the century-old technology of the internal combustion engine's camshaft and poppet valve system. An engine equipped with the CSRV can run on different fuels while reducing emissions and increasing efficiency; the need for maintenance is also reduced. CIL licenses its CSRV engine technology to makers of heavy-duty vehicles, automobiles, and industrial engines. Major customer Almont Energy (Canada) took first delivery of CSRV engines in 2010.

	Annual Growth	12/05	12/06	12/07	12/08	12/09
Sales ($ mil.)	(75.8%)	—	—	—	3.3	0.8
Net income ($ mil.)	—	—	—	—	0.9	(0.8)
Market value ($ mil.)	2.8%	—	—	—	99.2	101.9
Employees	0.0%	—	—	—	8	8

THE COBALT GROUP, INC.

2200 1st Ave. South, Ste. 400
Seattle, WA 98134
Phone: 206-269-6363
Fax: 206-269-6350
Web: www.cobaltgroup.com

CEO: John W. P. Holt
CFO: Jim Beach
HR: —
FYE: December 31
Type: Private

The Cobalt Group's Web sites and services come fully loaded. Cobalt provides Web-based marketing services to auto manufacturers and dealers to help them manage their businesses online. Services include Web site hosting, e-commerce applications, Web-based customer relationship management applications, data management, and best practices training and consulting. The company also provides automotive Internet marketing through its Dealix subsidiary, and its IntegraLink subsidiary collects automotive data from dealerships for manufacturers, direct-marketing firms, and others who work in the automotive industry. In addition, Cobalt also operates UsedCars.com, a place for used-vehicle buyers to connect with dealers.

COBALT INTERNATIONAL ENERGY, L.P.

NYSE: CIE

2 Post Oak Central, 1980 Post Oak Blvd., Ste. 1200
Houston, TX 77056
Phone: 713-579-9100
Fax: 713-579-9196
Web: www.cobaltintl.com

CEO: Joseph H. (Joe) Bryant
CFO: Rodney L. Gray
HR: —
FYE: December 31
Type: Public

Cobalt International Energy scours the deep blue seas in search of oil. An exploration and development company, Cobalt International owns interests in offshore properties located in the Gulf of Mexico and West Africa. The company's assets include majority and minority stakes in more than half-a-million acres in the Gulf and more than 2 million acres in blocks located off the coast of Gabon and Angola. It focuses primarily on searching for oil pockets encased beneath salt layers, which until recently was traditionally untapped geological territory in the oil industry. Founded in 2005, Cobalt International conducted its initial public offering (IPO) in 2009.

	Annual Growth	12/04	12/05	12/06	12/07	*12/08
Sales ($ mil.)	—	—	—	0.0	0.0	0.0
Net income ($ mil.)	—	—	—	(111.5)	(109.0)	(71.6)
Employees	—	—	—	—	—	54

*Most recent year available

COBIZ FINANCIAL INCORPORATED

NASDAQ (GS): COBZ

821 17th St.
Denver, CO 80202
Phone: 303-293-2265
Fax: —
Web: www.cobizfinancial.com

CEO: Steven Bangert
CFO: Lyne B. Andrich
HR: —
FYE: December 31
Type: Public

CoBiz Financial is reaching new heights in the Rockies and in the Valley of the Sun. It's the holding company for CoBiz Bank, which operates as Colorado Business Bank and Arizona Business Bank. The former operates more than 10 branches in the Denver, Boulder, and Vail areas; the latter has about a half-dozen branches in and around Phoenix. Catering to professionals, high-net-worth individuals, and small and midsized businesses, CoBiz's locations operate as separate community banks, each with a local president who has decision-making authority. CoBiz also offers investment banking services through Green Manning & Bunch and insurance through CoBiz Insurance, as well as investment services.

	Annual Growth	12/05	12/06	12/07	12/08	12/09
Assets ($ mil.)	6.3%	1,933.1	2,112.4	2,391.0	2,684.3	2,466.0
Net income ($ mil.)	—	20.0	22.8	23.0	1.3	(83.0)
Market value ($ mil.)	(28.6%)	670.3	810.3	546.7	358.1	174.6
Employees	4.8%	467	485	507	554	564

COBORN'S, INCORPORATED

1445 E. Hwy. 23, Bldg. A
St. Cloud, MN 56304
Phone: 320-252-4222
Fax: 320-252-0014
Web: www.cobornsinc.com

CEO: Chris Coborn
CFO: Curt Tillotson
HR: Greg Koenig
FYE: December 31
Type: Private

Coborn's hopes you'll shop at your convenience. The company runs more than 25 Coborn's and Cash Wise Foods stores in Minnesota and South Dakota, another 30 shops under the Holiday, Little Dukes, and Save-A-Lot banners, and online grocery shopping service CobornDelivers. It supplies its stores with baked goods, deli items, and meat from its own central bakery and manufacturing plant. Along with its grocery stores, the firm owns and operates convenience, liquor, and video stores, and pharmacies. Founded in 1921 when Chester Coborn started a single produce market, the company opened its first Cash Wise Foods store in 1979 and its first convenience store in 1986. Coborn's is owned by its employees.

	Annual Growth	12/04	12/05	12/06	12/07	12/08
Est. sales ($ mil.)	—	—	—	—	—	1,019.7
Employees	—	—	—	—	—	6,500

COBRA ELECTRONICS CORPORATION

NASDAQ (GM): COBR

6500 W. Cortland St.
Chicago, IL 60707
Phone: 773-889-8870
Fax: 773-794-1930
Web: www.cobra.com

CEO: James R. (Jim) Bazet
CFO: Michael Smith
HR: Lucy Vallicelli
FYE: December 31
Type: Public

Cobra Electronics' CB radios, radar detectors, and power inverters (capable of powering a laptop using a vehicle battery) are good buddies while your rig is on the road. Cobra manufactures handheld GPS navigators, marine and two-way radios, camera-equipped speed detectors, and micro inverters with a USB port for use with an iPod, BlackBerry, and other devices. Products are sold in the US, Canada, and Europe through consumer electronics stores, discount retailers, and truck stops. Cobra has boosted CB radio sales with limited-edition models co-branded with icons such as Harley-Davidson and Dale Earnhardt. Mackenzie Financial owns about 10% of the company.

	Annual Growth	12/05	12/06	12/07	12/08	12/09
Sales ($ mil.)	(5.7%)	133.1	153.7	155.9	124.7	105.2
Net income ($ mil.)	—	12.0	(1.6)	(4.4)	(18.8)	(10.3)
Market value ($ mil.)	(40.6%)	86.5	61.9	31.4	6.8	10.8
Employees	(0.2%)	151	181	177	132	150

⊞ COCA-COLA BOTTLING CO. CONSOLIDATED

NASDAQ (GM): COKE

4100 Coca-Cola Plaza
Charlotte, NC 28211
Phone: 704-557-4400
Fax: 704-551-4646
Web: www.cokeconsolidated.com

CEO: J. Frank Harrison III
CFO: James E. (Jamie) Harris
HR: Kevin A. Henry
FYE: December 31
Type: Public

Southerners like their drinks sweet, and for Coca-Cola Bottling Co. Consolidated (CCBCC), there's nothing sweeter than a Coke. CCBCC produces, bottles, and distributes beverages, principally the products of The Coca-Cola Company. Its distribution area is mainly in the southeastern US. The company is the #2 Coke bottler in the US (behind Coca-Cola Enterprises), serving areas in 11 US states — home to almost 19 million prospective and hopefully thirsty consumers. Coca-Cola Classic accounts for more than 50% of CCBCC's sales. The company does, however, own its own brands, including vitamin-enhanced Tum-E Yummies and Respect, and Country Breeze tea.

	Annual Growth	12/05	12/06	12/07	12/08	12/09
Sales ($ mil.)	1.1%	1,380.2	1,431.0	1,436.0	1,463.6	1,443.0
Net income ($ mil.)	13.4%	23.0	23.2	19.9	9.1	38.1
Market value ($ mil.)	5.9%	395.0	628.6	540.9	422.2	496.1
Employees	(0.8%)	6,200	5,700	5,800	6,200	6,000

⊞ An in-depth profile of this company is available to Hoover's Online members at hoovers.com.

395

COCA-COLA BOTTLING CO. UNITED, INC.

4600 East Lake Blvd.
Birmingham, AL 35217
Phone: 205-841-2653
Fax: 205-841-9168

CEO: Claude B. Nielsen
CFO: Hafiz Chandiwala
HR: Debbie Myles
FYE: December 31
Type: Private

Coca-Cola Bottling Co. United brings icy-cold Cokes to the sunny South. Founded in 1902, Coca-Cola Bottling United serves up "the real thing" in and around The Coca-Cola Company's home turf, serving consumers from Atlanta, Georgia, to Baton Rouge, Louisiana. The company is no slouch when it comes to production — it is the US's #3 Coca-Cola bottler (the world's #1 soft drink). Its brands include Coca-Cola Classic, Diet Coke, Fresca, Sprite, and Vanilla Coke. Coca-Cola Bottling Co. United serves accounts in Alabama, Georgia, Louisiana, Mississippi, South Carolina, and Tennessee.

	Annual Growth	12/04	12/05	12/06	12/07	12/08
Est. sales ($ mil.)	—	—	—	—	—	636.4
Employees	—	—	—	—	—	2,800

THE COCA-COLA BOTTLING COMPANY OF MEMPHIS, TENNESSEE

499 S. Hollywood St.
Memphis, TN 38111
Phone: 901-454-8700
Fax: 901-454-8751

CEO: Terry Ford
CFO: —
HR: Raymond E. (Ray) George
FYE: December 31
Type: Subsidiary

The Coca-Cola Bottling Company of Memphis, Tennessee, is a subsidiary of Coca-Cola Enterprises (CCE), the largest Coke bottler in the US. It bottles and distributes the company's line of soft drinks, bottled water, juices, and other beverages, as well as those of other beverage makers. The bottler is a part of CCE's East Business Unit. It serves parts of Alabama, Florida, Georgia, and Tennessee.

COCA-COLA BOTTLING COMPANY OF NORTHERN NEW ENGLAND, INC.

1 Executive Park Dr., Ste. 330
Bedford, NH 03110
Phone: 603-627-7871
Fax: 603-627-6108
Web: www.ccnne.com

CEO: Lawrence J. (Larry) Lordi
CFO: Bryan Riddell
HR: —
FYE: January 1
Type: Subsidiary

If you buy a Moxie in the upper half of New England, there's a good chance it was supplied by Coca-Cola Bottling Company of Northern New England. (Moxie is a regional brand favored by New Englanders, especially those in Maine, since 1876, when it was sold as a patent medicine known as Moxie Nerve Food.) In addition to Moxie, the company distributes products made by The Coca-Cola Company, Dr Pepper Snapple Group, Sunkist, and Nestlé. It supplies areas throughout all six New England states (Connecticut, Maine, Massachusetts, New Hampshire, Rhode Island, and Vermont), as well as New York State. The company, a subsidiary of Japan's Kirin Holdings, is one of the top Coca-Cola bottlers in the US.

	Annual Growth	1/04	1/05	1/06	1/07	1/08
Est. sales ($ mil.)	—	—	—	—	—	281.2
Employees	—	—	—	—	—	950

COCA-COLA BOTTLING COMPANY OF SOUTHERN CALIFORNIA

1334 S. Central Ave.
Los Angeles, CA 90021
Phone: 213-746-5555
Fax: 213-745-6141

CEO: Terry Fitch
CFO: Kevin Hagan
HR: Stacey Panayiotou
FYE: December 31
Type: Subsidiary

There's lots o' dark brown syrup at this company. And lots o' water. Lots o' aluminum cans and green glass bottles, too. Where are we? At the Coca-Cola Bottling Company of Southern California (CCBCSC), where they put the syrup and water into the bottles and cans of the world's top-selling soft drink. CCBCSC began bottling operations in Los Angeles in 1902; it now manufactures, bottles, and distributes Coca-Cola soft drinks in the southern portion of the Golden State, as well as its central coast, along with parts of southern Nevada. CCBCSC is also a divisional headquarters for its parent company, the world's largest bottler of Coke — Coca-Cola Enterprises.

THE COCA-COLA COMPANY
NYSE: KO

1 Coca-Cola Plaza
Atlanta, GA 30313
Phone: 404-676-2121
Fax: —
Web: www.thecoca-colacompany.com

CEO: Muhtar Kent
CFO: Gary P. Fayard
HR: Carolyn Jackson
FYE: December 31
Type: Public

Coke *is* it — *it* being the world's #1 soft-drink company. The Coca-Cola Company (TCCC) owns four of the top five soft-drink brands (Coca-Cola, Diet Coke, Fanta, and Sprite). Its other brands include Minute Maid, Powerade, and Dasani water. In North America it sells Groupe Danone's Evian; it also sells brands from Dr Pepper Snapple Group (Crush, Dr Pepper, and Schweppes) outside Australia, Europe, and North America. The firm makes or licenses more than 3,000 drinks under 500 brand names in some 200 nations. Although it does no bottling itself, Coke owns 34% of the world's #1 Coke bottler Coca-Cola Enterprises (CCE); 32% of Mexico's bottler Coca-Cola FEMSA; and 23% of European bottler Coca-Cola Hellenic Bottling.

	Annual Growth	12/05	12/06	12/07	12/08	12/09
Sales ($ mil.)	7.6%	23,104.0	24,088.0	28,857.0	31,944.0	30,990.0
Net income ($ mil.)	8.8%	4,872.0	5,080.0	5,981.0	5,807.0	6,824.0
Market value ($ mil.)	9.0%	92,997.2	111,315.2	141,583.7	104,440.2	131,501.9
Employees	14.0%	55,000	71,000	90,500	92,400	92,800

COCA-COLA ENTERPRISES INC.
NYSE: CCE

2500 Windy Ridge Pkwy.
Atlanta, GA 30339
Phone: 770-989-3000
Fax: 770-989-3790
Web: www.cokecce.com

CEO: John F. Brock
CFO: William W. (Bill) Douglas III
HR: Pamela O. (Pam) Kimmet
FYE: December 31
Type: Public

The scientists and the suits at The Coca-Cola Company (TCCC) concoct the secret syrup recipe and market the powerhouse brands, but Coca-Cola Enterprises (CCE) does much of the bottling and distribution of Coke's products. The world's #1 Coke bottler, CCE brings in 16% of worldwide sales of Coca-Cola beverages. CCE also bottles and distributes other beverages, including Canada Dry and Dr Pepper (both brands owned by Dr Pepper Snapple Group), Nestea (Nestlé), bottled waters, and juice. It sells soft drinks in 46 US states, Washington, DC, the US Virgin Islands, Canada, and six European countries. The company's territories consist of more than 420 million potential customers. The Coca-Cola Company owns 34% of CCE.

	Annual Growth	12/05	12/06	12/07	12/08	12/09
Sales ($ mil.)	3.7%	18,706.0	19,804.0	20,936.0	21,807.0	21,645.0
Net income ($ mil.)	9.2%	514.0	(1,143.0)	711.0	(4,394.0)	731.0
Market value ($ mil.)	2.5%	9,593.2	10,218.7	13,026.1	6,020.1	10,609.0
Employees	(1.0%)	73,000	74,000	73,000	72,000	70,000

COCA-COLA NORTH AMERICA

1 Coca-Cola Plaza
Atlanta, GA 30313
Phone: 404-676-2121
Fax: 404-676-6792
Web: www.thecoca-colacompany.com

CEO: J. Alexander M. (Sandy) Douglas Jr.
CFO: Duane Still
HR: Carolyn Jackson
FYE: December 31
Type: Subsidiary

Coca-Cola North America (CCNA), a division of The Coca-Cola Company, runs the soft drink giant's juice, water, and soda business in the US and Canada. Its brands include Coca-Cola, Barq's, Dasani, Evian, Minute Maid, Simply Orange, Fresca, smartwater, Sprite, and Odwalla. CCNA works with independent bottlers, including Coke's largest bottler, Coca-Cola Enterprises, to distribute its beverages. CCNA owns and operates nine still beverage production plants and four bottled water facilities. It also has one facility that manufactures juice concentrates for the foodservice sector — foodservice is a part of the division's operations. CCNA accounts for about a quarter of parent Coke's global sales.

CODEXIS, INC.

NASDAQ (GM): CDXS

200 Penobscot Dr.
Redwood City, CA 94063
Phone: 650-421-8100
Fax: 650-421-8102
Web: www.codexis.com

CEO: Alan Shaw
CFO: Robert J. (Bob) Lawson
HR: Andrea Danforth
FYE: December 31
Type: Public

The pharmaceutical and the biodiesel industries don't seem like they have much in common, but they both use the chemicals produced by Codexis. The company develops biocatalysts — chemicals used to manufacture other chemicals in a way that's easy on the environment. Its technology is used to make the active ingredients in pharmaceuticals and produce biofuel from plant material. Codexis has a research agreement with Shell to develop new ways of converting biomass to biofuel; Shell accounts for more than half of Codexis's sales. The company is also working within other markets to use its technology to manage CO2 emissions from coal-fired power plants and to treat wastewater. Codexis went public in 2010.

	Annual Growth	12/05	12/06	12/07	12/08	12/09
Sales ($ mil.)	62.8%	11.8	12.1	25.3	50.5	82.9
Net income ($ mil.)	—	(11.6)	(18.7)	(39.0)	(45.1)	(20.3)
Employees	12.3%	—	—	230	300	290

CODORUS VALLEY BANCORP, INC.

NASDAQ (GM): CVLY

105 Leader Heights Rd.
York, PA 17405
Phone: 717-747-1519
Fax: 717-741-9582
Web: www.peoplesbanknet.com

CEO: Larry J. Miller
CFO: Jann Allen Weaver
HR: —
FYE: December 31
Type: Public

Codorus Valley Bancorp is people oriented. The firm is the holding company for PeoplesBank, which operates more than a dozen branches in southeastern Pennsylvania's York County and Hunt Valley, Maryland. The bank offers a full range of commercial and consumer services, including checking and savings accounts and CDs. Some three-fourths of the bank's loan portfolio consists of business, industrial, and agricultural loans; residential mortgage, construction, land development, and consumer loans round out its lending activities. Subsidiary Codorus Valley Financial Advisors offers investment products, and its SYC Settlement Services provides real estate settlement services.

	Annual Growth	12/05	12/06	12/07	12/08	12/09
Assets ($ mil.)	17.0%	476.1	548.2	594.6	702.8	892.8
Net income ($ mil.)	(7.3%)	4.6	5.3	6.4	4.5	3.4
Market value ($ mil.)	(24.1%)	65.0	75.1	66.2	32.6	21.5
Employees	4.3%	181	189	204	212	214

COEUR D'ALENE MINES CORPORATION

NYSE: CDE

400 Coeur d'Alene Mines Bldg., 505 Front Ave.
Coeur d'Alene, ID 83816
Phone: 208-667-3511
Fax: 208-667-2213
Web: www.coeur.com

CEO: Dennis E. Wheeler
CFO: Mitchell J. Krebs
HR: Larry A. Nelson
FYE: December 31
Type: Public

Coeur d'Alene Mines gets to the heart of the matter when it comes to precious metals. A leading primary silver producer, the company holds interests in silver and gold properties in Africa, Australia, North America, and South America. It produces about 12 million ounces of silver and 45,000 ounces of gold annually. Coeur d'Alene has proved and probable reserves of about 250 million ounces of silver and 2 million ounces of gold. Coeur d'Alene produces most of its revenue from the Rochester mine in Nevada and the Cerro Bayo mine in Chile. Sales of silver account for about two-thirds of the company's revenue. Most of the minerals are sold to bullion-trading banks and to smelters.

	Annual Growth	12/05	12/06	12/07	12/08	12/09
Sales ($ mil.)	14.9%	172.3	216.6	215.3	189.5	300.6
Net income ($ mil.)	—	10.6	88.5	43.9	0.0	(31.9)
Market value ($ mil.)	(18.0%)	3,521.8	4,358.2	4,349.4	774.8	1,590.1
Employees	1.8%	1,206	931	1,047	1,034	1,294

COFFEE HOLDING CO., INC.

NASDAQ (GM): JVA

3475 Victory Blvd.
Staten Island, NY 10314
Phone: 718-832-0800
Fax: 718-832-0892
Web: www.coffeeholding.com

CEO: Andrew Gordon
CFO: Andrew Gordon
HR: —
FYE: October 31
Type: Public

Coffee Holding Co. brewed up the idea of selling a wide spectrum of raw and roasted Arabica coffee beans to coffee purveyors such as Green Mountain Roasters, as well as private-label coffees to foodservice suppliers. Coffee Holding imports its green coffee beans from Colombia, Brazil, Mexico, Kenya, and Uganda. In addition to producing private-label coffees for stores, the company also sells name brands including IL CLASSICO and S&W. Its Cafe Caribe espresso coffee targets the Hispanic market. The company has expanded its offerings through partnerships. The founding Gordon family, including CEO Andrew Gordon, owns about 60% of the company.

	Annual Growth	10/05	10/06	10/07	10/08	10/09
Sales ($ mil.)	15.8%	41.5	51.2	57.4	71.2	74.5
Net income ($ mil.)	28.8%	1.2	0.7	0.9	(2.6)	3.3
Market value ($ mil.)	(10.9%)	34.6	21.2	28.0	8.9	21.8
Employees	(6.7%)	74	79	83	87	56

COGDELL SPENCER INC.

NYSE: CSA

4401 Barclay Downs Dr., Ste. 300
Charlotte, NC 28209
Phone: 704-940-2900
Fax: 704-940-2957
Web: www.cogdell.com

CEO: Frank C. Spencer
CFO: Charles M. (Chuck) Handy
HR: —
FYE: December 31
Type: Public

Cogdell Spencer puts its money where your health is. The self-administered real estate investment trust (REIT) acquires, develops, and manages health care properties, including surgery centers, medical office buildings, and rehabilitation facilities, most of which are located on hospital campuses. It owns or manages about 110 properties, totaling nearly 6 million sq. ft. of space in a dozen states. The majority of its properties are located on hospital campuses in South Carolina, North Carolina, and Georgia. Subsidiary Erdman designs and builds health care facilities. Erdman has provided planning, engineering, construction, and related services for more than 5,000 properties throughout the US.

	Annual Growth	12/05	12/06	12/07	12/08	12/09
Sales ($ mil.)	135.2%	7.5	54.8	67.9	335.7	229.6
Net income ($ mil.)	—	(5.6)	(9.1)	(6.3)	(5.8)	(102.0)
Market value ($ mil.)	(23.9%)	723.0	920.3	683.2	400.7	242.3
Employees	54.3%	80	127	125	606	454

COGENT COMMUNICATIONS GROUP, INC.

NASDAQ (GS): CCOI

1015 31st St. NW
Washington, DC 20007
Phone: 202-295-4200
Fax: 202-295-9061
Web: www.cogentco.com

CEO: David (Dave) Schaeffer
CFO: Thaddeus G. (Tad) Weed
HR: —
FYE: December 31
Type: Public

Cogent Communications Group offers a compelling sales pitch: data at the speed of light. The company operates a fiber-optic IP network that serves customers in North America and Europe. It offers dedicated Internet access to businesses through Ethernet connections linking its facilities directly to customers' office buildings. The company's customers include financial services companies, universities, and law firms. Cogent also sells access to its network and provides colocation and modem management services to ISPs, hosting companies, and other big bandwidth users.

	Annual Growth	12/05	12/06	12/07	12/08	12/09
Sales ($ mil.)	14.9%	135.2	149.1	185.7	215.5	235.8
Net income ($ mil.)	—	(67.5)	(53.8)	(31.0)	26.8	(17.2)
Market value ($ mil.)	15.8%	246.3	727.6	1,063.5	292.9	442.3
Employees	14.1%	340	377	431	531	577

COGENT, INC.

NASDAQ (GS): COGT

209 Fair Oaks Ave.
South Pasadena, CA 91030
Phone: 626-799-8090
Fax: 626-799-8996
Web: www.cogentsystems.com

CEO: Ming Hsieh
CFO: Paul Kim
HR: —
FYE: December 31
Type: Public

Cogent knows the power of good security. The company provides Automated Fingerprint Identification Systems (AFIS) that governments, law enforcement agencies, and other organizations use to capture, analyze, and compare fingerprints. Cogent's offerings include proprietary fingerprint biometrics software, hardware, and professional services such as consulting, implementation, and systems integration. The US Department of Homeland Security is a major customer. Cogent has offices in Austria, Canada, China, Taiwan, the UK, and the US. Chairman, president, and CEO Ming Hsieh controls more than 55% of the company.

	Annual Growth	12/05	12/06	12/07	12/08	12/09
Sales ($ mil.)	(5.1%)	159.9	101.7	105.8	125.7	129.6
Net income ($ mil.)	(16.0%)	65.3	29.7	28.6	45.2	32.5
Market value ($ mil.)	(17.7%)	2,032.0	986.4	999.0	1,215.8	930.9
Employees	27.5%	164	195	260	365	434

COGENTRIX ENERGY, LLC

9405 Arrowpoint Blvd.
Charlotte, NC 28273
Phone: 704-525-3800
Fax: 704-529-5313
Web: www.cogentrix.com

CEO: Larry M. Kellerman
CFO: John O'Connor
HR: Linda Okowita
FYE: December 31
Type: Private

Tricks are for kids, but Cogentrix Energy serves up a power treat for customers, albeit a small one, through its electric generating facilities. The company develops, owns, and operates a handful of independent power plants, located primarily in the US. Cogentrix Energy once had a net operational generating capacity of about 4,900 MW from its stakes in 27 coal- and gas-fired facilities, but sold most of these after New York-based investment firm Goldman Sachs Group acquired the company in 2007. The investment firm has Cogentrix Energy looking for new energy opportunities beyond the US power plant industry.

COGNEX CORPORATION

NASDAQ (GS): CGNX

1 Vision Dr.
Natick, MA 01760
Phone: 508-650-3000
Fax: 508-650-3344
Web: www.cognex.com

CEO: Robert J. (Bob) Shillman
CFO: Richard A. Morin
HR: —
FYE: December 31
Type: Public

Cognex machines see what mere mortals cannot. The company is one of the world's largest producers of systems that, linked to a video camera, serve as eyes where human vision is insufficient. Semiconductor, consumer goods, health care, and automotive companies, among others, use the company's machine vision systems to position and identify products, gauge sizes, and locate defects. Customers include manufacturers such as Rexam and Sony. Cognex also offers consulting and educational services, as well as technical support for its products. Sales to customers located outside the US account for about two-thirds of sales.

	Annual Growth	12/05	12/06	12/07	12/08	12/09
Sales ($ mil.)	(5.1%)	216.9	238.4	225.7	242.7	175.7
Net income ($ mil.)	—	35.7	39.9	26.9	27.3	(4.9)
Market value ($ mil.)	(12.4%)	1,193.7	945.0	799.4	587.2	702.6
Employees	(0.4%)	740	760	799	832	729

COGNIS CORPORATION

5051 Estecreek Dr.
Cincinnati, OH 45232
Phone: 513-482-3000
Fax: 513-482-5503
Web: www.na.cognis.com

CEO: Paul S. Allen
CFO: Ralf Suenderman
HR: Deborah Davis
FYE: December 31
Type: Subsidiary

Cognis Corporation is the North American presence of global chemical manufacturer Cognis GmbH. The company focuses on specialty chemicals like personal care products, coating chemicals, and industrial chemicals used by the mining, pharmaceutical, and construction industries. Those operations are divided between business units Care Chemicals, Nutrition and Health, and Functional Products. Cognis North America accounts for almost a quarter of its parent's total sales and operates from 10 locations (four of which are manufacturing facilities) spread throughout the US and Canada. An investment consortium led by Permira and Goldman Sachs owns Cognis.

	Annual Growth	12/04	12/05	12/06	12/07	12/08
Est. sales ($ mil.)	—	—	—	—	—	800.0
Employees	—	—	—	—	—	800

COGNIZANT TECHNOLOGY SOLUTIONS

NASDAQ (GS): CTSH

500 Frank W. Burr Blvd., Glenpointe Centre West
Teaneck, NJ 07666
Phone: 201-801-0233
Fax: 201-801-0243
Web: www.cognizant.com

CEO: Francisco (Frank) D'Souza
CFO: Gordon J. Coburn
HR: Sriram Rajagopal
FYE: December 31
Type: Public

Cognizant Technology Solutions Corporation (CTS) remains mindful of the state of your technology. CTS provides application maintenance services, data warehousing, software development and integration, and reengineering services for legacy systems, primarily to midsized and large businesses. Its customers include IMS Health and First Data. Most of the company's software development centers and employees are located in India, although it has other development facilities in the US, Argentina, China, and Hungary. CTS serves clients in industries including financial services, health care, retail, and manufacturing. The company gets more than three-quarters of its revenues in North America.

	Annual Growth	12/05	12/06	12/07	12/08	12/09
Sales ($ mil.)	38.7%	885.8	1,424.3	2,135.6	2,816.3	3,278.7
Net income ($ mil.)	33.9%	166.3	232.8	350.1	430.8	535.0
Market value ($ mil.)	15.9%	7,525.9	11,551.6	10,162.3	5,407.5	13,572.7
Employees	34.0%	24,300	38,800	55,400	61,700	78,400

An in-depth profile of this company is available to Hoover's Online members at hoovers.com.

COHEN & COMPANY INC.

NYSE: COHN

2929 Arch St., 17th Fl.
Philadelphia, PA 19104
Phone: 215-701-9555
Fax: 215-701-8281
Web: www.cohenandcompany.com

CEO: James J. McEntee III
CFO: Joseph W. Pooler Jr.
HR: —
FYE: December 31
Type: Public

Cohen & Company is an investment firm with a focus on credit-related fixed income assets. The company's asset management division invests in domestic trusts, international hybrid securities and real estate debt, and other investment types; it manages some $16 billion in assets. Cohen & Company also has a capital markets division, which issues, sells, and trades corporate and securitized products. Formerly a specialty finance real estate investment trust named Alesco Financial, the company merged with external manager Cohen Brothers in late 2009. The combined company has access to greater capital resources, allowing it to pursue more investment opportunities in a distressed market.

	Annual Growth	12/05	12/06	12/07	12/08	12/09
Sales ($ mil.)	18.7%	46.3	230.6	818.2	628.0	91.8
Net income ($ mil.)	—	(4.7)	22.0	(1,261.3)	(144.7)	(11.7)
Market value ($ mil.)	(51.0%)	888.0	1,120.5	343.5	46.1	51.3
Employees	89.6%	11	—	136	—	142

COHEN & STEERS, INC.

NYSE: CNS

280 Park Ave.
New York, NY 10017
Phone: 212-832-3232
Fax: 212-832-3622
Web: www.cohenandsteers.com

CEO: Martin Cohen
CFO: Matthew S. (Matt) Stadler
HR: —
FYE: December 31
Type: Public

One of the largest managers of real estate funds in the US, Cohen & Steers administers about two dozen mutual funds, closed-end funds, and exchange-traded funds that are invested in real estate securities, global infrastructure, utilities, and large-cap value stocks. It also manages about 90 separate account portfolios for institutional investors and offers alternative investments such as hedged real estate securities portfolios. In 2009 the company sold its real estate investment banking practice, Cohen & Steers Capital Advisors (now CSCA Capital Advisors), to former managing directors of the unit. Cohen & Steers has more than $15 billion of assets under management.

	Annual Growth	12/05	12/06	12/07	12/08	12/09
Assets ($ mil.)	13.4%	198.5	285.1	332.2	286.1	328.7
Net income ($ mil.)	—	31.9	3.2	75.5	18.1	(0.3)
Market value ($ mil.)	5.2%	793.4	1,710.6	1,276.3	468.0	972.6
Employees	14.6%	117	178	220	202	202

COHEN FINANCIAL, L.P.

2 N. LaSalle St., Ste. 800
Chicago, IL 60602
Phone: 312-346-5680
Fax: 312-346-6669
Web: www.cohenfinancial.com

CEO: Jack M. Cohen
CFO: Pamela A. Kellam
HR: —
FYE: December 31
Type: Subsidiary

Cohen Financial is an investment bank that provides capital and other financial services to those in the commercial real estate industry. Cohen funds loans both directly and indirectly through a cadre of capital sources. Borrowers typically use loans to acquire, construct, or renovate industrial, multifamily, office, and retail properties. The firm spun off its investment management unit into a joint venture, Wrightwood Capital, which manages commercial real estate investments on behalf of foundations and endowments, institutions, private investors, and private and public pension funds. Founded in 1960, the company has nearly 10 offices in major US markets.

⊞ COHERENT, INC.

NASDAQ (GS): COHR

5100 Patrick Henry Dr.
Santa Clara, CA 95054
Phone: 408-764-4000
Fax: 408-764-4800
Web: www.coherentinc.com

CEO: John R. Ambroseo
CFO: Helene (Leen) Simonet
HR: Mark Rakic
FYE: September 30
Type: Public

Lord almighty, Coherent is just a hunk of burning light. The company specializes in light wave manipulation, called photonics, to manufacture and market all types of lasers. Operations straddle high-volume production of commercial lasers and components, and specialized, custom lasers. Products are used in a host of areas: microelectronics (semiconductor fabrication, packaging, flat-panel display and solar cell manufacture); scientific and government research involving physical and chemical processes; OEM components and bio-instrumentation; and materials processing industries, such as heavy manufacturing and cutting. Coherent's sales are primarily driven through its sales force to customers outside the US.

	Annual Growth	9/05	9/06	9/07	9/08	9/09
Sales ($ mil.)	(4.1%)	516.3	584.7	601.2	599.3	435.9
Net income ($ mil.)	—	39.9	45.4	16.0	23.4	(35.3)
Market value ($ mil.)	(5.5%)	739.9	875.8	810.6	898.3	589.3
Employees	(6.0%)	2,189	2,345	2,339	2,149	1,712

COHESANT INC.

Pink Sheets: COHY

23400 Commerce Park
Beachwood, OH 44122
Phone: 216-910-1700
Fax: —
Web: www.cohesant.com

CEO: Morris H. Wheeler
CFO: —
HR: —
FYE: November 30
Type: Public

Cohesant (formerly known as Cohesant Technologies) coheres to a narrower product portfolio these days. Its Cohesant Materials unit produces corrosion protection and other specialty coatings used in protecting, renewing, and rehabilitating infrastructure. The company provides licensee and rehabilitation and renewal services through its Cohesant Infrastructure Protection and Renewal unit (CIPAR). Cohesant produces solvent-free epoxy coating and grout products under the Raven and AquataPoxy brands. In early 2008 rival Graco acquired the company for $35 million.

	Annual Growth	11/05	11/06	11/07	11/08	11/09
Sales ($ mil.)	(3.2%)	—	12.0	11.5	11.6	10.9
Net income ($ mil.)	—	—	0.5	(0.7)	(9.7)	(1.0)
Employees	—	—	—	—	—	—

⊞ COHU, INC.

NASDAQ (GS): COHU

12367 Crosthwaite Circle
Poway, CA 92064
Phone: 858-848-8100
Fax: 858-848-8185
Web: www.cohu.com

CEO: James A. Donahue
CFO: Jeffrey D. Jones
HR: —
FYE: December 31
Type: Public

Cohu tries to blend various technologies into one coherent business. Of the company's three segments, the largest is Semiconductors (Delta Design and Rasco), which makes handling equipment that protects semiconductors during testing procedures. Customers include chip giants Advanced Micro Devices, Intel, and Texas Instruments, which together account for about half of company sales. The other segments include Electronics (closed-circuit television systems for surveillance, medical, and industrial applications) and Broadcast Microwave Services (microwave radios, antenna systems, and support equipment). The company derives about two-thirds of sales from customers outside the US.

	Annual Growth	12/05	12/06	12/07	12/08	12/09
Sales ($ mil.)	(8.0%)	238.9	270.1	241.4	199.7	171.3
Net income ($ mil.)	—	34.0	17.7	8.0	(5.4)	(28.2)
Market value ($ mil.)	(11.6%)	538.8	475.0	360.5	286.3	328.7
Employees	0.0%	1,000	1,100	1,000	1,100	1,000

⊞ An in-depth profile of this company is available to Hoover's Online members at hoovers.com.

399

⊞ COINMACH SERVICE CORP.

303 Sunnyside Blvd., Ste. 70   CEO: Robert M. (Bob) Doyle
Plainview, NY 11803   CFO: —
Phone: 516-349-8555   HR: —
Fax: 516-349-9125   FYE: March 31
Web: www.coinmachservicecorp.com   Type: Private

You won't find much dirty laundry at Coinmach Service. The leading US supplier of coin- and card-operated laundry equipment and related services helps its customers do millions of loads of laundry. Leasing laundry rooms in apartments and dormitories, Coinmach owns and operates about 900,000 washing machines and dryers in about 80,000 locations nationwide. It operates about 160 laundry centers under the Kwik Wash banner in Texas and Arizona. The company also runs Super Laundry, which supplies commercial laundry operators with industrial-grade equipment, and Appliance Warehouse, which rents washers and dryers to apartment communities and residents. Coinmach is owned by investment firm Babcock & Brown.

COINSTAR, INC.

NASDAQ (GS): CSTR

1800 114th Ave. SE   CEO: Paul D. Davis
Bellevue, WA 98004   CFO: J. Scott Di Valerio
Phone: 425-943-8000   HR: Dora Summers-Ewing
Fax: 425-637-0045   FYE: December 31
Web: www.coinstar.com   Type: Public

There's big money in spare change, and Coinstar has turned the previously underutilized "fourth wall" area between the cash registers and the door in retail stores into a potential profit center. Perhaps best-known for its eponymous coin-counting machines, the company underwent a major transformation in 2008 when it acquired RedBox, which, along with Coinstar's DVDXpress subsidiary, operates some 22,000 DVD rental kiosks at supermarkets, big-box retailers, drug and convenience stores, and restaurants across the US. Coinstar operates about 19,000 coin counting and cashing machines in the US, Canada, Ireland, and the UK that process approximately $3 billion in coins annually.

	Annual Growth	12/05	12/06	12/07	12/08	12/09
Sales ($ mil.)	25.6%	459.7	534.4	546.3	911.9	1,144.8
Net income ($ mil.)	26.6%	22.3	18.6	(22.3)	14.1	57.3
Market value ($ mil.)	5.0%	724.1	969.6	892.8	618.8	881.1
Employees	6.8%	2,000	1,900	1,900	—	2,600

COLAS INC.

163 Madison Ave., Ste. 500   CEO: Georges Ausseil
Morristown, NJ 07960   CFO: Dominique J. Leveille
Phone: 973-290-9082   HR: —
Fax: 973-290-9088   FYE: December 31
    Type: Subsidiary

There is nothing to drink here, just lots of gravel and asphalt. Colas Inc., the US arm of global road construction powerhouse Colas, paves roads in about a dozen states. The contractor serves both the public and private sectors, primarily in the industrial and retail markets, providing construction on roads, highways, airport runways, and commercial buildings. Sister company Barrett Paving Materials is also engaged in the paving of US roads. North of the border, Colas Canada represents the Canadian market. Colas Inc., together with the rest of the company's North American business units, account for about 17% of its parent's annual revenues.

	Annual Growth	12/04	12/05	12/06	12/07	12/08
Est. sales ($ mil.)	—	—	—	—	—	1,875.9
Employees	—	—	—	—	—	4,500

COLD STONE CREAMERY, INC.

9311 E. Via de Ventura   CEO: Daniel L. (Dan) Beem
Scottsdale, AZ 85258   CFO: Walt Schultz
Phone: 480-362-4800   HR: —
Fax: 480-362-4812   FYE: December 31
Web: www.coldstonecreamery.com   Type: Subsidiary

This chain of ice cream shops is known for using mineral assets. Cold Stone Creamery has more than 1,400 premium ice cream franchises across the US, as well as in a dozen other countries. True to its name, the company's ingredients are blended into the ice cream on a cold stone. Patrons can create their own flavors by choosing from a variety of mix-ins, such as candy, fruit, and cookie dough. The shops also offer yogurt, sorbet, and other frozen treats. A small number of locations are operated by the company. Founders Donald and Susan Sutherland opened their first Cold Stone Creamery in Tempe, Arizona, in 1988. The company is owned by multi-concept franchisor Kahala Corp.

⊞ COLDWATER CREEK, INC.

NASDAQ (GS): CWTR

1 Coldwater Creek Dr.   CEO: Dennis C. Pence
Sandpoint, ID 83864   CFO: James A. Bell
Phone: 208-263-2266   HR: Karen Horejs
Fax: 208-263-1582   FYE: January 31
Web: www.coldwatercreek.com   Type: Public

Women quench their thirst for classic, casual clothing and accessories from Coldwater Creek's stores, catalog, and website. The upscale multi-channel retailer sells mostly traditional apparel through some 355 full-line stores and about 35 retail outlets, targeting middle- and upper-income women 35 years of age and older. It also sells directly to consumers via its core Coldwater Creek catalog and online store. While Coldwater Creek got its start as a catalog operator, today its retail presence is felt more at the mall than the mailbox, with stores accounting for about 75% of sales. Coldwater Creek was founded in 1984 by Dennis and Ann Pence as a catalog operator and began opening stores in 1999.

	Annual Growth	1/06	1/07	1/08	1/09	1/10
Sales ($ mil.)	7.1%	788.2	1,054.6	1,151.5	1,024.2	1,038.6
Net income ($ mil.)	—	46.8	55.4	(2.5)	(26.0)	(56.1)
Market value ($ mil.)	(31.6%)	1,880.6	1,720.2	591.9	260.0	411.2
Employees	3.9%	8,170	11,577	13,171	11,200	9,531

⊞ COLDWELL BANKER REAL ESTATE CORPORATION

1 Campus Dr.   CEO: James R. (Jim) Gillespie
Parsippany, NJ 07054   CFO: —
Phone: 973-407-2000   HR: —
Fax: 973-496-7217   FYE: December 31
Web: www.coldwellbanker.com   Type: Subsidiary

To say the oldest real estate firm in the US was formed during a major shift in the market would be an understatement. Coldwell Banker was founded during a housing crisis following the 1906 California earthquake. Now a part of international real estate group Realogy Corporation, the firm's franchise members provide residential property brokerage services as well as refinancing and related support services. Upscale arm Coldwell Banker Previews International markets and sells luxury homes and resorts. There are more than 3,500 independently owned and operated Coldwell Banker offices in the US, Canada, Latin America, Europe, and Asia.

COLE HAAN

1 Cole Haan Dr.	CEO: Dave McTague
Yarmouth, ME 04096	CFO: —
Phone: 207-846-2500	HR: —
Fax: 207-846-6374	FYE: May 31
Web: www.colehaan.com	Type: Subsidiary

Cole Haan makes footwear and accessories, and is the more fashion-footed subsidiary of NIKE. The company operates about 110 Cole Haan stores in some 25 US states and Canada, as well as another 70-plus stores in Japan through Cole Haan Japan. It also sells its shoes, belts, hosiery, handbags, small leather goods, fine outerwear, and watches online and in stores run by other retailers. Cole Haan has branched out into high-end accessories (encroaching on Coach) and outerwear and has incorporated NIKE "Air Technology" into some of its shoes. Cole Haan outerwear is produced in Florence, Italy, factories by G-III Apparel Group. Cole Haan was founded in 1928 in Chicago by Trafton Cole and Eddie Haan.

COLEMAN NATURAL FOODS, LLC

1767 Denver West Marriott Blvd., Ste. 200	CEO: Mark McKay
Golden, CO 80401	CFO: —
Phone: 303-468-2920	HR: —
Fax: 303-277-9263	FYE: December 31
Web: www.colemannatural.com	Type: Private

Coleman Natural Foods cooked up a new recipe for a natural meat roll-up when it acquired and consolidated BC Natural Foods and KDSB Holdings into one multi-species meat company. Coleman Natural offers natural, organic, antibiotic-free, vegetarian-fed chicken and pork. It also provides processed meats such as sausage, hot dogs, and bacon, as well as ready-to-eat and frozen convenience meat products. The company's brand names include Coleman, Rocky, Rosie, and Hans. Coleman sells its meats to grocery retailers, specialty and natural food stores, and foodservice operations throughout the US. Its products may also be ordered through the company's website.

COLEMAN CABLE, INC.

NASDAQ (GM): CCIX

1530 Shields Dr.	CEO: G. Gary Yetman
Waukegan, IL 60085	CFO: Richard N. Burger
Phone: 847-672-2300	HR: Cliff Sanderson
Fax: 847-689-1192	FYE: December 31
Web: www.colemancable.com	Type: Public

Coleman Cable cuts the mustard when it comes to electrical wire and cable products. The company designs, manufactures, and supplies four core lines: industrial wire and cable, electronic wire, assembled wire and cable products, and fabricated bare wire. The mix runs from auto spark plug wires to coaxial cables for connecting audio-visual devices, rugged portable power distribution centers, and heavy-duty power strips. Nameplates feature Baron, Polar Solar, Royal, Seoprene, and Signal. Selling through OEMs and specialty distributors, Coleman taps automotive, construction, electronic, HVAC, irrigation, and voice and data markets. Manufacturing and warehouse facilities are planted in the US and Canada.

	Annual Growth	12/05	12/06	12/07	12/08	12/09
Sales ($ mil.)	9.9%	346.2	423.4	864.1	973.0	504.2
Net income ($ mil.)	—	11.1	29.4	14.9	(28.3)	(67.0)
Market value ($ mil.)	(40.0%)	—	—	163.9	78.6	59.0
Employees	(1.9%)	1,007	845	1,535	1,180	934

COLFAX CORPORATION

NYSE: CFX

8730 Stony Point Pkwy., Ste. 150	CEO: Clay H. Kiefaber
Richmond, VA 23235	CFO: G. Scott Faison
Phone: 804-560-4070	HR: Steven W. (Steve) Weidenmuller
Fax: 804-560-4076	FYE: December 31
Web: www.colfaxcorp.com	Type: Public

The cold, hard facts are that Colfax works hard to get its customers pumped up. The company makes fluid handling products, including centrifugal, gear, progressive cavity, and rotary screw pumps under such brands as Allweiler, Houttuin, Imo, Warren, and Zenith. It also makes valves and lubrication systems. Its products are used in cargo handling, oil transport, firefighting, chemical processing, and pipeline applications. Colfax counts Northrop Grumman, Alfa Laval, General Dynamics, GE, Siemens, Rolls-Royce, and the US Navy among its customers. Colfax has production plants in China, India, Germany, France, the Netherlands, Sweden, and the US; more than two-thirds of sales come from outside the US.

	Annual Growth	12/05	12/06	12/07	12/08	12/09
Sales ($ mil.)	11.0%	345.5	393.6	506.3	604.9	525.0
Net income ($ mil.)	15.5%	12.2	0.1	64.9	(0.6)	21.7
Market value ($ mil.)	15.9%	—	—	—	449.3	520.7
Employees	(9.1%)	2,002	2,002	2,059	2,200	1,365

THE COLEMAN COMPANY, INC.

3600 N. Hydraulic	CEO: Sam A. Solomon
Wichita, KS 67219	CFO: Daniel J. (Dan) Hogan
Phone: 316-832-2700	HR: —
Fax: 316-832-3060	FYE: December 31
Web: www.coleman.com	Type: Subsidiary

The Coleman Company makes what it takes to be a happy camper. As a leading maker of outdoor recreation gear, it also produces coolers, backpacks, footwear, camp stoves/grills, and other camping accessories, sold under the BackHome, Coleman, Campingaz, Exponent, and Peak 1 brands. Coleman has sales offices and distribution facilities worldwide and sells its products mainly through mass merchandisers, home centers, and other retail stores, as well as through its Web site and a network of Coleman Company Factory Outlet stores. Founded in 1900, Coleman is owned by Jarden Corporation.

COLGATE UNIVERSITY

13 Oak Dr.	CEO: Lyle D. Roelofs
Hamilton, NY 13346	CFO: David B. Hale
Phone: 315-228-1000	HR: Pamela Prescod-Caesar
Fax: 315-228-7798	FYE: May 31
Web: www.colgate.edu	Type: School

Colgate won't keep your teeth clean but it may prevent brain rot. The university is a liberal arts college with an enrollment of about 2,800 students. Most are undergrads, though the school has a small graduate program that offers master's degrees in arts and teaching. Colgate offers some 50 fields of study including biology, political science, and psychology. The school was founded in 1819 as the Baptist Education Society, a seminary in Hamilton, New York. Baptists in New York City, including soap maker William Colgate, consolidated their seminary with the Hamilton school a few years later. After nearly 70 years of involvement and service by the Colgate family, the school became known as Colgate in 1890.

	Annual Growth	5/04	5/05	5/06	5/07	5/08
Est. sales ($ mil.)	—	—	—	—	—	146.9
Employees	—	—	—	—	—	1,014

COLGATE-PALMOLIVE COMPANY

NYSE: CL

300 Park Ave.	CEO: Ian M. Cook
New York, NY 10022	CFO: Stephen C. Patrick
Phone: 212-310-2000	HR: Daniel B. Marsili
Fax: 212-310-2475	FYE: December 31
Web: www.colgate.com	Type: Public

Colgate-Palmolive takes a bite out of grime. The company is a top global maker and marketer of toothpaste and other soap and cleaning products. Many of its oral care products fall under the Colgate brand and include toothbrushes, mouthwash, and dental floss. Its Tom's of Maine unit covers the natural toothpaste niche. Personal and home care items include Ajax brand household cleaner, Palmolive dishwashing liquid, Softsoap shower gel, and Speed Stick deodorant. Colgate-Palmolive also offers pet nutrition products through subsidiary Hill's Pet Nutrition, which makes Science Diet and Prescription Diet pet foods. The company boasts operations in 70-plus countries and sells its products in more than 200 countries.

	Annual Growth	12/05	12/06	12/07	12/08	12/09
Sales ($ mil.)	7.7%	11,396.9	12,237.7	13,789.7	15,329.9	15,327.0
Net income ($ mil.)	14.1%	1,351.4	1,353.4	1,737.4	1,957.2	2,291.0
Market value ($ mil.)	10.6%	26,901.4	31,997.2	38,235.7	33,615.7	40,290.7
Employees	1.6%	35,800	34,700	36,000	36,600	38,100

COLLABERA INC.

25 Airport Rd.	CEO: Hiten Patel
Morristown, NJ 07960	CFO: Paul K. Kothari
Phone: 973-889-5200	HR: Kavita Rao
Fax: 973-292-1643	FYE: December 31
Web: www.collabera.com	Type: Private

Founded in 1991, Collabera furnishes information technology (IT) management and services to companies around the world in such industries as banking and financial services, manufacturing, logistics, telecommunications, media, insurance, and retail. The company's services include systems analysis and design, application development, staffing, e-commerce applications, enterprise resource planning software implementation, and data migration. Customers have included AT&T, Goldman Sachs, Johnson & Johnson, and Oracle. Collabera operates about two dozen offices in the US, Europe, and India.

COLLE & MCVOY, INC.

400 1st Ave. North, Ste. 700	CEO: Christine Fruechte
Minneapolis, MN 55401	CFO: Lisa Miller
Phone: 612-305-6000	HR: —
Fax: 612-305-6500	FYE: December 31
Web: www.collemcvoy.com	Type: Subsidiary

Colle & McVoy (doing business as Colle+McVoy) provides marketing communications including television, print, and interactive advertising; website design; direct mail; digital and social media marketing; public relations; and graphic design. The agency serves a variety of industries such as travel and leisure, agriculture, and retail. Customers have included DuPont, General Mills, Land O'Lakes, Yahoo!, and The Minnesota State Lottery. The firm was owned by Canadian shop Maxxcom until that company's acquisition by marketing communications agency network MDC Partners, which also owns the Crispin Porter + Bogusky ad agency.

	Annual Growth	12/04	12/05	12/06	12/07	12/08
Est. sales ($ mil.)	—	—	—	—	—	83.4
Employees	—	—	—	—	—	200

COLLECTIVE BRANDS, INC.

NYSE: PSS

3231 SE 6th Ave.	CEO: Matthew E. (Matt) Rubel
Topeka, KS 66607	CFO: Douglas G. (Doug) Boessen
Phone: 785-233-5171	HR: Angela Bass
Fax: 785-368-7510	FYE: January 31
Web: www.paylessshoesource.com	Type: Public

Collective Brands is banking on its collective efforts in shoe making and retailing. The holding company boasts a portfolio of premium and moderate footwear and accessories through its Performance + Lifestyle Group (PLG), a wide reach of more than 4,400 Payless ShoeSource outlets in about 20 countries, and an established licensing and brand management unit in Collective Licensing. Collective Brands was formed in 2007, when powerhouse Payless ShoeSource acquired Stride Rite, which is primarily a wholesaler to department stores and operates leased departments at Macy's stores. With brands such as Keds and Saucony, the company operates in the US, Canada, the Caribbean, Central and South America, and Puerto Rico.

	Annual Growth	1/06	1/07	1/08	1/09	1/10
Sales ($ mil.)	5.5%	2,667.3	2,796.7	3,035.4	3,442.0	3,307.9
Net income ($ mil.)	5.8%	70.5	122.0	42.7	(68.7)	88.3
Market value ($ mil.)	(5.2%)	1,567.9	2,185.2	1,134.1	686.8	1,266.7
Employees	2.2%	27,550	31,000	31,000	31,000	30,000

COLLECTORS UNIVERSE, INC.

NASDAQ (GM): CLCT

1921 E. Alton Ave.	CEO: Michael J. McConnell
Santa Ana, CA 92705	CFO: Joseph J. (Joe) Wallace
Phone: 949-567-1234	HR: —
Fax: 949-833-7955	FYE: June 30
Web: www.collectors.com	Type: Public

Before you sell that rare silver dollar or those old baseball cards, you might want to find out exactly what it is you have. Collectors Universe provides authentication, grading, and information services for sellers and buyers of coins, sports cards, stamps, autographs, and diamonds and colored gemstones. The company charges a fee — usually between $4 and $200 for collectibles; up to $2,500 for gemstones — to determine the authenticity, quality, and worth of an item. Coins and sports cards account for most of the company's business. Collectors Universe also publishes price guides, market reports, rarity reports, and other information in print form, as well as on its website.

	Annual Growth	6/05	6/06	6/07	6/08	6/09
Sales ($ mil.)	1.7%	33.6	36.9	40.5	42.0	35.9
Net income ($ mil.)	—	4.8	6.4	(0.5)	(15.6)	(16.9)
Market value ($ mil.)	(25.6%)	122.4	97.6	106.8	56.6	37.5
Employees	3.8%	186	228	294	288	216

THE COLLEGE BOARD

45 Columbus Ave.	CEO: W. Gaston Caperton III
New York, NY 10023	CFO: Thomas (Tom) Higgins
Phone: 212-713-8000	HR: —
Fax: 212-713-8143	FYE: June 30
Web: www.collegeboard.com	Type: Not-for-profit

The College Entrance Examination Board is a nonprofit association that serves high school students, parents, educators, and educational institutions nationwide. Its members — schools, colleges, universities, and other educational institutions — number 5,400. The College Board offers guidance counseling, financial aid, student assessment, standardized testing, workshops, and professional development courses. Among the tests the College Board administers are the Scholastic Assessment Test (SAT), College-Level Examination Program (CLEP), and the Advanced Placement Program (AP). The organization also studies education policy and makes recommendations. It was founded in 1900.

	Annual Growth	6/04	6/05	6/06	6/07	6/08
Est. sales ($ mil.)	—	—	—	—	—	574.2
Employees	—	—	—	—	—	1,130

THE COLLEGE OF WILLIAM & MARY

Richmond Rd.
Williamsburg, VA 23187
Phone: 757-221-4000
Fax: 757-221-2505
Web: www.wm.edu

CEO: W. Taylor Reveley III
CFO: Samuel E. Jones
HR: P. Geoffrey Feiss
FYE: June 30
Type: School

Not every Tom, Dick, and Harry gets into The College of William & Mary. The median SAT score for incoming freshmen is about 1350 (out of 1600). The second-oldest college in the US (Harvard is the oldest), William & Mary is a public university (though it retains its traditional "College" moniker) with an enrollment of about 7,700 students and an endowment of more than $575 million. Some 600 faculty members instruct students in more than 35 undergraduate programs and advanced degrees in about a dozen fields of study at schools of arts & sciences, business, education, law, and marine sciences. Among its notable alumni are three US presidents: Thomas Jefferson, James Monroe, and John Tyler.

COLLEXIS HOLDINGS, INC.

1418 Laurel St., Ste. 100
Columbia, SC 29201
Phone: 803-727-1113
Fax: 803-727-1118
Web: www.collexis.com

CEO: William D. (Bill) Kirkland
CFO: Mark Murphy
HR: —
FYE: June 30
Type: Subsidiary

Collexis Holdings provides the means to fish data out of a sea of information. The company makes software systems and applications that search within, and extract desired information from, digitized sources such as documents, websites, e-mails, and unstructured sources. Collexis' semantic search system is capable of searching through multiple sources simultaneously. Through its US and European operations, the company serves legal companies and governmental entities, as well as the university, medical, and biopharmaceutical research fields. Collexis has served such clients as Bristol-Myers Squibb, the US Department of Defense, and the World Health Organization. In 2010 the company was acquired by Elsevier.

	Annual Growth	6/04	6/05	6/06	6/07	6/08
Sales ($ mil.)	355.6%	—	—	—	0.9	4.1
Net income ($ mil.)	—	—	—	—	(4.6)	(11.3)
Employees	68.6%	—	—	—	35	59

COLLIERS INTERNATIONAL PROPERTY CONSULTANTS, INC.

50 Milk St., 20th Fl.
Boston, MA 02109
Phone: 617-722-0221
Fax: 617-722-0224
Web: www.colliers.com

CEO: Margaret Wigglesworth
CFO: —
HR: —
FYE: December 31
Type: Subsidiary

No matter where your business lives, Colliers International can help you find the best commercial property, *propiedad*, *propriété*, or *eigentum*. An affiliation of independently owned commercial real estate firms, Colliers International is one of the world's largest commercial real estate dealers, with more than 290 offices in about 60 countries. Colliers International agencies provide property brokerage, investment sales, development, and management and consulting services to tenants, owners, and investors. Altogether, the group's member firms manage more than 1.1 billion sq. ft. of space on six continents. A subsidiary of Canada-based property management firm FirstService acquired Colliers International in 2010.

	Annual Growth	12/04	12/05	12/06	12/07	12/08
Sales ($ mil.)	0.0%	—	—	—	1,600.0	1,600.0
Employees	25.8%	—	—	—	10,092	12,700

COLLINS STEWART LLC

350 Madison Ave.
New York, NY 10017
Phone: 212-402-8000
Fax: 212-402-5030
Web: www.collinsstewart.com/Geographies/USBusiness

CEO: John Abularrage
CFO: Martin Lynch
HR: Marie D'Epiro
FYE: December 31
Type: Subsidiary

Boutique investment banking firm Collins Stewart LLC (formerly C.E. Unterberg, Towbin) is the US arm of UK brokerage Collins Stewart plc. Serving more than 700 financial institutions and hedge funds, the company trades in and conducts research on US equities and derivatives. It also manages IPOs for technology and health care companies, makes markets in American Depositary Receipts, and trades foreign stocks and currency. Its research division focuses on the technology, health care, defense, and energy sectors. Collins Stewart has offices in New York City and San Francisco.

COLOMER USA

5344 Overmeyer Dr.
Jacksonville, FL 32254
Phone: 904-693-1200
Fax: 904-693-5365
Web: www.thecolomergroup.com

CEO: Gerard Schoor
CFO: —
HR: —
FYE: December 31
Type: Private

Colomer USA hopes to make *every* day a good hair day for its customers. Formerly Revlon Professional Products, the company makes and markets a variety of haircare products and specializes in ethnic haircare (primarily marketed to African-American and Hispanic consumers). Colomer USA operates under five divisions: consumer products, cosmetics, general US markets, multicultural, and professional products. Its brand names include American Crew, Intercosmo, Creme of Nature, African Pride, Revlon Realistic, Fabulaxer, Ginseng Miracle, 911, All Ways Natural, and HerbaRich. The haircare line was purchased from Revlon in 2000 by a group led by Colomer's chairman, Carlos Colomer, a former Revlon manager.

COLONIAL BANKSHARES, INC.

NASDAQ (GM): COBK

2745 S. Delsea Dr.
Vineland, NJ 08360
Phone: 856-205-0058
Fax: —
Web: www.colonialbankfsb.com

CEO: Edward J. Geletka
CFO: L. Joseph Stella III
HR: —
FYE: December 31
Type: Public

Community banking is a revolutionary idea for Colonial Bankshares. The holding company owns Colonial Bank, a regional thrift serving southern New Jersey from six locations. The bank offers products and services including checking and savings accounts, bank cards, loans, and brokerage. It uses funds from deposits to originate primarily real estate loans, with one- to four-family mortgages accounting for nearly 50% of its loan portfolio. It also writes construction, business, home equity, and consumer loans, as well as loans for other types of real estate. Mutual holding company Colonial Bankshares MHC owns about 55% of Colonial Bankshares; it owned 100% before the company's 2005 public stock offering.

	Annual Growth	12/05	12/06	12/07	12/08	12/09
Assets ($ mil.)	14.0%	336.9	383.6	457.9	530.6	568.5
Net income ($ mil.)	(6.1%)	1.8	1.6	1.2	1.3	1.4
Market value ($ mil.)	(8.9%)	46.8	62.4	45.1	34.9	32.2
Employees	8.5%	75	83	92	104	104

An in-depth profile of this company is available to Hoover's Online members at hoovers.com.

COLONIAL COMMERCIAL CORP.

OTC: CCOM

275 Wagaraw Rd.
Hawthorne, NJ 07506
Phone: 973-427-8224
Fax: 973-427-6981
Web: www.colonialcomm.com

CEO: William Pagano
CFO: William Salek
HR: —
FYE: December 31
Type: Public

Colonial Commercial Corp., through subsidiaries Universal Supply Group, The RAL Supply Group, American/Universal Supply, and S&A Supply, provides HVAC products, climate-control systems, and plumbing fixtures to mostly builders and HVAC contractors in New York and New Jersey. It supplies control system design, custom fabrication, technical support, training, and consultation services (but not installation) for engineers and installers. RAL Supply Group offers plumbing fixtures, water systems and water-treatment products, and heating and cooling equipment. About 85% of Colonial's sales come from the replacement market. Chairman Michael Goldman owns 28% of the company; CEO William Pagano, 16%.

	Annual Growth	12/05	12/06	12/07	12/08	12/09
Sales ($ mil.)	4.0%	66.7	71.5	82.4	85.6	78.1
Net income ($ mil.)	—	2.1	0.8	(0.1)	(1.0)	(3.3)
Market value ($ mil.)	(36.6%)	9.8	8.8	6.3	2.5	1.6
Employees	1.1%	159	154	215	177	166

THE COLONIAL COMPANY

5251 Hampstead High St., Ste. 200
Montgomery, AL 36116
Phone: 334-270-6565
Fax: 334-270-6599
Web: www.colonial-company.com

CEO: Purser L. McLeod
CFO: Bryan K. Tucker
HR: —
FYE: December 31
Type: Holding company

This firm is proud of its holding pattern. The Colonial Company is a holding company that invests in and manages private and public companies involved in real estate development and insurance. The company's diversified projects include residential construction (single-family and multi-family residences), shopping malls and centers, offices, insurance companies, and a golf course. Its Lowder New Homes division is one of the largest home builders in Alabama. The company also builds cabinets, serving home builders and renovators. Privately held by the Lowder family, The Colonial Company was founded in 1956.

COLONIAL GROUP INC.

101 N. Lathrop Ave.
Savannah, GA 31415
Phone: 912-236-1331
Fax: 912-235-3881
Web: www.colonialgroupinc.com

CEO: Robert H. Demere Jr.
CFO: Francis A. (Frank) Brown
HR: David (Dave) Deason
FYE: September 30
Type: Private

Colonial Group presides over an empire of oil and gas and shipping-related companies in the southeastern US. The group provides storage and distribution services (at more than 40 terminals) for liquid and dry bulk products including bulk chemicals, motor fuels, industrial fuel oil, and retail gas. It also provides ship bunkering, commercial shipping, and tug and barge services. Colonial Group also operates more than 70 gas stations and convenience stores in Georgia, North Carolina, and South Carolina through its Enmark Stations unit. In addition, subsidiary Georgia Kaolin Terminals provides storage facilities for customers in the US kaolin industry.

COLONIAL LIFE & ACCIDENT INSURANCE COMPANY

1200 Colonial Blvd.
Columbia, SC 29210
Phone: 803-798-7000
Fax: 803-213-7243
Web: www.coloniallife.com

CEO: Randall C. (Randy) Horn
CFO: David Parker
HR: Don Montgomery
FYE: December 31
Type: Subsidiary

Colonial Life & Accident Insurance steps in where traditional insurance companies leave off. Marketed under the Colonial Life brand, the company targets its supplemental insurance products to employees of companies who provide employer-sponsored benefits. Colonial Life's products include disability, accident, life, and cancer insurance. Operating in 49 states (all except New York) and in Washington, DC, the company has some 2.9 million policies in force with 60,000 business and organizational clients. Founded in 1939, Colonial Life was acquired in 1993 by Unum Corporation, and is now a subsidiary of Unum Group.

COLONIAL PIPELINE COMPANY

1185 Sanctuary Pkwy., Ste. 100
Alpharetta, GA 30004
Phone: 678-762-2200
Fax: 678-762-2813
Web: www.colpipe.com

CEO: Tim Felt
CFO: Tom Bundros
HR: —
FYE: December 31
Type: Private

With a reach that extends far beyond the original English colonies, Colonial Pipeline delivers about 100 million gallons of gasoline, diesel, home heating oil, aviation, and military fuels per day to cities and businesses across the eastern and southern US. The 5,520-mile Colonial system transports these fuels from Alabama, Louisiana, Mississippi, and Texas to 267 marketing terminals near major population centers in the Southeast and along the Eastern Seaboard. The company has shipper terminals in 12 states and the District of Columbia. Colonial Pipeline is owned by a consortium of companies, including Koch (28%), HUTTS (23%), Shell Pipeline (16%), and Industry Funds Management (16%).

	Annual Growth	12/04	12/05	12/06	12/07	12/08
Est. sales ($ mil.)	—	—	—	—	—	824.1
Employees	—	—	—	—	—	634

COLONIAL PROPERTIES TRUST

NYSE: CLP

2101 6th Ave. North, Ste. 750
Birmingham, AL 35203
Phone: 205-250-8700
Fax: 205-250-8890
Web: www.colonialprop.com

CEO: Thomas H. Lowder
CFO: C. Reynolds Thompson III
HR: Jennifer Wright
FYE: December 31
Type: Public

Whether you call it the South or the Sunbelt, Colonial Properties has much of it covered with its residential properties. The self-administered real estate investment trust (REIT) owns and operates nearly 120 multifamily apartment complexes with approximately 35,000 units, as well as some 22 million sq. ft. of office and retail space. Colonial Properties also offers third-party management services for commercial real estate clients. It is active in such markets as Atlanta and Savannah, Georgia; Charlotte and Raleigh, North Carolina; Austin, Dallas, and Fort Worth, Texas; Richmond, Virginia; and Charleston, South Carolina.

	Annual Growth	12/05	12/06	12/07	12/08	12/09
Sales ($ mil.)	(9.0%)	495.4	496.1	401.5	344.5	340.4
Net income ($ mil.)	(48.7%)	219.6	203.5	355.9	(46.6)	15.2
Market value ($ mil.)	(27.3%)	2,942.1	3,285.5	1,586.0	583.8	822.1
Employees	(11.6%)	1,700	1,550	1,250	1,166	1,037

COLONY BANKCORP, INC.

NASDAQ (GM): CBAN

115 S. Grant St.
Fitzgerald, GA 31750
Phone: 229-426-6000
Fax: 229-426-6039
Web: www.colonybank.com

CEO: Al D. Ross
CFO: Terry L. Hester
HR: —
FYE: December 31
Type: Public

Colony Bankcorp seems to be colonizing Georgia. The multibank holding company owns seven financial institutions doing business under variations of the Colony Bank name located throughout central and southern portions of the state. The banks operate more than 25 branches in all. They offer traditional fare such as checking and savings accounts, NOW and IRA accounts, and CDs. Real estate loans, including residential and commercial mortgages and construction and farmland loans, make up the largest portion of the company's loan portfolio, at more than 80%. The banks also issue business and consumer loans.

	Annual Growth	12/05	12/06	12/07	12/08	12/09
Assets ($ mil.)	4.2%	1,108.3	1,213.5	1,208.8	1,252.8	1,307.1
Net income ($ mil.)	—	9.0	10.2	8.5	2.0	(19.2)
Market value ($ mil.)	(34.5%)	211.0	149.5	128.4	67.8	38.9
Employees	(3.1%)	348	379	349	323	307

COLONY FINANCIAL, INC.

NYSE: CLNY

2450 Broadway, 6th Fl.
Santa Monica, CA 90404
Phone: 310-282-8820
Fax: —
Web: www.colonyfinancial.com

CEO: Richard B. Saltzman
CFO: Darren Tangen
HR: —
FYE: December 31
Type: Public

While most real estate investors are heading for the nearest exit, Colony Financial is knocking on the doors of opportunity. The real estate finance company, formed in June 2009 and immediately filed for an initial public offering, was established to acquire, originate, and manage commercial mortgage loans and other commercial real estate related debts. It is externally managed by affiliate Colony Financial Manager, a wholly owned subsidiary of Colony Capital. Colony Financial is using the approximately $250 million in proceeds from its initial public offering to acquire commercial real estate-related loans and assets; it may diversify as opportunities arise.

	Annual Growth	12/05	12/06	12/07	12/08	12/09
Sales ($ mil.)	—	—	—	—	—	1.1
Net income ($ mil.)	—	—	—	—	—	(0.4)
Market value ($ mil.)	—	—	—	—	—	298.0
Employees	—	—	—	—	—	—

COLOR SPOT NURSERIES, INC.

2575 Olive Hill Rd.
Fallbrook, CA 92028
Phone: 760-695-1430
Fax: 760-731-6762
Web: www.colorspot.com

CEO: Michael F. (Mike) Vukelich
CFO: Rodney Omps
HR: Trecia Pinchefsky
FYE: December 31
Type: Private

Color Spot Nurseries is firmly rooted in western soil. As one of the US's leading wholesale nurseries, Color Spot produces more than 1,000 types of plants, including bedding plants, shrubs, potted plants, ground cover, and Christmas trees. Color Spot supplies more than 2,000 retailers and commercial customers, including CVS, Lowe's, The Home Depot, and Wal-Mart. Its customers are primarily located in the western and southwestern US. The company operates about 10 production facilities split between California and Texas. Color Spot Nurseries was founded in 1983 by CEO Michael Vukelich.

COLORADO BAG 'N BAGGAGE LLC

2433 Curtis St.
Denver, CO 80205
Phone: 303-292-0033
Fax: —
Web: www.coloradobaggage.com

CEO: Peter (Pete) Paradise
CFO: Rob Kuppens
HR: —
FYE: December 31
Type: Private

Shopping for new luggage is part and parcel of the offerings from Colorado Bag 'N Baggage (formerly Bag'n Baggage). The company stocks luggage and travel goods from such manufacturers as Hartmann and Tumi, among many others. It also sells backpacks, business and travel accessories, business cases, luggage racks, travel organizers, and wallets from more than 25 mall-based stores in Colorado, Texas, Florida, and about a half-dozen other states. The company also does business as Houston Trunk Factory, Malm Luggage, and Colorado Baggage Co. Founded in Dallas in 1973, Bag 'N Baggage was acquired out of bankruptcy in 2008 by Colorado Baggage Company and given its current name.

COLORADO STATE UNIVERSITY

200 W. Lake St.
Fort Collins, CO 80523
Phone: 970-491-1101
Fax: 970-491-1958
Web: welcome.colostate.edu

CEO: Anthony A. (Tony) Frank
CFO: Rich Schweigert
HR: Thomas (Tom) Gorell
FYE: June 30
Type: School

Colorado State University (CSU) got its start as an agricultural college in 1870, six years before Colorado was even a state. The school still has agricultural and forestry programs and a first-rate veterinary medicine school, but it also offers degrees in liberal arts, business, engineering, and the sciences. True to its roots as a land-grant college, CSU engages the larger community in research and outreach, through statewide Cooperative Extension programs and centers like the Colorado Agricultural Experiment Station. Some 25,000 students are enrolled at CSU, about 80% of which are Colorado residents. Its student-faculty ratio is 18-to-1.

	Annual Growth	6/04	6/05	6/06	6/07	6/08
Est. sales ($ mil.)	—	—	—	—	—	562.9
Employees	—	—	—	—	—	1,306

COLUMBIA BANKING SYSTEM, INC.

NASDAQ (GS): COLB

1301 A St., Ste. 800
Tacoma, WA 98402
Phone: 253-305-1900
Fax: 253-305-0317
Web: www.columbiabank.com

CEO: Melanie J. Dressel
CFO: Gary R. Schminkey
HR: Kent L. Roberts
FYE: December 31
Type: Public

Columbia Banking System hopes money will flow through the Pacific Northwest via its three subsidiary banks. Columbia State Bank (also known as Columbia Bank) operates more than 80 branches in Washington, from Puget Sound to the timber country in the southwestern part of the state, as well as in northern Oregon, where it also operates as Bank of Astoria. Targeting individuals and local businesses, the bank offers standard retail services such as checking and savings accounts, CDs, IRAs, credit cards, loans, and mortgages. Subsidiary CB Financial Services offers investment products through a pact with third-party provider PrimeVest.

	Annual Growth	12/05	12/06	12/07	12/08	12/09
Assets ($ mil.)	7.7%	2,377.3	2,553.1	3,178.7	3,097.1	3,200.9
Net income ($ mil.)	—	29.6	32.1	32.4	6.0	(4.0)
Market value ($ mil.)	(13.2%)	806.8	992.4	840.1	337.1	457.2
Employees	2.4%	651	657	775	735	715

An in-depth profile of this company is available to Hoover's Online members at hoovers.com.

405

COLUMBIA DISTRIBUTING COMPANY, INC.

6840 N. Cutter Circle	CEO: Gregg Christiansen
Portland, OR 97217	CFO: Paul Meade
Phone: 503-289-9600	HR: —
Fax: 503-240-8389	FYE: December 31
Web: www.columbia-dist.com	Type: Private

One of the nation's largest suppliers of craft beers, Columbia Distributing also carries wine, soda, and other non-alcoholic beverages. Serving the US's Northwest region, it commands a 50% market share in the area. Its offerings include both domestic and imported labels. The Maletis family owns the business, which in 1989 took over and combined operations with Gold River Distributing. In 2008 the company (then called CoHo Distributing) acquired Mt. Hood Beverage and all three were combined under the name Columbia Distributing. The enterprise conducts operations in nearly 20 locations throughout Oregon and Washington.

COLUMBIA FALLS ALUMINUM COMPANY, LLC

2000 Alluminum Dr.	CEO: Charles D. Reali
Columbia Falls, MT 59912	CFO: Rob Vixie
Phone: 406-892-8400	HR: —
Fax: 406-892-8201	FYE: December 31
Web: www.cfaluminum.com	Type: Subsidiary

Columbia Falls Aluminum's smelting operations produce about 170,000 tons of aluminum annually. Its ingot, sheet, and bar products are sold to rolling mills and extrusion plants; its customers are located primarily in the US. Swiss natural resources conglomerate Glencore has owned Columbia Falls Aluminum since 1999. Among Glencore's other aluminum operations are Sherwin Alumina and Century Aluminum Company.

COLUMBIA HOUSE COMPANY

1 Penn Plaza, 250 W. 34th St., 5th Fl.	CEO: Stuart Goldfarb
New York, NY 10119	CFO: Fred Christensen
Phone: 212-287-0081	HR: —
Fax: —	FYE: December 31
Web: www.columbiahouse.com	Type: Private

DVDs are the name of the game for Columbia House. Initially a 50-50 joint venture between entertainment giants Sony and Time Warner, Columbia House is a club-based direct marketer of DVDs, with members in the US, Canada, and Mexico. The company sells more than 8,500 motion picture titles via mail order and online. Its TV on DVD club features a variety of television programming. Founded in 1997, the company is part of Direct Brands (formerly Direct Group North America), which is owned by Arizona-based investment firm Najafi Cos.

	Annual Growth	12/04	12/05	12/06	12/07	12/08
Est. sales ($ mil.)	—	—	—	—	—	401.9
Employees	—	—	—	—	—	2,300

COLUMBIA LABORATORIES, INC.

NASDAQ (GM): CBRX

354 Eisenhower Pkwy., 2nd Fl., Plaza I	CEO: Frank C. Condella Jr.
Livingston, NJ 07039	CFO: Lawrence A. (Larry) Gyenes
Phone: 973-994-3999	HR: —
Fax: 973-994-3001	FYE: December 31
Web: www.columbialabs.com	Type: Public

Not to be confused with *Colombia*, the drugs made by this Columbia are perfectly legal. Columbia Laboratories develops and markets women's health pharmaceutical products based upon its patented bioadhesive drug delivery technology. The company's progesterone gel products include Crinone 8% and Prochieve 8%, which are used to treat infertility and amenorrhea (loss of menstrual period). It also promotes Striant, an orally administered testosterone-replacement therapy for men. Columbia Laboratories' products in development include vaginal lidocaine to treat menstrual cramps. To raise much-needed capital Columbia has agreed to sell Watson Pharmaceuticals the rights to its progesterone products, including Crinone.

	Annual Growth	12/05	12/06	12/07	12/08	12/09
Sales ($ mil.)	10.0%	22.0	17.4	29.6	36.3	32.2
Net income ($ mil.)	—	(9.3)	(12.6)	(14.3)	(14.1)	(21.9)
Market value ($ mil.)	(30.6%)	305.1	334.6	148.9	83.3	70.9
Employees	3.5%	54	47	56	62	62

COLUMBIA SPORTSWEAR COMPANY

NASDAQ (GS): COLM

14375 NW Science Park Dr.	CEO: Timothy P. (Tim) Boyle
Portland, OR 97229	CFO: Thomas B. Cusick
Phone: 503-985-4000	HR: Susan G. Popp
Fax: 503-985-5800	FYE: December 31
Web: www.columbia.com	Type: Public

Gertrude Boyle is proud to be called one tough mother. The octogenarian chairwoman and star of Columbia Sportswear's popular "tough mother" and "tested tough" ads heads the top US skiwear seller and one of the world's biggest outerwear makers. The company popularized the Bugaboo jacket, a parka with weatherproof shell, and put Columbia on the map in upscale outerwear. Columbia also makes leather outerwear, sportswear, accessories, and boots and other rugged footwear. The company's brands include Mountain Hardwear, Sorel, Montrail, and Pacific Trail, among others. The Boyles (Gertrude; son Tim, president and CEO; and daughter Sarah Bany, director) own about 65% of Columbia Sportswear.

	Annual Growth	12/05	12/06	12/07	12/08	12/09
Sales ($ mil.)	1.9%	1,155.8	1,287.7	1,356.0	1,317.8	1,244.0
Net income ($ mil.)	(15.4%)	130.7	123.0	144.5	95.0	67.0
Market value ($ mil.)	(4.9%)	1,612.1	1,881.3	1,489.2	1,194.7	1,318.6
Employees	3.5%	2,712	2,810	3,057	3,163	3,113

COLUMBIA SUSSEX CORPORATION

740 Centre View Blvd.	CEO: William J. (Bill) Yung III
Crestview Hills, KY 41017	CFO: Theodore R. (Ted) Mitchel
Phone: 859-578-1100	HR: —
Fax: 859-578-1154	FYE: December 31
Web: www.columbiasussex.com	Type: Private

If you're looking for some hospitality, no need to travel to a South American country or a historic county in England. Columbia Sussex develops and manages about 70 hotels in some 30 states, as well as in Canada and the Caribbean. The company is a franchisee for national hotel brands, with hotels operating under established banners such as Hilton, Marriott, and Starwood. Properties include the Hilton Boston Financial District, the Hilton Head Marriott Resort & Spa, and the East Lansing Marriott at University Place. CEO William Yung and his family own Columbia Sussex. Yung founded the firm in 1972.

An in-depth profile of this company is available to Hoover's Online members at hoovers.com.

COLUMBIA UNIVERSITY

2960 Broadway
New York, NY 10027
Phone: 212-854-1754
Fax: 212-749-0397
Web: www.columbia.edu

CEO: Lee C. Bollinger
CFO: Anne Rollow Sullivan
HR: Kerri Jew
FYE: June 30
Type: School

Predating the American Revolution, Columbia University (founded as King's College in 1754) is the fifth-oldest institution of higher learning in the US. With a student population of more than 24,900 and a main campus spread across 36 acres in Manhattan, Columbia's 15 schools and colleges grant undergraduate and graduate degrees in about 100 disciplines, including its well-known programs in journalism, law, and medicine. The Ivy League university's more than 3,500-member faculty has boasted nearly 70 Nobel laureates, including former Vice President Al Gore. Columbia, which operates four sites in New York City and one in Paris, also has a strong reputation for research.

	Annual Growth	6/05	6/06	6/07	6/08	6/09
Sales ($ mil.)	4.9%	2,500.6	2,709.9	2,820.0	2,820.0	3,030.0
Employees	3.5%	12,631	13,904	14,113	14,113	14,520

COLUMBIA VENTURES CORPORATION

203 SE Park Plaza Dr., Ste. 270
Vancouver, WA 98684
Phone: 360-816-1840
Fax: 360-816-1841
Web: www.colventures.com

CEO: Kenneth D. Peterson Jr.
CFO: Richard A. (Rich) Roman
HR: —
FYE: December 31
Type: Holding company

Columbia Ventures Corporation (CVC) is hoping to recycle the business savvy it applied to the aluminum manufacturing business and use it to generate returns in the telecommunications field. The private equity firm was launched in 1987 to invest in an aluminum smelter plant in Washington state. It now owns a number of manufacturing facilities, including Columbia Commercial Building Products (aluminum windows) and Specialty Chemical Products LLC (silica extraction from crushed glass). In recent years the firm has turned its attention to international telecom providers; those holdings include One Communications, THUS Group, and Magnet Networks (Internet, telephone, and video provider in Ireland).

COLUMBUS MCKINNON CORPORATION

NASDAQ (GM): CMCO

140 John James Audubon Pkwy.
Amherst, NY 14228
Phone: 716-689-5400
Fax: 716-689-5644
Web: www.cmworks.com

CEO: Timothy T. (Tim) Tevens
CFO: Karen L. Howard
HR: Richard A. Steinberg
FYE: March 31
Type: Public

Columbus McKinnon gives new meaning to the question "Need a lift?" Through its operating units the company makes equipment for handling, lifting, and positioning materials. It markets its products under such brand names as Coffing, Duff-Norton, Shaw-Box, and Yale (NACCO Industries makes Yale forklifts). Columbus McKinnon's products, including hoists, chains, cranes, forged products, and industrial components, are sold mainly to construction, general manufacturing, and transportation markets. Hoists are the firm's biggest selling product, bringing in more than half of sales. In addition to OEMs, the company sells to hardware distributors and rental outlets. Some 70% of Columbus McKinnon's sales are in the US.

	Annual Growth	3/05	3/06	3/07	3/08	3/09
Sales ($ mil.)	4.2%	514.8	556.0	589.8	623.3	606.7
Net income ($ mil.)	—	16.7	59.8	34.1	37.3	(78.4)
Market value ($ mil.)	(10.5%)	260.3	514.7	427.9	592.1	166.7
Employees	(1.5%)	3,061	3,081	3,250	3,233	2,886

COLUMBUS SOUTHERN POWER COMPANY

1 Riverside Plaza
Columbus, OH 43215
Phone: 614-716-1000
Fax: 614-716-1823

CEO: Michael G. (Mike) Morris
CFO: —
HR: —
FYE: December 31
Type: Subsidiary

Columbus Southern Power may not have discovered that people in southern Ohio have a need for electricity, but it is obligated to provide it. The utility, founded in 1937, transmits and distributes electricity to 749,000 customers in central and southern Ohio, including the capital city of Columbus. The utility, a subsidiary of American Electric Power, operates 15,520 miles of electric transmission and distribution lines and has power plant interests that give it 3,200 MW of coal- and natural gas-fired generating capacity. It also sells bulk power to wholesale customers, such as municipal utilities and energy marketers.

	Annual Growth	12/04	12/05	12/06	12/07	12/08
Est. sales ($ mil.)	—	—	—	—	—	2,208.1
Employees	—	—	—	—	—	1,323

COMAG MARKETING GROUP, LLC

155 Village Blvd., 3rd Fl.
Princeton, NJ 08540
Phone: 609-524-1800
Fax: 609-524-1629
Web: www.i-cmg.com

CEO: James W. (Jay) Felts
CFO: Brad Erlenbach
HR: —
FYE: December 31
Type: Joint venture

Comag Marketing Group (CMG) encourages consumers to get between its clients' covers. The sales and marketing organization provides clients — mostly publishers of major US magazines — with sales, marketing, distribution, and promotional services. CMG also offers newsstand circulation services, helping retailers manage and merchandise its clients' products. The company reaches consumers at the point-of-sale in more than 175,000 outlets in the US and Canada and on newsstands in 100-plus countries worldwide. CMG, which operates from offices in New Jersey, New York, and North Carolina, is a joint venture of publishing giants Condé Nast and Hearst.

	Annual Growth	12/04	12/05	12/06	12/07	12/08
Est. sales ($ mil.)	—	—	—	—	—	47.9
Employees	—	—	—	—	—	340

COMARCO, INC.

NASDAQ (GM): CMRO

25541 Commercentre Dr.
Lake Forest, CA 92630
Phone: 949-599-7400
Fax: 949-599-1415
Web: www.comarco.com

CEO: Samuel M. Inman III
CFO: Winston E. Hickman
HR: —
FYE: January 31
Type: Public

Comarco is charging ahead with renewed focus. The company markets a line of battery chargers, called ChargeSource, designed for mobile phones, notebook computers, and a variety of other portable devices. It markets ChargeSource products through its retail partner, Kensington Computer Products (a division of ACCO Brands), which sells the products under its own label. Comarco previously operated two other businesses — emergency call box installation and maintenance and wireless network monitoring products — but it divested those operations between 2008 and 2009.

	Annual Growth	1/06	1/07	1/08	1/09	1/10
Sales ($ mil.)	(13.4%)	46.9	47.8	23.2	13.5	26.4
Net income ($ mil.)	—	6.3	1.8	(10.0)	(4.5)	(7.4)
Market value ($ mil.)	(31.2%)	86.8	56.0	39.7	7.0	19.4
Employees	(29.0%)	142	120	119	30	36

An in-depth profile of this company is available to Hoover's Online members at hoovers.com.

407

COMBE INCORPORATED

1101 Westchester Ave.
White Plains, NY 10604
Phone: 914-694-5454
Fax: 914-461-4402
Web: www.combe.com

CEO: Christopher B. (Chris) Combe
CFO: Douglas M. McGraime
HR: —
FYE: June 30
Type: Private

Combe makes powders and creams you're itching to buy. The company's products portfolio includes an array of items in the anti-itch niche, including Lanacane, Scalpicin, Gynecort, and Vagisil. Combe combats other human indignities, too, including loose dentures (Sea-Bond), stinky feet (Odor-Eaters), and gray hair (Grecian Formula, Just For Men). Combe's acquisition of J.B. Williams in 2002 added popular names Aqua Velva, Brylcreem, and Cepacol to its brands, among others. The family-owned firm was founded in 1949 by Ivan Combe, who created Clearasil in 1950 and made it the #1 acne medication before selling it off in 1960. Combe's products are sold in more than 60 countries.

COMBINED INSURANCE COMPANY OF AMERICA

1000 N. Milwaukee Ave.
Glenview, IL 60025
Phone: 847-953-2025
Fax: 847-953-8030
Web: www.combinedinsurance.com

CEO: Douglas R. (Doug) Wendt
CFO: Larry Cohen
HR: Todd Stevenson
FYE: December 31
Type: Subsidiary

Combined Insurance Company of America markets and underwrites a combination of supplemental accident, disability, health, and life insurance products. Combined Insurance's sales force of dedicated agents sell a variety of low-premium, low-limit accident and health products. Its Combined Worksite Solutions division markets exclusively to businesses while its Combined Select programs offer student insurance products. The company targets customers in the US, Europe, Canada, and Asia. Formerly a subsidiary of Aon Corporation, the company was acquired by ACE Limited in 2008.

COMBIMATRIX CORPORATION

NASDAQ (CM): CBMX

6500 Harbour Heights Pkwy., Ste. 303
Mukilteo, WA 98275
Phone: 425-493-2000
Fax: 425-493-2010
Web: www.combimatrix.com

CEO: Amit Kumar
CFO: Scott R. Burell
HR: —
FYE: December 31
Type: Public

Not only does CombiMatrix offer an array of products, it offers arrays as products. The company develops technology to make customizable microarrays for biotech and pharmaceutical firms and other researchers. The arrays are collections of short DNA strands arranged on either a semiconductor chip or glass slide, on which researchers perform experiments and monitor the reactions of genes. Such experiments are useful in the process of discovering and developing new drugs, as well as in the areas of molecular diagnostics, proteomic and genomic research, biosensors, and other fields.

	Annual Growth	12/05	12/06	12/07	12/08	12/09
Sales ($ mil.)	(11.5%)	8.0	5.7	6.0	6.3	4.9
Net income ($ mil.)	—	(12.4)	(20.0)	(12.6)	(15.0)	(17.6)
Market value ($ mil.)	(17.3%)	104.2	60.8	57.7	53.2	48.7
Employees	(6.9%)	92	56	57	59	69

COMCAST CABLE COMMUNICATIONS, LLC

1500 Market St.
Philadelphia, PA 19102
Phone: 215-665-1700
Fax: 215-981-7790
Web: www.comcast.com

CEO: Neil Smit
CFO: David A. (Dave) Scott
HR: Kenneth J. (Ken) Carrig
FYE: December 31
Type: Subsidiary

Capturing couch potatoes in 39 states from Connecticut to California, Comcast Cable Communications is the cable television component of parent Comcast Corporation. Comcast Cable has about 24 million basic cable customers, making it the largest US cable company (ahead of #2 Time Warner Cable). The company has about 16 million broadband Internet subscribers. Another approximately 7 million subscribers use Comcast's digital phone service to make calls over the Internet. Comcast Cable also oversees the regional sports and news network operations, as well as the advertising business, of its parent.

COMBINATORX, INCORPORATED

NASDAQ (GM): CRXX

245 1st St., 16th Fl.
Cambridge, MA 02142
Phone: 617-301-7000
Fax: 617-301-7010
Web: www.combinatorx.com

CEO: Mark H. N. Corrigan
CFO: Justin Renz
HR: —
FYE: December 31
Type: Public

CombinatoRx is looking for the right one-two punch combo. The company develops combinations of drugs to target multiple disease pathways rather than the traditional way of singling out genes or proteins for modification. CombinatoRx has chosen to work with compounds that have already received regulatory approval in the US, Europe, or Japan, with the hope of moving them more quickly and inexpensively through the drug development process. It has candidates in preclinical and clinical trial stages that could treat cancer, type 2 diabetes, rheumatoid arthritis, and other immuno-inflammatory diseases. CombinatoRx merged with privately held Neuromed Pharmaceuticals in late 2009.

	Annual Growth	12/05	12/06	12/07	12/08	12/09
Sales ($ mil.)	38.5%	4.7	13.3	14.9	14.1	17.3
Net income ($ mil.)	—	(29.5)	(34.3)	(53.3)	(65.1)	15.4
Market value ($ mil.)	(43.6%)	727.8	770.5	395.0	55.2	73.8
Employees	(14.4%)	95	144	164	73	51

[logo] COMCAST CORPORATION

NASDAQ (GS): CMCSA

1 Comcast Center
Philadelphia, PA 19103
Phone: 215-286-1700
Fax: —
Web: www.comcast.com

CEO: Brian L. Roberts
CFO: Michael J. Angelakis
HR: Ron Phillips
FYE: December 31
Type: Public

Commerce plus broadcasting equals Comcast. The company's core cable division is the largest provider in the US (ahead of #2 Time Warner Cable) with more than 24 million subscribers. Comcast derives the bulk of its revenue from television, Internet, and digital phone services offered in 39 states. It has about 16 million subscribers to its broadband Internet service, while its Comcast Digital Voice computer telephony service, has more than 7 million customers. Comcast also has cable programming interests, such as G4, VERSUS and The Golf Channel, and it owns entertainment channel E!. The company announced in late 2009 that it would form a joint venture with General Electric, giving it a 51% interest in NBC Universal.

	Annual Growth	12/05	12/06	12/07	12/08	12/09
Sales ($ mil.)	12.6%	22,255.0	24,966.0	30,895.0	34,256.0	35,756.0
Net income ($ mil.)	40.7%	928.0	2,533.0	2,587.0	2,547.0	3,638.0
Market value ($ mil.)	(0.6%)	48,757.6	79,626.1	51,522.7	47,628.9	47,572.5
Employees	7.5%	80,000	90,000	100,000	100,000	107,000

COMDATA CORPORATION

5301 Maryland Way
Brentwood, TN 37027
Phone: 615-370-7000
Fax: 615-370-7209
Web: www.comdata.com

CEO: Brett Rodewald
CFO: Randy Pitman
HR: Tracey Power
FYE: December 31
Type: Subsidiary

Comdata is into financial services for the long haul, literally speaking. The wholly owned subsidiary of Ceridian simplifies funds transfer for trucking companies and drivers by providing fleet charge cards and real-time reporting of transaction information. It also provides payroll services via cards and logistical consulting services for trucking companies. Other services that can be consolidated on Comdata Cards include quick fuel-ups via its point-of-sale and pay-at-the-pump technologies, repair charges, and travel reimbursement. The company goes beyond the transportation sector to offer retail, loyalty, and other card services to the aviation, retail, government, and restaurant and hospitality sectors.

COMERICA INCORPORATED

NYSE: CMA

Comerica Bank Tower, 1717 Main St.
Dallas, TX 75201
Phone: 800-925-2160
Fax: —
Web: www.comerica.com

CEO: Ralph W. Babb Jr.
CFO: Elizabeth S. Acton
HR: Megan D. Burkhart
FYE: December 31
Type: Public

If you have a cosigner, Comerica will be your copilot. The holding company owns Comerica Bank and is organized into three main segments: The Business Bank division is the largest, offering loans, deposits, and capital markets products to middle-market, large corporate, and government clients. The Retail Bank serves small businesses and consumers. Comerica's Wealth and Institutional Management arm provides private banking, investment management, financial advisory, investment banking, discount brokerage, insurance, and retirement services. Comerica has about 450 branches in about a dozen states across the US; Arizona, California, Florida, Michigan, and Texas are its primary markets.

	Annual Growth	12/05	12/06	12/07	12/08	12/09
Assets ($ mil.)	2.8%	53,013.0	58,001.0	62,331.0	67,548.0	59,249.0
Net income ($ mil.)	(62.5%)	861.0	893.0	686.0	213.0	17.0
Market value ($ mil.)	(15.0%)	10,008.0	10,346.6	7,675.3	3,500.0	5,213.8
Employees	(3.8%)	11,343	11,270	11,337	10,639	9,720

THE COMEX GROUP

8600 Park Meadows Dr., Ste. 300
Lone Tree, CO 80124
Phone: 720-873-3060
Fax: 720-873-3070
Web: www.thecomexgroup.com

CEO: Marcos Achar Levy
CFO: Marcos Achar Meyohas
HR: Dick Glassford
FYE: December 31
Type: Private

The Comex Group keeps adding colors to its palette. The company manufactures and distributes architectural paints and coatings through five regional operations/brands (Color Wheel, Frazee, General Paint, Parker Paint, and Kwal), and Duckback, a specialty coatings division. It sells its products mainly in the western US; though Color Wheel sells throughout Florida and the Southeast and General Paint covers western Canada. Each brand formulates its products especially for the climate in its home region. The company comprises the US and Canadian operations of Mexico's largest paints maker, Comex.

COMFORCE CORPORATION

NYSE Amex: CFS

415 Crossways Park Dr.
Woodbury, NY 11797
Phone: 516-437-3300
Fax: 516-396-9528
Web: www.comforce.com

CEO: John C. Fanning
CFO: Harry V. Maccarrone
HR: —
FYE: December 31
Type: Public

COMFORCE isn't the latest Chuck Norris movie. It's a staffing, consulting, and outsourcing company that provides clients with temporary employees for high-skills jobs in the information technology, telecommunications, and health care industries, and the tools to manage such contingent workforces. The company's PrO Unlimited subsidiary provides outsourced temporary workforce management services to *FORTUNE* 1000 companies. COMFORCE also provides payroll, funding, and outsourcing services to independent consulting and staffing firms through its financial outsourcing services division. The company has 28 offices (20 company-owned and eight licensed) throughout the US.

	Annual Growth	12/05	12/06	12/07	12/08	12/09
Sales ($ mil.)	1.1%	539.8	567.8	586.7	606.6	563.8
Net income ($ mil.)	—	6.3	4.1	6.0	5.9	(12.2)
Market value ($ mil.)	(14.7%)	40.0	41.0	38.1	15.6	21.2
Employees	(60.4%)	22,525	560	19,000	610	554

COMFORT SYSTEMS USA, INC.

NYSE: FIX

777 Post Oak Blvd., Ste. 500
Houston, TX 77056
Phone: 713-830-9600
Fax: 713-830-9696
Web: www.comfortsystemsusa.com

CEO: William F. (Bill) Murdy
CFO: William George III
HR: —
FYE: December 31
Type: Public

Comfort Systems USA alters ambient air automatically. The company sells and services commercial HVAC (heating, ventilation, and air conditioning) systems in apartments, health care facilities, office buildings, manufacturing plants, retail centers, and schools. The company maintains nearly 75 locations in about 65 cities throughout the US. In addition to HVAC services, Comfort Systems designs building automation control systems that integrate, monitor, and operate HVAC, lighting, and access control systems. Some company locations also offer fire protection, plumbing, and electrical services.

	Annual Growth	12/05	12/06	12/07	12/08	12/09
Sales ($ mil.)	5.8%	899.5	1,056.5	1,109.5	1,328.5	1,128.9
Net income ($ mil.)	—	(6.2)	28.7	32.5	49.7	34.2
Market value ($ mil.)	7.6%	349.8	480.5	485.9	405.3	469.1
Employees	(1.4%)	5,955	6,647	6,461	6,467	5,623

COMGLOBAL SYSTEMS, INC.

4250 Pacific Hwy., Ste. 111
San Diego, CA 92110
Phone: 619-321-6000
Fax: 619-523-3536
Web: www.comglobal.com

CEO: Frank F. Hewitt
CFO: —
HR: —
FYE: June 30
Type: Subsidiary

ComGlobal Systems gets high scores for military intelligence. The company provides a range of information technology services — including software development, systems engineering, and technical assistance — primarily for the US Navy and other Defense Department agencies. It specializes in developing classified applications used to support tactical data processing and so-called C4I systems (command, control, communications, computer, and intelligence). ComGlobal also provides related services such as systems engineering, rapid prototyping, network implementation, and testing and evaluation. The company operates as part of the systems engineering group of the North American arm of UK-based parent QinetiQ Group.

An in-depth profile of this company is available to Hoover's Online members at hoovers.com.

409

COMM BANCORP, INC.

NASDAQ (GM): CCBP

125 N. State St.
Clarks Summit, PA 18411
Phone: 570-586-0377
Fax: 570-587-4374
Web: www.combk.com

CEO: William F. Farber Sr.
CFO: Scott A. Seasock
HR: —
FYE: December 31
Type: Public

Comm Bancorp is the holding company for the Community Bank and Trust Company, which operates about 15 branches in northeastern Pennsylvania. Targeting individuals and small to midsized local businesses, the bank offers standard deposit services such as checking and savings accounts, money market accounts, CDs, and IRAs. Business loans make up the largest portion of the bank's loan portfolio, followed by commercial mortgages and residential mortgages. The bank writes a relatively fewer number of construction and consumer loans. Subsidiary Comm Realty manages the bank's foreclosed properties. The bank also has subsidiaries that offer insurance and asset management, commercial leasing, and title insurance.

	Annual Growth	12/05	12/06	12/07	12/08	12/09
Assets ($ mil.)	4.8%	543.6	540.4	549.0	604.0	656.8
Net income ($ mil.)	(62.8%)	5.2	6.3	6.9	5.7	0.1
Market value ($ mil.)	(15.0%)	72.0	73.7	75.6	60.3	37.6
Employees	(0.7%)	194	186	197	185	189

COMMAND CENTER, INC.

OTC: CCNI

3773 W. 5th Ave.
Post Falls, ID 83854
Phone: 208-773-7450
Fax: 208-773-7467
Web: www.commandlabor.com

CEO: Glenn Welstad
CFO: Ralph E. Peterson
HR: —
FYE: December 31
Type: Public

Command Center wouldn't mind being regarded as the George Patton of the temporary staffing market. The company operates about 80 temporary staffing stores across more than 20 US states that provide workers for event services, hospitality, light industrial, and office jobs. In addition, its Harborview unit designs software used in temporary staffing store operations. Command Center was formed in November 2005 when Temporary Financial Services acquired Command Staffing and Harborview Software, then changed its name. Currently, Command Center's executives own about 40% of the company.

	Annual Growth	12/05	12/06	12/07	12/08	12/09
Sales ($ mil.)	237.0%	0.4	71.3	98.7	79.2	51.6
Net income ($ mil.)	—	(0.2)	(2.4)	(26.0)	(17.6)	(6.0)
Market value ($ mil.)	(61.8%)	377.7	239.9	78.4	8.1	8.1
Employees	36.0%	45	57	290	175	154

COMMAND SECURITY CORPORATION

NYSE Amex: MOC

1133 Route 55, Ste. D
LaGrangeville, NY 12540
Phone: 845-454-3703
Fax: 845-454-0075
Web: www.commandsecurity.com

CEO: Edward S. Fleury
CFO: Barry I. Regenstein
HR: Robert Sagginario
FYE: March 31
Type: Public

At its customers' command are the security guards employed by Command Security. The company's guard services division provides security guards for commercial, governmental, and institutional clients. However, most of Command Security's business (more than half of sales) comes from its aviation services division. Although passenger screening services have been taken over by the US government, Command Security personnel are called upon for support services such as baggage-related security duties, document verification, and skycap and wheelchair escort services, in addition to general security tasks. Delta Air Lines, the company's largest customer, accounts for about 15% of sales.

	Annual Growth	3/05	3/06	3/07	3/08	3/09
Sales ($ mil.)	13.2%	79.7	85.2	93.8	119.4	130.8
Net income ($ mil.)	—	(0.4)	(0.1)	1.2	2.5	1.3
Market value ($ mil.)	12.5%	22.0	31.0	34.8	44.6	35.1
Employees	16.1%	3,300	3,400	3,650	4,500	6,000

COMMERCE BANCSHARES, INC.

NASDAQ (GS): CBSH

1000 Walnut
Kansas City, MO 64141
Phone: 816-234-2000
Fax: 816-234-2019
Web: www.commercebank.com

CEO: David W. Kemper
CFO: Charles G. (Chuck) Kim
HR: Sara E. Foster
FYE: December 31
Type: Public

C'mon to Commerce Bancshares if you're looking for the company that owns Commerce Bank, which operates approximately 370 branches in Missouri, Kansas, Illinois, Oklahoma, and Colorado. The bank focuses on retail and commercial banking services such as deposit accounts, mortgages, loans, and credit cards. Commerce Bank also has a wealth management division that offers portfolio management, trust, brokerage, and estate planning services, and manages proprietary mutual funds. In addition, the company has nonbank subsidiaries devoted to insurance, leasing, and private equity investments.

	Annual Growth	12/05	12/06	12/07	12/08	12/09
Assets ($ mil.)	6.9%	13,885.5	15,230.3	16,204.8	17,532.4	18,120.2
Net income ($ mil.)	(6.7%)	223.2	219.8	206.7	188.7	169.1
Market value ($ mil.)	(1.3%)	3,408.5	3,324.2	3,234.4	3,493.6	3,231.8
Employees	0.9%	5,059	4,478	4,520	5,340	5,239

COMMERCE ENERGY GROUP, INC.

600 Anton Blvd., Ste. 2000
Costa Mesa, CA 92626
Phone: 714-259-2500
Fax: 714-259-2501
Web: commerceenergy.com

CEO: C. Douglas (Doug) Mitchell
CFO: C. Douglas (Doug) Mitchell
HR: Helga Sherlock
FYE: July 31
Type: Subsidiary

Commerce Energy Group (formerly Commonwealth Energy) works for the common good of customer choice in terms of supplying electricity and natural gas. The company's primary subsidiary, Commerce Energy, Inc., is a non-regulated retail energy provider that operates under the trade name electricAmerica and serves more than 600,000 customers in California, Florida, Maryland, Michigan, New Jersey, New York, Nevada, Ohio, and Pennsylvania. In 2008 the company was acquired by Canada-based natural gas, electricity, and ethanol player Universal Energy Group.

COMMERCE GROUP CORP.

OTC: CGCO

6001 N. 91st St.
Milwaukee, WI 53225
Phone: 414-462-5310
Fax: 414-462-5312
Web: www.commercegroupcorp.com

CEO: Edward A. Machulak
CFO: —
HR: —
FYE: March 31
Type: Public

Commerce Group owns El Salvador's San Sebastian Gold Mine, which contains some 1.5 million ounces of gold reserves. Production at the mine has been suspended since 1999, however, while the company works to raise money to upgrade the facility's gold-processing equipment. Commerce Group also explores for other gold and silver mining opportunities in El Salvador. In 2009 the Commerce Group filed a motion for arbitration hearings with the government of El Salvador, which revoked the company's permits to explore the San Sebastian Gold Mine in 2006. The company has postponed all business activity pending the outcome of the arbitration.

	Annual Growth	3/05	3/06	3/07	3/08	3/09
Sales ($ mil.)	—	—	—	—	—	0.0
Net income ($ mil.)	—	—	—	—	—	(30.0)
Market value ($ mil.)	—	—	—	—	—	2.2
Employees	—	—	—	—	—	30

An in-depth profile of this company is available to Hoover's Online members at hoovers.com.

THE COMMERCE GROUP, INC.

211 Main St.
Webster, MA 01570
Phone: 508-943-9000
Fax: 508-949-4921
Web: www.commerceinsurance.com

CEO: Gerald Fels
CFO: Randall V. (Randy) Becker
HR: Cathleen M. Moynihan
FYE: December 31
Type: Subsidiary

When it comes to insurance, The Commerce Group means business. Its flagship Commerce Insurance is among the largest personal auto and homeowners insurers in Massachusetts — in part because of its affinity marketing programs with AAA clubs, and because they are required by law to accept nearly all personal auto insurance business submitted by its agencies. The group also offers earthquake, flood, business, and umbrella insurance. Commerce Group has expanded into New Hampshire, but Massachusetts accounts for more than 85% of the group's premiums. Personal auto insurance accounts for more than 70% of its business. Its Commerce West and American Commerce subsidiaries sell auto insurance in 15 western states.

COMMERCEFIRST BANCORP, INC.

NASDAQ (CM): CMFB

1804 West St., Ste. 200
Annapolis, MD 21401
Phone: 410-280-6695
Fax: 410-280-8565
Web: www.commerce1st.com

CEO: Richard J. (Rick) Morgan
CFO: Michael T. Storm
HR: —
FYE: December 31
Type: Public

CommerceFirst Bancorp is the holding company for CommerceFirst Bank, which opened in 2000 and now has five branches in central Maryland. Catering to small to midsized businesses and professional clients, it offers deposit products including checking and savings accounts, NOW and money market accounts, and certificates of deposit. The bank mainly uses funds from deposits to write business loans (including Small Business Administration loans) and mortgages. Executive officers and board members of CommerceFirst Bancorp collectively own more than 20% of the company.

	Annual Growth	12/05	12/06	12/07	12/08	12/09
Assets ($ mil.)	15.5%	112.5	141.3	148.8	166.6	200.4
Net income ($ mil.)	(8.5%)	1.0	1.3	1.1	0.3	0.7
Market value ($ mil.)	(19.5%)	24.9	24.9	20.2	9.8	10.5
Employees	17.5%	21	29	35	38	40

COMMERCIAL BANCSHARES, INC.

OTC: CMOH

118 S. Sandusky Ave.
Upper Sandusky, OH 43351
Phone: 419-294-5781
Fax: 419-294-2350
Web: www.csbanking.com

CEO: Robert E. Beach
CFO: Scott A. Oboy
HR: —
FYE: December 31
Type: Public

If Commercial Bancshares were planning to produce a commercial, it's quite probable the subject would be Commercial Savings Bank. The holding company owns the community bank, which serves northwestern Ohio from about 10 branches. The bank offers standard retail and business services, including checking and savings accounts, certificates of deposit, and loans. Commercial loans make up the largest portion of the bank's loan portfolio (more than two-thirds); other offerings include consumer finance loans, home equity loans, credit card loans, and residential mortgages.

	Annual Growth	12/05	12/06	12/07	12/08	12/09
Assets ($ mil.)	(0.8%)	303.4	273.7	266.2	259.8	294.3
Net income ($ mil.)	(10.3%)	1.7	1.8	(0.3)	1.3	1.1
Market value ($ mil.)	(22.0%)	30.5	30.7	29.3	15.9	11.3
Employees	(7.2%)	139	124	124	100	103

COMMERCIAL METALS COMPANY

NYSE: CMC

6565 N. MacArthur Blvd., Ste. 800
Irving, TX 75039
Phone: 214-689-4300
Fax: 214-689-5886
Web: www.commercialmetals.com

CEO: Murray R. McClean
CFO: William B. Larson
HR: James (Jim) Alleman
FYE: August 31
Type: Public

If companies have heart, Shakespeare might say Commercial Metals' is as true as steel. CMC manufactures, recycles, and sells steel. Its operations straddle five segments. CMC's Americas and international fabrication and distribution segments buy and sell primary and secondary metals, and fabricated and related metals. Fabrication includes a heat treating plant, producing fence posts, beams, and joists. CMC's Americas and international mills make steel products and copper tubing used in construction, energy, and transportation. A recycling segment runs 42 secondary metals processing plants that shred and pulverize scrap metal, for subsequent sale to steel mills. More than half of CMC's sales are in the US.

	Annual Growth	8/05	8/06	8/07	8/08	8/09
Sales ($ mil.)	0.8%	6,592.7	7,555.9	8,329.0	10,427.4	6,793.4
Net income ($ mil.)	(48.1%)	285.8	356.3	355.4	232.0	20.8
Market value ($ mil.)	3.1%	1,708.9	2,465.4	3,299.0	2,972.4	1,933.2
Employees	5.4%	11,027	11,734	12,730	15,276	13,586

COMMERCIAL NATIONAL FINANCIAL

NASDAQ (GM): CNAF

900 Ligonier St.
Latrobe, PA 15650
Phone: 724-539-3501
Fax: 724-537-9966
Web: www.cnbthebank.com

CEO: Gregg E. Hunter
CFO: Thomas D. Watters
HR: —
FYE: December 31
Type: Public

Commercial National Financial Corporation is the holding company for Commercial Bank & Trust of PA, which operates about 10 branches in western Pennsylvania's Westmoreland County. Targeting individuals and local businesses, the bank offers standard deposit services, as well as mutual funds, investment counseling, and brokerage and trust services. Commercial Bank & Trust of PA's loan portfolio consists mostly of residential mortgages (more than 55%) and commercial mortgages (about 30%), in addition to business, construction, consumer, and municipal loans. The bank was formed in 1934.

	Annual Growth	12/05	12/06	12/07	12/08	12/09
Assets ($ mil.)	3.9%	322.4	338.2	367.6	360.5	376.0
Net income ($ mil.)	10.7%	3.4	3.0	3.1	4.0	5.1
Market value ($ mil.)	(1.9%)	53.9	57.1	53.8	41.5	49.9
Employees	0.5%	110	112	107	110	112

COMMERCIAL VEHICLE GROUP, INC.

NASDAQ (GS): CVGI

7800 Walton Pkwy.
New Albany, OH 43054
Phone: 614-289-5360
Fax: 614-289-5367
Web: www.cvgrp.com

CEO: Mervin Dunn
CFO: Chad M. Utrup
HR: James F. Williams
FYE: December 31
Type: Public

CB radio lingo might have gone the way of mood rings, but Commercial Vehicle Group (CVG) is still a trucker's good buddy. The company makes components for the cabs of heavy-duty trucks that help keep drivers comfortable and safe. Products include seats and suspension seat systems, interior trim (instrument panels, door panels, headliners), mirrors, wiper systems, and controls. Its customers include heavy-duty truck manufacturers such as PACCAR, International Truck, and Daimler Trucks North America. Besides truck manufacturers, CVG sells its products to the fleet maintenance aftermarket and manufacturers of construction equipment and buses.

	Annual Growth	12/05	12/06	12/07	12/08	12/09
Sales ($ mil.)	(11.7%)	754.5	918.8	696.8	763.5	458.6
Net income ($ mil.)	—	49.4	58.0	(3.3)	(206.8)	(81.5)
Market value ($ mil.)	(24.8%)	531.6	617.1	410.5	26.3	169.6
Employees	(3.9%)	5,339	5,790	6,410	5,905	4,551

An in-depth profile of this company is available to Hoover's Online members at hoovers.com.

COMMONHEALTH

446 Interpace Parkway
Parsippany, NJ 07054
Phone: 973-352-1000
Fax: 973-352-1500
Web: www.commonhealth.com

CEO: Matthew (Matt) Giegerich
CFO: Robert Saporito
HR: Susan DiDonato
FYE: December 31
Type: Business segment

If a cure for the common cold is ever discovered, CommonHealth could help publicize it. A division of UK-based advertising giant WPP Group, CommonHealth provides advertising, marketing, market research, strategic planning, and media services primarily for customers in the health care industry. It operates through several main subsidiaries and divisions, including Altum, Carbon, Conectics, Earthborn, Ferguson, Noesis, Qi, and Valos. In addition, the company's EvoLogue unit acts as its core consumer business agency. CommonHealth's clients have included such big names as AstraZeneca, GlaxoSmithKline, Johnson & Johnson, and Pfizer.

COMMONWEALTH BRANDS, INC.

PO Box 51587
Bowling Green, KY 42102
Phone: 270-781-9100
Fax: 270-781-7651
Web: www.commonwealthbrands.com

CEO: Jonathan Cox
CFO: John Mercer
HR: —
FYE: September 30
Type: Subsidiary

Commonwealth Brands has struck USA Gold. The discount cigarette maker gains new customers as rising taxes and legal settlements increase the cost of smoking. It and other discount tobacco firms now control a double-digit percentage of the market. USA Gold is its best seller, but it also sells Malibu, Montclair, Sonoma, and Fortuna brands. The company is the exclusive distributor for Bali Shag, McClintock, Premier, and Rave smoking tobaccos. Founded in 1991 with six brands it bought from Brown & Williamson (now part of Reynolds American), the company has eschewed advertising, instead counting on discount pricing for its success. Houchens Industries sold the company to Imperial Tobacco for $1.9 billion.

	Annual Growth	9/04	9/05	9/06	9/07	9/08
Est. sales ($ mil.)	—	—	—	—	—	200.0
Employees	—	—	—	—	—	720

COMMONWEALTH BANKSHARES, INC.

NASDAQ (GM): CWBS

403 Boush St.
Norfolk, VA 23510
Phone: 757-446-6900
Fax: 757-446-6929
Web: www.bankofthecommonwealth.com

CEO: Edward J. Woodard Jr.
CFO: Cynthia A. Sabol
HR: —
FYE: December 31
Type: Public

Commonwealth Bankshares is the holding company for the Bank of the Commonwealth, which has nearly 20 branches in the Hampton Roads area of southeastern Virginia and northeastern North Carolina. The commercial bank attracts deposits from individuals and small to midsized businesses by offering checking and savings accounts, IRAs, and CDs. In addition, it has subsidiaries that offer residential mortgages, brokerage and investment services, and insurance. Commercial mortgages represent nearly half of the company's loan portfolio; construction and development loans are more than a quarter. The bank also originates business and consumer loans. The company plans for further expansion in North Carolina.

	Annual Growth	12/05	12/06	12/07	12/08	12/09
Assets ($ mil.)	23.5%	549.5	715.2	843.1	1,085.3	1,276.5
Net income ($ mil.)	—	6.6	10.1	11.2	(3.7)	(25.8)
Market value ($ mil.)	(47.7%)	156.0	172.2	109.6	49.4	11.7
Employees	8.4%	142	184	203	209	196

COMMONWEALTH EDISON COMPANY

440 S. LaSalle St.
Chicago, IL 60605
Phone: 312-394-4321
Fax: 312-394-2231
Web: www.comed.com

CEO: Frank M. Clark Jr.
CFO: Joseph R. (Joe) Trpik Jr.
HR: Michael T. Latino
FYE: December 31
Type: Subsidiary

Commonwealth Edison (ComEd) faces the not-so-common task of powering up Chicago. ComEd, a subsidiary of utility holding company Exelon, distributes electricity to 3.8 million homes and businesses in Chicago and surrounding areas of Northern Illinois, representing 70% of the state's population. The utility owns more than 70,000 circuit miles of transmission and distribution lines and 1,300 substations; it receives most of its power supply from sister company Exelon Generation. ComEd works with regional operator PJM Interconnection, which manages wholesale activities on the utility's transmission grid.

	Annual Growth	12/04	12/05	12/06	12/07	12/08
Est. sales ($ mil.)	—	—	—	—	—	6,136.0
Employees	—	—	—	—	—	6,000

COMMONWEALTH BIOTECHNOLOGIES, INC.

OTC: CBTE

601 Biotech Dr.
Richmond, VA 23235
Phone: 804-648-3820
Fax: 804-648-2641
Web: www.cbi-biotech.com

CEO: Bill Guo
CFO: —
HR: —
FYE: December 31
Type: Public

Working for the good of all, Commonwealth Biotechnologies (also known as CBI) provides research services and molecular chemicals used for the development of pharmaceuticals, vaccines, and other drug products. Through units Venturepharm-Asia and Mimotopes, the company provides early-stage drug discovery and biotech research services — mainly related to peptide and protein sequencing — to biotech and pharmaceutical companies, academic institutions, and government agencies in the US and the Asia/Pacific region. Founded in 1992, the company had recently offered a larger range of research services but has been restructuring to focus on its research chemical supply operations.

	Annual Growth	12/05	12/06	12/07	12/08	12/09
Sales ($ mil.)	(19.3%)	7.8	6.5	12.4	9.4	3.3
Net income ($ mil.)	—	0.1	(1.2)	(3.4)	(9.9)	(2.4)
Market value ($ mil.)	(46.8%)	47.6	21.2	25.3	2.6	3.8
Employees	(16.2%)	65	45	110	65	32

COMMONWEALTH OF PENNSYLVANIA STATE EMPLOYEES' RETIREMENT SYSTEM

30 N. 3rd St., Ste. 150
Harrisburg, PA 17101
Phone: 717-787-9657
Fax: 717-237-0346
Web: www.sers.state.pa.us

CEO: Leonard Knepp
CFO: Francis J. Donlevy
HR: Cheryl Krchnar
FYE: December 31
Type: Government-owned

Keystone State employees can rest assured the Pennsylvania State Employees Retirement System (SERS) is keeping a keen eye on their currency. SERS administers the statewide retirement and pension benefits fund for Pennsylvania's public employees. Serving more than 210,000 members, SERS is funded by a combination of employee contributions, employer contributions, and investment earnings. In addition to managing retirement accounts, the system provides retirees with health insurance. Established in 1923 by Governor Gifford Pinchot, the system has grown to manage more than $35 billion in assets.

COMMONWEALTH REIT

NYSE: CWH

400 Centre St.
Newton, MA 02458
Phone: 617-332-3990
Fax: 617-332-2261
Web: www.hrpreit.com

CEO: John A. Mannix
CFO: John C. Popeo
HR: —
FYE: December 31
Type: Public

CommonWealth REIT (formerly HRPT Properties Trust) is a real estate investment trust (REIT) that owns some 520 properties in more than 30 states, mainly in suburban areas of major metropolitan markets. About two-thirds are office properties, while the rest are industrial or other property types. Its portfolio comprises more than 65 million sq. ft. of space. CommonWealth is one of the largest industrial private land owners in Oahu. Other major markets include Boston, Philadelphia, the District of Columbia, and Southern California. Major tenants include GlaxoSmithKline and Flextronics. CommonWealth changed its name in 2010, while at the same time reducing the number of its outstanding shares by 75%.

	Annual Growth	12/05	12/06	12/07	12/08	12/09
Sales ($ mil.)	4.6%	710.8	795.8	840.0	835.5	849.7
Net income ($ mil.)	1.1%	157.4	247.7	122.0	244.6	164.7
Market value ($ mil.)	(11.1%)	2,674.3	3,191.1	1,997.3	870.8	1,671.8
Employees	13.5%	400	450	500	585	—

COMMSCOPE, INC.

NYSE: CTV

1100 CommScope Place SE
Hickory, NC 28603
Phone: 828-324-2200
Fax: 828-328-3400
Web: www.commscope.com

CEO: Frank M. Drendel
CFO: Jearld L. Leonhardt
HR: James L. Wright
FYE: December 31
Type: Public

CommScope doesn't need to be coaxed into making cable. The company makes coaxial, fiber-optic, and other cable products for data, voice, and video transmission; including high-bandwidth cable that provides telephone, cable TV, and Internet access through a single line. It develops radio frequency subsystems for wireless networks through its Andrew Solutions brand/division. SYSTIMAX and Uniprise brands encompass CommScope's network infrastructure products, including cabinets, antennas, software, and network design services for business applications. Telecommunications service providers and OEMs such as Anixter, Alcatel-Lucent, and Comcast are customers. CommScope makes about half of its sales outside the US.

	Annual Growth	12/05	12/06	12/07	12/08	12/09
Sales ($ mil.)	22.6%	1,337.2	1,623.9	1,930.8	4,016.6	3,024.9
Net income ($ mil.)	11.7%	50.0	111.5	204.8	(228.5)	77.8
Market value ($ mil.)	7.1%	1,901.3	2,878.9	4,648.0	1,467.8	2,505.8
Employees	29.8%	4,400	4,550	15,500	15,000	12,500

COMMUNICATION INTELLIGENCE CORPORATION

OTC: CICI

275 Shoreline Dr., Ste. 500
Redwood Shores, CA 94065
Phone: 650-802-7888
Fax: 650-802-7777
Web: www.cic.com

CEO: Guido D. DiGregorio
CFO: Francis V. (Frank) Dane
HR: —
FYE: December 31
Type: Public

If your intelligent communication involves hunting and pecking, try Communication Intelligence Corp. (CIC). The company's handwriting recognition software, including its SignatureOne and iSign products, recognizes character strokes of words from English, Chinese, and Western European languages and converts them to digital text. Industries served by CIC include banking, insurance, and financial services. Customers have included Charles Schwab and Wells Fargo.

	Annual Growth	12/05	12/06	12/07	12/08	12/09
Sales ($ mil.)	(11.5%)	3.1	2.3	2.1	2.4	1.9
Net income ($ mil.)	—	(4.0)	(3.3)	(3.4)	(3.3)	(10.8)
Market value ($ mil.)	(30.6%)	82.0	38.2	42.9	14.5	19.1
Employees	(5.0%)	27	23	25	23	22

COMMUNICATIONS SYSTEMS, INC.

NASDAQ (GM): JCS

10900 Red Circle Dr.
Minnetonka, MN 55343
Phone: 952-996-1674
Fax: 952-996-1693
Web: www.commsystems.com

CEO: Jeffrey K. Berg
CFO: David T. McGraw
HR: Karen J. Nesburg Bleick
FYE: December 31
Type: Public

Aptly named Communications Systems makes connectors and wiring systems for telecommunications networks. The company operates through subsidiaries. Its Suttle and Austin Taylor units make connectors, adapters, and other devices for voice, data, and video communications. Transition Networks makes converters that move data between copper wire and fiber-optic networks, LAN switches, and print servers. JDL Technologies provides schools and businesses with telecom network development services and software. Communications Systems sells directly and through distributors.

	Annual Growth	12/05	12/06	12/07	12/08	12/09
Sales ($ mil.)	0.0%	109.7	115.4	121.2	122.7	109.8
Net income ($ mil.)	7.5%	4.5	4.5	7.5	6.6	6.0
Market value ($ mil.)	0.3%	102.7	84.8	99.2	65.2	104.0
Employees	(2.4%)	473	505	499	462	429

COMMUNICATIONS TEST DESIGN, INC.

1373 Enterprise Dr.
West Chester, PA 19380
Phone: 610-436-5203
Fax: 610-429-3861
Web: www.ctdi.com

CEO: Gerald J. (Jerry) Parsons
CFO: Lawrence E. (Larry) Morgan
HR: Conrad Olie
FYE: December 31
Type: Private

Communications Test Design (CTDI) repairs, installs, tests, and manufactures telecommunications equipment. The company's main business is providing repair and maintenance services to wireless and wireline carriers and cable companies, as well as equipment makers such as Alcatel Lucent and Cisco. It also offers warehousing and distribution services, product quality testing, and equipment installation — from laying cable to installing customer premise equipment. Additionally, CTDI makes a line of broadband switching and access equipment and provides contract manufacturing services. The company was founded in 1975 by chairman and CEO Jerry Parsons, his father Donald, and brother Dick. CTDI is owned by the Parsons family.

	Annual Growth	12/04	12/05	12/06	12/07	12/08
Est. sales ($ mil.)	—	—	—	—	—	761.9
Employees	—	—	—	—	—	3,750

COMMUNITY BANK SHARES OF INDIANA, INC.

NASDAQ (CM): CBIN

101 W. Spring St.
New Albany, IN 47150
Phone: 812-944-2224
Fax: 812-949-6812
Web: www.cbinonline.com

CEO: James D. Rickard
CFO: Paul A. Chrisco
HR: Carl Page
FYE: December 31
Type: Public

Community Bank Shares of Indiana is the holding company for Your Community Bank and Scott County State Bank. The banks serve customers from about 20 locations in southern Indiana and Louisville, Kentucky. Both banks offer deposit products such as checking, money market, and savings accounts, as well as IRAs and CDs. Their lending activities center on commercial mortgages and residential real estate loans (each around 25% of the company's loan portfolio), but also include business, construction, and consumer (including home equity, home improvement, and auto) loans and credit cards. Community Bank Shares of Indiana is focused on organic growth within existing markets.

	Annual Growth	12/05	12/06	12/07	12/08	12/09
Assets ($ mil.)	5.4%	665.0	816.6	823.6	877.4	819.2
Net income ($ mil.)	—	3.7	4.1	3.5	0.8	(22.0)
Market value ($ mil.)	(26.8%)	74.8	73.9	58.4	38.5	21.4
Employees	1.1%	197	241	252	253	206

An in-depth profile of this company is available to Hoover's Online members at hoovers.com.

413

COMMUNITY BANK SYSTEM, INC.

NYSE: CBU

5790 Widewaters Pkwy.
DeWitt, NY 13214
Phone: 315-445-2282
Fax: 315-445-2997
Web: www.communitybankna.com

CEO: Mark E. Tryniski
CFO: Scott A. Kingsley
HR: Bernadette R. Barber
FYE: December 31
Type: Public

Community Bank System is right up front about what it is. The holding company owns Community Bank, which operates about 150 branches across nearly 30 counties in upstate New York and five counties in northeastern Pennsylvania, where it operates as First Liberty Bank and Trust. Focusing on small, underserved towns, the bank offers such services as checking and savings, money market, and NOW accounts. The bank's loan portfolio is divided nearly equally among business loans, residential mortgages, and consumer loans. Community Bank System also provides trust services, brokerage services, investment management, insurance products, and employee benefits plan administration.

	Annual Growth	12/05	12/06	12/07	12/08	12/09
Assets ($ mil.)	6.8%	4,152.7	4,497.8	4,697.5	5,174.6	5,402.8
Net income ($ mil.)	(5.0%)	50.8	38.4	42.9	45.9	41.4
Market value ($ mil.)	(3.8%)	747.0	761.9	658.2	807.9	639.7
Employees	5.3%	1,299	1,352	1,453	1,615	1,595

COMMUNITY BANKERS TRUST CORPORATION

NYSE Amex: BTC

4235 Innslake Dr., Ste. 200
Glen Allen, VA 23060
Phone: 804-934-9999
Fax: 804-934-9299
Web: www.cbtrustcorp.com

CEO: George M. Longest Jr.
CFO: Bruce E. Thomas
HR: —
FYE: December 31
Type: Public

Community Bankers Trust, formerly Community Bankers Acquisition, is the holding company for the Bank of Essex and TransCommunity Bank. Additional divisions of TransCommunity operate as Bank of Goochland, Bank of Powhatan, Bank of Louisa, and Bank of Rockbridge. The company grew in 2008 when it merged with former bank holding companies TransCommunity Financial and BOE Financial Services of Virginia. The company now includes about a dozen bank branches west and north of Richmond, Virginia. Subsidiaries offer securities and insurance products. Community Bankers Trust expanded into Georgia when it acquired the branches and deposits of The Community Bank, which was the 20th bank to fail in 2008.

	Annual Growth	3/05	3/06	3/07	*12/08	12/09
Assets ($ mil.)	1,352.9%	—	0.4	58.8	1,029.1	1,226.7
Net income ($ mil.)	—	—	0.0	1.1	1.2	(29.3)
Market value ($ mil.)	(33.0%)	—	—	155.9	64.4	70.0
Employees	31.8%	—	—	—	220	290

*Fiscal year change

COMMUNITY CAPITAL CORPORATION

NASDAQ (GM): CPBK

1402-C Hwy. 72 West
Greenwood, SC 29649
Phone: 864-941-8200
Fax: 864-941-8283
Web: www.comcapcorp.com

CEO: William G. Stevens
CFO: R. Wesley Brewer
HR: —
FYE: December 31
Type: Public

Community Capital is the holding company for CapitalBank, which operates about 20 branches in western South Carolina. Targeting individuals and small to midsized businesses, the bank provides standard deposit services such as checking and savings accounts, IRAs, and certificates of deposit. Residential real estate mortgages account for about 40% of its loan portfolio; construction loans are approximately 25%, as are commercial mortgages. Consumer and business loans round out its lending activities. The bank's Wealth Management Group provides investment management, retirement planning, fiduciary, and estate settlement services.

	Annual Growth	12/05	12/06	12/07	12/08	12/09
Assets ($ mil.)	5.8%	598.8	713.2	800.6	790.6	749.4
Net income ($ mil.)	—	7.1	5.8	6.9	2.4	(25.2)
Market value ($ mil.)	(37.7%)	190.8	177.6	148.7	72.4	28.8
Employees	(2.9%)	200	221	219	195	178

COMMUNITY CENTRAL BANK CORPORATION

NASDAQ (GM): CCBD

120 N. Main St.
Mt. Clemens, MI 48043
Phone: 586-783-4500
Fax: 586-783-9471
Web: www.communitycentralbank.com

CEO: David A. Widlak
CFO: Ray T. Colonius
HR: Debbie Reinhardt
FYE: December 31
Type: Public

The communities served by Community Central Bank Corporation are in the Detroit area — specifically Mt. Clemens, Grosse Pointe, and Rochester Hills. Founded in 1996, Community Central Bank operates branches that attract consumers, small to midsized businesses, and government entities. Standard services offered include checking, savings, NOW, and money market accounts, and CDs. Commercial real estate loans account for nearly 70% of the company's loan portfolio, followed by residential mortgages (about 20%), business loans, home equity lines, and consumer loans. In 2005 Community Central acquired River Place Financial Corp., a private bank previously owned by the descendants of brewery founder Julius Stroh.

	Annual Growth	12/05	12/06	12/07	12/08	12/09
Assets ($ mil.)	4.2%	462.0	505.0	520.3	557.0	543.8
Net income ($ mil.)	—	3.1	2.1	0.7	(2.0)	(14.6)
Market value ($ mil.)	(41.6%)	44.9	42.7	23.2	8.6	5.2
Employees	(0.6%)	91	90	81	89	89

COMMUNITY COFFEE COMPANY L.L.C.

3332 Partridge Ln., Bldg. A
Baton Rouge, LA 70809
Phone: 225-368-3900
Fax: 225-368-4507
Web: www.communitycoffee.com

CEO: Matthew C. (Matt) Saurage
CFO: Annette L. Vaccaro
HR: Daniel J. (Danny) Hebert
FYE: June 30
Type: Private

Community Coffee is a cuppa Joe with a Cajun patois, don't you know. Boasting that it makes the largest family-owned retail coffee brand (Community Coffee) in the US, the company sells its brew in grocery and convenience stores, restaurants, hotels, and offices throughout the southeastern US. And there's more brewing: Some 30 CC's Coffee Houses have sprung up in Louisiana since the original coffee shop opened in 1995 in New Orleans. The company also offers whole coffee beans, teas, chicory, and coffee-related gifts and accessories at its coffee houses as well as online. Community Coffee is owned by the descendants of Henry Norman Saurage, who founded it in 1919.

	Annual Growth	6/04	6/05	6/06	6/07	6/08
Est. sales ($ mil.)	—	—	—	—	—	148.3
Employees	—	—	—	—	—	1,000

COMMUNITY FINANCIAL CORPORATION

NASDAQ (CM): CFFC

38 N. Central Ave.
Staunton, VA 24401
Phone: 540-886-0796
Fax: 540-885-0643
Web: www.cbnk.com

CEO: Norman C. (Butch) Smiley III
CFO: R. Jerry Giles
HR: —
FYE: March 31
Type: Public

Community Financial is the holding company for Community Bank, originally organized as a Virginia building and loan association in 1928. The institution has a number of branches in the central portion of the state and two offices near the coast in Virginia Beach. Deposit options include checking, savings, NOW, and money market accounts; IRAs; and CDs. The bank also issues credit cards. Its loan portfolio is chiefly composed of real estate loans: Residential and commercial mortgages and construction loans account for some 70% of all loans. Consumer and business loans round out the loan portfolio.

	Annual Growth	3/05	3/06	3/07	3/08	3/09
Assets ($ mil.)	6.4%	399.6	422.6	463.1	491.2	512.7
Net income ($ mil.)	—	3.8	4.3	4.1	3.8	(5.8)
Market value ($ mil.)	(22.7%)	48.9	48.4	51.2	34.9	17.4
Employees	2.9%	138	143	135	134	155

COMMUNITY FIRST BANCORPORATION

OTC: CFOK

449 Hwy. 123 Bypass	CEO: Frederick D. Shepherd Jr.
Seneca, SC 29678	CFO: Frederick D. Shepherd Jr.
Phone: 864-886-0206	HR: —
Fax: 864-886-0912	FYE: December 31
Web: www.c1stbank.com	Type: Public

Community First Bancorporation puts financial matters first in the northwestern corner of South Carolina. The institution is the holding company for Community First Bank, which operates about five branches in Oconee and Anderson counties. The commercial bank offers traditional deposit products such as checking and savings accounts, CDs, and IRAs. Deposit funds are primarily used to originate single- to four-family mortgages and commercial mortgages. The bank also writes construction, consumer, and business loans. Community First Bank plans to continue to expand in Anderson County.

	Annual Growth	12/05	12/06	12/07	12/08	12/09
Assets ($ mil.)	11.3%	320.7	353.9	402.1	469.5	492.9
Net income ($ mil.)	(26.2%)	3.7	3.0	3.3	1.3	1.1
Market value ($ mil.)	(17.2%)	58.1	67.1	61.3	38.2	27.3
Employees	3.7%	76	73	90	92	88

COMMUNITY HEALTH SYSTEMS, INC.

NYSE: CYH

4000 Meridian Blvd.	CEO: Wayne T. Smith
Franklin, TN 37067	CFO: W. Larry Cash
Phone: 615-465-7000	HR: Linda K. Parsons
Fax: —	FYE: December 31
Web: www.chs.net	Type: Public

Community Health Systems (CHS) isn't much of a city dweller. The hospital operator prefers small-town America, owning or leasing some 120 hospitals mostly in rural areas or small cities in about 30 states. Its hospitals (which house roughly 18,000 beds) typically act as the sole or primary acute-health care provider in their service areas. They offer a variety of medical, surgical, and emergency services and generally have ancillary facilities that include doctors' offices, home health agencies, outpatient surgery centers, and diagnostic imaging facilities. CHS' Quorum Health subsidiary provides management services to non-affiliated hospitals.

	Annual Growth	12/05	12/06	12/07	12/08	12/09
Sales ($ mil.)	34.2%	3,738.3	4,365.6	7,127.5	10,840.1	12,107.6
Net income ($ mil.)	16.3%	167.5	168.3	30.3	218.3	306.4
Market value ($ mil.)	(1.8%)	3,637.7	3,465.0	3,497.3	1,383.3	3,377.7
Employees	25.1%	32,300	39,000	82,200	78,334	79,214

COMMUNITY HOSPITALS OF INDIANA, INC.

1500 N. Ritter Ave.	CEO: Michael C. (Mike) Blanchet
Indianapolis, IN 46219	CFO: Thomas P. Fischer
Phone: 317-355-1411	HR: Jill Parris
Fax: 317-351-7723	FYE: December 31
Web: www.ecommunity.com	Type: Not-for-profit

Community Hospitals of Indiana (also known as Community Health Network) keeps the residents of central Indiana in good health. The health care system includes four acute care hospitals, all operating under the Community Hospital moniker (including Community Hospital Anderson). It also runs The Indiana Heart Hospital, where Hoosiers can go to keep their tickers ticking. The Community Health Network, founded in 1956, has more than 950 staffed beds total. The network also includes more than 80 community care sites including physician practices, community clinics, surgery centers, occupational health facilities, a rehabilitation center, and home health practices.

	Annual Growth	12/04	12/05	12/06	12/07	12/08
Est. sales ($ mil.)	—	—	—	—	—	1,089.3
Employees	—	—	—	—	—	5,000

COMMUNITY PARTNERS BANCORP

NASDAQ (CM): CPBC

1250 Hwy. 35 South	CEO: William D. Moss
Middletown, NJ 07748	CFO: A. Richard Abrahamian
Phone: 732-706-9009	HR: —
Fax: —	FYE: December 31
Web: www.communitypartnersbancorp.com	Type: Public

Community Partners Bancorp is the holding company for Two River Community Bank and The Town Bank (a division of Two River). Through more than a dozen total branches located in eastern New Jersey, the two banks offer deposit services like checking and savings accounts, as well as a variety of lending services, to consumers and small to midsized businesses. The banks' combined loan portfolio consists mainly of commercial real estate loans (about 40%), commercial and industrial loans (25%), and construction loans (20%). Consumer and residential loans make up only about 10% of the portfolio. Two River's branches are located in Middletown, while Town Bank's are located in Westfield and Cranford.

	Annual Growth	12/05	12/06	12/07	12/08	12/09
Assets ($ mil.)	24.3%	268.3	520.5	525.1	570.2	640.0
Net income ($ mil.)	—	2.1	3.7	3.7	0.8	(5.1)
Market value ($ mil.)	(30.3%)	—	66.1	67.7	30.7	22.3
Employees	8.1%	—	125	137	140	158

COMMUNITY SHORES BANK CORPORATION

NASDAQ (CM): CSHB

1030 W. Norton Ave.	CEO: Heather D. Brolick
Muskegon, MI 49441	CFO: Tracey A. Welsh
Phone: 231-780-1800	HR: —
Fax: 231-780-1860	FYE: December 31
Web: www.communityshores.com	Type: Public

Community Shores Bank Corporation is the holding company for Community Shores Bank, which has about five branches that serve western Michigan's Muskegon and Ottawa counties. The bank provides deposit services such as checking and savings accounts, money market accounts, health savings accounts, CDs, and IRAs. Commercial operating and real estate loans to area businesses make up approximately three-quarters of the company's loan portfolio, which also includes residential real estate, consumer, and construction loans. The bank also offers investment products and services through an agreement with a third-party provider.

	Annual Growth	12/05	12/06	12/07	12/08	12/09
Assets ($ mil.)	1.0%	222.2	247.0	273.5	255.6	231.4
Net income ($ mil.)	—	1.2	1.3	(0.8)	(1.0)	(5.0)
Market value ($ mil.)	(52.1%)	22.2	19.6	8.8	2.9	1.2
Employees	3.7%	71	83	98	86	82

COMMUNITY TRUST BANCORP, INC.

NASDAQ (GS): CTBI

346 N. Mayo Trail	CEO: Jean R. Hale
Pikeville, KY 41501	CFO: Kevin J. Stumbo
Phone: 606-432-1414	HR: —
Fax: 606-437-3366	FYE: December 31
Web: www.ctbi.com	Type: Public

Even Pike County's Hatfields and McCoys might agree that Community Trust Bancorp is a good place to store your loot. One of Kentucky's largest bank holding companies, it's the parent of Community Trust Bank, which operates about 75 branches throughout the state and in southern West Virginia. The bank offers standard retail banking to area businesses and individuals, including checking and savings accounts, NOW accounts, and CDs. Loans secured by commercial and other real estate account for more than half of the bank's lending portfolio, which also includes commercial loans, consumer loans, and construction loans. The company provides trust services through subsidiary Community Trust and Investment Company.

	Annual Growth	12/05	12/06	12/07	12/08	12/09
Assets ($ mil.)	2.0%	2,849.2	2,969.8	2,902.7	2,954.5	3,086.7
Net income ($ mil.)	(7.6%)	34.4	39.1	36.6	23.1	25.1
Market value ($ mil.)	(5.6%)	468.3	632.4	419.2	559.6	372.3
Employees	(0.5%)	1,003	1,021	1,011	986	982

An in-depth profile of this company is available to Hoover's Online members at hoovers.com.

415

COMMUNITY VALLEY BANCORP

OTC: CVLL

2041 Forest Ave.
Chico, CA 95928
Phone: 530-899-2344
Fax: 530-891-3498
Web: www.communityvalleybancorp.com

CEO: John F. Coger
CFO: Barbara A. Crouse
HR: Beth Turner
FYE: December 31
Type: Public

Community Valley Bancorp is the holding company for Butte Community Bank, which serves individuals and businesses through more than a dozen branches in the northern California counties of Butte, Colusa, Shasta, Sutter, Tehema, and Yuba. Founded in 1990, it also operates loan production offices in Citrus Heights and Gridley. In addition to offering loans, the bank provides deposit products including CDs, and checking, savings, and retirement accounts. Sister subsidiary Butte Community Insurance Agency writes car, health, farm, and other policies. Other divisions offer payroll and financial services. Butte Community Bank is one of the largest US Department of Agriculture (USDA) lenders in the country.

	Annual Growth	12/05	12/06	12/07	12/08	12/09
Assets ($ mil.)	2.1%	494.8	550.0	580.6	595.2	538.5
Net income ($ mil.)	—	7.2	7.2	6.5	2.7	(27.5)
Market value ($ mil.)	(43.6%)	95.5	101.2	67.5	28.5	9.6
Employees	(1.9%)	275	306	291	278	255

COMMUNITY WEST BANCSHARES

NASDAQ (GM): CWBC

445 Pine Ave.
Goleta, CA 93117
Phone: 805-692-5821
Fax: 805-692-5835
Web: www.communitywest.com

CEO: Lynda J. Nahra
CFO: Charles G. Baltuskonis
HR: —
FYE: December 31
Type: Public

Community West Bancshares is the holding company for Community West Bank, which serves individuals and small to midsized businesses through five branches along California's Central Coast. Services include checking and savings accounts and CDs, as well as health savings accounts. Approximately 40% of the bank's loan portfolio is secured by manufactured housing loans; real estate mortgages account for more than 30%. A preferred Small Business Administration lender, Community West also writes SBA loans through offices in about a dozen other states.

	Annual Growth	12/05	12/06	12/07	12/08	12/09
Assets ($ mil.)	11.4%	444.4	516.6	609.8	657.0	684.2
Net income ($ mil.)	—	5.6	5.3	3.8	1.5	(5.8)
Market value ($ mil.)	(33.5%)	83.4	92.6	54.8	21.2	16.3
Employees	(3.0%)	147	163	159	148	130

COMMVAULT SYSTEMS, INC.

NASDAQ (GM): CVLT

2 Crescent Place
Oceanport, NJ 07757
Phone: 732-870-4000
Fax: 732-870-4525
Web: www.commvault.com

CEO: N. Robert (Bob) Hammer
CFO: Louis F. (Lou) Miceli
HR: William (Bill) Beattie
FYE: March 31
Type: Public

CommVault Systems wants to have a lock on data management. The company provides software that customers use to store and manage enterprise data. Its Simpana software suite handles such tasks as resource management, backup, archiving, data replication, disaster recovery, and search. The company's customers come from industries including manufacturing, financial services, health care, and transportation, as well as from the public sector. CommVault's strategic partners include systems integrators and professional services firms, distributors and resellers, and technology providers. It counts Dell and Hitachi Data Systems (HDS) among its key strategic partners.

	Annual Growth	3/06	3/07	3/08	3/09	3/10
Sales ($ mil.)	25.4%	109.5	151.1	198.3	234.5	271.0
Net income ($ mil.)	14.2%	10.8	64.3	20.8	12.3	18.4
Market value ($ mil.)	9.6%	—	699.3	535.3	473.5	921.6
Employees	60.0%	176	727	866	1,070	1,154

COMNET INTERNATIONAL COMPANY

1 Trans Am Plaza Dr., Ste. 520
Oakbrook Terrace, IL 60181
Phone: 630-615-2000
Fax: 630-678-2919
Web: www.comneti.com

CEO: Ravi Ravichandran
CFO: —
HR: —
FYE: December 31
Type: Subsidiary

COMNET International provides outsourced software development and other information technology services for the telecommunications industry. The company's IT services include consulting, application development, network design, product testing, and quality assurance. COMNET does software development from its offshore facility, India Comnet, in Chennai, India. In addition to the telecom industry, the company serves clients in such industries as banking and education. COMNET, founded in 1994 by president (and former owner) Ravi Ravichandran, is a subsidiary of Infinite Computer Solutions.

	Annual Growth	12/04	12/05	12/06	12/07	12/08
Est. sales ($ mil.)	—	—	—	—	—	23.5
Employees	—	—	—	—	—	300

COMPASS BANCSHARES, INC.

15 S. 20th St.
Birmingham, AL 35233
Phone: 205-297-3000
Fax: 205-297-7363
Web: www.bbvacompass.com

CEO: Manolo Sanchez
CFO: Isabel Goiri
HR: E. Lee Harris Jr.
FYE: December 31
Type: Subsidiary

The needle of this Compass points south. Compass Bancshares is the holding company for Compass Bank, which does business as BBVA Compass. The bank operates more than 720 branches in Alabama, Arizona, California, Colorado, Florida, New Mexico, and Texas. It provides standard corporate and retail banking services such as deposit accounts, credit cards, business and personal loans, and mortgages. BBVA Compass also offers wealth management services such as securities brokerage, mutual funds, insurance, annuities, pension fund management, and investment advisory. Compass Bancshares is a subsidiary of Spain-based banking giant Banco Bilbao Vizcaya Argentaria (BBVA).

COMPASS DIVERSIFIED HOLDINGS

NASDAQ (GS): CODI

61 Wilton Rd., 2nd Fl.
Westport, CT 06880
Phone: 203-221-1703
Fax: 203-221-8253
Web: www.compassdiversifiedtrust.com

CEO: Ihab Joseph (Joe) Massoud
CFO: James J. (Jim) Bottiglieri
HR: —
FYE: December 31
Type: Public

Compass Diversified Holdings helps companies navigate their way towards profitability. The holding company invests in and manages promising middle-market businesses. Its strategy is two-fold: help those companies in its portfolio grow and increase profits, and increase the size of its portfolio. The companies in its portfolio come from a variety of industries; they include human resources outsourcing firm Staffmark (formerly CBS Personnel) and promotional products maker HALO Holding. In 2008 Compass Diversified Holdings acquired a controlling interest in suspension products maker Fox Factory (dba Fox Racing Shox).

	Annual Growth	12/05	12/06	12/07	12/08	12/09
Sales ($ mil.)	44.8%	—	410.9	917.9	1,538.5	1,248.7
Net income ($ mil.)	—	—	(19.2)	40.4	78.3	(39.6)
Market value ($ mil.)	(9.4%)	—	718.2	623.9	471.1	534.3
Employees	5.4%	—	200	239	237	234

COMPASS GROUP USA, INC.

2400 Yorkmont Rd.
Charlotte, NC 28217
Phone: 704-329-4000
Fax: 704-329-4010
Web: www.cgnad.com

CEO: Gary R. Green
CFO: Thomas (Tom) Ondrof
HR: Vincent L. Berkeley Jr.
FYE: September 30
Type: Subsidiary

This company points the way to managed foodservices. Compass Group USA provides catering and dining services to corporate clients, educational and health care facilities, and sports and entertainment venues through a number of subsidiaries. Its operating units include Bon Appétit Management Co., Chartwells Educational Dining Services, and Morrison Management Specialists. Its Levy Restaurants unit also operates fine dining locations, as well as concessions at sports and entertainment venues. In addition, the company offers vending services and on-site dining. A division of UK-based Compass Group, Compass Group USA was formed in 1994 through the acquisition of Canteen Vending Services.

COMPASS MINERALS INTERNATIONAL, INC.

NYSE: CMP

9900 W. 109th St., Ste. 600
Overland Park, KS 66210
Phone: 913-344-9200
Fax: 913-338-7932
Web: www.compassminerals.com

CEO: Angelo C. Brisimitzakis
CFO: Rodney L. (Rod) Underdown
HR: Victoria Heider
FYE: December 31
Type: Public

Salt is Compass Minerals' true north. The company is one of the largest salt producers in North America. Its salt products include rock, evaporated, and solar salt and are used for applications such as water softening, road deicing, and food preparation. Highway deicing salt — generally sold to state, province, or municipal governments — accounts for almost half of its annual sales. Compass Minerals operates through subsidiaries North American Salt, Great Salt Lake Minerals (a top producer of the crop nutrient sulfate of potash), Sifto Canada, and Salt Union (based in the UK). It has seven manufacturing facilities and two salt mines in Canada, the UK, and the US.

	Annual Growth	12/05	12/06	12/07	12/08	12/09
Sales ($ mil.)	6.7%	742.3	660.7	857.3	1,167.7	963.1
Net income ($ mil.)	51.8%	30.9	55.0	80.0	159.5	163.9
Market value ($ mil.)	28.6%	803.0	1,032.7	1,341.6	1,919.5	2,198.7
Employees	4.4%	1,506	1,557	1,588	1,743	1,792

COMPELLENT TECHNOLOGIES, INC.

NYSE Arca: CML

7625 Smetana Ln.
Eden Prairie, MN 55344
Phone: 952-294-3300
Fax: 952-294-3333
Web: www.compellent.com

CEO: Philip E. (Phil) Soran
CFO: John R. (Jack) Judd
HR: —
FYE: December 31
Type: Public

Compellent Technologies can take a byte out of your storage woes. Storage Center, the company's main product, is a storage area network (SAN) that enables users to deposit, recover, and manage large amounts of data. The product combines software with standards-based hardware and has been purchased by more than 1,200 customers worldwide, in such industries as education, financial services, government, health care, insurance, retail, and transportation. Third-party hardware maintenance provider Anacomp offers storage equipment, network device, and peripheral repair services to Compellent's end users. The company gets most of its sales in the US.

	Annual Growth	12/05	12/06	12/07	12/08	12/09
Sales ($ mil.)	88.6%	9.9	23.3	51.2	90.9	125.3
Net income ($ mil.)	—	(9.1)	(6.8)	(7.8)	(0.4)	4.8
Market value ($ mil.)	37.3%	—	—	381.9	305.4	719.9
Employees	22.5%	172	153	212	290	387

COMPETITIVE TECHNOLOGIES, INC.

NYSE Amex: CTT

777 Commerce Dr., Ste. 100
Fairfield, CT 06825
Phone: 203-368-6044
Fax: 203-368-5399
Web: www.competitivetech.net

CEO: John B. Nano
CFO: John B. Nano
HR: —
FYE: July 31
Type: Public

It doesn't matter how great your invention is if you can't get it to market — that's where Competitive Technologies (CTT) comes in. The company helps individuals, corporations, government agencies, and universities commercialize their inventions. Clients such as Sony and the University of Illinois have used CTT's services, which include feasibility and marketability evaluations, as well as application for and enforcement of patents. CTT focuses on inventions in life and physical sciences as well as digital technologies. The company, established in 1971, also represents companies seeking to license technologies for commercial purposes.

	Annual Growth	7/05	7/06	7/07	7/08	7/09
Sales ($ mil.)	(61.9%)	14.2	5.2	4.2	1.2	0.3
Net income ($ mil.)	—	5.7	(2.4)	(8.9)	(6.0)	(3.5)
Market value ($ mil.)	(20.1%)	63.7	25.9	28.3	30.8	26.0
Employees	(13.4%)	16	20	15	12	9

COMPLETE PRODUCTION SERVICES, INC.

NYSE: CPX

11700 Old Katy Rd., Ste. 300
Houston, TX 77079
Phone: 281-372-2300
Fax: 281-372-2301
Web: www.completeproduction.com

CEO: Joseph C. Winkler III
CFO: Jose A. Bayardo
HR: Kenneth L. Nibling
FYE: December 31
Type: Public

Complete Production Services tries to live up to its name as it serves customers in Mexico, Western Canada, and the US (the Rocky Mountains, Arkansas, Louisiana, Oklahoma, Pennsylvania, and Texas). It is a major provider of specialized services and products that help oil and gas companies develop reserves, enhance production, and reduce costs. Focusing on hydrocarbon-rich basins in North America that have long-term growth potential, the company offers a range of oil field services, including drilling, completion and production services (intervention, downhole and wellsite services, and fluid handling), and product sales. It also has a used equipment refurbishment operation in Southeast Asia.

	Annual Growth	12/05	12/06	12/07	12/08	12/09
Sales ($ mil.)	8.7%	757.7	1,212.4	1,655.2	1,838.6	1,056.4
Net income ($ mil.)	—	53.9	139.1	161.6	(85.5)	(181.7)
Market value ($ mil.)	(15.0%)	—	1,648.1	1,397.0	633.6	1,010.6
Employees	3.9%	4,485	6,397	7,062	7,266	5,235

COMPREHENSIVE CARE CORPORATION

OTC: CHCR

3405 W. Dr. Martin Luther King Jr. Blvd., Ste. 101
Tampa, FL 33607
Phone: 813-288-4808
Fax: 813-288-4844
Web: www.compcare.com

CEO: Clark A. Marcus
CFO: Giuseppe (Joe) Crisafi
HR: —
FYE: December 31
Type: Public

Comprehensive Care makes sure that health insurance covers the mind as well as the body. Through its Comprehensive Behavioral Care subsidiary (CompCare, for short), the company manages behavioral health care, including psychiatric and substance abuse services, for commercial and government-run health plans in about a dozen states. For the most part it operates under capitation agreements, in which the plans pay CompCare a fixed monthly fee for each member. The firm maintains a network of about 3,500 behavioral health providers, through which it manages the care of private health plan members, as well as Medicare and Medicaid participants. Hythiam owns a controlling share in the firm.

	Annual Growth	5/05	5/06	*12/07	12/08	12/09
Sales ($ mil.)	(12.7%)	24.5	24.0	37.4	35.2	14.2
Net income ($ mil.)	—	(0.3)	(0.2)	(3.5)	(5.4)	(18.9)
Market value ($ mil.)	(30.4%)	73.2	82.0	21.7	19.5	17.2
Employees	(0.9%)	85	70	100	74	82

*Fiscal year change

An in-depth profile of this company is available to Hoover's Online members at hoovers.com.

417

COMPRESSCO PARTNERS, L.P.

101 Park Ave., 12th Fl.
Oklahoma City, OK 73102
Phone: 405-677-0221
Fax: 405-677-7046
Web: www.compressco.com

CEO: Ronald J. (Ron) Foster
CFO: Gary L. McBride
HR: —
FYE: December 31
Type: Private

Compressco Partners puts the pressure on before the natural gas and oil wells run dry. The company specializes in providing services to more than 400 natural gas and oil companies across 14 states to increase production and total recoverable reserves. The company offers compression, liquids separation, and gas metering services, as well as the GasJack units that perform these operations. It applies its services primarily to mature wells, but also on newer wells, which have declined in production. Compressco Partners, a subsidiary of TETRA Technologies, also provides well evaluations and well testing and monitoring services in Mexico.

COMPUCOM SYSTEMS, INC.

7171 Forest Ln.
Dallas, TX 75230
Phone: 972-856-3600
Fax: 972-856-5395
Web: www.compucom.com

CEO: James W. Dixon
CFO: Michael Simpson
HR: Timothy Shea
FYE: December 31
Type: Private

CompuCom Systems urges clients to leave the IT management to them. The company provides infrastructure management services encompassing desktops, servers, networks, data centers, and security. Its application services include consulting, implementation, and custom development. CompuCom also offers third-party hardware and software management services, handling the procurement, configuration, deployment, and support of products from such providers as Apple, Hewlett-Packard, IBM, Microsoft, and Oracle. The company markets primarily to midsized and large enterprises in North America. Court Square Capital Partners acquired CompuCom for $628 million in 2007.

	Annual Growth	12/04	12/05	12/06	12/07	12/08
Sales ($ mil.)	40.0%	—	—	—	1,500.0	2,100.0
Employees	42.9%	—	—	—	7,700	11,000

COMPUCREDIT HOLDINGS CORPORATION

NASDAQ (GS): CCRT

5 Concourse Pkwy., Ste. 400
Atlanta, GA 30328
Phone: 770-828-2000
Fax: 770-870-5183
Web: www.compucredit.com

CEO: David G. Hanna
CFO: J. Paul Whitehead III
HR: —
FYE: December 31
Type: Public

Suffering from a fiscal near-death experience? Let CompuCredit resuscitate you. CompuCredit operates in four segments: credit card receivables, in which it targets customers with low credit scores and charges them more for the risk; retail microloans, or payday loans, as they are more commonly known; auto financing; and charged-off credit card receivables, in which subsidiary Jefferson Capital Systems collects on debt other companies have written off. The company's retail operations include more than 500 payday loan stores under names including First American Cash Advance and First Southern Cash Advance. CompuCredit is considering a spin-off of its US and UK microloan business.

	Annual Growth	12/05	12/06	12/07	12/08	12/09
Assets ($ mil.)	(19.9%)	1,821.2	2,113.9	1,874.2	1,527.4	748.8
Net income ($ mil.)	—	171.4	107.5	(51.0)	(101.6)	(551.3)
Market value ($ mil.)	(45.8%)	1,842.8	1,907.5	478.2	265.0	159.6
Employees	(6.8%)	3,400	3,600	3,923	3,524	2,561

COMPUMED, INC.

OTC: CMPD

5777 W. Century Blvd., Ste. 1285
Los Angeles, CA 90045
Phone: 310-258-5000
Fax: 310-645-5880
Web: www.compumed.net

CEO: Maurizio Vecchione
CFO: Phuong Dang
HR: —
FYE: September 30
Type: Public

CompuMed won't comp your meds, but it might interpret your ECG. Through its CardioGram software, the telemedicine company provides online analyses of ECGs (electrocardiograms) for more than 1,000 hospitals, clinics, and other health care facilities throughout the US. The firm's ECG services are available 24 hours a day. CompuMed also rents and, to a lesser extent, sells ECG equipment. The company's additional product, OsteoGram, monitors osteoporosis by analyzing bone density; the test involves taking a hand X-ray and can be performed using standard X-ray equipment.

	Annual Growth	9/05	9/06	9/07	9/08	9/09
Sales ($ mil.)	(3.4%)	2.3	2.1	2.2	2.2	2.0
Net income ($ mil.)	—	(0.3)	(0.4)	(1.4)	(1.5)	(0.3)
Market value ($ mil.)	(21.7%)	10.8	9.5	13.5	7.6	4.1
Employees	(10.3%)	17	17	18	12	11

COMPUNET CLINICAL LABORATORIES, LLC

2308 Sandridge Dr.
Dayton, OH 45439
Phone: 937-296-0844
Fax: 937-296-1924
Web: www.compunetlab.com

CEO: Ed Doucette
CFO: John M. Manier
HR: Alan (Al) Turnbull
FYE: December 31
Type: Joint venture

If you're a Daytonian in need of a cholesterol check, CompuNet Clinical Laboratories has a vial with your name on it. The company provides comprehensive laboratory testing services to physicians, patients, hospitals, and managed care companies in and around Dayton, Ohio. It draws blood (and takes other patient samples) at some 30 specimen collection centers throughout its service area and processes them at one of its various laboratory locations including at its headquarters in Dayton and at Miami Valley Hospital. Founded in 1986, the company is a joint venture owned by Miami Valley Hospital, Quest Diagnostics, and a local pathology group.

	Annual Growth	12/04	12/05	12/06	12/07	12/08
Est. sales ($ mil.)	—	—	—	—	—	21.6
Employees	—	—	—	—	—	450

COMPUSA INC.

7795 W. Flagler St., Ste. 35
Miami, FL 33144
Phone: 305-415-2199
Fax: —
Web: www.compusa.com

CEO: Richard Leeds
CFO: Lawrence P. (Larry) Reinhold
HR: —
FYE: December 31
Type: Subsidiary

CompUSA has been rebooted after a major crash in 2008. The company operates about 30 stores, mostly in Florida, but also in several other states and Puerto Rico, as well as an e-commerce site. It sells computers and peripherals, TVs, gaming consoles, cameras, and other electronics and accessories. CompUSA is a division of Systemax, a multi-channel marketer of consumer electronics and digital media technology. In 2008 Systemax acquired CompUSA's brand, Web site, and retail outlets. Originally a pioneer in big-box computer sales, CompUSA is reformatting itself as a next-generation retailer.

COMPUTER GENERATED SOLUTIONS, INC.

3 World Financial Center, 200 Vesey St.
New York, NY 10281
Phone: 212-408-3800
Fax: 212-977-7474
Web: www.cgsinc.com

CEO: Philip (Phil) Friedman
CFO: Jeffrey (Jeff) White
HR: Paul Joseph
FYE: December 31
Type: Private

CGS (Computer Generated Solutions) provides IT products and services to multiple industries including apparel, education, government agencies, manufacturing, and professional services. The company produces several proprietary software suites, including BlueCherry, used by the apparel and footwear industry, which provides applications including customer relationship management (CRM), enterprise resource planning, and product lifecycle management; and Unlimited Mailbox, used in the government and education sectors to archive e-mail messages. CGS also provides outsourcing and training services. Its technology partners include Dell, IBM, Microsoft, and Quest Software. CEO Philip Friedman founded CGS in 1984.

	Annual Growth	12/04	12/05	12/06	12/07	12/08
Sales ($ mil.)	11.3%	112.9	111.0	135.0	164.0	173.0
Employees	12.9%	1,600	1,400	2,300	2,600	2,600

COMPUTER PROGRAMS AND SYSTEMS, INC.

NASDAQ (GS): CPSI

6600 Wall St.
Mobile, AL 36695
Phone: 251-639-8100
Fax: 251-639-8214
Web: www.cpsinet.com

CEO: J. Boyd Douglas
CFO: Darrell G. West
HR: —
FYE: December 31
Type: Public

Computer Programs and Systems, Inc. (CPSI) wants to make sure your neighborhood hospital isn't suffering from clogged information systems. CPSI develops, installs, and supports financial and clinical information management software and information technology systems for small and midsized hospitals in the US. The company, which targets community hospitals and small specialty hospitals, boasts a client base of more than 650 hospitals. Operating on UNIX and Windows platforms, CPSI's software enables health care providers to manage their patients, staff, finances, and facilities. The company also offers systems implementation, as well as billing, statement processing, and business office outsourcing services.

	Annual Growth	12/05	12/06	12/07	12/08	12/09
Sales ($ mil.)	4.1%	108.8	116.0	110.0	119.7	127.7
Net income ($ mil.)	1.0%	14.6	15.8	12.9	15.4	15.2
Market value ($ mil.)	2.7%	454.6	373.0	249.5	294.1	505.3
Employees	5.8%	858	941	709	886	1,077

[H] COMPUTER SCIENCES CORPORATION

NYSE: CSC

3170 Fairview Park Dr.
Falls Church, VA 22042
Phone: 703-876-1000
Fax: —
Web: www.csc.com

CEO: Michael W. (Mike) Laphen
CFO: Michael J. Mancuso
HR: Denise M. Peppard
FYE: March 31
Type: Public

CSC has mastered the art and science of computer technology. One of the world's leading providers of systems integration and other technology services, Computer Sciences Corporation (CSC) provides application development, data center management, communications and networking development, and business consulting. It also offers business process outsourcing (BPO) services in such areas as billing and payment processing, customer relationship management (CRM), and human resources. A major government and defense contractor, CSC generates about a third of its revenues from US federal agencies.

	Annual Growth	3/06	3/07	3/08	3/09	3/10
Sales ($ mil.)	2.5%	14,615.6	14,856.6	16,499.5	16,739.9	16,128.0
Net income ($ mil.)	6.4%	638.3	388.8	544.6	1,115.2	817.0
Market value ($ mil.)	(0.5%)	8,568.0	8,040.5	6,291.5	5,682.2	8,404.5
Employees	4.4%	79,000	79,000	89,000	92,000	94,000

[H] COMPUTER TASK GROUP, INCORPORATED

NASDAQ (CM): CTGX

800 Delaware Ave.
Buffalo, NY 14209
Phone: 716-882-8000
Fax: 716-887-7464
Web: www.ctg.com

CEO: James R. Boldt
CFO: Brendan M. Harrington
HR: Arthur W. (Bud) Crumlish
FYE: December 31
Type: Public

Computer Task Group (CTG) uses its IT expertise to take clients' computer systems to task. Serving primarily technology service providers, health care, manufacturing, and financial services clients, the company offers a wide range of professional technology services, including IT staffing, custom application development, and systems integration. It also provides strategic consulting services to assess its clients' technology needs, as well as project management and application outsourcing management services. CTG serves clients through offices in the US, Canada, and Europe. The company was founded in 1966.

	Annual Growth	12/05	12/06	12/07	12/08	12/09
Sales ($ mil.)	(1.6%)	294.5	327.3	325.3	353.2	275.6
Net income ($ mil.)	25.2%	2.4	3.5	4.2	7.8	5.9
Market value ($ mil.)	19.3%	71.6	86.1	100.3	58.4	145.2
Employees	(5.3%)	3,600	3,300	3,400	3,100	2,900

[H] COMPUWARE CORPORATION

NASDAQ (GS): CPWR

1 Campus Martius
Detroit, MI 48226
Phone: 313-227-7300
Fax: 313-227-7555
Web: www.compuware.com

CEO: Peter (Pete) Karmanos Jr.
CFO: Laura L. Fournier
HR: —
FYE: March 31
Type: Public

Compuware is more than aware of the power of diversity. The company's products include testing, development, and management software for programs running on mainframe computer systems, distributed computer networks, and Web-based systems. Compuware also makes application development, implementation, and support software for programmers, as well as file, data, and systems management tools. Compuware's service offerings include consulting, systems integration, custom programming, maintenance, and support. The company sells directly and through distributors to corporate and government customers.

	Annual Growth	3/05	3/06	3/07	3/08	3/09
Sales ($ mil.)	(3.0%)	1,231.8	1,205.4	1,213.0	1,229.6	1,090.5
Net income ($ mil.)	16.2%	76.5	143.0	158.1	134.4	139.6
Market value ($ mil.)	(2.2%)	1,637.3	1,780.6	2,158.1	1,669.2	1,498.6
Employees	(10.8%)	7,908	7,510	7,539	6,344	5,006

COMPX INTERNATIONAL INC.

NYSE: CIX

5430 LBJ Fwy., Ste. 1700, Three Lincoln Center
Dallas, TX 75240
Phone: 972-448-1400
Fax: 972-448-1445
Web: www.compxnet.com

CEO: David A. Bowers
CFO: Darryl R. Halbert
HR: —
FYE: December 31
Type: Public

CompX International tries to keep the workday smooth, theft-free, and painless. Through CompX's three divisions, Security Products, Furniture Components, and Marine Components, the company makes ball bearing slides, cabinet locks, and ergonomic computer support systems. Its primary customers are office furniture makers, but its components are used in recreational vehicles, ignition systems, vending equipment, mailboxes, appliances, and computer equipment. CompX's ball bearing slides are sold under names such as Dynaslide and Waterloo; its locks are sold under such names as National Cabinet Lock, Fort Lock, and Chicago Lock. NL Industries owns 87% of CompX International.

	Annual Growth	12/05	12/06	12/07	12/08	12/09
Sales ($ mil.)	(11.2%)	186.3	190.1	177.7	165.5	116.1
Net income ($ mil.)	—	0.4	11.7	9.0	(3.1)	(2.0)
Market value ($ mil.)	(17.1%)	198.2	249.4	180.9	65.3	93.6
Employees	(9.8%)	1,230	1,137	1,029	976	815

[H] An in-depth profile of this company is available to Hoover's Online members at hoovers.com.

419

COMSCORE, INC.

NASDAQ (GS): SCOR

11950 Democracy Dr., Ste. 600
Reston, VA 20190
Phone: 703-438-2000
Fax: 703-438-2051
Web: www.comscore.com

CEO: Magid M. Abraham
CFO: Kenneth (Ken) Tarpey
HR: —
FYE: December 31
Type: Public

comScore knows the score when it comes to measuring online audience behavior. The company provides data, analysis, and consultancy to some 1,100 clients looking to fortify their marketing, sales, and trading initiatives. Its global panel of more than 2 million Internet users measures and tracks consumer behaviors, demographics, and advertising responsiveness for clients in such industries as travel, pharmaceuticals, finance, and telecommunications. Branded products include comScore's Media Metrix suite of Web site and online advertising network measurement tools and comScore's Marketing Solutions products, which provide custom research and analysis from its panel. Clients include AT&T, Verizon, and Viacom.

	Annual Growth	12/05	12/06	12/07	12/08	12/09
Sales ($ mil.)	26.2%	50.3	66.3	87.2	117.4	127.7
Net income ($ mil.)	—	(4.0)	5.7	19.3	25.2	4.0
Market value ($ mil.)	(26.7%)	—	—	1,011.7	395.3	544.2
Employees	12.0%	377	377	452	581	593

COMSTOCK HOMEBUILDING COMPANIES, INC.

NASDAQ (GM): CHCI

11465 Sunset Hills Rd., Ste. 510
Reston, VA 20190
Phone: 703-883-1700
Fax: 703-760-1520
Web: www.comstockhomebuilding.com

CEO: Christopher (Chris) Clemente
CFO: Jeffrey R. (Jeff) Dauer
HR: —
FYE: December 31
Type: Public

While people take stock of their lives, Comstock takes stock of its portfolio. The homebuilder develops land and builds single-family homes, townhouses, and mid- and high-rise condominiums in and around Washington, DC. The company annually delivers some 200 homes with an average price of approximately $289,000. Its customer base includes first-time homebuyers, buyers looking to move up, empty nesters, and active retirees. The company also rents resdential properties under the Comstock Communities name. Average rent is appoximately $1,500 a month.

	Annual Growth	12/05	12/06	12/07	12/08	12/09
Sales ($ mil.)	(42.2%)	224.3	245.9	266.2	46.7	25.1
Net income ($ mil.)	—	27.6	(39.8)	(87.5)	(17.1)	(26.8)
Market value ($ mil.)	(51.0%)	264.2	107.7	12.4	3.2	15.3
Employees	(30.1%)	130	205	142	67	31

COMSTOCK RESOURCES, INC.

NYSE: CRK

5300 Town and Country Blvd., Ste. 500
Frisco, TX 75034
Phone: 972-668-8800
Fax: 972-668-8812
Web: www.comstockresources.com

CEO: M. Jay Allison
CFO: Roland O. Burns
HR: Roland O. Burns
FYE: December 31
Type: Public

Comstock Resources' stock in trade is producing natural gas and oil. The midsized independent oil and gas company in 2009 reported proved reserves of more than 725.7 billion cu. ft. of natural gas equivalent (94% in the form of natural gas) on its properties primarily located in two major areas — East Texas/North Louisiana, and South Texas. Comstock Resources operates 950 of the more than 1,640 producing wells in which it holds an interest. The company has grown through the drill bit (by exploiting existing reserves) and through complementary acquisitions.

	Annual Growth	12/05	12/06	12/07	12/08	12/09
Sales ($ mil.)	(1.0%)	303.3	511.9	687.1	590.3	291.1
Net income ($ mil.)	—	60.5	70.7	68.9	252.0	(36.5)
Market value ($ mil.)	7.4%	1,441.3	1,467.3	1,606.2	2,232.2	1,916.6
Employees	9.9%	89	130	138	135	130

COMSYS IT PARTNERS, INC.

4400 Post Oak Pkwy., Ste. 1800
Houston, TX 77027
Phone: 713-386-1400
Fax: 713-961-0719
Web: www.comsys.com

CEO: Larry L. Enterline
CFO: Amy Bobbitt
HR: Terry V. Bell
FYE: December 31
Type: Subsidiary

In need of a technical whiz? COMSYS IT Partners supplies temporary information technology (IT) personnel from more than 50 offices in the US, as well as from facilities in Canada and the UK. The company also helps companies recruit and hire permanent IT professionals and provides ad hoc project teams that develop and implement applications either on- or offsite. COMSYS IT Partners employs about 4,500 IT professionals and serves more than 1,000 customers in the finance, health care, pharmaceutical, telecom, manufacturing, and transportation industries, as well as government entities. It was acquired by global staffing services giant Manpower in 2010.

	Annual Growth	12/05	12/06	12/07	12/08	12/09
Sales ($ mil.)	(0.5%)	661.7	736.6	743.3	727.1	649.3
Net income ($ mil.)	45.5%	2.1	21.0	33.3	(65.2)	9.4
Employees	(5.1%)	5,661	4,297	4,986	4,516	4,596

COMTECH TELECOMMUNICATIONS CORP.

NASDAQ (GS): CMTL

68 S. Service Rd., Ste. 230
Melville, NY 11747
Phone: 631-962-7000
Fax: 631-962-7001
Web: www.comtechtel.com

CEO: Fred V. Kornberg
CFO: Michael D. Porcelain
HR: —
FYE: July 31
Type: Public

Comtech means contact. Through its subsidiaries, Comtech Telecommunications operates in three divisions: telecommunications transmission, mobile data communications, and radio-frequency (RF) microwave amplifiers. The company makes equipment used largely by the US government and related defense contractors. Other customers include satellite systems integrators, communications service providers, and oil companies. Its transmission equipment includes modems, frequency converters, high-power amplifiers, very-small-aperture terminal (VSAT) satellite transceivers and antennas, and microwave radios.

	Annual Growth	7/05	7/06	7/07	7/08	7/09
Sales ($ mil.)	17.5%	307.9	391.5	445.7	531.6	586.4
Net income ($ mil.)	7.8%	36.7	45.3	65.2	76.4	49.6
Market value ($ mil.)	(2.6%)	1,000.7	785.9	1,230.6	1,390.8	902.2
Employees	10.2%	1,090	1,228	1,230	1,350	1,607

COMTEL TELCOM ASSETS LP

433 Las Colinas Blvd. East, Ste. 1300
Irving, TX 75039
Phone: 972-910-1300
Fax: —
Web: www.excel.com

CEO: James Cashiola
CFO: —
HR: —
FYE: December 31
Type: Private

If it wasn't apparent from the name, Comtel Telcom Assets is in the communications game. The company, which does business as Excel Telecommunications, provides wholesale telecom services to residential customers, small businesses, and communications service resellers. Its consumer brands include Three Penny, Simply More, and Dime Deal. Commercial clients include corporate customer service call centers. Excel offers such services as local calling, domestic and international long-distance, VoIP computer telephony, Internet access, and toll-free numbers. The company also provides teleconferencing services. It operates from facilities in nine major US cities.

⊞ COMTEX NEWS NETWORK, INC.   OTC: CMTX

625 N. Washington St., Ste. 301   CEO: Chip Brian
Alexandria, VA 22314   CFO: Paul J. Sledz
Phone: 703-820-2000   HR: —
Fax: 703-820-2005   FYE: June 30
Web: www.comtexnews.net   Type: Public

Comtex News Network is a leading distributor of electronic news and alerts that specializes in the business and financial markets. The company gathers news and content from more than 10,000 national and international news agencies and publications, including PR Newswire, United Press International, and The Associated Press, and packages those feeds into several different product offerings. In addition to individual and institutional customers, Comtex supplies news to such information distributors as MarketWatch, Dow Jones' Factiva, and Thomson Financial.

	Annual Growth	6/05	6/06	6/07	6/08	6/09
Sales ($ mil.)	(5.4%)	8.0	7.7	7.1	7.1	6.4
Net income ($ mil.)	(38.5%)	0.7	(0.5)	(0.1)	0.7	0.1
Market value ($ mil.)	(3.8%)	2.2	13.4	3.2	3.9	1.9
Employees	4.3%	22	25	21	29	26

COMVERGE, INC.   NASDAQ (GM): COMV

120 Eagle Rock Rd., Ste. 190   CEO: R. Blake Young
East Hanover, NJ 07936   CFO: Michael D. (Mike) Picchi
Phone: 973-884-5970   HR: Mark Schaefer
Fax: 973-884-3504   FYE: December 31
Web: www.comverge.com   Type: Public

Comverge seeks a convergence of communications enabling the lights to stay on. The company provides demand management software and systems to electric utilities and other energy suppliers and sells automated meters and related equipment with communications links. The company's products are used by more than 500 utilities and energy providers in Asia, Latin America, the Middle East, and North America. US customers include Gulf Power, Buckeye Power, Duke Energy, Detroit Edison, and PEPCO. Its products include software and hardware that help control energy load, read meters remotely, manage billing, and detect theft and outages.

	Annual Growth	12/05	12/06	12/07	12/08	12/09
Sales ($ mil.)	43.3%	23.4	33.9	55.2	77.2	98.8
Net income ($ mil.)	—	(8.0)	(6.2)	(6.6)	(94.1)	(31.7)
Market value ($ mil.)	(40.3%)	—	—	791.7	123.2	282.6
Employees	55.5%	—	117	381	385	440

⊞ COMVERSE TECHNOLOGY, INC.   Pink Sheets: CMVT

810 7th Ave.   CEO: Andre Dahan
New York, NY 10019   CFO: Stephen M. (Steve) Swad
Phone: 212-739-1000   HR: Lance Miyamoto
Fax: —   FYE: January 31
Web: www.cmvt.com   Type: Public

Comverse Technology helps others converse. Through multiple subsidiaries, the company makes communications systems and software that its customers use to offer call answering, billing, voice and fax mail, communications surveillance, and other services. Comverse also makes digital monitoring systems for call centers and telecom software for information processing. Subsidiary Ulticom provides software used to enable call switching, database, and messaging systems and manage number, routing, and billing data. The company's customers include more than 500 communications and content service providers in 130-plus countries, including Sprint Nextel and Brazil's Sercomtel.

⊞ CONAGRA FOODS, INC.   NYSE: CAG

1 ConAgra Dr.   CEO: Gary M. Rodkin
Omaha, NE 68102   CFO: John F. Gehring
Phone: 402-240-4000   HR: Tim Jones
Fax: 402-240-4707   FYE: May 31
Web: www.conagrafoods.com   Type: Public

ConAgra Foods fills Americans' refrigerators, freezers, and pantries and, ultimately, their tummies. The company is a US top food producer, offering packaged and frozen foods. ConAgra's brands are a cornucopia of America's well-known foods, including Banquet, Chef Boyardee, Egg Beaters, Healthy Choice, Hunt's, Jiffy, Orville Redenbacher's, PAM, Slim Jim, and Van Camp's. It is also one of the country's largest foodservice suppliers, offering them convenience foods and ingredients. The company has sold off its agricultural segments and a number of noncore brands in order to concentrate on branded and value-added packaged foods.

	Annual Growth	5/05	5/06	5/07	5/08	5/09
Sales ($ mil.)	(3.3%)	14,566.9	11,579.4	12,028.2	11,605.7	12,731.2
Net income ($ mil.)	11.1%	641.5	533.8	764.6	930.6	978.4
Market value ($ mil.)	(8.2%)	11,651.4	10,069.6	11,361.7	10,506.3	8,282.9
Employees	(9.4%)	38,000	33,000	24,500	25,000	25,600

CONAIR CORPORATION

1 Cummings Point Rd.   CEO: Ronald T. Diamond
Stamford, CT 06902   CFO: Dennis Ling
Phone: 203-351-9000   HR: John Mayorek
Fax: —   FYE: December 31
Web: www.conair.com   Type: Private

Counterintelligence indicates that Conair has a place in many bathrooms and kitchens. The company operates through several divisions, including personal care and hair goods. Its personal care items, such as grooming and health and wellness appliances, are made under names Interplak, Travel Smart, and Allegro. Conair's hair goods business makes brushes, mirrors, and Scünci accessories, while its Rusk subsidiary caters to salons. Conair also makes Cuisinart and Waring kitchen items and sells its products through the likes of Bed Bath & Beyond, Target, and Wal-Mart in the US and online internationally. The manufacturer operates worldwide with offices in Canada, Mexico, Hong Kong, Europe, and other countries.

	Annual Growth	12/04	12/05	12/06	12/07	12/08
Sales ($ mil.)	8.7%	1,340.0	1,488.0	1,700.0	1,900.0	1,870.0
Net income ($ mil.)	—	—	—	—	—	146.0
Employees	5.3%	3,331	3,459	3,367	4,060	4,100

CONCENTRA INC.

5080 Spectrum Dr., Ste. 1200 West   CEO: James M. (Jim) Greenwood
Addison, TX 75001   CFO: Thomas E. (Tom) Kiraly
Phone: 972-364-8000   HR: Mark A. Solls
Fax: 972-387-0019   FYE: December 31
Web: www.concentra.com   Type: Private

Concentra concentrates on keeping employees healthy. The company's main business is providing occupational health care services through its network of more than 300 medical centers and about 260 workplace clinics in 40 states. Services provided at the centers include pre-employment screening, injury and urgent care, wellness checks, vaccinations, lab tests, and physical therapy. It also operates mobile health clinics and wellness programs. The company's Auto Injury Solutions division offers a suite of services to property/casualty insurers, including bill review, claims processing, and other services related to auto injury cases. Concentra is owned by private equity firm Welsh, Carson, Anderson & Stowe.

	Annual Growth	12/04	12/05	12/06	12/07	12/08
Sales ($ mil.)	(7.0%)	1,102.3	1,155.1	1,298.8	832.0	826.0
Employees	5.7%	10,370	11,285	11,585	—	—

CONCENTREK, INC.

263 Church St., Ste. B
Jenison, MI 49428
Phone: 616-988-5900
Fax: 616-988-5910
Web: www.concentrek.com

CEO: John R. Patterson
CFO: Roger Morse
HR: —
FYE: January 31
Type: Subsidiary

Concentrek concentrates on freight transportation management. The third-party logistics provider targets small to midsized freight shippers, generally manufacturers with complex distribution networks. Besides arranging the transportation of its customers' freight via a network of independent carriers, Concentrek offers consulting services intended to improve the efficiency of supply chains. It also offers Web-based tracking, data warehousing, procurement, route design, cross docking, and other order management services. The company is a unit of freight forwarder and logistics services provider UTi Worldwide, a global leader that operates in more than 140 countries. Concentrek was founded in 1999.

CONCEPTUS, INC.

NASDAQ (GM): CPTS

331 E. Evelyn
Mountain View, CA 94041
Phone: 650-628-4700
Fax: 650-610-8368
Web: www.conceptus.com

CEO: Mark M. Sieczkarek
CFO: Gregory E. Lichtwardt
HR: —
FYE: December 31
Type: Public

Though you might not think so from the name, Conceptus makes products to hinder conception, not help it along. The company makes and sells Essure, a birth control system that permanently blocks conception with a micro-coil device implanted in the fallopian tube. Essure can be inserted during an outpatient procedure that takes 15 minutes and does not require general anesthesia. Conceptus markets the product primarily to gynecologists in the US through a direct sales force and internationally through distributors in Australia, Canada, France, Spain, and the UK.

	Annual Growth	12/05	12/06	12/07	12/08	12/09
Sales ($ mil.)	57.8%	21.2	41.9	64.4	102.0	131.4
Net income ($ mil.)	—	(21.8)	(18.5)	(11.6)	(0.1)	7.9
Market value ($ mil.)	10.4%	391.6	660.7	597.1	472.3	582.2
Employees	18.3%	139	181	214	236	272

CONCHO RESOURCES INC.

NYSE: CXO

550 W. Texas Ave., Ste. 100
Midland, TX 79701
Phone: 432-683-7443
Fax: 432-683-7441
Web: www.conchoresources.com

CEO: Timothy A. Leach
CFO: Darin G. Holderness
HR: —
FYE: December 31
Type: Public

Concho Resources explores and develops properties, located primarily in the Permian Basin region of eastern New Mexico and West Texas, for the production of oil and gas. It also owns properties in North Dakota and Arkansas. More than half of the company's 550 billion cu. ft. in proved reserves is made up of crude oil, while the rest consists of natural gas. Concho Resources gets two-thirds of its sales from crude oil. Two customers, energy marketers Navajo Refining Company (60% of 2007 sales) and DCP Midstream (23%), account for a great majority of Concho's sales. The company has more than 85 producing wells in operation.

	Annual Growth	12/05	12/06	12/07	12/08	12/09
Sales ($ mil.)	77.5%	54.9	198.3	294.3	533.8	544.4
Net income ($ mil.)	—	2.0	19.7	25.4	278.7	(9.8)
Market value ($ mil.)	47.6%	—	—	1,886.8	2,089.1	4,110.5
Employees	37.3%	80	80	113	245	284

CONCUR TECHNOLOGIES, INC.

NASDAQ (GM): CNQR

18400 NE Union Hill Rd.
Redmond, WA 98052
Phone: 425-702-8808
Fax: 425-702-8828
Web: www.concur.com

CEO: S. Steven (Steve) Singh
CFO: Frank Pelzer
HR: —
FYE: September 30
Type: Public

Concur Technologies can help you make sure that all of your expense reports agree in perfect harmony with budgeting and accounting. The company offers expense and spend management software that enables businesses to automate and streamline the process for submitting and approving employee expense reports. Concur's software features Web-based modules for tracking, submitting, and processing reports for travel and entertainment costs, as well as applications to track employee requests for vendor payments. Concur licenses its software to clients primarily on a subscription basis.

	Annual Growth	9/05	9/06	9/07	9/08	9/09
Sales ($ mil.)	36.3%	71.8	97.1	129.1	215.5	247.6
Net income ($ mil.)	47.7%	5.4	34.2	8.2	17.2	25.7
Market value ($ mil.)	33.9%	617.0	725.7	1,572.1	1,908.3	1,983.1
Employees	29.2%	395	500	575	932	1,100

CONCURRENT COMPUTER CORPORATION

NASDAQ (GM): CCUR

4375 River Green Pkwy., Ste. 100
Duluth, GA 30096
Phone: 678-258-4000
Fax: 678-258-4300
Web: www.ccur.com

CEO: Dan Mondor
CFO: Emory O. Berry
HR: Suzanne Smith
FYE: June 30
Type: Public

Concurrent Computer hawks its wares worldwide. The company provides high-performance computing systems that can simulate a jet fighter or deliver a blockbuster. Digital cable and DSL service providers use its MediaHawk servers and software to offer their customers video-on-demand services. Concurrent also produces Linux-based systems that process large amounts of data instantaneously for such applications as military simulation and training, weather satellite data acquisition, and product design. The company's data collection suite allows customers to store and analyze data from disparate interactive television systems. About three-quarters of Concurrent's sales are in the US.

	Annual Growth	6/05	6/06	6/07	6/08	6/09
Sales ($ mil.)	(2.3%)	78.7	71.6	69.1	70.8	71.6
Net income ($ mil.)	—	(7.7)	(9.0)	(12.2)	0.3	(14.5)
Market value ($ mil.)	(28.0%)	177.0	217.9	149.4	56.8	47.6
Employees	(5.2%)	366	399	347	318	295

CONCURRENT TECHNOLOGIES CORPORATION

100 CTC Dr.
Johnstown, PA 15904
Phone: 814-269-2592
Fax: 814-269-6500
Web: www.ctc.com

CEO: Edward J. (Ed) Sheehan Jr.
CFO: Margaret A. DiVirgilio
HR: —
FYE: June 30
Type: Not-for-profit

Concurrent Technologies Corporation (CTC) can help you keep pace with all the current technologies. The company is a not-for-profit research and development company that provides a variety of IT services to both the public and private sectors. CTC's services include consulting, legacy migration, network design, project management, systems architecture, and systems integration; it serves clients in advanced materials and manufacturing, communications, computers, energy, environmental sustainability, and intelligence, to name a few fields. CTC got a new CEO for the first time in 20 years in 2009, when Ed Sheehan succeeded the retiring Dan DeVos. The company has an office in Canada, as well as offices throughout the US.

	Annual Growth	6/04	6/05	6/06	6/07	6/08
Est. sales ($ mil.)	—	—	—	—	—	238.2
Employees	—	—	—	—	—	1,458

THE CONDÉ NAST PUBLICATIONS

4 Times Square
New York, NY 10036
Phone: 212-286-2860
Fax: —
Web: www.condenast.com

CEO: Charles H. (Chuck) Townsend
CFO: John Bellando
HR: Jill H. Bright
FYE: December 31
Type: Subsidiary

While being *Wired* may hold a certain *Allure*, traditional publishing will always be in *Vogue* at Condé Nast Publications. Owned by newspaper publisher Advance Publications, Condé Nast publishes one of the most recognizable magazine portfolios in the industry, including fashion magazines *Allure* and *Vogue*, as well as cybermag *Wired*. It also produces newsstand stalwarts *GQ, The New Yorker,* and *Vanity Fair*, and newcomers such as *Lucky* (clothes and shopping). It runs websites such as Epicurious (food and fine dining) and Concierge (travel) through its Condé Nast Digital unit, and its Condé Nast International produces foreign versions of its titles for readers in Europe, Asia, Latin America, and South Africa.

CONERGY, INC.

1730 Camino Carlos Rey, Ste. 103
Santa Fe, NM 87507
Phone: 505-473-3800
Fax: 505-473-3830
Web: www.conergy.us

CEO: Kim McLawhorn
CFO: Anthony Fotopoulos
HR: Charlotte Kenzer
FYE: December 31
Type: Subsidiary

Conergy makes and distributes solar water pumps, installs small wind turbines, and distributes solar electric power components, including solar panels, batteries, and related electronics. The company also helps arrange financing for residential installations, since solar panels can be an expensive proposition to purchase. Conergy uses photovoltaic modules made by its German parent company and by Canadian Solar, SANYO Electric, and Suntech Power. Customers include Exelon, the South San Joaquin Irrigation District in California, and the US Army's Fort Carson in Colorado. The company is a subsidiary of Conergy AG.

	Annual Growth	12/04	12/05	12/06	12/07	12/08
Est. sales ($ mil.)	—	—	—	—	—	31.4
Employees	—	—	—	—	—	62

⊞ CONEXANT SYSTEMS, INC.　　NASDAQ (GS): CNXT

4000 MacArthur Blvd.
Newport Beach, CA 92660
Phone: 949-483-4600
Fax: —
Web: www.conexant.com

CEO: D. Scott Mercer
CFO: Jean Hu
HR: Michael H. (Mike) Vishny
FYE: September 30
Type: Public

Conexant Systems' chips help consumer electronics connect with pictures and sound. The fabless company has spun off several business units to focus on providing integrated circuits and subsystems for imaging, audio, video, and other media applications. Its system-on-chip products — which combine multiple functions on a single device — are found in multifunction printers, notebook computers, smartphones, fax machines, and surveillance gear. Conexant also makes embedded modems, decoders, and reference designs. The company sells to a broad range of top high-tech manufacturers, including Canon, Dell, Hewlett-Packard, Kodak, Panasonic, and Sony. About 95% of sales comes from the Asia/Pacific region, primarily China.

	Annual Growth	9/05	9/06	9/07	9/08	9/09
Sales ($ mil.)	(26.7%)	722.7	970.8	808.9	502.7	208.4
Net income ($ mil.)	—	(176.0)	(122.6)	(402.5)	(300.2)	(5.3)
Market value ($ mil.)	(37.5%)	1,453.2	1,623.7	974.2	325.6	222.5
Employees	(29.1%)	2,400	3,120	2,890	1,279	605

CONGOLEUM CORPORATION　　Pink Sheets: CGMC

3500 Quakerbridge Rd.
Mercerville, NJ 08619
Phone: 609-584-3000
Fax: 609-584-3522
Web: www.congoleum.com

CEO: Roger S. Marcus
CFO: Howard N. Feist III
HR: Robert Ingram
FYE: December 31
Type: Public

Congoleum's got your floors covered. The company specializes in making flooring products for residential and commercial use, including resilient sheet flooring (linoleum or vinyl flooring), do-it-yourself vinyl tile, and commercial flooring. Congoleum markets its products through a network of about a dozen distributors in more than 40 North American locations, as well as directly to large market retailers. Customers use its products for new construction, as well as commercial, remodeling, and manufactured housing applications. Distributors Mohawk Industries and LaSalle-Bristol together account for nearly two-thirds of Congoleum's sales. The company also buys sundries and accessories for resale.

	Annual Growth	12/05	12/06	12/07	12/08	12/09
Sales ($ mil.)	(13.2%)	237.6	219.5	204.3	172.6	134.9
Net income ($ mil.)	—	(21.6)	0.7	(0.7)	(14.6)	(15.2)
Market value ($ mil.)	(72.6%)	21.9	13.7	4.2	0.1	0.1
Employees	(11.0%)	833	823	753	613	523

⊞ CONMED CORPORATION　　NASDAQ (GS): CNMD

525 French Rd.
Utica, NY 13502
Phone: 315-797-8375
Fax: 315-797-0321
Web: www.conmed.com

CEO: Joseph J. (Joe) Corasanti
CFO: Robert D. Shallish Jr.
HR: Beth Bowers
FYE: December 31
Type: Public

Doctors and their patients get a charge out of CONMED's surgical equipment. The medical technology company develops and manufactures a wide range of surgical and medical procedure instruments. CONMED's products include electrosurgical systems, powered instruments, suction equipment, and endoscopic devices. Arthroscopic (joint surgery) products include reconstruction tools, scopes, implants, and fluid management systems. CONMED also manufactures patient monitoring products and medical accessories including scissors and staplers. Brands include Linvatec and Hall Surgical. The company sells its products in more than 100 countries through its sales divisions and local distributors.

	Annual Growth	12/05	12/06	12/07	12/08	12/09
Sales ($ mil.)	3.0%	617.3	646.8	694.3	742.2	694.7
Net income ($ mil.)	(21.6%)	32.0	(12.5)	41.5	44.6	12.1
Market value ($ mil.)	(0.9%)	690.4	674.7	674.4	698.6	665.3
Employees	3.1%	3,100	3,200	3,200	3,200	3,500

CONNECT DIRECT INC.

791 Middlefield Rd.
Redwood City, CA 94063
Phone: 650-306-9060
Fax: 650-306-9013
Web: www.connectdirect.com

CEO: Howard J. Sewell
CFO: Ann Corbin
HR: Ann Corbin
FYE: December 31
Type: Private

Connect Direct can hook you up — if direct marketing is what you need. The company provides direct marketing services primarily to small and midsized Internet firms and other technology companies. Although focused on such high-tech strategies as Web banner ads, paid search, and e-mail campaigns, Connect Direct also provides direct mail, event promotion, print media placement, and other traditional direct marketing services. In addition, the company provides strategic consulting, and its Campaign Connection software offers clients online access to marketing campaign results and analysis. Connect Direct was founded in 1990 by president and owner Howard Sewell.

	Annual Growth	12/04	12/05	12/06	12/07	12/08
Est. sales ($ mil.)	—	—	—	—	—	1.9
Employees	—	—	—	—	—	15

THE CONNECTICUT LIGHT AND POWER COMPANY

107 Selden St.	CEO: Jeffrey D. (Jeff) Butler
Berlin, CT 06037	CFO: David R. McHale
Phone: 860-947-2121	HR: —
Fax: 860-665-6276	FYE: December 31
Web: www.cl-p.com	Type: Subsidiary

Connecticut Light and Power Company (CL&P) keeps the folks in the Constitution State connected. CL&P provides electric utility services to more than 1.2 million customers (more than 90% residential) in nearly 150 Connecticut communities. The electric utility, a subsidiary of Northeast Utilities (NU), has more than 235 substations and owns and operates regulated transmission and distribution assets in its 4,400-sq.-mi. service territory. CL&P's transmission assets are monitored by ISO New England. To comply with deregulation mandates, CL&P has divested its generation assets.

	Annual Growth	12/04	12/05	12/06	12/07	12/08
Est. sales ($ mil.)	—	—	—	—	—	3,558.4
Employees	—	—	—	—	—	1,944

CONNECTICUT LOTTERY CORPORATION

777 Brook St.	CEO: Anne Noble
Rocky Hill, CT 06067	CFO: —
Phone: 860-713-2000	HR: Karen M. Mehigen
Fax: 860-713-2805	FYE: June 30
Web: www.ctlottery.org	Type: Government-owned

The Connecticut Lottery gives residents of the Constitution State a chance to amend their incomes. The organization operates a variety of scratch-off instant games and daily numbers games (Cash5, Play4). It also offers Classic Lotto twice-a-week jackpot games and the multistate Powerball Lottery. Revenues from the Connecticut Lottery are paid in prizes and to Connecticut's general fund, which finances services and programs in areas such as public health, public safety, and education. The Connecticut State Lottery began operating in 1971. It became a quasi-public corporation in 1996.

CONNECTICUT WATER SERVICE, INC.

NASDAQ (GS): CTWS

93 W. Main St.	CEO: Eric W. Thornburg
Clinton, CT 06413	CFO: David C. Benoit
Phone: 860-669-8636	HR: Kristen A. Johnson
Fax: 860-669-5579	FYE: December 31
Web: www.ctwater.com	Type: Public

A splash from Connecticut Water Service (CWS) might have helped Mark Twain's Yankee wake up from King Arthur's court. CWS's subsidiary Connecticut Water Company, through its three operating divisions — Connecticut Water, Crystal, and Unionville — serves more than 86,000 residential, commercial, and industrial customers in 54 Connecticut towns. The non-operating holding company's subsidiaries gather water from wells and reservoirs and produce 49 million gallons daily. They also offer fire protection and other water-related services. CWS's growth strategy is based on acquisitions.

	Annual Growth	12/05	12/06	12/07	12/08	12/09
Sales ($ mil.)	5.7%	47.5	46.9	59.0	61.3	59.4
Net income ($ mil.)	(0.2%)	10.3	7.0	8.8	9.4	10.2
Market value ($ mil.)	0.3%	211.1	196.0	203.0	203.4	213.4
Employees	4.2%	191	200	206	226	225

THE CONNELL COMPANY

200 Connell Dr.	CEO: Grover Connell
Berkeley Heights, NJ 07922	CFO: Terry Connell
Phone: 908-673-3700	HR: Maureen Waldron
Fax: 908-673-3800	FYE: December 31
Web: www.connellco.com	Type: Private

Add rice and stir. It's just one of the ingredients that go into The Connell Company. The diversified firm operates through a number of subsidiaries in a variety of businesses, including wholesale food ingredient distribution, international industrial equipment supply and leasing, real estate development and leasing, and business services. Its Connell Rice & Sugar subsidiary is a leading exporter and distributor of domestic rice, mainly serving markets in Japan, Korea, and the Middle East. Connell International exports industrial equipment to customers worldwide. Other units include Connell Real Estate & Development, Connell Finance, and Connell Mining Products. The family-owned business was started in 1926.

	Annual Growth	12/04	12/05	12/06	12/07	12/08
Est. sales ($ mil.)	—	—	—	—	—	284.5
Employees	—	—	—	—	—	620

CONN'S, INC.

NASDAQ (GS): CONN

3295 College St.	CEO: Timothy L. Frank
Beaumont, TX 77701	CFO: Michael J. Poppe
Phone: 409-832-1696	HR: Walter M. Broussard
Fax: 409-832-4344	FYE: January 31
Web: www.conns.com	Type: Public

Conn's has managed to outlive human life expectancy. With more than 115 years under its belt, the retailer sells appliances (refrigerators, freezers, washers, dryers) and consumer electronics (VCRs, DVD players, camcorders, LCD and plasma-screen TVs) through about 75 stores in Texas, Oklahoma, and southern Louisiana, and via its website. Conn's also offers home office equipment, lawn and garden products, and other home products such as bedding. The retailer began as a small plumbing and heating business in 1890. Conn's is about 50% owned by SF Holding Corp. (an investment arm of Stephens Group), which is considering various alternatives for the retailer, including taking the company private.

	Annual Growth	1/06	1/07	1/08	1/09	1/10
Sales ($ mil.)	4.5%	702.4	760.7	824.1	890.8	836.7
Net income ($ mil.)	(34.2%)	41.2	40.3	39.7	25.7	7.7
Market value ($ mil.)	(40.0%)	977.5	527.6	433.9	273.4	126.3
Employees	3.0%	2,800	2,950	2,900	3,235	3,150

⊞ CONOCOPHILLIPS

NYSE: COP

600 N. Dairy Ashford Rd.	CEO: James J. (Jim) Mulva
Houston, TX 77079	CFO: Sigmund L. (Sig) Cornelius
Phone: 281-293-1000	HR: Eugene L. (Gene) Batchelder
Fax: —	FYE: December 31
Web: www.conocophillips.com	Type: Public

Proudly combining two venerable names in the US oil industry, Conoco-Phillips is the #2 integrated oil and gas company in the US, behind Exxon Mobil.The company explores for oil and gas in more than 30 countries and has proved reserves of 10 billion barrels of oil equivalent (excluding its Syncrude oil sands assets). It has a global refining capacity of more than 2.6 million barrels per day and sells petroleum at 8,500 retail outlets in the US under the 76, Conoco, and Phillips 66 brands, and at 1,225 gas stations in Europe. Other operations include chemicals, gas gathering, fuels technology, and power generation.

	Annual Growth	12/05	12/06	12/07	12/08	12/09
Sales ($ mil.)	(4.4%)	183,364.0	167,578.0	194,495.0	246,182.0	152,840.0
Net income ($ mil.)	(22.7%)	13,617.0	15,550.0	11,891.0	(16,998.0)	4,858.0
Market value ($ mil.)	(3.2%)	86,590.3	107,084.5	131,418.5	77,094.9	76,008.4
Employees	(4.2%)	35,600	38,400	32,600	33,800	30,000

An in-depth profile of this company is available to Hoover's Online members at hoovers.com.

CONOCOPHILLIPS ALASKA, INC.

700 G St.	CEO: C. Doug Johnson
Anchorage, AK 99501	CFO: C. Doug Johnson
Phone: 907-276-1215	HR: Tim Kiehl
Fax: 907-263-4731	FYE: December 31
Web: www.conocophillipsalaska.com	Type: Subsidiary

ConocoPhillips Alaska is willing to don its long johns to bring natural gas and liquefied natural gas (LNG) to the lower 48. The company, a subsidiary of ConocoPhillips, owns stakes in two of Alaska's largest oil fields, Prudhoe Bay and Kuparuk, in the remote region of Alaska's North Slope, and is the state's largest oil producer. The region has more than 35 trillion cu. ft. of known gas resources. It is projected that Prudhoe Bay can provide more than 3 billion cu. ft. of natural gas per day. The company has 2.8 million undeveloped acres. ConocoPhillips Alaska produces about 244,000 barrels of oil per day, and 97 million cu. ft. of natural gas per day.

CONOLOG CORPORATION

NASDAQ (CM): CNLG

5 Columbia Rd.	CEO: Robert S. Benou
Somerville, NJ 08876	CFO: Robert S. Benou
Phone: 908-722-8081	HR: —
Fax: 908-722-5461	FYE: July 31
Web: www.conolog.com	Type: Public

Conolog makes small electronic and electromagnetic components that military, industrial, and utilities customers use for microwave, radio, and telephone transmission. Its products include transducers, receivers, electromagnetic-wave filters, and signal-processing equipment. Its products for commercial customers, electrical and industrial utilities in particular, are carried under the INIVEN brand name, taken from a company Conolog acquired in 1981. Leading customers include the US military and power utilities Bonneville Power Administration, NSTAR, and Tucson Electric Power.

	Annual Growth	7/05	7/06	7/07	7/08	7/09
Sales ($ mil.)	31.6%	0.5	0.5	0.5	1.2	1.5
Net income ($ mil.)	—	(3.0)	(3.3)	(8.1)	(7.0)	(2.4)
Market value ($ mil.)	(72.6%)	1,328.7	317.5	253.5	31.0	7.5
Employees	5.3%	13	14	15	15	16

CONRAD INDUSTRIES, INC.

Pink Sheets: CNRD

1100 Brashear Ave., Ste. 200	CEO: John P. (Johnny) Conrad Jr.
Morgan City, LA 70381	CFO: Cecil A. Hernandez
Phone: 985-702-0195	HR: Shane Alfred
Fax: 985-702-1126	FYE: December 31
Web: www.conradindustries.com	Type: Public

Like the story of Noah's Ark, Conrad Industries starts anew by rescuing the things its likes. Conrad Industries builds, converts, and repairs small to mid-sized vessels for commercial and government customers. More than half of the company's work is in constructing barges, liftboats, towboats, and tugboats. Its boat-conversion projects mainly involve lengthening vessel midbodies or modifying vessels to perform different functions. Conrad Industries operates shipyards along the Gulf Coast, in Louisiana and Texas. Conrad also offers fabrication of modular components, used on offshore drilling rigs, as well as storage and offloading of vessels. Established in 1948, the company is led by the founding Conrad family.

	Annual Growth	12/04	12/05	12/06	12/07	*12/08
Sales ($ mil.)	50.7%	37.1	64.6	121.8	168.5	191.1
Net income ($ mil.)	—	(7.1)	0.1	5.9	19.2	23.0
Market value ($ mil.)	42.9%	—	11.6	39.3	96.6	33.8
Employees	18.3%	275	384	520	498	539

*Most recent year available

CONSOL ENERGY INC.

NYSE: CNX

CNX Center, 1000 CONSOL Energy Dr.	CEO: J. Brett Harvey
Canonsburg, PA 15317	CFO: William J. Lyons
Phone: 724-485-4000	HR: —
Fax: —	FYE: December 31
Web: www.consolenergy.com	Type: Public

Consolation prizes don't interest CONSOL Energy. CONSOL is one of the US's largest coal mining companies, along with Peabody Energy and Arch Coal. The company has some 4.5 billion tons of proved reserves, mainly in northern and central Appalachia and the Illinois Basin, and produces about 59 million tons of coal annually. CONSOL primarily mines high BTU coal, which burns cleaner than lower grades. Customers include electric utilities and steel mills. CONSOL delivers coal using its own railroad cars, export terminals, and fleet of towboats and barges. The company also engages in natural gas exploration and production; its proved reserves total 1.9 trillion cu. ft.

	Annual Growth	12/05	12/06	12/07	12/08	12/09
Sales ($ mil.)	4.9%	3,810.4	3,715.2	3,762.2	4,486.3	4,621.9
Net income ($ mil.)	(1.8%)	580.9	408.9	267.8	442.5	539.7
Market value ($ mil.)	11.2%	7,355.9	7,252.1	16,142.8	6,450.8	11,240.4
Employees	2.5%	7,257	7,253	7,728	8,176	8,012

CONSOLIDATED COMMUNICATIONS

NASDAQ (CM): CNSL

121 S. 17th St.	CEO: Robert J. (Bob) Currey
Mattoon, IL 61938	CFO: Steven L. (Steve) Childers
Phone: 217-235-3311	HR: —
Fax: 217-258-7883	FYE: December 31
Web: www.consolidated.com	Type: Public

Consolidated Communications Holdings, Inc., is just what its name implies. The company encompasses operations based in Illinois, Pennsylvania, and Texas, providing voice and data telecommunications to business and residential customers. It operates rural local-exchange carriers that offer local access and long-distance, Internet access, business phone systems, and related services through about 247,000 local access lines and around 100,000 DSL lines in service. The company also offers directory publishing and carrier services. Operating subsidiaries include Illinois Consolidated Telephone Company (ICTC), Consolidated Communications of Fort Bend Company, and Consolidated Communications of Texas Company.

	Annual Growth	12/05	12/06	12/07	12/08	12/09
Sales ($ mil.)	6.0%	321.4	320.8	329.2	418.4	406.2
Net income ($ mil.)	—	(4.5)	13.3	11.4	5.3	25.9
Market value ($ mil.)	7.7%	387.4	623.3	593.5	354.3	521.3
Employees	(0.3%)	1,229	1,123	1,081	1,315	1,213

CONSOLIDATED CONTAINER COMPANY LLC

3101 Towercreek Pkwy., Ste. 300	CEO: Jeffrey M. Greene
Atlanta, GA 30339	CFO: Richard P. Sehring
Phone: 678-742-4600	HR: —
Fax: 678-742-4750	FYE: December 31
Web: www.cccllc.com	Type: Private

Sometimes rigid is good. Consolidated Container Company (CCC) is one of the largest manufacturers of rigid plastic packaging in the US. The company markets its myriad containers (used for milk, water, fertilizer, salsa, antifreeze, and more) to industries from dairy to water, agricultural, food, and industrial chemical. Custom packaging, project management, lab work, product integration, and logistics support are part of CCC's service lineup. CCC operates more than 70 blow-molded manufacturing plants in North America, which produce about 7 billion pieces annually. Customers include Dean Foods and Procter & Gamble. CCC is controlled by private equity Vestar Capital Partners.

	Annual Growth	12/04	12/05	12/06	12/07	12/08
Est. sales ($ mil.)	—	—	—	—	—	857.6
Employees	—	—	—	—	—	3,300

An in-depth profile of this company is available to Hoover's Online members at hoovers.com.

425

CONSOLIDATED EDISON COMPANY OF NEW YORK, INC.

4 Irving Place
New York, NY 10003
Phone: 212-460-4600
Fax: 212-477-2536
Web: www.coned.com

CEO: Kevin Burke
CFO: Robert N. Hoglund
HR: —
FYE: December 31
Type: Subsidiary

Consolidated Edison Company of New York (Con Edison of New York) keeps the nightlife pulsing in The Big Apple. The utility, a subsidiary of Consolidated Edison, distributes electricity throughout most of New York City and Westchester County. The company distributes electricity to 3.3 million residential and business customers in New York City; it also delivers natural gas to about 1.1 million customers. The utility also provides natural gas and steam services in portions of the New York metropolitan area. Con Edison of New York owns and operates more than 130,500 miles of overhead and underground power distribution lines.

	Annual Growth	12/04	12/05	12/06	12/07	12/08
Est. sales ($ mil.)	—	—	—	—	—	10,424.0
Employees	—	—	—	—	—	15,628

CONSOLIDATED EDISON, INC.

NYSE: ED

4 Irving Place
New York, NY 10003
Phone: 212-460-4600
Fax: 212-982-7816
Web: www.conedison.com

CEO: Kevin Burke
CFO: Robert N. Hoglund
HR: —
FYE: December 31
Type: Public

Utility holding company Consolidated Edison (Con Edison) is the night light for the city that never sleeps. Con Edison's main subsidiary, Consolidated Edison Company of New York, distributes electricity to 3.3 million residential and business customers in New York City; it also delivers natural gas to about 1.1 million customers. Subsidiary Orange and Rockland Utilities serves more than 400,000 electric and gas customers in three states. Con Edison's nonutility operations include retail and wholesale energy marketing, independent power production, and infrastructure project development.

	Annual Growth	12/05	12/06	12/07	12/08	12/09
Sales ($ mil.)	2.8%	11,690.0	12,137.0	13,120.0	13,583.0	13,032.0
Net income ($ mil.)	5.2%	719.0	737.0	929.0	1,196.0	879.0
Market value ($ mil.)	(0.5%)	13,063.7	13,554.3	13,774.3	10,977.1	12,809.9
Employees	1.7%	14,537	14,795	15,214	15,628	15,541

CONSOLIDATED ELECTRICAL DISTRIBUTORS, INC.

31356 Via Colinas, Ste. 107
Westlake Village, CA 91362
Phone: 818-991-9000
Fax: 818-991-6842
Web: www.cedcareers.com

CEO: H. Dean Bursch
CFO: Jeff C. Wofford
HR: —
FYE: December 31
Type: Private

Consolidated Electrical Distributors (CED) is an industry-leading consolidator of electrical equipment distributors. With more than 500 locations in 45 states, the automation and electric control wholesaler offers proximity and photoelectric sensors and circuit breakers. Other products include alarms and buzzers, power supplies, transformers, switches, wiring, and motor and temperature controls. The company serves residential and commercial construction, industrial facilities, and factories. Founded as The Electric Corporation of San Francisco, CED has grown through multiple acquisitions of distributors. It is owned by the Colburn family and operates under about 80 names.

	Annual Growth	12/04	12/05	12/06	12/07	12/08
Est. sales ($ mil.)	7.2%	2,600.0	2,800.0	3,280.0	3,900.0	3,430.0
Employees	4.5%	5,200	5,200	5,200	6,160	6,200

CONSOLIDATED GRAPHICS, INC.

NYSE: CGX

5858 Westheimer, Ste. 200
Houston, TX 77057
Phone: 713-787-0977
Fax: 713-787-5013
Web: www.consolidatedgraphics.com

CEO: Joe R. Davis
CFO: Jon C. Biro
HR: —
FYE: March 31
Type: Public

One of the leading commercial printers in North America, Consolidated Graphics unites many companies under one banner. The firm operates as a holding company while its printing subsidiaries exist as separate entities run by their own management teams. Operations include 70 sheetfed, web, and digital printing facilities in more than 25 states as well as Ontario, Canada, and the Czech Republic. Consolidated Graphics prints products such as annual reports, brochures, catalogs, corporate communications, direct-mail pieces, and point-of-purchase displays, among other items. The firm also provides fulfillment and mailing services for printed materials, as well as digital asset management and online print procurement.

	Annual Growth	3/06	3/07	3/08	3/09	3/10
Sales ($ mil.)	3.0%	879.0	1,006.2	1,095.4	1,145.1	990.9
Net income ($ mil.)	(22.2%)	38.5	50.7	59.3	(39.6)	14.1
Market value ($ mil.)	(5.6%)	585.3	831.5	629.4	142.8	465.0
Employees	1.6%	5,005	5,550	6,757	5,896	5,343

CONSOLIDATED METCO, INC.

5701 SE Columbia Way
Vancouver, WA 98661
Phone: 360-828-2599
Fax: —
Web: conmet.com

CEO: Edward (Ed) Oeltjen
CFO: John Waters
HR: Bryan Kenyon
FYE: January 31
Type: Subsidiary

Consolidated Metco (ConMet) looks to be a market heavy-weight, without the weight. The company manufactures lightweight components for heavy-duty commercial trucks. Its aluminum castings and assemblies include standard and preset wheel hubs and brake drums. ConMet offers structural plastics such as instrument panels and fairings, too. OEMs opt for the aluminum lineup as a way to simplify vehicle construction and reduce weight yet capture structural near-steel strength. ConMet parts can be found on heavy-duty truck brands Freightliner, as well as Daimler Trucks North America sister brands Sterling and Western Star, and Mack, Peterbilt, and Volvo. ConMet is a privately owned subsidiary of Amsted Industries.

CONSOLIDATED RESTAURANT OPERATIONS, INC.

12200 Stemmons Fwy., Ste. 100
Dallas, TX 75234
Phone: 972-241-5500
Fax: 972-888-8198
Web: www.croinc.com

CEO: John D. Harkey Jr.
CFO: Paul Hargett
HR: —
FYE: December 31
Type: Private

Consolidated Restaurant Operations (CRO) offers several dining concepts on its menu. The company is a full-service restaurant company with more than 85 locations encompassing more than half a dozen different dining concepts. Offering a range of Mexican favorites, its flagship El Chico chain operates in Texas, Oklahoma, and half a dozen other states. CRO also owns the upscale casual Cantina Laredo chain with about 30 locations. Other dining concepts include Cool River Cafe, Good Eats, and the upscale III Forks. The company also has more than 25 franchised restaurant locations. CRO is controlled by John Harkey, who started the restaurant business in 1998 with partners Gene Street and John Cracken.

	Annual Growth	12/04	12/05	12/06	12/07	12/08
Est. sales ($ mil.)	—	—	—	—	—	173.0
Employees	—	—	—	—	—	7,980

CONSOLIDATED-TOMOKA LAND CO.

NYSE Amex: CTO

1530 Cornerstone Blvd., Ste. 100
Daytona Beach, FL 32117
Phone: 386-274-2202
Fax: 386-274-1223
Web: www.consolidatedtomoka.com

CEO: William H. (Bill) McMunn
CFO: Bruce W. Teeters
HR: Linda Crisp
FYE: December 31
Type: Public

From golf courses and retail centers to timber and hay farms, Florida land developer Consolidated-Tomoka owns a chunk of the Sunshine State. The company's holdings include about 25 retail properties (tenants include CVS, Walgreen, and Best Buy), a couple of golf courses (including the national headquarters of the LPGA), and some 11,000 acres of agricultural land that the company is converting into other income properties. The company also holds subsurface oil, gas, and mineral interests on some 500,000 acres throughout Florida and properties in North Carolina and Georgia. Institutional investors own more than 45% of the company.

	Annual Growth	12/05	12/06	12/07	12/08	12/09
Sales ($ mil.)	(21.0%)	43.6	42.3	39.8	18.5	17.0
Net income ($ mil.)	(51.8%)	14.8	14.2	13.5	4.8	0.8
Market value ($ mil.)	(16.2%)	405.8	414.4	358.8	218.6	200.0
Employees	1.2%	20	25	17	25	21

CONSPIRACY ENTERTAINMENT HOLDINGS, INC.

OTC: CPYE

612 Santa Monica Blvd.
Santa Monica, CA 90401
Phone: 310-260-6150
Fax: 310-260-1450
Web: www.conspiracygames.com

CEO: Sirus Ahmadi
CFO: Keith Tanaka
HR: Keith Tanaka
FYE: December 31
Type: Public

Conspiracy Entertainment has all sorts of theories about capitalizing on the video game market. The company is a Los Angeles-based producer of kid-friendly, value-priced video games for play on the PC and on gaming consoles from Sony, Microsoft, and Nintendo. Conspiracy has co-published games featuring the Warner Bros. licensed characters of *Tiny Toons* and *Tom & Jerry*; other titles include *Amazing Live Sea Monkeys*, *Enclave*, and *Road Trip*. President and CEO Sirus Ahmadi owns about 40% of the company.

	Annual Growth	12/05	12/06	12/07	12/08	12/09
Sales ($ mil.)	61.8%	1.4	0.8	8.8	10.9	9.6
Net income ($ mil.)	—	1.1	(1.5)	(0.9)	0.3	(1.0)
Market value ($ mil.)	24.3%	3.4	6.8	9.0	6.5	8.1
Employees	31.6%	3	3	5	5	9

CONSTANT CONTACT, INC.

NASDAQ (GM): CTCT

1601 Trapelo Rd., Ste. 329
Waltham, MA 02451
Phone: 781-472-8100
Fax: 781-472-8101
Web: www.constantcontact.com

CEO: Gail F. Goodman
CFO: Robert P. (Bob) Nault
HR: Robert D. (Bob) Nicoson
FYE: December 31
Type: Public

Constant Contact makes sure businesses never lose touch with their most important customers. The company provides small businesses with Web-based marketing software and services for managing e-mail campaigns and online surveys. Its offerings include easy to use tools for creating, implementing, tracking, managing, and analyzing marketing materials. The company's customers include retailers, restaurants, and other businesses, as well as non-profit organizations, alumni associations, and churches; two-thirds of its clients have fewer than 10 employees. Constant Contact claims nearly 350,000 customers for its e-mail marketing products.

	Annual Growth	12/05	12/06	12/07	12/08	12/09
Sales ($ mil.)	72.1%	14.7	27.6	50.5	87.3	129.1
Net income ($ mil.)	—	(1.3)	(7.8)	(8.3)	(2.1)	(1.3)
Market value ($ mil.)	(13.7%)	—	—	613.0	377.8	456.2
Employees	58.1%	100	275	318	456	625

CONSTAR INTERNATIONAL INC.

NASDAQ (CM): CNST

1 Crown Way
Philadelphia, PA 19154
Phone: 215-552-3700
Fax: 215-552-3707
Web: www.constar.net

CEO: Ruth J. Mack
CFO: J. Mark Borseth
HR: David J. Waksman
FYE: December 31
Type: Public

Constar International's PET won't fetch your paper, but it will hold your water, soda, or peanut butter. Constar is one of North America's largest makers of polyethylene terephthalate (PET) plastic food and beverage containers. Its customers include soda kingpins PepsiCo and Coca-Cola, as well as food producers, such as ConAgra (Wesson Oil). Soft drink and water bottles remain the most common uses of PET packaging, but other applications, such as teas, juices, condiments, and beer, have also become popular. In addition, the company makes plastic closures and non-PET containers. It gets more than three-quarters of its sales in the US. Constar filed for Chapter 11 in 2008 and emerged from bankruptcy in 2009.

	Annual Growth	12/05	12/06	12/07	12/08	12/09
Sales ($ mil.)	(10.0%)	975.0	927.0	881.6	857.9	638.4
Net income ($ mil.)	—	(60.0)	(12.0)	(26.3)	(57.8)	89.1
Market value ($ mil.)	58.3%	6.1	12.3	7.1	0.1	38.5
Employees	(11.5%)	2,017	1,839	1,746	1,417	1,238

⊞ CONSTELLATION BRANDS, INC.

NYSE: STZ

207 HIght Point Dr., Bldg. 100
Victor, NY 14564
Phone: 585-678-7100
Fax: 585-218-3601
Web: www.cbrands.com

CEO: Robert S. (Rob) Sands
CFO: Robert (Bob) Ryder
HR: L. Denise Watson
FYE: February 28
Type: Public

Thinking about alcohol makes this company starry-eyed. Constellation Brands is a leading beer, wine, and spirits maker. It offers more than 100 brands, which it sells in some 150 countries. Its wine division, anchored by its domestic wine-making subsidiary Constellation Wines U.S., is a global leader in wine production, offering brands such as Robert Mondavi and Vendange, as well as such premium labels as Ravenswood and Simi. Its Crown Imports joint venture with Grupo Modelo imports Corona and Tsingtao beer, among other beer brands. Constellation Brands also markets premium spirits, including Black Velvet whiskey and SVEDKA vodka. North America accounts for about 70% of Constellation Brands' sales.

	Annual Growth	2/06	2/07	2/08	2/09	2/10
Sales ($ mil.)	(7.5%)	4,603.4	5,216.4	3,773.0	3,654.6	3,364.8
Net income ($ mil.)	(25.7%)	325.3	331.9	(613.3)	(301.4)	99.3
Market value ($ mil.)	(13.1%)	5,613.5	4,999.8	4,094.0	2,781.2	3,205.3
Employees	(6.6%)	7,900	9,200	8,200	6,600	6,000

CONSTELLATION ENERGY COMMODITIES GROUP, INC.

111 Market Place, Ste. 500
Baltimore, MD 21202
Phone: 410-470-3500
Fax: 410-468-3499
Web: www.constellation.com

CEO: Mayo A. Shattuck III
CFO: Andrew L. Good
HR: —
FYE: December 31
Type: Subsidiary

Constellation Energy Commodities Group is a leading source of wholesale power in deregulated US markets. The company holds the energy marketing and trading operations of parent Constellation Energy Group. Constellation Energy Commodities Group sells electricity, natural gas, coal, and other energy products under both short- and long-term contracts to energy users, including utilities and other energy marketers. The unit also provides risk management services. Constellation Energy Commodities Group's formerly diverse global portfolio included coal supply, freight management, and terminal logistics until it sold most of that business in 2009.

An in-depth profile of this company is available to Hoover's Online members at hoovers.com.

427

CONSTELLATION ENERGY GROUP, INC.

NYSE: CEG

100 Constellation Way
Baltimore, MD 21202
Phone: 410-470-2800
Fax: —
Web: www.constellation.com

CEO: Mayo A. Shattuck III
CFO: Jonathan W. (Jack) Thayer
HR: Shon J. Manasco
FYE: December 31
Type: Public

Constellation Energy Group's leading light is still utility Baltimore Gas and Electric (BGE), which distributes electricity and natural gas in central Maryland. The company trades and markets wholesale energy through subsidiary Constellation Energy Commodities Group, which is one of the top power marketers in North America. Constellation Energy also operates independent power plants with more than 8,200 MW of generating capacity through its Constellation Generation unit, and it competes in retail energy supply through Constellation NewEnergy. Other operations include HVAC services, appliance sales; nuclear plant development; and energy consulting services.

	Annual Growth	12/05	12/06	12/07	12/08	12/09
Sales ($ mil.)	(2.3%)	17,132.0	19,284.9	21,193.2	19,818.3	15,598.8
Net income ($ mil.)	63.5%	630.3	936.4	821.5	(1,314.4)	4,503.4
Market value ($ mil.)	(11.6%)	11,616.8	13,889.8	20,678.4	5,060.2	7,093.1
Employees	(7.5%)	9,850	9,645	10,200	10,200	7,200

CONSTELLATION ENERGY PARTNERS LLC

NYSE Arca: CEP

1801 Main St., Ste. 1300
Houston, TX 77002
Phone: 877-847-0008
Fax: —
Web: www.constellationenergypartners.com

CEO: Stephen R. Brunner
CFO: Charles C. (Chuck) Ward
HR: —
FYE: December 31
Type: Public

Constellation Energy Partners' domain is decidedly more terrestrial than stellar. A unit of Constellation Energy, it is a coalbed methane exploration and production company that operates in Alabama's Black Warrior Basin (one of the oldest and most lucrative coalbed methane basins in the US), the Cherokee Basin in Kansas and Oklahoma, and the Woodford Shale in the Arkoma Basin in Oklahoma. In 2009 Constellation Energy Partners reported proved reserves of 131.2 billion cu. ft. of natural gas equivalent. The company operated almost 90% of the 2,760 wells in which it holds an interest.

	Annual Growth	12/05	12/06	12/07	12/08	12/09
Sales ($ mil.)	53.0%	26.0	36.9	75.9	163.2	142.5
Net income ($ mil.)	—	11.9	16.0	14.2	7.3	(9.0)
Employees	54.3%	24	22	74	102	136

CONSTELLATION WINES U.S., INC.

235 N. Bloomfield Rd.
Canandaigua, NY 14424
Phone: 585-396-7600
Fax: —
Web: www.cwinesus.com

CEO: Jay Wright
CFO: Sue Bachorski
HR: —
FYE: August 31
Type: Subsidiary

You might say the company is the pathfinder star for a giant in the beverage business. Constellation Wines U.S. (CWUS) oversees the domestic winemaking operations of its parent, New York-based Constellation Brands. No matter the state of your pocketbook or level of wine connoisseurship, CWUS offers a complete range of US-made vintages. They include super-premium and luxury wines (Estancia, Inniskillin, Robert Mondavi Winery, Simi, and Wild Horse); premium wines (Blackstone, Woodbridge), emerging wines (Barossa, Red Guitar); and specialty and value wines (Arbor Mist, Cook's, Wild Irish Rose, Vendange).

CONSULATE HEALTH CARE, INC.

800 Concourse Pkwy. South, Ste. 200
Maitland, FL 32751
Phone: 407-571-1550
Fax: 407-571-1599
Web: www.consulatemgt.com

CEO: Joseph D. Conte
CFO: David A. Weidner
HR: Jo Anne Annichiarico
FYE: December 31
Type: Private

Consulate Health Care is a consummate elder care provider. The company offers long-term care, including assisted living, skilled nursing, and independent living services, to residents of its facilities in half a dozen states. Consulate owns, manages, and leases dozens of nursing homes and other long-term health care centers staffed with physicians, nurse practitioners, and physician assistants. It also provides rehabilitation, diagnostic imaging, hospice, and pharmacy services. In addition, Consulate offers Alzheimer's care and short-term transitional care programs for patients needing complex medical treatment. The company operates facilities in Florida, Maryland, Ohio, Pennsylvania, Tennessee, and Virginia.

CONSUMER PORTFOLIO SERVICES, INC.

NASDAQ (GM): CPSS

16355 Laguna Canyon Rd.
Irvine, CA 92618
Phone: 949-753-6800
Fax: 949-753-6805
Web: www.consumerportfolio.com

CEO: Charles E. Bradley Jr.
CFO: Jeffrey P. (Jeff) Fritz
HR: Missy Hennessey
FYE: December 31
Type: Public

Consumer Portfolio Services (CPS) buys, sells, and services auto loans made to consumers who probably don't have portfolios. The company finances vehicles for subprime borrowers who can't get traditional financing due to poor or limited credit. CPS purchases contracts from both new car and independent used car dealers in 45 states; the company then securitizes (bundles and sells) the financing contracts that it acquires. In recent years, the bulk of the contracts CPS acquires finance used vehicles. The company has operations in California, Florida, Illinois, and Virginia.

	Annual Growth	12/05	12/06	12/07	12/08	12/09
Assets ($ mil.)	(1.9%)	1,155.1	1,728.3	2,282.8	1,638.8	1,068.3
Net income ($ mil.)	—	3.4	13.2	13.9	(26.1)	(57.2)
Market value ($ mil.)	(32.8%)	100.5	113.8	58.6	6.9	20.5
Employees	(8.5%)	749	789	997	681	525

CONSUMERS BANCORP, INC.

OTC: CBKM

614 E. Lincoln Way
Minerva, OH 44657
Phone: 330-868-7701
Fax: 330-868-3460
Web: www.consumersbancorp.com

CEO: Ralph J. Lober II
CFO: Renee K. Wood
HR: —
FYE: June 30
Type: Public

You don't have to be a consumer to do business with Consumers — it's happy to serve businesses, as well. Consumers Bancorp is the holding company for Consumers National Bank, which has about 10 branches in eastern Ohio. The bank offers standard services, such as savings and checking accounts, CDs, and NOW accounts. Business loans make up more than half of the bank's loan portfolio; real estate, consumer, and construction loans round out its lending activities. CNB Investment Services, a division of the bank, offers insurance, brokerage, financial planning, and wealth management services through a third-party provider, UVEST. Chairman Laurie McClellan owns more than 20% of Consumers Bancorp.

	Annual Growth	6/05	6/06	6/07	6/08	6/09
Assets ($ mil.)	7.1%	191.2	203.6	202.0	233.1	251.9
Net income ($ mil.)	0.0%	2.0	1.2	1.3	1.8	2.0
Market value ($ mil.)	(7.0%)	34.6	26.9	21.4	25.0	25.8
Employees	(3.5%)	127	126	127	110	110

CONSUMERS ENERGY COMPANY

1 Energy Plaza	CEO: John G. Russell
Jackson, MI 49201	CFO: Thomas J. (Tom) Webb
Phone: 517-788-0550	HR: John M. Butler
Fax: 800-363-4806	FYE: December 31
Web: www.consumersenergy.com	Type: Subsidiary

Consumers Energy Company makes sure that the energy consumers in Michigan have the power to crank up their heaters and the gas to fire up their stoves. The company's operating area includes all 68 counties of Michigan's lower peninsula. All told, Consumers Energy has a generating capacity of about 9,600 MW (primarily fossil-fueled), and distributes electricity to 1.8 million customers and natural gas to 1.7 million customers. Included in the utility's arsenal of power production is electricity generated from fossil-fueled, nuclear, and hydroelectric power plants. Consumers Energy is a subsidiary and primary operating unit of CMS Energy.

	Annual Growth	12/04	12/05	12/06	12/07	12/08
Est. sales ($ mil.)	—	—	—	—	—	6,421.0
Employees	—	—	—	—	—	7,697

CONSUMERS UNION OF UNITED STATES, INC.

101 Truman Ave.	CEO: James A. (Jim) Guest
Yonkers, NY 10703	CFO: Richard B. (Rich) Gannon
Phone: 914-378-2000	HR: Richard (Rick) Lustig
Fax: 914-378-2900	FYE: May 31
Web: www.consumersunion.org	Type: Not-for-profit

Consumers Union of United States (CU) inspires both trust and fear. Best known for publishing *Consumer Reports* magazine, the independent not-for-profit organization also serves as a consumer watchdog through other print publications (newsletters and guides), TV and radio reports, and the Web (ConsumerReports.org). Its subscriber site rates products ranging from candy bars to cars. CU tests and rates thousands of products annually through its National Testing and Research Center, which conducts laboratory testing and survey research. CU accepts no advertising and derives income from the sale of *Consumer Reports* and other services, and from non-commercial contributions, grants, and fees.

THE CONTAINER STORE INC.

500 Freeport Pkwy.	CEO: William A. (Kip) Tindell
Coppell, TX 75019	CFO: Jodi L. Taylor
Phone: 972-538-6000	HR: —
Fax: 972-538-7623	FYE: March 31
Web: www.containerstore.com	Type: Private

With its packets, pockets, and boxes, The Container Store has the storage products niche well-contained. Its merchandise ranges from backpacks to recipe holders. The home organization pioneer operates about 50 stores in nearly 20 states, mostly in major cities in California, Colorado, New York, and Texas, as well as the District of Columbia. It also runs an e-commerce site. The company offers shipping across the US and to Canada, as well as same-day delivery in New York City. Stores carry more than 10,000 items; the firm's Elfa brand wire shelving (manufactured in Sweden) accounts for about 20% of sales. Founded in 1978, The Container Store is majority owned by private equity firm Leonard Green & Partners.

CONTANGO OIL & GAS COMPANY

NYSE Amex: MCF

3700 Buffalo Speedway, Ste. 960	CEO: Kenneth R. Peak
Houston, TX 77098	CFO: Kenneth R. Peak
Phone: 713-960-1901	HR: —
Fax: 713-960-1065	FYE: June 30
Web: contango.com	Type: Public

It takes two to tango but several more to make Contango, a successful independent oil and natural gas company. Contango Oil & Gas (named after a term used by oil and gas traders to describe anticipated rising prices in the futures market) explores for and acquires oil and gas properties in the Gulf of Mexico and in the Arkansas Fayetteville Shale. Contango, which holds proved reserves of about 369 billion cu. ft. of natural gas equivalent, has strategic exploration alliances with Juneau Exploration, Alta Resources, and others. CEO Kenneth Peak owns 15% of Contango.

	Annual Growth	6/05	6/06	6/07	6/08	6/09
Sales ($ mil.)	158.1%	4.3	0.9	18.7	116.5	190.7
Net income ($ mil.)	45.7%	12.4	(0.2)	(2.7)	256.9	55.9
Market value ($ mil.)	46.6%	145.2	223.1	572.4	1,467.9	670.4
Employees	3.9%	6	6	6	6	7

CONTECH CONSTRUCTION PRODUCTS INC.

9025 Centre Pointe Dr., Ste. 400	CEO: Ronald C. (Ron) Keating
West Chester, OH 45069	CFO: Jeffrey S. (Jeff) Lee
Phone: 513-645-7000	HR: Karen Luther
Fax: 513-645-7993	FYE: June 30
Web: www.contech-cpi.com	Type: Private

CONTECH Construction Products wants to see its business go down the drain. The company makes, distributes, and installs civil engineering products related to environmental storm water, drainage, bridges, walls, and earth stabilization. CONTECH sells to builders of commercial, industrial, and public projects, as well as large-scale residential communities. Products range from retaining walls and water-detention vaults to storm water pipes and bridges in a variety of types for vehicular or pedestrian use. CONTECH has dealers, distributors, or manufacturing plants in all 50 US states and a national sales organization of more than 350 people. Investment firm Apax Partners owns CONTECH.

CONTENTGUARD, INC.

222 N. Sepulveda Blvd., Ste. 1400	CEO: Rob Logan
El Segundo, CA 90245	CFO: —
Phone: 310-426-7930	HR: —
Fax: 310-322-3898	FYE: December 31
Web: www.contentguard.com	Type: Joint venture

ContentGuard plays watch dog to digital content rights. Spun off by Xerox in 2000, the company licenses digital rights management (DRM) technologies originally developed at Xerox's Palo Alto Research Center. ContentGuard's technology is designed to protect various types of digital content, including audio, video, text, games, software, electronics technology, personal financial data, and business information. Its DRM technology is especially attractive to media, entertainment, and publishing companies that attempt to prevent copyrighted material from being copied and distributed on the Internet without legal permission. The company is owned by Microsoft, Technicolor, and Time Warner.

An in-depth profile of this company is available to Hoover's Online members at hoovers.com.

429

CONTINENTAL AIRLINES, INC.

NYSE: CAL

1600 Smith St., Dept. HQSEO	CEO: Jeffery A. (Jeff) Smisek
Houston, TX 77002	CFO: Zane Rowe
Phone: 713-324-2950	HR: Dan Casey
Fax: 713-324-2687	FYE: December 31
Web: www.continental.com	Type: Public

If it's a continent, chances are it's accessible via Continental Airlines. The carrier serves about 135 US destinations and another 135 abroad from hubs in Cleveland; Houston; Newark, New Jersey; and Guam (hub of Continental Micronesia). Its network includes cities served by regional carriers operating as Continental Express and Continental Connection. Continental has about 340 mainline jets and 265 regional aircraft. It extends its offerings through code-sharing with fellow members of the Star Alliance, led by United Airlines, Lufthansa, and Air Canada. (Code-sharing allows airlines to sell tickets on one another's flights.) In May 2010 Continental agreed to merge with United in a $3 billion stock swap.

	Annual Growth	12/05	12/06	12/07	12/08	12/09
Sales ($ mil.)	2.9%	11,208.0	13,128.0	14,232.0	15,241.0	12,586.0
Net income ($ mil.)	—	(68.0)	369.0	459.0	(585.0)	(282.0)
Market value ($ mil.)	(4.2%)	2,974.7	5,760.9	3,107.4	2,522.2	2,502.7
Employees	(0.5%)	42,200	43,770	45,610	42,490	41,300

CONTINENTAL ENERGY CORPORATION

OTC: CPPXF

14001 Dallas Pkwy., Ste. 1200	CEO: Richard L. McAdoo
Dallas, TX 75240	CFO: Robert Rudman
Phone: 972-934-6774	HR: —
Fax: 972-934-6718	FYE: June 30
Web: www.continentalenergy.com	Type: Public

Continental Energy is a junior oil and gas exploration company with assets in Indonesia. The company has production-sharing contracts giving it exclusive petroleum exploration and production rights in two significant exploration concessions, the Bengara-II (with about 1.2 million acres) and the Yapen block. The exploration and production company also had a concession to develop the Bangkudulis Oil Field, but sold it in 2005. In 2007 Continental Energy set up a biofuels subsidiary, Continental Biofuels. Directors and officers own about 24% of the Continental Energy.

	Annual Growth	6/05	6/06	6/07	6/08	6/09
Sales ($ mil.)	—	—	—	—	—	0.0
Net income ($ mil.)	—	—	—	—	—	(3.1)
Market value ($ mil.)	—	—	—	—	—	7.6
Employees	—	—	—	—	—	14

CONTINENTAL GRAIN COMPANY CORP.

277 Park Ave.	CEO: Paul J. Fribourg
New York, NY 10172	CFO: Michael J. Zimmerman
Phone: 212-207-5930	HR: Teresa E. McCaslin
Fax: 212-207-5499	FYE: March 31
Web: www.continentalgrain.com	Type: Private

Continental Grain Company (CGC) is all over the food chain. The agribusiness company trades grain worldwide through subsidiaries including ContiAsia and ContiLatin. That grain is fed to chickens at subsidiary Wayne Farms, a major US poultry processor with 11 facilities and a capacity to process almost 2 billion pounds of poultry a year. CGC also has partnerships with Seaboard Corporation (called ContiSea), Charoen Pokphand, and Overseas Shipholding Group. In 2008 CGC formed Arlon, a private investment firm that manages three separate portfolios made up of diverse holdings. Chairman and CEO Paul Fribourg (a descendant of company founder Simon Fribourg) and his family own CGC.

CONTINENTAL MATERIALS CORPORATION

NYSE Amex: CUO

200 S. Wacker Dr., Ste. 4000	CEO: James G. Gidwitz
Chicago, IL 60606	CFO: Joseph J. Sum
Phone: 312-541-7200	HR: —
Fax: 312-541-8089	FYE: December 31
	Type: Public

Continental Materials divides its product plate between construction and heating, ventilation, and air conditioning (HVAC). Its construction products segment, which accounts for half of sales, produces ready-mix concrete, aggregates, metal doors, and related products. They are sold primarily to contractors, government entities, and consumers in Colorado. Continental Materials' HVAC segment makes wall furnaces, console heaters, fan coils, and evaporative air coolers that it markets to wholesale distributors and retail home centers throughout the Southwest region.

	Annual Growth	12/05	12/06	12/07	12/08	12/09
Sales ($ mil.)	(4.9%)	139.0	158.8	168.4	157.9	113.5
Net income ($ mil.)	—	2.8	2.0	(0.6)	0.0	(1.4)
Market value ($ mil.)	(21.3%)	46.5	42.3	41.2	25.6	17.8
Employees	(0.8%)	665	802	846	798	644

CONTINENTAL RESOURCES, INC.

175 Middlesex Tpke., Ste. 1	CEO: Mary Nardella
Bedford, MA 01730	CFO: James M. Bunt
Phone: 781-275-0850	HR: Cathy Shattuck
Fax: 781-533-0395	FYE: December 31
Web: www.continentalresources.com	Type: Private

Continental Resources' rivers of revenue cover a vast terrain of technology. The IT company's Test and Measurement division sells, rents, and leases new and used test instruments, such as spectrum analyzers, signal generators, and oscilloscopes. The Custom Computing Solutions division integrates computer systems and networks, and is one of the largest resellers of Oracle equipment in the US. The Enterico division focuses on selling IBM systems and servers. Continental Resources, also known as ConRes, also makes power supplies and converters through its Wall Industries subsidiary. The company was founded in 1962.

	Annual Growth	12/04	12/05	12/06	12/07	12/08
Est. sales ($ mil.)	—	—	—	—	—	355.5
Employees	—	—	—	—	—	372

CONTINENTAL RESOURCES, INC.

NYSE: CLR

302 N. Independence	CEO: Harold G. Hamm
Enid, OK 73702	CFO: John D. Hart
Phone: 580-233-8955	HR: —
Fax: 580-548-5253	FYE: December 31
Web: www.contres.com	Type: Public

The continental resources that Continental Resources searches for are oil and natural gas assets beneath the North American continent, in the Rocky Mountain, Mid-Continent, and Gulf Coast regions. The independent oil and gas exploration and production company has added reserves of 121.7 million barrels of oil equivalent through internal growth (aka "growing through the drill bit") between early 2004 and the end of 2008. In 2008 Continental Resources reported estimated proved reserves of 159.3 million barrels of oil equivalent. It holds more than 1.5 million net acres of leasehold properties.

	Annual Growth	12/05	12/06	12/07	12/08	12/09
Sales ($ mil.)	13.6%	375.8	483.7	582.2	960.5	626.2
Net income ($ mil.)	(22.2%)	194.3	253.1	28.6	321.0	71.3
Market value ($ mil.)	28.1%	—	—	4,441.2	3,520.0	7,289.9
Employees	9.3%	286	299	332	394	408

CONTINENTAL TIRE THE AMERICAS, LLC

1830 MacMillan Park Dr.	CEO: Matthias Schoenberg
Fort Mill, SC 29707	CFO: Tim Rogers
Phone: 704-583-4882	HR: —
Fax: —	FYE: December 31
Web: www.continentaltire.com	Type: Subsidiary

Continental Tire the Americas (CTA, formerly Continental Tire North America) rounds out tire production across the Atlantic for its German parent. The North American subsidiary of Germany-based tire and automotive component manufacturer Continental AG makes tires for cars, light- and heavy-duty trucks, motorhomes, commercial vehicles, SUVs, and agricultural and industrial vehicles (such as dozers and loaders). Brand names include Conti-Extreme, ContiTrac, ContiSport, ContiTouring, and ContiPremier. In addition to Continental-branded tires, the company also produces General, Euzkadi, and other private-brand tires that can be found in North America. Customers include BMW, Ford, Toyota, John Deere, Mack, and Volvo.

CONTINUCARE CORPORATION
NYSE Amex: CNU

7200 Corporate Center Dr., Ste. 600	CEO: Richard C. Pfenniger Jr.
Miami, FL 33126	CFO: Fernando L. Fernandez
Phone: 305-500-2000	HR: —
Fax: 305-500-2080	FYE: June 30
Web: www.continucare.com	Type: Public

Continucare keeps on caring for South and Central Florida's Medicare recipients. The company provides primary care medical services through a network of around 20 centers in Broward, Miami-Dade, and Hillsborough counties. It also provides practice management services to about 25 independent doctors' practices affiliated with Humana. A majority of the patients who seek care at Continucare clinics and practices are members of Medicare Advantage health plans; virtually all of the company's revenue comes from managed care contracts with HMOs operated by Humana, Vista Healthplan of South Florida, and Wellcare.

	Annual Growth	6/05	6/06	6/07	6/08	6/09
Sales ($ mil.)	25.8%	112.2	133.0	217.1	254.4	281.3
Net income ($ mil.)	(1.0%)	15.9	5.3	6.3	11.3	15.3
Market value ($ mil.)	(1.2%)	147.2	177.2	185.6	140.0	140.0
Employees	24.4%	255	266	563	589	610

CONTINUUM HEALTH PARTNERS, INC

1111 Amsterdam Ave.	CEO: Stanley Brezenoff
New York, NY 10025	CFO: Brendan C. Loughlin
Phone: 212-523-4000	HR: Kevin Molloy
Fax: —	FYE: December 31
Web: www.wehealnewyork.org	Type: Not-for-profit

Continuum Health Partners may be one of the largest health care systems serving the New York City area, but New Yorkers don't see its name splashed across its facilities. The medical facilities within its system include Beth Israel Medical Center, St. Luke's-Roosevelt Hospital, Long Island College Hospital, and the New York Eye and Ear Infirmary. Combined, the medical centers have more than 2,700 beds. Continuum Health Partners also operates group and private physician practices and ambulatory care centers in the New York metropolitan area, as well as home health, hospice, and community outreach programs.

CONTRAN CORPORATION

Three Lincoln Centre, 5430 LBJ Fwy., Ste. 1700	CEO: Steven L. (Steve) Watson
Dallas, TX 75240	CFO: Bobby D. O'Brien
Phone: 972-233-1700	HR: Keith A. Johnson
Fax: 972-448-1444	FYE: December 31
	Type: Private

Contran is a holding company that owns stakes of varying sizes in subsidiaries such as Valhi, Inc. (a publicly traded company about 95% controlled by Contran), which conducts diversified operations in chemicals (NL Industries and Kronos Worldwide), metals (Titanium Metals Corporation), waste management (Waste Control Specialties), computer support systems, and precision ball bearing slides and locking systems (CompX International). Contran also has a controlling interest in Keystone Consolidated Industries, a maker of fencing and wire products. Trusts benefiting chairman Harold Simmons' family (with Simmons as the sole trustee) own pretty much all of Contran.

CONTROL COMPONENTS INC.

22591 Avenida Empresa	CEO: Ian Whiting
Rancho Santa Margarita, CA 92688	CFO: —
Phone: 949-858-1877	HR: —
Fax: 949-858-1878	FYE: December 31
Web: www.ccivalve.com	Type: Subsidiary

Has all the pressure made you feel like you will explode? CCI is no therapist, but if your problem involves oil or gas extraction, the company's control valves can help you release some steam. CCI's trademark DRAG technology helps oil companies to extract oil and gas. The company also designs and manufactures corrosion resistant valves and related components for use in the power industry (fossil, nuclear, and combined heat and power generation plants) and pulp and paper plants. CCI was founded in 1961 by Richard Self and became a subsidiary of IMI in 1981. The company has manufacturing and service facilities in North America, Europe, and Asia.

CONVATEC

200 Headquarters Park Dr.	CEO: David I. Johnson
Skillman, NJ 08558	CFO: George Kegler
Phone: 908-904-2500	HR: Lucia L. Quinn
Fax: 908-904-2780	FYE: December 31
Web: www.convatec.com	Type: Private

ConvaTec winds its way around wicked wounds. The company makes wound cleansers, wound dressings, bandages, and wound hydration products. Its products are designed to foster the management and healing of wounds and address such issues as wound dryness and severity. ConvaTec's additional products include ostomy pouching systems, which allow patients with artificial openings (or stomas) to dispose of bodily waste into attachable pouches. The company also makes a line of skin care products, including shampoos, conditioners, body creams, and ointments. ConvaTec manufactures its products in the UK and the US and distributes them worldwide.

	Annual Growth	12/04	12/05	12/06	12/07	12/08
Est. sales ($ mil.)	—	—	—	—	—	294.7
Employees	—	—	—	—	—	3,500

An in-depth profile of this company is available to Hoover's Online members at hoovers.com.

CONVERGYS CORPORATION

NYSE: CVG

201 E. 4th St.
Cincinnati, OH 45202
Phone: 513-723-7000
Fax: 513-421-8624
Web: www.convergys.com

CEO: Jeffrey H. (Jeff) Fox
CFO: Earl C. Shanks
HR: Clark D. Handy
FYE: December 31
Type: Public

Convergys is conversant in the languages of outsourcing and relationship management. The company provides business process outsourcing (BPO) services designed to help its clients manage their customers and employees. Its customer unit provides inbound and outbound call handling for sales, marketing, and support through about 80 contact centers (and in about 35 languages). In addition, Convergys offers bill processing services and provisioning software to telecommunications companies through its information management unit. To focus on its primary operations, it sold its HR unit to NorthgateArinso in mid-2010. Convergys was formed as a division of Cincinnati Bell and spun off in 1998.

	Annual Growth	12/05	12/06	12/07	12/08	12/09
Sales ($ mil.)	2.3%	2,582.1	2,789.8	2,844.3	2,785.8	2,827.2
Net income ($ mil.)	—	122.6	166.2	169.5	(92.9)	(77.3)
Market value ($ mil.)	(9.3%)	1,960.1	2,940.8	2,035.6	792.7	1,329.4
Employees	(2.2%)	65,700	75,000	75,000	75,000	60,000

CONVERSE INC.

One High St.
North Andover, MA 01845
Phone: 978-983-3300
Fax: 978-983-3502
Web: www.converse.com

CEO: Michael Spillane
CFO: —
HR: —
FYE: May 31
Type: Subsidiary

With its roots as a popular basketball shoe worn by professionals, Converse has rebounded under NIKE as fashionable footwear and all-around cruiser for those off the court, too. Converse has sold some 750 million pairs of its classic Chuck Taylor All Star canvas basketball shoes, appealing to everyone from school kids to clothing designers. It licenses its name to sports apparel makers. Converse makes products under the names One Star and Jack Purcell that it sells through retailers such as Target and licensees in some 160 countries and its more than 40 stores. Converse operates as a separate unit from its parent's competing sports brands, reining in the kitsch value of Converse's vintage Chuck Taylor brand.

CONVERSION SERVICES INTERNATIONAL, INC.

NYSE Amex: CVN

100 Eagle Rock Ave.
East Hanover, NJ 07936
Phone: 973-560-9400
Fax: 973-560-9500
Web: www.csiwhq.com

CEO: Lori Cohen
CFO: William Hendry
HR: —
FYE: December 31
Type: Public

Conversion Services International (CSI) helps clients investigate data warehousing and business intelligence technologies. The company provides strategic and technology consulting, integrating products from such vendors as Business Objects, Cognos, MicroStrategy, and SAS Institute. Its customers, primarily located in the northeastern US, come mostly from the financial services, health care, pharmaceutical, and telecommunications industries. The company's client roster includes Amedisys, Bank of America, France Telecom, Goldman Sachs, Jaguar Cars, Pfizer, and Tiffany & Co.

	Annual Growth	12/05	12/06	12/07	12/08	12/09
Sales ($ mil.)	(3.2%)	27.6	25.7	21.5	19.7	24.2
Net income ($ mil.)	—	(4.5)	(9.6)	(10.2)	(10.5)	0.0
Market value ($ mil.)	(53.4%)	65.5	42.0	24.7	6.2	3.1
Employees	(17.1%)	199	87	145	138	94

CONVERTED ORGANICS INC.

NASDAQ (CM): COIN

137A Lewis Wharf
Boston, MA 02110
Phone: 617-624-0111
Fax: 617-624-0333
Web: www.convertedorganics.com

CEO: Edward J. (Ed) Gildea
CFO: David R. (Dave) Allen
HR: —
FYE: December 31
Type: Public

Converted Organics is not a group of new and fervent farmers but a company that is religiously developing a process to turn food into fertilizer. The company uses organic food waste as raw material to make all-natural soil amendment products — that is, fertilizers — that combine both disease suppression and nutrition characteristics. Converted Organics' manufacturing process uses heat and bacteria to transform food waste into a high-value natural fertilizer. That process is used at the company's two manufacturing facilities, one in New Jersey and the other in California. It sells its environmentally friendly products in the agribusiness, turf management, and retail markets.

	Annual Growth	12/05	12/06	12/07	12/08	12/09
Sales ($ mil.)	73.3%	—	—	—	1.5	2.6
Net income ($ mil.)	—	—	—	—	(16.2)	(21.1)
Market value ($ mil.)	(81.1%)	—	—	—	143.4	27.1
Employees	23.1%	—	—	—	39	48

CONVIO, INC.

NASDAQ (GM): CNVO

11501 Domain Dr., Ste. 200
Austin, TX 78758
Phone: 512-652-2600
Fax: 512-652-2699
Web: www.convio.com

CEO: Gene Austin
CFO: James R. (Jim) Offerdahl
HR: Angela G. (Angie) McDermott
FYE: December 31
Type: Public

Convio takes an approach *con brio* to helping not-for-profit organizations, institutions of higher education, and associations raise money, organize volunteer efforts, manage online content, and get their message out. The company's online Common Ground constituent relationship management (CRM) software and services connect potential donors and volunteers to groups they may support, and vice versa. It continues to expand the functionality to its software, adding modules for specialized efforts, such as tribute-based fundraising. Convio's clients include the AFL-CIO, The American Red Cross, the ASPCA, NPR, and the Texas Exes. Founded in 1999, the company completed an IPO in 2010.

	Annual Growth	12/05	12/06	12/07	12/08	12/09
Sales ($ mil.)	47.6%	13.3	21.5	43.1	57.0	63.1
Net income ($ mil.)	—	(5.8)	(5.0)	(10.5)	(3.7)	(2.1)
Employees	26.8%	135	301	320	—	349

CON-WAY FREIGHT INC.

110 Parkland Plaza
Ann Arbor, MI 48103
Phone: 734-769-0203
Fax: 734-214-5650
Web: freight.con-way.com

CEO: John G. Labrie
CFO: Michael D. (Mike) Yuenger
HR: Bruce H. Moss
FYE: December 31
Type: Subsidiary

A shipper picks a day, then Con-way hits the highway. Con-way Freight specializes in next-day and second-day less-than-truckload (LTL) freight transportation. (LTL carriers consolidate loads from multiple shippers into a single truckload.) The company operates throughout the US, and it extends its network throughout North America via Con-way Freight Canada and Con-way Mexico. Overall, Con-way Freight operates a fleet of about 8,300 tractors and 25,000 trailers from some 500 terminals. Con-way Freight is the main subsidiary of Con-way, which also owns supply chain management and truckload freight transportation businesses.

CON-WAY INC.

NYSE: CNW

2855 Campus Dr., Ste. 300
San Mateo, CA 94403
Phone: 650-378-5200
Fax: 650-357-9160
Web: www.con-way.com

CEO: Douglas W. Stotlar
CFO: Stephen L. (Steve) Bruffett
HR: Leslie P. Lundberg
FYE: December 31
Type: Public

Con-way (no relation to Twit-ty) provides trucking and logistics services. Con-way Freight, the company's less-than-truckload (LTL) unit, provides regional and inter-regional service throughout North America. (LTL carriers consolidate loads from multiple shippers into a single truckload.) Con-way Freight operates a fleet of about 8,300 tractors and some 25,000 trailers, utilizing five terminals. Con-way offers truckload transportation services through its Con-way Truckload subsidiary, which maintains a fleet of about 2,700 tractors and 8,100 trailers. Con-way's Menlo Worldwide Logistics unit provides contract logistics, freight brokerage, warehousing, and supply chain management services.

	Annual Growth	12/05	12/06	12/07	12/08	12/09
Sales ($ mil.)	0.6%	4,169.6	4,221.5	4,387.4	5,036.8	4,269.2
Net income ($ mil.)	—	223.0	270.4	152.9	73.7	(107.7)
Market value ($ mil.)	(11.1%)	2,781.6	2,191.8	2,067.4	1,323.9	1,737.4
Employees	5.9%	21,800	21,800	27,100	26,600	27,400

COOK COMPOSITES AND POLYMERS

820 E. 14th Ave.
Kansas City, MO 64116
Phone: 816-391-6000
Fax: 816-391-6122
Web: www.ccponline.com

CEO: Paul H. Colonna
CFO: Olivier Moulaert
HR: —
FYE: December 31
Type: Joint venture

The gelcoats are cookin' at Cook Composites and Polymers (CCP), the North American resins division of TOTAL's chemicals division. CCP is the world's #1 supplier of gelcoats and also manufactures powder coating and composite resins in addition to industrial cleaners and maintenance products. The company's products are used for marine, construction, and transportation applications. They go into such diverse products as furniture, cookware, showers and tubs, and in RV and truck panels. CCP has its headquarters in Kansas City and operates 13 other plants located throughout North America.

COOK GROUP INCORPORATED

750 Daniels Way
Bloomington, IN 47404
Phone: 812-339-2235
Fax: 800-554-8335
Web: www.cookgroup.com

CEO: Kem Hawkins
CFO: David Breedlove
HR: —
FYE: December 31
Type: Private

Cook Group makes sure you don't get a raw deal during surgery. Flagship subsidiary Cook Incorporated makes catheters, wire guides, stents, and other devices used in minimally invasive procedures. Cook Group operates a host of other medical subsidiaries that manufacture urological and gynecological devices, endoscopic accessories, cardiac rhythm management, and vascular products. Its industrial parts manufacturer Sabin makes plastic and metal parts used in Cook's medical products, while its K-Tube company manufactures hypodermic needles. The company, one of the world's largest privately held medical device firms, was founded by William Cook in 1963.

COOK INCORPORATED

750 Daniels Way
Bloomington, IN 47402
Phone: 812-339-2235
Fax: 800-554-8335
Web: www.cookincorporated.com

CEO: Kem Hawkins
CFO: —
HR: —
FYE: December 31
Type: Subsidiary

Cook Incorporated prepares the tools physicians use to keep people healthy worldwide. Among the many subsidiaries of the Cook Group, the company makes more than 50,000 medical device products. Its products include catheters, needles, wire guides, stents and stent grafts, and other minimally invasive devices. Its medical devices are primarily designed by, and custom-made for, physicians and are used for a variety of diagnostic, critical care, surgical, and therapeutic procedures. The company develops products in areas of care such as cardiology, radiology, anesthesiology, and women's health. Cook Incorporated was founded 1963 and is part of the Cook Medical division of the Cook Group.

COOKSON ELECTRONICS ASSEMBLY MATERIALS

1 Cookson Place
Providence, RI 02903
Phone: 401-228-8800
Fax: —
Web: alpha.cooksonelectronics.com

CEO: Richard J. Ertmann
CFO: Steven M. Adase
HR: —
FYE: December 31
Type: Business segment

Showing steadfast commitment to its customers, Cookson Electronics Assembly Materials solders on. The company manufactures solder products and related soldering materials used in electronics assembly. Its products include solder paste and preforms, squeegee blades, cored wire, and a complete line of lead-free products. Cookson Electronics Assembly Materials serves customers in the electronic equipment manufacturing, semiconductor, and photovoltaic solar module manufacturing industries. The company, which operates worldwide, is part of UK-based Cookson Group.

THE COOPER COMPANIES, INC.

NYSE: COO

6140 Stoneridge Mall Rd., Ste. 590
Pleasanton, CA 94588
Phone: 925-460-3600
Fax: —
Web: www.coopercos.com

CEO: Robert S. Weiss
CFO: Eugene J. (Gene) Midlock
HR: Ruby Varner
FYE: October 31
Type: Public

From eye care to lady care, The Cooper Companies has its customers covered. The global company makes specialty medical devices in two niche markets: vision care and gynecology. Its CooperVision subsidiary makes specialty contact lenses, including toric lenses for astigmatism, multifocal lenses for presbyopia (blurred vision), and cosmetic lenses. The company also offers lenses for more common vision problems such as nearsightedness and farsightedness. Subsidiary CooperSurgical specializes in women's health care; its wide range of products include bone densitometers (for diagnosing osteoporosis), surgery instruments, and fetal monitors.

	Annual Growth	10/05	10/06	10/07	10/08	10/09
Sales ($ mil.)	7.6%	806.6	859.0	950.6	1,063.2	1,080.4
Net income ($ mil.)	2.3%	91.7	66.2	(11.2)	65.5	100.5
Market value ($ mil.)	(20.1%)	3,206.1	2,684.0	1,956.1	767.5	1,304.5
Employees	(1.6%)	7,034	7,500	7,600	7,400	6,600

COOPER INDUSTRIES PLC

NYSE: CBE

600 Travis St., Ste. 5600
Houston, TX 77002
Phone: 713-209-8400
Fax: 713-209-8996
Web: www.cooperindustries.com

CEO: Kirk S. Hachigian
CFO: David A. Barta
HR: James P. Williams
FYE: December 31
Type: Public

Cooper Industries likes to keep customers from blowing a fuse. The company's electrical products segment makes circuit protection equipment, as well as lighting fixtures, wiring devices, and other power management and distribution equipment for residential, commercial, and industrial use. Its other main business segment manufactures power tools for the industrial market and hand tools for the do-it-yourself and commercial markets. Major electrical product and tool brands include Buss fuses, Capri conduits, Crescent pliers and wrenches, EMSA power transformers, Plumb hammers, and Weller soldering supplies. Cooper Industries gets about two-thirds of its sales in the US.

	Annual Growth	12/05	12/06	12/07	12/08	12/09
Sales ($ mil.)	1.7%	4,730.4	5,184.6	5,903.1	6,521.3	5,069.6
Net income ($ mil.)	27.9%	163.9	504.6	692.3	632.2	439.1
Market value ($ mil.)	4.0%	6,114.7	7,574.7	8,858.8	4,896.8	7,143.3
Employees	(0.6%)	28,903	30,561	31,504	31,202	28,255

COOPER LIGHTING, LLC

1121 Hwy. 74 South
Peachtree City, GA 30269
Phone: 770-486-4800
Fax: 770-486-4801
Web: www.cooperlighting.com

CEO: Neil A. Schrimsher
CFO: Heather Robinson
HR: Dan Hilinski
FYE: December 31
Type: Subsidiary

Cooper Lighting, a subsidiary of Cooper Industries Ltd., designs lighting and fixtures with commercial, residential, and utility applications. The company's products are primarily used in commercial buildings, homes, landscapes, shopping centers, and high-security areas and industrial plants. Cooper Lighting's brand names include AtLite, Fail-Safe, Halo, IRiS, Lumark, Streetworks, and Sure-Lites, among others. The Cooper Lighting SOURCE facilities offer continuing education lighting classes, which cover lighting fundamentals and lighting basics to landscape lighting for the lighting professional. Cooper Lighting's origins date back to 1958, when the manufacturer was founded as Halo Lighting Company.

COOPER TIRE & RUBBER COMPANY

NYSE: CTB

701 Lima Ave.
Findlay, OH 45840
Phone: 419-423-1321
Fax: 419-424-4212
Web: www.coopertire.com

CEO: Roy V. Armes
CFO: Bradley E. Hughes
HR: Brenda S. Harmon
FYE: December 31
Type: Public

Cooper Tire & Rubber is a real wheeler dealer. The company is the fourth-largest tire manufacturer in North America (behind the likes of Bridgestone, Michelin, and Goodyear). It makes and sells replacement tires mainly for passenger cars and light trucks but also for motorcycles, race cars, commercial, and off-road vehicles for North American and international markets. Cooper operates seven manufacturing facilities and over 35 distribution centers worldwide. Customers include tire dealers, wholesale distributors, and regional and national tire chains. Unlike some of its rivals, Cooper does not typically sell to automotive OEMs.

	Annual Growth	12/05	12/06	12/07	12/08	12/09
Sales ($ mil.)	6.6%	2,155.2	2,676.2	2,932.6	2,881.8	2,779.0
Net income ($ mil.)	—	(9.4)	(78.5)	93.1	(219.4)	83.6
Market value ($ mil.)	7.0%	938.1	875.6	1,015.2	377.2	1,227.7
Employees	9.4%	8,762	13,361	13,355	13,311	12,568

THE COOPER UNION FOR THE ADVANCEMENT OF SCIENCE AND ART

Cooper Square
New York, NY 10003
Phone: 212-353-4100
Fax: 212-353-4327
Web: www.cooper.edu

CEO: George Campbell Jr.
CFO: Robert E. Hawks
HR: —
FYE: June 30
Type: School

The Cooper Union for the Advancement of Science and Art was founded in 1859 by inventor and industrialist Peter Cooper, who created the US's first steam train engine and rose from poverty to build a fortune. Cooper's endowment continues to fund a full tuition scholarship for each of the 900 students who attend the college, which is located in the East Village in downtown New York City. The Cooper Union offers degree programs in art, architecture, and engineering, as well as a wide variety of lectures and continuing education courses for the public.

	Annual Growth	6/04	6/05	6/06	6/07	6/08
Est. sales ($ mil.)	—	—	—	—	—	39.4
Employees	—	—	—	—	—	642

COOPERATIVE REGIONS OF ORGANIC PRODUCERS POOL

1 Organic Way
LaFarge, WI 54639
Phone: 608-625-2602
Fax: 608-625-3025
Web: www.organicvalley.coop

CEO: George Siemon
CFO: Mike Bedessem
HR: —
FYE: December 31
Type: Cooperative

Cooperative Regions of Organic Producers Pool (CROPP) is one of the largest organic farmer cooperatives in the US. Its 1,341 farmer/members produce the co-op's Organic Valley Family of Farms brand of fluid and shelf-stable milk, along with cheese, butter, and soy milk. Beyond the dairy barn, the cooperative also offers organic citrus juices, produce, eggs, meats, and poultry. Organic Valley retail products are sold at food retailers, and its ingredients are marketed to other organic food processors. Wisconsin-headquartered CROPP's member/farmers are located in California, Florida, and the northeast, northwest, and midwest regions of the US.

	Annual Growth	12/04	12/05	12/06	12/07	12/08
Est. sales ($ mil.)	—	—	—	—	—	527.8
Employees	—	—	—	—	—	507

COOPER-STANDARD AUTOMOTIVE INC.

39550 Orchard Hill Place
Novi, MI 48375
Phone: 248-596-5900
Fax: 248-596-6535
Web: www.cooperstandard.com

CEO: James S. (Jim) McElya
CFO: Allen J. Campbell
HR: Kimberly (Kim) Dickens
FYE: December 31
Type: Private

There's nothing standard about Cooper-Standard Automotive. Straddling two divisions, North American and International, its manufacturing operations churn out noise, vibration, and heat (NVH) control systems, as well as interior sealing systems, under brands StanPro, ENVIsys, and Metzeler Technical Rubber Systems. It also makes fluid handling parts from sensors to tubes and hoses, used in heating and cooling, braking, fuel, and emissions systems. Cooper-Standard's some 70 facilities, in nearly 20 countries, cater to OEMs, such as Chrysler, Ford Motor, and GM. Goldman Sachs and Cypress Group hold a 50% stake; after a 10-month bankruptcy, the company emerged from Chapter 11 in mid-2010.

	Annual Growth	12/04	12/05	12/06	12/07	12/08
Sales ($ mil.)	8.7%	1,858.9	1,827.4	2,164.3	2,511.2	2,594.6
Net income ($ mil.)	—	83.3	8.8	(8.4)	(151.0)	(121.5)
Employees	7.3%	13,605	13,429	16,266	21,123	18,046

COOPERSURGICAL, INC.

95 Corporate Dr.
Trumbull, CT 06611
Phone: 203-601-5200
Fax: 203-601-1007
Web: www.coopersurgical.com

CEO: Nicholas J. Pichotta
CFO: —
HR: Joanne Augustine
FYE: October 31
Type: Subsidiary

CooperSurgical, a subsidiary of The Cooper Companies, makes and sells medical devices for gynecologists and other women's health care providers. Its extensive product line — marketed to doctors' offices, hospitals, and clinics — features bone density tests, fertility and surgical sterilization devices, neonatal respiratory products, obstetrics tools, and cancer screening products, among other things. The company was founded in 1990 and has expanded its product line and market share through regular acquisitions of smaller companies.

COOPERVISION, INC.

370 Woodcliff Dr., Ste. 200
Fairport, NY 14450
Phone: 585-385-6810
Fax: 585-385-6145
Web: www.coopervision.com

CEO: John A. Weber
CFO: —
HR: Anthony Damaschino
FYE: October 31
Type: Subsidiary

CooperVision wants you to be able to clearly see the benefits of its products. The company is a leading manufacturer of contact lenses, offering a wide range of lenses that address myriad vision problems and are offered in different replacement schedules (including daily, weekly, bi-weekly, and monthly). It specializes in lenses for astigmatism, presbyopia, and ocular dryness. CooperVision has distribution and manufacturing facilities in about 10 countries. The firm is part of The Cooper Companies, which operates through CooperVision and CooperSurgical (diagnostic products and surgical instruments for the women's health care market).

	Annual Growth	10/04	10/05	10/06	10/07	10/08
Est. sales ($ mil.)	—	—	—	—	—	329.6
Employees	—	—	—	—	—	660

COORSTEK, INC.

16000 Table Mountain Pkwy.
Golden, CO 80403
Phone: 303-271-7000
Fax: 303-271-7009
Web: www.coorstek.com

CEO: John K. Coors
CFO: Steve Rask
HR: Janet D. Comerford
FYE: December 31
Type: Private

CoorsTek is not your next-generation brewery. Rather, the company gets its buzz from producing precision-machined metals, technical ceramics, and engineered plastics. Products are used in the aerospace, automotive, computer, military contracting, power generation and distribution, and telecommunications industries, among others. CoorsTek — which once was a part of the Adolph Coors Company (now MillerCoors) — has focused on business acquisitions and product research and development to build its capacity and expertise in engineered ceramics and components, and assemblies for extreme-duty, high-technology applications. The company was taken private by CEO John Coors and his family in 2003.

COPANO ENERGY, L.L.C.

NASDAQ (GS): CPNO

2727 Allen Pkwy., Ste. 1200
Houston, TX 77019
Phone: 713-621-9547
Fax: 713-621-9545
Web: www.copanoenergy.com

CEO: R. Bruce Northcutt
CFO: Carl A. Luna
HR: —
FYE: December 31
Type: Public

Copano Energy hopes its business goes down the tubes. The natural gas pipeline and processing company operates and maintains a network of natural gas gathering and intrastate pipelines (totaling 6,200 miles) in Texas' Gulf Coast region and in Oklahoma and Wyoming. This includes 144 miles of pipelines owned by Webb/Duval Gatherers, an unconsolidated general partnership 62.5%-owned by Copano Energy. The company also provides natural gas processing operations through its Houston Central Processing plant and 200 miles of natural gas liquids (NGL) pipelines (Brenham, Markham, and Sheridan).

	Annual Growth	12/05	12/06	12/07	12/08	12/09
Sales ($ mil.)	2.3%	747.7	860.3	1,141.7	1,629.1	820.0
Net income ($ mil.)	(6.5%)	30.4	65.1	63.2	58.2	23.2
Market value ($ mil.)	5.2%	1,278.4	1,951.2	2,380.1	764.1	1,565.6
Employees	12.6%	206	225	322	347	331

⊞ COPART, INC.

NASDAQ (GS): CPRT

4665 Business Center Dr.
Fairfield, CA 94534
Phone: 707-639-5000
Fax: 707-639-5196
Web: www.copart.com

CEO: A. Jayson Adair
CFO: William E. Franklin
HR: Thomas E. Wylie
FYE: July 31
Type: Public

What happens after cars are totaled in wrecks or natural disasters? How about stolen cars recovered *after* the insurance settlement? Perhaps Copart happens — it takes junked cars and auctions them for insurers, auto dealers, and car rental agencies. The buyers are mostly rebuilders, licensed dismantlers, and used-car dealers and exporters. It has replaced live auctions with Internet auctions using a platform known as Virtual Bidding Second Generation (VB2 for short). Copart also provides services such as towing and storage to buyers and other salvage companies, as well as an online database and search engine for used parts. The company has more than 150 storage facilities throughout North America and the UK.

	Annual Growth	7/05	7/06	7/07	7/08	7/09
Sales ($ mil.)	12.9%	457.1	528.6	560.7	784.8	743.1
Net income ($ mil.)	8.4%	102.1	96.9	136.3	156.9	141.1
Market value ($ mil.)	9.6%	2,061.7	2,245.4	2,370.2	3,696.9	2,976.2
Employees	2.9%	2,421	2,133	2,536	2,975	2,713

COPPER KING MINING CORPORATION

Pink Sheets: CPRK

1208 South 200
West Milford, UT 84751
Phone: 435-387-5053
Fax: —
Web: www.wuccompany.com

CEO: Mark Dotson
CFO: Mark McMillin
HR: —
FYE: December 31
Type: Public

Copper King Mining is in the business of developing mining claims in Utah. It entered that business with the 2008 acquisition of Western Utah Mining Company, a diversified minerals operation. Following the acquisition, Western Utah's management took over the executive positions at Copper King Mining. Its development projects lay in the Milford Mineral Belt and contain precious metals, tungsten, and molybdenum in addition to copper. The company, under the name International Broadcasting Corporation, had previously produced online content focused on business news.

⊞ An in-depth profile of this company is available to Hoover's Online members at hoovers.com.

435

COPYTELE, INC.

OTC: COPY

900 Walt Whitman Rd.
Melville, NY 11747
Phone: 631-549-5900
Fax: 631-549-5974
Web: www.copytele.com

CEO: Denis A. Krusos
CFO: Henry P. Herms
HR: —
FYE: October 31
Type: Public

CopyTele has an original take on display and communications technology. The company licenses technology used in thin, low-voltage phosphor displays. A licensing agreement with Videocon Industries allows the India-based consumer electronics company to develop televisions utilizing CopyTele's technology. CopyTele also provides secure communications products. Its stand-alone devices provide encryption for secure voice, fax, and data communication. Boeing, the exclusive distributor for many of the company's security products, uses CopyTele's encryption products on the Thuraya satellite communications network, which is employed by the US military.

	Annual Growth	10/05	10/06	10/07	10/08	10/09
Sales ($ mil.)	28.8%	0.4	0.5	0.5	2.1	1.1
Net income ($ mil.)	—	(4.5)	(7.6)	(5.5)	(5.8)	(16.5)
Market value ($ mil.)	3.2%	76.3	86.6	132.0	70.4	86.6
Employees	0.7%	33	31	33	20	34

CORAL GRAPHIC SERVICES, INC.

840 S. Broadway
Hicksville, NY 11801
Phone: 516-576-2100
Fax: 516-576-2153
Web: www.coralgraphics.com

CEO: Dave Liess
CFO: —
HR: —
FYE: December 31
Type: Subsidiary

Coral Graphic Services provides commercial printing services from facilities in Kentucky, New York, and Virginia. The company offers prepress, printing (including digital printing), and finishing services. Specialties include book components, such as covers, inserts, and jackets, that incorporate such graphic effects as die cutting, embossing, and foil stamping. Coral Graphics also produces annual reports, corporate brochures, and various forms of marketing materials, including posters. The company is a unit of arvato, a Germany-based printing and customer relationship management services company that itself is part of the Bertelsmann media conglomerate.

	Annual Growth	12/04	12/05	12/06	12/07	12/08
Est. sales ($ mil.)	—	—	—	—	—	21.7
Employees	—	—	—	—	—	226

⊞ CORBIS CORPORATION

710 2nd Ave., Ste. 200
Seattle, WA 98104
Phone: 206-373-6000
Fax: 206-373-6100
Web: www.corbis.com

CEO: Gary Shenk
CFO: Barry Allen
HR: Vivian Farris
FYE: December 31
Type: Private

If a picture is worth a thousand words, then Corbis has lots to say. The company's archive of more than 100 million images is one of the largest in the world, along with that of rival Getty Images. Corbis licenses its images — contemporary and archival photography, art, illustrations, and footage — for commercial and editorial use in print and electronic media. Customers can find and license images via the company's website. Corbis also offers artist representation (matching photographers with assignments) and GreenLight rights services (securing rights to images controlled by third parties). Microsoft co-founder Bill Gates owns Corbis, which he founded in 1989.

CORCEPT THERAPEUTICS INCORPORATED

NASDAQ (GM): CORT

149 Commonwealth Dr.
Menlo Park, CA 94025
Phone: 650-327-3270
Fax: 650-327-3218
Web: www.corcept.com

CEO: Joseph K. Belanoff
CFO: Caroline M. Loewy
HR: Mark Strem
FYE: December 31
Type: Public

Corcept Therapeutics wants to help people who are beyond blue. The biotechnology firm is exploring treatments that regulate the presence of Cortisol, a steroid hormone associated with some psychiatric and metabolic disorders. It is developing its lead candidate Corlux, a version of the compound mifepristone (commonly known as RU-486 or the "abortion pill"), as a means to regulate release patterns of cortisol in patients with psychotic depression, as well as those experiencing weight gain from taking other antipsychotic medications. The company is also investigating whether the drug may treat Cushing's Syndrome, a disorder caused by high levels of cortisol in the blood.

	Annual Growth	12/05	12/06	12/07	12/08	12/09
Sales ($ mil.)	—	—	0.3	0.5	0.2	0.0
Net income ($ mil.)	—	—	(24.9)	(11.6)	(20.1)	(20.2)
Market value ($ mil.)	31.2%	—	82.4	207.1	68.4	186.3
Employees	28.9%	—	14	21	31	30

CORDIS CORPORATION

14201 NW 60th Ave.
Miami Lakes, FL 33014
Phone: 786-313-2000
Fax: 786-313-2080
Web: www.cordis.com

CEO: Seth H.Z. Fischer
CFO: Joseph Prati
HR: —
FYE: December 31
Type: Subsidiary

Cordis is Johnson & Johnson's hearty subsidiary. The company develops products to treat circulatory system diseases including congestive heart failure and cerebral aneurysms. Cordis is divided into five units: Cordis Cardiology focuses on cardiovascular disease management; Cordis Endovascular for treatment of vascular and liver diseases; Conor Medsystem provides controlled vascular drug delivery technologies; Biosense Webster develops medical sensor and electrophysiology technology for cardiovascular use; and the Biologics Delivery Systems division makes cardiac mapping equipment used to improve the delivery of biological therapies. Cordis was founded in 1959 and bought by Johnson & Johnson in 1996.

	Annual Growth	12/04	12/05	12/06	12/07	12/08
Est. sales ($ mil.)	—	—	—	—	—	175.0
Employees	—	—	—	—	—	2,079

CORE MOLDING TECHNOLOGIES, INC.

NYSE Amex: CMT

800 Manor Park Dr.
Columbus, OH 43228
Phone: 614-870-5000
Fax: —
Web: www.coremt.com

CEO: Kevin L. Barnett
CFO: Herman F. Dick Jr.
HR: —
FYE: December 31
Type: Public

The core business of Core Molding Technologies is reinforced plastic parts. Through compression molding, sprayup, hand layup, and vacuum-assisted resin infusion molding, the company makes truck components (air deflectors, fenders, hoods) and personal watercraft parts (decks, hulls, and engine hatches, made primarily for Yamaha). Navistar International owns about 10% of Core Molding Technologies and accounts for more than half of its sales. Other major customers include heavy-duty truck manufacturers Daimler Trucks North America and PACCAR (Peterbilt trucks; about one-quarter of sales). The company's sales are confined to North America.

	Annual Growth	12/05	12/06	12/07	12/08	12/09
Sales ($ mil.)	(10.6%)	130.5	162.3	122.7	116.7	83.3
Net income ($ mil.)	(36.9%)	6.3	10.4	3.7	5.6	1.0
Market value ($ mil.)	(21.7%)	53.5	67.5	49.4	18.2	20.1
Employees	(12.3%)	1,377	1,379	942	933	813

CORE-MARK HOLDING COMPANY, INC.

NASDAQ (GS): CORE

395 Oyster Point Blvd., Ste. 415
South San Francisco, CA 94080
Phone: 650-589-9445
Fax: 650-952-4284
Web: www.coremark.com

CEO: J. Michael (Mike) Walsh
CFO: Stacy Loretz-Congdon
HR: —
FYE: December 31
Type: Public

Core-Mark Holding Company is the phoenix of smokes and snacks distributors. It's the sole entity to emerge from the ashes of the Fleming Companies' 2003 bankruptcy. From about 25 distribution facilities, Core-Mark distributes packaged consumables (including cigarettes, tobacco, candy, snacks, grocery items, perishables, nonalcoholic beverages, and health and beauty aids) to 24,000 convenience retailers, mass merchandisers, and drug, liquor, and specialty stores. Cigarettes account for more than two-thirds of sales. Core-Mark's largest customers include Couche-Tard and Valero; each has a dedicated distribution facility. The firm serves customers in all 50 US states and five Canadian provinces.

	Annual Growth	12/05	12/06	12/07	12/08	12/09
Sales ($ mil.)	7.5%	4,891.1	5,314.4	5,560.9	6,044.9	6,531.6
Net income ($ mil.)	34.9%	14.3	20.6	24.1	17.9	47.3
Market value ($ mil.)	0.8%	341.4	358.0	307.3	230.3	352.7
Employees	5.6%	3,430	3,745	4,035	4,181	4,267

COREMETRICS, INC.

1840 Gateway Dr., Ste. 320
San Mateo, CA 94404
Phone: 650-762-1400
Fax: 650-762-1499
Web: www.coremetrics.com

CEO: Joe Davis
CFO: Terry Schmid
HR: Terry Schmid
FYE: December 31
Type: Private

Want to know who's clicking on your website, and where, and how? Coremetrics provides Web-based analytics and precision marketing software that companies use to analyze the behavior of their online customers and website visitors. The company's software captures and stores site visitor activity data, then converts the data into individual visitor profiles that give online marketers, information technology managers, and e-commerce company executives insight into how their websites are being used. Customers have included Bank of America, Columbia House, Motorola, and Williams-Sonoma.

CORGENIX MEDICAL CORPORATION

OTC: CONX

11575 Main St.
Broomfield, CO 80020
Phone: 303-457-4345
Fax: 303-457-4519
Web: www.corgenix.com

CEO: Douglass T. (Doug) Simpson
CFO: William H. Critchfield
HR: —
FYE: June 30
Type: Public

Corgenix Medical wants to take a peek inside you. The company makes *in vitro* diagnostics to detect autoimmune, liver, and vascular diseases. Its line of more than 50 diagnostics are used by reference labs, hospitals and clinics, researchers, and other medical facilities around the world. It sells directly to customers in the US and the UK and through independent distributors elsewhere. To expand its product line, Corgenix Medical has released an aspirin resistance diagnostic, and it is developing new tests to diagnose fibromyalgia (pain disorder) and cardiovascular disease. It is also developing tests that detect potential bioterrorism agents using grant funding from the National Institutes of Health.

	Annual Growth	6/05	6/06	6/07	6/08	6/09
Sales ($ mil.)	9.7%	5.6	6.6	7.4	8.4	8.1
Net income ($ mil.)	—	(0.6)	(1.6)	(2.4)	(2.1)	(1.6)
Market value ($ mil.)	(26.2%)	9.9	13.0	9.0	9.0	2.9
Employees	2.6%	37	49	40	40	41

CORINTHIAN COLLEGES, INC.

NASDAQ (GS): COCO

6 Hutton Centre Dr., Ste. 400
Santa Ana, CA 92707
Phone: 714-427-3000
Fax: 714-724-5111
Web: www.cci.edu

CEO: Peter C. Waller
CFO: Kenneth S. Ord
HR: Beth A. Wilson
FYE: June 30
Type: Public

Corinthian Colleges believes more in marketable skills than in ivory towers. One of the largest for-profit, post-secondary education companies in North America, Corinthian Colleges focuses on career-oriented students. It has more than 100,000 students enrolled in about 100 schools in the US and another 20 schools in Ontario. Corinthian Colleges' institutions operate under the Everest College and the WyoTech (for automotive training) brand names. The majority of Corinthian's students are enrolled in associate's degree or diploma programs, but the schools also offer bachelor's and master's degrees. Additionally, Corinthian Colleges offers some 20 online degrees through Everest College.

	Annual Growth	6/05	6/06	6/07	6/08	6/09
Sales ($ mil.)	7.9%	963.6	966.6	933.2	1,068.7	1,307.8
Net income ($ mil.)	4.2%	58.4	41.5	7.2	21.3	68.8
Market value ($ mil.)	7.3%	1,125.4	1,265.5	1,435.6	1,023.1	1,492.0
Employees	7.9%	8,185	9,500	8,950	10,000	11,100

CORMEDIX, INC.

NYSE Amex: CRMD

745 Route 202-206, Ste. 303
Summit, NJ 08807
Phone: 908-517-9500
Fax: 908-429-4307
Web: www.cormedix.com

CEO: John C. Houghton
CFO: Brian Lenz
HR: —
FYE: December 31
Type: Public

CorMedix believes the way to a healthy heart is through the kidney — and vice versa. The biopharmaceutical company develops medications for the treatment and prevention of cardiorenal disease (kidney and related cardiac dysfunctions), including a liquid and gel used to prevent infection and clotting that can occur during intravenous treatments, such as dialysis and chemotherapy. Also, in an agreement with Shiva Biomedical, the company is developing a new formulation of the drug deferipone, to be used in the prevention of kidney damage in high-risk patients. The company expects to market its products worldwide. CorMedix, controlled by a group of its officers, went public in early 2010.

	Annual Growth	12/05	12/06	12/07	12/08	12/09
Sales ($ mil.)	—	—	—	0.0	0.0	0.0
Net income ($ mil.)	—	—	—	(7.2)	(9.0)	(8.1)
Employees	33.3%	—	—	—	3	4

CORN PRODUCTS INTERNATIONAL, INC.

NYSE: CPO

5 Westbrook Corporate Center
Westchester, IL 60154
Phone: 708-551-2600
Fax: 708-551-2700
Web: www.cornproducts.com

CEO: Ilene S. Gordon
CFO: Cheryl K. Beebe
HR: Diane J. Frisch
FYE: December 31
Type: Public

Sweet sodas and diet desserts alike get their taste from Corn Products International. The company makes food ingredients and industrial products from corn and other starch-based raw materials. Its customers include food, beverage, pharmaceutical, and paper manufacturers. More than half of its sales come from sweeteners, including high-fructose corn syrup, which is used by just about every beverage maker and a good many food companies as well, to sweeten their products. The company also produces corn starch (a thickener for processed foods), corn oil, and corn gluten (for animal feed). Corn Products International operates manufacturing plants throughout Africa, Asia, and North and South America.

	Annual Growth	12/05	12/06	12/07	12/08	12/09
Sales ($ mil.)	11.7%	2,360.0	2,621.0	3,391.0	3,944.0	3,672.0
Net income ($ mil.)	(17.8%)	90.0	124.0	198.0	267.0	41.0
Market value ($ mil.)	5.2%	1,797.5	2,598.9	2,765.2	2,170.8	2,199.3
Employees	3.7%	7,000	7,600	7,100	7,800	8,100

An in-depth profile of this company is available to Hoover's Online members at hoovers.com.

CORNELL COMPANIES, INC.
NYSE: CRN

1700 West Loop South, Ste. 1500
Houston, TX 77027
Phone: 713-623-0790
Fax: 713-623-2853
Web: www.cornellcompanies.com

CEO: James E. Hyman
CFO: John R. Nieser
HR: —
FYE: December 31
Type: Public

Stone walls do not a prison make, nor iron bars a cage — unless correctional institutions are your living. Cornell Companies designs, builds, and operates secure, community-based incarceration and treatment facilities. It runs more than 70 adult and juvenile systems comprising about 20,000 beds, serving federal, state, and local government agencies in 15 US states. Cornell's adult and juvenile facilities (including halfway houses) provide General Equivalency Diploma (GED) programs, job training and placement, recovery-recreational activities, health care, mental health and drug counseling, and life skills training. In 2010 Cornell agreed to a $685 million offer by The GEO Group to acquire the Texas company.

	Annual Growth	12/05	12/06	12/07	12/08	12/09
Sales ($ mil.)	7.3%	310.8	360.9	360.6	386.7	412.4
Net income ($ mil.)	200.9%	0.3	11.9	11.9	22.2	24.6
Market value ($ mil.)	13.2%	205.9	273.1	347.4	276.9	338.2
Employees	(0.6%)	4,513	4,653	4,439	4,409	4,407

CORNELL UNIVERSITY

Cornell University Campus, Day Hall Lobby
Ithaca, NY 14853
Phone: 607-254-4636
Fax: 607-255-5396
Web: www.cornell.edu

CEO: David J. Skorton
CFO: Joanne M. DeStefano
HR: Mary G. Opperman
FYE: June 30
Type: School

To excel at Cornell, you'll need every one of your brain cells. The Ivy League university has been educating young minds since its founding in 1865. Its more than 20,000 students can select undergraduate, graduate, and professional courses from 11 colleges and schools. In addition to its Ithaca, New York, campus the university has medical programs in New York City and Doha, Qatar. Cornell's faculty includes a handful of Nobel laureates, and the university has a robust research component studying everything from animal health to space to waste management; the university's 20 libraries hold more than 7 million volumes. Notable alumni include author E. B. White and US Supreme Court Justice Ruth Bader Ginsburg.

	Annual Growth	6/04	6/05	6/06	6/07	6/08
Sales ($ mil.)	3.0%	2,509.9	2,546.3	2,504.0	2,677.8	2,826.4
Employees	3.3%	13,677	14,073	14,226	—	15,558

CORNERSTONE BANCORP
OTC: CTOT

1670 E. Main St.
Easley, SC 29640
Phone: 864-306-1444
Fax: 864-306-1473
Web: www.cornerstonenatlbank.com

CEO: J. Rodger Anthony
CFO: Jennifer M. Champagne
HR: —
FYE: December 31
Type: Public

Cornerstone Bancorp has laid the groundwork for three banking branches in northwestern South Carolina. The institution is the holding company for Cornerstone National Bank, which offers traditional products and services, including checking and savings accounts, money market accounts, CDs, and credit cards. Commercial real estate loans comprise the largest portion of its lending portfolio; other offerings include residential mortgages, business and industrial loans, real estate construction, and consumer loans. Cornerstone National Bank has three offices in Easley, Greenville, and Powdersville, South Carolina. Cornerstone Bancorp also has an insurance agency that operates as Crescent Financial Services.

	Annual Growth	12/05	12/06	12/07	12/08	12/09
Assets ($ mil.)	13.6%	113.3	127.6	140.5	163.9	189.0
Net income ($ mil.)	—	1.1	1.7	1.6	0.2	(1.4)
Market value ($ mil.)	(33.0%)	—	28.7	23.9	19.1	8.6
Employees	(1.8%)	—	38	38	38	36

CORNERSTONE BANCSHARES, INC.
OTC: CSBQ

835 Georgia Ave.
Chattanooga, TN 37402
Phone: 423-385-3000
Fax: 423-385-3100
Web: www.cscbank.com

CEO: Nathaniel F. (Frank) Hughes
CFO: —
HR: —
FYE: December 31
Type: Public

Cornerstone Bancshares is the holding company for Cornerstone Community Bank, which operates about five locations in Chattanooga, Tennessee and surrounding communities, in addition to two loan production offices in Knoxville, Tennessee, and Dalton, Georgia. The bank offers standard retail and commercial services, including checking and savings accounts, money market accounts, and CDs. Its lending activities primarily consist of commercial real estate loans, residential mortgages, real estate construction loans, and business and agricultural loans. Another subsidiary of Cornerstone Bancshares, Eagle Financial, purchases accounts receivable and acts as a conduit lender.

	Annual Growth	12/05	12/06	12/07	12/08	12/09
Assets ($ mil.)	13.3%	323.6	374.9	444.4	471.8	532.4
Net income ($ mil.)	—	4.3	5.8	0.9	2.5	(8.2)
Market value ($ mil.)	(34.3%)	73.5	104.3	68.9	33.2	13.7
Employees	3.1%	93	107	116	121	105

CORNERSTONE BRANDS, INC.

5568 West Chester Rd.
West Chester, OH 45069
Phone: 513-603-1400
Fax: 513-603-1124
Web: www.hsni.com/cornerstone.cfm

CEO: Mark Ethier
CFO: James B. (Jim) Pekarek
HR: Thomas J. (Tom) Wonderly
FYE: December 31
Type: Subsidiary

Cornerstone Brands' foundation is split between more than a half dozen direct marketers. Formed in 1995, it serves as a holding company for catalog operators: Ballard Designs, Frontgate, Garnet Hill, Improvements, Smith+Noble, The Territory Ahead (formerly owned by Lands' End), and TravelSmith. Its companies sell home and leisure goods and casual apparel through catalogs and seven e-commerce sites primarily aimed at affluent, well-educated consumers ages 35 to 60. Cornerstone Brands mails more than 200 million catalogs annually and runs about two dozen retail stores. It is owned by multi-channel retailer HSN, which separated from IAC/InterActiveCorp in 2008.

	Annual Growth	12/04	12/05	12/06	12/07	12/08
Est. sales ($ mil.)	—	—	—	—	—	278.9
Employees	—	—	—	—	—	1,600

CORNERSTONE PROMOTION, INC.

71 W. 23rd St., Fl. 13
New York, NY 10010
Phone: 212-741-7100
Fax: 212-741-4747
Web: www.cornerstonepromotion.com

CEO: Rob Stone
CFO: Jason Fenton
HR: —
FYE: December 31
Type: Private

Cornerstone Promotion is a marketing and branding firm that serves the music, film, technology, and fashion industries by specializing in urban and alternative lifestyles. The firm uses viral marketing and other nontraditional marketing disciplines to influence the cool trendsetters and early adopters. Cornerstone Promotion has provided brand consulting, radio promotion, field marketing, digital marketing, and event marketing services for such clients as Levi Strauss & Co., Coca-Cola, Converse, and Proctor & Gamble. Music industry veterans Rob Stone and Jon Cohen launched the firm in 1996, with Sprite as a major customer. Cornerstone Promotion operates from offices in Chicago, Los Angeles, and New York.

	Annual Growth	12/04	12/05	12/06	12/07	12/08
Est. sales ($ mil.)	—	—	—	—	—	2.3
Employees	—	—	—	—	—	30

CORNERSTONE THERAPEUTICS INC.

NASDAQ (CM): CRTX

1255 Crescent Green Dr., Ste. 250
Cary, NC 27518
Phone: 919-678-6611
Fax: 866-443-3092
Web: www.crtx.com

CEO: Craig A. Collard
CFO: David Price
HR: —
FYE: December 31
Type: Public

Cornerstone Therapeutics (formerly Critical Therapeutics) wants to help clear things up for the allergic, the asthmatic, the congested, and the inflamed. The drug company is focused on developing and commercializing therapeutic products to prevent and treat acute inflammation and other respiratory ailments. Its marketed products include AlleRx, Balacet, Deconsal, Spectracef, and Zyflo CR. Cornerstone Therapeutics was formed by the 2008 merger of Critical Therapeutics and privately held respiratory therapy firm Cornerstone BioPharma. Italian drugmaker Chiesi Farmaceutici owns a majority stake in the company.

	Annual Growth	12/05	12/06	12/07	12/08	12/09
Sales ($ mil.)	105.0%	6.2	13.1	12.9	64.9	109.6
Net income ($ mil.)	—	(47.1)	(48.8)	(37.0)	9.0	10.2
Market value ($ mil.)	(46.0%)	1,838.2	522.3	325.1	67.8	156.2
Employees	(1.9%)	175	61	80	107	162

CORNING CABLE SYSTEMS LLC

800 17th St. NW
Hickory, NC 28601
Phone: 828-901-5000
Fax: 828-325-5060
Web: www.corningcablesystems.com

CEO: Clark S. Kinlin
CFO: Ann Schading
HR: Susan Scholten Lemley
FYE: December 31
Type: Subsidiary

Corning Cable Systems believes that fiber is an important part of an industrial diet. The company makes fiber-optic cables and networking products for voice, data, and video network applications. Corning Cable Systems manufactures cables, connectors, and related hardware; it also provides network design, installation, and maintenance services. The company offers its products and services to both public and private networks and to equipment manufacturers. Corning Cable Systems operates within Corning's Telecommunications segment, which accounts for about one-third of its parent company's annual sales.

⊞ CORNING INCORPORATED

NYSE: GLW

1 Riverfront Plaza
Corning, NY 14831
Phone: 607-974-9000
Fax: 607-974-8091
Web: www.corning.com

CEO: Wendell P. Weeks
CFO: James B. Flaws
HR: Christine M. Pambianchi
FYE: December 31
Type: Public

Corning is cookin' up some great technology. Once known mainly for its kitchenware and lab products, the company designs and produces material components for five industries: display technologies (flat-screen televisions, laptops, computer monitors), environmental technologies (mobile emission control systems), telecommunications (optical fiber, cable), life sciences (biosensors for drug research), and specialty materials (semiconductors, optical sensors for aerospace and defense). More than half of Corning's sales are derived in the Asia/Pacific region, principally from Taiwan and Japan. Corning has more than 45 manufacturing and processing facilities around the world.

	Annual Growth	12/05	12/06	12/07	12/08	12/09
Sales ($ mil.)	4.2%	4,579.0	5,174.0	5,860.0	5,948.0	5,395.0
Net income ($ mil.)	36.1%	585.0	1,855.0	2,150.0	5,257.0	2,008.0
Market value ($ mil.)	(0.4%)	30,684.6	29,201.8	37,442.7	14,874.1	30,138.3
Employees	(2.5%)	26,000	24,500	24,800	27,000	23,500

CORNING NATURAL GAS CORPORATION

OTC: CNIG

330 W. William St.
Corning, NY 14830
Phone: 607-936-3755
Fax: 607-962-2844
Web: www.corninggas.com

CEO: Michael I. (Mike) German
CFO: Firouzeh Sarhangi
HR: Stanley G. (Jerry) Sleve
FYE: September 30
Type: Public

Corning Natural Gas has cornered the market for natural gas supply in Corning, New York. The company is a regulated transmission and distribution utility serving 14,500 residential and business customers in Corning and surrounding areas; the company also sells gas wholesale to two nearby communities (Elmira and Bath). It has about 586,000 decatherms of natural gas storage capacity, and 400 miles of gas distribution pipelines and 15,000 miles of service pipelines in its service area. In 2009 Corning Natural Gas had four major customers, venerable industrial concern Corning Incorporated, New York State Electric & Gas, Bath Electric, Gas & Water Systems, and Fortuna Energy.

	Annual Growth	9/05	9/06	9/07	9/08	9/09
Sales ($ mil.)	0.9%	22.9	26.9	24.3	25.8	23.7
Net income ($ mil.)	3.9%	0.6	(3.6)	0.3	1.0	0.7
Market value ($ mil.)	0.1%	15.7	16.3	16.6	17.2	15.7
Employees	(3.1%)	60	48	51	54	53

COROPLAST, INC.

4501 Spring Valley Rd.
Dallas, TX 75244
Phone: 972-392-2241
Fax: 972-392-2242
Web: www.coroplast.com

CEO: Ken Vandervelde
CFO: Ken Vandervelde
HR: —
FYE: December 31
Type: Subsidiary

If stupid people wore signs so you wouldn't rely on them — as suggested by comedian Bill Engvall — Coroplast would be a household name. The company is North America's largest manufacturer of corrugated plastic sheet for sign substrate and returnable packaging markets. Its lineup touts a range of colors, graphics, and additives for flame resistance, UV protection, corrosive inhibitors, and other functional buffers. Coroplast caters to blue chip customers through a network of independent distributors. Exxon tapped the line to supply its name change from Esso/Humble Oil at stations across North America. Coroplast is a division of Great Pacific Enterprises, a US subsidiary of Canadian giant Jim Pattison Group.

	Annual Growth	12/04	12/05	12/06	12/07	12/08
Est. sales ($ mil.)	—	—	—	—	—	75.0
Employees	—	—	—	—	—	151

THE CORPORATE EXECUTIVE BOARD COMPANY

NASDAQ (GS): EXBD

1919 N. Lynn St.
Arlington, VA 22209
Phone: 571-303-3000
Fax: 571-303-5014
Web: www.executiveboard.com

CEO: Thomas L. Monahan III
CFO: Richard S. Lindahl
HR: Melody L. Jones
FYE: December 31
Type: Public

Don't fear the competition; learn from them. So says The Corporate Executive Board Company (CEB), a provider of business research and analysis services to more than 4,500 companies worldwide. Its 40-plus program areas cover "best practices" in such areas as finance, human resources, information technology, operations, and sales and marketing. Unlike consulting firms, which engage with one client at a time, CEB operates on a membership-based business model. Members subscribe to one or more of the company's programs and participate in the research and analysis, thus sharing expertise with others. Besides reports on best practices, CEB offers seminars, customized research briefs, and decision-support tools.

	Annual Growth	12/05	12/06	12/07	12/08	12/09
Sales ($ mil.)	5.2%	362.2	460.6	532.7	558.4	442.9
Net income ($ mil.)	(11.7%)	75.1	79.2	80.6	50.8	45.6
Market value ($ mil.)	(29.0%)	3,073.3	3,004.7	2,059.1	755.8	781.8
Employees	(1.7%)	1,865	2,279	2,440	2,430	1,742

⊞ An in-depth profile of this company is available to Hoover's Online members at hoovers.com.

439

CORPORATE OFFICE PROPERTIES TRUST
NYSE: OFC

6711 Columbia Gateway Dr., Ste. 300
Columbia, MD 21046
Phone: 443-285-5400
Fax: 443-285-7650
Web: www.copt.com

CEO: Randall M. (Rand) Griffin
CFO: Stephen E. Riffee
HR: Holly G. Edington
FYE: December 31
Type: Public

The name says "corporate" but it's really about the government. A real estate investment trust (REIT), Corporate Office Properties Trust owns and manages some 250 properties totaling some 19 million sq. ft. of leasable space. The REIT focuses on large suburban business parks near federal government hubs and military installations. More than three-quarters of its assets are located in the Baltimore/Washington, DC corridor; other major markets include Colorado Springs, Colorado; Philadelphia; San Antonio; and central New Jersey. The company also has interests in 20 additional office properties through joint ventures, as well as properties under development and land.

	Annual Growth	12/05	12/06	12/07	12/08	12/09
Sales ($ mil.)	23.6%	329.1	361.4	410.2	588.0	767.5
Net income ($ mil.)	12.1%	38.8	48.5	33.2	57.8	61.3
Market value ($ mil.)	0.8%	2,094.3	2,974.2	1,856.3	1,809.1	2,158.6
Employees	10.4%	257	313	351	372	382

CORRECTIONAL MEDICAL SERVICES, INC.

12647 Olive Blvd.
St. Louis, MO 63141
Phone: 314-919-8501
Fax: 314-919-8864
Web: www.cmsstl.com

CEO: Richard H. (Dick) Miles
CFO: —
HR: —
FYE: December 31
Type: Private

Prison inmates can't really shop around for health plans, but depending on where they are held, they may have access to Correctional Medical Services (CMS). More than a quarter of a million incarcerated people rely on CMS, which operates on-site medical units in more than 330 prisons and jails in some 20 states across the US. Its 6,000 doctors, nurses, and other staff provide primary and specialty medical care (including dental care, mental health and substance abuse services), pharmacy services, and medical records management. The company, which was founded in 1979, has statewide health care contracts with more than 10 state prison systems.

CORRECTIONS CORPORATION OF AMERICA
NYSE: CXW

10 Burton Hills Blvd.
Nashville, TN 37215
Phone: 615-263-3000
Fax: 615-263-3140
Web: www.correctionscorp.com

CEO: Damon T. Hininger
CFO: Todd J. Mullenger
HR: Brian D. Collins
FYE: December 31
Type: Public

Corrections Corporation of America (CCA) has locked up a big share of the private prison market. The company operates more than 60 correctional, detention, and juvenile facilities with a capacity of some 87,000 beds in about 20 states and Washington, DC. CCA contracts with federal, state, and local authorities to manage the facilities, over 40 of which are company-owned. CCA also owns two facilities that are managed by other companies. Federal correctional and detention authorities account for about 40% of CCA's sales. The company also provides rehabilitation, education programs, health care food services, recreational programs, and religious services for inmates of its facilities.

	Annual Growth	12/05	12/06	12/07	12/08	12/09
Sales ($ mil.)	8.8%	1,192.6	1,331.1	1,478.8	1,598.9	1,670.0
Net income ($ mil.)	32.6%	50.1	105.2	133.4	150.9	155.0
Market value ($ mil.)	13.1%	1,704.9	2,572.1	3,356.3	1,860.7	2,792.2
Employees	3.0%	15,500	16,000	16,600	17,400	17,425

CORRIGENT SYSTEMS INC.

101 Metro Dr., Ste. 680
San Jose, CA 95110
Phone: 408-392-9292
Fax: 408-392-9294
Web: www.corrigent.co.il

CEO: Izhak Tamir
CFO: Uri Shalom
HR: Inbar Rozenberg
FYE: December 31
Type: Subsidiary

Corrigent Systems designs and manufactures optical communications network equipment. The company (which does business as Orckit-Corrigent) makes products that are designed to enable Ethernet and Sonet functionality over IP networks. Orckit-Corrigent targets telecom carriers that deliver data, video, and other services using optical transmission technology. The company's top customer, KDDI, is one of Japan's largest telecommunications service providers. It has partnerships with other manufacturers including Oki. Corrigent is a subsidiary of Tel Aviv-based broadband networking equipment maker Orckit Communications.

CORT BUSINESS SERVICES CORPORATION

11250 Waples Mill Rd., Ste. 500
Fairfax, VA 22030
Phone: 703-968-8500
Fax: 703-968-8502
Web: www.cort1.com

CEO: Paul N. Arnold
CFO: Debbie (Deb) Rosenberg
HR: Edie Cardwell
FYE: December 31
Type: Subsidiary

If you need to furnish an office or temporary residence, buying furniture often doesn't make sense: moving furniture is expensive, office needs may change, and furniture may become worn or dated. These simple facts made CORT Business Services the country's #1 furniture renter. A subsidiary of Wesco Financial (which is 80% owned by Berkshire Hathaway), CORT rents office and residential furniture — along with trade show and special event furnishings — online, by phone, and from about 250 US locations. CORT, which offers such well-known brands as HON, Lane, Bassett, Chromcraft, United Chair, and National Office Furniture, also offers space planning and design services, and sells previously rented furniture.

CORTEX PHARMACEUTICALS, INC.
NYSE Amex: COR

15231 Barranca Pkwy.
Irvine, CA 92618
Phone: 949-727-3157
Fax: 949-727-3657
Web: www.cortexpharm.com

CEO: Mark A. Varney
CFO: Maria S. Messinger
HR: —
FYE: December 31
Type: Public

Cortex Pharmaceuticals develops drugs to treat neurodegenerative and psychiatric disorders. Its research focuses on the AMPA receptor, which facilitates communication between nerve cells; the firm's Ampakine compounds may enhance this receptor's activity. Cortex's tends to develop candidates and then license the technologies to larger firms for diseases that require clinical and commercialization infrastructure to develop drugs for large markets (Alzheimer's disease, for instance). In turn, it will focus its internal research efforts on developing more compounds for niche markets, which require a smaller sales organization and more limited clinical trials.

	Annual Growth	12/05	12/06	12/07	12/08	12/09
Sales ($ mil.)	—	—	—	—	—	0.0
Net income ($ mil.)	—	—	—	—	—	(8.4)
Market value ($ mil.)	—	—	—	—	—	7.1
Employees	—	—	—	—	—	13

CORTLAND BANCORP
OTC: CLDB

194 W. Main St.
Cortland, OH 44410
Phone: 330-637-8040
Fax: 330-638-3018
Web: www.cortland-banks.com

CEO: James M. Gasior
CFO: David J. Lucido
HR: Stephen A. Telego Sr.
FYE: December 31
Type: Public

Cortland Bancorp is the place to keep your bucks in the Buckeye State. Cortland Bancorp is the holding company for Cortland Savings and Banking Company (aka Cortland Banks), a community-oriented institution serving northeastern Ohio from about 15 banking locations. Cortland Banks offers standard banking services including checking and savings accounts, debit cards, and business and consumer loans. More than half of Cortland's loan portfolio is composed of commercial mortgages. Other offerings include discount brokerage and trust services.

	Annual Growth	12/05	12/06	12/07	12/08	12/09
Assets ($ mil.)	2.0%	459.7	471.8	492.7	493.4	497.3
Net income ($ mil.)	—	4.3	4.6	4.3	2.4	(6.3)
Market value ($ mil.)	(29.7%)	78.6	80.2	53.5	42.6	19.2
Employees	(0.6%)	174	185	177	175	170

⊞ CORVEL CORPORATION
NASDAQ (GS): CRVL

2010 Main St., Ste. 600
Irvine, CA 92614
Phone: 949-851-1473
Fax: 949-851-1469
Web: www.corvel.com

CEO: Daniel J. Starck
CFO: Scott R. McCloud
HR: —
FYE: March 31
Type: Public

CorVel has carved out a niche providing medical cost containment for workers' compensation programs, group health plans, and auto insurers. CorVel helps insurers, third-party administrators, and self-insured employers keep down medical costs associated with workers' compensation claims and to get employees back on the job as soon as is practicable. Among other things, CorVel reviews medical bills to make sure they are in line with state fee schedules, using its automated online MedCheck software. It also maintains a preferred provider organization (PPO) and provides case management and vocational rehabilitation services. Clients access CorVel's range of services through its CareMC Web portal.

	Annual Growth	3/05	3/06	3/07	3/08	3/09
Sales ($ mil.)	1.6%	291.0	266.5	274.6	301.9	310.1
Net income ($ mil.)	17.3%	10.2	9.8	18.6	23.4	19.3
Market value ($ mil.)	9.2%	171.8	177.5	365.7	369.8	244.4
Employees	(2.4%)	2,980	2,323	2,631	2,705	2,700

COSCO AMERICAS, INC.

100 Lighting Way, Ste. 101
Secaucus, NJ 07094
Phone: 201-422-0500
Fax: 201-617-8060
Web: www.coscoamericas.com

CEO: Wan Min
CFO: Huang Jian
HR: Jim Kemp
FYE: December 31
Type: Subsidiary

COSCO Americas, Inc. (CAI) represents the interests of its parent, marine transportation giant China Ocean Shipping (Group) Company, known as COSCO, in North and South America. In addition to serving as a shipping agent, CAI provides services related to sales, fuel supply, and technical consulting, as well as inland transportation of freight — in other words, whatever is necessary to facilitate the movement of containerized and bulk cargo by the parent company. Overall, CAI operates from about 80 offices in Argentina, Brazil, Canada, Chile, Panama, Peru, Uruguay, and the US. The unit was established in 1982.

COSI, INC.
NASDAQ (GM): COSI

1751 Lake Cook Rd., Ste. 600
Deerfield, IL 60015
Phone: 847-597-8800
Fax: 847-597-8884
Web: www.getcosi.com

CEO: James F. (Jim) Hyatt
CFO: William E. (Bill) Koziel
HR: Becky Iliff
FYE: December 31
Type: Public

Cosi's recipe calls for one part coffee house, one part sandwich shop, and one part cocktail bar. The company operates and franchises about 150 eclectic Così cafés in almost 20 states offering premium and specialty coffees and made-to-order sandwiches. Its menu also features breakfast items (including its bagel-inspired Squagels), salads, soups, and desserts. Most of the company's restaurants also offer dinner and drinks after 5 p.m., while its Così Downtown units (primarily located in non-residential business districts) close in the evening. Cosi also offers delivery and catering services. About 100 of the locations are company owned while the rest are franchised.

	Annual Growth	12/05	12/06	12/07	12/08	12/09
Sales ($ mil.)	0.3%	117.2	126.9	134.6	135.6	118.6
Net income ($ mil.)	—	(13.1)	(12.3)	(20.8)	(16.2)	(11.1)
Market value ($ mil.)	(47.3%)	427.9	262.4	115.5	14.8	33.0
Employees	(3.1%)	2,727	4,210	2,918	2,514	2,409

COSINE COMMUNICATIONS, INC.
Pink Sheets: COSN

61 E. Main
Los Gatos, CA 95030
Phone: 408-399-6494
Fax: —
Web: www.cosinecom.com

CEO: Terry R. Gibson
CFO: Terry R. Gibson
HR: —
FYE: December 31
Type: Public

CoSine Communications is trying to switch businesses. The company was a manufacturer of switches and software that telecom service providers used to manage their Internet protocol networks, but the company shuttered its operations and ceased its support services in 2004. CoSine had agreed to be acquired by telecom equipment maker Tut Systems, but the deal fell through in 2005. CoSine is seeking to acquire an operating business.

	Annual Growth	12/05	12/06	12/07	12/08	12/09
Sales ($ mil.)	—	3.3	1.4	0.0	0.0	0.0
Net income ($ mil.)	—	(1.2)	0.4	0.4	0.0	(0.6)
Market value ($ mil.)	(5.4%)	24.2	33.5	27.7	17.7	19.4
Employees	—	1	1	0	—	—

COSMETIC ESSENCE, INC.

2182 Rte. 35 South
Holmdel, NJ 07733
Phone: 732-888-7788
Fax: 732-888-6086
Web: www.cosmeticessence.com

CEO: Andy Brewer
CFO: Barry C. Nuss
HR: Ely Bar-Ness
FYE: December 31
Type: Subsidiary

Time isn't the only thing that is of the essence in the world of cosmetics. A contract manufacturer, Cosmetic Essence specializes in the formulation, manufacturing, and filling of personal care products. The company also offers packaging design and distribution services. Its product lines consist of color cosmetics, creams and lotions, perfumes, bath and hair care items, and household supplies. Customers include leading branded manufacturers and major retailers nationwide. Until 2009 Cosmetic Essence was owned by private investment firm Onex.

⊞ An in-depth profile of this company is available to Hoover's Online members at hoovers.com.

441

COST PLUS, INC.

NASDAQ (GS): CPWM

200 4th St.
Oakland, CA 94607
Phone: 510-893-7300
Fax: 510-893-3681
Web: www.costplusworldmarket.com

CEO: Barry J. Feld
CFO: Jane L. Baughman
HR: Joan S. Fujii
FYE: January 31
Type: Public

Cost Plus adorns dining rooms and picnics with wicker, wine, and cheese. The retailer's 270 Cost Plus World Market and World Market stores sell furniture, rugs, baskets, ceramics, and other home decor, as well as exotic food and beverages. Designed to resemble upscale world markets, Cost Plus' stores are often located near major malls in about 30 states. The company targets women ages 25 to 55. Much of what it sells is imported from more than 50 countries; many of its 10,000-plus items are proprietary and are sold under its World Market private label. The retailer, which had aims of doubling its store network, has suffered from declining sales and is putting its expansion plans on hold.

	Annual Growth	1/06	1/07	1/08	1/09	1/10
Sales ($ mil.)	(2.7%)	970.4	1,040.3	1,023.9	1,000.4	869.5
Net income ($ mil.)	—	20.2	(22.5)	(55.5)	(102.7)	(63.3)
Market value ($ mil.)	(50.2%)	431.8	227.5	88.3	21.2	26.5
Employees	(1.8%)	6,170	6,741	6,705	6,251	5,745

COSTAR GROUP, INC.

NASDAQ (GS): CSGP

2 Bethesda Metro Center, 10th Fl.
Bethesda, MD 20814
Phone: 301-215-8300
Fax: 301-718-2444
Web: www.costar.com

CEO: Andrew C. Florance
CFO: Brian J. Radecki
HR: Craig F. Gomez
FYE: December 31
Type: Public

CoStar has all the dirt on the commercial real estate industry. A provider of commercial real estate information, CoStar has a proprietary database of some 3.2 million properties in the US, the UK, and France. The database contains information on nearly 9 billion sq. ft. of sale and lease listings. It also has more than 7 million digital images of buildings, floor plans, and maps. CoStar additionally offers property research, tenant profiling, and its *CoStar Advisor* newsletter. Clients include government agencies, real estate brokerages, real estate investment trusts (REITs), and property owners and managers. Most of CoStar's sales come from subscription fees.

	Annual Growth	12/05	12/06	12/07	12/08	12/09
Sales ($ mil.)	11.8%	134.3	158.9	192.8	212.4	209.7
Net income ($ mil.)	30.2%	6.5	12.4	16.0	24.6	18.7
Market value ($ mil.)	(0.8%)	893.1	1,108.1	977.5	681.5	864.2
Employees	7.5%	1,076	1,308	1,335	1,178	1,438

COSTCO WHOLESALE CORPORATION

NASDAQ (GS): COST

999 Lake Dr.
Issaquah, WA 98027
Phone: 425-313-8100
Fax: —
Web: www.costco.com

CEO: James D. (Jim) Sinegal
CFO: Richard A. Galanti
HR: Ross Hunt
FYE: August 31
Type: Public

Wal-Mart isn't the biggest in *every* business. Costco Wholesale is the largest wholesale club operator in the US (ahead of Wal-Mart's SAM'S CLUB). The company operates about 565 membership warehouse stores serving some 56 million cardholders in some 40 US states and Puerto Rico, Canada, Japan, Mexico, South Korea, Taiwan, the UK, and Australia primarily under the Costco Wholesale name. Stores offer discount prices on an average of about 4,000 products (many in bulk packaging), ranging from alcoholic beverages and appliances to fresh food, pharmaceuticals, and tires. Certain club memberships also offer products and services such as car and home insurance, mortgage and real estate services, and travel packages.

	Annual Growth	8/05	8/06	8/07	8/08	8/09
Sales ($ mil.)	7.8%	52,935.2	60,151.2	64,400.2	72,483.0	71,422.0
Net income ($ mil.)	0.5%	1,063.1	1,103.2	1,082.8	1,282.7	1,086.0
Market value ($ mil.)	4.1%	19,118.0	20,611.3	27,201.3	29,540.4	22,457.0
Employees	4.7%	118,000	127,000	127,000	137,000	142,000

COTTON INCORPORATED

6399 Weston Pkwy.
Cary, NC 27513
Phone: 919-678-2220
Fax: 919-678-2230
Web: www.cottoninc.com

CEO: J. Berrye Worsham
CFO: —
HR: —
FYE: December 31
Type: Association

Battling both boll weevils and synthetic fibers, Cotton Incorporated bolsters the US cotton industry through its research and marketing efforts. To the public, Cotton Inc. is known for its white-on-brown "Seal of Cotton" logo — recognized by about 75% of Americans — and its advertising slogan, "The fabric of our lives." Founded in 1970, Cotton Inc. is funded by US growers of upland cotton, cotton importers, and cotton-product makers. Its board consists of representatives from each cotton-growing state, all of whom are themselves cotton producers. Cotton Incorporated is overseen by the US Department of Agriculture.

	Annual Growth	12/04	12/05	12/06	12/07	12/08
Est. sales ($ mil.)	—	—	—	—	—	78.0
Employees	—	—	—	—	—	157

COTY INC.

2 Park Ave., 17th Fl.
New York, NY 10016
Phone: 212-479-4300
Fax: 866-336-6064
Web: www.coty.com

CEO: Bernd Beetz
CFO: Sérgio Messias Pedreiro
HR: Nancy Halligan
FYE: June 30
Type: Subsidiary

Sarah Jessica Parker, Beyoncé, and Celine Dion all go to Coty to smell good. It is the world's leading maker of mass-market fragrances for men and women. Coty scents have turned heads since François Coty created his first perfume, La Rose Jacqueminot, in 1904. Its boudoir includes moderately priced fragrances and colognes sold by mass retailers and prestige brands found in department stores. Coty's brands include Jennifer Lopez, JOOP!, Jovan, Rimmel, Stetson, and Vivienne Westwood. Coty went upmarket in 2005 with its purchase of the prestige Calvin Klein fragrance brand, now its #1 seller. Coty is owned by Germany's Joh. A. Benckiser GmbH, which bought Coty to operate its fragrance and cosmetics businesses.

COUNTRY MUTUAL INSURANCE COMPANY, INC.

1705 N. Towanda
Bloomington, IL 61702
Phone: 309-821-3000
Fax: 309-557-3232
Web: www.countryfinancial.com

CEO: John D. Blackburn
CFO: David A. Magers
HR: —
FYE: December 31
Type: Subsidiary

COUNTRY Mutual Insurance sells property/casualty insurance in both rural and urban settings. The company, a member of CC Services (known as COUNTRY Financial), sells residential, farm, automobile, and corporate insurance to individuals and businesses. The company provides policies in some 25 states in the midwestern, western, northeastern, and southeastern US. Its subsidiaries include COUNTRY Preferred Insurance Company, COUNTRY Casualty Insurance Company, and Modern Service Insurance Company. Founded in 1925, COUNTRY Mutual sells insurance products through a network of affiliated and independent agents.

	Annual Growth	12/04	12/05	12/06	12/07	12/08
Est. sales ($ mil.)	—	—	—	—	—	1,803.8
Employees	—	—	—	—	—	4,500

COUNTRY VILLA SERVICE CORP.

5120 W. Goldleaf Cir., Ste. 400
Los Angeles, CA 90056
Phone: 310-574-3733
Fax: 310-301-9343
Web: countryvillahealth.com

CEO: Stephen E. Reissman
CFO: Joe Saltzburg
HR: —
FYE: December 31
Type: Private

Some Californians wind up at a Country Villa upon retirement. Country Villa Service Corp., which does business as Country Villa Health Service, operates about 50 skilled nursing and assisted living centers across California. Services include sub-acute, complex, and long-term care, as well as rehabilitation, hospice, AIDS, and Alzheimer's programs. The company also offers outsourced management services to hospital and freestanding skilled nursing facilities, including billing, recruitment, and clinical and operational support. In addition, Country Villa offers free training to become a nursing assistant. The family-owned company was founded in 1969.

COURTROOM TELEVISION NETWORK LLC

600 3rd Ave.
New York, NY 10016
Phone: 212-973-2800
Fax: 212-973-3210
Web: www.trutv.com

CEO: Steven R. (Steve) Koonin
CFO: —
HR: Drenda Jones
FYE: December 31
Type: Subsidiary

You might say this TV channel is courting the truth. Courtroom Television Network operates truTV, a cable channel that reaches more than 90 million US homes with a programming slate heavy on reality-based shows. Focused mostly on crime and justice, the network's shows include *Disorder in the Court*, *Smoking Gun Presents*, and *Speeders*. truTV also offers real-life courtroom coverage during the day during its *In Session* programming block. In addition to television programming, truTV distributes videos and an archive of notorious criminals online. Courtroom Television Network operates as part of Turner Broadcasting System, the cable programming arm of media giant Time Warner.

⊞ COURIER CORPORATION
NASDAQ (GS): CRRC

15 Wellman Ave.
N. Chelmsford, MA 01863
Phone: 978-251-6000
Fax: 978-251-8228
Web: www.courier.com

CEO: James F. Conway III
CFO: Peter M. Folger
HR: —
FYE: September 30
Type: Public

Courier dispatches books for playing, praying, and puzzling over. One of the largest book printers in the US, Courier manufactures a variety of hard and soft cover books for educational, religious, and specialty trade publishers and organizations. The firm's book printing operations, which account for about 85% of sales, produce more than 175 million books per year and serve more than 500 customers; its largest clients include Bible distributor The Gideons International and publishing giant Pearson, which each account for about 22% of sales. A book publisher itself, Courier offers books for niche markets through subsidiaries Creative Homeowner, Dover Publications, and Research & Education Association.

	Annual Growth	9/05	9/06	9/07	9/08	9/09
Sales ($ mil.)	2.3%	227.0	269.1	294.6	280.3	248.8
Net income ($ mil.)	—	22.1	28.4	25.7	(0.4)	(3.1)
Market value ($ mil.)	(20.2%)	448.9	445.7	422.6	244.3	181.8
Employees	2.0%	1,479	1,724	1,830	1,825	1,603

COUSINS PROPERTIES INCORPORATED
NYSE: CUZ

191 Peachtree St. NE, Ste. 3600
Atlanta, GA 90909
Phone: 404-407-1000
Fax: 404-407-1002
Web: www.cousinsproperties.com

CEO: Lawrence L. (Larry) Gellerstedt III
CFO: James A. (Jim) Fleming
HR: Lawrence B. Gardner
FYE: December 31
Type: Public

Cousins Properties manages a *primo* brood of office, multifamily, and retail holdings. The real estate investment trust (REIT) invests in, develops, and manages commercial and residential properties, primarily in the Southeast. Its portfolio (some of which is owned through joint ventures) includes 7.5 million sq. ft. of office space, about a dozen shopping centers, 25 residential properties, and nearly 10,000 acres of land. Most properties are located in Atlanta; other core markets include California, Florida, and Texas. Deloitte & Touche, American Cancer Society, and Bank of America are among its major tenants.

	Annual Growth	12/05	12/06	12/07	12/08	12/09
Sales ($ mil.)	9.6%	155.7	169.9	165.4	214.7	224.9
Net income ($ mil.)	(12.2%)	49.7	232.7	32.9	22.5	29.5
Market value ($ mil.)	(27.9%)	2,854.5	3,557.6	2,229.1	1,397.0	769.6
Employees	(3.6%)	448	488	470	435	387

COURT SQUARE CAPITAL PARTNERS

Park Avenue Plaza, 55 E. 52nd St., 34th Fl.
New York, NY 10055
Phone: 212-752-6110
Fax: 212-752-6184
Web: www.courtsquare.com

CEO: Byron L. Knief
CFO: —
HR: —
FYE: December 31
Type: Private

Court Square Capital Partners is courting technology, health care, industrial and media companies. Spun off from Citigroup in 2006, the private equity and venture capital firm (formerly Citicorp Venture Capital) specializes in buyouts of middle-market companies. (In order to avoid potential conflicts of interest with its customers or its other investment funds, Citigroup no longer has equity in the firm.) Court Square Capital manages approximately $6 billion of capital commitments and takes an active role with its investments, helping to improve operational efficiency and often making add-on acquisitions. The firm has been involved in more than 150 transactions over the last 20 years.

⊞ COVAD COMMUNICATIONS GROUP, INC.

110 Rio Robles
San Jose, CA 95134
Phone: 408-952-6400
Fax: 408-952-7687
Web: www.covad.com

CEO: Patrick J. (Pat) Bennett
CFO: Jeffrey (Jeff) Bailey
HR: —
FYE: December 31
Type: Private

Covad Communications converts conventional copper wires for quick connectivity. The company uses digital subscriber line (DSL) and T-1 technologies to provide broadband Internet access largely on a wholesale basis to customers in 235 metropolitan markets spanning 44 US states. Covad's main clients are Internet service providers (ISPs) — such as EarthLink, AT&T, and AOL — and other resellers. In addition to its wholesale business, the company offers wired and wireless broadband access and Voice over Internet Protocol (VoIP) service directly to small and midsized businesses. Covad is owned by private buy-out specialist Platinum Equity. Covad plans to merge with MegaPath in 2010.

	Annual Growth	12/04	12/05	12/06	12/07	12/08
Est. sales ($ mil.)	—	—	—	—	—	123.6
Employees	—	—	—	—	—	967

⊞ An in-depth profile of this company is available to Hoover's Online members at hoovers.com.

443

COVANCE INC.

NYSE: CVD

210 Carnegie Center
Princeton, NJ 08540
Phone: 609-452-4440
Fax: 609-452-9375
Web: www.covance.com

CEO: Joseph L. (Joe) Herring
CFO: William E. Klitgaard
HR: Donald Kraft
FYE: December 31
Type: Public

Behind every great big drug company stands a great big contract research organization (CRO), and Covance is one of the biggest. Covance helps pharmaceutical and biotech companies worldwide develop new drugs by providing preclinical testing services, as well as designing and carrying out human clinical trials to determine if the drugs are safe and effective. Services include toxicology studies, biostatistical analysis, clinical laboratory testing, and post-marketing studies. Among the company's customers are pharmaceutical, biotech, and medical device companies; Covance also offers laboratory testing services to companies in the chemical, agrochemical, and food industries.

	Annual Growth	12/05	12/06	12/07	12/08	12/09
Sales ($ mil.)	11.9%	1,250.5	1,406.1	1,631.5	1,827.1	1,962.6
Net income ($ mil.)	10.1%	119.6	145.0	175.9	196.8	175.9
Market value ($ mil.)	3.0%	3,139.8	3,809.9	5,601.9	2,976.9	3,529.2
Employees	9.0%	7,300	8,100	8,700	9,600	10,320

COVANTA ENERGY CORPORATION

40 Lane Rd.
Fairfield, NJ 07004
Phone: 973-882-9000
Fax: 973-882-7234
Web: www.covantaholding.com

CEO: Anthony J. (Tony) Orlando
CFO: Thomas E. (Tom) Bucks
HR: Michael A. Wright
FYE: December 31
Type: Subsidiary

The power ball is back in Covanta Energy's court. The major operating arm of Covanta Holding, the power producer has interests in 60 power plants located in the Americas, Asia, and Europe. Its plants use a variety of fuels, including municipal solid waste, wood waste (biomass), landfill gas, water (hydroelectric), natural gas, coal, and heavy fuel. Covanta Energy has 30 waste to energy plants worldwide. These specialized plants can convert 16 million tons of waste into more than 8 million MW hours of electricity annually and create 10 billion pounds of steam that are sold to a variety of industries.

COVANTA HOLDING CORPORATION

NYSE: CVA

40 Lane Rd.
Fairfield, NJ 07004
Phone: 973-882-9000
Fax: 973-882-7076
Web: www.covantaholding.com

CEO: Anthony J. (Tony) Orlando
CFO: Thomas E. (Tom) Bucks
HR: —
FYE: December 31
Type: Public

Covanta Holding has seen the light: waste can result in power. Led by Covanta Energy), the company is a leader in the waste-to-energy market. Covanta Holding owns or operates 60 energy generation facilities (50 in the US) which use municipal solid waste and biomass, as well as fossil fuels and hydroelectric sources, to generate power. Related business include four landfills, and waste and biomass procurement business programs. Internationally, Covanta Holding also is engaged in independent power production, and it operates an insurance business in California. Chairman Samuel Zell holds about 10% in the company through his SZ Investments unit.

	Annual Growth	12/05	12/06	12/07	12/08	12/09
Sales ($ mil.)	12.2%	978.8	1,268.5	1,433.1	1,664.3	1,550.5
Net income ($ mil.)	14.4%	59.3	105.8	130.5	139.3	101.6
Market value ($ mil.)	4.7%	2,344.1	3,430.6	4,305.3	3,418.1	2,815.7
Employees	3.3%	3,600	3,300	3,500	3,700	4,100

COVENANT TRANSPORTATION GROUP, INC.

NASDAQ (GS): CVTI

400 Birmingham Hwy.
Chattanooga, TN 37419
Phone: 423-821-1212
Fax: 423-821-5442
Web: www.covenanttransport.com

CEO: David R. Parker
CFO: Richard B. Cribbs
HR: Jon W. Huston
FYE: December 31
Type: Public

Truckload freight carrier Covenant Transportation Group promises its customers speedy service on long-haul and regional routes. The company operates a fleet of about 3,300 tractors and 8,270 trailers, including both dry vans and temperature-controlled units (through its Southern Refrigerated Transport subsidiary). In addition to for-hire transportation, Covenant offers dedicated contract carriage, in which drivers and equipment are assigned long-term to a customer or route, and freight brokerage services. Averaging about 800 miles per length of haul, the company gets business from manufacturers, retailers, and other transportation companies; among its top customers are Georgia-Pacific, Wal-Mart, and UPS.

	Annual Growth	12/05	12/06	12/07	12/08	12/09
Sales ($ mil.)	(2.2%)	643.1	683.8	712.5	773.9	588.7
Net income ($ mil.)	—	5.7	(1.4)	(16.7)	(53.4)	(25.0)
Market value ($ mil.)	(25.9%)	199.0	162.3	95.7	28.5	59.9
Employees	(3.7%)	5,712	4,817	5,052	5,279	4,912

COVENTRY HEALTH CARE, INC.

NYSE: CVH

6705 Rockledge Dr., Ste. 900
Bethesda, MD 20817
Phone: 301-581-0600
Fax: 301-493-0731
Web: www.coventryhealthcare.com

CEO: Allen F. Wise
CFO: John J. Stelben
HR: Patrisha L. Davis
FYE: December 31
Type: Public

Coventry Health Care wants to measure up in the tough world of managed care. Through numerous local health plans, the firm provides health care coverage to more than 5 million members, primarily in the Midwest, Mid-Atlantic, and Southeast. It offers HMO, PPO, and point-of-service (POS) plans to employer groups, as well as Medicare Advantage, Medicare prescription drug coverage, Medicaid managed care plans, and other coverage directly to individuals. Its Specialty unit administers (but doesn't underwrite) workers' compensation programs, providing services such as bill review and case management to insurers and employers; it also administers network rental and pharmacy benefit programs.

	Annual Growth	12/05	12/06	12/07	12/08	12/09
Sales ($ mil.)	20.4%	6,611.2	7,733.8	9,879.5	11,913.6	13,903.5
Net income ($ mil.)	(16.6%)	501.6	560.0	626.1	381.9	242.3
Market value ($ mil.)	(19.2%)	8,426.6	7,404.3	8,765.4	2,201.3	3,593.4
Employees	10.0%	9,830	10,250	15,000	15,800	14,400

COVER-ALL TECHNOLOGIES INC.

OTC: COVR

55 Lane Rd., Ste. 300
Fairfield, NJ 07004
Phone: 973-461-5200
Fax: 973-461-5257
Web: www.cover-all.com

CEO: John W. Roblin
CFO: Ann F. Massey
HR: —
FYE: December 31
Type: Public

Cover-All Technologies keeps insurers covered. The company offers software and services for carriers, agents, and brokers in the property/casualty insurance industry. Cover-All's software, which the company licenses and offers as a hosted application, automates insurance rating and policy issuance. Its My Insurance Center site, an Internet-based portal for insurance professionals, helps agents with policy quoting, rating, issuance, and billing; provides quick access to policy information; and offers applications for managing insurance agencies. The company also provides product customization, data integration, and other support services that keep the software up-to-date on industry information and regulations.

	Annual Growth	12/05	12/06	12/07	12/08	12/09
Sales ($ mil.)	18.7%	7.3	7.3	9.8	13.5	14.5
Net income ($ mil.)	—	(1.4)	(1.0)	1.2	4.6	3.9
Market value ($ mil.)	19.5%	13.6	19.6	34.2	22.3	27.8
Employees	(1.0%)	50	45	44	48	48

⊞ COVISTA COMMUNICATIONS, INC.

Pink Sheets: CVST

4803 Hwy. 58 North, Ste. 200
Chattanooga, TN 37416
Phone: 423-648-9700
Fax: 423-648-9705
Web: www.covista.com

CEO: Henry G. Luken III
CFO: —
HR: Jackie Barry
FYE: January 31
Type: Public

Covista Communications offers alternative telecommunications services to business and residential customers, mostly in Georgia, New Jersey, New York, Pennsylvania, and Tennessee. Once primarily a long-distance provider, the company has added local service in some markets; it also provides Internet and data networking services. In addition to commercial and residential service, Covista sells wholesale termination services and colocation facilities to telecom carriers. The company operates its own switching facilities in Chattanooga, Tennessee; Dallas; and Minneapolis.

COWEN GROUP, INC.

NASDAQ (GM): COWN

1221 Avenue of the Americas
New York, NY 10020
Phone: 646-562-1000
Fax: 646-562-1861
Web: www.cowen.com

CEO: Peter A. Cohen
CFO: Stephen A. Lasota
HR: William H. Dibble
FYE: December 31
Type: Public

Ever herd of Cowen Group? The firm offers alternative investments such as hedge funds, funds of funds, and real estate funds through Ramius, with which it merged in 2009. Ramius has approximately $8 billion of assets under management. Another subsidiary, Cowen and Company, represents the firm's investment banking and brokerage practice, which mainly entails strategic advisory and corporate finance services for small to midsized companies in the alternative energy, aerospace and defense, consumer goods, health care, media, technology, and real estate industries. It also conducts equities research in those sectors.

	Annual Growth	12/05	12/06	12/07	12/08	12/09
Assets ($ mil.)	5.1%	785.3	684.4	349.0	207.5	959.4
Net income ($ mil.)	—	12.1	37.9	(11.3)	(72.2)	(55.3)
Market value ($ mil.)	(34.6%)	—	1,579.0	710.0	474.8	442.0
Employees	2.3%	529	537	527	449	580

COWLITZ BANCORPORATION

NASDAQ (GM): CWLZ

927 Commerce Ave.
Longview, WA 98632
Phone: 360-423-9800
Fax: 360-423-3562
Web: www.cowlitzbancorp.com

CEO: Richard J. Fitzpatrick
CFO: Gerald L. Brickey
HR: —
FYE: December 31
Type: Public

Cowlitz Bancorporation is the holding company for Cowlitz Bank and its Bay Bank division, which serve southwestern Washington and the Seattle and Portland, Oregon, areas through about 10 branches and loan production offices. Targeting small and midsized businesses and individuals, the banks provide checking and savings accounts, IRAs, CDs, and other standard retail products. They mainly use deposits to originate commercial mortgages, business loans, and construction loans. The company also originates long-term residential real estate loans through its Bay Mortgage division.

	Annual Growth	12/05	12/06	12/07	12/08	12/09
Assets ($ mil.)	10.5%	370.1	468.4	514.2	587.4	552.4
Net income ($ mil.)	—	3.0	4.8	0.1	(8.1)	(34.8)
Market value ($ mil.)	(53.0%)	74.1	86.4	60.2	30.2	3.6
Employees	(1.7%)	119	135	142	114	111

⊞ COX COMMUNICATIONS, INC.

1400 Lake Hearn Dr.
Atlanta, GA 30319
Phone: 404-843-5000
Fax: —
Web: www.cox.com

CEO: Patrick J. (Pat) Esser
CFO: Mark F. Bowser
HR: Mae A. Douglas
FYE: December 31
Type: Subsidiary

Cox Communications carries the complete collection of cable capacity. The company provides basic cable service to more than 6 million customers, including about 3 million digital cable subscribers and 3.5 million Internet access subscribers, making it the third-largest US cable company, behind Comcast and Time Warner Cable. Cox also provides telecommunications services as a competitive local-exchange carrier (CLEC) and it offers wireless services in some markets. In addition, the company offers voice and data communications services to businesses, and it has investments in television programming and broadband technology companies. Cox Communications is a subsidiary of media conglomerate Cox Enterprises.

⊞ COX ENTERPRISES, INC.

6205 Peachtree Dunwoody Rd.
Atlanta, GA 30328
Phone: 678-645-0000
Fax: 678-645-1079
Web: www.coxenterprises.com

CEO: Jimmy W. Hayes
CFO: John M. Dyer
HR: Charlie Chance
FYE: December 31
Type: Private

Cox Enterprises is a family-owned holding company with operations spanning cable TV, broadcasting, publishing, and auctions. Its flagship subsidiary, Cox Communications, is the #3 cable system operator (behind Comcast and Time Warner Cable) serving more than 6 million customers with TV, Internet, and digital phone services. Its Manheim unit is the largest wholesale vehicle auction company in the US, with about 145 locations. Cox's media operations, overseen by Cox Media Group, include Cox Newspapers (eight daily papers), Cox Television (about 15 local stations), and Cox Radio (more than 80 stations). Cox also owns a majority stake in AutoTrader.com, an online used car listing service.

	Annual Growth	12/04	12/05	12/06	12/07	12/08
Sales ($ mil.)	7.5%	11,552.0	12,000.0	13,200.0	15,033.0	15,400.0
Employees	0.0%	77,000	77,000	80,000	81,693	77,000

COX TARGET MEDIA, INC.

8605 Largo Lakes Dr.
Largo, FL 33773
Phone: 727-399-3000
Fax: 727-399-3171
Web: www.coxtarget.com

CEO: Greg Bicket
CFO: Jeff Heinicka
HR: —
FYE: December 31
Type: Subsidiary

This company homes in on consumers and hits them in the mailbox. Cox Target Media (CTM) is a leading provider of direct mail and direct response marketing services. Its primary operating unit, Valpak Direct Marketing Systems, helps companies reach new customers through mailings of its Valpak coupon booklet and Valpak.com website. The company also offers custom designed direct response marketing services using direct mail and online campaigns. CTM is a subsidiary of newspaper publisher Cox Newspapers, one of the main operating subsidiaries of media conglomerate Cox Enterprises. In 2008 Cox Enterprises announced plans to sell Valpak and several Cox Newspapers properties.

An in-depth profile of this company is available to Hoover's Online members at hoovers.com.

445

CP KELCO

1000 Parkwood Circle, Ste. 1000
Atlanta, GA 30339
Phone: 678-247-7300
Fax: 678-247-2797
Web: www.cpkelco.com

CEO: Donald (Don) Rubright
CFO: —
HR: Thomas K. (Tom) Johnson
FYE: December 31
Type: Subsidiary

Don't worry, teachers. CP Kelco has brought enough gum for the entire class. The company's products include carrageenan, gellan gum, xanthan gum, and microparticulated whey protein. CP Kelco, a subsidiary of J. M. Huber, makes additives used to give food, industrial, personal care, and pharmaceutical products (everything from jam and ketchup to paint and cosmetics) the desired texture, viscosity, and stability. Other markets that serve as customers include the pulp and paper (which uses cellulose derivatives) and oilfield drilling industries (additives for drilling fluids). The company operates from manufacturing facilities in Asia, Europe, and the Americas.

	Annual Growth	12/04	12/05	12/06	12/07	12/08
Est. sales ($ mil.)	—	—	—	—	—	357.6
Employees	—	—	—	—	—	2,500

CPEX PHARMACEUTICALS, INC.

NASDAQ (CM): CPEX

2 Holland Way
Exeter, NH 03833
Phone: 603-658-6100
Fax: 603-658-6101
Web: www.cpexpharm.com

CEO: John A. Sedor
CFO: Robert P. (Bob) Hebert
HR: —
FYE: December 31
Type: Public

CPEX Pharmaceuticals has set out on its own to seek its fortunes in the drug industry. The company is developing prescription drugs using its CPE-215 drug delivery technology, which allows for drug absorption via the skin, nasal mucosa, and eyes. Auxilium Pharmaceuticals licensed the technology for its FDA-approved testosterone replacement gel Testim. And CPEX is using the technology to develop its own product, an intranasal insulin called Nasulin that is undergoing clinical trials. Formerly a unit of generic drugmaker Bentley Pharmaceuticals, the company was spun off in 2008 into a separate, publicly traded entity.

	Annual Growth	12/05	12/06	12/07	12/08	12/09
Sales ($ mil.)	32.3%	6.1	8.4	11.1	15.6	18.7
Net income ($ mil.)	—	(1.1)	(4.2)	(4.9)	(2.9)	(3.0)
Market value ($ mil.)	13.0%	—	—	—	24.8	28.0
Employees	6.5%	—	—	15	18	17

CPI AEROSTRUCTURES, INC.

NYSE Amex: CVU

60 Heartland Blvd.
Edgewood, NY 11717
Phone: 631-586-5200
Fax: 631-586-5840
Web: www.cpiaero.com

CEO: Edward J. Fred
CFO: Vincent (Vince) Palazzolo
HR: —
FYE: December 31
Type: Public

To build an aircraft, some assembly is required, and CPI Aerostructures is ready. CPI Aero delivers contract production of structural aircraft subassemblies, chiefly for the US Air Force and other US military customers. Military products include skin panels, flight control surfaces, leading edges, wing tips, engine components, cowl doors, and nacelle and inlet assemblies. The lineup is used on military aircraft, such as the C-5A Galaxy and C-130 Hercules cargo jets, E-3 Sentry AWACs jet, and T-38 Talon jet trainer. As a subcontractor to OEMs, CPI Aero also makes aprons and engine mounts for commercial aircraft, such as business jets. Government prime and subcontracts represent a majority of CPI Aero's sales.

	Annual Growth	12/05	12/06	12/07	12/08	12/09
Sales ($ mil.)	14.5%	25.5	17.9	28.0	35.6	43.9
Net income ($ mil.)	27.0%	1.5	(1.3)	1.9	2.6	3.9
Market value ($ mil.)	(12.1%)	65.9	47.4	57.0	36.0	39.4
Employees	6.0%	72	61	65	85	91

CPI CORP.

NYSE: CPY

1706 Washington Ave.
St. Louis, MO 63103
Phone: 314-231-1575
Fax: 314-231-8150
Web: www.cpicorp.com

CEO: Renato Cataldo Jr.
CFO: Dale E. Heins
HR: Dan Duggan
FYE: January 31
Type: Public

CPI gets the picture. One of the largest preschool portrait photographers in North America, the company operates some 3,050 photographic studios in the US, Canada, and Puerto Rico, mainly in Sears and Wal-Mart stores. The firm operates about 1,000 Sears Portrait Studios (SPS) in Sears and Sears Grand outlets. CPI's 2007 purchase of rival Portrait Corporation of America (PCA) brought 2,000-plus photo studios under the PictureMe Portrait Studio (PMPS) name inside Wal-Mart stores throughout North America and Mexico into the picture. All of the company's studios, with the exception of some locations in Canada, use digital imaging technology and offer a choice of poses and print sizes, as well as photo accessories.

	Annual Growth	1/06	1/07	1/08	1/09	1/10
Sales ($ mil.)	9.7%	292.0	293.8	424.0	462.5	422.4
Net income ($ mil.)	21.2%	6.4	16.3	3.6	(7.7)	13.8
Market value ($ mil.)	(9.3%)	192.5	522.2	196.4	66.7	130.2
Employees	11.6%	7,100	7,700	12,854	12,298	11,000

CPI INTERNATIONAL, INC.

NASDAQ (GS): CPII

811 Hansen Way
Palo Alto, CA 94303
Phone: 650-846-2900
Fax: 650-846-3276
Web: www.cpii.com

CEO: O. Joe Caldarelli
CFO: Joel A. Littman
HR: —
FYE: September 30
Type: Public

CPI International makes broadcast and wireless components, such as satellite communications transmitters, amplifiers, sensors, X-ray equipment, power supplies, transmitters, and microwave components. Its radio-frequency (RF) and microwave components go into a great deal of military hardware (governments account for about half of sales), including Aegis-class cruisers and destroyers, electronic warfare decoys, Patriot missile systems, and fighter aircraft. CPI International sells in more than 90 countries, with the US providing nearly two-thirds of sales. Competitor Comtech Telecommunications plans to buy CPI.

	Annual Growth	9/05	9/06	9/07	9/08	9/09
Sales ($ mil.)	0.9%	320.7	339.7	351.1	370.0	332.9
Net income ($ mil.)	14.4%	13.7	17.2	22.5	20.4	23.5
Market value ($ mil.)	(5.3%)	—	220.5	318.3	242.5	187.4
Employees	(2.8%)	1,700	1,610	1,700	1,650	1,520

CPS ENERGY

145 Navarro St.
San Antonio, TX 78205
Phone: 210-353-2000
Fax: 210-353-3021
Web: www.citypublicservice.com

CEO: Milton B. Lee
CFO: Paula Gold-Williams
HR: —
FYE: January 31
Type: Government-owned

And the award for being the energy distributor for the seventh-largest city in the US goes to . . . CPS Energy (formerly City Public Service Board of San Antonio, Texas). Serving more than 690,000 electricity customers and almost 320,000 natural gas customers, the utility operates in a nearly 1,600 sq.-mile service territory. CPS Energy also has a generating capacity of 5,100 MW from its 16 fossil-fueled power plants and its ownership interests in the South Texas Nuclear Project and the Desert Sky Wind Farm in West Texas. As a municipally owned utility, CPS Energy is exempt from retail competition in Texas; the exemption took effect for investor-owned utilities in 2002.

	Annual Growth	1/04	1/05	1/06	1/07	1/08
Est. sales ($ mil.)	—	—	—	—	—	1,860.7
Employees	—	—	—	—	—	3,716

CPS TECHNOLOGIES CORPORATION

OTC: CPSH

111 S. Worcester St.
Norton, MA 02766
Phone: 508-222-0614
Fax: 508-222-0220
Web: www.alsic.com

CEO: Grant C. Bennett
CFO: Grant C. Bennett
HR: —
FYE: December 31
Type: Public

CPS Technologies makes thermal management components for electronics using aluminum silicon carbide (ALSiC) metal matrix composites. Products include substrates, baseplates, and heat spreaders that are used by customers in motor controller and wireless communications component applications. CPS is working with the US Army on using its composite technology in armor for military vehicles. The company also licenses its technology to other manufacturers; revenue from licenses and royalties, however, has dwindled away to virtually nothing. CPS Technologies makes more than two-thirds of its sales to locations outside the US, although the majority of its customers are actually based in the US.

	Annual Growth	12/05	12/06	12/07	12/08	12/09
Sales ($ mil.)	15.9%	7.2	11.9	12.4	14.8	13.0
Net income ($ mil.)	18.9%	0.3	1.8	0.9	1.5	0.6
Market value ($ mil.)	2.3%	13.3	18.9	32.8	17.5	14.5
Employees	10.7%	94	133	135	133	141

C. R. BARD, INC.

NYSE: BCR

730 Central Ave.
Murray Hill, NJ 07974
Phone: 908-277-8000
Fax: 908-277-8240
Web: www.crbard.com

CEO: Timothy M. Ring
CFO: Todd C. Schermerhorn
HR: Bronwen K. Kelly
FYE: December 31
Type: Public

C. R. Bard is no upstart in the world of medical devices. The company has been in the business for more than a century and introduced the Foley urological catheter (still one of its top sellers) in 1934. Its products fall into four general therapeutic categories: vascular, urology, oncology, and surgical specialties. Among other things, the company makes stents, catheters, and guidewires used in angioplasties and other vascular procedures; urology catheters and products used to treat urinary incontinence; and catheters for delivering chemotherapy treatments. Its line of specialty surgical tools, made by subsidiary Davol, includes devices used in laparoscopic and orthopedic procedures and for hernia repair.

	Annual Growth	12/05	12/06	12/07	12/08	12/09
Sales ($ mil.)	9.4%	1,771.3	1,985.5	2,202.0	2,452.1	2,534.9
Net income ($ mil.)	8.1%	337.1	272.1	406.4	416.5	460.1
Market value ($ mil.)	4.3%	6,268.8	7,890.2	9,015.2	8,012.9	7,408.1
Employees	5.4%	8,900	9,400	10,200	11,000	11,000

C.R. ENGLAND, INC.

4701 W. 2100 South
Salt Lake City, UT 84120
Phone: 801-972-2712
Fax: 801-977-6703
Web: www.crengland.com

CEO: Dean D. England
CFO: Keith Wallace
HR: Thom Pronk
FYE: December 31
Type: Private

London might have its cool, foggy days, but the England of C.R. England is always chilly. Truckload freight carrier C.R. England hauls refrigerated and dry cargo throughout the US. The company also serves parts of Canada and, through alliances, parts of Mexico. C.R. England's fleet includes some 3,500 tractors and about 5,700 trailers. Besides for-hire freight hauling, C.R. England offers dedicated contract carriage, in which drivers and equipment are assigned to a customer long-term; logistics services, including freight brokerage; and intermodal railroad service. C.R. England was founded in 1920 by Chester Rodney England and is run by his descendants.

	Annual Growth	12/04	12/05	12/06	12/07	12/08
Est. sales ($ mil.)	—	—	—	—	—	829.8
Employees	—	—	—	—	—	4,500

CRA INTERNATIONAL, INC.

NASDAQ (GS): CRAI

200 Clarendon St., Ste. T-33
Boston, MA 02116
Phone: 617-425-3000
Fax: 617-425-3132
Web: www.crai.com

CEO: Paul A. Maleh
CFO: Wayne D. Mackie
HR: Elizabeth Ramos
FYE: November 30
Type: Public

Whether you need an expert to help you run your business, testify for you in court, or evaluate the finances of an acquisition candidate, CRA International wants to help. The company, which operates under the Charles River Associates trade name, employs about 600 consultants offering economic and business counsel from more than 20 offices, mainly in North America but also in Europe, the Middle East, and Asia. Its practices are organized into three areas: finance (valuation and accounting, insurance, and risk management); litigation and applied economics (competition, intellectual property, trade, and transfer pricing); and business consulting. Clients include government agencies and law firms, among others.

	Annual Growth	11/05	11/06	11/07	11/08	11/09
Sales ($ mil.)	0.5%	295.5	349.9	394.6	376.8	301.6
Net income ($ mil.)	(25.0%)	24.6	27.4	32.6	8.7	7.8
Market value ($ mil.)	(13.5%)	491.5	570.0	510.7	320.1	274.6
Employees	(3.8%)	906	733	1,049	823	777

CRACKER BARREL OLD COUNTRY STORE

NASDAQ (GS): CBRL

305 Hartmann Dr.
Lebanon, TN 37088
Phone: 615-444-5533
Fax: 615-443-9476
Web: www.crackerbarrel.com

CEO: Michael A. (Mike) Woodhouse
CFO: Sandra B. (Sandy) Cochran
HR: Robert J. Harig
FYE: July 31
Type: Public

This company has gotten ahead in the restaurant business by holding on to a bit of the past. Cracker Barrel Old Country Store, Inc., owns and operates more than 590 of its flagship restaurants known for their country kitsch, rustic decor, and down-home cooking. The eateries, located in more than 40 states, offer mostly standard American fare, such as chicken, ham, and roast beef dishes, but they are most popular as breakfast spots. Each Cracker Barrel features a retail area where patrons can buy hand-blown glassware, cast iron cookware, and woodcrafts, as well as jellies and old-fashioned candies. Most of the restaurants are found along interstate highways and target hungry travelers.

	Annual Growth	7/05	7/06	7/07	7/08	7/09
Sales ($ mil.)	(2.0%)	2,567.5	2,643.0	2,351.6	2,384.5	2,367.3
Net income ($ mil.)	(15.1%)	126.6	116.3	162.1	65.6	65.9
Market value ($ mil.)	(7.4%)	897.2	748.3	880.2	553.6	661.0
Employees	(3.2%)	75,029	74,031	64,000	65,000	66,000

CRAFT BREWERS ALLIANCE, INC.

NASDAQ (GM): HOOK

292 N. Russell St.
Portland, OR 97227
Phone: 503-331-7270
Fax: 503-331-7373
Web: www.craftbrewers.com

CEO: Terry E. Michaelson
CFO: Mark D. Moreland
HR: Stacia Bird
FYE: December 31
Type: Public

Beer is a real craft for these brewers. Craft Brewers Alliance markets and sells the beers of The Redhook Ale Brewery (Seattle), Widmer Brothers Brewing Company (Portland, Oregon), Kona Brewing Company (Kona, Hawaii), and Goose Island Beer Company (Chicago). The Alliance, which is headquartered in Portland, offers approximately 30 craft beers that are available regionally and nationally. Its brands include Longhammer IPA, Wider Hefeweizen, Longboard Island Lager, and Oatmeal Stout. The company's beers are distributed nationally though a partnership with beverage giant Anheuser-Busch, which also owns about 36% of Craft Brewers Alliance.

	Annual Growth	12/05	12/06	12/07	12/08	12/09
Sales ($ mil.)	43.5%	31.1	35.7	41.5	79.8	131.7
Net income ($ mil.)	—	(1.2)	0.5	(0.9)	(33.3)	0.9
Market value ($ mil.)	(6.7%)	54.1	88.8	113.5	20.5	41.0
Employees	19.5%	196	205	221	400	400

An in-depth profile of this company is available to Hoover's Online members at hoovers.com.

447

CRAFTMADE INTERNATIONAL, INC.

NASDAQ (GM): CRFT

650 S. Royal Ln., Ste. 100
Coppell, TX 75019
Phone: 972-393-3800
Fax: 972-304-3753
Web: www.craftmade.com

CEO: J. Marcus Scrudder
CFO: C. Brett Burford
HR: —
FYE: June 30
Type: Public

Craftmade International is no celebrity, but it is accustomed to fans and bright lights. The company designs and distributes Craftmade brand ceiling fans, as well as lights for home use. Operating through subsidiaries Woodard, Prime/Home Impressions, and Trade Source International, the company sells more than 70 fan models, separate light kits, doorbells, and accessories. It also offers bathstrip and outdoor lighting, lamps, and Woodard brand outdoor furniture. Asian manufacturers produce most Craftmade lines, sold to specialty retailers and mass merchandisers, including Lowe's, Costco, Bed Bath & Beyond, and Wal-Mart. Craftmade also owns a 50% stake in Design Trends, a Chinese distributor of lamps and shades.

	Annual Growth	6/05	6/06	6/07	6/08	6/09
Sales ($ mil.)	6.4%	116.8	118.1	103.3	137.6	149.7
Net income ($ mil.)	—	6.4	7.1	5.9	2.1	(1.1)
Market value ($ mil.)	(39.7%)	92.4	95.6	97.6	37.1	12.2
Employees	18.3%	130	131	141	320	255

CRAIGSLIST, INC.

1381 9th Ave.
San Francisco, CA 94122
Phone: 415-566-6394
Fax: 415-504-6394
Web: www.craigslist.org

CEO: Jim Buckmaster
CFO: —
HR: —
FYE: December 31
Type: Private

Just who is this Craig fellow, and why is his list so popular? Online community bulletin board craigslist was founded by computer programmer Craig Newmark, who in 1995 began informing people about events around San Francisco through a list server. The service later evolved into a Web forum for locals in metropolitan areas across the globe to post listings for jobs, housing, companionship and dating, the sale of goods and services, events, and additional community information. The firm charges businesses a fee to post job openings on about 20 major city sites; brokered apartment listings in New York City; and certain therapeutic and adult services listings. Auction firm eBay owns about 20% of craigslist.

	Annual Growth	12/04	12/05	12/06	12/07	12/08
Est. sales ($ mil.)	—	—	—	—	—	0.9
Employees	—	—	—	—	—	12

CRAIN COMMUNICATIONS INC

1155 Gratiot Ave.
Detroit, MI 48207
Phone: 313-446-6000
Fax: 313-446-1616
Web: www.crain.com

CEO: Rance E. Crain
CFO: Thomas M. (Tom) Marantette Jr.
HR: Laura Anger
FYE: December 31
Type: Private

These Crains have been whooping it up in the publishing business for a long time. Crain Communications is a leading publisher of trade journals and weekly business newspapers with about 30 titles serving audiences mostly in the North America and Europe. Its portfolio covers such areas as the automotive industry (*Automotive News, AutoWeek*), the financial sector (*Business Insurance, InvestmentNews*), and media (*Advertising Age*). Crain also publishes business journals in four major US cities (Chicago, Cleveland, Detroit, and New York City). The family-owned company was started by G. D. Crain in 1916.

CRANE CO.

NYSE: CR

100 First Stamford Place
Stamford, CT 06902
Phone: 203-363-7300
Fax: 203-363-7295
Web: www.craneco.com

CEO: Eric C. Fast
CFO: Andrew L. Krawitt
HR: Elise M. Kopczick
FYE: December 31
Type: Public

In many cultures the crane is a symbol of longevity, and this Crane, indeed, reflects such endurance. Founded in 1855, the company makes a wide variety of engineered industrial products through its five business segments: Aerospace & Electronics (sensing and control systems), Engineered Materials (plastic composites, substrates), Merchandising Systems (vending machines), Fluid Handling (valves and pumps), and Controls (diagnostic, measurement, and control devices). Crane products have applications in aerospace, military and defense, recreational vehicle, construction, transportation, automated merchandising, petrochemical, chemical, and power generation industries.

	Annual Growth	12/05	12/06	12/07	12/08	12/09
Sales ($ mil.)	1.6%	2,061.2	2,256.9	2,619.2	2,604.3	2,196.3
Net income ($ mil.)	(0.4%)	136.0	165.9	(62.3)	135.2	133.9
Market value ($ mil.)	(3.5%)	2,083.6	2,164.5	2,534.3	1,018.5	1,808.9
Employees	(1.0%)	10,400	11,870	12,000	12,000	10,000

CRAWFORD & COMPANY

NYSE: CRD

1001 Summit Blvd.
Atlanta, GA 30319
Phone: 404-256-0830
Fax: 404-300-1905
Web: www.crawfordandcompany.com

CEO: Jeffrey T. (Jeff) Bowman
CFO: W. Bruce Swain Jr.
HR: —
FYE: December 31
Type: Public

Crawford & Company is an international insurance services firm providing claims adjustment and risk management services to insurers and self-insured companies. Services include workers' compensation and property/casualty claims investigation, evaluation, and resolution; statistical and financial reporting; and medical case management. Subsidiaries provide class-action settlement services, property damage repairs, and computer-based risk management information services. Crawford & Company has more than 700 offices in more than 60 countries. Members of the Crawford family own a majority of the firm.

	Annual Growth	12/05	12/06	12/07	12/08	12/09
Sales ($ mil.)	5.2%	854.8	900.4	1,051.3	1,135.9	1,048.2
Net income ($ mil.)	—	12.9	15.0	16.1	32.3	(115.7)
Market value ($ mil.)	(9.1%)	302.2	383.0	217.7	762.8	206.7
Employees	4.1%	7,525	9,280	8,967	2,362	8,852

CRAY INC.

NASDAQ (GM): CRAY

901 5th Ave., Ste. 1000
Seattle, WA 98164
Phone: 206-701-2000
Fax: 206-701-2500
Web: www.cray.com

CEO: Peter J. Ungaro
CFO: Brian C. Henry
HR: Linda J. Howitson
FYE: December 31
Type: Public

Cray makes computers that aren't just good — they're super. Its massively parallel and vector supercomputers provide the firepower behind research ranging from weather forecasting and scientific research to design engineering and classified government projects. The company also provides maintenance and support services, and it sells data storage products from partners including BlueArc, LSI, and Quantum. Many of Cray's sales are to US government agencies and commercial customers that serve those agencies; it also targets schools and industrial companies. The company primarily utilizes a direct sales force.

	Annual Growth	12/05	12/06	12/07	12/08	12/09
Sales ($ mil.)	9.0%	201.1	221.0	186.2	282.9	284.0
Net income ($ mil.)	—	(64.3)	(12.1)	(5.7)	(31.3)	(0.6)
Market value ($ mil.)	4.8%	188.8	421.6	212.6	73.8	227.8
Employees	2.6%	787	768	800	829	872

CRAYOLA LLC

1100 Church Ln.
Easton, PA 18044
Phone: 610-253-6271
Fax: 610-250-5768
Web: www.crayola.com

CEO: Mike Perry
CFO: Smith Holland
HR: Michelle Powers
FYE: December 31
Type: Subsidiary

The company that has cornered the market on colors is Crayola, with its top 10 most popular Crayon colors: blue, red, violet, green, carnation pink, black, turquoise blue, blue green, periwinkle, and magenta. Previously named Binney & Smith, Crayola's a subsidiary of Hallmark Cards. It produces about 3 billion crayons a year, as well as other Crayola art products for children, such as markers and craft and activity kits. Crayola also makes Silly Putty, the iconic silicone putty with utility; and inkTank pens and markers for adults. The firm's products are packaged in many languages and sold worldwide. Edwin Binney and C. Harold Smith sold their first Crayola crayons in 1903, when a box of eight cost a nickel.

CREATIVE ARTISTS AGENCY, LLC

2000 Avenue of the Stars
Los Angeles, CA 90067
Phone: 424-288-2000
Fax: 424-288-2900
Web: www.caa.com

CEO: Richard Lovett
CFO: —
HR: —
FYE: December 31
Type: Private

Arguably the most powerful talent agency in the business, Creative Artists Agency (CAA) represents clients working in film, music, television, theater, sports, and literature. The firm's client list reads like a who's who of A-list stars, including such luminaries as Steven Spielberg, Tom Cruise, Brad Pitt, George Clooney, Oprah Winfrey, LeBron James, David Beckham, Will Ferrell, and now Ryan Seacrest. Other heavy-hitting clients include corporations such as Coca-Cola and toymaker Mattel. Supplemental services include strategic counsel, financing, and consulting. Its Intelligence Group/Youth Intelligence unit tracks and conducts behavior research for consumers from ages 8 to 39. CAA was founded in 1975.

CREDIT ACCEPTANCE CORPORATION

NASDAQ (GS): CACC

25505 W. Twelve Mile Rd., Ste. 3000
Southfield, MI 48034
Phone: 248-353-2700
Fax: 248-827-8553
Web: www.creditacceptance.com

CEO: Brett A. Roberts
CFO: Kenneth S. Booth
HR: —
FYE: December 31
Type: Public

In the world of Credit Acceptance Corporation (CAC), to purchase a car is not an impossible dream for problem borrowers — just an expensive reality. Working with more than 3,000 independent and franchised automobile dealers in the US, CAC provides capital for auto loans to people with substandard credit. The company also provides other services to dealers, including payment servicing, receivables management, marketing, and service contracts. It originates more than 1.7 million loans per year; Texas is the company's largest market. Founder and chairman Donald Foss owns more than 60% of Credit Acceptance.

	Annual Growth	12/05	12/06	12/07	12/08	12/09
Assets ($ mil.)	17.4%	619.4	725.2	942.2	1,139.4	1,176.2
Net income ($ mil.)	19.1%	72.6	58.6	54.9	67.2	146.3
Market value ($ mil.)	27.2%	499.4	1,033.9	641.2	425.0	1,305.9
Employees	4.1%	777	788	971	1,048	911

CREDIT SUISSE (USA), INC.

11 Madison Ave.
New York, NY 10010
Phone: 212-325-2000
Fax: 212-325-6665
Web: www.credit-suisse.com/us/en

CEO: Robert S. (Rob) Shafir
CFO: Paul O'Keefe
HR: —
FYE: December 31
Type: Subsidiary

Credit Suisse (USA) is one of the top US investment banks, offering securities underwriting and trading, mergers and acquisitions advice, research, private equity investment, and risk management products. The company also provides asset management and private banking services; Credit Suisse Private Banking USA operates more than 15 offices throughout the country. Investment bank Donaldson, Lufkin & Jenrette is among its predecessors. Credit Suisse (USA) is a wholly owned subsidiary of Swiss banking powerhouse Credit Suisse Group.

	Annual Growth	12/04	12/05	12/06	12/07	12/08
Est. sales ($ mil.)	—	—	—	—	—	9.6
Employees	—	—	—	—	—	10,899

CREDITRISKMONITOR.COM, INC.

OTC: CRMZ

704 Executive Blvd., Ste. A
Valley Cottage, NY 10989
Phone: 845-230-3000
Fax: 845-267-4110
Web: www.creditriskmonitor.com

CEO: Jerome S. (Jerry) Flum
CFO: Lawrence (Larry) Fensterstock
HR: Lawrence (Larry) Fensterstock
FYE: December 31
Type: Public

Need to monitor credit risk? CreditRiskMonitor.com provides online financial information and news about some 40,000 public companies, marketing the service to corporate credit managers, who use the data to make credit decisions. Subscribers get access to such information as company background, financial statements, trend reports, and comparative analysis, in addition to proprietary credit scores. The firm also provides access to information on more than 20 million foreign and private companies through affiliations with third-party providers. CreditRiskMonitor.com was formed in 1999 after it bought Market Guide's credit information database. Chairman and CEO Jerry Flum owns more than 60% of the firm.

	Annual Growth	12/05	12/06	12/07	12/08	12/09
Sales ($ mil.)	19.7%	3.8	4.3	5.0	5.9	7.8
Net income ($ mil.)	14.2%	1.0	0.0	0.4	0.4	1.7
Market value ($ mil.)	22.4%	13.0	23.7	19.0	6.6	29.2
Employees	108.8%	3	37	43	50	57

CREDO PETROLEUM CORPORATION

NASDAQ (GS): CRED

1801 Broadway, Ste. 900
Denver, CO 80202
Phone: 303-297-2200
Fax: 303-297-2204
Web: www.credopetroleum.com

CEO: Marlis E. Smith Jr.
CFO: Alford B. Neely
HR: —
FYE: October 31
Type: Public

CREDO Petroleum believes strongly in fossil fuels: It explores for, produces, and markets natural gas and crude oil in the US Gulf Coast, Midcontinent, and Rocky Mountain regions. The company has traditionally concentrated on shallow and medium-depth properties (7,000-9,000 ft.), but in recent years it has launched projects in Kansas and South Texas (where it is drilling to well depths ranging from 10,000 to 17,000 ft.). In 2008 the company reported estimated proved reserves of 15.5 billion cu. ft. of gas and 710,000 barrels of oil. Subsidiary United Oil operates the company's properties in Oklahoma, and CREDO Petroleum's other subsidiary, SECO Energy, owns royalty interests in the Rocky Mountains.

	Annual Growth	10/05	10/06	10/07	10/08	10/09
Sales ($ mil.)	(7.5%)	13.8	16.5	17.0	17.3	10.1
Net income ($ mil.)	—	5.2	5.9	6.1	6.0	(14.5)
Market value ($ mil.)	(13.6%)	177.3	132.2	98.8	88.9	98.9
Employees	2.0%	12	12	12	13	13

An in-depth profile of this company is available to Hoover's Online members at hoovers.com.

449

CREE, INC.

NASDAQ (GS): CREE

4600 Silicon Dr.
Durham, NC 27703
Phone: 919-313-5300
Fax: 919-313-5558
Web: www.cree.com

CEO: Charles M. (Chuck) Swoboda
CFO: John T. Kurtzweil
HR: —
FYE: June 30
Type: Public

Cree has its name in lights. Its blue, green, and near-ultraviolet light-emitting diodes (LEDs) — made from silicon carbide (SiC) and gallium nitride (GaN) — are used in products such as dashboard lights, architectural light fixtures, market tickers, and video screens, including the giant screen in New York City's Times Square. Cree also sells SiC wafers, which work better at higher temperatures and voltages than standard silicon devices, and SiC and GaN materials. Its power and radio-frequency (RF) products include Schottky diodes and transistors. Leading customers include Seoul Semiconductor, Arrow Electronics, and Sumitomo. Cree sells products globally, but Asia accounts for more than two-thirds of sales.

	Annual Growth	6/05	6/06	6/07	6/08	6/09
Sales ($ mil.)	9.9%	389.1	423.0	394.1	493.3	567.3
Net income ($ mil.)	(24.1%)	91.1	76.7	57.3	33.4	30.3
Market value ($ mil.)	3.7%	2,737.7	2,553.9	2,778.5	2,451.8	3,160.1
Employees	24.5%	1,322	1,364	2,578	3,168	3,172

CRESCENT BANKING COMPANY

NASDAQ (CM): CSNT

7 Caring Way
Jasper, GA 30143
Phone: 678-454-2266
Fax: 678-454-2282
Web: www.crescentbank.com

CEO: J. Donald Boggus Jr.
CFO: Leland W. Brantley Jr.
HR: —
FYE: December 31
Type: Public

This crescent gives a whole new meaning to the term "dough boy." Crescent Banking Company is the holding company of Crescent Bank & Trust, which serves north-central Georgia from about a dozen branches and loan offices. The bank offers standard services such as checking and savings accounts, money market accounts, CDs, and IRAs. It mainly uses funds from deposits to originate loans in its market area. Real estate construction and land development loans account for more than half of its total portfolio, which also consists of real estate mortgages (about 40%), as well as agricultural, business, and consumer installment loans.

	Annual Growth	12/05	12/06	12/07	12/08	12/09
Assets ($ mil.)	9.0%	704.1	779.7	920.3	1,039.0	993.9
Net income ($ mil.)	—	4.1	7.3	6.4	(31.7)	(35.5)
Market value ($ mil.)	(58.3%)	95.9	125.7	68.5	22.8	2.9
Employees	(2.1%)	196	199	112	194	180

CRESCENT ELECTRIC SUPPLY COMPANY

7750 Dunleith Dr.
East Dubuque, IL 61025
Phone: 815-747-3145
Fax: 815-747-7720
Web: www.cesco.com

CEO: Martin S. (Marty) Burbridge
CFO: James R. (Jim) Etheredge Sr.
HR: Dan Philippi
FYE: December 31
Type: Private

Crescent Electric Supply Company (Cesco) always plays it straight with its customers. The company was founded in 1919 by Titus Schmid and later became a lamp agent for General Electric. Today Crescent Electric distributes electrical supplies from leading manufacturers, such as GE Lighting, Hubbell, Siemens, and Thomas & Betts. The company also offers bin management and other inventory services. Orders can be placed through Crescent Electric's online order system at any hour of the day. Customers include Caterpillar, Deere, and various government agencies. Members of the Schmid family continue to own Crescent Electric Supply.

CRESCENT FINANCIAL CORPORATION

NASDAQ (CM): CRFN

1005 High House Rd.
Cary, NC 27513
Phone: 919-460-7770
Fax: 919-460-2512
Web: www.crescentstatebank.com

CEO: Michael G. Carlton
CFO: Bruce W. Elder
HR: —
FYE: December 31
Type: Public

This Crescent helps your financial health take shape. Crescent Financial is the holding company for Crescent State Bank, which operates some 15 branches in central North Carolina. The community bank offers standard products and services, including checking and savings accounts, certificates of deposit, and credit cards. Commercial mortgages make up about half of its loan portfolio; construction loans make up more than a quarter. The company, which was founded in 1998, also writes business loans, home equity loans, and residential mortgages. Its Crescent Investment Services division offers financial planning products and services, including retirement plans, mutual funds, insurance, and other investments.

	Annual Growth	12/05	12/06	12/07	12/08	12/09
Assets ($ mil.)	25.9%	410.8	697.9	835.5	968.3	1,032.8
Net income ($ mil.)	—	3.1	4.9	6.2	2.0	(30.2)
Market value ($ mil.)	(28.3%)	115.7	111.9	91.5	36.6	30.6
Employees	13.8%	99	129	134	144	166

CRESCENT RESOURCES, LLC

400 S. Tryon St., Ste. 1300
Charlotte, NC 28285
Phone: 980-321-6000
Fax: —
Web: www.crescent-resources.com

CEO: Andrew Hede
CFO: Kevin H. Lambert
HR: Barbara R. Bailey
FYE: December 31
Type: Subsidiary

Commercial property developments? That's the way Crescent rolls. Crescent Resources manages land holdings, mostly in the Southeast and Southwest US, and uses them to develop commercial and residential real estate. Its holdings include office buildings, industrial projects, and retail developments. Residential properties such as single-family home communities, condominiums, and apartments are developed by its Crescent Communities arm. It also invests in tracts of land to sell off in pieces. Commercial clients have included General Electric, BellSouth, Lanier Worldwide, and CIGNA. Crescent emerged from Chapter 11 bankruptcy protection in June 2010 after eliminating more than $1 billion of debt.

CRESTRON ELECTRONICS, INC.

15 Volvo Dr.
Rockleigh, NJ 07647
Phone: 201-767-3400
Fax: 201-767-1903
Web: www.crestron.com

CEO: George Feldstein
CFO: —
HR: Martin DeVaney
FYE: June 30
Type: Private

Crestron Electronics doesn't mind if its customers have control issues. The company provides the hardware and the software used to control audio and video systems, as well as computer networks, security systems, and environmental systems, such as temperature and lighting. Its products include amplifiers, controllers, management software, remotes, touchpanels, tuners, cabling, and cabinet enclosures. It markets to businesses, consumers, government agencies, and schools worldwide; the company's commercial customers include airports, hotels and casinos, museums, restaurants, and retailers. Crestron was established in 1971 by George Feldstein, the company's president and CEO. It is owned by the Feldstein family.

CRETE CARRIER CORPORATION

400 NW 56th St.
Lincoln, NE 68528
Phone: 402-475-9521
Fax: 402-479-2075
Web: www.cretecarrier.com

CEO: Tonn M. Ostergard
CFO: Dean Troester
HR: Jane Goertzen
FYE: September 30
Type: Private

Holding company Crete Carrier Corporation's flagship business, Crete Carrier, provides dry van truckload freight transportation services in the 48 contiguous states. It operates from some two dozen terminals, mainly in the midwestern and southeastern US. The company's Shaffer Trucking unit transports temperature-controlled cargo, and Hunt Transportation (no relation to J.B. Hunt Transport Services) hauls heavy equipment and other cargo on flatbed trailers. Overall, the companies operate more than 5,300 tractors and more than 12,400 trailers. Family-owned Crete Carrier was founded in 1966 by chairman Duane Acklie; president and CEO Tonn Ostergard is his son-in-law.

CREXUS INVESTMENT CORP.

NYSE: CXS

1211 Avenue of the Americas, Ste. 2902
New York, NY 10036
Phone: 212-696-0100
Fax: 212-696-9809
Web: www.crexusinvestment.com

CEO: Kevin Riordan
CFO: Daniel Wickey
HR: —
FYE: December 31
Type: Public

CreXus Investment is looking to put its money where other people do business. As a mortgage real estate investment trust (REIT), the company focuses on buying commercial real estate debt, mortgage-backed securites, and other commercial-related debt. Having gone public in late 2009, the company plans to build its commercial portfolio using capital raised from its shareholders; it also intends to invest in residential mortgage-backed securites and construction loans. CreXus is managed by Fixed Income Discount Advisory Company, a subsidiary of Annaly Capital Management.

	Annual Growth	12/05	12/06	12/07	12/08	12/09
Sales ($ mil.)	—	—	—	—	—	0.3
Net income ($ mil.)	—	—	—	—	—	(1.0)
Market value ($ mil.)	—	—	—	—	—	253.0
Employees	—	—	—	—	—	—

CRI CATALYST CO.

16825 Northchase Dr., Ste. 1110
Houston, TX 77060
Phone: 281-874-2490
Fax: 281-874-2499
Web: www.cri-catalysts.com

CEO: Alan Del Paggio
CFO: —
HR: —
FYE: December 31
Type: Subsidiary

Chemically speaking, CRI Catalyst (CRICC) is known for its chain reactions. The company, a part of Royal Dutch Shell's Catalyst Technology unit, manages catalyst development centers, research laboratories, support groups, and manufacturing plants. Along with its CRI Asia Pacific subsidiary the company provides flue gas treatment catalysts used to reduce harmful emissions produced at chemical and petrochemical facilities. CRICC provides services such as silver management and silver recovery for the production of ethylene oxide. It also supplies base metal and platinum group catalysts for the chemical and petrochemical industries.

CRICKET COMMUNICATIONS, INC.

5887 Copley Dr.
San Diego, CA 92111
Phone: 858-882-6000
Fax: 858-882-6010
Web: www.mycricket.com

CEO: Stewart D. (Doug) Hutcheson
CFO: Walter Z. Berger
HR: Leonard C. (Len) Stephens
FYE: December 31
Type: Subsidiary

Cricket Communications may not know a bowler from a batsman, but it can get you off a sticky wicket if you need wireless service. The primary operating subsidiary of Leap Wireless International, the company provides local wireless service to about 4 million customers in 30 US states. Sales are made in part through partnerships with such retailers as Best Buy and Target. Its service is used primarily by youth and minority callers who do most of their calling from within the company's network. Cricket's core products are flat-rate monthly plans for unlimited local and domestic long-distance calling. It also offers prepaid roaming services and resells cell phones from such manufacturers as Samsung and Kyocera.

CRIMSON EXPLORATION, INC.

OTC: CXPO

717 Texas Ave., Ste. 2900
Houston, TX 77002
Phone: 713-236-7400
Fax: 713-236-4424
Web: www.crimsonexploration.com

CEO: Allan D. Keel
CFO: E. Joseph Grady
HR: —
FYE: December 31
Type: Public

Independent oil and gas company Crimson Exploration has operations that extend from the Gulf (of Mexico) to the West (Texas and points beyond). The company owns and operates more than 140 wells located primarily in the Permian Basin of West Texas and in East Texas. It also operates in Colorado and Louisiana. In 2007 Crimson Exploration reported estimated proved reserves of 91.2 billion cu. ft. of natural gas, 2.9 million barrels of oil, and 3.6 million barrels of natural gas liquids. The company is targeting strategic expansion through acquisitions in its existing areas of operation and in other oil producing regions across the US.

	Annual Growth	12/05	12/06	12/07	12/08	12/09
Sales ($ mil.)	58.7%	17.7	21.7	109.5	186.8	112.4
Net income ($ mil.)	—	(3.5)	1.9	(0.4)	46.2	(34.1)
Market value ($ mil.)	(16.5%)	346.3	240.5	708.0	119.3	168.5
Employees	25.3%	30	33	67	81	74

CRISPIN PORTER + BOGUSKY

3390 Mary St., Ste. 300
Miami, FL 33133
Phone: 305-859-2070
Fax: 305-854-3419
Web: www.cpbgroup.com

CEO: Jeff Hicks
CFO: —
HR: —
FYE: December 31
Type: Private

Creativity plus a full-service ad agency equals Crispin Porter + Bogusky. The agency provides media planning and buying, research, and creative services plus production for print and broadcast. Its work (known for its eccentricity) includes the Truth campaign (youth smoking prevention) for the American Legacy Foundation, Coca-Cola's Coke Zero product, and Burger King's Internet sensation, the Subservient Chicken (in which users can get an online chicken to do just about anything). The agency has also handled MillerCoors' "Man Laws" campaign. Crispin Porter has offices in Boulder, Colorado; Los Angeles; Miami; and London. Marketing and advertising conglomerate MDC Partners owns the agency.

An in-depth profile of this company is available to Hoover's Online members at hoovers.com.

451

CRM HOLDINGS, LTD.

NASDAQ (GS): CRMH

112 Delafield St.
Poughkeepsie, NY 12601
Phone: 845-452-4100
Fax: 845-473-6154
Web: www.crmholdingsltd.com

CEO: James J. Scardino
CFO: Joseph F. Taylor
HR: —
FYE: December 31
Type: Public

CRM Holdings offers a wide range of workers' compensation products and services. The firm offers management services to about half a dozen workers' compensation self-insured groups in California and New York. CRM provides each group (made up of employers within a given industry) with comprehensive services, including assistance in forming the groups, underwriting, risk assessment, and case management services. CRM also acts as a broker by placing excess coverage for the groups, and it reinsures part of this coverage through subsidiary Twin Bridges. Additionally, the firm provides traditional workers' compensation insurance in about 10 states through subsidiary Majestic Insurance Company.

	Annual Growth	12/05	12/06	12/07	12/08	12/09
Assets ($ mil.)	54.9%	83.9	306.4	379.4	444.2	482.9
Net income ($ mil.)	—	7.3	14.3	20.1	(1.5)	(46.8)
Market value ($ mil.)	(59.9%)	221.7	151.7	133.6	29.0	5.7
Employees	5.4%	165	245	268	218	204

CROCS, INC.

NASDAQ (GS): CROX

6328 Monarch Park Place
Niwot, CO 80503
Phone: 303-848-7000
Fax: 303-468-4266
Web: www.crocs.com

CEO: John P. McCarvel
CFO: Russell C. (Russ) Hammer
HR: —
FYE: December 31
Type: Public

Crocs has taken its bite out of the footwear industry. Its colorful slip-on shoes have gained popularity in the watersports arena and in mainstream fashion. Its shoes, branded as Crocs, are made of proprietary closed-cell resin and designed for men, women, and children; Jibbitz are their decorative add-on charms. The firm operates manufacturing facilities in Mexico, Italy, and China and boasts distribution centers worldwide. Crocs sells through retailers such as Dillard's, Nordstrom, and The Sports Authority, as well as through about 180 of its own stores and kiosks worldwide. Crocs has expanded on both domestic and international fronts and through acquisitions.

	Annual Growth	12/05	12/06	12/07	12/08	12/09
Sales ($ mil.)	56.2%	108.6	354.7	847.3	721.6	645.8
Net income ($ mil.)	—	17.0	64.4	168.2	(185.1)	(42.1)
Market value ($ mil.)	(35.7%)	—	1,853.2	3,158.1	106.4	493.3
Employees	33.2%	1,130	2,900	5,300	3,700	3,560

CROGHAN BANCSHARES, INC.

OTC: CHBH

323 Croghan St.
Fremont, OH 43420
Phone: 419-332-7301
Fax: 419-355-2266
Web: www.croghan.com

CEO: Steven C. Futrell
CFO: Kendall W. Rieman
HR: —
FYE: December 31
Type: Public

Croghan Bancshares is helping to share the wealth in the Buckeye state. The firm is the holding company for Croghan Colonial Bank, which has about 10 branches in northern Ohio. Founded in 1888, the bank provides standard products and services, including checking and savings accounts, money market accounts, certificates of deposit, and credit cards, Its lending activities primarily consist of residential and commercial mortgages and, to a lesser extent, agricultural, business, construction, and consumer loans. In addition, the bank offers wealth management, investments, estate planning, private banking, and trust services.

	Annual Growth	12/05	12/06	12/07	12/08	12/09
Assets ($ mil.)	1.1%	461.9	458.9	455.1	460.5	482.0
Net income ($ mil.)	(14.1%)	5.7	5.5	5.5	4.4	3.1
Market value ($ mil.)	(11.6%)	63.7	60.9	59.6	42.6	39.0
Employees	(4.0%)	172	168	164	161	146

CROSS COUNTRY HEALTHCARE, INC.

NASDAQ (GS): CCRN

6551 Park of Commerce Blvd. NW
Boca Raton, FL 33487
Phone: 561-998-2232
Fax: 800-768-8128
Web: www.crosscountryhealthcare.com

CEO: Joseph A. Boshart
CFO: Emil Hensel
HR: Lori Schutte
FYE: December 31
Type: Public

Cross Country Healthcare is one of the largest health care staffing firms in the US. Under several brands, the company places traveling nurses and other health care professionals through more than 5,000 contracts with acute care hospitals, pharmaceutical companies, nursing homes, schools, and other related facilities across the nation. The firm coordinates travel and housing arrangements for its nurses, whose assignments usually last about three months at a time. Cross Country also provides health care education, training, and recruiting services for doctors and health care executives. Subsidiaries and brands include Assignment America, Allied Health Group, NovaPro, Med-Staff, TravCorps, and Cejka Search.

	Annual Growth	12/05	12/06	12/07	12/08	12/09
Sales ($ mil.)	(2.7%)	645.4	655.2	718.3	734.2	578.2
Net income ($ mil.)	(18.0%)	14.8	16.6	24.6	(142.9)	6.7
Market value ($ mil.)	(13.7%)	552.9	676.6	441.6	272.6	307.3
Employees	(10.4%)	6,598	6,616	6,285	5,893	4,253

CROSS TIMBERS ROYALTY TRUST

NYSE: CRT

901 Main St., 17th Fl.
Dallas, TX 75283
Phone: 214-209-2400
Fax: 214-209-2431
Web: www.crosstimberstrust.com

CEO: Nancy G. Willis
CFO: Louis G. Baldwin
HR: —
FYE: December 31
Type: Public

Cross Timbers Royalty Trust distributes royalties from oil and natural gas properties in Texas, Oklahoma, and New Mexico. The trust, which was formed in 1991, does not operate or control any of its properties. Instead, it owns stakes in wells located primarily in gas properties in the San Juan Basin of northwestern New Mexico. The trust's estimated proved gas reserves are 1.7 million barrels of oil and 27.7 billion cu. ft. of gas. XTO Energy (formerly Cross Timbers Oil), which markets the trust's oil and gas, distributed all of its trust units as a dividend to its stockholders in 2003.

	Annual Growth	12/05	12/06	12/07	12/08	12/09
Sales ($ mil.)	(13.2%)	20.6	25.8	20.2	31.3	11.7
Net income ($ mil.)	(13.6%)	20.3	25.4	19.8	30.9	11.3
Market value ($ mil.)	(8.9%)	293.4	303.7	247.5	167.1	202.3
Employees	—	—	—	—	—	—

CROSSMARK, INC.

5100 Legacy Dr.
Plano, TX 75024
Phone: 469-814-1000
Fax: 469-814-1355
Web: www.crossmark.com

CEO: John Thompson
CFO: Don Martin
HR: Brice Coleman
FYE: December 31
Type: Private

CROSSMARK helps its clients in the consumer packaged goods industry get its products into stores and then out of stores. The company supports its customers with planning promotional events, and provides headquarter sales (securing distribution in retail outlets), in-store merchandising, sales support, and supply chain optimization services for supermarkets, convenience stores, and drug stores, along with other specialty trade channels. CROSSMARK has more than 45 offices throughout the US, Australia, Canada, and New Zealand. The privately owned company is the result of a 1995 merger between three former businesses: The Gordon Company, SALES MARK/ALPHA ONE, and The Phillips Company.

CROSSROADS SYSTEMS, INC.

Pink Sheets: CRDS

11000 N. Mopac Expwy.
Austin, TX 78759
Phone: 512-349-0300
Fax: 512-349-0304
Web: www.crossroads.com

CEO: Robert C. (Rob) Sims
CFO: Jennifer Ray-Crane
HR: —
FYE: October 31
Type: Public

Crossroads Systems sets up shop where business and information intersect. The company provides storage networking equipment and business information assurance (BIA) systems used to manage and protect critical data. Its products include DBProtector (database security), FileMigrator Agent (migrating files from servers to network-attached storage), ReadVerify Appliance (monitoring tape media and the condition of disk drives), and ShareLoader (protecting data on desktop and laptop PCs and in remote offices). Crossroads Systems sells directly to manufacturers, such as EMC and Hewlett-Packard, and through distributors, including Bell Microproducts. The company was founded in 1996.

CROSSTEX ENERGY, INC.

NASDAQ (GS): XTXI

2501 Cedar Springs Rd., Ste. 100
Dallas, TX 75201
Phone: 214-953-9500
Fax: 214-953-9501
Web: www.crosstexenergy.com

CEO: Barry E. Davis
CFO: William W. Davis
HR: —
FYE: December 31
Type: Public

Crosstex Energy Inc. owns and controls the general partner of natural gas company Crosstex Energy, L.P. Crosstex Energy's energy sources and markets are found along the Gulf Coast, from Texas to Florida. It is engaged in natural gas gathering, processing, transmission, and marketing, and its treating division focuses on cleaning natural gas of carbon dioxide and hydrogen sulfide to enable the gas to meet pipeline quality requirements. The company buys natural gas from independent producers. Crosstex Energy's assets include 3,300 miles of natural pipeline, 10 processing plants, three fractionators, and 225 gas treating plants. Chieftain Capital Management owns about 18% of the company.

	Annual Growth	12/05	12/06	12/07	12/08	12/09
Sales ($ mil.)	(16.7%)	3,033.0	3,141.8	3,860.4	4,907.0	1,459.1
Net income ($ mil.)	15.1%	49.1	16.3	12.2	24.2	86.1
Market value ($ mil.)	(26.8%)	979.0	1,476.0	1,734.5	181.6	281.8
Employees	(2.1%)	496	610	700	780	456

CROSSTEX ENERGY, L.P.

NASDAQ (GS): XTEX

2501 Cedar Springs, Ste. 100
Dallas, TX 75201
Phone: 214-953-9500
Fax: 214-953-9501
Web: www.crosstexenergy.com

CEO: Barry E. Davis
CFO: William W. Davis
HR: Jennifer K. Johnson
FYE: December 31
Type: Public

Across the Gulf of Mexico region of the US, Crosstex Energy is hard at work pushing natural gas. The company gathers, transports, treats, and processes natural gas through more than 3,300 miles of natural pipeline, 10 processing plants, three fractionators, and 225 gas treating plants. Its revenues are generated through the purchase and resale of natural gas from more than 40 independent producers located along the US Gulf Coast from Texas to Florida. Through its treating division, Crosstex cleans carbon dioxide and hydrogen sulfide from natural gas, enabling it to meet pipeline quality requirements. Crosstex Energy Inc. owns and controls the general partner of Crosstex Energy.

	Annual Growth	12/05	12/06	12/07	12/08	12/09
Sales ($ mil.)	(16.7%)	3,033.0	3,139.3	3,860.4	4,907.0	1,459.1
Net income ($ mil.)	52.7%	19.2	(4.9)	13.9	10.8	104.5
Market value ($ mil.)	(29.1%)	1,695.5	1,982.5	1,543.2	217.4	427.8
Employees	(2.1%)	496	610	700	780	456

CROTHALL SERVICES GROUP, INC.

955 Chesterbrook Blvd., Ste. 300
Wayne, PA 19087
Phone: 610-249-0420
Fax: 610-249-0439
Web: www.crothall.com

CEO: Bobby Kutteh
CFO: Daniel E. (Dan) Gatti
HR: Raj Pragasam
FYE: September 30
Type: Subsidiary

Cleanliness isn't next to *anything* for Crothall Services Group. As a subsidiary of foodservice provider Compass Group, Crothall provides laundry and other facilities upkeep services to hospitals and health care providers in North America. In addition to keeping hospitals supplied with clean linens, it has a patient transport service and assists companies with their on-site laundry facilities, offering consulting services and operating personnel. Crothall's list of 1,500 clients has included the Cleveland Clinic Foundation and the Baylor Health Care System, but it has also worked with customers in the education (Case Western University) and hospitality (Ritz-Carlton Naples) sectors.

	Annual Growth	9/04	9/05	9/06	9/07	9/08
Est. sales ($ mil.)	—	—	—	—	—	417.6
Employees	—	—	—	—	—	13,000

CROWE HORWATH LLP

330 E. Jefferson Blvd.
South Bend, IN 46624
Phone: 574-232-3992
Fax: 574-236-8692
Web: www.crowehorwath.com

CEO: Chuck Allen
CFO: Jim Fulton
HR: Julie Wood
FYE: March 31
Type: Partnership

If your company has something to crow about, Crowe Horwath is sure to find out. Crowe Horwath, one of the top 10 accounting firms in the US, has some 25 offices in about a dozen states, primarily in the Midwest and South. The firm offers auditing and assurance, benefit plan services, financial advice, forensic services, tax consulting, and more to governments, auto dealerships, and clients in such industries as agriculture, construction, education, financial services, health care, manufacturing, and distribution. Affiliates provide investment banking services and wealth management services. Crowe Horwath is the largest member of global accounting group Crowe Horwath International.

	Annual Growth	3/04	3/05	3/06	3/07	3/08
Est. sales ($ mil.)	—	—	—	—	—	361.6
Employees	—	—	—	—	—	2,073

CROWLEY MARITIME CORPORATION

9487 Regency Sq. Blvd.
Jacksonville, FL 32225
Phone: 904-727-2200
Fax: 904-727-2501
Web: www.crowley.com

CEO: Thomas B. (Tom) Crowley Jr.
CFO: William A. (Bill) Pennella
HR: William A. (Bill) Pennella
FYE: December 31
Type: Private

Crowley Maritime has pushed and pulled its way into prominence as a tug and barge operator. The company's Liner Services unit provides scheduled transportation of containers, trailers, and other cargo, mainly among ports in the Bahamas, the Caribbean, Central America, Cuba, Haiti, Puerto Rico, and the US. Other units transport oil and chemical products and oil field equipment and provide ship assist/escort, marine salvage and emergency, towing, logistics, ship management, and fuel distribution services. Overall, the company's fleet includes more than 200 vessels. Founded in 1892 Crowley Maritime is owned by members of the founding Crowley family, including chairman/CEO Thomas Crowley, and company employees.

	Annual Growth	12/04	12/05	12/06	12/07	12/08
Sales ($ mil.)	18.3%	999.7	1,190.8	1,467.7	1,620.0	1,955.0
Employees	0.2%	4,268	4,257	4,074	4,171	4,300

An in-depth profile of this company is available to Hoover's Online members at hoovers.com.

453

CROWN CASTLE INTERNATIONAL CORP.

NYSE: CCI

1220 Augusta Dr., Ste. 500	CEO: W. Benjamin (Ben) Moreland
Houston, TX 77057	CFO: James A. (Jay) Brown
Phone: 713-570-3000	HR: Lisa Davidson
Fax: 713-570-3100	FYE: December 31
Web: www.crowncomm.net	Type: Public

Crown Castle International rules over a kingdom of radio towers. Its subsidiaries and joint ventures provide broadcast, data, and wireless communications infrastructure services in Australia, Puerto Rico, and the US. The company's clients include AT&T Mobility, Optus, Sprint Nextel (23% of sales), Verizon Wireless, and Vodafone Australia. They lease antenna space on Crown Castle's about 24,000 owned or managed towers. The company has sites primarily in the US and Puerto Rico, and has about 1,600 towers in Australia. It also designs networks, selects and develops sites, and installs antennas. Crown Castle gets most of its revenues in the US.

	Annual Growth	12/05	12/06	12/07	12/08	12/09
Sales ($ mil.)	25.6%	676.8	788.2	1,385.5	1,526.5	1,685.4
Net income ($ mil.)	—	(392.5)	(41.9)	(222.8)	(48.9)	(114.3)
Market value ($ mil.)	9.7%	7,815.7	9,381.2	12,082.3	5,105.9	11,338.8
Employees	11.2%	785	1,160	1,200	1,300	1,200

CROWN CRAFTS, INC.

NASDAQ (CM): CRWS

916 S. Burnside Ave.	CEO: E. Randall Chestnut
Gonzales, LA 70737	CFO: Olivia W. Elliott
Phone: 225-647-9100	HR: —
Fax: 225-647-8331	FYE: March 31
Web: www.crowncrafts.com	Type: Public

Prospects for new opportunities keep Crown Crafts drooling. Operating through its subsidiaries, Hamco and Crown Crafts Infant Products, it designs and sells textile products for infants and juveniles including baby bibs, burp cloths, bathing accessories, and bedding. Crown Crafts, founded in 1957, has sought to regain profitability by selling or shuttering its US manufacturing operations and relying on foreign contractors, mainly in China, to make its goods. Its products are sold in department and specialty stores, mass retailers, catalog houses, and outlet stores.

	Annual Growth	3/05	3/06	3/07	3/08	3/09
Sales ($ mil.)	1.0%	83.9	72.6	72.0	74.9	87.4
Net income ($ mil.)	—	2.4	8.0	7.6	4.4	(17.1)
Market value ($ mil.)	38.4%	4.8	5.9	44.2	33.6	17.6
Employees	(7.1%)	215	202	145	150	160

CROWN EQUIPMENT CORPORATION

44 S. Washington St.	CEO: James F. Dicke II
New Bremen, OH 45869	CFO: Kent W. Spille
Phone: 419-629-2311	HR: Randall W. (Randy) Niekamp
Fax: 419-629-2900	FYE: March 31
Web: www.crown.com	Type: Private

The jewels in the crown of Crown Equipment Corporation are electric and engine lift trucks used for maneuvering goods in warehouses and distribution centers. A market leader, the company's products include narrow-aisle stacking equipment, and powered pallet trucks. The engine lift truck line features forklifts with differing tons. Its equipment can move 4-ton loads and stack pallets nearly 45 ft. high. Crown Equipment sells its products globally through dealers and distributors. The company, founded in 1945 by Carl and Allen Dicke, has evolved from making temperature controls for coal furnaces to building 85% of the parts for its material-handling equipment. The Dicke family still controls Crown Equipment.

CROWN HOLDINGS, INC.

NYSE: CCK

1 Crown Way	CEO: John W. Conway
Philadelphia, PA 19154	CFO: Timothy J. Donahue
Phone: 215-698-5100	HR: —
Fax: 215-676-7245	FYE: December 31
Web: www.crowncork.com	Type: Public

Crown Holdings knows how to keep a lid on profits. The company is a global manufacturer of consumer packaging; steel and aluminum food and beverage cans, and related packaging are Crown's primary lines. Its portfolio includes aerosol cans, and various metal closures marketed under brands Liftoff, SuperEnd, and Easylift, as well as specialty packaging, such as novelty containers and industrial cans. Crown also supplies can-making equipment and parts. Its roster of customers includes Coca-Cola, Cadberry Schweppes, Heinz, Nestlé, SC Johnson, Unilever, and Procter & Gamble, which owns Gillette, another customer. Crown operates 139 plants throughout 41 countries, with some 75% of net sales from outside the US.

	Annual Growth	12/05	12/06	12/07	12/08	12/09
Sales ($ mil.)	3.5%	6,908.0	6,982.0	7,727.0	8,305.0	7,938.0
Net income ($ mil.)	—	(362.0)	309.0	528.0	226.0	334.0
Market value ($ mil.)	7.0%	3,163.9	3,389.1	4,155.4	3,110.5	4,144.0
Employees	(3.9%)	24,000	21,700	21,800	21,300	20,500

CROWN MEDIA HOLDINGS, INC.

NASDAQ (GM): CRWN

12700 Ventura Blvd., Ste. 200	CEO: William J. (Bill) Abbott
Studio City, CA 91604	CFO: Brian C. Stewart
Phone: 818-755-2400	HR: —
Fax: 818-755-2564	FYE: December 31
Web: www.hallmarkchannel.com	Type: Public

Family-friendly TV is the jewel in this Crown. Crown Media Holdings owns and operates the Hallmark Channel, a cable network that specializes in family-oriented TV fare. It features mostly third-party programming, including such TV series as *7th Heaven, Little House on the Prairie,* and *Matlock,* as well as made-for-TV movies, feature films, and miniseries. The channel reaches about 85 million US homes. Crown Media also operates the Hallmark Movie Channel, a 24-hour channel that primarily offers feature films and miniseries; it reaches about 15 million homes. Hallmark Cards controls about 95% of the company.

	Annual Growth	12/05	12/06	12/07	12/08	12/09
Sales ($ mil.)	9.1%	197.4	201.2	234.4	281.8	279.6
Net income ($ mil.)	—	(215.5)	(386.9)	(159.0)	(37.2)	(22.6)
Market value ($ mil.)	(36.9%)	960.9	380.4	681.1	298.6	151.9
Employees	(3.8%)	186	158	176	178	159

CRUISE LINE HOLDINGS CO.

8052 NW 14th St.	CEO: Robin (Rob) Norris
Miami, FL 33126	CFO: Ares Michaelides
Phone: 786-845-7300	HR: —
Fax: 305-477-4522	FYE: December 31
Web: www.starboardcruise.com	Type: Subsidiary

Turn to Cruise Line Holdings for your onboard booty. The company, which does business as Miami Cruiseline Services and Starboard Cruise Services, is part of the Selective Retailing segment of luxury goods company LVMH Moët Hennessy Louis Vuitton. The firm sells duty-free retail luxury goods, such as perfume, cosmetics, apparel, souvenirs, giftware, fine jewelry, watches, and accessories, as well as liquor, tobacco, and food aboard nearly 100 ships worldwide operated by some 10 cruise lines, including Carnival and Royal Caribbean. Cruise Line Holdings was founded in 1963 and acquired by LVMH in 2000.

CRUM & FORSTER HOLDINGS CORP.

305 Madison Ave.
Morristown, NJ 07962
Phone: 973-490-6600
Fax: 973-490-6940
Web: www.cfins.com

CEO: Douglas M. (Doug) Libby
CFO: Mary Jane Robertson
HR: Stephen M. (Steve) Mulready
FYE: December 31
Type: Subsidiary

Crum & Forster looks out for the best interests of employers. Through its subsidiaries, the company offers an array of property/casualty insurance products to businesses, including general liability, automobile, property, and workers' compensation coverage. Crum & Forster also offers The Defender, a broad commercial umbrella policy. The company's specialty policies include management protection, crime insurance, and e-commerce risk protection coverage. Crum & Forster also provides risk management services. The company's products are sold through some 1,400 independent brokers across the US. Crum & Forster is a subsidiary of Fairfax Financial Holdings.

	Annual Growth	12/04	12/05	12/06	12/07	12/08
Sales ($ mil.)	4.2%	—	—	1,476.8	1,563.6	1,602.3
Net income ($ mil.)	3.2%	—	—	312.3	293.2	332.8
Employees	77.9%	—	—	400	1,373	1,266

CRYO-CELL INTERNATIONAL, INC.

OTC: CCEL

700 Brooker Creek Blvd., Ste. 1800
Oldsmar, FL 34677
Phone: 813-749-2100
Fax: 813-855-4745
Web: www.cryo-cell.com

CEO: Mercedes Walton
CFO: Jill M. Taymans
HR: —
FYE: November 30
Type: Public

Cryo-Cell International freezes the ties that bind. Cryo-Cel collects and cryogenically stores umbilical cord blood stem cells, giving expectant parents some insurance in case disease (such as diabetes, heart disease, or stroke) should strike in the future. Specimens collected in the US are processed and stored at Cryo-Cell's facility in Oldsmar, Florida. The company also offers services through subsidiaries in certain countries in Asia, Europe, Latin America, and the Middle East. Cryo-Cell markets its services directly to consumers online through its website and by providing information and education to obstetricians, pediatricians, childbirth educators, and other health care providers.

	Annual Growth	11/05	11/06	11/07	11/08	11/09
Sales ($ mil.)	3.0%	14.5	17.2	17.5	17.3	16.3
Net income ($ mil.)	8.8%	1.0	(2.8)	(5.0)	(0.8)	1.4
Market value ($ mil.)	(16.3%)	42.0	30.0	14.9	6.8	20.6
Employees	(2.4%)	54	66	65	45	49

⊞ CRYOLIFE, INC.

NYSE: CRY

1655 Roberts Blvd., NW
Kennesaw, GA 30144
Phone: 770-419-3355
Fax: 770-426-0031
Web: www.cryolife.com

CEO: Steven G. (Steve) Anderson
CFO: D. Ashley Lee
HR: —
FYE: December 31
Type: Public

CryoLife preserves lives, as well as the cardiovascular tissues that keep life going. The company takes human heart valves and blood vessels from deceased volunteer donors, processes them, and stores them in liquid nitrogen freezers (a process called cryopreservation). It then ships them to surgeons nationwide, who implant them during cardiac and vascular repair procedures. For some preserved tissue, the company uses its proprietary SynerGraft technology, which reduces the presence of donor cells and makes the tissue more compatible with the recipient. CryoLife also develops implantable biomaterials, including BioGlue, an adhesive used to seal internal surgical wounds.

	Annual Growth	12/05	12/06	12/07	12/08	12/09
Sales ($ mil.)	12.7%	69.3	81.3	94.8	105.1	111.7
Net income ($ mil.)	—	(19.5)	0.4	7.2	32.9	8.7
Market value ($ mil.)	17.7%	95.7	219.2	227.8	278.2	183.9
Employees	3.4%	363	388	405	435	415

CRYSTAL RIVER CAPITAL, INC.

OTC: CYRV

3 World Financial Center, 200 Vesey St., 10th Fl.
New York, NY 10281
Phone: 212-549-8400
Fax: 212-549-8304
Web: www.crystalriverreit.com

CEO: Rodman L. Drake
CFO: Craig J. Laurie
HR: —
FYE: December 31
Type: Public

Crystal River Capital has no crystal ball, but it hopes its investment decisions prove to be far-sighted. The real estate investment trust (REIT) invests in commercial real estate and residential and commercial mortgage-backed securities. Formed in 2005, the company is managed and advised by Hyperion Brookfield Asset Management, a subsidiary of Toronto-based Brookfield Asset Management. The economic crisis led to big problems for the REIT, which was unable to refinance or leverage against its portfolio. With no extra cash for new investments, it began looking for options. Brookfield offered to buy Crystal River in 2010; the company also received a competing offer from Laurel Canyon Partners.

	Annual Growth	12/05	12/06	12/07	12/08	12/09
Sales ($ mil.)	—	76.6	209.0	243.6	139.4	(36.1)
Net income ($ mil.)	—	13.9	46.9	(345.9)	(307.1)	(88.3)
Market value ($ mil.)	(74.6%)	—	635.9	359.7	13.5	10.5
Employees	—	—	—	—	—	—

CSB BANCORP, INC.

OTC: CSBB

91 N. Clay St.
Millersburg, OH 44654
Phone: 330-674-9015
Fax: —
Web: www.csb1.com

CEO: Eddie L. Steiner
CFO: Paula J. Meiler
HR: Julie A. Jones
FYE: December 31
Type: Public

CSB Bancorp is the holding company for The Commercial and Savings Bank, which serves Holmes and Tuscarawas counties and surrounding areas of east-central Ohio from about a dozen branches. Founded in 1879, the bank offers traditional products such as checking and savings accounts and CDs, as well as credit cards, trust services, estate planning, and corporate and individual retirement plans. Its loan portfolio is composed mostly of residential and commercial mortgages; the bank also originates business, construction, and consumer installment loans. CSB Bancorp bought another area community bank, the three-branch Indian Village Community Bank, in 2008.

	Annual Growth	12/05	12/06	12/07	12/08	12/09
Assets ($ mil.)	8.9%	321.0	327.2	350.3	424.7	450.7
Net income ($ mil.)	4.1%	2.9	3.1	3.5	3.5	3.4
Market value ($ mil.)	(7.7%)	57.4	52.0	48.5	41.0	41.7
Employees	3.0%	141	135	133	150	159

CSC HOLDINGS, INC.

1111 Stewart Ave.
Bethpage, NY 11714
Phone: 516-803-2300
Fax: 516-803-3134
Web: www.cablevision.com

CEO: James L. Dolan
CFO: Michael P. Huseby
HR: —
FYE: December 31
Type: Subsidiary

CSC Holdings is the main operating company of Cablevision Systems Corporation, one of the top US cable and entertainment companies. Its core business is centered around its cable television network that serves about 3 million customers in the New York City area. The company's iO digital video service is used by about 3 million subscribers. Subsidiary Rainbow Media is an entertainment programming company that owns nationwide cable channels such as American Movie Classics and the Independent Film Channel, as well as regional programming interests. CSC's Newsday segment oversees print and online publishing interests. Chairman Charles Dolan and his family control 70% of Cablevision's shares.

	Annual Growth	12/04	12/05	12/06	12/07	12/08
Est. sales ($ mil.)	—	—	—	—	—	7,230.1
Employees	—	—	—	—	—	16,705

⊞ An in-depth profile of this company is available to Hoover's Online members at hoovers.com.

455

CSG SYSTEMS INTERNATIONAL, INC.

NASDAQ (GS): CSGS

9555 Maroon Cir.
Englewood, CO 80112
Phone: 303-200-2000
Fax: 303-804-4965
Web: www.csgsystems.com

CEO: Peter E. Kalan
CFO: Randy R. Wiese
HR: Suzanne Broski
FYE: December 31
Type: Public

CSRs love CSG. CSG Systems International makes life a little easier for customer service representatives (CSRs) with its customer care and billing software and services. Designed for clients that handle a high volume of transactions, the company offers outsourced transaction processing and customer service systems that are used to establish customer accounts, process orders, manage and mail monthly statements, perform marketing analysis, and other functions. The company serves primarily North American cable TV, direct broadcast satellite, online services, and telecom companies. CSG's clients include Time Warner and Comcast.

	Annual Growth	12/05	12/06	12/07	12/08	12/09
Sales ($ mil.)	7.3%	377.3	383.1	419.3	472.1	500.7
Net income ($ mil.)	(5.0%)	53.2	59.8	60.8	61.8	43.3
Market value ($ mil.)	(3.8%)	760.1	910.3	501.3	594.9	650.1
Employees	7.6%	1,540	1,685	1,877	2,066	2,066

CSK AUTO CORPORATION

645 E. Missouri Ave., Ste. 400
Phoenix, AZ 85012
Phone: 602-265-9200
Fax: 602-631-7321
Web: www.cskauto.com

CEO: Ted F. Wise
CFO: Thomas G. (Tom) McFall
HR: —
FYE: December 31
Type: Subsidiary

CSK Auto likes people who look under their own hoods. The retailer of automotive parts and accessories sells mainly to do-it-yourselfers but also to auto professionals and commercial installers. CSK Auto operates some 1,340 stores in 20-plus mostly western states under the names Checker Auto Parts, Schuck's Auto Supply, Kragen Auto Parts, and Murray's Discount Auto Stores. Kragen Auto Parts runs more than 500 stores, mostly in California; Checker Auto Parts operates about 490 stores throughout the West and Hawaii; and Schucks' some 220 stores are in Washington, Oregon, Idaho, Alaska, and California. CSK Auto is now a subsidiary of O'Reilly Automotive, which bought it in 2008 for about $500 million, plus debt.

CSL BEHRING, LLC

1020 1st Ave.
King of Prussia, PA 19406
Phone: 610-878-4000
Fax: 610-878-4009
Web: www.cslbehring.com

CEO: Peter Turner
CFO: Karen Neave
HR: Kathy Quay
FYE: June 30
Type: Subsidiary

Take away the red and white blood cells from blood and you get plasma, a protein-rich fluid. CSL Behring is among the world's largest fully integrated plasma collection companies. Through subsidiary CSL Plasma (formerly ZLB Plasma), the company collects plasma through dozens of facilities in the US and Germany. CSL Behring then develops plasma-based protein biotherapeutics to treat a range of health ailments, including bleeding disorders (such as hemophilia), immune system deficiencies, and respiratory disease (including emphysema). Biotherapeutics are also used in critical care settings for surgical and wound healing applications. CSL Behring is a subsidiary of Australian biopharmaceutical firm CSL Limited.

CSL PLASMA INC.

5201 Congress Ave., Ste. 220
Boca Raton, FL 33487
Phone: 561-981-3700
Fax: 561-912-3005
Web: www.cslplasma.com

CEO: Randy L. Furby
CFO: —
HR: —
FYE: December 31
Type: Subsidiary

CSL Plasma (formerly ZLB Plasma Services) employees don't mind being in a bloody business. CSL Plasma, a subsidiary of CSL Behring (which itself is part of CSL Limited), collects donations of blood plasma across the US through about 60 donation centers in 25 states; it also has about 10 collection locations in Germany. The company collects approximately 3 million liters of plasma each year. The plasma is used by the company's parent to manufacture therapies for bleeding disorders such as hemophilia, as well as blood clots, immune deficiencies, burns, shock, and other conditions. It also operates laboratory testing facilities and logistics centers.

CSP INC.

NASDAQ (GM): CSPI

43 Manning Rd.
Billerica, MA 01821
Phone: 978-663-7598
Fax: 978-663-0150
Web: www.cspi.com

CEO: Alexander R. Lupinetti
CFO: Gary W. Levine
HR: —
FYE: September 30
Type: Public

CSP knows IT. The company provides information technology services, including the resale and integration of computer hardware and software, through its MODCOMP subsidiary. Other services include maintenance and custom software development. MODCOMP serves clients in Germany, the UK, and the US; industries served include financial services, manufacturing, and telecommunications. CSP's systems segment develops and builds computer signal processing systems for aerospace and defense markets. Its MultiComputer product line includes systems used for radar, sonar, surveillance, and other applications; sales are made directly in the US and through distributors and resellers to customers in Asia, India, and Europe.

	Annual Growth	9/05	9/06	9/07	9/08	9/09
Sales ($ mil.)	9.7%	57.5	68.9	94.0	76.8	83.4
Net income ($ mil.)	—	0.8	2.0	4.0	(0.4)	(3.8)
Market value ($ mil.)	(15.6%)	25.6	31.2	27.7	18.9	13.0
Employees	0.5%	147	138	135	157	150

CSS INDUSTRIES, INC.

NYSE: CSS

1845 Walnut St., Ste. 800
Philadelphia, PA 19103
Phone: 215-569-9900
Fax: 215-569-9979
Web: www.cssindustries.com

CEO: Christopher J. Munyan
CFO: Vincent A. Paccapaniccia
HR: William G. Kiesling
FYE: March 31
Type: Public

Every day is Christmas at CSS Industries, maker of seasonal and everyday decorative products such as gift wrap, gift bags, ribbons, bows, stationery, and cards, as well as floral, craft, and packaging items. The company also makes dye for Easter eggs (Dudley's), valentines for classroom exchange, and Halloween makeup and costumes. Customers include mass-merchandise retailers, warehouse clubs, and drug and food chains, primarily in the US and Canada (Wal-Mart and Target account for a combined 37% of sales.) Originally founded as a furniture and department store retailer in 1923, the company shifted gears in the mid-1980s through acquisitions, such as The Paper Magic Group, Berwick Offray, and C.R. Gibson.

	Annual Growth	3/06	3/07	3/08	3/09	3/10
Sales ($ mil.)	(3.9%)	525.5	530.7	498.3	482.4	448.5
Net income ($ mil.)	—	21.8	23.9	25.4	17.0	(23.7)
Market value ($ mil.)	(11.5%)	316.9	362.7	338.4	164.5	194.5
Employees	(4.7%)	3,400	2,700	2,200	2,100	2,800

CSX CORPORATION
NYSE: CSX

500 Water St., 15th Fl.
Jacksonville, FL 32202
Phone: 904-359-3200
Fax: 904-633-3450
Web: www.csx.com

CEO: Michael J. Ward
CFO: Oscar Munoz
HR: Lisa A. Mancini
FYE: December 31
Type: Public

CSX banks on the railway as the right way to make money. Its main subsidiary, CSX Transportation (CSXT), operates a major rail system (some 21,000 route miles) in the eastern US. The freight carrier links 23 states, 70 ports, the District of Columbia, and two Canadian provinces. Freight hauled by the company includes a wide variety of merchandise (food, chemicals, consumer goods), coal, automotive products, and intermodal containers. CSX's rail segment, which accounts for about 90% of the company's sales, also includes units that operate motor vehicle distribution centers and bulk cargo terminals. Subsidiary CSX Intermodal arranges the transportation of freight by combinations of road and rail carriers.

	Annual Growth	12/05	12/06	12/07	12/08	12/09
Sales ($ mil.)	1.2%	8,618.0	9,566.0	10,030.0	11,255.0	9,041.0
Net income ($ mil.)	0.2%	1,145.0	1,310.0	1,336.0	1,365.0	1,152.0
Market value ($ mil.)	17.6%	9,880.5	13,401.1	17,118.2	12,638.2	18,873.6
Employees	(3.7%)	35,000	36,000	35,000	34,000	30,088

CT CORPORATION SYSTEM

111 8th Ave., 13th Fl.
New York, NY 10011
Phone: 212-894-8940
Fax: —
Web: www.ctadvantage.com

CEO: Richard Flynn
CFO: Joseph (Joe) D'Avanzo
HR: —
FYE: December 31
Type: Subsidiary

CT helps Inc.'s and Corp.'s dot their i's and cross their t's. The company assists large and small businesses and their lawyers in their efforts to comply with the various rules that govern the existence of corporate entities. CT's services include acting as a registered agent and handling and managing corporate, Uniform Commercial Code, and SEC filings. The company operates from more than 40 offices throughout the US, as well as through a network of correspondents. Subsidiary CT Tymetrix makes software used to manage law practices. CT, which traces its roots to 1892 when it was established as The Corporation Trust Company, is a unit of Netherlands-based publisher Wolters Kluwer.

	Annual Growth	12/04	12/05	12/06	12/07	12/08
Est. sales ($ mil.)	—	—	—	—	—	500.0
Employees	—	—	—	—	—	1,563

CTI GROUP (HOLDINGS) INC.
OTC: CTIG

333 N. Alabama St., Ste. 240
Indianapolis, IN 46204
Phone: 317-262-4666
Fax: 317-262-4849
Web: www.ctigroup.com

CEO: John Birbeck
CFO: Manfred (Fred) Hanuschek
HR: —
FYE: December 31
Type: Public

CTI Group (Holdings) helps companies act on their transactions. The company provides software and services for billing, customer care, and telemanagement. Targeting service providers in the telecom, information technology, financial, cable, and health care industries, CTI offers software that analyzes billing data (SmartBill), automates telecommunications spending, manages electronic invoicing, and handles call accounting. The company also offers professional services and outsourced call center management, output processing, training, support, and marketing services.

	Annual Growth	12/05	12/06	12/07	12/08	12/09
Sales ($ mil.)	0.6%	15.3	12.8	21.3	22.5	15.7
Net income ($ mil.)	—	0.5	(1.1)	(1.5)	0.8	(1.3)
Market value ($ mil.)	(34.7%)	9.6	8.8	8.2	3.8	1.8
Employees	9.9%	94	146	129	138	137

CTI INDUSTRIES CORPORATION
NASDAQ (CM): CTIB

22160 N. Pepper Rd.
Barrington, IL 60010
Phone: 847-382-1000
Fax: 847-382-1219
Web: www.ctiindustries.com

CEO: Howard W. Schwan
CFO: Stephen M. Merrick
HR: Bertha Vertiz
FYE: December 31
Type: Public

Ballooning profits would be most welcome at CTI Industries Corporation. The company's metalized and latex balloons are decorated with messages and cartoon characters, such as Garfield and Miss Spider. It sells balloons and novelty inflatable items to distributors, retailers, grocers, and florists. CTI Industries also makes wrapping and custom film for commercial and industrial uses such as food packaging (candy wrappers) and dunnage bags (inflatable pouches used as cushioning during shipping). Its top three customers account for about 50% of sales. Chairman John Schwan and EVP Stephen Merrick each own approximately 27% of CTI. John's brother, president Howard Schwan, owns another 10% of the company.

	Annual Growth	12/05	12/06	12/07	12/08	12/09
Sales ($ mil.)	9.1%	29.2	35.4	36.5	45.0	41.3
Net income ($ mil.)	—	(0.3)	1.9	0.1	1.2	1.0
Market value ($ mil.)	(5.9%)	8.1	13.5	10.6	5.8	6.3
Employees	5.8%	280	89	84	330	351

CTM MEDIA HOLDINGS, INC.
Pink Sheets: CTMM

11 Largo Dr. South
Stamford, CT 06907
Phone: 203-323-5161
Fax: 203-973-0319
Web: www.ctmmediagroup.com

CEO: Marc E. Knoller
CFO: Leslie B. Rozner
HR: —
FYE: July 31
Type: Public

CTM Media Holdings is not embarrassed by tourists. The company distributes travel-related print and online advertising and information. Offerings include visitor maps, brochures, and other destination guides. Its publications are found in strategically located display stands, primarily located in hotels, attractions, restaurants, and rest stops along high traffic throughways and interstates. In addition, CTM Media publishes books and comics through its IDW Publishing subsidiary. The company was founded in 1983 as Creative Theatre Marketing. Previously known as IDT Capital, the company was spun off from telecommunications firm IDT Corporation in 2009.

	Annual Growth	7/04	7/05	7/06	7/07	*7/08
Sales ($ mil.)	41.7%	—	—	—	23.0	32.6
Net income ($ mil.)	—	—	—	—	(0.3)	(5.3)
Employees	—	—	—	—	—	165

*Most recent year available

CTS CORPORATION
NYSE: CTS

905 N. West Blvd.
Elkhart, IN 46514
Phone: 574-293-7511
Fax: 574-293-6146
Web: www.ctscorp.com

CEO: Vinod M. Khilnani
CFO: Donna L. Belusar
HR: Vernon Pitcher
FYE: December 31
Type: Public

CTS is all about electronics. The company's two segments, Electronics Manufacturing Services (EMS) and Components and Sensors, provide products and manufacturing services to the aerospace, automotive, communications, computer, medical equipment, and military contracting industries, among others. Products include automotive sensors, oscillators, quartz crystals, resistors, and switches. CTS also makes radio-frequency modules for wireless phones, pointing sticks for notebook computer keyboards, and ceramics for use in Global Positioning System (GPS) devices. Customers include Hewlett-Packard and Motorola. More than half of the company's sales comes from the US.

	Annual Growth	12/05	12/06	12/07	12/08	12/09
Sales ($ mil.)	(5.2%)	617.5	655.6	685.9	691.7	499.0
Net income ($ mil.)	—	22.2	24.2	25.4	29.9	(34.0)
Market value ($ mil.)	(3.4%)	375.8	533.5	337.4	187.2	326.9
Employees	(3.1%)	4,902	4,977	4,746	5,044	4,316

An in-depth profile of this company is available to Hoover's Online members at hoovers.com.

457

CUBIC CORPORATION

NYSE: CUB

9333 Balboa Ave.
San Diego, CA 92123
Phone: 858-277-6780
Fax: 858-277-1878
Web: www.cubic.com

CEO: Walter J. Zable
CFO: William W. Boyle
HR: Bernard A. (Bernie) Kulchin
FYE: September 30
Type: Public

Cubic equips people to fight their way through the line, be it a subway or a firing line. For the latter, it designs, manufactures, and installs combat simulation and training products; for the former, automatic fare collection (AFC) systems. Cubic's defense segment, which caters to the armed forces of the US and its allies, also makes communications systems and surveillance equipment. Military education and support services are the focus of its mission segment. On the transit side, Cubic's AFC systems are installed at public authorities — bus, light rail, ferry, and parking — in London to New York, San Francisco to Sydney, and Washington, DC. The US government accounts for more than half of Cubic's sales.

	Annual Growth	9/05	9/06	9/07	9/08	9/09
Sales ($ mil.)	6.0%	804.4	821.4	889.9	881.1	1,016.7
Net income ($ mil.)	48.0%	11.6	24.1	41.6	36.9	55.7
Market value ($ mil.)	23.2%	457.7	523.5	1,127.5	657.4	1,055.3
Employees	0.5%	6,000	6,000	6,000	7,000	6,125

CUBIST PHARMACEUTICALS, INC.

NASDAQ (GS): CBST

65 Hayden Ave.
Lexington, MA 02421
Phone: 781-860-8660
Fax: 781-240-0256
Web: www.cubist.com

CEO: Michael W. (Mike) Bonney
CFO: David W. J. McGirr
HR: Maureen H. Powers
FYE: December 31
Type: Public

Fighting infection is a modern art form at Cubist Pharmaceuticals. The company is developing antimicrobial agents that aim to treat drug-resistant infections typically found in hospitals and other health care institutions. Its flagship product Cubicin is an intravenous antibiotic that is FDA-approved to fight staph infections of the skin and blood; it has also received regulatory approval in Europe and a handful of non-European countries to treat certain kinds of infections. Cubist markets the drug in the US using its own sales force. It has agreements with numerous other firms to develop and market the drug internationally; its partners include Novartis for Europe, Merck for Japan, and AstraZeneca for China.

	Annual Growth	12/05	12/06	12/07	12/08	12/09
Sales ($ mil.)	46.9%	120.6	194.7	294.6	433.6	562.1
Net income ($ mil.)	—	(31.9)	(0.4)	48.1	169.8	79.6
Market value ($ mil.)	(2.8%)	1,240.4	1,057.6	1,197.8	1,410.9	1,107.8
Employees	12.9%	369	410	489	554	600

THE CULINARY INSTITUTE OF AMERICA

1946 Campus Dr.
Hyde Park, NY 12538
Phone: 845-452-9600
Fax: 845-451-1067
Web: www.ciachef.edu

CEO: L. Timothy Ryan
CFO: Charles A. O'Mara
HR: David Jaskiewicz
FYE: May 31
Type: School

At this CIA they work on countertops, not counterterrorism. The Culinary Institute of America (CIA) offers bachelor's and associate degrees in Culinary Arts Management and Baking and Pastry Arts Management, as well as continuing education, conferences, travel programs, and e-learning. The independent, not-for-profit educational organization enrolls some 2,700 students and employs more than 125 chef-instructors and other faculty members representing 16 countries. The CIA operates campuses in Hyde Park, New York; St. Helena, California; and San Antonio, Texas. Notable graduates include media personalities Anthony Bourdain and Rocco DiSpirito and Steve Ellis, founder of Chipotle Mexican Grill.

	Annual Growth	5/04	5/05	5/06	5/07	5/08
Est. sales ($ mil.)	—	—	—	—	—	118.1
Employees	—	—	—	—	—	810

CULLEN/FROST BANKERS, INC.

NYSE: CFR

100 W. Houston St.
San Antonio, TX 78205
Phone: 210-220-4011
Fax: 210-220-4325
Web: www.frostbank.com

CEO: Richard W. (Dick) Evans Jr.
CFO: Phillip D. Green
HR: Emily A. Skillman
FYE: December 31
Type: Public

One of the largest independent bank holding companies based in Texas, Cullen/Frost Bankers owns Frost National Bank through a second-tier holding company, the New Galveston Company. The community-oriented bank serves individuals and local businesses, as well as clients in neighboring parts of Mexico, through more than 100 branches in Texas metropolitan areas. It offers commercial and consumer deposit products and loans, trust and investment management services, mutual funds, insurance, capital markets and brokerage services, and correspondent banking. Subsidiaries include Frost Insurance Agency, Frost Brokerage Services, Frost Investment Advisors, and investment banking arm Frost Securities.

	Annual Growth	12/05	12/06	12/07	12/08	12/09
Assets ($ mil.)	8.5%	11,741.4	13,224.2	13,485.0	15,034.1	16,288.0
Net income ($ mil.)	2.0%	165.4	193.6	212.1	207.3	179.0
Market value ($ mil.)	(1.8%)	3,250.0	3,379.5	3,067.1	3,068.4	3,027.2
Employees	3.2%	3,386	3,652	3,781	3,892	3,834

CULLIGAN INTERNATIONAL COMPANY

9399 W. Higgins Rd.
Rosemont, IL 60018
Phone: 847-430-2800
Fax: 847-430-1524
Web: www.culligan.com

CEO: Mark Seals
CFO: Maria Henry
HR: Janet Snow-Godfrey
FYE: June 30
Type: Private

"Hey Culligan Man!" To be sure, the phrase made famous by an ad campaign still rings in the ears of Culligan International workers. Formerly a subsidiary of Veolia Environnement, Culligan produces filters for tap water, household water softeners, microfiltration products, desalination systems, and portable deionization services for commercial and industrial users. The franchised "Culligan Man" noted in the advertising phrase delivers bottled water and water systems to consumers and businesses through more than 800 Culligan company-owned and franchised dealers in more than 90 countries. Buyout firm Clayton, Dubilier & Rice owns the company.

CULP, INC.

NYSE: CFI

1823 Eastchester Dr.
High Point, NC 27265
Phone: 336-889-5161
Fax: 336-889-7246
Web: www.culpinc.com

CEO: Franklin N. Saxon
CFO: Kenneth R. Bowling
HR: Teresa Huffman
FYE: April 30
Type: Public

Culp just wants to keep on ticking. The company is one of the world's largest makers of furniture upholstery fabrics and mattress fabrics (known as ticking). Its upholstery fabrics include wovens (jacquards and dobbies), knits, screen-prints, and velvets (woven and tufted). Its fabrics are used in upholstering residential and commercial furniture such as recliners, sofas, and love seats. Its ticking is used for covering mattresses and box springs. Major customers include furniture makers Bassett, Furniture Brands International, and La-Z-Boy (12% of sales), and mattress makers Sealy and Serta. US customers account for about 80% of sales. Culp has eight manufacturing plants in the US, Canada, and China.

	Annual Growth	4/05	4/06	4/07	4/08	4/09
Sales ($ mil.)	(8.2%)	286.5	261.1	250.5	254.0	203.9
Net income ($ mil.)	—	(17.9)	(11.8)	(1.3)	5.4	(38.8)
Market value ($ mil.)	(1.1%)	60.8	60.0	116.3	90.9	58.2
Employees	(13.8%)	1,900	1,300	1,140	1,087	1,047

An in-depth profile of this company is available to Hoover's Online members at hoovers.com.

CULVER FRANCHISING SYSTEM, INC.

1240 Water St.
Prairie du Sac, WI 53578
Phone: 608-643-7980
Fax: 608-643-7982
Web: www.culvers.com

CEO: Craig C. Culver
CFO: Joseph (Joe) Koss
HR: —
FYE: December 31
Type: Private

If you think ButterBurgers are better burgers, then you're probably a fan of Culver's. Culver Franchising System operates a chain of about 400 Culver's quick-service restaurants popular for their signature ButterBurgers (hamburgers served on a grilled buttered bun) and frozen custard. The chain's menu also includes chicken, fish, and pork sandwiches; salads; and dinner items such as shrimp and Norwegian Cod. Culver's has locations in Wisconsin and about 15 other states. Nearly all of the restaurants are operated by franchisees. President Craig Culver and his family started the business in 1984.

	Annual Growth	12/04	12/05	12/06	12/07	12/08
Est. sales ($ mil.)	—	—	—	—	—	45.8
Employees	—	—	—	—	—	290

CUMBERLAND FARMS, INC.

100 Crossing Blvd.
Framingham, MA 01702
Phone: 508-270-1400
Fax: —
Web: www.cumberlandfarms.com

CEO: Joseph H. (Joe) Petrowski
CFO: Jayne Conway
HR: Patricia A. Firing
FYE: September 30
Type: Private

Once a one-cow dairy, Cumberland Farms now operates a network of about 1,000 convenience stores and gas stations in about a dozen eastern seaboard states from Maine to Florida. The company operates its own grocery distribution and bakery operations to supply its stores, as well. Cumberland owns a two-thirds limited partnership in petroleum wholesaler Gulf Oil, giving it the right to use and license Gulf trademarks in Delaware, New Jersey, New York, most of Ohio, Pennsylvania, and the New England states. The first convenience-store operator in New England, Cumberland was founded in 1939 by Vasilios and Aphrodite Haseotes. The Haseotes' children, including chairman Lily Haseotes Bentas, own the company.

CUMBERLAND GENERAL STORE, LLC

P.O. Box 4468
Alpharetta, GA 30023
Phone: 678-240-0407
Fax: 678-240-0410
Web: www.cumberlandgeneral.com

CEO: Tim Seanor
CFO: —
HR: —
FYE: December 31
Type: Private

When you say retro at Cumberland General Store, you're really talking the 80s — the 1880s, to be more precise. Cumberland General Store markets items that would be appropriate for a rural home or farm in the 19th century. The company sells appliances, hardware, toys, kitchen supplies, and other products (that typically require little or no electricity) from a single store in Alpharetta, Georgia, as well as through its well-known catalog and online. Customers include back-to-nature enthusiasts, residents of areas without electricity, and producers of period movies and television shows. In 2005 the store and company moved from Crossville, Tennessee, to its current location in Georgia.

	Annual Growth	12/04	12/05	12/06	12/07	12/08
Est. sales ($ mil.)	—	—	—	—	—	0.3
Employees	—	—	—	—	—	1

CUMBERLAND PHARMACEUTICALS INC.

NASDAQ (GS): CPIX

2525 West End Ave., Ste. 950
Nashville, TN 37203
Phone: 615-255-0068
Fax: 615-255-0094
Web: www.cumberlandpharma.com

CEO: A. J. Kazimi
CFO: David L. Lowrance
HR: —
FYE: December 31
Type: Public

Cumberland Pharmaceuticals wants to make your search for the right drugs less cumbersome. The specialty pharmaceutical company focuses on acquiring, developing, and commercializing branded prescription drugs. Targeting the hospital acute care and gastroenterology segments, Cumberland's FDA-approved drugs include Acetadote for the treatment of acetaminophen poisoning; Kristalose, a prescription strength laxative; and Caldolor (neé Amelior), the first injectable dosage form of ibuprofen. The company also has several projects in early-stage development. Acetadote and Kristalose are marketed through Cumberland's own hospital and gastroenterology sales forces. The company went public in an IPO in mid-2009.

	Annual Growth	12/05	12/06	12/07	12/08	12/09
Sales ($ mil.)	42.0%	10.7	17.8	28.1	35.1	43.5
Net income ($ mil.)	11.6%	2.0	4.4	4.0	4.8	3.1
Market value ($ mil.)	—	—	—	—	—	277.7
Employees	48.5%	—	33	43	53	108

CUMMINS INC.

NYSE: CMI

500 Jackson St.
Columbus, IN 47201
Phone: 812-377-5000
Fax: 812-377-3334
Web: www.cummins.com

CEO: Theodore M. (Tim) Solso
CFO: Patrick J. (Pat) Ward
HR: —
FYE: December 31
Type: Public

Cummins is in it for the long haul, on the road, rail, or river. The company is the world's leader in the manufacture of large diesel engines. Cummins engines also power school buses, medium-duty trucks, pickups (primarily Dodge Rams), and equipment for mining and construction. Cummins claims just under one-third of the North American market for heavy-duty truck engines. The company also makes power generation products such as its Onan generator sets and Stamford alternators. Other products and brands include Fleetguard (filtration), Kuss (fuel filters), and Holset (turbochargers). Among its customers are OEMs PACCAR, Daimler, Chrysler, Komatsu, and Case. Cummins nets more than half of its sales outside the US.

	Annual Growth	12/05	12/06	12/07	12/08	12/09
Sales ($ mil.)	2.2%	9,918.0	11,362.0	13,048.0	14,342.0	10,800.0
Net income ($ mil.)	(6.1%)	550.0	715.0	739.0	755.0	428.0
Market value ($ mil.)	19.6%	4,499.5	5,926.1	12,773.9	5,361.5	9,198.6
Employees	1.0%	33,500	34,600	37,800	39,800	34,900

CUMMINS-AMERICAN CORPORATION

852 Feehanville Dr.
Mount Prospect, IL 60056
Phone: 847-299-9550
Fax: 847-299-4940
Web: www.cumminsallison.com

CEO: John E. Jones
CFO: John Diedrich
HR: Joan Cantrell
FYE: December 31
Type: Private

Cummins-American knows how to bring the money in and sort it out. The company owns Glenview State Bank, which offers personal and business banking services through around 10 branches in Chicago's northern suburbs. Cummins-American's other main subsidiary, Cummins-Allison, makes a variety of coin and currency sorters, counters, wrappers, and scanners; check signers, imprinters, and endorsers; and paper shredders and perforators. It also produces cash management software. These products are sold around the world to banks, government agencies, and the retail, gaming, and vending industries. The family of chairman and CEO John Jones owns a majority of the company.

An in-depth profile of this company is available to Hoover's Online members at hoovers.com.

459

CUMULUS MEDIA INC.

NASDAQ (GS): CMLS

14 Piedmont Ctr., Ste. 1400
Atlanta, GA 30305
Phone: 404-949-0700
Fax: 404-443-0743
Web: www.cumulus.com

CEO: Lewis W. (Lew) Dickey Jr.
CFO: Joseph Patrick (J.P.) Hannan
HR: —
FYE: December 31
Type: Public

Cumulus Media reigns over an empire of radio stations. The company is the #2 radio station ownership group in the US (behind Clear Channel), with more than 300 owned or operated stations in almost 60 midsized markets throughout the country. In each of its markets, Cumulus has built clusters of stations that realize cost savings through shared administrative and sales operations. In addition to its core mid-market stations, Cumulus, through a partnership with a group of private equity firms, owns about 30 stations in such large markets as Atlanta, Dallas, and San Francisco. Chairman and CEO Lewis Dickey, along with his family, has more than 45% control of Cumulus Media.

	Annual Growth	12/05	12/06	12/07	12/08	12/09
Sales ($ mil.)	(6.0%)	327.8	334.3	328.3	311.5	256.0
Net income ($ mil.)	—	(213.4)	(44.6)	(223.8)	(361.7)	(126.7)
Market value ($ mil.)	(34.5%)	521.4	436.5	337.8	104.6	95.8
Employees	(9.7%)	3,392	3,400	3,300	2,700	2,255

CUNA MUTUAL INSURANCE SOCIETY

5910 Mineral Point Rd.
Madison, WI 53705
Phone: 608-238-5851
Fax: —
Web: www.cunamutual.com

CEO: Jeff Post
CFO: Gerald (Jerry) Pavelich
HR: David Sargent
FYE: December 31
Type: Mutual company

CUNA Mutual knows a thing or two about credit unions, having served them and their members since 1935. The company provides insurance (such as credit insurance and health benefit packages) for the credit unions themselves, as well as consumer products like homeowners and crop insurance that the institutions can offer to their members. Participants in CUNA Mutual's MemberCONNECT program, for instance, can offer auto and homeowners insurance provided jointly by CUNA and its partner Liberty Mutual. CUNA also provides credit unions with software and marketing support for bringing in new members and advisory services for growing their investments. It operates throughout the US and in some foreign markets.

	Annual Growth	12/05	12/06	12/07	12/08	12/09
Assets ($ mil.)	(0.2%)	14,574.0	15,046.2	15,201.9	13,218.0	14,446.0
Net income ($ mil.)	(19.9%)	124.0	186.6	183.6	(149.0)	51.0
Employees	(4.9%)	5,500	5,500	4,500	4,500	4,500

CURAGEN CORPORATION

NASDAQ (GM): CRGN

322 E. Main St.
Branford, CT 06405
Phone: 203-481-1104
Fax: 203-483-2552
Web: www.curagen.com

CEO: Elizabeth Crowley
CFO: —
HR: Nathalie Richard
FYE: December 31
Type: Public

In the war against cancer, CuraGen is looking for the ultimate weapon. The drug company's main focus is on developing an antibody therapy to treat metastatic melanoma and breast cancer. The anticancer compound (called CR011) is a monoclonal antibody that is combined with a cell-killing drug using technology from Seattle Genetics. In addition to CR011, CuraGen has a portfolio of early-stage compounds in the areas of oncology and inflammatory disease, including a preclinical candidate for ovarian cancer and renal cell carcinoma. In 2009 CuraGen was acquired by fellow biotech company Celldex Therapeutics.

	Annual Growth	12/04	12/05	12/06	12/07	*12/08
Sales ($ mil.)	(33.9%)	6.3	2.8	39.6	0.1	1.2
Net income ($ mil.)	—	(90.4)	(73.2)	(59.8)	25.4	24.8
Market value ($ mil.)	(49.7%)	0.0	0.0	0.0	0.0	0.0
Employees	(56.7%)	454	666	255	33	16

*Most recent year available

CURIS, INC.

NASDAQ (GM): CRIS

45 Moulton St.
Cambridge, MA 02138
Phone: 617-503-6500
Fax: 617-503-6501
Web: www.curis.com

CEO: Daniel R. (Dan) Passeri
CFO: Michael P. (Mike) Gray
HR: —
FYE: December 31
Type: Public

Curis's cancer patients and Sega's gamers might one day have an unlikely hero in common: Sonic the Hedgehog. Drug development firm Curis is studying hedgehog signaling pathways (including the sonic hedgehog pathway, named after the Sega mascot) to find treatments for cancer, neurological disease, and cardiovascular conditions. Such signaling pathways regulate tissue growth and repair, and the company is looking for ways to either stimulate them or slow them down as a means of treating disease. Curis is collaborating with Genentech to develop cancer drugs using hedgehog pathways. The company also has internal development programs for cancer treatments using other signaling pathways.

	Annual Growth	12/05	12/06	12/07	12/08	12/09
Sales ($ mil.)	9.4%	6.0	14.9	16.4	8.4	8.6
Net income ($ mil.)	—	(14.9)	(8.8)	(7.0)	(12.1)	(9.8)
Market value ($ mil.)	(2.3%)	269.2	95.3	74.1	56.7	245.8
Employees	(16.5%)	68	51	42	34	33

CURRENT USA, INC.

1025 E. Woodmen Rd.
Colorado Springs, CO 80920
Phone: 719-594-4100
Fax: 719-531-2283
Web: www.currentinc.com

CEO: Tim Arland
CFO: Kirby Heck
HR: Paul Andersen
FYE: December 31
Type: Subsidiary

Current USA is a leading direct marketer of greeting cards and gift wrap, scrapbooking supplies, stationery, and home decorating items. It sells under the brands Times to Cherish (scrapbooking supplies), Colorful Images (personalized address labels and other paper products), Lillian Vernon (gifts and home decor), and, of course, Current. The company also operates an outlet store in Colorado and a fundraising business that lets not-for-profit groups sell its products and share the proceeds. Founded in the 1950s, Current USA was initially run out of the basement of founders Orin and Miriam Loo. The company, which was family owned and operated until 1986, is a subsidiary of printing giant Taylor.

CURTISS-WRIGHT CORPORATION

NYSE: CW

10 Waterview Blvd., 2nd Fl.
Parsippany, NJ 07054
Phone: 973-541-3700
Fax: 973-541-3699
Web: www.curtisswright.com

CEO: Martin R. Benante
CFO: Glenn E. Tynan
HR: —
FYE: December 31
Type: Public

Once an aeronautical pioneer — its engines powered the B-17 bomber and *The Spirit of St. Louis* — Curtiss-Wright makes lower-visibility products these days. Curtiss-Wright comprises three business segments. Flow Control makes special valves for military and commercial applications, including nuclear submarines, nuclear power plants, and refineries. Motion Control makes actuation systems that control wing flaps and bomb-bay doors, and stabilize aiming systems; products include sensors and electronic controls, along with ruggedized computer systems for military ground vehicles. Metal Treatment technologies help prevent premature fatigue and corrosion failures. The US Government generates 42% of revenues.

	Annual Growth	12/05	12/06	12/07	12/08	12/09
Sales ($ mil.)	12.5%	1,130.9	1,282.2	1,592.1	1,830.1	1,809.7
Net income ($ mil.)	6.0%	75.3	80.6	104.3	109.4	95.2
Market value ($ mil.)	3.5%	1,252.0	1,700.5	2,302.3	1,531.3	1,436.4
Employees	6.6%	5,892	6,233	7,500	8,000	7,600

CURVES INTERNATIONAL, INC.

100 Ritchie Rd.
Waco, TX 76712
Phone: 254-399-9285
Fax: 254-399-6623
Web: www.curves.com

CEO: H. Gary Heavin
CFO: Ronnie Glaesmann
HR: Steffanie Huffstatler
FYE: December 31
Type: Private

Curves International is turning heads with its successful women's gym franchise. With more than 4 million members, the company operates one of the nation's fastest-growing franchise systems by targeting busy women with limited time for exercise. It franchises some 10,000 Curves for Women fitness centers worldwide (in the US and more than 70 additional countries). The centers offer 30-minute fitness work-out sessions featuring strength and cardio training. The company was founded in 1992 when husband-and-wife Gary (CEO) and Diane Heavin opened a center in Harlingen, Texas. The company began franchise operations in 1995.

	Annual Growth	12/04	12/05	12/06	12/07	12/08
Sales ($ mil.)	—	—	—	—	—	2,000.0
Employees	—	—	—	—	—	—

CUSHMAN & WAKEFIELD, INC.

1290 Avenue of the Americas
New York, NY 10104
Phone: 212-841-7500
Fax: 212-841-5002
Web: www.cushmanwakefield.com

CEO: Glenn J. Rufrano
CFO: Robert P. Rozek
HR: Charlene Pickus
FYE: December 31
Type: Subsidiary

Cushman & Wakefield heeds the maxim, "Buy land — they aren't making any more." With some 220 offices in about 60 countries, it serves the real estate needs of corporations and financial institutions around the globe. In addition to property management and brokerage services, Cushman & Wakefield also provides research and analysis on markets worldwide, portfolio optimization, supply chain management, and owner and investor services. Its Sonnenbeck-Goldman subsidiary offers real estate investment banking and is part of the company's Global Capital Markets platform. Italy-based investment firm Ifil (part of EXOR) bought the 72% stake of Cushman & Wakefield owned by the Rockefeller Group.

	Annual Growth	12/04	12/05	12/06	12/07	12/08
Est. sales ($ mil.)	—	—	—	—	—	242.7
Employees	—	—	—	—	—	12,035

CUSTOM SENSORS & TECHNOLOGIES, INC.

14501 Princeton Ave.
Moorpark, CA 93021
Phone: 805-552-3599
Fax: 805-552-3577
Web: cst.schneider-electric.com

CEO: Eric Pilaud
CFO: —
HR: —
FYE: December 31
Type: Subsidiary

Custom Sensors & Technologies (CST) is taking a custom approach to the sensor business. The company makes electronic sensors, controls, and actuators used in factory and process automation, aerospace and defense equipment, telecommunications gear, and a wide range of transportation applications. CST's products, which include DC motors, optical encoders, servo systems, and trackballs, help determine exact positions and link the actions of precision mechanisms, such as automotive stability-enhancement systems. CST is a global business unit of Schneider Electric, and is composed of several industry-branded business segments.

CUTERA, INC.

NASDAQ (GS): CUTR

3240 Bayshore Blvd.
Brisbane, CA 94005
Phone: 415-657-5500
Fax: 415-330-2444
Web: www.cutera.com

CEO: Kevin P. Connors
CFO: Ronald J. Santilli
HR: Stacie Rodgers
FYE: December 31
Type: Public

Cutera has a handle on hairy situations and a firm plan for flabby faces. The firm makes lasers for medical and aesthetic use in doctors' offices and spas. Its FDA-approved devices are marketed under the names CoolGlide, Solera, and Xeo and are used for hair removal and treatments to reduce pigmented lesions (age and sun spots), wrinkles, and veins. Its Titan line of products uses deep tissue heating to firm up saggy skin. The company markets its products through a direct sales force and a distributor (PSS World Medical) in the US and relies on a small sales group and distributors in more than 30 other countries.

	Annual Growth	12/05	12/06	12/07	12/08	12/09
Sales ($ mil.)	(8.2%)	75.6	100.7	101.7	83.4	53.7
Net income ($ mil.)	—	13.8	2.1	10.5	(2.9)	(17.7)
Market value ($ mil.)	(24.6%)	355.0	363.6	211.4	119.4	114.6
Employees	(1.2%)	195	221	273	244	186

CVB FINANCIAL CORP.

NASDAQ (GS): CVBF

701 N. Haven Ave., Ste. 350
Ontario, CA 91764
Phone: 909-980-4030
Fax: 909-481-2131
Web: www.cbbank.com

CEO: Christopher D. (Chris) Myers
CFO: Edward J. Biebrich Jr.
HR: David M. Krebs
FYE: December 31
Type: Public

CVB Financial is into the California Vibe, Baby. The holding company's Citizens Business Bank offers community banking services to primarily small and midsized businesses, but also consumers through some 50 locations in nine central and southern California counties. Its deposit products include checking, money market, and savings accounts, as well as CDs. Commercial real estate loans account for about half of the bank's loan portfolio, which is rounded out by business, consumer, and construction loans; residential mortgages; dairy and livestock loans; and municipal lease financing.

	Annual Growth	12/05	12/06	12/07	12/08	12/09
Assets ($ mil.)	5.6%	5,423.0	6,094.3	6,294.0	6,649.7	6,739.8
Net income ($ mil.)	(1.9%)	70.6	71.9	60.6	63.1	65.4
Market value ($ mil.)	(12.5%)	1,570.1	1,397.3	1,099.1	1,264.9	918.4
Employees	3.5%	719	752	766	776	825

CVD EQUIPMENT CORPORATION

OTC: CVV

1860 Smithtown Ave.
Ronkonkoma, NY 11779
Phone: 631-981-7081
Fax: 631-981-7095
Web: www.cvdequipment.com

CEO: Leonard A. Rosenbaum
CFO: Glen R. Charles
HR: —
FYE: December 31
Type: Public

CVD Equipment has expanded well beyond the chemical vapor deposition (CVD) equipment that gave it its name. Its Chemical Vapor Deposition unit makes gear that performs its namesake function, depositing precise layers of chemicals onto semiconductor wafers during chip manufacturing. The Stainless Design Concepts unit makes gas and chemical delivery control systems for handling the ultrapure materials used in chip fabrication. The Equipment Consulting Services group advises semiconductor manufacturers on equipment purchases, and refurbishes used equipment. CVD's Conceptronic unit makes equipment used in chip packaging and board fabrication. Exports account for about 20% of sales.

	Annual Growth	12/05	12/06	12/07	12/08	12/09
Sales ($ mil.)	(1.4%)	11.2	13.4	13.6	18.1	10.6
Net income ($ mil.)	(15.9%)	0.4	0.6	0.8	0.6	0.2
Market value ($ mil.)	9.3%	13.9	27.2	18.9	14.8	19.8
Employees	1.0%	119	108	115	151	124

An in-depth profile of this company is available to Hoover's Online members at hoovers.com.

461

CVR ENERGY, INC.

NYSE: CVI

2277 Plaza Dr., Ste. 500
Sugar Land, TX 77479
Phone: 281-207-3200
Fax: —
Web: www.cvrenergy.com

CEO: John J. (Jack) Lipinski
CFO: Edward A. (Ed) Morgan
HR: Harry S. Nichols Jr.
FYE: December 31
Type: Public

CVR Energy puts its energy into two primary refinery products — petroleum and nitrogen fertilizer. The company operates a 115,000 barrels-per-day-throughput-capacity oil refinery in Coffeyville, Kansas, and a crude oil gathering system in Kansas and Oklahoma. It also has asphalt and refined fuels storage and terminalling plants in Phillipsburg, Kansas. The company is controlled by Coffeyville Acquisitions, a partnership of GS Capital Partners, the private equity arm of Goldman Sachs, and the private equity investment firm Kelso & Company.

	Annual Growth	12/05	12/06	12/07	12/08	12/09
Sales ($ mil.)	21.2%	1,454.3	3,037.6	2,966.9	5,016.1	3,136.3
Net income ($ mil.)	—	(119.2)	191.6	(56.8)	163.9	69.4
Market value ($ mil.)	(47.6%)	—	—	2,153.1	345.3	592.2
Employees	(4.5%)	570	577	428	475	474

⊞ CVS CAREMARK CORPORATION

NYSE: CVS

1 CVS Dr.
Woonsocket, RI 02895
Phone: 401-765-1500
Fax: 401-762-9227
Web: www.cvs.com

CEO: Thomas M. (Tom) Ryan
CFO: David M. (Dave) Denton
HR: Lisa Bisaccia
FYE: December 31
Type: Public

Size matters to CVS Caremark (formerly CVS), the nation's second-largest drugstore chain and its third-largest pharmacy benefits manager. With about 7,090 retail and specialty drugstores under the CVS and Longs Drug banners, it trails archrival Walgreen by about 400 stores. CVS has grown rapidly through a string of acquisitions that included the Eckerd chain, stores from Albertsons, and most recently Longs Drug Stores (2008). In 2007 CVS purchased prescription benefits management (PBM) firm Caremark Rx for about $26.5 billion. Caremark was combined with CVS's PBM and specialty pharmacy unit PharmaCare Management Services to form Caremark Pharmacy Services.

	Annual Growth	12/05	12/06	12/07	12/08	12/09
Sales ($ mil.)	27.8%	37,006.2	43,813.8	76,329.5	87,471.9	98,729.0
Net income ($ mil.)	31.8%	1,224.7	1,368.9	2,637.0	3,212.1	3,696.0
Market value ($ mil.)	5.1%	35,954.6	42,064.9	54,095.1	39,111.8	43,834.1
Employees	18.8%	148,000	176,000	200,000	215,000	295,000

THE CW NETWORK, LLC

3300 Olive Ave.
Burbank, CA 91505
Phone: 818-977-2500
Fax: 818-954-7667
Web: www.cwtv.com

CEO: Dawn Ostroff
CFO: Rich Vokulich
HR: —
FYE: December 31
Type: Joint venture

This company hopes to prove there's room on the small screen for more than just the Big Four. Launched in 2006, The CW Network is a national TV network that reaches almost 95% of the country with prime-time programming aimed mostly at the young-adult audience segment. Its top shows include *America's Next Top Model*, *Gossip Girl*, and *Smallville*. The CW also broadcasts children's programming on Saturday mornings. Local stations owned by Tribune Company and CBS Corporation anchor the network's affiliate group. The CW is a 50-50 joint venture between CBS and Time Warner's Warner Bros. Entertainment unit.

	Annual Growth	12/04	12/05	12/06	12/07	12/08
Est. sales ($ mil.)	—	—	—	—	—	26.5
Employees	—	—	—	—	—	250

CYANOTECH CORPORATION

NASDAQ (CM): CYAN

73-4460 Queen Kaahumanu Hwy., Ste. 102
Kailua-Kona, HI 96740
Phone: 808-326-1353
Fax: 808-329-4533
Web: www.cyanotech.com

CEO: David I. Rosenthal
CFO: Deanna Spooner
HR: —
FYE: March 31
Type: Public

Cyanotech transforms the scum of the earth into health products. The majority of the company's sales come from Spirulina Pacifica, a nutritional supplement made from tiny blue-green vegetable algae and sold as powder, flakes, and tablets. The firm also produces BioAstin, an astaxanthin-based dietary supplement full of antioxidants. Cyanotech produces the microalgae used in its product lines at a 90-acre production facility on the Kona Coast of Hawaii. It sells them primarily to health food and dietary supplement makers. In order to focus on its nutritional supplement business, the company has discontinued some other product lines, including NatuRose, an algae-based pigmentation used to color farm-raised fish.

	Annual Growth	3/05	3/06	3/07	3/08	3/09
Sales ($ mil.)	5.1%	11.4	11.1	9.7	11.4	13.9
Net income ($ mil.)	21.8%	0.5	(0.3)	(7.4)	(1.1)	1.1
Market value ($ mil.)	(19.9%)	25.6	15.1	8.6	8.2	10.6
Employees	0.8%	64	62	64	53	66

CYBERONICS, INC.

NASDAQ (GM): CYBX

Cyberonics Bldg., 100 Cyberonics Blvd.
Houston, TX 77058
Phone: 281-228-7200
Fax: 281-218-9332
Web: www.cyberonics.com

CEO: Daniel J. (Dan) Moore
CFO: Gregory H. (Greg) Browne
HR: —
FYE: April 30
Type: Public

Cyberonics makes the first medical device to be cleared by the FDA for treating epilepsy. The company's VNS Therapy System is a pacemaker-like device implanted under the collarbone with a lead attached to the vagus nerve in the neck. The device delivers intermittent signals to the brain, dubbed vagus nerve stimulation (VNS), to control epileptic seizures. The signals can be programmed by a physician using a computer, and patients can stop or start signals with a hand-held magnet. The system is also approved for use in Australia, Canada, the EU, and some Asian and Latin American countries. The VNS system is being studied as a potential treatment for conditions such as bulimia and Alzheimer's disease.

	Annual Growth	4/05	4/06	4/07	4/08	4/09
Sales ($ mil.)	8.6%	103.4	123.4	131.0	121.2	143.6
Net income ($ mil.)	—	(12.2)	(59.1)	(51.2)	(10.3)	26.7
Market value ($ mil.)	(23.0%)	1,047.1	643.2	607.3	439.0	367.8
Employees	(9.6%)	660	645	547	438	440

⊞ CYBEROPTICS CORPORATION

NASDAQ (GM): CYBE

5900 Golden Hills Dr.
Minneapolis, MN 55416
Phone: 763-542-5000
Fax: 763-542-5100
Web: www.cyberoptics.com

CEO: Kathleen P. (Kitty) Iverson
CFO: Jeffrey A. Bertelsen
HR: —
FYE: December 31
Type: Public

CyberOptics keeps a close eye on the printed circuit board market. The company makes noncontact sensors and integrated systems that use proprietary laser and optics technology to measure the characteristics and placement of electronic components during and after the assembly of printed circuit boards. Product lines include LaserAlign sensors, which ensure accurate component placement, and Process Insight, real-time statistical process control software. CyberOptics also makes the SE 300 Ultra quality control system, which measures solder paste deposition; the machine generates almost one-quarter of sales. Customers outside the US account for about three-quarters of sales.

	Annual Growth	12/05	12/06	12/07	12/08	12/09
Sales ($ mil.)	(10.5%)	42.2	57.1	58.8	45.5	27.1
Net income ($ mil.)	—	7.2	6.4	5.0	(6.7)	(6.8)
Market value ($ mil.)	(16.0%)	92.3	86.8	82.0	35.6	45.9
Employees	(2.1%)	170	179	186	179	156

CYBERSOURCE CORPORATION

NASDAQ (GS): CYBS

1295 Charleston Rd.
Mountain View, CA 94043
Phone: 650-965-6000
Fax: 650-625-9145
Web: www.cybersource.com

CEO: Michael A. Walsh
CFO: Steven D. Pellizzer
HR: Gregory T. (Greg) Pappas
FYE: December 31
Type: Public

When it comes to moving money through cyberspace, CyberSource could be the place to start. The company provides electronic payment systems and software to merchants that accept point-of-sale, phone, and Web-based payments. Its systems enable credit card and electronic check processing, as well as reoccurring bill payments. The company also offers security-based services, such as online and credit card fraud screening, as well as software that assists merchants with tax payment processes and regulatory compliance. CyberSource designs products for small businesses and midsized to large corporations, including those in the airline, media, retail, and telecom industries. Visa agreed to buy the company in 2010.

	Annual Growth	12/05	12/06	12/07	12/08	12/09
Sales ($ mil.)	51.4%	50.5	70.3	117.0	229.0	265.1
Net income ($ mil.)	4.6%	9.2	14.4	2.4	10.7	11.0
Market value ($ mil.)	32.1%	467.5	780.6	1,258.8	849.3	1,424.5
Employees	35.0%	185	247	496	614	614

CYBEX INTERNATIONAL, INC.

NASDAQ (GM): CYBI

10 Trotter Dr.
Medway, MA 02053
Phone: 508-533-4300
Fax: 508-533-5500
Web: www.ecybex.com

CEO: John Aglialoro
CFO: Arthur W. Hicks Jr.
HR: —
FYE: December 31
Type: Public

Cybex International won't get you to cyberspace but it can help you get a second glance at the grocery store. The firm makes premium-priced strength-building gear and cardio fitness equipment sold to commercial markets, including health clubs, hotels, and schools, and to consumers via independent retailers. Cybex's selection of products includes stationary bikes, treadmills, free weights, and single- and multi-station strength-training equipment. It sells its products through about 70 distributors worldwide. The firm's Cybex UK subsidiary provides sales and distribution throughout Europe. Chairman John Aglialoro and his wife, director Joan Carter, own nearly 50% of Cybex through investment company UM Holdings.

	Annual Growth	12/05	12/06	12/07	12/08	12/09
Sales ($ mil.)	1.3%	114.6	126.9	146.5	147.9	120.5
Net income ($ mil.)	—	0.1	20.1	9.8	(9.1)	(2.4)
Market value ($ mil.)	(25.0%)	63.3	102.7	78.1	31.5	20.0
Employees	1.4%	528	547	608	556	558

CYCLE COUNTRY ACCESSORIES CORP.

NYSE Amex: ATC

1701 38th Ave. West
Spencer, IA 51301
Phone: 712-262-4191
Fax: 712-262-0248
Web: www.cyclecountry.com

CEO: Jeffrey M. (Jeff) Tetzlaff
CFO: —
HR: —
FYE: September 30
Type: Public

Cycle Country Accessories turns ATVs into beasts of burden. The company makes all-terrain vehicle (ATV) accessories, such as snowplow blades, lawnmowers, spreaders, sprayers, tillage equipment, winch mounts, and wheel covers for Honda, Yamaha, Kawasaki, Suzuki, Polaris, Arctic Cat, and other ATV models. Cycle Country also makes hubcaps for golf carts, riding lawnmowers, and light-duty trailers. Its products are sold through 20 distributors in the US and more than 30 other countries. The company also makes pull-behind implements and other accessories for riding mowers under the Weekend Warrior brand, and offers contract manufacturing services. Cycle Country makes most of its sales in the US.

	Annual Growth	9/05	9/06	9/07	9/08	9/09
Sales ($ mil.)	(12.0%)	17.2	16.5	14.2	17.5	10.3
Net income ($ mil.)	—	0.8	0.6	0.4	(0.4)	(6.8)
Market value ($ mil.)	(31.9%)	17.0	11.8	9.3	6.2	3.6
Employees	(12.0%)	120	102	104	104	72

CYGNE DESIGNS, INC.

Pink Sheets: CYDS

10866 Washington Blvd.
Culver City, CA 90232
Phone: 800-974-0797
Fax: —

CEO: Samuel J. (Jay) Furrow Jr.
CFO: Nomaan Yousef
HR: —
FYE: January 31
Type: Public

Cygne (pronounced "see-nya") Designs has had its wings clipped in recent years. The firm, whose name is French for "swan," designs and makes private-label women's casual and professional apparel. While it formerly feathered its nest with customers Ann Taylor and Limited Brands, today it almost exclusively caters to Limited Brands' former subsidiary, New York & Company, which sells its apparel under its own label, as well as JCPenney, Kohl's, Target, and AEO. It also makes Hippie, Hint Jeans, and Voyou brands. Hubert Guez, personally and through his partnership with Diversified Apparel Resources and the Guez Living Trust, owns some 77% of the its stock. Cygne's former chairman Bernard Manuel owns nearly 19%.

	Annual Growth	1/04	1/05	1/06	1/07	*1/08
Sales ($ mil.)	37.1%	27.1	29.0	58.5	118.8	95.8
Net income ($ mil.)	—	0.4	0.3	(5.4)	(0.2)	(63.9)
Employees	(50.8%)	1,191	812	719	700	70

*Most recent year available

CYIOS CORPORATION

OTC: CYIO

1300 Pennsylvania Ave. NW, Ste. 700
Washington, DC 20004
Phone: 202-204-3006
Fax: 202-315-3458
Web: www.cyios.com

CEO: Timothy W. (Tim) Carnahan
CFO: Jodie Buckler
HR: Susan Schaffer
FYE: December 31
Type: Public

CYIOS is a holding company for two operating subsidiaries. The first, which has the same name as the parent company and is referred to as CYIOS DC, is a provider of information technology (IT) systems integration services for agencies within the Department of Defense. The second subsidiary, CKO, offers an online office management software product called XO Office software. The company had previously provided telecommunications services as WorldTeq, but has ceased those operations. CEO Tim Carnahan owns 67% of the company.

	Annual Growth	12/05	12/06	12/07	12/08	12/09
Sales ($ mil.)	(4.7%)	2.3	1.7	2.2	1.5	1.9
Net income ($ mil.)	—	(0.3)	(0.9)	0.3	0.1	0.0
Market value ($ mil.)	(40.5%)	10.0	3.7	6.3	1.1	1.2
Employees	(6.2%)	22	22	17	12	17

CYMER, INC.

NASDAQ (GS): CYMI

17075 Thornmint Ct.
San Diego, CA 92127
Phone: 858-385-7300
Fax: 858-385-7100
Web: www.cymer.com

CEO: Robert P. (Bob) Akins
CFO: Paul B. Bowman
HR: —
FYE: December 31
Type: Public

Simon says, "Cymer makes lasers." The company is the top manufacturer of excimer lasers, light sources used by chip makers to pattern advanced semiconductors. Its products enable semiconductor manufacturers to produce smaller, faster microchips. Cymer also supplies deep-ultraviolet light sources to lithography tool manufacturers ASML, Canon, and Nikon, who integrate the light source into their wafer steppers and scanners, which they supply to chip makers. Cymer has installed more than 3,300 light sources around the world in wafer fabrication facilities (fabs) run by IBM Microelectronics, Intel, Samsung Electronics, and Texas Instruments, among others. The company gets almost two-thirds of its sales in Asia.

	Annual Growth	12/05	12/06	12/07	12/08	12/09
Sales ($ mil.)	(5.4%)	383.6	543.9	521.7	459.0	307.7
Net income ($ mil.)	(34.3%)	46.6	95.6	88.4	36.5	8.7
Market value ($ mil.)	2.0%	1,068.4	1,322.3	1,171.3	659.2	1,154.7
Employees	(1.8%)	879	975	1,022	994	816

CYNOSURE, INC.

NASDAQ (GM): CYNO

5 Carlisle Rd.
Westford, MA 01886
Phone: 978-256-4200
Fax: 978-256-6556
Web: www.cynosurelaser.com

CEO: Michael R. Davin
CFO: Timothy W. Baker
HR: —
FYE: December 31
Type: Public

Beauty may be skin deep, but that's just deep enough for Cynosure to help. The company makes laser and pulsed-light devices used to perform non-invasive aesthetic procedures to remove hair, treat varicose veins, remove tattoos, and reduce the appearance of birthmarks, freckles, and cellulite. Folks who want to go deeper can opt for its minimally invasive procedures to remove unwanted fat using lasers. Cynosure's systems are marketed under such names as Apogee, Cynergy, and Smartlipo. Its customers include doctors and health spas served by distributors in more than 60 countries.

	Annual Growth	12/05	12/06	12/07	12/08	12/09
Sales ($ mil.)	6.6%	56.3	78.4	124.3	139.7	72.8
Net income ($ mil.)	—	4.2	(0.6)	14.5	10.2	(22.8)
Market value ($ mil.)	(13.9%)	265.1	201.2	336.3	116.0	146.0
Employees	8.5%	184	213	295	288	255

CYPRESS BIOSCIENCE, INC.

NASDAQ (GM): CYPB

4350 Executive Dr., Ste. 325
San Diego, CA 92121
Phone: 858-452-2323
Fax: 858-452-1222
Web: www.cypressbio.com

CEO: Jay D. Kranzler
CFO: Sabrina Martucci Johnson
HR: —
FYE: December 31
Type: Public

Cypress Bioscience explores the swampy waters of functional somatic syndromes, a group of chronic symptom-based disorders that are, on the whole, poorly understood. The biotech company's primary target is fibromylagia, a condition marked by pain, stiffness, and fatigue that tends to affect adult women. Cypress Bioscience licensed a drug called milnacipran (branded as Savella) from French drugmaker Pierre Fabre as a potential therapy for fibromyalgia. Developed with partner Forest Laboratories, Savella was approved by the FDA in 2009. Cypress Bioscience has also partnered with Collegium Pharmaceutical to develop reformulations and analogs of milnacipran.

	Annual Growth	12/05	12/06	12/07	12/08	12/09
Sales ($ mil.)	34.3%	8.4	4.3	13.9	17.2	27.3
Net income ($ mil.)	—	(8.6)	(8.2)	3.5	(18.2)	(28.3)
Market value ($ mil.)	(0.0%)	221.8	297.4	423.3	262.5	221.4
Employees	77.8%	15	15	23	145	150

CYPRESS SEMICONDUCTOR CORPORATION

NYSE: CY

198 Champion Ct.
San Jose, CA 95134
Phone: 408-943-2600
Fax: 408-943-4730
Web: www.cypress.com

CEO: T. J. Rodgers
CFO: Brad W. Buss
HR: —
FYE: December 31
Type: Public

In Silicon Valley, it's perfectly logical for a giant Cypress to put its roots down in pure silicon. Cypress Semiconductor makes more than 400 types of integrated circuits; its nonmemory products include programmable logic devices, clock and timing chips, Universal Serial Bus (USB) microcontrollers, and specialty products for the computer and data communications markets. It also makes memory chips, especially static random-access memories (SRAMs). Customers include computer, networking, and telecommunications equipment makers such as Cisco Systems, EMC, Logitech, Motorola, and Sony. Customers outside the US account for more than 80% of sales.

	Annual Growth	12/05	12/06	12/07	12/08	12/09
Sales ($ mil.)	(6.8%)	886.4	1,091.6	1,596.4	765.7	667.8
Net income ($ mil.)	—	(92.2)	39.5	394.3	(430.3)	(150.4)
Market value ($ mil.)	46.9%	371.7	440.1	939.9	732.8	1,731.3
Employees	(8.3%)	5,100	5,800	7,900	4,100	3,600

CYPRESS SHARPRIDGE INVESTMENTS, INC.

NYSE: CYS

65 E. 55th St.
New York, NY 10022
Phone: 212-705-0160
Fax: 212-705-0199
Web: www.cypresssharpridge.com

CEO: Kevin E. Grant
CFO: Frances R. Spark
HR: —
FYE: December 31
Type: Public

Cypress Sharpridge Investments is a real estate investment trust (REIT) created to invest in Fannie Mae-, Freddie Mac-, and Ginnie Mae-guaranteed residential mortgage-backed securities (RMBS), primarily collateralized by adjustable-rate mortgage loans. Investment funds are secured through major commercial banks, brokerage firms, specialty investors, and other asset management companies. It holds a portfolio valued at some $690 million. Founded in 2006, the REIT is externally managed by Cypress Sharpridge Advisors, a joint venture between private equity firm The Cypress Group and Sharpridge Capital Management.

	Annual Growth	12/05	12/06	12/07	12/08	12/09
Sales ($ mil.)	16.1%	—	48.1	88.6	(7.4)	75.3
Net income ($ mil.)	299.6%	—	1.0	(29.7)	(39.2)	63.8
Market value ($ mil.)	—	—	—	—	—	253.6
Employees	12.8%	—	11	12	14	—

CYTEC INDUSTRIES INC.

NYSE: CYT

5 Garret Mountain Plaza
West Paterson, NJ 07424
Phone: 973-357-3100
Fax: 973-357-3065
Web: www.cytec.com

CEO: Shane D. Fleming
CFO: David M. Drillock
HR: Marilyn R. Charles
FYE: December 31
Type: Public

Cytec Industries covers its business bases. The company produces the building-block chemicals from which it makes engineered materials (composites and adhesives for the aerospace industry), specialty chemicals (resins and coatings for metal, plastic, and wood), and additives used in industrial processes. Cytec also sells its building-block chemicals (acrylonitrile, melamine, and sulfuric acid) to third parties. Cytec Engineered Materials includes aerospace products such as advanced composites and structural adhesives. The Specialty Chemicals unit's products are used in mining, drilling, and the manufacture of pharmaceuticals. The unit combines Cytec's Performance Chemicals and Surface Specialties segments.

	Annual Growth	12/05	12/06	12/07	12/08	12/09
Sales ($ mil.)	(1.2%)	2,925.7	3,329.5	3,503.8	3,639.9	2,789.5
Net income ($ mil.)	—	59.1	196.1	206.5	(198.8)	(2.5)
Market value ($ mil.)	(6.5%)	2,332.1	2,766.8	3,015.1	1,039.0	1,783.2
Employees	(5.6%)	7,300	6,700	6,800	6,700	5,800

CYTOKINETICS, INCORPORATED

NASDAQ (GM): CYTK

280 E. Grand Ave.
South San Francisco, CA 94080
Phone: 650-624-3000
Fax: 650-624-3010
Web: www.cytokinetics.com

CEO: Robert I. Blum
CFO: Sharon A. Barbari
HR: David W. Cragg
FYE: December 31
Type: Public

Cytokinetics studies the cytoskeleton to get to the heart of the problem. The biopharmaceutical firm's development pipeline includes a lead drug candidate — in oral and intravenous formulations — designed for the treatment of heart failure based on a cytoskeletal protein in the heart muscle. It is being developed in collaboration with Amgen. Several other candidates are targeting multiple types of cancer; early clinical trials of these anti-cancer candidates were supported by GlaxoSmithKline and the National Cancer Institute. Cytokinetics is responsible for additional clinical development but may seek future strategic alliances to help advance this set of drugs into later-stage trials.

	Annual Growth	12/05	12/06	12/07	12/08	12/09
Sales ($ mil.)	74.0%	8.9	3.1	13.6	12.4	81.5
Net income ($ mil.)	—	(42.3)	(57.1)	(48.9)	(56.4)	24.5
Market value ($ mil.)	(18.3%)	421.1	481.6	304.6	183.5	187.4
Employees	(7.3%)	150	148	161	110	111

CYTOMEDIX, INC.

NYSE Amex: GTF

416 Hungerford Dr., Ste. 330
Rockville, MD 20850
Phone: 240-499-2680
Fax: 240-499-2690
Web: www.cytomedix.com

CEO: Martin P. Rosendale
CFO: Andrew Maslan
HR: —
FYE: December 31
Type: Public

Here's a concept — using the body's own faculties to heal wounds. Cytomedix has developed and markets an autologous platelet therapy, which uses a patient's own blood plasma to promote healing. Its AutoloGel System includes a centrifuge and blood draw kit. The centrifuge is used to separate key blood components, including platelets and growth factors, which are then combined with reagents to make a topical gel. When applied to a wound, the gel spurs the body's own healing process. AutoloGel has received FDA approval to treat chronic exuding wounds such as diabetic ulcers. Other products in Cytomedix' pipeline include an anti-inflammatory peptide that may help treat such diseases as rheumatoid arthritis.

	Annual Growth	12/05	12/06	12/07	12/08	12/09
Sales ($ mil.)	8.8%	1.5	1.9	1.9	2.1	2.1
Net income ($ mil.)	—	(6.5)	(2.3)	(5.0)	(7.7)	(3.4)
Market value ($ mil.)	(35.4%)	88.3	38.7	66.9	7.1	15.4
Employees	11.5%	11	12	12	15	17

CYTORI THERAPEUTICS, INC.

NASDAQ (GM): CYTX

3020 Callan Rd.
San Diego, CA 92121
Phone: 858-458-0900
Fax: 858-458-0994
Web: www.cytoritx.com

CEO: Christopher J. Calhoun
CFO: Mark E. Saad
HR: —
FYE: December 31
Type: Public

Attention lovers of liposuction: Cytori Therapeutics needs your fat. The firm (formerly known as MacroPore Biosurgery) is developing therapies using regenerative adult stem cells derived from adipose, otherwise known as fat tissue. Cytori's Celution is an adipose tissue extraction system that is marketed in Europe and Asia for reconstructive surgery purposes. The company is developing therapies based on the Celution system intended to treat cardiovascular disease, spine and orthopedic injuries, pelvic health conditions, and gastrointestinal disorders. Cytori has a joint venture with Olympus Corporation to develop future products based on its Celution system.

	Annual Growth	12/05	12/06	12/07	12/08	12/09
Sales ($ mil.)	27.3%	5.6	7.9	6.0	4.5	14.7
Net income ($ mil.)	—	(26.5)	(25.4)	(28.7)	(30.0)	(23.2)
Market value ($ mil.)	(7.4%)	374.1	294.8	272.7	162.7	275.0
Employees	(9.2%)	137	133	143	126	93

CYTRX CORPORATION

NASDAQ (CM): CYTR

11726 San Vicente Blvd., Ste. 650
Los Angeles, CA 90049
Phone: 310-826-5648
Fax: 310-826-6139
Web: www.cytrx.com

CEO: Steven A. Kriegsman
CFO: John Y. Caloz
HR: —
FYE: December 31
Type: Public

With its molecular chaperones, CytRx keeps an eye on the suspicious activities of proteins. The drug developer is working on small molecule therapies using its chaperone amplification technology, a method of boosting a certain corrective response in cells to protein misfires that cause disease. Its lead drug candidate is arimoclomol, a potential treatment for the neurodegenerative disorder Lou Gehrig's disease; it is also developing the compound as a treatment for stroke. Another candidate, iroxanadine, is undergoing clinical trials for the treatment of diabetic ulcers. In 2008 CytRx spun off its research programs related to RNA interference (RNAi) into publicly traded biotech firm RXi Pharmaceuticals.

	Annual Growth	12/05	12/06	12/07	12/08	12/09
Sales ($ mil.)	162.5%	0.2	2.1	7.5	6.3	9.5
Net income ($ mil.)	—	(15.1)	(16.8)	(21.9)	(27.0)	(4.8)
Market value ($ mil.)	2.1%	112.4	208.4	309.9	32.7	122.2
Employees	(14.4%)	28	25	27	35	15

CYVEILLANCE, INC.

CYVEILLANCE, INC.

1555 Wilson Blvd., Ste. 406
Arlington, VA 22209
Phone: 703-351-1000
Fax: 703-312-0536
Web: www.cyveillance.com

CEO: Panos Anastassiadis
CFO: Richard D. Rose
HR: —
FYE: December 31
Type: Subsidiary

Cyveillance helps clients keep a watchful eye for digital intruders. The company provides corporate customers with information technology services that monitor Internet traffic for security issues such as identity theft, fraud, and brand abuse. Its subscription-based services are also used to guard against malware and viruses by providing dynamically updated lists of malicious websites. Cyveillance's customers come from a wide variety of industries such as financial services, manufacturing, telecommunications, health care, pharmaceuticals, transportation, and technology. Cyveillance was founded in 1997. The company was acquired in 2009 by UK-based technical and engineering services provider QinetiQ.

	Annual Growth	12/04	12/05	12/06	12/07	12/08
Est. sales ($ mil.)	—	—	—	—	—	8.8
Employees	—	—	—	—	—	125

DAC TECHNOLOGIES GROUP INTERNATIONAL, INC.

OTC: DAAT

12120 Colonial Glenn Rd., Ste. 6200
Little Rock, AR 72210
Phone: 501-661-9100
Fax: 501-661-9108
Web: www.dactec.com

CEO: David A. Collins
CFO: Robert C. Goodwin
HR: —
FYE: December 31
Type: Public

This company's aim is to give gun owners a clean shot. DAC Technologies Group International manufactures more than 50 different GunMaster brand gun cleaning kits, as well as gun maintenance and safety products, such as trigger locks and gun safes. Its gun-related business rings up more than two-thirds of DAC's sales. The company also makes game processing equipment, aluminum camping tables and other items for the hunting and camping markets, as well as a line of household cleaning dusters. DAC also has a licensing agreement with Olin Corp. to market some of its gun cleaning items under the Winchester brand name for sale at Wal-Mart. (The retail giant accounts for about 55% of DAC's sales.)

	Annual Growth	12/05	12/06	12/07	12/08	12/09
Sales ($ mil.)	2.3%	13.4	15.5	14.8	17.0	14.7
Net income ($ mil.)	(15.9%)	1.2	0.8	0.3	0.4	0.6
Market value ($ mil.)	(24.8%)	13.6	13.2	4.9	2.0	4.3
Employees	4.7%	10	11	11	12	12

DADA ENTERTAINMENT, LLC

DADA ENTERTAINMENT, LLC

14 Penn Plaza, Ste. 501
New York, NY 10122
Phone: 646-217-0458
Fax: —
Web: www.dada-ent.com

CEO: Massimiliano (Max) Pellegrini
CFO: Sheldra Khahaifa
HR: Janet Slavinsky
FYE: December 31
Type: Joint venture

Dada Entertainment is music to the ears of anyone who wants music (and other things) on the go. Available on a subscription basis to mobile phone and PC users, the company provides Web-based music content such as ringtones, audio and video clips, and full-length songs (for MP3s), as well as social networking services, wallpapers, and mobile games. The company serves users in the US and Canada, and its services are compatible with most US mobile phone operators, including AT&T, Sprint, T-Mobile, Alltel, and others. Formed in 2007, the company is a 50/50 joint venture between Dada USA, the US division of Italian-based DADA S.p.A., and Sony Music Entertainment.

	Annual Growth	12/04	12/05	12/06	12/07	12/08
Est. sales ($ mil.)	—	—	—	—	—	0.6
Employees	—	—	—	—	—	35

An in-depth profile of this company is available to Hoover's Online members at hoovers.com.

DAHL'S FOODS, INC.

4343 Merle Hay Rd.
Des Moines, IA 50310
Phone: 515-278-1657
Fax: 515-278-0012
Web: www.dahlsfoods.com

CEO: David Sinnwell
CFO: —
HR: Debra Jones
FYE: December 31
Type: Private

Dahl's Foods is a dominant force in the Iowa grocery market. It operates about 10 Dahl's Foods supermarkets in the Des Moines metropolitan area. The company prides itself on offering low prices and good service. All Dahl's locations have in-store pharmacies and cafés while some operate convenience stores, gas stations, and coffee shops. The regional grocery chain also added in-store Quick Care Clinics to several of its locations in partnership with Mercy Medical Center. Founded by W.T. Dahl in 1931, the grocery company was sold to its employees (organized under the name Foods Inc.) in 1970.

DAILY EXPRESS, INC.

1072 Harrisburg Pike
Carlisle, PA 17013
Phone: 717-243-5757
Fax: 717-240-2193
Web: www.dailyexp.com

CEO: Todd R. Long
CFO: Harry C. Smith
HR: Erik Thompson
FYE: December 31
Type: Private

Daily Express moves freight not seen every day. The trucking company carries mostly oversized loads (construction machinery, industrial equipment, even gigantic telescope mirrors) on various-sized trailers. Delivery of wind turbine components, a Daily Express specialty, has given the company a boost — high energy prices have caused headaches for most freight companies but have ramped up demand for alternative energy production, giving Daily Express extra business. The company's fleet consists of more than 700 trailers. It operates throughout the US from a network of about 10 terminals, primarily east of the Mississippi. An affiliate, Plant Site Logistics, provides transportation management services.

	Annual Growth	12/04	12/05	12/06	12/07	12/08
Est. sales ($ mil.)	—	—	—	—	—	99.5
Employees	—	—	—	—	—	200

DAILY JOURNAL CORPORATION

NASDAQ (GM): DJCO

915 E. 1st St.
Los Angeles, CA 90012
Phone: 213-229-5300
Fax: 213-229-5481
Web: www.dailyjournal.com

CEO: Gerald L. Salzman
CFO: Gerald L. Salzman
HR: —
FYE: September 30
Type: Public

Legal matters dominate the news in these papers. Daily Journal Corporation is a leading newspaper publisher with more than a dozen papers serving markets primarily in California. Its flagship papers include the *Los Angeles Daily Journal* and the *San Francisco Daily Journal*, which offer in-depth coverage of legal cases and court matters in addition to general interest news. The company also publishes legal affairs magazine *California Lawyer*, operates subscription-based access to court case and real estate information, and publishes a legal directory for California. Chairman Charles Munger (who also serves as vice chairman of Berkshire Hathaway) and Ira Marshall control 40% of Daily Journal Corporation.

	Annual Growth	9/05	9/06	9/07	9/08	9/09
Sales ($ mil.)	4.2%	34.3	32.4	35.1	40.6	40.4
Net income ($ mil.)	16.8%	4.3	2.4	5.3	7.1	8.0
Market value ($ mil.)	7.2%	63.6	56.0	58.1	57.7	83.9
Employees	(4.9%)	275	275	255	240	225

DAILY NEWS, L.P.

450 W. 33rd St.
New York, NY 10001
Phone: 212-210-2100
Fax: 212-643-7831
Web: www.nydailynews.com

CEO: Marc Z. Kramer
CFO: Tom Peck
HR: Jeff Zomper
FYE: December 31
Type: Private

This daily news might not always be fit to print, but it at least keeps New Yorkers entertained. Daily News, L.P., publishes New York City's *Daily News*, the big city tabloid that goes toe-to-toe with the *New York Post* (owned by Rupert Murdoch's News Corporation) by penning over-the-top headlines and sensational stories. The paper, founded in 1919, is distributed primarily in the Five Boroughs and boasts a circulation of more than 540,000. It also distributes news and features online through its website. The *Daily News* is owned by real estate magnate Mortimer Zuckerman, who also owns news magazine *U.S. News & World Report*.

DAIMLER BUSES NORTH AMERICA INC.

165 Base Rd.
Oriskany, NY 13424
Phone: 315-223-5100
Fax: 315-768-6520
Web: www.dcbusna.com

CEO: Andreas Strecker
CFO: Harry Rendel
HR: —
FYE: December 31
Type: Subsidiary

Daimler Buses North America won't throw you under the bus. The company (formerly Orion Bus), a part of Daimler AG, makes vehicles that range from 30 to 40 feet in length and that can operate on natural gas as well as conventional fuels. The company is also developing a diesel-electric hybrid version of its Orion VII model that will reportedly be ready in 2010. Daimler Buses North America, which has a manufacturing facility in Mississauga, Ontario, and another in Oriskany, New York, sells its vehicles throughout the US and Canada.

DAIMLER FINANCIAL SERVICES AMERICAS, LLC

36455 Corporate Dr.
Farmington Hills, MI 48331
Phone: 248-991-6700
Fax: 248-957-2997
Web: www.daimlerfinancialservices.com/na

CEO: Franz-Josef Reiner
CFO: Brian Stevens
HR: Jeremy Gump
FYE: December 31
Type: Subsidiary

Daimler Financial Services Americas provides financing for dealers and buyers of Daimler-brand cars and trucks in the US, Canada, Argentina, Brazil, and Mexico. Doing business as Mercedes-Benz Financial and Daimler Truck Financial, the company finances dealer inventories, consumer loans and leases, and commercial and municipal truck fleets. Its loan portfolio weighs in at more than $30 billion. Through an agreement with Visa, Daimler Financial Services Americas offers Mercedes Benz-branded credit cards that offer purchase rewards that customers can use toward parts, service, accessories, monthly payments, and lease-end fees. The company is a subsidiary of Daimler Financial Services AG.

DAIMLER TRUCKS NORTH AMERICA LLC

4747 N. Channel Ave.
Portland, OR 97217
Phone: 503-745-8000
Fax: 503-745-8921
Web: www.daimler-trucksnorthamerica.com

CEO: Martin Daum
CFO: Juergen Kritschgau
HR: —
FYE: December 31
Type: Subsidiary

What moves you? For Daimler Trucks North America (DTNA), it's a rhetorical question. The subsidiary of German automaker Daimler AG is North America's #1 heavy-duty truck maker for long hauls. In addition to the familiar Freightliner brand, DTNA makes commercial vehicles under the Western Star nameplate, and manufactures school buses under the Thomas Built brand. Operations include Freightliner Custom Chassis, which makes chassis for motor homes, delivery vans, and buses, and Detroit Diesel, a builder of medium- and heavy-duty diesel engines and components. DTNA offers customers access to capital as well as roadway conveniences, too, through partnerships with Daimler Truck Financial and TravelCenters of America.

⊞ DAIRY FARMERS OF AMERICA, INC.

10220 N. Ambassador Dr.
Kansas City, MO 64153
Phone: 816-801-6455
Fax: 816-801-6456
Web: www.dfamilk.com

CEO: Richard P. (Rick) Smith
CFO: David Meyer
HR: Annette Regan
FYE: December 31
Type: Cooperative

The members of Dairy Farmers of America (DFA) are partners in cream. DFA is one of the world's largest dairy cooperatives, with some 17,000 member/farmers nationwide. Some 1.8 million cows belonging to member/farmers produce about 62 billion pounds of milk a year, which DFA markets. Along with fresh and shelf-stable fluid milk, the co-op produces cheese, butter, dried whey, dried milk powder, and other dairy products for industrial, wholesale, and retail customers worldwide. It also offers contract manufacturing services. The co-op has some 30 manufacturing sites located throughout the country. DFA, which netted more than $8 billion in sales in 2009, is a major supplier to US dairy powerhouse, Dean Foods.

	Annual Growth	12/04	12/05	12/06	12/07	12/08
Sales ($ mil.)	6.9%	8,953.5	8,908.6	7,898.8	11,100.0	11,700.0
Net income ($ mil.)	—	—	—	—	—	61.7
Employees	0.0%	—	—	4,000	4,000	4,000

DAIWA CORPORATION

12851 Midway Place
Cerritos, CA 90703
Phone: 562-802-9589
Fax: 562-404-6212
Web: www.daiwa.com

CEO: Taka Inagaki
CFO: Gene Taniguchi
HR: —
FYE: March 31
Type: Subsidiary

Daiwa Corporation hopes you'd rather be fishing. The company is the US distribution and customer support subsidiary of Tokyo-based fishing tackle and sportswear maker Daiwa Seiko. Its products include rods, reels, line, and lures. Daiwa also makes and sells such goods as cases, clothing, equipment racks, luggage, and other accessories. It sells its tackle through boating and sporting goods retailers, including Boater's World and Academy Sports & Outdoors, in the US, Canada, and Central and South America. The company also provides equipment maintenance and repair services.

DAK AMERICAS LLC

5925 Carnegie Blvd., Ste. 500
Charlotte, NC 28209
Phone: 704-940-7500
Fax: 704-940-7501
Web: www.dakamericas.com

CEO: Hector Camberos
CFO: Jorge P. Young
HR: —
FYE: December 31
Type: Subsidiary

DAK Americas manufactures products that are high in fiber and contain resins, but it has nothing to do with your breakfast cereal. The company's three units are DAK Resins, DAK Fibers, and DAK Monomers. Its primary products are PET resins, polyester staple fibers, and terephthalic acid (TPA) monomers, all used in the production of various textiles to make apparel, home furnishings, and items such as tea bags and diapers. DAK Americas maintains manufacturing facilities in the Carolinas in the US as well as in Mexico. Alpek, a subsidiary of Mexican industrial giant Alfa, S.A. de C.V., owns DAK Americas.

DAKOTA BEEF LLC

507 E. Hwy. 34
Howard, SD 57349
Phone: 605-772-5339
Fax: 605-772-5378
Web: www.dakotabeefcompany.com

CEO: Daniel J. Feinberg
CFO: Trish Peterson
HR: —
FYE: December 31
Type: Private

You might say this company has a steak in the organic meat business. Dakota Beef is a leading supplier of organic beef and beef products that are free of antibiotics and growth hormones. It sources its beef from certified organic producers and operates a 33,000-sq.-ft., certified-organic processing plant capable of handling more than 100 head of cattle each day. The company supplies cuts of meat and ground beef to food wholesalers, retailers, and manufacturers including Costco and Whole Foods Market. It also sells beef online to individual consumers. Dakota Beef was founded in 2003.

	Annual Growth	12/04	12/05	12/06	12/07	12/08
Est. sales ($ mil.)	—	—	—	—	—	19.9
Employees	—	—	—	—	—	65

DAKOTA GROWERS PASTA COMPANY, INC.

1 Pasta Ave.
Carrington, ND 58421
Phone: 701-652-2855
Fax: 701-652-3552
Web: www.dakotagrowers.com

CEO: Timothy J. Dodd
CFO: Edward O. Irion
HR: —
FYE: July 31
Type: Subsidiary

Dakota Growers Pasta Company is trying to put an *al dente* in the noodle market. It is a supplier of branded and private-label pasta products and flours to retail, foodservice, and food ingredient companies in North America. Its mills have an annual capacity to grind more than 12 million bushes of grain; its production facilities can produce 500 million pound of pasta (and makes more than 100 different shapes). Brand names include Dreamfields, Pasta Growers, Pasta Sanita, Primo Piatto, and Zia Briosa. Under license, the company distributes Ronzoni, Prince, Creamette, and Mrs. Weiss pasta brands to the foodservice sector. In 2010 Dakota Growers was acquired by Canada-based grain giant Viterra.

DAKOTA, MINNESOTA & EASTERN RAILROAD CORPORATION

140 N. Phillips Ave.
Sioux Falls, SD 57104
Phone: 605-782-1200
Fax: 605-782-1299
Web: www.dmerail.com

CEO: J. Edward (Ed) Terbell
CFO: Kurt V. Feaster
HR: Traci Lund
FYE: December 31
Type: Subsidiary

Dakota, Minnesota & Eastern Railroad (DM&E), one of the largest regional railroads in the US, operates about 1,100 miles of track in South Dakota, Minnesota, Iowa, Wyoming, and Nebraska. Sister company Iowa, Chicago & Eastern Railroad (IC&E), with 1,400 miles of line in Illinois, Iowa, Minnesota, Missouri, and Wisconsin, was consolidated into the DM&E in 2008. The railroad transports a variety of goods, including coal, grain products (including ethanol), and steel. Rival Canadian Pacific Railway acquired DM&E and IC&E in 2007 for $1.5 billion. (After review, the US Surface Transportation Board approved the deal in late 2008.)

	Annual Growth	12/04	12/05	12/06	12/07	12/08
Est. sales ($ mil.)	—	—	—	—	—	102.5
Employees	—	—	—	—	—	975

⊞ DAKTRONICS, INC.

NASDAQ (GS): DAKT

201 Daktronics Dr.
Brookings, SD 57006
Phone: 605-692-0200
Fax: 605-697-4700
Web: www.daktronics.com

CEO: James B. (Jim) Morgan
CFO: William R. (Bill) Retterath
HR: Carla S. Gatzke
FYE: April 30
Type: Public

Daktronics always knows the score. The company designs and manufactures electronic display systems. Its products include scoreboards, game timers, shot clocks, and animation displays for sports facilities; advertising and information displays for businesses; and electronic messaging displays used by transportation departments for motorist alerts. Other applications include airport information, securities trading, and outdoor advertising signs. Daktronics converted many of its products to light-emitting diode (LED) technology, which is brighter than other light sources and uses less electricity. The company makes most of its sales in the US.

	Annual Growth	4/05	4/06	4/07	4/08	4/09
Sales ($ mil.)	26.1%	230.3	309.4	433.2	499.7	581.9
Net income ($ mil.)	13.9%	15.7	21.0	24.4	26.2	26.4
Market value ($ mil.)	(2.9%)	418.0	804.0	935.4	607.3	371.2
Employees	21.1%	1,630	2,100	3,200	3,400	3,500

DALE JARRETT RACING ADVENTURE, INC.

OTC: DJRT

120A N. Main Ave.
Newton, NC 28658
Phone: 828-466-8837
Fax: 828-465-5088
Web: www.racingadventure.com

CEO: Timothy B. (Tim) Shannon
CFO: Timothy B. (Tim) Shannon
HR: —
FYE: December 31
Type: Public

Gentlemen, start your engines! Dale Jarrett Racing Adventure brings the thrills (but hopefully not the spills) of NASCAR racing to doctors, lawyers, Indian chiefs — and even average joes, assuming they have enough "fuel" to foot the bill. The company gives racing fans the opportunity to race on a major track. Packages range from riding three laps in the passenger seat with a professional driver to 60 laps of actual driving at speeds of up to 165 mph (after instruction). Events are held at racetracks around the country (including Talladega Superspeedway and Atlanta Motor Speedway). The Dale Jarrett Racing Adventure was founded in 1998 when CEO Tim Shannon approached NASCAR driver Dale Jarrett with the concept.

	Annual Growth	12/05	12/06	12/07	12/08	12/09
Sales ($ mil.)	11.7%	1.8	2.1	2.7	2.7	2.8
Net income ($ mil.)	—	(0.3)	0.1	(0.9)	(0.3)	(0.1)
Market value ($ mil.)	(36.1%)	7.4	4.8	10.0	1.1	1.2
Employees	0.0%	7	7	7	7	7

DALLAS COUNTY HOSPITAL DISTRICT

5201 Harry Hines Blvd.
Dallas, TX 75235
Phone: 214-590-8000
Fax: 214-590-8096
Web: www.parklandhospital.com

CEO: Ron J. Anderson
CFO: John F. Dragovits
HR: Candy Knowles
FYE: October 1
Type: Not-for-profit

Dallas County Hospital District may do business as Parkland Health and Hospital System (PHHS), but many people know it as Parkland Memorial Hospital, the hospital where JFK died. Parkland Memorial sits at the heart of the health system and is Dallas' only public hospital. PHHS manages a network of community clinics, as well as Parkland Community Health Plan, a regional HMO for Medicaid and CHIP (Children's Health Insurance Program) members. The system also offers HEALTHplus, a medical assistance program for uninsured Dallas County residents. Parkland Memorial Hospital has more than 700 beds and is the primary teaching institution of The University of Texas Southwestern Medical Center.

	Annual Growth	10/04	10/05	10/06	10/07	10/08
Est. sales ($ mil.)	—	—	—	—	—	34.2
Employees	—	—	—	—	—	6,200

DALLAS COWBOYS FOOTBALL CLUB, LTD.

1 Cowboys Pkwy.
Irving, TX 75063
Phone: 972-556-9900
Fax: 972-556-9304
Web: www.dallascowboys.com

CEO: Jerral W. (Jerry) Jones
CFO: —
HR: —
FYE: February 28
Type: Private

Proclaiming itself "America's Team," this football franchise certainly has the loyalty of many Texans. Dallas Cowboys Football Club operates the famed Dallas Cowboys professional football franchise, one of the most popular teams in the National Football League and the winner of five Super Bowl titles (a mark it shares with the San Francisco 49ers). The team was founded in 1960 by Clint Murchison Jr. and Bedford Wynne and competed for the NFL championship twice in that decade (losing both times to the Green Bay Packers). Dallas has been home to such Hall of Fame players as Troy Aikman, Michael Irvin, and Roger Staubach, as well as famed head coach Tom Landry. Oilman Jerry Jones has owned the team since 1989.

	Annual Growth	2/04	2/05	2/06	2/07	2/08
Sales ($ mil.)	7.0%	205.0	231.0	235.0	242.0	269.0
Employees	—	—	—	—	—	—

DALLAS/FORT WORTH INTERNATIONAL AIRPORT

3200 E. Airfield Dr.
DFW Airport, TX 75261
Phone: 972-574-8888
Fax: —
Web: www.dfwairport.com

CEO: Jeffrey P. (Jeff) Fegan
CFO: Christopher A. Poinsatte
HR: Sherry Vidal-Brown
FYE: September 30
Type: Government-owned

Yes, many things *are* bigger in Texas, and Dallas/Fort Worth International Airport (DFW) is no exception. Covering some 30 square miles, DFW is one of the world's largest airports by land mass. The facility includes seven runways, three control towers, five terminals, and about 150 gates. Nearly 60 million passengers pass through DFW annually. Aside from typical airport fare, DFW also houses private warehouse and distribution centers, a 36-hole golf course, as well as a Grand Hyatt and a Hyatt Regency hotel. Opened in 1974, the airport complex is owned by the cities of Dallas and Fort Worth and is situated approximately halfway between them.

	Annual Growth	9/04	9/05	9/06	9/07	9/08
Est. sales ($ mil.)	—	—	—	—	—	567.6
Employees	—	—	—	—	—	1,700

An in-depth profile of this company is available to Hoover's Online members at hoovers.com. ⊞

DAL-TILE CORPORATION

7834 C.F. Hawn Fwy.	CEO: Harold G. Turk
Dallas, TX 75217	CFO: Michael F. McGlothlin
Phone: 214-398-1411	HR: Paul Adams
Fax: 214-309-4835	FYE: December 31
Web: www.daltile.com	Type: Subsidiary

Dal-Tile International never fails to floor its customers: A subsidiary of Mohawk Industries, the company is the US's largest and best-known maker of ceramic tile. Dal-Tile — which sells its floor, wall, quarry, and mosaic tiles under the Daltile, Mohawk, and American Olean brand names — manufactures ceramic, porcelain, and natural stone tiles at eight plants in the US and Mexico and sells them through more than 250 company-operated sales service centers in the US and Canada, and through independent distributors and retailers such as The Home Depot and Lowe's. Customers include architects, builders, developers, and homeowners.

DANA CLASSIC FRAGRANCES, INC.

400 Lyster Ave.	CEO: Emil Giliotti
Saddle Brook, NJ 07663	CFO: Joseph C. Sienkiewicz
Phone: 201-881-8550	HR: —
Fax: 973-416-0499	FYE: March 31
Web: danaclassics.com	Type: Private

Resurrecting established fragrances makes sense to Dana Classic Fragrances. The company makes, markets, and distributes some 50 classic fragrance brands, taking older products that may have fallen on hard times and updating them for current generations of consumers. Among its products are the classic 1970s women's scent Love's Baby Soft, as well as Navy, Toujours Moi, Tabu, and Chantilly. For men, the company sells British Sterling, Canoe, and English Leather, among other brands. Dana Classic Fragrances sells its products online and through major drug stores, mid-range department stores such as Sears, and other mass-market retailers. The company is owned by the private equity firm Patriarch Partners.

	Annual Growth	3/04	3/05	3/06	3/07	3/08
Est. sales ($ mil.)	—	—	—	—	—	34.1
Employees	—	—	—	—	—	80

DANA HOLDING CORPORATION

NYSE: DAN

3939 Technology Dr.	CEO: James E. Sweetnam
Maumee, OH 43537	CFO: James A. (Jim) Yost
Phone: 419-887-3000	HR: Robert H. Marcin
Fax: —	FYE: December 31
Web: www.dana.com	Type: Public

When it comes to building cars, it starts with the parts. Dana manufactures many of the parts car makers use to piece together new vehicles. Its core products include axles and driveshafts, as well as sealing (gaskets, cover modules), thermal (cooling and heat transfer), and structural (frames, cradles, side rails) products. Among its largest customers are OEMs such as Ford, Toyota, Nissan, GM, and Hyundai. The company also supplies companies that make commercial and off-highway vehicles, such as PACCAR, Deere, Sandvik, and Navistar. Dana filed for Chapter 11 bankruptcy protection from creditors in 2006 and emerged in 2008. Customers outside of the US account for more than half of sales.

	Annual Growth	12/05	12/06	12/07	12/08	12/09
Sales ($ mil.)	(11.7%)	8,611.0	8,504.0	8,721.0	8,095.0	5,228.0
Net income ($ mil.)	—	(1,609.0)	(739.0)	(551.0)	18.0	(436.0)
Market value ($ mil.)	1,364.9%	—	—	—	103.6	1,517.3
Employees	(14.1%)	44,000	45,000	35,000	29,000	24,000

DANAHER CORPORATION

NYSE: DHR

2099 Pennsylvania Ave. NW, 12th Fl.	CEO: H. Lawrence (Larry) Culp Jr.
Washington, DC 20006	CFO: Daniel L. Comas
Phone: 202-828-0850	HR: Kevin A. Klau
Fax: 202-828-0860	FYE: December 31
Web: www.danaher.com	Type: Public

If you've ever used Craftsman hand tools or bought something with a bar code on it, then odds are you've been in touch with Danaher's business. Its Professional Instrumentation segment produces environmental and electronic testing technology; Industrial Technologies makes motion control equipment and devices that read bar codes; Medical Technologies makes dental products and medical instrumentation devices; and Danaher's Tools and Components manufactures hand and automotive specialty tools and accessories under brand names like Sears' Craftsman. The two Rales brothers, Steven (board chairman) and Mitchell (executive committee chairman), together own approximately 20% of the company.

	Annual Growth	12/05	12/06	12/07	12/08	12/09
Sales ($ mil.)	8.8%	7,984.7	9,596.4	11,025.9	12,697.5	11,184.9
Net income ($ mil.)	6.4%	897.8	1,122.0	1,369.9	1,317.6	1,151.7
Market value ($ mil.)	7.8%	18,108.8	23,517.4	28,484.5	18,378.2	24,413.4
Employees	3.9%	40,000	45,000	50,000	50,300	46,600

D&H DISTRIBUTING CO.

2525 N. 7th St.	CEO: Israel (Izzy) Schwab
Harrisburg, PA 17110	CFO: Robert J. Miller Jr.
Phone: 717-236-8001	HR: —
Fax: 717-255-7838	FYE: April 30
Web: www.dandh.com	Type: Private

D&H Distributing sells computer and electronics products in the US and Canada. Its product portfolio includes computers and peripherals, electronic components, data storage devices, printing and imaging equipment, software, mobile devices, gaming systems, home appliances, surveillance systems, and digital music players. Clients include small and large resellers and retailers, system builders, and college bookstores. D&H also targets schools and government agencies. Suppliers include Hewlett-Packard, Intel, and Microsoft. D&H Distributing is owned by its employees.

DANFOSS TURBOCOR COMPRESSORS, INC.

1769 E. Paul Dirac Dr.	CEO: Ricardo Schneider
Tallahassee, FL 32310	CFO: —
Phone: 850-504-4800	HR: —
Fax: 850-575-2126	FYE: December 31
Web: www.turbocor.com	Type: Joint venture

Danfoss Turbocor is not only cool, it's green. The company makes the world's first oil-free compressor designed for the commercial heating, ventilation, air conditioning, and refrigeration (HVACR) industry. Using a combination of aerospace, magnetic bearing, and digital electronic technologies, its compressors are used in air- and water-cooled chillers and rooftop units; they are roughly 33% more energy efficient than conventional compressors. Hotels, hospitals, industrial facilities, office buildings, and schools are primary users of its products. The company mainly sells them to HVACR retrofit contractors and original equipment manufacturers. Danfoss Turbocor maintains offices in the US, Canada, and Europe.

	Annual Growth	12/04	12/05	12/06	12/07	12/08
Est. sales ($ mil.)	—	—	—	—	—	12.1
Employees	—	—	—	—	—	60

🔳 DANIEL J. EDELMAN, INC.

200 E. Randolph Dr., 63rd Fl.	CEO: Richard W. Edelman
Chicago, IL 60601	CFO: Victor (Vic) Malanga
Phone: 312-240-3000	HR: Michelle Deese
Fax: 312-240-2900	FYE: June 30
Web: www.edelman.com	Type: Private

If image truly is everything, then Edelman may be one of the most indispensable companies around. Daniel J. Edelman, which does business simply as Edelman, is the largest independent agency in the industry, conducting work for heavy hitters such as Wal-Mart and Microsoft. With more than 50 offices worldwide, the company provides its services to five industries through about 20 practice areas (including financial communications and investor relations, corporate affairs, marketing, litigation, and public affairs). Edelman has fiercely guarded its independent status, despite the business world's ever-increasing trend toward consolidation. The company was founded in 1952 by chairman and owner Daniel Edelman.

THE DANNON COMPANY, INC.

100 Hillside Ave.	CEO: Gustavo Valle
White Plains, NY 10603	CFO: Antoine Remy
Phone: 914-872-8400	HR: Tony Cicio
Fax: 914-872-1565	FYE: December 31
Web: www.dannon.com	Type: Subsidiary

Yes, it's curdled milk with bacteria with a bit of jam added, but Dannon has lifted yogurt from health-food obscurity into a supermarket staple. The Dannon Company vies with General Mills, maker of Yoplait, for the #1 spot as the US's top yogurt producer (the two have traded off the honor in recent years). Dannon's approximately 100 flavors, styles, and sizes of yogurts come in regular, low-fat, and nonfat varieties, as well as in liquid ("drinkable") and smoothie forms. To better attract children, Dannon makes Danimals yogurt in kid-friendly packaging; to better attract moms, it continues to launch ever more indulgent and even fluffier yogurts. Dannon is a subsidiary of France's Groupe Danone.

DANVERS BANCORP, INC.

NASDAQ (GS): DNBK

1 Conant St.	CEO: Kevin T. Bottomley
Danvers, MA 01923	CFO: L. Mark Panella
Phone: 978-777-2200	HR: Judy Tenaglia
Fax: —	FYE: December 31
Web: www.danversbank.com	Type: Public

Danvers Bancorp is the holding company for Danversbank, which serves eastern Massachusetts from about 30 branches. Founded in 1850, the bank offers deposit services such as checking and savings accounts, in addition to loan services targeted to both consumers and businesses. Commercial and industrial loans dominate its loan portfolio, followed by commercial mortgages, residential mortgages, and construction loans. Wealth management services are offered through an arrangement with Raymond James Financial. In 2009, Danvers Bancorp acquired Beverly National Bancorp and its eight Beverly National Bank locations in a $62 million stock swap. Beverly National was merged into Danversbank in early 2010.

	Annual Growth	12/05	12/06	12/07	12/08	12/09
Assets ($ mil.)	20.6%	1,180.4	1,262.6	1,448.3	1,727.8	2,499.7
Net income ($ mil.)	0.0%	5.3	4.2	4.4	(2.7)	5.3
Market value ($ mil.)	(2.8%)	—	—	—	288.2	280.0
Employees	10.8%	267	267	262	292	402

DARA BIOSCIENCES, INC.

NASDAQ (CM): DARA

8601 Six Forks Rd., Ste. 160	CEO: Richard A. Franco Sr.
Raleigh, NC 27615	CFO: Ann A. Rosar
Phone: 919-872-5578	HR: —
Fax: —	FYE: December 31
Web: www.darabiosciences.com	Type: Public

Metabolism out of whack? DARA BioSciences is working on it. The drug development company is testing drugs for metabolic diseases such as diabetes. However, it was not always thus for the company. Formerly called Point Therapeutics, the firm failed in its previous efforts to advance lead cancer drug talabostat and was forced to regroup and consider its options. The company turned to its preclinical pipeline, which included a potential diabetes drug, and then in 2008 executed a reverse merger with privately held DARA BioSciences, which brought along a complementary set of metabolic compounds, as well as programs focused on neuropathic pain and psoriasis.

	Annual Growth	12/05	12/06	12/07	12/08	12/09
Sales ($ mil.)	—	—	—	—	0.0	0.0
Net income ($ mil.)	—	—	—	—	(11.6)	(3.3)
Market value ($ mil.)	(11.8%)	—	—	—	24.5	21.6
Employees	0.0%	—	—	—	5	5

🔳 DARDEN RESTAURANTS, INC.

NYSE: DRI

1000 Darden Center Dr.	CEO: Clarence Otis Jr.
Orlando, FL 32837	CFO: C. Bradford (Brad) Richmond
Phone: 407-245-4000	HR: Jack Snow
Fax: 407-245-5389	FYE: May 31
Web: www.dardenrestaurants.com	Type: Public

This company has cornered not one but two dining markets: seafood and "Hospitaliano." Darden Restaurants is the #1 casual-dining operator (in terms of revenue), with more than 1,770 restaurants in the US and Canada. Its flagship chains include seafood-segment leader Red Lobster and top Italian-themed concept Olive Garden. Both chains cater to families, with mid-priced menu items, themed interiors, and primarily suburban locations. Darden also operates the LongHorn Steakhouse chain, with more than 320 outlets. In addition, the company operates a small chain of tropical-themed Bahama Breeze restaurants that offer Caribbean-inspired food, along with a casual grill and wine bar concept called Seasons 52.

	Annual Growth	5/05	5/06	5/07	5/08	5/09
Sales ($ mil.)	8.1%	5,278.1	5,720.6	5,567.1	6,626.5	7,217.5
Net income ($ mil.)	6.4%	290.6	338.2	201.4	377.2	372.2
Market value ($ mil.)	2.7%	4,566.5	4,978.5	6,406.9	4,815.4	5,085.3
Employees	4.5%	150,100	157,300	157,000	179,000	179,000

DARIGOLD, INC.

1130 Rainier Ave., South	CEO: John Underwood
Seattle, WA 98144	CFO: John Wells
Phone: 206-284-7220	HR: Duane Harris
Fax: 206-722-2569	FYE: March 31
Web: www.darigold.com	Type: Subsidiary

Churning out dairy foods since 1918, Darigold is the processing and marketing subsidiary of the Northwest Dairy Association. With 10 processing plants, Darigold makes and distributes fluid milk, butter, cottage cheese, yogurt, and other cultured dairy products under both private labels and the Darigold brand name. The company retired its dba name WestFarm Foods in 2006. Darigold offers its products to wholesale and retail food companies, as well as foodservice operators; however most of its sales are generated from selling dairy ingredients to other food manufacturers. It numbers Albertsons, Fred Meyer, and Safeway among its retail customers.

DARLING INTERNATIONAL INC.

NYSE: DAR

251 O'Connor Ridge Blvd., Ste. 300
Irving, TX 75038
Phone: 972-717-0300
Fax: 972-717-1588
Web: www.darlingii.com

CEO: Randall C. Stuewe
CFO: John O. Muse
HR: —
FYE: December 31
Type: Public

It's not the most darling of businesses — in fact it's messy and it's stinky — but Darling International, the largest publicly traded rendering operation in the US, is willing to do it. The company collects and processes animal by-products and used cooking grease from approximately 110,000 restaurants, butcher shops, grocery stores, and independent meat and poultry processors throughout the US. Its rendering operations produce yellow grease, tallow, and meat, bone, and blood meal, which Darling sells in the US as well as internationally to makers of soap, rubber, oils, pet and livestock feed, and chemicals.

	Annual Growth	12/05	12/06	12/07	12/08	12/09
Sales ($ mil.)	17.9%	308.9	407.0	645.3	807.5	597.8
Net income ($ mil.)	52.6%	7.7	5.1	45.5	54.6	41.8
Market value ($ mil.)	20.5%	327.3	454.3	953.0	452.6	690.9
Employees	13.2%	1,110	1,830	1,830	1,870	1,820

⊞ DART CONTAINER CORPORATION

500 Hogsback Rd.
Mason, MI 48854
Phone: 517-676-3800
Fax: 517-676-3883
Web: www.dartcontainer.com

CEO: Robert C. Dart
CFO: Kevin Fox
HR: Kenneth Petersen
FYE: December 31
Type: Private

Dart Container is a world cup winner — not in soccer, but in foam cups and containers. It commands about half of the global market in foam cups. To make its products, Dart touts a secret molding method for expandable polystyrene. The foodservice lineup includes not just cups but lids, dinnerware, and cutlery, which is marketed through a global distribution network to hospitals, schools, and restaurants, as well as retailers. Self-sufficient, Dart builds its own molding machinery, and uses Dart trucks to deliver products from plants in the US, Canada, Mexico, Argentina, the UK, and Australia. Its recycled polystyrene is sold to manufacturers of such durables as insulation and egg cartons. Dart is family-owned.

	Annual Growth	12/04	12/05	12/06	12/07	12/08
Est. sales ($ mil.)	2.9%	1,250.0	1,388.0	1,510.0	1,540.0	1,400.0
Employees	14.2%	5,000	5,200	5,640	5,840	8,500

DARTMOUTH COLLEGE

207 Parkhurst Hall
Hanover, NH 03755
Phone: 603-646-1110
Fax: 603-646-2266
Web: www.dartmouth.edu

CEO: Jim Yong Kim
CFO: Adam M. Keller
HR: Adam M. Keller
FYE: June 30
Type: School

Part of the esteemed Ivy League, Dartmouth is a private, four-year liberal arts college with an enrollment of some 5,700 students. It has an undergraduate college and graduate schools of business, engineering, and medicine, plus about 20 graduate programs in the arts and sciences. It is also home to a number of centers and institutes including Children's Hospital at Dartmouth; Dartmouth Center on Addiction, Recovery, and Education; and Center for Integrated Space Weather Modeling. Notable alumni include Daniel Webster, Robert Frost, Theodore "Dr. Seuss" Geisel, and Nelson Rockefeller.

	Annual Growth	6/04	6/05	6/06	6/07	6/08
Est. sales ($ mil.)	—	—	—	—	—	670.8
Employees	—	—	—	—	—	5,000

DASSAULT FALCON JET CORP.

200 Riser Rd.
Little Ferry, NJ 07643
Phone: 201-440-6700
Fax: 201-541-4515
Web: www.falconjet.com

CEO: John Rosanvallon
CFO: J. Morgan Young
HR: Robert Basso
FYE: December 31
Type: Subsidiary

Helping the rich, famous, or merely busy soar to new heights, Dassault Falcon Jet sells and supports the Falcon 50EX, 900DX, 900EX EASy, 7X, 2000, and 2000EX EASy business jets. A subsidiary of Dassault Aviation, the company offers engine maintenance, spare parts and tools distribution, parts exchange, special equipment testing, and operational assistance services, as well as pilot, maintenance, and cabin crew training. More than 1,650 Falcon jets have flown into the wild blue yonder since Dassault began production in 1963. The company builds its aircraft in France, then flies them to its facilities in the US for painting and installation of interiors and amenities.

	Annual Growth	12/04	12/05	12/06	12/07	12/08
Est. sales ($ mil.)	—	—	—	—	—	1,530.0
Employees	—	—	—	—	—	3,000

DASSAULT SYSTÈMES SIMULIA CORP.

Rising Sun Mills, 166 Valley St.
Providence, RI 02909
Phone: 401-276-4400
Fax: 401-276-4408
Web: www.simulia.com

CEO: Scott A. Berkey
CFO: Jim Lambert
HR: Denise Hempe
FYE: December 31
Type: Subsidiary

Dassault Systèmes Simulia Corp. (which operates as SIMULIA) makes engineering analysis software that simulates the physical response of structures and solid bodies to load, temperature, contact, impact, and other stresses. Its finite element analysis tools are widely used in the aerospace, automotive, consumer goods, electronics, and manufacturing industries, among other fields. The company also provides related engineering, legal, technical consulting, and training services. The company was founded in 1978 as Hibbitt, Karlsson & Sorensen. In 2005 Dassault Systèmes acquired the company for approximately $413 million in cash.

DASSAULT SYSTÈMES SOLIDWORKS CORP.

300 Baker Ave.
Concord, MA 01742
Phone: 978-371-5011
Fax: 978-371-7303
Web: www.solidworks.com

CEO: Hugh Jefferson (Jeff) Ray III
CFO: David Stott
HR: Richard E. (Dick) Morgan
FYE: December 31
Type: Subsidiary

Dassault Systèmes SolidWorks wants to put some meat on your designs. A subsidiary of France's Dassault Systèmes, SolidWorks offers 3-D mechanical design software that helps engineers speed up product development, translate designs into 3-D models, and communicate product ideas more effectively for customers and collaborators. The company's solid modeling suite includes features for animation, analyzing designs, and publishing 3-D designs on the Web. Customers range from consumer products makers to automotive and aerospace companies. Founded in 1993, SolidWorks was acquired by Dassault Systèmes in 1997.

⊞ An in-depth profile of this company is available to Hoover's Online members at hoovers.com.

471

DATA DOMAIN, INC.

2421 Mission College Blvd.
Santa Clara, CA 95054
Phone: 408-980-4800
Fax: 408-980-8620
Web: www.datadomain.com

CEO: Frank Slootman
CFO: Michael P. (Mike) Scarpelli
HR: —
FYE: December 31
Type: Subsidiary

Data Domain keeps datasets down to reasonable sizes. The company develops de-duplication appliances for data backup systems and other storage applications. Based on proprietary compression technology, its systems identify redundant files to reduce the amount of data that has to be stored. Its customers include enterprises in the defense, entertainment, finance, health care, legal, media, and retail sectors. The company also generates revenue from maintenance and support services. In 2009 Data Domain was acquired by data storage systems leader EMC.

DATA I/O CORPORATION

NASDAQ (CM): DAIO

6464 185th Ave. NE, Ste. 101
Redmond, WA 98052
Phone: 425-881-6444
Fax: 425-869-7423
Web: www.dataio.com

CEO: Frederick R. (Fred) Hume
CFO: Joel S. Hatlen
HR: —
FYE: December 31
Type: Public

Data I/O knows the chip-programming business inside and out. The company makes programming systems used by electronics makers to tailor their integrated circuits (ICs) to suit a broad range of products. Data I/O makes both automated and non-automated programming systems. The automated models are used for high-volume applications; the non-automated programming systems include both single-site systems that program one device at a time and multisite systems for increased output. Industrial giant Siemens is a leading client, among 1,200-plus customers around the world. More than three-quarters of sales are outside the US.

	Annual Growth	12/05	12/06	12/07	12/08	12/09
Sales ($ mil.)	(10.1%)	28.3	28.8	26.8	27.6	18.5
Net income ($ mil.)	—	0.6	0.0	0.8	5.1	(0.8)
Market value ($ mil.)	1.5%	37.7	32.3	58.8	21.5	40.0
Employees	(8.3%)	130	129	97	93	92

DATACARD CORPORATION

11111 Bren Rd. West
Minnetonka, MN 55343
Phone: 952-933-1223
Fax: 952-931-0418
Web: www.datacard.com

CEO: Todd G. Wilkinson
CFO: Kurt Ishaug
HR: —
FYE: March 31
Type: Private

Datacard has a full deck of financial and identification products. The company, which does business as Datacard Group, offers card printers, laminators, digital cameras, engravers, mail handlers, and software that organizations use to manage, customize, and issue personalized credit and ID cards. Datacard products are used by financial institutions (credit cards, smart cards), corporations (badges), and government agencies (passports, national ID cards) in more than 120 countries. Established in 1969, the company also offers consulting, graphic design, and systems integration services. The Quandt family of Germany, which also controls BMW, owns Datacard.

DATACOLOR INC.

5 Princess Rd.
Lawrence, NJ 08648
Phone: 609-924-2189
Fax: 609-895-7414
Web: www.datacolor.com

CEO: Albert Busch
CFO: Mark Leuchtmann
HR: Gary Brennan
FYE: September 30
Type: Business segment

Datacolor takes its cue from hue. The company makes instruments and software that control color measuring, matching, and quality control for use in textile, paint, automotive, printing, photography, and home theater applications. Its Spyder brand targets the consumer market. Datacolor also offers a variety of services, including calibration of spectrophotometers, on-site consulting, product training, and education in color theory. The company sells directly to consumers online and through resellers. It also integrates its products with those of partners such as Lectra, Fongs, and Lawer. Established in 1970, Datacolor is a subsidiary of Datacolor AG (formerly Eichhof Holdings), a Swiss firm.

DATALINK CORPORATION

NASDAQ (GM): DTLK

8170 Upland Cir.
Chanhassen, MN 55317
Phone: 952-944-3462
Fax: 952-944-7869
Web: www.datalink.com

CEO: Paul F. Lidsky
CFO: Gregory T. Barnum
HR: Mary E. West
FYE: December 31
Type: Public

Datalink serves up storage system smorgasbords. The company builds and implements high-end, custom-designed data storage systems for large corporations. Datalink's storage systems include disk- and tape-based storage devices, storage networking components, and data management software. The company employs an open-system standard, building its offerings from products made by leading manufacturers such as Brocade Communications Systems, EMC, and Hitachi Data Systems. Datalink also provides support and maintenance services. Datalink markets its products directly to customers in the US.

	Annual Growth	12/05	12/06	12/07	12/08	12/09
Sales ($ mil.)	11.1%	117.1	146.0	177.8	195.6	178.1
Net income ($ mil.)	—	(2.9)	8.5	1.2	3.4	(0.6)
Market value ($ mil.)	2.8%	51.5	99.8	48.9	42.4	57.4
Employees	20.2%	147	160	199	208	307

DATALOGIC SCANNING, INC.

959 Terry St.
Eugene, OR 97402
Phone: 541-683-5700
Fax: 541-345-7140
Web: www.scanning.datalogic.com

CEO: William L. (Bill) Parnell Jr.
CFO: Chet Galka
HR: Rhone E. Lee
FYE: December 31
Type: Subsidiary

Datalogic Scanning is helping to replace the "cha-ching" of cash registers with the beeping of bar code scanners. The company's retail, commercial, and industrial bar code scanners speed up retail checkout, inventory management, shipping, parcel sorting, and other functions. Datalogic's software provides detailed analysis of its scanner products, allowing for easier maintenance and increased performance. Long an expert in bar code data collection, the company also develops products for the radio-frequency identification (RFID) market. Customers include American Express, Blockbuster, Disneyland, FedEx, IBM, Medtronic, Safeway, Tellabs, and the US military. Datalogic Scanning is a subsidiary of Datalogic SpA.

	Annual Growth	12/04	12/05	12/06	12/07	12/08
Est. sales ($ mil.)	—	—	—	—	—	255.0
Employees	—	—	—	—	—	809

DATARAM CORPORATION

NASDAQ (GM): DRAM

186 Princeton Rd.
West Windsor, NJ 08550
Phone: 609-799-0071
Fax: 609-799-6734
Web: www.dataram.com

CEO: John H. Freeman
CFO: Mark E. Maddocks
HR: —
FYE: April 30
Type: Public

Dataram wants you to remember your DRAMs. The company makes add-in memory boards and memory modules that expand the capacity of computer servers and workstations running under the UNIX and Windows operating systems. Its products, which use DRAM memory devices, are compatible with systems from companies such as Sun Microsystems, Hewlett-Packard, IBM, Dell, and SGI (now named Silicon Graphics International), and with microprocessors made by AMD and Intel. Sun Microsystems licensed Dataram to sell memory components for its computer hardware products. About 70% of Dataram's sales comes from customers in the US.

	Annual Growth	4/05	4/06	4/07	4/08	4/09
Sales ($ mil.)	(20.8%)	65.7	41.8	38.4	30.9	25.9
Net income ($ mil.)	—	6.7	2.8	0.8	1.6	(3.1)
Market value ($ mil.)	(25.1%)	37.5	51.6	37.6	29.3	11.8
Employees	2.2%	100	102	95	89	109

DATASCENSION, INC.

OTC: DSEN

532 Pima Canyon Ct.
Las Vegas, NV 89144
Phone: 702-233-6785
Fax: 714-276-9080
Web: www.datascension.com

CEO: Lou Persico
CFO: David Lieberman
HR: Harold Fallas
FYE: December 31
Type: Public

Datascension helps other companies gather information by providing call center services. It conducts interviews, designs surveys and databases, stores and mines data, and processes documents for its clients, mostly market research firms. The company offers telephone interviewing services in both English and Spanish. Datascension also assists other companies with the process of setting up and launching new call centers offshore. It works with a concentrated number of clients; in 2009, Synovate, Nielsen, Admax Media, Sandelman & Associates, and Market Cast collectively accounted for almost 50% of its revenue. Datascension, which is also known as DSEN, owns offices in California and Costa Rica.

	Annual Growth	12/05	12/06	12/07	12/08	12/09
Sales ($ mil.)	10.9%	9.8	14.8	20.3	18.1	14.8
Net income ($ mil.)	—	1.8	(0.2)	(0.9)	(6.5)	(0.5)
Market value ($ mil.)	(37.3%)	5.1	7.9	13.5	0.2	0.8
Employees	16.2%	551	1,000	1,500	1,200	1,003

DATATEL, INC.

4375 Fair Lakes Ct.
Fairfax, VA 22033
Phone: 703-968-9000
Fax: 703-968-4573
Web: www.datatel.com

CEO: John F. Speer III
CFO: Kevin M. Boyce
HR: —
FYE: December 31
Type: Private

Datatel doesn't care if you're a Bruin, a Hurricane, or a Longhorn, as long as you've got data that needs managing. The company, which serves higher education institutions, provides software that manages information about students, finances, financial aid, human resources, and advancement. The company's software streamlines such processes as enterprise resource planning, e-recruitment, and alumni communications, serving more than 700 institutions throughout North America. Datatel was founded in 1968 by Ken Kendrick and Tom Davidson; they sold the company in 2005 to members of their executive team (backed by Thoma Cressey Equity Partners and Trident Capital). In 2009 Hellman & Friedman purchased Datatel.

	Annual Growth	12/04	12/05	12/06	12/07	12/08
Sales ($ mil.)	9.2%	—	—	108.0	122.7	128.8
Employees	(1.4%)	—	—	547	550	532

DATATRAK INTERNATIONAL, INC.

Pink Sheets: DATA

6150 Parkland Blvd., Ste. 100
Mayfield Heights, OH 44124
Phone: 440-443-0082
Fax: 440-442-3482
Web: www.datatrak.net

CEO: Laurence P. (Larry) Birch
CFO: Raymond J. Merk
HR: —
FYE: December 31
Type: Public

Researchers rely on DATATRAK to keep track of their clinical data. The company develops online, hosted electronic data capture (EDC) software for the biotechnology, medical device, contract research, and pharmaceutical industries. Its software speeds up the process of gathering data during clinical trials by collecting and electronically transmitting trial data from remote research sites to sponsors. DATATRAK also offers project management, site assessment, training, and hosting services. Its products have been used to support hundreds of clinical trials involving patients in more than 50 countries.

	Annual Growth	12/04	12/05	12/06	12/07	*12/08
Sales ($ mil.)	(6.1%)	11.3	15.7	17.7	10.6	8.8
Net income ($ mil.)	—	0.8	2.5	(4.5)	(10.9)	(16.8)
Market value ($ mil.)	(58.8%)	100.1	136.9	68.8	21.9	2.9
Employees	(11.0%)	75	110	122	81	47

*Most recent year available

DATAWATCH CORPORATION

NASDAQ (CM): DWCH

271 Mill Rd.
Chelmsford, MA 01824
Phone: 978-441-2200
Fax: 978-441-1114
Web: www.datawatch.com

CEO: Kenneth P. (Ken) Bero
CFO: Murray P. Fish
HR: —
FYE: September 30
Type: Public

Datawatch keeps close tabs on data. The company makes enterprise information management software that includes data mining, business intelligence, and help desk management applications. Its products include Monarch, for extracting and manipulating data from ASCII or HTML files; Monarch Data Pump, a data replication and migration tool used to populate and refresh data marts and data warehouses; and Monarch RMS, Web-based report mining and analysis. Its 35,000 customers have included the likes of Aetna, Ford, McDonald's, and the US Postal Service.

	Annual Growth	9/05	9/06	9/07	9/08	9/09
Sales ($ mil.)	(2.3%)	21.5	20.8	25.3	23.0	19.6
Net income ($ mil.)	—	0.8	(0.6)	1.7	0.7	(4.9)
Market value ($ mil.)	(9.5%)	20.8	15.2	26.4	10.4	14.0
Employees	(5.6%)	127	136	121	118	101

🔲 DAVE & BUSTER'S, INC.

2481 Mañana Dr.
Dallas, TX 75220
Phone: 214-357-9588
Fax: 214-350-0941
Web: www.daveandbusters.com

CEO: Stephen M. (Steve) King
CFO: Brian A. Jenkins
HR: Margo L. Manning
FYE: January 31
Type: Private

Fun and games collide with food and drink at these nightspots. Dave & Buster's owns and operates about 55 entertainment complexes in 25 states and Canada that offer casual dining, full bar service, and a cavernous game room. The adult fun centers feature the latest in video games and motion simulators, as well as games of skill played for prizes. For dining, Dave & Buster's offers a menu that features traditional American fare such as burgers, seafood, and steak. Partners David Corriveau and James "Buster" Corley opened the first Dave & Buster's in 1982. Private equity firm Oak Hill Capital Partners acquired the company in 2010.

	Annual Growth	1/04	1/05	1/06	1/07	1/08
Sales ($ mil.)	10.3%	362.8	390.3	463.5	510.2	536.3
Net income ($ mil.)	—	10.9	12.9	4.3	(11.6)	(8.8)
Employees	9.2%	5,810	7,400	7,500	7,500	8,248

An in-depth profile of this company is available to Hoover's Online members at hoovers.com.

473

THE DAVEY TREE EXPERT COMPANY

1500 N. Mantua St.
Kent, OH 44240
Phone: 330-673-9511
Fax: 330-673-9843
Web: www.davey.com

CEO: Karl J. Warnke
CFO: David E. Adante
HR: Gordon L. Ober
FYE: December 31
Type: Private

Business at The Davey Tree Expert Company is as strong as an oak. The company's roots extend back to 1880 when John Davey founded the horticultural services firm, which branched into residential, commercial, utility, and other natural resource management services. With offices in the US and Canada, Davey's services include treatment, planting, and removal of trees, shrubs, and other plants; landscaping; tree surgery; and the application of fertilizers, herbicides, and insecticides. It also provides line clearing for public utilities, urban and utility forestry research and development, and environmental planning. Pacific Gas and Electric accounts for about 10% of sales. Davey has been employee-owned since 1979.

	Annual Growth	12/04	12/05	12/06	12/07	12/08
Sales ($ mil.)	10.6%	398.6	431.6	467.5	506.1	595.8
Net income ($ mil.)	11.5%	12.3	13.3	14.0	18.1	19.0
Employees	6.8%	5,000	5,200	5,500	5,600	6,500

THE DAVID J. JOSEPH COMPANY

300 Pike St.
Cincinnati, OH 45202
Phone: 513-419-6200
Fax: 513-419-6222
Web: www.djj.com

CEO: Keith B. Grass
CFO: James H. (Jim) Goetz
HR: Judith G. (Judy) Smith
FYE: December 31
Type: Subsidiary

Since it has been in business since the 19th century, it's probably fair to say that The David J. Joseph Company (DJJ) has been in a scrap or two. One of the largest scrap-metal brokerage operations in the US, DJJ recycles both ferrous (iron and steel) and nonferrous metals (copper, aluminum, lead, and brass) worldwide. To accomplish this feat, the company operates about 60 scrap processing centers (including 15 car shredders) and about a dozen trading offices in the US. Its shredders can process up to a million car hulks each year. DJJ had been a subsidiary of Dutch energy and retail firm SHV Holdings, but US steel minimill titan Nucor acquired the company in 2008 for $1.1 billion.

DAVID'S BRIDAL, INC.

1001 Washington St.
Conshohocken, PA 19428
Phone: 610-943-5000
Fax: 610-943-5048
Web: www.davidsbridal.com

CEO: Robert D. (Bob) Huth
CFO: Gene S. Morphis
HR: Fred A. Postelle
FYE: January 31
Type: Private

From prom night to the big day itself, David's Bridal wants to be there. With more than 300 stores nationwide and in Puerto Rico, the company is the largest retail chain specializing in bridal gowns. All gowns are available off the rack and are priced to meet most budgets. David's Bridal also sells invitations and gifts, veils and bridal accessories, and apparel for formal occasions, such as communions and Quinceañeras. Besides its brick-and-mortar locations, David's Bridal boasts an online catalog and spotlights the latest trends through its Style Council blogs and podcasts, which debuted during 2009. David's Bridal is owned by Leonard Green & Partners.

DAVIDSON COLLEGE

209 Ridge Rd.
Davidson, NC 28035
Phone: 704-894-2000
Fax: 704-894-2502
Web: www.davidson.edu

CEO: Thomas W. Ross Sr.
CFO: Karen L. Goldstein
HR: Kim Ball
FYE: June 30
Type: School

The 1,700 students at Davidson College account for about a fifth of the population in a small North Carolina town with the same name. Located just north of Charlotte, the liberal arts school offers 20 majors and 12 minors in areas such as anthropology, art, economics, history, and philosophy. It also offers pre-professional programs in medicine, law, business, ministerial, and management. Students are bound by a strict honor code that allows self-scheduled, unproctored exams and prohibits students from cheating and stealing. The school was founded in 1837 by Presbyterian ministers and named for Revolutionary War commander William Davidson. The college is supported by a more than $485 million endowment.

	Annual Growth	6/04	6/05	6/06	6/07	6/08
Est. sales ($ mil.)	—	—	—	—	—	98.5
Employees	—	—	—	—	—	800

DAVIDSON COMPANIES

8 3rd St. North
Great Falls, MT 59401
Phone: 406-727-4200
Fax: 406-791-7238
Web: www.dadco.com

CEO: William A. (Bill) Johnstone
CFO: Tom Nelson
HR: Dan McLaughlin
FYE: September 30
Type: Private

Employee-owned Davidson Companies offers investment banking, asset management, and travel services through five subsidiaries. The company's flagship firm, D.A. Davidson & Co., was founded in 1935 and offers investment banking services such as merger and acquisition advisory, capital raising, institutional sales and trading, and fundamental research. Davidson Companies provides brokerage, trust, wealth management, and financial planning services for private clients through Davidson Trust Co. and Davidson Investment Advisors. Davidson Travel is a full-service travel agency. Davidson Companies has more than 50 offices in some 15 states, though it is mainly active in the Northwest.

	Annual Growth	9/04	9/05	9/06	9/07	9/08
Sales ($ mil.)	17.4%	120.9	108.9	187.0	212.0	230.0
Employees	8.3%	800	866	—	—	—

DAVIDSON PERSONNEL, INC.

2302 Martin, Ste. 150
Irvine, CA 92612
Phone: 949-955-3114
Fax: 949-955-3609
Web: www.davidsonstaffing.com

CEO: Jennifer Evans
CFO: —
HR: —
FYE: December 31
Type: Subsidiary

Davidson Personnel has a line on legal, corporate, and technical hiring in Southern California. The company, which operates as Davidson Staffing, is made up of its units Davidson Attorneys, Davidson Legal Staffing, Davidson Corporate Staffing, and Davidson Technical Staffing (primarily for law firms and IT companies). The company provides temporary and contract staff, as well as permanent placements, and provides criminal background screening for all candidates. It serves Orange County, Los Angeles, San Diego, the San Francisco Bay area, and Oakland. Davidson Personnel was founded in 1987 by Sue Davidson. It was a subsidiary of MPS Group, which was acquired by global staffing rival Adecco in 2010.

	Annual Growth	12/04	12/05	12/06	12/07	12/08
Est. sales ($ mil.)	—	—	—	—	—	1.5
Employees	—	—	—	—	—	24

DAVIS POLK & WARDWELL LLP

450 Lexington Ave.
New York, NY 10017
Phone: 212-450-4000
Fax: 212-701-5800
Web: www.dpw.com

CEO: John R. Ettinger
CFO: —
HR: Jacqueline Nuñez
FYE: December 31
Type: Partnership

Founded in 1849, Davis Polk & Wardwell is one of the oldest law firms in the US. Having built a notable corporate practice early on, it helped J. P. Morgan (now JPMorgan Chase) form General Electric. With more than 700 lawyers, the firm is known for its skill in litigation, securities, and mergers and acquisitions; other practice areas include real estate, tax, technology, and trusts and estates. Davis Polk has served such high-profile clients as AT&T, Comcast, General Motors, and Philip Morris. In addition, more than one-third of the firm's clients are non-US companies or governments. Davis Polk has 10 offices in seven countries.

DAVIS VISION INC.

159 Express St.
Plainview, NY 11803
Phone: 516-932-9500
Fax: 516-932-7551
Web: www.davisvision.com

CEO: Steve Holden
CFO: Lawrence (Larry) Gable
HR: —
FYE: December 31
Type: Subsidiary

Davis Vision is a managed vision and eye care provider that serves about 55 million eye plan members through thousands of employer client groups. The company operates across the US through benefits contracts with companies, government agencies, unions, and insurance companies. In addition to covering eye exams and eyewear, Davis Vision offers discounted laser vision-correction surgery. Its centralized laboratories fill some 6,000 custom ophthalmic orders daily. Davis Vision also provides customers with a mail-order contact lens replacement service called Lens 123. The company was founded as a family optical business in 1917; today it is a subsidiary of Highmark.

DAVITA INC.

NYSE: DVA

1551 Wewatta Street
Denver, CO 80202
Phone: 303-405-2100
Fax: —
Web: www.davita.com

CEO: Kent J. Thiry
CFO: Luis Borgen
HR: Laura A. Mildenberger
FYE: December 31
Type: Public

DaVita — an Italian phrase that means "gives life" — provides life-sustaining dialysis treatments to patients suffering from end-stage renal disease (also known as chronic kidney failure). As one of the country's largest chains of outpatient dialysis centers, the company operates or provides administrative services to about 1,500 centers across the US. The firm also offers home-based dialysis services, as well as inpatient dialysis in some 700 hospitals. DaVita also operates clinical laboratories that specialize in routine testing of dialysis patients, and its DaVita Clinical Research business conducts research trials with dialysis patients.

	Annual Growth	12/05	12/06	12/07	12/08	12/09
Sales ($ mil.)	19.7%	2,973.9	4,880.7	5,264.2	5,660.2	6,108.8
Net income ($ mil.)	16.6%	228.6	289.7	381.8	374.2	422.7
Market value ($ mil.)	3.8%	5,261.5	5,909.8	5,854.8	5,150.3	6,103.1
Employees	3.8%	28,000	28,900	31,000	32,500	32,500

DAWN FOOD PRODUCTS, INC.

3333 Sargent Rd.
Jackson, MI 49201
Phone: 517-789-4400
Fax: 517-789-4465
Web: www.dawnfoods.com

CEO: Carrie L. Jones-Barber
CFO: Jerry Baglien
HR: Tom Harmon
FYE: December 31
Type: Private

They don't wait for the sun to come up at this company; the ovens are always fired up at Dawn Food Products. The company provides a comprehensive array of pre-baked and fully baked grain-based products, such as cakes, muffins, cookies, donuts, and artisan breads, as well as all the fixings for bakery production, including bases, fillings, flavorings, frozen dough, icings, ingredients, and mixes for other companies in the baking sector. Its customers include food manufacturers, foodservice companies, institutional bakeries, and restaurants. It also manufactures retail bakery goods, including Weight Watchers products.

DAWSON GEOPHYSICAL COMPANY

NASDAQ (GS): DWSN

508 W. Wall St., Ste. 800
Midland, TX 79701
Phone: 432-684-3000
Fax: 432-684-3030
Web: www.dawson3d.com

CEO: Stephen C. Jumper
CFO: Christina W. Hagan
HR: Olga Smoot
FYE: September 30
Type: Public

The oil industry can be shaky at times, but Dawson Geophysical always looks for good vibrations. The company, founded in 1952, provides data acquisition and data processing services including the analysis of 2-D and 3-D seismic data to assess potential underground oil and gas deposits. Dawson Geophysical's customers, both major and independent oil and gas operators, use the data in exploration and development activities. The company's 3-D seismic data acquisition crews work in the lower 48 states; data processing is performed by geophysicists at the firm's computer center in Midland, Texas.

	Annual Growth	9/05	9/06	9/07	9/08	9/09
Sales ($ mil.)	20.2%	116.7	168.6	257.8	324.9	244.0
Net income ($ mil.)	0.5%	10.0	15.9	27.2	35.0	10.2
Market value ($ mil.)	(2.5%)	236.5	232.2	606.0	365.0	214.1
Employees	4.1%	803	1,023	1,345	1,436	942

DAXOR CORPORATION

NYSE Amex: DXR

350 5th Ave., Ste. 7120
New York, NY 10118
Phone: 212-330-8500
Fax: 212-244-0806
Web: www.daxor.com

CEO: Joseph Feldschuh
CFO: David Frankel
HR: —
FYE: December 31
Type: Public

They might not give you a toaster with that new account, but Daxor's blood and sperm banks are open to attract new, uh, deposits. The company offers blood banking through subsidiary Scientific Medical Systems and operates sperm banks through its Idant division. Its main business, however, has been the development and commercialization of a blood volume analyzer, the BVA-100, which hospitals and other health care providers use to diagnose and treat heart and kidney failure, anemia, and other conditions, as well as to manage blood transfusions. The BVA-100 measures a patient's blood volume within 90 minutes.

	Annual Growth	12/05	12/06	12/07	12/08	12/09
Sales ($ mil.)	6.9%	1.3	1.5	1.9	1.8	1.7
Net income ($ mil.)	—	(1.3)	(0.8)	10.6	15.1	5.8
Market value ($ mil.)	(8.6%)	73.3	63.1	62.1	65.4	51.2
Employees	(2.8%)	46	41	40	36	41

THE DAY & ZIMMERMANN GROUP

1500 Spring Garden St.	CEO: Harold L. (Hal) Yoh III
Philadelphia, PA 19130	CFO: Joseph W. (Joe) Ritzel
Phone: 215-299-8000	HR: Silvana Battaglia
Fax: 215-299-8030	FYE: December 31
Web: www.dayzim.com	Type: Private

Day & Zimmermann offers services as distinct as day and night. Its family of companies provide engineering and construction, design, plant maintenance, security, staffing, munitions decommissioning, validation, and asset management services worldwide. A top global contractor, Day & Zimmermann provides operations, contract support, and maintenance services to US and foreign governments, as well as commercial customers. Its Day & Zimmerman NPS unit maintains half of the US's nuclear plants. Staffing subsidiary Yoh Services specializes in filling IT, engineering, and health care positions. Founded in 1901, Day & Zimmermann is owned and managed by the Yoh family, which has headed the firm for three generations.

	Annual Growth	12/04	12/05	12/06	12/07	12/08
Sales ($ mil.)	14.5%	—	1,600.0	1,900.0	2,200.0	2,400.0
Employees	6.3%	—	20,000	23,000	24,000	24,000

DAYS INNS WORLDWIDE, INC.

1 Sylvan Way	CEO: Ken Greene
Parsippany, NJ 07054	CFO: —
Phone: 973-753-6000	HR: —
Fax: —	FYE: December 31
Web: www.daysinn.com	Type: Subsidiary

Here's a chain that won't charge you an arm and a leg to put your head on a pillow for a day or two. Days Inns Worldwide is a leading franchiser of economy hotels, with about 1,850 locations in more than a dozen countries, including the US (all 50 states), Canada, China, and the UK. The properties typically offer affordable rooms with such amenities as cable television, complimentary newspaper service, and swimming pools, and attract budget-minded families and business travelers. Some locations also provide continental breakfast and pet-friendly rooms. Days Inns is owned by hospitality firm Wyndham Worldwide.

DAYSTAR TECHNOLOGIES, INC.

	NASDAQ (CM): DSTI
2972 Stender Way	CEO: Magnus Ryde
Santa Clara, CA 95054	CFO: —
Phone: 408-907-4600	HR: —
Fax: 408-907-4637	FYE: December 31
Web: www.daystartech.com	Type: Public

Old Sol, otherwise known as the sun, is the "day star" providing energy through the solar cells of this company. DayStar Technologies makes energy-generating and storing devices out of copper, indium, gallium, and selenium, dubbed CIGS solar cells. The company is developing manufacturing processes for its thin-film photovoltaic foil CIGS solar cells that will be cheaper to produce than conventional polycrystalline silicon solar cells, which currently dominate the market. DayStar got out of the business of installing and maintaining solar panels for residences. Running out of cash in 2009, the company warned that it may have to seek Chapter 11 protection from creditors if it is unable to raise capital.

	Annual Growth	12/05	12/06	12/07	12/08	12/09
Sales ($ mil.)	—	—	—	—	—	0.0
Net income ($ mil.)	—	—	—	—	—	(25.0)
Market value ($ mil.)	—	—	—	—	—	15.5
Employees	—	—	—	—	—	41

DAYTON FREIGHT LINES, INC.

6450 Poe Ave.	CEO: Thomas L. Cronin Jr.
Dayton, OH 45414	CFO: Bryan Brown
Phone: 937-264-4060	HR: —
Fax: 937-890-4846	FYE: December 31
Web: www.daytonfreight.com	Type: Private

Carrying freight in Big Ten country, Dayton Freight Lines is a less-than-truckload (LTL) carrier operating in 11 states in the North-Central US. (LTL carriers consolidate freight from multiple shippers into a single truckload.) The company operates a fleet of about 900 tractors and 2,100 trailers from a network of more than 40 terminals. Outside its home territory, Dayton Freight offers service in the rest of the US, Canada, Puerto Rico, and Guam through alliances with other carriers, including A. Duie Pyle, Oak Harbor Freight Lines, and Southeastern Freight Lines. Founded in 1981, Dayton Freight is owned by the Cronin family, which includes President and CEO Thomas L. Cronin Jr. and EVP Michael D. Cronin.

DAYTON SUPERIOR CORPORATION

7777 Washington Village Dr., Ste. 130	CEO: Eric R. (Rick) Zimmerman
Dayton, OH 45459	CFO: Edward J. Puisis
Phone: 937-428-6360	HR: Kenneth Tynes
Fax: 937-428-9560	FYE: December 31
Web: www.daytonsuperior.com	Type: Private

Superior products are all in a day's work for Dayton Superior. The company makes metal accessories and forms for keeping concrete and masonry nonresidential structures in place while under construction. Dayton Superior's sales come largely from lines comprising concrete accessories, such as anchoring and bracing for walls and bridge support framework. It also makes masonry products, welded dowel assemblies, paving products, and corrosion-preventing epoxy coatings and other chemicals. The company's rental equipment includes concrete forming systems and shoring systems. In 2009 Dayton Superior emerged from Chapter 11 bankruptcy protection as a private company burdened by less debt and lower interest expenses.

	Annual Growth	12/04	12/05	12/06	12/07	12/08
Sales ($ mil.)	3.3%	418.6	419.0	479.3	483.0	475.9
Net income ($ mil.)	—	(48.7)	(114.7)	(18.0)	(6.7)	(11.9)
Employees	(4.7%)	1,700	1,700	1,600	1,700	1,400

DB PROFESSIONALS, INC.

620 SW 5th Ave., Ste. 610	CEO: Shankar Viswanathan
Portland, OR 97204	CFO: —
Phone: 503-226-6586	HR: —
Fax: 503-226-6786	FYE: December 31
Web: www.dbpi.com	Type: Subsidiary

DB Professionals approaches your databases and other enterprise technology in a very professional manner. The company provides a variety of systems integration and other information technology consulting services including project management, enterprise architecture, network engineering, systems design, project management, systems integration, application development, and network engineering. It also specializes in IT staffing for companies in need of technical assistance. DB Professionals' customers come from industries such as financial services, manufacturing, health care, telecommunications, and retail. The company is a subsidiary of CDC Software.

	Annual Growth	12/04	12/05	12/06	12/07	12/08
Est. sales ($ mil.)	—	—	—	—	—	17.9
Employees	—	—	—	—	—	130

DC SHOES, INC.

1333 Keystone Way, Unit A
Vista, CA 92081
Phone: 760-599-2999
Fax: 760-597-2511
Web: www.dcshoes.com

CEO: Craig Stephenson
CFO: —
HR: Carol Sherman
FYE: October 31
Type: Subsidiary

Having developed its own version of the culture club, DC Shoes was among the first to capitalize on the skateboard, snowboard, and adventure sports niche market. The company designs technical footwear for skateboarding and snowboarding, as well as casual apparel, accessories, and other sports gear. In addition to its standalone retail shops in New York and Los Angeles, DC Shoes markets its products online and through such retailers as Macy's and Pacific Sunwear. Co-founders Damon Way and Ken Block sold the firm to Quiksilver in 2004 to the tune of $87 million. Quiksilver, which had been under pressure to sell assets to help alleviate its debt, appears content to keep DC Shoes in its closet.

DCB FINANCIAL CORP

110 Riverbend Ave.
Lewis Center, OH 43035
Phone: 740-657-7000
Fax: 740-657-7901
Web: www.dcbfinancialcorp.com

OTC: DCBF
CEO: David J. Folkwein
CFO: John A. Ustaszewski
HR: Brian E. Stanfill
FYE: December 31
Type: Public

DCB Financial is the holding company for The Delaware County Bank and Trust, which serves individual and commercial customers through some 20 branches in central Ohio. The bank offers traditional deposit products and services including checking and savings accounts, safe deposit facilities, and IRAs. Its loan portfolio includes commercial mortgages, residential mortgages, and other commercial and consumer loans; the company has increasingly focused on construction loans. The Delaware County Bank and Trust also provides financial services such as brokerage and wealth management.

	Annual Growth	12/05	12/06	12/07	12/08	12/09
Assets ($ mil.)	(0.6%)	690.9	681.9	680.8	712.6	675.0
Net income ($ mil.)	—	7.6	7.4	0.1	0.3	(4.2)
Market value ($ mil.)	(30.4%)	105.9	109.7	59.5	32.9	24.9
Employees	1.0%	207	224	228	243	215

DCI MARKETING INC.

2727 W. Good Hope Rd.
Milwaukee, WI 53209
Phone: 414-228-7000
Fax: 414-228-3421
Web: www.dcimarketing.com

CEO: Joseph (Joe) Asfour
CFO: Terry Matchulat
HR: Coreen Foster
FYE: December 31
Type: Subsidiary

DCI Marketing provides retail point-of-purchase (POP) display design, product development, and marketing services. Catering primarily to auto dealers, the company assists customers including Mazda, Motorola, Harley-Davidson, and Subaru with the development of retail displays and marketing communication strategies including direct mail and Web and mobile marketing. The firm also offers architectural and engineering services to retailers. Besides the auto industry, DCI draws clients from sectors such as consumer electronics, packaged goods, gaming, and wireless communications. Founded in 1944 by Lloyd Sauer, the company is part of the Cannon Merchandising unit owned by UK-based engineering firm IMI.

DCP MIDSTREAM PARTNERS, LP

370 17th St., Ste. 2775
Denver, CO 80202
Phone: 303-633-2900
Fax: 303-605-2225
Web: www.dcppartners.com

NYSE: DPM
CEO: Mark A. Borer
CFO: Angela A. Minas
HR: —
FYE: December 31
Type: Public

DCP Midstream Partners is the publicly traded entity of DCP Midstream LLC, one of the largest natural gas gatherers in North America and also the largest producer and one of the largest marketers of natural gas liquids (NGLs). Following the spin off of Spectra Energy from Duke Energy, Spectra Energy assumed Duke Energy's 50% holding in DCP (ConocoPhillips holds the other 50%). It also engages in natural gas compressing, treating, processing, transporting, and selling. DCP Midstream LLC also transports and sells NGLs and distributes propane wholesale. It operates six natural gas gathering systems (primarily in Arkansas, Louisiana, Oklahoma, and Texas), three NGL pipelines, and eight propane storage terminals.

	Annual Growth	12/05	12/06	12/07	12/08	12/09
Sales ($ mil.)	4.7%	785.2	795.7	877.8	1,288.9	942.4
Net income ($ mil.)	—	38.0	33.0	(15.8)	125.7	(18.1)
Market value ($ mil.)	4.8%	847.9	1,195.7	1,590.2	325.3	1,023.4
Employees	40.3%	64	118	155	148	248

DCT INDUSTRIAL TRUST INC.

518 17th St., Ste. 800
Denver, CO 80202
Phone: 303-597-2400
Fax: 303-228-2201
Web: www.dctindustrial.com

NYSE: DCT
CEO: Philip L. Hawkins
CFO: Stuart B. Brown
HR: —
FYE: December 31
Type: Public

DCT Industrial Trust is in da house! (The warehouse, that is.) The real estate investment trust (REIT) owns, develops, and manages bulk distribution warehouses, light industrial properties, and service centers located in high-density, high-volume markets in about 15 US states and Mexico. It owns interests in or manages about 450 buildings totaling some 75 million sq. ft. Bulk distribution warehouses account for a majority of the company's rentable space. Companies in the manufacturing, wholesale and retail trade, and transportation and warehousing sectors make up most of DCT's clients. Major tenants include CEVA Logisitics, Bridgestone, Technicolor, and UPS.

	Annual Growth	12/05	12/06	12/07	12/08	12/09
Sales ($ mil.)	17.5%	127.9	219.1	260.2	251.6	244.0
Net income ($ mil.)	—	(12.0)	(158.0)	14.2	9.1	(21.7)
Market value ($ mil.)	(24.8%)	—	2,491.7	1,965.9	1,068.5	1,060.0
Employees	(0.8%)	90	64	78	81	87

DDB WORLDWIDE COMMUNICATIONS GROUP INC.

437 Madison Ave.
New York, NY 10022
Phone: 212-415-2000
Fax: 212-415-3414
Web: www.ddb.com

CEO: Charles E. (Chuck) Brymer
CFO: Keith Bremer
HR: —
FYE: December 31
Type: Subsidiary

Advertising is whassup at DDB Worldwide Communications Group. One of the world's top creative ad agencies, DDB has produced memorable spots for such brands as McDonald's ("I'm lovin' it"), Avis ("We Try Harder"), Budweiser ("Whassup"), and Life Cereal ("Hey, Mikey"). It offers such services as brand building and consulting, campaign planning and management, and effectiveness measurement services in addition to creative ad development. The firm operates through more than 200 offices in about 90 countries. Founded in 1949 by Ned Doyle, Maxwell Dane, and William Bernbach, DDB is one of the flagship agencies of global media conglomerate Omnicom Group.

An in-depth profile of this company is available to Hoover's Online members at hoovers.com.

477

DDD GROUP PLC

London AIM: DDD

3000 Ocean Park Blvd., Ste. 1025
Santa Monica, CA 90405
Phone: 310-566-3340
Fax: 310-566-3380
Web: www.ddd.com

CEO: Christopher (Chris) Yewdall
CFO: —
HR: —
FYE: December 31
Type: Public

DDD Group has a multi-dimensional view of digital content. The company licenses 3D imaging software through its Dynamic Digital Depth subsidiaries. Its offerings include software for converting 2D digital content into stereoscopic 3D images, as well as conversion and consulting services. Advertisers, broadcasters, scientists, and software developers are among the customers that utilize DDD Group's technology to enhance their products. Though its corporate headquarters is in the US, DDD trades on the London Stock Exchange. It also has offices in Australia.

	Annual Growth	12/05	12/06	12/07	12/08	12/09
Sales ($ mil.)	14.1%	1.3	0.6	0.7	0.9	2.2
Net income ($ mil.)	—	(2.0)	(3.4)	(2.4)	(2.0)	(1.5)
Market value ($ mil.)	(0.7%)	35.1	36.9	26.9	9.1	34.0
Employees	7.5%	18	18	24	23	24

DDI CORP.

NASDAQ (GM): DDIC

1220 N. Simon Circle
Anaheim, CA 92806
Phone: 714-688-7200
Fax: 714-688-7400
Web: www.ddiglobal.com

CEO: Mikel H. Williams
CFO: J. Michael (Mike) Dodson
HR: —
FYE: December 31
Type: Public

DDi takes a dynamic approach to manufacturing. DDi provides time-critical, customized electronics design, fabrication, and assembly services for makers of communications and networking gear, computers, medical instruments, and military equipment. The company produces complete electronics systems, as well as subsystems, such as printed circuit boards (PCBs), backpanels, and wire harnesses. Its more than 1,000 customers include electronics manufacturers, such as Intel and Tyco Electronics. Nearly half of orders are filled within 10 days, and some are turned around in 24 hours. DDi derives over 90% of its business from customers in North America.

	Annual Growth	12/05	12/06	12/07	12/08	12/09
Sales ($ mil.)	(3.8%)	184.6	198.1	181.1	190.8	158.0
Net income ($ mil.)	—	(64.0)	(7.2)	0.7	(33.4)	1.8
Market value ($ mil.)	(7.4%)	132.0	143.0	111.8	61.2	97.1
Employees	3.5%	1,400	1,300	1,300	1,230	1,604

D. E. SHAW & CO., L.P.

120 W. 45th St., 39th Fl., Tower 45
New York, NY 10036
Phone: 212-478-0000
Fax: 212-478-0100
Web: www.deshaw.com

CEO: Max Stone
CFO: Christopher Zaback
HR: —
FYE: December 31
Type: Private

D. E. Shaw & Co. hopes to find the formula for investment success. The firm, known for its critical thinking and scientific analysis, applies quantitative trading strategies, as well as human research and analysis, to manage hedge funds and other investments. It invests in public and private securities, commodities, real estate, and companies involved in technology, health care, and financial services. D. E. Shaw & Co. also makes venture capital investments and acquires assets of distressed companies. The firm has nearly $30 billion in invested and committed capital. It operates from more than a dozen offices in North America, Europe, the Middle East, and Asia.

DEALER TIRE LLC

3711 Chester Ave.
Cleveland, OH 44114
Phone: 216-432-0088
Fax: 216-881-7923
Web: www.dealertire.com

CEO: Scott Mueller
CFO: Pete Waters
HR: Pete Crowley
FYE: December 31
Type: Private

Dealer Tire tirelessly makes deals to meet the tire needs of America's car dealers. The company is the only US tire dealer focused exclusively on delivering tires and accessories direct from OEMs to auto dealers nationwide. Dealer Tire is a factory-authorized tire supplier to more than 6,000 dealerships, primarily those of leading German and Japanese automakers. It assists OEMs with their tire programs as well as builds replacement tire and customer satisfaction strategies at its car dealerships. Tire brands distributed by the company include BF-Goodrich, Continental, Dunlop, Goodyear, Michelin, Pirelli, and Yokohama. Dealer Tire is led by its founder's grandsons, CEO Scott Mueller, and president Dean Mueller.

DEALERTRACK HOLDINGS, INC.

NASDAQ (GS): TRAK

1111 Marcus Ave., Ste. M04
Lake Success, NY 11042
Phone: 516-734-3600
Fax: 516-734-3809
Web: www.dealertrack.com

CEO: Mark F. O'Neil
CFO: Eric D. Jacobs
HR: Ana M. Herrera
FYE: December 31
Type: Public

DealerTrack Holdings helps car dealers play their cards right in the financing game. The company provides Web-based software that links automotive dealerships with banks, finance companies, credit unions, credit reporting agencies, and other players in the car sales and financing process. DealerTrack connects clients in the US and Canada to its network of auto dealers, financing sources, and other service and information providers. The company, which generates revenues through subscriptions and transaction-based fees, also offers tools that automate credit application processing, ensure document legal compliance, and execute electronic financing contracts.

	Annual Growth	12/05	12/06	12/07	12/08	12/09
Sales ($ mil.)	17.0%	120.2	173.3	233.8	242.7	225.6
Net income ($ mil.)	—	4.5	19.3	19.8	1.7	(4.3)
Market value ($ mil.)	(2.7%)	845.6	1,185.7	1,349.0	479.2	757.3
Employees	22.2%	539	670	1,000	1,100	1,200

DEAN & DELUCA

560 Broadway
New York, NY 10012
Phone: 212-226-6800
Fax: 800-781-4050
Web: www.deandeluca.com

CEO: Mark Daley
CFO: Justin P. Seamonds
HR: —
FYE: January 31
Type: Private

You could go to Manhattan's tony SoHo neighborhood for a taste of Dean & DeLuca, but increasingly, you don't have to. The purveyor of pricey gourmet foods, wines, cheeses, baked goods, and high-end kitchenware operates about 15 specialty markets and cafes in select US cities and is growing rapidly in Japan. The company opened its first cafe in the Middle East, located in Dubai, in early 2008 and now has a store in Kuwait. Dean & DeLuca also offers its goods through consumer and corporate gift catalogs, as well as online. It has operated in Japan since 2003 through a distribution agreement with ITOCHU there. Joel Dean and Giorgio DeLuca opened their first market in SoHo in 1977.

DEAN FOODS COMPANY

NYSE: DF

2515 McKinney Ave., Ste. 1200
Dallas, TX 75201
Phone: 214-303-3400
Fax: 214-303-3499
Web: www.deanfoods.com

CEO: Gregg L. Engles
CFO: John F. (Jack) Callahan Jr.
HR: Paul T. Moskowitz
FYE: December 31
Type: Public

Dean Foods has become the king of milk by taking over other dairies' thrones. A leading US producer of fluid milk and other dairy products, Dean has grown and continues to grow through acquisitions. Its retail and foodservice dairy products are sold under more than 50 national, regional, and private-label brands, including Borden, Pet, Country Fresh, and Meadow Gold. In addition, the company manufactures coffee creamers (International Delight), dips and yogurt, ice cream, butter, cottage cheese, and specialty dairy products (lactose-free and organic milk, soy milk, and flavored milks). Dean owns and operates a number of smaller dairy companies, including Horizon Organic, Berkeley Farms, and Garelick Farms.

	Annual Growth	12/05	12/06	12/07	12/08	12/09
Sales ($ mil.)	1.5%	10,505.6	10,098.6	11,821.9	12,454.6	11,158.4
Net income ($ mil.)	(8.8%)	329.1	225.4	131.4	183.8	227.8
Market value ($ mil.)	(16.8%)	6,835.9	7,674.5	4,694.0	3,261.8	3,274.5
Employees	0.1%	27,030	26,348	25,585	25,820	27,157

DEAN HEALTH SYSTEMS, INC.

1808 W. Beltline Hwy.
Madison, WI 53713
Phone: 608-250-1075
Fax: 608-250-1441
Web: www.deancare.com

CEO: Craig Samitt
CFO: Steven R. Caldwell
HR: —
FYE: December 31
Type: Private

Dean Health Systems manages a school of medical professionals. The multi-specialty physicians group is affiliated with St. Mary's Hospital in Madison, Wisconsin. It operates about 70 clinics and other facilities throughout the southern part of the state. Most of its clinics provide primary care services such as family and internal medicine, as well as specialty care in such areas as cardiology, mental health, and orthopedics. The firm also operates several outpatient surgery centers, pharmacy locations, ophthalmology clinics, and fitness centers. Established in 1904, Dean Health is 95% physician-owned, with the remainder controlled by SSM Healthcare, the parent of St. Mary's Hospital.

DEARBORN BANCORP, INC.

NASDAQ (GM): DEAR

1360 Porter St.
Dearborn, MI 48124
Phone: 313-565-5700
Fax: 313-561-2291
Web: www.fidbank.com

CEO: Michael J. Ross
CFO: Jeffrey L. Karafa
HR: —
FYE: December 31
Type: Public

Frankly, my Dearborn, they do give a damn. Dearborn Bancorp is the holding company for Fidelity Bank (formerly Community Bank of Dearborn). The bank has about 30 branches and lending centers in suburban Detroit and points west, offering checking and savings accounts, money market accounts, and CDs. Lending activities include commercial mortgages (more than 70% of the company's loan portfolio), as well as residential, business, consumer, and construction loans. Dearborn Bancorp also has a subsidiary that provides auditing and consulting services to other community banks. Community Bank of Dearborn changed its name after its parent company acquired Fidelity Bank in 2007.

	Annual Growth	12/05	12/06	12/07	12/08	12/09
Assets ($ mil.)	8.7%	706.5	855.9	1,047.0	1,121.9	986.5
Net income ($ mil.)	—	7.5	7.8	3.2	(31.9)	(61.2)
Market value ($ mil.)	(62.1%)	172.6	146.1	59.4	12.8	3.6
Employees	7.8%	151	161	225	205	204

DEARBORN MID-WEST CONVEYOR CO.

20334 Superior Rd.
Taylor, MI 48180
Phone: 734-288-4400
Fax: 734-288-1914
Web: www.dmwcc.com

CEO: Frank Warmoth
CFO: Sherry Gavito
HR: —
FYE: December 31
Type: Subsidiary

In the march toward automation, Dearborn Mid-West Conveyor (DMW) steps to a faster beat. The company designs, manufactures, and installs a range of material handling systems. Its lineup divides between bulk materials handling, auto, parcel post, and industrial manufacturing systems. The short list includes conveyors, belts and feeders, chutes, and systems for assembly, storage, sorting, and transfer. DMW sells largely to OEMs such as Ford and Chrysler, and the U.S. Postal Service. It makes materials handling equipment as well for agricultural and mining operations, rail and shipping facilities, and power plants. DMW is owned by private equity firms Knox Lawrence International and Falcon Investment Advisors.

DEARBORN WHOLESALE GROCERS L.P.

2801 S. Western Ave.
Chicago, IL 60608
Phone: 773-254-4300
Fax: 773-847-3838
Web: www.dearbornwholesale.com

CEO: Sherwin Friedman
CFO: Peter Westerberg
HR: —
FYE: June 30
Type: Private

Dearborn Wholesale Grocers is a full-service food distributor for retail food outlets primarily in the Chicago area. The family-owned company delivers more than 23,000 items including frozen and refrigerated foods, tobacco, health and beauty products, and general merchandise to supermarkets, convenience stores, and delis. It supplies more than 7,000 locations in Illinois, Indiana, Michigan, and Wisconsin. Dearborn Wholesale also operates four Cash & Carry stores in Chicago and another in Milwaukee. The business traces its roots back to 1919 when the Friedman family acquired wholesale grocery business C. Moon and Sons.

DEB SHOPS, INC.

9401 Blue Grass Rd.
Philadelphia, PA 19114
Phone: 215-676-6000
Fax: 215-698-7151
Web: www.debshops.com

CEO: Diane M. Paccione
CFO: Barry J. Susson
HR: —
FYE: January 31
Type: Private

Deb Shops just, like, knows fashion, totally, you know? Targeting fashion-conscious juniors, teens, and plus-sized misses, Deb Shops sells moderately priced accessories, coats, dresses, lingerie, shoes, and sportswear through more than 340 stores nationwide. The retailer also sells apparel online. The DEB chain makes up almost all of the company's stores. About half of all DEB stores contain plus-size departments. Other chains include CSO (outlet stores) and Tops 'N Bottoms (apparel for young men and juniors). Founded in 1932 as Joy Hosiery, Deb Shops was acquired by investment firm Lee Equity Partners (LEP) for about $395 million in 2007.

An in-depth profile of this company is available to Hoover's Online members at hoovers.com.

479

DEBEVOISE & PLIMPTON LLP

919 3rd Ave.
New York, NY 10022
Phone: 212-909-6000
Fax: 212-909-6836
Web: www.debevoise.com

CEO: Martin F. (Rick) Evans
CFO: Jeffrey Miller
HR: Catherine Fagan
FYE: December 31
Type: Partnership

A leading advocate for the interests of domestic and international businesses, Debevoise & Plimpton has about 750 lawyers in more than half a dozen offices in the US, Europe, and the Asia/Pacific region. Corporate law represents the firm's largest practice area, but its expertise also spans litigation, tax, and trusts and estates. High-profile clients have included American Airlines, AXA Financial, MetLife, the NFL, and PriceWaterhouseCoopers. Eli Debevoise (a descendant of Eli Whitney) helped found the firm in 1931; after Francis Plimpton (father of author George Plimpton) joined in 1933, the firm's name was changed to Debevoise & Plimpton.

DEBT RESOLVE, INC.

NYSE Amex: DRV

707 Westchester Ave., Ste. L7
White Plains, NY 10604
Phone: 914-949-5500
Fax: 914-428-3044
Web: www.debtresolve.com

CEO: James G. Brakke
CFO: David Rainey
HR: Nancy Hutter
FYE: December 31
Type: Public

Debt Resolve isn't intimidated by mountains of debt. The company provides a hosted software service that allows credit card companies and collection agencies to collect money from consumers who are past due on their credit card bills. The online service, branded as DebtResolve, uses an Internet-based bidding system that allows debtors and creditors to agree on acceptable repayment schedules. Customers include banks and other credit originators, credit card issuers, and third-party collection agencies, as well as assignees and buyers of consumer debt.

	Annual Growth	12/05	12/06	12/07	12/08	12/09
Sales ($ mil.)	—	0.0	0.1	2.8	0.2	0.1
Net income ($ mil.)	—	(5.4)	(21.7)	(12.6)	(10.5)	(13.1)
Market value ($ mil.)	(58.7%)	—	203.5	53.3	0.6	14.4
Employees	(26.4%)	17	116	33	5	5

DECHERT LLP

Cira Centre, 2929 Arch St.
Philadelphia, PA 19104
Phone: 215-994-4000
Fax: 215-994-2222
Web: www.dechert.com

CEO: Barton J. (Bart) Winokur
CFO: —
HR: Mary Ann Christ
FYE: December 31
Type: Partnership

The Dechert law firm might have a single name on its shingle, but it's no solo practice. The firm's 1,000-plus lawyers practice from a dozen offices in the US (mainly in eastern states) and about five more in Europe. Dechert focuses on work related to business transactions, government relations (involving both the US and the European Union), litigation, and tax. Within those broad areas, the firm's specialties include asset management, corporate and securities, intellectual property, product liability, and real estate finance. Dechert draws clients from industries such as energy, financial services, media, retail, and technology. The firm was founded in 1875.

	Annual Growth	12/04	12/05	12/06	12/07	12/08
Sales ($ mil.)	(2.5%)	—	—	—	836.5	816.0
Employees	—	—	—	—	—	—

⊞ DECKERS OUTDOOR CORPORATION

NASDAQ (GS): DECK

495-A S. Fairview Ave.
Goleta, CA 93117
Phone: 805-967-7611
Fax: 805-967-7862
Web: www.deckers.com

CEO: Angel R. Martinez
CFO: Thomas A. George
HR: Graciela Montgomery
FYE: December 31
Type: Public

There's no business like shoe business for Deckers Outdoor. It makes and markets Teva sports sandals — a cross between a hiking boot and a flip-flop. They're used for walking, hiking, and rafting, among other pursuits. While imitations flood the market, the company distinguishes Teva from its numerous competitors by avoiding distribution in off-price outlets. Other product lines include Simple and TSUBO (casual footwear), as well as iconic UGG (sheepskin boots/shoes). Deckers Outdoor's products are made by independent contractors in Asia, Australia, and New Zealand. It sells them through 10 US retail stores, independent distributors, catalogs, the Internet, and two company-owned outlets in the UK.

	Annual Growth	12/05	12/06	12/07	12/08	12/09
Sales ($ mil.)	32.4%	264.8	304.4	448.9	689.4	813.2
Net income ($ mil.)	38.4%	31.8	31.5	66.4	73.9	116.8
Market value ($ mil.)	38.5%	356.2	773.2	1,999.8	1,030.1	1,311.9
Employees	45.2%	225	276	370	780	1,000

DECORATOR INDUSTRIES, INC.

NYSE Amex: DII

10011 Pines Blvd., Ste. 201
Pembroke Pines, FL 33024
Phone: 954-436-8909
Fax: 954-436-1778
Web: www.decoratorindustries.com

CEO: William A. Johnson
CFO: Michael K. Solomon
HR: Diana Hinton
FYE: December 31
Type: Public

Travelers can sleep easier, thanks to Decorator Industries. The firm makes and sells window coverings that keep the light out, and bedspreads and comforters that keep the warmth in. Products include draperies, curtains, blinds, valance boards, pillows, cushions, and more. Decorator Industries sells its merchandise to manufactured home builders, makers of recreational vehicles (RVs), and to hotels, motels, and other customers nationwide. CMH Manufacturing accounted for more than 15% of company's sales in 2009. Sales to Fleetwood Enterprises, maker of RVs and manufactured housing, generated about 13% of its 2008 sales. Decorator Industries was established in 1953. William Bassett owns about 11% of the company.

	Annual Growth	12/05	12/06	12/07	12/08	12/09
Sales ($ mil.)	(22.1%)	50.5	52.2	46.1	39.6	18.6
Net income ($ mil.)	—	1.4	0.4	(0.8)	(2.6)	(3.0)
Market value ($ mil.)	(42.5%)	25.1	23.1	13.3	2.0	2.7
Employees	(27.7%)	731	650	600	270	200

DECORIZE, INC.

OTC: DCZI

1938 E. Phelps
Springfield, MO 65802
Phone: 417-879-3326
Fax: 417-879-3330
Web: www.decorize.com

CEO: Stephen R. (Steve) Crowder
CFO: Daniel (Dan) Graham
HR: —
FYE: June 30
Type: Public

Rather than standardize, Decorize wants to spice things up in your living space. The company, founded in 2000, manufactures and wholesales imported home furnishings. In addition to furniture, Decorize imports accent pieces including lamps, frames, vases, mirrors, and baskets. It sources its wares directly to retailers from factories in China, Indonesia, the Philippines, and India. Decorize consolidated its brands in recent years. Products marketed to independent retailers (76% of 2008 revenue) maintain the GuildMaster brand, while products targeting large retailers (24% of 2008 revenue) are marketed under the Decorize brand name. Customers include Klaussner Furniture, Dillard's, OfficeMax, and Williams-Sonoma.

	Annual Growth	6/04	6/05	6/06	6/07	*6/08
Sales ($ mil.)	5.9%	12.1	10.8	9.2	15.9	15.2
Net income ($ mil.)	—	(4.4)	(2.6)	(2.2)	(0.7)	(0.6)
Employees	42.9%	133	131	324	432	554

*Most recent year available

An in-depth profile of this company is available to Hoover's Online members at hoovers.com. ⊞

DEEP DOWN, INC.

OTC: DPDW

8827 W. Sam Houston Pkwy. North, Ste. 100
Houston, TX 77040
Phone: 281-517-5000
Fax: 281-517-5001
Web: www.deepdowninc.com

CEO: Ronald E. (Ron) Smith
CFO: Eugene L. Butler
HR: —
FYE: December 31
Type: Public

Deep down, Deep Down understands itself to be in the subsea sector. The company (formerly medical equipment provider Mediquip Holdings) acquired Deep Down in a reverse merger, taking on that company's subsea service business as well as its name. An umbilical and flexible pipe installation engineering and installation management company, Deep Down also fabricates component parts for subsea distribution systems and assemblies that specialize in the development of offshore subsea fields. The company's product include umbilicals, flowlines, distribution systems, pipeline terminations, controls, winches, and launch and retrieval systems. It serves clients in the Gulf of Mexico and internationally.

	Annual Growth	1/06	*12/06	12/07	12/08	12/09
Sales ($ mil.)	89.1%	2.3	1.0	19.4	35.8	29.4
Net income ($ mil.)	—	(3.3)	(3.3)	1.0	(4.3)	(16.1)
Market value ($ mil.)	(40.1%)	195.9	43.6	190.1	31.0	25.2
Employees	62.2%	23	49	94	169	159

*Fiscal year change

DEERE & COMPANY

NYSE: DE

1 John Deere Place
Moline, IL 61265
Phone: 309-765-8000
Fax: 309-765-5671
Web: www.deere.com

CEO: Samuel R. (Sam) Allen
CFO: James M. Field
HR: Mertroe B. (Mert) Hornbuckle
FYE: October 31
Type: Public

Deere & Company interested in seeing its customers go to seed and grow. The company, one of the world's largest makers of farm equipment, is also a leading producer of construction, forestry, and commercial and residential lawn care equipment. Deere operates through three business segments: Agriculture & Turf and Construction & Forestry make up its Equipment Operations; the Credit division is part of Financial Services. Deere, which is famous for its "Nothing Runs Like A Deere" brand marketing campaign, operates factories and sales offices around the world. With the majority of its sales made in North America, Deere counts over 2,500 distribution branches throughout the US and Canada.

	Annual Growth	10/05	10/06	10/07	10/08	10/09
Sales ($ mil.)	1.3%	21,930.5	22,147.8	24,082.2	28,437.6	23,112.4
Net income ($ mil.)	(11.9%)	1,446.8	1,693.8	1,821.7	2,052.8	873.5
Market value ($ mil.)	10.7%	12,889.6	18,083.2	32,903.7	16,381.8	19,351.4
Employees	2.0%	47,400	46,500	52,000	56,700	51,300

DEERE-HITACHI CONSTRUCTION MACHINERY CORPORATION

1000 Deere Hitachi Rd.
Kernersville, NC 27285
Phone: 336-996-8100
Fax: 336-996-8200
Web: www.hitachiconstruction.com

CEO: Alan L. Seeba
CFO: Bryan Swerbinsky
HR: —
FYE: December 31
Type: Joint venture

Don't dig your grave with your own knife and fork — Deere-Hitachi Construction Machinery (DHCM) produces and sells the machines that will do the job. Offering both new and used equipment, its lineup includes compact excavators, rigid frame trucks, forestry excavators, and mining excavators and shovels. DHCM was formed in 1988 as a 50/50 joint venture between Deere & Company and Hitachi subsidiary Hitachi Construction Machinery Co. The venture leverages the manufacturing and marketing muscle of the two companies, streamlining operations and customer support across North, Central, and South America. DHCM is one of a series of deals between manufacturing giants fueling global construction equipment expansion.

	Annual Growth	12/04	12/05	12/06	12/07	12/08
Est. sales ($ mil.)	—	—	—	—	—	103.7
Employees	—	—	—	—	—	900

DEERFIELD CAPITAL CORP.

NYSE: DFR

1 O'Hare Center, 9th Fl., 6250 N. River Rd.
Rosemont, IL 60018
Phone: 773-380-1600
Fax: 773-380-1601
Web: www.deerfieldcapital.com

CEO: Jonathan W. Trutter
CFO: Francis P. Straub III
HR: —
FYE: December 31
Type: Public

Specialty finance company Deerfield Capital Corp. grazes on a green pasture of investments. Through its subsidiary, Deerfield Capital Management (DCM), the company invests in and manages client assets such as residential mortgage-backed securities (RMBS), bank loans, government securities, and asset-backed securities. DCM has nearly $10 billion of assets under management. Deerfield offers its clients some 27 investment products, which include separately managed accounts and a private investment fund. Deerfield Capital Management is acquiring Charlotte-based investment manager Nova Credit Investment Management.

	Annual Growth	12/05	12/06	12/07	12/08	12/09
Assets ($ mil.)	(45.6%)	8,203.8	9,250.0	7,788.0	996.9	720.2
Net income ($ mil.)	9.9%	45.9	71.6	(96.2)	(757.4)	66.9
Market value ($ mil.)	(57.2%)	884.4	1,092.9	516.4	23.0	29.7
Employees	(15.6%)	132	148	130	67	67

DEI HOLDINGS, INC.

Pink Sheets: DEIX

1 Viper Way
Vista, CA 92081
Phone: 760-598-6200
Fax: 760-598-6400
Web: www.deiholdings.com

CEO: James E. (Jim) Minarik
CFO: Kevin P. Duffy
HR: —
FYE: December 31
Type: Public

If it is protected by one of these Vipers, you may want to step away from the vehicle. Formerly Directed Electronics, DEI Holdings is one of the world's top manufacturers of auto security systems, including products sold under such brands as Viper, Python, and Hornet. It also makes keyless entry and remote start systems for automobiles and offers GPS tracking systems. In addition, the company's Polk Audio and Definitive Technology units are leading makers of car audio equipment, including speakers and amplifiers. DEI sells its products in more than 70 countries in North America, Europe, and Asia.

	Annual Growth	12/04	12/05	12/06	12/07	*12/08
Sales ($ mil.)	(34.5%)	—	—	—	401.1	262.9
Net income ($ mil.)	—	—	—	—	(140.0)	(55.0)
Employees	—	—	—	—	—	—

*Most recent year available

DEL FRISCO'S RESTAURANT GROUP, LLC

224 East Douglas, Ste. 700
Wichita, KS 67202
Phone: 316-264-8899
Fax: 316-264-2093
Web: www.delfriscos.com

CEO: Mark S. Mednansky
CFO: Jon W. Howie
HR: M. Orloff
FYE: December 31
Type: Private

You might say this company has a one-two punch for meat and potato lovers. Del Frisco's Restaurant Group operates two upscale steakhouse chains, Del Frisco's Double Eagle Steak House and Sullivan's Steakhouse, with about 25 locations in 15 states. Its more than half dozen Del Frisco's locations offer upscale dining in a contemporary surrounding, while its somewhat less pricey Sullivan's chain features an atmosphere reminiscent of a Chicago-style steakhouse. Both concepts serve premium cuts of beef along with seafood, lamb, and pork dishes, and both offer an extensive wine list. The company is controlled by Dallas-based private equity firm Lone Star Funds.

An in-depth profile of this company is available to Hoover's Online members at hoovers.com.

481

DEL GLOBAL TECHNOLOGIES CORP.   OTC: DGTC

11550 W. King St.	CEO: John J. Quicke
Franklin Park, IL 60131	CFO: Mark A. Zorko
Phone: 847-288-7000	HR: —
Fax: 847-288-7011	FYE: July 31
Web: www.delglobal.com	Type: Public

Del Global Technologies can see the beauty of the inner You. The firm makes medical and dental X-ray systems used by hospitals and doctors, dentists, and veterinarians. It sells its products through distributors worldwide under the Villa, Del, Universal, and DynaRad brand names and provides some of its dental products under private-label agreements. Through its RFI subsidiary, Del Global Technologies also makes precision electronic components and subassemblies for makers of everything from weapons systems to satellites to MRI machines; RFI's brands include Filtron, Sprague, and Stanley.

	Annual Growth	7/05	7/06	7/07	7/08	7/09
Sales ($ mil.)	(1.4%)	84.9	83.0	104.2	108.3	80.4
Net income ($ mil.)	—	0.4	0.1	3.8	3.0	(4.1)
Market value ($ mil.)	(31.3%)	61.3	39.8	56.8	34.1	13.6
Employees	(6.3%)	341	314	331	310	263

DEL MONTE FOODS COMPANY   NYSE: DLM

1 Market @ The Landmark	CEO: Richard G. Wolford
San Francisco, CA 94105	CFO: David L. Meyers
Phone: 415-247-3000	HR: Richard W. Muto
Fax: 415-247-3565	FYE: April 30
Web: www.delmonte.com	Type: Public

How does Del Monte's garden grow? Very well indeed. It is one of the US's largest manufacturers of branded canned fruit, vegetables, and soups and broths. Its flagship products (canned corn, green beans, peas, peaches, pears, and pineapples) are purchased mostly from US growers. The company makes tomato-based foods such as ketchup and tomato sauce. Its retail brands include College Inn, Del Monte, and Contadina. Del Monte makes pets grow too, with a stable of pet-food and -treat brands, including 9Lives, Gravy Train, Milk-Bone, and Meow Mix. The company also makes private-label products and food ingredients for other food manufacturers, and offers products to foodservice operators.

	Annual Growth	4/05	4/06	4/07	4/08	4/09
Sales ($ mil.)	3.3%	3,180.9	2,998.6	3,414.9	3,736.8	3,626.9
Net income ($ mil.)	9.9%	117.9	169.9	112.6	133.1	172.3
Market value ($ mil.)	(7.8%)	2,071.0	2,315.3	2,303.4	1,791.1	1,499.2
Employees	(25.5%)	17,500	16,700	18,200	18,100	5,400

DEL TACO HOLDINGS, INC.

25521 Commercentre Dr.	CEO: Paul J. B. Murphy III
Lake Forest, CA 92630	CFO: Steven L. (Steve) Brake
Phone: 949-462-9300	HR: Arlene Petokas
Fax: 949-462-7444	FYE: December 31
Web: www.deltaco.com	Type: Private

This taco stand caters to the burger and fries crowd, as well as the burrito fans. Formerly Sagittarius Brands, Del Taco Holdings operates the Del Taco fast food chain, the #2 quick-service Mexican brand in the US (behind YUM! Brand's Taco Bell division). The restaurants offer tacos, burritos, and quesadillas, along with such traditional fast-food fare as hamburgers, french fries, and shakes. The chain was founded in 1964 and has more than 500 locations found mostly in California and about 15 other western states. About 290 of the eateries are company-owned while the rest are franchised. Formed in 2004, Del Taco Holdings is backed by investors led by Charlesbank Capital Partners and Leonard Green & Partners.

DELAWARE MANAGEMENT HOLDINGS, INC.

2005 Market St.	CEO: Patrick P. (Pat) Coyne
Philadephia, PA 19103	CFO: Philip N. Russo
Phone: 215-255-2300	HR: —
Fax: —	FYE: December 31
Web: www.delawareinvestments.com	Type: Subsidiary

Delaware Management Holdings, which does business as Delaware Investments, provides investment management services to institutional and individual clients. The company manages some 40 mutual funds with value, core, and growth equity, fixed income, and international strategies. Other products for consumers include managed accounts, insurance, and retirement plans. Delaware Investments also offers separate accounts and mutual funds to its more than 500 institutional clients, including corporations, retirement plans, endowments, foundations, and financial institutions. Macquarie Group bought the company in 2010 for nearly $430 million in cash.

	Annual Growth	12/04	12/05	12/06	12/07	12/08
Est. sales ($ mil.)	—	—	—	—	—	9.4
Employees	—	—	—	—	—	34

DELAWARE NORTH COMPANIES, INC.

40 Fountain Plaza	CEO: Jeremy M. Jacobs Sr.
Buffalo, NY 14202	CFO: Christopher J. Feeney
Phone: 716-858-5000	HR: Eileen Morgan
Fax: 716-858-5479	FYE: December 31
Web: www.delawarenorth.com	Type: Private

This company makes few concessions when it comes to selling hot dogs and sodas at the ball game. Delaware North is a leading provider of foodservices and hospitality at airports, sports stadiums, and tourist destinations throughout the US and in a handful of other countries. Its Sportservice division operates concessions at more than 50 major and minor league sporting arenas, while its Travel Hospitality Services division runs concessions and retail operations at more than 25 airports. In addition, Delaware North provides hospitality services at several tourist destinations, and it operates Boston's TD Garden arena. The family-owned company was founded in 1915 by brothers Charles, Louis, and Marvin Jacobs.

	Annual Growth	12/04	12/05	12/06	12/07	12/08
Sales ($ mil.)	6.7%	1,700.0	2,000.0	2,040.0	2,000.0	2,200.0
Employees	13.6%	30,000	40,000	50,000	40,000	50,000

DELCATH SYSTEMS, INC.   NASDAQ (CM): DCTH

600 5th Ave., 23rd Fl.	CEO: Eamonn P. Hobbs
New York, NY 10020	CFO: David A. McDonald
Phone: 212-489-2100	HR: —
Fax: 212-489-2102	FYE: December 31
Web: www.delcath.com	Type: Public

A cancer-stricken liver might be one lonely little organ, thanks to Delcath Systems. The development-stage company's technology allows blood infused with chemotherapy drugs to be pumped directly to the liver and then filtered before being returned to the general circulation system. By isolating the liver, Delcath's system is designed to protect other parts of the body from side effects and allow stronger doses of drugs to be used to treat liver cancer and malignant melanoma that has spread to the liver. The system is undergoing clinical trials to gain FDA approval. Delcath is also developing the system for use in treating other cancers and viral hepatitis.

	Annual Growth	12/05	12/06	12/07	12/08	12/09
Sales ($ mil.)	—	—	—	—	0.0	0.0
Net income ($ mil.)	—	—	—	—	(6.9)	(22.1)
Market value ($ mil.)	329.4%	—	—	—	44.4	190.5
Employees	183.3%	—	—	—	6	17

DELEK US HOLDINGS, INC.   NYSE: DK

7102 Commerce Way
Brentwood, TN 37027
Phone: 615-771-6701
Fax: 615-224-1185
Web: www.delekus.com

CEO: Ezra Uzi Yemin
CFO: Mark B. Cox
HR: Kathy Roadarmel
FYE: December 31
Type: Public

Delek US Holdings takes a delectable approach to the petroleum business — with a tasty balance of refining, fuel marketing, and retail operations. The company operates a 60,000 barrels-per-day refinery in Tyler, Texas. Delek US Holdings' marketing segment sells refined products on a wholesale basis in west Texas through company-owned and third-party operated terminals. On the retail side, its MAPCO Express business operates 482 convenience store/gas stations under the MAPCO Express, East Coast, Discount Food Mart and other banners in the southeastern US. Israeli-based conglomerate Delek Group owns 73.4% of the company.

	Annual Growth	12/05	12/06	12/07	12/08	12/09
Sales ($ mil.)	7.0%	2,031.9	3,207.7	4,097.1	4,615.2	2,666.7
Net income ($ mil.)	(67.7%)	64.4	93.0	96.4	26.5	0.7
Market value ($ mil.)	(25.4%)	—	890.6	1,099.3	287.5	370.1
Employees	8.0%	2,634	3,064	3,708	3,692	3,578

DELHAIZE AMERICA, INC.

2110 Executive Dr.
Salisbury, NC 28145
Phone: 704-633-8250
Fax: 704-636-5024
Web: www.delhaizegroup.com

CEO: Pierre-Olivier Beckers
CFO: Carol M. Herndon
HR: Ronald C. (Ron) Hodge
FYE: December 31
Type: Subsidiary

Belgian food retailer Delhaize "Le Lion" has a big cub — Delhaize America. A holding company for its growing number of US supermarket subsidiaries, Delhaize America runs one of the Southeast's biggest supermarket chains, Food Lion (about 1,320 stores located mainly in the Carolinas and Virginia, but also in eight other eastern seaboard states). It also operates the Hannaford Bros. supermarket chain (about 165 stores in New England and New York), and 70 Harveys supermarkets. In Florida, the firm has converted all of its grocery stores to the Sweetbay format. Parent Delhaize Group formed Delhaize America in 1999. The international food retailer bought the rest of Delhaize America in 2001.

	Annual Growth	12/04	12/05	12/06	12/07	12/08
Est. sales ($ mil.)	—	—	—	—	—	17,289.2
Employees	—	—	—	—	—	109,000

DELIA*S, INC.   NASDAQ (GM): DLIA

50 W. 23rd St.
New York, NY 10010
Phone: 212-590-6200
Fax: 212-590-6300
Web: www.delias.com

CEO: Walter Killough
CFO: David J. Dick
HR: —
FYE: January 31
Type: Public

If you think getting your teenager out of the mall will keep money in your pocket, think again: dELiA*s has her covered — or almost covered — with bare-midriff peasant tops, short shorts, and barely-there sandals, not to mention Feng Shui necklaces and iridescent lip gloss. The multi-channel retailer sells trendy clothing, accessories, and home furnishings to girls ages 12 to 19 (known as the Millennials) through about 100 dELiA*s stores, a catalog, and its website. The stores, located in about 30 states along the East Coast and in the Midwest, offer apparel and accessories under the dELiA*s and Alloy brands, and to a lesser extent national brands. Youth marketer Alloy spun off dELiA*s in 2005.

	Annual Growth	1/06	1/07	1/08	1/09	1/10
Sales ($ mil.)	(0.3%)	226.7	257.6	274.3	215.6	223.9
Net income ($ mil.)	—	(12.0)	5.8	(2.3)	17.2	(10.4)
Market value ($ mil.)	(33.8%)	291.2	322.8	73.6	62.3	56.0
Employees	16.3%	1,605	1,673	1,960	2,273	2,941

DELL INC.   NASDAQ (GS): DELL

1 Dell Way
Round Rock, TX 78682
Phone: 512-338-4400
Fax: 512-283-6161
Web: www.dell.com

CEO: Michael S. Dell
CFO: Brian T. Gladden
HR: Andrew C. (Andy) Esparza
FYE: January 31
Type: Public

Dell wants its name to ring from the desktop to the data center. One of the world's top suppliers of PCs, the company offers a broad range of technology products for the consumer, education, enterprise, and government sectors. In addition to a full line of desktop and notebook PCs, Dell offers network servers, data storage systems, printers, Ethernet switches, and peripherals, such as displays and projectors. It also markets third-party software and hardware. The company's growing services unit provides asset recovery, financing, infrastructure consulting, support, systems integration, and training. Dell generates nearly half of its revenues outside the US.

	Annual Growth	1/06	1/07	1/08	1/09	1/10
Sales ($ mil.)	(1.4%)	55,908.0	57,420.0	61,133.0	61,101.0	52,902.0
Net income ($ mil.)	(20.4%)	3,572.0	2,583.0	2,947.0	2,478.0	1,433.0
Market value ($ mil.)	(18.5%)	57,380.9	47,416.1	39,232.8	18,598.4	25,254.7
Employees	9.8%	66,100	90,500	88,200	78,900	96,000

DELMARVA POWER & LIGHT COMPANY

800 King St.
Wilmington, DE 19801
Phone: 302-451-5500
Fax: 302-283-6090
Web: www.delmarva.com

CEO: David M. (Dave) Velazquez
CFO: A. J. Kamerick
HR: —
FYE: December 31
Type: Subsidiary

Delmarva Power & Light (formerly Conectiv) has a delmarvellous proposition — connecting people to its energy supply network. The company is engaged in the transmission and distribution of electricity in Delaware and a portion of Maryland (the Eastern Shore); it delivers electricity to almost 500,000 customers. Delmarva Power & Light also provides natural gas (in Delaware) to more than 121,000 customers. The company has refocused on its core utility operations after several years of engagement in non-regulated energy activities. Delmarva Power & Light is a subsidiary of Pepco Holdings.

DELOITTE & TOUCHE LLP

Paramount Bldg., 1633 Broadway
New York, NY 10019
Phone: 212-489-1600
Fax: 212-489-1687
Web: www.deloitte.com

CEO: Nick Tommasino
CFO: —
HR: W. Stanton (Stan) Smith
FYE: May 31
Type: Subsidiary

Deloitte & Touche LLP touches on all aspects of accounting in the US. The firm is the accounting arm of Deloitte LLP, the US affiliate of international Big Four accounting firm Deloitte Touche Tohmatsu. Deloitte & Touche LLP offers auditing and management consulting services (the bulk of its revenues) and related services. Specialization areas include services for Asian businesses and mergers and acquisitions advisory services. Deloitte & Touche LLP has about 9,000 CPAs and operations in some 90 US cities. Deloitte LLP also manages other US subsidiaries that offer tax, consulting, and financial advisory services.

An in-depth profile of this company is available to Hoover's Online members at hoovers.com.

483

DELOITTE CONSULTING LLP

1633 Broadway	CEO: Punit Renjen
New York, NY 10019	CFO: John Kocjan
Phone: 212-618-4000	HR: Mike Fucci
Fax: 212-618-4500	FYE: May 31
Web: www.deloitte.com/dtt/section_node/0,1042,sid%253D26551,00.html	Type: Subsidiary

One of the world's largest consulting firms, Deloitte Consulting serves customers in industries such as aviation, consumer products and services, energy, financial services, health care, manufacturing, and technology, as well as government agencies. The firm's areas of expertise include human resources, information technology services, outsourcing, and strategy and operations. Along with accounting firm Deloitte & Touche, Deloitte Consulting is a unit of Deloitte LLP, which in turn is an affiliate of global accounting powerhouse Deloitte Touche Tohmatsu. Other Deloitte LLP units offer financial advisory and tax services.

DELOITTE LLP

Paramount Bldg., 1633 Broadway	CEO: Barry Salzberg
New York, NY 10019	CFO: —
Phone: 212-489-1600	HR: —
Fax: 212-489-1687	FYE: May 31
Web: www.deloitte.com/view/en_US/us	Type: Private

Deloitte LLP is the US member of Deloitte Touche Tohmatsu, one of the big four global accounting firms. It operates through four primary subsidiaries: Deloitte & Touche LLP, Deloitte Consulting, Deloitte Financial Advisory Services, and Deloitte Tax. The companies offer audit and enterprise risk services, consulting, tax advice and preparation, and financial advisory services. Industry specializations include automotive, banking, consumer products, life sciences, oil and gas, federal government, and technology. The company has 100 offices in about 90 US cities, employing some 8,900 CPAs. Deloitte's first US office dates back to New York City in 1900.

DELOITTE TOUCHE TOHMATSU

1633 Broadway	CEO: James H. (Jim) Quigley
New York, NY 10019	CFO: Jeffrey P. (Jeff) Rohr
Phone: 212-489-1600	HR: Peter May
Fax: 212-489-1687	FYE: May 31
Web: www.deloitte.com/global	Type: Private

This company is "deloitted" to make your acquaintance, particularly if you're a big business in need of accounting services. Deloitte Touche Tohmatsu (or Deloitte) is one of accounting's Big Four, along with Ernst & Young, KPMG, and PricewaterhouseCoopers. Deloitte operates through some 150 independent firms around the world, including US-based Deloitte LLP and its accountng arm, Deloitte & Touche LLP. Each independent member firm works in a specific geographic area offering audit, tax, consulting, and financial advisory services, in addition to human resources and technology services. Deloitte Touche Tohmatsu coordinates its member firms but does not provide services to clients.

	Annual Growth	5/05	5/06	5/07	5/08	5/09
Sales ($ mil.)	9.4%	18,200.0	20,000.0	23,100.0	27,400.0	26,100.0
Employees	8.6%	121,283	135,000	146,600	165,000	168,651

DELPHAX TECHNOLOGIES INC.

Pink Sheets: DLPX

6100 W. 110th St.	CEO: Dieter P. Schilling
Bloomington, MN 55438	CFO: Gregory S. Furness
Phone: 952-939-9000	HR: Les B. Weibye
Fax: 952-939-1151	FYE: September 30
Web: www.delphax.com	Type: Public

You don't have to be an oracle to know that Delphax Technologies doesn't like blank checks. The company makes digital print production systems based on its patented electron-beam imaging (EBI) technology for continuous roll-fed and cut-sheet printing applications. Its machines print addresses and numbers on checks, as well as print payroll and accounts payable checks with audit trail capabilities. Delphax's Imaggia II can print up to 300 pages per minute. Its Foliotronic finishing systems bind financial forms into books. Harland Clarke and RR Donnelly are the company's largest customers. While Delphax sells its products globally to more than 50 countries, about 80% of its sales are from the US.

DELPHI AUTOMOTIVE, LLP

5725 Delphi Dr.	CEO: Rodney O'Neal
Troy, MI 48098	CFO: Keith D. Stipp
Phone: 248-813-2000	HR: Kevin M. Butler
Fax: 248-813-2673	FYE: December 31
Web: www.delphi.com	Type: Private

Delphi has taken the long and winding road alone after being spun off from General Motors in 1999. A leading maker of auto parts, Delphi makes nearly everything mechanical and electrical/electronic that goes into cars. Its business divisions include Electrical/Electronic Architecture (vehicle electrical systems), Powertrain (engine, fuel, and emissions systems), Electronics & Safety (sensors, guidance systems, navigation and entertainment systems), and Thermal Systems (climate control, radiators, heat exchangers). Delphi operates in 32 countries worldwide. In a deal that gave control of the company to its lenders, Delphi Automotive, LLP (formerly Delphi Corp.) emerged from bankruptcy a private company in 2009.

	Annual Growth	12/04	12/05	12/06	12/07	12/08
Sales ($ mil.)	(10.9%)	28,622.0	26,947.0	26,392.0	22,283.0	18,060.0
Net income ($ mil.)	—	(4,753.0)	(2,340.0)	(5,467.0)	(3,065.0)	3,037.0
Employees	(5.7%)	185,200	184,200	171,400	169,500	146,600

DELPHI FINANCIAL GROUP, INC.

NYSE: DFG

1105 N. Market St., Ste. 1230	CEO: Robert Rosenkranz
Wilmington, DE 19899	CFO: Thomas W. Burghart
Phone: 302-478-5142	HR: —
Fax: 302-427-7663	FYE: December 31
Web: www.delphifin.com	Type: Public

One doesn't need an oracle to see that Delphi Financial Group knows a thing or two about employee benefits and insurance. Through Reliance Standard Life and Safety National Casualty, Delphi sells life, disability, excess workers' compensation, and personal accident insurance to small and mid-sized businesses. Its Matrix Absence Management subsidiary provides disability and absence management services to larger employers. The company also offers asset accumulation products, mainly annuities, to individuals and groups. Delphi Financial products are sold through independent brokers and agents.

	Annual Growth	12/05	12/06	12/07	12/08	12/09
Assets ($ mil.)	7.0%	5,276.2	5,670.5	6,094.8	5,953.9	6,921.4
Net income ($ mil.)	(3.3%)	113.3	142.1	164.5	36.7	99.1
Market value ($ mil.)	(7.6%)	1,660.5	2,190.3	1,909.9	998.3	1,211.0
Employees	11.4%	1,170	1,410	1,551	1,700	1,800

⊞ DELTA AIR LINES, INC.

NYSE: DAL

1030 Delta Blvd.	CEO: Richard H. Anderson
Atlanta, GA 30320	CFO: Hank Halter
Phone: 404-715-2600	HR: Michael H. (Mike) Campbell
Fax: 404-715-5042	FYE: December 31
Web: www.delta.com	Type: Public

Just as a delta is a symbol for change in math, Delta Air Lines symbolizes the changing mathematics of the airline industry. Delta became the world's largest airline by traffic after its $2.8 billion acquisition of Northwest Airlines in 2008. Through its regional carriers (including subsidiary Comair), the combined company serves more than 365 destinations in more than 65 countries, and it operates a mainline fleet of about 800 aircraft. Delta is a founding member of the SkyTeam marketing and code-sharing alliance (allowing airlines to sell tickets on one another's flights and thus extend their networks), which includes carriers such as Air France and KLM.

	Annual Growth	12/05	12/06	12/07	12/08	12/09
Sales ($ mil.)	14.7%	16,191.0	17,171.0	19,154.0	22,697.0	28,063.0
Net income ($ mil.)	—	(3,818.0)	(6,203.0)	1,612.0	(8,922.0)	(1,237.0)
Market value ($ mil.)	(12.6%)	—	—	11,724.2	9,023.5	8,960.5
Employees	9.8%	55,700	51,300	55,044	84,306	81,106

DELTA APPAREL, INC.

NYSE Amex: DLA

2750 Premiere Pkwy., Ste. 100	CEO: Robert W. (Bob) Humphreys
Duluth, GA 30097	CFO: Deborah H. (Deb) Merrill
Phone: 678-775-6900	HR: —
Fax: 678-775-6992	FYE: June 30
Web: www.deltaapparel.com	Type: Public

Delta Apparel has been there, done that, and made the T-shirt. The company manufactures knitted cotton and polyester/cotton T-shirts, tank tops, and sweatshirts primarily for the screen-printing industry. Delta Apparel sells its casual and athletic tops and caps nationwide to distributors, screen printers, sporting goods stores, mass merchants, traditional and upscale department stores, college bookstores, the US military, and online. The company's garments are finished at facilities in the US (specifically North Carolina), Mexico, El Salvador, and Honduras. In 2009 it entered the hat business by acquiring Gekko Brands and custom apparel design by purchasing Art Gun Technologies.

	Annual Growth	6/05	6/06	6/07	6/08	6/09
Sales ($ mil.)	11.7%	228.1	270.1	312.4	322.0	355.2
Net income ($ mil.)	(12.7%)	11.2	14.8	5.7	(0.5)	6.5
Market value ($ mil.)	(14.6%)	110.1	146.0	154.6	31.1	58.6
Employees	12.2%	4,100	4,000	6,200	6,400	6,500

DELTA DENTAL OF CALIFORNIA

100 1st St.	CEO: Gary D. Radine
San Francisco, CA 94105	CFO: Michael J. Castro
Phone: 415-972-8300	HR: Richard (Rick) Doering
Fax: 415-972-8466	FYE: December 31
Web: www.deltadentalins.com	Type: Not-for-profit

Delta Dental of California doesn't just help keep the mouths of movie stars clean. The not-for-profit company is a member of the Delta Dental Plans Association and has affiliates nationwide. Delta Dental of California provides dental coverage through HMOs, preferred provider plans (PPOs), and such government programs as the TRICARE Retiree Dental Program and California's Healthy Families Program. The company serves more than 17 million enrollees in California; its programs cover more than one-third of California residents. It also provides dental benefits administration support to employers.

	Annual Growth	12/04	12/05	12/06	12/07	12/08
Sales ($ mil.)	—	—	—	—	—	5,900.0
Employees	—	—	—	—	—	3,600

DELTA DENTAL PLANS ASSOCIATION

1515 W. 22nd St., Ste. 1200	CEO: Kim Volk
Oak Brook, IL 60523	CFO: —
Phone: 630-574-6001	HR: —
Fax: 630-574-6999	FYE: December 31
Web: www.deltadental.com	Type: Association

Delta Dental is responsible for miles of smiles. Established in 1966, Delta Dental Plans Association is the largest dental benefits provider in the nation. The not-for-profit company provides dental benefits and related administrative services to approximately 54 million people through its nationwide network of independent affiliates. The association has some 40 affiliates that contract with nearly 90,000 large and small employer groups to provide dental benefits through HMO, PPO, and POS (Point of Service) plans. The Delta Dental Premier plan offers access to about 130,000 contracted dentists.

	Annual Growth	12/04	12/05	12/06	12/07	12/08
Est. sales ($ mil.)	—	—	—	—	—	3.1
Employees	—	—	—	—	—	30

DELTA MUTUAL, INC.

OTC: DLTM

14301 N. 87th St., Ste. 310	CEO: Daniel R. Peralta
Scottsdale, AZ 85260	CFO: Michael Gilburd
Phone: 480-221-1989	HR: —
Fax: 480-584-6138	FYE: December 31
Web: www.deltamutual.com	Type: Public

Delta Mutual tried to clean up during the Internet boom by providing online mortgage services. Today, it really does clean up. Literally. This development stage company has shifted its direction to being an environmental services provider. Delta Mutual offers waste processing and reclamation technology and equipment, as well as energy-efficient construction technologies to low-cost housing development projects. Its operations are concentrated in the US, the Asia/Pacific region, the Middle East, and Puerto Rico. In 2008 the company acquired American Hedge Fund LLC, a limited liability company that intends to make investments in South America.

	Annual Growth	12/05	12/06	12/07	12/08	12/09
Sales ($ mil.)	—	—	—	—	0.0	0.0
Net income ($ mil.)	—	—	—	—	(4.6)	0.9
Market value ($ mil.)	(25.6%)	—	—	—	11.5	8.6
Employees	(33.3%)	—	—	—	3	2

DELTA NATURAL GAS COMPANY, INC.

NASDAQ (GM): DGAS

3617 Lexington Rd.	CEO: Glenn R. Jennings
Winchester, KY 40391	CFO: John B. Brown
Phone: 859-744-6171	HR: —
Fax: 859-744-6552	FYE: June 30
Web: www.deltagas.com	Type: Public

Delta digs blue grass and natural gas. Delta Natural Gas provides gas to some 36,000 retail customers in central and southeastern Kentucky and has 2,500 miles of gathering, transmission, and distribution lines. It also provides transportation services to wholesale customers and operates an underground gas storage field. The regulated utility buys almost all of its gas supply from interstate gas marketers. Delta Natural Gas's production subsidiary, Enpro, has interests in 35 producing gas wells and it has proved developed reserves of 3 billion cu. ft. of natural gas. Other subsidiaries include Delta Resources and Delgasco, which purchase gas from marketers and resell it to utilities and large customers.

	Annual Growth	6/05	6/06	6/07	6/08	6/09
Sales ($ mil.)	5.8%	84.2	117.2	98.2	112.7	105.6
Net income ($ mil.)	1.0%	5.0	5.0	5.3	6.8	5.2
Market value ($ mil.)	(3.4%)	86.1	81.6	86.4	87.0	75.0
Employees	0.5%	152	156	157	158	155

⊞ An in-depth profile of this company is available to Hoover's Online members at hoovers.com.

DELTA PETROLEUM CORPORATION

NASDAQ (GM): DPTR

370 17th St., Ste. 4300
Denver, CO 80202
Phone: 303-293-9133
Fax: 303-298-8251
Web: www.deltapetro.com

CEO: John R. Wallace
CFO: Kevin K. Nanke
HR: Peggy (Peg) Griffith
FYE: December 31
Type: Public

An independent oil and gas exploration and production company, Delta Petroleum has been dealt a good hand in estimated proved reserves in the Rocky Mountains and the Gulf Coast. In 2008 it reported reserves of 884.4 billion cu. ft. of natural gas equivalent, 95% of which is in the Rocky Mountains. The company also has major assets in the Gulf Coast region. It has oil and gas leasehold properties covering approximately 893,000 net undeveloped acres. Delta Petroleum holds 49.8% of contract driller DHS Holding, which in 2008 owned 19 drilling rigs (of 10,000 to 25,000 feet drilling capacity), of which three were active.

	Annual Growth	6/05	*12/06	12/07	12/08	12/09
Sales ($ mil.)	17.5%	95.7	181.4	164.2	271.2	182.4
Net income ($ mil.)	—	15.1	(5.1)	(149.3)	(452.0)	(349.7)
Market value ($ mil.)	(47.9%)	3,992.9	6,549.3	5,330.5	1,346.0	294.1
Employees	(4.5%)	95	122	128	160	79
						*Fiscal year change

DELTAGEN, INC.

Pink Sheets: DGEN

1900 S. Norfold St., Ste. 105
San Mateo, CA 94403
Phone: 650-345-7600
Fax: —
Web: www.deltagen.com

CEO: Robert J. Driscoll
CFO: Daniel (Dan) Ratto
HR: —
FYE: December 31
Type: Public

Disney's not the only one with a knockout mouse; in fact, Deltagen has a database full of them. The company provides information about gene functions to biopharmaceutical companies by creating mouse models with specific genes deleted, or knocked out. Deltagen can then study the function and potential relevance of the genes for the development of new drugs. The company stores everything it learns in a database it calls DeltaBase and sells access to that information to companies such as Pfizer, GlaxoSmithKline, and Merck. The drug companies use the information to select and validate promising targets; they also buy customized knockout mice from Deltagen to test the efficacy of their drug candidates.

DELTATHREE, INC.

OTC: DDDC

224 West 35th St., Ste. 1004, 10th Fl.
New York, NY 10001
Phone: 212-500-4850
Fax: 212-500-4888
Web: www.deltathree.com

CEO: Efraim (Efi) Baruch
CFO: Ziv Zviel
HR: —
FYE: December 31
Type: Public

Deltathree supplies the pipes that make phone calls via the Internet possible. The company manages an international voice over Internet Protocol (VoIP) network that offers distribution through both service provider and reseller channels. It offers phone service through its direct-to-consumer website under the iConnectHere (or ICH) and joip brands. Using the company's software and network connection, customers can place calls from their computers to traditional telephones. Deltathree also provides operational management services such as account provisioning, billing, and payment processing. The company's backbone network connects points in New Jersey; Atlanta, Georgia; and Frankfurt, Germany.

	Annual Growth	12/05	12/06	12/07	12/08	12/09
Sales ($ mil.)	(10.6%)	29.7	38.0	29.5	20.2	19.0
Net income ($ mil.)	—	(0.9)	0.5	(9.3)	(11.9)	(3.2)
Market value ($ mil.)	(40.3%)	210.2	91.0	29.0	1.2	26.7
Employees	(26.5%)	147	144	148	43	43

DELTEK, INC.

NASDAQ (GS): PROJ

13880 Dulles Corner Ln.
Herndon, VA 20171
Phone: 703-734-8606
Fax: 703-734-1146
Web: www.deltek.com

CEO: Kevin T. Parker
CFO: Michael P. Corkery
HR: Holly C. Kortright
FYE: December 31
Type: Public

Deltek provides project management software designed to meet the needs of professional services firms and project-based businesses. Its applications handle expense reporting, HR administration, materials management, customer management, and sales force automation. Deltek integrates tools from partners such as Cognos and Microsoft with its own software, and it also provides consulting and implementation services. Deltek targets such industries as aerospace, construction, engineering, and information technology. It also serves government agencies and government contractors, an area of strength for Deltek where it holds a large market share. Donald and Kenneth deLaski (father and son) co-founded Deltek in 1983.

	Annual Growth	12/05	12/06	12/07	12/08	12/09
Sales ($ mil.)	14.8%	153.0	228.3	278.2	289.4	265.8
Net income ($ mil.)	25.2%	8.7	15.3	22.5	23.5	21.4
Market value ($ mil.)	(28.5%)	—	—	1,026.1	312.6	524.2
Employees	(1.5%)	1,212	1,041	1,255	1,240	1,140

⊞ DELTIC TIMBER CORPORATION

NYSE: DEL

210 E. Elm St.
El Dorado, AR 71730
Phone: 870-881-9400
Fax: 870-881-6454
Web: www.deltic.com

CEO: Ray C. Dillon
CFO: Kenneth D. Mann
HR: —
FYE: December 31
Type: Public

Money doesn't grow on trees? Deltic Timber might beg to differ. The company annually harvests some 580,000 tons of timber from the more than 440,000 acres of timberlands that it owns, primarily in Arkansas and northern Louisiana. The company's two sawmills convert the timber (mainly southern pine) into softwood lumber products; this is then sold to wholesale distributors, lumber treaters, and truss manufacturers for use in residential construction to make roof trusses, laminated beams, and decking. In addition to its timber and lumber businesses, Deltic Timber develops real estate in central Arkansas and manufactures medium density fiberboard (MDF) through its Del-Tin Fiber joint venture.

	Annual Growth	12/05	12/06	12/07	12/08	12/09
Sales ($ mil.)	(9.7%)	168.4	153.1	128.3	129.5	112.0
Net income ($ mil.)	(28.9%)	14.5	11.3	11.1	4.4	3.7
Market value ($ mil.)	(2.9%)	648.2	697.2	643.6	571.8	577.2
Employees	(0.9%)	481	464	465	466	464

⊞ DELUXE CORPORATION

NYSE: DLX

3680 Victoria St. North
Shoreview, MN 55126
Phone: 651-483-7111
Fax: 651-481-4163
Web: www.deluxe.com

CEO: Lee J. Schram
CFO: Terry D. Peterson
HR: Julie M. Loosbrock
FYE: December 31
Type: Public

When money can move at the speed of a mouse click, Deluxe wants to do more than keep its revenues in check. The company is a leading printer of checks in the US, serving the nation's banks, credit unions, and financial services companies. Checks and business forms account for the majority of Deluxe's sales; it sells checkbook covers and address labels, as well as stationery, greeting cards, stored-value gift cards, labels, and packaging supplies online. Deluxe also provides Web design services through its Hostopia.com unit. The company's Direct Checks division is the nation's #1 direct-to-consumer seller of personal and business checks under the brands Checks Unlimited and Designer Checks.

	Annual Growth	12/05	12/06	12/07	12/08	12/09
Sales ($ mil.)	(5.9%)	1,716.3	1,639.7	1,606.4	1,468.7	1,344.2
Net income ($ mil.)	(10.9%)	157.5	101.0	143.5	101.6	99.4
Market value ($ mil.)	(16.3%)	1,547.3	1,293.7	1,688.5	768.0	759.3
Employees	(7.5%)	8,310	8,396	7,991	7,172	6,089

DELUXE ENTERTAINMENT SERVICES GROUP, INC.

5433 Fernwood Ave.
Hollywood, CA 90027
Phone: 323-960-3600
Fax: 323-960-7016
Web: www.bydeluxe.com

CEO: Cyril Drabinsky
CFO: —
HR: —
FYE: June 30
Type: Subsidiary

There's nothing standard about this company's movie production services. Deluxe Entertainment Services Group operates through three business segments: Film Labs (processes 35mm film for the motion picture industry); Creative Services (post-production work); and Film Distribution (delivers prints to film studios). Clients include all major Hollywood studios. Since 1943 Deluxe has received 10 Academy Awards for technical achievement. The company can trace its history back to 1919, when Fox Film Corporation built Deluxe Laboratory on its lot for film processing and printing. Deluxe Entertainment Services is a subsidiary of MacAndrews & Forbes Holdings Inc. (the holding company for billionaire Ronald Perelman).

DEMAND MEDIA, INC.

1333 2nd St., Ste. 100
Santa Monica, CA 90401
Phone: 310-394-6400
Fax: 310-394-6499
Web: www.demandmedia.com

CEO: Richard M. Rosenblatt
CFO: Charles S. Hilliard
HR: Nicolas Schoenlaub
FYE: March 31
Type: Private

Demand Media knows that Web branding is in demand. The company operates through a variety of Web-related enterprises that exist to help drive Web traffic to its clients' sites. Subsidiaries include domain-name wholesaler eNom and Internet blogging service Pluck. Other Demand Media Web sites include niche Web content provider eHow and humor site Cracked.com. The company also operates Trails.com, which it acquired with the purchase of travel, sports, and outdoors content provider Hillclimb Media, and produces online video through its Demand Studios business. Demand Media was founded in 2006 by former MySpace.com chairman Richard Rosenblatt and Shawn Colo of Spectrum Equity Investors.

DEMANDTEC, INC.

1 Circle Star Way, Ste. 200
San Carlos, CA 94070
Phone: 650-226-4600
Fax: 650-556-1190
Web: www.demandtec.com

NASDAQ (GM): DMAN
CEO: Daniel R. (Dan) Fishback
CFO: Mark A. Culhane
HR: —
FYE: February 28
Type: Public

The laws of supply and demand become a little more high-tech in DemandTec's hands. The company makes software that helps manufacturers and suppliers predict consumer demand and develop strategies for pricing and promotions. Designed to help clients improve their planning and profitability, the company's consumer demand management (CDM) software is available in versions tailored to the needs of retailers and consumer products manufacturers. Its applications include tools for managing pricing, promotions, and markdowns. The company's customers include Best Buy, Coca-Cola, General Mills, and Office Depot.

	Annual Growth	2/06	2/07	2/08	2/09	2/10
Sales ($ mil.)	24.9%	32.5	43.5	61.3	75.0	79.1
Net income ($ mil.)	—	(2.8)	(1.5)	(4.5)	(5.0)	(11.8)
Market value ($ mil.)	(24.0%)	—	—	304.0	220.5	175.8
Employees	12.8%	—	218	251	329	313

DEMATIC CORP.

507 Plymouth Ave. NE
Grand Rapids, MI 49505
Phone: 616-913-7700
Fax: 616-913-7701
Web: www.dematic.us

CEO: John Baysore
CFO: Daniel Killeen
HR: Herbert Fitzon
FYE: September 30
Type: Subsidiary

When it comes to handling with care, Dematic has the right system. Formerly Rapistan, and Siemens Logistics and Assembly, the company designs and manufactures an array of logistic and automated material handling solutions, including sorting and conveyor systems, warehouse control software, and direct order fulfillment and picking systems. Making warehouses more productive and less costly, Dematic caters to a host of industries, from beverages (Suncoast Beverage, an Anheuser-Busch distributor) to apparel (Pacific Sunwear), retailers (Walgreens and WalMart), and wholesalers (JTM). The company has installed over 4,000 material handling systems across the world. Dematic is the North American arm of Dematic GmbH.

DEMOULAS SUPER MARKETS INC.

875 East St.
Tewksbury, MA 01876
Phone: 978-851-8000
Fax: 978-640-8390

CEO: Arthur Demoulas
CFO: Donald Mulligan
HR: —
FYE: December 31
Type: Private

The Demoulas supermarket chain is ripe with family history all rolled up into numerous Market Baskets. Demoulas Super Markets runs 60-plus grocery stores under the Market Basket banner in Massachusetts and New Hampshire. One store still operates under the "DeMoulas" banner. The grocery retailer also manages real estate interests. Market Basket supermarkets are typically located in shopping centers with other retail outlets, including properties owned by the company through its real estate arm, Retail Management and Development (RMD), Inc. Begun as a mom-and-pop grocery store, the Demoulas sons transformed the chain into a traditional, yet modern, concept. The business is run by CEO Arthur Demoulas.

	Annual Growth	12/04	12/05	12/06	12/07	12/08
Sales ($ mil.)	9.5%	1,950.0	2,000.0	2,200.0	2,500.0	2,800.0
Employees	10.1%	—	12,000	13,000	13,000	16,000

DENBURY RESOURCES INC.

5100 Tennyson Pkwy., Ste. 1200
Plano, TX 75024
Phone: 972-673-2000
Fax: 972-673-2150
Web: www.denbury.com

NYSE: DNR
CEO: Phil Rykhoek
CFO: Mark C. Allen Sr.
HR: Whitney Shelley
FYE: December 31
Type: Public

Denbury Resources has long since buried its oil and gas operations in its native Canada to try its luck in the Deep South. The independent exploration and production company has estimated proved reserves of 250.5 million barrels of oil equivalent in Mississippi; onshore Alabama; the Barnett Shale play near Fort Worth, Texas; and in properties in Southeast Texas. In Mississippi it owns the top reserves of CO_2 used for tertiary oil recovery (hydrocarbon recovery using advanced techniques) east of the Mississippi River. CO_2 is transported to wellheads where it is used to force oil from abandoned wells. To expand its market share, in 2010 Denbury Resources acquired rival Encore Acquisition for $4.5 billion.

	Annual Growth	12/05	12/06	12/07	12/08	12/09
Sales ($ mil.)	12.0%	560.7	731.5	972.0	1,365.7	882.5
Net income ($ mil.)	—	166.5	202.5	253.1	388.4	(75.2)
Market value ($ mil.)	6.8%	2,988.3	3,645.5	7,805.3	2,865.0	3,883.0
Employees	15.9%	460	596	686	797	830

An in-depth profile of this company is available to Hoover's Online members at hoovers.com.

487

DENDREON CORPORATION

NASDAQ (GM): DNDN

3005 1st Ave.
Seattle, WA 98121
Phone: 206-256-4545
Fax: 206-256-0571
Web: www.dendreon.com

CEO: Mitchell H. Gold
CFO: Gregory T. (Greg) Schiffman
HR: Richard J. (Rich) Ranieri
FYE: December 31
Type: Public

Dendreon wants to boost your immunity from the start. It is developing therapeutic vaccines that help the body's immune system fight cancer by targeting dendritic cells, which initiate an immune response to disease-causing antigens. Lead candidate Provenge, a therapeutic vaccine that targets prostate cancer, received FDA approval in 2010. Dendreon is also working on a therapeutic vaccine called Neuvenge as a treatment for breast, colon, and ovarian cancers; and it has research programs investigating cancer-fighting monoclonal antibodies and small molecule drugs.

	Annual Growth	12/05	12/06	12/07	12/08	12/09
Sales ($ mil.)	(15.9%)	0.2	0.3	0.7	0.1	0.1
Net income ($ mil.)	—	(81.5)	(91.6)	(99.3)	(71.6)	(220.2)
Market value ($ mil.)	48.4%	733.0	564.0	841.2	619.4	3,554.1
Employees	23.5%	208	232	194	198	484

⊞ DENNY'S CORPORATION

NASDAQ (CM): DENN

203 E. Main St.
Spartanburg, SC 29319
Phone: 864-597-8000
Fax: 864-597-8780
Web: www.dennys.com

CEO: Debra Smithart-Oglesby
CFO: F. Mark Wolfinger
HR: Jill A. Van Pelt
FYE: December 31
Type: Public

Feel like getting slammed for breakfast? The home of the Grand Slam Breakfast, Denny's is one of the leading full-service, family-style restaurant chains in the US, with about 1,550 of its signature eateries located across the country. Typically open 24 hours a day, the chain is best known for its menu of breakfast items, including eggs, pancakes, and combination plates carrying such names as All-American Slam, Lumberjack Slam, and the aforementioned Grand Slam Breakfast. Denny's also serves standard American fare (burgers, sandwiches, steak) for lunch and dinner. The company owns and operates about 230 of its restaurants, while the rest are franchised or operate under licensing agreements.

	Annual Growth	12/05	12/06	12/07	12/08	12/09
Sales ($ mil.)	(11.2%)	978.7	994.0	939.4	760.3	608.1
Net income ($ mil.)	—	(7.3)	30.1	34.7	14.7	41.6
Market value ($ mil.)	(14.1%)	399.9	467.3	372.1	197.5	217.3
Employees	(20.1%)	27,000	27,000	21,000	15,000	11,000

DENON ELECTRONICS (USA), LLC

100 Corporate Dr.
Mahwah, NJ 07430
Phone: 201-762-6500
Fax: 201-762-6670
Web: www.usa.denon.com

CEO: Stephen Baker
CFO: —
HR: —
FYE: March 31
Type: Subsidiary

Turn up the volume with Denon. Denon Electronics (USA) sells the Denon brand of home entertainment products. The company makes and markets such consumer electronic goods as CD and DVD players, headphones, home theater systems, stereo tuners and amplifiers, and turntables. In 2009, it has been boosting its Blue-ray products. Denon Electronics (USA) sells its products through stereo and electronics retailers in the US. The company is owned by D&M Holdings, which in 2008 combined its Denon and Boston Acoustics brands under a single management team (led by Joe Stinziano) in a bid to reduce costs. The move has allowed it to integrate the sales and marketing operations of both companies.

DENSO INTERNATIONAL AMERICA, INC.

24777 Denso Dr.
Southfield, MI 48033
Phone: 248-350-7500
Fax: 248-213-2337
Web: www.densocorp-na.com

CEO: Steve Y. Sekiguchi
CFO: Art A. Shimmura
HR: —
FYE: March 31
Type: Subsidiary

DENSO International America is the holding company for DENSO's North American operations. The company oversees about 30 joint venture and affiliate companies — mostly in the US, but also in Mexico and Canada. In addition to manufacturing everything from radiators and fuel injectors to alternators and air conditioners, DENSO International has significant research and development operations that focus on developing energy-efficient and eco-friendly products. The company's customers include Toyota, General Motors, Ford Motor, Honda of America, Cummins, Deere & Company, Volvo Trucks, Mercedes-Benz U.S. International, and Harley-Davidson.

DENSO MANUFACTURING MICHIGAN, INC.

1 Denso Rd.
Battle Creek, MI 49037
Phone: 269-965-3322
Fax: 269-965-8399
Web: www.densocorp-na-dmmi.com

CEO: Junichi Soh
CFO: —
HR: —
FYE: March 31
Type: Subsidiary

DENSO Manufacturing Michigan (DMMI) doesn't make the Great Lake State, but it does make part of what makes Michigan famous. The company, a subsidiary of Japan's DENSO CORPORATION, is a manufacturer of automotive heating and cooling components, and systems, including car heater assemblies, condensers, cooling unit assemblies, evaporators, oil coolers, and radiators. Customers are major auto OEMs, such as Toyota, Honda, Mitsubishi, GM, and Chrysler. DMMI was established in 1986; its facility is located on more than 85 acres, operating a million square feet of manufacturing, warehouse, and administrative floor space. A conservative employer, DMMI has avoided workforce reductions even during the economic recession.

⊞ DENTSPLY INTERNATIONAL INC.

NASDAQ (GS): XRAY

221 W. Philadelphia St.
York, PA 17405
Phone: 717-845-7511
Fax: 717-849-4760
Web: www.dentsply.com

CEO: Bret W. Wise
CFO: William R. Jellison
HR: Rachel P. McKinney
FYE: December 31
Type: Public

Open wider, please, so that DENTSPLY International can fit more of its products in your mouth. The company manufactures a range of dental goods, from anesthetics, pastes, and tooth whiteners to artificial teeth, crown and bridge materials, and implants. DENTSPLY also makes dental equipment, including root canal instruments, ultrasonic polishers, X-ray viewers, and other orthodontic appliances. The company manufactures its various products under more than 100 brand names. More than half of its products are sold through domestic and international distributors, but DENTSPLY also sells directly to dentists, dental labs, and dental schools in more than 120 countries.

	Annual Growth	12/05	12/06	12/07	12/08	12/09
Sales ($ mil.)	5.9%	1,715.1	1,810.5	2,009.8	2,193.7	2,159.9
Net income ($ mil.)	56.8%	45.4	223.7	259.7	283.9	274.3
Market value ($ mil.)	7.0%	3,928.8	4,368.6	6,588.8	4,133.0	5,147.2
Employees	3.8%	8,000	8,500	8,900	9,400	9,300

DENTSU AMERICA, INC.

32 Avenue of the Americas, 16th Fl.
New York, NY 10013
Phone: 212-397-3333
Fax: 212-261-4286
Web: www.dentsuamerica.com

CEO: Timothy P. (Tim) Andree
CFO: Vincent Legg
HR: —
FYE: December 31
Type: Subsidiary

A full service agency, Dentsu America (formerly DCA Advertising) provides branding and marketing services through offices in New York City and Palo Alto, California. The company is a subsidiary of global advertising conglomerate and #1 ad firm in Japan, Dentsu. Dentsu America has provided integrated marketing, including print and television campaigns, for diverse clients including imaging systems manufacturer Canon U.S.A., New York University's medical center, international aid organization UNICEF, India's Department of Tourism, publisher HarperCollins, and car maker Toyota.

DEPUY INC.

325 Paramount Dr.
Raynham, MA 02767
Phone: 508-880-8100
Fax: 508-880-8122
Web: www.depuy.com

CEO: Michael F. Mahoney
CFO: Peter (Pete) Batesko III
HR: Kathleen (Kate) McDaniel
FYE: December 31
Type: Subsidiary

DePuy makes it possible for orthopedic patients to stand up straight and take a step in the right direction. A subsidiary of Johnson & Johnson, DePuy's businesses develop and market orthopedic joint reconstruction, spinal care products, and neurosurgical devices. As one of the world's largest suppliers of orthopedic products, DePuy's products include hip replacements; knee, shoulder, and spinal implants; internal and external fixator products for bone fractures; and operating room equipment and supplies. The company's products are used primarily by orthopedic specialists and neurosurgeons to treat patients with musculoskeletal defects resulting from diseases, deformities, trauma, or accidents.

DEPOMED, INC.

NASDAQ (GM): DEPO

1360 O'Brien Dr.
Menlo Park, CA 94025
Phone: 650-462-5900
Fax: 650-462-9993
Web: www.depomedinc.com

CEO: Carl A. Pelzel
CFO: Tammy L. Cameron
HR: Kera Alexander
FYE: December 31
Type: Public

For comedians and Depomed, it's all about the delivery. The drug company makes proprietary drug therapies using its patented delivery technology AcuForm, an extended-release technology that stretches out the time a pill stays in the stomach, thus reducing the number of necessary doses and potential side effects. Depomed's internal development efforts have yielded two FDA-approved and marketed products: Glumetza, an extended-release formulation of common diabetes drug metformin, and ProQuin XR, an extended-release version of antibiotic ciprofloxacin, used to treat urinary tract infections.

	Annual Growth	12/05	12/06	12/07	12/08	12/09
Sales ($ mil.)	90.3%	4.4	9.6	65.6	34.8	57.7
Net income ($ mil.)	—	(24.5)	(39.7)	49.2	(15.3)	(22.0)
Market value ($ mil.)	(13.6%)	314.2	180.7	170.7	86.4	175.4
Employees	(5.1%)	90	105	73	81	73

DERMA SCIENCES, INC.

OTC: DSCI

214 Carnegie Center, Ste. 300
Princeton, NJ 08540
Phone: 609-514-4744
Fax: 609-514-0502
Web: www.dermasciences.com

CEO: Edward J. (Ed) Quilty
CFO: John E. Yetter
HR: —
FYE: December 31
Type: Public

Time may eventually heal all wounds, but in the meantime there's Derma Sciences. The company has three product lines: sprays, ointments, and dressings for basic and chronic skin wounds (burns, abrasions, bedsores, and venous ulcers); wound closure strips and fasteners; and skin care products such as lotions, soaps, and bath sponges. The company's direct sales force sells its products, which are designed for use in nursing homes, hospitals, and other health care facilities, to distributors and large institutions in the US; it also sells internationally through distribution agreements, primarily in Canada, Europe, and Latin America.

	Annual Growth	12/05	12/06	12/07	12/08	12/09
Sales ($ mil.)	19.9%	23.5	27.9	34.1	50.2	48.5
Net income ($ mil.)	—	(0.9)	0.7	(2.3)	(4.0)	(1.1)
Market value ($ mil.)	8.8%	28.9	44.6	68.2	29.9	40.4
Employees	6.9%	133	139	188	187	174

THE DEPOSITORY TRUST & CLEARING CORPORATION

55 Water St., 22nd Fl.
New York, NY 10041
Phone: 212-855-1000
Fax: 212-855-8440
Web: www.dtcc.com

CEO: Donald F. Donahue
CFO: Ellen Fine Levine
HR: Anthony J. Portannese
FYE: December 31
Type: Private

It's clear that securities trading just wouldn't be the same without The Depository Trust & Clearing Corporation (DTCC). Its subsidiaries provide the infrastructure for clearing, settlement, and custody of most US securities transactions. DTCC was established in 1999 when operating companies The Depository Trust Company (DTC) and the National Securities Clearing Company (NSCC) — both of which were founded in the 1970s — were combined under a single holding structure. DTC is the world's largest securities depository and a clearinghouse for trading settlement; NSCC processes most broker-to-broker equity, corporate, and municipal bond trades in the US.

	Annual Growth	12/04	12/05	12/06	12/07	12/08
Est. sales ($ mil.)	—	—	—	—	—	706.2
Employees	—	—	—	—	—	2,658

DESERET MANAGEMENT CORPORATION

60 E. South Temple, Ste. 575
Salt Lake City, UT 84111
Phone: 801-538-0651
Fax: 801-538-0655
Web: www.deseretmanagement.com

CEO: Mark H. Willes
CFO: Dale G. Bailey
HR: Claire H. Averett
FYE: December 31
Type: Holding company

While the Church of Jesus Christ of Latter-day Saints handles the spiritual, Deseret Management takes care of the worldly. The holding company oversees a portfolio of for-profit ventures for the Mormon Church, including Bonneville International Corporation (radio and TV stations), Deseret Book Company (inspirational publishing), and Salt Lake City's *Deseret Morning News* newspaper. Its holdings also include life insurance and financial services provider Beneficial Life Insurance and contract foodservices and corporate catering provider Temple Square Hospitality. Deseret Management also has real estate holdings through other subsidiaries. The Mormon Church formed the holding company in 1966.

An in-depth profile of this company is available to Hoover's Online members at hoovers.com.

489

DESERT SCHOOLS FEDERAL CREDIT UNION

148 N. 48th St.
Phoenix, AZ 85034
Phone: 602-433-7000
Fax: —
Web: www.desertschools.org

CEO: Susan C. Frank
CFO: Mark Wiete
HR: David Strachan
FYE: December 31
Type: Not-for-profit

One of the largest credit unions in Arizona, Desert Schools Federal Credit Union operates about 60 branch locations in the Phoenix area, serving more than 325,000 members. Established in 1939 by a group of 15 teachers, the credit union offers banking products and services, including checking and savings accounts, IRAs, and CDs; it also provides online banking services. Subsidiary Desert Schools Financial Services sells insurance products and investment services. Membership is available to any individual living, working, or attending church or school in Gila, Maricopa, and Pinal counties.

	Annual Growth	12/04	12/05	12/06	12/07	12/08
Assets ($ mil.)	9.1%	2,212.1	2,570.0	2,885.0	3,019.9	3,136.7
Net income ($ mil.)	—	28.0	35.7	39.7	29.5	(39.2)
Employees	6.8%	1,000	1,134	1,300	1,300	1,300

DESIGN WITHIN REACH, INC.

Pink Sheets: DWRI

225 Bush St., 20th Fl.
San Francisco, CA 94104
Phone: 415-676-6500
Fax: 415-676-6871
Web: www.dwr.com

CEO: John D. Edelman
CFO: Ted Upland
HR: —
FYE: December 31
Type: Public

Design Within Reach (commonly referred to as DWR) may be just out of reach for the average Joe's pocketbook. The company sells upscale modern home furnishings (such as sofas, chairs, tables, and beds) as well as kitchen cabinets, bathtubs, fixtures, lighting, rugs, and related accessories. Its designs have been featured on decorating TV series such as *Trading Spaces* and books such as *Trading Up: The New American Luxury*. The company operates about 70 stores, including two DWR: Tools for Living locations and two outlets, in some 25 states and in Canada. Its goods are also marketed through a catalog and its Web site. The firm was founded by designer Rob Forbes in 1998.

	Annual Growth	12/04	12/05	12/06	12/07	*12/08
Sales ($ mil.)	10.4%	120.6	158.2	178.1	193.9	178.9
Net income ($ mil.)	—	3.7	(2.1)	(8.3)	0.3	(24.0)
Market value ($ mil.)	(53.5%)	435.1	158.5	147.4	110.7	20.3
Employees	12.0%	269	356	407	442	423

*Most recent year available

DESTINATION MATERNITY CORPORATION

NASDAQ (GM): DEST

456 N. 5th St.
Philadelphia, PA 19123
Phone: 215-873-2200
Fax: 215-873-0869
Web: www.mothersvork.com

CEO: Edward M. (Ed) Krell
CFO: Judd P. Tirnauer
HR: Julie Marini
FYE: September 30
Type: Public

Career women need work clothes — even when they are moms-to-be. Destination Maternity Corporation (formerly Mothers Work) offers value-priced to high-end career, casual, and special-occasion maternity apparel through three chains (A Pea in the Pod, Destination Maternity, and Motherhood Maternity). It operates more than 1,080 retail locations, including some 720 mall-based and outlet stores and some 360 leased spaces in department stores (Boscov's, Macys) in the US, Guam, Canada, and Puerto Rico. It also sells online and through catalogs. Most of its merchandise is designed by the company and manufactured by third-party contractors. Rebecca Matthias and her husband, Dan, founded Mothers Work in 1982.

	Annual Growth	9/05	9/06	9/07	9/08	9/09
Sales ($ mil.)	(1.4%)	561.6	602.7	581.4	564.6	531.3
Net income ($ mil.)	—	(0.2)	9.1	(0.4)	(1.4)	(40.7)
Market value ($ mil.)	16.0%	63.4	305.0	118.3	88.0	114.9
Employees	(2.1%)	5,104	4,987	4,871	4,664	4,684

DETREX CORPORATION

Pink Sheets: DTRX

24901 Northwestern Hwy., Ste. 410
Southfield, MI 48075
Phone: 248-358-5800
Fax: 248-799-7192
Web: www.detrex.com

CEO: Thomas E. (Tom) Mark
CFO: Steven J. (Steve) Quinlan
HR: Bob Querrie
FYE: December 31
Type: Public

Detrex Corporation has one word for you: *plastics*. OK, three words: *plastics* and *specialty chemicals*. Detrex's subsidiary Harvel Plastics, which accounts for more than two-thirds of Detrex's sales, makes PVC and CPVC pipe and custom extrusions. Detrex's other division, The Elco Corporation, makes lubricant additives (such as hydraulic fluid additives), fine chemicals, and semiconductor grade hydrochloric acid. The company has operations throughout the US and customers in 50 countries, though a clear majority of Detrex's sales are in the US. Those customers include manufacturers of appliances, automobiles, and farm implements. Summit Capital Partners owns 37% of Detrex.

DETROIT DIESEL CORPORATION

13400 Outer Dr. West
Detroit, MI 48239
Phone: 313-592-5000
Fax: 313-592-7323
Web: www.detroitdiesel.com

CEO: Martin Daum
CFO: Andrew M. (Andy) Williamson
HR: —
FYE: December 31
Type: Subsidiary

Detroit Diesel Corporation (DDC) says keep on truckin' so it can continue making diesel engines. DDC sells its diesel engines to the truck, auto, and marine markets. The Series 60, a heavy-duty diesel engine with electronic controls, is its best seller. Detroit Diesel has built more than 5 million engines in its history; more than 1 million of those engines were Series 60 models. DDC also remanufactures two- and four-cycle engines. It markets its engines directly and through a worldwide network of some 800 authorized distributor and dealer locations. Most sales are made directly to truck makers in the US. Detroit Diesel is a brand affiliate of Daimler Trucks North America.

THE DETROIT EDISON COMPANY

2000 2nd Ave.
Detroit, MI 48226
Phone: 313-235-4000
Fax: 313-235-8055
Web: my.dteenergy.com

CEO: Anthony F. Earley Jr.
CFO: David E. Meador
HR: —
FYE: December 31
Type: Subsidiary

Ford Motors is not the only powerhouse operating in Detroit. Detroit Edison generates and distributes electricity to 2.2 million customers in Michigan. The utility, a unit of regional power player DTE Energy, has more than 11,000 MW of generating capacity from its interests in fossil-fueled, nuclear, and hydroelectric power plants. It operates more than 44,000 circuit miles of distribution lines and owns and operates about 680 distribution substations. Detroit Edison also sells excess power to wholesale customers and provides coal transportation services.

	Annual Growth	12/04	12/05	12/06	12/07	12/08
Est. sales ($ mil.)	—	—	—	—	—	4,874.0
Employees	—	—	—	—	—	4,674

DETWILER FENTON & CO.

Pink Sheets: DMCD

225 Franklin St., 20th Fl.
Boston, MA 02110
Phone: 617-451-0100
Fax: 617-747-0800
Web: www.dmcos.com

CEO: Peter D. Fenton
CFO: Stephen D. Martino
HR: —
FYE: December 31
Type: Public

Detwiler Fenton (formerly Detwiler, Mitchell & Co.) performs wealth management and equities research services. Focusing on private clients, the company provides brokerage, portfolio management, mutual funds, and alternative investments. Its institutional research department specializes in the communications, manufacturing, software, and semiconductor industries. Subsidiary James Mitchell & Co. offers insurance, annuities, investments, group benefits, and retirement planning to individuals and small businesses. Messrs. Detwiler and Fenton control Detwiler Fenton.

⊞ DEUTSCH, INC.

111 8th Ave.
New York, NY 10011
Phone: 212-981-7600
Fax: 212-981-7525
Web: www.deutschinc.com

CEO: Linda Sawyer
CFO: Tom Entrup
HR: Robin Lander
FYE: December 31
Type: Subsidiary

Advertising is the big idea at Deutsch. The firm, led by advertising-guru-turned-television-personality Donny Deutsch, offers creative development and brand marketing services through offices in New York and Los Angeles. Clients have included DIRECTV, Anheuser-Busch, Kodak, and Johnson & Johnson. Deutsch also does interactive and direct marketing work, as well as event marketing. The agency creates branded entertainment through its media unit. Founded in 1969, Deutsch is a subsidiary of global advertising conglomerate Interpublic Group. It enhances its geographical presence by working closely with Lowe & Partners Worldwide, another Interpublic agency.

DEUTSCHE BANK BERKSHIRE MORTGAGE, INC.

7575 Irvine Center Dr., Ste. 200
Irvine, CA 92618
Phone: 949-754-6300
Fax: —
Web: www.cre.db.com

CEO: Steve Wendel
CFO: —
HR: —
FYE: December 31
Type: Business segment

Deutsche Bank Berkshire Mortgage (DBBM) doesn't fund homes in the hoity-toity western Massachusetts region. Instead, it's one of the nation's largest commercial real estate lenders. DBBM originates and underwrites loans, while its DB Mortgage Services affiliate handles servicing and asset management. The company specializes in loans backed by Fannie Mae, Freddie Mac, and the Federal Housing Administration, and secured by multifamily and commercial real estate, including affordable housing, student housing, senior housing, hotels, and office, retail, and industrial properties. DBBM is a part of Deutsche Bank's Commercial Real Estate Group.

DEUTSCHE BANK SECURITIES INC.

60 Wall St.
New York, NY 10005
Phone: 212-250-2500
Fax: 212-797-4664
Web: www.db.com/index_e.htm

CEO: Richard Bryne
CFO: —
HR: —
FYE: December 31
Type: Subsidiary

Deutsche Bank Securities is the US investment banking and securities arm of German banking colossus Deutsche Bank. The company offers a range of financial services including underwriting, financial advisory, and mergers and acquisitions assistance. Deutsche Bank Securities also provides investment products, brokerage, and financial advice to wealthy individual investors through its Deutsche Bank Alex. Brown division. The company has underwritten the initial public offerings for companies including MAP Pharmaceuticals and NYSE.

	Annual Growth	12/04	12/05	12/06	12/07	12/08
Est. sales ($ mil.)	—	—	—	—	—	23.0
Employees	—	—	—	—	—	200

DEVCON INTERNATIONAL CORP.

3880 N. 28th Terrace
Hollywood, FL 33020
Phone: 954-926-5200
Fax: —
Web: www.devcon-security.com

CEO: Robert C. Farenhem
CFO: Ann MacDonald
HR: —
FYE: December 31
Type: Private

Devcon International wants to pave its way to a secure future. The company is focused on its Devcon Security Services subsidiary, which provides electronic security services, primarily in Florida and the New York City metropolitan area. Products include burglary, fire, medical, environmental, video and CCTV (closed-circuit television), and security access systems. The company provides services to more than 140,000 residential and commercial clients. Devcon International in 2009 voluntarily deregistered its common stock, delisting from the NASDAQ Stock Market and ceasing to file statements with the SEC.

DEVELOPERS DIVERSIFIED REALTY CORPORATION

NYSE: DDR

3300 Enterprise Pkwy.
Beachwood, OH 44122
Phone: 216-755-5500
Fax: 216-755-1500
Web: www.ddrc.com

CEO: Scott A. Wolstein
CFO: David J. Oakes
HR: Nan R. Zieleniec
FYE: December 31
Type: Public

Developers Diversified Realty (DDR) is a self-administered real estate investment trust (REIT) that acquires, develops, renovates, leases, and manages retail and office properties. Its portfolio includes about 670 community shopping centers, more than 30 enclosed malls and other retail properties, as well as about a half dozen office and industrial centers and more than 2,000 acres of undeveloped land. Almost half of its shopping centers are owned through joint ventures. Altogether, the firm owns or manages approximately 153 million sq. ft. of leasable space in 45 states, as well as Brazil, Canada, and Puerto Rico.

	Annual Growth	12/05	12/06	12/07	12/08	12/09
Sales ($ mil.)	1.5%	772.1	857.5	996.9	973.2	819.3
Net income ($ mil.)	—	194.5	181.2	207.2	(57.8)	(412.8)
Market value ($ mil.)	(31.6%)	10,597.8	14,188.2	8,630.2	1,099.9	2,315.4
Employees	7.1%	548	641	773	768	722

⊞ An in-depth profile of this company is available to Hoover's Online members at hoovers.com.

491

DEVELOPMENT DIMENSIONS INTERNATIONAL, INC.

1225 Washington Pike
Bridgeville, PA 15017
Phone: 412-257-0600
Fax: 412-257-2942
Web: www.ddiworld.com

CEO: William C. (Bill) Byham
CFO: William D. (Bill) Koch
HR: —
FYE: August 31
Type: Private

Development Dimensions International (DDI) helps businesses hire, develop, and retain talent. The company provides consulting services in areas such as talent assessment, selection system design and implementation, and leadership development for front line, middle management, and senior executives. In addition, DDI offers services in performance and succession management, work analysis, and workforce development. The company serves customers in industries such as manufacturing, health care, technology, finance, and telecommunications. The company serves multinational clients through more than 40 offices in about 25 countries. William Byham and Douglas Bray founded DDI in 1970.

	Annual Growth	8/04	8/05	8/06	8/07	8/08
Sales ($ mil.)	—	—	—	—	—	192.0
Employees	—	—	—	—	—	1,276

DEVEREUX FOUNDATION

444 Devereux Dr.
Villanova, PA 19085
Phone: 610-520-3000
Fax: 610-542-3136
Web: www.devereux.org

CEO: Robert Q. (Bob) Kreider
CFO: Robert C. Dunne
HR: Timothy Dillon
FYE: December 31
Type: Foundation

Devereux Foundation endeavors to make a difference in the lives of people with behavioral, psychological, intellectual, or neurological problems. A not-for-profit organization, Devereux serves children, adolescents, adults and their families through some 15 centers in about a dozen states. Its offerings include hospitalization, group homes, respite care, family counseling, and vocational training. Devereux also conducts behavioral health research and provides consulting services for other organizations with similar concerns. The group's work began in 1912 when a Philadelphia educator, Helena Devereux, started working with three special education students in her parents' house.

	Annual Growth	12/04	12/05	12/06	12/07	12/08
Est. sales ($ mil.)	—	—	—	—	—	384.9
Employees	—	—	—	—	—	6,000

DEVON ENERGY CORPORATION

NYSE: DVN

20 N. Broadway
Oklahoma City, OK 73102
Phone: 405-235-3611
Fax: 405-552-4550
Web: www.devonenergy.com

CEO: John Richels
CFO: Jeffrey A. (Jeff) Agosta
HR: Frank W. Rudolph
FYE: December 31
Type: Public

Independent oil and gas producer Devon Energy puts its energy into oil and gas finds far from England's southern coast. It has exploration and production assets in North Texas, Oklahoma, Wyoming, and western Canada. In 2008 Devon Energy reported proved reserves of 429 million barrels of oil, 9.9 trillion cu. ft. of natural gas, and 325 million barrels of natural gas liquids. That year the company drilled a record 2,441 gross wells with an overall 98% rate of success. Devon Energy is the largest producer and largest lease holder in the Barnett Shale area of North Texas.

	Annual Growth	12/05	12/06	12/07	12/08	12/09
Sales ($ mil.)	(7.1%)	10,741.0	10,578.0	11,362.0	15,211.0	8,015.0
Net income ($ mil.)	—	2,930.0	2,846.0	3,606.0	(2,148.0)	(2,479.0)
Market value ($ mil.)	4.1%	27,949.1	29,978.1	39,733.9	29,365.8	32,847.2
Employees	7.3%	4,075	4,600	5,000	5,500	5,400

⊞ DEVRY INC.

NYSE: DV

3005 Highland Pkwy.
Downers Grove, IL 60515
Phone: 630-571-7700
Fax: —
Web: www.devryinc.com

CEO: Daniel M. Hamburger
CFO: Richard M. (Rick) Gunst
HR: Donna N. Jennings
FYE: June 30
Type: Public

It isn't exactly Ivy League, but DeVry is in the big leagues of technical, health care, and business schools. The for-profit company offers professional, undergraduate, and graduate programs through several subsidiary schools. Flagship DeVry University, with about 100 US locations and another in Canada, specializes in business and technology education. Its Keller Graduate School of Management unit offers MBA and other graduate programs. Most of DeVry University's courses are also available online. The company also offers health care education through Ross University (in the Caribbean), Chamberlain College of Nursing, Apollo College, and Western Career College. In all, DeVry has about 70,000 students.

	Annual Growth	6/05	6/06	6/07	6/08	6/09
Sales ($ mil.)	16.9%	781.3	843.3	933.5	1,091.8	1,461.5
Net income ($ mil.)	57.8%	26.7	43.1	76.2	125.5	165.6
Market value ($ mil.)	25.9%	1,417.6	1,565.1	2,423.5	3,819.7	3,564.7
Employees	15.7%	5,700	4,800	5,400	6,755	10,200

DEWEY & LEBOEUF LLP

1301 Avenue of the Americas
New York, NY 10019
Phone: 212-259-8000
Fax: 212-259-6333
Web: www.deweyleboeuf.com

CEO: Steven H. Davis
CFO: Joel I. Sanders
HR: Howard Adler
FYE: September 30
Type: Partnership

International law firm Dewey & LeBoeuf has 1,200 lawyers in about 25 offices worldwide in 15 countries. One of the leading law firms headquartered in New York, Dewey & LeBoeuf's areas of expertise include antitrust, bankruptcy, government investigations, real estate, tax, and trade law, as well as mergers and acquisitions. The firm is the result of the October 2007 merger between law firms Dewey Ballantine and LeBoeuf, Lamb, Greene & MacRae. Dewey Ballantine was initially founded in 1909; the Dewey in the name refers to former partner Thomas Dewey, a three-term New York governor and two-time Republican presidential nominee in the 1940s. LeBoeuf, Lamb was established in 1929.

THE DEWEY ELECTRONICS CORPORATION

OTC: DEWY

27 Muller Rd.
Oakland, NJ 07436
Phone: 201-337-4700
Fax: 201-337-3976
Web: www.deweyelectronics.com

CEO: John H. D. Dewey
CFO: —
HR: —
FYE: June 30
Type: Public

The Dewey Electronics Corporation powers the military and powders the slopes. The company's electronics segment, which accounts for nearly all of Dewey's sales, provides the US Army with diesel-operated tactical generator sets, and produces underwater speed and distance measuring instrumentation for the US Navy. The US Department of Defense and its various agencies provide around 72% of sales. Dewey's HEDCO division designs, manufactures, and services the Snow Cub brand of snowmaking equipment, which it has sold to more than 300 ski resorts around the world. The family of late CEO Gordon Dewey owns about 37% of the company.

	Annual Growth	6/05	6/06	6/07	6/08	6/09
Sales ($ mil.)	15.7%	6.2	7.3	5.4	9.6	11.1
Net income ($ mil.)	—	0.0	(0.6)	(1.7)	0.1	0.1
Market value ($ mil.)	(26.6%)	8.0	5.3	3.8	4.1	2.3
Employees	0.0%	34	36	29	39	34

DEX ONE CORPORATION

NYSE: DEXO

1001 Winstead Dr.
Cary, NC 27513
Phone: 919-297-1600
Fax: 919-297-1285
Web: www.dexone.com

CEO: W. Kirk Liddell II
CFO: Steven M. (Steve) Blondy
HR: Gretchen Zech
FYE: December 31
Type: Public

You might say this company provides directory assistance. Dex One (formerly R.H. Donnelley) is one of the largest publishers of print and online directories in the US. It distributes directories in nearly 30 states, serving more than 500,000 local and national advertisers. In addition, Dex One provides such marketing products as print directories (Dex yellow and white pages), Internet Yellow Pages (DexKnows.com), and directory assistance via phone (1-800-Call-Dex). It also owns Business.com, and provides marketing services such as keyword and search engine optimization. The company emerged from bankruptcy in 2010.

	Annual Growth	12/05	12/06	12/07	12/08	12/09
Sales ($ mil.)	23.2%	956.6	1,895.9	2,680.3	2,616.8	2,202.4
Net income ($ mil.)	—	67.5	(237.7)	46.9	(2,298.3)	(6,453.3)
Market value ($ mil.)	(91.1%)	3,082.0	3,137.5	1,824.6	18.5	0.2
Employees	13.6%	2,100	4,400	4,700	3,800	3,500

DEXCOM, INC.

NASDAQ (GM): DXCM

6340 Sequence Dr.
San Diego, CA 92121
Phone: 858-200-0200
Fax: 858-200-0201
Web: www.dexcom.com

CEO: Terrance H. (Terry) Gregg
CFO: Jess Roper
HR: Cathy Alsaro
FYE: December 31
Type: Public

DexCom offers alternatives to diabetic fingertip tests. The company develops and markets glucose monitoring systems that measure and wirelessly transmit blood sugar levels from a sensor on the patient to a small receiver. Patients can access blood glucose trends and real-time information by pressing a button, and are alerted when levels are too high or too low. Diabetics can insert sensors themselves for the short-term continuous monitoring systems, which can be used for three to seven days. Products are marketed directly and through distributor representatives to physicians, endocrinologists, and diabetes educators in the US and select international markets.

	Annual Growth	12/05	12/06	12/07	12/08	12/09
Sales ($ mil.)	138.1%	—	2.2	4.6	9.8	29.7
Net income ($ mil.)	—	—	(46.6)	(45.9)	(55.2)	(53.5)
Market value ($ mil.)	(6.5%)	—	566.3	507.2	158.5	463.5
Employees	14.0%	—	260	252	304	385

DEY, L.P.

2751 Napa Valley Corporate Dr.
Napa, CA 94558
Phone: 707-224-3200
Fax: 707-224-9264
Web: www.dey.com

CEO: Carolyn Myers
CFO: Pamela R. Marrs
HR: —
FYE: December 31
Type: Subsidiary

Dey helps people breathe easier. The company, a subsidiary of generic drugmaker Mylan, makes prescription drugs for the treatment of allergies and respiratory diseases. Dey markets EpiPen autoinjectors, used by patients to self-administer epinephrine for severe allergic reactions. Its premeasured unit-dose inhalation products include treatments for asthma and chronic obstructive pulmonary disease (COPD). These treatments, called bronchodilators, are used in air-driven breathing devices called nebulizers and include branded DuoNeb and Perforomist products. It also offers several non-branded generic nebulizer treatments. A direct sales force markets Dey's products to doctors, pharmacies, and wholesalers.

D.F. STAUFFER BISCUIT COMPANY

360 S. Belmont St.
York, PA 17405
Phone: 717-843-9016
Fax: 717-843-0592
Web: www.stauffers.net

CEO: Taka Kataoka
CFO: Doug Dutton
HR: Donna Mummert
FYE: December 31
Type: Subsidiary

Lions and tigers and bears, oh my! D.F. Stauffer Biscuit's products include packaged animal crackers, sandwich cookies, and sugar wafers. It also makes (non-sweet) animal crackers for soup. With nearly 20 oven lines at four production sites, the company is able to bake more than 250 tons of its products every day. Stauffer's cookies are available worldwide. The company's Web site allows customers to buy products or play games online, and also has a handy animal-cracker identifier to ensure that visitors will never be left wondering what kind of animal they're munching on. Baking up edible its critters since 1871, D.F. Stauffer Biscuit Company is a subsidiary of Japanese candy company Meiji Seika Kaisha.

	Annual Growth	12/04	12/05	12/06	12/07	12/08
Est. sales ($ mil.)	—	—	—	—	—	126.0
Employees	—	—	—	—	—	650

DG FASTCHANNEL, INC.

NASDAQ (GM): DGIT

750 W. John Carpenter Fwy., Ste. 700
Irving, TX 75039
Phone: 972-581-2000
Fax: 972-581-2001
Web: www.dgfastchannel.com

CEO: Scott K. Ginsburg
CFO: Omar A. Choucair
HR: —
FYE: December 31
Type: Public

Commercials don't signify bathroom breaks for DG FastChannel (formerly Digital Generation Systems, which did business as DG Systems). The company provides digital distribution services for advertisers, agencies, newspaper publishers, and TV and radio broadcasters. Ad agencies and other content providers route their clients' audio and video spots to radio and TV stations and other traditional media outlets through DG FastChannel's nationwide digital distribution network. Electronic transmissions are made across the Internet and via satellite. Chairman and CEO Scott Ginsburg owns about 15% of the company, which became DG FastChannel in 2006 after purchasing competitor FastChannel Network for $37.5 million.

	Annual Growth	12/05	12/06	12/07	12/08	12/09
Sales ($ mil.)	34.5%	58.4	68.7	97.7	157.1	190.9
Net income ($ mil.)	—	(1.1)	(0.6)	10.4	15.1	20.5
Market value ($ mil.)	50.8%	153.4	382.8	728.2	354.4	793.2
Employees	23.6%	317	376	552	770	739

DGSE COMPANIES, INC.

NYSE Amex: DGC

11311 Reeder Rd.
Dallas, TX 75229
Phone: 972-484-3662
Fax: 972-241-0646
Web: www.dgse.com

CEO: L. S. Smith
CFO: John Benson
HR: —
FYE: December 31
Type: Public

Attracted to things gold and shiny? If so, DGSE Companies is for you. The firm buys and sells jewelry, bullion, rare coins, fine watches, and collectibles to retail and wholesale customers across the US through its various websites and retail stores in California, Texas, and South Carolina. The company's eight e-commerce sites let customers buy and sell jewelry and bullion interactively, and obtain current precious-metal prices. In all, more than 7,500 items are available for sale on DGSE websites, including $2 million in diamonds. DGSE also owns Fairchild Watches, a leading vintage watch wholesaler, and the rare coin dealer Superior Galleries. The company sold its pair of pawn shops in Dallas, Texas, in 2009.

	Annual Growth	12/05	12/06	12/07	12/08	12/09
Sales ($ mil.)	24.5%	35.6	44.1	63.0	105.2	85.4
Net income ($ mil.)	—	0.5	0.6	0.9	(7.9)	(0.3)
Market value ($ mil.)	(8.3%)	19.6	25.0	51.6	16.7	13.9
Employees	11.0%	54	50	93	102	82

An in-depth profile of this company is available to Hoover's Online members at hoovers.com.

493

DHL EXPRESS (USA), INC.

1200 S. Pine Island Rd., Ste. 600	CEO: Ian D. Clough
Plantation, FL 33324	CFO: Rafael Estevez
Phone: 954-888-7000	HR: Michael Munn
Fax: 954-888-7310	FYE: December 31
Web: www.dhl-usa.com	Type: Subsidiary

DHL Express (USA) is the US arm of express delivery giant DHL, which itself is a subsidiary of Germany's Deutsche Post. The operations of DHL Express (USA) are coordinated with those of other DHL express delivery units; overall, DHL serves some 120,000 locations in more than 220 countries and territories worldwide. Besides its express delivery operations, DHL offers supply chain management and freight forwarding services. In order to cut costs and improve DHL Express (USA)'s operating efficiency, in early 2009 Deutsche Post ceased all of its air and ground services within the US. DHL Express (USA) still offers international shipping services to and from the US.

DHL GLOBAL FORWARDING

1200 S. Pine Island Rd., Ste. 140	CEO: Hans Toggweiler
Plantation, FL 33324	CFO: Dagmar Hennes
Phone: 954-888-7000	HR: —
Fax: 954-888-7301	FYE: December 31
Web: www.us.danzas.com	Type: Business segment

DHL Global Forwarding can arrange to keep cargo rolling through the land, sailing over the sea, or flying in the air. The company provides freight forwarding services, including customs brokerage, and logistics services, including warehousing and distribution. (As a freight forwarder, DHL Global Forwarding buys transportation capacity from carriers and resells it to customers.) The company is part of the DHL empire, which also includes units that focus on express delivery, supply chain management, and overland transport within Europe. DHL, in turn, is a unit of express delivery and logistics services giant Deutsche Post.

DHL GLOBAL MAIL

2700 S. Commerce Pkwy., Ste. 400	CEO: Thomas Kipp
Weston, FL 33331	CFO: Terry Hilsman
Phone: 954-903-6300	HR: Beth Day
Fax: 317-455-2289	FYE: December 31
Web: www.dhlglobalmail.com	Type: Subsidiary

DHL Global Mail doesn't actually deliver the mail, but the company does work to speed its arrival. A provider of mail processing and distribution services for business customers, DHL Global Mail operates from more than 20 terminals throughout North America. The company takes mail from its customers that is bound for various destinations, sorts it, and gets it to the post office distribution facility closest to its destination. It also provides international distribution services to some 200 countries through affiliates; in total, DHL Global Mail's international network consists of about 50 processing facilities. The company is part of the mail business segment of its parent, German postal service Deutsche Post.

THE DIAGEO CHATEAU & ESTATE WINES COMPANY

240 Gateway Rd. West	CEO: Sandra LeDrew
Napa, CA 94558	CFO: —
Phone: 707-299-2600	HR: —
Fax: —	FYE: June 30
Web: www.diageowines.com	Type: Subsidiary

You might find the aromas of orange and jasmine complemented by spicy pepper along with lingering herb notes at Diageo Chateau & Estate Wines. A subsidiary of alcoholic drinks powerhouse Diageo, the company produces and markets a corking good list of wines, including Beaulieu Vineyard, Jade Mountain, Sterling Vineyards, and the wines of the Chalone Vineyard. Its imported offerings include the French wines of Barton & Guestier. Diageo's portfolio of wines comes from its vineyards in California and the Bordeaux, Burgundy, and other wine-making regions of France. Chateau & Estate Wines was purchased by Diageo in 2001.

DIAGEO NORTH AMERICA, INC.

801 Main Ave.	CEO: Ivan M. Menezes
Norwalk, CT 06851	CFO: Catherine K. (Cathy) Jessup
Phone: 203-229-2100	HR: Eliana Zem
Fax: 203-229-8901	FYE: June 30
Web: www.diageo.com	Type: Subsidiary

A subsidiary of Diageo plc, one of the world's largest producers of alcoholic drinks, Diageo North America makes up the largest portion (about 40%) of its parent company's total sales. North America is also Diageo's largest market by volume. In the US, the company asks distributors to dedicate people exclusively to the sale of Diageo brands. Its well-known libations include Baileys Irish Cream liqueur, Captain Morgan rum, Crown Royal Canadian whiskey, José Cuervo tequila, Johnnie Walker Scotch whisky, Smirnoff vodka, Sterling Vineyards wines, Tanqueray gin, and beer from Guinness and Red Stripe. Diageo North America owns production facilities in the US and Canada, as well as vineyards in Northern California.

⊞ THE DIAL CORPORATION

15501 N. Dial Blvd.	CEO: Bradley A. (Brad) Casper
Scottsdale, AZ 85260	CFO: Ian Parrish
Phone: 480-754-3425	HR: —
Fax: —	FYE: December 31
Web: www.dialcorp.com	Type: Subsidiary

Don't look for dirt on The Dial Corporation. The company has built a business keeping itself and its customers squeaky clean and as fresh as a daisy. The manufacturer boasts one of the top-selling soaps in the US and counts several leading brands in each of its two core product segments: laundry and home care (with product names Purex, Zout, 20 Mule Team, Combat, Soft Scrub, and Renuzit) and beauty and personal care (with its Dial soaps, body-washes, and hand sanitizers; Tone, Coast, Dry Idea, Soft & Dri, and Right Guard). Dial, a subsidiary of Henkel KGaA since 2004, is known for its "Aren't You Glad You Use Dial?" slogan, which was first used in 1953.

DIALYSIS CORPORATION OF AMERICA

1302 Concourse Dr., Ste. 204
Linthicum, MD 21090
Phone: 410-694-0500
Fax: 410-694-0596
Web: www.dialysiscorporation.com

CEO: Stephen W. Everett
CFO: Andrew J. Jeanneret
HR: —
FYE: December 31
Type: Private

Dialysis Corporation of America (DCA) is out to keep America's blood clean. The company operates about 35 outpatient dialysis clinics in more than half a dozen US states, providing life-sustaining services to patients with chronic kidney failure (also known as end-stage renal disease). DCA also provides inpatient dialysis through contracts with about a dozen hospitals, all of them in markets where it has outpatient facilities; and, through its dialysis clinics, DCA provides training and support to patients who use peritoneal dialysis at home. The company was acquired by privately-held US Renal Care for about $112 million in 2010.

	Annual Growth	12/05	12/06	12/07	12/08	12/09
Sales ($ mil.)	21.5%	45.4	62.5	74.2	86.8	98.9
Net income ($ mil.)	11.2%	1.9	3.0	3.1	2.8	2.9
Employees	8.5%	493	601	653	550	682

DIAMOND FOODS, INC.

NASDAQ (GS): DMND

600 Montgomery St., 17th Fl.
San Francisco, CA 94111
Phone: 415-912-3180
Fax: —
Web: www.diamondfoods.com

CEO: Michael J. Mendes
CFO: Steven M. (Steve) Neil
HR: Stephen E. Kim
FYE: July 31
Type: Public

Shy, you ask? Not a bit. Diamond Foods is always coming out of its shell. The company sells a wide array of tree nuts and value-added nut products. Walnuts accounted for 47% of its 2009 sales, but Diamond also offers almonds, Brazil nuts, hazelnuts, pecans, pine nuts, and peanuts for use in home cooking, snack foods, in-shell eating, and as ingredients for other food manufacturers. The company, whose primary brands are Diamond and Emerald, also sells nuts to restaurants and other foodservice operators. In addition to US markets, Diamond Foods also does business internationally, mainly in Germany, Japan, the Netherlands, South Korea, Spain, and Turkey.

	Annual Growth	7/05	7/06	7/07	7/08	7/09
Sales ($ mil.)	7.4%	428.3	477.2	522.6	531.5	570.9
Net income ($ mil.)	(40.0%)	182.8	7.3	8.4	14.8	23.7
Market value ($ mil.)	6.2%	368.3	255.1	274.0	404.4	468.9
Employees	6.3%	670	768	754	628	855

DIAMOND HILL INVESTMENT GROUP, INC.

NASDAQ (GM): DHIL

325 John H. McConnell Blvd., Ste. 200
Columbus, OH 43215
Phone: 614-255-3333
Fax: 614-255-3363
Web: www.diamond-hill.com

CEO: Roderick H. (Ric) Dillon Jr.
CFO: James F. (Jim) Laird Jr.
HR: —
FYE: December 31
Type: Public

Diamond Hill Investment Group takes a shine to investing. Operating through flagship subsidiary Diamond Hill Capital Management, the firm oversees approximately $5 billion in assets, most of it invested in mutual funds. Serving institutional and individual clients, the company administers several mutual funds and sells them mainly through independent investment advisors, broker-dealers, financial planners, investment consultants, and third-party marketing firms. It also manages separate accounts and hedge funds.

	Annual Growth	12/05	12/06	12/07	12/08	12/09
Assets ($ mil.)	33.6%	12.7	37.2	53.3	44.5	40.5
Net income ($ mil.)	32.5%	3.7	8.1	9.9	3.3	11.4
Market value ($ mil.)	19.7%	86.8	232.1	202.6	180.2	178.0
Employees	33.1%	21	32	42	57	66

DIAMOND MANAGEMENT & TECHNOLOGY

NASDAQ (GM): DTPI

875 N. Michigan Ave., Ste. 3000
Chicago, IL 60611
Phone: 312-255-5000
Fax: 312-255-6000
Web: www.diamondconsultants.com

CEO: Adam J. Gutstein
CFO: Karl E. Bupp
HR: Edmund (Ed) Brady III
FYE: March 31
Type: Public

At Diamond Management & Technology Consultants, Inc., gems come in the form of advice. The firm specializes in providing clients with strategic and operational assistance regarding the use of technology in their businesses. Diamond focuses on helping companies in industries such as financial services, health care, insurance, and telecommunications. The firm also performs work for clients in the public sector, and its enterprise practice seeks out business from companies in a variety of industries, including manufacturers and retailers of consumer products. Employing more than 460 consultants, Diamond operates from six offices in the US, the UK, and India.

	Annual Growth	3/05	3/06	3/07	3/08	3/09
Sales ($ mil.)	(5.5%)	219.8	163.7	190.3	205.1	175.0
Net income ($ mil.)	—	33.0	(10.6)	31.4	21.1	(8.4)
Market value ($ mil.)	(36.9%)	437.5	290.8	317.7	175.3	69.3
Employees	(6.4%)	751	554	613	626	577

DIAMOND OFFSHORE DRILLING, INC.

NYSE: DO

15415 Katy Fwy., Ste. 100
Houston, TX 77094
Phone: 281-492-5300
Fax: 281-492-5316
Web: www.diamondoffshore.com

CEO: Lawrence R. (Larry) Dickerson
CFO: Gary T. Krenek
HR: R. Lynn Charles
FYE: December 31
Type: Public

This Diamond is an oiler's best friend. Diamond Offshore Drilling is a contract offshore oil and gas driller capable of descending the deep blue to depths of 10,000 feet. A leading US drilling contractor, Diamond Offshore has about 50 rigs, including 32 semisubmersibles, 13 jack-up rigs (mobile drilling platforms), and one drillship. Operating in waters off six of the world's continents, Diamond Offshore contracts with almost 50 oil and gas companies; Brazil's PETROBRAS is its major customer. The company also provides project management and other drilling-related services. Loews Corp. owns 50.4% of the company.

	Annual Growth	12/05	12/06	12/07	12/08	12/09
Sales ($ mil.)	31.3%	1,221.0	2,052.6	2,567.7	3,544.1	3,631.3
Net income ($ mil.)	51.6%	260.3	706.8	846.5	1,311.0	1,376.2
Market value ($ mil.)	9.1%	9,670.7	11,113.8	19,741.7	8,194.2	13,683.0
Employees	5.1%	4,500	4,800	5,400	5,700	5,500

DIAMOND RESORTS HOLDINGS, LLC

3865 W. Cheyenne Ave.
North Las Vegas, NV 89032
Phone: 702-804-8600
Fax: 702-304-7066
Web: www.diamondresorts.com

CEO: Stephen J. Cloobeck
CFO: David Palmer
HR: —
FYE: September 30
Type: Private

Diamond Resorts Holdings, formerly Sunterra Corporation, can take you to some of the sunniest places on Earth. The time-share vacation company, which does business as Diamond Resorts International, owns or manages more than 150 resorts in Asia, Australia, the Caribbean, Europe, and North America. Some 380,000 owners and members vacation at the company's resorts through the purchase of either vacation intervals (generally a one-week stay) or vacation points (redeemable for varying lengths of stay). CEO Stephen Cloobeck controls the company.

	Annual Growth	9/04	9/05	9/06	9/07	9/08
Est. sales ($ mil.)	—	—	—	—	—	99.0
Employees	—	—	—	—	—	5,100

An in-depth profile of this company is available to Hoover's Online members at hoovers.com.

DIAMONDHEAD CASINO CORPORATION
OTC: DHCC

1301 Seminole Blvd., Ste. 142
Largo, FL 33770
Phone: 727-674-0055
Fax: —

CEO: Deborah A. Vitale
CFO: Robert Zimmerman
HR: —
FYE: December 31
Type: Public

Diamondhead Casino Corporation owns more than 400 acres of land on Mississippi's St. Louis Bay, where it plans to develop a casino resort. The company previously owned and operated four "cruise-to-nowhere" casino gambling ships in Florida but sold the vessels between 1999 and 2001 to focus on its Diamondhead, Mississippi, casino plans. Currently Diamondhead Casino Corporation has no operations and four employees who are seeking the various permits, authorizations, and financing required to develop a casino. Chairman and CEO Deborah Vitale owns more than 10% of the company through an employee stock trust.

	Annual Growth	12/05	12/06	12/07	12/08	12/09
Sales ($ mil.)	—	—	—	—	0.0	0.0
Net income ($ mil.)	—	—	—	—	(3.1)	(1.1)
Market value ($ mil.)	0.2%	—	—	—	20.5	20.5
Employees	0.0%	—	—	—	4	4

DIAMONDROCK HOSPITALITY COMPANY
NYSE: DRH

6903 Rockledge Dr., Ste. 800
Bethesda, MD 20817
Phone: 240-744-1150
Fax: —
Web: www.drhc.com

CEO: Mark W. Brugger
CFO: Sean M. Mahoney
HR: —
FYE: December 31
Type: Public

If diamonds are a girl's best friend, then DiamondRock Hospitality must be an investor's best friend. Operating as an umbrella partnership real estate investment trust (UPREIT), DiamondRock primarily functions through its taxable REIT subsidiary Bloodstone TRS. It owns (but does not operate) about 20 upper upscale full-service hotels with more than 9,500 rooms in North America, with an emphasis on such markets as New York, Los Angeles, Chicago, Boston, and Atlanta. Its hotels are all operated under brands owned by Marriott International, Starwood Hotels & Resorts Worldwide, and Hilton Worldwide.

	Annual Growth	12/05	12/06	12/07	12/08	12/09
Sales ($ mil.)	25.9%	229.5	491.9	710.9	693.2	575.7
Net income ($ mil.)	—	(7.3)	35.2	68.3	52.9	(11.1)
Market value ($ mil.)	(8.3%)	1,570.2	2,364.6	1,966.7	665.6	1,112.0
Employees	6.5%	14	17	18	17	18

DIAPULSE CORPORATION OF AMERICA
Pink Sheets: DIAC

321 E. Shore Rd.
Great Neck, NY 11023
Phone: 516-466-3030
Fax: 516-829-8069
Web: www.diapulse.com

CEO: David M. Ross
CFO: —
HR: —
FYE: December 31
Type: Public

Energize! Diapulse Corporation of America makes and sells its Diapulse Wound Treatment System, a machine that generates non-thermal electromagnetic energy for the treatment of post-operative pain and edema for soft-tissue wounds such as bed sores, diabetic ulcers, and venous ulcers. Buyers of the Diapulse system include hospitals, assisted-living and long-term care facilities, clinics, physicians, and individual patients who use the equipment at home. Diapulse Corp. both rents and sells its technology, and the equipment is covered by Medicare and many insurance plans. Chairman and CEO David Ross owns 40% of the company.

DIASYS CORPORATION
Pink Sheets: DYXC

81 W. Main St.
Waterbury, CT 06702
Phone: 203-755-5083
Fax: 203-755-5105
Web: www.diasys.com

CEO: Frederic H. Neikrug
CFO: Morris Silverman
HR: —
FYE: June 30
Type: Public

Diagnostic testing company DiaSys plays detective with patient specimens. The company makes instruments, reagents, consumables, and test kits used in routine urinalysis and detection of parasites. Its R/S and FE series workstations are automated instrumentation systems that analyze urine and fecal samples. The company markets its products in North America through a direct sales force and distribution contracts with the likes of Cardinal HealthCare, Thermo Fisher Scientific, and Broadlane. Internationally, it sells directly in the UK and through independent distributors elsewhere. Hospital and clinical laboratories are its primary customers.

DICE HOLDINGS, INC.
NYSE: DHX

1040 Avenue of the Americas, 16th Fl.
New York, NY 10018
Phone: 212-725-6550
Fax: 212-725-6559
Web: www.diceholdingsinc.com

CEO: Scot W. Melland
CFO: Michael P. Durney
HR: —
FYE: December 31
Type: Public

Dice Holdings rolls along with websites devoted to employee recruiting and career development. Through its flagship website, Dice.com, it provides job postings and career-related resources for technology professionals in the US. Dice also operates ClearanceJobs.com, for people with US government security clearances; eFinancialCareers.com, aimed at the financial services industry; AllHealthcareJobs.com, targeting health care workers; and JobsintheMoney.com, for accounting and finance professionals. It also puts on job fairs. Most of the company's revenue comes from employers, who pay to post job listings and view resumes. Investment firms General Atlantic and Quadrangle Group own a controlling stake in Dice Holdings.

	Annual Growth	12/05	12/06	12/07	12/08	12/09
Sales ($ mil.)	59.5%	17.0	83.7	142.4	155.0	110.0
Net income ($ mil.)	—	(1.7)	6.8	15.5	15.4	13.5
Market value ($ mil.)	(9.5%)	—	—	501.3	256.0	410.9
Employees	7.0%	202	329	308	283	265

DICKINSON FINANCIAL CORPORATION II

1100 Main St., Ste. 350
Kansas City, MO 64105
Phone: 816-471-9800
Fax: 816-412-0022
Web: www.bankmw.com

CEO: Paul P. Holewinski
CFO: Dennis P. Ambroske
HR: —
FYE: December 31
Type: Private

Drop and give me a twenty. Dickinson Financial is the holding company for flagship subsidiary Bank Midwest, as well as SunBank, Southern Commerce Bank, and a group of military banks: Armed Forces Bank, Armed Forces Bank of California, and Academy Bank. Bank Midwest operates about 70 branches in Kansas and Missouri, including the Kansas City and St. Louis metropolitan areas. SunBank and Southern Commerce Bank have about a dozen branches apiece in Arizona and Florida, respectively. Academy Bank has more than 50 locations in Colorado; the other two military banks have about 60 locations on or around military bases in nearly 20 states.

	Annual Growth	12/05	12/06	12/07	12/08	12/09
Assets ($ mil.)	10.1%	4,022.2	4,704.9	5,579.0	6,080.4	5,918.6
Net income ($ mil.)	—	75.8	106.9	105.4	(3.4)	(334.2)
Employees	1.9%	1,901	2,002	2,179	2,226	2,046

An in-depth profile of this company is available to Hoover's Online members at hoovers.com.

DICK'S SPORTING GOODS, INC.

NYSE: DKS

345 Court St.
Coraopolis, PA 15108
Phone: 724-273-3400
Fax: 724-227-1902
Web: www.dickssportinggoods.com

CEO: Edward W. (Ed) Stack
CFO: Timothy E. (Tim) Kullman
HR: Kathryn (Kathy) Sutter
FYE: January 31
Type: Public

See Dick's shoppers run, putt, dunk, drive, dribble — and buy. Fast-growing Dick's Sporting Goods operates about 420 stores in some 40 states. The stores contain on average five smaller shops ("stores within a store") featuring sporting goods, apparel, and footwear for leisure pursuits, ranging from football, golf, and cycling to hunting and camping. Dick's also sells its products online. In addition to brands such as NIKE and adidas, Dick's carries Ativa, Walter Hagen, and others exclusive to the firm. The company also operates 90 Golf Galaxy (acquired in 2007) stores in 30 states. Dick's was founded in 1948 when Dick Stack, father of company chairman and CEO Edward Stack, opened a bait and tackle store.

	Annual Growth	1/06	1/07	1/08	1/09	1/10
Sales ($ mil.)	13.9%	2,625.0	3,114.2	3,888.4	4,130.1	4,412.8
Net income ($ mil.)	16.7%	73.0	112.6	155.0	(35.1)	135.4
Market value ($ mil.)	5.0%	2,111.8	2,957.2	3,734.2	1,264.6	2,569.5
Employees	8.6%	18,100	19,920	26,400	27,600	25,200

⊞ DIEBOLD, INCORPORATED

NYSE: DBD

5995 Mayfair Rd.
North Canton, OH 44720
Phone: 330-490-4000
Fax: 330-490-3794
Web: www.diebold.com

CEO: Thomas W. Swidarski
CFO: Bradley C. (Brad) Richardson
HR: Sheila M. Rutt
FYE: December 31
Type: Public

Cash is king at Diebold. The company is one of the leading producers of automated teller machines (ATMs). In addition, Diebold offers remote teller systems, cash dispensers, and check cashing machines. Originally a manufacturer of safes, the company is still active in its original market, offering products that include vaults and security systems for financial institutions. Diebold also provides electronic voting machines through its Procomp Industria Eletronica subsidiary in Brazil. Its services range from product maintenance to installation consulting and plan design. Diebold, which has operations in about 90 countries, gets around three-quarters of its sales in the Americas.

	Annual Growth	12/05	12/06	12/07	12/08	12/09
Sales ($ mil.)	1.2%	2,587.0	2,906.2	2,964.8	3,170.1	2,718.3
Net income ($ mil.)	(24.0%)	96.7	86.5	39.5	88.6	32.3
Market value ($ mil.)	(7.0%)	2,505.9	3,073.1	1,911.1	1,852.4	1,876.2
Employees	2.9%	14,603	15,451	16,942	16,658	16,397

DIEDRICH COFFEE, INC.

28 Executive Park, Ste. 200
Irvine, CA 92614
Phone: 949-260-1600
Fax: 949-260-1610
Web: www.diedrich.com

CEO: Sean M. McCarthy
CFO: Sean M. McCarthy
HR: —
FYE: June 30
Type: Subsidiary

This company keeps caffeine lovers buzzing. Diedrich Coffee is a leading coffee producer and wholesale supplier that distributes coffee products to retailers and foodservice customers. The company produces a variety of specialty coffee blends and flavors under the brands Coffee People, Diedrich Coffee, and Gloria Jean's. Its primary product is K-Cup single serving portion packs, produced under license for Keurig's single-service coffee machines. Diedrich Coffee produces and distributes fresh roasted coffee from its facility in California. In 2010 the company was acquired by Green Mountain Coffee Roasters.

	Annual Growth	6/05	6/06	6/07	6/08	6/09
Sales ($ mil.)	4.4%	52.5	59.4	36.6	46.3	62.3
Net income ($ mil.)	(42.5%)	14.6	(7.8)	(1.8)	(13.8)	1.6
Employees	(34.5%)	815	951	223	220	150

DIERBERGS MARKETS INC.

16690 Swingley Ridge Rd.
Chesterfield, MO 63017
Phone: 636-532-8884
Fax: 636-812-1603
Web: www.dierbergs.com

CEO: Gregory (Greg) Dierberg
CFO: Connie Hawley
HR: —
FYE: December 31
Type: Private

Dierbergs Markets has a taste of what folks in St. Louis like to eat. Dierbergs operates about two dozen upscale supermarkets in the St. Louis area, where rival Schnuck Markets is the market leader. Dierbergs' stores offer food, drugs, photo processing, and video centers, as well as cooking schools, banks, self-service checkout, Krispy Kreme donuts, and made-to-order Chinese food at some locations. The company also offers online grocery shopping. Dierbergs Florist and Gifts, affiliated with FTD, offers gift baskets and floral services at its stores and over the Internet for local and international delivery. Founded as a trading outpost in 1854, the Dierberg family has owned and operated Dierbergs since 1914.

⊞ DIGI INTERNATIONAL INC.

NASDAQ (GS): DGII

11001 Bren Rd. East
Minnetonka, MN 55343
Phone: 952-912-3444
Fax: 952-912-4952
Web: www.digi.com

CEO: Joseph T. (Joe) Dunsmore
CFO: Brenda L. Mueller
HR: Tracy L. Roberts
FYE: September 30
Type: Public

Digi serves up peripherals on a serial platter. Digi International makes serial cards and ports for connecting peripherals to networks. It also sells networking devices that utilize the USB (Universal Serial Bus) interface. The company's products are used in point-of-sale (POS) systems, as well as industrial automation, medical, hospitality, and building automation applications. Digi manufactures microprocessors and software used to connect electronic devices to networks. The company sells directly and through resellers and distributors, such as Tech Data. Digi International gets more than half of its sales in North America.

	Annual Growth	9/05	9/06	9/07	9/08	9/09
Sales ($ mil.)	7.3%	125.2	144.7	173.3	185.1	165.9
Net income ($ mil.)	(30.6%)	17.7	11.1	19.8	12.4	4.1
Market value ($ mil.)	(5.6%)	267.5	336.5	355.0	254.3	212.4
Employees	7.1%	481	549	564	663	634

DIGI-KEY CORPORATION

701 Brooks Ave. South
Thief River Falls, MN 56701
Phone: 218-681-6674
Fax: 218-681-3380
Web: www.digikey.com

CEO: Ronald Stordahl
CFO: Marie Finney
HR: Rick Trontvet
FYE: December 31
Type: Private

Digi-Key holds more than one key to electronics distribution. The company distributes electronic components to businesses and consumers mainly in the US, Canada, Europe, and Japan. Digi-Key uses an entirely in-house sales force and does business by means of telemarketing and a catalog featuring more than 300,000 products from 400-plus manufacturers, such as 3M, Freescale, and Texas Instruments. Its products, ranging from AC line cords to zinc-oxide non-linear resistors, also are available through a downloadable catalog featured on the company's Web site. Founded in 1971 by CEO and owner Ronald Stordahl, Digi-Key takes its name from the ham radio digital electronic keyer kit he developed and sold in college.

	Annual Growth	12/04	12/05	12/06	12/07	12/08
Est. sales ($ mil.)	—	—	—	—	—	83.4
Employees	—	—	—	—	—	2,000

⊞ An in-depth profile of this company is available to Hoover's Online members at hoovers.com.

497

DIGIMARC CORPORATION

NASDAQ (GM): DMRC

9405 SW Gemini Dr.
Beaverton, OR 97008
Phone: 503-469-4800
Fax: 503-469-4777
Web: www.digimarc.com

CEO: Bruce Davis
CFO: Michael E. McConnell
HR: —
FYE: December 31
Type: Public

Digimarc makes its mark on media. The company provides digital watermarking software that embeds code in printed and digital content, including photographs, music, movies, and television content. Customers — which include movie studios, record labels, broadcasters, creative professionals, and government agencies — use Digimarc's software to control copyrights, deter piracy, license online content, and manage digital assets. The company generates revenue from software development, consulting services, and technology licensing and subscription fees. Licensees include Microsoft, The Nielsen Company, and THOMSON.

	Annual Growth	12/05	12/06	12/07	12/08	12/09
Sales ($ mil.)	19.8%	—	11.1	13.0	19.8	19.1
Net income ($ mil.)	—	—	(2.7)	0.1	1.5	(2.8)
Market value ($ mil.)	49.6%	—	—	—	73.2	109.5
Employees	(3.1%)	—	—	99	87	93

DIGIRAD CORPORATION

NASDAQ (GM): DRAD

13950 Stowe Dr.
Poway, CA 92064
Phone: 858-726-1600
Fax: 858-726-1700
Web: www.digirad.com

CEO: Todd P. Clyde
CFO: Richard B. Slansky
HR: —
FYE: December 31
Type: Public

Digirad gives doctors the nuclear option and curbside service. The firm makes and sells nuclear imaging equipment and provides mobile imaging services. Nuclear imaging uses low-level radioactive drugs introduced into a patient's bloodstream to detect heart disease, cancer, and neurological disorders. The company leases its equipment and provides staffing through its Digirad Imaging Solutions (DIS) unit which allows doctors to offer imaging in their offices with less capital investment. DIS also provides mobile cardiovascular ultrasound services. Digirad sells its larger solid state cameras to doctors' offices, hospitals, and imaging centers, through a direct sales force and distributors in the US.

	Annual Growth	12/05	12/06	12/07	12/08	12/09
Sales ($ mil.)	0.5%	68.2	71.9	73.9	80.4	69.6
Net income ($ mil.)	—	(9.6)	(6.3)	(1.4)	(6.9)	0.6
Market value ($ mil.)	(15.0%)	76.6	78.5	69.3	11.0	40.0
Employees	(9.0%)	601	371	457	460	413

DIGITAL ALLY, INC.

NASDAQ (CM): DGLY

7311 West 130th St., Ste. 170
Overland Park, KS 66213
Phone: 913-814-7774
Fax: 913-814-7775
Web: www.digitalallyinc.com

CEO: Stanton E. Ross
CFO: Thomas J. Heckman
HR: —
FYE: December 31
Type: Public

Digital video systems manufacturer Digital Ally is an ally to police and other law enforcement that want more than a paper record of their traffic stops. Targeted to city, state, and commercial law enforcement agencies, the company designs and manufactures specialized digital video cameras, including a rearview mirror with a built-in digital video camera (used to capture video from inside police vehicles), as well as a portable digital video flashlight, which can be used to record routine traffic stops, sobriety tests, and other law enforcement/civilian interactions. The company also offers a version of their video camera that can be worn on law enforcement officers' uniforms. Digital Ally was formed in 2004.

	Annual Growth	12/05	12/06	12/07	12/08	12/09
Sales ($ mil.)	86.0%	—	4.1	19.4	32.6	26.4
Net income ($ mil.)	—	—	(3.4)	4.5	3.4	(1.1)
Market value ($ mil.)	(47.0%)	—	—	119.2	50.4	33.5
Employees	40.7%	—	37	72	117	103

DIGITAL ANGEL CORPORATION

NASDAQ (CM): DIGA

490 Villaume Ave.
South St. Paul, MN 55075
Phone: 651-455-1621
Fax: 651-455-0413
Web: www.digitalangel.com

CEO: Joseph J. (Joe) Grillo
CFO: Lorraine M. Breece
HR: —
FYE: December 31
Type: Public

Digital Angel (formerly known as Applied Digital Solutions) can help you find your way. The company develops miniaturized radio frequency identification devices used in military and commercial applications, as well as for tracking companion animals and locating and monitoring livestock. Digital Angel was best known for its microchip technology — marketed through the company's VeriChip (now PositiveID) subsidiary — which were computer chips that could be embedded under the skin and read by a remote sensor to check vital signs and diagnose medical problems. As part of a larger effort to divest itself of underperforming units, the company sold its 45% stake in the company to R&R Consulting Partners in late 2008.

	Annual Growth	12/05	12/06	12/07	12/08	12/09
Sales ($ mil.)	(18.8%)	113.7	122.7	117.4	78.2	49.5
Net income ($ mil.)	—	(10.2)	(27.2)	(32.0)	(58.1)	(12.4)
Market value ($ mil.)	(57.4%)	641.8	403.9	94.3	14.0	21.0
Employees	(5.6%)	307	314	419	364	244

DIGITAL POWER CORPORATION

NYSE Amex: DPW

41324 Christy St.
Fremont, CA 94538
Phone: 510-657-2635
Fax: 510-353-4023
Web: www.digipwr.com

CEO: Amos Kohn
CFO: Assaf (Assi) Itshayek
HR: —
FYE: December 31
Type: Public

Digital Power is a real switch hitter. The company makes power supplies, such as AC/DC switchers and DC/DC converters, for OEMs in the industrial, medical, military, and telecommunications markets. Its products protect electronic components and circuits from power surges while converting a single input voltage into different output voltages. Most of Digital Power's products, which can be easily modified to meet the specific needs of its 400 customers, are made by subcontractors in China and Mexico. UK-based subsidiary Digital Power Limited, doing business as Gresham Power Electronics, makes AC/DC power supplies, uninterruptible power supplies, and power inverters; it accounts for more than half of sales.

	Annual Growth	12/05	12/06	12/07	12/08	12/09
Sales ($ mil.)	(5.5%)	10.9	12.6	12.2	11.9	8.7
Net income ($ mil.)	—	0.0	0.1	0.1	0.6	(0.1)
Market value ($ mil.)	11.6%	5.8	8.5	9.2	6.0	9.0
Employees	0.8%	32	33	33	33	33

DIGITAL REALTY TRUST, INC.

NYSE: DLR

560 Mission St., Ste. 2900
San Francisco, CA 94105
Phone: 415-738-6500
Fax: 415-738-6501
Web: www.digitalrealtytrust.com

CEO: Michael F. Foust
CFO: A. William Stein
HR: —
FYE: December 31
Type: Public

Technically, Digital Realty Trust puts its chips in real estate. The real estate investment trust (REIT) owns properties that are leased to companies in the technology sector. Its portfolio includes about 75 properties in the US and Europe, including data centers, data communications hubs, offices, and manufacturing properties. Altogether, the REIT owns some 13 million sq. ft. of rentable space, including space held for redevelopment. Digital Realty Trust focuses on properties in hot tech markets, including the Silicon Valley, Chicago, the New York/New Jersey corridor, and Dallas. Savvis Communications and Qwest Communications are the company's largest tenants.

	Annual Growth	12/05	12/06	12/07	12/08	12/09
Sales ($ mil.)	32.2%	208.8	281.9	395.2	527.4	637.1
Net income ($ mil.)	94.7%	6.1	31.4	40.6	67.7	87.7
Market value ($ mil.)	22.1%	1,762.5	2,665.9	2,988.3	2,558.4	3,915.9
Employees	49.4%	53	109	153	210	264

DIGITAL RIVER, INC.
NASDAQ (GS): DRIV

9625 W. 76th St., Ste. 150
Eden Prairie, MN 55344
Phone: 952-253-1234
Fax: 952-253-8497
Web: www.digitalriver.com

CEO: Joel A. Ronning
CFO: Thomas M. Donnelly
HR: —
FYE: December 31
Type: Public

Digital River helps keep the e-commerce flowing. The company provides technology and services that enable its clients to sell their products on the Web without building an e-commerce platform from the ground up. Using its own proprietary server technology, Digital River offers Web development and hosting, transaction processing, fulfillment, and fraud screening services to tens of thousands of customers operating online retail and distribution businesses. It also provides its customers with Web traffic data that allows them to better market their online presence. Security software client Symantec accounted for 22% of total sales in 2009.

	Annual Growth	12/05	12/06	12/07	12/08	12/09
Sales ($ mil.)	16.3%	220.4	307.6	349.3	394.2	403.8
Net income ($ mil.)	(2.1%)	54.3	60.8	70.8	63.6	49.8
Market value ($ mil.)	(2.4%)	1,178.4	2,210.5	1,310.3	982.6	1,069.4
Employees	6.9%	948	1,086	1,265	1,335	1,239

DIGITALGLOBE, INC.
NYSE: DGI

1601 Dry Creek Dr., Ste. 260
Longmont, CO 80503
Phone: 303-684-4000
Fax: 303-682-3848
Web: www.digitalglobe.com

CEO: Jill D. Smith
CFO: Yancey L. Spruill
HR: —
FYE: December 31
Type: Public

DigitalGlobe has its eye on you. The company provides satellite imagery that is used for a variety of applications, including mapping, urban planning, oil exploration, land management, and disaster assessment. DigitalGlobe's products include standard images, panchromatic images, multispectral images, and color infrared images, as well as mosaics and digital elevation models. The company's customers come from fields such as agriculture, civil government, oil and gas exploration, and military intelligence. DigitalGlobe's images and services are incorporated into popular mapping applications such as Google Maps and Microsoft Virtual Earth, as well as into GPS systems from Garmin and Nokia.

	Annual Growth	12/04	12/05	12/06	12/07	*12/08
Sales ($ mil.)	61.4%	—	65.4	106.8	151.7	275.2
Net income ($ mil.)	—	—	(28.7)	9.2	95.8	53.8
Employees	13.2%	—	—	—	410	464

*Most recent year available

DIGITAS INC.

33 Arch St.
Boston, MA 02110
Phone: 617-867-1000
Fax: 617-867-1111
Web: www.digitasinc.com

CEO: Laura W. Lang
CFO: Joe Tomasulo
HR: Len Dolce
FYE: December 31
Type: Subsidiary

This company knows the important bits (and bytes) about interactive marketing. Digitas provides digital communications and direct marketing services through several operating agencies: Digitas Health, iBase, Prodigious, Worldwide, Webformance, and Publicis Modem (formerly Modem Media). Operating from about 30 offices spanning 16 countries, the agency offers Web site design, e-mail management, and demand generation services which enable clients to build marketing campaigns across a plethora of media channels. It has worked with such big clients as American Express, Kraft, General Motors, Procter & Gamble, and MillerCoors. Digitas is a subsidiary of French advertising conglomerate Publicis.

DILLARD'S, INC.
NYSE: DDS

1600 Cantrell Rd.
Little Rock, AR 72201
Phone: 501-376-5200
Fax: 501-399-7831
Web: www.dillards.com

CEO: William (Bill) Dillard II
CFO: James I. Freeman
HR: —
FYE: January 31
Type: Public

Tradition is trying to catch up with the times at Dillard's. Sandwiched between retail giant Macy's and discount chains, such as Kohl's, Dillard's is rethinking its strategy and trimming its store count. The department store chain operates some 310 locations (down from 330 in 2005) in about 30 states, covering the Sunbelt and the central US. Its stores cater to middle- and upper-middle-income women, selling name-brand and private-label merchandise with a focus on apparel and home furnishings. Women's apparel and accessories account for more than a third of sales. Founded in 1938 by William Dillard, family members, through the W. D. Company, control nearly all of the company's voting shares and run the company.

	Annual Growth	1/06	1/07	1/08	1/09	1/10
Sales ($ mil.)	(5.2%)	7,708.0	7,810.1	7,370.8	6,988.4	6,226.6
Net income ($ mil.)	(13.3%)	121.5	245.6	53.8	(241.1)	68.5
Market value ($ mil.)	(10.6%)	1,775.4	2,354.0	1,360.0	298.2	1,135.2
Employees	(5.6%)	52,056	51,385	49,938	49,000	41,300

DILLON COMPANIES, INC.

2700 E. 4th Ave.
Hutchinson, KS 67504
Phone: 620-665-5511
Fax: 620-669-3160
Web: www.dillons.com

CEO: John E. Bays
CFO: Steve Richardson
HR: —
FYE: January 31
Type: Subsidiary

Dillon Companies, which began as J.S. Dillon and Sons Stores, has been selling bread to America's breadbasket bread since 1921. The regional supermarket chain has 100-plus stores under several banners; Dillon Stores in Kansas and Oklahoma; Baker's and Food-4-Less in Nebraska; Gerbes in Missouri; and City Market and King Soopers in Colorado and Wyoming. In addition to traditional supermarket fare, Dillon's supermarkets have in-store pharmacies and many sell gas in the parking lot. Dillon Companies is losing market share to discounters, including Wal-Mart Supercenters, which has Dillon's parent company Kroger to become the #1 seller of groceries in the US. The company was acquired by Kroger in 1983.

DILLON SUPPLY CO.

216 S. West St.
Raleigh, NC 27601
Phone: 919-838-4200
Fax: 919-838-4251
Web: www.dillonsupply.com

CEO: Dean Wagoner
CFO: Jeff Bell
HR: Mary Cribb
FYE: December 31
Type: Subsidiary

If opportunity knocks only once, Dillon Supply has the equipment to take advantage of it. A one-stop source, the company distributes all kinds of industrial, construction, and materials handling equipment. To do so, its work is divided between eight divisions: industrial and maintenance equipment, repair and overhaul machines; safety and janitorial supplies; storage and handling hardware; cutting tools, abrasives, and lubricants; industrial coatings; pipe, valve, and fittings; steel products (beams, angles, flats, tubing); and forklift trucks. Customers include the Army Corps of Engineers, and industries large and small. Founded in 1914, Dillon Supply operates as a subsidiary of supply giant Descours Et Cabaud.

An in-depth profile of this company is available to Hoover's Online members at hoovers.com.

499

DIME COMMUNITY BANCSHARES, INC.

NASDAQ (GS): DCOM

209 Havemeyer St.
Brooklyn, NY 11211
Phone: 718-782-6200
Fax: 718-486-7535
Web: www.dimewill.com

CEO: Vincent F. Palagiano
CFO: Kenneth J. Mahon
HR: —
FYE: December 31
Type: Public

Hey brother, Dime Community Bancshares could spare some change, if you qualify. It is the holding company for The Dime Savings Bank of Williamsburgh, which operates about two dozen branches in Brooklyn, Queens, the Bronx, and in Nassau County, New York. Founded in 1864 as a state-chartered mutual savings bank, it offers standard deposit products and services, including checking, savings, and money market accounts. Multifamily residential and commercial real estate mortgages account for about 95% of the company's loan portfolio. Bank subsidiaries include brokerage Havemeyer Investments and two real estate investment trusts (REITs). Employees own nearly 10% of the company.

	Annual Growth	12/05	12/06	12/07	12/08	12/09
Assets ($ mil.)	6.0%	3,126.2	3,173.4	3,501.2	4,055.6	3,952.3
Net income ($ mil.)	(7.8%)	36.2	30.6	22.4	28.0	26.2
Market value ($ mil.)	(5.3%)	504.7	483.9	441.1	459.4	405.2
Employees	2.2%	397	409	414	453	433

⊞ DINEEQUITY, INC.

NYSE: DIN

450 N. Brand Blvd., 7th Fl.
Glendale, CA 91203
Phone: 818-240-6055
Fax: 818-637-3131
Web: dineequity.com

CEO: Julia A. Stewart
CFO: John F. (Jack) Tierney
HR: John Jakubek
FYE: December 31
Type: Public

This company shows an equal bias for breakfast, lunch, and dinner. DineEquity is one of the leading chain restaurant companies in the US with two flagship concepts, IHOP (the International House of Pancakes) and Applebee's Neighborhood Grill and Bar (operated through subsidiary Applebee's Services). The #3 family-style diner chain behind Denny's and Waffle House, IHOP has about 1,450 mostly franchised restaurants that are open 24 hours a day. The chain is best known for its breakfast menu, but it also offers standard family fare for lunch and dinner. Applebee's is the #1 casual-dining chain, with about 2,000 locations in the US and 20 other countries, offering a wide variety of appetizers and entrees.

	Annual Growth	12/05	12/06	12/07	12/08	12/09
Sales ($ mil.)	42.0%	348.0	349.6	484.6	1,613.6	1,414.0
Net income ($ mil.)	(8.0%)	43.9	44.6	(0.5)	(154.5)	31.4
Market value ($ mil.)	(15.2%)	840.7	944.4	655.5	207.2	435.3
Employees	124.8%	897	972	32,300	25,248	22,900

DINEWISE, INC.

OTC: DWIS

500 Bi-County Blvd., Ste. 400
Farmingdale, NY 11735
Phone: 631-694-1111
Fax: 631-694-4064
Web: www.dinewise.com

CEO: Paul A. Roman
CFO: Thomas (Tom) McNeill
HR: —
FYE: December 31
Type: Public

For Americans who would rather dial than cook, DineWise delivers meals directly to the door in 48 US states. The direct marketer serves up flash-frozen, chef-prepared meals for time-pressed cooks to microwave at home. DineWise also offers diet meals, as well as meals tailored to fit special needs, including diabetic and low-sodium regimens. Complete meals include entrees, sides, and vegetables. Customers can order by phone, catalog, or by using its website. Founded in 1959 as Colorado Prime Foods, the firm changed its name to DineWise in 2006 and went public. Colorado Prime, best know for its beef, remains a core part of the business. In 2009 DineWise acquired Home Bistro Foods, its largest direct competitor.

DIODES INCORPORATED

NASDAQ (GS): DIOD

15660 Dallas Pkwy., Ste. 850
Dallas, TX 75248
Phone: 972-385-2810
Fax: —
Web: www.diodes.com

CEO: Keh-Shew Lu
CFO: Richard D. White
HR: —
FYE: December 31
Type: Public

Diodes Incorporated knows how important it is to be discrete in business. The company manufactures discrete semiconductors — fixed-function devices that are much less complex than integrated circuits. Diodes' products are used by makers of automotive, computing, consumer electronics, and telecommunications gear. The company makes hundreds of products (including diodes, transistors, and rectifiers) that vary in voltage, current, and switching speeds. Customers include Delphi, Intel, Nortel Networks, and Samsung Electronics. Lite-On Semiconductor, a company that is part of Taiwan's Lite-On Technology, owns about 20% of Diodes. Lite-On Semiconductor is also Diodes' biggest customer and its biggest supplier.

	Annual Growth	12/05	12/06	12/07	12/08	12/09
Sales ($ mil.)	19.3%	214.8	343.3	401.2	432.8	434.4
Net income ($ mil.)	(31.1%)	33.3	48.1	59.7	39.0	7.5
Market value ($ mil.)	(0.4%)	907.9	1,037.4	1,318.8	265.8	895.2
Employees	21.2%	1,621	2,268	2,612	3,067	3,501

⊞ DIONEX CORPORATION

NASDAQ (GS): DNEX

1228 Titan Way
Sunnyvale, CA 94085
Phone: 408-737-0700
Fax: 408-730-9403
Web: www.dionex.com

CEO: Frank R. Witney
CFO: Craig A. McCollam
HR: —
FYE: June 30
Type: Public

Dionex's instruments keep the contaminants away while scientists play. The company makes and services instruments and related accessories that are used for substance analysis, including identifying contaminants in everything from drinking water to industrial chemicals. Dionex leads the market for ion chromatography instruments, devices used by chemists to isolate and quantify charged molecules in complex chemical mixtures. It also specializes in high-performance liquid chromatography (used to separate and identify biological molecules such as amino acids, carbohydrates, and proteins), sample extraction, and sample handling automation equipment. The company gets about 70% of its sales outside the US.

	Annual Growth	6/05	6/06	6/07	6/08	6/09
Sales ($ mil.)	8.4%	279.3	291.3	327.3	377.5	385.0
Net income ($ mil.)	5.1%	45.5	35.7	45.3	52.8	55.5
Market value ($ mil.)	8.8%	768.3	963.2	1,250.9	1,169.5	1,075.4
Employees	7.1%	1,064	1,135	1,193	1,351	1,400

DIRECT ENERGY TEXAS

12 Greenway Plaza, Ste. 600
Houston, TX 77046
Phone: 713-877-3500
Fax: 713-877-3799
Web: www.directenergy.com/texas/home

CEO: Chris Weston
CFO: Nathan Kroker
HR: Janice Thomson
FYE: December 31
Type: Subsidiary

Direct Energy Texas flips the switch for cowboys on the ranch and on the field. The energy retailer sells electric and natural gas service primarily in Dallas, Fort Worth, and Houston. Direct Energy Texas manages accounts and provides customer service to about 1 million residential and business clients. The Dallas Cowboys NFL team is a top customer. In addition to offering electricity derived from fossil fuels, Direct Energy Texas also taps power from wind farm operators like Airtricity, and offers its customers HVAC and other services. The company is one of Toronto-based Direct Energy's US bases of operations along with Connecticut, Illinois, Michigan, New York, and Ohio. Centrica is the firm's ultimate parent.

DIRECT GENERAL CORPORATION

1128 Murfreesboro Rd., Ste. 103
Nashville, TN 37217
Phone: 615-399-0600
Fax: 800-541-0856
Web: www.direct-general.com

CEO: Daniel (Dan) Tarantin
CFO: J. Todd Hagely
HR: Kim W. Nowell
FYE: December 31
Type: Subsidiary

Tickets, accidents, and credit problems are no problem for insurance provider Direct General Corporation. Founded in 1991, Direct General offers non-standard personal automobile coverage and motorcycle insurance through such subsidiaries as Direct General Insurance, Cash Register Auto, Right Choice Insurance, and Florida No Fault. Direct General also offers a bit of term life insurance and premium financing products. It has also branched out into offering tax preparation services. Direct General sells its products through more than 400 locally-based sales offices in 13 southern states. The company was acquired by private investment partnerships Calera Capital and TPG Capital in 2007.

DIRECT INSITE CORP.

OTC: DIRI

80 Orville Dr.
Bohemia, NY 11716
Phone: 631-873-2900
Fax: 631-563-8085
Web: www.directinsite.com

CEO: James A. Cannavino
CFO: Michael J. Beecher
HR: Dawn Valenti
FYE: December 31
Type: Public

Direct Insite helps give its customers insight into their customers. The company's hosted software and services provide data mining and analysis, reporting, electronic invoice management, and electronic bill presentment and payment functions. Its products are used to manage such functions as customer service workflows, order processing, dispute resolution, and accounts payable and receivable. Direct Insite serves clients in more than 60 countries, with its applications available in 15 languages and all major currencies. IBM is responsible for 51% of the company's sales, while EDS accounts for 46%.

	Annual Growth	12/05	12/06	12/07	12/08	12/09
Sales ($ mil.)	3.0%	8.9	8.9	10.1	9.6	10.0
Net income ($ mil.)	—	(1.0)	0.3	2.1	4.2	1.7
Market value ($ mil.)	11.3%	7.1	9.2	23.9	12.4	10.8
Employees	(9.1%)	57	39	37	39	39

DIRECT SELLING ASSOCIATION

1275 Pennsylvania Ave. NW, Ste. 800
Washington, DC 20004
Phone: 202-347-8866
Fax: 202-347-0055
Web: www.dsa.org

CEO: Neil H. Offen
CFO: —
HR: —
FYE: December 31
Type: Group

Direct Selling Association promotes the business interests of Avon ladies, Fuller Brush men, and Tupperware peddlers everywhere. The organization represents more than 200 companies that make and distribute a variety of goods and services directly to consumers including Discovery Toys, Herbalife, and The Longaberger Company. All member companies pledge to follow the group's code of ethics, which includes a ban on deceptive practices. Some 90% of direct sellers conduct their business on a part-time basis. DSA provides its members with a research center, publications, seminars, and an annual meeting. The group was formed as the Agents Credit Association in 1910.

	Annual Growth	12/04	12/05	12/06	12/07	12/08
Est. sales ($ mil.)	—	—	—	—	—	6.5
Employees	—	—	—	—	—	28

⊞ DIRECTV

NASDAQ (GS): DTV

2230 E. Imperial Hwy.
El Segundo, CA 90245
Phone: 310-964-5000
Fax: 310-535-5225
Web: www.directv.com

CEO: Michael D. (Mike) White
CFO: Patrick T. (Pat) Doyle
HR: Larry D. Hunter
FYE: December 31
Type: Public

DIRECTV takes television straight to the masses — no wires attached. The company (formerly the The DIRECTV Group) operates the largest direct broadcast satellite (DBS) service in the US, ahead of #2 DISH Network, and in direct competition with cable providers Comcast and Time Warner. In addition to its more than 18 million US customers, the company serves more than 6 million subscribers in Latin America under the DIRECTV and Sky brands. Its services include high-definition and video-on-demand (VOD) programming. Phone companies such as Verizon bundle its video services with their own voice and Internet packages. Liberty Media owns 55% of DIRECTV's stock.

	Annual Growth	12/05	12/06	12/07	12/08	12/09
Sales ($ mil.)	13.1%	13,164.5	14,755.5	17,246.0	19,693.0	21,565.0
Net income ($ mil.)	31.6%	335.9	1,420.1	1,451.0	1,521.0	1,007.0
Market value ($ mil.)	24.0%	12,832.3	22,665.5	21,011.5	20,820.6	30,308.5
Employees	26.2%	9,200	11,200	12,300	19,600	23,300

DISCOUNT TIRE CO. INC.

20225 N. Scottsdale Rd.
Scottsdale, AZ 85255
Phone: 480-606-6000
Fax: 480-951-8619
Web: www.discounttire.com

CEO: Tom Englert
CFO: Christian Roe
HR: —
FYE: December 31
Type: Private

Concerned about that upcoming "re-tire-ment"? Discount Tire Co., one of the largest independent tire dealers in the US, can provide several options. With about 780 company-owned stores in more than 20 states, the company sells such leading tire brands as Michelin, Goodyear, and Uniroyal, as well as wheels from Enkei, Konig, and TSW. Discount Tire operates mostly in the West, Midwest, Southwest, and Southeast. Some of the company's West Coast stores operate as America's Tire Co. because of a name conflict. Customers can search for tires by make and model on the company's Web site. Chairman and owner Bruce Halle founded the company in 1960 with six tires — four of them recaps.

	Annual Growth	12/04	12/05	12/06	12/07	12/08
Sales ($ mil.)	9.6%	1,670.0	1,856.0	2,060.0	2,310.0	2,410.0
Employees	5.2%	9,500	10,100	10,980	11,630	11,652

DISCOVER FINANCIAL SERVICES

NYSE: DFS

2500 Lake Cook Rd.
Riverwoods, IL 60015
Phone: 224-405-0900
Fax: 224-405-4993
Web: www.discoverfinancial.com

CEO: David W. Nelms
CFO: Roy A. Guthrie
HR: —
FYE: November 30
Type: Public

Seems cardholders aren't the only ones getting paid to discover. Discover Financial Services is best known for issuing Discover-brand credit cards, which are used by more than 25 million members. The company's cards, which include several levels of business and consumer cards, repay cardholders a percentage of the purchase price each time they use their cards. But there's more to this business than just plastic. Discover Financial Services also offers banking services and runs the PULSE Network ATM system. Morgan Stanley spun off Discover Financial Services in 2007. A similar move had been announced in 2005, but Morgan Stanley pulled the plug on that earlier attempt amid market turmoil.

	Annual Growth	11/05	11/06	11/07	11/08	11/09
Assets ($ mil.)	14.3%	26,943.9	29,067.2	37,376.1	39,892.4	46,021.0
Net income ($ mil.)	21.9%	577.9	1,076.6	588.6	927.8	1,276.2
Market value ($ mil.)	(5.7%)	—	—	9,446.2	5,563.3	8,407.5
Employees	(9.1%)	—	14,000	12,800	11,900	10,500

An in-depth profile of this company is available to Hoover's Online members at hoovers.com.

501

DISCOVERY COMMUNICATIONS, INC.
NASDAQ (GS): DISCA

1 Discovery Place
Silver Spring, MD 20910
Phone: 240-662-2000
Fax: 240-662-1868
Web: corporate.discovery.com

CEO: David M. Zaslav
CFO: Bradley E. (Brad) Singer
HR: Adria Alpert-Romm
FYE: December 31
Type: Public

This company helps people discover nature and science programming right from their living rooms. Discovery Communications, Inc. (DCI) is a leading operator of cable channels focused primarily on such topics as history, natural and physical science, and technology. Its portfolio is anchored by the Discovery Channel, which reaches about 100 million US homes and is broadcast in more than 170 other countries. DCI also runs Animal Planet, the Military Channel, Science Channel, and TLC (The Learning Channel). In addition, the company offers video-on-demand and publishes content online through its Discovery.com and AnimalPlanet.com Web sites; other online destinations include HowStuffWorks.com and Petfinder.com.

	Annual Growth	12/05	12/06	12/07	12/08	12/09
Sales ($ mil.)	50.0%	694.5	688.1	707.2	3,443.0	3,516.0
Net income ($ mil.)	102.4%	33.3	(46.0)	(68.4)	317.0	559.0
Market value ($ mil.)	22.2%	3,907.7	4,150.1	6,484.4	4,025.7	8,719.6
Employees	3.7%	3,800	4,500	3,600	4,000	4,400

DISCOVERY LABORATORIES, INC.
NASDAQ (GM): DSCO

2600 Kelly Rd., Ste. 100
Warrington, PA 18976
Phone: 215-488-9300
Fax: 215-488-9301
Web: www.discoverylabs.com

CEO: W. Thomas Amick
CFO: John G. Cooper
HR: Kathryn A. Cole
FYE: December 31
Type: Public

If you're waiting to exhale, Discovery Laboratories may be able to help. The biotechnology company focuses on treatments for respiratory disorders, particularly for babies in intensive care. Its lead candidate, Surfaxin, is under FDA review for the prevention of respiratory distress syndrome in premature infants. Discovery Labs bases its therapies on surfactants, which are naturally produced by the lungs and essential for breathing. Its Aerosurf product is a surfactant therapy in aerosol form, developed as an alternative to endotracheal intubation and conventional mechanical ventilation. Other potential disease targets include acute lung injury, asthma, chronic obstructive pulmonary disease, and cystic fibrosis.

	Annual Growth	12/05	12/06	12/07	12/08	12/09
Sales ($ mil.)	—	—	—	—	4.6	0.0
Net income ($ mil.)	—	—	—	—	(39.1)	(30.2)
Market value ($ mil.)	(43.9%)	—	—	—	177.0	99.3
Employees	(34.7%)	—	—	—	118	77

DISH NETWORK CORPORATION
NASDAQ (GS): DISH

9601 S. Meridian Blvd.
Englewood, CO 80112
Phone: 303-723-1000
Fax: 303-723-1999
Web: www.dishnetwork.com

CEO: Charles W. (Charlie) Ergen
CFO: Robert E. Olson
HR: Stephen W. Wood
FYE: December 31
Type: Public

DISH Network serves up fare intended to whet everyone's appetite for televised entertainment. The #2 provider of direct broadcast satellite TV service in the US (behind DIRECTV), the company serves about 14 million subscribers; customers include home viewers as well as business clients in such industries as hospitality, restaurant, and retail. DISH provides premium movies, SIRIUS satellite radio, and many local, international, and pay-per-view options in addition to basic video programming. It offers bundled voice and Internet services through partnerships with such voice and data communications providers as EarthLink and Qwest. Co-founder and CEO Charlie Ergen controls about 83% of the company's voting power.

	Annual Growth	12/05	12/06	12/07	12/08	12/09
Sales ($ mil.)	8.5%	8,425.5	9,818.5	11,090.4	11,617.2	11,664.2
Net income ($ mil.)	(19.5%)	1,514.5	608.3	756.1	902.9	635.5
Market value ($ mil.)	(4.0%)	10,957.1	15,331.0	15,206.1	4,966.6	9,301.7
Employees	3.9%	21,000	21,000	23,000	26,000	24,500

DISNEY PUBLISHING WORLDWIDE

44 S. Broadway
White Plains, NY 10601
Phone: 212-633-4400
Fax: 212-633-4809
Web: disneybooks.disney.go.com

CEO: R. Russell Hampton Jr.
CFO: Rajmohan P. (Raj) Murari
HR: Robin Eletto
FYE: September 30
Type: Subsidiary

Just because these tomes come from the Magic Kingdom doesn't mean they are magic books. Disney Publishing Worldwide is the children's publishing arm of Walt Disney's Consumer Products division. Most of its books and magazines are based on characters and content licensed from other parts of the Disney media empire. Its Disney Global Book Group publishes titles based on Disney characters and franchises such as Winnie the Pooh and Mickey Mouse Clubhouse, while its Global Children's Magazines business produces magazines such as *Disney Princess* and *Disney and Me*. Disney Publishing sells more than 250 million books and 400 million magazines each year. Titles are available in some 85 languages and 75 countries.

DITECH NETWORKS, INC.
NASDAQ (GM): DITC

825 E. Middlefield Rd.
Mountain View, CA 94043
Phone: 650-623-1300
Fax: 650-564-9599
Web: www.ditechcom.com

CEO: Todd G. Simpson
CFO: William J. (Bill) Tamblyn
HR: —
FYE: April 30
Type: Public

Echoes can be fun when bouncing your name off a canyon wall, but not during an urgent phone call. Ditech Networks' echo cancellation equipment regulates the distracting echoes that can occur in long distance, satellite, and wireless phone calls. It has also developed voice processing products for VoIP networks. The company primarily markets through a direct sales force in the US; it utilizes resellers and distributors overseas. Ditech's largest customers include telecommunications service providers Verizon Wireless, Intercall, and Orascom Telecom. Customers outside the US provide more than half of the company's sales.

	Annual Growth	4/05	4/06	4/07	4/08	4/09
Sales ($ mil.)	(33.3%)	94.1	54.9	84.0	35.1	18.6
Net income ($ mil.)	—	71.1	(0.9)	5.3	(94.7)	(26.8)
Market value ($ mil.)	(45.7%)	298.0	248.2	229.2	75.1	25.8
Employees	(13.1%)	184	216	224	148	105

DIVERSEY, INC.

8310 16th St.
Sturtevant, WI 53177
Phone: 262-631-4001
Fax: 262-631-4282
Web: www.diversey.com

CEO: Edward F. (Ed) Lonergan
CFO: Norman Clubb
HR: James W. (Jim) Larson
FYE: December 31
Type: Private

The industrial-strength version of S.C. Johnson & Son, Diversey (formerly JohnsonDiversey) split from the well-known company in 1999 to make commercial cleaning, hygiene, pest control, and food sanitation products for retailers, building service contractors, hospitality providers, and food service operators. It's the #2 global industrial and institutional cleaning products company behind Ecolab. Diversey also provides safety and hygiene training and consulting. Europe generates more than half of the firm's sales, which span some 160 countries. Following a recapitalization deal in late 2009, the Johnson family controls 50% of the firm while private equity firm Clayton Dubilier & Rice (CD&R) holds a 46% stake.

	Annual Growth	12/04	12/05	12/06	12/07	12/08
Sales ($ mil.)	1.1%	3,169.3	3,310.3	2,928.3	3,130.0	3,315.9
Net income ($ mil.)	—	13.7	(166.6)	118.3	(86.6)	(11.8)
Employees	(2.6%)	12,000	12,000	11,000	11,500	10,800

DIVERSIFIED THERMAL SOLUTIONS, INC.

Pink Sheets: DVTS

4126 Delp St., Ste. 200
Memphis, TN 38118
Phone: 901-365-7650
Fax: 901-365-9617
Web: www.dthermal.com

CEO: B. Grant Hunter
CFO: J. Terry Medovitch
HR: —
FYE: December 31
Type: Public

When the heat is on, companies look to Diversified Thermal Solutions to protect their heat-generating equipment. The company manufactures refractory products, such as clay and brick, for the linings of high-temperature furnaces and reactors. Diversified Thermal Solutions is expanding in the Southeast and Northeast of the US, primarily targeting non-ferrous industries such as aluminum, incineration, paper, and petrochemical operations. Prior to the refractory business, the company was involved in providing international long distance communications service. President and CEO B. Grant Hunter controls more than a third of Diversified Thermal Solutions.

DIVX, INC.

NASDAQ (GS): DIVX

4780 Eastgate Mall
San Diego, CA 92121
Phone: 858-882-0600
Fax: 858-882-0601
Web: www.divx.com

CEO: Kevin C. Hell
CFO: Dan L. Halvorson
HR: —
FYE: December 31
Type: Public

FX from DVDs benefit from DivX, a digital media format for content playback, creation, and distribution. The company's video compression-decompression (or codec) software library has been downloaded more than 300 million times. The firm has built on the success of this technology by distributing the DivX software through its own website, and through licenses with consumer video hardware original equipment manufacturers (OEMs) such as Samsung and Philips. CEO Kevin Hell and former executives Darrius Thompson, Joe Bezdek, Tay Nguyen, and Gej Vashisht-Rota founded DivX in 2000. The firm has agreed to be acquired by Sonic Solutions, a maker of software used in formatting and making DVDs, CDs, and other media.

	Annual Growth	12/05	12/06	12/07	12/08	12/09
Sales ($ mil.)	20.9%	33.0	59.3	84.9	93.9	70.6
Net income ($ mil.)	(54.3%)	2.3	16.4	9.2	10.0	0.1
Market value ($ mil.)	(37.5%)	—	758.8	460.5	172.0	185.5
Employees	16.1%	189	108	389	301	343

THE DIXIE GROUP, INC.

NASDAQ (GM): DXYN

104 Nowlin Ln., Ste. 101
Chattanooga, TN 37421
Phone: 423-510-7000
Fax: 706-876-5896
Web: www.thedixiegroup.com

CEO: Daniel K. Frierson
CFO: Jon A. Faulkner
HR: W. Derek Davis
FYE: December 31
Type: Public

The Dixie Group takes its business to the rug. Once a textile manufacturer, the company has evolved into a maker of high-end carpets and rugs, as well as yarns used in manufacturing them. Dixie channels broadloom carpets worldwide to customers in retail and replacement markets, and home and commercial building trades. The company's line bears the Dixie Home, Masland Carpets & Rugs, Fabrica International, and Candlewick Yarn labels. Offered mainly through select retailers, its Dixie Home brand touts stylish, cost-sensitive broadloom flooring. Masland's original design carpets straddle the commercial contract and residential marketplace. Supplying home decorators, Fabrica features luxury carpets and custom rugs.

	Annual Growth	12/05	12/06	12/07	12/08	12/09
Sales ($ mil.)	(10.6%)	318.5	331.1	320.8	282.7	203.5
Net income ($ mil.)	—	10.1	7.7	6.3	(31.4)	(42.1)
Market value ($ mil.)	(33.4%)	177.0	162.4	106.8	19.7	34.8
Employees	(8.5%)	1,500	1,500	1,500	1,250	1,050

DJO INCORPORATED

1430 Decision St.
Vista, CA 92081
Phone: 760-727-1280
Fax: 800-936-6569
Web: www.djoglobal.com

CEO: Leslie H. (Les) Cross
CFO: Vickie L. Capps
HR: Thomas A. Capizzi
FYE: December 31
Type: Private

DJO is tryin' to make you to go through rehab so you can go, go, go. The company develops and manufactures medical devices used in orthopedic rehabilitation. As one of the world's largest orthopedic medical device makers, its external product lines range from knee braces and traction systems to electrotherapy pain management systems and continuous passive motion devices. DJO also makes implantable joint replacement products, including knee, shoulder, hip, and spinal implants. Its products are sold globally under a host of brand names, including Aircast, Empi, Chattanooga, Cefar-Compex, Ormed, DonJoy, and ProCare. The company sells its products directly and through dealers.

	Annual Growth	12/04	12/05	12/06	12/07	12/08
Est. sales ($ mil.)	—	—	—	—	—	370.4
Employees	—	—	—	—	—	4,848

D. L. RYAN COMPANIES, LTD.

50 Danbury Rd.
Wilton, CT 06897
Phone: 203-210-3000
Fax: 203-210-7926
Web: www.ryanpartnership.com

CEO: Tom Libonate
CFO: Lester Preston
HR: —
FYE: December 31
Type: Private

Independent agency D. L. Ryan Companies, also known as Ryan Partnership, provides services such as direct, interactive, promotional, and retail marketing, as well as offerings designed to help customers reach the Latino and young adult markets. The agency specializes in serving companies in the consumer packaged goods and pharmaceutical industries; clients over the years have included such industry leaders as Campbell's Soup, Frito-Lay, Heineken, and Unilever. Ryan Partnership operates from about half a dozen offices in the US and Canada. It handles business in other regions as a member of The Contact Group, a network of independent agencies.

DLA PIPER

6225 Smith Ave.
Baltimore, MD 21209
Phone: 410-580-3000
Fax: 410-580-3001
Web: www.dlapiper.com

CEO: Sir Nigel Knowles
CFO: Raymond Dearchs
HR: Clarissa Peterson
FYE: December 31
Type: Partnership

One of the world's largest law firms, DLA Piper has about 3,500 lawyers operating in Asia, Europe, the Middle East, and the US. The firm's network of more than 65 offices spans about 30 countries. DLA Piper serves corporate clients through a broad range of practices divided into about a dozen key groups; specialties include mergers and acquisitions, intellectual property, regulatory and government affairs, and technology and media. Clients have included Life Technologies, British Midland Airways, and Trident Microsystems. The firm was formed in 2005 when Maryland-based Piper Rudnick merged with California-based Gray Cary Ware & Freidenrich and UK firm DLA.

	Annual Growth	12/04	12/05	12/06	12/07	12/08
Sales ($ mil.)	3.8%	—	—	—	1,134.5	1,178.0
Employees	—	—	—	—	—	—

DEL LABORATORIES, INC.

726 RexCorp Plaza
Uniondale, NY 11553
Phone: 516-844-2020
Fax: —
Web: www.dellabs.com

CEO: Harvey P. Alstodt
CFO: —
HR: —
FYE: June 30
Type: Subsidiary

Beauty is a science at Del Laboratories. The company makes a variety of personal care products, including cosmetics (lipsticks, powders), nail colors, hair removers, beauty implements (tweezers, eyelash curlers), and skin care products (creams, scrubs). Del Labs' beauty supplies are marketed under the Sally Hansen, LaCross, and N.Y.C. New York Color brand names. Its products are available at mass merchandisers (Wal-Mart, Target) and major drugstore chains (CVS, Walgreen) throughout North America, as well as online. The company also distributes its goods to more than 40 other countries. Del Labs is owned by fragrance-and-beauty giant Coty.

DNP PHOTO IMAGING AMERICA CORP.

101 Uhland Rd., Ste. 210
San Marcos, TX 78666
Phone: 512-753-7280
Fax: 512-753-7299
Web: www.dnpphoto.com

CEO: Brett Cameron
CFO: —
HR: —
FYE: December 31
Type: Subsidiary

DNP Photo Imaging America develops and markets systems used to reproduce, correct, and reorder film and digital photos. The company's kiosks and countertop photo systems are used by consumers at retail locations such as drug and grocery stores. Its professional digital minilabs are used in photo labs to process film and digital images. Formerly called Pixel Magic Imaging, the company was established in 1992. In 2004 two Japanese firms, Dai Nippon Printing and Altech ADS, purchased a controlling stake in Pixel Magic. The company changed its name to DNP Photo Imaging America in 2007.

DMG INFORMATION

3 Stamford Landing, Ste. 400, 46 Southfield Ave.
Stamford, CT 06902
Phone: 203-973-2940
Fax: 203-973-2995
Web: www.dmginfo.com

CEO: Suresh Kavan
CFO: Paul Sykes
HR: —
FYE: September 30
Type: Subsidiary

DMG Information (DMGI) is an investment vehicle of UK-based media firm Daily Mail and General Trust (DMGT). It invests in established companies that provide business-to-business information and analytical tools for the real estate, financial services, energy trading, education, mapping, and other sectors. With operations in the US, Europe, and India, DMGI's companies combine large databases with proprietary software to provide information related to topics such as historical land use (Environmental Data Resources), student recruitment and enrollment (Hobsons), asset securitization (Lewtan Technologies), real estate transactions (Real Capital Analytics), and commercial mortgages and related securities (Trepp).

DO IT BEST CORP.

6502 Nelson Rd.
Fort Wayne, IN 46803
Phone: 260-748-5300
Fax: 260-748-5620
Web: www.doitbestcorp.com

CEO: Robert N. (Bob) Taylor
CFO: David W. (Dave) Dietz
HR: Daniel B. (Dan) Starr
FYE: June 30
Type: Cooperative

If you're building a house or fixing one up, you might as well Do it Best — at least that's the hope of one of the hardware industry's largest cooperatives. Do it Best boasts more than 4,100 member-owned stores in 45-plus countries worldwide, but primarily the US. Besides the usual tools and building materials, merchandise includes automotive items, bicycles, camping gear, housewares, office supplies, and small appliances. Customers can also have products specially shipped to their local stores through Do It Best's e-commerce site. The co-op's buying power enables members to offer items at competitive prices. Formerly named Hardware Wholesalers, Do it Best was founded in 1945.

	Annual Growth	6/04	6/05	6/06	6/07	6/08
Sales ($ mil.)	—	—	—	—	—	2,546.4
Net income ($ mil.)	—	—	—	—	—	0.6
Employees	—	—	—	—	—	—

DNB FINANCIAL CORPORATION

OTC: DNBF

4 Brandywine Ave.
Downingtown, PA 19335
Phone: 610-269-1040
Fax: 610-873-5298
Web: www.dnb4you.com

CEO: William S. Latoff
CFO: Gerald F. Sopp
HR: —
FYE: December 31
Type: Public

DNB Financial Corporation is the holding company for DNB First, a bank with about a dozen branches in Chester and Delaware counties in southeastern Pennsylvania. Founded in 1861, the bank serves area consumers, but mainly lends to small and midsized businesses, with mortgages secured by commercial property (approximately 35% of its loan portfolio), commercial operating loans (more than 25%), and equipment leases representing most of its financing activity. The bank also writes residential mortgages and consumer loans. Deposit products include checking, savings, and money market accounts.

DOCTOR'S ASSOCIATES INC.

325 Bic Dr.
Milford, CT 06461
Phone: 203-877-4281
Fax: —
Web: www.subway.com

CEO: Frederick A. (Fred) DeLuca
CFO: David Worroll
HR: —
FYE: December 31
Type: Private

You don't have to go underground to catch this Subway. Doctor's Associates operates the Subway chain of sandwich shops, the second-largest quick-service chain behind McDonald's. It boasts more than 31,000 locations in 90 countries, with more US locations than the Golden Arches. Virtually all Subway restaurants are franchised and offer such fare as hot and cold sub sandwiches, turkey wraps, and salads. Subways are located in freestanding buildings, as well as in airports, convenience stores, sports facilities, and other locations. Doctor's Associates is owned by co-founders Fred DeLuca and Peter Buck, who opened the first Subway in 1965.

	Annual Growth	12/05	12/06	12/07	12/08	12/09
Assets ($ mil.)	7.6%	473.0	525.2	545.8	533.4	634.2
Net income ($ mil.)	(8.1%)	2.1	1.7	1.8	0.8	1.5
Market value ($ mil.)	(23.5%)	47.2	50.2	42.1	24.2	16.2
Employees	(3.8%)	152	139	138	135	130

	Annual Growth	12/04	12/05	12/06	12/07	12/08
Est. sales ($ mil.)	—	—	—	—	—	926.6
Employees	—	—	—	—	—	700

DOCUMENT CAPTURE TECHNOLOGIES, INC.   OTC: DCMT

1798 Technology Dr., Ste. 178
San Jose, CA 95110
Phone: 408-436-9888
Fax: 408-436-6151
Web: www.docucap.com

CEO: David P. Clark
CFO: Carolyn (Martha) Ellis
HR: —
FYE: December 31
Type: Public

Document Capture Technologies (formerly known as Sysview Technology and Syscan Imaging) is a developer of contact image sensor (CIS) modules used in such office equipment as fax machines and PC scanners. The company's line of portable image scanners are sold under the TravelScan and DocketPORT brand names. Customers for the company's CIS modules include such vendors as CardScan, Datacolor, Digimarc, OMRON, and Nuance Communications. Document Capture Technologies has engaged the investment firm of Oppenheimer & Co. to advise the company on ways to enhance shareholder value, including potential sales, mergers, combinations, and partnerships.

	Annual Growth	12/05	12/06	12/07	12/08	12/09
Sales ($ mil.)	10.2%	7.8	12.5	15.0	11.6	11.5
Net income ($ mil.)	—	(2.7)	(5.2)	(1.1)	(0.1)	(0.3)
Market value ($ mil.)	(15.2%)	12.0	11.1	15.3	9.1	6.2
Employees	(4.1%)	26	36	14	15	22

DOCUMENT SECURITY SYSTEMS, INC.   NYSE Amex: DMC

28 E. Main St., Ste. 1525
Rochester, NY 14614
Phone: 585-325-3610
Fax: 585-325-2977
Web: www.documentsecurity.com

CEO: Patrick White
CFO: Patrick White
HR: —
FYE: December 31
Type: Public

Document Security Systems (DSS) caters to those who are insecure about their security, particularly on paper. The company develops anti-counterfeiting products. Its offerings include technology that prevents documents from being accurately scanned or copied and authentication coding that can be used in conjunction with a handheld reader to verify that a document is genuine. DSS also sells paper that displays words such as "void" or "unauthorized copy" if it goes through a copier, fax machine, or scanner. The company considers document security to be its core business, so it has been unloading units with unrelated objectives.

	Annual Growth	12/05	12/06	12/07	12/08	12/09
Sales ($ mil.)	55.3%	1.7	4.8	6.0	6.6	9.9
Net income ($ mil.)	—	(2.8)	(4.8)	(7.0)	(8.3)	(4.0)
Market value ($ mil.)	(33.7%)	224.7	197.2	115.3	32.5	43.5
Employees	50.2%	22	58	62	85	112

THE DOLAN COMPANY   NYSE: DM

222 S. 9th St., Ste. 2300
Minneapolis, MN 55402
Phone: 612-317-9420
Fax: 612-321-0563
Web: www.dolanmedia.com

CEO: James P. (Jim) Dolan
CFO: Vicki J. Duncomb
HR: —
FYE: December 31
Type: Public

Helping law firms is a big part of the process for this publisher. Formerly Dolan Media Company, The Dolan Company is a diversified professional services provider with a significant interest in local business news publishing. Through subsidiary National Default Exchange (NDeX), the company offers mortgage default processing services to lenders, loan servicers, and law firms around the country. Its Counsel Press and DiscoverReady units provide services for law firms, including outsourced document management to support litigation discovery. In addition, Dolan's publishing business includes a portfolio of more than 40 daily and weekly newspapers serving mostly markets on the East Coast and in the Midwest.

	Annual Growth	12/05	12/06	12/07	12/08	12/09
Sales ($ mil.)	35.5%	77.9	111.6	152.0	189.9	262.9
Net income ($ mil.)	—	(7.5)	(20.3)	(54.0)	14.3	30.8
Market value ($ mil.)	(40.8%)	—	—	884.1	199.7	309.4
Employees	34.9%	574	1,177	1,237	1,812	1,903

DOLBY LABORATORIES, INC.   NYSE: DLB

100 Potrero Ave.
San Francisco, CA 94103
Phone: 415-558-0200
Fax: 415-863-1373
Web: www.dolby.com

CEO: Kevin J. Yeaman
CFO: Murray J. Demo
HR: Andrew Dahlkemper
FYE: September 30
Type: Public

Talk about having a sound business model. Dolby Laboratories is the market leader in developing sound processing and noise reduction systems for use in professional and consumer audio and video equipment. Though it does make some of its own products, Dolby mostly licenses its technology to other manufacturers. (Licensing accounts for more than 80% of revenue.) The firm has about 1,600 patents and more than 960 trademarks worldwide. In film, the Dolby Digital format has become the de facto audio standard; its systems equip movie screens around the globe. The company has expanded into digital audio compression. American engineer and physicist Ray Dolby and his family own the company.

	Annual Growth	9/05	9/06	9/07	9/08	9/09
Sales ($ mil.)	21.7%	328.0	391.5	482.0	640.2	719.5
Net income ($ mil.)	46.8%	52.3	89.5	142.8	199.5	243.0
Market value ($ mil.)	24.3%	1,815.0	2,251.8	3,949.9	3,991.9	4,332.2
Employees	8.3%	825	864	976	1,153	1,135

Ⓗ DOLE FOOD COMPANY, INC.   NYSE: DOLE

1 Dole Dr.
Westlake Village, CA 91362
Phone: 818-879-6600
Fax: 818-879-6615
Web: www.dole.com

CEO: David A. DeLorenzo
CFO: Joseph S. Tesoriero
HR: Sue Hagen
FYE: December 31
Type: Public

Fans of bananas and other fresh fruit might find this company to be a-peel-ing. Dole Food is the world's largest producer of fresh fruit and vegetables, known best as a top grower of bananas, pineapples, and other tropical varieties of fruit. The company's 200 products are sourced, grown, processed, marketed, and distributed in more than 90 countries worldwide. It peddles its products to supermarkets, mass merchandisers, wholesalers, and foodservice operators worldwide. In addition to fresh fruits and vegetables, Dole produces sliced fruit, fresh salads, canned fruit, and frozen, bottled, and canned juices. The company traces its roots back to 1851, when James Dole founded a pineapple growing and canning company in Hawaii.

	Annual Growth	12/04	12/05	12/06	12/07	*12/08
Sales ($ mil.)	9.4%	5,316.2	5,870.6	6,171.5	6,931.0	7,620.0
Net income ($ mil.)	(2.2%)	134.4	—	(89.0)	(57.5)	122.8
Employees	4.3%	64,000	72,000	75,000	87,000	75,800

*Most recent year available

DOLLAR FINANCIAL CORP.   NASDAQ (GS): DLLR

1436 Lancaster Ave., Ste. 300
Berwyn, PA 19312
Phone: 610-296-3400
Fax: 610-296-7844
Web: www.dfg.com

CEO: Jeffrey A. (Jeff) Weiss
CFO: Randall (Randy) Underwood
HR: —
FYE: June 30
Type: Public

If your wallet is flat and payday is far away, Dollar Financial will tide you over. Through its subsidiary Dollar Financial Group, the company owns more than 1,000 check-cashing and payday loan stores (and franchises about 200 additional locations) in North America and Europe. The stores operate under such names as Money Mart, Loan Mart, and Cash Advance. In addition to check cashing and short-term loans, the stores offer money wiring services, money orders, and reloadable Visa and Mastercard debit cards to customers who choose not to use, or don't have access to, traditional banks or financial institutions. The company also provides legal document processing services through its We The People retail locations.

	Annual Growth	6/05	6/06	6/07	6/08	6/09
Assets ($ mil.)	24.2%	387.9	551.8	833.6	947.2	922.6
Net income ($ mil.)	—	(0.4)	7.0	(32.2)	51.2	1.8
Market value ($ mil.)	6.4%	261.6	438.0	693.5	367.7	335.5
Employees	3.7%	3,909	4,226	4,795	5,490	4,522

DOLLAR GENERAL CORPORATION

NYSE: DG

100 Mission Ridge
Goodlettsville, TN 37072
Phone: 615-855-4000
Fax: 615-855-5252
Web: www.dollargeneral.com

CEO: Richard W. (Rick) Dreiling
CFO: David M. Tehle
HR: Robert D. (Bob) Ravener
FYE: January 31
Type: Public

Dollar General's at ease with living off the crumbs of Wal-Mart. The retailer commands a chain of more than 8,700 discount stores in 35 states, primarily in the southern and eastern US, the Midwest, and the Southwest. Offering basic household items, such as cleaning supplies and health and beauty aids, as well as some apparel and food, it targets low-, middle-, and fixed-income customers. Stores are generally located in small towns off the radar of giant discounters. Its big-city stores (about 30% of its total) are situated in lower-income neighborhoods. About 35% of its merchandise is priced at $1 or less. Two years after being taken private by affiliates of KKR and Goldman Sachs, the chain went public in 2009.

	Annual Growth	1/06	1/07	1/08	1/09	1/10
Sales ($ mil.)	8.3%	8,582.2	9,169.8	9,495.2	10,457.7	11,796.4
Net income ($ mil.)	(0.8%)	350.2	137.9	(12.8)	108.2	339.4
Employees	5.5%	64,500	69,500	71,500	77,200	79,800

DOLLAR THRIFTY AUTOMOTIVE GROUP, INC.

NYSE: DTG

5330 E. 31st St.
Tulsa, OK 74135
Phone: 918-660-7700
Fax: 918-669-2934
Web: www.dtag.com

CEO: Scott L. Thompson
CFO: H. Clifford Buster III
HR: —
FYE: December 31
Type: Public

Thrifty drivers looking to get the most for a buck might look to Dollar Thrifty Automotive Group (DTG), which rents cars under the Dollar Rent A Car and Thrifty Car Rental brands. Combined, Dollar and Thrifty rent cars from some 600 locations (down from 830) in North America, about half of which are run by franchisees. Both brands target the airport rental market; Thrifty also maintains off-airport locations. The combined DTG fleet of some 100,000 vehicles is made up mainly Ford, Chrysler, and GM cars. Although the brands retain their separate identities, key operations and administrative functions have been consolidated under the company umbrella. DTG in 2010 agreed to be acquired by Hertz Global Holdings.

	Annual Growth	12/05	12/06	12/07	12/08	12/09
Sales ($ mil.)	0.4%	1,522.5	1,660.7	1,760.8	1,698.0	1,546.2
Net income ($ mil.)	(6.3%)	58.4	51.7	1.2	(340.4)	45.0
Market value ($ mil.)	(8.2%)	1,033.2	1,306.5	678.3	31.2	733.6
Employees	(8.1%)	8,400	8,500	8,500	6,800	6,000

DOLLAR TREE, INC.

NASDAQ (GS): DLTR

500 Volvo Pkwy.
Chesapeake, VA 23320
Phone: 757-321-5000
Fax: 757-321-5111
Web: www.dollartree.com

CEO: Bob Sasser
CFO: Kevin S. Wampler
HR: James E. Fothergill
FYE: January 31
Type: Public

Dollars may not grow on trees, but outlets of Dollar Tree's stores seem to. The company operates more than 3,800 Dollar Tree, Deal$, and Dollar Bills discount stores in 48 states, which sell a changing mix of housewares, toys, seasonal items, food, health and beauty aids, gifts, and books — most priced at $1 or less. About 40% of its merchandise is imported, primarily from China. The stores are located in high-traffic strip centers anchored by mass merchandisers and supermarkets, malls, and in small towns. Dollar Tree bought the Deal$ chain in 2006 and the Greenbacks chain in 2003. Founded in 1986 as Dollar Tree Stores, the company reorganized and changed its name to Dollar Tree, Inc. in 2008.

	Annual Growth	1/06	1/07	1/08	1/09	1/10
Sales ($ mil.)	11.4%	3,393.9	3,969.4	4,242.6	4,644.9	5,231.2
Net income ($ mil.)	16.5%	173.9	192.0	201.3	229.5	320.5
Market value ($ mil.)	18.9%	2,103.6	2,667.7	2,375.9	3,622.8	4,200.5
Employees	9.9%	37,400	42,200	42,600	45,840	54,480

DOMINICK'S FINER FOODS, LLC

711 Jorie Blvd.
Oak Brook, IL 60523
Phone: 630-891-5000
Fax: 630-891-5210
Web: www.dominicks.com

CEO: Donald Keprta
CFO: —
HR: Dwayne Howard
FYE: December 31
Type: Subsidiary

Dominick's Finer Foods is a member of the big Safeway family. The company is the second-largest supermarket operator in the metropolitan Chicago area (after the SUPERVALU-owned Jewel-Osco supermarket chain). Dominick's has about 80 stores, including many large "Lifestyle" stores with upscale deli and bakery departments and expanded produce areas, floral departments, and in-store cafes. The rest are mostly conventional supermarkets. Dominick's also operates a commissary that produces its prepared foods. Supermarket giant Safeway, which bought Dominick's in 1998, has decided to keep the chain, which was on the block in the early 2000s, but failed to attract a buyer.

	Annual Growth	12/04	12/05	12/06	12/07	12/08
Est. sales ($ mil.)	—	—	—	—	—	1,952.8
Employees	—	—	—	—	—	18,000

DOMINION ENTERPRISES

150 Granby St.
Norfolk, VA 23510
Phone: 757-351-7000
Fax: 757-314-2500
Web: www.dominionenterprises.com

CEO: Jack J. Ross
CFO: Teresa S. Blevins
HR: Sunny R. Sonner
FYE: December 31
Type: Private

Dominion Enterprises can help you sell what you've got, no matter what it is. The company publishes classified advertising, and provides information resources in the real estate, apartment, specialty vehicle, employment, and travel industries. Its more than 450 magazine titles include *Boat Trader*, *The Employment Guide*, and *For Rent*. Dominion Enterprises also operates more than 45 websites, such as Homes.com, ForRent.com, and TraderOnline.com. In addition, the company owns businesses that offer Internet marketing, website design and hosting, lead generation, customer relationship management software, and data capture and distribution services. Dominion Enterprises is owned by Landmark Media Enterprises.

DOMINION RESOURCES BLACK WARRIOR TRUST

NYSE: DOM

901 Main St., Ste. 1700
Dallas, TX 75202
Phone: 214-209-2400
Fax: 214-209-2431
Web: www.dom-dominionblackwarriortrust.com

CEO: Ron E. Hooper
CFO: —
HR: —
FYE: December 31
Type: Public

Dominion Resources Black Warrior Trust knows that when the wells get old, financial warriors (aka shareholders) don't give up on the economic possibilities. The trust holds royalty interests in 532 natural gas producing wells and is set to terminate when these wells no longer produce enough gas to be profitable. The trust receives, then distributes to shareholders, 65% of the gross proceeds that Dominion Resources (via its subsidiary Dominion Black Warrior Basin) earns by selling the natural gas from its wells in the Black Warrior Basin of Alabama. In 2008 the trust had proved reserves of 22.6 billion cu. ft. of natural gas equivalent.

DOMINION RESOURCES, INC.
NYSE: D

120 Tredegar St.
Richmond, VA 23219
Phone: 804-819-2000
Fax: 804-819-2233
Web: www.dom.com

CEO: Thomas F. Farrell II
CFO: Mark F. McGettrick
HR: Roy Grier
FYE: December 31
Type: Public

And darkness shall have no dominion, as far as Dominion Resources is concerned. Through its Dominion Virginia Power the company transmits and distributes electricity to 2.4 million customers and natural gas to 1.7 million customers in five states. Its Dominion Generation unit manages the company's regulated and non-regulated power plants (27,500 MW of owned or controlled capacity); subsidiary Dominion Energy trades and markets energy, oversees 12,000 miles of natural gas pipelines, and operates underground gas storage facilities (941 billion cu. ft. of capacity). Dominion is one of the largest producers and transporters of energy in the US.

	Annual Growth	12/05	12/06	12/07	12/08	12/09
Sales ($ mil.)	(4.3%)	18,041.0	16,482.0	15,674.0	16,290.0	15,131.0
Net income ($ mil.)	5.8%	1,039.0	1,380.0	2,697.0	1,834.0	1,304.0
Market value ($ mil.)	0.2%	23,007.7	24,986.6	28,282.7	21,362.6	23,198.4
Employees	0.7%	17,400	17,500	17,000	18,000	17,900

DOMINO'S PIZZA, INC.
NYSE: DPZ

30 Frank Lloyd Wright Dr.
Ann Arbor, MI 48106
Phone: 734-930-3030
Fax: —
Web: www.dominos.com

CEO: J. Patrick Doyle
CFO: Wendy A. Beck
HR: Patricia A. (Patti) Wilmot
FYE: December 31
Type: Public

This company knows the rules of the pizza delivery game. Domino's Pizza runs the world's #2 pizza chain (behind YUM! Brands' Pizza Hut division), with about 9,000 delivery locations in more than 60 countries. (The chain includes about 5,000 stores in the US.) Domino's menu features several different styles of pizza with a wide array of topping options, as well as additional items such as bread sticks, cheese bread, and chicken wings. Its stores are principally delivery locations and generally do not have any dine-in seating. The company owns and operates more than 450 locations in the US, while the rest are franchised. Private equity firm Bain Capital owns nearly 30% of the company.

	Annual Growth	12/05	12/06	12/07	12/08	12/09
Sales ($ mil.)	(1.8%)	1,511.6	1,437.3	1,462.9	1,425.1	1,404.1
Net income ($ mil.)	(7.4%)	108.3	106.2	37.9	54.0	79.7
Market value ($ mil.)	(23.3%)	1,429.8	1,654.3	781.6	278.3	495.1
Employees	(6.8%)	13,500	13,300	12,500	10,500	10,200

DON MIGUEL MEXICAN FOODS, INC.

1501 W. Orangewood Ave.
Orange, CA 92868
Phone: 714-634-8441
Fax: 714-937-0493
Web: www.donmiguel.com

CEO: John Signorino
CFO: Michael Chaignot
HR: —
FYE: November 30
Type: Private

Don Miguel Mexican Foods makes tastebuds say "Olé!" The company manufactures and sells refrigerated and frozen Mexican meals and snacks for the retail market. Its products include frozen burritos, tacos, quesadillas, taquitos, tamales, party trays, and family-style dinner entrees, all of which are sold under the Don Miguel brand name. The company's manufacturing facility is in Dallas (it closed the Anaheim, California plant in 2006). Don Miguel is owned by private investment firm TSG Consumer Partners (formerly The Shansby Group).

DONALDSON COMPANY, INC.
NYSE: DCI

1400 W. 94th St.
Minneapolis, MN 55431
Phone: 952-887-3131
Fax: 952-887-3155
Web: www.donaldson.com

CEO: William M. (Bill) Cook
CFO: Thomas R. (Tom) VerHage
HR: Sandra N. Joppa
FYE: July 31
Type: Public

Grime fighter Donaldson is cleaning up the industrial world. The company makes filtration systems designed to remove contaminants from air and liquids. Donaldson's engine products business makes air intake and exhaust systems, liquid-filtration systems, and replacement parts; products are sold to manufacturers of construction, mining, and transportation equipment, as well as parts distributors and fleet operators. The company's industrial products include dust, fume, and mist collectors and air filtration systems used in industrial gas turbines, computer disk drives, and manufacturers' clean rooms. Donaldson has more than 100 locations worldwide, including 40 manufacturing plants.

	Annual Growth	7/05	7/06	7/07	7/08	7/09
Sales ($ mil.)	4.0%	1,595.7	1,694.3	1,918.8	2,232.5	1,868.6
Net income ($ mil.)	4.5%	110.6	132.3	150.7	172.0	131.9
Market value ($ mil.)	3.9%	2,513.3	2,537.2	2,807.2	3,479.9	2,932.2
Employees	(1.3%)	11,180	11,500	12,000	12,700	10,600

DONATOS PIZZERIA, LLC

935 Taylor Station Rd.
Columbus, OH 43230
Phone: 614-416-7700
Fax: 614-416-7701
Web: www.donatos.com

CEO: James E. (Jim) Grote
CFO: Doug Kourie
HR: Mary Rauchenstein
FYE: December 31
Type: Private

You might say this company knows how to toss around some dough. Donatos Pizzeria operates and franchises more than 175 Donatos Pizza restaurants in about half a dozen states, primarily in Ohio and surrounding areas. The chain serves several varieties of specialty pizza, along with sub sandwiches, salads, and desserts. Most Donatos locations offer dine-in seating, as well as carry-out, delivery, and take-and-bake pizzas; some also offer catering services for group events. About two-thirds of the pizza joints are company-owned. CEO Jim Grote and his family own the business, which he founded in 1963.

	Annual Growth	12/04	12/05	12/06	12/07	12/08
Est. sales ($ mil.)	—	—	—	—	—	47.7
Employees	—	—	—	—	—	2,200

DONEGAL GROUP INC.
NASDAQ (GS): DGICA

1195 River Rd.
Marietta, PA 17547
Phone: 717-426-1931
Fax: 717-426-7009
Web: www.donegalgroup.com

CEO: Donald H. Nikolaus
CFO: Jeffrey D. Miller
HR: Kevin G. Burke
FYE: December 31
Type: Public

"Risk" is Donegal Group's middle name. Through about five subsidiaries, including Atlantic States Insurance and Southern Insurance Company of Virginia, Donegal Group provides clients in 18 mid-Atlantic, midwestern, and southeastern states with personal, farm, and commercial property/casualty insurance products. The group's personal insurance offerings range from auto and boat policies to homeowners and fire coverage; its commercial insurance products include business owners, multiperil, and workers' compensation. Donegal Group has a joint banking venture with Donegal Mutual Insurance, which owns about 65% of the company; the venture, federal savings bank Province Bank, has three branches in Pennsylvania.

	Annual Growth	12/05	12/06	12/07	12/08	12/09
Assets ($ mil.)	4.6%	781.4	831.7	834.1	880.1	935.6
Net income ($ mil.)	(15.5%)	36.9	40.2	38.3	25.5	18.8
Market value ($ mil.)	(2.8%)	444.6	499.6	437.9	427.7	396.3
Employees	—	—	—	—	—	410

An in-depth profile of this company is available to Hoover's Online members at hoovers.com.

507

DONNA KARAN INTERNATIONAL INC.

550 7th Ave.	CEO: Mark Weber
New York, NY 10018	CFO: Patricia (Tisha) Kalberer
Phone: 212-789-1500	HR: Christina Nichols
Fax: —	FYE: December 31
Web: www.donnakaran.com	Type: Subsidiary

Known for clothes both classic and comfortable, Donna Karan International (DKI) defines the metropolitan flair that bridges the difference between stylishly casual and conventional. The firm designs and sells men's and women's clothes, including suits, sportswear, accessories, and shoes, under the Donna Karan New York, DKNY, DKNY Jeans, and DKNY Active labels. DKI sells to upscale department and specialty stores and through its own retail stores. It also licenses third parties to run most of its international stores. Fashion leviathan LVMH holds a majority stake in Donna Karan, although designer Karan still remains in creative control of its fashion lines and helps maintain her namesake brand.

	Annual Growth	12/04	12/05	12/06	12/07	12/08
Est. sales ($ mil.)	—	—	—	—	—	95.8
Employees	—	—	—	—	—	2,060

DOONEY & BOURKE INC.

1 Regent St.	CEO: Frederick Bourke
Norwalk, CT 06855	CFO: Philip Kinsley
Phone: 203-853-7515	HR: —
Fax: 203-853-9926	FYE: December 31
Web: www.dooney.com	Type: Private

With young rocker-types (Jonas Brothers), actresses (like Emma Roberts), and general trendsetters seen spotted with its products, this late 20-something company is hardly showing its age. Dooney & Bourke makes high-end handbags and accessories, mostly for women but also for men. They're sold in department stores (Macy's and Nordstrom), online, and by catalog. The company operates about 10 of its own stores internationally, including seven locations in a handful of US states and a flagship shop in Manhattan. Best-known for its distinctive initial-covered purses, Dooney & Bourke also makes cell phone and iPod cases, as well as jewelry, luggage, apparel, shoes, totes, wallets, and assorted accessories.

	Annual Growth	12/04	12/05	12/06	12/07	12/08
Est. sales ($ mil.)	—	—	—	—	—	6.2
Employees	—	—	—	—	—	104

DOPACO, INC.

100 Arrandale Blvd.	CEO: Robert Cauffman
Exton, PA 19341	CFO: Rick Scanlan
Phone: 610-269-1776	HR: Don Heisey
Fax: 610-524-9188	FYE: December 31
Web: www.dopaco.com	Type: Subsidiary

If your two favorite words in meal planning are "take-out," invite Dopaco to dinner. Dopaco manufactures take-out containers for customers in the food service industry. Its lineup includes folding cartons, hot and cold beverage cups and accompanying lids and carriers, as well as cartons for fries, and clamshells and food trays for pizza and hot dogs. The company also touts customized packaging design services to meet menu and marketing requirements. Major customers include Jack in the Box, Burger King, McDonald's, and Wendy's. Based near Philadelphia, Dopaco has six plants in North America, and joint ventures in the US, Australia, Indonesia, and China. It is a subsidiary of Canadian paper-maker Cascades Inc.

DORAL FINANCIAL CORPORATION NYSE: DRL

1451 Franklin D. Roosevelt Ave.	CEO: Glen R. Wakeman
San Juan, PR 00920	CFO: Robert E. Wahlman
Phone: 787-474-6700	HR: Lesbia Blanco
Fax: —	FYE: December 31
Web: www.doralfinancial.com	Type: Public

The Caribbean is home to more than just sun and fun. Doral Financial offers mortgage, retail, and business banking in Puerto Rico. Traditionally known as a mortgage-banking concern, the company has refocused its efforts to become a broader based community banking institution. The company's Doral Bank has about 40 branches in the Commonwealth. In addition to mortgages, the company offers construction, business, consumer, and other loans. Besides providing mortgage banking services through Doral Bank, the company sells insurance products through Doral Insurance Agency. A group of institutional investors led by Irving Place Capital (formerly Bear Stearns Merchant Banking) owns 90% of the company.

	Annual Growth	12/05	12/06	12/07	12/08	12/09
Assets ($ mil.)	(12.3%)	17,298.7	11,856.4	9,304.4	10,138.9	10,232.0
Net income ($ mil.)	—	13.2	(223.9)	(170.9)	(318.3)	(21.1)
Market value ($ mil.)	(63.8%)	14,264.1	3,862.1	1,213.8	504.6	244.2
Employees	(16.0%)	2,317	1,278	1,371	1,199	1,154

DORCHESTER MINERALS, L.P. NASDAQ (GM): DMLP

3838 Oak Lawn Ave., Ste. 300	CEO: William Casey McManemin
Dallas, TX 75219	CFO: H. C. Allen Jr.
Phone: 214-559-0300	HR: —
Fax: 214-559-0301	FYE: December 31
	Type: Public

The stakeholders of Dorchester Minerals are enjoying the benefits of three natural resource exploitation enterprises which came together as one. The oil and gas exploration company was formed by the 2003 merger of oil trust Dorchester Hugoton with Republic Royalty and Spinnaker Royalty. Dorchester Minerals' holdings include about 141,600 net acres in Texas and 62,850 net acres in Montana. The company holds assets (producing and nonproducing mineral, royalty, overriding royalty, net profits, and leasehold interests) in properties in 574 counties in 25 states. In 2009 Dorchester Minerals reported proved reserves of 60.3 billion cu. ft. of natural gas and 3.3 million barrels of oil and condensate.

	Annual Growth	12/05	12/06	12/07	12/08	12/09
Sales ($ mil.)	(14.0%)	79.8	74.9	65.4	89.9	43.6
Net income ($ mil.)	(19.9%)	52.8	50.2	43.0	66.8	21.7
Market value ($ mil.)	(4.4%)	781.3	675.8	617.5	486.8	652.8
Employees	(7.5%)	26	19	27	18	19

DOREL JUVENILE GROUP, INC.

2525 State St.	CEO: Dave Taylor
Columbus, IN 47201	CFO: Steve Willeke
Phone: 812-372-0141	HR: Tim Ferguson
Fax: 812-372-0893	FYE: December 31
Web: www.djgusa.com	Type: Subsidiary

Getting little ones around town safely is Dorel Juvenile Group's primary push. The global firm makes infant car seats, strollers, high chairs, changing tables, monitors, and toddler beds and cribs. Dorel Juvenile's own brands include Cosco, Maxi-Cosi, and Safety 1st and in Europe Bébé Confort, Maxi-Cosi, Quinny, Monbébé, Babidéal, Baby Relax, and Safety 1st. It licenses other big-name brands, such as Eddie Bauer, Playskool, and Disney Baby. Dorel Juvenile is a unit of Canadian company Dorel Industries. It was formed in 2000 when Safety 1st was acquired and its operations were folded into Dorel's existing juvenile operation, Cosco. The company has been expanding internationally.

DORLAND CORPORATION

1 S. Broad, 11th Fl.	CEO: Maryellen Royle
Philadelphia, PA 19107	CFO: —
Phone: 215-625-0111	HR: Sharon Rundberg
Fax: 215-625-9037	FYE: December 31
Web: www.dorland.com	Type: Subsidiary

Dorland helps its medical clients get a foot in the door when it comes to attracting potential customers. The agency provides global marketing, medical education, public relations, and strategic consulting to its clients in the health care industry. Its customers include health care providers, medical device makers, and pharmaceutical companies. Dorland gets out the message with films and videos, interactive Web and conference call presentations, print advertising, and public relations campaigns. John Dorland founded the firm in 1883 as a travel and resort advertising agency. It is owned by public relations consultancy Huntsworth PLC and resides within that firm's Huntsworth Health division.

	Annual Growth	12/04	12/05	12/06	12/07	12/08
Est. sales ($ mil.)	—	—	—	—	—	32.8
Employees	—	—	—	—	—	130

DORMA GROUP NORTH AMERICA

Dorma Dr., Drawer AC	CEO: Larry O'Toole
Reamstown, PA 17567	CFO: Daniel P. (Dan) Conner
Phone: 717-336-3881	HR: Scott Haden
Fax: 717-336-2106	FYE: June 30
Web: www.dorma-usa.com	Type: Subsidiary

Opening doors for others is the DORMA Group North America way. The company, a subsidiary of German building products maker DORMA Holding operates through its own divisions in the US, Canada, and Mexico. The company supplies automatic door systems, controls, and components mostly for commercial buildings and facilities. Its principal products include revolving doors marketed under the name Crane Revolving Door, automatic doors, and door hardware (closers, locks, key systems and electronic-access controls). Operable walls and accordion partitions are sold by its Modernfold division. DORMA Glas designs and manufactures products for tempered glass entrances.

DORMAN PRODUCTS, INC.

NASDAQ (GM): DORM

3400 E. Walnut St.	CEO: Richard N. Berman
Colmar, PA 18915	CFO: Mathias J. Barton
Phone: 215-997-1800	HR: Penny Boyer
Fax: 215-997-8577	FYE: December 31
Web: www.dormanproducts.com	Type: Public

Got parts? Dorman does. From its stock of 92,000 products, Dorman Products (formerly R&B, Inc.) is a leading supplier of OEM automotive hardware and replacement parts and brake parts to the automotive aftermarket. It also supplies household hardware and organization products to mass merchants. About 90% of Dorman's revenue comes from parts sold under the company's brand names, which include AutoGrade, FirstStop, and Symmetry. Dorman sells to retailers such as AutoZone and O'Reilly and to distributors and parts manufacturers for resale under private labels. Brothers Richard and Steven Berman (CEO and president, respectively) and their families own more than a third of Dorman's shares.

	Annual Growth	12/05	12/06	12/07	12/08	12/09
Sales ($ mil.)	7.9%	278.1	295.8	327.7	342.3	377.4
Net income ($ mil.)	11.6%	17.1	13.8	19.2	17.8	26.5
Market value ($ mil.)	13.4%	168.3	192.2	253.6	234.3	278.1
Employees	3.2%	879	961	1,005	966	997

DOSKOCIL MANUFACTURING COMPANY, INC.

4209 Barnett Blvd.	CEO: Larry Rambold
Arlington, TX 76017	CFO: Gary Kohlschmidt
Phone: 817-467-5116	HR: Chris Yu
Fax: 817-472-9810	FYE: June 30
Web: www.petmate.com	Type: Private

Doskocil Manufacturing has dogs, cats, and birds covered. The company, which does business as Petmate, is one of the nation's leading providers of non-food pet care products. It makes kennels, bedding, feeders, litter boxes, scratching posts, and related supplies for dogs and cats under the Petmate brand. Its Aspen Pet Products division offers up chew toys, treats, collars, bird perches, and other accessories under the Booda and Aspen Pet names. Products are sold by mass merchandisers, pet supply stores, and online retailers, including Wal-Mart, Ace Hardware, PETCO, PetSmart, and Amazon.com. Owned by private investment firm Westar Capital, the firm was founded in 1961 by Ben Doskocil.

	Annual Growth	6/04	6/05	6/06	6/07	6/08
Est. sales ($ mil.)	—	—	—	—	—	176.2
Employees	—	—	—	—	—	630

DOT FOODS, INC.

1 Dot Way	CEO: John M. Tracy
Mount Sterling, IL 62353	CFO: William H. (Bill) Metzinger
Phone: 217-773-4411	HR: Dana Chapman
Fax: 217-773-3321	FYE: December 31
Web: www.dotfoods.com	Type: Private

Dot Foods, the largest foodservice redistributor in the US, started out in business as one station wagon that hauled dairy goods around and went by the name of Associated Dairy Products. The company now owns more than 700 trucks (through its Dot Transportation division) that distribute some 70,000 products including food, flatware, serveware, and janitorial supplies from 500 manufacturers to its customers — more than 3,300 foodservice distributors. Dot has nine distribution facilities located across the country. Its edotfoods unit offers ordering and fulfillment services online. The company also sells food ingredients to dairies, bakeries, confectioners, meat processors, and other food manufacturers.

	Annual Growth	12/04	12/05	12/06	12/07	12/08
Sales ($ mil.)	12.6%	1,930.0	2,164.0	2,490.0	2,810.0	3,100.0
Employees	6.8%	2,500	2,746	2,916	3,168	3,248

DOT HILL SYSTEMS CORP.

NASDAQ (GM): HILL

2200 Faraday Ave., Ste. 100	CEO: Dana W. Kammersgard
Carlsbad, CA 92008	CFO: Hanif I. Jamal
Phone: 760-931-5500	HR: —
Fax: 760-931-5527	FYE: December 31
Web: www.dothill.com	Type: Public

Dot Hill Systems attacks data storage problems. The company makes RAID (redundant array of independent disks) storage products. Dot Hill targets enterprises in data-intensive industries such as financial services and telecommunications with its storage area networks (SANs) offerings. In addition to entry-level and and mid-range storage systems, the company provides storage system and data management software. Most of the company's sales are to OEM partners, which include Fujitsu Technology Solutions, Hewlett-Packard, NetApp, and Oracle. It primarily sells its products on a private-label basis. Dot Hill generates the majority of its revenues in the US, but it maintains offices in Europe and Asia.

	Annual Growth	12/05	12/06	12/07	12/08	12/09
Sales ($ mil.)	0.1%	233.8	239.2	207.1	272.9	234.4
Net income ($ mil.)	—	26.6	(80.8)	(60.2)	(25.8)	(13.6)
Market value ($ mil.)	(27.6%)	379.0	215.0	132.9	43.8	103.9
Employees	0.9%	275	269	261	266	285

An in-depth profile of this company is available to Hoover's Online members at hoovers.com.

509

DOTS, LLC

30300 Emerald Valley Pkwy.
Glenwillow, OH 44139
Phone: 440-349-7900
Fax: 440-349-7001
Web: www.dots.com

CEO: Robert A. (Bob) Glick
CFO: —
HR: —
FYE: December 31
Type: Private

DOTS operates 420-plus women's clothing and accessory stores in more than two dozen states, mostly along the East Coast and in the Midwest. The stores, which target female shoppers between the ages of 18 and 45, sell low-priced fashion apparel and accessories for the junior, misses, and plus-size markets. The fast-growing company has been opening new stores in some big markets, including Texas and Georgia. Overall, the apparel and accessories chain is aiming to open 150 new stores by 2010. William Blair Capital Partners owns a sizable equity interest in DOTS, which has plans for continued national expansion, including California eventually.

DOUBLE EAGLE PETROLEUM CO.

NASDAQ (GS): DBLE

1675 Broadway, Ste. 2200
Denver, CO 80202
Phone: 303-794-8445
Fax: 303-794-8451
Web: www.dble.us

CEO: Richard D. (Dick) Dole
CFO: Kurtis S. Hooley
HR: —
FYE: December 31
Type: Public

It's double or nothing for Double Eagle Petroleum (formerly Double Eagle Petroleum and Mining), which gambles on hitting pay dirt as it explores for and produces oil and gas in the Rocky Mountains of Utah and Wyoming. Double Eagle owns interests in 888 producing wells, and natural gas accounts for more than 95% of the oil and gas independent's production and reserves. The company has proved reserves of more than 413,000 barrels of oil and 71.3 billion cu. ft. of natural gas, and leases acreage in seven states. Double Eagle sells its oil and gas on the spot market.

	Annual Growth	12/05	12/06	12/07	12/08	12/09
Sales ($ mil.)	21.6%	20.5	19.0	17.2	49.6	44.8
Net income ($ mil.)	(26.0%)	4.0	2.1	(11.6)	10.4	1.2
Market value ($ mil.)	(32.2%)	226.8	272.9	175.2	78.0	48.0
Employees	14.4%	14	17	15	26	24

⊞ DOUBLECLICK INC.

111 8th Ave., 10th Fl.
New York, NY 10011
Phone: 212-271-2542
Fax: 212-287-1203
Web: www.doubleclick.com

CEO: Henrique De Castro
CFO: —
HR: —
FYE: December 31
Type: Subsidiary

Help with online advertising is only a DoubleClick away. The company provides targeted online display advertising placement and scheduling services for both advertisers and website publishers through its DART suite of products and services. DoubleClick's technology products allow its advertising and media clients to track, target, deliver, and run their digital advertising campaigns. The company also offers consulting services, case studies, and research reports related to online advertising. Overall, DoubleClick has more than 30 offices and data centers across the US, Europe, and the Asia/Pacific region. DoubleClick is a unit of Internet search giant Google, which acquired the company in 2008.

DOUBLE-TAKE SOFTWARE, INC.

NASDAQ (GM): DBTK

257 Turnpike Rd., Ste. 210
Southborough, MA 01772
Phone: 508-229-8483
Fax: 508-229-0866
Web: www.doubletake.com

CEO: Dean F. Goodermote
CFO: S. Craig Huke
HR: Monica Sanders
FYE: December 31
Type: Public

Double-Take Software helps companies take a second look at their data protection. The company provides data-replication-and-storage software designed to help businesses protect and manage data assets. Its core Double-Take product line features data backup and disaster recovery software for a variety of systems; the company also offers professional services such as consulting, implementation, and support. Double-Take's customers come from fields such as education, financial and legal services, government, health care, manufacturing, retail, and telecommunications. In May 2010 it agreed to be acquired by private equity firm Thoma Bravo for about $242 million.

	Annual Growth	12/05	12/06	12/07	12/08	12/09
Sales ($ mil.)	19.6%	40.7	60.8	82.8	96.3	83.2
Net income ($ mil.)	—	(3.8)	6.8	20.1	17.6	13.5
Market value ($ mil.)	(8.1%)	—	272.4	459.4	189.7	211.3
Employees	6.9%	296	301	354	392	387

DOUBLETREE CORPORATION

9336 Civic Center Dr.
Beverly Hills, CA 90210
Phone: 310-278-4321
Fax: 310-205-7678
Web: www.doubletree.com

CEO: Christopher J. (Chris) Nassetta
CFO: Steven R. (Steve) Goldman
HR: —
FYE: December 31
Type: Subsidiary

Look to the two trees for one good night's sleep. Doubletree Hotels is a chain of more than 200 full-service hotels in the mid-market to upscale segment. The hotels, located primarily in the US, are also found in Canada and Latin America. The chain also includes Doubletree Guest Suites (all-suite hotels) and Doubletree Club (moderately priced format). The company was formed in 1993 by combining Guest Quarters (Boston) and Doubletree Hotels (Phoenix), and was acquired by Hilton Hotels (now Hilton Worldwide) in 1999. Investment firm The Blackstone Group purchased Hilton in 2007 in a deal worth more than $20 billion. As a result, Doubletree operates as one of about 10 brands in the Hilton Family of Hotels.

	Annual Growth	12/04	12/05	12/06	12/07	12/08
Est. sales ($ mil.)	—	—	—	—	—	464.6
Employees	—	—	—	—	—	13,800

DOUGLAS DYNAMICS, INC.

NYSE: PLOW

7777 N. 73rd St.
Milwaukee, WI 53233
Phone: 414-354-2310
Fax: —
Web: www.douglasdynamics.com

CEO: James L. Janik
CFO: Robert McCormick
HR: —
FYE: December 31
Type: Public

Unlike many, Douglas Dynamics isn't afraid of a blizzard. A holding company, Douglas Dynamics, Inc. operates through Douglas Dynamics LLC, which makes snowplows and sand and salt spreading equipment for light trucks and other vehicles. One of the biggest manufacturers in its industry, the company targets its products to municipalities, private citizens, and professional snowplowers, and sells under the Western, Fisher, and Blizzard brands. Most of its customers are located in the midwestern and eastern US and throughout Canada; it sells its products through network of more than 720 distributors. Douglas Dynamics, which traces its roots back to the 1970s, filed an initial public offering in 2010.

	Annual Growth	12/05	12/06	12/07	12/08	12/09
Sales ($ mil.)	6.1%	—	145.8	140.1	180.1	174.3
Net income ($ mil.)	265.9%	—	0.2	(1.1)	11.5	9.8
Employees	0.0%	—	—	—	562	562

DOUGLAS EMMETT, INC.

NYSE: DEI

808 Wilshire Blvd., Ste. 200
Santa Monica, CA 90401
Phone: 310-255-7700
Fax: 310-255-7888
Web: www.douglasemmett.com

CEO: Jordan L. Kaplan
CFO: William Kamer
HR: —
FYE: December 31
Type: Public

Office Space is more than the name of a cult movie to Douglas Emmett. The self-administered and self-managed real estate investment trust (REIT) invests in commercial real estate in Southern California and Hawaii. It owns more than 50 commercial properties (totaling 11.9 million sq. ft.), mostly in the heart of Hollywood and surrounding areas. Its office holdings account for some 90% of all revenues. The REIT also owns some 3,000 apartment units in tony neighborhoods of West Los Angeles and Honolulu. Douglas Emmett's portfolio includes some of the most notable addresses on the West Coast, including the famed Sherman Oaks Galleria, Burbank's Studio Plaza, and office tower 100 Wilshire.

	Annual Growth	12/05	12/06	12/07	12/08	12/09
Sales ($ mil.)	9.7%	393.8	433.7	518.2	608.1	571.1
Net income ($ mil.)	—	(16.5)	(37.0)	(13.0)	(28.0)	(27.1)
Market value ($ mil.)	(18.8%)	—	3,250.1	2,763.6	1,596.3	1,741.8
Employees	7.3%	400	400	480	500	530

DOV PHARMACEUTICAL, INC.

Pink Sheets: DOVP

150 Pierce St.
Somerset, NJ 08873
Phone: 732-907-3600
Fax: 732-907-3799
Web: www.dovpharm.com

CEO: Barbara G. Duncan
CFO: Barbara G. Duncan
HR: —
FYE: December 31
Type: Public

DOV Pharmaceutical is all lovey-dovey with neurotransmitter receptors. The biopharmaceutical company primarily focuses on products that treat central nervous system disorders. One of its lead candidates is a triple reuptake inhibitor called DOV 21,947, designed to treat depression and obesity. Its bicifadine and diltiazem candidates are undergoing clinical trials for post-surgical pain and hypertension, respectively. Indiplon, which is supposed to treat insomnia, is under discussion with the FDA and may be subject to additional requirements before it can be commercialized. The company has agreed to be acquired by Euthymics Bioscience for about $2 million.

DOVER CORPORATION

NYSE: DOV

280 Park Ave., Fl. 34W
New York, NY 10017
Phone: 212-922-1640
Fax: 212-922-1656
Web: www.dovercorporation.com

CEO: Robert A. (Bob) Livingston
CFO: Brad M. Cerepak
HR: Jay L. Kloosterboer
FYE: December 31
Type: Public

The "D" in Dover could stand for diversity. Dover manages over 30 companies that make equipment ranging from car wash systems to aerospace components. Dover operates in four segments: Industrial Products (material handling and mobile equipment); Engineered Systems (product identification and refrigeration systems); Fluid Management (fluid and gas control, movement, measurement, and monitoring products); and Electronic Technologies (micro-components for hearing aids and electronics, automated assembly and testing equipment, and RF/microwave filters). The company maintains a highly decentralized management culture, with a president for each division as well as for each subsidiary company.

	Annual Growth	12/05	12/06	12/07	12/08	12/09
Sales ($ mil.)	(1.3%)	6,078.4	6,511.6	7,226.1	7,568.9	5,775.7
Net income ($ mil.)	(8.6%)	510.1	561.8	661.1	590.8	356.4
Market value ($ mil.)	0.7%	7,561.9	9,154.9	8,607.7	6,148.1	7,771.0
Employees	(1.9%)	31,650	33,000	33,400	32,300	29,300

DOVER DOWNS GAMING & ENTERTAINMENT, INC.

NYSE: DDE

1131 N. DuPont Hwy.
Dover, DE 19901
Phone: 302-674-4600
Fax: 302-857-3253
Web: www.doverdowns.com

CEO: Denis McGlynn
CFO: Timothy R. Horne
HR: —
FYE: December 31
Type: Public

Dover Downs Gaming & Entertainment is betting on being the first stop for gamblers in the First State. Spun off from Dover Motorsports, the company operates three facilities, all in Dover, Delaware, adjacent to Dover Motorsports' Dover Downs International Speedway. Dover Downs Casino, a 165,000 square-foot facility, is home to more than 3,000 video slot machines; Dover Downs Hotel and Conference Center is a 500-room luxury hotel featuring ballroom, concert hall, banquet, fine dining, meeting room, and spa facilities; and Dover Downs Raceway features harness racing and simulcast horse race betting. Dover Downs' video slot operations are operated and administered by the Delaware State Lottery Office.

	Annual Growth	12/05	12/06	12/07	12/08	12/09
Sales ($ mil.)	1.8%	216.9	236.5	242.4	239.1	232.8
Net income ($ mil.)	(18.8%)	26.0	25.3	26.1	19.5	11.3
Market value ($ mil.)	(20.4%)	304.1	431.1	362.7	102.5	121.9
Employees	0.5%	922	888	906	898	941

DOVER MOTORSPORTS, INC.

NYSE: DVD

1131 N. DuPont Hwy.
Dover, DE 19901
Phone: 302-883-6500
Fax: 302-672-0100
Web: www.dovermotorsportsinc.com

CEO: Denis McGlynn
CFO: Timothy R. Horne
HR: Janie Libby
FYE: December 31
Type: Public

This company makes its money when rubber meets the pavement at one of its tracks. Dover Motorsports is a leading operator of racetracks that host more than a dozen top auto racing events each year. Its tracks include Gateway International Raceway near St. Louis, Memphis Motorsports Park, Nashville Superspeedway, and its flagship Dover International Speedway in Delaware. The tracks hold events sponsored by all the major US racing leagues, including NASCAR, the Indy Racing League, and the National Hot Rod Association, though stock car racing accounts for 70% of sales. Chairman Henry Tippie controls more than 50% of the company as executor of the estate of the late chairman John Rollins.

	Annual Growth	12/05	12/06	12/07	12/08	12/09
Sales ($ mil.)	(6.0%)	91.0	91.3	86.1	84.3	70.9
Net income ($ mil.)	—	4.6	(35.3)	3.7	(5.7)	(5.9)
Market value ($ mil.)	(23.5%)	224.4	195.1	240.6	47.8	76.8
Employees	(8.4%)	139	146	145	144	98

DOVER SADDLERY, INC.

NASDAQ (GM): DOVR

525 Great Rd.
Littleton, MA 01460
Phone: 978-952-8062
Fax: 978-952-8065
Web: www.doversaddlery.com

CEO: Stephen L. Day
CFO: Michael W. Bruns
HR: —
FYE: December 31
Type: Public

Dover Saddlery is an upscale specialty retailer and direct marketer of equestrian products. The company's specialty is English-style riding gear, and its selection features riding apparel, tack, and stable supplies, as well as horse health care products. Its brand-name products include names such as Ariat, Grand Prix, Hermes, Mountain Horse, Passier, Prestige, and Smith Brothers. Dover sells through catalogs, a website, and more than 10 retail stores in the northeastern US and Texas, operating under the Dover Saddlery and Smith Brothers banners. The company was founded in 1975 by US Equestrian Team members, including company directors Jim and Dave Powers.

	Annual Growth	12/05	12/06	12/07	12/08	12/09
Sales ($ mil.)	5.0%	62.7	73.0	81.4	78.0	76.2
Net income ($ mil.)	3.0%	0.8	1.4	0.8	(13.8)	0.9
Market value ($ mil.)	(30.2%)	50.0	44.5	22.0	7.1	11.8
Employees	12.0%	330	472	502	519	520

An in-depth profile of this company is available to Hoover's Online members at hoovers.com.

511

DOW AGROSCIENCES LLC

9330 Zionsville Rd.
Indianapolis, IN 46268
Phone: 317-337-3000
Fax: —
Web: www.dowagro.com

CEO: Antonio Galindez
CFO: Gordon Slack
HR: Nick Gray
FYE: December 31
Type: Subsidiary

Dow AgroSciences, a subsidiary of Dow Chemical, doesn't want its customers to be bugged. The subsidiary makes insecticides, herbicides, and fungicides for agricultural applications, as well as for residential pest control. It also develops genetically modified (GM) seeds under the Mycogen and Phytogen names. Dow AgroSciences splits its operations into five product lines: plant genetics and biotechnology (in addition to seeds the unit has developed food products like the heart-healthy Natreon canola oil), weed management, disease management, pest management, and urban pest management. It has operations in more than 50 countries around the world.

DOW JONES & COMPANY, INC.

1 World Financial Center, 200 Liberty St. # 8
New York, NY 10281
Phone: 212-416-2000
Fax: 413-592-4783
Web: www.dj.com

CEO: Leslie F. (Les) Hinton
CFO: Stephen Daintith
HR: Gregory (Greg) Giangrande
FYE: December 31
Type: Subsidiary

This company covers the news from Wall Street to Main Street. Dow Jones & Company is a leading provider of news and information with a portfolio of newspapers and magazines anchored by *The Wall Street Journal*, the #1 daily paper in the US, with a circulation of more than 2 million. Dow Jones also publishes international editions of the *Journal*, serving readers in Asia and Europe. Its Dow Jones Local Media Group, meanwhile, runs a collection of local papers serving smaller communities on the East and West coasts. Beyond newspapers, Dow Jones owns business magazine *Barron's*, financial news site MarketWatch, *SmartMoney* magazine, and research service Factiva. The company is a subsidiary of News Corporation.

THE DOW CHEMICAL COMPANY

NYSE: DOW

2030 Dow Center
Midland, MI 48674
Phone: 989-636-1000
Fax: 989-636-1830
Web: www.dow.com

CEO: Andrew N. Liveris
CFO: William H. (Bill) Weideman
HR: Gregory M. Freiwald
FYE: December 31
Type: Public

Dow Chemical is a leader in the production of plastics, chemicals, hydrocarbons, and agrochemicals. The largest chemical company in the US and #2 worldwide (ahead of ExxonMobil and behind BASF), Dow also makes performance plastics (engineering plastics, polyurethanes, and materials for Dow Automotive). Other products include materials for packaging (such as its Styrofoam brand insulation), fibers, and films, as well as performance chemicals like acrylic acid. The company also manufactures commodity chemicals (chloralkalies and glycols) and agrochemicals. Its Hydrocarbons and Energy unit makes olefins and aromatics, raw materials for other chemicals. Dow also owns half of silicone products maker Dow Corning.

	Annual Growth	12/05	12/06	12/07	12/08	12/09
Sales ($ mil.)	(0.8%)	46,307.0	49,124.0	53,513.0	57,514.0	44,875.0
Net income ($ mil.)	(37.9%)	4,535.0	3,724.0	2,887.0	579.0	676.0
Market value ($ mil.)	(10.9%)	50,607.7	46,080.5	45,526.2	17,427.4	31,909.9
Employees	5.3%	42,413	42,578	45,856	46,102	52,195

DPAC TECHNOLOGIES CORP.

OTC: DPAC

5675 Hudson Industrial Pkwy.
Hudson, OH 44236
Phone: 330-655-9000
Fax: 330-655-9070
Web: www.dpactech.com

CEO: Steven D. (Steve) Runkel
CFO: Stephen J. (Steve) Vukadinovich
HR: —
FYE: December 31
Type: Public

DPAC Technologies takes networking to the air. Through its Quatech division, the company provides device connectivity and wireless networking products. Its offerings include the Airborne line of wireless LAN modules, which are made to be easily embedded into existing designs for electronic gear. The company also has a line of plug-and-play wireless device servers and Ethernet bridges. Its device connectivity operations design multi-port serial adapters and boards. DPAC Technologies sells through distributors, systems integrators, resellers, and manufacturers. The company gets about three-quarters of its sales in the US.

	Annual Growth	12/05	12/06	12/07	12/08	12/09
Sales ($ mil.)	(25.0%)	—	—	12.1	9.2	6.8
Net income ($ mil.)	—	—	—	(0.8)	(0.8)	(1.1)
Market value ($ mil.)	(13.4%)	—	—	1.8	1.1	1.3
Employees	(29.3%)	—	—	38	29	19

DOW CORNING CORPORATION

2200 W. Salzburg Rd.
Midland, MI 48686
Phone: 989-496-4000
Fax: 989-496-4393
Web: www.dowcorning.com

CEO: Stephanie A. Burns
CFO: Joseph D. (Don) Sheets
HR: Alan E. Hubbard
FYE: December 31
Type: Joint venture

Dow Corning knows about cooperation. The company began as a joint venture of chemical titan Dow and glass giant Corning in 1943 and ranks among the longest-lasting partnerships of its kind in the US. Dow Corning produces more than 7,000 silicone-based products such as adhesives, insulating materials, and lubricants for aerospace, automotive, and electrical uses. Because silicone does not conduct electricity, it is also used in its hard polycrystalline form (silicon) as the material on which semiconductors are built. Its products are also used in the production of photovoltaic cells used to produce solar energy. With plants worldwide, the company sells more than half of its products outside the US.

	Annual Growth	12/04	12/05	12/06	12/07	12/08
Sales ($ mil.)	12.7%	3,372.6	3,878.7	4,391.6	4,940.0	5,450.0
Net income ($ mil.)	32.7%	238.3	506.5	668.4	—	738.7
Employees	5.4%	—	—	9,000	10,000	10,000

DPI SPECIALTY FOODS, INC.

1007 Church St., Ste. 314
Evanston, IL 60201
Phone: 847-492-8036
Fax: 847-492-8039
Web: www.distribution-plus.com

CEO: Jim DeKeyser
CFO: Kevin Carmody
HR: Bart McGuinn
FYE: December 31
Type: Subsidiary

DPI Specialty Foods is a leading wholesale food distributor that delivers gourmet, organic, and ethnic food, and other specialized products. The company offers more than 55,000 items through its five main distribution centers and delivers goods to customers throughout the US. It serves foodservice operators, retail grocers, and customers in other food sectors. In addition to supplying food and other goods, DPI offers its customers technology support, marketing, merchandising, and sales services. The company, founded in 1989, is controlled by the Irish Dairy Board.

DPL INC.
NYSE: DPL

1065 Woodman Dr.
Dayton, OH 45432
Phone: 937-224-6000
Fax: 937-259-7147
Web: www.dplinc.com

CEO: Paul M. Barbas
CFO: Frederick J. (Fred) Boyle
HR: Daniel J. (Dan) McCabe
FYE: December 31
Type: Public

When it's dark in Dayton, DPL turns on the lights. The holding company's main subsidiary, regulated utility Dayton Power and Light (DP&L), which was established in 1911, brightens the night for more than 515,000 electricity customers in 24 counties in west central Ohio. Nonregulated subsidiary DPL Energy markets wholesale power generated at DPL's 10 power plants, which produce about 3,700 MW of primarily coal-fired generating capacity. It also sells power to affiliate DPL Energy Resources to meet the electric requirements of its retail customers. Other activities include street lighting and financial support services.

	Annual Growth	12/05	12/06	12/07	12/08	12/09
Sales ($ mil.)	5.5%	1,284.9	1,393.5	1,515.7	1,601.6	1,588.9
Net income ($ mil.)	6.6%	177.6	139.6	221.8	244.5	229.1
Market value ($ mil.)	1.5%	3,093.7	3,304.2	3,526.6	2,716.6	3,282.8
Employees	3.4%	1,381	1,452	1,562	1,588	1,581

DPR CONSTRUCTION, INC.

1450 Veterans Blvd.
Redwood City, CA 94063
Phone: 650-474-1450
Fax: 650-474-1451
Web: www.dprinc.com

CEO: Douglas E. (Doug) Woods
CFO: Gary Wohl
HR: Jorinne Jackson
FYE: December 31
Type: Private

From bio labs to wafer fabs, the projects of DPR Construction reflect the focus of its commercial building operations. The general contractor/construction manager builds projects for the biotechnology, pharmaceutical, health care, education, and semiconductor markets. DPR also specializes in corporate offices, entertainment facilities (theme parks and studios), energy-efficient projects, and warehouse and distribution centers. Clients have included Apple, Banner Health, Pixar Animation, Scripps Research Institute, and the American Red Cross. Head of the company Doug Woods, former CEO Peter Nosler, and secretary/treasurer Ron Davidowski (the D, P, and R) founded the firm in 1990.

	Annual Growth	12/04	12/05	12/06	12/07	12/08
Sales ($ mil.)	3.7%	—	—	1,580.0	1,470.0	1,700.0
Employees	(4.5%)	—	—	2,200	2,100	—

⊞ D.R. HORTON, INC.
NYSE: DHI

301 Commerce St., Ste. 500
Fort Worth, TX 76102
Phone: 817-390-8200
Fax: 817-390-1715
Web: www.drhorton.com

CEO: Donald J. (Don) Tomnitz
CFO: William W. (Bill) Wheat
HR: —
FYE: September 30
Type: Public

When this Horton heard a Who, it built the little guy a house. D.R. Horton builds single-family homes designed for the entry-level and move-up markets. Homes range from 1,000 sq. ft. to 5,000 sq. ft., with an average selling price of about $213,400; luxury homes cost up to $700,000. In fiscal 2009 the company sold some 16,700 homes, a 37% drop from the previous year. D.R. Horton operates in about 30 states and provides mortgage financing (through DHI Mortgage) as well as title services. One of the top homebuilders in the US, D.R. Horton has suffered along with its competitors as a result of the housing market bust, the subprime mortgage crisis, the global credit crunch, and years of industry-wide overbuilding.

	Annual Growth	9/05	9/06	9/07	9/08	9/09
Sales ($ mil.)	(28.3%)	13,863.7	15,051.3	11,296.5	6,646.1	3,657.6
Net income ($ mil.)	—	1,470.5	1,233.3	(712.5)	(2,633.6)	(545.3)
Market value ($ mil.)	(25.1%)	11,525.0	7,620.8	4,076.1	4,142.9	3,630.6
Employees	(24.3%)	8,900	8,772	6,231	3,800	2,926

DR PEPPER SNAPPLE GROUP, INC.
NYSE: DPS

5301 Legacy Dr.
Plano, TX 75024
Phone: 972-673-7000
Fax: 972-673-7980
Web: www.drpeppersnapplegroup.com

CEO: Larry D. Young
CFO: Martin M. (Marty) Ellen
HR: Lawrence N. Solomon
FYE: December 31
Type: Public

In this case, it's a snap decision about what doctor to choose. Dr Pepper Snapple Group (DPS) is the bottler and distributor of Dr Pepper soda and Snapple drinks for North America. Serving Canada, Mexico, and the US, the company offers a large portfolio of non-alcoholic beverages including flavored, carbonated soft drinks and non-carbonated soft drinks, along with ready-to-drink non-carbonated teas, juices, juice drinks, and mixers. Among its brands are Dr Pepper and Snapple of course, along with A&W Root Beer, Hawaiian Punch, Mott's, and Schweppes. It has some old favorites as well, including Vernors, Squirt, and Royal Crown Cola. DPS is the #3 soda business in North America, after #1 Coke and #2 Pepsi.

	Annual Growth	12/05	12/06	12/07	12/08	12/09
Sales ($ mil.)	14.6%	3,205.0	4,735.0	5,748.0	5,710.0	5,531.0
Net income ($ mil.)	3.3%	487.0	510.0	497.0	(312.0)	555.0
Market value ($ mil.)	74.2%	—	—	—	3,992.5	6,953.0
Employees	42.2%	—	6,605	20,000	20,000	19,000

DRAFTFCB

101 E. Erie St.
Chicago, IL 60611
Phone: 312-425-5000
Fax: —
Web: www.draftfcb.com

CEO: Laurence J. Boschetto
CFO: Neil Miller
HR: Beverly Popielarz
FYE: December 31
Type: Subsidiary

DraftFCB hopes its advertising shop gets off on the right Foote. The result of a merger between direct marketer Draft, Inc. and advertising agency Foote, Cone & Belding, DraftFCB specializes in integrated marketing and advertising with an emphasis on branding, interactive, emerging media, multimedia, and database technology. Headquartered in Chicago and New York, the agency's network includes offices in about 100 countries serving clients such as Hewlett-Packard, Verizon, Computer Associates, Kellogg, and the United States Postal Service. The agency is a subsidiary of Interpublic, the world's third-largest advertising conglomerate.

DRAKA ELEVATOR PRODUCTS, INC.

2151 N. Church St.
Rocky Mount, NC 27802
Phone: 252-984-5100
Fax: 252-972-6001
Web: www.drakaep.com

CEO: John S. Moore
CFO: James Taverner
HR: Lindsay Tripp
FYE: December 31
Type: Subsidiary

With Draka Elevator Products around, there's no need for draconian measures to find parts for your elevator system. Draka manufactures elevator cables and wire rope and sells a variety of hoistway hardware, kits, and elevator electromechanical parts. It also makes components for escalator systems and offers customized products such as power-conducting cables, coaxial cable units, and other instrumentation wires and cables. Draka Elevator Products is part of Draka Cableteq, which in turn is a subsidiary of big Netherlands-based cabling company Draka Holding.

DRAKE BEAM MORIN, INC.

750 3rd Ave., 28th Fl.	CEO: Robert L. Gasparini
New York, NY 10017	CFO: —
Phone: 212-692-7700	HR: —
Fax: 212-297-0426	FYE: December 31
Web: www.dbm.com	Type: Private

Drake Beam Morin (DBM) is always in transition. The company provides strategic human resources services, focusing on employee selection, development, retention, and transition. DBM is best known for outplacement and transition services, which help corporate clients plan for workforce reductions and assist former employees in finding new positions. It aids clients in improving hiring practices through workshops, research studies, and online hiring site JobScout. DBM also offers executive coaching and training to optimize workforce effectiveness and offers research, analysis, and consulting to increase employee retention. Operating through 200 worldwide locations, the company was founded in 1967.

DREAMWORKS STUDIOS

100 Universal City Plaza Dr., Bldg. 5121	CEO: Stacey Snider
Universal City, CA 91608	CFO: Larry Wasserman
Phone: 818-733-9300	HR: —
Fax: —	FYE: December 31
Web: www.dreamworksstudios.com	Type: Private

Stephen Spielberg has long since realized his dream. The filmmaker's DreamWorks Studios is a producer of movies and TV shows (*I Love You, Man*; *The United States of Tara*.). The company was founded in 1994 by Spielberg, animation guru Jeffrey Katzenberg, and recording industry maven David Geffen as a diversified media firm. It struggled with any business beyond filmed entertainment, and later shed its arcade business and a music label. Moneymaker DreamWorks Animation was spun off to shareholders as a separate company in 2004. DreamWorks Studios was formerly owned by Paramount Pictures; it parted ways with that studio in 2008 and now operates through a financing partnership with Reliance Entertainment.

DREAMS, INC.

NYSE Amex: DRJ

2 S. University Dr., Ste. 325	CEO: Ross Tannenbaum
Plantation, FL 33324	CFO: Dorothy Sillano
Phone: 954-377-0002	HR: Kymberly Jackson
Fax: 954-475-8785	FYE: December 31
Web: www.dreamscorp.com	Type: Public

Talk about a dream team: Troy Aikman, Emmitt Smith, Randy Moss, and Jerry Rice. These sports heroes mean money to Dreams. The company owns and operates about 20 Field of Dreams and FansEdge stores across the US — in addition to some 10 franchised stores — that sell signed balls, jerseys, photos, plaques, and other collectibles, which it licenses from the NFL, MLB, NHL, NBA, NCAA, and NASCAR. It also reaches shoppers via the *FansEdge* catalog and online (including FansEdge.com and ProSportsMemorabilia.com). Dreams' Mounted Memories division makes and distributes sports memorabilia, while its Greene Organization handles special appearances, endorsements, and other off-field activities for athletes.

	Annual Growth	3/06	3/07	*12/07	12/08	12/09
Sales ($ mil.)	19.0%	42.7	56.0	59.7	82.0	85.5
Net income ($ mil.)	(46.8%)	2.5	1.0	0.8	(1.6)	0.2
Market value ($ mil.)	12.3%	38.5	127.9	67.9	14.7	61.1
Employees	15.1%	180	255	328	466	316

*Fiscal year change

THE DREES COMPANY

211 Grandview Dr., Ste. 300	CEO: David Drees
Fort Mitchell, KY 41017	CFO: Mark Williams
Phone: 859-578-4200	HR: Effie McKeehan
Fax: 859-341-5854	FYE: March 31
Web: www.dreeshomes.com	Type: Private

The Drees Company is a leading homebuilder in Cincinnati and one of the top private builders in the US. First-time home buyers and move-up customers may choose from homes that range from about $100,000 to more than $1 million. Drees also builds condominiums, town homes, and patio homes. It sells luxury homes through its Zaring Premier Homes division and more modest houses under the Marquis Homes name. The company purchases land to develop as homesites in Florida, Indiana, Kentucky, North Carolina, Ohio, Tennessee, Texas, and the Washington, DC, area. Drees also offers financing through its First Equity Mortgage subsidiary, which has closed more than $1 billion in loans over the years.

	Annual Growth	3/04	3/05	3/06	3/07	3/08
Sales ($ mil.)	(3.9%)	978.0	1,183.0	1,120.0	1,104.9	833.0
Employees	(11.1%)	1,200	1,339	1,226	900	750

DREAMWORKS ANIMATION SKG INC.

NASDAQ (GM): DWA

1000 Flower St.	CEO: Jeffrey Katzenberg
Glendale, CA 91201	CFO: Lewis W. (Lew) Coleman
Phone: 818-695-5000	HR: Dan Satterthwaite
Fax: 818-695-9944	FYE: December 31
Web: www.dreamworksanimation.com	Type: Public

While live action isn't a nightmare for DreamWorks Animation SKG, this company definitely prefers CGI. DreamWorks Animation has produced about 20 computer-animated family-friendly features — including box office hits such as the 3-D adventure film *How to Train Your Dragon* and the wildly successful movies in the *Shrek* series (the record-breaking *Shrek 2* remains the highest-grossing animated film, as well as the fifth-highest grossing film of all time in the domestic box office). Other titles include *Monsters vs. Aliens* and *Madagascar: Escape 2 Africa*. The studio's movies are distributed and marketed by Paramount Pictures. In 2004 former parent DreamWorks spun off DreamWorks Animation as a separate company.

	Annual Growth	12/05	12/06	12/07	12/08	12/09
Sales ($ mil.)	11.9%	462.3	394.8	767.2	650.1	725.2
Net income ($ mil.)	9.6%	104.6	15.1	218.4	142.5	151.0
Market value ($ mil.)	12.9%	2,144.7	2,575.2	2,230.2	2,205.8	3,488.6
Employees	11.0%	1,280	1,300	1,450	1,700	1,940

THE DRESS BARN, INC.

NASDAQ (GS): DBRN

30 Dunnigan Dr.	CEO: David R. Jaffe
Suffern, NY 10901	CFO: Armand Correia
Phone: 845-369-4500	HR: David Montieth
Fax: 845-369-4829	FYE: July 31
Web: www.dressbarn.com	Type: Public

Although its name is evocative of *Green Acres,* The Dress Barn caters to women who have more to do and less to spend than Mrs. Douglas. The retailer operates more than 2,400 stores, including about 120 Dress Barn locations, 35 Dress Barn Woman shops, and 685 combined Dress Barn/Dress Barn Woman stores. It also has about 900 Justice shops and 720 Maurices locations. The retailer's Dress Barn, Dress Barn Woman (larger sizes), and combination stores sell in-season, moderate- to better-quality women's apparel and accessories at discount prices and cater to professional women in their mid-30s to mid-50s. The Dress Barn opened its doors in 1962. In November 2009 it acquired Tween Brands and its Justice banner.

	Annual Growth	7/05	7/06	7/07	7/08	7/09
Sales ($ mil.)	10.6%	1,000.3	1,300.3	1,426.6	1,444.2	1,494.2
Net income ($ mil.)	7.3%	52.6	79.0	101.2	74.1	69.7
Market value ($ mil.)	6.3%	975.4	1,726.7	1,454.7	1,290.7	1,247.5
Employees	4.1%	12,000	12,800	13,200	13,700	14,100

DRESSER, INC.

15455 Dallas Pkwy., Ste. 1100
Addison, TX 75001
Phone: 972-361-9800
Fax: 972-361-9903
Web: www.dresser.com

CEO: John P. Ryan
CFO: Marty R. Kittrell
HR: Robbie Marshall
FYE: December 31
Type: Private

Is your energy business all dressed up with no place to flow? Not if Dresser can help it. The company, formerly Dresser Industries (and once a part of Halliburton), makes flow control products (valves, actuators, meters, fittings, and the like for oil and gas exploration), measurement systems (gas pumps and point of sale terminals made by business unit Dresser Wayne), power and compression systems (Waukesha engines, fuel testing systems), and infrastructure products (Roots blowers and compressors, piping systems, and pumps). Dresser serves companies in the oil and gas, power generation, water and wastewater, and other industries. The company has a presence in more than 100 countries.

	Annual Growth	12/04	12/05	12/06	12/07	12/08
Sales ($ mil.)	3.0%	1,991.7	1,700.0	1,830.0	2,000.0	2,240.0
Employees	(7.3%)	8,800	6,500	6,100	6,400	6,500

DRESSER-RAND GROUP INC.

NYSE: DRC

10205 Westheimer Rd., West 8 Tower, Ste. 1000
Houston, TX 77042
Phone: 713-354-6100
Fax: 713-354-6110
Web: www.dresser-rand.com

CEO: Vincent R. (Vince) Volpe Jr.
CFO: Mark E. Baldwin
HR: Elizabeth C. (Beth) Powers
FYE: December 31
Type: Public

Dresser-Rand might get you pretty steamed, but that's part of its job. The company is a leading maker of industrial rotating equipment that includes steam and gas turbines, centrifugal and reciprocating compressors, hot gas expanders, and control systems. It makes new and replacement units and offers aftermarket repair and upgrades for its own and third-party products. Dresser-Rand serves customers in the oil and gas, power, chemical, and petrochemical markets through 12 manufacturing and nearly 40 service facilities in about 30 countries. About 90% of sales comes from energy infrastructure and oilfield projects. BP, Chevron, Royal Dutch Shell, Exxon Mobil, and Dow Chemical are among its blue-chip customers.

	Annual Growth	12/05	12/06	12/07	12/08	12/09
Sales ($ mil.)	17.3%	1,208.2	1,501.5	1,665.0	2,194.7	2,289.6
Net income ($ mil.)	54.4%	37.1	78.8	106.7	197.7	210.8
Market value ($ mil.)	6.9%	1,995.6	2,019.5	3,222.8	1,423.7	2,608.8
Employees	3.7%	5,277	5,612	6,000	6,400	6,100

🔲 DREW INDUSTRIES INCORPORATED

NYSE: DW

200 Mamaroneck Ave.
White Plains, NY 10601
Phone: 914-428-9098
Fax: 914-428-4581
Web: www.drewindustries.com

CEO: Fredric M. (Fred) Zinn
CFO: Joseph S. Giordano III
HR: —
FYE: December 31
Type: Public

Drew Industries knows that when one door closes, another one opens — and that goes for windows too. The company supplies aluminum and vinyl windows and doors for recreational vehicles (72% of sales) and manufactured homes (28%) through 29 facilities in 12 states. The company's Kinro subsidiary produces windows, doors, and screens. Its Lippert Components subsidiary makes axles, ramps, and chassis parts, as well as specialty trailers for hauling boats and snowmobiles. Customers include manufactured homebuilders Clayton Homes and Champion Enterprises and RV makers Fleetwood Enterprises and Thor Industries.

	Annual Growth	12/05	12/06	12/07	12/08	12/09
Sales ($ mil.)	(12.2%)	669.1	729.2	668.6	510.5	397.8
Net income ($ mil.)	—	33.6	31.0	39.8	11.7	(24.1)
Market value ($ mil.)	(7.5%)	619.8	571.8	602.4	263.8	454.0
Employees	(9.4%)	4,541	3,690	3,499	2,223	3,054

🔲 DREYER'S GRAND ICE CREAM HOLDINGS, INC.

5929 College Ave.
Oakland, CA 94618
Phone: 510-652-8187
Fax: 510-450-4621
Web: www.dreyersinc.com

CEO: Mike Mitchell
CFO: Steve Barbour
HR: Tim Gates
FYE: December 31
Type: Subsidiary

This company takes a licking and keeps on selling — Dreyer's Grand Ice Cream is the leading US ice cream producer. The company manufactures premium ice creams and other frozen dairy desserts under its namesake Dreyer's and its Edy's brands for distribution to food retailers and foodservice purveyors throughout the US and some 25 overseas markets. In addition, Dreyer's distributes Nestlé's Häagen-Dazs and ice cream novelties; it also operates the Häagen-Dazs Shoppe Company, which franchises ice cream parlors worldwide. Dreyer's is a subsidiary of Swiss food giant Nestlé.

THE DREYFUS CORPORATION

200 Park Ave.
New York, NY 10166
Phone: 212-922-6000
Fax: 212-922-6585
Web: www.dreyfus.com

CEO: Jon Baum
CFO: Gary Pierce
HR: —
FYE: December 31
Type: Subsidiary

No lion! Dreyfus takes pride in its pecuniary prowess. The company, which sports a leonine logo, provides mutual fund management, investment advice, and related services to retail and institutional investors. Known for its fixed-income and money market funds, the subsidiary of The Bank of New York Mellon administers some 200 mutual fund portfolios, investing in equities, money market instruments, and corporate, municipal, and government debt. It has approximately $450 billion of assets under management. Founded in 1951, Dreyfus claims to be the first mutual fund company to target retail investors via advertising (in 1957).

	Annual Growth	12/04	12/05	12/06	12/07	12/08
Est. sales ($ mil.)	—	—	—	—	—	107.7
Employees	—	—	—	—	—	1,100

DRI CORPORATION

NASDAQ (CM): TBUS

13760 Noel Rd., Ste. 830
Dallas, TX 75240
Phone: 214-378-8992
Fax: 214-378-8437
Web: www.digrec.com

CEO: David L. Turney
CFO: Stephen P. Slay
HR: —
FYE: December 31
Type: Public

DRI drives transportation technology. The company designs automatic voice announcement systems and electronic destination signs for mass transit operators, as well as vehicle location systems. Its Talking Bus announcement systems broadcast stops and transfer information for buses, subways, trains and other private and commercial vehicles. The company also makes electronic destination signs that display transit information for buses. DRI counts vehicle makers, transit operators, and state and local governments among its customers. The company operates through subsidiaries in the US (Digital Recorders, TwinVision) and abroad (Mobitec).

	Annual Growth	12/05	12/06	12/07	12/08	12/09
Sales ($ mil.)	16.1%	45.3	51.3	57.9	70.6	82.3
Net income ($ mil.)	—	(5.9)	(3.9)	0.7	1.5	2.0
Market value ($ mil.)	1.7%	18.1	14.0	28.7	12.9	19.3
Employees	7.2%	185	198	186	212	244

🔲 An in-depth profile of this company is available to Hoover's Online members at hoovers.com.

515

DRIL-QUIP, INC.

NYSE: DRQ

13550 Hempstead Hwy.
Houston, TX 77040
Phone: 713-939-7711
Fax: 713-939-8063
Web: www.dril-quip.com

CEO: Larry E. Reimert
CFO: Jerry M. Brooks
HR: —
FYE: December 31
Type: Public

Dril-Quip equips the folks with the drills — the oil and gas industry. Its products include drilling and production riser systems, subsea and surface wellheads and production trees, mudline hanger systems, and specialty connectors and pipe. Dril-Quip's offshore rig equipment includes drilling and completion riser systems, wellhead connectors, and diverters. The company, which specializes in deep-water or severe-condition equipment, also provides installation, reconditioning, and tool-rental services. Dril-Quip has major manufacturing plants in Brazil, Singapore, the UK, and the US.

	Annual Growth	12/05	12/06	12/07	12/08	12/09
Sales ($ mil.)	12.2%	340.8	442.7	495.6	542.8	540.2
Net income ($ mil.)	34.0%	32.6	86.9	107.9	105.6	105.1
Market value ($ mil.)	24.4%	939.6	1,559.1	2,216.0	816.6	2,248.7
Employees	8.9%	1,514	1,709	1,890	2,051	2,130

DRINKS AMERICAS HOLDINGS, LTD.

OTC: DKAM

372 Danbury Rd., Ste. 163
Wilton, CT 06897
Phone: 203-762-7000
Fax: 203-762-8992
Web: www.drinksamericas.com

CEO: J. Patrick Kenny
CFO: —
HR: —
FYE: April 30
Type: Public

Image sells for Drinks Americas Holdings. The company markets and distributes alcoholic and non-alcoholic beverages using the faces and names of such entertainers and celebrities as Donald Trump (vodka), Willie Nelson (bourbon whiskey), and Paul Newman (sparkling fruit juice). It also makes ready-to-drink tea, beer, rum, tequila, and the first ultra-premium sake made in the US. Its subsidiary, Drinks Global Imports, imports premium wines from Europe and Australia. The company sells its beverages to a network of North American distributors for resale to supermarkets and liquor, drug, and convenience stores. Southern Wine & Spirits is its largest alcohol distributor. CEO Patrick Kenny owns 18% of the company.

	Annual Growth	4/05	4/06	4/07	4/08	4/09
Sales ($ mil.)	4.5%	2.1	1.6	6.1	4.5	2.5
Net income ($ mil.)	—	(4.3)	(4.4)	(9.4)	(6.3)	(5.0)
Market value ($ mil.)	(37.8%)	223.2	189.7	305.8	55.8	33.5
Employees	(14.7%)	17	15	17	17	9

DRIVETIME AUTOMOTIVE, INC.

4020 E. Indian School Rd.
Phoenix, AZ 85018
Phone: 602-852-6600
Fax: 602-852-6686
Web: www.drivetime.com

CEO: Raymond C. (Ray) Fidel
CFO: Mark G. Sauder
HR: —
FYE: December 31
Type: Private

In this story the ugly duckling changes into DriveTime Automotive. Formerly known as Ugly Duckling, the company is a used-car dealership chain that primarily targets low-income customers and those with credit problems. To cater to subprime clients, it's a "buy here-pay here" dealer, meaning it finances and services car loans rather than using outside lenders. DriveTime operates about 80 dealerships located in almost 20 metropolitan areas in 10 mostly southern and western states. It reconditions cars at about a dozen facilities. The cars undergo a 53-point inspection and are run through Experian AutoCheck, an auto history database. DriveTime, owned by chairman Ernest Garcia II, filed to go public in early 2010.

DRS TECHNOLOGIES, INC.

5 Sylvan Way
Parsippany, NJ 07054
Phone: 973-898-1500
Fax: 973-898-4730
Web: www.drs.com

CEO: Mark S. Newman
CFO: Richard A. Schneider
HR: Andrea J. Mandel
FYE: December 31
Type: Subsidiary

Methods used to track military activity are complex, but DRS Technologies makes the tasks manageable with electronic systems that process, display, and store complex military and aerospace data. The company's offerings include surveillance and radar systems, ruggedized computers, weapons targeting systems, flight recorders, communications systems, thermal imaging systems, air combat training systems, and video recorders for defense and aerospace applications. While the vast majority of sales are derived from US government agencies (primarily the DoD), as well as the US military, DRS also serves foreign allies. In 2008 Italy-based aviation firm Finmeccanica bought DRS for $5.2 billion.

DRUGSTORE.COM, INC.

NASDAQ (GM): DSCM

411 108th Ave. NE, Ste. 1400
Bellevue, WA 98004
Phone: 425-372-3200
Fax: 425-372-3800
Web: www.drugstore.com

CEO: Dawn G. Lepore
CFO: Tracy Wright
HR: Robert Hargadon
FYE: December 31
Type: Public

Drugstore.com hopes it has the right Rx for e-commerce success. The e-tailer sells name-brand and private-label health and beauty items as well as prescription and over-the-counter (OTC) drugs through its website and by telephone. A partnership with GNC Corporation allows drugstore.com to offer the retailer's vitamins and wellness products online. It also sells high-end cosmetics and skin care items through its beauty.com unit. The company markets contact lenses through its Vision Direct subsidiary and customized nutritional supplement programs through its Custom Nutrition Services subsidiary. Founded in 1998, the company has yet to turn a profit on a consistent basis.

	Annual Growth	12/05	12/06	12/07	12/08	12/09
Sales ($ mil.)	0.8%	399.4	415.8	445.7	366.6	412.8
Net income ($ mil.)	—	(20.9)	(13.0)	(11.5)	(8.3)	(1.4)
Market value ($ mil.)	2.0%	301.5	387.2	349.1	131.2	326.9
Employees	2.3%	780	732	850	814	855

DRUMMOND COMPANY, INC.

1000 Urban Center Dr., Ste. 300
Birmingham, AL 35242
Phone: 205-945-6300
Fax: 205-945-6440
Web: www.drummondco.com

CEO: Garry N. Drummond Sr.
CFO: Jack Stilwell
HR: —
FYE: December 31
Type: Private

Drummond does business from the ground down. The company operates the Shoal Creek underground coal mine in Alabama and the Pribbenow surface coal mine in Colombia. Drummond's ABC Coke unit produces foundry coke, which is used mainly in the automotive, construction, and sugar industries, at a plant in Alabama. It controls more than 2 billion tons of reserves and sells around 30 million annually. In addition, Drummond develops housing communities and office parks in Alabama, California, and Florida. H. E. Drummond began his company in 1935 on land homesteaded by his mother; eventually his five sons entered the business. The Drummond family still owns and manages the company.

	Annual Growth	12/04	12/05	12/06	12/07	12/08
Sales ($ mil.)	16.9%	—	1,798.0	1,770.0	1,890.0	2,870.0
Employees	5.6%	—	5,100	5,100	5,600	6,000

DRYCLEAN USA, INC.

NYSE Amex: DCU

290 NE 68th St.
Miami, FL 33138
Phone: 305-754-4551
Fax: 305-754-8010
Web: www.drycleanusa.com

CEO: Michael S. Steiner
CFO: Venerando J. Indelicato
HR: —
FYE: June 30
Type: Public

DRYCLEAN USA is anything but hard pressed. The firm franchises and licenses more than 400 retail dry cleaners in three US states, the Caribbean, and Latin America. However, most of its sales are generated by subsidiary Steiner-Atlantic, which sells coin-operated laundry machines, steam boilers, and other laundry equipment; most are sold under the Aero-Tech, Green-Jet, and Multi-Jet names to some 750 customers that include DRYCLEAN USA, independent dry cleaners, hotels, cruise lines, and hospitals. Other divisions offer business brokerage and turn-key development of new dry cleaning businesses. Founded in 1963 under the name Metro-Tel Corp., the company changed its name to DRYCLEAN USA in 1999.

	Annual Growth	6/05	6/06	6/07	6/08	6/09
Sales ($ mil.)	6.0%	18.4	20.4	22.7	22.7	23.2
Net income ($ mil.)	(8.1%)	0.7	0.8	0.9	0.6	0.5
Market value ($ mil.)	(22.5%)	17.9	12.9	14.1	6.3	6.5
Employees	(4.6%)	35	35	34	33	29

DS WATERS OF AMERICA, INC.

5660 New Northside Dr., Ste. 500
Atlanta, GA 30328
Phone: 770-933-1400
Fax: 770-956-9495
Web: www.water.com

CEO: Stewart E. Allen
CFO: Dillon K. Schickli
HR: —
FYE: December 31
Type: Private

Whether your glass is half empty or half full, DS Waters of America fills it up. The largest water-cooler delivery company in the US, the company delivers to homes and offices, owning some 25 manufacturing sites across some 40 US states. Regional brands offered by the company include Alhambra, Belmont Springs, Crystal Springs, Hinckley Springs, Kentwood Springs, Sierra Springs, and Sparkletts. The company also operates a national coffee and tea delivery service under the Roast2Coast banner and sells water filtration systems. Founded in 2003, DS Waters has grown through the acquisition of regional brands and is owned by private investment fund Kelso & Co.

DSC LOGISTICS

1750 S. Wolf Rd.
Des Plaines, IL 60018
Phone: 800-372-1960
Fax: 847-390-7276
Web: www.dsclogistics.com

CEO: Ann M. Drake
CFO: Dave Copeland
HR: Janice Miller
FYE: December 31
Type: Private

DSC Logistics knows the ABCs of supply chain management. The third-party logistics company manages services such as warehousing, transportation, and packaging for its customers; it also offers logistics consulting services. DSC maintains a network of about 20 logistics centers spread throughout the US; overall, the company's facilities offer about 15 million sq. ft. of storage space. Customers have included Georgia-Pacific, J.R. Simplot, and Kimberly-Clark. DSC founder Jim McIlrath, the father of CEO Ann Drake, started the company as Dry Storage Corporation in 1960 after a former boss refused to offer dry storage along with refrigerated storage services.

	Annual Growth	12/04	12/05	12/06	12/07	12/08
Est. sales ($ mil.)	—	—	—	—	—	164.9
Employees	—	—	—	—	—	1,787

DSM DYNEEMA LLC

1101 Hwy. 27 South
Stanley, NC 28164
Phone: 704-862-5000
Fax: —
Web: www.dyneema.com

CEO: Feike Sijbesma
CFO: Rolf-Dieter Schwalb
HR: —
FYE: December 31
Type: Subsidiary

DSM Dyneema finds dynamic uses for a deeply durable fiber. The company, a unit of the Dutch specialty chemicals maker DSM N.V., makes specialized polyethylene fiber (marketed as Dyneema) for use in bullet-resistant armor, bomb disposal suits, heavy-duty marine cables, fishing nets, ropes, and safety gloves. The company estimates that Dyneema, which it calls "the world's strongest fiber," is up to 15 times stronger than steel. With its Dyneema Purity line, DSM Dyneema also uses its lightweight material in medical and dental applications such as surgical cables and orthopedic sutures.

	Annual Growth	12/04	12/05	12/06	12/07	12/08
Est. sales ($ mil.)	—	—	—	—	—	11.9
Employees	—	—	—	—	—	156

DSM RESINS U.S. INC.

31 Columbia Nitrogen Rd.
Augusta, GA 30903
Phone: 706-849-6700
Fax: 706-849-6777
Web: www.dsm.com/en_US/html/about/resins.htm

CEO: John Leonard
CFO: Kathy L. Griffis
HR: Mike Griggs
FYE: December 31
Type: Subsidiary

Dutch specialty chemicals company DSM entered its own Age of Resin in 1983 when it created DSM Resins. The company supplies polyester resins for powder, can, and coil coatings, as well as resins for the decorative, protective and maintenance, industrial coatings, and stereolithography markets. DSM Resins structures its activities into four main business units: DSM Powder Coating Resins, DSM NeoResins+ (specialty resins), DSM Desotech (high-performance ultraviolet light formulates), and DSM Composite Resins. Since 2008 the company has opened a number of manufacturing facilities around the world, helping advance the unit's green agenda with products that lower emissions and are used in composites materials.

DSP GROUP, INC.

NASDAQ (GS): DSPG

2580 N. 1st St., Ste. 460
San Jose, CA 95131
Phone: 408-986-4300
Fax: 408-986-4323
Web: www.dspg.com

CEO: Ofer Elyakim
CFO: Dror Levy
HR: Tali Chen
FYE: December 31
Type: Public

DSP Group loves the sound of its own voice . . . chips. The company's name derives from the digital signal processors (DSPs) and related speech compression software it develops; these products convert speech and other audio data into digital values for telephone answering devices, PCs, wireless products, and consumer electronics. DSP's top customers include the Tomen Electronics distribution unit of Japan's Toyota Tsusho (one-quarter of sales), Philips, Sony, and VTech (21% of sales). Panasonic Mobile Communications accounts for most of the sales made through Tomen Electronics, and 13% of DSP Group's revenues. The company gets most of its sales in the Asia/Pacific region.

	Annual Growth	12/05	12/06	12/07	12/08	12/09
Sales ($ mil.)	3.2%	187.2	216.9	248.8	305.8	212.2
Net income ($ mil.)	—	29.5	22.4	(4.8)	(212.4)	(8.4)
Market value ($ mil.)	(31.2%)	580.1	502.3	282.4	185.6	130.3
Employees	8.9%	291	319	502	448	409

DST SYSTEMS, INC.

NYSE: DST

333 W. 11th St.
Kansas City, MO 64105
Phone: 816-435-1000
Fax: 816-435-8618
Web: www.dstsystems.com

CEO: Thomas A. (Tom) McDonnell
CFO: Kenneth V. Hager
HR: Stephen C. Hooley
FYE: December 31
Type: Public

The feeling is mutual at DST Systems. A leading provider of information processing software and services for the mutual fund industry, DST's Financial Services segment processes millions of mutual fund accounts and offers software, systems, and processing services for banks, investment firms, and insurance companies. The company's Output Solutions unit manages statement and bill mailings and customer communications. Its applications and services are used to address a wide range of tasks including business process management, investment management, customer care, and health care claims processing and administration. DST Systems gets most of its sales in the US.

	Annual Growth	12/05	12/06	12/07	12/08	12/09
Sales ($ mil.)	(3.1%)	2,515.1	2,235.8	2,302.5	2,285.4	2,217.9
Net income ($ mil.)	(13.1%)	424.6	272.9	874.7	242.9	241.6
Market value ($ mil.)	(7.7%)	2,798.7	2,925.7	3,856.3	1,774.2	2,034.4
Employees	1.6%	10,500	10,500	11,000	10,900	11,200

DSW INC.

NYSE: DSW

810 DSW Dr.
Columbus, OH 43219
Phone: 614-237-7100
Fax: —
Web: www.dsw.com

CEO: Michael R. (Mike) MacDonald
CFO: Douglas J. (Doug) Probst
HR: —
FYE: January 31
Type: Public

While you don't have to watch out for trees in this jungle, you may want to watch your back. DSW sells discounted brand-name footwear for style-conscious men and women through some 300 stores in about three dozen states, as well as online. In addition to more than 2,000 styles of dress, casual, and athletic shoes, stores offer a complementary array of handbags, hosiery, and accessories. It also operates about 375 leased departments inside stores operated by other retailers. Prior to its 2005 IPO, DSW was a wholly owned subsidiary of holding company Retail Ventures, which still owns more than 60% of its stock.

	Annual Growth	1/06	1/07	1/08	1/09	1/10
Sales ($ mil.)	8.8%	1,144.1	1,279.1	1,405.6	1,462.9	1,602.6
Net income ($ mil.)	10.1%	37.2	65.5	53.8	26.9	54.7
Market value ($ mil.)	(2.6%)	1,173.3	1,759.8	810.3	438.1	1,057.9
Employees	19.2%	4,950	5,800	8,500	10,000	10,000

DTE ENERGY COMPANY

NYSE: DTE

1 Energy Plaza
Detroit, MI 48226
Phone: 313-235-4000
Fax: 313-235-8055
Web: www.dteenergy.com

CEO: Anthony F. Earley Jr.
CFO: David E. Meador
HR: Larry E. Steward
FYE: December 31
Type: Public

Detroit's economy may be lackluster, but DTE Energy still provides a reliable spark. The holding company's main subsidiary, Detroit Edison, distributes electricity to some 2.1 million customers in southeastern Michigan. The utility's power plants (mainly fossil-fueled) have a generating capacity of more than 11,060 MW. The company's Michigan Consolidated Gas (MichCon) unit distributes natural gas to 1.2 million customers. DTE Energy's nonregulated operations (in 25 US states) include energy marketing and trading; coal transportation and procurement; energy management services for commercial and industrial customers; independent and on-site power generation; and gas exploration, production, and processing.

	Annual Growth	12/05	12/06	12/07	12/08	12/09
Sales ($ mil.)	(2.9%)	9,022.0	9,022.0	8,506.0	9,329.0	8,014.0
Net income ($ mil.)	(0.2%)	540.0	432.0	971.0	546.0	535.0
Market value ($ mil.)	0.2%	7,273.6	8,152.7	7,403.3	6,007.2	7,341.0
Employees	(2.7%)	11,410	10,527	10,262	10,471	10,244

DTS, INC.

NASDAQ (GS): DTSI

5220 Las Virgenes Rd.
Calabasas, CA 91302
Phone: 818-436-1000
Fax: 818-436-1999
Web: www.dtsonline.com

CEO: Jon E. Kirchner
CFO: Melvin L. (Mel) Flanigan
HR: Sharon K. Faltemier
FYE: December 31
Type: Public

DTS (formerly Digital Theater Systems) surrounds movie lovers with sound. The company's multi-channel audio systems are used throughout the world in movie theaters, as well as consumer electronics such as audio/video receivers, DVD and Blu-ray HD players, personal computers, car audio products, video game consoles, and home theater systems. In 2008 the company sold its image processing, enhancement, and restoration services business, DTS Digital Cinema, in order to focus on licensing its technology in consumer audio products. DTS has licensing agreements with all the world's major consumer electronics manufacturers (Sony, Panasonic, and Philips).

	Annual Growth	12/05	12/06	12/07	12/08	12/09
Sales ($ mil.)	0.8%	75.3	78.3	53.1	60.2	77.7
Net income ($ mil.)	7.6%	7.9	3.0	(20.4)	11.4	10.6
Market value ($ mil.)	23.3%	257.4	420.6	444.6	319.1	594.9
Employees	(10.3%)	314	325	159	193	203

DUANE READE INC.

440 9th Ave.
New York, NY 10001
Phone: 212-273-5700
Fax: 212-244-6527
Web: www.duanereade.com

CEO: John A. Lederer
CFO: John K. Henry
HR: Vincent A. Scarfone
FYE: December 31
Type: Subsidiary

Duane Reade — the Big Apple of drugstores — has been swallowed by a big fish: Walgreen. Named after the two streets where its first store was located, Duane Reade is the region's market leader with 150 stores (more than twice that of its nearest competitor) in densely-populated Manhattan. New York City's other boroughs and the surrounding New York and New Jersey suburbs account for the rest. The stores sell prescription drugs, but more than 50% of the chain's sales come from items such as over-the-counter medications, food and beverages, and health and beauty aids. Duane Reade's stores vary greatly in size (500 to 12,700 sq. ft.). Oak Hill Capital Partners sold Duane Reade to Walgreen in April 2010.

	Annual Growth	12/04	12/05	12/06	12/07	12/08
Sales ($ mil.)	2.6%	1,598.4	1,589.5	1,584.8	1,686.8	1,774.0
Net income ($ mil.)	—	(52.1)	(100.4)	(79.4)	(87.8)	(72.8)
Employees	1.9%	6,300	6,100	6,100	6,700	6,800

THE DUCHOSSOIS GROUP, INC.

845 N. Larch Ave.
Elmhurst, IL 60126
Phone: 630-279-3600
Fax: 630-530-6091
Web: www.duch.com

CEO: Craig J. Duchossois
CFO: Michael E. Flannery
HR: Melanie Ditore
FYE: December 31
Type: Private

The only thing this family of companies has in common is the Duchossois family, the third-generation owners of The Duchossois Group, Inc. The holding company, pronounced "deshy-swa," focuses its investment interests in the consumer products, technology and services sectors. The Chamberlain Group, a subsidiary, is the world's top maker of residential and commercial door openers and a leading maker of access control products. AMX LLC performs systems integration, while other companies offer AV equipment, Internet-based access control, and lighting products. The Duchossois Group also owns an early-stage IT venture capital fund and holds a minority stake in horse racetrack Churchill Downs.

DUCKWALL-ALCO STORES, INC.

NASDAQ (GM): DUCK

401 Cottage Ave.
Abilene, KS 67410
Phone: 785-263-3350
Fax: 785-263-7531
Web: www.duckwall.com

CEO: Richard E. Wilson
CFO: Donny Johnson
HR: Daniel J. Curoe
FYE: January 31
Type: Public

Some retailers prize locations where they can battle competitors toe-to-toe; Duckwall-ALCO prizes locations the big national discount chains, such as Wal-Mart and Target, wouldn't even consider. The retailer runs about 210 ALCO and ALCO Market Place discount stores and some 50 Duckwall variety stores in small towns in about two dozen states in the central US. ALCO stores, situated in towns with populations of 5,000 or fewer, account for about 95% of the company's sales. Product lines include apparel, crafts, electronics, fabrics, furniture, hardware, and toys. The smaller Duckwall stores carry about a third of ALCO's merchandise and are located in about 10 states in towns with populations below 2,500.

	Annual Growth	1/06	1/07	1/08	1/09	1/10
Sales ($ mil.)	3.0%	435.0	475.3	499.0	490.0	488.7
Net income ($ mil.)	12.1%	1.9	5.7	(0.2)	(5.0)	3.0
Market value ($ mil.)	(17.3%)	99.5	135.5	86.8	33.0	46.7
Employees	(3.6%)	4,800	4,800	4,675	4,200	4,150

DUCOMMUN INCORPORATED

NYSE: DCO

23301 Wilmington Ave.
Carson, CA 90745
Phone: 310-513-7280
Fax: 310-513-7279
Web: www.ducommun.com

CEO: Anthony J. (Tony) Reardon
CFO: Joseph P. (Joe) Bellino
HR: Rosalie F. Rogers
FYE: December 31
Type: Public

Plans are always up in the air at Ducommun (rhymes with "uncommon"). The company makes aerostructures and electromechanical components for commercial and military aircraft, as well as missile and space programs. Ducommun AeroStructures manufactures structures and assemblies such as aircraft wing spoilers and helicopter blades using shaped aluminum, composites, and titanium. Ducommun Technologies makes electromechanical components such as switch assemblies, actuators, gyroscopes, keyboard panels, and avionics racks. Its Miltec subsidiary designs missile and aerospace systems. Products destined for military applications account for more than half of sales. Aircraft giant Boeing represents about 30% of sales.

	Annual Growth	12/05	12/06	12/07	12/08	12/09
Sales ($ mil.)	14.6%	249.7	319.0	367.3	403.8	430.7
Net income ($ mil.)	(10.6%)	16.0	14.3	19.6	13.1	10.2
Market value ($ mil.)	(3.3%)	223.8	239.7	398.1	175.0	196.0
Employees	8.5%	1,353	1,740	1,865	2,048	1,872

DUFF & PHELPS CORPORATION

NYSE: DUF

55 E. 52nd St., Fl. 31
New York, NY 10055
Phone: 212-871-2000
Fax: —
Web: www.duffandphelps.com

CEO: Noah Gottdiener
CFO: Jacob L. Silverman
HR: —
FYE: December 31
Type: Public

Duff & Phelps provides investment banking and advisory services for clients including corporations, law firm, investment vehicles, and government entities. The group's financial advisory segment provides valuation, tax services, and dispute and legal management consulting services. Its investment banking segment offers global restructuring and M&A advisory and transaction opinions. The company's corporate finance consulting business, its newest segment, specializes in portfolio valuation, financial engineering, strategic value advisory, and due diligence. Duff & Phelps has more than 20 offices in North America, Europe, and Asia; the US accounts for some 90% of all revenues.

	Annual Growth	12/05	12/06	12/07	12/08	12/09
Sales ($ mil.)	48.7%	78.2	259.3	90.7	392.0	382.0
Net income ($ mil.)	—	(12.5)	10.5	(6.4)	5.2	28.7
Market value ($ mil.)	(3.7%)	—	—	818.1	794.8	759.1
Employees	9.1%	—	870	1,070	1,236	1,131

DUKANE CORPORATION

2900 Dukane Dr.
St. Charles, IL 60174
Phone: 630-584-2300
Fax: 630-584-5154
Web: www.dukcorp.com

CEO: Michael W. Ritschdorff
CFO: Brad Johnson
HR: —
FYE: December 31
Type: Private

"Death by PowerPoint" isn't pretty, but its remedy is at hand with Dukane's advanced technologies. The diversified manufacturer and marketer's Audio Visual division plies an array of video projectors, cameras, screens, and flat-panel monitors. The lineup is sold to a wide range of customers looking for some visual aid, from business to government, schools, and churches. Microprocessor-controlled ultrasonic joining equipment, for plastics assembly, is supplied by Dukane's Intelligent Assembly. This division courts big assembly operations, such as automotive, aerospace, and appliance, as well as smaller operations like electronics and toys. Founded in 1922 by J. McWilliams "Mac" Stone Sr., Dukane was acquired in an MBO in 2005.

DUKE CONSTRUCTION LIMITED PARTNERSHIP

600 E. 96th St., Ste. 100
Indianapolis, IN 46240
Phone: 317-808-6000
Fax: 317-808-6791
Web: www.dukeconstructiononline.com

CEO: Steven R. (Steve) Kennedy
CFO: —
HR: —
FYE: December 31
Type: Subsidiary

Duke Construction has its dukes up and is ready to hammer away at its next building project. The construction arm of publicly traded developer Duke Realty, the company provides an array of commercial construction services to office, industrial, and health care markets. It offers design/build, construction management, and general contracting services to customers such as Lenovo and Kimberly-Clark. The economic downturn has affected Duke Construction, and its parent halted all new developments in 2008. It also withdrew from the retail and national build-to-suit business. Duke is looking to focus future developments and construction on the health care industry.

DUKE ENERGY CORPORATION

NYSE: DUK

526 S. Church St.
Charlotte, NC 28202
Phone: 704-594-6200
Fax: 704-382-3814
Web: www.duke-energy.com

CEO: James E. (Jim) Rogers
CFO: Lynn J. Good
HR: Jennifer L. Weber
FYE: December 31
Type: Public

Duke Energy is a John Wayne-sized power business. The company has 4 million electric customers and about 500,000 gas customers in the South and Midwest. Its US Franchised Electric and Gas unit operates primarily through its Duke Energy Carolinas, Duke Energy Ohio, Duke Energy Indiana and Duke Energy Kentucky regional businesses. The company has 35,000 MW of electric generating capacity in the Midwest and the Carolinas, including 7,550 MW of commercial power generation (not counting renewables). Duke Energy International has more than 4,000 MW of generation capacity, primarily in Latin America. While it is focused on energy operations, Duke also has stakes in insurance, real estate, and telecom businesses.

	Annual Growth	12/05	12/06	12/07	12/08	12/09
Sales ($ mil.)	(6.6%)	16,746.0	15,184.0	12,720.0	13,207.0	12,731.0
Net income ($ mil.)	(12.2%)	1,828.0	1,863.0	1,500.0	1,295.0	1,085.0
Market value ($ mil.)	1.9%	20,985.9	25,389.5	26,485.9	19,710.2	22,599.0
Employees	(2.2%)	20,400	25,600	17,800	18,250	18,680

An in-depth profile of this company is available to Hoover's Online members at hoovers.com.

519

DUKE REALTY CORPORATION
NYSE: DRE

600 E. 96th St., Ste. 100
Indianapolis, IN 46240
Phone: 317-808-6000
Fax: 317-808-6770
Web: www.dukerealty.com

CEO: Dennis D. (Denny) Oklak
CFO: Christie B. Kelly
HR: Denise K. Dank
FYE: December 31
Type: Public

Duke Realty's got something of a suburban empire on its hands. The self-managed and self-administered real estate investment trust (REIT) owns and develops suburban office, industrial, and health care properties primarily in the Midwest and East, where it focuses on metropolitan markets. Offices account for about 60% of its property holdings; industrial properties comprise about 40%. In addition to more than 760 rental properties totaling more than 135 million sq. ft., the company owns 5,000 acres of undeveloped land. Duke Realty's service operations include construction and development, asset and property management, and leasing.

	Annual Growth	12/05	12/06	12/07	12/08	12/09
Sales ($ mil.)	14.3%	788.1	908.8	923.2	996.1	1,344.1
Net income ($ mil.)	—	355.7	204.1	279.5	114.0	(271.5)
Market value ($ mil.)	(22.3%)	7,492.2	9,174.6	5,850.2	2,458.5	2,730.0
Employees	(2.4%)	1,100	1,250	1,400	1,200	1,000

DUKE UNIVERSITY

207 Allen Bldg.
Durham, NC 27708
Phone: 919-684-8111
Fax: —
Web: www.duke.edu

CEO: Richard H. (Dick) Brodhead
CFO: B. Hofler Milam
HR: Kyle Cavanaugh
FYE: June 30
Type: School

Duke University is home to more than 13,400 Blue Devils who attend undergraduate- and graduate-level classes in nine schools and colleges. Trinity College of Art and Sciences, the Fuqua School of Business, and the Pratt School of Engineering are among the most well known; its law and medical schools are also highly regarded nationally. The private institution has an endowment of about $6 billion. Notable alumni include Richard Nixon, Melinda French Gates, Elizabeth Dole, and talk show host Charlie Rose. Founded in 1838 as Trinity College, Duke adopted its present name in 1924 after American Tobacco Co. magnate James Duke established the Duke Endowment.

DUKE UNIVERSITY HEALTH SYSTEM

3701 Duke Medical Center
Durham, NC 27706
Phone: 919-684-8111
Fax: —
Web: dukehealth.org

CEO: Victor J. Dzau
CFO: Kenneth C. Morris
HR: —
FYE: June 30
Type: Private

More than a campus infirmary, the Duke University Health System operates the Duke University Hospital and other medical, educational, and research facilities on the Duke University grounds. Duke University Hospital has about 950 acute, pediatric, and psychiatric patient beds and specializes in trauma care, diagnostics, and cardiac and endoscopic surgeries. The system also includes two community hospitals, Durham Regional Hospital (370 beds) and Duke Raleigh Hospital (185 beds), and other area health clinics. Duke University Health System's facilities provide such services as primary and specialty care, home and hospice care, clinical research, physician and nurse training, and public education programs.

	Annual Growth	6/04	6/05	6/06	6/07	6/08
Est. sales ($ mil.)	7.9%	1,400.0	1,500.0	1,584.0	1,700.0	1,900.0
Employees	42.1%	—	10,391	30,551	30,000	29,826

DULCICH, INC.

16797 SE 130th Ave.
Clackamas, OR 97015
Phone: 503-905-4500
Fax: 503-905-2491
Web: www.pacseafood.com

CEO: Frank D. Dulcich
CFO: —
HR: —
FYE: December 31
Type: Private

Dulcich, Inc., which does business as the Pacific Seafood Group, is always fishing for acquisitions. The Oregon-based company has built its business by snapping up competitors, giving it a wide array of offerings. Its more than 1,800 different products range from shellfish (clams, crab, lobster, mussels, oysters, scallops) to finfish (catfish, cod, flounder, sable, salmon, swordfish, trout, and tuna). In addition to fresh and frozen seafood, the company offers value-added products, including battered, breaded, marinated, and smoked fish. Pacific Seafood operates distribution and processing centers from Alaska to Mexico, and throughout the western US. It exports products to Asia, Europe, and the Middle East.

	Annual Growth	12/04	12/05	12/06	12/07	12/08
Est. sales ($ mil.)	—	—	—	—	—	150.6
Employees	—	—	—	—	—	1,000

THE DUN & BRADSTREET CORPORATION
NYSE: DNB

103 JFK Pkwy.
Short Hills, NJ 07078
Phone: 973-921-5500
Fax: 973-921-6056
Web: www.dnb.com

CEO: Sara S. Mathew
CFO: Anastasios G. (Tasos) Konidaris
HR: Maria Renna Sharpe
FYE: December 31
Type: Public

For The Dun & Bradstreet Corporation, there's no business like "know" business. The company, known as D&B, is one of the world's leading suppliers of business information, services, and research. Its database contains statistics on more than 150 million companies in over 200 countries, including the largest volume of business-credit information in the world. The company's risk management segment (the largest segment, accounting for two-thirds of revenues) sells that information and integrates it into software products and Web-based applications. D&B also offers marketing information and purchasing-support services. The company acquired Hoover's, the publisher of this profile, in 2003.

	Annual Growth	12/05	12/06	12/07	12/08	12/09
Sales ($ mil.)	4.0%	1,443.6	1,531.3	1,599.2	1,726.3	1,687.0
Net income ($ mil.)	9.8%	221.2	240.7	298.1	310.6	322.0
Market value ($ mil.)	5.9%	3,374.1	4,171.7	4,466.0	3,890.1	4,251.3
Employees	3.5%	4,350	4,400	4,900	4,900	5,000

DUNBAR ARMORED, INC.

50 Schilling Rd.
Hunt Valley, MD 21031
Phone: 410-584-9800
Fax: 410-229-1765
Web: www.dunbararmored.com

CEO: Kevin R. Dunbar
CFO: Juergen Laue
HR: Dominick Valencia
FYE: December 31
Type: Private

Dunbar Armored gets paid to take the money and run — to the bank. The company provides armored transportation to major banks and retailers through some 80 branch locations throughout the US. It also offers armored air transport, ATM and bank vault services, cash handling, and other security services. Dunbar Armored operates through six subsidiaries: Dunbar Alarm Systems (electronic alarm and monitoring), Dunbar BankPak (security containers), Dunbar Cash Vault Services (money rooms), Dunbar Global Logistics (transportation services), and Dunbar Guard Services (trained and uniformed security guards). The company is owned by the Dunbar family.

DUNCAN ENERGY PARTNERS L.P.

NYSE: DEP

1100 Louisiana St., 10th Fl.
Houston, TX 77002
Phone: 713-381-6500
Fax: 713-381-6668
Web: www.deplp.com

CEO: W. Randall Fowler
CFO: Bryan F. Bulawa
HR: —
FYE: December 31
Type: Public

Duncan Energy Partners (DEP) goes deep and wide to make its money. The company, a spinoff from Enterprise Products Partners, finds, stores, and transports natural gas and other petrochemicals. Its operations include Mont Belvieu Caverns (33 salt-dome storage "tanks" with a 100-million-barrel capacity), the 1,000-mile-long Acadian Gas pipeline in Louisiana, propylene pipelines between Texas and Louisiana, and a 297-mile-long intrastate natural gas liquids (NGLs) pipeline. Exxon Mobil accounts for about 10% of DEP's revenues. In 2008 the company greatly boosted its assets, acquiring stakes in three midstream energy companies from its parent for $730 million.

	Annual Growth	12/05	12/06	12/07	12/08	12/09
Sales ($ mil.)	0.7%	953.4	924.5	797.0	1,598.1	979.3
Net income ($ mil.)	23.1%	39.7	55.3	19.2	47.9	91.1
Market value ($ mil.)	4.3%	—	—	1,259.5	784.6	1,370.2
Employees	—	0	0	0	0	1,900

DUNE ENERGY, INC.

NYSE Amex: DNE

2 Shell Plaza, 777 Walker St., Ste. 2450
Houston, TX 77002
Phone: 713-229-6300
Fax: 713-229-6388
Web: www.duneenergy.com

CEO: James A. Watt
CFO: Frank T. Smith Jr.
HR: —
FYE: December 31
Type: Public

Like sand piling up in a windblown sand dune, Dune Energy is looking to pile up profits from its Texas and Louisiana oil and gas properties. The oil and gas exploration and production independent has leases on 100,000 gross acres across 23 producing oil and natural gas fields along the Texas and Louisiana Gulf Coast. In 2008 Dune Energy reported proved reserves of 8.2 million barrels of oil and 83.8 billion cu. ft. of natural gas. It has a more than two-year current drilling inventory for its properties along the Gulf Coast. Swiss bank UBS owns 35% of the company; Russian gas company ITERA's Tierra Holdings BV unit, 33%.

	Annual Growth	12/05	12/06	12/07	12/08	12/09
Sales ($ mil.)	104.6%	3.7	7.6	84.3	146.6	64.9
Net income ($ mil.)	—	(1.6)	(43.9)	(28.4)	(141.1)	(59.1)
Market value ($ mil.)	(64.5%)	574.9	471.6	412.9	36.4	9.1
Employees	44.5%	11	11	60	52	48

⊞ DUNKIN' BRANDS, INC.

130 Royall St.
Canton, MA 02021
Phone: 781-737-3000
Fax: 781-737-4000
Web: www.dunkinbrands.com

CEO: Nigel Travis
CFO: Kate S. Lavelle
HR: Christine Deputy
FYE: August 31
Type: Private

Doughnuts and ice cream make sweet bedfellows at Dunkin' Brands. The company is a leading multi-concept quick-service franchisor that operates both the Dunkin' Donuts and Baskin-Robbins chains. It has about 15,000 franchise locations operating in more than 40 countries. With more than 9,000 units in 30 countries (about 6,400 in North America), Dunkin' Donuts is the world's leading chain of doughnut shops. Baskin-Robbins is a top ice cream and frozen snacks outlet with its more than 6,000 locations (2,600 in the US). Dunkin' Brands is owned by a group of private investment firms including Bain Capital, The Carlyle Group, and Thomas H. Lee Partners.

DUNKIN' DONUTS NORTHEAST DISTRIBUTION CENTER, INC.

150 Depot St.
Bellingham, MA 02019
Phone: 508-553-2600
Fax: 508-422-3866

CEO: David Liguori
CFO: Kevin Cardullo
HR: Katherine (Kate) Norton-Edge
FYE: December 31
Type: Cooperative

When it's time to make the donuts, this is where you'll find the supplies. Dunkin' Donuts Northeast Distribution Center is one of several member-owned cooperative distribution hubs serving Dunkin' Donuts and Baskin-Robbins franchisees around the country. The company supplies thousands of store locations in New England and upstate New York with ingredients and other food products, as well as restaurant equipment and supplies. The cooperative was founded by owners of 250 Dunkin' Donuts franchises in 1982. Both the Dunkin' Donuts and Baskin-Robbins chains are owned by Dunkin' Brands.

	Annual Growth	12/04	12/05	12/06	12/07	12/08
Est. sales ($ mil.)	—	—	—	—	—	498.5
Employees	—	—	—	—	—	425

DUNN-EDWARDS CORPORATION

4885 E. 52nd Place
Los Angeles, CA 90058
Phone: 323-771-3330
Fax: 323-826-2650
Web: www.dunnedwards.com

CEO: Ken Edwards
CFO: Robert Hill
HR: Gary Jones
FYE: December 31
Type: Private

If you want to paint the town red, it's a "Dunn" deal. From two manufacturing facilities in California and Arizona, Dunn-Edwards makes numerous paints and coatings, as well as paint-related products ranging from ladders to spray equipment. The company operates 100 retail outlets and caters to architects, designers, home builders, and property managers in the Southwest; it also serves do-it-yourselfers, though professionals account for 90% of sales. Founded in 1925 by Frank Dunn, Dunn-Edwards is owned lock, stock, and bucket by the employees and the Edwards family. Among the places coated with Dunn-Edwards paint are the Staples Center and Mann's Chinese Theater in Los Angeles and Caesars Palace in Las Vegas.

DUPONT AUTOMOTIVE

950 Stephenson Hwy.
Troy, MI 48083
Phone: 248-583-8000
Fax: 248-583-4556
Web: automotive.dupont.com

CEO: Boo Ching (BC) Chong
CFO: —
HR: —
FYE: December 31
Type: Association

DuPont Automotive has a hand in building your car from beginning to end. It has been working with the auto industry for nearly a century, providing everything from the glass in a sunroof down to the rubber in the tires, from thermoplastic front end systems to the R&D involved in producing tail lights. The $6 billion unit of DuPont operates from more than 100 plants and labs in more than 70 countries and is the largest provider of coatings to the automotive industry. The company's plants make coatings and plastics and provides compounding services to the auto industry in North America, Asia, and Europe.

⊞ An in-depth profile of this company is available to Hoover's Online members at hoovers.com.

521

DUPONT FABROS TECHNOLOGY, INC.

NYSE: DFT

1212 New York Ave. NW, Ste. 900
Washington, DC 20005
Phone: 202-728-0044
Fax: 202-728-0220
Web: www.dft.com

CEO: Hossein Fateh
CFO: Mark L. Wetzel
HR: Kathy Murphy
FYE: December 31
Type: Public

DuPont Fabros Technology owns, develops, operates, and manages wholesale data centers — the facilities that house, power, and cool computer servers for such technology companies as Facebook, Google, Microsoft, and Yahoo!. The company establishes its rental rates based on the amount of power reserved for tenant use and the square footage they occupy. As a wholesale provider, the company targets clients with high power requirements and a preference for long-term leases. DuPont Fabros Technology develops its wholesale data centers to compete with more traditional colocation models in which managed services are bundled with power and cooling. Wholesale customers typically install and maintain their own servers.

	Annual Growth	12/05	12/06	12/07	12/08	12/09
Sales ($ mil.)	—	0.0	54.8	25.9	173.7	200.3
Net income ($ mil.)	—	(0.6)	0.8	(99.3)	19.1	1.8
Market value ($ mil.)	(4.2%)	—	—	884.6	93.4	811.9
Employees	11.9%	—	50	52	67	70

DUPONT POWDER COATINGS USA, INC.

9800 Genard Rd.
Houston, TX 77041
Phone: 713-939-4000
Fax: 713-939-4027
Web: www.dupontpowder.com

CEO: Dave Lazzeri
CFO: William (Bill) Rising
HR: Andy Brink
FYE: December 31
Type: Subsidiary

DuPont Powder Coatings USA wants to make sure your cold steel doesn't stay that way. The subsidiary of DuPont's coatings unit makes more than 500 types of decorative and protective coatings that adhere to most metal finishes. Its products are used in the construction industry as coatings for rebar and in the oil and gas industry as a finish for both small- and large-diameter pipes. DuPont Powder Coatings pioneered such coating technologies as UV curing. It also makes coatings for the automotive OEM market. DuPont Powder Coatings operates manufacturing facilities primarily in Asia, Europe, and the Americas. The company was called Herberts-O'Brien until it was acquired by DuPont in 1998.

	Annual Growth	12/04	12/05	12/06	12/07	12/08
Est. sales ($ mil.)	—	—	—	—	—	150.0
Employees	—	—	—	—	—	400

DUQUESNE LIGHT COMPANY

411 7th Ave.
Pittsburgh, PA 15219
Phone: 412-393-6000
Fax: 412-393-5517
Web: www.duquesnelight.com

CEO: Andrew M. Chapman
CFO: Mark E. Kaplan
HR: Maureen Meehan
FYE: December 31
Type: Subsidiary

Duquesne Light is the first and last resort for light for many in the Keystone State. The company, founded in 1880, provides electricity to about 580,000 customers in southwestern Pennsylvania over its 17,000-mile transmission and distribution system. The utility, a subsidiary of Duquesne Light Holdings (formerly DQE) acts as a generation Provider of Last Resort (POLR) for customers who do not choose an alternative supplier. In 2006 Duquesne Light Holdings expanded its a generating capacity, acquiring Atlantic City Electric's 108 MW ownership interests in the Keystone and Conemaugh coal-fired power plants.

	Annual Growth	12/04	12/05	12/06	12/07	12/08
Est. sales ($ mil.)	—	—	—	—	—	723.2
Employees	—	—	—	—	—	1,400

DUQUESNE LIGHT HOLDINGS, INC.

411 7th Ave.
Pittsburgh, PA 15219
Phone: 412-393-6000
Fax: 412-393-5517
Web: www.duquesnelight.com

CEO: Andrew M. Chapman
CFO: Stevan R. Schott
HR: —
FYE: December 31
Type: Private

As energy markets deregulated, the venerable Duquesne Light Holdings (founded 1880) restructured PDQ. Its principal subsidiary, regulated utility Duquesne Light, distributes electricity to 580,000 customers in southwestern Pennsylvania. The company had divested noncore assets to concentrate on its power utility and energy services businesses; it changed its name in 2003 to mark the shift. In 2007 a consortium led by Macquarie Infrastructure Partners and Diversified Utilities and Energy Trust acquired Duquesne Light for about $3 billion in cash and debt.

DURA AUTOMOTIVE SYSTEMS, INC.

2791 Research Dr.
Rochester Hills, MI 48309
Phone: 248-299-7500
Fax: 248-299-7501
Web: www.duraauto.com

CEO: Timothy D. (Tim) Leuliette
CFO: Jeffrey M. (Jeff) Stafeil
HR: Theresa L. Skotak
FYE: December 31
Type: Private

You wouldn't be able to keep the pedal to the metal without Dura Automotive Systems' driver control systems. The company is a leading supplier of pedal systems, parking brake mechanisms, manual and automatic transmission gear shifter systems, and auto cables. Dura also makes door and window systems and trim, as well as engineered assemblies such as tailgate latches and seating adjustment controls. The company sells to every auto OEM in Europe, Japan, and North America. Customers include Ford, Volkswagen, GM, Chrysler, and BMW. Dura has about 33 manufacturing facilities in 16 countries. In December 2009 private equity firm Patriarch Partners bought a majority interest in Dura for about $125 million.

	Annual Growth	12/04	12/05	12/06	12/07	12/08
Est. sales ($ mil.)	—	—	—	—	—	1,894.7
Employees	—	—	—	—	—	15,350

DURECT CORPORATION

NASDAQ (GM): DRRX

2 Results Way
Cupertino, CA 95014
Phone: 408-777-1417
Fax: 408-777-3577
Web: www.durect.com

CEO: James E. Brown
CFO: Matthew J. (Matt) Hogan
HR: —
FYE: December 31
Type: Public

DURECT wants your medicine to go DURECTly where it's needed. It is developing drug-delivery systems to provide long-term therapy for such conditions as chronic pain, heart disease, cancer, and neurological disorders. Drug delivery technologies provided by DURECT include SABER, a controlled-release injectable; TRANSDUR, a transdermal patch; ORADUR, a sustained release oral gel-cap; DUROS, an osmotic implant; and DURIN, a biodegradable implant. Its R&D efforts are conducted independently and collaboratively. DURECT sells biodegradable polymers (Lactel) and osmotic pumps (ALZET) to pharmaceutical and medical research firms through direct sales representatives and distributors.

	Annual Growth	12/05	12/06	12/07	12/08	12/09
Sales ($ mil.)	(4.0%)	28.6	21.9	30.7	27.1	24.3
Net income ($ mil.)	—	(18.1)	(33.3)	(24.3)	(43.9)	(30.3)
Market value ($ mil.)	(16.5%)	440.0	385.3	558.0	294.2	214.4
Employees	(2.1%)	138	170	179	171	127

DÜRR SYSTEMS, INC.

40600 Plymouth Rd.
Plymouth, MI 48170
Phone: 734-459-6800
Fax: 734-459-5837
Web: www.durr.com/en/company/divisions.html

CEO: Dave Meynell
CFO: Mateusz Novakowski
HR: —
FYE: December 31
Type: Subsidiary

Dürr Systems (also known as Paint and Assembly Systems) wants everyone to choose a car color, and it does not have to be black. Dürr Systems is the US unit of Dürr Inc., a wholly owned subsidiary of Dürr AG. Dürr Systems is a leading global supplier of mass-production paint shops for car manufacturers and suppliers, and also designs and installs automobile manufacturing assembly systems. In addition, Dürr Systems designs and manufactures air-exhaust purification systems for a range of industries. Dürr AG has operations in several countries in Europe, Latin America, and Asia.

DUSA PHARMACEUTICALS, INC.

NASDAQ (GM): DUSA

25 Upton Dr.
Wilmington, MA 01887
Phone: 978-657-7500
Fax: 978-657-9193
Web: www.dusapharma.com

CEO: Robert F. (Bob) Doman
CFO: Richard C. Christopher
HR: —
FYE: December 31
Type: Public

DUSA Pharmaceuticals has seen the light. The company develops photodynamic and and photodetection therapies for treating and diagnosing a variety of dermatological conditions using a combination of drugs and light. In the US, DUSA markets its Levulan Kerastick brand topical solution, a product that is used in combination with the BLU-U light to treat actinic keratoses, or precancerous skin lesions caused by sun exposure. On its own, BLU-U is also FDA approved to treat moderate acne. DUSA's 2006 acquisition of Sirius Laboratories expanded the company's product line for acne to include ClindaReach, a topical prescription.

	Annual Growth	12/05	12/06	12/07	12/08	12/09
Sales ($ mil.)	27.4%	11.3	25.6	27.7	29.5	29.8
Net income ($ mil.)	—	(15.0)	(31.3)	(14.7)	(6.3)	(2.5)
Market value ($ mil.)	(38.4%)	259.7	103.7	49.9	25.3	37.4
Employees	6.8%	66	85	83	86	86

DUTKO WORLDWIDE

412 1st St. SE, Ste. 100
Washington, DC 20003
Phone: 202-484-4884
Fax: 202-484-0109
Web: www.dutkoworldwide.com

CEO: Mark S. Irion
CFO: —
HR: —
FYE: December 31
Type: Subsidiary

One of the top lobbying firms in the US, Dutko Worldwide extends its reach not only through about 10 offices in its home country, but also with almost five European outposts. The firm provides policy expertise on the federal, state, and local levels of government, as well as advisory and research services related to public opinion and media relations. It helps clients, which have included Abbott Laboratories and GlaxoSmithKline, shape and navigate policy issues in such areas as health care, energy, transportation, homeland security, and telecommunications. Founded in 1981, Dutko was acquired in December 2009 by UK-based public relations firm Huntsworth for $34 million.

DVL, INC.

OTC: DVLN

70 E. 55th St., 7th Fl.
New York, NY 10022
Phone: 212-350-9900
Fax: 212-350-9911

CEO: Alan E. Casnoff
CFO: Neil H. Koenig
HR: —
FYE: December 31
Type: Public

As far as DVL is concerned, making money is all in the family. The commercial finance company owns and services commercial mortgages held by more than 40 affiliated limited partnerships (in which it is general partner). DVL's partnerships hold some 1.9 million sq. ft. of commercial, industrial, and office space; a percentage of its income comes from tenant rental payments. Retail giant Wal-Mart is its largest tenant. The company also owns residual interests in securitized portfolios and offers real estate asset management and administrative services for its partnerships.

	Annual Growth	12/05	12/06	12/07	12/08	12/09
Sales ($ mil.)	0.5%	9.3	9.4	11.0	10.2	9.5
Net income ($ mil.)	(4.7%)	1.7	1.8	2.3	1.5	1.4
Market value ($ mil.)	(12.2%)	7.2	5.8	6.7	3.6	4.3
Employees	0.0%	10	10	10	10	10

DWS INVESTMENTS DISTRIBUTORS, INC.

222 S. Riverside Plaza
Chicago, IL 60606
Phone: 312-537-7000
Fax: —
Web: www.dws-investments.com

CEO: Axel Schwarzer
CFO: —
HR: —
FYE: December 31
Type: Business segment

Mutual funds are DWS Investments' bread and butter. Formerly DWS Scudder, the firm is the US retail asset management division of Deutsche Asset Management (DeAM), which in turn is part of German banking giant Deutsche Bank. The company's products include defined-contribution retirement plans, individual retirement accounts (IRAs), variable annuities, closed-end funds, and money market funds, in addition to its family of more than 70 mutual funds. DWS Investments serves large corporations, financial institutions, governments, and foundations, as well as individual investors. The firm has more than $80 billion of client assets under management.

DXP ENTERPRISES, INC.

NASDAQ (GS): DXPE

7272 Pinemont
Houston, TX 77040
Phone: 713-996-4700
Fax: 713-996-4701
Web: www.dxpe.com

CEO: David R. Little
CFO: Mac McConnell
HR: —
FYE: December 31
Type: Public

DXP Enterprises is well-equipped to meet its customers' needs. The company distributes maintenance, repair, and operating (MRO) equipment and products, primarily to the oil and gas, petrochemical, and wood products industries. It also distributes centrifugal pumps, rotary gear pumps, plunger pumps, and other fluid-handling equipment as well as bearings and power transmission equipment, general mill (cutting tools) and safety supplies, and electrical products (wire conduit). DXP's MRO unit also provides system design, fabrication, and repair services. DXP's electrical contractor division sells a range of electrical products including wire conduit, wiring devices, electrical fittings and boxes, and tools.

	Annual Growth	12/05	12/06	12/07	12/08	12/09
Sales ($ mil.)	33.2%	185.4	279.8	444.5	736.9	583.2
Net income ($ mil.)	—	5.5	11.9	17.3	25.9	(42.4)
Market value ($ mil.)	11.0%	118.1	240.7	320.6	200.7	179.5
Employees	34.5%	519	763	1,603	1,874	1,697

An in-depth profile of this company is available to Hoover's Online members at hoovers.com.

523

DYAX CORP.

NASDAQ (GM): DYAX

300 Technology Sq.
Cambridge, MA 02139
Phone: 617-225-2500
Fax: 617-225-2501
Web: www.dyax.com

CEO: Gustav A. Christensen
CFO: George Migausky
HR: Tony Yerardi
FYE: December 31
Type: Public

Dyax is arming the war against disease. The biopharmaceutical company develops drugs from its proprietary bacteriophage (phage) display binding technology that rapidly identifies proteins, peptides, and antibodies it can use to treat disease. Using phages to identify useful genetic codes, it primarily focuses on oncology and inflammation remedies. Dyax's lead drug candidate, DX-88, may be used to treat hereditary angioedema and to reduce blood loss during cardiopulmonary bypass surgeries — it is currently undergoing clinical trials. The company has numerous other products in its discovery and development pipeline, including key candidate DX-2240, which is designed to inhibit cancerous tumor growth.

	Annual Growth	12/05	12/06	12/07	12/08	12/09
Sales ($ mil.)	2.1%	19.9	12.8	26.1	43.4	21.6
Net income ($ mil.)	—	(30.9)	(50.3)	(56.3)	(66.5)	(62.4)
Market value ($ mil.)	(10.4%)	514.8	296.0	357.5	355.6	331.2
Employees	(4.3%)	144	161	177	164	121

DYCOM INDUSTRIES, INC.

NYSE: DY

11770 US Hwy. 1, Ste. 101
Palm Beach Gardens, FL 33408
Phone: 561-627-7171
Fax: 561-627-7709
Web: www.dycomind.com

CEO: Steven E. Nielsen
CFO: H. Andrew (Drew) DeFerrari
HR: —
FYE: July 31
Type: Public

The telecommunications industry dials Dycom Industries for construction and engineering assistance. Operating through more than two dozen subsidiaries, the company primarily designs, builds, and maintains coaxial, copper, and fiber-optic cable systems for local and long-distance phone companies and cable television operators. Dycom also provides wiring services for businesses and government agencies, installs and maintains electrical lines for utilities, and locates underground wires and pipelines for excavators. AT&T, Comcast, and Verizon Communications together account for nearly half of sales.

	Annual Growth	7/05	7/06	7/07	7/08	7/09
Sales ($ mil.)	2.9%	986.6	1,023.7	1,137.8	1,230.0	1,106.9
Net income ($ mil.)	—	24.3	18.2	41.9	21.7	(53.2)
Market value ($ mil.)	(15.0%)	943.2	695.4	1,080.4	613.5	492.1
Employees	2.9%	8,228	9,352	10,899	10,746	9,231

DYLAN'S CANDYBAR, LLC

315 E. 62nd St., 6th Fl.
New York, NY 10065
Phone: 212-620-2700
Fax: —
Web: www.dylanscandybar.com

CEO: Dylan Lauren
CFO: —
HR: —
FYE: January 31
Type: Private

Dylan's Candy Bar is a Candyland of wonders for the well-heeled on Manhattan's Upper East Side and beyond. Founded in 2001 by Dylan Lauren (daughter of designer Ralph Lauren), and candy store veteran Jeff Rubin (no longer associated with the company), Dylan's Candy Bar has hit the big time. Boasting three stories of candy (more than 5,000 types) and apparel, a ten-foot artificial chocolate bunny, and staircases laden with gummy candies, the candy retailer's Manhattan location has become a tourist draw in its own right. It also sports a cafe, bar, and private party rooms. Dylan's, which has five locations in New York, Florida, and Texas, aspires to open stores in London and Tokyo eventually.

DYNA GROUP INTERNATIONAL, INC.

Pink Sheets: DGIX

1661 S. Seguin Ave.
New Braunfels, TX 78130
Phone: 830-620-4400
Fax: 830-620-8430
Web: www.gap1.com

CEO: Roger R. Tuttle
CFO: Sandra K. Tristan
HR: Carla Keffer-Barres
FYE: December 31
Type: Public

Pewter is like gold to Dyna Group. Through wholly owned subsidiary Great American Products, the company produces pewter products, mostly collectibles, that are centrifugally cast in rubber molds. The company's products include belt buckles, key chains, picture frames, magnets, glassware, and bar accessories, as well as keepsake boxes. Dyna Group has licensing agreements with NASCAR, the NFL, MLB, the NBA, the NHL, and other sports leagues. Dyna Group maintains a manufacturing facility in New Braunfels, Texas, but also outsources some manufacturing to companies in Mexico. CEO Roger Tuttle founded the company in 1972.

DYNACQ HEALTHCARE, INC.

NASDAQ (CM): DYII

10304 Interstate 10 East, Ste. 369
Houston, TX 77029
Phone: 713-378-2000
Fax: 713-673-6416
Web: www.dynacq.com

CEO: Chiu M. Chan
CFO: Philip S. Chan
HR: —
FYE: August 31
Type: Public

Dynacq Healthcare is a holding company that owns and operates acute-care specialty hospitals providing electively scheduled surgeries, such as bariatric (weight loss) and orthopedic surgeries and pain management procedures. Dynacq operates Vista Hospital in Garland, Texas, and Surgery Specialty Hospitals of America in Pasadena, Texas (suburbs of Dallas and Houston, respectively). Most of the Dynacq's revenues come from workers' compensation insurance and commercial insurers on an out-of-network basis. Chairman and CEO Chiu Moon Chan owns more than half of Dynacq.

	Annual Growth	8/05	8/06	8/07	8/08	8/09
Sales ($ mil.)	(2.8%)	55.3	36.0	42.8	60.3	49.4
Net income ($ mil.)	—	(5.1)	(6.4)	4.1	8.4	(0.5)
Market value ($ mil.)	(8.9%)	70.5	28.4	89.5	68.9	48.6
Employees	(9.1%)	412	332	271	272	281

DYNAMEX INC.

NASDAQ (GS): DDMX

5429 LBJ Fwy., Ste. 1000
Dallas, TX 75240
Phone: 214-560-9000
Fax: 214-560-9349
Web: www.dynamex.com

CEO: James L. Welch
CFO: Ray E. Schmitz
HR: Doris Oloton
FYE: July 31
Type: Public

Dynamex knows the dynamics of same-day delivery. The company provides both scheduled and on-demand delivery of time-sensitive items such as medical supplies, financial documents, and office products. It has built its delivery services around its network of ground couriers concentrating on intracity deliveries. Most of its drivers are independent contractors, and it uses third-party air and ground carriers to provide same-day intercity services. Dynamex also enables customers to outsource certain logistics functions, including the management of dedicated vehicle fleets and facilities such as mailrooms and inventory-tracking call centers.

	Annual Growth	7/05	7/06	7/07	7/08	7/09
Sales ($ mil.)	5.8%	321.1	358.4	413.8	455.8	402.1
Net income ($ mil.)	(5.9%)	11.2	12.4	15.0	15.8	8.8
Market value ($ mil.)	(3.1%)	172.2	203.8	233.8	273.2	151.6
Employees	(30.1%)	6,290	6,300	2,000	2,000	1,500

DYNAMIC MATERIALS CORPORATION

NASDAQ (GS): BOOM

5405 Spine Rd.
Boulder, CO 80301
Phone: 303-665-5700
Fax: 303-604-1897
Web: www.dynamicmaterials.com

CEO: Yvon Pierre Cariou
CFO: Richard A. (Rick) Santa
HR: Philippe Roquette
FYE: December 31
Type: Public

Dynamic Materials Corporation (DMC) has an explosive personality when it comes to working with metal. Formerly Explosive Fabricators, the company uses explosives to metallurgically bond, or "clad," metal plates; the process usually joins a corrosion-resistant alloy with carbon steel, metals that do not bond easily. Its clad metal plates are central to making heavy-duty pressure vessels and heat exchangers used in industries from alternative energy to shipbuilding. In addition to explosive metalworking, DMC produces and sells oilfield components used to knock open oil and gas wells. Its subsidiary, AMK Welding, machines and welds parts for commercial and military aircraft engines and power-generation turbines.

	Annual Growth	12/05	12/06	12/07	12/08	12/09
Sales ($ mil.)	20.1%	79.3	113.5	165.2	232.6	164.9
Net income ($ mil.)	(4.9%)	10.4	20.8	24.6	24.1	8.5
Market value ($ mil.)	(9.6%)	389.0	364.2	763.3	250.3	259.8
Employees	20.1%	181	230	446	408	377

DYNAMICS RESEARCH CORPORATION

NASDAQ (GM): DRCO

60 Frontage Rd.
Andover, MA 01810
Phone: 978-289-1500
Fax: 978-470-0201
Web: www.drc.com

CEO: James P. Regan
CFO: David Keleher
HR: Steven P. (Steve) Wentzell
FYE: December 31
Type: Public

Research is this company's middle name. No, really. Dynamics Research Corporation (DRC) provides computer-based systems development, engineering, management, and logistics support services to the US government and its contractors, state and local agencies, and corporate customers. Most of its business comes from various agencies within the Department of Defense, including the US Air Force, Army, and Navy. Its Metrigraphics division produces precision components — including optical discs and fine line circuits — for commercial manufacturing customers in the computing, telecom, and medical markets. Subsidiary Kadix Systems provides consulting services for defense and homeland security agencies.

	Annual Growth	12/05	12/06	12/07	12/08	12/09
Sales ($ mil.)	(2.7%)	300.4	259.0	229.6	242.8	268.7
Net income ($ mil.)	(2.7%)	11.4	4.0	7.1	(1.3)	10.2
Market value ($ mil.)	(9.0%)	153.4	96.8	107.4	79.4	105.3
Employees	(5.2%)	1,822	1,500	1,400	1,500	1,470

DYNAPAC USA, INC.

16435 IH 35 North
Selma, TX 78154
Phone: 210-474-5770
Fax: 210-474-5780
Web: www.dynapac.com

CEO: Bruce Truesdale
CFO: Peter Doemel
HR: Connie Nivens
FYE: December 31
Type: Subsidiary

Dynapac USA is rolling along in the compaction and paving machinery business. A division of Sweden-based Dynapac AB, its products primarily include compactors, cutters and grinders, pavers, planers, poker vibrators, rollers, rammers, and submersible pumps for use in road building and civil construction. Dynapac also offers service, spare parts, and training. Formerly a subsidiary of Metso Minerals Industries, Dynapac was taken private by Nordic investment firm Altor in 2004. Dynapac has eight production facilities in Brazil, China, France, Germany, Sweden, and the US, and has sales operations in 16 countries worldwide. Dynapac AB was purchased by Atlas Copco in 2007.

DYNASIL CORPORATION OF AMERICA

OTC: DYSL

385 Cooper Rd.
West Berlin, NJ 08091
Phone: 856-767-4600
Fax: 856-767-6813
Web: www.dynasil.com

CEO: Craig T. Dunham
CFO: Richard A. (Rich) Johnson
HR: —
FYE: September 30
Type: Public

Dynasil Corporation of America likes playing with the dynamics of silica. The company manufactures custom synthetic-fused silica and quartz products primarily used in industrial optical materials. Its products include filters, lenses, prisms, reflectors, windows, and mirrors. Customers use the company's fabricated optical products in lasers, aircraft, optical equipment, analytical instruments, semiconductors, and electronics. Manufacturers Corning, Schott Glass Technologies, and General Electric supply the company with some fused silica, fused quartz, and optical materials. Dynasil sells its products in the US and overseas.

	Annual Growth	9/05	9/06	9/07	9/08	9/09
Sales ($ mil.)	61.2%	5.1	6.9	10.8	17.1	34.4
Net income ($ mil.)	68.2%	0.2	0.5	0.5	1.2	1.6
Market value ($ mil.)	29.4%	8.9	10.1	20.2	20.8	25.1
Employees	42.0%	47	75	80	184	191

DYNATRONICS CORPORATION

NASDAQ (CM): DYNT

7030 Park Centre Dr.
Salt Lake City, UT 84121
Phone: 801-568-7000
Fax: 801-568-7711
Web: www.dynatronics.com

CEO: Kelvyn H. Cullimore Jr.
CFO: Terry M. Atkinson
HR: —
FYE: June 30
Type: Public

Dynatronics makes medical equipment to keep active people on the go. Its products include electrotherapy, ultrasound, and infrared light therapy equipment; medical supplies such as wraps, braces, bandages, walking aids, and training equipment; rehabilitation therapy tables; and aesthetic products sold under the Synergie brand. Its Synergie Aesthetic Massage System (AMS) uses vacuum massage for cosmetic weight loss, and its Synergie Peel is a microdermabrasion device that reduces wrinkles. The company's products are sold through several distribution channels, including directly through its own distributors, through independent dealers, and via catalog.

	Annual Growth	6/05	6/06	6/07	6/08	6/09
Sales ($ mil.)	12.3%	20.4	19.5	17.8	32.6	32.4
Net income ($ mil.)	(38.5%)	0.7	0.2	(0.1)	(8.4)	0.1
Market value ($ mil.)	(24.3%)	26.5	16.2	14.4	9.5	8.7
Employees	2.6%	138	289	177	183	153

DYNAVAX TECHNOLOGIES CORPORATION

NASDAQ (CM): DVAX

2929 7th St., Ste. 100
Berkeley, CA 94710
Phone: 510-848-5100
Fax: 510-848-1327
Web: www.dynavax.com

CEO: Dino Dina
CFO: —
HR: Cecilia Vitug
FYE: December 31
Type: Public

Dynavax Technologies is trying to reprogram the way the body reacts to disease. The firm focuses on immunostimulatory sequences (ISS), short strands of DNA found to strengthen the immune system. The company's lead candidate in clinical trials is HEPLISAV, a hepatitis B vaccine. Dynavax is working on other candidates that might lead to treatments for asthma, colorectal cancer, and hepatitis C. Partnerships are key to its work with other candidates. Dynavax has partnered with AstraZeneca to research preclinical work on a treatment for asthma and chronic obstructive pulmonary disease, while Symphony Dynamo has poured in money to fund the company's colorectal cancer and hepatitis C research.

	Annual Growth	12/05	12/06	12/07	12/08	12/09
Sales ($ mil.)	28.7%	14.7	4.8	14.1	37.1	40.3
Net income ($ mil.)	—	(20.6)	(52.1)	(60.0)	(20.8)	(30.6)
Market value ($ mil.)	(23.8%)	364.5	794.7	442.4	72.7	122.9
Employees	14.0%	77	153	173	155	130

An in-depth profile of this company is available to Hoover's Online members at hoovers.com.

525

DYNAVOX INC.

NASDAQ (GS): DVOX

2100 Wharton St., Ste. 400
Pittsburgh, PA 15203
Phone: 412-381-4883
Fax: 412-381-5241
Web: www.dynavoxtech.com

CEO: Edward L. (Ed) Donnelly Jr.
CFO: Kenneth D. Misch
HR: —
FYE: June 30
Type: Public

DynaVox makes communication available to all. The company provides speech generation communication devices used by persons with speech, learning, and physical disabilities; it also develops text-to-speech software. Its products, which come in various keyboard- and touchscreen-based form factors, are used by children and adults impacted by amyotrophic lateral sclerosis, autism, cerebral palsy, mental retardation, Parkinson's disease, stroke, and traumatic brain injury. In addition to hardware and software, the company provides technical and reimbursement support services. DynaVox completed an IPO in 2010.

	Annual Growth	6/05	6/06	6/07	6/08	6/09
Sales ($ mil.)	17.4%	—	—	66.2	81.4	91.2
Net income ($ mil.)	34.0%	—	—	4.9	7.3	8.8
Employees	—	—	—	—	—	364

DYNCORP INTERNATIONAL INC.

NYSE: DCP

3190 Fairview Park Dr., Ste. 700
Falls Church, VA 22042
Phone: 571-722-0210
Fax: 571-722-0252
Web: www.dyn-intl.com

CEO: William L. (Bill) Ballhaus
CFO: Michael J. Thorne
HR: Dianne Walker
FYE: March 31
Type: Public

DynCorp International works behind the scenes to support military and diplomatic efforts on the front lines. Training police officers overseas for US government agencies is the company's core business, along with interpreting and translating services. The US's Department of State and the Department of Defense (DoD) are its largest customers, representing almost all sales. As a result, DynCorp nets about 73% of its business in the Middle East. Contracts with commercial entities and foreign governments make up the balance. In April 2010 DynCorp agreed to be acquired by an affiliate of Cerberus for an estimated $1.5 billion.

	Annual Growth	3/06	3/07	3/08	3/09	3/10
Sales ($ mil.)	16.2%	1,967.0	2,082.3	2,139.8	3,101.1	3,585.3
Net income ($ mil.)	86.0%	7.2	27.0	48.0	69.8	86.1
Market value ($ mil.)	(8.7%)	—	849.7	939.2	750.6	647.0
Employees	11.6%	14,400	14,600	16,800	22,500	22,300

⊞ DYNEGY INC.

NYSE: DYN

1000 Louisiana St., Ste. 5800
Houston, TX 77002
Phone: 713-507-6400
Fax: 713-507-6808
Web: www.dynegy.com

CEO: Bruce A. Williamson
CFO: Holli C. Nichols
HR: Julius Cox
FYE: December 31
Type: Public

Power dynamo Dynegy (short for "dynamic energy") provides wholesale power, capacity, and ancillary services to a broad range of customers (utilities, cooperatives, municipalities and other energy operations) in 13 states, in the Midwest, the Northeast, and on the West Coast. The company's power generation portfolio consists of 18 power plants (in six states) fueled by coal, fuel oil, and natural gas, and have a generation capacity of 12,300 MW. Originally a natural gas trader, the company has refocused in recent years on the wholesale electricity market.

	Annual Growth	12/05	12/06	12/07	12/08	12/09
Sales ($ mil.)	1.6%	2,313.0	2,017.0	3,103.0	3,549.0	2,468.0
Net income ($ mil.)	—	108.0	(334.0)	264.0	174.0	(1,262.0)
Market value ($ mil.)	(21.8%)	2,912.3	4,356.4	4,296.2	1,203.4	1,089.1
Employees	19.5%	1,371	1,339	1,800	2,000	2,800

DYNEX CAPITAL, INC.

NYSE: DX

4551 Cox Rd., Ste. 300
Glen Allen, VA 23060
Phone: 804-217-5800
Fax: 804-217-5860
Web: www.dynexcapital.com

CEO: Thomas B. (Tom) Akin
CFO: Stephen J. Benedetti
HR: Alison G. Griffin
FYE: December 31
Type: Public

Dynex Capital is a real estate investment trust (REIT) that invests in loans and fixed-income securities backed by single-family residential and commercial mortgage loans. The company isn't too picky, investing in both investment-grade and subprime loans and adjustable-rate and fixed-rate loans. However, citing competition and a "lack of compelling opportunities" in a volatile marketplace, the company makes few new investments and has been slimming down its balance sheet by selling off assets, including all of its manufactured home lending and delinquent property-tax receivable portfolios.

	Annual Growth	12/05	12/06	12/07	12/08	12/09
Sales ($ mil.)	(17.6%)	86.0	50.9	31.7	40.8	39.6
Net income ($ mil.)	16.4%	9.6	4.9	8.9	15.1	17.6
Market value ($ mil.)	6.1%	104.3	107.2	134.1	98.9	132.0
Employees	(8.5%)	20	17	11	13	14

DYNO NOBEL INC.

2650 Decker Lake Blvd., Ste. 300
Salt Lake City, UT 84119
Phone: 801-364-4800
Fax: 801-321-6706
Web: www.dynonobel.com

CEO: Brian Wallace
CFO: Shaun Love
HR: Ric Mullis
FYE: December 31
Type: Subsidiary

Dyno Nobel Inc. is the North American unit of explosives maker Dyno Nobel. The company, which operates more than 50 manufacturing and distribution facilities throughout the continent, is North America's leading supplier of explosives. Primary customers include mining, construction, and industrial quarry companies. Its former parent company, the Norwegian private equity firm Industrie Kapital, divided the parent company in 2005 and sold the Australian and North American operations to Macquarie Bank. Rival Orica acquired the other operations. Dyno Nobel remains the world's second-largest explosives producer behind Orica, though it was acquired by Australian agrochem maker Incitec Pivot in 2008.

DYNTEK, INC.

Pink Sheets: DYNE

19700 Fairchild Rd., Ste. 230
Irvine, CA 92612
Phone: 949-271-6700
Fax: 949-271-6799
Web: www.dyntek.com

CEO: Ron Ben-Yishay
CFO: Karen S. Rosenberger
HR: —
FYE: June 30
Type: Public

DynTek sees a bright future in technology services. The company, previously a provider of medication and services to diabetes patients, now provides a variety of information technology services to local and state governments, schools, and commercial enterprises. Its services include technology procurement, systems integration, business process outsourcing, network engineering, and technical support. While its marketing emphasis focuses on its IT services business, the bulk of its sales are derived from the resale of hardware and software from partners such as Cisco, IBM, Microsoft, and Novell.

An in-depth profile of this company is available to Hoover's Online members at hoovers.com. ⊞

E! ENTERTAINMENT TELEVISION, INC.

5750 Wilshire Blvd.
Los Angeles, CA 90036
Phone: 323-954-2400
Fax: 323-954-2661
Web: www.eentertainment.com

CEO: Ted Harbert
CFO: —
HR: —
FYE: December 31
Type: Private

Telling the true stories of Hollywood fuels this network. E! Entertainment Television operates a cable-TV network reaching more than 80 million US homes with a mix of celebrity gossip, entertainment news, and reality-based programming. Its schedule includes such shows as *The Girls Next Door* (featuring *Playboy* publisher Hugh Hefner and his three girlfriends) and *Keeping Up with the Kardashians* (presenting the life of socialite Kim Kardashian and her family), as well as its *True Hollywood Story* series about celebrity scandals. The company also runs sister channel Style Network that reaches more than 50 million homes with fashion and lifestyle programming. E! Entertainment is owned by cable provider Comcast.

E1 MUSIC

740 Broadway, 7th Fl.
New York, NY 10003
Phone: 212-353-8800
Fax: 212-228-0660
Web: www.kochrecords.com

CEO: Michael Koch
CFO: —
HR: —
FYE: December 31
Type: Subsidiary

E1 Music, formerly KOCH Records, is a leading independent diversified music company in North America, founded by Michael Koch. The company began as a small classical label in 1990, but has since expanded to cover a wide range of genres, including jazz, rock, R&B, hip hop, country music, and children's titles. E1 Music releases music from artists such as Robert Earl Keen, Carole King, Ringo Starr, and The Wiggles. The company also has music publishing operations. E1 Music is a subsidiary of Entertainment One. The parent company changed the music subsidiary's name from KOCH Records in 2009 following a corporate restructuring.

E. GLUCK CORPORATION

29-10 Thomson Ave.
Long Island City, NY 11101
Phone: 718-784-0700
Fax: 718-482-2702
Web: www.egluck.com

CEO: Eugen Gluck
CFO: Renee Jacobs Prager
HR: Robert Noblin
FYE: December 31
Type: Private

E. Gluck wonders, "Do you have the time?" The company makes quartz watches that bear monikers such as Anne Klein, Nine West, and its own Armitron. Its timepieces also feature characters from Disney, Mattel, and Warner Bros, as well as the designer labels of Lucky Brand and JLO by Jennifer Lopez. E. Gluck uses edgy styling, microfiber bands, and digital colors to attract younger customers, as well as interchangeable bracelets and bezels (and even diamonds) for the more sophisticated set. Its watches, which carry a lifetime guarantee on working parts, are sold through jewelers, department stores, and specialty retailers. Owner and CEO Eugen Gluck founded the company in 1955.

EADS NORTH AMERICA, INC.

1616 N. Fort Myer Dr., Ste. 1600
Arlington, VA 22209
Phone: 703-236-3300
Fax: 703-236-3301
Web: www.eadsnorthamerica.com

CEO: Sean C. O'Keefe
CFO: Christopher Emerson
HR: David M. Fink
FYE: December 31
Type: Subsidiary

EADS North America (EADS), a subsidiary of the Netherlands-based European Aeronautic Defence and Space Company (EADS N.V.), is the holding company for the North American activities of its parent. Business concerns include fixed-wing and rotorcraft, defense systems, security and public safety, avionics and controls, test equipment and services, space, and communications. EADS North America serves the US military, the Border Patrol, the FBI, and local law enforcement agencies. Its business operations include American Eurocopter, Airbus Military North America (formerly EADS CASA), Supply & Services, Test & Services, Defense & Security, Fairchild Controls Corporation, PlantCML, and TYX.

	Annual Growth	12/04	12/05	12/06	12/07	12/08
Est. sales ($ mil.)	—	—	—	—	—	950.0
Employees	—	—	—	—	—	1,702

EAGLE BANCORP

OTC: EBMT

1400 Prospect Ave.
Helena, MT 59601
Phone: 406-442-3080
Fax: 406-457-4035
Web: www.americanfederalsavingsbank.com

CEO: Peter J. Johnson
CFO: Clinton J. Morrison
HR: —
FYE: June 30
Type: Public

Eagle Bancorp hopes to soar majestically over the competition. The holding company (unrelated to the Maryland company of the same name) owns American Federal Savings Bank, a thrift that serves businesses and residents of southwestern Montana through five branches. American Federal primarily writes mortgages on one- to four-family residences (these comprise more than half of its loan book); the rest of its portfolio consists of home equity loans, commercial mortgages, and consumer, business, and construction loans. The bank's deposit products include checking, money market, and savings accounts; CDs; and IRAs. Mutual holding company Eagle Financial MHC owns a majority of Eagle Bancorp.

	Annual Growth	6/05	6/06	6/07	6/08	6/09
Assets ($ mil.)	8.8%	206.4	226.2	244.7	279.9	289.7
Net income ($ mil.)	9.0%	1.7	1.8	1.8	2.1	2.4
Market value ($ mil.)	(1.7%)	32.2	34.0	35.1	29.0	30.1
Employees	4.9%	71	74	80	80	86

EAGLE BANCORP, INC.

NASDAQ (CM): EGBN

7815 Woodmont Ave.
Bethesda, MD 20814
Phone: 301-986-1800
Fax: 301-986-8529
Web: www.eaglebankmd.com

CEO: Ronald D. (Ron) Paul
CFO: James H. Langmead
HR: —
FYE: December 31
Type: Public

For those nest eggs that need a little help hatching, holding company Eagle Bancorp would recommend its community-oriented EagleBank subsidiary. The bank serves businesses and individuals through about 15 branches in Washington, DC, and its suburbs. Deposit products include checking, savings, and money market accounts; certificates of deposit; and IRAs. Commercial, residential, and construction real estate loans combined represent 70% of its loan portfolio, which also includes business (it has significant expertise as a Small Business Administration lender), consumer, and home equity loans.

	Annual Growth	12/05	12/06	12/07	12/08	12/09
Assets ($ mil.)	28.0%	672.3	773.5	846.4	1,496.8	1,805.5
Net income ($ mil.)	8.5%	7.5	8.0	7.7	7.4	10.4
Market value ($ mil.)	(10.3%)	317.9	310.6	216.0	112.9	205.6
Employees	12.8%	145	171	173	235	235

EAGLE BULK SHIPPING INC.

NASDAQ (GS): EGLE

477 Madison Ave., Ste. 1405
New York, NY 10022
Phone: 212-785-2500
Fax: 212-785-3311
Web: www.eagleships.com

CEO: Sophocles N. Zoullas
CFO: Alan S. Ginsberg
HR: —
FYE: December 31
Type: Public

Some eagles soar through the skies, but Eagle Bulk Shipping rides the waves. The company owns a fleet of about 20 Handymax dry bulk carriers that it charters to customers, typically on one- to three-year contracts. Most of its vessels are classified as Supramaxes — large Handymaxes, essentially. The Supramaxes range in capacity from 50,000 to 60,000 deadweight tons (DWT) and feature on-board cranes for cargo loading and unloading. Overall, the company's fleet has a carrying capacity of more than 1.1 million DWT. Cargo carried by charterers of Eagle Bulk Shipping's vessels includes cement, coal, fertilizer, grain, and iron ore.

	Annual Growth	12/05	12/06	12/07	12/08	12/09
Sales ($ mil.)	36.1%	56.1	104.6	124.8	185.4	192.6
Net income ($ mil.)	49.3%	6.7	33.8	52.2	61.6	33.3
Market value ($ mil.)	(25.3%)	989.1	1,077.3	1,649.5	423.7	307.5
Employees	17.8%	295	339	387	495	568

EAGLE EXPLORATION COMPANY

OTC: EGXP

93 Spyglass Dr.
Littleton, CO 80123
Phone: 303-797-6816
Fax: —

CEO: Raymond N. Joeckel
CFO: Paul M. Joeckel
HR: —
FYE: March 31
Type: Public

Eagle Exploration is digging its talons into some big nests. The company was originally hatched as an oil and gas exploration firm but turned its eye towards real estate in the early 1990s. Eagle Exploration now operates as a property investment and development firm. The company is a member of a consortium that has invested in 320 acres of undeveloped land north of Denver for residential development. Eagle Exploration also owns stakes in some oil and gas properties and related assets (still its sole source of revenue). CEO Raymond Joeckel and his family have a controlling stake in the company.

	Annual Growth	3/04	3/05	3/06	3/07	*3/08
Sales ($ mil.)	0.0%	0.1	0.0	0.1	0.0	0.1
Net income ($ mil.)	—	(0.1)	(0.2)	(0.2)	0.2	(0.1)
Market value ($ mil.)	(14.7%)	0.5	0.7	0.6	0.7	0.3
Employees	(15.9%)	2	2	2	2	1

*Most recent year available

EAGLE MATERIALS INC.

NYSE: EXP

3811 Turtle Creek Blvd., Ste. 1100
Dallas, TX 75219
Phone: 214-432-2000
Fax: 214-432-2100
Web: www.eaglematerials.com

CEO: Steven R. (Steve) Rowley
CFO: D. Craig Kesler
HR: —
FYE: March 31
Type: Public

Eagle Materials is perched near the top of the building materials business. The company produces and distributes gypsum wallboard and cement (each accounting for about 40% of revenues), ready-mix concrete and aggregates, and recycled paperboard. It sells its products to residential, commercial, and industrial construction customers throughout the US. Eagle operates about 20 plants and manufacturing facilities. It also has about 140 railcars for shipping its wallboard products to customers across the country. Eagle Materials is a spinoff of mega-homebuilder Centex Corporation, which founded the company in 1963. It became a separate company in 2004.

	Annual Growth	3/06	3/07	3/08	3/09	3/10
Sales ($ mil.)	(14.1%)	859.7	922.4	749.6	602.2	467.9
Net income ($ mil.)	(34.9%)	161.0	202.7	97.8	41.8	29.0
Market value ($ mil.)	(19.7%)	2,797.9	1,958.4	1,560.0	1,064.1	1,164.6
Employees	(4.2%)	1,600	1,600	1,600	2,000	1,350

EAGLE ROCK ENERGY PARTNERS, L.P.

NASDAQ (GM): EROC

16701 Greenspoint Park Dr., Ste. 200
Houston, TX 77060
Phone: 281-408-1200
Fax: 281-408-1399
Web: www.eaglerockenergy.com

CEO: Joseph A. (Joe) Mills
CFO: Jeffrey P. (Jeff) Wood
HR: —
FYE: December 31
Type: Public

The Eagles were into soft rock, whereas Eagle Rock Energy Partners digs the production, gathering, compressing, treating, processing, transporting, and selling of natural gas. It owns 5,200 miles of natural gas gathering pipelines. The company also fractionates and transports natural gas liquids (NGLs) and earns fees and royalties from its holdings in oil and gas properties. Eagle Rock Energy Partners has primary assets in Alabama, Louisiana, Mississippi, and Texas, and has proved reserves of 116.9 billion cu. ft. of natural gas of equivalent. Directors own 30% of the company through Eagle Rock Holdings, L.P. which is controlled by investment firm Natural Gas Resources.

	Annual Growth	12/05	12/06	12/07	12/08	12/09
Sales ($ mil.)	69.7%	73.7	501.8	910.5	1,743.3	610.5
Net income ($ mil.)	—	2.7	(23.3)	(145.6)	87.5	(171.3)
Market value ($ mil.)	(34.3%)	—	1,140.4	1,022.3	263.4	323.8
Employees	23.9%	150	163	270	348	353

EAGLEPICHER CORPORATION

5850 Mercury Dr., Ste. 250
Dearborn, MI 48126
Phone: 313-749-5500
Fax: 313-749-5502
Web: www.epcorp.com

CEO: David L. Treadwell
CFO: Patrick S. (Pat) Aubry
HR: Benjamin A. DePompei
FYE: December 30
Type: Private

EaglePicher products are small but powerful. Its EaglePicher Technologies subsidiary makes a wide range of batteries and battery storage systems used in aerospace, defense, and commercial applications. Its products are used in the International Space Station and Hubble Space Telescope, as well as in other spacecraft and satellites. EaglePicher Medical Power makes batteries used in pacemakers and other implantable medical devices. Beyond batteries, the company's Wolverine Advanced Materials unit makes gaskets, brake shims, and other parts used to reduce noise and vibration in automotive and industrial products, and its EP Minerals unit produces diatomaceous earth and mineral-based filtration products.

E. & J. GALLO WINERY

600 Yosemite Blvd.
Modesto, CA 95354
Phone: 209-341-3111
Fax: —
Web: www.gallo.com

CEO: Joseph E. (Joe) Gallo
CFO: Doug Vilas
HR: —
FYE: December 31
Type: Private

E. & J. Gallo Winery brings merlot to the masses. The company is one of the world's largest winemakers, thanks in part to its low-end jug and box brands, including Carlo Rossi and Boone's Farm brands. The vintner owns seven wineries and some 15,000 acres of California vineyards; it also contracts with other growers to meet its supply demands. It is the leading US exporter of California wine, selling its some 60 brands in more than 90 countries across the globe. Among its premium wines and imports are those of Gallo Family Vineyards Sonoma Reserve and the Italian wine Ecco Domani. For those who prefer a little more kick to their imbibing, Gallo offers a number of distilled beverages, including brandy and gin.

	Annual Growth	12/04	12/05	12/06	12/07	12/08
Est. sales ($ mil.)	(9.6%)	3,000.0	2,700.0	2,700.0	3,150.0	2,000.0
Employees	4.4%	—	4,400	4,600	5,000	5,000

An in-depth profile of this company is available to Hoover's Online members at hoovers.com.

E & S INTERNATIONAL ENTERPRISES, INC

7801 Hayvenhurst Ave	CEO: Philip Asherian
Van Nuys, CA 91406	CFO: Mark Barron
Phone: 818-887-0700	HR: —
Fax: 818-702-6344	FYE: December 31
Web: www.esintl.com	Type: Private

E & S International Enterprises (also known as ESI) has its fingers in a lot of pies. The company manufactures and sells a variety of consumer products through its subsidiaries. Once a consumer electronics distributor, the company has expanded its product line to include such items as sporting goods, mobile phone batteries, and appliances. It also acts as a broker between manufacturers and retailers, sometimes handling warranty and support functions for the makers. ESI is also in the business of acquiring commercial and residential real estate. The company was founded in 1945 as an electronics distributor.

	Annual Growth	12/04	12/05	12/06	12/07	12/08
Est. sales ($ mil.)	—	—	—	—	—	69.7
Employees	—	—	—	—	—	177

EARLE M. JORGENSEN COMPANY

10650 Alameda St.	CEO: R. Neil McCaffery
Lynwood, CA 90262	CFO: E. Gilbert Leon Jr.
Phone: 323-567-1122	HR: Inger Dickinson
Fax: 323-563-5500	FYE: March 31
Web: www.emjmetals.com	Type: Subsidiary

One of the largest steel distributors in North America, Earle M. Jorgensen primarily sells bars, tubing, and plate products made from carbon, alloy, and stainless steel; aluminum; and brass. Customers include companies in the construction and farm equipment, general machining, industrial equipment, oil and gas, and transportation industries; machining companies account for more than a quarter of sales. The company operates a network of about 40 service centers and processing facilities in the US and Canada. It is a subsidiary of service center giant Reliance Steel & Aluminum.

	Annual Growth	3/04	3/05	3/06	3/07	3/08
Est. sales ($ mil.)	—	—	—	—	—	1,789.8
Employees	—	—	—	—	—	1,800

EARTH FARE, INC.

145 Cane Creek Industrial Park Dr., Ste. 150	CEO: Jack Murphy
Fletcher, NC 28732	CFO: Gary Jones
Phone: 828-281-4800	HR: Jennifer Dotson
Fax: 828-254-7556	FYE: December 31
Web: www.earthfare.com	Type: Private

The destination for shoppers looking for organic milk, soy, and antibiotic-free poultry is Earth Fare, naturally. The regional organic and natural foods supermarket chain operates more than 15 stores in the Carolinas, Georgia, and Tennessee. Its stores are smaller (the largest is 28,000 sq. ft.) than those of its conventional supermarket competitors and national natural foods chains like Whole Foods Market. Even so, Earth Fare stores offer about 26,000 natural and organic products, house cafes and juice bars, sell vitamins and herbs, and offer deli service and cooking classes. Earth Fare was founded in 1975 by Roger Derrough as a single Dinner for the Earth store. Derrough owns Earth Fare with other investors.

EARTH SEARCH SCIENCES, INC.   OTC: ESSE

306 Stoner Loop Rd., Ste. 6	CEO: Larry F. Vance
Lakeside, MT 59922	CFO: Tami J. Story
Phone: 406-751-5200	HR: —
Fax: 406-752-7433	FYE: March 31
Web: www.earthsearch.com	Type: Public

The technology used by Earth Search Sciences (ESSI) is rooted in the stars, not the ground. The company has developed remote sensing instruments (using what is called hyperspectral remote sensing technology) based on NASA's Airborne Visible and Infra-Red Imaging Spectrometer (AVIRIS). The instruments designed by ESSI collect and analyze data for use in oil and gas exploration, mining, hazardous material remediation, and ecosystem monitoring, among other things. The company has served customers in the private, military, and government sectors. Chairman and CEO Larry Vance owns 74% of the company.

	Annual Growth	3/05	3/06	3/07	3/08	3/09
Sales ($ mil.)	—	—	—	—	—	0.0
Net income ($ mil.)	—	—	—	—	—	(8.5)
Market value ($ mil.)	—	—	—	—	—	4.0
Employees	—	—	—	—	—	4

EARTHLINK, INC.   NASDAQ (GS): ELNK

1375 Peachtree St.	CEO: Rolla P. Huff
Atlanta, GA 30309	CFO: Bradley A. (Brad) Ferguson
Phone: 404-815-0770	HR: Stacie Hagan
Fax: 404-892-7616	FYE: December 31
Web: www.earthlink.net	Type: Public

As one of the largest ISPs in the US, EarthLink provides Internet connections to about 3 million consumer and small-business subscribers in that area of the planet. It provides premium broadband access to about one-third of those customers. The company also offers such services as VoIP computer telephony and Web hosting. Earthlink provides broadband access over cable lines through agreements with network operators including Time Warner Cable, Bright House, and Comcast, while DSL access is made available over lines owned by Covad, AT&T, Verizon, and Qwest. Subsidiary New Edge Networks implements and manages private data networks in addition to providing Internet access and Web hosting for businesses.

	Annual Growth	12/05	12/06	12/07	12/08	12/09
Sales ($ mil.)	(13.5%)	1,290.1	1,301.3	1,216.0	955.6	723.7
Net income ($ mil.)	19.1%	142.8	5.0	(135.1)	189.6	287.1
Market value ($ mil.)	(7.0%)	1,199.0	766.2	763.0	729.5	896.8
Employees	(22.6%)	1,732	2,210	998	754	623

EAST PENN MANUFACTURING CO., INC.

Deka Road	CEO: Daniel Langdon
Lyon Station, PA 19536	CFO: Christopher E. Pruitt
Phone: 610-682-6361	HR: —
Fax: 610-682-4781	FYE: May 31
Web: www.eastpenn-deka.com	Type: Private

East Penn Manufacturing charged forward to become one of the US's leading makers of lead-acid batteries for the stationary, industrial, automotive, commercial, marine, and specialty markets. Under the Deka brand, the company manufactures batteries that provide juice to everything from cell phone transmitters to cars and trucks to wheelchairs and mining tractors. East Penn, which also has a facility in Iowa and exports worldwide, makes battery cables, starter cables, terminals, and other accessories. OEM customers include Daimler Trucks North America, Deere & Company, and Harley-Davidson. East Penn chairman DeLight Breidegam Jr. controls the company, which he and his father founded in 1946.

EAST TEXAS MEDICAL CENTER REGIONAL HEALTHCARE SYSTEM

1000 S. Beckham Ave.	CEO: Elmer G. Ellis
Tyler, TX 75701	CFO: Byron Hale
Phone: 903-597-0351	HR: —
Fax: 903-535-6100	FYE: October 31
Web: www.etmc.org	Type: Not-for-profit

East Texas Medical Center (ETMC) Regional Healthcare System helps meet the health care needs of residents of the Piney Woods. The not-for-profit health system operates about a dozen hospitals across eastern Texas, along with behavioral, rehabilitation, and home health care businesses. Its flagship 450-bed Tyler location serves as the hub and referral center for satellite medical centers located in more rural locations. The system also features numerous primary care and outpatient clinics throughout the region. In addition, ETMC operates an emergency ambulance service subsidiary and a clinical laboratory, which provide services to the facilities of ETMC Regional Healthcare System.

	Annual Growth	10/04	10/05	10/06	10/07	10/08
Est. sales ($ mil.)	—	—	—	—	—	877.0
Employees	—	—	—	—	—	7,600

EAST WEST BANCORP, INC.

NASDAQ (GS): EWBC

135 N. Los Robles Ave.	CEO: Dominic Ng
Pasadena, CA 91101	CFO: Irene Oh
Phone: 626-768-6000	HR: —
Fax: 626-799-3167	FYE: December 31
Web: www.eastwestbank.com	Type: Public

East West Bancorp is the holding company for East West Bank, which operates more than 110 branches in California, mainly in and around Los Angeles and the San Francisco Bay area. The bank also has more than 25 additional branches in the Atlanta, Boston, Houston, New York, and Seattle metropolitan areas, as well as locations in China, Hong Kong, and Taiwan. It caters to the Chinese-American community and provides international banking and trade financing to importers/exporters doing business in the Asia/Pacific region. East West Bank offers multilingual service in English, Cantonese, Mandarin, Spanish, and Vietnamese.

	Annual Growth	12/05	12/06	12/07	12/08	12/09
Assets ($ mil.)	25.5%	8,278.3	10,823.7	11,852.2	12,422.8	20,559.2
Net income ($ mil.)	(6.7%)	108.4	143.4	161.2	(49.7)	82.0
Market value ($ mil.)	(18.9%)	5,398.6	5,240.3	3,584.8	2,362.7	2,337.6
Employees	25.6%	1,078	1,312	1,361	1,346	2,679

EASTER SEALS, INC.

230 W. Monroe St., Ste. 1800	CEO: Gerard P. Mattimore
Chicago, IL 60606	CFO: —
Phone: 312-726-6200	HR: —
Fax: 312-726-1494	FYE: August 31
Web: www.easter-seals.org	Type: Not-for-profit

A year-round effort that has nothing to do with Easter, seals, or flowers, the National Easter Seal Society annually helps more than 1.3 million children and adults with disabilities through over 550 service centers in the US, Puerto Rico, Canada, and Australia. The organization offers medical rehabilitation, job training, child care, and adult day services. It began in 1907 as the National Society for Crippled Children and launched its first "seal" campaign around Easter in 1934. Supporters placed stickers or seals depicting the lily, a symbol of renewal, on letters and envelopes. The campaign was so successful and the symbol so associated with the organization that it changed its name in 1967.

	Annual Growth	8/04	8/05	8/06	8/07	8/08
Est. sales ($ mil.)	—	—	—	—	—	92.8
Employees	—	—	—	—	—	200

EASTERN AMERICAN NATURAL GAS TRUST

NYSE: NGT

919 Congress Ave., Ste. 500	CEO: Michael J. (Mike) Ulrich
Austin, TX 78701	CFO: —
Phone: 800-852-1422	HR: —
Fax: 512-479-2553	FYE: December 31
	Type: Public

Shareholders of Eastern American Natural Gas Trust know all about the clean-burning, royalty-producing attributes of natural gas. The trust receives royalty interests from 650 producing natural gas wells in West Virginia and Pennsylvania and operated by Eastern American Energy. The trust distributes the royalties to its shareholders quarterly. As a grantor trust, Eastern American Natural Gas Trust does not pay federal income taxes, and the production on some of its wells qualifies for tax credits because the wells are located on hard-to-drill formations. The trust, which in 2008 reported proved reserves of 12.9 billion cu. ft. of natural gas equivalent on its properties, will be liquidated no later than 2013.

EASTERN BANK CORPORATION

265 Franklin St.	CEO: Richard E. Holbrook
Boston, MA 02110	CFO: Charles M. Johnston
Phone: 617-897-1008	HR: Edward J. Saras
Fax: 617-897-1105	FYE: December 31
Web: www.easternbank.com	Type: Mutual company

Mutually owned Eastern Bank has more than 80 branches throughout Massachusetts. Founded in 1818, the bank offers retail and commercial banking products, including checking and savings accounts, investments, and credit cards. Its lending activities focus on commercial loans and leases, residential mortgages, and consumer loans. The bank also provides wealth management services and offers mutual funds and alternative investments through a third-party provider. Insurance agency subsidiary Eastern Insurance offers personal and commercial coverage, group health and life insurance, employee benefit plans, and 401(k) administration through more than 25 locations.

	Annual Growth	12/04	12/05	12/06	12/07	12/08
Assets ($ mil.)	6.6%	5,125.5	6,259.4	6,580.0	6,794.8	6,616.0
Net income ($ mil.)	(34.6%)	43.1	49.2	72.4	62.6	7.9
Employees	2.5%	1,462	1,519	1,459	1,469	1,613

THE EASTERN COMPANY

NYSE Amex: EML

112 Bridge St.	CEO: Leonard F. Leganza
Naugatuck, CT 06770	CFO: John L. Sullivan III
Phone: 203-729-2255	HR: —
Fax: 203-723-8653	FYE: December 31
Web: www.easterncompany.com	Type: Public

The Eastern Company has latched on to the security industry. The company's security products group makes coin acceptors used in laundry facilities, smart card payment systems, and keyless locks sold under such brands as Sesamee, Presto, and Huski. It also manufactures industrial hardware, including latches, locks, and hinges, used by the transportation industry. Eastern owns a foundry that makes metal anchoring devices to support underground mine roofs, clamps for construction, and railroad brake system components. The company sells mainly to manufacturers, distributors, and locksmiths through its operations in the US, Canada, China, Mexico, and Taiwan.

	Annual Growth	12/05	12/06	12/07	12/08	12/09
Sales ($ mil.)	0.8%	109.1	138.5	156.3	135.9	112.7
Net income ($ mil.)	(31.0%)	4.4	9.7	10.1	4.5	1.0
Market value ($ mil.)	0.8%	78.9	117.9	111.2	52.2	81.5
Employees	(1.8%)	642	695	741	696	597

EASTERN INSURANCE HOLDINGS, INC.

NASDAQ (GM): EIHI

25 Race Ave.
Lancaster, PA 17603
Phone: 717-396-7095
Fax: 717-399-3781
Web: www.easterninsuranceholdings.com

CEO: Bruce M. Eckert
CFO: Kevin M. Shook
HR: —
FYE: December 31
Type: Public

Through its operating subsidiaries, Eastern Insurance Holdings sells workers' compensation and some group benefits coverage to companies with fewer than 300 employees. It sells its workers' compensation products in Delaware, Maryland, and Pennsylvania through subsidiaries Eastern Alliance and Allied Eastern. Eastern Insurance Holdings' Eastern Re unit, based in the Cayman Islands, provides workers' compensation products through "rent-a-captive" arrangements to self-insured groups; it also provides specialty reinsurance for underground storage and non-hazardous waste transportation insurance programs. Subsidiary Eastern Life and Heath Insurance underwrites group benefits, including dental, life, and disability.

	Annual Growth	12/05	12/06	12/07	12/08	12/09
Assets ($ mil.)	19.8%	190.2	368.2	385.5	377.3	391.5
Net income ($ mil.)	(14.9%)	16.0	8.3	18.7	(17.4)	8.4
Market value ($ mil.)	(16.0%)	—	141.1	159.8	77.8	83.5
Employees	7.5%	148	136	163	207	198

EASTERN LIGHT CAPITAL, INCORPORATED

NYSE Amex: ELC

100 Pine St., Ste. 560
San Francisco, CA 94111
Phone: 415-693-9500
Fax: 415-693-9501
Web: www.caitreit.com

CEO: Richard J. Wrensen
CFO: Richard J. Wrensen
HR: —
FYE: December 31
Type: Public

Eastern Light Capital (ELC) is a real estate investment trust (REIT) focused on loans rather than properties. The company formerly originated and purchased (through mortgage banks and brokers) non-conforming first and second home mortgages and home equity loans collateralized mainly by properties in California. ELC suspended those operations in 2006, but continues to hold such investments in it portfolio, which consists primarily of loans that do not meet the purchasing standards set by Fannie Mae, Freddie Mac, and other government-sponsored housing enterprises. ELC is exploring investments in other REIT-compliant assets. WrenCap Funding, a subsidiary, invests in exchange-listed securities.

	Annual Growth	12/05	12/06	12/07	12/08	12/09
Sales ($ mil.)	(43.0%)	3.8	2.5	1.1	0.7	0.4
Net income ($ mil.)	—	(0.2)	(1.3)	(2.9)	—	(2.8)
Market value ($ mil.)	(15.1%)	2.6	2.9	1.4	—	1.4
Employees	(32.3%)	19	16	4	4	4

EASTERN MOUNTAIN SPORTS, INC.

1 Vose Farm Rd.
Peterborough, NH 03458
Phone: 603-924-9571
Fax: 603-924-9138
Web: www.emsonline.com

CEO: William O. (Will) Manzer
CFO: Robert (Bob) Mayerson
HR: —
FYE: January 31
Type: Private

Eastern Mountain Sports (EMS) can prepare you for a life of climb. EMS sells a wide range of outdoor gear and apparel from about 70 stores in a dozen East Coast states and its website. Outdoor enthusiasts can purchase or rent tents, sleeping bags, and other equipment — choosing from brands such as Patagonia, Columbia, The North Face, and Teva. EMS offers outdoor skills clinics, provides guides for hire, and arranges day and overnight trips. It also operates climbing, skiing, kayaking, and mountain biking schools. EMS was founded in 1967.

	Annual Growth	1/04	1/05	1/06	1/07	1/08
Est. sales ($ mil.)	—	—	—	—	—	29.3
Employees	—	—	—	—	—	400

EASTERN VIRGINIA BANKSHARES, INC.

NASDAQ (GM): EVBS

330 Hospital Rd.
Tappahannock, VA 22560
Phone: 804-443-8400
Fax: 804-445-1047
Web: www.evb.org

CEO: Joe A. Shearin
CFO: Douglas C. Haskett II
HR: M. Robin Jett
FYE: December 31
Type: Public

Founded in 1997, Eastern Virginia Bankshares is the holding company for EVB, a community bank that operates more than two dozen branches in — believe it or not — eastern Virginia. Targeting individuals and local business customers, the bank offers such standard retail services as checking and savings accounts, money market accounts, CDs, IRAs, and credit cards. Residential mortgages make up nearly half of the company's loan portfolio, which also includes commercial real estate, construction, business, and consumer loans. Subsidiary EVB Financial Services owns interests in companies that offer investments and insurance.

	Annual Growth	12/05	12/06	12/07	12/08	12/09
Assets ($ mil.)	10.2%	763.9	851.4	926.7	1,051.4	1,126.3
Net income ($ mil.)	—	6.7	7.2	8.8	3.1	(8.8)
Market value ($ mil.)	(24.0%)	127.1	134.6	101.1	52.6	42.4
Employees	1.6%	296	296	305	317	315

EASTGROUP PROPERTIES, INC.

NYSE: EGP

190 E. Capitol St., Ste. 400
Jackson, MS 39201
Phone: 601-354-3555
Fax: 601-352-1441
Web: www.eastgroup.net

CEO: David H. Hoster II
CFO: N. Keith McKey
HR: —
FYE: December 31
Type: Public

EastGroup Properties points its compass all across the Sunbelt. The self-administered real estate investment trust (REIT) invests in, develops, and manages industrial properties, with a particular emphasis on Florida, Texas, Arizona, and California. EastGroup specializes in operating multi-tenant distribution and bulk distribution facilities, from 5,000 to 50,000 sq. ft. in size, located near major transportation hubs. Its portfolio includes more than 200 industrial properties and one office building, totaling more than 27 million sq. ft. of leasable space. The REIT has developed build-to-suit projects for clients including United Stationers Supply Company and Dal-Tile Corporation.

	Annual Growth	12/05	12/06	12/07	12/08	12/09
Sales ($ mil.)	8.0%	126.5	133.6	150.7	168.6	172.4
Net income ($ mil.)	5.1%	22.2	29.2	29.7	34.1	27.1
Market value ($ mil.)	(4.0%)	1,216.6	1,442.9	1,127.4	958.5	1,031.3
Employees	2.8%	61	64	63	70	68

EASTMAN CHEMICAL COMPANY

NYSE: EMN

200 S. Wilcox Dr.
Kingsport, TN 37662
Phone: 423-229-2000
Fax: 423-229-2145
Web: www.eastman.com

CEO: James P. (Jim) Rogers
CFO: Curtis E. Espeland
HR: —
FYE: December 31
Type: Public

Eastman Chemical can recall its past through photos — it was once part of film giant Eastman Kodak. The company has developed into a major producer of chemicals, fibers, and plastics. Among Eastman's operating segments are its CASPI (coatings, adhesives, specialty polymers, and inks), Specialty Plastics (engineering polymers), and Fibers (acetate tow and textile fibers) units. Its Performance Polymers segment is the #1 maker of polyethylene terephthalate (PET), a plastic used to make packaging for soft drinks, food, and water. The largest segment manufactures Performance Chemicals and Intermediates. Eastman's products go into such items as food and medical packaging, films, and toothbrushes.

	Annual Growth	12/05	12/06	12/07	12/08	12/09
Sales ($ mil.)	(8.0%)	7,059.0	7,450.0	6,830.0	6,726.0	5,047.0
Net income ($ mil.)	(29.7%)	557.0	409.0	300.0	346.0	136.0
Market value ($ mil.)	4.0%	3,734.8	4,293.6	4,422.5	2,295.6	4,361.0
Employees	(4.5%)	12,000	11,000	10,800	10,500	10,000

An in-depth profile of this company is available to Hoover's Online members at hoovers.com.

531

EASTMAN KODAK COMPANY

NYSE: EK

343 State St.
Rochester, NY 14650
Phone: 585-724-4000
Fax: 585-724-1089
Web: www.kodak.com

CEO: Antonio M. Perez
CFO: Frank S. Sklarsky
HR: Essie L. Calhoun
FYE: December 31
Type: Public

When Kodak made Brownies, folks began to say cheese. The inventor of the Brownie camera (1900), Kodak has retouched its image from a top maker of photographic film to a provider of imaging technology products and services to the photographic and graphic communications markets. The firm reorganized its business to focus less on film sales and more on sales of digital cameras and imaging systems. It operates through three segments: Consumer Digital Imaging Group; Film, Photofinishing, and Entertainment Group; and Graphic Communications Group. Kodak's multiyear shift to become a digital technology business spurred the company in 2009 to discontinue its iconic Kodachrome color film, which had logged sales declines.

	Annual Growth	12/05	12/06	12/07	12/08	12/09
Sales ($ mil.)	(14.6%)	14,268.0	13,274.0	10,301.0	9,416.0	7,606.0
Net income ($ mil.)	—	(1,314.0)	(601.0)	676.0	(442.0)	(215.0)
Market value ($ mil.)	(34.8%)	6,286.8	6,931.6	5,875.8	1,767.8	1,133.8
Employees	(20.7%)	51,100	40,900	26,900	24,400	20,250

EASTON-BELL SPORTS, INC.

7855 Haskell Ave., Ste. 200
Van Nuys, CA 91406
Phone: 818-902-5800
Fax: —
Web: www.eastonbellsports.com

CEO: Paul E. Harrington
CFO: Mark A. Tripp
HR: Jackelyn E. Werblo
FYE: December 31
Type: Private

Afraid your favorite athlete might take a knockin' on the noggin? Easton-Bell Sports (EBS) products can help soften the blow. A leading maker of helmets and other sporting goods used by professional and recreational athletes, EBS caters to the baseball, softball, football, and hockey markets, as well as to cycling, snowsports, and powersports enthusiasts. The company's items are sold under the Easton, Bell, Giro, and Riddell names, among others. It also owns the licensing rights for the MacGregor golf brand. EBS's products are sold at national chains the likes of Wal-Mart and to local retailers. A subsidiary of RBG Holdings, EBS was created by the merger of Riddell Bell and Easton Sports in 2006.

EASYLINK SERVICES INTERNATIONAL

NASDAQ (CM): ESIC

6025 The Corners Pkwy., Ste. 100
Norcross, GA 30092
Phone: 678-533-8000
Fax: —
Web: www.easylink.com

CEO: Thomas J. Stallings
CFO: Glen E. Shipley
HR: —
FYE: July 31
Type: Public

EasyLink Services International Corporation makes sure clients get the message. The company provides electronic data interchange (EDI) and telex software and services through its Supply Chain Messaging division. Its data translation systems allow trading partners with incompatible information systems to exchange invoices, purchase orders, shipping notices, and other documents. EasyLink's On Demand Messaging segment provides a document delivery system that handles fax, e-mail, and messaging communications. The company offers services ranging from consulting and training to outsourced document processing. EasyLink gets three-quarters of its sales in North America.

	Annual Growth	7/05	7/06	7/07	7/08	7/09
Sales ($ mil.)	50.4%	16.7	19.8	21.9	92.2	85.4
Net income ($ mil.)	—	0.2	3.0	2.7	16.3	(11.2)
Market value ($ mil.)	(2.2%)	55.6	104.4	83.4	90.7	50.9
Employees	28.3%	108	134	368	359	293

EAT AT JOE'S LTD.

OTC: JOES

670 White Plains Rd., Ste. 120
Scarsdale, NY 10583
Phone: 914-725-2700
Fax: 914-725-8663

CEO: Joseph (Joe) Fiore
CFO: Joseph (Joe) Fiore
HR: —
FYE: December 31
Type: Public

Eat At Joe's operates a themed casual-dining restaurant at the Philadelphia airport that offers breakfast, lunch, and dinner. The concept features such interior appointments as 1950s-era Harley-Davidsons, booths resembling 1957 Chevy interiors, and tabletop jukeboxes. Patrons can choose from such menu items as hot dogs, burgers, and meatloaf. CEO Joseph Fiore owns more than 60% of Eat at Joe's.

	Annual Growth	12/05	12/06	12/07	12/08	12/09
Sales ($ mil.)	0.0%	1.3	1.4	1.4	1.6	1.3
Net income ($ mil.)	—	(0.4)	(0.5)	(0.6)	(1.0)	0.3
Market value ($ mil.)	(12.4%)	1.8	1.6	1.3	0.4	1.1
Employees	(6.9%)	12	12	14	11	9

EATON CORPORATION

NYSE: ETN

1111 Superior Ave. East, Eaton Center
Cleveland, OH 44114
Phone: 216-523-5000
Fax: 216-523-4787
Web: www.eaton.com

CEO: Alexander M. (Sandy) Cutler
CFO: Richard H. Fearon
HR: James W. (Jim) McGill
FYE: December 31
Type: Public

When it comes to diversification, Eaton favors an all-you-can-eat approach. The manufacturer has made dozens of acquisitions (as well as divestitures) in its long and storied history. The company's product lines include electrical power distribution and control equipment, hydraulic products for use in mobile and industrial applications, aerospace propulsion systems, and truck safety systems. It is also one of the world's largest manufacturers of grips for golf clubs. Electrical power management is its leading line of business these days, accounting for about half of Eaton's sales. Geographically, the company makes more than half of its sales within the US.

	Annual Growth	12/05	12/06	12/07	12/08	12/09
Sales ($ mil.)	1.7%	11,115.0	12,370.0	13,033.0	15,376.0	11,873.0
Net income ($ mil.)	(16.8%)	805.0	950.0	994.0	1,058.0	385.0
Market value ($ mil.)	(1.3%)	11,244.3	12,593.5	16,248.8	8,331.4	10,662.7
Employees	4.4%	59,000	60,000	64,000	75,000	70,000

EATON VANCE CORP.

NYSE: EV

255 State St.
Boston, MA 02109
Phone: 617-482-8260
Fax: —
Web: www.eatonvance.com

CEO: Thomas E. (Tom) Faust Jr.
CFO: Robert J. (Bob) Whelan
HR: —
FYE: October 31
Type: Public

A veritable supermarket of investing, Eaton Vance offers more than 100 mutual funds and manages investments for institutional and wealthy individual clients. Its investment specialties include tax-managed equity funds, municipal bond funds, floating-rate bank-loan funds, closed-end funds, and equity funds. Its Eaton Vance Distributors unit markets and sells its funds, separate accounts, and retail managed accounts via sales associates in the US, Europe, and Latin America, as well as a network of brokers, independent financial advisors, banks, and insurance firms. Altogether, Eaton Vance has approximately $160 billion of assets under management.

	Annual Growth	10/05	10/06	10/07	10/08	10/09
Assets ($ mil.)	11.2%	702.5	668.2	966.8	968.4	1,075.1
Net income ($ mil.)	(5.0%)	159.9	160.0	142.8	195.7	130.1
Market value ($ mil.)	3.4%	2,946.2	3,677.1	5,926.7	2,606.2	3,363.2
Employees	8.8%	757	869	5,900	1,061	1,059

EAU TECHNOLOGIES, INC.

OTC: EAUI

1890 Cobb International Blvd., Ste. A
Kennesaw, GA 30152
Phone: 678-388-9492
Fax: 770-424-8684
Web: www.eau-x.com

CEO: Wade R. Bradley
CFO: Brian D. Heinhold
HR: —
FYE: December 31
Type: Public

Of all the vowels, O is EAU's bread and butter (as in H2O). Using water electrolysis technology, EAU Technologies (formerly Electric Aquagenics Unlimited) makes equipment and process systems that clean and disinfect surfaces and foods. Its Empowered Water generators are sold and leased to companies in search of improved cleaning and sanitizing. The firm's water-based, nontoxic products reduce bacteria, viruses, spores, and molds in food processing, living surfaces, and other environments. Director Peter Ullrich, individually and through his Water Science firm, is EAU Technologies largest shareholder. Water Science is also EAU's biggest customer and it licenses EAU technology in Latin America.

	Annual Growth	12/05	12/06	12/07	12/08	12/09
Sales ($ mil.)	0.0%	0.7	1.9	0.9	0.4	0.7
Net income ($ mil.)	—	(13.2)	(8.5)	(10.9)	(6.7)	(3.4)
Market value ($ mil.)	(44.2%)	51.6	18.0	23.0	6.0	5.0
Employees	(32.7%)	44	29	16	13	9

EBARA TECHNOLOGIES, INC.

51 Main Ave.
Sacramento, CA 95838
Phone: 916-920-5451
Fax: 916-830-1900
Web: www.ebaratech.com

CEO: Mitsuhiko Shirakashi
CFO: Ray Campbell
HR: —
FYE: March 31
Type: Subsidiary

Ebara Technologies takes it seriously when its parent says, "keep your room clean." Ebara manufactures cleanroom equipment necessary in semiconductor production. Through its two divisions, Components and Semiconductor Equipment, Ebara provides cleaning and ozone, systems, exhaust systems, chemical mechanical polishing systems, wafer plating, heaters, and other equipment used in the electronics industry for silicon wafer processing. It also offers solar exhaust management products. Ebara Technologies has sales offices throughout the US, and sales and production facilities in Asia and Europe. Founded in 1990, the company is a part of Ebara Corporation's Precision Machinery Group.

EBAY INC.

NASDAQ (GS): EBAY

2145 Hamilton Ave.
San Jose, CA 95125
Phone: 408-376-7400
Fax: 408-516-8811
Web: www.ebay.com

CEO: John J. Donahoe
CFO: Robert H. (Bob) Swan
HR: Elizabeth L. (Beth) Axelrod
FYE: December 31
Type: Public

"I got it on eBay" is barreling its way into the lexicon of the new millennium and placing a cyber-grin on the corporate face of online auctioneer extraordinaire eBay. Trading $2,000 worth of goods every second, the company offers an online forum for selling merchandise worldwide, from fine antiques to the latest video games. eBay, which generates revenue through listing and selling fees and through advertising, boasts more than 90 million active users. It also sees gains from its online payments division, comprising PayPal and Bill Me Later, and other e-commerce platforms, including StubHub and Half.com. In November 2009 eBay sold a majority stake in its Skype Internet phone service to an investor group.

	Annual Growth	12/05	12/06	12/07	12/08	12/09
Sales ($ mil.)	17.7%	4,552.4	5,969.7	7,672.3	8,541.3	8,727.4
Net income ($ mil.)	21.9%	1,082.0	1,125.6	348.3	1,779.5	2,389.1
Market value ($ mil.)	(14.1%)	56,487.2	39,300.6	43,378.3	18,245.3	30,753.0
Employees	6.8%	12,600	13,200	15,000	16,200	16,400

EBIX, INC.

NASDAQ (GM): EBIX

5 Concourse Pkwy., Ste. 3200
Atlanta, GA 30328
Phone: 678-281-2020
Fax: 678-281-2019
Web: www.ebix.com

CEO: Robin Raina
CFO: Robert (Bob) Kerris
HR: —
FYE: December 31
Type: Public

Ebix knows a lot about the insurance biz. The company sells insurance industry software products and professional services to property/casualty insurers, brokerages, and individuals in Asia, Australia, Europe, and North America. The company's EbixExchange service acts as an online auction house where buyers and carriers can exchange bids for auto, home, health, life, and other types of insurance, while paying Ebix a fee on each transaction. Ebix also provides agency management software that includes workflow and customer relationship management (CRM) capabilities, as well as other back-office functions, for insurance brokers and insurance carriers.

	Annual Growth	12/05	12/06	12/07	12/08	12/09
Sales ($ mil.)	41.9%	24.1	29.3	42.8	74.8	97.7
Net income ($ mil.)	73.3%	4.3	6.0	12.7	27.3	38.8
Market value ($ mil.)	65.0%	77.0	108.8	285.0	279.2	570.3
Employees	43.0%	229	292	391	637	958

EBSCO INDUSTRIES INC.

5724 Hwy. 280 East
Birmingham, AL 35242
Phone: 205-991-6600
Fax: 205-995-1636
Web: www.ebscoind.com

CEO: F. Dixon Brooke Jr.
CFO: Richard L. (Rick) Bozzelli
HR: John C. Thompson
FYE: June 30
Type: Private

Few portfolios are more diverse than that of EBSCO Industries (short for Elton B. Stephens Company). Among the conglomerate's more than 40 information services, manufacturing, and sales subsidiaries are magazine subscription and fulfillment firms, a fishing lure manufacturer, a rifle manufacturer, a specialty office and computer furniture retailer, and a real estate company. Its main businesses revolve around the publishing industry: EBSCO operates a subscription management agency and is one of the largest publishers of digital information. It has a database of more than 300,000 title listings from more than 78,000 publishers worldwide. The family of founder Elton B. Stephens Sr. owns the company.

EBY-BROWN COMPANY, LLC

280 W. Shuman Blvd., Ste. 280
Naperville, IL 60566
Phone: 630-778-2800
Fax: 630-778-2830
Web: www.eby-brown.com

CEO: Richard W. (Dick) Wake
CFO: Mark Smetana
HR: Laura Brush
FYE: September 30
Type: Private

Eby-Brown makes its money on such vices as munchies and nicotine. The company is a leading convenience store supplier that distributes more than 16,000 products to some 13,000 retail locations in 30 states, mostly east of the Mississippi. It operates about half a dozen distribution centers that supply such items as beverages, candy and snack foods, frozen and refrigerated foods, tobacco products, and general merchandise. In addition, the company offers advertising and promotion services for its customers. The family-owned Eby-Brown was founded in 1887 by the Wake family.

An in-depth profile of this company is available to Hoover's Online members at hoovers.com.

533

ECB BANCORP, INC.

NASDAQ (GM): ECBE

35050 US Hwy. 264
Engelhard, NC 27824
Phone: 252-925-9411
Fax: 252-925-8491
Web: www.ecbbancorp.com

CEO: A. Dwight Utz
CFO: Thomas M. Crowder
HR: —
FYE: December 31
Type: Public

ECB Bancorp Enjoys Community Banking. The holding company owns The East Carolina Bank, which serves individuals, small to midsized businesses, and local governments through about 20 branches in eastern North Carolina and the Outer Banks. The bank, which opened in a barbershop in 1920, provides checking, savings, money market, NOW, and individual retirement accounts, plus certificates of deposit. It mainly originates real estate loans (approximately 75% of its loan portfolio), including residential and commercial mortgages and construction and land development loans. The East Carolina Bank also writes commercial, consumer, and credit card loans.

	Annual Growth	12/05	12/06	12/07	12/08	12/09
Assets ($ mil.)	12.9%	547.7	624.1	643.9	841.9	888.7
Net income ($ mil.)	(25.6%)	4.9	5.6	4.8	3.4	1.5
Market value ($ mil.)	(19.8%)	76.7	92.9	72.9	45.6	31.7
Employees	2.3%	203	195	218	229	222

ECC CAPITAL CORPORATION

Pink Sheets: ECRO

1733 Alton Pkwy.
Irvine, CA 92606
Phone: 949-955-8700
Fax: 866-405-6836
Web: www.ecccapital.com

CEO: Steven G. Holder
CFO: Roque A. Santi
HR: —
FYE: December 31
Type: Public

ECC Capital refused to conform — to credit scoring criteria. The real estate investment trust (REIT) originates and purchases non-conforming residential real estate loans. Subsidiary Performance Credit, which used to act as a wholesale originator of nonconforming loans, now provides financing to ECC Capital's clients. The company is licensed in California, Georgia, Illinois, Massachusetts, Minnesota, Mississippi, and New Hampshire. In 2007 ECC Capital sold its wholesale mortgage banking subsidiary Encore Credit to Bear Stearns. Concurrent with that transaction, the REIT also sold its portfolio of direct-to-consumer loans to ResCap. It is now seeking a buyer for the remainder of its securitized assets.

ECHELON CORPORATION

NASDAQ (GM): ELON

550 Meridian Ave.
San Jose, CA 95126
Phone: 408-938-5200
Fax: 408-790-3800
Web: www.echelon.com

CEO: Robert R. (Bob) Maxfield
CFO: Oliver R. (Chris) Stanfield
HR: Jill Hollister
FYE: December 31
Type: Public

Echelon wants to take control systems to the next level. The company designs hardware and software that link and automate industrial equipment, building environments, and devices ranging from light switches to conveyor belts. Its open-source operating system, LonWorks Network Services, lets equipment interact through local networks and the Internet. Echelon's hardware — transceivers, routers, network interfaces — can sense, monitor, and control such equipment as automatic doors, security systems, and railcars. Echelon also provides an automated electricity metering system called Networked Energy Services (NES).

	Annual Growth	12/05	12/06	12/07	12/08	12/09
Sales ($ mil.)	8.6%	74.4	57.3	137.6	134.0	103.3
Net income ($ mil.)	—	(19.7)	(24.4)	(14.5)	(25.8)	(32.0)
Market value ($ mil.)	10.2%	323.2	330.3	852.1	336.5	477.2
Employees	4.9%	269	283	319	325	326

ECHO GLOBAL LOGISTICS, INC.

NASDAQ (GM): ECHO

600 W. Chicago Ave., Ste. 725
Chicago, IL 60610
Phone: 800-354-7993
Fax: 888-796-4445
Web: www.echo.com

CEO: Douglas R. (Doug) Waggoner
CFO: David B. (Dave) Menzel
HR: Debbie Bowen
FYE: December 31
Type: Public

By land, air, or sea, Echo Global Logistics can help you deliver the goods. The company provides a wide range of transportation services, including truckload, small parcel, domestic air, international, and expedited services. In order to facilitate the shipping process, the firm also offers assistance with logistics such as claims processing, rate negotiation, and shipment execution and tracking. In addition, its Evolved Transportation Manager (ETM) software analyzes clients' transportation needs and helps reduce costs, as well as manages all procedures in shipping. Established in 2005, Echo Global Logistics serves more than 4,600 customers in the manufacturing and consumer products industries, among others.

	Annual Growth	12/05	12/06	12/07	12/08	12/09
Sales ($ mil.)	144.2%	7.3	33.2	95.5	202.8	259.6
Net income ($ mil.)	—	(0.5)	(0.2)	1.7	2.9	5.2
Market value ($ mil.)	—	—	—	—	—	276.7
Employees	64.5%	—	—	245	553	663

ECHO METRIX, INC.

OTC: EHMI

6800 Jericho Tpke., Ste. 208E
Syosset, NY 11791
Phone: 516-802-0223
Fax: 516-802-0228
Web: www.sentryparentalcontrols.com

CEO: Jeffrey Greene
CFO: Erica Zalbert
HR: —
FYE: December 31
Type: Public

Echo Metrix (formerly SearchHelp) makes sure children are always under a watchful eye. The company provides parental control software designed to monitor the activity of children while they surf the Web, send instant messages, or chat online. Its Sentry At Home software alerts parents via e-mail or mobile phone when established usage guidelines are violated. The company's Sentry Remote software allows parents to monitor their children's online activities in real-time and remotely shut down their computers. Echo Metrix also developed an application for tracking registered sex offenders, but it decided to discontinue that line in 2008.

	Annual Growth	12/05	12/06	12/07	12/08	12/09
Sales ($ mil.)	—	1.7	0.3	0.1	0.1	0.0
Net income ($ mil.)	—	(3.8)	(4.0)	(6.3)	(5.2)	(4.5)
Market value ($ mil.)	(36.1%)	36.5	21.9	16.2	10.5	6.1
Employees	(8.5%)	10	9	9	9	7

ECHO THERAPEUTICS, INC.

OTC: ECTE

10 Forge Pkwy.
Franklin, MA 02038
Phone: 508-553-8850
Fax: 508-553-8760
Web: www.echotx.com

CEO: Patrick T. (Pat) Mooney
CFO: Harry G. Mitchell
HR: —
FYE: December 31
Type: Public

Echo Therapeutics (formerly Sontra Medical) tries not to scratch the surface. The company develops instruments for transdermal (through the skin) drug delivery and diagnostics. Its devices use gentle abrasion and ultrasound technologies to painlessly introduce drugs without breaking the skin. The firm's SonoPrep technology is being developed for use in glucose monitoring under the name Symphony. Echo is also developing Azone, a transdermal technology used for reformulated drugs already on the market. Lead Azone product candidate Durhalieve treats dermatoses and is under review by the FDA. The company acquired private transdermal therapeutics firm Echo Therapeutics in 2007 and took on the acquired firm's name.

	Annual Growth	12/05	12/06	12/07	12/08	12/09
Sales ($ mil.)	59.7%	0.2	0.1	0.1	0.0	1.3
Net income ($ mil.)	—	(5.7)	(5.3)	(13.2)	(10.6)	(11.0)
Market value ($ mil.)	(22.4%)	136.7	6.1	48.0	11.6	49.4
Employees	(14.9%)	21	5	16	13	11

ECHOSTAR CORPORATION

NASDAQ (GS): SATS

90 Inverness Circle E.	CEO: Michael T. Dugan
Englewood, CO 80112	CFO: Bernard L. (Bernie) Han
Phone: 303-706-4444	HR: —
Fax: —	FYE: December 31
Web: www.echostar.com	Type: Public

EchoStar is thinking outside the set-top box. Spun off from DISH Network at the beginning of 2008, the company provides set-top boxes to direct-to-home satellite service providers. Its set-top portfolio includes standard and high-definition devices, some of which incorporate digital video recorders. Other products include satellite dishes, remote controls, and analog-to-digital converters. In addition to its traditional business, the company plans to launch a fixed satellite service business using its fleet of eight owned or leased in-orbit satellites. EchoStar also owns Sling Media, which provides equipment that allows consumers to remotely manage and watch TV programming on their PCs or handheld devices.

	Annual Growth	12/05	12/06	12/07	12/08	12/09
Sales ($ mil.)	5.9%	1,513.7	29.1	1,544.1	2,150.5	1,903.6
Net income ($ mil.)	—	(44.9)	(20.9)	(85.3)	(944.0)	364.7
Market value ($ mil.)	3.4%	—	—	1,601.9	1,265.0	1,713.3
Employees	17.0%	—	1,500	1,500	2,100	2,400

ECI TELECOM DATA NETWORKING DIVISION

1300 Omega Dr.	CEO: Anthony (Tony) Scarfo
Pittsburgh, PA 15205	CFO: —
Phone: 412-809-4200	HR: —
Fax: 412-809-4201	FYE: July 31
Web: dnd.ecitele.com	Type: Subsidiary

ECI Telecom Data Networking Division, a business unit of networking and switching equipment maker ECI Telecom, provides edge routing equipment. The company's ST-series routers are used by cable system operators, ISPs, and telecommunications carriers to provide data, video, and voice services, such as Internet protocol television (IPTV) and VoIP. The products, which combine switching and routing functions, are compatible with a variety of network connection methods, including virtual private network (VPN), ATM, frame relay, and Ethernet. Founded in 1999 as Laurel Networks by former employees of Fore Systems, the company was acquired by ECI Telecom in 2005 for $88 million.

ECKO.COMPLEX, LLC

40 W. 23rd St., 2nd Fl.	CEO: Seth Gerszberg
New York, NY 10010	CFO: James P. (Jim) Reilly
Phone: 917-262-1002	HR: —
Fax: —	FYE: December 31
Web: www.marceckoenterprises.com	Type: Private

G-Unit may not be well-known worldwide, but the brand has street cred to burn. Ecko.Complex, dba Marc Ecko Enterprises (MEE), is an edgy fashion firm that appeals to street-savvy youths, extreme sports fans, and hip-hop stars. The company's rhinoceros logo graces apparel, shoes, eyewear, and other accessories. Its brand portfolio includes *ecko unltd., eckored, Marc Ecko Cut & Sew, G-Unit, and Zoo York. Products are sold in the firm's roughly 90 retail and outlet stores in the US and Puerto Rico as well as through department and specialty stores worldwide. In addition to branded fashions, MEE is involved in entertainment production. Chairman Marc Ecko started the firm in 1993 with six T-shirts.

ECLIPSYS CORPORATION

NASDAQ (GS): ECLP

3 Ravinia Dr.	CEO: Philip M. Pead
Atlanta, GA 30346	CFO: Chris E. Perkins
Phone: 404-847-5000	HR: John J. McAuley
Fax: 404-847-5700	FYE: December 31
Web: www.eclipsys.com	Type: Public

Eclipsys wants to help you get out from underneath the shadow of disorganized health care. The company's software helps health care organizations manage and automate clinical, administrative, and financial functions, including patient information access, medical records and clinical documentation, prescription ordering, billing, reimbursement, and performance analysis. Its products also include tools for application integration and decision support. In addition to its software offerings, Eclipsys also sells third-party hardware, including desktop and network products. In 2010 the company agreed to merge with Allscripts in a deal valued at about $1.3 billion.

	Annual Growth	12/05	12/06	12/07	12/08	12/09
Sales ($ mil.)	7.9%	383.3	427.5	477.5	515.8	519.2
Net income ($ mil.)	52.4%	0.5	4.1	41.1	99.5	2.7
Market value ($ mil.)	(0.5%)	1,087.5	1,181.2	1,454.1	815.2	1,064.0
Employees	8.5%	2,020	2,220	2,400	2,800	2,800

⊞ ECOLAB INC.

NYSE: ECL

370 Wabasha St. North	CEO: Douglas M. (Doug) Baker Jr.
St. Paul, MN 55102	CFO: Steven L. Fritze
Phone: 651-293-2233	HR: Michael L. Meyer
Fax: 651-293-2092	FYE: December 31
Web: www.ecolab.com	Type: Public

Ecolab cleans up by cleaning up. The company offers cleaning, sanitation, pest-elimination, and maintenance products and services to hospitality, institutional, and industrial customers. Its institutional division is its largest, accounting for half of sales, and serves hotels, health care facilities, schools, and commercial and institutional laundries. Other divisions focus on products for textile care, water care, food and beverage, and pest control; its Kay unit provides cleaning supplies to quick-service restaurants. Ecolab makes most of its products, although it does sell some products made by other manufacturers. It does about half of its business outside the US, operating in more than 75 countries.

	Annual Growth	12/05	12/06	12/07	12/08	12/09
Sales ($ mil.)	6.8%	4,534.8	4,895.8	5,469.6	6,137.5	5,900.6
Net income ($ mil.)	6.9%	319.5	368.6	427.2	448.1	417.3
Market value ($ mil.)	5.3%	8,464.4	10,548.4	11,951.0	8,203.0	10,403.7
Employees	3.7%	22,404	23,130	26,052	26,568	25,931

ECOLLEGE.COM

4900 S. Monaco St., Ste. 200	CEO: Matthew Leavy
Denver, CO 80237	CFO: —
Phone: 303-873-7400	HR: —
Fax: 303-873-7449	FYE: December 31
Web: www.ecollege.com	Type: Subsidiary

You don't have to eat dorm food if you go to college online. eCollege.com is propelling higher education into cyberspace by creating online campuses for universities and high schools. The company sets up online academic communities replete with computer-based courses, testing, online registration, and other student services. Customers include career colleges, community colleges, school districts, and universities. eCollege.com also has corporate clients who use its services to build online training courses for employees. The company, acquired by educational publisher Pearson in 2007, is a subsidiary of Pearson Education and does business as Pearson eCollege.

⊞ An in-depth profile of this company is available to Hoover's Online members at hoovers.com.

535

ECOLOGY AND ENVIRONMENT, INC.

NASDAQ (GM): EEI

Buffalo Corporate Center, 368 Pleasant View Dr.	CEO: Kevin S. Neumaier
Lancaster, NY 14086	CFO: H. John Mye III
Phone: 716-684-8060	HR: —
Fax: 716-684-0844	FYE: July 31
Web: www.ene.com	Type: Public

Every day is Earth Day at environmental consulting and testing company Ecology and Environment. The company, which has completed 35,000 projects in 83 countries, provides engineering, permitting, and environmental support for all kinds of energy development, including offshore energy, power plants, pipelines, and renewables. Services include environmental impact assessments, air pollution control, wastewater analyses, and site-planning. It offers hazardous waste site evaluations and field assessments across the US and provides cleanups of Superfund sites and emergency response to hazardous waste spills for the EPA. The four founders of Ecology and Environment control about 64% of the company.

	Annual Growth	7/05	7/06	7/07	7/08	7/09
Sales ($ mil.)	18.5%	74.5	81.8	103.5	110.5	146.9
Net income ($ mil.)	—	(1.6)	2.5	3.1	1.8	5.2
Market value ($ mil.)	23.5%	27.4	40.2	50.5	46.3	63.7
Employees	12.0%	700	801	870	1,000	1,100

ECVISION INC.

485A Rte. 1 South, Ste. 340	CEO: Thomas K. Ng
Iselin, NJ 08830	CFO: —
Phone: 732-582-3900	HR: —
Fax: 973-624-9219	FYE: December 31
Web: www.ecvision.com	Type: Subsidiary

ecVision eyes all sorts of opportunity in software for retail and other markets, primarily in international trade. The company provides software and Web-based applications to automate trade transactions of retailers, manufacturers, and other customers, including J. C. Penney and MAST Industries. ecVision also provides a variety of professional services, such as consulting, implementation, outsourcing, and support. The company has strategic partnerships with Microsoft, Oracle, and Hewlett-Packard, as well as with resellers and distributors. ecVision has offices in China, Hong Kong, and the US. It is owned by private equity partnership Fung Capital USA Investment, which is in turn controlled by Li & Fung.

	Annual Growth	12/04	12/05	12/06	12/07	12/08
Est. sales ($ mil.)	—	—	—	—	—	1.4
Employees	—	—	—	—	—	11

EDAC TECHNOLOGIES CORPORATION

NASDAQ (CM): EDAC

1806 New Britain Ave.	CEO: Dominick A. Pagano
Farmington, CT 06032	CFO: Glenn L. Purple
Phone: 860-677-2603	HR: Carol Foley
Fax: 860-674-2718	FYE: December 31
Web: www.edactechnologies.com	Type: Public

Operating through its Gros-Ite and Apex Machine Tool subsidiaries, EDAC Technologies designs and produces tools, gauges, and other equipment and parts used by the aerospace industry in the manufacture and inspection of jet engines. EDAC's specialties include jet turbine cases made from difficult-to-machine alloys, such as aluminum, titanium, and high-nickel alloys. Gros-Ite makes and repairs a variety of spindles, which are integral parts of machine tools used in a wide range of manufacturing industries. EDAC's manufacturing facilities include computerized, numerically controlled (CNC) machining centers. The company also provides grinding, welding, painting, and assembly services.

	Annual Growth	12/05	12/06	12/07	12/08	12/09
Sales ($ mil.)	11.8%	35.0	38.3	50.0	44.7	54.6
Net income ($ mil.)	23.2%	3.3	1.6	3.4	1.1	7.6
Market value ($ mil.)	(4.3%)	17.9	14.8	47.4	8.7	15.0
Employees	13.3%	209	228	223	224	345

EDCI HOLDINGS, INC.

NASDAQ (CM): EDCI

825 8th Ave., 23rd Fl.	CEO: Clarke H. Bailey
New York, NY 10019	CFO: Michael D. Nixon
Phone: 212-333-8400	HR: —
Fax: —	FYE: December 31
Web: www.edcllc.com	Type: Public

This company helps Hollywood get its entertainment into consumers' hands. EDCI Holdings (formerly Entertainment Distribution Company) is a leading provider of manufacturing and distribution services to movie and music companies. It manufactures and distributes pre-recorded CDs and DVDs in Europe through its manufacturing and distribution center in Germany. The company sold its US assets in 2008. In addition to its traditional manufacturing and supply chain management services, EDCI Holdings offers distribution and delivery services for interactive content and other digital media.

	Annual Growth	12/05	12/06	12/07	12/08	12/09
Sales ($ mil.)	(8.5%)	267.8	348.5	384.6	238.4	187.9
Net income ($ mil.)	—	8.0	(9.7)	(16.2)	(21.7)	(2.8)
Market value ($ mil.)	(34.8%)	218.7	172.3	45.1	24.2	39.5
Employees	(22.3%)	2,193	2,200	2,000	1,100	800

EDD HELMS GROUP, INC.

Pink Sheets: EDDH

17850 NE 5th Ave.	CEO: W. Edd Helms Jr.
Miami, FL 33162	CFO: Dean A. Goodson
Phone: 305-653-2520	HR: —
Fax: 305-651-5527	FYE: May 31
Web: www.eddhelms.com	Type: Public

Like a friend's sentiment in your junior high yearbook, the Edd Helms Group wants you to "stay cool." The contracting group provides electrical and HVAC maintenance and retrofitting services for commercial, marine (primarily private yachts), and residential customers in South Florida. It also offers temporary power and lighting installation for tradeshows and conventions; the group markets its temporary power services for emergency power restoration in emergency situations such as hurricanes. Additionally, the group provides structural and radio frequency services for wireless and cellular towers. CEO and founder W. Edd Helms, Jr., owns 84% of the company.

EDDIE BAUER LLC

10401 NE 8th St., Ste. 500	CEO: Neil S. Fiske Jr.
Bellevue, WA 98004	CFO: —
Phone: 425-755-6544	HR: —
Fax: 425-755-7696	FYE: December 31
Web: www.eddiebauer.com	Type: Private

Nonagenarian Eddie Bauer is looking to the future with a focus on the past. The multi-channel retailer operates about 370 stores throughout North America, as well as a catalog and website. The company sells outerwear, apparel, and accessories for active outdoorsmen and women. It also licenses its name for eyewear, furniture, bicycles, and Ford SUVs and has stores in Japan through a joint venture there. A descendant of former top US direct retailer Spiegel, Eddie Bauer has struggled to find its niche in today's crowded marketplace. Eddie Bauer Holdings, formed in a 2005 reorganization, filed for Chapter 11 bankruptcy protection in June 2009 and was sold at auction to investment firm Golden Gate Capital (GGC).

	Annual Growth	12/04	12/05	12/06	12/07	12/08
Sales ($ mil.)	(3.0%)	1,157.9	593.7	1,013.4	1,044.4	1,023.4
Net income ($ mil.)	—	43.7	(22.8)	(212.0)	(101.7)	(165.5)
Employees	(14.4%)	—	11,826	9,613	9,629	7,427

EDENTIFY, INC.

Pink Sheets: EDFY

74 W. Broad St., Ste. 350
Bethlehem, PA 18018
Phone: 610-814-6830
Fax: 610-814-6836
Web: www.edentify.us

CEO: Terrence M. DeFranco
CFO: —
HR: —
FYE: December 31
Type: Public

Edentify aims to end identity crimes. The development-stage company owns intellectual property related to the prevention of identity theft. Its technology includes both data analysis and monitoring and biometrics-based systems. It is targeting such customers as government entities, health care providers, and financial services companies. Edentify's biometric technology includes facial and voice recognition systems, combined with inner-lip analysis. Edentify acquired Budgethotels Network in 2005 through a reverse stock split. Budgethotels' InfoCenter business (travel-related display advertising and lodging reservations) was spun off to shareholders as part of the transaction.

EDGAR ONLINE, INC.

NASDAQ (GM): EDGR

50 Washington St.
Norwalk, CT 06854
Phone: 203-852-5666
Fax: 203-852-5667
Web: www.edgar-online.com

CEO: Philip D. Moyer
CFO: Ronald P. (Ron) Fetzer
HR: —
FYE: December 31
Type: Public

Need the inside scoop on companies that file documents with the SEC? Just ask EDGAR. EDGAR Online (whose name is an acronym for Electronic Data Gathering Analysis and Retrieval) provides electronic SEC filings. Its subscription-based EDGAR Pro service offers unlimited access to filings and has searching, filtering, and downloading tools; its less expensive EDGAR Access has limited access. Its I-Metrix Professional product offers complex data analysis. EDGAR Online also provides digital data feeds to corporations for use in intranet, extranet, and other applications. Other revenue comes from ads and e-commerce. EDGAR Online was the first company to publish real-time SEC filings online for individual investors.

	Annual Growth	12/05	12/06	12/07	12/08	12/09
Sales ($ mil.)	7.8%	14.2	16.2	17.9	19.5	19.2
Net income ($ mil.)	—	(5.6)	(5.9)	(7.4)	(2.7)	(0.9)
Market value ($ mil.)	(4.7%)	49.1	94.3	91.6	33.7	40.4
Employees	(0.3%)	90	87	78	90	89

EDGEWATER TECHNOLOGY, INC.

NASDAQ (GM): EDGW

20 Harvard Mill Sq.
Wakefield, MA 01880
Phone: 781-246-3343
Fax: 781-246-5903
Web: www.edgewater.com

CEO: Shirley Singleton
CFO: Timothy R. (Tim) Oakes
HR: Kristin Zaepfel
FYE: December 31
Type: Public

Edgewater Technology is on the cutting edge of technology management consulting. The company provides management consulting, designs customized software applications, and helps enterprises optimize business processes. Its managed services division allows clients to outsource management and maintenance of IT facilities. The company has expertise in such markets as financial services, health care, insurance, and higher education. It targets middle-market clients and divisions of large (Global 2000) firms. Its clients include Chiron, Merrill, TJX, and MIT.

	Annual Growth	12/05	12/06	12/07	12/08	12/09
Sales ($ mil.)	3.8%	43.1	60.1	68.5	73.7	50.1
Net income ($ mil.)	—	1.6	3.2	8.8	(47.0)	(3.8)
Market value ($ mil.)	(15.8%)	72.2	74.8	89.4	31.7	36.4
Employees	(4.3%)	282	303	367	298	237

EDIETS.COM, INC.

NASDAQ (CM): DIET

1000 Corporate Dr., Ste. 600
Fort Lauderdale, FL 33334
Phone: 954-360-9022
Fax: 954-360-9095
Web: www.ediets.com

CEO: Kevin N. McGrath
CFO: Thomas J. (Tom) Hoyer
HR: —
FYE: December 31
Type: Public

eDiets.com is banking on your losing proposition. The company's website allows fat-fighting clients in several countries to enter information and receive a customized, software-generated program to help them lose weight. Some of its 20 plans include the Atkins Nutritional Approach, the Glycemic Impact Diet, and the Slim-Fast Optima Diet. eDiets.com also offers support message boards, an e-newsletter, expert nutrition advice, vitamins, and eDiets DeliciouslyYours nationwide meal-delivery service. Its eDiets Corporate Services unit licenses its brand to companies and their employees for health programs. It operates eDiets Europe overseas. Investment firm Prides Capital Partners owns about 55% of eDiets.com.

	Annual Growth	12/05	12/06	12/07	12/08	12/09
Sales ($ mil.)	(23.8%)	53.7	48.8	29.7	23.9	18.1
Net income ($ mil.)	—	1.3	(4.1)	(9.4)	(19.8)	(12.1)
Market value ($ mil.)	(32.1%)	210.1	133.2	202.5	120.1	44.6
Employees	(13.0%)	150	108	103	95	86

E.DIGITAL CORPORATION

OTC: EDIG

16770 W. Bernardo Dr.
San Diego, CA 92127
Phone: 866-502-8234
Fax: 858-304-3023
Web: www.edigital.com

CEO: Alfred H. (Fred) Falk
CFO: Robert Putnam
HR: —
FYE: March 31
Type: Public

e.Digital believes that the future is digital. The company provides engineering services, product reference designs, and technology platforms to customers focusing on the digital video and audio markets. e.Digital, however, plans to focus future growth on selling its eVU mobile entertainment device, which features a 7-inch LCD screen, dual stereo headphone jacks, embedded credit card reader, and touch screen capabilities. The eVu is geared towards customers in the airline, health care, military, and travel and leisure industries.

	Annual Growth	3/05	3/06	3/07	3/08	3/09
Sales ($ mil.)	26.8%	4.3	3.3	1.8	5.6	11.1
Net income ($ mil.)	—	(2.4)	(3.1)	(3.1)	(1.7)	2.9
Market value ($ mil.)	(3.9%)	54.5	43.0	68.9	45.9	46.5
Employees	(10.2%)	20	16	17	15	13

EDISON INTERNATIONAL

NYSE: EIX

2244 Walnut Grove Ave.
Rosemead, CA 91770
Phone: 626-302-2222
Fax: 626-302-2517
Web: www.edison.com

CEO: Theodore F. (Ted) Craver Jr.
CFO: W. James (Jim) Scilacci Jr.
HR: Diane L. Featherstone
FYE: December 31
Type: Public

Edison International has been around the world, but the company's largest subsidiary is Southern California Edison (SCE), which distributes electricity to a population of more than 13 million people in central, coastal, and Southern California; it is the leading purchaser of renewable energy in the US. The utility's system consists of about 12,000 circuit miles of transmission lines and more than 113,500 circuit miles of distribution lines. SCE also has 5,500 MW of generating capacity from interests in nuclear, hydroelectric, and fossil-fueled power plants. Edison created an international portfolio through Edison Mission Energy (EME), but it has pulled back on almost all of its non-US operations.

	Annual Growth	12/05	12/06	12/07	12/08	12/09
Sales ($ mil.)	1.1%	11,852.0	12,622.0	13,113.0	14,112.0	12,361.0
Net income ($ mil.)	(4.5%)	1,138.0	1,180.0	1,098.0	1,215.0	945.0
Market value ($ mil.)	(5.5%)	14,208.6	14,817.9	17,388.5	10,465.1	11,331.7
Employees	5.0%	15,838	16,139	17,275	18,291	19,244

An in-depth profile of this company is available to Hoover's Online members at hoovers.com.

537

EDISON MISSION ENERGY

18101 Von Karman Ave., Ste. 1700	CEO: Ronald L. Litzinger
Irvine, CA 92612	CFO: John P. Finneran Jr.
Phone: 949-752-5588	HR: Jenene Wilson
Fax: 949-263-9162	FYE: December 31
Web: www.edison.com	Type: Subsidiary

Edison Mission Energy (EME) once wanted to conquer the nonregulated energy sector around the world, but now it'll settle for a piece of the US market. The company, a subsidiary of Edison International, has interests in 36 power plants in the US and one in Turkey (Doga project) that give it a net physical generating capacity of more than 11,000 MW. EME sells power through contracts with large utilities, regional distributors, and other energy companies; it also trades energy on the open markets. In 2008, 75% of the company's power was generated by coal plants, 15% by natural gas, and 10% by wind energy.

	Annual Growth	12/04	12/05	12/06	12/07	12/08
Est. sales ($ mil.)	—	—	—	—	—	2,811.0
Employees	—	—	—	—	—	1,794

EDISONLEARNING, INC.

485 Lexington Ave., 2nd Fl.	CEO: Jeffrey S. (Jeff) Wahl
New York, NY 10017	CFO: David J. Duffy
Phone: 212-419-1600	HR: Anne Miller
Fax: 212-419-1764	FYE: June 30
Web: www.edisonlearning.com	Type: Private

Light bulbs switch on daily at EdisonLearning (formerly Edison Schools). The company works with school districts and administrators to help improve school performance. The company manages the operations of public and charter K-12 schools, ranging from curriculum decisions to community relations. EdisonLearning focuses on retaining quality teachers, engaging students and families, individualized instruction, and achievement-driven management. The company's offerings include online tutoring programs, hybrid instructional environments, and school design. EdisonLearning has partnerships with some 125 schools in the US and the UK, serving some 350,000 students. The company was founded in 1992.

EDUCATE, INC.

1001 Fleet St.	CEO: Jeffrey H. Cohen
Baltimore, MD 21202	CFO: Kevin E. (Ken) Shaffer
Phone: 410-843-8000	HR: Troy Albright
Fax: —	FYE: December 31
Web: www.educate-inc.com	Type: Private

For Educate, the name says it all. Its portfolio of companies features Sylvan Learning Center, which offers tutoring to students in pre-K through 12th grade. Certified teachers provide personalized instruction in reading, writing, math, study skills, and test prep for state assessment and college entrance exams via more than 1,100 primarily franchised Sylvan centers throughout the US and Canada. Educate also offers online tutoring services for Sylvan students. In addition, Educate operates in Europe through more than 1,000 Schülerhilfe centers that offer tutoring in Germany and Austria.

	Annual Growth	12/04	12/05	12/06	12/07	12/08
Est. sales ($ mil.)	—	—	—	—	—	354.7
Employees	—	—	—	—	—	10,161

EDUCATION MANAGEMENT CORPORATION
NASDAQ (GS): EDMC

210 6th Ave., 33rd Fl.	CEO: Todd S. Nelson
Pittsburgh, PA 15222	CFO: Edward H. West
Phone: 412-562-0900	HR: Roberta L. Troike
Fax: 412-562-0598	FYE: June 30
Web: www.edumgt.com	Type: Public

Worried that traditional higher education could leave you enlightened but unemployed? Education Management Corporation believes it has the solution. Founded in 1962, the company operates The Art Institutes, with more than 40 locations across the US and Canada, in addition to Argosy University, South University, and Brown Mackie College. The schools offer associate's degrees, certificate programs, undergraduate and graduate-level programs, and doctoral degrees. Education Management's institutions boast a total student enrollment of around 136,000 at more than 90 locations. The company went public in 2009.

	Annual Growth	6/05	6/06	6/07	6/08	6/09
Sales ($ mil.)	18.5%	1,019.3	1,170.2	1,363.7	1,684.2	2,011.5
Net income ($ mil.)	0.7%	101.6	80.7	32.4	66.0	104.4
Employees	(1.8%)	12,150	8,800	10,100	11,400	11,300

EDUCATION REALTY TRUST, INC.
NYSE: EDR

530 Oak Court Dr., Ste. 300	CEO: Randall L. (Randy) Churchey
Memphis, TN 38117	CFO: Randall H. (Randy) Brown
Phone: 901-259-2500	HR: Susan B. Arrison
Fax: 901-259-2594	FYE: December 31
Web: www.educationrealty.com	Type: Public

This company can give your college student a home away from home. Education Realty Trust, a self-administered real estate investment trust (REIT), develops, buys, owns, and operates residential communities for university students. It owns about 40 communities in some 20 states, consisting of approximately 25,000 beds in more than 7,800 units. Through its Allen & O'Hara Education Services subsidiary, the REIT manages another 20 student housing properties owned by others. Education Realty Trust communities offer private rooms as well as amenities such as Internet access, fitness centers, game rooms, dining facilities, swimming pools — and even study rooms.

	Annual Growth	12/05	12/06	12/07	12/08	12/09
Sales ($ mil.)	10.6%	89.8	119.3	120.0	139.9	134.2
Net income ($ mil.)	—	(15.5)	(12.2)	(5.5)	(7.9)	(7.3)
Market value ($ mil.)	(21.7%)	733.8	840.8	639.9	297.2	275.5
Employees	4.7%	1,038	1,065	1,196	1,259	1,249

EDUCATIONAL DEVELOPMENT CORPORATION
NASDAQ (GM): EDUC

10302 E. 55th Place	CEO: Randall W. White
Tulsa, OK 74146	CFO: Marilyn R. Welborn
Phone: 918-622-4522	HR: Marilyn R. Welborn
Fax: 918-665-7919	FYE: February 28
Web: www.edcpub.com	Type: Public

Educational Development Corporation (EDC) likes being in a bind, as long as the cover appeals to youngsters. The company is the exclusive US distributor of a line of about 1,400 children's books published by the UK's Usborne Publishing Limited. EDC's Home Business Division markets the books to individuals using independent sales reps who sell through personal websites, home parties, direct sales, and book fairs; this division also distributes books to public and school libraries. EDC's Publishing Division distributes the Usborne line to a network of book, toy, and other retail stores. The company also offers more than 60 Usborne Kid Kits, which combine books with related materials such as toys.

	Annual Growth	2/06	2/07	2/08	2/09	2/10
Sales ($ mil.)	(2.5%)	31.8	31.4	30.5	29.4	28.7
Net income ($ mil.)	(5.7%)	2.4	2.4	2.3	1.9	1.9
Market value ($ mil.)	(6.7%)	31.1	29.6	22.1	13.9	23.6
Employees	(0.9%)	81	82	79	78	78

EDUCATIONAL TESTING SERVICE

Rosedale Road
Princeton, NJ 08541
Phone: 609-921-9000
Fax: 609-734-5410
Web: www.ets.org

CEO: Kurt M. Landgraf
CFO: Frank R. Gatti
HR: Yvette Donado
FYE: June 30
Type: Not-for-profit

For college-bound high school students, taking the SAT is as much a rite of passage as getting a driver's license. Founded in 1947, Educational Testing Service (ETS), creates and administers the Scholastic Assessment Test (SAT) and is one of the world's largest private testing and research organizations. The not-for-profit group develops and administers more than 50 million achievement, admissions, academic, and professional tests a year at nearly 10,000 locations in more than 180 countries. It also develops recognition programs for corporations and not-for-profit entities. ETS's research unit conducts education-focused analysis and policy studies; test-development firm Prometric is a for-profit subsidiary.

	Annual Growth	6/04	6/05	6/06	6/07	6/08
Est. sales ($ mil.)	—	—	—	—	—	850.3
Employees	—	—	—	—	—	2,600

EDWARD DON & COMPANY

2500 S. Harlem Ave.
North Riverside, IL 60546
Phone: 708-442-9400
Fax: 708-442-0436
Web: www.don.com

CEO: Steven R. (Steve) Don
CFO: James P. (Jim) Jones
HR: Andre Mills
FYE: December 31
Type: Private

Edward Don & Company sells just about everything to kitchen managers, including the kitchen sink. A leading foodservice equipment supplier, the company provides more than 12,000 products to restaurants, hospitals, schools, and other institutional foodservice operators. It operates six distribution facilities across the country that deliver such goods as catering and cooking equipment, flatware, tableware, paper goods, cleaning products and sanitation supplies. Edward Don also designs and builds full-service kitchens for customers in the foodservice industry. The family-owned company was founded in 1921.

EDWARDS LIFESCIENCES CORPORATION

NYSE: EW

1 Edwards Way
Irvine, CA 92614
Phone: 949-250-2500
Fax: 949-250-2525
Web: www.edwards.com

CEO: Michael A. Mussallem
CFO: Thomas M. Abate
HR: Robert C. Reindl
FYE: December 31
Type: Public

Edwards Lifesciences has its heart in the right place. Named for the co-inventor of the first artificial heart valve, Miles "Lowell" Edwards, the company is a spin-off of Baxter International. Its main products are still heart valve devices, including valves made from animal tissue and annuloplasty rings that repair damaged valves. The company also makes monitoring systems that measure heart function during surgery; various types of cannulae (surgical tubes used for drainage, delivery, or filtration); and embolectomy catheters that remove blood clots from peripheral arteries. Edwards Lifesciences markets its products worldwide through a direct sales force and distributors.

	Annual Growth	12/05	12/06	12/07	12/08	12/09
Sales ($ mil.)	7.3%	997.9	1,037.0	1,091.1	1,237.7	1,321.4
Net income ($ mil.)	30.4%	79.3	130.5	113.0	128.9	229.1
Market value ($ mil.)	20.2%	2,357.5	2,665.1	2,605.6	3,113.3	4,920.6
Employees	4.3%	5,400	5,550	5,600	6,200	6,400

EDWIN WATTS GOLF, LLC

20 Hill Ave.
Fort Walton Beach, FL 32548
Phone: 850-244-2066
Fax: 850-244-5217
Web: www.edwinwatts.com

CEO: Edwin (Ed) Watts
CFO: Linda K. Barr
HR: —
FYE: December 31
Type: Private

Golfers often hit Edwin Watts before hitting the links. Named for its founder, Edwin Watts Golf is a leading golf specialty retail chain in the US. The company operates about 70 golf specialty stores in 10 mostly southeastern states and Texas. Its stores sell clubs, golf balls, bags, training aids, and more. The company also sells golf equipment by catalog and online, and it operates a club leasing program for novices and golfers who like to try out state-of-the-art gear. Edwin Watts Golf was founded in 1968 as a small pro shop at the municipal golf course in Fort Walton Beach, Florida, by brothers Edwin and Ronnie Watts. It is owned by an affiliate of investment firm Sun Capital Partners.

EESTECH, INC.

OTC: EESH

1105 N. Market St., Ste. 1300
Wilmington, DE 19801
Phone: 302-427-2360
Fax: —
Web: eestechinc.com

CEO: Murray Bailey
CFO: Murray Bailey
HR: —
FYE: December 31
Type: Public

A development-stage company, EESTech (formerly Aqua Dyne) wants to join the wave of water purification and clean energy providers. Through its evaporation-based JetWater System, the company recovers distilled drinking water from seawater or water polluted with minerals. Rather than relying on membranes, the JetWater system uses thermal technology — heat — to remove impurities. EESTech promotes Hybrid Coal and Gas Turbine (HCGT) technology, which can use biomass or a combination of methane from underground coal mines and waste coal as the fuel source for power plants. It is also exploring capturing carbon dioxide from power stations.

EF JOHNSON TECHNOLOGIES, INC.

NASDAQ (GM): EFJI

1440 Corporate Dr.
Irving, TX 75038
Phone: 972-819-0700
Fax: 972-819-0639
Web: www.efjohnsontechnologies.com

CEO: Michael E. Jalbert
CFO: Jana A. Bell
HR: Michael B. Gamble
FYE: December 31
Type: Public

EF Johnson makes sure certain communications remain on the QT. The company makes radio and radio-security systems for police departments, government agencies, the military, and service providers. Its primary EFJohnson-branded products include handheld and mobile radios, base stations, and signal repeaters. Sold as aftermarket add-ons, its Transcrypt-branded products include security modules that encrypt and decode radio and wireless phone signals to prevent eavesdropping. The company's 3eTI line consists of secure Wi-Fi and software products for federal government and military agencies, and enterprise and industrial customers. In 2010 Francisco Partners agreed to buy EF Johnson for about $28 million in cash.

	Annual Growth	12/05	12/06	12/07	12/08	12/09
Sales ($ mil.)	(0.6%)	94.6	96.7	154.6	126.3	92.3
Net income ($ mil.)	—	22.5	(6.8)	(37.7)	(20.9)	(12.2)
Market value ($ mil.)	(42.5%)	269.1	179.0	72.9	35.5	29.4
Employees	(0.5%)	272	375	377	290	267

An in-depth profile of this company is available to Hoover's Online members at hoovers.com.

539

EFTEC NORTH AMERICA, L.L.C.

2710 Bellingham Dr., Ste. 100
Troy, MI 48083
Phone: 248-585-2200
Fax: 248-585-3699
Web: www.eftec.com

CEO: Jay Scripter
CFO: John Lavoie
HR: Kathleen Ward
FYE: November 30
Type: Subsidiary

It's not just nuts and bolts that hold your car together. It's also products like EFTEC North America's adhesives and sealants that are responsible for bonding together the myriad parts of an automobile. The company and its sister, EFTEC AG, provide sealants, adhesives, and coatings to the auto industry. Other operations include the manufacture of mineral wool, waxes, PVC products, and elastomers. EFTEC North America's customers include Audi, General Motors, and Mercedes-Benz. The two EFTECs existed as a joint venture between EMS-CHEMIE and H.B. Fuller until 2007 when EMS bought out Fuller's portion of the JV.

EGON ZEHNDER INTERNATIONAL

350 Park Ave., 8th Fl.
New York, NY 10022
Phone: 212-519-6000
Fax: 212-519-6060
Web: www.egonzehnder.com

CEO: Damien O'Brien
CFO: Laurent de Meeûs
HR: Isabelle Langlois-Loris
FYE: October 31
Type: Private

Egon Zehnder International gives corporate engines a tune-up (and supplies replacement parts). Operating through some 385 consultants across more than 60 offices in almost 40 countries, Egon Zehnder is one of the world's largest senior-level executive recruitment firms, along with Heidrick & Struggles and Korn/Ferry. It also specializes in management appraisals and corporate governance. The firm operates through such practice groups as technology, life sciences, consumer, and financial services. Egon Zehnder's clients include both start-up companies and large corporations, as well as government, educational, and cultural organizations. Founded by Egon Zehnder in 1964, the company is owned by its partners.

EGAIN COMMUNICATIONS CORPORATION

OTC: EGAN

345 E. Middlefield Rd.
Mountain View, CA 94043
Phone: 650-230-7500
Fax: 650-230-7600
Web: www.egain.com

CEO: Ashutosh (Ashu) Roy
CFO: Eric N. Smit
HR: —
FYE: June 30
Type: Public

eGain helps eBusinesses offer eService to their eCustomers. eGain Communications offers call center software that integrates online and telephone communications with other data sources. The company's software suite includes applications for routing e-mails, giving customers self-service options, enabling live Web chat, and providing call center agents with customer information. In addition, eGain provides such services as consulting, hosting, maintenance, implementation, and support. Its customers have included AT&T, Cox Newspapers, and Hewlett-Packard.

	Annual Growth	6/05	6/06	6/07	6/08	6/09
Sales ($ mil.)	12.9%	20.4	22.6	22.5	30.1	33.2
Net income ($ mil.)	—	(0.8)	(1.1)	(7.7)	(4.1)	2.2
Market value ($ mil.)	(6.3%)	14.4	28.8	22.1	17.5	11.1
Employees	48.9%	51	57	76	279	251

EGPI FIRECREEK, INC.

OTC: EFCR

6564 Smoke Tree Ln.
Scottsdale, AZ 85253
Phone: 480-948-6581
Fax: 480-443-1403
Web: www.egpifirecreek.com

CEO: Dennis R. Alexander
CFO: Dennis R. Alexander
HR: —
FYE: December 31
Type: Public

The fire in EGPI Firecreek's belly is for oil and gas exploration and production and traffic systems. Once dependent on the sale of private leisure and commercial vessels, EGPI Firecreek has refocused on US oil and gas activities. The company produces and sells oil and natural gas from wells in Sweetwater County, Wyoming, and Knox County, Texas. It had a strategic alliance with Sahara Group, an oil and gas concern with expertise in Eastern Europe, North Africa, Russia, Turkey, and Ukraine, but wound this down in 2008. In 2009 in a diversification move, EGPI Firecreek subsidiary Asian Ventures Corp. acquired M3 Lighting as the company expanded into light and traffic fixture manufacturing.

	Annual Growth	12/05	12/06	12/07	12/08	12/09
Sales ($ mil.)	128.9%	—	0.1	0.5	0.0	1.2
Net income ($ mil.)	—	—	(4.2)	(1.5)	3.3	(3.4)
Market value ($ mil.)	(67.6%)	—	308.4	72.6	10.9	10.5
Employees	—	—	—	—	—	—

EGAMES, INC.

Pink Sheets: EGAM

2000 Cabot Blvd. West, Ste. 110
Langhorne, PA 19047
Phone: 215-750-6606
Fax: —
Web: www.egames.com

CEO: Gerald W. (Jerry) Klein
CFO: Thomas W. (Tom) Murphy
HR: —
FYE: June 30
Type: Public

eGames is taking a G-rated (or should that be E-rated?) approach to PC entertainment. The company markets video games usually rated E (for everyone) that are easy to use and nonviolent. Its titles, which include *Bowling Mania* and *MahJongg Master,* typically sell for $20 or less and are marketed in North America under such brand names as eGames, Home Office Help, and RealAge. eGames sells its products at national retail chains (Wal-Mart, Target, Best Buy, K-Mart), office supply stores, and warehouse clubs (Office Max, Sam's Club); it also sells through wholesale distributor Atari, Take-Two Interactive, and various inventory liquidators. In addition, the company offers online games through its eGames.com website.

EHARMONY.COM, INC.

888 E. Walnut Ave.
Pasadena, CA 91101
Phone: 626-795-4814
Fax: 626-585-4040
Web: www.eharmony.com

CEO: Gregory L. (Greg) Waldorf
CFO: John Powers
HR: Jim Lambert
FYE: December 31
Type: Private

Looking to settle down harmoniously? eharmony.com (which does business as eHarmony) is an online service that attempts to match compatible singles who are looking for long-term relationships. The company focuses on helping clients find their "soul mate" by giving them a detailed questionnaire emphasizing compatibility matching and communication. (It has patented its "Compatibility Matching System.") The site counts more than 20 million registered users in all 50 states and 190 countries. The company was founded in 2000 by Dr. Neil Clark Warren, an evangelical Christian who practiced for years as a clinical psychologist. Investors include Technology Crossover Ventures, Sequoia Capital, and Fayez Sarofim & Co.

	Annual Growth	12/04	12/05	12/06	12/07	12/08
Est. sales ($ mil.)	—	—	—	—	—	6.8
Employees	—	—	—	—	—	119

EHEALTH, INC.

NASDAQ (GM): EHTH

440 E. Middlefield Rd.	CEO: Gary L. Lauer
Mountain View, CA 94043	CFO: Stuart M. Huizinga
Phone: 650-584-2700	HR: —
Fax: 650-961-2153	FYE: December 31
Web: www.ehealthinsurance.com	Type: Public

eHealth brought e-commerce to the insurance business. The company sells health insurance online through its eHealthInsurance Services subsidiary to more than 600,000 individual, family, and small business members. The company is licensed to sell in all 50 states and Washington, DC, and it has partnerships with some 180 health insurance carriers. It offers more than 10,000 products online — including health, dental, and vision insurance products from the likes of Aetna, Humana, Kaiser Permanente, and Wellpoint, as well as more than 40 Blue Cross and Blue Shield licensees. The company was founded in 1997.

	Annual Growth	12/05	12/06	12/07	12/08	12/09
Sales ($ mil.)	34.0%	41.8	61.3	87.8	111.7	134.9
Net income ($ mil.)	—	(0.4)	16.5	31.6	14.2	15.3
Market value ($ mil.)	(6.5%)	—	473.1	755.4	312.4	386.5
Employees	15.5%	292	357	437	482	520

E. I. DU PONT DE NEMOURS AND COMPANY

NYSE: DD

1007 Market St.	CEO: Ellen J. Kullman
Wilmington, DE 19898	CFO: Nicholas C. (Nick) Fanandakis
Phone: 302-774-1000	HR: Maritza J. Poza-Grise
Fax: 302-999-4399	FYE: December 31
Web: www.dupont.com	Type: Public

E. I. du Pont de Nemours wants to cover your house, feed your crops, and coat your car. The #3 US chemical maker (behind Dow and ExxonMobil Chemicals) operates through six business units. These segments produce crop protection chemicals and genetically modified seeds, coatings (automotive finishes and coatings), electronic materials (LCDs and sensors), films and resins for packaging and other uses, performance chemicals (fluorine products and white pigments), and safety and security materials (under brand names like Tyvek, Kevlar, and Corian). In the last decade, the company slimmed down substantially, exiting the pharmaceutical and fibers businesses, and is now focusing on biotech and safety and protection.

	Annual Growth	12/05	12/06	12/07	12/08	12/09
Sales ($ mil.)	(2.2%)	28,491.0	28,982.0	29,378.0	30,529.0	26,109.0
Net income ($ mil.)	(3.8%)	2,053.0	3,148.0	2,988.0	2,007.0	1,755.0
Market value ($ mil.)	(5.7%)	38,506.8	44,133.3	39,947.4	22,922.9	30,506.4
Employees	(0.8%)	60,000	59,000	60,000	60,000	58,000

EILEEN FISHER, INC.

2 Bridge St.	CEO: Eileen Fisher
Irvington, NY 10533	CFO: Kenneth Pollak
Phone: 914-591-5700	HR: —
Fax: 914-591-8824	FYE: December 31
Web: www.eileenfisher.com	Type: Private

Eileen Fisher — the woman and the company — cares about customer's comfort as well as their sense of fashion. The company makes and sells upscale women's business and casual clothing, including apparel made from organic and natural fabrics. Fisher's unfussy, forgivingly-tailored, solid color, apparel is sold through more than 40 of its namesake boutiques and outlets in about 15 states, as well as through upscale department and specialty stores (including Nordstrom, Saks Fifth Avenue, and Neiman Marcus) nationwide and in Canada. It also offers personal shopping services for US customers. After working in the fields of graphic arts and interior design, Eileen Fisher founded the company in 1984 in New York.

	Annual Growth	12/04	12/05	12/06	12/07	12/08
Est. sales ($ mil.)	—	—	—	—	—	272.9
Employees	—	—	—	—	—	900

EINSTEIN NOAH RESTAURANT GROUP, INC.

NASDAQ (GM): BAGL

555 Zang St., Ste. 300	CEO: Jeffrey J. (Jeff) O'Neill
Lakewood, CO 80228	CFO: Emanuel P. N. (Manny) Hilario
Phone: 303-568-8000	HR: Michael (Mike) Serchia
Fax: 303-568-8039	FYE: December 31
Web: www.einsteinnoah.com	Type: Public

Bagels and coffee are key ingredients for this company. Einstein Noah Restaurant Group is the largest bagel shop operator in the US, with more than 690 company-owned and franchised locations in more than 35 states. Its flagship chain, Einstein Bros. Bagels, offers more than a dozen varieties of fresh-made bagels and spreads, along with coffee, pastries, and a menu of sandwiches and salads at its more than 530 outlets. In addition to Einstein Bros., New World operates the Noah's New York Bagels and Manhattan Bagel chains. About 430 of the bagel shops are company-owned, while the rest are operated by franchisees or licensees. Investment firm Greenlight Capital controls about 65% of Einstein Noah.

	Annual Growth	12/05	12/06	12/07	12/08	12/09
Sales ($ mil.)	1.2%	389.1	390.0	402.9	413.5	408.6
Net income ($ mil.)	—	(14.0)	(6.9)	12.6	21.1	72.0
Market value ($ mil.)	21.6%	74.1	123.6	299.0	94.7	161.9
Employees	(2.6%)	7,830	8,109	7,190	7,698	7,054

EISAI INC.

100 Tice Blvd.	CEO: Hajime Shimizu
Woodcliff Lake, NJ 07677	CFO: —
Phone: 201-692-1100	HR: —
Fax: 201-692-1804	FYE: March 31
Web: www.eisai.com	Type: Subsidiary

Eisai Inc. develops and markets pharmaceuticals to treat a variety of ills. As the US production arm of Eisai Co., its roster includes Alzheimer's treatment Aricept, Aciphex for acid reflux, anti-seizure medication Banzel, anticoagulant Fragmin, and anti-convulsant Zonegran. In recent years it has become increasingly focused on oncology discovery, research, and clinical capabilities, primarily through acquisitions. Eisai Inc. also maintains an extensive pipeline of potential drugs to address epilepsy and severe infection. The company supplies its products to health care professionals, pharmacies, and hospitals through a vast network of distributors that include AmerisourceBergen, Cardinal Health, and Kinray.

EKA CHEMICALS INC.

1775 W. Oak Commons Ct.	CEO: Byron Smith
Marietta, GA 30062	CFO: Michel Gregoire
Phone: 770-578-0858	HR: Steve Shiflet
Fax: 770-578-1359	FYE: December 31
	Type: Subsidiary

Eka helps supply the American pulp and paper industry. The US arm of Eka Chemicals (a subsidiary of Akzo Nobel), Eka operates through offices in Georgia, Mississippi, New York, Washington, and Wisconsin. In addition to bleaching and water treatment chemicals, it markets specialty products like colloidal silica (which is used by the electronics industry) and high-purity alkalies. Akzo Nobel has declared pulp and paper chemicals to be strategic areas of focus.

An in-depth profile of this company is available to Hoover's Online members at hoovers.com.

541

EL DORADO FURNITURE CORPORATION

4200 NW 167th St.
Miami, FL 33054
Phone: 305-624-9700
Fax: 305-624-8772
Web: www.eldoradofurniture.com

CEO: Luis Capó
CFO: Ivan Trabal
HR: Henry E. Hererro
FYE: December 31
Type: Private

The road to El Dorado Furniture is covered in sand. The company sells home furnishings in South Florida through about a dozen retail showrooms in Broward, Dade, and Palm Beach counties. It offers wood, upholstered, and leather furniture for every room in the house, as well as mattresses, bedding, and decorative accents. Stores are designed to look like a small town, with building facades situated along a main street; locations also feature cafes. El Dorado, one of the largest Hispanic-owned retail enterprises in the US, was founded in 1967 and is still operated by the Capó family.

	Annual Growth	12/04	12/05	12/06	12/07	12/08
Est. sales ($ mil.)	—	—	—	—	—	166.5
Employees	—	—	—	—	—	725

EL PASO CORPORATION

NYSE: EP

El Paso Bldg., 1001 Louisiana St.
Houston, TX 77002
Phone: 713-420-2600
Fax: 713-420-4417
Web: www.elpaso.com

CEO: Douglas L. (Doug) Foshee
CFO: John R. (J. R.) Sult
HR: —
FYE: December 31
Type: Public

Out in the West Texas town of El Paso, this company fell in love with the natural gas industry. Founded in 1928 in its namesake city, El Paso Corp. is primarily engaged in gas transportation and storage, oil and gas exploration and production, and gas gathering and processing. Operator of the largest gas transportation system in the US, El Paso has interests in 42,000 miles of interstate pipeline. Subsidiary El Paso Exploration and Production has estimated proved reserves of 2.3 trillion cu. ft. of natural gas equivalent in Brazil, Egypt, and the US. The company also has interests in global energy projects and markets wholesale energy commodities.

	Annual Growth	12/05	12/06	12/07	12/08	12/09
Sales ($ mil.)	3.6%	4,017.0	4,281.0	4,648.0	5,363.0	4,631.0
Net income ($ mil.)	—	(602.0)	475.0	1,110.0	(823.0)	(474.0)
Market value ($ mil.)	(5.2%)	8,557.5	10,753.2	12,132.5	5,510.3	6,917.8
Employees	(3.3%)	5,700	5,050	4,992	5,344	4,991

EL PASO ELECTRIC COMPANY

NYSE: EE

Stanton Tower, 100 N. Stanton
El Paso, TX 79901
Phone: 915-543-5711
Fax: 915-521-4787
Web: www.epelectric.com

CEO: David W. Stevens
CFO: David G. Carpenter
HR: —
FYE: December 31
Type: Public

El Paso Electric creates currents along the Rio Grande River. The utility transmits and distributes electricity to some 363,000 customers in West Texas and southern New Mexico. More than half of the company's sales come from its namesake city and nearby Las Cruces, New Mexico. The firm has more than 1,500 MW of nuclear and fossil-fueled generating capacity. El Paso Electric also purchases power from other utilities and marketers, and sells wholesale power in Texas and New Mexico, as well as in Mexico. Its largest customers include military installations, such as Fort Bliss in Texas and White Sands Missile Range and Holloman Air Force Base in New Mexico.

	Annual Growth	12/05	12/06	12/07	12/08	12/09
Sales ($ mil.)	0.7%	803.9	816.5	877.4	1,038.9	828.0
Net income ($ mil.)	16.3%	36.6	61.4	74.8	77.6	66.9
Market value ($ mil.)	(0.9%)	920.7	1,066.5	1,119.0	791.6	887.5
Employees	0.0%	1,000	1,000	1,000	1,000	1,000

EL PASO PIPELINE PARTNERS, L.P.

NYSE: EPB

1001 Louisiana St.
Houston, TX 77002
Phone: 713-420-2600
Fax: 713-420-4417
Web: www.eppipelinepartners.com

CEO: James C. (Jim) Yardley
CFO: John R. (J. R.) Sult
HR: —
FYE: December 31
Type: Public

While El Paso Pipeline Partners might seem like the way El Paso gets great Mexican food across the border, it's actually a natural gas pipeline and storage company. The firm, which consists primarily of Wyoming Interstate Company (WIC) and partial interests in Colorado Interstate Gas Company (CIG) and Southern Natural Gas Company (SNG), has 12,500 miles of pipeline, and storage facilities totaling 89 billion cubic feet. Parent El Paso Corp. owns the remainder of CIG and SNG. El Paso Pipeline Partners' customers include local distribution companies, industrial users, electricity generators, and natural gas marketing and trading companies. El Paso Corporation controls about 74% of the company.

	Annual Growth	12/05	12/06	12/07	12/08	12/09
Sales ($ mil.)	60.5%	81.0	97.0	110.0	141.1	537.6
Net income ($ mil.)	64.7%	38.0	65.0	66.0	114.5	279.5
Market value ($ mil.)	1.8%	—	—	3,521.0	2,192.7	3,648.9
Employees	—	—	—	0	0	—

EL POLLO LOCO HOLDINGS, INC.

3535 Harbor Blvd., Ste. 100
Costa Mesa, CA 92626
Phone: 714-599-5000
Fax: —
Web: www.elpolloloco.com

CEO: Stephen E. (Steve) Carley
CFO: Gary C. Campanaro
HR: Jeanne A. Scott
FYE: December 31
Type: Private

You might say this company is trying to fuel a chicken craze. El Pollo Loco Holdings operates and franchises more than 400 fast-casual restaurants operating under the El Pollo Loco banner. Specializing in Mexican-style chicken dishes, the chain's menu includes chicken burritos and tacos, as well as complete chicken dinners and sides. Most El Pollo Loco outlets are found in the Los Angeles area and other markets in California. A small number can be found in more than a dozen other states including Arizona, Nevada, and Texas. About 250 of the restaurants are operated by franchisees. Juan Francisco Ochoa started the chain in Mexico in 1975. El Pollo Loco is owned by private equity firm Trimaran Capital.

ELAMEX, S.A. DE C.V.

Pink Sheets: ELAMF

1800 Northwestern Dr.
El Paso, TX 79912
Phone: 915-298-3061
Fax: 915-298-3065
Web: www.elamex.com

CEO: David E. Stewart
CFO: Mark Zimmerman
HR: —
FYE: December 31
Type: Public

It may sound nutty, but Elamex has a sweet tooth for candy. The company manufactures candy and packaged nuts through its subsidiary, Mount Franklin Foods. Mount Franklin operates Sunrise Confections in Juarez, Mexico, and Azar Nut Company in El Paso, Texas. Sunrise makes Sunrise and private-label branded sugar-based candies, including starlight mints, orange slices, spice drops, jelly beans, and gummies, which are sold at grocery store, drug store, mass merchandising, convenience store, and foodservice operators. Azar offers walnuts, pecans, almonds, sunflower seeds, and trail mixes in packaged and bulk form to the retail food and foodservice sectors.

ELAN PHARMACEUTICALS

800 Gateway Blvd.   CEO: Ted Yednock
San Francisco, CA 94080   CFO: —
Phone: 650-877-0900   HR: —
Fax: 650-877-7669   FYE: December 31
Web: www.elan.com   Type: Subsidiary

Elan Pharmaceuticals is part of the the brains behind the brawn of Irish drug-maker Elan Corporation. The US-based subsidiary provides research and discovery services, such as the identification and development of new drug candidates, to its parent, which specializes in treatments for neurological and autoimmune diseases, severe pain, and infectious diseases. The company investigates possible treatments for diseases such as Alzheimer's disease, Parkinson's disease, and multiple myeloma. The subsidiary also handles marketing of Elan's approved products in the US, including multiple sclerosis/Crohn's disease treatment Tysabri in a partnership with Biogen Idec.

ELANTAS PDG, INC

5200 N. Second St.   CEO: Susan W. Graham
St. Louis, MO 63147   CFO: —
Phone: 314-621-5700   HR: —
Fax: 314-436-1030   FYE: December 31
Web: www.elantas.com/pdg   Type: Subsidiary

ELANTAS PDG has a long business pedigree when it comes to making protective and performance-enhancing electronic coatings, varnishes, and resins. Although scholars might take issue, the company claims that "founder P. D. George coined the word 'Pedigree' in 1919 to denote quality." Etymology aside, the company — which is owned by German conglomerate ALTANA — makes wire coatings, insulating varnishes, and encapsulating resins designed to insulate, protect, and improve the performance of wires and other electronic components. ELANTAS PDG (formerly called P. D. George Corporation) also makes resins used in other electronic products and applications, including banding tape, adhesives, and laminating resins.

	Annual Growth	12/04	12/05	12/06	12/07	12/08
Est. sales ($ mil.)	—	—	—	—	—	100.0
Employees	—	—	—	—	—	185

▥ ELAVON, INC.

1 Concourse Pkwy., Ste. 300   CEO: Stuart C. Harvey Jr.
Atlanta, GA 30328   CFO: Jamie Walker
Phone: 678-731-5000   HR: —
Fax: —   FYE: December 31
Web: www.elavon.com   Type: Subsidiary

Nothing makes Elavon more elated than customers who say, "Put it on my card." The firm is a major processor of credit and debit card transactions in the US, Europe, Puerto Rico, and Canada. Elavon offers point-of-sale (POS) authorization for all major credit cards, accounting and clearing services, and dispute resolution. The company, a subsidiary of U.S. Bancorp, also provides its customers with sales, leasing, and maintenance of POS terminals connected to its network. Elavon serves more than 1 million customers including small merchants, large organizations, and financial institutions. Transactions also can be authorized around the world in more than 85 currencies and converted in nearly 50 currencies.

▥ ELCOM INTERNATIONAL, INC.   Pink Sheets: ELCO

10 Oceana Way   CEO: Mark Stephenson
Norwood, MA 02062   CFO: David Elliott
Phone: 781-501-4000   HR: —
Fax: —   FYE: December 31
Web: www.elcom.com   Type: Public

If only sales were as easy for Elcom to procure as the products bought and sold with its software. Elcom International's PECOS (Professional Electronic Commerce Online System) software enables clients to automate procurement functions such as pricing, invoicing, and payment. Its application suite, which Elcom offers as either a licensed or hosted application, includes tools for managing the order cycle, creating rapid requisitions, and building electronic marketplaces to conduct online transactions with suppliers and distributors. Elcom also provides integration services for suppliers and buyers to help them manage catalog information and other content.

ELDERHOSTEL, INC.

11 Ave. de Lafayette   CEO: James A. (Jim) Moses
Boston, MA 02111   CFO: David Stahl
Phone: 617-426-7788   HR: —
Fax: —   FYE: September 30
Web: www.elderhostel.org   Type: Not-for-profit

No, it's not a cheap place for older folks to stay whilst backpacking around the world. But Elderhostel does provide a wide variety of educational travel programs to adults ages 55 and over. The not-for-profit organization offers about 8,000 educational tours throughout the US and in more than 90 countries, from Africa to Antarctica. Programs are taught by professors, local scholars, and museum professionals and include lectures, field trips, and hands-on activities. Participants experience and learn about art, literature, music, nature, and traditional cultures. Elderhostel was founded in 1975 by world traveler and social activist Marty Knowlton and University of New Hampshire administrator David Bianco.

ELDORADO ARTESIAN SPRINGS, INC.   OTC: ELDO

1783 Dogwood St.   CEO: Douglas A. Larson
Louisville, CO 80027   CFO: Cathleen M. Shoenfeld
Phone: 303-499-1316   HR: —
Fax: 303-499-1339   FYE: March 31
Web: www.eldoradosprings.com   Type: Public

If Cortez had sought a wealth of water instead of streets of gold, he might have headed for Eldorado Artesian Springs. The company bottles water from springs it owns in the foothills of the Rocky Mountains. About 70% of its sales comes from home and office delivery of three and five gallon bottles of its natural spring water (and water cooler rentals); it also supplies smaller bottles to wholesalers and distributors for retail sale. Eldorado's water is distributed primarily in Colorado but also in regions of bordering states. In addition to its bottled water business, the company owns and operates a resort on its property.

	Annual Growth	3/05	3/06	3/07	3/08	3/09
Sales ($ mil.)	4.2%	—	7.9	8.2	8.5	9.3
Net income ($ mil.)	—	—	0.0	0.1	(0.3)	(0.2)
Market value ($ mil.)	(14.2%)	—	10.6	11.4	13.1	5.8
Employees	1.5%	—	67	69	74	71

ELECSYS CORPORATION

NASDAQ (CM): ESYS

846 N. Mart-Way Ct.
Olathe, KS 66061
Phone: 913-647-0158
Fax: 913-647-0132
Web: www.elecsyscorp.com

CEO: Karl B. Gemperli
CFO: Todd A. Daniels
HR: —
FYE: April 30
Type: Public

Many companies elect Elecsys to make their electronics. Elecsys is a contract manufacturer of electronic assemblies and displays. Through subsidiary DCI, Inc., the company makes custom electronic assemblies — including printed circuit boards, electronic modules, LCDs, and light-emitting diodes (LEDs) — for OEMs in the aerospace, communications, medical, and other industries. Five customers account for about a quarter of the company's sales. In 2007 Elecsys acquired the assets of Radix International, a supplier of ultra-rugged handheld computers and portable printers. DCI previously manufactured most of Radix's product line on a contract basis.

	Annual Growth	4/05	4/06	4/07	4/08	4/09
Sales ($ mil.)	15.5%	12.3	14.7	19.8	23.4	21.9
Net income ($ mil.)	0.0%	0.7	1.7	1.0	0.7	0.7
Market value ($ mil.)	2.7%	12.3	14.8	21.6	24.6	13.7
Employees	8.0%	97	106	129	158	132

ELECTRIC & GAS TECHNOLOGY, INC.

Pink Sheets: ELGT

3233 W. Kingsley Rd.
Garland, TX 75041
Phone: 972-840-3223
Fax: 972-271-8925
Web: www.elgt.com

CEO: Daniel A. Zimmerman
CFO: Daniel A. Zimmerman
HR: Daniel A. Zimmerman
FYE: July 31
Type: Public

Oil and water may not mix, but electric and metal does — in the business plan of Electric & Gas Technology (EGTI). EGTI operates as a holding company. Its subsidiary Logic Metals Technology offers contract precision sheet metal fabrication of electronic metal enclosures and equipment panels. The company caters to communications and electronics industries, as well as a variety of aesthetic design applications. The father and son team, Chairman S. Mort Zimmerman and CEO Daniel Zimmerman control the company.

ELECTRIC BOAT CORPORATION

75 Eastern Point Rd.
Groton, CT 06340
Phone: 860-433-3000
Fax: 860-433-1400
Web: www.gdeb.com

CEO: John P. Casey
CFO: John V. Leonard Jr.
HR: Robert H. Nardone
FYE: December 31
Type: Subsidiary

Electric Boat is not a float in the Disney Electric Light Parade. Electric Boat designs, builds, and maintains nuclear attack and ballistic-missile submarines for the US Navy. A subsidiary of defense giant General Dynamics, Electric Boat was established in 1899 and won its first US Navy contract the next year. It has delivered the lead ship of the Virginia class (USS Virginia-SSN774) and its third and final Seawolf-class submarine (Jimmy Carter-SSN23) to the US Navy, and is working on several Virginia-class submarines with Northrop Grumman. Electric Boat continues to provide support and maintenance for Seawolf-, Ohio-, and Los Angeles-class submarines. Electric Boat operates in Connecticut and Rhode Island.

ELECTRIC ENERGY, INC.

2100 Portland Rd.
Joppa, IL 62953
Phone: 618-543-7531
Fax: 618-543-7420

CEO: Robert L. (Bob) Powers
CFO: —
HR: —
FYE: December 31
Type: Private

It does not take a genius to figure out what business Electric Energy (EEI) is involved in. The company generates 1,000 MW of electric capacity at its coal-fired power plant in Joppa, Illinois (which began operating in 1953), and 74 MW at it natural gas-fired facility (which commenced operations in 2000) at the same location. The independent producer sells its power output to its shareholders. The Missouri-based utility holding company Ameren holds an 80% stake in EEI; Kentucky Utilities (a subsidiary of LG&E Energy) owns the remaining 20% of the company.

	Annual Growth	12/04	12/05	12/06	12/07	12/08
Est. sales ($ mil.)	—	—	—	—	—	514.3
Employees	—	—	—	—	—	263

ELECTRO RENT CORPORATION

NASDAQ (GM): ELRC

6060 Sepulveda Blvd.
Van Nuys, CA 91411
Phone: 818-787-2100
Fax: 818-786-4354
Web: www.electrorent.com

CEO: Daniel Greenberg
CFO: Craig R. Jones
HR: Peter M. Shapiro
FYE: May 31
Type: Public

Electro Rent isn't the electronica version of the popular Broadway musical — the company rents, leases, and resells electronic test and measurement equipment, computers, and related equipment. The company's suppliers include Agilent Technologies, Olympus, and Tektronix, while its computer products come from such manufacturers as Dell, Hewlett-Packard, IBM, and Toshiba. Electro Rent provides new and used equipment to government agencies and companies in the electronics and military/aerospace industries. The company gets most of its sales in the US.

	Annual Growth	5/05	5/06	5/07	5/08	5/09
Sales ($ mil.)	4.9%	107.6	114.8	125.3	144.5	130.5
Net income ($ mil.)	(16.5%)	24.3	22.2	21.0	21.1	11.8
Market value ($ mil.)	(4.8%)	281.4	395.1	345.1	338.1	231.1
Employees	5.4%	240	284	301	—	296

ELECTRO SCIENTIFIC INDUSTRIES, INC.

NASDAQ (GM): ESIO

13900 NW Science Park Dr.
Portland, OR 97229
Phone: 503-641-4141
Fax: 503-671-5551
Web: www.esi.com

CEO: Nicholas (Nick) Konidaris
CFO: Paul Oldham
HR: Tracey Jerijervi
FYE: March 31
Type: Public

Electro Scientific Industries (ESI) and its subsidiaries use science — and a lot of engineering — to help its customers produce electronics on an industrial, high-volume scale. The company's manufacturing and test equipment is used to make and inspect electronic components in automotive electronics, PCs, and wireless communications gear. Its offerings include yield improvement systems, circuit fine-tuning equipment, and miniature capacitor test products. ESI also makes electronic packaging equipment, as well as machine vision systems to inspect and verify chip and circuit board quality. ESI's customers include Canon, Hynix Semiconductor, Kulicke and Soffa, Kyocera, Samsung Electronics, and STMicroelectronics.

	Annual Growth	5/06	5/07	*3/08	3/09	3/10
Sales ($ mil.)	(7.9%)	207.0	250.8	247.2	157.3	148.9
Net income ($ mil.)	—	20.8	23.5	16.6	(51.0)	(12.0)
Market value ($ mil.)	(10.2%)	548.3	569.3	452.4	163.2	356.5
Employees	(0.9%)	603	585	—	567	581

*Fiscal year change

ELECTROLUX HOME CARE PRODUCTS NORTH AMERICA

807 N. Main St.
Bloomington, IL 61701
Phone: 309-828-2367
Fax: 309-823-5203
Web: www.eureka.com

CEO: Russell S. (Russ) Minick
CFO: Jan Wolansky
HR: Jan Dahlman
FYE: December 31
Type: Subsidiary

No one knows if Fred Wardell exclaimed "Eureka!" when he came up with the idea for a vacuum company, but that's what he named it in 1909. The vacuum cleaner company stuck with its birth name until 2004, when it was rechristened Electrolux Home Care Products North America by Sweden-based AB Electrolux. The name change coincided with its parent's reacquisition of the Electrolux name in North America. The company makes and markets more than 130 vacuum models under brand names Electrolux, Sanitaire, Beam, and Eureka. Its products include uprights, canisters, built-in systems, hand-held and battery-powered vacuums, wet-dry vacs, stick models, and others. They're typically sold through Lowe's, Sears, and Wal-Mart.

ELECTROLUX HOME PRODUCTS - NORTH AMERICA

250 Bobby Jones Expwy.
Martinez, GA 30907
Phone: 706-228-6615
Fax: —
Web: www.electroluxusa.com

CEO: Kevin Scott
CFO: Marty O'Gorman
HR: —
FYE: December 31
Type: Business segment

Electrolux Home Products is the North American marketing and distribution arm of Sweden-based — and #1 appliance maker — AB Electrolux. Electrolux also is a top brand in US markets. The company makes home appliances (including refrigerators, microwave ovens, stoves, electric and gas cooktops, dishwashers, laundry equipment, and vacuums) and outdoor products (such as lawn mowers and gas grills). Its brands include namesake Electrolux, as well as Frigidaire, Eureka, Poulan, and Weed Eater. Products are sold through mass merchandisers, department stores, and home improvement retailers, including Best Buy, Lowe's, Sears, and Target. Electrolux Home Products generates about 30% of its parent's revenue.

	Annual Growth	12/04	12/05	12/06	12/07	12/08
Est. sales ($ mil.)	—	—	—	—	—	5,056.5
Employees	—	—	—	—	—	22,000

ELECTRO-MOTIVE DIESEL, INC.

9301 W. 55th St.
La Grange, IL 60525
Phone: 800-255-5355
Fax: 708-387-6660
Web: www.emdiesels.com

CEO: John Hamilton
CFO: Michael P. O'Donnell
HR: —
FYE: December 31
Type: Private

What do manufacturer Electro-Motive Diesel (EMD) and 1970s band Grand Funk Railroad have in common? They both do the locomotion! EMD designs, builds, sells, and services diesel-electric locomotives for commercial railroad use, including commuter, freight, industrial, intercity passenger, and mining. The company has the largest installed base of diesel-electric locomotives in the world; its products are sold in more than 70 countries. EMD also provides diesel engines to the marine propulsion, oil drilling rigs, and power generation markets. The company was founded in 1922 as Electro-Motive Engineering. Formerly part of GM, the company is held by private-equity firms Greenbriar Equity and Berkshire Partners.

	Annual Growth	12/04	12/05	12/06	12/07	12/08
Est. sales ($ mil.)	28.8%	—	1,030.0	1,710.0	1,830.0	2,200.0
Employees	7.3%	—	2,640	2,640	2,740	3,260

ELECTRONIC ARTS INC.

NASDAQ (GS): ERTS

209 Redwood Shores Pkwy.
Redwood City, CA 94065
Phone: 650-628-1500
Fax: 650-628-1422
Web: www.ea.com

CEO: John S. Riccitiello
CFO: Eric F. Brown
HR: Gabrielle Toledano
FYE: March 31
Type: Public

Electronic Arts (EA) has a knack for the craft of creating video games. EA is a leading video game publisher, with popular titles such as *Madden NFL*, *The Sims*, *Need for Speed*, *Spore*, and *Medal of Honor*. It also distributes titles for third-party labels (including *Rock Band*) and publishes games based on Hollywood franchises such as *The Lord of the Rings*, *The Godfather*, *Harry Potter*, and *Batman*. EA develops its games for PCs and console systems and portable devices from Sony, Nintendo, and Microsoft. In 2008 the company offered $2 billion to purchase Take-Two Interactive, publisher of the *Grand Theft Auto* franchise; Take-Two rejected the offer.

	Annual Growth	3/05	3/06	3/07	3/08	3/09
Sales ($ mil.)	7.7%	3,129.0	2,951.0	3,091.0	3,665.0	4,212.0
Net income ($ mil.)	—	504.0	236.0	76.0	(454.0)	(1,088.0)
Market value ($ mil.)	(23.0%)	16,913.6	17,874.0	16,449.8	16,306.1	5,941.7
Employees	10.5%	6,100	7,200	7,900	9,000	9,100

ELECTRONIC CLEARING HOUSE, INC.

730 Paseo Camarillo
Camarillo, CA 93010
Phone: 805-419-8700
Fax: 805-419-8694
Web: www.echo-inc.com

CEO: Charles J. (Chuck) Harris
CFO: Alice L. Cheung
HR: —
FYE: September 30
Type: Subsidiary

This Clearing House doesn't deliver gigantic checks to your door but, if you're a merchant, it could determine if that big check you received from a customer is legit. Electronic Clearing House (ECHO) provides transaction and processing services related to credit and debit card payments. Its XpressCheX and National Check Network (NCN) units provide check-related services, including authorization, guarantee, conversion, collection, and verification; the NCN database compiles consumer checking account data from more than 250 collection agencies. ECHO's clients include more than 100,000 retail merchants, as well as banks and technology firms. The company was acquired by Intuit for about $131 million in 2008.

ELECTRONIC CONTROL SECURITY, INC.

OTC: EKCS

790 Bloomfield Ave., Bldg. C-1
Clifton, NJ 07012
Phone: 973-574-8555
Fax: 973-574-8562
Web: www.anti-terrorism.com

CEO: Arthur Barchenko
CFO: Arthur Barchenko
HR: Natalie Barchenko
FYE: June 30
Type: Public

Electronic Control Security (ECSI) is a leading provider of integrated security systems for government and commercial facilities worldwide. Its products include command and control, intrusion detection, and sensing and surveillance systems used at airports, military bases, ports, and other sensitive facilities such as embassies and power plants. ECSI also provides risk assessment and other security consulting services. Its customers include a number of government agencies, such as the US Department of Energy and the Department of Defense. In addition to offices in the US, the company has operations in the Middle East and Latin America.

	Annual Growth	6/05	6/06	6/07	6/08	6/09
Sales ($ mil.)	(12.6%)	6.0	8.8	5.6	2.9	3.5
Net income ($ mil.)	—	(0.1)	(1.7)	(1.1)	(0.9)	(0.7)
Market value ($ mil.)	(45.3%)	16.9	5.6	10.6	2.0	1.5
Employees	(15.9%)	28	27	21	18	14

ELECTRONIC SYSTEMS TECHNOLOGY, INC.

OTC: ELST

415 N. Quay St., Bldg. B1
Kennewick, WA 99336
Phone: 509-735-9092
Fax: 509-783-5475
Web: www.esteem.com

CEO: T. L. Kirchner
CFO: Jon Correio
HR: —
FYE: December 31
Type: Public

Electronic Systems Technology (EST) makes wireless modems that it markets under the ESTeem brand. EST targets the modems for applications in industrial automation, the military, and public safety. The ESTeem line includes Ethernet radios that can be used for handling video and voice over Internet protocol (VoIP) transmissions. EST buys parts from Hitachi, Intersil, Integrated Microelectronics, Motorola, Mitsubishi, Murata Manufacturing, Rakon, and Toko America for its products. Assembly of EST's products is farmed out to Manufacturing Services.

	Annual Growth	12/05	12/06	12/07	12/08	12/09
Sales ($ mil.)	(5.7%)	2.4	2.6	3.0	2.1	1.9
Net income ($ mil.)	—	0.1	0.2	0.3	(0.2)	0.0
Market value ($ mil.)	(2.6%)	3.1	3.3	4.4	1.6	2.8
Employees	(3.1%)	17	14	16	15	15

ELECTRONICS FOR IMAGING, INC.

NASDAQ (GS): EFII

303 Velocity Way
Foster City, CA 94404
Phone: 650-357-3500
Fax: 650-357-3907
Web: www.efi.com

CEO: Guy Gecht
CFO: Gordon Heneweer
HR: Jackie Cimino
FYE: December 31
Type: Public

Electronics For Imaging (EFI) wants to take control of your color. The company makes hardware and software systems for commercial and enterprise digital printing and print management. EFI's Fiery line includes stand-alone print servers, as well as print controllers that copier and printer vendors such as Canon, Konica Minolta, Ricoh, and Xerox integrate into their equipment. EFI's Print MIS software provides supply chain and customer relationship management from print job submission to fulfillment. Its ink jet products include superwide format printers (VUTEk) and industrial printers (Jetrion). The company gets more than half of its sales in the Americas.

	Annual Growth	12/05	12/06	12/07	12/08	12/09
Sales ($ mil.)	(3.8%)	468.5	564.6	620.6	560.4	401.1
Net income ($ mil.)	—	(4.1)	(0.2)	26.8	(113.4)	(2.2)
Market value ($ mil.)	(16.4%)	1,204.9	1,203.5	1,017.9	432.9	587.3
Employees	1.5%	1,723	1,889	2,018	2,021	1,827

ELECTRO-OPTICAL SCIENCES, INC.

NASDAQ (CM): MELA

3 W. Main St., Ste. 201
Irvington, NY 10533
Phone: 914-591-3783
Fax: 914-591-3785
Web: www.eo-sciences.com

CEO: Joseph V. Gulfo
CFO: Richard I. Steinhart
HR: —
FYE: December 31
Type: Public

Electro-Optical Sciences can detect whether that mole is a sign of a more serious medical condition — melanoma. The company's lead product is a hand-held imaging device called MelaFind, which captures images of suspicious skin lesions, compares them to other malignant and benign lesions stored in a database, and provides information about whether they should be biopsied. MelaFind is in pivotal clinical trials for its ability to detect skin cancer at an early stage. Electro-Optical Sciences is seeking FDA approval, so that it can begin commercially marketing the point-of-care product to primary care physicians, dermatologists, and plastic surgeons in the US and through partnerships abroad.

	Annual Growth	12/05	12/06	12/07	12/08	12/09
Sales ($ mil.)	—	—	—	—	0.0	0.0
Net income ($ mil.)	—	—	—	—	(17.6)	(18.5)
Market value ($ mil.)	207.8%	—	—	—	77.1	237.4
Employees	17.1%	—	—	—	41	48

ELECTRO-SENSORS, INC.

NASDAQ (CM): ELSE

6111 Blue Circle Dr.
Minnetonka, MN 55343
Phone: 952-930-0100
Fax: 952-930-0130
Web: www.electro-sensors.com

CEO: Bradley D. Slye
CFO: Bradley D. Slye
HR: —
FYE: December 31
Type: Public

Electro-Sensors supports the manufacturing process with sensitive loving care. The company's Product Monitoring Division, which accounts for the bulk of sales, makes computerized systems that monitor and regulate the production speed of industrial machinery. Products are sold worldwide. Electro-Sensors also has an AutoData Systems unit, which makes software that reads hand-printed characters, check marks, and bar code information from scanned or faxed forms. The unit has an exclusive license to use a neural network algorithm developed by PPT Vision. Its software sells mostly in North America and Western Europe. Electro-Sensors director and secretary Peter Peterson and his family own 38% of the company.

	Annual Growth	12/05	12/06	12/07	12/08	12/09
Sales ($ mil.)	4.8%	4.9	5.8	7.1	6.7	5.9
Net income ($ mil.)	(21.7%)	0.8	1.7	1.2	0.6	0.3
Market value ($ mil.)	(2.9%)	14.1	17.6	19.9	10.8	12.6
Employees	2.5%	29	29	33	32	32

ELEGANT ILLUSIONS, INC.

Pink Sheets: EILL

542 Lighthouse Ave., Ste. 5
Pacific Grove, CA 93950
Phone: 831-649-1814
Fax: 831-649-1001
Web: www.elegantillusions.com

CEO: James Cardinal
CFO: Gavin Gear
HR: James Cardinal
FYE: December 31
Type: Public

You can't believe all you see at Elegant Illusions, but you can believe in some of it. The jewelry company operates about a dozen stores in nine US states and on St. Croix, US Virgin Islands. Most of its locations sell copies of fine jewelry, although a couple sell the real deal. Elegant Illusions also boasts two fine jewelry stores and an art gallery in New Orleans. Its faux jewelry includes different styles of rings, earrings, and pendants featuring lab-created emeralds, rubies, sapphires, and opals in 14-carat gold and white gold settings. Executives James Cardinal and married couple Gavin and Tamara Gear are majority owners. The Gears started the firm at a former hot dog stand on Cannery Row in San Francisco.

ELEMENT K CORPORATION

500 Canal View Blvd.
Rochester, NY 14623
Phone: 585-240-7500
Fax: 585-295-4650
Web: www.elementk.com

CEO: Paul Krause
CFO: William Jacques
HR: Donna Maxwell
FYE: December 31
Type: Subsidiary

Element K . . . That would be potassium, right? Element K doesn't teach chemistry, but it does offer business and technology-related training programs. The company develops, builds, and manages training learning products for corporate, government, university, and individual clients. Element K offers self-paced online courses, print materials, and certification and accreditation programs in thousands of topics including networking, leadership skills, and compliance. Founded in 1982, Element K was acquired by global learning company NIIT in 2006.

An in-depth profile of this company is available to Hoover's Online members at hoovers.com.

ELEMENTIS SPECIALTIES, INC.

329 Wyckoffs Mill Rd.
Hightstown, NJ 08520
Phone: 609-443-2000
Fax: 609-443-2422
Web: www.elementis-specialties.com

CEO: David Dutro
CFO: Gregory (Greg) Cappucci
HR: —
FYE: December 31
Type: Subsidiary

Elementis Specialties focuses on the elements of specialty chemicals. The company manufactures additives that improve the various properties of products made by the coatings, building products, and cosmetics industries. A subsidiary of Elementis plc, it manufactures rheological additives that affect thinning, thickening, and flow in products like cosmetics, coatings, and drilling fluids. The company also makes a line of pigment dispersions and a variety of other specialty additives and polymers. Although its parent is based in the UK, Elementis Specialties makes its home in New Jersey and has operations worldwide. It generates more than half of its additives sales by supplying the US paints and coatings market.

ELG HANIEL METALS CORP.

369 River Rd.
McKeesport, PA 15132
Phone: 412-672-9200
Fax: 412-672-0824
Web: www.elg.de/locations/usa.en.html

CEO: Simon Merrills
CFO: David Reichenecker
HR: Shirley Lippai
FYE: December 31
Type: Subsidiary

In the one-man's-trash-is-another-man's-treasure category, scrappy ELG Haniel Metals has made a mint from the business of metal-morphosis. US-based ELG Metals recycles stainless steel and specialty metal alloys that make use of nickel, cadmium, titanium, and copper. The company operates from half a dozen locations throughout the US. It's a subsidiary of German metals trader and scrap processor ELG Haniel and provides almost a quarter of its total sales.

	Annual Growth	12/04	12/05	12/06	12/07	12/08
Est. sales ($ mil.)	—	—	—	—	—	48.3
Employees	—	—	—	—	—	235

⊞ ELI LILLY AND COMPANY

NYSE: LLY

Lilly Corporate Center, 893 S. Delaware
Indianapolis, IN 46285
Phone: 317-276-2000
Fax: 317-276-4878
Web: www.lilly.com

CEO: John C. Lechleiter
CFO: Derica W. Rice
HR: Patricia A. Martin
FYE: December 31
Type: Public

Eli Lilly hopes everything will come up roses for you, healthwise. Although best known for its popular antidepressant Prozac, the company develops medicines for a wide variety of ailments. Its top drugs include neurological therapies Zyprexa (schizophrenia and bipolar disorder) and Cymbalta (depression), cancer treatments Gemzar and Alimta, and endocrinology (hormone-related) products such as Humalog insulin and osteoporosis medication Evista. The company also makes cardiovascular therapies and anti-infective agents, as well as animal health products. Lilly sells its products in some 130 countries.

	Annual Growth	12/05	12/06	12/07	12/08	12/09
Sales ($ mil.)	10.5%	14,645.3	15,691.0	18,633.5	20,378.0	21,836.0
Net income ($ mil.)	21.3%	2,001.6	2,662.7	2,953.0	(2,071.9)	4,328.8
Market value ($ mil.)	(10.9%)	65,256.2	60,078.6	61,566.2	46,437.0	41,178.6
Employees	(1.3%)	42,600	41,500	40,600	40,500	40,360

ELITE MODEL MANAGEMENT CORPORATION

404 Park Ave. South, 9th Fl.
New York, NY 10016
Phone: 212-529-9700
Fax: 212-475-0572
Web: www.elitemodel.com

CEO: Jane Stewart
CFO: Jeff Loveland
HR: Chrysa Nakis
FYE: December 31
Type: Private

Who says modeling agents are a bunch of elitists? Elite Model Management does. The New York-based agency created the term "supermodel" in the 1980s and helped launch the careers of some of the world's most well-known models, including Gisele Bundchen, Cindy Crawford, Claudia Schiffer, Naomi Campbell, and Linda Evangelista. The company manages the careers of some 800 models globally; those who earn top dollar are in the Elite+ division. Elite Model Management boasts the Elite Model Look, an international model-scouting contest that attracts more than 300,000 participants who are looking to be discovered. Creative World Management owns the company.

	Annual Growth	12/04	12/05	12/06	12/07	12/08
Est. sales ($ mil.)	—	—	—	—	—	9.3
Employees	—	—	—	—	—	22

ELITE PHARMACEUTICALS, INC.

NYSE Amex: ELI

165 Ludlow Ave.
Northvale, NJ 07647
Phone: 201-750-2646
Fax: 201-750-2755
Web: www.elitepharma.com

CEO: Jerry I. Treppel
CFO: Carter A. Ward
HR: —
FYE: March 31
Type: Public

Elite Pharmaceuticals isn't above peddling generics. Subsidiary Elite Laboratories develops generic versions of existing controlled-release drugs whose patents are about to expire. Its commercial products include allergy therapeutics Lodrane 24 and Lodrane 24D, which are marketed by ECR Pharmaceuticals. Products in various stages of testing and preclinical development include oxycodone pain medications, anti-infectives, and treatments for gastrointestinal disorders. Elite Laboratories also provides contract research and development services for other drugmakers.

	Annual Growth	3/05	3/06	3/07	3/08	3/09
Sales ($ mil.)	66.4%	0.3	0.6	1.1	1.4	2.3
Net income ($ mil.)	—	(5.9)	(6.9)	(11.8)	(13.9)	(6.6)
Market value ($ mil.)	(58.5%)	368.5	208.5	194.3	77.0	10.9
Employees	(9.6%)	18	26	41	34	12

ELIZABETH ARDEN, INC.

NASDAQ (GS): RDEN

2400 SW 145th Ave., 2nd Fl.
Miramar, FL 33027
Phone: 954-364-6900
Fax: 954-364-6910
Web: www.elizabetharden.com

CEO: E. Scott Beattie
CFO: Stephen J. Smith
HR: Lita Cunningham
FYE: June 30
Type: Public

Sweet scents and more are behind Elizabeth Arden's red door. The firm owns and licenses prestige and mass-market celebrity, lifestyle, and designer fragrances and distributes some 300 prestige fragrance brands. Fragrance accounts for more than 75% of the company's sales. Older, established brands include Elizabeth Arden, Red Door, 5th avenue, and Elizabeth Taylor's White Diamonds. Scents targeted at younger customers include the Hilary Duff and Juicy Couture brands. Skin care products and makeup (Ceramide, Intervene, and PREVAGE) account for the balance of the company's sales. Third-party manufacturer Cosmetic Essence makes Elizabeth Arden products, and a separate firm runs its Red Door salons.

	Annual Growth	6/05	6/06	6/07	6/08	6/09
Sales ($ mil.)	3.8%	920.5	954.5	1,127.5	1,141.1	1,070.2
Net income ($ mil.)	—	37.6	32.8	37.3	19.9	(6.2)
Market value ($ mil.)	(21.8%)	673.8	515.1	698.8	437.3	251.5
Employees	2.0%	2,350	2,650	2,850	2,525	2,546

ELKAY MANUFACTURING COMPANY

2222 Camden Ct.
Oak Brook, IL 60523
Phone: 630-574-8484
Fax: 630-574-5012
Web: www.elkay.com

CEO: Timothy J. (Tim) Jahnke
CFO: Timothy J. (Tim) Bondy
HR: Vicki Slomka
FYE: December 31
Type: Private

Someone's in the kitchen with Dinah, and it's Elkay Manufacturing. Elkay makes sinks, cabinets, countertops, drinking fountains, faucets, water coolers, and water filtration products. The family-owned company sells residential and commercial products such as stainless steel sinks under such names as Harmony, The Mystic, and Elite Gourmet. It also offers kitchen accessories (colanders, cutting boards, soap dispensers). Elkay's cabinet brands include Yorktowne, Medallion, and MasterCraft. Elkay is the parent of a dozen privately held companies and one joint venture, Elkay Pacific Rim. The company was founded in 1920 by the Katz family to make sinks for butlers' pantries and sculleries.

	Annual Growth	12/04	12/05	12/06	12/07	12/08
Est. sales ($ mil.)	—	—	—	—	—	739.0
Employees	—	—	—	—	—	4,300

ELKEM HOLDING, INC.

Airport Office Park, Bldg. 2, 400 Rouser Rd.
Coraopolis, PA 15108
Phone: 412-299-7200
Fax: 412-299-7225

CEO: Geir Kvernmo
CFO: Albert Woodrich
HR: David Renfrew
FYE: December 31
Type: Subsidiary

Elkem Holding is the North American holding company for Norwegian metals company Elkem AS. Among its operating subsidiaries are Elkem Metals Co. and Elkem Materials. The group's operations supply silicon metal, ferrosilicon, carbon products, and microsilica to customers. Silicon metal is used by the chemical (silicones), electronics (semiconductors), and aluminum (metal alloys) industries. Elkem Holding has production plants in the US and Canada. Norwegian industrial conglomerate Orkla owns Elkem.

	Annual Growth	12/04	12/05	12/06	12/07	12/08
Est. sales ($ mil.)	—	—	—	—	—	91.0
Employees	—	—	—	—	—	337

ELKHART PRODUCTS CORPORATION

1255 Oak St.
Elkhart, IN 46515
Phone: 574-264-3181
Fax: 574-264-0103
Web: www.elkhartproducts.com

CEO: Dale A. Dieckbernd
CFO: —
HR: Elaine S. Laux
FYE: December 31
Type: Subsidiary

"What hath Elkhart Products wrought?" Wrot copper fittings for plumbing, that's what. Elkhart Products manufactures wrot copper and cast fittings, including couplings, elbows, tees, hangers, and adapters, used by plumbing and industrial flow control markets in the US and Canada. The company also serves the automotive and air conditioning and refrigeration industries and provides custom tubular fabrication work. Formerly a subsidiary of Amcast Industrial Corporation (which acquired Elkhart Products in 1983), the company was sold to Aalberts Industries N.V. in 2004. Aalberts Industries has more than 150 industrial services and flow control production facilities worldwide.

ELLIOTT COMPANY

901 N. 4th St.
Jeanette, PA 15644
Phone: 724-527-2811
Fax: 724-600-8525
Web: www.elliott-turbo.com

CEO: Antonio (Tony) Casillo
CFO: Eugene J. O'Sullivan
HR: —
FYE: March 31
Type: Subsidiary

Elliott Company (formerly known as Elliott Turbomachinery) is a manufacturer of power generating equipment. Products include bow thrusters, air and gas compressors, control systems, and steam turbines; services include field service, parts supply, and turbine remanufacturing. The company serves customers in the chemical, oil and gas, petrochemical, and power industries, among others. Elliot was founded in 1895 as the Chicago Boiler Company, and relocated to Pennsylvania in 1914. The company was owned by Carrier for 30 years before going private in a management buyout. Since 2000, Elliott has been a subsidiary of Ebara Corporation.

	Annual Growth	3/04	3/05	3/06	3/07	3/08
Est. sales ($ mil.)	—	—	—	—	—	355.1
Employees	—	—	—	—	—	1,297

ELLORA ENERGY INC.

5665 Flatiron Pkwy.
Boulder, CO 80301
Phone: 303-444-8881
Fax: 303-417-1000
Web: www.elloraenergy.com

CEO: T. Scott Martin
CFO: E. Lon McCain
HR: —
FYE: December 31
Type: Private

Ellora Energy doesn't cave in — it drills deep for profits. An oil and gas exploration and development company, the firm owns properties in the Haynesville Play and other assets in East Texas (including adjacent property in western Louisiana), and in Kansas (the Hugoton field). The company has built up a land base of 910,000 gross acres with about 1,060 identified drilling locations. In 2008 Ellora Energy reported that it was operating 426 gross (319 net) producing wells and controlled proved reserves of approximately 194 billion cu. ft. of natural gas equivalent. Investment firm Yorktown Energy Partners owns about 64% of the company.

	Annual Growth	12/04	12/05	12/06	12/07	12/08
Sales ($ mil.)	55.5%	24.3	53.1	56.6	82.1	142.0
Net income ($ mil.)	29.2%	6.0	10.8	10.2	3.0	16.7
Employees	24.2%	—	47	—	—	90

ELMA ELECTRONIC INC.

44350 Grimmer Blvd.
Fremont, CA 94538
Phone: 510-656-3400
Fax: 510-656-3783
Web: www.elma.com/us

CEO: Fred Ruegg
CFO: Peter Brunner
HR: —
FYE: December 31
Type: Subsidiary

If Nigel's amp goes to 11, it's because Elma Electronic made the knob to crank it up. Founded in 1986, the US subsidiary of Elma Electronic AG manufactures and distributes an array of electronic enclosures, backplanes, and server racks. It also makes passive electronic components, from rotary switches to knobs and light-emitting diodes. Elma Electronic's slate of services includes component customization, design, engineering, manufacture, systems integration, and verification. Subsidiary operation Elma Bustronic offers custom backplane applications, and Optima EPS makes electronic enclosures. The company courts industries worldwide in telecommunications, medical electronics, industrial control, defense, and aerospace.

ELMER'S PRODUCTS, INC.

1 Easton Oval
Columbus, OH 43219
Phone: 614-985-2600
Fax: 614-985-2605
Web: www.elmers.com

CEO: James L. Hamling
CFO: Doug A. Kramer
HR: —
FYE: December 31
Type: Subsidiary

Elmer's knows that when a product works, people stick with it. Elmer's Products makes more than 200 adhesive items, including glues for wood, school, and all-purpose, as well as the top instant adhesive in the US — Krazy Glue. Besides its sticky business, Elmer's markets brands such as X-Acto (knives), Bienfang (papers), Conte (crayons), ColorLoco (markers), GiddyUp (arts and crafts goods), and Scientific Explorer (educational kits). Products are sold by retailers worldwide and online. The company was founded in 1947 when former parent Borden debuted its white Cascorez Glue, which was renamed Elmer's Glue-All after Elmer, the spouse of Borden icon Elsie the Cow. Elmer's is owned by investment giant Berwind.

E-LOAN, INC.

6230 Stoneridge Mall Rd.
Pleasanton, CA 94588
Phone: 925-847-6200
Fax: 925-847-0831
Web: www.eloan.com

CEO: Mark E. Lefanowicz
CFO: Alberto J. Paracchini
HR: Cecily Carel
FYE: December 31
Type: Subsidiary

E-LOAN has E-LIMINATED its direct-to-consumer lending activities and now only provides access to CDs and savings accounts through its website. The struggling division of Banco Popular North America (BPNA) stopped issuing new auto, home, and other types of loans in 2008 after it faced significant losses amid illiquid credit markets, declining mortgage originations, and a spike in foreclosures. E-LOAN attempted to restructure itself in 2007 and it cut 40% of its workforce. But a year later, its parent company, Puerto Rico's Popular, announced that it would scale back its US operations. All of E-LOAN'S functions were transferred to BPNA and Popular's processing unit, EVERTEC, in mid-2009.

THE ELMIRA SAVINGS BANK, FSB

NASDAQ (CM): ESBK

333 E. Water St.
Elmira, NY 14901
Phone: 607-734-3374
Fax: 607-732-4007
Web: www.elmirasavingsbank.com

CEO: Michael P. Hosey
CFO: Jason T. Sanford
HR: Bradley V. Serva
FYE: December 31
Type: Public

The Elmira Savings Bank is a community bank that serves individuals and small to midsized businesses through about a dozen branch offices in upstate New York's Cayuga, Chemung, Steuben, and Tompkins counties. The bank offers traditional deposit products such as checking and savings accounts, CDs, and IRAs. With these funds, it mainly originates residential and commercial mortgages, business loans, and auto and other consumer loans. The bank offers investments and financial planning through its ESB Advisory Services subsidiary. Elmira Savings Bank was organized in 1869.

	Annual Growth	12/05	12/06	12/07	12/08	12/09
Assets ($ mil.)	10.6%	333.3	371.5	453.7	—	499.0
Net income ($ mil.)	12.6%	2.8	(0.3)	2.1	3.0	4.5
Market value ($ mil.)	(4.8%)	39.2	48.0	34.2	—	32.2
Employees	13.0%	101	98	129	—	—

ELOYALTY CORPORATION

NASDAQ (GM): ELOY

150 Field Dr., Ste. 250
Lake Forest, IL 60045
Phone: 847-582-7000
Fax: 847-582-7001
Web: www.eloyalty.com

CEO: Kelly D. Conway
CFO: William B. (Bill) Noon
HR: —
FYE: December 31
Type: Public

eLoyalty hopes its services and tools make customers feel like eRoyalty. The company is a customer relationship management (CRM) services provider. It offers management consulting, systems integration, and managed services aimed at developing and implementing strategies. eLoyalty's services are designed to integrate customer contacts generated from a variety of sources, including information gathered from e-mails, call centers, field sales, and Internet channels. It also offers systems designed to measure financial and operating metrics associated with CRM programs.

	Annual Growth	12/05	12/06	12/07	12/08	12/09
Sales ($ mil.)	6.5%	79.0	89.8	102.1	91.2	101.6
Net income ($ mil.)	—	(7.6)	(11.1)	(18.7)	(20.9)	(10.6)
Market value ($ mil.)	(9.6%)	152.0	276.9	197.1	38.2	101.5
Employees	3.7%	373	406	445	421	431

ELO TOUCHSYSTEMS, INC.

301 Constitution Dr.
Menlo Park, CA 94025
Phone: 650-361-4700
Fax: 650-361-4747
Web: www.elotouch.com

CEO: Mark Mendenhall
CFO: Brian O'Sullivan
HR: Amelia Generalis
FYE: September 30
Type: Subsidiary

Elo TouchSystems makes touchscreen products, including LCD monitors, touchscreen overlays, touch sensors, and touchscreen computers. Used in kiosks, point-of-sale systems, process control equipment, and office automation systems, the company's touch system products are marketed to customers in the education, gaming, government, financial, hospitality, industrial, medical, retail, and transportation sectors. It sells directly and through distributors to customers worldwide. Founded in 1971, Elo TouchSystems is a subsidiary of Tyco Electronics.

ELSTER AMERICAN METER COMPANY

2221 Industrial Rd.
Nebraska City, NE 68410
Phone: 402-873-8200
Fax: 402-873-7616
Web: www.elster-americanmeter.com

CEO: Roy Sutterfield
CFO: —
HR: Faris Anderson
FYE: December 31
Type: Private

Elster American Meter's products have been ticking for more than 170 years. The specialty manufacturer, formerly known as American Meter, makes natural gas meters, regulators, shutoff devices, filters, test equipment, and accessories, and provides services including metering, data collection and transfer, and evaluation. The company is a unit of the Elster Group, which has some 70 natural gas measurement and control subsidiaries worldwide. Elster American Meter introduced the synthetic molded, convoluted diaphragm that established new industry standards for long-term accuracy and reliability. Founded in 1836, the company pioneered the shift to aluminum-case meters as a replacement for cast iron.

An in-depth profile of this company is available to Hoover's Online members at hoovers.com.

549

ELXSI CORPORATION

Pink Sheets: ELXS

3600 Rio Vista Ave., Ste. A
Orlando, FL 32805
Phone: 407-849-1090
Fax: 407-849-0625
Web: www.bickfords.com

CEO: Alexander M. (Sandy) Milley
CFO: David M. Doolittle
HR: Beverly Hall
FYE: December 31
Type: Public

This restaurant operator comes with a side of technology. ELXSI Corporation's hospitality division operates about 15 family-style restaurants in New England, while its CUES division manufactures sewer inspection equipment. The eateries operate under the Bickford's Grille brand and offer casual dining with an emphasis on breakfast items served throughout the day. Its equipment manufacturing operation makes remote-control video cameras and robotic cutting devices used by municipalities and contractors. ELXSI is controlled by chairman and CEO Alexander Milley.

EMAGIN CORPORATION

NYSE Amex: EMAN

10500 NE 8th St., Ste. 1400
Bellevue, WA 98004
Phone: 425-749-3600
Fax: 425-749-3601
Web: www.emagin.com

CEO: Andrew Sculley
CFO: Paul C. Campbell
HR: —
FYE: December 31
Type: Public

eMagin is imagining eye-opening technology. The company develops virtual imaging and organic light-emitting diodes (OLEDs) that can be used in applications ranging from wearable PCs and virtual imaging devices to more mundane products such as DVD headset systems, video games, and high-definition televisions. The technology also extends to military uses. eMagin's products use microcircuits and displays to magnify images of text or video. Subsidiary Virtual Vision develops near-eye and virtual image display products, including headset viewer systems. eMagin markets to OEMs and directly to customers in the government, industrial, and medical sectors.

	Annual Growth	12/05	12/06	12/07	12/08	12/09
Sales ($ mil.)	59.3%	3.7	8.2	17.6	18.7	23.8
Net income ($ mil.)	—	(16.5)	(15.3)	(18.5)	(1.9)	4.3
Market value ($ mil.)	(24.2%)	112.1	20.5	25.2	10.6	37.0
Employees	(10.1%)	98	67	65	59	64

EMAK WORLDWIDE, INC.

Pink Sheets: EMAK

6330 San Vicente Blvd.
Los Angeles, CA 90048
Phone: 323-932-4300
Fax: 323-932-4400
Web: emak.com

CEO: James L. (Jim) Holbrook Jr.
CFO: Michael W. (Mike) Sanders
HR: Duane V. Johnson
FYE: December 31
Type: Public

Marketer EMAK Worldwide has a few notions about promotions. Through its many agencies and divisions, the company plans and implements promotional programs using licensed popular characters from studios such as Warner Bros. and Universal. It then designs and arranges for the manufacturing of a variety of items, such as figurines and plush toys, for its clients' campaigns. Promotional items account for the majority of its sales, and long-time customer Burger King typically accounts for 48% of its revenue. To supplement its promotions offerings, EMAK has expanded its marketing services to include event and collaborative marketing, as well as retail and environmental design services.

EMBLEMHEALTH, INC.

55 Water St.
New York, NY 10041
Phone: 646-447-5000
Fax: 646-447-3011
Web: www.emblemhealth.com

CEO: Anthony L. Watson
CFO: —
HR: —
FYE: December 31
Type: Private

EmblemHealth is the parent company of two not-for-profit health insurance companies, Group Health Incorporated (GHI) and the Health Insurance Plan of Greater New York (HIP). Collectively, the two health insurers cover some 4 million New Yorkers, primarily state government and New York City employees; the two companies cover upwards of 90% of Big Apple city workers and retirees. Both provide a variety of managed health plans to their members, including prescription drug and dental coverage, and Medicare plans. GHI and HIP joined together under the EmblemHealth banner in 2006, with the intention of merging into a single insurer that would convert to a for-profit, publicly traded company.

	Annual Growth	12/05	12/06	12/07	12/08	12/09
Sales ($ mil.)	7.4%	7,160.1	7,781.2	8,147.4	8,612.1	9,519.7
Net income ($ mil.)	(40.5%)	124.8	238.9	100.7	(117.0)	15.6
Employees	(3.8%)	—	—	5,400	4,800	5,000

EMC CORPORATION

NYSE: EMC

176 South St.
Hopkinton, MA 01748
Phone: 508-435-1000
Fax: 508-555-1212
Web: www.emc.com

CEO: Joseph M. (Joe) Tucci
CFO: David I. Goulden
HR: John T. (Jack) Mollen
FYE: December 31
Type: Public

EMC bytes data storage problems and swallows every bit. The company is a leading provider of RAID (redundant array of independent disks) storage systems. Banks, government agencies, ISPs, manufacturers, and retailers use EMC's systems to store and retrieve massive amounts of information. It also markets a line of network attached storage (NAS) file servers, and a wide array of software designed to manage, protect, and share data. EMC is the majority owner of virtualization specialist VMware, and its RSA division provides security software. The company gets more than half of its sales in the US.

	Annual Growth	12/05	12/06	12/07	12/08	12/09
Sales ($ mil.)	9.8%	9,664.0	11,155.1	13,230.2	14,876.2	14,025.9
Net income ($ mil.)	(1.0%)	1,133.2	1,227.4	1,665.7	1,345.6	1,088.1
Market value ($ mil.)	6.4%	27,997.4	27,134.0	38,090.4	21,522.2	35,911.5
Employees	13.0%	26,500	31,100	37,700	42,100	43,200

EMC INSURANCE GROUP INC.

NASDAQ (GS): EMCI

717 Mulberry St.
Des Moines, IA 50309
Phone: 515-345-2902
Fax: 515-345-2895
Web: www.emcins.com

CEO: Bruce G. Kelley
CFO: Mark E. Reese
HR: —
FYE: December 31
Type: Public

EMC Insurance Group may be publicly traded, but in its heart it's a mutual insurance company. Subsidiaries EMCASCO Insurance, Illinois EMCASCO, and Dakota Fire Insurance sell property/casualty lines including automobile, property, liability, and workers' compensation insurance, primarily to small and midsized businesses. EMC Underwriters offers excess and surplus lines of insurance. EMC Reinsurance sells property/casualty treaty reinsurance. The group operates throughout the US, primarily in the Midwest; Iowa accounts for nearly 15% of premiums. Employers Mutual Casualty, a multiple-line property/casualty insurance company, owns 57% of EMC Insurance Group.

	Annual Growth	12/05	12/06	12/07	12/08	12/09
Assets ($ mil.)	1.1%	1,113.7	1,206.2	1,202.7	1,108.1	1,165.8
Net income ($ mil.)	1.4%	43.0	53.5	42.5	(1.7)	45.4
Market value ($ mil.)	1.9%	261.9	448.1	310.9	336.9	282.5
Employees	—	0	2,156	2,169	2,169	2,157

EMCARE HOLDINGS INC.

1717 Main St., Ste. 5200
Dallas, TX 75201
Phone: 214-712-2000
Fax: 214-712-2444
Web: www.emcare.com

CEO: Todd G. Zimmerman
CFO: Thomas Sutherland
HR: Karen D. Thornton
FYE: August 31
Type: Subsidiary

EmCare works well under pressure. The company is the largest provider of contracted emergency department staffing and management to more than 400 hospitals in 40 states. EmCare manages emergency services for hospitals, including recruiting and hiring medical directors, doctors, and nurses and monitoring their performance. The company is expanding its hospitalist services — staffing hospitals with acute-care specialists. Emcare also provides anesthesiology services to surgery centers and teleradiology services to smaller regional hospitals. Other services include such administrative functions as billing, record keeping, and staff scheduling. EmCare is a subsidiary of Emergency Medical Services.

	Annual Growth	8/04	8/05	8/06	8/07	8/08
Est. sales ($ mil.)	—	—	—	—	—	1,000.0
Employees	—	—	—	—	—	8,002

EMCLAIRE FINANCIAL CORP.

OTC: EMCF

612 Main St.
Emlenton, PA 16373
Phone: 724-867-2311
Fax: 724-867-1614
Web: www.emclairefinancial.com

CEO: William C. Marsh
CFO: —
HR: —
FYE: December 31
Type: Public

Emclaire Financial is the holding company for the Farmers National Bank of Emlenton, which operates about a dozen branches in northwestern Pennsylvania. Serving area consumers and businesses, the bank offers standard deposit products and services, including checking and savings accounts, money market accounts, and CDs. The bank is mainly a real estate lender, with commercial mortgages, residential first mortgages, and home equity loans and lines of credit making up most of its loan portfolio. Emclaire Financial also owns title insurance and real estate settlement services provider Emclaire Settlement Services.

	Annual Growth	12/05	12/06	12/07	12/08	12/09
Assets ($ mil.)	14.1%	275.5	300.6	311.7	375.7	467.5
Net income ($ mil.)	(12.8%)	2.6	2.0	2.7	1.5	1.5
Market value ($ mil.)	(15.1%)	38.1	41.9	36.9	33.6	19.8
Employees	1.8%	111	101	103	104	119

⊞ EMCOR GROUP, INC.

NYSE: EME

301 Merritt Seven, 6th Fl.
Norwalk, CT 06851
Phone: 203-849-7800
Fax: 203-849-7900
Web: www.emcorgroup.com

CEO: Frank T. MacInnis
CFO: Mark A. Pompa
HR: —
FYE: December 31
Type: Public

The core of EMCOR Group is electrical and mechanical construction. One of the world's largest specialty construction firms, EMCOR designs, installs, operates, and maintains complex mechanical and electrical systems. These include systems for power generation and distribution, lighting, voice and data communications, fire protection, plumbing, and heating, ventilation, and air-conditioning (HVAC). It also provides facilities services, including management and maintenance support. Through about 75 subsidiaries and joint ventures, the company serves various commercial, industrial, institutional, and utility customers. EMCOR operates primarily in the US (some 85% of sales), Canada, and the UK.

	Annual Growth	12/05	12/06	12/07	12/08	12/09
Sales ($ mil.)	4.2%	4,714.5	5,021.0	5,927.2	6,785.2	5,547.9
Net income ($ mil.)	28.4%	60.0	86.6	126.8	182.2	163.1
Market value ($ mil.)	12.4%	1,119.5	1,884.9	1,566.9	1,487.3	1,783.7
Employees	(1.0%)	26,000	27,000	29,000	28,000	25,000

EMCORE CORPORATION

NASDAQ (GM): EMKR

10420 Research Rd. SE, Bldg. 1
Albuquerque, NM 87123
Phone: 505-332-5000
Fax: 505-332-5038
Web: www.emcore.com

CEO: Hong Q. Hou
CFO: John M. Markovich
HR: Monica Van Berkel
FYE: September 30
Type: Public

EMCORE is both compound and complex. The company's offerings include compound semiconductor-based components and subsystems — chips made from complex materials, such as gallium arsenide (GaAs) and gallium nitride (GaN), as opposed to traditional silicon. Compound semiconductors support a range of high-tech devices, including photovoltaic solar cells, and optical components used in high-speed telecommunications networks. Solar power and fiber optics customers include Alcatel-Lucent, Boeing, Cisco Systems, Fujitsu, General Dynamics, Hewlett-Packard, Lockheed Martin, Motorola, Northrop Grumman, Sycamore Networks, Tellabs, and the US government. North America accounts for more than half of EMCORE's sales.

	Annual Growth	9/05	9/06	9/07	9/08	9/09
Sales ($ mil.)	8.4%	127.6	143.5	169.6	239.3	176.4
Net income ($ mil.)	—	(13.1)	54.9	(58.7)	(80.9)	(136.1)
Market value ($ mil.)	(32.0%)	512.2	497.9	807.4	415.5	109.3
Employees	1.9%	650	750	738	1,006	700

EMD CHEMICALS INC.

480 S. Democrat Rd.
Gibbstown, NJ 08027
Phone: 856-423-6300
Fax: 856-423-4389
Web: www.emdchemicals.com

CEO: Deon Vos
CFO: Klaus Rueth
HR: Gail Colatrella
FYE: December 31
Type: Subsidiary

EMD Chemicals is a North American affiliate of German pharmaceutical giant Merck KGaA (not to be confused with American pharmaceutical giant Merck & Co.; they've been separate and unrelated since 1917). EMD Chemicals provides specialty chemicals for pharmaceutical, biotech, cosmetic, automotive, plastics, electronics, and other industrial applications. The company's Lab Chemicals business makes high purity chemicals and analytical reagents for laboratory applications; its Life Science Solutions unit manufactures bulk ingredients for pharmaceutical, food, and cosmetic producers; and the Industrial Pigments division produces effect pigments for coatings, cosmetics, and the automotive industry.

EMD SERONO, INC

1 Technology Place
Rockland, MA 02370
Phone: 781-982-9000
Fax: —
Web: www.emdserono.com

CEO: Fereydoun Firouz
CFO: Stefan Rupp
HR: Megan Wherry
FYE: December 31
Type: Subsidiary

EMD Serono develops a potpourri of prescription pharmaceuticals used for the treatment of neurological, metabolic, and fertility disorders and diseases such as multiple sclerosis (MS), lupus, and HIV. The Massachusetts-based company conducts research and development programs in the US and markets products that include Gonal-f, Luveris, Ovidrel, Rebif, and Zorbtive in the US and Canada. The company has manufacturing and marketing agreements with other pharmaceutical firms, including Pfizer (MS) and CuraScript (fertility). EMD Serono is the North American operating subsidiary of Merck Serono S.A.

⊞ An in-depth profile of this company is available to Hoover's Online members at hoovers.com.

EMDEON INC.

NYSE: EM

3055 Lebanon Pike, Ste. 1000
Nashville, TN 37214
Phone: 615-932-3000
Fax: 615-231-7972
Web: www.emdeon.com

CEO: George I. Lazenby IV
CFO: Bob A. Newport Jr.
HR: Ann Wallbrech
FYE: December 31
Type: Public

Emdeon wants to make the servicing of medical accounts a little easier. The company offers products and services designed to simplify and streamline health care billing for insurance companies, health care systems, and doctors. It also offers discounted office supplies online, provides automated billing and document mailing services, insurance card printing, and has products specifically for dental and pharmaceutical offices. Major customers include CSC, Veriquest, Synergy, and Blue Cross and Blue Shield of North Carolina. Emdeon, which is jointly owned by General Atlantic and Hellman & Friedman, went public in 2009.

	Annual Growth	12/05	12/06	12/07	12/08	12/09
Sales ($ mil.)	7.4%	690.1	751.1	808.5	853.6	918.4
Net income ($ mil.)	(38.1%)	65.5	60.8	16.0	9.2	9.6
Market value ($ mil.)	—	—	—	—	—	1,758.4
Employees	(3.4%)	—	—	2,250	2,200	2,100

EMERALD DAIRY, INC.

OTC: EMDY

11990 Market St., Ste. 205
Reston, VA 20190
Phone: 703-867-9247
Fax: —
Web: www.emeralddairy.com

CEO: Yang Yong Shan
CFO: Shu Kaneko
HR: —
FYE: December 31
Type: Public

Emerald Dairy's formula for success is turning milk into milk powder. The company produces milk powder (infant formula and enriched milk powders for children and adults), as well as rice and soybean powders. Its product line includes two brands: Xing An Ling, which is marketed to low-end customers, and Yi Bai, which is marketed to middle and high-end customers. Producing more than 9,000 tons of milk powder annually, the dairy distributes its products to more than 5,800 retail stores located in 20 of China's 30 provinces. Emerald Dairy gets its milk supply through contracting with local dairy farmers. Chairman and CEO Yong Shan Yang owns 47% of Emerald, John Winfield owns 10%, and Farallon Partners owns 9%.

	Annual Growth	12/05	12/06	12/07	12/08	12/09
Sales ($ mil.)	33.5%	—	18.8	29.6	44.3	44.7
Net income ($ mil.)	15.9%	—	2.7	3.6	2.3	4.2
Market value ($ mil.)	(61.3%)	—	—	395.3	23.1	59.3
Employees	26.0%	—	—	867	1,110	1,376

EMERGENCY MEDICAL SERVICES CORPORATION

NYSE: EMS

6200 S. Syracuse Way, Ste. 200
Greenwood Village, CO 80111
Phone: 303-495-1200
Fax: 303-495-1466
Web: www.emsc.net

CEO: William A. (Bill) Sanger
CFO: Randel G. (Randy) Owen
HR: Kimberly Norman
FYE: December 31
Type: Public

Municipalities and hospitals can't call 911 when *they* have an emergency — but they *can* call Emergency Medical Services Corporation. The holding company is the parent of AMR Inc., the largest private ambulance service in the US, and EmCare Holdings, a leading medical staffing firm that specializes in filling emergency rooms with doctors and nurses. AMR has approximately 3,300 contracts with clients (cities, government agencies, health care providers, and insurance companies) in more than 35 states for emergency and non-emergency transport services. EmCare provides staffing services to more than 450 hospitals and physician groups in 40 states. Private investment firm Onex controls the company.

	Annual Growth	12/05	12/06	12/07	12/08	12/09
Sales ($ mil.)	11.6%	1,655.5	1,934.2	2,107.0	2,409.9	2,569.7
Net income ($ mil.)	54.7%	20.1	39.1	59.8	84.8	115.2
Market value ($ mil.)	41.8%	588.5	921.4	1,286.0	1,607.9	2,378.2
Employees	(1.9%)	18,644	18,038	18,015	18,331	17,276

EMERGENT BIOSOLUTIONS INC.

NYSE: EBS

2273 Research Blvd., Ste. 400
Rockville, MD 20850
Phone: 301-795-1800
Fax: 301-795-1899
Web: www.emergentbiosolutions.com

CEO: Fuad El-Hibri
CFO: R. Don Elsey
HR: —
FYE: December 31
Type: Public

Emergent BioSolutions protects your thorax against anthrax. The company develops and produces vaccines that treat or protect against infectious diseases and bio-agents. The company supplies BioThrax (the US's only FDA-approved anthrax vaccine) primarily to the departments of Defense and Health and Human Services (HHS). Its biodefense unit is also developing a post-exposure treatment for anthrax and a preventive vaccine for botulinum toxin. For commercial markets, Emergent BioSolutions is working on therapies and vaccines for such infectious diseases as typhoid, tuberculosis, hepatitis B, and chlamydia. Chairman and CEO Fuad El-Hibri controls half of the company.

	Annual Growth	12/05	12/06	12/07	12/08	12/09
Sales ($ mil.)	15.8%	130.7	152.7	182.9	178.6	234.8
Net income ($ mil.)	18.4%	15.8	22.8	22.9	20.7	31.1
Market value ($ mil.)	6.8%	—	346.4	157.1	810.5	421.8
Employees	8.5%	470	494	560	587	652

EMERGING VISION, INC.

OTC: ISEE

520 8th Ave., 23rd Fl.
New York City, NY 10018
Phone: 646-737-1500
Fax: —
Web: www.emergingvision.com

CEO: Glenn Spina
CFO: Brian P. Alessi
HR: Laura Hoffman
FYE: December 31
Type: Public

It's all coming back into focus at Emerging Vision. The firm owns and franchises about 140 optical outlets under the Sterling Optical, Site For Sore Eyes, Kindy Optical, and Singer Specs names in about a dozen states, the District of Columbia, the US Virgin Islands, and Canada. All but 11 of the locations are franchised. The company also runs a specialized HMO (VisionCare of California). Refocusing on its optical operations to boost brand awareness, Emerging Vision has scrapped plans to sell its chain of retail stores and establish itself as an online supply chain serving optical businesses. Former director Benito Fernandez, who launched a 2004 proxy battle for the company, owns about 40% of the firm.

	Annual Growth	12/05	12/06	12/07	12/08	12/09
Sales ($ mil.)	45.1%	14.0	21.7	49.6	71.8	62.1
Net income ($ mil.)	—	0.3	1.9	0.4	(0.1)	(2.5)
Market value ($ mil.)	(2.4%)	14.2	23.2	25.8	9.0	12.9
Employees	(0.8%)	128	146	134	116	124

EMERITUS CORPORATION

NYSE: ESC

3131 Elliott Ave., Ste. 500
Seattle, WA 98121
Phone: 206-298-2909
Fax: 206-301-4500
Web: www.emeritus.com

CEO: Daniel R. Baty
CFO: Robert C. Bateman
HR: —
FYE: December 31
Type: Public

The Emeritus Corporation honors the retirement set. The company operates assisted-living communities for senior citizens who don't need the more intensive care provided by nursing homes, but may need some help with daily activities such as feeding, bathing, housekeeping, and managing their medications. Emeritus' communities also organize social and recreational activities for residents, and most of them provide special services (called Join Their Journey programs) to support residents with Alzheimer's disease or other forms of dementia. Emeritus owns, leases, or manages some 300 communities in more than 35 states across the US, some under the Summerville name.

	Annual Growth	12/05	12/06	12/07	12/08	12/09
Sales ($ mil.)	23.4%	387.7	421.9	545.6	769.4	898.7
Net income ($ mil.)	—	12.3	(14.6)	(48.7)	(104.8)	(54.8)
Market value ($ mil.)	(2.7%)	823.1	976.4	988.1	394.1	736.7
Employees	19.5%	8,548	10,100	16,205	18,671	17,409

⊞ EMERSON ELECTRIC CO.
NYSE: EMR

8000 W. Florissant Ave.	CEO: David N. Farr
St. Louis, MO 63136	CFO: Frank J. Dellaquila
Phone: 314-553-2000	HR: M.G. Rohret
Fax: 314-553-3527	FYE: September 30
Web: www.emerson.com	Type: Public

Ralph Waldo Emerson once said, "Make yourself necessary to somebody," and Emerson Electric follows that adage. The company, generally known as just Emerson, makes a host of electrical, electromechanical, and electronic products, many of which are used to control gases, liquids, and electricity. Emerson pursues an active, aggressive acquisition strategy (with select divestitures along the way) in building up its global business with dozens of subsidiaries. The company gathers its 60-plus business units and divisions under eight Emerson Brands. It has more than 250 manufacturing locations, with about 165 locations outside of the US. Foreign operations make up more than half of Emerson's sales.

	Annual Growth	9/05	9/06	9/07	9/08	9/09
Sales ($ mil.)	4.9%	17,305.0	20,133.0	22,572.0	24,807.0	20,915.0
Net income ($ mil.)	4.9%	1,422.0	1,845.0	2,136.0	2,412.0	1,724.0
Market value ($ mil.)	2.8%	27,038.8	31,580.4	40,083.7	30,721.8	30,187.0
Employees	3.1%	114,200	127,800	137,700	140,700	129,000

EMERSON NETWORK POWER-EMBEDDED COMPUTING, INC.

2900 S. Diablo Way, Ste. 190	CEO: Jay L. Geldmacher
Tempe, AZ 85282	CFO: —
Phone: 602-438-5720	HR: —
Fax: 602-438-5825	FYE: September 30
Web: www.emerson.com/sites/Network_Power/en-US/Pages/Home.aspx	Type: Subsidiary

Emerson Network Power-Embedded Computing, Inc. (dba Emerson Network Power) makes some powerful products for a broad range of applications. The company makes standard and custom power supplies including switches, rectifiers, breaker interface panels, AC/DC and DC/DC power supplies, and related accessories. Its products are used in computing, medical, networking and telecommunications, process control, and test instrumentation applications. One of the largest manufacturers of power supplies in the world, Emerson Network Power, also a company brand, is a subsidiary of Emerson Electric. It has manufacturing and direct sales force operations in Asia, Europe, and North America. The US represents about 40% of sales.

⊞ EMERSON RADIO CORP.
NYSE Amex: MSN

85 Oxford Dr.	CEO: Adrian C. C. Ma
Moonachie, NJ 07074	CFO: Greenfield Pitts
Phone: 973-884-5800	HR: —
Fax: —	FYE: March 31
Web: www.emersonradio.com	Type: Public

Emerson Radio caters to the crowd that thinks a new stereo or microwave oven shouldn't cost an arm and a leg. The company designs and distributes a wide range of consumer electronics and houseware products that are sold primarily at mass merchants, such as Wal-Mart and Target, and toy retailers under the Emerson, Girl Power, H.H. Scott, and Olevia brand names, among others. Emerson's products include shelf stereo systems, televisions, DVD players, digital clock radios, telephones, microwaves, and coffee makers. Through an agreement with Apple, the company manufactures a line of iPod compatible devices, as well. Emerson Radio was founded in 1948.

	Annual Growth	3/05	3/06	3/07	3/08	3/09
Sales ($ mil.)	(11.1%)	320.7	233.8	284.4	223.2	200.6
Net income ($ mil.)	—	5.9	16.6	3.5	(9.0)	(4.8)
Market value ($ mil.)	(38.6%)	95.5	101.5	86.8	31.2	13.6
Employees	(23.9%)	379	115	125	170	127

EMI MUSIC NORTH AMERICA

150 5th Ave.	CEO: Colin Finkelstein
New York, NY 10010	CFO: Paul Kahn
Phone: 212-786-8000	HR: Kristine Muscara
Fax: 212-786-8343	FYE: March 31
	Type: Business segment

EMI Music North America wants to be your first — and last — stop for popular music. The North American operations of major record label EMI Group is the home of two of the top pop labels in the US — Capitol Records and Virgin Records — producing music from such artists as Coldplay, Janet Jackson, and Lenny Kravitz. Its roster of R&B and hip-hop artists includes Faith Evans, the Beastie Boys, and Jermaine Dupri. Other labels that fall under the EMI Music North America umbrella include Blue Note, Manhattan Records, and Chordant. EMI Music North America was formed in 2007 when EMI Music reorganized the business into three geographic divisions: International, UK & Ireland, and North America.

EMI MUSIC PUBLISHING

75 9th Ave.	CEO: Roger Faxon
New York, NY 10011	CFO: Thomas F. Kelly
Phone: 212-492-1200	HR: Anne Roche
Fax: —	FYE: March 31
Web: www.emimusicpub.com	Type: Business segment

EMI Music Publishing is looking after the business part of the music business. The division of UK-based recording giant EMI Group is the world's largest music publisher, administering the rights to more than a million songs. Its collection includes classics and standards such as "Blue Moon," "I Left My Heart in San Francisco," and "Santa Claus Is Comin' to Town," as well as more recent hits including "Crazy in Love," "Genie in a Bottle," and "Smells Like Teen Spirit." The company collects royalties for including its songs on CDs, as well as live performance fees. EMI Music Publishing also licenses its music for use in movies, television shows, and advertising.

EMIGRANT BANK

5 E. 42nd St.	CEO: Howard P. Milstein
New York, NY 10017	CFO: —
Phone: 212-850-4521	HR: —
Fax: 212-850-4372	FYE: December 31
Web: www.emigrant.com	Type: Private

Emigrant Bank has built its business around the huddled masses longing to save. The bank, which also has four regional Emigrant Savings Bank affiliates in the Bronx, Brooklyn, Queens, and Long Island, serves retail and commercial customers in the New York metropolitan area from some 35 branches. It offers online banking nationwide through its EmigrantOnline service. The bank provides standard products such as checking and savings accounts, CDs, IRAs, and credit and debit cards. New York Private Bank & Trust is Emigrant Bank's wealth management division; Emigrant Financial Services offers mutual funds and life insurance. Emigrant Mortgage originates home loans in about a dozen eastern states.

⊞ An in-depth profile of this company is available to Hoover's Online members at hoovers.com.

553

EMISPHERE TECHNOLOGIES, INC.

OTC: EMIS

240 Cedar Knolls Rd.
Cedar Knolls, NJ 07927
Phone: 973-532-8000
Fax: 914-347-2498
Web: www.emisphere.com

CEO: Michael V. Novinski
CFO: Michael R. (Mike) Garone
HR: Daria M. Palestina
FYE: December 31
Type: Public

Needle prick, be gone. Development-stage Emisphere Technologies is offering an alternative to traditional injection of certain drugs with an oral drug delivery technology called eligen, which is designed to improve the way certain therapeutic molecules (such as proteins, carbohydrates, and peptides) are administered to and absorbed by the body. With collaborative partners, including Novartis, Roche, and Genta, Emisphere is developing oral formulations that incorporate eligen to deliver drugs that treat such health problems as osteoporosis, diabetes, growth disorders, and cardiovascular disease. Emisphere was formed in 1986.

	Annual Growth	12/05	12/06	12/07	12/08	12/09
Sales ($ mil.)	(58.9%)	3.5	7.3	4.1	0.3	0.1
Net income ($ mil.)	—	(18.1)	(41.8)	(16.9)	(24.4)	(21.2)
Market value ($ mil.)	(29.7%)	186.3	227.1	117.2	33.9	45.5
Employees	(38.4%)	118	111	86	20	17

EMMIS COMMUNICATIONS CORPORATION

NASDAQ (GS): EMMS

1 Emmis Plaza, 40 Monument Circle, Ste. 700
Indianapolis, IN 46204
Phone: 317-266-0100
Fax: 317-631-3750
Web: www.emmis.com

CEO: Jeffrey H. (Jeff) Smulyan
CFO: Patrick M. Walsh
HR: Traci L. Thomson
FYE: February 28
Type: Public

Emmis Communications is a leading diversified media company with interests in radio and publishing. It owns and operates more than 20 radio stations serving more than a half dozen markets in the US, including clusters of stations in Chicago, Los Angeles, and New York City. Emmis also owns Network Indiana, which syndicates programming to more than 70 affiliate stations, and it has radio stations in Belgium and other parts of Europe. In addition to broadcasting, the company owns a portfolio of regional magazines and specialty publications, including *Atlanta, Los Angeles,* and *Texas Monthly.* CEO Jeffrey Smulyan, who controls about 70% of Emmis, is taking the company private.

	Annual Growth	2/06	2/07	2/08	2/09	2/10
Sales ($ mil.)	(11.0%)	387.4	359.5	361.2	333.9	242.6
Net income ($ mil.)	—	357.8	113.6	(1.4)	(275.0)	(118.5)
Market value ($ mil.)	(51.6%)	619.4	311.0	112.0	11.7	34.1
Employees	(11.1%)	1,940	1,900	1,565	1,370	1,210

EMORY UNIVERSITY

201 Dowman Dr.
Atlanta, GA 30322
Phone: 404-727-6123
Fax: 404-727-5997
Web: www.emory.edu

CEO: James W. (Jim) Wagner
CFO: Eric Bymaster
HR: Ozzie Harris
FYE: August 31
Type: School

"Have a Coke and a smile" means a little more to Emory University than it does to the rest of the world. The school, which boasts some 12,500 students and 3,600 faculty members, was transformed from Emory College to Emory University in 1915 by a $1 million donation from Coca-Cola Company owner Asa Candler. The university offers undergraduate, graduate, and professional degrees in a wide range of fields, including medicine, theology, law, nursing, and business. Oxford College offers liberal arts courses and is sited on the university's original campus. Founded in 1836, the private university also maintains several research centers and operates a joint venture with HCA to offer managed health care.

	Annual Growth	8/04	8/05	8/06	8/07	8/08
Est. sales ($ mil.)	—	—	—	—	—	2,887.1
Employees	—	—	—	—	—	19,319

EMPI, INC.

CEO: Les Cross

599 Cardigan Rd.
St. Paul, MN 55126
Phone: 651-415-9000
Fax: 651-414-7414
Web: www.empi.com

CEO: Les Cross
CFO: Jim Webber
HR: Anna Skar
FYE: December 31
Type: Subsidiary

Empi empathizes with patients who have pain, swelling, spasms, and muscle weakness. The company makes and markets a wide range of medical products, including non-pharmaceutical pain management and orthopedic electrotherapy devices. Empi's product brands include the Saunders cervical traction device used for spinal decompression therapy, the SporTX electrotherapy device for injury swelling reduction, and Minnova, a device that stimulates the pelvic floor to treat urinary incontinence. Empi sells to rehabilitation clinics and medical device distributors nationwide, as well as abroad. The company is a division of medical device maker DJO.

	Annual Growth	12/04	12/05	12/06	12/07	12/08
Est. sales ($ mil.)	—	—	—	—	—	185.0
Employees	—	—	—	—	—	780

THE EMPIRE DISTRICT ELECTRIC COMPANY

NYSE: EDE

602 Joplin St.
Joplin, MO 64801
Phone: 417-625-5100
Fax: 417-625-5146
Web: www.empiredistrict.com

CEO: William L. (Bill) Gipson
CFO: Gregory A. Knapp
HR: —
FYE: December 31
Type: Public

Empire District Electric (EDE) has the sovereign authority to light up its territory. The utility transmits and distributes electricity to a population base of more than 450,000 (or about 215,000 direct customers) in southwestern Missouri and adjacent areas of Arkansas, Kansas, and Oklahoma. It also supplies water to three Missouri towns and natural gas throughout most of the state. EDE's interests in fossil-fueled and hydroelectric power plants give it a generating capacity of 1,257 MW; it also buys and sells power on the wholesale market. In addition, the company is pursuing nonregulated opportunities such as leasing capacity on its fiber-optic network.

	Annual Growth	12/05	12/06	12/07	12/08	12/09
Sales ($ mil.)	6.5%	386.2	413.5	490.2	518.2	497.2
Net income ($ mil.)	14.8%	23.8	39.3	33.2	39.7	41.3
Market value ($ mil.)	(2.0%)	816.1	991.1	914.4	706.5	751.9
Employees	(3.8%)	851	705	733	733	730

EMPIRE ENERGY CORPORATION INTERNATIONAL

Pink Sheets: EEGC

4500 College Blvd., Ste. 240
Leawood, KS 66211
Phone: 913-663-2310
Fax: 913-663-2239
Web: www.empireenergy.com

CEO: Malcolm R. Bendall
CFO: John C. Garrison
HR: —
FYE: December 31
Type: Public

Empire Energy Corporation International has put a lot of energy into the search for oil and gas in a once far-flung region of Her Majesty's former empire — Australia. Oil and gas independent Empire Energy previously owned oil and gas interests in Texas, Wyoming, and Nicaragua. However, in 2005 the company acquired Australian oil and gas explorer Great South Land Minerals and began to focus on developing oil and gas assets in Tasmania. Empire Energy is investing in developing a potential 3-million-barrel oil deposit on 15,000 sq. km. of leasehold property. The company also controls 47% of Chinese food canner Pacific Rim Foods.

	Annual Growth	12/05	12/06	12/07	12/08	12/09
Sales ($ mil.)	—	—	—	—	—	0.0
Net income ($ mil.)	—	—	—	—	—	(13.2)
Market value ($ mil.)	—	—	—	—	—	9.8
Employees	—	—	—	—	—	15

EMPIRE MERCHANTS LLC

19-50 48th St.	CEO: E. Lloyd Sobel
Astoria, NY 11105	CFO: Terence Arlotta
Phone: 718-726-2500	HR: —
Fax: 718-726-4428	FYE: March 31
Web: www.empiremerchants.com	Type: Joint venture

Not easily shaken by competition, Empire Merchants (formerly Charmer Industries) has not stirred from its spot as a leading wine and liquor wholesaler in New York state. The company distributes an array of wines, spirits, and champagnes to licensed liquor stores throughout the region. Empire Merchants is as a joint venture between Quaker Equities and Charmer-Sunbelt Group, one of the largest wine and spirits wholesalers in the US. Charmer-Sunbelt in 2007 combined its metro New York operations with those of Quaker's Peerless Importers to form Empire Merchants. It is owned by the Drucker, Magliocco, and Merinoff families.

EMPIRE RESORTS, INC.

NASDAQ (GM): NYNY

204 Route 17B	CEO: Joseph A. D'Amato
Monticello, NY 12701	CFO: —
Phone: 845-807-0001	HR: —
Fax: 845-791-1402	FYE: December 31
Web: www.empireresorts.com	Type: Public

Empire Resorts has taken up permanent residence in New York's playground. The company operates Catskills-area harness horseracing track Monticello Gaming and Raceway, which features pari-mutuel wagering and more than 1,500 video gaming machines (VGMs). The property, located 90 miles northwest of New York City, also includes a clubhouse, entertainment lounge, bar, and food court. Its VGMs are owned by the State of New York and are overseen by the state's Division of the Lottery, which distributes a percentage of VGM revenue to Empire Resorts. Other company revenues primarily come from wagering fees, admission fees, program and racing form sales, and food and beverages sales.

	Annual Growth	12/05	12/06	12/07	12/08	12/09
Sales ($ mil.)	(6.1%)	86.8	98.1	75.7	67.3	67.6
Net income ($ mil.)	—	(18.5)	(7.1)	(24.6)	(10.6)	(10.6)
Market value ($ mil.)	(26.9%)	514.1	602.4	236.9	75.7	146.6
Employees	(4.3%)	380	370	340	351	319

EMPIRE RESOURCES, INC.

Pink Sheets: ERSO

One Parker Plaza, 400 Kelby Street	CEO: Nathan Kahn
Fort Lee, NJ 07024	CFO: Sandra R. Kahn
Phone: 201-944-2200	HR: Deborah Waltuch
Fax: 201-944-2226	FYE: December 31
Web: www.empireresources.com	Type: Public

When it comes to aluminum, Empire Resources is especially resourceful. The company distributes semifinished aluminum products, including sheet, foil, wire, plate, and coil. Products are sold primarily to manufacturers of appliances, automobiles, packaging, and housing materials. Empire Resources provides a variety of related services, including sourcing of aluminum products, storage and delivery, and handling foreign exchange transactions. Company president and CEO Nathan Kahn and CFO Sandra Kahn, who are husband and wife, own some 40% of Empire Resources.

	Annual Growth	12/04	12/05	12/06	12/07	*12/08
Sales ($ mil.)	19.2%	212.6	358.5	426.0	475.5	429.0
Net income ($ mil.)	(5.1%)	4.8	9.5	8.7	4.5	3.9
Employees	29.7%	30	50	65	80	85

*Most recent year available

EMPIRE SOUTHWEST, LLC

1725 S. Country Club Dr.	CEO: Jeffrey S. (Jeff) Whiteman
Mesa, AZ 85210	CFO: —
Phone: 480-633-4000	HR: —
Fax: 480-633-4489	FYE: October 31
Web: www.empire-cat.com	Type: Private

With CAT-like tread, Empire Southwest has created a heavy equipment sales, rental, and leasing empire in the US Southwest. One of the largest Caterpillar dealerships in the US, Empire Southwest operates through five divisions: hydraulic service, machinery, power systems, precision machining, and transport. The company's equipment includes backhoes, compactors, dozers, front shovels, loaders, pipelayers, telehandlers, and tractors. It also handles equipment used for mining and forestry projects. Empire Southwest also carries batteries, power generators, engines, and tools, and has a service department.

	Annual Growth	10/04	10/05	10/06	10/07	10/08
Est. sales ($ mil.)	—	—	—	—	—	945.0
Employees	—	—	—	—	—	1,320

EMPIRE TODAY, LLC

333 Northwest Ave.	CEO: Steve Silvers
Northlake, IL 60164	CFO: —
Phone: 847-583-3000	HR: —
Fax: 847-583-3094	FYE: —
Web: www.empirecarpet.com	Type: Private

Whether you come from a Berber family or prefer plush padding, Empire Today will take care of your home and office flooring needs. The company sells and installs carpets and hard-surface flooring, as well as blinds and shades and acrylic shower and bathtub liners and replacements. Rather than selling its products from retail stores, the company makes house (and office) calls — taking samples to customers' homes, providing free estimates, and often offering next-day installation. Empire operates in more than 35 metropolitan areas in the US and Canada. Seymour Cohen founded Empire Plastic Covers in 1959 to sell plastic slip covers. It added home improvement services over the years and became Empire Today in 2007.

EMPLOYERS HOLDINGS, INC.

NYSE: EIG

10375 Professional Circle	CEO: Douglas D. Dirks
Reno, NV 89521	CFO: William E. Yocke
Phone: 775-327-2700	HR: —
Fax: 888-527-3422	FYE: December 31
Web: www.eig.com	Type: Public

Because workers' compensation is nothing to gamble with, small business owners can turn to Employers Holdings. The Reno-based holding company provides workers' compensation services, including claims management, loss prevention consulting, and care management to small businesses in low hazard industries including retailers and restaurants. The company provides workers' compensation through its Employer Insurance Company of Nevada (EICN) and Employers Compensation Insurance Company. Employers Holdings also operates Employers Occupational Health, which provides care management and claim dispute resolution services, and Elite Insurance Services, a managing general agency that provides administrative services.

	Annual Growth	12/05	12/06	12/07	12/08	12/09
Assets ($ mil.)	4.4%	3,094.2	3,195.7	3,191.2	3,756.7	3,676.7
Net income ($ mil.)	(11.9%)	137.6	171.6	120.3	101.8	83.0
Market value ($ mil.)	(4.2%)	—	—	713.9	705.0	655.4
Employees	11.1%	617	635	671	150	941

An in-depth profile of this company is available to Hoover's Online members at hoovers.com.

555

EMRISE CORPORATION

NYSE Arca: ERI

611 Industrial Way
Eatontown, NJ 07724
Phone: 732-389-0355
Fax: 732-460-0214
Web: www.emrise.com

CEO: Carmine T. Oliva
CFO: D. John Donovan
HR: —
FYE: December 31
Type: Public

The sun doesn't set on EMRISE. Through its worldwide subsidiaries, the company makes electronic components and communications equipment for customers in the aerospace, military, and telecommunications industries. Its CXR Larus units produce network transmission and access equipment and a range of testing gear. EMRISE's EEC Corporation subsidiary manufactures power converters, digital and rotary switches, and subsystem assemblies. The company counts BAE SYSTEMS, EMS Technologies, Harris, ITT, Motorola, Raytheon, Rockwell Collins, and Thales Air Defence among its top clients. EMRISE gets more than half of its sales outside the US, principally in the UK.

	Annual Growth	12/05	12/06	12/07	12/08	12/09
Sales ($ mil.)	7.0%	41.0	46.4	51.3	59.5	53.8
Net income ($ mil.)	(6.3%)	1.3	(3.6)	(1.9)	(7.4)	1.0
Market value ($ mil.)	(37.6%)	51.3	40.2	23.4	15.5	7.8
Employees	0.5%	329	305	300	360	335

EMS TECHNOLOGIES, INC.

NASDAQ (GS): ELMG

660 Engineering Dr.
Norcross, GA 30092
Phone: 770-263-9200
Fax: 770-263-9207
Web: www.ems-t.com

CEO: Neilson A. (Neil) Mackay
CFO: Gary B. Shell
HR: Michael R. Robertson
FYE: December 31
Type: Public

EMS Technologies' wireless systems can help you communicate, whether you're walking the warehouse floor or floating in space. The company's LXE unit makes handheld and vehicle-mounted computers used for logistics management and other applications. EMS also makes microwave-based communications hardware for military contractors through its Defense & Space unit. Its Aviation unit makes aeronautical satellite antennas and earth station antennas and control terminals used for emergency management. The company's EMS Sky Connect business provides telephony and flight tracking services for aircraft over the Iridium Satellite network. Customers based in the US account for more than two-thirds of EMS's sales.

	Annual Growth	12/05	12/06	12/07	12/08	12/09
Sales ($ mil.)	3.8%	310.0	261.1	287.9	335.0	360.0
Net income ($ mil.)	—	(11.4)	33.0	18.7	20.5	(20.1)
Market value ($ mil.)	(4.9%)	270.9	306.6	462.9	396.0	222.0
Employees	0.0%	1,300	900	1,100	1,200	1,300

EMTEC, INC.

OTC: ETEC

525 Lincoln Dr. West, 5 Greentree Center, Ste. 117
Marlton, NJ 08053
Phone: 856-552-4204
Fax: 856-552-4298
Web: www.emtecinc.com

CEO: Dinesh R. Desai
CFO: Gregory P. Chandler
HR: Stephen C. Donnelly
FYE: August 31
Type: Public

Emtec provides information technology services, including data management, security consulting, and infrastructure design and implementation. The company resells computer hardware and software from leading providers such as Cisco Systems, Dell, Hewlett-Packard, IBM, Lenovo, Microsoft, and Oracle. It serves federal government agencies including the US Department of Defense, Department of Justice, and Department of Homeland Security; other customers include state government agencies, as well as corporate and educational organizations. The company was founded in 1964.

	Annual Growth	3/05	*8/06	8/07	8/08	8/09
Sales ($ mil.)	18.7%	112.7	224.5	217.0	211.2	223.8
Net income ($ mil.)	(10.9%)	2.7	0.2	(2.3)	1.3	1.7
Market value ($ mil.)	(9.8%)	21.4	15.7	11.5	15.6	14.2
Employees	39.1%	153	208	213	574	572

*Fiscal year change

E-MU SYSTEMS, INC.

1500 Green Hills Rd.
Scotts Valley, CA 95066
Phone: 831-438-1921
Fax: —
Web: www.emu.com

CEO: Bill Wrightson
CFO: —
HR: Christine Silver
FYE: June 30
Type: Subsidiary

Electronic music becomes a synthesis of art and science with the help of this company. E-MU Systems is a leading manufacturer of digital audio recording systems, MIDI controllers, electronic synthesizers, and monitor speakers for the professional audio market. Its digital recording systems can be used with both desktop and laptop computers to capture performances and create master mixes, while its keyboards allow musicians to create performances from synthesized instrument sounds. Products are sold online and through musical equipment retailers, such as Guitar Center and Sam Ash. Founded in 1971, the company is a subsidiary of digital audio products maker Creative Technology.

	Annual Growth	6/04	6/05	6/06	6/07	6/08
Est. sales ($ mil.)	—	—	—	—	—	0.1
Employees	—	—	—	—	—	1

EMULEX CORPORATION

NYSE: ELX

3333 Susan St.
Costa Mesa, CA 92626
Phone: 714-662-5600
Fax: 714-241-0792
Web: www.emulex.com

CEO: James M. (Jim) McCluney
CFO: Michael J. Rockenbach
HR: Susan H. Bowman
FYE: June 30
Type: Public

Emulex provides the ties that bind in storage networks. The company is a leading provider of Fibre Channel host bus adapters (HBAs). Its LightPulse cards are used to connect storage devices in traditional direct-attached storage configurations, as well as storage area network (SAN) and network-attached storage (NAS) systems. Emulex also develops HBAs based on the Fibre Channel over Ethernet (FCoE) protocol. Emulex sells its products directly to OEMs and through resellers and distributors. Its customers include equipment manufacturers such as Dell, EMC, Fujitsu, IBM (22% of sales), and Hewlett-Packard (17%). The company gets more than 60% of its sales outside the US.

	Annual Growth	6/05	6/06	6/07	6/08	6/09
Sales ($ mil.)	0.2%	375.7	402.8	470.2	488.3	378.2
Net income ($ mil.)	(43.1%)	71.6	40.5	29.4	(7.1)	7.5
Market value ($ mil.)	(14.5%)	1,481.2	1,319.7	1,771.5	945.0	793.3
Employees	(4.0%)	528	618	746	853	448

EN POINTE TECHNOLOGIES, INC.

18701 S. Figueroa St.
Gardena, CA 90248
Phone: 310-337-5200
Fax: 310-258-2301
Web: www.enpointe.com

CEO: Attiazaz (Bob) Din
CFO: Javed Latif
HR: —
FYE: September 30
Type: Private

En Pointe Technologies makes sure product procurement stays on point. The company provides hardware and software fulfillment and support services. Its online AccessPointe catalog features products from hundreds of providers, including Cisco Systems, Dell, Hewlett-Packard, IBM, and Lenovo. En Pointe's hardware-related services include asset tagging, configuration, imaging, inventory management, deployment, and packing. It also provides software consulting and license compliance monitoring, as well as deployment and help desk services. In 2009 En Pointe was taken private by CEO Attiazaz (Bob) Din and his wife, Naureen Din.

ENABLE HOLDINGS, INC.

OTC: ENAB

1140 W. Thorndale Ave.
Itasca, IL 60143
Phone: 773-272-5000
Fax: 773-272-4000
Web: www.enableholdings.com

CEO: Patrick L. (Pat) Neville
CFO: Miguel (Mike) Martinez Jr.
HR: —
FYE: December 31
Type: Public

Got excess inventory? This company wants to do your bidding. Enable Holdings (formerly uBid.com Holdings) is a multi-channel seller of refurbished and closeout merchandise that hosts both online and live auctions. In addition, its RedTag.com site offers merchandise at a fixed price, instead of through an auction process. Through its Dibu Trading Company, the company helps businesses sell entire inventories in a single transaction. Enable's merchandise includes computers, automobiles, and other consumer goods from some 200 product categories, and comes directly from manufacturers such as Hewlett-Packard, IBM, and Sony. The company also licenses auction software to third party companies.

	Annual Growth	12/05	12/06	12/07	12/08	12/09
Sales ($ mil.)	(32.0%)	84.6	66.6	43.1	31.6	18.1
Net income ($ mil.)	—	(9.0)	(7.6)	(7.0)	(16.0)	(7.5)
Market value ($ mil.)	(58.3%)	—	54.2	14.8	5.1	3.9
Employees	(18.9%)	95	78	79	72	41

ENBRIDGE ENERGY MANAGEMENT, L.L.C.

NYSE: EEQ

1100 Louisiana St., Ste. 3300
Houston, TX 77002
Phone: 713-821-2000
Fax: 713-821-2230
Web: www.enbridgemanagement.com

CEO: Stephen J. J. (Steve) Letwin
CFO: Mark A. Maki
HR: —
FYE: December 31
Type: Public

Enbridge Energy Management, bridging the gap over a complex structure of pipeline partnerships, manages and controls the business of Enbridge Energy Partners (formerly Lakehead Pipe Line Partners). The company's only asset is its 10% limited partner interest and 2% general partner interest in Enbridge Energy Partners, which owns the US part of North America's longest liquid petroleum pipeline (Lakehead System) and also has interests in natural gas gathering, treating, processing, and transmission operations in East Texas. Enbridge Energy Company, a wholly owned subsidiary of Enbridge Inc., holds a 17% stake in the company, and serves as the general partner of Enbridge Energy Partners.

	Annual Growth	12/05	12/06	12/07	12/08	12/09
Sales ($ mil.)	—	12.0	44.6	32.0	51.8	0.0
Net income ($ mil.)	15.1%	12.4	28.7	31.4	24.2	21.8
Market value ($ mil.)	32.0%	286.8	627.1	724.0	360.9	870.5
Employees	—	0	0	0		

ENBRIDGE ENERGY PARTNERS, L.P.

NYSE: EEP

1100 Louisiana St., Ste. 3300
Houston, TX 77002
Phone: 713-821-2000
Fax: 713-821-2232
Web: www.enbridgepartners.com

CEO: Stephen J. J. (Steve) Letwin
CFO: Mark A. Maki
HR: —
FYE: December 31
Type: Public

Heading up petroleum transportation around the Great Lakes is Enbridge Energy Partners, which owns the 1,900-mile US portion of the world's longest liquid petroleum pipeline. When combined with the Canadian segment (owned and operated by Enbridge Inc.), the pipeline system spans some 3,500 miles across North America. Other midstream assets include 5,300 miles of crude oil gathering and transportation lines and 28.9 million barrels of crude oil storage and terminaling capacity, and 11,700 miles of natural gas gathering and transportation pipelines. Enbridge Energy Management owns a 14% stake in the company. In 2008 Enbridge Inc. boosted its overall stake in the partnership to 27%.

	Annual Growth	12/05	12/06	12/07	12/08	12/09
Sales ($ mil.)	(3.0%)	6,476.9	6,509.0	7,282.6	10,060.0	5,731.8
Net income ($ mil.)	38.5%	89.2	284.9	249.5	403.2	328.0
Market value ($ mil.)	5.2%	4,277.8	4,812.7	4,924.8	2,484.8	5,231.7
Employees	—	0	0	0	—	—

ENBRIDGE (U.S.) INC.

1100 Louisiana St., Ste. 3300
Houston, TX 77002
Phone: 713-821-2000
Fax: 713-821-2230
Web: www.enbridge-us.com

CEO: Stephen J. J. (Steve) Letwin
CFO: —
HR: —
FYE: December 31
Type: Subsidiary

Enbridge (U.S.), a subsidiary of Canada's Enbridge, provides oil and gas pipeline transportation services. The company holds interests in a range of US pipeline assets, including Alliance Pipeline, Enbridge Pipelines (Toledo), Mustang Pipe Line Partners, and Vector Pipeline. Enbridge (U.S.) is also an affiliate of Enbridge Energy Company. In 2007 Enbridge (U.S.) and ExxonMobil Pipeline Company began to jointly pursue the development of the Texas Access Pipeline, a proposed heavy crude oil pipeline, which when completed will provide 445,000 barrels per day of new capacity from the Patoka, Illinois, oil terminal to Texas Gulf Coast refineries.

ENCANA OIL & GAS (USA) INC.

370 17th St., Ste. 1700
Denver, CO 80202
Phone: 303-623-2300
Fax: 303-623-2400
Web: www.encana.com

CEO: Randall K. (Randy) Eresman
CFO: Sherri A. Brillon
HR: R. William (Bill) Oliver
FYE: December 31
Type: Subsidiary

EnCana Oil & Gas (USA) is a south of the border chip off the block of a Canadian energy giant. The company is an exploration and production subsidiary of integrated oil firm EnCana Corporation. EnCana Oil & Gas (USA) explores for and produces oil in its four key natural gas resource plays (about 90% of its total US natural gas production) located at Jonah and Piceance in the US Rockies (Wyoming and northwest Colorado) and the Fort Worth and East Texas basins. It also owns stakes in natural gas gathering and processing assets, mainly in Colorado, Texas, Utah, and Wyoming. EnCana Oil & Gas (USA)'s oil and gas production averaged about 1,713 million cu. ft. per day in 2008.

ENCISION INC.

OTC: ECIA

6797 Winchester Cir.
Boulder, CO 80301
Phone: 303-444-2600
Fax: 303-444-2693
Web: www.encision.com

CEO: John R. (Jack) Serino
CFO: Marcia K. McHaffie
HR: —
FYE: March 31
Type: Public

Encision enables doctors to make the cut during surgery. The company makes instruments for use in laparoscopic surgical procedures, including electrodes, graspers, monitors, and scissor inserts. Encision's products, sold under the brand name AEM Surgical Instruments, work like conventional electrosurgical instruments but incorporate proprietary technology that reduces the risk of accidental damage to surrounding tissues caused by stray electrosurgical energy. The company has been working to expand its marketing and distribution network, using independent distributors and sales representatives, as well as agreements with group purchasing organizations such as Novation and Premier.

	Annual Growth	3/05	3/06	3/07	3/08	3/09
Sales ($ mil.)	12.1%	8.1	9.1	11.0	12.1	12.8
Net income ($ mil.)	—	(0.6)	(0.3)	(0.1)	(0.2)	0.2
Employees	13.1%	33	35	46	50	54

ENCOMPASS HOLDINGS, INC.

Pink Sheets: ECMH

1005 Terminal Way, Ste. 110
Reno, NV 89502
Phone: 530-355-7674
Fax: —
Web: www.encompassholdings.com

CEO: J. Scott Webber
CFO: —
HR: —
FYE: June 30
Type: Public

Surf's up at Encompass Holdings! The investment firm owns Aqua Xtremes, which makes water sports equipment including the XBoard brand of jet-powered surfboards. It also owns Nacio Systems, which provides outsourced IT services including e-commerce, customer relationship management, and software audits. Xtremes subsidiary Xtreme Engines and its majority-owned Rotary Engine Technologies are developing an engine for the XBoard. Encompass Holdings plans to spin off Nacio Systems (it will retain a stake) and continues to look for further investment opportunities in varied industries.

ENCOMPASS INSURANCE COMPANY

3100 Sanders Rd., Ste. K4
Northbrook, IL 60062
Phone: 847-402-5000
Fax: 847-402-3175
Web: www.encompassinsurance.com

CEO: Cynthia H. Young
CFO: Laura Dunne
HR: —
FYE: December 31
Type: Subsidiary

Encompass Insurance does not encompass businesses. The company, formerly known as CNA Personal Insurance, specializes in personal insurance. As one of the largest personal brands in the US, it has more than 1.2 million customers in 42 states. The company offers its products through more than 2,800 independent agents. Products include auto, collectible auto, boat, and homeowners coverage, as well as its Universal Security Policy (combining personal insurance policies into one). Encompass Insurance is a subsidiary of auto insurance giant Allstate Insurance Company, part of the Allstate Corporation.

ENCORE, INC.

999 N. Sepulveda Blvd., Ste. 700
El Segundo, CA 90245
Phone: 310-768-1800
Fax: 310-768-1822
Web: www.encoreusa.com

CEO: Calvin (Cal) Morrell
CFO: —
HR: —
FYE: December 31
Type: Subsidiary

Encore just knows you'll want to play it again, Sam. The company publishes educational and entertainment software games. Encore's products — which are designed for use on PCs and console games, as well as over the Internet — can be found in retail stores across the US. Publishing brands include *Hoyle*, *Marine Aquarium*, *Family Tree Maker*, *3D Home Architect*, and the Riverdeep family of brands. CEO Michael Bell founded the company in a basement with his college roommate in 1994. Navarre Corporation, a distributor and publisher of entertainment goods, owns Encore.

	Annual Growth	12/04	12/05	12/06	12/07	12/08
Est. sales ($ mil.)	—	—	—	—	—	4.7
Employees	—	—	—	—	—	52

ENCORE BANCSHARES, INC.

NASDAQ (GM): EBTX

9 Greenway Plaza, Ste. 1000
Houston, TX 77046
Phone: 713-787-3100
Fax: —
Web: www.encorebank.com

CEO: James S. D'Agostino Jr.
CFO: L. Anderson Creel
HR: Nancy L. Smith
FYE: December 31
Type: Public

Encore! Encore! Encore Bancshares is taking its bows as the holding company for Encore Bank. Encore operates around a dozen branches in Houston and a handful more in southwestern Florida, offering traditional retail banking products to businesses and individuals. It also provides mortgages and other loans and wealth management, and insurance to its customers through subsidiaries Town & Country Insurance Agency, Encore Trust Company, and Linscomb & Williams. The bank caters to wealthy clients (hence its focus on the Houston area and southwest Florida, two of the wealthiest regions in the US) with private bankers and relationship managers.

	Annual Growth	12/05	12/06	12/07	12/08	12/09
Assets ($ mil.)	5.6%	1,316.6	1,336.8	1,401.2	1,587.8	1,635.4
Net income ($ mil.)	(21.7%)	4.8	7.5	7.4	(8.1)	1.8
Market value ($ mil.)	(36.7%)	—	—	227.9	125.4	91.4
Employees	(0.7%)	318	318	309	303	309

ENCORE CAPITAL GROUP, INC.

NASDAQ (GS): ECPG

8875 Aero Dr., Ste. 200
San Diego, CA 92123
Phone: 858-560-2600
Fax: —
Web: www.mcmcg.com

CEO: J. Brandon Black
CFO: Paul J. Grinberg
HR: —
FYE: December 31
Type: Public

Credit junkies, beware: Encore Capital Group has your number. The firm and its Midland Credit Management subsidiary purchase, at a discount, charged-off receivables that credit card issuers and other lenders have given up on. The group then does its best to collect the money via phone, direct mail, third-party collection agencies, and legal action. Utilizing a "friendly, but firm approach" its account managers evaluate customers' ability to pay, then develop tailored payment programs; the company also uses skip-tracers to track down stubborn debtors. Subsidiary Ascension Capital Group provides bankruptcy services to the finance industry.

	Annual Growth	12/05	12/06	12/07	12/08	12/09
Sales ($ mil.)	9.3%	221.8	255.1	254.0	255.9	316.4
Net income ($ mil.)	1.5%	31.1	24.0	15.0	18.8	33.0
Market value ($ mil.)	0.1%	407.0	295.6	227.1	168.9	408.2
Employees	13.5%	905	893	1,000	1,100	1,500

ENCORE ENERGY PARTNERS LP

NYSE: ENP

777 Main St., Ste. 1400
Fort Worth, TX 76102
Phone: 817-877-9955
Fax: —
Web: www.encoreenp.com

CEO: Phil Rykhoek
CFO: Mark C. Allen Sr.
HR: —
FYE: December 31
Type: Public

Encore Energy Partners is banking on a second trip to the well. The partnership acquires, exploits, and develops existing oil and natural gas properties. Encore Energy's primary assets consist of oil and natural gas properties in the Big Horn Basin of Wyoming and Montana, the Permian Basin of West Texas, and the Williston Basin of North Dakota. In 2008 the company reported estimated proved reserves of 16.6 million barrels of oil and 56.5 billion cu. ft. of natural gas. Encore Energy's strategy is to leverage its relationship with parent Denbury Resources to develop additional properties.

	Annual Growth	12/05	12/06	12/07	12/08	12/09
Sales ($ mil.)	72.7%	16.9	12.7	79.7	187.4	150.5
Net income ($ mil.)	—	11.6	7.6	(25.3)	172.5	(40.3)
Market value ($ mil.)	4.9%	—	—	816.1	588.5	898.7
Employees	—	—	—	0	394	421

ENCORE ENERGY SYSTEMS, INC.

Pink Sheets: ENCS

5190 Neil Rd., Ste. 430
Reno, NV 89502
Phone: 662-253-5766
Fax: 662-510-0151
Web: www.encoreenergyinc.com

CEO: Jack R. Tarry
CFO: —
HR: —
FYE: June 30
Type: Public

Encore Energy Systems, through its DeMarco Energy subsidiary, makes patented geothermal water-air heating/cooling systems. Its Energy Miser geothermal heat pump system uses municipal water mains or other piping loops to heat, cool, and provide hot water for commercial buildings. The Energy Miser transfers thermal energy — to cool, it removes heat from inside buildings to exterior heat sinks; to heat, the process is reversed. It also sells a line of BioGreen Power Generation Systems, which feature multi-fuel capabilities using diesel, bio-diesel, vegetable oils, and even waste motor oils and transmission fluids. The firm was initially founded in 1978 and became incorporated in 1983.

ENCORE WIRE CORPORATION

NASDAQ (GS): WIRE

1410 Millwood Rd.
McKinney, TX 75069
Phone: 972-562-9473
Fax: 972-542-4744
Web: www.encorewire.com

CEO: Daniel L. Jones
CFO: Frank J. Bilban
HR: Brad Rattan
FYE: December 31
Type: Public

Encore Wire likes to keep customers applauding and calling for more — more wire, that is. A low-cost manufacturer of copper electrical building wire and cable, Encore produces NM-B cable, a sheathed cable used to wire homes, apartments, and pre-fabricated housing, and UF-B cable, an underground feeder cable for outside lighting and remote residential building connections. Its 7,000 stock-keeping units include THWN-2 cable, an insulated feeder, circuit, and branch wiring for commercial and industrial buildings, and other wires like armored cable. The company sells to wholesale electrical distributors and select retail home-improvement centers. It is the only public copper building wire company in the US.

	Annual Growth	12/05	12/06	12/07	12/08	12/09
Sales ($ mil.)	(3.8%)	758.1	1,249.3	1,184.8	1,081.1	649.6
Net income ($ mil.)	(48.2%)	50.1	115.1	30.8	39.8	3.6
Market value ($ mil.)	(1.9%)	527.3	509.9	368.8	439.2	488.1
Employees	(0.6%)	686	755	762	753	669

ENCORIUM GROUP, INC.

NASDAQ (CM): ENCO

400 Berwyn Park, 899 Cassatt Rd., Ste. 115
Berwyn, PA 19312
Phone: 610-989-4208
Fax: —
Web: www.encorium.com

CEO: Kai E. Lindevall
CFO: Philip L. (Phil) Calamia
HR: Nicole Haraczka
FYE: December 31
Type: Public

Encorium Group aims to make its research clients say "Encore!" The contract research organization (CRO) manages all stages of clinical trials for pharmaceutical, biotech, and medical device firms worldwide using both full-time and contract personnel. It provides program design, trial and data management, biostatistical analysis, medical and regulatory services, and quality assurance. The company also provides technology solutions, including interactive speech recognition systems and Internet data systems. In response to financial difficulties, Encorium has restructured and sold off its primary US subsidiary. It is focusing on its international CRO operations.

	Annual Growth	12/05	12/06	12/07	12/08	12/09
Sales ($ mil.)	13.7%	12.7	17.7	36.8	35.9	21.2
Net income ($ mil.)	—	(1.5)	(0.5)	(2.8)	(21.1)	(3.9)
Market value ($ mil.)	(40.7%)	59.1	143.9	46.4	7.3	7.3
Employees	17.7%	84	264	275	235	161

⊞ ENCYCLOPÆDIA BRITANNICA, INC.

331 N. La Salle St.
Chicago, IL 60610
Phone: 312-347-7159
Fax: 312-294-2104
Web: corporate.britannica.com

CEO: Jorge Cauz
CFO: Richard Anderson
HR: William J. Bowe
FYE: December 31
Type: Private

Encyclopædia Britannica thinks it knows everything, and it probably does. In addition to its flagship 32-volume *Encyclopædia Britannica* (first published in 1768), the company publishes reference works (*Great Books of the Western World*), atlases (*Britannica's Student Atlas*), and other titles (*The American Presidency*). It publishes dictionaries (*Merriam Webster's Collegiate Dictionary*) through its Merriam-Webster subsidiary. The company's Britannica Online School Edition is a reference site for students and teachers. Most of the company's products are available online (Britannica.com), as well as on CD-ROM and DVD. Swiss financier Jacob Safra (a nephew of the late banking king Edmond Safra) owns the company.

	Annual Growth	12/04	12/05	12/06	12/07	12/08
Est. sales ($ mil.)	—	—	—	—	—	50.1
Employees	—	—	—	—	—	439

ENDEAVOUR INTERNATIONAL CORPORATION

NYSE Amex: END

1001 Fannin, Ste. 1600
Houston, TX 77002
Phone: 713-307-8700
Fax: —
Web: www.endeavourcorp.com

CEO: William L. (Bill) Transier
CFO: J. Michael (Mike) Kirksey
HR: —
FYE: December 31
Type: Public

Like famous British explorer Captain James Cook's vessel, the *Endeavour*, Endeavour International has been on quite a journey in the pursuit of new discoveries. The exploration and production company is buying up stakes in mature North Sea fields that the oil majors are moving away from. In a major strategic move, in 2008 Endeavour International began opening up a second core area, the US, and started buying stakes in oil and gas properties in Louisiana, New Mexico, and Texas. In 2008 Endeavour International reported proved and probable reserves of 32.2 million barrels of oil equivalent.

	Annual Growth	12/05	12/06	12/07	12/08	12/09
Sales ($ mil.)	12.6%	38.7	54.1	176.1	260.4	62.3
Net income ($ mil.)	—	(31.4)	(6.8)	(49.1)	56.5	(41.0)
Market value ($ mil.)	(24.4%)	536.7	372.5	218.0	81.3	175.7
Employees	(4.6%)	52	60	60	66	43

ENDECA TECHNOLOGIES INC.

101 Main St.
Cambridge, MA 02142
Phone: 617-674-6000
Fax: 617-674-6001
Web: www.endeca.com

CEO: Steve Papa
CFO: Daniel (Dan) Demmer
HR: —
FYE: December 31
Type: Private

Endeca Technologies doesn't want Internet surfers to drown in a sea of information. The company's enterprise search software categorizes and organizes search results, enabling users to narrow their choices when browsing online catalogs, information portals, and corporate intranets. Endeca also offers tools for e-commerce searches and business intelligence analytics. Endeca targets clients in the media and publishing, financial services, manufacturing and distribution, government, and retail industries; customers include Bank of America, Barnes & Noble, IBM, and Wal-Mart.

	Annual Growth	12/04	12/05	12/06	12/07	12/08
Est. sales ($ mil.)	—	—	—	—	—	108.2
Employees	—	—	—	—	—	450

⊞ An in-depth profile of this company is available to Hoover's Online members at hoovers.com.

559

ENDO PHARMACEUTICALS HOLDINGS INC.

NASDAQ (GS): ENDP

100 Endo Blvd.
Chadds Ford, PA 19317
Phone: 610-558-9800
Fax: 610-558-8979
Web: www.endo.com

CEO: David P. Holveck
CFO: Alan G. Levin
HR: Larry Cunningham
FYE: December 31
Type: Public

Endo Pharmaceuticals wants the pain to end, preferably through the drugs it acquires and markets. The pharmaceutical company has a portfolio of both branded and generic prescription products for pain management. Its best-selling drug is Lidoderm, a lidocaine patch that treats nerve pain caused by shingles; it accounts for about two-thirds of the company's revenue. Endo also sells well-known pain meds Percodan and Percocet, as well as migraine therapy Frova. Its generics include morphine and oxycodone tablets. The company markets its drugs in the US through its own domestic sales force; however, it outsources almost everything else, from manufacturing to distribution to clinical development acitivities.

	Annual Growth	12/05	12/06	12/07	12/08	12/09
Sales ($ mil.)	15.5%	820.2	909.7	1,085.6	1,260.5	1,460.8
Net income ($ mil.)	7.1%	202.3	137.8	227.4	261.7	266.3
Market value ($ mil.)	(9.3%)	3,518.2	3,206.6	3,100.8	3,009.0	2,385.8
Employees	20.3%	710	1,024	1,208	1,216	1,487

ENDOLOGIX, INC.

NASDAQ (GM): ELGX

11 Studebaker
Irvine, CA 92618
Phone: 949-595-7200
Fax: 949-457-9561
Web: www.endologix.com

CEO: John McDermott
CFO: Robert J. (Bob) Krist
HR: —
FYE: December 31
Type: Public

Medical device company Endologix strengthens weak arteries with its PowerLink Systems, which use a catheter and stent cage to treat abdominal aortic aneurysm (or weakening of the aortic wall). The device, which reduces blood pressure on the weakened portion of the aorta, offers a less-invasive alternative to conventional surgery. Endologix sells the products in the US through its own team of sales representatives and in Europe through distributors (including LeMaitre Vascular). The company has also licensed some legacy technologies to Guidant.

	Annual Growth	12/05	12/06	12/07	12/08	12/09
Sales ($ mil.)	64.8%	7.1	14.7	27.8	37.7	52.4
Net income ($ mil.)	—	(15.5)	(17.5)	(15.1)	(12.0)	(2.4)
Market value ($ mil.)	(6.5%)	335.8	170.3	136.3	58.4	256.9
Employees	10.1%	134	164	168	190	197

ENDURANCE SPECIALTY HOLDINGS LTD.

NYSE: ENH

767 Third Ave., 5th Fl.
New York, NY 10017
Phone: 212-209-6500
Fax: 212-209-6501
Web: www.endurance.bm

CEO: David S. Cash
CFO: Michael J. McGuire
HR: —
FYE: December 31
Type: Public

Endurance Specialty Holdings hopes it has what it takes to endure the rough and tumble world of commercial insurance and reinsurance. The company's insurance underwriting operations include crop and livestock insurance, health care liability coverage for hospitals, and professional coverage for corporate officers, as well as general property/casualty lines. The company offers various property/casualty reinsurance policies, with a focus on catastrophe coverage. Other reinsurance offerings include marine, aerospace, and surety lines. Endurance Specialty is domiciled in Bermuda and has additional offices in the US and the UK.

	Annual Growth	12/05	12/06	12/07	12/08	12/09
Assets ($ mil.)	4.8%	6,352.5	6,925.6	7,270.7	7,272.5	7,666.7
Net income ($ mil.)	—	(223.2)	482.6	505.6	98.6	536.1
Market value ($ mil.)	0.9%	1,934.8	1,974.2	2,252.1	1,647.6	2,009.2
Employees	18.5%	396	484	727	776	781

ENDWAVE CORPORATION

NASDAQ (GM): ENWV

130 Baytech Dr.
San Jose, CA 95134
Phone: 408-522-3100
Fax: 408-522-3197
Web: www.endwave.com

CEO: John J. Mikulsky
CFO: Curt P. Sacks
HR: —
FYE: December 31
Type: Public

Endwave is riding the wireless tide. The company designs components and subsystems for broadband wireless systems. Telecom equipment makers such as Nokia Siemens Networks (70% of sales) and Nera Networks (18%) use Endwave's radio-frequency (RF) modules and transceivers in cellular, point-to-point, and point-to-multipoint network access gear. The company also manufactures RF amplifiers, converters, and oscillators. Northrop Grumman Information Systems supplies Endwave with chips. The company gets nearly all of its sales from European customers.

	Annual Growth	12/05	12/06	12/07	12/08	12/09
Sales ($ mil.)	(20.5%)	48.7	62.2	56.5	58.3	19.5
Net income ($ mil.)	—	(0.9)	(1.3)	(5.4)	(14.8)	6.6
Market value ($ mil.)	(32.5%)	111.6	102.6	68.9	22.7	23.1
Employees	(21.3%)	141	151	214	228	54

🔲 ENER1, INC.

NASDAQ (GM): HEV

500 W. Cypress Creek Rd., Ste. 100
Fort Lauderdale, FL 33309
Phone: 954-556-4020
Fax: 954-556-4031
Web: www.ener1.com

CEO: Charles Gassenheimer
CFO: Gerard A. (Jerry) Herlihy
HR: —
FYE: December 31
Type: Public

Ener1 is an energy-related technology holding company. The company develops products related to fuel cells and solar cells for the consumer, industrial, and military markets. Its NanoEner subsidiary develops nanotechnology-based products. Its EnerFuel unit develops fuel cell components and provides related testing services. Ener1 also owns EnerDel (previously a joint venture with Delphi), which develops lithium power technologies and products for stored energy and battery power — primary cells (non-rechargeable), rechargeable cells, battery packs, and electronics. EnerDel is providing lithium-ion batteries for Volvo Car's prototype electric vehicles.

	Annual Growth	12/05	12/06	12/07	12/08	12/09
Sales ($ mil.)	331.9%	0.1	0.1	0.3	6.8	34.8
Net income ($ mil.)	—	28.1	(41.3)	(51.7)	(43.0)	(51.0)
Market value ($ mil.)	23.4%	343.1	202.3	708.2	898.6	796.8
Employees	69.8%	62	73	104	486	515

ENERGAS RESOURCES, INC.

OTC: EGSRE

800 NE 63rd St., 3rd Fl.
Oklahoma City, OK 73105
Phone: 405-879-1752
Fax: 405-879-0175
Web: www.energasresources.com

CEO: George G. Shaw
CFO: George G. Shaw
HR: —
FYE: January 31
Type: Public

Turning subterranean natural gas into a useful energy is the goal of exploration and development independent Energas Resources. Operating through its A.T. Gas Gathering Systems and TGC subsidiaries, the company is primarily focused on exploring and producing in the Arkoma Basin in Oklahoma, and the Powder River Basin in Wyoming. Energas Resources has proved reserves of 22,143 barrels of oil and 1.9 billion cu. ft. of natural gas. In 2007 the company sold most of its assets in the shallow Devonian Shale natural gas strata in the Appalachian Basin of Kentucky. President George Shaw owns about 24% of the company.

	Annual Growth	1/06	1/07	1/08	1/09	1/10
Sales ($ mil.)	(36.1%)	1.2	0.6	0.4	0.3	0.2
Net income ($ mil.)	—	(1.6)	(1.5)	(1.5)	(2.5)	(1.9)
Market value ($ mil.)	(52.3%)	52.7	3.1	2.7	4.2	2.7
Employees	(20.5%)	10	10	—	4	4

ENERGEN CORPORATION

NYSE: EGN

605 Richard Arrington Jr. Blvd. North
Birmingham, AL 35203
Phone: 205-326-2700
Fax: 205-326-2704
Web: www.energen.com

CEO: James T. McManus II
CFO: Charles W. (Chuck) Porter Jr.
HR: William K. (Bill) Bibb
FYE: December 31
Type: Public

Energen's natural gas distribution business puts the energy out in Dixie, but the company also takes it in through gas and oil exploration operations that extend into the Southwest. The diversified energy company generates more than half of its sales from its regulated utility, Alabama Gas Corporation (Alagasco), which distributes natural gas to approximately 413,150 residential and more than 33,900 commercial and industrial customers. Energen has oil and gas exploration and production operations in the Southwest through subsidiary Energen Resources; the unit has estimated proved reserves of 1.6 trillion cu. ft. of natural gas equivalent.

	Annual Growth	12/05	12/06	12/07	12/08	12/09
Sales ($ mil.)	6.3%	1,128.4	1,394.0	1,435.1	1,568.9	1,440.4
Net income ($ mil.)	10.3%	173.0	273.6	309.2	321.9	256.3
Market value ($ mil.)	6.5%	2,610.8	3,374.1	4,617.0	2,108.3	3,364.1
Employees	0.2%	1,500	1,530	1,542	1,530	1,515

ENERGIZER HOLDINGS, INC.

NYSE: ENR

533 Maryville University Dr.
St. Louis, MO 63141
Phone: 314-985-2000
Fax: 314-985-2205
Web: www.energizer.com

CEO: Ward M. Klein
CFO: Daniel J. Sescleifer
HR: Peter J. Conrad
FYE: September 30
Type: Public

Energizer Holdings keeps going, and going . . . and leading the battery market in the process. Known for its pink bunny marketing icon, the company was spun off in 2000 by pet food maker Nestlé Purina PetCare (formerly Ralston Purina). Its popular Energizer and Eveready battery products — which include alkaline, carbon zinc, lithium, miniature, and specialty batteries — are sold in more than 165 countries. Its e2 Lithium and e2 Titanium batteries provide additional power for portable electronics. Other products include flashlights, razors, shaving cream, moist wipes, and feminine care products. Wal-Mart makes up about 21% of sales. Energizer gets more than half of sales from the US.

	Annual Growth	9/05	9/06	9/07	9/08	9/09
Sales ($ mil.)	7.5%	2,989.8	3,076.9	3,365.1	4,331.0	3,999.8
Net income ($ mil.)	1.0%	286.4	260.9	321.4	329.3	297.8
Market value ($ mil.)	4.0%	3,971.1	5,041.9	7,763.5	5,641.4	4,646.2
Employees	1.1%	14,848	14,800	14,800	16,410	15,500

ENERGY BRANDS INC.

17-20 Whitestone Expwy.
Whitestone, NY 11357
Phone: 718-746-0087
Fax: 718-747-1748
Web: www.energybrands.com

CEO: Brent Hastie
CFO: Wadih Khayat
HR: —
FYE: December 31
Type: Subsidiary

Energy Brands (also known as glacèau) is proud of its liquid assets. The company's main brands are vitaminwater, which comes in more than a dozen flavors and is fortified with such nutrients as folic acid, magnesium, vitamin B-12, and zinc; vitaminenergy, a nutrient-enhanced energy drink; smartwater, a no-calorie, vapor-distilled, electrolyte-enriched beverage; and fruitwater, a flavored version of smartwater but sweetened with fructose. Energy Brands' products are available worldwide. Energy Brands is a subsidiary of Coca-Cola.

ENERGY CONVERSION DEVICES, INC.

NASDAQ (GS): ENER

2956 Waterview Dr.
Rochester Hills, MI 48309
Phone: 248-293-0440
Fax: 248-844-1214
Web: www.ovonic.com

CEO: Mark D. Morelli
CFO: William C. (Kriss) Andrews
HR: Gary M. Glandon
FYE: June 30
Type: Public

Energy Conversion Devices (ECD) gets a charge out of its technology. ECD makes storage products that generate and store power or store information electronically. Subsidiary United Solar Ovonic, which accounts for more than 95% of sales, makes flexible solar panels mainly for roofs, but also for telecom, lighting, and other uses. The Ovonic Materials Division licenses its optical memory storage technology to the likes of Sony and Toshiba. It also produces materials for use in NiMH and other batteries; Sanyo licenses its battery technology. ECD's largest customers are EDF En Developpement, Solardis-Soprasolar, Centrosolar AG, and Advanced Green Technologies, a unit of Advanced Roofing.

	Annual Growth	6/05	6/06	6/07	6/08	6/09
Sales ($ mil.)	19.2%	156.6	102.4	113.6	255.9	316.3
Net income ($ mil.)	(29.6%)	50.9	(18.6)	(25.2)	3.9	12.5
Market value ($ mil.)	(10.8%)	1,024.2	1,667.1	1,410.4	3,370.0	647.5
Employees	24.6%	746	964	1,204	1,768	1,800

ENERGY FOCUS, INC.

NASDAQ (GM): EFOI

32000 Aurora Rd.
Solon, OH 44139
Phone: 440-715-1300
Fax: 440-715-1314
Web: www.energyfocusinc.com

CEO: Joseph G. (Joe) Kaveski
CFO: Nicholas G. Berchtold
HR: Donna Prunetti
FYE: December 31
Type: Public

The Illuminator may be coming to a theater near you, but it isn't a movie. It's Energy Focus, a designer and manufacturer of energy-efficient fiber-optic, light-emitting diode, ceramic metal halide, and high-intensity discharge lighting systems. Serving the commercial/industrial and pool lighting markets, Energy Focus' systems illuminate cinemas, shopping malls, parking garages, performing arts centers, restaurants, pools/spas, and homes. Its lighting products include acrylic accent fixtures, downlight fixtures, spotlights, solar retrofits, and display-case lighting. Energy Focus sells its products in the US, Asia, and Europe through independent sales reps, distributors, and swimming pool manufacturers.

	Annual Growth	12/05	12/06	12/07	12/08	12/09
Sales ($ mil.)	(18.5%)	28.3	27.0	22.9	23.0	12.5
Net income ($ mil.)	—	(7.4)	(9.6)	(11.3)	(14.4)	(11.0)
Market value ($ mil.)	(47.7%)	196.1	149.3	166.2	26.4	14.7
Employees	(11.5%)	127	160	102	92	78

ENERGY FUTURE HOLDINGS CORP.

1601 Bryan St.
Dallas, TX 75201
Phone: 214-812-4600
Fax: —
Web: www.energyfutureholdings.com

CEO: John F. Young
CFO: Paul M. Keglevic
HR: Kim Koonce
FYE: December 31
Type: Private

Energy Future Holdings (formerly TXU) has seen the future and it works — powered by electricity. The company is the largest nonregulated retail electric provider in Texas (TXU Energy), with 2.1 million customers, and through its Luminant unit it has a generating capacity of more than 15,510 MW from its interests in nuclear and fossil-fueled power plants in the state. Energy Future Holdings has regulated power transmission and distribution operations through 80%-owned Oncor Electric Delivery. Oncor operates the largest regulated distribution and transmission system in Texas, providing power to more than 3.1 million electric delivery points over more than 117,000 miles of transmission and distribution lines.

	Annual Growth	12/04	12/05	12/06	12/07	12/08
Sales ($ mil.)	42.2%	—	—	—	7,992.0	11,364.0
Net income ($ mil.)	—	—	—	—	(637.0)	(9,838.0)
Employees	7.2%	—	—	—	7,600	8,150

ENERGY NORTHWEST

76 N. Power Plant Loop
Richland, WA 99352
Phone: 509-372-5000
Fax: 509-372-5205
Web: www.energy-northwest.com

CEO: Joseph V. (Vic) Parrish
CFO: Albert E. (Al) Mouncer
HR: Cheryl M. Whitcomb
FYE: June 30
Type: Government-owned

The name says its all. Energy Northwest provides electricity to public utility districts (PUDs) and municipalities in the northwestern US. The company, which is owned by the utilities it serves, has interests in nuclear, hydroelectric, wind, and solar power generation facilities. Energy Northwest is a joint operating agency comprised of about 30 member public utilities from across the state of Washington. Its four electricity generating stations are Columbia Generating Station, Nine Canyon Wind Project, Packwood Lake Hydroelectric Project, and the White Bluffs Solar Station. The company has a total generating capacity of 1,400 MW.

	Annual Growth	6/04	6/05	6/06	6/07	6/08
Est. sales ($ mil.)	—	—	—	—	—	455.1
Employees	—	—	—	—	—	1,100

ENERGY PARTNERS, LTD.

NYSE: EPL

201 St. Charles Ave., Ste. 3400
New Orleans, LA 70170
Phone: 504-569-1875
Fax: 504-569-1874
Web: www.eplweb.com

CEO: Gary C. Hanna
CFO: Tiffany J. Thom
HR: —
FYE: December 31
Type: Public

It pays for Energy Partners to have friends in the oil and gas business. The independent explorer and producer focuses on the deep and shallow waters of the Gulf of Mexico and the Gulf Coast. It partners with big oil companies to explore for reserves on properties the majors have left behind; Energy Partners earns an interest in the new reserves and production. Buffered by a major economic downturn and by 2008 hurricanes that damaged Energy Partners' oil and gas pipelines, disrupting production, in May 2009 the company filed for Chapter 11 bankruptcy protection. It emerged from Chapter 11 in September 2009.

	Annual Growth	12/05	12/06	12/07	12/08	12/09
Sales ($ mil.)	(17.0%)	402.9	449.5	454.6	356.3	191.6
Net income ($ mil.)	—	73.1	(50.4)	(80.0)	(52.2)	(57.1)
Market value ($ mil.)	(60.6%)	14,157.7	15,866.5	7,673.4	877.1	342.6
Employees	(12.2%)	170	179	163	156	101

ENERGY RECOVERY, INC.

NASDAQ (GM): ERII

1908 Doolittle Dr.
San Leandro, CA 94577
Phone: 510-483-7370
Fax: 510-483-7371
Web: www.energyrecovery.com

CEO: G.G. Pique
CFO: Thomas D. (Tom) Willardson
HR: MariaElena Ross
FYE: December 31
Type: Public

Desalination makes seawater potable; Energy Recovery makes desalination practical. The company designs, develops, and manufactures energy recovery devices for use in sea water reverse osmosis (SWRO) desalination plants. The SWRO process is energy intensive, using high pressure to drive salt water through membranes to produce fresh water. The company's primary product, the PX Pressure Exchanger, helps recapture and recycle up to 98% of the energy available in the high-pressure reject stream, a by-product of the SWRO process. The PX can reduce the energy consumption of a desalination plant by up to 60% compared with a plant lacking an energy recovery device. Energy Recovery completed an IPO in mid-2008.

	Annual Growth	12/05	12/06	12/07	12/08	12/09
Sales ($ mil.)	44.8%	10.7	20.1	35.4	52.1	47.0
Net income ($ mil.)	42.4%	0.9	2.4	5.8	8.7	3.7
Market value ($ mil.)	(9.2%)	—	—	—	397.3	360.6
Employees	39.3%	—	—	67	89	130

ENERGY TRANSFER EQUITY, L.P.

NYSE: ETE

3738 Oak Lawn Ave.
Dallas, TX 75219
Phone: 214-981-0700
Fax: 214-981-0703
Web: www.energytransfer.com

CEO: Kelcy L. Warren
CFO: John W. McReynolds
HR: —
FYE: December 31
Type: Public

Energy Transfer Equity transfers some of its equity in order to get more out of its midstream energy assets. The company acts as the general partner of Energy Transfer Partners, which sells more than 600 million gallons of propane a year to more than 1 million customers from 440 service centers in 40 states. It also operates more than 17,500 miles of natural gas pipelines. Through its Energy Transfer Partners GP unit, Energy Transfer Equity owns a 2% general partnership stake in Energy Transfer Partners and 33% of common stock. Energy Transfer Equity is managed by general partner LE GP, LLC.

	Annual Growth	8/05	8/06	8/07	*12/08	12/09
Sales ($ mil.)	(3.2%)	6,168.8	7,859.1	6,792.0	9,293.4	5,417.3
Net income ($ mil.)	31.8%	146.7	107.1	319.4	375.0	442.5
Market value ($ mil.)	4.1%	—	6,043.9	8,193.1	3,613.9	6,817.5
Employees	20.6%	2,642	3,900	5,316	5,430	5,581

*Fiscal year change

ENERGY TRANSFER PARTNERS, L.P.

NYSE: ETP

3738 Oak Lawn Ave.
Dallas, TX 75219
Phone: 214-981-0700
Fax: 214-981-0703
Web: www.energytransfer.com

CEO: Kelcy L. Warren
CFO: Martin Salinas Jr.
HR: —
FYE: December 31
Type: Public

Energy Transfer Partners distributes natural gas and propane across the US. The company operates more than 7,800 miles of intrastate natural gas gathering and transmission pipelines, and about 2,700 miles of interstate pipelines, and related storage assets. It sells about 570 million gallons of propane a year to more than 1 million customers through 440 retail outlets in 40 states. Energy Transfer Partners also operates about 7,000 miles of gas gathering pipelines, three gas processing plants and more than 20 gas treating and/or conditioning facilities. Energy Transfer Equity controls about 33% of the company.

	Annual Growth	8/05	8/06	8/07	*12/08	12/09
Sales ($ mil.)	(3.2%)	6,168.8	7,859.1	6,792.0	9,293.9	5,417.3
Net income ($ mil.)	22.7%	349.4	515.9	676.1	866.0	791.5
Market value ($ mil.)	5.0%	7,074.0	9,116.4	9,952.2	6,504.1	8,600.1
Employees	15.0%	3,193	3,898	5,316	5,430	5,581

*Fiscal year change

ENERGY WEST, INCORPORATED

NASDAQ (GM): EWST

1 1st Ave. South
Great Falls, MT 59401
Phone: 406-791-7500
Fax: 406-791-7560
Web: www.ewst.com

CEO: Richard M. Osborne
CFO: Thomas J. Smith
HR: —
FYE: December 31
Type: Public

Energy West keeps the West (and the East) warm. The company's energy marketing subsidiary, Energy West Resources, primarily sells natural gas to industrial and commercial customers in Maine, Montana, North Carolina and Wyoming. Energy West's regulated natural gas utility businesses serve 36,000 customers in the four states. Energy West also has gas gathering and production operations; it owns the Shoshone interstate and the Glacier gathering natural gas pipelines located in Montana and Wyoming, and has stakes in 165 natural gas producing wells.

	Annual Growth	6/05	6/06	6/07	6/08	*12/09
Sales ($ mil.)	(1.7%)	76.7	84.3	59.4	76.8	71.5
Net income ($ mil.)	48.5%	1.4	2.3	6.2	3.3	6.8
Market value ($ mil.)	14.3%	36.6	36.5	60.9	65.3	62.5
Employees	11.6%	111	100	76	108	172

*Fiscal year change

ENERGY XXI (BERMUDA) LIMITED

NASDAQ (CM): EXXI

Canon's Court, 22 Victoria St.
Hamilton, HM EX, Bermuda
Phone: 441-295-2244
Fax: —
Web: www.energyxxi.com

CEO: John D. Schiller Jr.
CFO: David West Griffin
HR: Kerry McDonough
FYE: June 30
Type: Public

Energy XXI would like to deliver twice the energy and then some. The oil and natural gas exploration and production company has proved reserves of more than 50 million barrels of oil equivalent. Its properties include about 135,000 acres of land along the Gulf of Mexico, mostly in (or near) the state of Louisiana. Nearly 80% of the company's assets are offshore. Energy XXI spends about half of its production dollars exploring for new sources of oil and gas; it spends the rest exploiting resources previously overlooked by other companies. Global energy giant Shell accounts for more than 60% of the company's sales. Energy XXI, which was formed in 2005, grows by acquiring producing companies or properties.

	Annual Growth	6/05	6/06	6/07	6/08	6/09
Sales ($ mil.)	109.6%	—	47.1	341.3	643.2	433.8
Net income ($ mil.)	—	—	6.9	24.1	26.9	(571.6)
Market value ($ mil.)	(71.5%)	—	—	1,615.1	1,751.8	130.8
Employees	29.3%	—	55	80	114	119

ENERGYSOLUTIONS, INC.

NYSE: ES

423 W. 300 South, Ste. 200
Salt Lake City, UT 84101
Phone: 801-649-2000
Fax: 801-321-0453
Web: www.energysolutions.com

CEO: Val J. Christensen
CFO: Mark C. McBride
HR: Terry Aubie
FYE: December 31
Type: Public

Environmental services company EnergySolutions wants to solve the problem posed by what's left over after electricity has been generated from nuclear fuel. The company provides nuclear waste management services, including nuclear facility decommissioning and decontamination, spent fuel handling, and waste disposal. EnergySolutions provides its services primarily to the United Kingdom Nuclear Decommissioning Authority (the company's largest revenue generator), the US Department of Energy, the US Department of Defense, and a number industrial companies.

	Annual Growth	12/05	12/06	12/07	12/08	12/09
Sales ($ mil.)	47.0%	348.2	427.1	1,092.6	1,791.6	1,623.9
Net income ($ mil.)	(19.0%)	118.0	26.9	(8.9)	45.2	50.8
Market value ($ mil.)	(43.9%)	—	—	2,388.6	500.0	751.4
Employees	0.0%	5,000	1,500	5,000	5,000	5,000

ENERJEX RESOURCES, INC.

OTC: EJXR

27 Corporate Woods, Ste. 350, 10975 Grandview Dr.
Overland Park, KS 66210
Phone: 913-754-7754
Fax: 913-754-7755
Web: www.enerjexresources.com

CEO: C. Stephen (Steve) Cochennet
CFO: Dierdre P. (Dede) Jones
HR: —
FYE: March 31
Type: Public

When other oil companies have given up, EnerJex Resources steps in and injects some capital. The oil and gas exploration and production company works primarily in eastern Kansas, buying producing properties that it feels are undervalued or that were abandoned by other oil companies when oil prices were below $10 a barrel. The company, which has proved reserves of 1.2 million barrels of oil equivalent, holds full or partial interest in half a dozen oil, gas, and oil and gas projects across Kansas. It uses enhanced drilling techniques to recover additional oil and gas from already explored fields.

	Annual Growth	3/05	3/06	3/07	3/08	3/09
Sales ($ mil.)	700.0%	—	—	0.1	3.6	6.4
Net income ($ mil.)	—	—	—	(2.0)	(4.8)	(5.3)
Market value ($ mil.)	15.8%	—	—	4.7	5.1	6.2
Employees	32.3%	—	—	8	9	14

ENERLUME ENERGY MANAGEMENT CORP.

OTC: ENLU

2 Broadway
Hamden, CT 06518
Phone: 203-248-4100
Fax: 203-230-8667
Web: www.enerlumeenergymanagementcorp.com

CEO: John Ekregen
CFO: —
HR: —
FYE: June 30
Type: Public

This former host wants to save you money on your energy costs. Formerly Host America, EnerLume Energy Management is a manufacturer of electronic devices designed to save energy and reduce electricity costs. Its EnerLume-EM energy management system regulates the power consumption of fluorescent lighting fixtures, allowing businesses to cut energy costs without sacrificing lighting levels. The programmable devices can also be used to switch office lighting on and off. EnerLume sells its products through a network of distribution partners. The company's RS Services subsidiary provides electrical construction contracting services.

	Annual Growth	6/04	6/05	6/06	6/07	*6/08
Sales ($ mil.)	(30.6%)	26.8	30.8	37.0	7.2	6.2
Net income ($ mil.)	—	(4.9)	(9.7)	(12.9)	(6.1)	(7.4)
Market value ($ mil.)	(37.2%)	78.3	43.4	14.7	30.0	12.1
Employees	(37.5%)	387	415	413	381	59

*Most recent year available

ENERNOC, INC.

NASDAQ (GM): ENOC

75 Federal St., Ste. 300
Boston, MA 02110
Phone: 617-224-9900
Fax: 617-224-9910
Web: www.enernoc.com

CEO: Timothy G. (Tim) Healy
CFO: Timothy Weller
HR: —
FYE: December 31
Type: Public

EnerNOC knocks on the door of large energy customers and kindly asks them to dim the lights. Not literally of course, but the company has added its technology to utility companies' traditional demand response model. Rather than manually calling up their largest end users, EnerNOC's Network Operations Center (NOC) remotely monitors their customers' energy assets and has the capability to adjust their electrical use (whether it's dimming lights, adjusting the A/C, or turning on emergency generators). It caters to commercial, industrial, and institutional organizations, as well as electric power grid operators and utilities. EnerNOC also assists customers in buying energy in a cost-effective manner.

	Annual Growth	12/05	12/06	12/07	12/08	12/09
Sales ($ mil.)	110.0%	9.8	26.1	60.8	106.1	190.7
Net income ($ mil.)	—	(1.7)	(5.8)	(23.6)	(36.7)	(6.8)
Market value ($ mil.)	(21.3%)	—	—	1,208.8	183.2	748.2
Employees	33.7%	131	131	253	345	418

ENERSYS INC.

NYSE: ENS

2366 Bernville Rd.
Reading, PA 19605
Phone: 610-208-1991
Fax: 610-372-8457
Web: www.enersysinc.com

CEO: John D. Craig
CFO: Michael J. Schmidtlein
HR: —
FYE: March 31
Type: Public

EnerSys' battery operations are charging off in different directions. The company makes stationary industrial batteries that provide uninterruptible power and backup power for electronic systems and motive power batteries for big equipment, such as forklifts. Other products include battery chargers and accessories. Its Hawker subsidiary makes batteries with industrial and military applications. Company management and Morgan Stanley acquired Yuasa's Motive Power and Stationary Power operations and renamed the company EnerSys. The battery manufacturer sells directly and through distributors to more than 10,000 customers around the world. Customers in Europe account for about half of sales.

	Annual Growth	3/06	3/07	3/08	3/09	3/10
Sales ($ mil.)	5.3%	1,283.3	1,504.5	2,026.6	1,972.9	1,579.4
Net income ($ mil.)	19.4%	30.7	45.2	59.7	84.6	62.3
Market value ($ mil.)	15.6%	676.8	842.6	1,173.2	594.4	1,209.5
Employees	1.0%	7,500	7,800	8,600	7,500	7,800

An in-depth profile of this company is available to Hoover's Online members at hoovers.com.

ENESCO, LLC

225 Windsor Dr.
Itasca, IL 60143
Phone: 630-875-5300
Fax: 630-875-5350
Web: www.enesco.com

CEO: Matt Bousquette
CFO: Anthony G. (Tony) Testolin
HR: —
FYE: December 31
Type: Private

Enesco collects from collectibles. The company is a global marketer of porcelain and cold-cast collectibles (figurines, cottages), giftware (ornaments, music boxes, plush animals), garden accessories, and home décor (tableware, sculpture). It offers about 25,000 products, including the Cherished Teddies line of figurines, for sale in the US, Canada, Europe, Australia, and Asia. Enesco's products also include licensed brands, such as Boyds Bears, Disney, Gund, and Pooh & Friends. Its Gregg Gift division makes faith-based items. It sells through more than 44,000 retailers and catalogs. The company is owned by Tinicum Capital Partners.

ENFATICO

285 Madison Ave.
New York, NY 10017
Phone: 212-294-8600
Fax: 212-294-8610
Web: www.enfatico.com

CEO: Torrence Boone
CFO: Joseph (Joe) Scangamor
HR: Jack Reynolds
FYE: December 31
Type: Subsidiary

Enfatico, which means "emphatically" in musical notation, is ready to make its mark in marketing. The creative agency, a subsidiary of global communications services giant WPP Group, is a start-up born out of a relationship with computer technology behemoth Dell. Enfatico is the new name for Project Da Vinci, a marketing services firm that was built with Dell to consolidate marketing efforts that were previously handled by more than 800 agencies. Enfatico has established operations through more than a dozen offices in the Americas, Asia, Australia, and Europe. Enfatico was folded into WPP's Young & Rubicam Brands in April 2009.

ENGLOBAL CORPORATION

NASDAQ (GM): ENG

654 N. Sam Houston Pkwy. East, Ste. 400
Houston, TX 77060
Phone: 281-878-1000
Fax: 281-878-1010
Web: www.englobal.com

CEO: Edward L. (Edd) Pagano
CFO: Robert W. (Bob) Raiford
HR: Robert J. Church
FYE: December 31
Type: Public

ENGlobal hopes to engineer its way into the hearts of energy companies throughout the world. The company provides engineering and systems services, procurement, construction management, inspection, and control system automation services to the pipeline and process divisions of major oil and gas companies. It also designs and installs control and instrumentation systems for energy companies. Subsidiary ENGlobal Land (formerly WRC Corporation) provides land management, environmental compliance, and other services. Other subsidiaries include ENGlobal Automation Group (EAG), which offers control system automation products, and Analyzer Technology, which provides online process analyzer systems.

	Annual Growth	12/05	12/06	12/07	12/08	12/09
Sales ($ mil.)	10.1%	233.6	303.1	363.2	493.3	343.5
Net income ($ mil.)	(29.3%)	4.8	(3.5)	12.5	18.3	1.2
Market value ($ mil.)	(21.9%)	230.5	176.5	311.8	89.2	85.9
Employees	3.8%	1,724	2,100	2,443	2,302	1,999

ENHERENT CORP.

OTC: ENHT

101 Eisenhower Pkwy., Ste. 300
Roseland, NJ 07068
Phone: 973-795-1290
Fax: 973-795-1311
Web: www.enherent.com

CEO: Pamela A. Fredette
CFO: Arunava De
HR: Lori Stanley
FYE: December 31
Type: Public

Little "e," big on "IT." Information technology (IT) consultancy enherent provides software development and technical staffing. Its software integrates Web-enabled communication and transaction applications with legacy systems, as well as other enterprise information systems. Through its staffing business, enherent provides technical personnel and project management services. Targeting *FORTUNE* 1000 companies, enherent's customers come from industries such as financial services, health care, and manufacturing, and include AIG, Bank of America, New England Motor Freight, GlaxoSmithKline, and Wachovia Securities.

	Annual Growth	12/05	12/06	12/07	12/08	12/09
Sales ($ mil.)	(20.7%)	27.3	30.1	30.7	27.4	10.8
Net income ($ mil.)	—	(0.7)	(0.3)	0.4	(0.4)	(1.3)
Market value ($ mil.)	(44.2%)	6.5	3.2	5.6	1.4	0.6
Employees	(30.7%)	269	272	213	119	62

ENNIS, INC.

NYSE: EBF

2441 Presidential Pkwy.
Midlothian, TX 76065
Phone: 972-775-9801
Fax: 972-775-9820
Web: www.ennis.com

CEO: Keith S. Walters
CFO: Richard L. Travis Jr.
HR: Richard Maresh
FYE: February 28
Type: Public

Ennis is in the forms and fashion business. It makes a variety of custom business forms and promotional products (Post-it Notes, presentation products, advertising specialty items). It also sells printed bank forms, secure and negotiable documents, and apparel. Most of its sales, however, come from custom items. The firm sells its products throughout the US — to end users and forms distributors and resellers. It operates about 40 manufacturing plants in 16 states, as well as in Mexico and Canada. Ennis runs about 30 subsidiaries, including Adams McClure (retail promotions), Northstar Computer Forms (bank forms), and Alstyle Apparel. Founded in 1909, Ennis became a publicly traded company in 1960.

	Annual Growth	2/06	2/07	2/08	2/09	2/10
Sales ($ mil.)	(1.9%)	559.4	584.7	610.6	584.0	517.7
Net income ($ mil.)	(3.4%)	40.5	41.6	44.6	(32.8)	35.2
Market value ($ mil.)	(6.0%)	510.7	668.1	413.3	211.8	398.0
Employees	(2.0%)	5,950	6,383	6,256	5,836	5,492

ENOVA SYSTEMS, INC.

NYSE Amex: ENA

1560 W. 190th St.
Torrance, CA 90501
Phone: 310-527-2800
Fax: 310-527-7888
Web: www.enovasystems.com

CEO: Michael (Mike) Staran
CFO: Jarett Fenton
HR: —
FYE: December 31
Type: Public

Enova Systems makes commercial digital power management systems for controlling and monitoring electric power in automobiles and stationary power generators. Products include hybrid-electric drive systems, electric drive motors, electric motor controllers, hybrid drive systems, battery care units, safety disconnect units, generator units, fuel cell management units, and fuel cell power conditioning units. The company counts EDO, First Auto Works of China, Ford Motor, Hyundai Motor, Navistar International, and Volvo/Mack among its customers. Enova gets more than half of its sales outside the US, primarily in China.

	Annual Growth	12/05	12/06	12/07	12/08	12/09
Sales ($ mil.)	(2.1%)	6.1	1.7	9.2	6.4	5.6
Net income ($ mil.)	—	(2.1)	(4.8)	(9.3)	(12.9)	(7.0)
Market value ($ mil.)	(15.0%)	111.5	97.0	150.7	12.6	58.1
Employees	0.7%	33	43	74	54	34

ENPRO INDUSTRIES, INC.

NYSE: NPO

5605 Carnegie Blvd., Ste. 500
Charlotte, NC 28209
Phone: 704-731-1500
Fax: 704-731-1511
Web: www.enproindustries.com

CEO: Stephen E. (Steve) Macadam
CFO: William (Bill) Dries
HR: Robert P. McKinney
FYE: December 31
Type: Public

When it comes to making engines, engineered products, and sealing systems, EnPro is a real pro. The company's Sealing Products segment offers gaskets, metal and non-metal seals, compression packing, rotary lip seals, elastomeric seals, hydraulic components, expansion joints, and PTFE parts. Its Engineered Products segment makes bearings, air compressors, vacuum pumps, diesel and natural gas engines, and industrial tooling systems under GGB and Compressor Products International brands. The company's Engine Products and Services segment makes heavy-duty, medium-speed diesel and natural gas engines under the Fairbanks Morse Engine brand name. EnPro Industries nets a little more than half of its sales in the US.

	Annual Growth	12/05	12/06	12/07	12/08	12/09
Sales ($ mil.)	(1.1%)	838.6	928.4	1,030.0	1,167.8	803.0
Net income ($ mil.)	—	58.6	(158.9)	37.7	53.5	(139.3)
Market value ($ mil.)	(0.5%)	554.1	682.8	630.2	442.9	543.0
Employees	(0.6%)	4,200	4,400	4,700	5,100	4,100

⊞ ENRON CREDITORS RECOVERY CORP.

4 Houston Center, 1331 Lamar, Ste. 1600
Houston, TX 77010
Phone: 713-853-6161
Fax: —
Web: www.enron.com

CEO: Richard Lydeker
CFO: Richard Lydeker
HR: —
FYE: December 31
Type: Private

Enron Creditors Recovery Corp. is a shell of the former Enron Corp. (once the world's #1 energy trader) and is shelling out the remaining assets of the bankrupt Enron to creditors. Once the largest buyer and seller of natural gas and electricity in the US, Enron also traded numerous other commodities. Enron has sold its North American power utility and gas pipeline assets, and its global interests in utilities and power plants. Between 2004 and the end of 2009 Enron Creditors Recovery Corp. paid out about $21.6 billion to Enron's creditors and remains embroiled in litigation stemming from Enron's collapse.

	Annual Growth	12/04	12/05	12/06	12/07	12/08
Est. sales ($ mil.)	—	—	—	—	—	2,901.8
Employees	—	—	—	—	—	10,000

THE ENSIGN GROUP, INC.

NASDAQ (GM): ENSG

27101 Puerta Real, Ste. 450
Mission Viejo, CA 92691
Phone: 949-487-9500
Fax: —
Web: www.ensigngroup.net

CEO: Christopher R. Christensen
CFO: Suzanne D. Snapper
HR: —
FYE: December 31
Type: Public

The Ensign Group hangs its insignia at dozens of senior living facilities in the western US. Most of its facilities (which Ensign either owns or operates under lease agreements) are nursing homes, but it also operates a number of assisted-living facilities and has assisted-living wings at some of its nursing centers. The company has a decentralized operating structure, with its portfolio of homes organized into five regional operating companies, each with its own management team. In turn, each home operates under local, and largely independent, management. The Ensign Group went public in 2007.

	Annual Growth	12/05	12/06	12/07	12/08	12/09
Sales ($ mil.)	15.8%	300.9	358.6	411.3	469.4	542.0
Net income ($ mil.)	15.3%	18.4	22.5	20.5	27.5	32.5
Market value ($ mil.)	3.3%	—	—	298.6	347.1	318.7
Employees	8.8%	5,506	5,435	5,603	6,153	7,718

ENSIGN UNITED STATES DRILLING INC.

1700 Broadway, Ste. 777
Denver, CO 80290
Phone: 303-292-1206
Fax: 303-292-5843
Web: www.ensignusd.com

CEO: Bob Geddes
CFO: Steve Hunt
HR: Tuss Erickson
FYE: December 31
Type: Subsidiary

Ensign United States Drilling (formerly Caza Drilling) serves oil and gas companies exploring in the western US. A subsidiary of Ensign Energy Services, the company provides contract drilling services primarily in the Rocky Mountain region. It claims to be the second-largest and most active land-based drilling contractor in the Rockies. Ensign United States has 56 drilling rigs in operation in Colorado, Nebraska, Oklahoma, North Dakota, Utah, and Wyoming. In California the drilling contractor operates more than 20 drilling rigs, primarily in the San Joaquin, Los Angeles, and Sacramento basins.

ENTECH SOLAR, INC.

OTC: ENSL

13301 Park Vista Blvd., Ste. 100
Fort Worth, TX 76177
Phone: 817-379-0100
Fax: 817-379-0300
Web: www.entechsolar.com

CEO: David Gelbaum
CFO: Chas Michel
HR: —
FYE: December 31
Type: Public

Entech Solar (formerly WorldWater & Solar Technologies) aims to shine brightly in the solar energy market. The company designs, makes, and markets solar energy systems that provide electricity and thermal energy for commercial, industrial, and utility applications. Its products include ThermoVolt System (a proprietary concentrating photovoltaic and thermal technology that produces both electricity and thermal energy), and Solar Volt System (which uses a concentrating photovoltaic technology that produces cost-competitive electricity). Entech Solar also makes energy-efficient skylights and provides engineering services.

	Annual Growth	12/05	12/06	12/07	12/08	12/09
Sales ($ mil.)	2.4%	2.0	17.3	18.5	30.8	2.2
Net income ($ mil.)	—	(10.2)	(8.2)	(14.4)	(29.3)	(35.5)
Market value ($ mil.)	(25.5%)	104.5	125.4	630.4	94.9	32.2
Employees	(5.8%)	33	45	93	57	26

ENTEGEE, INC.

70 Blanchard Rd., Ste. 102
Burlington, MA 01803
Phone: 781-221-5800
Fax: 781-221-4544
Web: www.entegee.com

CEO: Robert L. Cecchini
CFO: Neil Harrington
HR: Carol Bibeault
FYE: December 31
Type: Subsidiary

When businesses need help with engineering and technical projects, Entegee is ready. The company's staffing division places engineering and technical professionals — including assemblers, designers, drafters, programmers, and technical writers — with clients such as defense contractors, government agencies, and manufacturing and engineering companies. In addition, Entegee offers consulting and project-based services and outsourced engineering and drafting. It operates throughout the US from a network of about 20 offices. Entegee was a unit of MPS Group, which was acquired by global staffing rival Adecco in 2010.

	Annual Growth	12/04	12/05	12/06	12/07	12/08
Est. sales ($ mil.)	—	—	—	—	—	318.1
Employees	—	—	—	—	—	14,713

⊞ An in-depth profile of this company is available to Hoover's Online members at hoovers.com.

ENTEGRIS, INC.

NASDAQ (GS): ENTG

129 Concord Rd.
Billerica, MA 01821
Phone: 978-436-6500
Fax: 978-436-6735
Web: www.entegris.com

CEO: Gideon Argov
CFO: Gregory B. (Greg) Graves
HR: John J. (Joe) Murphy
FYE: December 31
Type: Public

Entegris products are integral to making semiconductors and computer disk drives. The company makes more than 15,000 products used to transport and protect semiconductor and disk drive materials during processing. Its semiconductor products include wafer carriers, storage boxes, and chip trays, as well as chemical delivery products, such as pipes, fittings, and valves. Its disk drive offerings include shippers, stamper cases, and transport trays. Top customers for Entegris include ASML, MEMC, SUMCO, Taiwan Semiconductor Manufacturing, and Tokyo Electron. The Asia/Pacific region generates more than half of sales.

	Annual Growth	8/05	*12/06	12/07	12/08	12/09
Sales ($ mil.)	2.1%	367.1	678.7	626.2	554.7	398.6
Net income ($ mil.)	—	9.4	63.5	44.4	(517.0)	(57.8)
Market value ($ mil.)	(15.7%)	1,372.5	1,421.1	1,133.4	287.6	693.5
Employees	(3.3%)	2,750	3,000	3,022	3,225	2,400

*Fiscal year change

ENTELOS, INC.

London AIM: ENTL

110 Marsh Dr.
Foster City, CA 94404
Phone: 650-572-5400
Fax: 650-572-5401
Web: www.entelos.com

CEO: Jim Neal
CFO: —
HR: —
FYE: December 31
Type: Public

Computers can get viruses, so why can't they get cancer or heart disease? Entelos makes it possible. Using its PhysioLab technology, the company develops computer models of diseases that drug makers and other researchers can use to design drugs and other therapies more effectively. The disease models integrate known genomic and proteomic data with physiologic, environmental, and other information collected from clinical trials, case studies, and other sources. Entelos has developed PhysioLab models for asthma, diabetes, obesity, and rheumatoid arthritis. The models are built in partnership with such firms as Eli Lilly, PDL Biopharma, and UCB Pharma.

ENTERASYS NETWORKS, INC.

50 Minuteman Rd.
Andover, MA 01810
Phone: 978-684-1000
Fax: 978-684-1658
Web: www.enterasys.com

CEO: Christopher (Chris) Crowell
CFO: Terry Schmid
HR: —
FYE: October 31
Type: Private

Enterasys Networks provides companies with a sense of security. The company designs routers and switches for use in corporate networks. It also provides network management and security software and access points used to build wireless networks. The company's service offerings include network installation, maintenance, support, and outsourcing. It markets to the commercial, government, education, and health care markets. Its client roster includes such diverse organizations as the City of Anaheim, The Goodyear Tire & Rubber Company, and The University of North Carolina at Chapel Hill. Enterasys is privately held by a group led by equity firms The Gores Group and Tennenbaum Capital Partners.

	Annual Growth	10/04	10/05	10/06	10/07	10/08
Sales ($ mil.)	0.9%	—	—	324.0	328.0	330.0
Employees	4.3%	—	—	735	750	800

ENTERCOM COMMUNICATIONS CORP.

NYSE: ETM

401 City Ave., Ste. 809
Bala Cynwyd, PA 19004
Phone: 610-660-5610
Fax: 610-660-5620
Web: www.entercom.com

CEO: David J. Field
CFO: Stephen F. (Steve) Fisher
HR: Noreen McCormack
FYE: December 31
Type: Public

The signals from Entercom Communications come through loud and clear. The company is among the largest radio broadcasters in the US, with more than 100 stations clustered in more than 20 markets, including Boston, Denver, Kansas City, and Seattle. Operating a number of stations in one market allows the company to combine such back office functions as finance and accounting, as well as advertising sales and marketing. Its stations program a variety of formats, including oldies, country, and adult contemporary, as well as talk, sports, and news. The Field family, including founder and chairman Joseph Field, controls more than 60% of Entercom.

	Annual Growth	12/05	12/06	12/07	12/08	12/09
Sales ($ mil.)	(3.7%)	432.5	440.5	468.4	438.8	372.4
Net income ($ mil.)	(48.8%)	78.4	48.0	(8.4)	(516.7)	5.4
Market value ($ mil.)	(30.1%)	1,102.5	1,047.1	508.7	45.7	262.7
Employees	(0.7%)	2,380	2,812	2,343	2,300	2,310

ENTERGY ARKANSAS, INC.

425 W. Capitol Ave., 40th Fl.
Little Rock, AR 72201
Phone: 501-377-4000
Fax: 501-377-4448
Web: www.entergy-arkansas.com

CEO: Hugh T. McDonald
CFO: Leo P. Denault
HR: Terry R. Seamons
FYE: December 31
Type: Subsidiary

When Jim "Dandy" Mangrum sings "When Electricity Came to Arkansas," Entergy Arkansas can say it's been at it for "nearly 100 years." The utility is the largest power provider in the Natural State. Entergy Arkansas serves about 687,000 residential, commercial, industrial, and government customers in 63 eastern and central Arkansas counties. Residential customers account for about 84% of total clients. The Entergy subsidiary also has interests in fossil-fueled, nuclear, and hydroelectric power generation facilities with almost 4,500 MW of capacity, and it offers energy conservation and management programs.

	Annual Growth	12/04	12/05	12/06	12/07	12/08
Est. sales ($ mil.)	—	—	—	—	—	2,328.3
Employees	—	—	—	—	—	1,526

⊞ ENTERGY CORPORATION

NYSE: ETR

639 Loyola Ave.
New Orleans, LA 70113
Phone: 504-576-4000
Fax: 504-576-4428
Web: www.entergy.com

CEO: J. Wayne Leonard
CFO: Leo P. Denault
HR: E. Renae Conley
FYE: December 31
Type: Public

If Entergy had an Entergizer bunny for a mascot, it would stay fully charged (with a safe, radioactive glow). The integrated utility holding company's subsidiaries distribute electricity to 2.7 million customers in four southern states (Arkansas, Louisiana, Mississippi, and Texas) and provide natural gas to 189,000 customers in Louisiana. Entergy operates more than 15,500 miles of high-voltage transmission lines and 1,550 transmission substations. In addition, the company has interests in regulated and nonregulated power plants in North America that have a combined generating capacity of about 30,000 MW. An advocate of nuclear power, Entergy is one of the largest nuclear power generators in the US.

	Annual Growth	12/05	12/06	12/07	12/08	12/09
Sales ($ mil.)	1.5%	10,106.2	10,932.2	11,484.4	13,093.8	10,745.7
Net income ($ mil.)	7.9%	923.8	1,132.6	1,134.8	1,240.5	1,251.1
Market value ($ mil.)	4.5%	12,993.3	17,473.3	22,621.4	15,733.9	15,489.8
Employees	1.6%	14,100	13,800	14,322	14,669	15,000

ENTEROMEDICS INC.
NASDAQ (GM): ETRM

2800 Patton Rd.
St. Paul, MN 55113
Phone: 651-634-3003
Fax: —
Web: www.enteromedics.com

CEO: Mark B. Knudson
CFO: Gregory S. (Greg) Lea
HR: —
FYE: December 31
Type: Public

EnteroMedics is trying to quiet those grumbling hunger pangs. The development-stage medical device company uses neuroblocking technology called VBLOC therapy to combat obesity. Its initial product in development, the Maestro System, is a device laparoscopically implanted near the diaphragm that uses electrical impulses to limit the expansion of the stomach, thereby producing a feeling of prolonged fullness. The Maestro System is in US and international clinical trials, with FDA approval and commercial sales anticipated by 2010. EnteroMedics plans to build a direct sales force to market the product to bariatric surgeons and weight management specialists.

	Annual Growth	12/05	12/06	12/07	12/08	12/09
Sales ($ mil.)	—	—	—	—	0.0	0.0
Net income ($ mil.)	—	—	—	—	(37.9)	(31.9)
Market value ($ mil.)	(61.6%)	—	—	—	65.5	25.1
Employees	(35.8%)	—	—	—	53	34

ENTERPRISE BANCORP, INC.
NASDAQ (GM): EBTC

222 Merrimack St.
Lowell, MA 01852
Phone: 978-459-9000
Fax: 978-656-5813
Web: www.enterprisebankandtrust.com

CEO: John P. (Jack) Clancy Jr.
CFO: James A. Marcotte
HR: —
FYE: December 31
Type: Public

Enterprising entrepreneurs might consider seeking financial assistance from Enterprise Bancorp. The holding company is parent to Enterprise Bank and Trust, a full-service commercial bank that specializes in lending to growing businesses, corporations, partnerships, and not-for-profits. Business loans (some 85% of the bank's loan portfolio) include commercial mortgage, construction, and working capital loans; revolving lines of credit; and equipment financing and asset-based lending products. Through about 15 branches (primarily located in northeastern Massachusetts' Middlesex County), the bank also offers consumer loans, deposit products, investment management, trust, and other services.

	Annual Growth	12/05	12/06	12/07	12/08	12/09
Assets ($ mil.)	9.2%	918.5	979.3	1,057.7	1,180.5	1,304.0
Net income ($ mil.)	(1.5%)	8.4	9.2	9.9	5.5	7.9
Market value ($ mil.)	(8.4%)	143.2	148.3	116.5	104.1	100.8
Employees	4.5%	269	282	286	307	321

ENTERPRISE FINANCIAL SERVICES CORP
NASDAQ (GM): EFSC

150 N. Meramec Ave.
Clayton, MO 63105
Phone: 314-725-5500
Fax: 314-812-4025
Web: www.enterprisebank.com

CEO: Peter F. Benoist
CFO: Frank H. Sanfilippo
HR: Mark Murtha
FYE: December 31
Type: Public

Enterprise Financial Services wants you to boldly bank where many have banked before. It's the holding company for Enterprise Bank & Trust, which primarily targets closely held businesses and their owners, but also serves individuals in the St. Louis and Kansas City metropolitan areas. Through about a dozen branches, Enterprise Bank & Trust offers standard products such as checking, savings, and money market accounts and CDs. Loans to businesses, including commercial mortgages and operating loans, make up most of the company's lending activities. The bank also originates consumer, construction, and residential mortgage loans.

	Annual Growth	12/05	12/06	12/07	12/08	12/09
Assets ($ mil.)	16.4%	1,287.0	1,535.6	1,999.1	2,270.2	2,365.7
Net income ($ mil.)	—	11.3	15.5	17.6	4.4	(48.0)
Market value ($ mil.)	(23.6%)	336.9	483.9	353.7	226.4	114.5
Employees	4.2%	261	329	364	348	308

ENTERPRISE GP HOLDINGS L.P.
NYSE: EPE

1100 Louisiana, 10th Fl.
Houston, TX 77002
Phone: 713-381-6500
Fax: 713-381-8200
Web: www.enterprisegp.com

CEO: Ralph S. Cunningham
CFO: W. Randall Fowler
HR: —
FYE: December 31
Type: Public

It has taken a lot of enterprise to put Enterprise GP Holdings on top. It owns Enterprise Products GP, LLC, the general partner and 2% owner of Enterprise Products Partners L.P. Enterprise Products Partners is a leading player in the North American natural gas, natural gas liquids (NGLs), and crude oil industries, with a range of processing, transportation, and storage services. Enterprise GP Holdings also holds the general partner and limited partner interests in Energy Transfer Equity, L.P. Chairman Dan Duncan controls about 78% of Enterprise GP Holdings.

	Annual Growth	12/05	12/06	12/07	12/08	12/09
Sales ($ mil.)	20.1%	12,257.0	13,991.0	26,713.8	35,469.6	25,510.9
Net income ($ mil.)	38.6%	55.3	99.4	109.0	164.1	204.1
Market value ($ mil.)	0.8%	5,250.4	5,146.0	5,153.0	2,426.2	5,424.4
Employees	16.6%	2,600	2,920	0	4,500	4,800

⊞ ENTERPRISE PRODUCTS PARTNERS L.P.
NYSE: EPD

1100 Louisiana St., 10th Fl.
Houston, TX 77002
Phone: 713-381-6500
Fax: 713-381-8200
Web: www.epplp.com

CEO: Michael A. Creel
CFO: W. Randall Fowler
HR: —
FYE: December 31
Type: Public

Both enterprising and productive, Enterprise Products Partners is the leading player in the North American natural gas, natural gas liquids (NGL), and crude oil industries, with a range of processing, transportation, and storage services. Operations include natural gas processing, NGL fractionation, petrochemical services, and crude oil transportation. The hub of the company's business is Houston's Mont Belvieu refinery complex. In a major expansion move, in 2009 the company acquired rival TEPPCO Partners L.P. As a result, Enterprise has 48,000 miles of pipelines, and 200 million of crude oil, refined products, and NGL storage capacity. Chairman Dan Duncan holds a 34.5% stake in Enterprise.

	Annual Growth	12/05	12/06	12/07	12/08	12/09
Sales ($ mil.)	20.1%	12,257.0	13,991.0	16,950.1	21,905.7	25,510.9
Net income ($ mil.)	24.9%	423.7	599.7	533.7	954.0	1,030.9
Market value ($ mil.)	6.9%	15,349.0	18,526.2	20,380.1	13,252.2	20,079.6
Employees	10.4%	2,600	3,000	3,200	3,500	—

ENTERTAINMENT PROPERTIES TRUST
NYSE: EPR

30 West Pershing Rd., Ste. 201
Kansas City, MO 64108
Phone: 816-472-1700
Fax: 816-472-5794
Web: www.eprkc.com

CEO: David M. Brain
CFO: Mark A. Peterson
HR: —
FYE: December 31
Type: Public

Entertainment Properties Trust invests in places to play. The self-administered real estate investment trust (REIT) owns some 95 movie megaplex theaters and nine theater-anchored entertainment retail centers around the US and Canada. Entertainment Properties also owns other recreational properties, including a ski resort in Ohio and wineries in California. In a more recent twist, the company began to diversify its holdings by acquiring public charter schools. However, movie megaplexes remain the featured attraction at Entertainment Properties. The company, founded in 1997, buys properties from theater operators and leases them back to the original owners. Many of its theaters are leased to AMC Entertainment.

	Annual Growth	12/05	12/06	12/07	12/08	12/09
Sales ($ mil.)	13.1%	165.5	196.6	237.8	287.8	270.9
Net income ($ mil.)	(3.5%)	69.1	82.3	104.7	130.0	(11.9)
Market value ($ mil.)	(3.5%)	1,747.6	2,506.2	2,015.6	1,278.0	1,512.6
Employees	14.1%	13	13	16	22	22

⊞ An in-depth profile of this company is available to Hoover's Online members at hoovers.com.

567

ENTORIAN TECHNOLOGIES INC.

Pink Sheets: ENTN

8900 Shoal Creek Blvd., Ste. 125
Austin, TX 78757
Phone: 512-454-9531
Fax: 512-454-9409
Web: www.entorian.com

CEO: Stephan B. Godevais
CFO: W. Kirk Patterson
HR: —
FYE: December 31
Type: Public

Entorian Technologies is trading memory for ruggedized computers. Previously a manufacturer of high-density memory modules, in 2009 the company shifted its focus to re-engineering and ruggedizing Dell notebooks and servers through its Augmentix subsidiary. Its ruggedized products are used in environments where computers and other electronics are subjected to heavy wear and tear, including military applications, field service and sales, industrial manufacturing, and for emergency responders. Entorian sells its ruggedized notebooks directly to Dell, which then markets them in North America and Europe; its ruggedized servers are sold directly to end users and channel partners.

	Annual Growth	12/05	12/06	12/07	12/08	12/09
Sales ($ mil.)	(3.7%)	52.5	55.6	40.9	55.9	45.1
Net income ($ mil.)	—	(7.5)	(0.5)	(40.0)	(42.6)	0.5
Market value ($ mil.)	(50.1%)	345.5	239.4	91.1	13.5	21.4
Employees	(43.4%)	457	504	416	158	47

ENTRADE, INC.

Pink Sheets: ETAD

500 Central Ave.
Northfield, IL 60093
Phone: 847-784-3300
Fax: 847-441-7652

CEO: Peter R. Harvey
CFO: Richard E. Mandra
HR: —
FYE: December 31
Type: Public

Entrade was entranced by the online B2B portal craze, but it's now bidding on the auction business. Formerly ARTRA GROUP, it's focused on developing its Nationwide Auction Systems, once the leading asset liquidation business in the US. Nationwide specializes in the disposal of surplus property, such as vehicles, equipment, excess inventory, and repossessions. Nationwide has facilities in California. Entrade is looking to enhance the unit's business through Internet technology. The firm continues to have equity positions in several online B2B portals, like AssetTRADE and AssetControl. In 2007 Entrade, through Nationwide, bought Cogent Financial Group.

ENTRAVISION COMMUNICATIONS CORPORATION

NYSE: EVC

2425 Olympic Blvd., Ste. 6000 West
Santa Monica, CA 90404
Phone: 310-447-3870
Fax: 310-447-3899
Web: www.entravision.com

CEO: Walter F. Ulloa
CFO: Christopher T. Young
HR: Alexander K. LaBrie
FYE: December 31
Type: Public

This company wants to be the whole enchilada for advertisers trying to reach the US Hispanic market. Entravision Communications is the #2 Spanish-language media company in the country (behind Univision Communications) with about 50 television stations and 50 radio stations located mostly in the Southwest. It is the largest affiliate of Univision's two Spanish-language television networks, Univision and TeleFutura; Entravision's TV portfolio also includes a small number of stations affiliated with The CW Network, FOX, and MyNetworkTV. On the radio, the company offers a variety of programming formats, including music, news, sports, and talk radio.

	Annual Growth	12/05	12/06	12/07	12/08	12/09
Sales ($ mil.)	(9.4%)	281.0	291.8	250.0	232.3	189.2
Net income ($ mil.)	—	(9.7)	(134.6)	(43.1)	(487.9)	(50.1)
Market value ($ mil.)	(16.9%)	601.6	694.5	661.6	131.8	287.3
Employees	(6.1%)	1,148	1,111	1,168	1,035	892

ENTREMED, INC.

NASDAQ (GM): ENMD

9640 Medical Center Dr.
Rockville, MD 20850
Phone: 240-864-2600
Fax: 240-864-2601
Web: www.entremed.com

CEO: Cynthia W. Hu
CFO: Kathy R. Wehmeir-Davis
HR: —
FYE: December 31
Type: Public

EntreMed wants to get in between cancer and the blood vessels that feed it. The biotech pharmaceutical company develops drugs that inhibit angiogenesis, or the growth of new blood vessels. Its lead candidate, ENMD-2076, inhibits aurora kinases which regulate cell division and are linked to several cancers. The company has several other product candidates in its pipeline, but has placed them on the shelf until further funding is available. EntreMed receives royalties from sales of Thalomid, Celgene's multiple myeloma therapy. Celgene owns about a quarter of EntreMed.

	Annual Growth	12/05	12/06	12/07	12/08	12/09
Sales ($ mil.)	(2.6%)	5.9	6.9	7.4	7.5	5.3
Net income ($ mil.)	—	(16.3)	(49.9)	(22.4)	(23.9)	(8.2)
Market value ($ mil.)	(19.9%)	196.9	160.4	121.8	16.4	81.2
Employees	(23.6%)	41	57	57	21	14

ENTROPIC COMMUNICATIONS, INC.

NASDAQ (GM): ENTR

6290 Sequence Dr.
San Diego, CA 92121
Phone: 858-768-3600
Fax: 858-768-3601
Web: www.entropic.com

CEO: Patrick C. Henry
CFO: David Lyle
HR: Suzanne (Suzy) Zoumaras
FYE: December 31
Type: Public

Entropic Communications is far from sluggish when it comes to broadband. The fabless semiconductor company designs specialized chipsets for video and broadband multimedia applications. Entropic is targeting digital home entertainment networks linked by coaxial cable connections, a market being promoted by cable TV services providers and others. The company's c.LINK technology enables networking among high-definition TVs, digital video recorders, and set-top boxes. Actiontec Electronics (20% of sales), Jabil, and Motorola (36%) are leading customers. The Asia/Pacific region accounts for most sales.

	Annual Growth	12/05	12/06	12/07	12/08	12/09
Sales ($ mil.)	136.8%	3.7	41.5	122.5	146.0	116.3
Net income ($ mil.)	—	(12.3)	(7.1)	(32.0)	(136.4)	(13.2)
Market value ($ mil.)	(35.1%)	—	—	522.6	35.9	220.4
Employees	45.2%	59	220	281	297	262

ENTRUST, INC.

One Lincoln Centre, 5400 LBJ Freeway
Dallas, TX 75240
Phone: 972-728-0447
Fax: 972-728-0440
Web: www.entrust.com

CEO: F. William (Bill) Conner
CFO: David Wagner
HR: —
FYE: December 31
Type: Private

Entrust has a multi-layered approach to data security. The company's software and services ensure the privacy of electronic communications and transactions across corporate networks and the Internet. Its applications are used to authenticate users via smart cards, passwords, and biometric devices, controlling access to information in e-mail, databases, Web pages, and business applications. Entrust's services include consulting, deployment, and security systems management. It targets customers worldwide in such industries as health care and financial services, as well as US government agencies. Clients have included Aon, Credit Suisse, and NASA. The company is controlled by private equity firm Thoma Bravo.

	Annual Growth	12/04	12/05	12/06	12/07	12/08
Sales ($ mil.)	2.3%	91.0	98.1	95.2	99.7	99.7
Net income ($ mil.)	—	1.1	6.4	(15.4)	(6.2)	(1.0)
Employees	(4.3%)	491	475	503	455	411

ENTRX CORPORATION

Pink Sheets: ENTX

800 Nicollet Mall, Ste. 2690
Minneapolis, MN 55402
Phone: 612-333-0614
Fax: 612-338-7332
Web: metalclad.com

CEO: Peter L. Hauser
CFO: Brian D. Niebur
HR: Jerri Hartline
FYE: December 31
Type: Public

The *raison d'être* of Entrx as of late has been to insulate and abate. The company provides insulation and asbestos abatement services through subsidiary Metalclad Insulation. Operating primarily in California, it installs insulation on pipes, ducts, furnaces, boilers, and other industrial equipment. It also maintains and removes insulation and sells specialty insulation products to public utilities, oil, petrochemical, and heavy construction companies. Metalclad's customers have included Jacobs Engineering Group and Southern California Edison .

	Annual Growth	12/05	12/06	12/07	12/08	12/09
Sales ($ mil.)	6.8%	14.7	19.5	22.4	27.8	19.1
Net income ($ mil.)	—	(1.7)	2.1	0.6	0.3	(0.1)
Market value ($ mil.)	0.0%	1.3	1.2	3.0	1.6	1.3
Employees	(8.8%)	26	28	17	19	18

ENVESTNET, INC.

35 E. Wacker Dr., Ste. 2400
Chicago, IL 60601
Phone: 312-827-2800
Fax: 312-827-2801
Web: www.envestnet.com

CEO: Judson (Jud) Bergman
CFO: Pete D'Arrigo
HR: —
FYE: December 31
Type: Private

Envestnet provides managed account services for more than 10,000 financial institutions and investment advisers. Used by brokers, banks, insurance companies, registered investment advisers, and certified public accountants, the company's online financial planning programs allow advisers to generate proposals and manage client accounts. The firm also affords access to mutual funds, alternative investments, and financial research, and, through subsidiary Portfolio Management Consultants, offers tools that enable advisers to build customized portfolios for investors. Envestnet has approximately $38 billion of assets under management and administration. The company filed an initial public offering in March 2010.

ENVIRO VORAXIAL TECHNOLOGY, INC.

OTC: EVTN

821 NW 57th Place
Fort Lauderdale, FL 33309
Phone: 954-958-9968
Fax: 954-958-8057
Web: www.evtn.com

CEO: Alberto DiBella
CFO: Alberto DiBella
HR: —
FYE: December 31
Type: Public

Enviro Voraxial Technology has a voracious appetite for developing equipment to separate solids and liquids with different specific gravities. The company's Voraxial Separator can be used for wastewater treatment, grit and sand separation, oil and water separation, marine-oil-spill cleanup, bilge and ballast treatment, stormwater treatment, and food-processing-waste treatment. The separator is capable of processing volumes as low as three gallons per minute, as well as volumes of more than 10,000 gallons per minute, with only one moving part. Chairman and CEO Alberto DiBella, officers, and directors control almost 35% of the company.

	Annual Growth	12/05	12/06	12/07	12/08	12/09
Sales ($ mil.)	49.5%	0.1	0.3	0.3	0.1	0.5
Net income ($ mil.)	—	(1.1)	(0.8)	(1.9)	(1.5)	(0.8)
Market value ($ mil.)	(4.7%)	14.7	14.1	15.4	12.9	12.1
Employees	4.7%	5	5	6	6	6

ENVIRONMENTAL POWER CORPORATION

Pink Sheets: EPGR

120 White Plains Rd., 6th Fl.
Tarrytown, NY 10591
Phone: 914-631-1435
Fax: 914-631-1436
Web: www.environmentalpower.com

CEO: Richard E. Kessel
CFO: Michael E. Thomas
HR: —
FYE: December 31
Type: Public

Cow manure is not just a waste product, it is the energy behind Environmental Power's quest for making clean, reliable, and cost-effective power. Operating through subsidiary Microgy Cogeneration Systems, the company holds an exclusive license to market an animal waste-to-energy conversion technology in North America. This unit not only has several projects in development stages, it has also moved some of its plants into commercial operations in Texas and Wisconsin. Microgy's plants can produce methane, marketable biogas, compressed natural gas, liquefied natural gas, renewable electrical energy or thermal energy, and other by-products.

	Annual Growth	12/05	12/06	12/07	12/08	12/09
Sales ($ mil.)	(46.1%)	55.8	53.9	1.2	2.9	4.7
Net income ($ mil.)	—	(11.4)	(18.4)	(17.4)	(16.0)	(36.1)
Market value ($ mil.)	(59.5%)	110.0	139.0	71.8	9.9	3.0
Employees	0.8%	30	47	41	44	31

ENVIRONMENTAL SYSTEMS RESEARCH INSTITUTE, INC.

380 New York St.
Redlands, CA 92373
Phone: 909-793-2853
Fax: 909-307-3025
Web: www.esri.com

CEO: Jack Dangermond
CFO: Thomas G. (Tom) Pickett
HR: Cathy Mueller
FYE: December 31
Type: Private

For Environmental Systems Research Institute, success stems from thinking globally and mapping locally. The company, known as ESRI, is a leading developer of geographic information systems (GIS) software used to create and label digital maps, publish maps on the Internet, and build related databases. ESRI has customers in fields such as government, forestry, oil and gas, and transportation. The company's ArcGIS products include applications in containing oil spills, planning land use, monitoring rainforest depletion, and routing emergency vehicles, among other uses. ESRI was founded in 1969 by president Jack Dangermond and VP Laura Dangermond, who own the company.

ENVIRONMENTAL TECTONICS CORPORATION

OTC: ETCC

125 James Way
Southampton, PA 18966
Phone: 215-355-9100
Fax: 215-357-4000
Web: www.etcusa.com

CEO: William F. Mitchell
CFO: Duane D. Deaner
HR: —
FYE: February 28
Type: Public

Environmental Tectonics Corporation (ETC) believes virtual environments can teach us a lot about real life. Through its aircrew training systems segment, the company makes software-driven flight simulators, disaster simulators, and motion-based simulation rides for the amusement industry. Its NASTAR center provides space training and research services. ETC's industrial business segment makes steam and gas sterilizers, hyperbaric chambers (used for high-altitude training, decompression, and wound care), and environmental sampling and analysis chambers. The company's major customers include L-3 Communications, the Royal Malaysian Air Force, the UK Ministry of Defence, and the US Army Corps of Engineers.

	Annual Growth	2/06	2/07	2/08	2/09	2/10
Sales ($ mil.)	13.9%	25.1	17.4	22.7	36.7	42.3
Net income ($ mil.)	—	(6.7)	(8.9)	(13.9)	(2.0)	6.5
Market value ($ mil.)	(13.5%)	46.5	32.2	16.8	11.8	26.0
Employees	5.2%	223	257	259	240	273

ENXNET, INC.

OTC: EXNT

11333 E. Pine St., Ste. 75
Tulsa, OK 74116
Phone: 918-592-0015
Fax: 918-592-0016
Web: www.enxnet.com

CEO: Ryan Corley
CFO: Stephen (Steve) Hoelscher
HR: —
FYE: March 31
Type: Public

EnXnet licenses and markets emerging multimedia technologies, including video compression and content storage. It has acquired the licensing rights to a video compression technology called ClearVideo, used for distribution, downloading, and streaming of video and audio content over the Internet. Other technologies and products include DVDPlus, a media storage product that combines a CD and DVD on the same disc, gift cards, and CD/DVD anti-theft technologies. CEO Ryan Corley owns a majority stake in the company.

	Annual Growth	3/05	3/06	3/07	3/08	3/09
Sales ($ mil.)	—	0.4	0.0	0.0	0.0	0.0
Net income ($ mil.)	—	(0.7)	(0.7)	(1.0)	(0.8)	(0.7)
Market value ($ mil.)	4.1%	5.9	65.6	30.4	17.8	7.0
Employees	8.8%	5	4	4	4	7

ENZO BIOCHEM, INC.

NYSE: ENZ

527 Madison Ave.
New York, NY 10022
Phone: 212-583-0100
Fax: —
Web: www.enzo.com

CEO: Elazar Rabbani
CFO: Barry W. Weiner
HR: —
FYE: July 31
Type: Public

For Enzo Biochem, antisense is perfectly sensible. The biotech company's Enzo Therapeutics subsidiary is developing antisense technology, a kind of gene therapy that switches off disease-causing genes, to fight such diseases as HIV, hepatitis, and Crohn's disease. This work is funded by two other subsidiaries. Enzo Clinical Labs provides diagnostic testing services in the New York City area. Enzo Life Sciences makes reagents used by pharmaceutical and biotech companies, as well as academic institutions, in biomedical research. Enzo Biochem has collaborative partnerships with academic and research centers such as the University of Connecticut and the Hadassah University Hospital in Jerusalem.

	Annual Growth	7/05	7/06	7/07	7/08	7/09
Sales ($ mil.)	19.9%	43.4	39.8	52.9	77.8	89.6
Net income ($ mil.)	—	3.0	(15.7)	(13.3)	(10.7)	(23.6)
Market value ($ mil.)	(25.8%)	637.4	489.6	485.4	539.8	193.7
Employees	15.8%	342	340	454	510	614

ENZON PHARMACEUTICALS, INC.

NASDAQ (GM): ENZN

685 Rte. 202/206
Bridgewater, NJ 08807
Phone: 908-541-8600
Fax: 908-575-9457
Web: www.enzon.com

CEO: Ralph del Campo
CFO: Craig A. Tooman
HR: Paul S. Davit
FYE: December 31
Type: Public

Enzon Pharmaceuticals has deadly diseases PEGged. The firm's proprietary PEGylation process enhances existing pharmaceutical treatments by attaching a customized molecule to the drug; the attachment of the molecule ensures the treatment's longevity in the patient's blood by allowing the drug to avoid the immune system's response. Enzon produced a number of marketed drugs using the technology; however, following the sale of its specialty pharmaceuticals business to a US subsidiary of Italian drug firm Sigma-Tau Group for more than $300 million, Enzon's operations consist of collecting royalties on its PEG and Locked Nucleic Acid (LNA) technologies, as well as developing other pipeline and technology platforms.

	Annual Growth	6/05	*12/06	12/07	12/08	12/09
Sales ($ mil.)	2.6%	166.3	185.7	185.6	196.9	184.6
Net income ($ mil.)	—	(89.6)	21.3	83.1	(2.7)	0.7
Market value ($ mil.)	12.9%	380.7	499.9	559.8	342.5	618.6
Employees	0.9%	306	359	371	351	317

*Fiscal year change

EOG RESOURCES, INC.

NYSE: EOG

1111 Bagby, Sky Lobby 2
Houston, TX 77002
Phone: 713-651-7000
Fax: 713-651-6995
Web: www.eogresources.com

CEO: Mark G. Papa
CFO: Timothy K. Driggers
HR: Patricia L. Edwards
FYE: December 31
Type: Public

EOG Resources hogs a resource — natural gas. The independent oil and gas company is engaged in exploring for natural gas and crude oil and developing, producing, and marketing those resources. In 2009 EOG, an independent offspring of the once powerful Enron, reported estimated proved reserves of 10.8 trillion cu. ft. equivalent, including 8.9 trillion cu. ft. of natural gas reserves and 313 million barrels of crude oil, condensate, and natural gas liquid (NGL) reserves. The company operates in major production basins in Canada, offshore Trinidad, the US, the UK sector of the North Sea, and in China (Sichuan basin).

	Annual Growth	12/05	12/06	12/07	12/08	12/09
Sales ($ mil.)	7.3%	3,607.0	3,904.4	4,038.5	6,386.5	4,787.0
Net income ($ mil.)	(18.8%)	1,259.6	1,299.9	1,089.9	2,436.9	546.6
Market value ($ mil.)	7.3%	18,573.8	15,809.4	22,593.9	16,854.9	24,631.8
Employees	10.7%	1,400	1,570	1,800	2,100	2,100

EON COMMUNICATIONS CORPORATION

NASDAQ (CM): EONC

185 Martinvale Ln.
San Jose, CA 95119
Phone: 408-694-9500
Fax: 408-694-9600
Web: www.eoncc.com

CEO: James W. (Jim) Hopper
CFO: Lee M. Bowling
HR: —
FYE: July 31
Type: Public

eOn Communications knows it's been ages since you've had a good customer service experience. The company's products integrate voice and Internet communications for large call centers and e-commerce customer contact centers. eOn's communications servers feature automatic call distribution, e-mail queuing, and customer identification. It also sells the Millennium voice switching hardware platform, a private branch exchange (PBX) system with computer telephony integration. Customers include Lillian Vernon and Rockhurst University. Chairman and president David Lee owns about 30% of eOn.

	Annual Growth	7/05	7/06	7/07	7/08	7/09
Sales ($ mil.)	(16.1%)	21.4	12.0	10.7	7.0	10.6
Net income ($ mil.)	—	(2.0)	1.4	(1.3)	(3.5)	(0.3)
Market value ($ mil.)	(39.6%)	17.7	16.8	11.6	1.9	2.3
Employees	(22.9%)	173	79	92	43	61

E.ON U.S. LLC

220 W. Main St.
Louisville, KY 40232
Phone: 502-627-2000
Fax: 502-627-3609
Web: www.eon-us.com/about_eonus.asp

CEO: Victor A. (Vic) Staffieri
CFO: S. Bradford (Brad) Rives
HR: Paula H. Pottinger
FYE: December 31
Type: Subsidiary

E.ON U.S. (formerly LG&E Energy) may not be a Kentucky colonel, but it's a major power source in the state. Its regulated utilities, Louisville Gas and Electric and Kentucky Utilities, distribute electricity to 908,000 customers and natural gas to more than 318,000 customers in Kentucky and Virginia. The utilities have a combined generating capacity of 7,600 MW, primarily from coal-fired facilities. E.ON U.S.'s nonregulated businesses include international gas distribution and independent power production. E.ON U.S. is a subsidiary of German energy conglomerate E.ON. In 2010 PPL agreed to buy E.ON U.S. for $7.2 billion.

EPIC SYSTEMS CORPORATION

1979 Milky Way
Verona, WI 53593
Phone: 608-271-9000
Fax: 608-271-7237
Web: www.epic.com

CEO: Judith R. Faulkner
CFO: —
HR: —
FYE: December 31
Type: Private

Epic Systems tells a grand tale of health care technology. The company provides health care management software that integrates financial and clinical information across inpatient, ambulatory, and payer technology systems. Epic's software offerings include scheduling and registration tools, billing and managed care administration applications, inpatient and outpatient core clinical systems, electronic medical records applications, and applications for managing hospital pharmacy, emergency, surgery, radiology, laboratory, and intensive care departments. The company was founded in 1979 and is employee-owned.

EPICEPT CORPORATION

NASDAQ (CM): EPCT

777 Old Saw Mill River Rd.
Tarrytown, NY 10591
Phone: 914-606-3500
Fax: 914-606-3501
Web: www.epicept.com

CEO: John V. Talley
CFO: Robert W. Cook
HR: —
FYE: December 31
Type: Public

EpiCept has made leukemia remission its entire mission. Its lead cancer drug candidate, Ceplene, is designed for use in adult patients who have had a complete remission from acute myeloid leukemia, but who are still at risk for relapse. It has been approved for use, along with interleukin-2, as a remission maintenance therapy in the EU, and it is awaiting approval in the US. The company's pipeline includes other cancer candidates, as well as topical analgesics for both acute and chronic pain. However, EpiCept has put all drug-discovery work on the back burner to focus on bringing Ceplene to market.

	Annual Growth	12/05	12/06	12/07	12/08	12/09
Sales ($ mil.)	(15.9%)	0.8	2.1	0.3	0.3	0.4
Net income ($ mil.)	—	(7.2)	(65.5)	(28.7)	(25.4)	(38.8)
Market value ($ mil.)	(26.0%)	—	189.7	168.4	84.9	76.9
Employees	(16.5%)	35	34	32	20	17

⊞ EPICOR SOFTWARE CORPORATION

NASDAQ (GS): EPIC

18200 Von Karman Ave., Ste. 1000
Irvine, CA 92612
Phone: 949-585-4000
Fax: 949-585-4091
Web: www.epicor.com

CEO: L. George Klaus
CFO: Michael Pietrini
HR: —
FYE: December 31
Type: Public

Epicor Software hopes the middle of the road proves paved with gold. The company provides enterprise resource planning software for midsized businesses. Epicor's software integrates back-office applications for manufacturing, distribution, and accounting with customer relationship management functions, including sales, marketing, and customer support. The company's software also includes collaborative applications that link employees, distributors, and suppliers, encompassing operations such as supply chain management, sourcing, and procurement. In October 2008 Elliott Associates (which holds a 10% stake in the company) made an unsolicited bid to acquire Epicor. Epicor's board of directors rejected the offer.

	Annual Growth	12/05	12/06	12/07	12/08	12/09
Sales ($ mil.)	9.1%	289.4	384.1	429.8	487.9	409.6
Net income ($ mil.)	—	52.0	23.8	41.3	1.0	(1.2)
Market value ($ mil.)	(14.3%)	892.0	852.8	743.6	303.0	481.0
Employees	7.7%	1,887	2,178	2,907	2,645	2,539

EPICORE BIONETWORKS INC.

Pink Sheets: EBN

4 Lina Ln.
Eastampton, NJ 08060
Phone: 609-267-9118
Fax: 609-267-9336
Web: www.epicorebionetworks.com

CEO: William P. (Bill) Long
CFO: Keith Blackman
HR: —
FYE: June 30
Type: Public

Epicore BioNetworks puts the earth at the core of its scientific creations. The company manufactures environmentally sensitive biotechnology products for commercial, industrial, and consumer applications, and specialty animal feeds. It mixes natural bacteria, enzymes, microbes, and other biodegradable, non-toxic ingredients to create products for diverse industries like agriculture, cleaning and sanitation, food processing and nutrition, and environmental remediation. Those products include water treatment chemicals, agrochemicals, and sanitizers and deodorizers. Epicore is a major supplier of products to the aquaculture industry, especially to the shrimp industries in Asia and in Latin America.

	Annual Growth	6/05	6/06	6/07	6/08	6/09
Sales ($ mil.)	13.9%	1.9	2.0	3.1	3.2	3.2
Net income ($ mil.)	41.4%	0.1	0.1	0.5	0.5	0.4
Market value ($ mil.)	(1.3%)	2.4	1.6	4.2	2.4	2.2
Employees	—	—	—	—	—	—

EPIQ SYSTEMS, INC.

NASDAQ (GS): EPIQ

501 Kansas Ave.
Kansas City, KS 66105
Phone: 913-621-9500
Fax: 913-321-1243
Web: www.epiqsystems.com

CEO: Tom W. Olofson
CFO: Elizabeth M. (Betsy) Braham
HR: —
FYE: December 31
Type: Public

EPIQ Systems wants to make bankruptcy as quick and painless as possible. The company provides case and document management software for bankruptcy, class action, mass tort, and other legal proceedings. Its software automates tasks including legal notice and claims management, funds distribution, and government reporting. EPIQ's software line includes products for Chapter 7 liquidations, Chapter 13 individual debt reorganizations, and Chapter 11 reorganizations. The company, which caters primarily to law firms and bankruptcy trustees as opposed to debtors and creditors, also offers case management services and software for class action, mass tort, and bankruptcy case administration.

	Annual Growth	12/05	12/06	12/07	12/08	12/09
Sales ($ mil.)	16.3%	130.8	224.2	174.4	236.1	239.1
Net income ($ mil.)	7.6%	10.9	35.1	6.9	13.8	14.6
Market value ($ mil.)	3.1%	452.7	414.4	637.6	612.0	512.4
Employees	2.4%	500	500	500	550	550

EPLUS INC.

NASDAQ (GM): PLUS

13595 Dulles Technology Dr.
Herndon, VA 20171
Phone: 703-984-8400
Fax: 703-984-8600
Web: www.eplus.com

CEO: Phillip G. (Phil) Norton
CFO: Elaine D. Marion
HR: —
FYE: March 31
Type: Public

ePlus wants to rate an A-plus from its customers by meeting their hardware and software needs. The company resells and leases products from top IT infrastructure providers. Its offerings include security, storage, and networking products, as well as consulting and systems integration services. The company also offers supply chain management software and services; its proprietary applications include procurement, asset management, spend analytics, and document management tools. ePlus markets its products and services to midsized and large businesses, government agencies, and schools. The company gets nearly all of its sales in the US.

	Annual Growth	3/05	3/06	3/07	3/08	3/09
Sales ($ mil.)	4.9%	575.8	647.3	791.6	849.3	698.0
Net income ($ mil.)	(15.7%)	25.3	(0.5)	17.4	16.4	12.8
Market value ($ mil.)	0.0%	96.9	118.2	87.9	76.4	97.1
Employees	0.7%	637	680	649	658	656

EPOCH HOLDING CORPORATION

NASDAQ (CM): EPHC

640 5th Ave., 18th Fl.
New York, NY 10019
Phone: 212-303-7200
Fax: 212-202-4948
Web: www.eipny.com

CEO: William W. Priest
CFO: Adam Borak
HR: Andrea Tasker Glogoff
FYE: June 30
Type: Public

Epoch Holding is the holding company of Epoch Investments Partners (EIP), which manages investments for retirement plans, mutual fund clients, endowments, foundations, and other high-net-worth clients. EIP has approximately $6.6 billion of assets under management, including some $4 billion added since the beginning of 2006. Among its largest customers (about 15% of sales) is Canadian management company CI Investments, for which Epoch acts as subadvisor. Formerly known as J Net Enterprises, the company was once one of Nevada's largest gaming-machine operators and even tried its hand at Internet-based e-commerce before acquiring EIP in 2004.

	Annual Growth	6/05	6/06	6/07	6/08	6/09
Assets ($ mil.)	43.4%	13.0	13.6	39.4	54.3	55.0
Net income ($ mil.)	—	(7.7)	(5.7)	7.9	9.0	5.9
Market value ($ mil.)	19.1%	97.9	115.7	305.0	207.5	196.8
Employees	13.2%	28	38	43	46	46

EPOLIN, INC.

OTC: EPLN

358-364 Adams St.
Newark, NJ 07105
Phone: 973-465-9495
Fax: 973-465-5353
Web: www.epolin.com

CEO: Greg Amato
CFO: James Ivchenko
HR: —
FYE: February 28
Type: Public

Welders and army tank drivers alike owe their continued ability to see to Epolin. The company develops near-infrared dyes used in the manufacture of eyewear for protection against lasers (used in range finders in tanks) and face shields used by welders. Epolin also makes intermediates for the specialty chemical industry. Additionally, Epolin sells its dyes as security inks for credit cards, drug and food labels, and official documents. Products are sold in 20 countries; the US accounts for about 80% of sales. Founder Murray Cohen stepped down as CEO in 2006; he remains as chairman and chief scientist. Former sales exec Greg Amato replaced Cohen. Epolin is exploring options that could include selling the company.

	Annual Growth	2/05	2/06	2/07	2/08	2/09
Sales ($ mil.)	1.7%	2.9	3.7	3.6	3.6	3.1
Net income ($ mil.)	(12.0%)	0.5	0.6	0.6	0.7	0.3
Market value ($ mil.)	(2.4%)	6.4	8.6	8.5	7.6	5.8
Employees	0.0%	10	10	10	10	10

EPSILON DATA MANAGEMENT, LLC

4401 Regent Blvd.
Irving, TX 75063
Phone: 972-582-9600
Fax: 972-582-9700
Web: www.epsilon.com

CEO: Bryan J. Kennedy
CFO: Paul Dundon
HR: Jane Huston
FYE: December 31
Type: Subsidiary

Companies looking for positive marketing results can call on this firm. Epsilon Data Management is a leading provider of direct marketing and customer relationship management services. It helps develop database marketing and consumer loyalty programs, as well as marketing communications for traditional direct mail and interactive media campaigns. In addition, Epsilon offers data collection and analysis and database integration services. The agency, a unit of credit and transaction services provider Alliance Data Systems, operates through offices in Boston, Dallas, St. Louis, and Washington, DC. It was established in 1969.

EPSON AMERICA, INC.

3840 Kilroy Airport Way
Long Beach, CA 90806
Phone: 562-981-3840
Fax: 562-290-5220
Web: www.epson.com

CEO: John Lang
CFO: Alan Pound Sr.
HR: —
FYE: March 31
Type: Subsidiary

When it comes to digital images, Epson America snaps, scans, prints, and projects. A subsidiary of Japanese giant Seiko Epson, the company manufactures digital cameras, document cameras, home theater systems, personal and professional flatbed scanners, printers, and projectors. Its printer line includes personal ink jet and high-volume impact printers, as well as wide-format and point-of-sale devices. It also offers printing and photography software, and supplies such as print cartridges and paper. Epson America, which represents Seiko Epson in North America and South America, was founded in 1975.

EPSON PORTLAND INC.

3950 NW Aloclek Place
Hillsboro, OR 97124
Phone: 503-645-1118
Fax: 503-617-6746
Web: www.epi.epson.com

CEO: David (Dave) Graham
CFO: —
HR: —
FYE: December 31
Type: Subsidiary

Epson Portland Inc. (EPI) manufactures products such as ink cartridges for its Japanese parent, Seiko Epson. The company also refurbishes optical components used in LCD projectors, manufactures injection-molded plastic parts, and assembles products for Epson's Photo Business Printing Systems. Also part of EPI is the Epson Imaging Technology Center (EITC), which operates from facilities in Bellevue, Washington, and San Jose, California. EITC develops software for Epson products sold in the US and Europe. EPI's products are distributed by Epson America.

EQT CORPORATION

NYSE: EQT

225 North Shore Dr.
Pittsburgh, PA 15212
Phone: 412-553-5700
Fax: 412-553-7781
Web: www.eqt.com

CEO: David L. Porges
CFO: Philip P. (Phil) Conti
HR: Charlene Petrelli
FYE: December 31
Type: Public

Integrated natural gas company EQT Corporation (formerly Equitable Resources) hopes to get its fair share of the natural gas market. EQT's Distribution unit provides gas to about 276,000 customers in Pennsylvania, West Virginia, and Kentucky. EQT Midstream operates 10,650 miles of natural gas-gathering pipeline and 970 miles of transmission lines. EQT Production exploits proved reserves of 4.1 trillion cu. ft. of natural gas equivalent in the Appalachian region, operating some 13,000 active wells and drilling more than 700 new wells in 2009. EQT Production sells its natural gas products to Appalachian-area utilities and industrial customers and to marketers, including EQT Energy, its own gas marketing affiliate.

	Annual Growth	12/05	12/06	12/07	12/08	12/09
Sales ($ mil.)	0.3%	1,253.7	1,267.9	1,361.4	1,576.5	1,269.8
Net income ($ mil.)	(11.9%)	260.1	220.3	257.5	255.6	156.9
Market value ($ mil.)	4.6%	5,267.7	5,994.2	7,649.6	4,816.9	6,305.7
Employees	9.5%	1,250	1,340	1,400	1,680	1,800

EQUIBASE COMPANY LLC

821 Corporate Dr.
Lexington, KY 40503
Phone: 859-224-2860
Fax: 859-224-2870
Web: www.equibase.com

CEO: Alan Marzelli
CFO: —
HR: —
FYE: December 31
Type: Joint venture

Equibase knows its ponies. The company is the official horseracing information and statistics keeper for the thoroughbred racing industry and supplies information to a variety of media, including the industry's daily publisher, *Daily Racing Form*. The company's database of information covers more than 140 tracks and 1,400 simulcast locations throughout North America. Equibase's website offers handicapping information and services. Its Virtual Stable service notifies fans with real-time results for horses they wish to follow. Equibase is a joint venture between The Jockey Club and the Thoroughbred Racing Associations of North America.

	Annual Growth	12/04	12/05	12/06	12/07	12/08
Est. sales ($ mil.)	—	—	—	—	—	2.6
Employees	—	—	—	—	—	30

EQUIFAX INC.

NYSE: EFX

1550 Peachtree St. NW
Atlanta, GA 30309
Phone: 404-885-8000
Fax: 404-885-8988
Web: www.equifax.com

CEO: Richard F. (Rick) Smith
CFO: Lee Adrean
HR: Coretha M. Rushing
FYE: December 31
Type: Public

Ever get the feeling you're beeing watched? You could be feeling the gaze of Equifax. One of the country's big three credit bureaus (Experian and TransUnion are the others), Equifax provides credit scores, history information, and risk analysis. The company also provides credit card marketing and fraud detection services, and offers database marketing and credit-scoring software. Subsidiary TALX provides outsourced payroll and human resources services in the US. Equifax's customers include financial institutions, retailers, automotive dealers, and mortgage companies. The group operates in North America, Latin America, and Europe, but the majority of its revenues come from the US.

	Annual Growth	12/05	12/06	12/07	12/08	12/09
Sales ($ mil.)	6.0%	1,443.4	1,546.3	1,843.0	1,935.7	1,824.5
Net income ($ mil.)	(1.3%)	246.5	274.5	272.7	272.8	233.9
Market value ($ mil.)	(5.1%)	4,813.8	5,140.5	4,603.6	3,357.8	3,911.1
Employees	9.4%	4,600	4,960	7,000	6,500	6,600

EQUINIX, INC.

NASDAQ (GS): EQIX

301 Velocity Way, 5th Fl.
Foster City, CA 94404
Phone: 650-513-7000
Fax: 650-513-7900
Web: www.equinix.com

CEO: Stephen M. (Steve) Smith
CFO: Keith D. Taylor
HR: Keri Crask
FYE: December 31
Type: Public

In the Internet game, Equinix is the neutral playing field. Founded in 1998, the company provides data and network hosting and colocation facilities (it calls them Internet Business Exchanges, or IBXs) where ISPs, telecommunications carriers, and content providers can locate equipment and interconnect networks and operations. The company also offers colocation-related services that include providing clients with cabinets, operating space, and storage. Its clients include such firms as Apple, eBay, IBM, and Bank of America. Equinix operates dozens of IBXs in almost 20 major international markets, including Chicago, Hong Kong, Los Angeles, New York, and Tokyo.

	Annual Growth	12/05	12/06	12/07	12/08	12/09
Sales ($ mil.)	41.3%	221.1	286.9	419.4	704.7	882.5
Net income ($ mil.)	—	(42.6)	(6.8)	(5.2)	131.5	69.4
Market value ($ mil.)	27.0%	1,621.9	3,009.1	4,021.8	2,116.5	4,223.9
Employees	24.8%	537	616	911	1,115	1,301

EQUINOX HOLDINGS, INC.

895 Broadway
New York, NY 10003
Phone: 212-677-0180
Fax: —
Web: www.equinoxfitness.com

CEO: Harvey Spevak
CFO: Larry M. Segall
HR: —
FYE: December 31
Type: Private

Equinox Holdings (doing business as Equinox Fitness Clubs) hopes you go to the gym more than twice a year. The company owns and operates about 50 full-service, upscale fitness clubs in select US cities, about 30 of which are in New York City. Beyond the monthly membership fee, Equinox gyms earn revenue from its cafés, spa services, and on-site stores that sells sportswear. Equinox opened its first club in New York in 1991 and was originally owned by North Castle Partners. The company was bought by New York real estate developer Related for $505 million in 2006. Many of Related's new developments now have an Equinox Fitness Club in the building.

EQUISTAR CHEMICALS, LP

1221 McKinney St., Ste. 700
Houston, TX 77010
Phone: 713-652-7200
Fax: 713-652-4151
Web: www.equistarchem.com

CEO: James L. (Jim) Gallogly
CFO: C. Kent Potter
HR: —
FYE: December 31
Type: Subsidiary

Someone's got to build the building blocks too, you know? Equistar Chemicals, a subsidiary of LyondellBasell, does just that. Its primary product is ethylene, which is the world's most-used petrochemical and the basis for any number of other chemicals, plastics, and synthetics. Among the company's other products are propylene, butadiene, polyethylene, polypropylene, ethylene oxide, ethylene glycol, benzene, and toluene. Polyethylene is used in plastic bags and bottles; polypropylene is used in plastic caps, rigid packaging, automotive components, and carpet. Equistar's US operations were a part of LyondellBasell's Chapter 11 filing in early 2009.

	Annual Growth	12/04	12/05	12/06	12/07	12/08
Est. sales ($ mil.)	—	—	—	—	—	13,037.0
Employees	—	—	—	—	—	3,330

EQUITY LIFESTYLE PROPERTIES, INC.

NYSE: ELS

2 N. Riverside Plaza, Ste. 800
Chicago, IL 60606
Phone: 312-279-1400
Fax: 312-279-1710
Web: www.mhchomes.com

CEO: Thomas P. Heneghan
CFO: Michael B. Berman
HR: —
FYE: December 31
Type: Public

Snow birds and empty nesters flock to communities developed and owned by Equity LifeStyle Properties. The real estate investment trust (REIT) owns and operates lifestyle-oriented residential properties aimed at retirees, vacationers, and second home owners. Other properties also focus on providing affordable housing for families. It leases developed areas for factory-built homes, cottages, cabins, and recreational vehicles. The REIT's portfolio includes more than 300 properties containing 110,000 lots in nearly 30 states and Canada. Its properties are similar to site-built residential subdivisions, with centralized entrances, utilities, gutters, curbs, and paved streets.

	Annual Growth	12/05	12/06	12/07	12/08	12/09
Sales ($ mil.)	6.1%	386.5	412.8	413.5	652.1	489.9
Net income ($ mil.)	—	(2.3)	16.6	32.1	18.3	56.3
Market value ($ mil.)	3.2%	1,356.4	1,659.1	1,392.1	1,169.3	1,538.4
Employees	20.9%	1,500	1,400	1,600	3,000	3,200

An in-depth profile of this company is available to Hoover's Online members at hoovers.com.

EQUITY OFFICE PROPERTIES TRUST

2 N. Riverside Plaza, Ste. 2100	CEO: Christopher Peatross
Chicago, IL 60606	CFO: —
Phone: 312-466-3300	HR: Laura Klimenko
Fax: 312-454-0332	FYE: December 31
Web: www.equityoffice.com	Type: Subsidiary

All else being equal, Equity Office is one of the largest commercial landlords in the US. The company owns more than 60 million sq. ft. of premiere Class A office space in the country's top markets, including Boston, Manhattan, Los Angeles, and Northern California. Former chairman Sam "Grave Dancer" Zell founded Equity Office in 1976. After a fierce bidding war against Vornado Realty, The Blackstone Group acquired Equity Office for some $39 billion in 2007; it was one of the largest private equity transactions ever. Blackstone combined the newly acquired portfolio with its own holdings, which included assets purchased from CarrAmerica and Trizec Properties.

EQUITY ONE, INC.
NYSE: EQY

1600 NE Miami Gardens Dr.	CEO: Jeffrey S. (Jeff) Olson
North Miami Beach, FL 33179	CFO: Mark Langer
Phone: 305-947-1664	HR: Mark Langer
Fax: 305-947-1734	FYE: December 31
Web: www.equityone.net	Type: Public

Equity One wants to be #1. The number one shopping center owner, that is. A real estate investment trust (REIT), Equity One acquires, develops, and manages shopping centers, with many properties located in Florida and in the Boston area. Its portfolio consists primarily of shopping centers anchored by supermarkets and drug stores totaling around 19 million sq. ft.; including land and other holdings, Equity One's portfolio comprises some 180 properties. Florida is Equity One's largest market. Publix (which leases nearly 15% of the company's space), Kroger, and Winn-Dixie are its biggest tenants. Chairman Chaim Katzman controls the REIT through his Israeli real estate firm Gazit-Globe.

	Annual Growth	12/05	12/06	12/07	12/08	12/09
Sales ($ mil.)	1.8%	253.0	233.4	246.6	239.0	271.4
Net income ($ mil.)	(3.2%)	92.7	177.0	69.4	35.0	81.4
Market value ($ mil.)	(8.6%)	2,138.4	2,465.9	2,130.1	1,637.1	1,495.6
Employees	(11.3%)	259	217	155	159	160

🕮 EQUITY RESIDENTIAL
NYSE: EQR

2 N. Riverside Plaza	CEO: David J. Neithercut
Chicago, IL 60606	CFO: Mark J. Parrell
Phone: 312-474-1300	HR: John Powers
Fax: 312-454-8703	FYE: December 31
Web: www.equityapartments.com	Type: Public

The "Grave Dancer" is also the lord of the rents. Sam Zell (whose moniker springs from his buying and turning around moribund properties) is at the head of the conga line at Equity Residential, the nation's #1 apartment owner by sales and units. (The company bypassed rival AIMCO in terms of units owned in 2009.) Equity Residential wholly or partially owns some 550 communities with about 140,000 units, comprising garden units, mid- and high rises, and military housing. A real estate investment trust (REIT), Equity Residential also provides property leasing, development, management, financial, and other support operations. The company focuses on growth regions throughout the US.

	Annual Growth	12/05	12/06	12/07	12/08	12/09
Sales ($ mil.)	(0.1%)	1,954.9	1,990.4	2,038.1	2,103.2	1,943.7
Net income ($ mil.)	(18.4%)	861.8	1,072.8	989.6	420.1	382.0
Market value ($ mil.)	(3.6%)	11,068.7	14,359.3	10,318.9	8,437.3	9,557.8
Employees	(9.1%)	6,000	5,200	4,800	4,700	4,100

ER SOLUTIONS, INC.

800 SW 39th St.	CEO: Steve Hunter
Renton, WA 98057	CFO: —
Phone: 206-322-4500	HR: —
Fax: 206-322-4838	FYE: December 31
Web: www.convergentusa.com/ERS	Type: Subsidiary

Companies send their ailing accounts receivable to ER. A subsidiary of Convergent Resources (CRI), one of the largest collections companies in the US, ER Solutions (ERS) provides receivables collections services to creditors in the retail, telecommunications, and utilities industries. Utilizing a mixture of state-of-the-art technology and old-fashioned diplomacy, the company tracks down delinquent customers and encourages voluntary repayment of debt. It also provides customer service both for outbound communications (contacting customers to remind them of their debt and payment options), and inbound customer relations.

	Annual Growth	12/04	12/05	12/06	12/07	12/08
Est. sales ($ mil.)	—	—	—	—	—	81.2
Employees	—	—	—	—	—	730

ERESEARCHTECHNOLOGY, INC.
NASDAQ (GS): ERES

30 S. 17th St.	CEO: Michael J. McKelvey
Philadelphia, PA 19103	CFO: Keith D. Schneck
Phone: 215-972-0420	HR: Valerie Mattern
Fax: 215-972-0414	FYE: December 31
Web: www.ert.com	Type: Public

eResearchTechnology (eRT) e-cares about your e-clinical e-trial. The firm offers support services and software to help streamline the clinical trials process that drugs and medical devices must pass to earn regulatory approval. eRT's products automate all aspects of the process, from setup and data gathering to analysis and FDA application preparation. Customers include drugmakers, medical device firms, and contract research organizations (CROs). Flagship product EXPeRT ensures cardiac safety by collecting, processing, and interpreting electrocardiogram (ECG) data. eRT also provides site support including ECG equipment rentals and sales. The firm markets its products through a global sales force.

	Annual Growth	12/05	12/06	12/07	12/08	12/09
Sales ($ mil.)	2.0%	86.8	86.4	98.7	133.1	93.8
Net income ($ mil.)	(8.7%)	15.4	8.3	15.3	25.0	10.7
Market value ($ mil.)	(20.6%)	736.9	328.4	576.8	323.6	293.3
Employees	(0.1%)	355	341	356	415	353

ERGON, INC.

2829 Lakeland Dr., Ste. 2000	CEO: Leslie B. Lampton Sr.
Jackson, MS 39232	CFO: A. Patrick (Pat) Busby
Phone: 601-933-3000	HR: Daphne Williams
Fax: 601-933-3350	FYE: December 31
Web: www.ergon.com	Type: Private

When it comes to work, Ergon (named after the Greek word for work) has it covered. Ergo, Ergon operates in six major business segments: asphalt and emulsions, information technology (embedded computing), oil and gas, real estate, refining and marketing, and transportation and terminaling. In addition to providing a range of petroleum products and services, the company manufactures and markets computer technology services and sells road maintenance systems, including emulsions and special coatings. Ergon also provides truck, rail, and marine transport services and sells residential and commercial real estate properties.

	Annual Growth	12/04	12/05	12/06	12/07	12/08
Est. sales ($ mil.)	19.3%	2,680.0	3,000.0	4,110.0	4,490.0	5,430.0
Employees	2.1%	2,300	2,500	2,500	2,500	2,500

ERHC ENERGY INC.

OTC: ERHE

5444 Westheimer Rd., Ste. 1570
Houston, TX 77056
Phone: 713-626-4700
Fax: 713-626-4704
Web: www.erhc.com

CEO: Peter C. Ntephe
CFO: Sylvan Odobulu
HR: —
FYE: September 30
Type: Public

Oil, out of Africa, is the hope of ERHC Energy (formerly Environmental Remediation Holding Corporation), an independent oil and gas company whose sole assets are two West African oil and gas exploration concessions: in the Joint Development Zone between the Sao Tome and Nigeria; and in the Exclusive Economic Zone in Sao Tome. ERHC is teaming up with larger oil and gas companies (such as Noble Energy and Pioneer Natural Resources) to help it develop its holdings. The company is also hoping to acquire interests in high-potential non-producing international prospects in known oil-producing areas. Former chairman and CEO Emeka Offor, the owner of Chrome Oil Services and Chrome Energy, controls about 40% of ERHC.

	Annual Growth	9/05	9/06	9/07	9/08	9/09
Sales ($ mil.)	—	—	—	—	—	0.0
Net income ($ mil.)	—	—	—	—	—	(7.7)
Market value ($ mil.)	—	—	—	—	—	519.9
Employees	—	—	—	—	—	6

ERICKSON AIR-CRANE INCORPORATED

5550 SW Macadam Ave., Ste. 200
Portland, OR 97239
Phone: 503-505-5800
Fax: 541-664-7613
Web: www.ericksonaircrane.com

CEO: Udo Rieder
CFO: Charles E. (Chuck) Ryan
HR: Mary Walden
FYE: December 31
Type: Private

Erickson Air-Crane owns, operates, and maintains a fleet of more than 15 heavy-duty S-64 Aircrane helicopters. The craft are capable of lifting up to 25,000 pounds and are used in power line construction, logging, and oil and gas support applications. The S-64 Helitanker is equipped with a 2,650-gallon tank for use in firefighting. Customers include fire departments, forest managers, and heavy construction companies around the world. Erickson has international subsidiaries operating in North America, Europe, and the Asia/Pacific region. The company also manufactures the S-64 under a contract with Sikorsky. Erickson, which was founded in 1971 by Jack Erickson, filed an initial public offering in 2010.

ERICSSON INC.

6300 Legacy Dr.
Plano, TX 75024
Phone: 972-583-0000
Fax: —
Web: www.ericsson.com/US

CEO: Angel Ruiz
CFO: Emil Nilsson
HR: Paul Miesse
FYE: December 31
Type: Subsidiary

Ericsson is Swede on North America. The subsidiary of Sweden-based global wireless network equipment leader Telefonaktiebolaget LM Ericsson oversees the North American business of its parent company. Its core network products are antennas, transmitters, switching systems, and other gear used to build wireless networks. Ericsson primarily serves telecom network operators, transportation companies, utilities providers, and broadcasters. It also makes multimedia products that enable such services as Internet television, as well as satellite equipment, optical equipment, and wireless software. Services include consulting and network build-out. The company makes mobile phones through joint venture Sony Ericsson.

ERIE INDEMNITY COMPANY

NASDAQ (GS): ERIE

100 Erie Insurance Place
Erie, PA 16530
Phone: 814-870-2000
Fax: 814-870-3126
Web: www.erie-insurance.com

CEO: Terrence W. Cavanaugh
CFO: Marcia A. Dall
HR: Christina Marsh
FYE: December 31
Type: Public

Erie Indemnity may be near a lake, but it prefers pools. Founded in 1925 as an auto insurer, it now provides underwriting and sales and policy administration services to Erie Insurance Exchange, a reciprocal insurance exchange that pools the underwriting of several property/casualty insurance firms. Most of its revenues come from the management fees it charges the exchange, but it also writes a bit of property/casualty insurance of its own through subsidiaries. Its reach includes coverage in about a dozen eastern states and it markets its products through some 8,800 independent agents. The company is the only publicly traded part of the Erie Insurance Group, which also includes Erie Family Life Insurance.

	Annual Growth	12/05	12/06	12/07	12/08	12/09
Assets ($ mil.)	(3.7%)	3,101.3	3,039.4	2,878.6	2,613.4	2,666.5
Net income ($ mil.)	(17.2%)	231.1	204.0	212.9	69.2	108.5
Market value ($ mil.)	(7.5%)	3,044.5	3,318.0	2,969.5	2,153.5	2,233.0
Employees	(2.2%)	4,600	4,300	4,100	4,200	4,200

ERIE INSURANCE GROUP

100 Erie Insurance Place
Erie, PA 16530
Phone: 814-870-2000
Fax: 814-870-3126
Web: www.erie-insurance.com

CEO: Terrence W. Cavanaugh
CFO: Marcia A. Dall
HR: —
FYE: December 31
Type: Holding company

Formed in 1925 as a Pennsylvania auto insurer, Erie Insurance Group has rolled down lots of other roads since then, offering personal auto, property, and life insurance through its subsidiaries Erie Family Life Insurance and publicly traded Erie Indemnity. The group also offers commercial coverage (including auto, liability, and workers' compensation) for smaller businesses. Doing business in a dozen eastern states, Erie Insurance Group sells its products through thousands of independent agencies. The company has slowly but steadily expanded its territory, choosing to concentrate on growth in areas it already serves.

	Annual Growth	12/04	12/05	12/06	12/07	12/08
Est. sales ($ mil.)	—	—	—	—	—	3,566.5
Employees	—	—	—	—	—	3,500

ERNST & YOUNG LLP

5 Times Sq., 14th Fl.
New York, NY 10036
Phone: 212-773-3000
Fax: 212-773-6350
Web: www.ey.com/global/content.nsf/US

CEO: James S. (Jim) Turley
CFO: —
HR: Sam Fouad
FYE: June 30
Type: Partnership

Ernst & Young LLP is earnest about its chosen profession. The firm is the US arm of Ernst & Young Global, one of the Big Four accounting firms, which include rivals KPMG, PricewaterhouseCoopers, and Deloitte Touche Tohmatsu. Ernst & Young provides assurance, tax, transactions, and advisory services to public and private companies in a wide variety of industries from about 80 offices throughout the US, including Puerto Rico. Ernst & Young LLP is part of the Americas division of the global accountancy network. Arthur Young and Alwin C. Ernst founded the two accounting firms that were later combined to form Ernst & Young.

	Annual Growth	6/04	6/05	6/06	6/07	6/08
Est. sales ($ mil.)	—	—	—	—	—	1,653.2
Employees	—	—	—	—	—	27,000

An in-depth profile of this company is available to Hoover's Online members at hoovers.com.

575

EROOMSYSTEM TECHNOLOGIES, INC.

OTC: ERMS

1072 Madison Ave.	CEO: David A. Gestetner
Lakewood, NJ 08701	CFO: —
Phone: 732-730-0116	HR: —
Fax: 732-810-0380	FYE: December 31
Web: www.eroomsystem.com	Type: Public

eRoomSystem Technologies is keeping tabs for hotels. The company provides computer-based refreshment centers for the hospitality industry. Its eRoomSystem products track beverage and other refreshment purchases and automatically charge lodgers' accounts. The eRoomSystem generates reports on sales statistics, inventory control, and restocking requirements. The company's other products include room safes that feature reprogrammable electronic combinations. Through revenue-sharing agreements the company installs its systems and takes a cut of the sales they generate.

	Annual Growth	12/05	12/06	12/07	12/08	12/09
Sales ($ mil.)	(18.7%)	1.6	1.3	1.2	0.9	0.7
Net income ($ mil.)	—	0.2	0.2	0.4	0.1	(0.1)
Market value ($ mil.)	6.3%	4.3	2.9	4.5	4.5	5.5
Employees	43.6%	4	3	2	4	17

ESB FINANCIAL CORPORATION

NASDAQ (GS): ESBF

600 Lawrence Ave.	CEO: Charlotte A. Zuschlag
Ellwood City, PA 16117	CFO: Charles P. Evanoski
Phone: 724-758-5584	HR: John T. Stunda
Fax: 724-758-0576	FYE: December 31
Web: www.esbbank.com	Type: Public

ESB Financial is the holding company for ESB Bank, which provides banking services to individuals and businesses in western Pennsylvania. The bank has some two dozen branch locations in Allegheny, Beaver, Butler, and Lawrence counties; its offerings include standard retail services such as checking and savings accounts, CDs, and credit cards. The company's lending activities consist of residential mortgages (about half of its loan portfolio), as well as construction, commercial real estate, business, and consumer loans. Bank subsidiary ESB Financial Services provides financial planning services and investment products through a partnership with Raymond James Financial.

	Annual Growth	12/05	12/06	12/07	12/08	12/09
Assets ($ mil.)	1.4%	1,852.8	1,922.7	1,880.2	1,974.8	1,960.7
Net income ($ mil.)	6.9%	9.2	10.6	7.7	10.2	12.0
Market value ($ mil.)	4.2%	135.0	132.3	120.3	129.2	159.0
Employees	1.2%	282	282	286	284	296

ESCALADE, INCORPORATED

NASDAQ (GM): ESCA

817 Maxwell Ave.	CEO: Robert J. Keller
Evansville, IN 47711	CFO: Deborah J. Meinert
Phone: 812-467-4449	HR: Gary Allan
Fax: 812-467-1303	FYE: December 31
Web: www.escaladeinc.com	Type: Public

Escalade isn't in the business of making high-end SUVs, but rather helping its customers get their game on as the world's largest producer of tables for table tennis under the Ping-Pong and STIGA brand names. The company's other sporting goods include pool tables, hockey and soccer tables, play systems, archery, darts, and fitness equipment. These products are sold under the Goalrilla, Silverback, USWeight, and Woodplay names, as well as private labels. Escalade also peddles office products through its Martin Yale unit, which makes and markets data shredders, paper trimmers, and folding machines that are sold worldwide under brand names (Intimus, Master, Mead Hatcher) and private labels.

	Annual Growth	12/05	12/06	12/07	12/08	12/09
Sales ($ mil.)	(11.1%)	185.6	191.5	185.6	148.7	116.0
Net income ($ mil.)	(38.5%)	11.9	8.5	9.3	(7.5)	1.7
Market value ($ mil.)	(32.2%)	149.4	136.2	115.9	9.5	31.5
Employees	(7.1%)	805	891	864	739	600

ESCALON MEDICAL CORP.

NASDAQ (CM): ESMC

565 E. Swedesford Rd., Ste. 200	CEO: Richard J. DePiano
Wayne, PA 19087	CFO: Robert M. O'Connor
Phone: 610-688-6830	HR: —
Fax: 610-688-3641	FYE: June 30
Web: www.escalonmed.com	Type: Public

Escalon Medical keeps blood and eyes healthy. The company develops and markets blood testing products and ophthalmic medical devices. Its Drew Scientific division makes instruments and consumables for blood cell counting and analysis, including diabetes testing and hematology equipment. In the area of ophthalmology, the company makes ultrasound systems (through subsidiary Sonomed), intraocular gases, and other products used in eye exams and surgeries. Additionally, Escalon sells vascular access products (such as catheters, monitors, and needles) that help locate hard-to-reach blood vessels for injections.

	Annual Growth	6/05	6/06	6/07	6/08	6/09
Sales ($ mil.)	6.5%	26.9	29.8	38.8	30.2	34.6
Net income ($ mil.)	—	2.4	(2.0)	5.9	(15.1)	(13.0)
Market value ($ mil.)	(24.6%)	50.5	38.0	29.8	22.1	16.3
Employees	1.0%	180	179	179	161	187

ESCO CORPORATION

2141 NW 25th Ave.	CEO: Steven D. (Steve) Pratt
Portland, OR 97210	CFO: Gene K. Huey
Phone: 503-228-2141	HR: Nick Blauwiekel
Fax: 503-226-8071	FYE: December 31
Web: www.escocorp.com	Type: Private

ESCO is well ensconced as a global manufacturer of engineered metal parts, castings, and components for industrial machinery. The company's two operating groups are Engineered Products and Turbine Technologies. It employs about 4,500 personnel and operates some 25 manufacturing facilities. ESCO provides such services as contract manufacturing, engineering, and supply chain management, as well as specialized services to the aerospace, construction, industrial, mining, and power generation markets. Customers include Bucyrus, Caterpillar, and Komatsu. ESCO was founded in Portland, Oregon, by C. F. Swigert in 1913 as an Electric Steel Foundry; its products at that time included trolley car replacement parts.

☐ ESCO TECHNOLOGIES INC.

NYSE: ESE

9900A Clayton Rd., Ste. 200	CEO: Victor L. (Vic) Richey Jr.
St. Louis, MO 63124	CFO: Gary E. Muenster
Phone: 314-213-7200	HR: Deborah J. Hanlon
Fax: 314-213-7250	FYE: September 30
Web: www.escotechnologies.com	Type: Public

Diversified manufacturing company ESCO Technologies focuses on three business segments: Utility Solutions (automation and communication devices for utilities), Filtration/Fluid Flow, and RF Shielding and Test. ESCO's communications equipment includes meter-reading technology and video surveillance systems used to monitor industrial applications. The company's filters are used in industrial applications, fuel systems, medical applications, and appliances. Test products include electromagnetic compatibility (EMC) equipment such as antennas, probes, turntables, and calibration equipment, as well as radio-frequency (RF) shielding products.

	Annual Growth	9/05	9/06	9/07	9/08	9/09
Sales ($ mil.)	9.6%	429.1	458.9	527.5	623.8	619.1
Net income ($ mil.)	3.2%	43.5	31.3	33.7	46.7	49.4
Market value ($ mil.)	(5.8%)	1,324.2	1,217.6	879.1	1,273.9	1,042.0
Employees	(2.5%)	2,365	2,685	2,700	2,200	2,140

ESCORT, INC.

5440 West Chester Rd.
West Chester, OH 45069
Phone: 513-870-8500
Fax: 513-870-8509
Web: www.escortinc.com

CEO: John Larson
CFO: Mark Carr
HR: —
FYE: December 31
Type: Private

Escort has built a business to help escort its customers safely past radar guns. The company, best known for manufacturing laser and radar detectors, primarily sells its products under its flagship Passport brand. It also makes the SOLO battery-operated radar and laser detector, as well as the Road Tech detector through a joint venture with Harley-Davidson. Escort launched its RedLine radar and laser detector in 2009. The product rollout follows the launch in 2007 of its global positioning system version of Passport, which offers TrueLock to eliminate false alerts. Falconhead Capital LLC owns a majority stake in the company.

ESI INTERNATIONAL, INC.

901 N Glebe Rd., Ste. 200
Arlington, VA 22203
Phone: 703-558-3000
Fax: 703-558-3001
Web: www.esi-intl.com

CEO: John Elsey
CFO: Mike Kyathfield
HR: Marcia Riley
FYE: December 31
Type: Subsidiary

ESI International wants to build brighter project managers. The company provides project and contract management training and consulting services, focusing on *FORTUNE* Global 500 companies and US government agencies. Established in 1981, ESI offers open enrollment and online courses (with classes ranging from two to five days), as well as on-site training; its consulting services include appraisal of project management capabilities and project execution support. ESI offers more than 100 courses in 18 different languages. Outside the US, ESI has offices in Brazil, Germany, South Africa, Spain, Sweden, the United Arab Emirates, and the UK. The company is a unit of UK-based magazine publisher Informa.

ESPEY MFG. & ELECTRONICS CORP.

NYSE Amex: ESP

233 Ballston Ave.
Saratoga Springs, NY 12866
Phone: 518-245-4400
Fax: 518-245-4421
Web: www.espey.com

CEO: Mark St. Pierre
CFO: David A. O'Neil
HR: Peggy A. Murphy
FYE: June 30
Type: Public

Espey is on a power trip. Espey Mfg. & Electronics makes electronic equipment for high-voltage applications, including specialized electronic power supplies, transformers, and electronic system components. Its transformers and electronic systems include high-power radar transmitters, antennas, and iron-core products such as magnetic amplifiers and audio filters. The company's products are used by industrial and military customers in radar, missile guidance and control, communications, aircraft navigation, and nuclear submarine control. Customers include General Electric, Lockheed Martin, Raytheon, and the US government. Exports account for more than 20% of Espey's sales.

	Annual Growth	6/05	6/06	6/07	6/08	6/09
Sales ($ mil.)	9.7%	18.8	20.9	27.7	25.7	27.2
Net income ($ mil.)	28.2%	1.0	1.6	2.5	3.4	2.7
Market value ($ mil.)	0.0%	35.6	38.7	55.8	44.0	35.6
Employees	(0.4%)	171	175	180	167	168

ESPN, INC.

ESPN Plaza, 935 Middle St.
Bristol, CT 06010
Phone: 860-766-2000
Fax: —
Web: espn.go.com

CEO: George W. Bodenheimer
CFO: Christine Driessen
HR: —
FYE: September 30
Type: Joint venture

ESPN is a superstar of the sports broadcasting world. The company is the leading cable sports broadcaster, reaching about 100 million US viewers per month with its stable of channels, including ESPN, ESPN2, and ESPN Classic. The 24-hour networks carry a variety of live sporting events, as well as programs devoted to news and analysis. ESPN also creates original programming for TV and radio, and lends content for ESPN.com, one of the most popular sports sites on the Internet. Its international operations extend the ESPN brand to another 200 countries. ESPN is 80% owned by Walt Disney (through ABC); media conglomerate Hearst has a 20% stake.

ESSA BANCORP, INC.

NASDAQ (GS): ESSA

200 Palmer St.
Stroudsburg, PA 18360
Phone: 570-421-0531
Fax: 570-476-6258
Web: www.essabank.com

CEO: Gary S. Olson
CFO: Allan A. Muto
HR: Thomas J. Grayuski
FYE: September 30
Type: Public

ESSA Bancorp is the holding company for ESSA Bank & Trust, which offers deposits and loans to consumers and businesses in eastern Pennsylvania. One-to four-family residential mortgages dominate the bank's lending activities, representing more than 80% of its loan portfolio. Commercial real estate loans account for 10%, while home equity loans and lines of credit make up ESSA's other significant loan segments. In addition to its lending and deposit services, the bank also offers financial and investment services through a third-party firm. Founded in 1916, ESSA operates more than a dozen branches in Monroe and Northampton counties.

	Annual Growth	9/05	9/06	9/07	9/08	9/09
Assets ($ mil.)	12.3%	656.1	725.8	910.4	993.5	1,042.1
Net income ($ mil.)	10.0%	4.5	4.0	(5.1)	6.1	6.6
Market value ($ mil.)	8.8%	—	—	158.3	197.3	187.5
Employees	4.3%	—	170	185	184	193

⊞ ESSELTE CORPORATION

225 Broadhollow Rd., Ste. 300
Melville, NY 11747
Phone: 800-645-6051
Fax: —
Web: www.esselte.com

CEO: Gary J. Brooks
CFO: Richard A. (Rich) Douville
HR: James (Jim) O'Leary
FYE: December 31
Type: Private

Type it, print it, staple it, drop it in a folder, and store it in a filing cabinet — Esselte is there for each step. With more than 20,000 products, the company is a leading manufacturer of office supplies worldwide. Esselte makes paper-based filing and document management items (files, binders, folders, covers), workspace products (staplers, letter trays), and computer accessories under the Esselte, Leitz, Oxford, Pendaflex, and Xyron brands. Customers range from wholesalers and direct marketers to office superstores and mass retailers, including Wal-Mart, Target, and Staples. Founded in 1913 in Stockholm, Sweden Esselte is controlled by the Boston-based private equity firm J. W. Childs Associates.

ESSENCE COMMUNICATIONS, INC.

135 W. 50th St., 4th Floor
New York, NY 10020
Phone: 212-522-1212
Fax: —
Web: www.essence.com

CEO: Michelle Ebanks
CFO: —
HR: —
FYE: December 31
Type: Subsidiary

Essence Communications, Inc. (ECI) is out to capture the essence of African-American culture through publishing, fashion, and entertainment. The company publishes *ESSENCE*, a magazine geared toward African-American women, which has a monthly circulation of more than 1 million and a readership of 8.5 million. ECI also publishes books and online content (Essence.com), and has licensing operations. In addition, the company hosts the Essence Music Festival, which is held every Fourth of July weekend, and has featured superstars such as Prince, Beyoncé, Mary J. Blige, and Lionel Richie. The first issue of ESSENCE hit the newsstands in 1970. ECI is a subsidiary of Time Inc.

ESSEX INSURANCE COMPANY, INC.

4521 Highwoods Pkwy.
Glen Allen, VA 23060
Phone: 804-273-1400
Fax: 804-273-1435
Web: www.essexinsurance.com

CEO: Brad Dickler
CFO: —
HR: —
FYE: December 31
Type: Subsidiary

Essex Insurance, dba Markel Essex, offers excess and surplus insurance — which isn't the stuff left lying around, it's the insurance coverage companies seek when three other insurers have already turned them down. A subsidiary of specialty insurance provider Markel Corporation, Markel Essex provides coverage for light-to-medium loss exposures typically avoided by standard property/casualty insurers. Offerings include coverage on such niches as short-line railroad, driving schools, logging trucks, and daycares. Its basic products include product liability, truck physical damage, inland and ocean marine, and motor-truck cargo insurance. Some 400 general agents and brokers market its products.

	Annual Growth	12/04	12/05	12/06	12/07	12/08
Est. sales ($ mil.)	—	—	—	—	—	331.8
Employees	—	—	—	—	—	340

ESSEX PROPERTY TRUST, INC.

925 E. Meadow Dr.
Palo Alto, CA 94303
Phone: 650-494-3700
Fax: 650-494-8743
Web: www.essexproperties.com

NYSE: ESS

CEO: Keith R. Guericke
CFO: Michael T. Dance
HR: Suzanne M. Golden
FYE: December 31
Type: Public

Essex is collecting its own kingdom of hamlets on the West Coast. Essex Property Trust acquires, develops, redevelops, and manages apartment communities, focusing on the metropolitan areas of Los Angeles, San Francisco, and Seattle. The self-managed and self-administered real estate investment trust (REIT) owns more than 130 residential communities with approximately 27,000 apartment units; about half are located in Southern California. Essex also owns a handful of office buildings in its home state. The REIT adds to its portfolio through acquisition and through the development and renovation of properties.

	Annual Growth	12/05	12/06	12/07	12/08	12/09
Sales ($ mil.)	5.9%	327.3	348.1	388.5	412.9	411.4
Net income ($ mil.)	(9.4%)	79.7	62.7	115.6	65.4	53.7
Market value ($ mil.)	(2.4%)	2,775.5	3,890.8	2,934.7	2,310.4	2,518.1
Employees	3.4%	820	869	917	930	938

ESSILOR OF AMERICA, INC.

13515 N Stemmons Fwy.
Dallas, TX 75234
Phone: 972-241-4141
Fax: —
Web: www.essilorusa.com

CEO: Hubert Sagnieres
CFO: Kevin A. Rupp
HR: Leslie Wilemon
FYE: December 31
Type: Subsidiary

Essilor of America can help you see more clearly now. The company makes and distributes optical lenses under the Airwear, Crizal, DEFINITY, Transitions, and Varilux brand names, among others. Its Essilor Laboratories of America business, a wholesale laboratory network, provides services and a variety of lens brands to opticians, optometrists and ophthalmologists across the US. Essilor of America is a subsidiary of Paris-based Essilor International, which operates about 250 prescription laboratories that manufacture corrective lenses worldwide. The company has been expanding its operations through acquisitions in recent years. In 2010 it acquired Signet Armorlite.

	Annual Growth	12/04	12/05	12/06	12/07	12/08
Est. sales ($ mil.)	—	—	—	—	—	1.5
Employees	—	—	—	—	—	8,500

ESSROC CEMENT CORP.

3251 Bath Pike
Nazareth, PA 18064
Phone: 610-837-6725
Fax: 610-837-9614
Web: www.essroc.com

CEO: Rodolfo Danielli
CFO: Glenn R. Dalrymple
HR: —
FYE: December 31
Type: Subsidiary

Essroc Cement likes to mix it up. The company operates about a dozen cement plants and other facilities in the US, Canada, and Puerto Rico, and has an annual capacity of more than 6.5 million metric tons of cement. Essroc makes bulk and packaged cement products, including portland cement, ready-mix concrete, and masonry cement. Its AXIM Concrete Technologies subsidiary creates concrete admixtures used to improve the performance quality of cement. Essroc's brands include BRIXMENT, Saylor's PLUS, and VELVET masonry. Its BRAVO line includes masonry chemical products. Founded in 1866 by David Saylor as Coplay Cement, the company is now a part of the Italian cement and building materials group, Italcementi.

⊞ THE ESTÉE LAUDER COMPANIES INC.

767 5th Ave.
New York, NY 10153
Phone: 212-572-4200
Fax: —
Web: www.elcompanies.com

NYSE: EL

CEO: Fabrizio Freda
CFO: Richard W. Kunes
HR: Amy DiGeso
FYE: June 30
Type: Public

The firm's Estée and Bobbi are counted among some of the closest friends to women worldwide. Estée Lauder sells cosmetics, fragrances, and skin care products, with brands including upscale Estée Lauder and Clinique, professional Bobbi Brown *essentials*, and luxurious Tom Ford Collection. The company's lines are sold in department stores, company stores, and by specialty retailers, as well as online. The firm operates a chain of freestanding retail stores (primarily for its M.A.C, Origins, and Aveda brands). The founding Lauder family controls about 75% of its voting shares. CEO Fabrizio Freda, a veteran of Procter & Gamble, joined the firm in 2008.

	Annual Growth	6/05	6/06	6/07	6/08	6/09
Sales ($ mil.)	3.7%	6,336.3	6,463.8	7,037.5	7,910.8	7,323.8
Net income ($ mil.)	(14.4%)	406.1	244.2	449.2	473.8	218.4
Market value ($ mil.)	(4.4%)	7,788.1	7,696.5	9,057.9	9,245.0	6,502.3
Employees	7.2%	23,700	26,200	28,500	32,000	31,300

ESTERLINE TECHNOLOGIES CORPORATION

NYSE: ESL

500 108th Ave. NE, Ste. 1500
Bellevue, WA 98004
Phone: 425-453-9400
Fax: 425-453-2916
Web: www.esterline.com

CEO: R. Bradley (Brad) Lawrence
CFO: Robert D. George
HR: Marcia J. Mason
FYE: October 31
Type: Public

Esterline Technologies has a trio of aerospace & defense and commercial business segments: Avionics & Controls, Sensors & Systems, and Advanced Materials. Avionics & Controls makes interface systems (switches, indicators, keyboards, displays, GPS systems) for aircraft and military vehicles, communications systems, and medical equipment. Sensors & Systems operations include temperature and pressure sensors, as well as power switching, data communications, and fluid control devices. Advanced Materials makes elastomer products and, through the defense group, ordnance and military countermeasures. Esterline Technologies also offers aftermarket parts and service, which have higher sales margins than OEM sales.

	Annual Growth	10/05	10/06	10/07	10/08	10/09
Sales ($ mil.)	14.3%	835.4	972.3	1,266.6	1,483.2	1,425.4
Net income ($ mil.)	19.9%	58.0	55.6	92.3	120.5	119.8
Market value ($ mil.)	2.8%	1,130.3	1,131.9	1,644.6	1,082.3	1,264.3
Employees	7.4%	6,700	8,150	9,361	9,699	8,901

ESTES EXPRESS LINES, INC.

3901 W. Broad St.
Richmond, VA 23230
Phone: 804-353-1900
Fax: 804-353-8001
Web: www.estes-express.com

CEO: Robey W. (Rob) Estes Jr.
CFO: Gary D. Okes
HR: Thomas Donahue
FYE: December 31
Type: Private

Estes Express Lines is a multiregional less-than-truckload (LTL) freight hauler. (LTL carriers consolidate freight from multiple shippers into a single trailer.) The company operates a fleet of about 7,700 tractors and 22,000 trailers from a network of about 200 terminals throughout the US. Estes Express offers service in Canada through ExpressLINK alliance partner TST Overland Express; it works with other companies to offer service in the Caribbean and in Mexico. In addition, it Estes Forwarding Worldwide subsidiary provides ocean and air freight forwarding services. Founded by W.W. Estes in 1931, the company is owned and operated by the Estes family.

	Annual Growth	12/04	12/05	12/06	12/07	12/08
Sales ($ mil.)	10.3%	1,000.0	1,149.0	1,447.2	1,394.6	1,480.0
Employees	(0.1%)	—	13,051	13,824	12,374	13,000

ESURANCE INC.

650 Davis St.
San Francisco, CA 94111
Phone: 415-875-4500
Fax: 415-875-4501
Web: www.esurance.com

CEO: Gary C. Tolman
CFO: Jonathan Adkisson
HR: —
FYE: December 31
Type: Subsidiary

Esurance was an early pioneer selling car insurance to Internet-savvy customers, and it remains one of the leading issuers of auto insurance online. The company offers quote comparisons and sells personal auto policies directly from its website and through select online agents. It also provides online access to accounts and makes telephone agents available for offline questions. Esurance sells auto insurance to customers in 30 states, with California and Florida its leading markets. Subsidiaries Esurance Insurance Company and Esurance Property and Casualty Insurance underwrite the company's auto policies. Esurance has been a subsidiary of White Mountains Insurance Group since 2000.

ETELOS, INC.

OTC: ETLO

1900 O'Farrell St., Ste. 320
San Mateo, CA 94403
Phone: 425-458-4510
Fax: 425-458-4511
Web: www.etelos.com

CEO: Daniel J. A. (Danny) Kolke
CFO: —
HR: Randall G. Clark
FYE: December 31
Type: Public

Etelos is developing into a provider of Web applications tools with a higher profile. The company completed a reverse merger in 2008 with Tripath Technology, a bankrupt chip design firm, and became a publicly held venture in the process. Pursuing the software-as-a-service market, where companies offer applications as a resource on the Internet rather than as packages that need to be installed and maintained at a customer's facilities, Etelos offers what it calls a "platform as a service" for developing Web apps, a Web-based service that developers can access. Its Etelos Marketplace service allows developers to distribute, license, and support Web applications.

	Annual Growth	12/05	12/06	12/07	12/08	12/09
Sales ($ mil.)	(12.6%)	—	0.3	0.3	0.1	0.2
Net income ($ mil.)	—	—	(1.5)	(4.0)	(19.3)	(6.8)
Market value ($ mil.)	126.3%	—	—	0.0	8.0	18.1
Employees	(6.7%)	—	16	34	14	13

ETHAN ALLEN INTERIORS INC.

NYSE: ETH

Ethan Allen Drive
Danbury, CT 06811
Phone: 203-743-8000
Fax: 203-743-8298
Web: www.ethanallen.com

CEO: M. Farooq Kathwari
CFO: David R. Callen
HR: —
FYE: June 30
Type: Public

Furniture maker Ethan Allen Interiors (the holding company for Ethan Allen Inc.) has some revolutionary ideas for your home's living room and other areas. Named after the American patriot, the vertically integrated firm has about 10 furniture factories, including a couple of saw mills. The company's products include case goods (wood furniture, such as beds, dressers, and tables), upholstery items (sofas, recliners), and accessories (wall decor, lighting). They're sold at some 290 Ethan Allen stores located primarily in the US. About half of its stores are operated by independent dealers who are required to deal exclusively in Ethan Allen products and follow company guidelines.

	Annual Growth	6/05	6/06	6/07	6/08	6/09
Sales ($ mil.)	(8.2%)	949.0	1,066.4	1,005.3	980.0	674.3
Net income ($ mil.)	—	79.3	85.7	69.2	58.1	(52.7)
Market value ($ mil.)	(25.4%)	975.6	1,064.1	997.2	716.2	301.6
Employees	(9.5%)	6,400	6,400	6,000	5,800	4,300

ETHICON ENDO-SURGERY, INC.

4545 Creek Rd.
Cincinnati, OH 45242
Phone: 513-337-7000
Fax: 513-337-7912
Web: www.ethiconendo.com

CEO: Kevin Lobo
CFO: —
HR: —
FYE: December 31
Type: Subsidiary

When surgeons need to stock up on tools, Ethicon Endo-Surgery has an endless supply on hand. A subsidiary of Johnson & Johnson, the company makes surgical devices and equipment for open surgeries and minimally invasive procedures. Its products include endoscopic tools, adjustable gastric bands, breast biopsy systems, and the Harmonic Scalpel, which cuts and coagulates tissue using ultrasonic technology to minimize damage during surgery. The company also operates the Endo-Surgery Institute, an educational facility in Cincinnati, as well as additional training centers in Germany and Japan. Ethicon Endo-Surgery markets its products in more than 50 countries worldwide.

An in-depth profile of this company is available to Hoover's Online members at hoovers.com.

579

ETHICON, INC.

Route 22 West
Somerville, NJ 08876
Phone: 908-218-0707
Fax: 908-218-2471
Web: www.ethiconinc.com

CEO: Alex Gorsky
CFO: —
HR: —
FYE: December 31
Type: Subsidiary

Johnson & Johnson subsidiary Ethicon has the operating room all sewn up. The company's Ethicon Products division is a leading maker of sutures and wound-closure products, including absorbable and non-absorbable sutures, Dermabond skin glue, surgical mesh products, and wound drains. Another division, Ethicon Biosurgery, provides a line of absorbable hemostats and other products that help control bleeding during surgery, while the Biopatch unit offers infection-resistant wound dressings. Ethicon Women's Health and Urology makes surgical grafts, devices, and equipment under the Gynecare brand. Ethicon also makes hospital disinfection products through its Advanced Sterilization Products unit.

⊞ E*TRADE FINANCIAL CORPORATION

NASDAQ (GS): ETFC

135 E. 57th St.
New York, NY 10022
Phone: 646-521-4300
Fax: 212-826-2803
Web: www.etrade.com

CEO: Steven J. Freiberg
CFO: Bruce P. Nolop
HR: Karen Wall
FYE: December 31
Type: Public

E*TRADE wants you to use its services for E*VERYTHING financial. A top online brokerage, the company has more than 2.5 million retail account holders who can trade stock over the Internet (the majority of transactions) and by phone. It also offers mutual funds, options, fixed-income products, exchange-traded funds, and portfolio management services. For corporate clients, the company performs market making, trade clearing, and employee stock option plan administration services. Subsidiary E*TRADE Bank offers deposits, savings, and credit cards online, as well as at some 30 financial centers in major US cities; customers can transfer funds between their banking and brokerage accounts in real-time.

	Annual Growth	12/05	12/06	12/07	12/08	12/09
Sales ($ mil.)	(10.1%)	2,637.3	3,921.6	2,440.7	3,149.0	1,721.4
Net income ($ mil.)	—	428.8	628.9	(1,441.8)	(511.8)	(1,297.8)
Market value ($ mil.)	(46.1%)	45,899.3	49,331.9	7,811.2	2,530.4	3,872.6
Employees	(2.3%)	3,400	4,100	3,800	3,249	3,100

EUPA INTERNATIONAL CORP.

Pink Sheets: EUPI

89 N. San Gabriel Blvd.
Pasadena, CA 91107
Phone: 626-793-2688
Fax: 626-286-7127

CEO: Yun-Chang Tsai
CFO: Kung-Chieh Huang
HR: —
FYE: December 31
Type: Public

As the US arm of Tsann Kuen Enterprise (TKE), Eupa International wants to make a TKO in the nation's appliances market. Previously named Access Network Corporation, Eupa makes consumer electronics and home appliances. The manufacturer provides market research, design, sales, and customer support for products, such as coffee makers, irons, toaster ovens, and vacuum cleaners. In addition Eupa is becoming the major supplier of TKE products to brand name distributors in Asia and Europe. TKE owns about 67% of Eupa through its wholly owned subsidiary Tsann Kuen USA.

EURAMAX INTERNATIONAL, INC.

5445 Triangle Pkwy., Ste. 350
Norcross, GA 30092
Phone: 770-449-7066
Fax: 770-449-7354
Web: www.euramax.com

CEO: Mitchell B. Lewis
CFO: R. Scott Vansant
HR: —
FYE: December 31
Type: Private

Euramax International takes aluminum building materials to the max. Operating through multiple subsidiaries, the company supplies metal fabricated components to distributors, OEMs, contractors, and home centers in North America and Europe. In addition to aluminum, its products are produced out of traditional building materials — steel, vinyl, and copper — primarily in the US, and to a lesser extent, in Canada and Europe. Core lines are coated coils, and systems for roofs, walls, windows, and doors, as well as rain-carrying and patio products. Its market for steel roofing, siding, and trim extends to commercial and building construction industries. Euramax also offers RV makers aluminum doors, windows, and sidewalls.

EURO RSCG WORLDWIDE, INC.

350 Hudson St.
New York, NY 10014
Phone: 212-886-2000
Fax: 212-886-2016
Web: www.eurorscg.com

CEO: David Jones
CFO: Jean-Marc Antoni
HR: —
FYE: December 31
Type: Subsidiary

This Euro coaxes consumers to spend their dollars and cents on ad campaigns. Euro RSCG Worldwide operates one of the world's leading creative advertising agency networks, with more than 230 offices in about 75 countries. It offers creative ad design and campaign management, branding and other marketing services, and public relations services. Euro RSCG also provides specialized communications and marketing services for companies in the health care industry through Euro RSCG Life. Its Euro RSCG 4D unit is a leading direct marketing and interactive services agency. Clients have included Air France, IBM, and Schering-Plough. Euro RSCG is the primary advertising agency network of French holding company Havas.

⊞ EUROMARKET DESIGNS, INC.

1250 Techny Rd.
Northbrook, IL 60062
Phone: 847-272-2888
Fax: 847-272-5366
Web: www.crateandbarrel.com

CEO: Barbara A. Turf
CFO: Diane M. Pearse
HR: Susie Muellman
FYE: February 28
Type: Private

Think you've never bought anything from Euromarket Designs? Think again. The retailer, which does business under the Crate & Barrel name, pioneered the fashionable-yet-homey look for contemporary interiors, offering furniture, housewares, and linens in *au courant* colors and styles. It operates some 160 Crate & Barrel locations (including a dozen outlet stores) in 30 states and also peddles products through its catalogs and website. Euromarket Designs' other retailing ventures include CB2 (modern home furnishings) and The Land of Nod (furniture and toys for children). The company was founded by Carole and Gordon Segal in 1962. It is majority-owned by Germany-based Otto, the world's largest mail-order merchant.

EURONET WORLDWIDE, INC.

NASDAQ (GS): EEFT

4601 College Blvd., Ste. 300
Leawood, KS 66211
Phone: 913-327-4200
Fax: 913-327-1921
Web: www.euronetworldwide.com

CEO: Michael J. (Mike) Brown
CFO: Rick L. Weller
HR: —
FYE: December 31
Type: Public

Euronet Worldwide might soon have the whole world in its net — thanks to its network of ATMs and other electronic financial services. Banks, card issuers, and other institutions pay the firm for managing transactions at more than 10,000 ATMs and some 400,000 point-of-sale terminals in 100 countries across Africa, Europe, India, and the Middle East. The company operates in three segments: its aforementioned EFT (electronic funds transfer) services; epay, which provides prepaid mobile phone cards and other prepaid products and collection services; and money transfer, which performs global money transfer and bill pay services.

	Annual Growth	12/05	12/06	12/07	12/08	12/09
Sales ($ mil.)	18.1%	531.2	629.2	917.6	1,045.7	1,032.7
Net income ($ mil.)	3.8%	27.4	46.3	53.5	(195.1)	31.8
Market value ($ mil.)	(5.7%)	1,415.4	1,511.6	1,527.4	591.1	1,117.5
Employees	30.7%	926	1,098	2,500	2,500	2,700

EV ENERGY PARTNERS, L.P.

NASDAQ (GS): EVEP

1001 Fannin St., Ste. 800
Houston, TX 77002
Phone: 713-651-1144
Fax: 713-651-1260
Web: www.evenergypartners.com

CEO: John B. Walker
CFO: Michael E. (Mike) Mercer
HR: —
FYE: December 31
Type: Public

EV Energy Partners is a natural gas and oil exploration and production company, which operates in the Appalachian Basin, primarily in West Virginia and Ohio, as well as in Louisiana, Michigan, Oklahoma, and Texas. In 2007 EV Energy Partners reported estimated proved reserves of 250 billion cu. ft. of natural gas and 4.5 million barrels of oil. Its base in the Appalachian Basin puts EV Energy Partners in close proximity to the nation's major consuming markets, allowing for stronger pricing power. EV Energy Partners was formed in 2006 by Canadian energy industry investment group EnerVest, which owns 71% of EV Energy Partners' general partner.

	Annual Growth	12/05	12/06	12/07	12/08	12/09
Sales ($ mil.)	28.9%	44.2	7.8	100.8	205.7	121.9
Net income ($ mil.)	(44.8%)	15.1	3.4	11.2	225.5	1.4
Market value ($ mil.)	8.8%	—	634.3	879.5	397.0	818.0
Employees	14.0%	332	360	465	500	560

EV3 INC.

NASDAQ (GS): EVVV

9600 54th Ave. North, Ste. 100
Plymouth, MN 55442
Phone: 763-398-7000
Fax: 763-398-7200
Web: www.ev3.net

CEO: Robert J. (Bob) Palmisano
CFO: Shawn McCormick
HR: Gregory Morrison
FYE: December 31
Type: Public

Here's what the "ev" in ev3 stands for: endovascular. The "3" refers to the three systems the catheter maker targets: peripheral vascular, neurovascular, and cardiovascular. ev3 develops, manufactures, and sells catheter-based medical devices used to treat vascular diseases, especially disorders in the heart and brain. ev3's products include stents, microcatheters, guidewires, embolic coils, and stroke reduction devices. The company sells more than 100 products in more than 60 countries through a direct sales team and distributors. Among its customers are radiologists, cardiologists, neurosurgeons, and vascular surgeons. ev3 is being acquired by medical equipment firm Covidien for $2.6 billion.

	Annual Growth	12/05	12/06	12/07	12/08	12/09
Sales ($ mil.)	35.4%	133.7	202.4	284.2	422.1	449.1
Net income ($ mil.)	—	(110.0)	(52.4)	(165.7)	(335.6)	41.9
Market value ($ mil.)	(2.5%)	1,668.3	1,950.1	1,438.5	690.4	1,509.8
Employees	11.3%	880	975	1,600	1,250	1,350

EVANS & SUTHERLAND COMPUTER

Pink Sheets: ESCC

770 Komas Dr.
Salt Lake City, UT 84108
Phone: 801-588-1000
Fax: 801-588-4500
Web: www.es.com

CEO: David H. (Dave) Bateman
CFO: Paul L. Dailey Jr.
HR: Bob Morishita
FYE: December 31
Type: Public

Evans & Sutherland Computer Corporation (E&S) makes products that can impartially be described as stellar. The company provides hardware and software used in digital planetariums and other theaters. Its products include laser projectors, domed projection screens, and complete planetarium packages. The company also produces planetarium content. E&S sells its visual systems to theaters and schools; its domes are additionally marketed to casinos, theme parks, and military contractors. The company counts Disney, Griffith Observatory, IMAX, Texas A&M University, and Universal Studios among its customers. E&S gets more than half of its sales in the US.

	Annual Growth	12/05	12/06	12/07	12/08	12/09
Sales ($ mil.)	(23.6%)	73.6	15.0	26.2	37.7	25.1
Net income ($ mil.)	—	(1.1)	22.0	(6.3)	(4.0)	(7.8)
Market value ($ mil.)	(62.2%)	54.3	46.6	13.2	6.7	1.1
Employees	(21.6%)	268	118	124	126	101

EVANS BANCORP, INC.

NASDAQ (GM): EVBN

1 Grimsby Dr.
Hamburg, NY 14075
Phone: 716-926-2000
Fax: 716-926-2005
Web: www.evansbancorp.com

CEO: David J. Nasca
CFO: Gary A. Kajtoch
HR: —
FYE: December 31
Type: Public

Evans National Bank wants to take care of Buffalo's bills. The Evans Bancorp subsidiary operates about a dozen branches in western New York (including Buffalo). The bank primarily uses funds gathered from deposits to originate commercial and residential real estate loans (more than 70% of its loan portfolio) and to invest in securities. Subsidiaries include ENB Insurance Agency, which sells property/casualty insurance; ENB Associates, offering mutual funds and annuities to bank customers; and Evans National Leasing, which provides financing for business equipment throughout the US. Evans Bancorp aquired the assets and single branch of the failed Waterford Village Bank in Clarence, New York, in 2009.

	Annual Growth	12/05	12/06	12/07	12/08	12/09
Assets ($ mil.)	7.2%	468.5	473.9	442.7	529.0	619.4
Net income ($ mil.)	(38.2%)	4.8	4.9	3.4	4.9	0.7
Market value ($ mil.)	(13.9%)	58.6	55.7	44.7	42.8	32.1
Employees	4.9%	186	194	209	229	225

EVCI CAREER COLLEGES HOLDING CORP.

Pink Sheets: EVCI

1 Van Der Donck St., 2nd Fl.
Yonkers, NY 10701
Phone: 914-623-0700
Fax: 914-964-8222
Web: www.evcinc.com

CEO: John J. McGrath
CFO: Henry Hetherington
HR: —
FYE: December 31
Type: Public

EVCI provides on-campus college education through three institutions: the Interboro Institute, Technical Career Institutes, and Pennsylvania School of Business. Interboro (2,700 students) offers associate degrees to students who have GEDs or did not graduate from high school. Students earn an associate of occupational studies degree in areas such as accounting, medical assistant, executive assistant, paralegal studies, ophthalmic dispensing, and security. Technical Career (3,000 students) degrees include office technology, facilities management technology, and industrial technology. The Pennsylvania School of Business (325 students) offers training in office and medical billing operations, among others.

An in-depth profile of this company is available to Hoover's Online members at hoovers.com.

581

EVENFLO COMPANY, INC.

1801 Commerce Dr.
Piqua, OH 45356
Phone: 937-415-3300
Fax: 937-415-3112
Web: www.evenflo.com

CEO: Perry Odak
CFO: Mike Katafiasz
HR: Dennis Pregent
FYE: December 31
Type: Private

Those having a baby say hello to Evenflo. Named for a nursing device patented in 1935, the veteran company offers hundreds of items for the well-equipped baby and tot, including car seats, strollers, portable cribs, bath items, baby monitors, and feeding and safety products under the names Evenflo, ExerSaucer, and Snugli, among others. Its website offers parenting resources with safety recalls and child care information. Evenflo has international sales operations in Canada, Mexico, and the Philippines. The firm sells its products through specialty retailers and big box stores, such as Target and Wal-Mart. An affiliate of private equity firm Weston Presidio bought Evenflo from Harvest Partners in early 2007.

EVERBANK FINANCIAL CORPORATION

501 Riverside Ave.
Jacksonville, FL 32202
Phone: 904-281-6000
Fax: 904-281-6165
Web: www.everbank.com

CEO: Robert M. Clements
CFO: W. Blake Wilson
HR: —
FYE: December 31
Type: Private

EverBank Financial helps bank accounts stay evergreen. The privately held holding company owns home loan servicer EverHome Mortgage, which manages some 340,000 loans, and EverBank, which offers community banking services through more than a dozen branches in Florida. The company has a mortgage production joint venture with priceline.com, and provides online banking through EverBank Direct. It also offers wholesale residential and commercial real estate lending. EverBank got a boost in 2008 when private investment firm Sageview Capital contributed over $100 million to the company.

	Annual Growth	12/04	12/05	12/06	12/07	12/08
Est. sales ($ mil.)	—	—	—	—	—	498.3
Employees	—	—	—	—	—	1,500

EVERCORE PARTNERS INC.

NYSE: EVR

55 E. 52nd St., 43rd Fl.
New York, NY 10055
Phone: 212-857-3100
Fax: 212-857-3101
Web: www.evercore.com

CEO: Ralph L. Schlosstein
CFO: Robert B. Walsh
HR: Robert B. Walsh
FYE: December 31
Type: Public

Evercore Partners provides financial, restructuring, and mergers and acquisitions advisory services to corporate clients. Subsidiary Evercore Asset Management serves institutional investors and focuses on small- and mid-cap equities. Subsidiary Protego, a boutique investment bank founded by Pedro Aspe, Mexico's former Minister of Finance, specializes in financing municipal infrastructure and energy projects in Mexico. Evercore Europe provides services from its London office. The company also has a venture capital fund. As a boutique investment firm, Evercore believes that it operates without the conflicts of interest that plague larger firms that both underwrite and invest in their clients.

	Annual Growth	12/05	12/06	12/07	12/08	12/09
Sales ($ mil.)	25.7%	125.6	209.7	321.6	224.9	313.1
Net income ($ mil.)	—	63.2	3.8	(34.5)	(4.7)	(1.6)
Market value ($ mil.)	(6.2%)	—	631.4	369.2	214.0	520.9
Employees	29.3%	120	247	290	335	335

EVEREST RE GROUP, LTD.

NYSE: RE

477 Martinsville Rd.
Liberty Corner, NJ 07938
Phone: 908-604-3000
Fax: 908-604-3322
Web: www.everestre.com

CEO: Joseph V. (Joe) Taranto
CFO: Dominic J. (Dom) Addesso
HR: Barry H. Smith
FYE: December 31
Type: Public

Everest Re Group is in peak form; it's the holding company for Everest Reinsurance Company (Everest Re), an underwriter of property & casualty reinsurance and insurance. Everest Re markets to US and international insurance companies directly and through independent brokers. Under its reinsurance arrangements, Everest Re assumes risks of policies written by other insurance companies. The company offers specialized underwriting in several areas, including property/casualty, marine, aviation, and surety, as well as medical malpractice, directors and officers liability, and professional errors and omissions liability.

	Annual Growth	12/05	12/06	12/07	12/08	12/09
Assets ($ mil.)	2.2%	16,474.5	17,107.6	17,999.5	16,846.6	18,001.3
Net income ($ mil.)	—	(218.7)	840.8	839.3	(18.8)	807.0
Market value ($ mil.)	(3.9%)	5,912.9	5,780.9	5,915.8	4,486.4	5,048.5
Employees	6.5%	670	736	779	858	863

EVEREST REINSURANCE COMPANY

477 Martinsville Rd.
Liberty Corner, NJ 07938
Phone: 908-604-3000
Fax: 908-604-3322
Web: www.everestre.com

CEO: Joseph V. (Joe) Taranto
CFO: —
HR: —
FYE: December 31
Type: Subsidiary

Everest Reinsurance, part of the Everest Re Group, provides property/casualty reinsurance and insurance in the US through a handful of subsidiaries. Its Everest National Insurance underwrites property/casualty insurance in 47 states. While not technically a niche provider, Everest Security Insurance sells auto insurance only in Alabama, Georgia, and South Carolina. Everest Indemnity Insurance writes excess and surplus lines in 49 states, the District of Columbia, and Puerto Rico. Everest Insurance Company of Canada no longer writes new business, and is operating in run-off. Formed in 1973, the company also offers actuarial support, claims management, and loss control services.

	Annual Growth	12/04	12/05	12/06	12/07	12/08
Est. sales ($ mil.)	—	—	—	—	—	3,527.6
Employees	—	—	—	—	—	377

EVERGREEN ENERGY INC.

NYSE Arca: EEE

55 Madison St., Ste. 745
Denver, CO 80206
Phone: 303-293-2992
Fax: 303-293-8430
Web: www.evgenergy.com

CEO: Thomas H. Stoner Jr.
CFO: Diana L. Kubik
HR: Victoria Yeung
FYE: December 31
Type: Public

Evergreen Energy wants to fuel the advancement of efficient, environmentally friendly power generation. The company, operating through subsidiaries, deploys a process known as K-Fuel that uses heat and pressure to transform low-energy value coal and other feedstocks into high-energy fuel for power plants. After low-grade coal has been through the K-Fuel process, it can be used without causing power plants to violate pollution standards. Evergreen's C-Lock process, which it calls GreenCert, is a Web-based platform that tracks carbon emissions to be used to quantify carbon emission credits.

	Annual Growth	12/05	12/06	12/07	12/08	12/09
Sales ($ mil.)	166.8%	1.0	36.7	48.7	58.9	50.7
Net income ($ mil.)	—	(23.3)	(51.5)	(204.7)	—	(58.5)
Market value ($ mil.)	(62.6%)	3,450.4	2,003.0	446.9	—	67.5
Employees	19.1%	72	216	—	208	145

EVERGREEN HOLDINGS, INC.

3850 Three Mile Ln.	CEO: Delford M. (Del) Smith
McMinnville, OR 97128	CFO: John A. Irwin
Phone: 503-472-9361	HR: —
Fax: 503-472-1048	FYE: February 28
Web: www.evergreenaviation.com	Type: Holding company

Through subsidiary Evergreen International Aviation, Evergreen Holdings soars over green lands. Evergreen International Aviation itself operates through several units, including Evergreen International Airlines, which transports cargo for government and commercial customers with a fleet of Boeing 747 freighters. Evergreen Aviation Ground Logistics Enterprise provides ground handling services at US airports. Other Evergreen units offer helicopter transportation services; maintain, repair, and overhaul aircraft; sell and lease aircraft; and engage in farming. Del Smith, a former Air Force pilot and crop duster, owns a controlling stake in the company, which he founded in 1960.

EVERGREEN INVESTMENT MANAGEMENT COMPANY, LLC

30 Dan Rd.	CEO: Peter Cieszko
Canton, MA 02021	CFO: —
Phone: 617-338-3200	HR: —
Fax: 617-210-2786	FYE: December 31
Web: www.evergreeninvestments.com	Type: Subsidiary

Love may be soft as an easy chair, but this Evergreen knows that money — and lots of it — really provides comfort. Evergreen Investment Management (Evergreen Investments for short) manages about 75 stock, bond, and money market mutual funds for more than 3 million individual and institutional investors. In addition, the company offers alternative investments (hedge funds, private equity, real estate), closed-end funds, separately managed accounts, customized portfolios, IRAs, variable annuities, and financial advisory services. Evergreen's former parent, Wachovia, was bought by banking giant Wells Fargo in 2008. It has more than $160 billion of assets under management.

	Annual Growth	12/04	12/05	12/06	12/07	12/08
Est. sales ($ mil.)	—	—	—	—	—	244.5
Employees	—	—	—	—	—	1,800

EVERGREEN SHIPPING AGENCY (AMERICA) CORP.

1 Evertrust Plaza	CEO: Thomas Chen
Jersey City, NJ 07302	CFO: —
Phone: 201-761-3000	HR: —
Fax: 201-761-3011	FYE: December 31
Web: www.evergreen-shipping.us	Type: Subsidiary

Evergreen Shipping Agency (America), formerly known as Evergreen America, serves as the US agent for its Taiwan-based parent, shipping giant Evergreen Marine Corporation, as well as two other shipping lines, Italia Marittima and Hatsu Marine Limited. As a shipping agent, the company provides ground-based administrative services and coordinates inland transportation of marine freight. The company has about five logistics centers in the US and one in Canada, and it operates through agents in Latin America. Evergreen Shipping Agency (America) was founded in 1968.

EVERGREEN SOLAR, INC.

NASDAQ (GM): ESLR

138 Bartlett St.	CEO: Richard M. Feldt
Marlboro, MA 01752	CFO: Michael (Mike) El-Hillow
Phone: 508-357-2221	HR: Gary T. Pollard
Fax: 508-229-0747	FYE: December 31
Web: www.evergreensolar.com	Type: Public

In the theater of alternative energy, Evergreen Solar is a rising star. Using a proprietary, low-cost silicon wafer manufacturing technology — String Ribbon — the company makes and markets solar power products, including solar cells, panels, and systems. Residential and commercial applications for Evergreen's solar modules (assemblies of photovoltaic solar cells) range from highway call boxes to street and billboard lighting, and on-grid and off-grid rural electrification. It sells solar panels made by its Sovello affiliate under the Evergreen brand. Customers include Donauer Solartechnik, Krannich Solartechnik, and SunPower Systems. Evergreen Solar gets about half of its sales in Germany.

	Annual Growth	12/05	12/06	12/07	12/08	12/09
Sales ($ mil.)	57.7%	44.0	103.1	69.9	112.0	271.8
Net income ($ mil.)	—	(17.3)	(26.7)	(16.6)	(84.9)	(265.2)
Market value ($ mil.)	(38.6%)	2,215.7	1,574.9	3,592.9	663.7	314.1
Employees	25.9%	290	330	400	801	729

EVERLAST WORLDWIDE INC.

183 Madison Ave., Ste. 1701	CEO: Adam Geisler
New York, NY 10016	CFO: Gary J. Dailey
Phone: 212-239-0990	HR: Ronnie Kornblum
Fax: 212-239-4261	FYE: December 31
Web: www.everlast.com	Type: Subsidiary

Everlast Worldwide has been a real contender in the business world, with one foot in the ring and one foot in the closet. Everlast trunks and boxing gloves have outfitted pugilists from Jack Dempsey to Muhammad Ali; its name is a fixture in and out of the ring. Having extended its reach into mixed martial arts, Everlast Worldwide also licenses its name for distribution overseas and to makers of children's wear, footwear, watches, exercise equipment, gym bags, and other products. Everlast Worldwide sells its products through department and sporting goods stores, as well as through online and catalog retailers. The company was acquired by Brands Holdings, a unit of Sports Direct International, in late 2007.

EVOLUTION PETROLEUM CORPORATION

NYSE Amex: EPM

2500 CityWest Blvd., Ste. 1300	CEO: Robert S. Herlin
Houston, TX 77042	CFO: Sterling H. McDonald
Phone: 713-935-0122	HR: —
Fax: 713-935-0199	FYE: June 30
Web: www.evolutionpetroleum.com	Type: Public

Petroleum evolved from old living forms, and Evolution Petroleum evolved from Natural Gas Systems (which was formed in 2003). The crude oil and natural gas exploration company operates oil and gas producing fields in Louisiana. Its strategy is to acquire already-established properties and to redevelop them, thereby making the fields more profitable. One method it uses is gas flooding, which uses carbon dioxide to free up trapped oil deposits. In 2007 the company reported proved reserves of 1.7 million barrels of oil equivalent and probable reserves of up to 16 million barrels of oil equivalent.

	Annual Growth	6/05	6/06	6/07	6/08	6/09
Sales ($ mil.)	39.7%	1.6	2.9	1.9	4.3	6.1
Net income ($ mil.)	—	(2.2)	24.6	(1.8)	(1.6)	(2.6)
Market value ($ mil.)	11.2%	46.2	78.7	82.3	165.6	70.6
Employees	38.4%	3	3	6	12	11

An in-depth profile of this company is available to Hoover's Online members at hoovers.com.

583

EVOLVING SYSTEMS, INC.

NASDAQ (CM): EVOL

9777 Pyramid Ct., Ste. 100
Englewood, CO 80112
Phone: 303-802-1000
Fax: 303-802-1420
Web: www.evolving.com

CEO: Thaddeus (Thad) Dupper
CFO: Brian R. Ervine Sr.
HR: —
FYE: December 31
Type: Public

Evolving Systems offers software for the ever-evolving telecommunications industry. The company provides applications used by telecom companies to automate and manage parts of their network operations, including tools for managing and monitoring number inventory, as well as applications that allow users to route calls and messages to various devices. The company also provides local number portability software that allows telephone customers to keep the same phone number when changing to a new carrier. Evolving Systems has expanded its international operations in Africa, Asia, and Central America and added products for managing SIM cards.

	Annual Growth	12/05	12/06	12/07	12/08	12/09
Sales ($ mil.)	(0.8%)	39.5	33.8	36.0	37.8	38.2
Net income ($ mil.)	—	(2.8)	(16.8)	0.6	2.9	4.8
Market value ($ mil.)	10.3%	42.3	23.5	59.7	16.0	62.6
Employees	1.8%	227	227	226	238	244

EVONIK CYRO LLC

379 Interpace Pkwy.
Parsippany, NJ 07054
Phone: 973-541-8000
Fax: 973-541-8445
Web: www.cyro.com

CEO: John Rolando
CFO: Robert S. (Bob) Wurst
HR: Keith Baumann
FYE: December 31
Type: Subsidiary

Evonik Cyro's scope includes the manufacturing of all manner of acrylics. The company is a part of Evonik Methacrylates, the performance polymers unit of German specialty chemicals company EvonikDegussa. Evonik Cyro produces acrylic sheets and film and methyl methacrylates. Among the markets it serves and end uses of its own products: signage, sporting goods, jet and helicopter windows, hockey rink protective walls, office equipment, medical devices, and flat-panel displays.

	Annual Growth	12/04	12/05	12/06	12/07	12/08
Est. sales ($ mil.)	—	—	—	—	—	400.0
Employees	—	—	—	—	—	700

EVONIK DEGUSSA CORPORATION

379 Interpace Pkwy.
Parsippany, NJ 07054
Phone: 973-541-8000
Fax: 973-541-8013
Web: www.degussa-nafta.com

CEO: Tom Bates
CFO: James Hickey
HR: Thomas P. (Tom) Ayers
FYE: December 31
Type: Subsidiary

Evonik Degussa Corporation is the North America arm of German chemical giant Evonik Degussa GmbH. Like its parent, it operates through six divisions, the biggest of which are Industrial Chemicals (chlorides and peroxides) and Inorganic Materials (silicon products and carbon black). The other units are Consumer Specialties, Health and Nutrition, Coatings and Additives, and Performance Polymers. Products range from amino acids and building protection coatings to another of its specialties: specialty acrylic products including its best known brand, Plexiglas. In addition to the automotive industry, Evonik Degussa serves makers of coatings, pharmaceuticals, and plastics.

EVONIK STOCKHAUSEN, INC.

2401 Doyle St.
Greensboro, NC 27406
Phone: 336-333-3500
Fax: 336-333-7934
Web: www.stockhausen-inc.com

CEO: Reinhold Brand
CFO: Carsten Schminke
HR: Barry DuBois
FYE: December 31
Type: Subsidiary

What makes a baby's bottom so smooth, anyway? Well, Evonik Stockhausen's absorbent polymers are used in diapers to take the wetness away from the skin, so maybe that's it. The company also manufactures chemicals for skin care treatments (synthetic detergents and heavy-duty cleaners). Stockhausen's US manufacturing facilities are located in North Carolina and Louisiana. Brand names include Favor (superabsorbers used in diapers and other products), Stoko (for skin care and cleaning products), and Creasorb (fluid management products). The company is the American branch of Evonik Degussa subsidiary Evonik Stockhausen GmbH.

EVRAZ INC. NA

1000 SW Broadway, Ste. 2200
Portland, OR 97205
Phone: 503-223-9228
Fax: —
Web: www.evrazincna.com

CEO: Michael T. (Mike) Rehwinkel
CFO: Robin A. Gantt
HR: Marshall Hamilton
FYE: December 31
Type: Subsidiary

The Russians have come to the North American steel market in the form of Evraz Inc. NA. The company is the North American unit of Russian steel giant Evraz, holding businesses acquired since 2006. Evraz Inc. NA consists of tubular goods producer Evraz Oregon Steel Tubular, steel plate manufacturer Claymont Steel, and Canadian steel tube operations that formerly had belonged to IPSCO. Evraz entered the North American market with the acquisition of Oregon Steel Mills in 2006 and has kept the acquisitions coming ever since. In mid-2008, when it closed the IPSCO deal, the company decided to gather all of these businesses under one umbrella — thus the formation of Evraz Inc. NA.

E.W. HOWELL CO., INC.

113 Crossways Park Dr.
Woodbury, NY 11797
Phone: 516-921-7100
Fax: 516-921-0119
Web: www.ewhowell.com

CEO: Howard L. Rowland
CFO: —
HR: —
FYE: December 31
Type: Subsidiary

E.W. Howell is a midsized New York general contractor and construction management firm that is a regional leader in retail construction. With offices in Manhattan and Long Island, E.W. Howell also builds hospitals, labs, libraries, office interiors, schools, and restaurants. Clients have included Bergdorf Goodman, Target, and Columbia University. It typically bids on projects in the private sector but also selectively competes within the public sector. Established in 1891, E.W. Howell began as a builder of homes for such well-heeled East Coast families as the Huttons and the Guggenheims. The Howells left the firm in the 1980s, and Japanese construction group Obayashi acquired the company in 1989.

THE E. W. SCRIPPS COMPANY

NYSE: SSP

312 Walnut St.
Cincinnati, OH 45202
Phone: 513-977-3000
Fax: 513-977-3721
Web: www.scripps.com

CEO: Richard A. (Rich) Boehne
CFO: Timothy E. (Tim) Stautberg
HR: Mary Minser
FYE: December 31
Type: Public

You might say this media company tries to be appealing to both newspaper readers and television viewers. The E. W. Scripps Company is a venerable newspaper publisher with a portfolio of more than 15 dailies, including *The Commercial Appeal* (Memphis, Tennessee), the *Knoxville News Sentinel* (Tennessee), and the *Ventura County Star* (California). Scripps also owns 10 local TV stations, most of which are affiliated with broadcast networks ABC and NBC. In addition, subsidiaries Scripps Howard News Service and United Media distribute syndicated news and other content, including columnists, editorial cartoons, and such comic strips as *Dilbert* and *Peanuts*. The Scripps family controls the company through various trusts.

	Annual Growth	12/05	12/06	12/07	12/08	12/09
Sales ($ mil.)	(24.8%)	2,513.9	2,498.1	2,517.1	1,001.8	802.4
Net income ($ mil.)	—	249.2	353.2	(1.6)	(476.6)	(209.6)
Market value ($ mil.)	(10.9%)	629.8	654.9	590.3	125.8	396.2
Employees	(15.0%)	9,600	9,000	8,500	6,000	5,000

EXACT SCIENCES CORPORATION

NASDAQ (GM): EXAS

100 Campus Dr.
Marlborough, MA 01752
Phone: 508-683-1200
Fax: 508-683-1201
Web: www.exactlabs.com

CEO: Kevin T. Conroy
CFO: Maneesh K. Arora
HR: —
FYE: December 31
Type: Public

Guesstimates aren't good enough when diagnosing a deadly cancer, so EXACT Sciences aims for accuracy. The firm develops non-invasive tests for the early detection of colorectal cancer and precancerous lesions. Its products isolate DNA in stool samples, using its Effipure technology, then identify genetic mutations associated with cancer. Colorectal cancer is a common (and one of the deadliest) cancers, and EXACT believes its method is superior to existing diagnostic methods because it may be able to discern colorectal cancer in its early stages, when it is most treatable. However, facing several product development setbacks, the company is undergoing a strategic reorganization.

	Annual Growth	12/05	12/06	12/07	12/08	12/09
Sales ($ mil.)	2.8%	4.3	4.8	2.9	(0.9)	4.8
Net income ($ mil.)	—	(14.5)	(12.9)	(12.0)	(9.7)	(9.1)
Market value ($ mil.)	11.3%	88.6	113.5	129.1	22.9	135.9
Employees	(21.1%)	49	22	14	4	19

EXACT SOFTWARE NORTH AMERICA, INC.

35 Village Rd.
Middleton, MA 01949
Phone: 978-560-6900
Fax: 978-560-6901
Web: www.exactamerica.com

CEO: Mitchell (Mitch) Alcon
CFO: Alex N. Braverman
HR: —
FYE: December 31
Type: Subsidiary

Exact Software North America wants to give its customers an exact view of their operations and clients. The company, which was called Macola before its acquisition by Dutch software maker Exact Holding, provides small to mid-sized businesses with enterprise resource planning (ERP), customer relationship management (CRM), and related software. These applications help companies track and manage their interactions with customers — even when both supplier and customer have widely scattered operations — as well as the interactions between various parts of their own operations.

EXACTECH, INC.

NASDAQ (GM): EXAC

2320 NW 66th Ct.
Gainesville, FL 32653
Phone: 352-377-1140
Fax: 352-378-2617
Web: www.exac.com

CEO: William (Bill) Petty
CFO: Joel C. Phillips
HR: Betty B. Petty
FYE: December 31
Type: Public

Back off, lawman — Exactech's joints are medicinal. Hospitals, surgeons, and clinics worldwide use the company's knee and hip devices to replace joints weakened by injury or disease. Its Optetrak knee implants and AcuMatch hip implant system either partially or totally replace patients' damaged joints. It also markets Opteform and Optefil, bone allograft materials used to correct bone defects and damage. Exactech markets its products through independent dealers in the US and primarily through distributors in some 25 other countries. Chairman, president, and CEO William Petty and his family own about a third of Exactech, which was founded in 1985 by an orthopedic surgeon.

	Annual Growth	12/05	12/06	12/07	12/08	12/09
Sales ($ mil.)	18.1%	91.0	102.4	124.2	161.7	177.3
Net income ($ mil.)	5.9%	6.6	7.8	8.9	11.1	8.3
Market value ($ mil.)	10.9%	147.3	183.2	267.1	216.8	222.8
Employees	17.5%	214	215	265	390	408

EXACTTARGET, INC.

20 N. Meridian St.
Indianapolis, IN 46204
Phone: 317-423-3928
Fax: 317-396-1592
Web: www.exacttarget.com

CEO: Scott D. Dorsey
CFO: Traci M. Dolan
HR: C. Todd Richardson
FYE: December 31
Type: Private

ExactTarget aims to be the Google of the Midwest. The company offers a wide blend of e-mail marketing software used for creating marketing campaigns. Its agency and retailer software helps customers create and personalize e-mails, build lists, and track the results of their campaigns. Utilizing the software-as-a-service (SaaS) model, ExactTarget partners with other sales and marketing systems supplied by salesforce.com, Microsoft Dynamics, Omniture, and WebTrends. Its clients span many industries and include CareerBuilder, Charles Schwab, Wellpoint, and firms with fewer than 150 employees. ExactTarget was founded in 2000 by president and CEO Scott Dorsey and GM Peter McCormick.

	Annual Growth	12/04	12/05	12/06	12/07	12/08
Est. sales ($ mil.)	—	—	—	—	—	27.4
Employees	—	—	—	—	—	275

EXAR CORPORATION

NASDAQ (GM): EXAR

48720 Kato Rd.
Fremont, CA 94538
Phone: 510-668-7000
Fax: 510-668-7001
Web: www.exar.com

CEO: Pedro P. (Pete) Rodriguez
CFO: Kevin Bauer
HR: Diane Hill
FYE: March 31
Type: Public

Exar seeks excellence in the exacting world of high-speed communications chips. The fabless semiconductor company's digital, analog, and mixed-signal integrated circuits are used in broadband networking equipment — especially telecommunications infrastructure gear — as well as in video and imaging devices, such as medical instrumentation, digital still cameras, and scanners. Exar's customers include Alcatel-Lucent, Apple, Cisco Systems, Fujitsu, Hewlett-Packard, IBM, LG Electronics, Motorola, NEC, Nokia Siemens Networks, and Samsung Electronics. The company derives three-quarters of its sales outside the US.

	Annual Growth	3/05	3/06	3/07	3/08	3/09
Sales ($ mil.)	19.0%	57.4	67.0	68.5	89.7	115.1
Net income ($ mil.)	—	5.3	7.8	8.0	(195.9)	(73.0)
Market value ($ mil.)	(17.4%)	587.1	625.7	580.1	360.6	273.4
Employees	8.3%	268	255	234	404	368

An in-depth profile of this company is available to Hoover's Online members at hoovers.com.

585

EXCEL TRUST, INC.

NYSE: EXL

17140 Bernardo Center Dr., Ste. 300
San Diego, CA 92128
Phone: 858-613-1800
Fax: 858-487-9890
Web: www.excelreit.com

CEO: Gary B. Sabin
CFO: James Y. Nakagawa
HR: —
FYE: December 31
Type: Public

Excel Trust likes to buy retail space off the clearance rack. Based in San Diego, the self-managed, self-administered real estate investment trust has a penchant for acquiring high-value retail properties at a reduced cost — including anchored and "power" shopping centers and freestanding retail properties — located in the Northwest, Northeast, and the Sunbelt regions. Excel went public in 2010. The company raised some $194 million in order to acquire more properties. Excel owns about 20 retail and commercial properties totaling more than 1 million sq. ft. of leasable space. Tenants include Walgreens, Publix, and Dollar Tree.

	Annual Growth	12/05	12/06	12/07	12/08	12/09
Sales ($ mil.)	5.4%	—	—	4.5	3.8	5.0
Net income ($ mil.)	41.4%	—	—	0.1	(0.4)	0.2
Employees	—	—	—	—	—	20

EXCELLUS BLUECROSS BLUESHIELD

165 Court St.
Rochester, NY 14647
Phone: 585-454-1700
Fax: 585-238-4233
Web: www.excellusbcbs.com

CEO: David H. Klein
CFO: Emil D. Duda
HR: Ellen Wilson
FYE: December 31
Type: Subsidiary

Excellus BlueCross BlueShield aims to excel as a provider of health insurance plans. The insurance firm serves some 2 million members in over 30 counties in upstate New York. Its offerings include HMO, PPO, managed care, and low-cost health plans for individuals, families, and businesses large and small, as well as Medicare and supplemental dental plans. Excellus BlueCross BlueShield operates through four regional divisions: Central New York, Central New York Southern Tier, Rochester, and Utica. The company is a subsidiary of the not-for-profit organization The Lifetime Healthcare Companies, and is a licensee of the Blue Cross and Blue Shield Association.

EXCHANGE BANK

OTC: EXSR

545 4th St.
Santa Rosa, CA 95401
Phone: 707-524-3000
Fax: 707-579-4745
Web: www.exchangebank.com

CEO: C. William Reinking
CFO: Greg Jahn
HR: David Rapoport
FYE: December 31
Type: Public

In Santa Rosa there may be no refunds, but there *are* exchanges. Exchange Banks, that is. Serving personal and business customers throughout Sonoma County, California, Exchange Bank offers standard deposit products such as checking and savings accounts; Visa credit cards; online banking; a variety of loans including home, auto, and boat; and trust and investment management services. Representing more than 60% of the total, the bank's loan portfolio is dominated by real estate (both commercial and residential); business loans represent about 25%. The bank has had just six presidents since its inception in 1890.

EXCO RESOURCES, INC.

NYSE: XCO

12377 Merit Dr., Ste. 1700, LB 82
Dallas, TX 75251
Phone: 214-368-2084
Fax: 214-368-2087
Web: www.excoresources.com

CEO: Douglas H. Miller
CFO: Stephen F. Smith
HR: Joe D. Ford
FYE: December 31
Type: Public

EXCO Resources puts extra effort into oil and gas exploration and production operations in Colorado, Ohio, Oklahoma, Louisiana, Pennsylvania, Texas, and West Virginia. The company has pursued a strategy of growth through the drill bit coupled with selective acquisitions. In 2008 the oil and gas explorer reported proved reserves of 1.9 trillion cu. ft. of natural gas equivalent. EXCO Resources holds stakes in more than 11,970 gross wells. In 2009 EXCO Resources signed up British gas giant BG Group to help it develop EXCO's Haynesville shale gas assets located in East Texas and North Louisiana.

	Annual Growth	12/05	12/06	12/07	12/08	12/09
Sales ($ mil.)	68.8%	72.2	355.8	846.1	1,490.3	585.8
Net income ($ mil.)	—	16.0	139.0	49.7	(1,733.5)	(496.8)
Market value ($ mil.)	7.9%	—	3,592.5	3,288.7	1,924.8	4,510.2
Employees	26.4%	314	471	689	892	802

EXEL, INC.

570 Polaris Pkwy., Ste. 200 C
Westerville, OH 43082
Phone: 614-865-8500
Fax: 614-865-8875
Web: www.exel.com

CEO: James J. (Jim) Damman
CFO: Bruce Wise
HR: —
FYE: December 31
Type: Subsidiary

For Exel, the goal is to excel at expediting freight transportation. The company arranges for its customers' freight to be hauled in truckload and less-than-truckload (LTL) quantities; in addition, it oversees intermodal freight transportation, which involves the use of both trucks and trains. Through its numerous affiliates, Exel provides services such as international freight forwarding, warehousing, and package delivery. The company is part of the US arm of the DHL Exel Supply Chain business unit of DHL, the global express delivery and logistics giant. DHL itself is a subsidiary of Germany's Deutsche Post.

	Annual Growth	12/04	12/05	12/06	12/07	12/08
Est. sales ($ mil.)	—	—	—	—	—	694.9
Employees	—	—	—	—	—	320

EXELIXIS, INC.

NASDAQ (GS): EXEL

210 E. Grand Ave.
South San Francisco, CA 94080
Phone: 650-837-7000
Fax: 650-837-8300
Web: www.exelixis.com

CEO: George A. Scangos
CFO: Frank L. Karbe
HR: —
FYE: December 31
Type: Public

We've come a long way, baby, but we still have a lot in common with the fruit fly. Exelixis, a pharmaceutical research and development firm, got its start analyzing genetic data from fruit flies and other organisms as a means to speed the development of drugs and other products. Its early genomic work has yielded a pipeline of drug candidates primarily in the area of cancer therapies, as well as some potential treatments for metabolic and cardiovascular diseases. The company's drug candidates in clinical trials include treatments for solid tumors, thyroid cancer, and non-small cell lung cancer. Development and licensing partners include Bristol-Myers Squibb, Genentech, GlaxoSmithKline, and Sanofi-Aventis.

	Annual Growth	12/05	12/06	12/07	12/08	12/09
Sales ($ mil.)	18.9%	76.0	98.7	113.5	117.9	151.8
Net income ($ mil.)	—	(84.4)	(101.5)	(86.4)	(162.9)	(135.2)
Market value ($ mil.)	(6.0%)	1,022.8	977.2	937.0	545.1	800.2
Employees	5.3%	550	651	735	676	676

EXELON CORPORATION

NYSE: EXC

10 S. Dearborn St., 52nd Fl.
Chicago, IL 60603
Phone: 312-394-7398
Fax: 312-394-8941
Web: www.exeloncorp.com

CEO: John W. Rowe
CFO: Matthew F. Hilzinger
HR: Ruth Ann M. Gillis
FYE: December 31
Type: Public

The City of Brotherly Love meets the Windy City in utility holding company Exelon. The company distributes electricity to 5.4 million customers in northern Illinois (including Chicago) and southeastern Pennsylvania (including Philadelphia) through subsidiaries Commonwealth Edison (ComEd) and PECO Energy. PECO also distributes natural gas to 485,000 customers. Subsidiary Exelon Generation holds the company's power plants, whose production capacity is just about 25,000 MW. About two-thirds of Generation's power is nuclear. Exelon Power Team is a top wholesale energy marketer, and Exelon Energy markets retail power and offers other energy-related services.

	Annual Growth	12/05	12/06	12/07	12/08	12/09
Sales ($ mil.)	3.0%	15,357.0	15,655.0	18,916.0	18,859.0	17,318.0
Net income ($ mil.)	29.4%	965.0	1,592.0	2,736.0	2,737.0	2,707.0
Market value ($ mil.)	(2.1%)	35,103.2	40,883.2	53,929.6	36,734.8	32,282.5
Employees	3.0%	17,200	17,200	17,800	19,610	19,329

EXIDE TECHNOLOGIES

NASDAQ (GM): XIDE

13000 Deerfield Pkwy., Bldg. 200
Milton, GA 30004
Phone: 678-566-9000
Fax: 678-566-9188
Web: www.exide.com

CEO: Gordon A. Ulsh
CFO: Phillip A. Damaska
HR: George S. Jones Jr.
FYE: March 31
Type: Public

Exide Technologies hopes you'll get a charge out of its products. The company makes and recycles automotive and industrial batteries for retailers such as Wal-Mart and NAPA, and for transportation manufacturers like Fiat and Toyota. The company also makes batteries for boats, farm equipment, golf carts, hybrid vehicles, and wheelchairs. Industrial applications include computer, locomotive, photovoltaic (solar power), power plant, and telecommunications systems. Classic, Marathon, NASCAR Extreme, Sunlyte, and Super Crank make up some of the company's brand names. Operations outside the US account for nearly two-thirds of sales.

	Annual Growth	3/06	3/07	3/08	3/09	3/10
Sales ($ mil.)	(1.2%)	2,819.9	2,939.8	3,696.7	3,322.3	2,685.8
Net income ($ mil.)	—	(172.7)	(105.9)	32.1	(69.5)	(11.8)
Market value ($ mil.)	19.1%	216.2	659.2	990.3	226.8	435.4
Employees	(7.2%)	13,982	13,862	13,027	12,081	10,349

EXLSERVICE HOLDINGS, INC.

NASDAQ (GS): EXLS

350 Park Ave., 10th Fl.
New York, NY 10022
Phone: 212-277-7100
Fax: 212-277-7111
Web: www.exlservice.com

CEO: Rohit Kapoor
CFO: Vishal Chhibbar
HR: Amitabh Hajela
FYE: December 31
Type: Public

Have an extra-large task you'd rather not take on? Outsource it to ExlService Holdings. The company, known as EXL, offers business process outsourcing (BPO), research and analytics, and consulting services. EXL's BPO offerings, which generate most of its sales, include claims processing, collections, customer support, and finance and accounting. Customers come mainly from the banking, financial services, and insurance industries, but also from sectors such as utilities and telecommunications. Two UK-based customers, insurer Norwich Union and natural gas supplier Centrica, together account for about 35% of EXL's sales.

	Annual Growth	12/05	12/06	12/07	12/08	12/09
Sales ($ mil.)	26.8%	74.0	121.8	179.9	181.7	191.0
Net income ($ mil.)	21.9%	7.1	14.1	27.0	14.4	15.7
Market value ($ mil.)	(4.8%)	—	613.7	673.2	250.0	529.4
Employees	10.0%	7,300	8,200	10,000	9,995	10,700

EXPEDIA, INC.

NASDAQ (GS): EXPE

333 108th Ave., NE
Bellevue, WA 98004
Phone: 425-679-7200
Fax: 425-679-7240
Web: www.expediainc.com

CEO: Dara Khosrowshahi
CFO: Michael B. Adler
HR: —
FYE: December 31
Type: Public

These days, expediting your vacation begins online. As the market leader in online travel services (ahead of rivals Orbitz, Priceline, and Travelocity), Expedia offers Web-based trip-planning tools that allow users to book airline tickets, hotel reservations, car rentals, cruises, and vacation packages. Its portfolio of brands includes flagship Expedia.com, accommodations manager Hotels.com, travel discounter Hotwire, search engine TripAdvisor, corporate travel unit Egencia, luxury package provider Classic Vacations, and Chinese travel service eLong (55% stake), among others. Launched in 1996, the company serves travelers in North America, Europe, and the Asia/Pacific region.

	Annual Growth	12/05	12/06	12/07	12/08	12/09
Sales ($ mil.)	8.7%	2,119.5	2,237.6	2,665.3	2,937.0	2,955.4
Net income ($ mil.)	7.0%	228.7	244.9	295.9	(2,517.8)	299.5
Market value ($ mil.)	1.8%	6,805.6	5,959.2	8,981.4	2,340.5	7,308.4
Employees	3.8%	6,850	6,600	7,150	8,050	7,960

EXPEDITORS INTERNATIONAL

NASDAQ (GS): EXPD

1015 3rd Ave., 12th Fl.
Seattle, WA 98104
Phone: 206-674-3400
Fax: 206-682-9777
Web: www.expeditors.com

CEO: Peter J. Rose
CFO: Bradley S. (Brad) Powell
HR: Samuel R. Bokor
FYE: December 31
Type: Public

Need your goods moved expeditiously? Freight forwarder Expeditors International of Washington, Inc., can help. As a freight forwarder, the company purchases air and ocean cargo space on a volume basis and resells that space to its customers at lower rates than they could obtain directly from the carriers. The company also acts as a customs broker for air and ocean freight shipped by its customers and offers supply chain management services. Expeditors operates from more than 250 facilities in more than 50 countries worldwide. Approximately half of the company's sales come from Asia. Customers include global businesses engaged in retailing/wholesaling, electronics, and manufacturing.

	Annual Growth	12/05	12/06	12/07	12/08	12/09
Sales ($ mil.)	1.2%	3,901.8	4,626.0	5,235.2	5,633.9	4,092.3
Net income ($ mil.)	2.4%	218.6	235.1	269.2	301.0	240.2
Market value ($ mil.)	0.7%	7,186.1	8,622.0	9,511.9	7,082.8	7,402.1
Employees	3.2%	10,600	11,600	12,310	12,580	12,010

EXPERIAN INFORMATION SOLUTIONS, INC.

475 Anton Blvd.
Costa Mesa, CA 92626
Phone: 714-830-7000
Fax: 714-830-2449
Web: www.experian.com

CEO: Donald A. (Don) Robert
CFO: Paul Brooks
HR: —
FYE: March 31
Type: Subsidiary

Experian Information Solutions, also known as Experian Americas, is the US-based arm of global credit reporting agency Experian plc. The unit provides credit reporting and lead generation services utilizing its database of more than 215 million US consumers and some 15 million US businesses. Clients include retailers, financial services firms, utilities, not-for-profits, and small businesses. The company also provides addresses for more than 20 billion pieces of promotional mail every year. Services include skip tracing and collections, direct marketing, sales prospecting, demographic information, and more. Experian Americas has about a dozen offices across the US.

An in-depth profile of this company is available to Hoover's Online members at hoovers.com.

587

EXPONENT, INC.

NASDAQ (GS): EXPO

149 Commonwealth Dr.
Menlo Park, CA 94025
Phone: 650-326-9400
Fax: 650-326-8072
Web: www.exponent.com

CEO: Paul R. Johnston
CFO: Richard L. Schlenker Jr.
HR: Gregory P. Klein
FYE: December 31
Type: Public

Exponent has found success in failure. The science and engineering consulting firm specializes in analyzing and solving complex problems and preventing disasters and product failures. Exponent's 640 scientists, physicians, engineers, and business consultants assess environmental risks, regulatory issues, and workplace hazards for government agencies and clients from such industries as transportation, construction, and manufacturing. Established in 1967, its work has included analyzing such disasters as the Exxon Valdez oil spill and the bombing of the Murrah Federal Building in Oklahoma City. Exponent operates through more than 20 facilities in China, Germany, the UK, and the US.

	Annual Growth	12/05	12/06	12/07	12/08	12/09
Sales ($ mil.)	10.1%	155.2	168.5	205.1	228.8	227.9
Net income ($ mil.)	11.7%	14.2	14.2	20.3	23.2	22.1
Market value ($ mil.)	18.4%	196.7	258.6	374.8	416.9	385.8
Employees	3.0%	785	835	875	937	883

EXPRESS PARENT LLC

NYSE: EXPR

1 Limited Pkwy.
Columbus, OH 43230
Phone: 614-415-4000
Fax: 614-415-7440
Web: www.expressfashion.com

CEO: Michael A. Weiss
CFO: Matthew C. (Matt) Mollering
HR: Elliott R. Tobias
FYE: January 31
Type: Public

Right from the runway is the Express way. Express operates more than 570 stores in the US that sell trendy private-label apparel and accessories targeted to men and women between the ages of 20 and 30. (Its fashions are styled to have an international influence and modern appeal.) Express also sells denim and lingerie and operates an online store. Amid declining sales, Express shuttered stores and converted about 500 of its locations to dual-gender outlets that carry both men's and women's fashions. Limited Brands, which launched Express in 1980, sold a majority stake in the chain to the San Francisco-based private equity firm Golden Gate Capital (GGC) in 2007. In early 2010 GGC filed to take Express public.

	Annual Growth	1/06	1/07	1/08	1/09	1/10
Sales ($ mil.)	(1.0%)	1,794.0	1,748.9	1,796.3	1,737.0	1,721.1
Net income ($ mil.)	62.6%	—	17.5	(10.5)	(29.0)	75.3
Employees	0.0%	—	—	—	17,000	17,000

EXPRESS-1 EXPEDITED SOLUTIONS, INC.

NYSE Amex: XPO

429 Post Rd.
Buchanan, MI 49107
Phone: 269-695-2700
Fax: 269-695-7458
Web: www.express-1.com

CEO: Michael R. (Mike) Welch
CFO: John D. Welch
HR: —
FYE: December 31
Type: Public

Express-1 Expedited Solutions specializes in arranging expedited ground transportation. Customers' freight is transported throughout the US by independent contractors, who give the company's Express-1 unit access to a fleet of vehicles that includes cargo vans, trucks, and tractor-trailers. In addition to for-hire hauling, the company provides dedicated service — delivery of parts from a major Ford distribution facility in Evansville, Indiana, to dealers with a 250-mile radius. Express-1 Expedited offers domestic and international freight forwarding through Concert Group Logistics, which it acquired in 2008, as well as a variety of supply chain management services, through Bounce Logistics.

	Annual Growth	12/05	12/06	12/07	12/08	12/09
Sales ($ mil.)	25.9%	39.8	42.2	52.8	109.5	100.1
Net income ($ mil.)	—	(5.8)	3.9	2.2	3.2	1.7
Market value ($ mil.)	17.1%	21.8	40.7	39.4	36.8	41.0
Employees	1.9%	127	129	132	150	137

EXPRESS EMPLOYMENT PROFESSIONALS

8516 Northwest Expwy.
Oklahoma City, OK 73162
Phone: 405-840-5000
Fax: 405-717-5669
Web: www.expresspros.com

CEO: Robert A. Funk
CFO: —
HR: Carol Lane
FYE: December 31
Type: Private

When you need a worker fast, Express Employment Professionals delivers. Formerly known as Express Personnel Services, the professional staffing company provides work for some 350,000 employees from about 600 offices across Australia, Canada, South Africa, and the US. In addition to temporary staffing, it offers workplace services (consulting, training, development) through Express Business Solutions. Founded in 1983, the company is owned by founders William Stoller (vice chairman) and Robert Funk (CEO).

	Annual Growth	12/04	12/05	12/06	12/07	12/08
Sales ($ mil.)	5.1%	—	1,550.0	1,800.0	2,000.0	1,800.0
Employees	5.3%	—	300,000	350,000	375,000	350,000

⊞ EXPRESS SCRIPTS, INC.

NASDAQ (GS): ESRX

1 Express Way
St. Louis, MO 63121
Phone: 314-996-0900
Fax: —
Web: www.express-scripts.com

CEO: George Paz
CFO: Jeffrey L. Hall
HR: —
FYE: December 31
Type: Public

Express Scripts knows that its customers like their drugs fast. One of the largest pharmacy benefits management (PBM) companies in North America, Express Scripts administers the prescription drug benefits of millions of health plan members in the US and Canada. Members have access to a network of about 60,000 retail pharmacies, as well as the company's own mail-order pharmacies. Express Scripts processes claims for about 750 million prescriptions per year, designs drug plans, and offers such services as disease management programs and consumer drug data analysis. Clients include HMOs and other health insurers, self-insured businesses, and union benefit plans.

	Annual Growth	12/05	12/06	12/07	12/08	12/09
Sales ($ mil.)	11.1%	16,266.0	17,660.0	18,273.6	21,978.0	24,748.9
Net income ($ mil.)	19.9%	400.0	474.4	567.8	776.1	827.6
Market value ($ mil.)	19.8%	11,482.6	9,810.9	20,005.5	15,067.2	23,683.2
Employees	6.5%	11,100	11,300	11,820	10,820	14,270

EXPRESSJET HOLDINGS, INC.

NYSE: XJT

700 N. Sam Houston Pkwy. West, Ste. 200
Houston, TX 77067
Phone: 832-353-1000
Fax: 832-353-1008
Web: www.expressjet.com

CEO: Thomas M. (Tom) Hanley
CFO: Phung Ngo-Burns
HR: —
FYE: December 31
Type: Public

ExpressJet Holdings' main subsidiary, ExpressJet Airlines operates as Continental Express, a regional carrier for Continental Airlines, and as United Express for UAL's United Airlines — helping both airlines to reach markets that would be inefficient to serve with larger aircraft. Its Corporate Aviation division offers charter service arrangements, and sister company ExpressJet Services provides ground-handling and aircraft MRO services. Its fleet of over 240 Embraer regional jets fly from Continental and United hubs (Chicago, Cleveland, Houston, Newark, Denver, Los Angeles, San Francisco, and Washington, DC) to approximately 130 destinations in the US, Canada, Mexico, and the Caribbean.

	Annual Growth	12/05	12/06	12/07	12/08	12/09
Sales ($ mil.)	(18.5%)	1,562.8	1,679.6	1,685.5	1,318.2	688.3
Net income ($ mil.)	—	98.0	92.6	(70.2)	(88.2)	(3.3)
Market value ($ mil.)	(50.6%)	1,372.6	1,374.3	420.8	28.8	81.8
Employees	(4.4%)	6,700	4,980	8,000	5,400	5,600

EXTERRAN HOLDINGS, INC.

NYSE: EXH

16666 Northchase Dr.
Houston, TX 77060
Phone: 713-335-7000
Fax: 281-854-3051
Web: www.exterran.com

CEO: Ernie L. Danner
CFO: J. Michael Anderson
HR: —
FYE: December 31
Type: Public

Applying pressure is Exterran Holding's forte — the company rents and repairs compressors and carries out natural gas compression services for oil and gas companies. Its three businesses are contract operations, fabrication, and aftermarket services. It has a global fleet of about 11,600 mobile compressors (90% contracted in North America) ranging from 8 to 4,750 horsepower. The company provides fabrication services and equipment for oil and natural gas processing and transportation applications. The firm's aftermarket services support the surface production and processing needs of customers. Exterran Holdings is a majority owner of Exterran Partners, which contracts compressor units in the US.

	Annual Growth	12/05	12/06	12/07	12/08	12/09
Sales ($ mil.)	45.0%	613.6	947.7	2,540.5	3,178.7	2,715.6
Net income ($ mil.)	—	55.4	87.7	34.6	(947.3)	(545.5)
Market value ($ mil.)	(15.0%)	2,596.1	3,921.3	5,164.4	1,344.8	1,354.2
Employees	13.7%	6,650	8,800	10,700	12,600	11,100

EXTERRAN PARTNERS, L.P.

NASDAQ (GS): EXLP

16666 Northchase Dr.
Houston, TX 77060
Phone: 281-836-7000
Fax: —
Web: www.exterran.com

CEO: Ernie L. Danner
CFO: David S. Miller
HR: —
FYE: December 31
Type: Public

Exterran Partners is the largest operator of contract compression equipment in the US. Its services include designing, installing, operating, repairing, and maintaining compression equipment. The company operates a fleet of nearly 2,500 compressor units, comprising more than 1 million horsepower. Universal Compression Holdings held a 50% stake in the company (spun off in 2006) until Universal Compression merged with Hanover Compressors to form Exterran Holdings in 2007. Exterran Partners and Exterran Holdings manage their respective US compression fleets as one pool of compression equipment in order to more easily fulfill their respective customers' needs. Exterran Holdings holds a majority stake in Exterran Partners.

	Annual Growth	12/05	12/06	12/07	12/08	12/09
Sales ($ mil.)	29.9%	—	—	107.7	163.7	181.7
Net income ($ mil.)	(12.7%)	—	—	19.4	29.8	14.8
Market value ($ mil.)	(16.7%)	—	—	562.4	197.4	390.5
Employees	—	—	—	—	—	—

EXTRA SPACE STORAGE INC.

NYSE: EXR

2795 E. Cottonwood Pkwy., Ste. 400
Salt Lake City, UT 84121
Phone: 801-562-5556
Fax: 801-562-5579
Web: www.extraspace.com

CEO: Spencer F. Kirk
CFO: Kent W. Christensen
HR: Bruce Boucher
FYE: December 31
Type: Public

Is your closet bursting at the seams? Looking for a little extra space? Extra Space Storage has your back. The self-administered, self-managed real estate investment trust (REIT) buys, develops, and manages self-storage properties. It wholly owns, owns in joint-venture partnerships, or operates for third parties about 700 facilities totaling approximately 50 million sq. ft. of rentable space in more than 30 states and Washington, DC. It offers both groundfloor and multifloor facilities, and leases to some 300,000 tenants nationwide. Extra Space Storage operates in two segments: property management and rental operations.

	Annual Growth	12/05	12/06	12/07	12/08	12/09
Sales ($ mil.)	20.1%	134.7	197.3	238.9	273.3	280.5
Net income ($ mil.)	—	(5.0)	14.9	34.6	46.9	32.0
Market value ($ mil.)	(6.9%)	1,342.9	1,592.3	1,246.1	899.9	1,007.2
Employees	0.7%	1,943	1,835	1,853	1,947	2,001

EXTREME NETWORKS, INC.

NASDAQ (GM): EXTR

3585 Monroe St.
Santa Clara, CA 95051
Phone: 408-579-2800
Fax: 408-579-3000
Web: www.extremenetworks.com

CEO: Bob L. Corey
CFO: Bob L. Corey
HR: —
FYE: June 30
Type: Public

Extreme Networks hopes you switch to its products. The company designs and markets three switch families — Alpine, Black Diamond, and Summit — using custom semiconductor components to address network switching needs from desktops to network cores. Designed to replace software-based routers, its Layer 3 switches are used by enterprise customers and network service providers to build and upgrade LANs, WANs, and metro-area networks. The company, which outsources the manufacturing of its products to Flextronics and other companies, also offers load-balancing Web switches and software for switch management and configuration. Customers outside North America account for more than half of Extreme's sales.

	Annual Growth	6/05	6/06	6/07	6/08	6/09
Sales ($ mil.)	(3.3%)	383.3	358.6	342.8	361.8	335.6
Net income ($ mil.)	(31.7%)	12.9	8.5	(14.2)	8.4	2.8
Market value ($ mil.)	(16.3%)	366.3	374.4	364.5	255.6	180.0
Employees	(1.5%)	834	847	825	861	786

⊞ EXXON MOBIL CORPORATION

NYSE: XOM

5959 Las Colinas Blvd.
Irving, TX 75039
Phone: 972-444-1000
Fax: 972-444-1350
Web: www.exxon.mobil.com

CEO: Rex W. Tillerson
CFO: Donald D. (Don) Humphreys
HR: Lucille J. Cavanaugh
FYE: December 31
Type: Public

It's not necessarily the oil standard, but Exxon Mobil is the world's largest integrated oil company (ahead of Royal Dutch Shell and BP). Exxon Mobil engages in oil and gas exploration, production, supply, transportation, and marketing worldwide. In 2009 it reported proved reserves of 23 billion barrels of oil equivalent, as well as major holdings in oil sands through Imperial Oil. Exxon Mobil's 37 refineries in 20 countries have a throughput capacity of 6.3 million barrels per day. The company supplies refined products to almost 28,000 gas stations in 100 countries. Exxon Mobil is also a major petrochemical producer.

	Annual Growth	12/05	12/06	12/07	12/08	12/09
Sales ($ mil.)	(4.3%)	370,680.0	377,635.0	404,552.0	477,359.0	310,586.0
Net income ($ mil.)	(14.5%)	36,130.0	39,500.0	40,610.0	45,220.0	19,280.0
Market value ($ mil.)	5.0%	263,889.7	360,011.8	440,160.6	375,045.6	320,360.3
Employees	(0.9%)	83,700	82,100	80,800	79,900	80,700

EXXONMOBIL CHEMICAL COMPANY

13501 Katy Fwy.
Houston, TX 77079
Phone: 281-870-6000
Fax: 281-870-6661
Web: www.exxonmobilchemical.com

CEO: Stephen D. (Steve) Pryor
CFO: —
HR: —
FYE: December 31
Type: Subsidiary

No surprise that a subsidiary of the world's #1 oil company, Exxon Mobil, is among the world's top chemical companies. ExxonMobil Chemical ranks #1 or #2 in making many petrochemicals, including benzene and toluene, as well as polyolefins such as polypropylene (PP) and high-density and linear low-density polyethylene (HDPE and LLDPE, respectively). The company also is a major producer of olefins (such as ethylene and propylene, used to make polyolefins), aromatics (toluene and xylene used in paints and agrochemicals), and plastics (such as thermoplastic elastomers). ExxonMobil uses its polyolefins to make films for packaging and labeling and also licenses some of its process technology. It operates globally.

An in-depth profile of this company is available to Hoover's Online members at hoovers.com.

589

EYE CARE CENTERS OF AMERICA, INC.

11103 West Ave.
San Antonio, TX 78213
Phone: 210-340-3531
Fax: 210-524-6996
Web: www.ecca.com

CEO: David L. Holmberg
CFO: Jennifer L. Kelley Taylor
HR: Robert T. Cox
FYE: December 31
Type: Subsidiary

Eye Care Centers of America is clearly focused on becoming the top eyewear chain. It owns or manages more than 400 optical stores in nearly 40 states. Its stores — operating under the EyeMasters name and a host of others (Binyon's, Hour Eyes, Stein Optical, Visionworks, and Vision World) — sell contact lenses, prescription eyewear, and sunglasses. The firm offers contacts and eyeglass frames under its own and designer brands, as well as one-hour service, on-site processing labs, and independent optometrists. Founded in 1984, the firm is a subsidiary of HVHC, itself a subsidiary of health care provider Highmark.

	Annual Growth	12/04	12/05	12/06	12/07	12/08
Est. sales ($ mil.)	—	—	—	—	—	537.6
Employees	—	—	—	—	—	5,400

EYEBLASTER, INC.

135 W. 18th St., 5th Fl.
New York, NY 10011
Phone: 646-202-1320
Fax: 212-686-9208
Web: www.eyeblaster.com

CEO: Gal Trifon
CFO: Sarit Firon
HR: —
FYE: December 31
Type: Private

Eyeblaster isn't afraid to get in your face with online advertising. Advertisers and media agencies use the company's campaign management software to create and administer rich media content, including online, mobile, and in-game advertisements. Its portfolio also includes analytics tools for monitoring and measuring such metrics as display time and interaction rate. Eyeblaster provides professional services ranging from custom development and testing to data tracking and analysis. The company's products have been used in advertisements for Ameritrade, Microsoft, Pfizer, and Virgin Mobile, among others. Eyeblaster filed for an IPO in 2010.

	Annual Growth	12/05	12/06	12/07	12/08	12/09
Sales ($ mil.)	36.4%	18.8	27.7	44.7	63.8	65.1
Net income ($ mil.)	38.0%	2.7	3.7	7.4	6.2	9.8
Employees	24.4%	117	157	224	—	280

EYEMED VISION CARE LLC

4000 Luxottica Place
Mason, OH 45040
Phone: 513-765-4321
Fax: 513-765-6388
Web: www.eyemedvisioncare.com

CEO: Kerry Bradley
CFO: Jack S. Dennis
HR: Mildred Curtis
FYE: December 31
Type: Subsidiary

EyeMed Vision Care delivers the visuals. A subsidiary of Italian eyewear maker Luxottica, the company administers managed vision care plans to about 160 million members through a nationwide network of providers that includes optometrists, ophthalmologists, opticians, and retailers (including Luxottica subsidiaries LensCrafters and Pearle Vision). EyeMed offers several different plans, all of which provide various levels of discounts on exams and vision products such as eyeglass frames and lenses, contact lenses, and other eye care services. The company has a diverse customer base that includes large corporations (Cintas), government entities (the State of New York), and health insurers (Health Net).

EZCORP, INC.

NASDAQ (GS): EZPW

1901 Capital Pkwy.
Austin, TX 78746
Phone: 512-314-3400
Fax: 512-314-3404
Web: www.ezcorp.com

CEO: Joseph L. (Joe) Rotunda
CFO: Daniel M. (Danny) Chism
HR: Robert A. Kasenter
FYE: September 30
Type: Public

No mere pawn in the game, EZCORP is one of the largest operators of pawnshops in the US. It operates some 370 EZPAWN and Value Pawn locations in the US; it operates another 60 stores in Mexico under the banners Empeño Fácil and Empeñe Su Oro. The stores offer such standard pawnshop fare as second-hand jewelry, tools, electronics, sports equipment, and musical instruments. The company's inventory is built from items forfeited by customers who used them as collateral for small, short-term, high-interest loans. EZCORP also offers customers unsecured loans, commonly referred to as payday loans or payroll advances, through some of its pawnshops and from its more than 470 EZMONEY stores.

	Annual Growth	9/05	9/06	9/07	9/08	9/09
Assets ($ mil.)	31.4%	165.4	197.9	251.2	308.7	492.5
Net income ($ mil.)	46.7%	14.8	29.3	37.9	52.4	68.5
Market value ($ mil.)	26.4%	263.2	633.9	662.2	924.3	671.6
Employees	12.7%	2,700	3,100	3,200	3,300	4,350

EZENIA! INC.

OTC: EZEN

14 Celina Ave., Ste. 17-18
Nashua, NH 03063
Phone: 603-589-7600
Fax: —
Web: www.ezenia.com

CEO: Khoa D. Nguyen
CFO: Thomas J. McCann
HR: Thomas J. McCann
FYE: December 31
Type: Public

Ezenia! is defensive about online communications. Serving the US defense industry, the company makes video and multimedia conferencing equipment and related software that connects users over both local and wide area networks. Its products enable multiple users to connect from distance locations in order to interact as a group. Its core software product, InfoWorkSpace, features chat rooms, instant messaging, Web cam technologies, and data storage capabilities. Serving both commercial and government organizations, the company counts the Department of Defense and defense contractors like General Dynamics and SAIC among its customers. Ezenia! was founded in 1991; CEO Khoa D. Nguyen owns about 13% of the company.

	Annual Growth	12/05	12/06	12/07	12/08	12/09
Sales ($ mil.)	(28.2%)	13.2	13.2	9.0	6.7	3.5
Net income ($ mil.)	—	3.8	3.9	(4.5)	(3.1)	(3.4)
Market value ($ mil.)	(54.9%)	35.3	29.8	10.0	0.9	1.5
Employees	(15.0%)	46	47	37	38	24

F5 NETWORKS, INC.

NASDAQ (GS): FFIV

401 Elliott Ave. West
Seattle, WA 98119
Phone: 206-272-5555
Fax: 206-272-5556
Web: www.f5.com

CEO: John McAdam
CFO: Andy Reinland
HR: —
FYE: September 30
Type: Public

F5 Networks wants to help your network take a load off. The company's products include application delivery controllers (ADC) and software that are used for network load balancing, availability assurance, and security assessment. The company also provides file virtualization, WAN optimization, and remote access products. It also offers services such as network monitoring, performance analysis, and training. F5 targets a variety of industries, including telecommunications, manufacturing, financial services, and e-commerce. The company counts Blue Cross and Blue Shield of Kansas, Microsoft, and Toshiba America among its customers. F5 Networks gets the majority of its sales in the Americas.

	Annual Growth	9/05	9/06	9/07	9/08	9/09
Sales ($ mil.)	23.4%	281.4	394.0	525.7	650.2	653.1
Net income ($ mil.)	15.3%	51.7	66.0	77.0	74.3	91.5
Market value ($ mil.)	16.2%	1,742.0	2,152.7	2,980.7	1,873.8	3,176.2
Employees	20.1%	792	1,068	1,582	1,694	1,646

FACEBOOK, INC.

1601 S. California Ave.
Palo Alto, CA 94304
Phone: 650-543-4800
Fax: 650-543-4801
Web: www.facebook.com

CEO: Mark Zuckerberg
CFO: David A. Ebersman
HR: Lori Goler
FYE: December 31
Type: Private

When it comes to social networking, it's wise to put your best face forward. Facebook is the latest star of the online social networking craze. Users post photos and information about themselves and connect with one another through online profiles. The site was launched in 2004 by Harvard undergraduate Mark Zuckerberg, as an online version of the Harvard Facebook. (The name comes from books of freshmen's faces, majors, and hometowns that are distributed to incoming students.) It began by connecting students, but later opened its service to the general public. Microsoft has a deal to be the exclusive provider of advertising to Facebook. Investors include Paypal co-founder Peter Thiel and Accel Partners.

	Annual Growth	12/04	12/05	12/06	12/07	12/08
Est. sales ($ mil.)	—	—	—	—	—	0.8
Employees	—	—	—	—	—	850

FACET BIOTECH CORPORATION

1400 Seaport Blvd.
Redwood City, CA 94063
Phone: 650-454-1000
Fax: —
Web: www.facetbiotech.com

CEO: Faheem Hasnain
CFO: Andrew L. Guggenhime
HR: —
FYE: December 31
Type: Subsidiary

Facet Biotech conducts forward-facing research in the biotechnology industry. The drug development company is engaged in the pursuit of antibody (protein) therapies for immune system diseases and cancers. Its research is based on a humanization technology for mouse monoclonal antibodies (MAbs, or single-source proteins) that triggers an immunological response against diseased cells. Facet Biotech is developing treatments for solid cancer tumors, multiple sclerosis, and multiple myeloma (bone marrow cancer). The company was spun off from PDL BioPharma in late 2008 and was snapped up by new parent Abbott Laboratories in 2010.

	Annual Growth	12/05	12/06	12/07	12/08	12/09
Sales ($ mil.)	11.4%	29.9	51.4	26.7	18.3	46.1
Net income ($ mil.)	—	(166.2)	(186.7)	(227.3)	(161.8)	(141.7)
Employees	(24.2%)	—	—	329	327	189

FACILITY GROUP, INC.

2233 Lake Park Dr., Ste. 500
Smyrna, GA 30080
Phone: 770-437-2700
Fax: 770-437-3900
Web: www.facilitygroup.com

CEO: W. Ennis Parker Jr.
CFO: —
HR: —
FYE: December 31
Type: Group

Facility Group wants to facilitate every phase of your construction project. The privately owned and operated group provides planning, architectural and engineering, and program and construction management services. It manages more than $700 million in projects and targets several commercial and industrial markets, including the food and beverage, distribution, justice, and education sectors. Clients have included The Coca-Cola Company, Russell Stover Candies, Bright Horizons, the US Army Corps of Engineers, Trinchero Family Estates (formerly Sutter Home Winery), and Ampacet. Facility Group, which was established in 1986, operates from offices located throughout the US.

	Annual Growth	12/04	12/05	12/06	12/07	12/08
Est. sales ($ mil.)	—	—	—	—	—	400.0
Employees	—	—	—	—	—	150

🔲 FACTORY CARD & PARTY OUTLET CORP.

2727 Diehl Rd.
Naperville, IL 60563
Phone: 630-579-2000
Fax: 630-579-2400
Web: www.factorycard.com

CEO: Gary W. Rada
CFO: Timothy J. (Tim) Benson
HR: Debra Smetana
FYE: January 31
Type: Subsidiary

Factory Card & Party Outlet takes the work out of partying. The retailer operates about 170 discount stores in some 20 states, primarily in the Midwest and along the eastern seaboard, as well as an e-commerce site. Greeting cards, beginning at 49 cents apiece, account for only part of the company's offerings, which also include gift wrap and ribbon, party supplies (invitations, party favors, candles, and piñatas), balloons, and novelty and celebratory items for birthdays, holidays, weddings, graduations, and other special occasions. Factory Card & Party Outlet is owned by party retail and wholesale giant Amscan Holdings, the owner of rivals Party City and Party America, which acquired the company in 2007.

FACTORY MUTUAL INSURANCE COMPANY

1301 Atwood Ave.
Johnston, RI 02919
Phone: 401-275-3000
Fax: 401-275-3029
Web: www.fmglobal.com

CEO: Shivan S. Subramaniam
CFO: Jeffrey A. Burchill
HR: Enzo Rebula
FYE: December 31
Type: Mutual company

If you're looking to protect your corporation, turn your insurance dial to FM Global. Factory Mutual Insurance (operating as FM Global) provides commercial and industrial property/casualty insurance and a variety of risk management services. It provides specialized products for ocean cargo and machinery equipment, as well as property loss prevention engineering and research. FM Global operates through such subsidiaries as Affiliated FM Insurance, FM Global Cargo, and Mutual Boiler Re. In addition to the US, the company has offices in Asia, Australia, Canada, Europe, and South America.

	Annual Growth	12/04	12/05	12/06	12/07	12/08
Assets ($ mil.)	4.5%	9,484.4	11,090.1	12,267.8	13,030.1	11,306.6
Net income ($ mil.)	—	557.7	634.6	736.9	927.8	(318.0)
Employees	1.6%	4,700	4,700	4,900	4,500	5,000

🔲 FACTSET RESEARCH SYSTEMS INC.

NYSE: FDS

601 Merritt 7
Norwalk, CT 06851
Phone: 203-810-1000
Fax: 203-810-1001
Web: www.factset.com

CEO: Philip A. Hadley
CFO: Maurizio Nicolelli
HR: —
FYE: August 31
Type: Public

Analysts, portfolio managers, and investment bankers know FactSet Research Systems has the scoop. The company offers global financial and economic information for investment analysis. FactSet complements its data with a variety of software for use in downloading and manipulating the data. (Its products can be fully integrated with Microsoft applications such as Excel and PowerPoint.) Among the company's applications are tools for presentations, data warehousing, portfolio analysis, and report writing. Revenues are derived from month-to-month subscriptions to services, databases, and financial applications. More than 80% of revenue comes from investment managers; investment banking clients account for the rest.

	Annual Growth	8/05	8/06	8/07	8/08	8/09
Sales ($ mil.)	18.8%	312.6	387.4	475.8	575.5	622.0
Net income ($ mil.)	19.2%	71.8	82.9	109.6	125.0	144.9
Market value ($ mil.)	12.0%	1,632.6	2,057.0	2,795.4	2,925.1	2,567.3
Employees	24.7%	1,226	1,431	1,653	1,934	2,962

🔲 An in-depth profile of this company is available to Hoover's Online members at hoovers.com.

591

FAIR ISAAC CORPORATION

NYSE: FICO

901 Marquette Ave., Ste. 3200
Minneapolis, MN 55402
Phone: 612-758-5200
Fax: 612-758-5201
Web: www.fico.com

CEO: Mark N. Greene
CFO: Thomas A. Bradley
HR: Richard S. Deal
FYE: September 30
Type: Public

Fair or not, Fair Isaac (now known as FICO) has a lot to say about whether you get a loan. A leading developer of credit scoring systems, the firm offers statistics-based predictive tools for the consumer credit industry. FICO is the progenitor of the FICO Score, a three-digit number based on a complex set of factors to determine a borrower's creditworthiness. Customers include credit card companies, retailers, commercial lenders, insurers, health care, and telecommunications service providers in some 80 countries worldwide. FICO's analytic and decision-management products and services include applicant scoring for insurers and financial risk and database management products for financial concerns.

	Annual Growth	9/05	9/06	9/07	9/08	9/09
Sales ($ mil.)	(5.7%)	798.7	825.4	822.2	744.8	630.7
Net income ($ mil.)	(16.6%)	134.5	103.5	104.7	84.0	65.1
Market value ($ mil.)	(16.8%)	2,045.6	1,669.8	1,648.8	1,052.5	981.2
Employees	(7.1%)	2,796	2,737	2,824	2,480	2,086

THE FAIRCHILD CORPORATION

Pink Sheets: FCHDQ

1750 Tysons Blvd., Ste. 1400
McLean, VA 22102
Phone: 703-478-5800
Fax: 703-478-5775
Web: www.fairchild.com

CEO: Philip S. Sassower
CFO: Michael L. McDonald
HR: —
FYE: September 30
Type: Public

The Fairchild Corporation aims to keep those who prefer two wheels to four safe with its Fairchild Sports USA (FSUSA) line of protective clothing, helmets, and accessories for motorcyclists. FSUSA also makes private-label items for Harley-Davidson, Yamaha, and Honda. Fairchild Corporation also owns a 49% stake in some 95 PoloExpress retail shops in Germany and Switzerland that sell motorcycle clothing, helmets, and accessories as well as camping gear. Ailing Fairchild filed for Chapter 11 bankruptcy protection in March 2009 and sold its Banner Aerospace group of businesses to Greenwich AeroGroup in June 2009.

FAIRCHILD SEMICONDUCTOR INTERNATIONAL, INC.

NYSE: FCS

82 Running Hill Rd.
South Portland, ME 04106
Phone: 207-775-8100
Fax: 207-761-6139
Web: www.fairchildsemi.com

CEO: Mark S. Thompson
CFO: Mark S. Frey
HR: Kevin B. London
FYE: December 31
Type: Public

Fairchild Semiconductor International is hardly a babe in the woods when it comes to making chips. One of the world's oldest chip companies, Fairchild makes semiconductors for tens of thousands of customers in the automotive, computer, consumer electronics, industrial, and telecommunications markets. Its diversified product line includes logic chips, discrete power and signal components, optoelectronics, nonvolatile memory chips, and many types of analog and mixed-signal chips. The company also provides foundry (contract semiconductor manufacturing) services for other chip makers, such as Samsung Electronics and National Semiconductor. Operations in Asia account for about three-quarters of Fairchild's sales.

	Annual Growth	12/05	12/06	12/07	12/08	12/09
Sales ($ mil.)	(4.5%)	1,425.1	1,651.1	1,670.2	1,574.2	1,187.5
Net income ($ mil.)	—	(241.2)	83.4	64.0	(167.4)	(60.2)
Market value ($ mil.)	(12.3%)	2,124.0	2,111.5	1,812.5	614.2	1,254.8
Employees	(1.0%)	8,929	9,344	9,691	9,771	8,563

FAIRFIELD RESIDENTIAL LLC

5510 Morehouse Dr., Ste. 200
San Diego, CA 92121
Phone: 858-457-2123
Fax: 858-457-3982
Web: www.fairfield-residential.net

CEO: Christopher E. Hashioka
CFO: Jim Hribar
HR: —
FYE: December 31
Type: Private

Affordable housing need not look like affordable housing. That's one of the ideas that drive multifamily housing owner and developer Fairfield Residential. The company builds and renovates apartment communities, including mixed-use urban developments, university housing, luxury apartments, and tax credit affordable housing. Active throughout the US, Fairfield also helps investors locate, acquire, and/or sell multifamily property investment opportunities. The company provides property management and marketing services for some 60,000 residential units. Falling victim to the nation's troubled real estate market, Fairfield filed for Chapter 11 bankruptcy protection in late 2009.

FAIRMONT HOMES, INC.

502 S. Oakland Ave.
Nappanee, IN 46550
Phone: 574-773-7941
Fax: 574-773-2185
Web: www.fairmonthomes.com

CEO: James Foster (Jim) Shea
CFO: Chuck Kroft
HR: Rick Jones
FYE: December 31
Type: Private

As a maker of recreational vehicles as well as manufactured housing, Fairmont Homes puts the mobile in mobile homes. The company produces more than 400 different single- and multi-section homes under the Fairmont, Friendship, and Century brands. Its homes, which range in size from from less than 800 sq. ft. to more than 2,300 sq. ft., are sold through retailers mainly in the midwestern and northeastern US. The company's parts and accessories suppliers include Moen (bathroom fixtures), Pella (windows), and Whirlpool (appliances). James Shea Sr. started Fairmont Homes in 1971 and established subsidiary Gulf Stream Coach, a builder of RVs, in 1983.

	Annual Growth	12/04	12/05	12/06	12/07	12/08
Est. sales ($ mil.)	—	—	—	—	—	94.1
Employees	—	—	—	—	—	490

FAIRPOINT COMMUNICATIONS, INC.

521 E. Morehead St., Ste. 500
Charlotte, NC 28202
Phone: 704-344-8150
Fax: 704-344-8121
Web: www.fairpoint.com

CEO: David L. Hauser
CFO: Lisa R. Hood
HR: —
FYE: December 31
Type: Private

When the country mouse calls the city mouse, she might just be using FairPoint Communications. The company serves about 2 million subscribers through more than 30 local-exchange carriers in 18 US states. It concentrates largely on rural and small urban markets located mainly in the Northeast and the Midwest, but the company's service areas extend to the South and the Northwest. FairPoint provides local and long-distance phone services, as well as DSL and TV Internet access to residential and business customers. It also offers Web hosting and domain name registration. Burdened with about $2.7 billion in debt, FairPoint filed for Chapter 11 protection from creditors in 2009.

	Annual Growth	12/05	12/06	12/07	12/08	12/09
Sales ($ mil.)	43.9%	262.8	270.1	283.5	1,274.6	1,126.8
Net income ($ mil.)	—	28.9	31.1	6.0	(68.5)	(241.4)
Employees	45.8%	900	952	1,087	4,071	4,066

FAIRVIEW HEALTH SERVICES

2450 Riverside Ave.	CEO: Mark A. Eustis
Minneapolis, MN 55454	CFO: James M. Fox
Phone: 612-672-6000	HR: Paula H. Phillippe
Fax: 612-672-7186	FYE: December 31
Web: www.fairview.org	Type: Not-for-profit

It's fair to say that when it comes to health care, Fairview Health Services takes the long view. The not-for-profit health care system serves Minnesota's Twin Cities and surrounding communities. Fairview Health Services is affiliated with the medical school of the University of Minnesota and counts among its seven hospitals the University of Minnesota Medical Center. Its hospitals house some 2,500 beds and provide comprehensive medical and surgical services. The health system also operates a network of primary and specialty care clinics that also provide preventative and wellness care. Additionally, Fairview Health operates retail pharmacies and nursing homes and provides home health care and rehabilitation.

	Annual Growth	12/04	12/05	12/06	12/07	12/08
Est. sales ($ mil.)	—	—	—	—	—	2,566.6
Employees	—	—	—	—	—	18,000

FALCON OIL & GAS LTD.

TSX Venture: FO

1875 Lawrence St., Ste. 1400	CEO: Marc A. Bruner
Denver, CO 80202	CFO: Evan L. Wasoff
Phone: 303-893-1800	HR: —
Fax: 303-572-8927	FYE: December 31
Web: www.falconoilandgas.com	Type: Public

Falcon Oil & Gas has spread its wings and focused its energy on searching for oil and gas. It operates in Romania (through JVX Exploration) where it has has the right to explore and drill wells on property that covers 575,260 acres and is adjacent to Hungary's two largest oil fields. The company licenses are in south-central Hungary near the town of Szolnok. Falcon operates in Hungary (through TXM Oil and Gas Exploration) where it is focusing on an underground geologic formation called the Mako Trough. Falcon Oil & Gas also holds interests in four non-producing properties in Alberta, Canada.

	Annual Growth	12/05	12/06	12/07	12/08	12/09
Sales ($ mil.)	0.0%	0.1	0.1	0.2	0.1	0.1
Net income ($ mil.)	—	(4.2)	(20.3)	(12.8)	(35.9)	(63.9)
Market value ($ mil.)	(29.6%)	379.4	2,288.4	207.8	168.6	93.3
Employees	18.6%	—	18	—	40	30

FALCON PHARMACEUTICALS, LTD.

6201 South Fwy.	CEO: Kevin J. Buehler
Fort Worth, TX 76134	CFO: —
Phone: 817-293-0450	HR: —
Fax: 800-777-2799	FYE: December 31
Web: www.falconpharma.com	Type: Subsidiary

Falcon Pharmaceuticals has a keen eye for alternatives. The company specializes in making generic equivalents of ophthalmic drugs that treat a range of eye conditions, as well as otic (ear) and nasal ailments. Its lead product, Timolol GFS, is a generic equivalent of Merck's glaucoma treatment Timoptic-XE gel. The company also offers anti-infective, steroid, anti-viral, anti-allergy, and anesthetic pharmaceutical products without the markup typically associated with brand names. Falcon Pharmaceuticals is a subsidiary of eye care products company Alcon.

FALCON RIDGE DEVELOPMENT, INC.

OTC: FCNR

5111 Juan Tabo Blvd. NE	CEO: Fred M Montano
Albuquerque, NM 87111	CFO: Karen Y. Duran
Phone: 505-856-6043	HR: —
Fax: —	FYE: September 30
Web: www.falconridgedev.com	Type: Public

Falcon Ridge Development is hoping to hatch a second life in real estate. Formerly a maker of color-measuring devices, the company exited that business to buy and develop raw land in New Mexico into communities with residential, retail, and commercial properties. In 2007 Falcon Ridge established subsidiaries to build houses and sell houses and mortgages. It owns rights to a 140-acre parcel in the small town of Belen (near Albuquerque), although it has stopped all development activities there in light of the struggling real estate market and its own lack of capital.

	Annual Growth	1/04	1/05	1/06	9/07	*9/08
Sales ($ mil.)	(15.9%)	0.2	0.2	0.0	0.0	0.1
Net income ($ mil.)	—	(2.7)	(0.5)	(0.4)	(1.3)	(4.6)
Market value ($ mil.)	(98.5%)	—	—	—	33.6	0.5
Employees	(15.9%)	4	3	3	3	2

*Most recent year available

FALCONSTOR SOFTWARE, INC.

NASDAQ (GM): FALC

2 Huntington Quadrangle, Ste. 2S01	CEO: ReiJane Huai
Melville, NY 11747	CFO: James Weber
Phone: 631-777-5188	HR: —
Fax: 631-501-7633	FYE: December 31
Web: www.falconstor.com	Type: Public

FalconStor Software watches data like a hawk. The company provides network storage management software and related services. Its IPStor software is used to manage storage provisioning and virtualization, data availability, replication, and disaster recovery functions in disk-based systems. FalconStor also offers consulting, engineering, implementation, and maintenance services. Ranging from small and midsized businesses to large enterprises, the company's customers come from fields such as health care, financial services, education, and information technology. FalconStor sells predominantly through distributors, manufacturers, and resellers.

	Annual Growth	12/05	12/06	12/07	12/08	12/09
Sales ($ mil.)	21.6%	41.0	55.1	77.4	87.0	89.5
Net income ($ mil.)	—	2.3	(3.4)	12.7	1.2	(3.1)
Market value ($ mil.)	(13.9%)	336.1	393.4	512.1	126.4	184.7
Employees	18.1%	279	340	414	505	542

FALKEN TIRE CORPORATION

13649 Valley Blvd.	CEO: Hideo Honda
Fontana, CA 92335	CFO: Dan Sullivan
Phone: 800-723-2553	HR: —
Fax: 800-950-2561	FYE: December 31
Web: www.falkentire.com	Type: Subsidiary

Just like the theme song from *Rawhide*, Falken Tire keeps on *rollin', rollin', rollin'*. The company, a subsidiary of Japan-based Sumitomo Rubber Industries, makes and distributes tires that run the gamut from original equipment replacement tires for passenger cars to those found on light trucks/SUVs (including tires for off-road use) and even race cars. Falken's other product offerings include high-performance wheels for cars, trucks, and SUVs, as well as all-season tires geared toward the consumer automotive aftermarket. Falken tires are sold by independent dealers throughout the US and Canada. Wheel brands include Aviator, Marquis, and Solaris; tire brands include Azenis, Sinsera, and Ziex.

FALLON WORLDWIDE

901 Marquette Ave., Ste. 2400
Minneapolis, MN 55402
Phone: 612-758-2345
Fax: 612-758-2346
Web: www.fallon.com

CEO: Patrick (Pat) Fallon
CFO: Steve Waring
HR: —
FYE: December 31
Type: Subsidiary

This company might be able to lend a hand if your brand has fallen on hard times. Fallon Worldwide is a leading creative ad agency, serving such clients as Travelers Insurance, Sony, Holiday Inn, Purina, and NBC, and operating through offices in Minneapolis, London, and Tokyo. In addition to creative development, the firm offers marketing and branding services, brand and corporate identity consulting, and campaign planning services. Fallon also provides interactive marketing services and website development. The agency was founded as Fallon McElligott Rice in 1981 by partners Pat Fallon, Tom McElligott, and Nancy Rice. Fallon is a subsidiary of Paris-based advertising conglomerate Publicis.

FAMILY CHRISTIAN STORES, INC.

5300 Patterson Ave. SE
Grand Rapids, MI 49530
Phone: 616-554-8700
Fax: 616-554-8608
Web: www.familychristian.com

CEO: Cliff Bartow
CFO: John Pindred
HR: Steve Biondo
FYE: January 31
Type: Private

The latest from Nora Roberts or Stephen King is no match for a perennial bestseller found in large supply at Family Christian Stores. A leading Christian retailer in the US, Family Christian Stores boasts about 300 stores in about 35 states. The company sells a variety of Christian-themed merchandise, including Bibles and other Christian books, music, software, gifts, cards, videos, apparel, and church supplies. Customers can also buy products through the company's catalog and website. Family Christian has grown through new store openings and acquisitions (including chains Joshua's Christian Stores and Shepherd Shoppe). The investment firm Madison Dearborn owns a majority stake in Family Christian Stores.

⊞ FAMILY DOLLAR STORES, INC.

NYSE: FDO

10401 Monroe Rd.
Matthews, NC 28105
Phone: 704-847-6961
Fax: 704-847-0189
Web: www.familydollar.com

CEO: Howard R. Levine
CFO: Kenneth T. (Ken) Smith
HR: Bryan E. Venberg
FYE: August 31
Type: Public

Penny-pinching moms are important to Family Dollar Stores. The nation's #2 dollar store (behind Dollar General) targets women shopping for a family earning less than $40,000 a year. It operates about 6,665 stores in some 45 states and the District of Columbia. Consumables (food, health and beauty aids, and household items) account for more than 60% of sales; the stores also sell apparel, shoes, and linens. Family Dollar emphasizes small-format neighborhood stores near its low- and middle-income customers in rural and urban areas. Most merchandise (national brands, Family Dollar private labels, and unbranded items) costs less than $10. Family Dollar was founded in 1959 by the father of CEO Howard Levine.

	Annual Growth	8/05	8/06	8/07	8/08	8/09
Sales ($ mil.)	6.2%	5,824.8	6,394.8	6,834.3	6,983.6	7,400.6
Net income ($ mil.)	7.6%	217.5	195.1	242.9	233.1	291.3
Market value ($ mil.)	11.1%	2,685.3	3,453.8	3,955.0	3,366.0	4,090.0
Employees	2.9%	42,000	44,000	44,000	44,000	47,000

FAMOUS DAVE'S OF AMERICA, INC.

NASDAQ (GM): DAVE

12701 Whitewater Dr., Ste. 200
Minnetonka, MN 55343
Phone: 952-294-1300
Fax: 952-294-1301
Web: www.famousdaves.com

CEO: Christopher O'Donnell
CFO: Diana G. Purcel
HR: Jackie Kane Ottoson
FYE: December 31
Type: Public

Barbecue made this Dave famous. Famous Dave's of America operates and franchises about 170 barbecue restaurants in some 35 states, primarily Minnesota, Illinois, California, and Wisconsin. The eateries serve St. Louis-style ribs, Georgia chopped pork, and Texas brisket. Most restaurants resemble 1930s-era roadhouse shacks, although others follow the decor of a hunting lodge or a Chicago-style blues club featuring live music. The company also distributes barbecue sauce, seasonings, and prepared meats through grocery stores and other retail outlets. Famous Dave's owns and operates almost 50 of its restaurants and franchises the rest.

	Annual Growth	12/05	12/06	12/07	12/08	12/09
Sales ($ mil.)	7.4%	102.4	116.6	125.9	140.4	136.0
Net income ($ mil.)	6.7%	4.4	4.9	6.1	0.4	5.7
Market value ($ mil.)	(14.6%)	99.2	145.1	119.3	25.5	52.8
Employees	7.8%	2,000	2,600	2,800	3,100	2,700

FAMOUS UNCLE AL'S HOT DOGS & GRILLE, INC.

OTC: FDOG

100 Mill Plain Rd.
Danbury, CT 06811
Phone: 203-616-2930
Fax: —
Web: www.famousunclealshotdogs.com

CEO: Paul Esposito
CFO: —
HR: —
FYE: December 31
Type: Public

Famous Uncle Al's Hot Dogs & Grille operates a chain of about 10 franchised quick-service restaurants in Arizona, Connecticut, Florida, Nevada, and Virginia that specialize in hot dogs and sausage sandwiches. The eateries also serve a variety of Italian-style sandwiches, burgers, and fries. CEO Paul Esposito and president Dean Valentino together control more than 30% of the company.

	Annual Growth	12/05	12/06	12/07	12/08	12/09
Sales ($ mil.)	—	—	0.3	0.2	0.1	0.0
Net income ($ mil.)	—	—	(1.0)	(1.5)	(0.6)	(0.1)
Market value ($ mil.)	(85.9%)	—	—	4.5	0.7	0.1
Employees	(30.7%)	—	3	3	3	1

FANDANGO INC.

12200 W. Olympic Blvd., Ste. 150
Los Angeles, CA 90064
Phone: 310-451-7690
Fax: 310-451-7861
Web: www.fandango.com

CEO: Chuck Davis
CFO: Daniel V. (Dan) Murray
HR: Bethany Ellis
FYE: January 1
Type: Private

Better than cutting ahead in line, Fandango lets you skip the line. The firm provides advance movie tickets and show time information via the Internet (at Fandango.com), phone (at 1-800-FANDANGO), and wireless mobile (mobile.fandango.com). Customers can use credit cards to guarantee tickets, which they pick up at the theater. Fandango also offers print-at-home tickets and is supported by more than 20 movie exhibitors, including Cinemark and Regal Entertainment Group, providing tickets to some 16,000 screens across the US. A group of exhibitors formed Fandango in 2000; cable firm Comcast purchased it in 2007. Fandango operates as part of Comcast Interactive Media, alongside sites such as Plaxo and DailyCandy.

F & M BANK CORP.

OTC: FMBM

205 S. Main St.
Timberville, VA 22853
Phone: 540-896-8941
Fax: 540-896-2840
Web: www.farmersandmerchants.biz

CEO: Dean W. Withers
CFO: Neil W. Hayslett
HR: Ellen C. Branner
FYE: December 31
Type: Public

F & M Bank has deep roots in Virginia's Shenandoah Valley. Founded in 1908, the holding company operates about 10 Farmers & Merchants Bank branches in the northern Virginia counties of Rockingham and Shenandoah. Farmers & Merchants caters to individuals and businesses. It provides typical deposit products, including checking and savings accounts, CDs, and IRAs. Some 40% of its loans are mortgages; it also writes agricultural, business, construction, and consumer loans. The company offers insurance, brokerage, and financial services through TEB Life Insurance and Farmers & Merchants Financial Services.

	Annual Growth	12/05	12/06	12/07	12/08	12/09
Assets ($ mil.)	11.7%	346.3	375.9	386.7	472.1	539.2
Net income ($ mil.)	(19.7%)	4.8	4.5	4.5	3.2	2.0
Market value ($ mil.)	(3.0%)	59.7	64.6	71.3	69.5	52.8
Employees	4.9%	114	133	137	134	138

FANSTEEL INC.

Pink Sheets: FELI

1746 Commerce Rd.
Creston, IA 50801
Phone: 641-782-8521
Fax: 641-782-4844
Web: www.fansteel.com

CEO: Curtis J. (Curt) Zamec II
CFO: Earl F. White
HR: —
FYE: December 31
Type: Public

Fansteel is a big fan of steel and other performance metals, such as tungsten carbide, titanium, special alloys, and other metals. The company's Advanced Structures segment (63% of sales) produces aluminum and magnesium sand castings, closed die forgings, and machined components. Its Metal Components segment (37%) makes powdered metal components, engineered investment castings, and custom assemblies. United Technologies represents over 20% of sales, while Navistar International accounts for about 7%. Other customers include companies in the aerospace, agricultural equipment, automotive, defense, electrical appliances, fluid controls, lawn and garden, industrial hardware, and power tools industries.

	Annual Growth	12/04	12/05	12/06	12/07	*12/08
Sales ($ mil.)	9.9%	54.8	56.3	67.5	74.8	79.9
Net income ($ mil.)	—	54.1	(1.4)	(5.3)	(2.5)	(0.7)
Market value ($ mil.)	(22.0%)	3.3	4.5	0.6	0.3	1.2
Employees	5.1%	—	—	685	720	—

*Most recent year available

FANUC ROBOTICS AMERICA, INC.

3900 W. Hamlin Rd.
Rochester Hills, MI 48309
Phone: 248-377-7000
Fax: 248-276-4133
Web: www.fanucrobotics.com

CEO: Richard E. (Rick) Schneider
CFO: Steve Stanko
HR: —
FYE: March 31
Type: Subsidiary

FANUC Robotics America makes intelligent robots that automate industrial manufacturing. Its robotic devices automate such processes as assembly, cleaning, dispensing, grinding, packaging, painting, polishing, and welding. Customers include Corning, Rubbermaid, Ford, and General Motors. FANUC Robotics America supplies equipment to the aerospace, agriculture, automotive, consumer goods, electronics, food and beverage, glass, machine tools, medical devices, paper and printing, pharmaceuticals, plastics, and textile industries, among others. It also provides engineering, service support, analysis, and system maintenance. The company operates facilities in Brazil, Canada, Mexico, and the US.

FAO SCHWARZ INC.

875 Avenue of the Americas, 20th Fl.
New York, NY 10001
Phone: 212-644-9400
Fax: 212-308-6094
Web: www.fao.com

CEO: Jerry Storch
CFO: —
HR: —
FYE: January 31
Type: Private

Famed toy store FAO Schwarz is a kid pleaser. The toy seller operates two retail locations: its landmark store on New York's Fifth Avenue and one in The Forum Shops at Caesars Palace in Las Vegas. The company also boasts some 260 shops within selected Macy's locations. FAO Schwarz sells its unique, hard-to-find toys (such as life-size stuffed bears and $50,000 kid-size Ferraris) through its relaunched catalog and website. The toy retailer's flagship stores log foot traffic from more than 3 million visitors each year. Being a kid itself, FAO Schwarz has a sweet tooth, with its sweets shop called FAO Schweetz, an add-on at its New York store. Toy titan Toys "R" Us added FAO Schwarz to its toy chest in 2009.

FAR EAST ENERGY CORPORATION

OTC: FEEC

363 N. Sam Houston Pkwy., Ste. 380
Houston, TX 77060
Phone: 832-598-0470
Fax: 832-598-0479
Web: www.fareastenergy.com

CEO: Michael R. McElwrath
CFO: Bruce N. Huff
HR: —
FYE: December 31
Type: Public

Far East Energy is engaged in coalbed methane gas exploration and production in China, and in the development of related technologies. The company works with ConocoPhillips and China United Coalbed Methane Company to acquire and explore assets across China. Far East Energy's Shanxi coalbed methane project, when fully developed, could sustain more than 3,000 horizontal gas wells, making it one of the world's largest coalbed methane projects. The company has drilled five coalbed methane gas exploration wells in Shanxi, and six in its other major project area in Yunnan Province. It holds more than 1.3 million acres of leasehold properties.

	Annual Growth	12/05	12/06	12/07	12/08	12/09
Sales ($ mil.)	—	—	—	—	0.0	0.0
Net income ($ mil.)	—	—	—	—	(22.6)	(13.8)
Market value ($ mil.)	162.9%	—	—	—	32.5	85.4
Employees	(6.5%)	—	—	—	31	29

FAR EAST NATIONAL BANK

2 California Plaza, 350 S. Grand Ave., Ste. 4100
Los Angeles, CA 90071
Phone: 213-687-1200
Fax: 213-687-8511
Web: www.fareastnationalbank.com

CEO: Frederick Copeland
CFO: —
HR: —
FYE: December 31
Type: Subsidiary

Far East National Bank serves California's Asian-American community through about a dozen branches in Southern California and the San Francisco Bay area. It also has representative offices in China and Vietnam. The bank offers traditional banking services such as checking, savings, and investment accounts, and business, commercial real estate, and residential mortgage loans. It also has divisions devoted to treasury services and international banking. Far East Capital Corporation, a subsidiary of the bank, provides capital raising and advisory services to high-growth companies in California and the Pacific Rim. Founded in 1974, Far East National Bank is owned by Taiwan's SinoPac Financial Holdings.

	Annual Growth	12/04	12/05	12/06	12/07	12/08
Est. sales ($ mil.)	—	—	—	—	—	126.8
Employees	—	—	—	—	—	354

An in-depth profile of this company is available to Hoover's Online members at hoovers.com.

595

FAREWAY STORES, INC.

2300 E. 8th St.
Boone, IA 50036
Phone: 515-432-2623
Fax: 515-433-4416
Web: www.fareway.com

CEO: F. William Beckwith
CFO: Craig A. Shepley
HR: Mike Mazour
FYE: March 31
Type: Private

Fareway Stores makes the green through groceries. The regional grocery chain operates under the Fareway banner, primarily in Iowa but also in Illinois, Nebraska, and now Minnesota. Its 95 locations average about 25,000 sq. ft. Eschewing such amenities as video rentals and dry-cleaning services, Fareway Stores sticks to the basics — lots of meat (all cut to order) and groceries only — counts on low prices and customer service to compete with supercenter operators, such as Wal-Mart. Former Safeway workers Paul Beckwith and Fred Vitt founded Fareway in 1938; the Beckwith family controls the company. Because of the founders' biblical beliefs, the stores are closed on Sundays.

FARLEY'S & SATHERS CANDY COMPANY, INC.

1 Sather Plaza
Round Lake, MN 56167
Phone: 507-945-8181
Fax: 507-945-8343
Web: www.farleysandsathers.com

CEO: Liam C. Killeen
CFO: Tammy Koller
HR: Theresa Neuberger
FYE: December 31
Type: Private

Farley's & Sathers Candy Company went on a buying spree. The Minnesota-based company makes non-chocolate confections including Chuckles, JujyFruits, and Jujubes (all acquired from Hershey Foods in 2002), along with Now and Later, Mighty Bite, and Intense Fruit Chews candies (acquired from Kraft Foods in 2002 as well). Farley's also makes RainBlo, Jujyfruits, Super Bubble, and Hot Dog! bubble gums (which it bought from Hershey in 2003). Offering 900 different candy items, it produces some 42 million pounds of sweet treats a year, which are distributed throughout the US. The company, which dates back to 1870, is owned by investment firm Catterton Partners.

	Annual Growth	12/04	12/05	12/06	12/07	12/08
Est. sales ($ mil.)	—	—	—	—	—	400.0
Employees	—	—	—	—	—	1,600

FARM CREDIT SERVICES OF MID-AMERICA, ACA

1601 UPS Dr.
Louisville, KY 40223
Phone: 502-420-3700
Fax: 502-420-3456
Web: www.e-farmcredit.com

CEO: Donald W. (Donnie) Winters
CFO: Paul C. Bruce Jr.
HR: —
FYE: December 31
Type: Cooperative

If Old McDonald's farm is in Indiana, Kentucky, Ohio, or Tennessee, he might have a loan-loan-here and a loan-loan-there from Farm Credit Services of Mid-America. The cooperative association, one of the largest in the National Farm Credit System, provides lending and other financial services to these states' farmers and rural homeowners. Borrowers use Farm Credit's products to purchase real estate, homes, livestock, and farming equipment, and to fund capital improvements, and operating and living expenses. It has a loan volume of about $12 billion and serves some 85,000 customers through nearly 100 offices located throughout its service area.

	Annual Growth	12/04	12/05	12/06	12/07	12/08
Est. sales ($ mil.)	—	—	—	—	—	674.1
Employees	—	—	—	—	—	740

FARM PROGRESS COMPANIES, INC.

255 38th Ave., Ste. P
Saint Charles, IL 60174
Phone: 630-690-5600
Fax: 630-462-2202
Web: www.farmprogress.com

CEO: Jeff Lapin
CFO: Michael Barb
HR: —
FYE: June 30
Type: Subsidiary

Farm Progress Companies is sowing the seeds of agricultural publishing. The company publishes about two dozen magazines, including flagship title *Prairie Farmer* (first published in 1841), as well as *American Agriculturist*, *Southern Farmer*, and *Western Farmer-Stockman*. In addition, Farm Progress Companies' network of Web sites offers breaking news, weather, blogs, e-commerce services, classified advertising, and other resources to the agricultural community. The company also produces events (the Farm Progress Show) and offers custom publishing and marketing services. Farm Progress Companies is owned by Australian newspaper publisher Fairfax Media.

⊞ FARMER BROS. CO.

NASDAQ (GM): FARM

20333 S. Normandie Ave.
Torrance, CA 90502
Phone: 310-787-5200
Fax: 310-787-5246
Web: www.farmerbroscousa.com

CEO: Roger M. (Rocky) Laverty III
CFO: Jeffrey A. (Jeff) Wahba
HR: —
FYE: June 30
Type: Public

Farmer Bros. knows beans about farming, but it knows about coffee beans. The company roasts and packages coffee and sells it mainly to institutional foodservice providers, such as restaurants, hotels, and hospitals. It also serves other foodservice operators, including fast-food outlets and convenience stores. It distributes related or "allied" coffee products such as filters, cups, and creamers, as well as teas, spices, and soup bases to those same customers. Farmer Bros. distributes more than 400 products from about 100 branch warehouses in major US cities in more than a dozen states. Its Brewmatic division makes coffee dispensers. Coffee products accounted for about 50% of the company's 2009 sales.

	Annual Growth	6/05	6/06	6/07	6/08	6/09
Sales ($ mil.)	14.6%	198.4	207.5	216.3	266.5	341.7
Net income ($ mil.)	—	(5.4)	4.8	6.8	(7.9)	(33.3)
Market value ($ mil.)	0.7%	359.8	343.3	365.7	341.8	369.8
Employees	19.6%	1,084	1,091	1,233	1,256	2,218

FARMERS CAPITAL BANK CORPORATION

NASDAQ (GS): FFKT

202 W. Main St.
Frankfort, KY 40601
Phone: 502-227-1600
Fax: 502-227-1692
Web: www.farmerscapital.com

CEO: Lloyd C. Hillard Jr.
CFO: C. Douglas Carpenter
HR: Linda L Faulconer
FYE: December 31
Type: Public

Farmers Capital has found some green in the Bluegrass State. Its five bank subsidiaries — Citizens Bank of Northern Kentucky, Farmers Bank & Capital Trust, First Citizens Bank, LNB, and United Bank — operate more than 35 branches in northern and central Kentucky. Serving individuals and local businesses, they offer standard retail services such as checking and savings accounts, CDs, and trust activities. Residential mortgages and commercial real estate loans together account for around 80% of the company's loan portfolio. Nonbank subsidiaries of Farmers Capital provide leasing, insurance, and data processing services.

	Annual Growth	12/05	12/06	12/07	12/08	12/09
Assets ($ mil.)	6.7%	1,672.6	1,824.4	2,068.2	2,202.2	2,171.6
Net income ($ mil.)	—	15.8	21.4	15.6	4.4	(44.7)
Market value ($ mil.)	(24.1%)	227.0	252.0	199.4	180.3	75.5
Employees	(1.0%)	570	585	578	579	547

FARMERS GROUP, INC.

4680 Wilshire Blvd.
Los Angeles, CA 90010
Phone: 323-932-3200
Fax: —
Web: www.farmers.com

CEO: F. Robert (Bob) Woudstra
CFO: Scott R. Lindquist
HR: —
FYE: December 31
Type: Subsidiary

Don't expect to see tractors in the parking lot of Farmers Group. The US subsidiary of Zurich Financial Services provides insurance management services to the members of the Farmers Insurance Exchange, Truck Insurance Exchange, and Fire Insurance Exchange — which together form one of the leading US property/casualty insurers. Farmers Group does not own the exchanges, but acts as the companies' attorneys-in-fact. It chooses risks, distributes policy statements to customers, collects premiums, and provides other non-claims related services. Farmers Group is also the holding company of Farmers New World Life Insurance, and specialty insurer Foremost Insurance.

FARMERS NATIONAL BANC CORP.

OTC: FMNB

20 S. Broad St.
Canfield, OH 44406
Phone: 330-533-3341
Fax: 330-533-0451
Web: www.fnbcanfield.com

CEO: Frank L. Paden
CFO: Carl D. Culp
HR: —
FYE: December 31
Type: Public

Farmers National Banc is willing to help even nonfarmers grow their seed income into thriving bounties of wealth. The institution is the holding company for Farmers National Bank of Canfield, which provides commercial and personal banking from some 20 branches in northeastern Ohio. The bank offers traditional products and services including checking accounts, savings accounts, credit cards, and loans and mortgages. Farmers National Banc's lending portfolio is composed of real estate mortgages, consumer loans, and commercial loans. The company bought wealth management and trust services provider Butler Wick Trust (since renamed Farmers National Trust) from United Community Financial for some $12 million in 2009.

	Annual Growth	12/05	12/06	12/07	12/08	12/09
Assets ($ mil.)	5.2%	827.1	821.6	798.2	880.4	1,014.8
Net income ($ mil.)	(8.0%)	8.1	7.2	5.9	5.7	5.8
Market value ($ mil.)	(22.6%)	172.7	142.9	104.3	48.8	62.0
Employees	(3.0%)	294	284	274	260	260

FARMERS NEW WORLD LIFE INSURANCE COMPANY

3003 77th Ave. SE
Mercer Island, WA 98040
Phone: 206-232-8400
Fax: 206-236-6672
Web: www.farmers.com/life_insurance.html

CEO: Thomas J. White
CFO: Katherine P. (Kathy) Cody
HR: —
FYE: December 31
Type: Subsidiary

Individuals hoping to reap the rich rewards of life may discover Farmers New World Life Insurance without crossing treacherous oceans. The company is the primary life insurance subsidiary of Farmers Group, a top provider of personal property/casualty insurance in the US. Farmers New World Life Insurance offers a range of individual life insurance products, including universal, term, and whole life policies, as well fixed and variable annuities. The products of Farmers New World Life Insurance (which operates under the Farmers Life brand) are marketed through the Farmers Group's agency force. The company was founded in 1910.

	Annual Growth	12/04	12/05	12/06	12/07	12/08
Est. sales ($ mil.)	—	—	—	—	—	1,020.7
Employees	—	—	—	—	—	800

FARMLAND DAIRIES, LLC

520 Main Ave.
Wallington, NJ 07057
Phone: 973-777-2500
Fax: 973-777-7648
Web: www.farmlanddairies.com

CEO: Martin J. (Marty) Margherio
CFO: Terri Webe
HR: Peter Clifford
FYE: December 31
Type: Subsidiary

Farmland Dairies (formerly Parmalat USA) has happy cows once again. The company got caught up in the 2003 bankruptcy scandal of its then-parent, Italy's Parmalat Finaziaria, but emerged in 2005 hale and healthy as Farmland. Its brand names include Clinton's, Farmland, Parmalat, Lil' Milk, and Welsh Farms. In addition to fresh and shelf-stable milk, Farmland also makes ice cream mixes, cream, half and half, fruit drinks and juices, and Pomi brand shelf-stable tomatoes and tomato sauces. Available throughout the US, the company's milk and milk products are market leaders in the New York and New Jersey metro areas. Farmland Dairies was bought by Grupo Lala in 2009.

FARMLAND FOODS, INC.

11500 NW Ambassador Dr., Ste. 500
Kansas City, MO 64153
Phone: 816-243-2700
Fax: 816-243-3356
Web: www.farmlandfoods.com

CEO: James C. (Jim) Sbarro
CFO: Shelly Phalen
HR: Mark Garrett
FYE: December 31
Type: Subsidiary

Farmland Foods hopes to put all sorts of meaty morsels on dining tables far and wide. With customers in the Americas, Europe, Asia, Africa, the Middle East, and Australasia, the company sells a variety of meat products under the Farmland label, including bacon, ham, pork, hot dogs, deli and lunch meats, sausage, and beef. The company also sells its offerings carrying other brand names, including Roegelein (deli meats), and Ohse (hot dogs, sandwich meats, bacon). Its foodservice division specializes in delivering a variety of meat offerings to the US foodservice industry. Farmland is a subsidiary of Smithfield Foods.

	Annual Growth	12/04	12/05	12/06	12/07	12/08
Est. sales ($ mil.)	—	—	—	—	—	1,796.6
Employees	—	—	—	—	—	6,123

FARNER-BOCKEN COMPANY

1751 Hwy. 30 East
Carroll, IA 51401
Phone: 712-792-3503
Fax: 712-792-3513
Web: www.farnerbocken.com

CEO: John J. Norgaard
CFO: Paul Francis
HR: —
FYE: April 30
Type: Private

Farner-Bocken is a full-line wholesale distributor that serves primarily convenience stores in more than a dozen midwestern and western states. It supplies more than 14,000 items, including food, candy, tobacco products, and other nationally branded retail grocery goods. It also distributes frozen prepared foods and foodservice equipment and supplies to restaurants and institutional foodservice operators. In addition to food products, Farner-Bocken offers business support services, including accounting, merchandising, and technology support. William Farner and Donald Bocken started the family-owned company in 1939.

FARO TECHNOLOGIES, INC.

NASDAQ (GM): FARO

250 Technology Park
Lake Mary, FL 32746
Phone: 407-333-9911
Fax: 407-333-4181
Web: www.faro.com

CEO: Jay W. Freeland
CFO: Keith S. Bair
HR: John E. Townsley
FYE: December 31
Type: Public

FARO Technologies is putting the Arm on companies around the world — and they like it. With the touch of its mechanical arm, FARO's measuring systems can facilitate reverse engineering of an undocumented part or a competitor's product. The portable FaroArm, FARO Laser ScanArm, and FARO Gage are jointed devices that simulate the human arm's movement. Along with the FARO Laser Scanner LS, and Laser Tracker, inspections and measurements are integrated with companion CAM2, 3-D software. Aerospace, automotive, and heavy equipment companies such as Boeing, Caterpillar, General Motors, and Siemens use FARO Arm units in their factories. Customers located outside the Americas account for over 60% of sales.

	Annual Growth	12/05	12/06	12/07	12/08	12/09
Sales ($ mil.)	4.1%	125.6	152.4	191.6	209.2	147.7
Net income ($ mil.)	—	8.2	8.2	18.1	14.0	(10.6)
Market value ($ mil.)	1.8%	322.7	387.9	438.5	272.0	345.9
Employees	2.8%	657	641	780	959	734

FASHION BUG RETAIL COMPANIES, INC.

450 Winks Ln.
Bensalem, PA 19020
Phone: 215-245-9100
Fax: 215-633-4640
Web: www.fashionbug.com

CEO: Jay H. Levitt
CFO: Michele Pascoe
HR: Donna D. Desilets
FYE: January 31
Type: Business segment

When women get the bug to shop they hop on over to Fashion Bug, a chain of about 900 shops in more than 40 states. The specialty apparel retailer sells low- to moderate-priced plus-size and misses fashionable clothing to women ages 30 to 50. Fashion Bug stores are located mainly in strip shopping centers and average about 8,700 sq. ft. Customers can also shop online at fashionbug.com. In addition to casual and career apparel, Fashion Bug sells footwear and accessories, bridal attire, and Bundle of Joy maternity clothing. The chain also offers its own Fashion Bug credit card. Founded in the 1960s, today Fashion Bug is owned by Charming Shoppes and accounts for about a third of its parent company's revenue.

	Annual Growth	1/04	1/05	1/06	1/07	1/08
Sales ($ mil.)	(1.7%)	—	1,045.0	1,049.0	1,058.0	993.0
Employees	—	—	—	—	—	—

⊞ FASTENAL COMPANY

NASDAQ (GS): FAST

2001 Theurer Blvd.
Winona, MN 55987
Phone: 507-454-5374
Fax: 507-453-8049
Web: www.fastenal.com

CEO: Willard D. (Will) Oberton
CFO: Daniel L. (Dan) Florness
HR: Reyne K. Wisecup
FYE: December 31
Type: Public

Some might say it has a screw loose, but things are really pretty snug at Fastenal. The company operates about 2,350 stores in all 50 US states, Canada, China, Mexico, the Netherlands, Puerto Rico, and Singapore. Its stores stock about 690,000 products in about a dozen categories, including threaded fasteners such as screws, nuts, and bolts. Other sales come from fluid-transfer parts for hydraulic and pneumatic power; janitorial, electrical, and welding supplies; material handling items; metal-cutting tool blades; and power tools. Its customers are typically construction, manufacturing, and other industrial professionals. Fastenal Company was founded by its chairman Bob Kierlin in 1967 and went public in 1987.

	Annual Growth	12/05	12/06	12/07	12/08	12/09
Sales ($ mil.)	6.1%	1,523.3	1,809.3	2,061.8	2,340.4	1,930.3
Net income ($ mil.)	2.5%	166.8	199.0	232.6	279.7	184.4
Market value ($ mil.)	1.6%	5,769.0	5,289.8	5,959.1	5,138.0	6,139.0
Employees	6.7%	9,306	10,415	12,013	13,634	12,045

FAUQUIER BANKSHARES, INC.

NASDAQ (CM): FBSS

10 Courthouse Sq.
Warrenton, VA 20186
Phone: 540-347-2700
Fax: 540-349-9533
Web: www.fauquierbank.com

CEO: Randy K. Ferrell
CFO: Eric P. Graap
HR: —
FYE: December 31
Type: Public

Fauquier Bankshares is the holding company for The Fauquier Bank, which operates about 10 branches in northern Virginia, southwest of Washington, DC. The bank targets individual and regional business customers, offering standard retail products such as checking, savings, and money market accounts, and CDs. Its lending activities consist mostly of residential and commercial mortgages (about 40% and 30% of its loan portfolio, respectively). Its wealth management division provides investment management, trust, estate, retirement, insurance, and brokerage services. Through subsidiary Fauquier Bank Services it has equity ownership in Bankers Insurance, Bankers Investments Group, and Bankers Title Shenandoah.

	Annual Growth	12/05	12/06	12/07	12/08	12/09
Assets ($ mil.)	4.3%	481.2	521.8	489.9	514.5	568.5
Net income ($ mil.)	(12.1%)	5.7	5.6	5.0	3.7	3.4
Market value ($ mil.)	(16.1%)	90.6	90.7	61.8	46.3	44.8
Employees	2.0%	147	147	128	156	—

FAURECIA EXHAUST SYSTEMS, INC.

543 Matzinger Rd.
Toledo, OH 43612
Phone: 419-727-5000
Fax: 419-727-5025

CEO: Michael T. Heneka
CFO: —
HR: —
FYE: December 31
Type: Subsidiary

Faurecia Exhaust Systems, formerly AP Automotive Systems, ends each day exhausted but rewarded. A subsidiary of France-based automotive company Faurecia (automotive seating and interiors, exhaust systems, front-end modules), the company is one of the leading makers of auto exhaust systems for the global auto industry. Faurecia Exhaust Systems turns out complete exhaust systems, mufflers, tailpipes, and other exhaust system components for such automakers as Ford, General Motors, Volvo, and Volkswagen. The company has operations in the US as well as in Mexico, the Netherlands, South Africa, and Sweden.

FAURECIA INTERIOR SYSTEMS, INC.

2050 Auburn Rd.
Auburn Hills, MI 48326
Phone: 248-409-3500
Fax: 248-409-3501

CEO: Yann Delabrière
CFO: —
HR: —
FYE: December 31
Type: Subsidiary

A subsidiary of French auto parts supplier Faurecia, Faurecia Interior Systems manufactures central consoles, door panels, instrument panels, seats, and soundproofing molding for motor vehicles. Faurecia Interior Systems has operations in Michigan and South Carolina. PSA Peugeot Citroën, France's leading maker of automobiles, controls 71% of Faurecia. In addition to Citroën and Peugeot, Faurecia's customers for vehicle interior modules include Adam Opel, BMW, Chrysler, Dodge, Volkswagen, and Volvo Car.

FAYGO BEVERAGES, INC.

3579 Gratiot Ave.
Detroit, MI 48207
Phone: 313-925-1600
Fax: 313-571-7611
Web: www.faygo.com

CEO: Alan A. (Al) Chittaro
CFO: —
HR: —
FYE: April 30
Type: Subsidiary

Faygo Beverages believes in flavor. Old-fashioned flavor — its products are made with cane sugar (rather than high-fructose corn syrup) and are packaged in genuine glass bottles. The company manufactures some 50 fruit-flavored sodas, cola, ginger ale, root beer, and creme soda under the Faygo name. It also makes Fago non-alcoholic mixers (club soda and tonic water). Although it is best known for its "pop," the beverage maker offers Ohana brand iced tea, lemonade, and fruit punch. The wide range of Faygo pop flavors include Blueberry, Vanilla Creme, Redpop, Dr. Faygo, Moon Mist, and Black Cherry. The company, whose products are available throughout the US, is a subsidiary of National Beverage Corp.

FBL FINANCIAL GROUP, INC.
NYSE: FFG

5400 University Ave.
West Des Moines, IA 50266
Phone: 515-225-5400
Fax: 515-226-6053
Web: www.fblfinancial.com

CEO: James E. (Jim) Hohmann
CFO: James P. (Jim) Brannen
HR: Mark Mincks
FYE: December 31
Type: Public

Insurance holding company FBL Financial Group is the parent of Farm Bureau Life and EquiTrust Life. Through these subsidiaries the firm sells life insurance, annuities, and investment products to farmers, ranchers, and agricultural businesses. Farm Bureau Life sells its insurance and annuities through an exclusive network of some 2,000 agents in the Midwest and West. EquiTrust Life's annuity products are sold through about 20,000 independent agents across the US. The company markets its products through an affiliation with the American Farm Bureau Federation. The Iowa Farm Bureau Federation owns about two-thirds of the company.

	Annual Growth	12/05	12/06	12/07	12/08	12/09
Assets ($ mil.)	8.9%	10,153.9	12,154.0	14,003.0	14,060.8	14,259.3
Net income ($ mil.)	(1.0%)	72.7	90.0	86.2	(18.1)	69.8
Market value ($ mil.)	(13.3%)	1,009.9	1,202.8	1,062.8	475.5	570.0
Employees	(2.8%)	1,923	1,858	1,818	1,866	1,714

FBR CAPITAL MARKETS CORPORATION
NASDAQ (GS): FBCM

1001 Nineteenth St. North, 18th Fl.
Arlington, VA 22209
Phone: 703-312-9500
Fax: 703-312-9501
Web: www.fbrcm.com

CEO: Richard J. Hendrix
CFO: Bradley J. Wright
HR: —
FYE: December 31
Type: Public

Don't confuse FDR and FBR: One was a beloved US president, while the other loves dead presidents. FBR Capital Markets provides investment banking, institutional brokerage, and fee-based asset management services for institutional and corporate clients and wealthy individuals. It also invests its own capital in merchant banking transactions alongside its clients. The company focuses on the financial services, insurance, and energy industries as well as real estate and health care. Arlington Asset Investment Corporation (formerly FBR Group) created FBR Capital in 2006. Arlington Asset spun off some of its stake in FBR Capital in an IPO the following year, and had liquidated its holdings by 2009.

	Annual Growth	12/05	12/06	12/07	12/08	12/09
Sales ($ mil.)	(23.8%)	575.4	418.6	484.9	275.7	193.8
Net income ($ mil.)	—	48.1	(9.8)	5.2	(194.7)	(27.7)
Market value ($ mil.)	(19.7%)	—	—	596.0	302.4	384.5
Employees	(4.1%)	702	751	758	568	595

FD AMERICAS PUBLIC AFFAIRS

1101 K St. NW, 9th Fl.
Washington, DC 20005
Phone: 202-346-8800
Fax: 202-346-8804
Web: www.fdpublicaffairsamericas.com

CEO: Edward Reilly
CFO: —
HR: —
FYE: December 31
Type: Subsidiary

A unit of UK-based strategic and financial communications consultancy FD, FD Americas Public Affairs (formerly Dittus Communications) offers public relations, marketing communications, and issue advocacy services. The firm provides the usual corporate services (media relations, corporate communications, and crisis management) plus public affairs services (issues management, legislative strategy, grassroots organizing and coalition building) as well as marketing, creative, and design services. Clients have included Kraft Foods, Dell, the US Department of Energy, and International Paper. The firm was founded in 1993.

FECHHEIMER BROTHERS COMPANY, INC.

4545 Malsbary Rd.
Cincinnati, OH 45242
Phone: 513-793-5400
Fax: 513-793-7819
Web: www.fechheimer.com

CEO: Bob Getto
CFO: Dan Dudley
HR: Jeanne Bossart
FYE: December 31
Type: Subsidiary

When you see Fechheimer Brothers Company products, you might not be having the best of days. Founded in 1842, it's a subsidiary of billionaire Warren Buffett's Berkshire Hathaway. The firm is a leading uniform manufacturer that outfits those who are employed in public service industries, such as corrections, fire and EMS, military, police, postal, and umpires, as well as military school students. Brand names include Flying Cross by Fechheimer and Urban Defender (battle dress uniforms). Fechheimer Brothers Company owns manufacturing plants in (Hodgenville) Kentucky, (Grantsville) Maryland, and (Jefferson) Pennsylvania.

FEDERAL AGRICULTURAL MORTGAGE CORPORATION
NYSE: AGM

1133 21st St. NW, Ste. 600
Washington, DC 20036
Phone: 202-872-7700
Fax: 202-872-7713
Web: www.farmermac.com

CEO: Michael A. Gerber
CFO: Timothy L. (Tim) Buzby
HR: —
FYE: December 31
Type: Public

Farmer Mac (Federal Agricultural Mortgage Corporation) is Fannie Mae and Freddie Mac's country cousin. Like its city-slicker kin, it provides liquidity in its markets (agricultural real estate and rural housing mortgages) by buying loans from lenders and then securitizing the loans into Farmer Mac Guaranteed Securities. Farmer Mac buys both conventional loans and those guaranteed by the US Department of Agriculture. About 40% of Farmer Mac's outstanding loans are secured by real estate in the southwestern US; the Northwest and the Upper Midwest account for nearly 20% apiece. More than 40% of its loans are for crops, some 25% for livestock facilities, and about another 20% for permanent plantings.

	Annual Growth	12/05	12/06	12/07	12/08	12/09
Assets ($ mil.)	9.1%	4,340.6	4,953.7	4,977.6	5,107.3	6,138.8
Net income ($ mil.)	35.6%	29.5	32.0	6.7	(150.4)	99.6
Market value ($ mil.)	(30.4%)	303.7	275.3	267.0	35.5	71.1
Employees	3.6%	46	45	42	43	53

FEDERAL HOME LOAN BANK OF ATLANTA

1475 Peachtree St., NE
Atlanta, GA 30309
Phone: 404-888-8000
Fax: 404-888-5648
Web: www.fhlbatl.com

CEO: Jill Spencer
CFO: Steven J. Goldstein
HR: Cathy Callaway Adams
FYE: December 31
Type: Member-owned banking authority

Where do banks in the southeastern US bank? Federal Home Loan Bank of Atlanta. More than 1,200 commercial banks, credit unions, insurance companies, and thrifts in the southeast bank at the institution, which calls itself FHLBank Atlanta. It's one of 12 Federal Home Loan Banks in the Federal Home Loan Bank System and is cooperatively owned by its member institutions, ranging in size from organizations with less than $5 million in assets to "super-regionals" with more than $125 billion. Institutions are required to purchase capital stock in the bank to be members. A government-sponsored enterprise, the bank funds residential mortgages and community development loans.

	Annual Growth	12/04	12/05	12/06	12/07	12/08
Assets ($ mil.)	11.7%	134,012.6	143,238.9	140,758.4	189,746.1	208,564.3
Net income ($ mil.)	(3.6%)	294.1	344.1	414.2	444.9	253.8
Employees	4.2%	—	339	349	362	383

FEDERAL HOME LOAN MORTGAGE CORPORATION   NYSE: FRE

8200 Jones Branch Dr.
McLean, VA 22102
Phone: 703-903-2000
Fax: 703-903-4045
Web: www.freddiemac.com

CEO: Charles E. (Ed) Haldeman Jr.
CFO: Ross J. Kari
HR: Paul G. George
FYE: December 31
Type: Public

Freddie Mac (officially the Federal Home Loan Mortgage Corporation) is a government-sponsored enterprise that, along with its sister agency the Federal National Mortgage Association (Fannie Mae), creates liquidity in the residential mortgage market by guaranteeing, purchasing, securitizing, and investing in home loans. The company buys conventional residential mortgages from mortgage bankers, mitigating risk and letting them provide mortgages to those who otherwise wouldn't qualify. It also provides assistance for affordable rental housing. In September 2008 the government seized the company, crippled by the mortgage crisis, in one of the largest government interventions in business since the Great Depression.

	Annual Growth	12/05	12/06	12/07	12/08	12/09
Assets ($ mil.)	1.1%	806,222.0	813,081.0	794,368.0	850,963.0	841,784.0
Net income ($ mil.)	—	2,189.0	2,211.0	(3,094.0)	(50,119.0)	(21,553.0)
Market value ($ mil.)	(61.3%)	42,419.1	44,074.4	22,115.1	473.8	954.2
Employees	1.8%	5,038	5,535	5,000	5,012	5,408

FEDERAL NATIONAL MORTGAGE ASSOCIATION   NYSE: FNM

3900 Wisconsin Ave. NW
Washington, DC 20016
Phone: 202-752-7000
Fax: —
Web: www.fanniemae.com

CEO: Michael J. (Mike) Williams
CFO: David M. Johnson
HR: —
FYE: December 31
Type: Public

The Federal National Mortgage Association, or Fannie Mae, has helped more than 50 million low- to middle-income families realize the American Dream. Like its brother Freddie Mac, the government-supported enterprise (GSE) provides liquidity in the mortgage market by buying mortgages from lenders and packaging them for resale, transferring risk from lenders and allowing them to offer mortgages to those who may not otherwise qualify. The company owns or guarantees about $3.1 trillion in home loans, or more than a quarter of all outstanding mortgages in the US. Due to losses caused largely by the subprime mortgage crisis, the federal government seized both Fannie and Freddie in September 2008.

	Annual Growth	12/05	12/06	12/07	12/08	12/09
Assets ($ mil.)	1.0%	834,168.0	843,936.0	882,547.0	912,404.0	869,141.0
Net income ($ mil.)	—	6,294.0	4,047.0	(2,035.0)	(58,298.0)	(72,022.0)
Market value ($ mil.)	(60.6%)	54,538.5	66,360.2	44,672.2	849.2	1,318.5
Employees	1.7%	5,600	6,600	5,700	5,800	6,000

FEDERAL REALTY INVESTMENT TRUST   NYSE: FRT

1626 E. Jefferson St.
Rockville, MD 20852
Phone: 301-998-8100
Fax: 301-998-3700
Web: www.federalrealty.com

CEO: Donald C. (Don) Wood
CFO: Andrew P. Blocher
HR: —
FYE: December 31
Type: Public

It's a safe bet that Federal Realty Investment Trust makes a federal case of shopping centers. The real estate investment trust (REIT) owns or has majority interest in some 80 retail properties, including community and neighborhood shopping centers and mixed-use complexes, totaling more than 18 million sq. ft. The company's key markets are densely populated, affluent areas in the Mid-Atlantic and Northeast, but it also has properties in California and Texas. Tenants include Bed Bath & Beyond, Kohl's, and Whole Foods. Rather than acquiring other real estate firms, the REIT tends to grow by acquiring and renovating existing, primarily grocery-anchored shopping centers.

	Annual Growth	12/05	12/06	12/07	12/08	12/09
Sales ($ mil.)	6.7%	410.3	451.0	485.9	520.5	531.0
Net income ($ mil.)	(2.4%)	114.6	118.7	195.5	129.8	103.9
Market value ($ mil.)	2.8%	3,721.0	5,215.0	5,040.1	3,808.8	4,154.8
Employees	(1.2%)	394	335	155	409	376

FEDERAL SCREW WORKS   Pink Sheets: FSCR

20229 Nine Mile Rd.
St. Clair Shores, MI 48080
Phone: 586-443-4200
Fax: 586-443-4210
Web: www.federalscrew.com

CEO: Thomas ZurSchmiede
CFO: W. T. ZurSchmiede Jr.
HR: —
FYE: June 30
Type: Public

Although many US residents might think so, Federal Screw Works (FSW) is not a division of the Internal Revenue Service. *This* Federal Screw Works is a manufacturer of fasteners and related items, primarily for the automotive industry. The company produces high-volume lots to the specifications of manufacturers. Nonautomotive sales are mainly to makers of durable goods. FSW's products include locknuts, bolts, piston pins, studs, bushings, shafts, and other machined, cold-formed, hardened, and ground-metal parts. It maintains five manufacturing facilities, all of which are located in Michigan.

FEDERAL SIGNAL CORPORATION   NYSE: FSS

1415 W. 22nd St., Ste. 1100
Oak Brook, IL 60523
Phone: 630-954-2000
Fax: 630-954-2030
Web: www.federalsignal.com

CEO: William H. (Bill) Osborne
CFO: William G. Barker III
HR: Jennifer L. Sherman
FYE: December 31
Type: Public

Federal Signal products protect people, property, and the environment. The company's business groups — environmental solutions, safety and security systems, and fire rescue — make various products for municipal, governmental, industrial, and institutional markets. Offerings include street sweepers, sewer cleaners, and water blasting equipment for environmental cleanup; emergency communications, lightbars and sirens, and public warning systems for public safety; and aerial platforms for firefighting and utility maintenance. In 2010 Federal Signal formed FSTech, expanding into intelligent transport systems (ITS). More than half of the company's sales come from the US.

	Annual Growth	12/05	12/06	12/07	12/08	12/09
Sales ($ mil.)	(10.2%)	1,156.9	1,211.6	1,268.1	958.8	752.5
Net income ($ mil.)	—	(4.6)	22.7	54.9	(95.6)	23.1
Market value ($ mil.)	(20.4%)	749.0	800.4	559.9	409.7	300.4
Employees	(17.1%)	5,500	5,400	5,500	3,300	2,600

FEDERAL-MOGUL CORPORATION

NASDAQ (GS): FDML

26555 Northwestern Hwy.
Southfield, MI 48033
Phone: 248-354-7700
Fax: 248-354-8950
Web: www.federalmogul.com

CEO: José Maria Alapont
CFO: Alan Haughie
HR: Pascal Goachet
FYE: December 31
Type: Public

For Federal-Mogul, the sum of the parts is greater than the whole. The company makes components used in cars, trucks, and commercial vehicles, as well as in energy, industrial, and other transportation equipment. Its products include pistons, spark plugs, ignition coils, bearings, gaskets, seals, and brake pads sold under brand names such as Champion, Federal-Mogul, FelPro, Glyco, and Moog. Federal-Mogul has manufacturing and distribution facilities in 33 countries worldwide; customers include global automakers such as BMW, General Motors, Ford, and Volkswagen. Federal-Mogul also distributes its own and others' auto parts to aftermarket customers. About 60% of sales come from outside the US.

	Annual Growth	12/05	12/06	12/07	12/08	12/09
Sales ($ mil.)	(4.0%)	6,286.0	6,326.4	6,913.9	6,865.6	5,330.0
Net income ($ mil.)	—	(334.2)	(549.6)	1,412.3	(467.9)	(45.0)
Market value ($ mil.)	163.3%	35.6	57.9	—	418.4	1,711.0
Employees	(1.7%)	41,700	43,100	50,000	43,400	39,000

FEDERATED INSURANCE COMPANIES

121 E. Park Sq.
Owatonna, MN 55060
Phone: 507-455-5200
Fax: 507-455-5452
Web: www.federatedinsurance.com

CEO: Jeffrey E. Fetters
CFO: Gregory J. Stroik
HR: Bryan Brose
FYE: December 31
Type: Mutual company

Federated Insurance is a mutual firm with a clear focus. The company provides multiple lines of business insurance coverage and risk management to employers in automotive repair and sales, building construction, printers, funeral homes, and jewelers, among others. Its products and services include workers' compensation, automotive, group life and health, and retirement planning. Federated Insurance markets its products both directly and through an independent sales force in 48 states and Washington, DC. It maintains offices in eight states. Since its founding in 1904, the company has worked closely with trade associations to develop and endorse its insurance programs.

	Annual Growth	12/04	12/05	12/06	12/07	12/08
Est. sales ($ mil.)	—	—	—	—	—	107.1
Employees	—	—	—	—	—	179

FEDERATED INVESTORS, INC.

NYSE: FII

Federated Investors Tower, 1001 Liberty Ave.
Pittsburgh, PA 15222
Phone: 412-288-1900
Fax: 412-288-1171
Web: www.federatedinvestors.com

CEO: J. Christopher Donahue
CFO: Thomas R. Donahue
HR: —
FYE: December 31
Type: Public

One of the country's largest money market fund managers, Federated Investors provides investment advisory and administrative services to more than 150 mutual funds and to separate accounts. The company's products are distributed through some 5,300 investment advisers, financial institutions, corporations, pension funds, and government entities. Money market funds make up the majority of Federated Investors' approximately $350 billion in assets under management. Chairman John Donahue and his family (including his son, president and CEO J. Christopher) own about 10% of Federated Investors, but control all of its votes.

	Annual Growth	12/05	12/06	12/07	12/08	12/09
Assets ($ mil.)	0.4%	896.6	810.3	841.0	846.6	912.4
Net income ($ mil.)	6.8%	160.3	197.7	217.5	224.3	208.5
Market value ($ mil.)	(7.2%)	3,823.7	3,487.1	4,249.0	1,750.8	2,838.9
Employees	1.2%	1,305	1,243	1,270	1,381	1,368

FEDEX CORPORATION

NYSE: FDX

942 S. Shady Grove Rd.
Memphis, TN 38120
Phone: 901-818-7500
Fax: 901-395-2000
Web: www.fedex.com

CEO: Frederick W. (Fred) Smith
CFO: Alan B. Graf Jr.
HR: —
FYE: May 31
Type: Public

Holding company FedEx hopes its package of subsidiaries will keep delivering significant market share. Its FedEx Express unit is the world's #1 express transportation provider, delivering about 3.4 million packages daily to more than 220 countries and territories. It maintains a fleet of about 655 aircraft and more than 51,000 motor vehicles and trailers. To complement the express delivery business, FedEx Ground provides small-package ground delivery in North America, and less-than-truckload (LTL) carrier FedEx Freight hauls larger shipments. FedEx Office stores offer a variety of document-related and other business services and serve as retail hubs for other FedEx units.

	Annual Growth	5/05	5/06	5/07	5/08	5/09
Sales ($ mil.)	4.9%	29,363.0	32,294.0	35,214.0	37,953.0	35,497.0
Net income ($ mil.)	(49.0%)	1,449.0	1,806.0	2,016.0	1,125.0	98.0
Market value ($ mil.)	(11.3%)	28,005.4	34,222.3	34,958.3	28,722.7	17,360.1
Employees	(13.5%)	250,000	260,000	280,000	290,000	140,000

FEDEX GROUND PACKAGE SYSTEM, INC.

1000 FedEx Dr.
Coraopolis, PA 15018
Phone: 412-269-1000
Fax: 412-747-4290
Web: www.fedex.com/us/ground/main

CEO: David F. (Dave) Rebholz
CFO: Gretchen G. Smarto
HR: Roman M. Hlutkowsky
FYE: May 31
Type: Subsidiary

When it doesn't absolutely, positively have to be there overnight, there's FedEx Ground Package System. A unit of air express giant FedEx, FedEx Ground provides ground delivery of small packages (up to 150 pounds) throughout the continental US and Canada. The company serves Alaska, Hawaii, and Puerto Rico through alliances. Deliveries are generally made within one to seven business days, depending on distance. The company offers both business-to-business and home delivery services across 32 hubs with a fleet of more than 22,000 motorized vehicles, most of which are operated by independent contractors. FedEx Ground handles an average of more than 3.4 million shipments per day from a network of about 30 hubs.

FEDEX NATIONAL LTL, INC.

1144 Griffin Rd.
Lakeland, FL 33805
Phone: 863-687-4545
Fax: 863-687-4599
Web: www.fedex.com/us/national/main

CEO: Mike Moss
CFO: Charlotte A. Kozlin
HR: Steve Newhouse
FYE: December 31
Type: Subsidiary

One of the largest less-than-truckload (LTL) carriers of general commodities in the US, FedEx National LTL (formerly Watkins Motor Lines) goes coast to coast. (LTL carriers combine freight from multiple shippers into a single truckload.) FedEx National LTL's specialty resides in serving the long-haul LTL freight market sector, which involves delivery windows of three days and more. Owned by express giant FedEx, the company is a unit within its FedEx Freight segment, which operates from a network of about 480 terminals in the US and Canada. Overall, FedEx Freight maintains a fleet of about 59,000 vehicles and trailers.

An in-depth profile of this company is available to Hoover's Online members at hoovers.com.

FEDEX OFFICE AND PRINT SERVICES, INC.

3 Galleria Tower, 13155 Noel Rd., Ste. 1600
Dallas, TX 75240
Phone: 214-550-7000
Fax: 214-550-7001
Web: www.fedex.com/us/officeprint/main

CEO: Brian D. Philips
CFO: Leslie Benners
HR: Tracy Brightman
FYE: May 31
Type: Subsidiary

A unit of express delivery giant FedEx, FedEx Office and Print Services (formerly FedEx Kinko's Office and Print Services) has duplicated its business formula many times. The company operates about 1,950 business service centers in the US and seven other countries worldwide. FedEx Office stores provide high-speed Internet access, videoconferencing, presentation support, and more. The stores serve as drop-off points for items to be delivered by sister companies FedEx Express and FedEx Ground. FedEx Office also sells office supplies and rents computers and videoconferencing rooms. Primarily targeting small business and home office clients, the company also provides services to individuals and corporations.

FEED THE CHILDREN, INC.

333 N. Meridian Ave.
Oklahoma City, OK 73107
Phone: 405-942-0228
Fax: 405-945-4177
Web: www.feedthechildren.org

CEO: Travis Arnold
CFO: Christy Tharp
HR: Richard Gray
FYE: June 30
Type: Not-for-profit

Tuppence a bag might feed some birds, but it takes more to feed growing children. Feed The Children (FTC) is a not-for-profit Christian charity that distributes food, medicine, clothing, and other necessities. In the US, FTC accepts bulk contributions of surplus food from businesses, packages it in various ways at six main facilities nationwide, and distributes it to food banks, homeless shelters, churches, and other organizations that help feed the hungry. In more than 110 countries overseas FTC works with organizations such as schools, orphanages, and churches to provide food, medical supplies, clothing, and educational support to the needy. Larry and Frances Jones founded FTC in 1979.

FEDFIRST FINANCIAL CORPORATION

NASDAQ (CM): FFCO

Donner at 6th St.
Monessen, PA 15062
Phone: 724-684-6800
Fax: 724-684-4851
Web: www.firstfederal-savings.com

CEO: Patrick G. O'Brien
CFO: Robert C. (Bob) Barry Jr.
HR: DaCosta Smith III
FYE: December 31
Type: Public

FedFirst Financial wants to be first in the hearts of its customers. It is the holding company for First Federal Savings Bank, a community-oriented thrift serving southwestern Pennsylvania. From about 10 branches, the bank offers traditional products and services, including checking and savings accounts, money markets accounts, and IRAs. Residential mortgages secured by homes in the Pittsburgh metropolitan area make up more than three-quarters of a lending portfolio that also includes multi-family and commercial mortgages and construction, business, and consumer loans. Majority-owned by mutual holding company FedFirst Financial MHC since 2005, FedFirst Financial now plans to convert to a stock holding company.

	Annual Growth	12/05	12/06	12/07	12/08	12/09
Assets ($ mil.)	6.4%	276.1	283.5	305.3	349.8	353.3
Net income ($ mil.)	—	(0.1)	0.3	(2.0)	(2.1)	0.6
Market value ($ mil.)	(21.4%)	56.2	61.4	57.1	27.1	21.5
Employees	(0.8%)	94	89	93	95	91

FEI COMPANY

NASDAQ (GM): FEIC

5350 NE Dawson Creek Dr.
Hillsboro, OR 97124
Phone: 503-726-7500
Fax: 503-726-7509
Web: www.feicompany.com

CEO: Don R. Kania
CFO: Raymond A. (Ray) Link
HR: Jim D. Higgs
FYE: December 31
Type: Public

FEI finds defects PDQ. The company makes structural process management systems that use ion beams to analyze and diagnose submicron structures in semiconductors, data storage components, and biological and industrial compounds. FEI makes focused ion beam and dual beam electron microscopes that analyze integrated circuits (ICs). It also makes scanning and transmission electron microscopes that detect defects in ICs and analyze biological specimens and materials. FEI is targeting applications in nanotechnology R&D, while still getting sales from semiconductor and data storage companies. Customers outside the US account for about two-thirds of sales.

	Annual Growth	12/05	12/06	12/07	12/08	12/09
Sales ($ mil.)	7.8%	427.2	479.5	592.5	599.2	577.3
Net income ($ mil.)	—	(78.2)	20.0	58.3	24.3	22.6
Market value ($ mil.)	5.1%	728.3	1,001.9	943.4	716.6	887.5
Employees	1.6%	1,674	1,683	1,866	1,830	1,781

FEDWAY ASSOCIATES INCORPORATED

River Terminal Development, Bldg. 56, Hackensack Ave.
Kearny, NJ 07032
Phone: 973-624-6444
Fax: 973-578-8969
Web: www.fedway.com

CEO: Richard Leventhal
CFO: Michael Dokachev
HR: —
FYE: June 30
Type: Private

If you live in New Jersey, you know that Fedway does it the right way. The company is a major wine and spirits wholesaler that has been operating in the Garden State for more than 25 years. Fedway Associates operates a 300,000-sq.-ft. warehouse that can send out as many as 25,000 cases of wine and spirits per day. The company wholesales such high-end brand names as Grey Goose and Bombay Sapphire vodkas in its home state. One of the largest liquor distributors in New Jersey, it has sales and marketing agreements with many major producers, as well as other distributors, including Southern Wine & Spirits of America.

FELCOR LODGING TRUST INCORPORATED

NYSE: FCH

545 E. John Carpenter Fwy., Ste. 1300
Irving, TX 75062
Phone: 972-444-4900
Fax: 972-444-4949
Web: www.felcor.com

CEO: Richard A. (Rick) Smith
CFO: Andrew J. Welch
HR: —
FYE: December 31
Type: Public

FelCor Lodging welcomes weary North American travelers. One of the top hotel real estate investment trusts (REIT) in the US, FelCor owns roughly 90 hotels with some 25,000 rooms in nearly two dozen states and Canada. Most are upscale hotels operating under the Embassy Suites, Holiday Inn, Doubletree, Sheraton, Westin, Renaissance, and Hilton brands, with a concentration of its portfolio located in Florida, California, and Texas. FelCor's properties are managed by Hilton Worldwide, InterContinental Hotels, Marriott International, and Starwood Hotels & Resorts.

	Annual Growth	12/05	12/06	12/07	12/08	12/09
Sales ($ mil.)	(7.0%)	1,212.2	991.0	1,021.9	1,129.8	908.7
Net income ($ mil.)	—	(251.6)	51.0	89.0	(119.2)	(109.1)
Market value ($ mil.)	(32.4%)	1,126.0	1,428.9	1,020.0	120.4	235.5
Employees	(2.7%)	76	74	72	69	68

An in-depth profile of this company is available to Hoover's Online members at hoovers.com.

FELDMAN MALL PROPERTIES, INC.
OTC: FMLP

1065 Avenue of the Americas, 19th Fl.
New York, NY 10018
Phone: 212-221-2620
Fax: 212-221-7376
Web: www.feldmanmall.com

CEO: —
CFO: —
HR: —
FYE: December 31
Type: Public

Even shopping malls in a slump can be whipped back into tip top shape. In fact, it's Feldman Mall Properties' specialty. The real estate investment trust (REIT) buys underperforming malls in an attempt to turn them into more attractive and profitable venues. Founded in 2004 to continue the business of mall management firm Feldman Equities of Arizona, the company owns or has stakes in about a half-dozen mall properties spanning 2.5 million rentable sq. ft. in Arizona, Florida, Illinois, Ohio, Pennsylvania, and Texas. Feldman's renovation techniques include architectural redesign, square footage increase, and the addition of more in-demand tenants. Its top tenant is Loews Cineplex.

FELLOWES, INC.

1789 Norwood Ave.
Itasca, IL 60143
Phone: 630-893-1600
Fax: 630-893-1683
Web: www.fellowes.com

CEO: James (Jamie) Fellowes
CFO: Brian Cooper
HR: Lyn Bulman
FYE: March 31
Type: Private

Fellowes (formerly Fellowes Manufacturing) produces office products that can organize or obliterate. The leading maker of paper shredders (such as Powershred and Intellishred), it also makes binding and laminating machines, records storage products, ergonomic workspace supplies, desk organizers, and computer accessories. The company offers fashionable cases for mobile phones and iPods through its license with surf gear maker Body Glove International. Fellowes' products are sold through office supply retailers and mass merchants, as well as online. Still owned and run by the Fellowes family, the firm was started in 1917 when Harry Fellowes paid $50 for Bankers Box, a maker of storage boxes for bank records.

	Annual Growth	3/04	3/05	3/06	3/07	3/08
Est. sales ($ mil.)	—	—	—	—	—	600.0
Employees	—	—	—	—	—	2,800

THE FEMALE HEALTH COMPANY
NYSE Amex: FHC

515 N. State St., Ste. 2225
Chicago, IL 60654
Phone: 312-595-9123
Fax: 312-595-9122
Web: www.femalehealth.com

CEO: O. B. Parrish
CFO: Donna Felch
HR: —
FYE: September 30
Type: Public

Move over, Trojan Man! Here comes The Female Health Company (FHC), maker of condoms for women. The polyurethane female condom is the only female contraceptive that is FDA-approved for preventing both pregnancy and sexually transmitted diseases, including HIV/AIDS. The firm's condoms are sold in more than 115 countries worldwide (under the FC and FC2 names), including South Africa, Brazil, the US, the UK, and Zimbabwe. Outside the US, many of its products bear the Femidom name, among others. FHC also provides low-cost female condoms in Africa through an agreement with the Joint United Nations Programme on HIV/AIDS (UNAIDS). It sponsors the Female Health Foundation, which provides women with health education.

	Annual Growth	9/05	9/06	9/07	9/08	9/09
Sales ($ mil.)	25.2%	11.2	14.8	19.3	25.6	27.5
Net income ($ mil.)	—	(1.4)	0.3	1.7	5.0	6.5
Market value ($ mil.)	32.1%	45.6	36.5	64.6	83.7	138.8
Employees	(18.2%)	123	159	166	168	55

FENDER MUSICAL INSTRUMENTS CORPORATION

8860 E. Chaparral Rd., Ste. 100
Scottsdale, AZ 85250
Phone: 480-596-9690
Fax: 480-596-1384
Web: www.fender.com

CEO: William (Bill) Mendello
CFO: James Broenen
HR: Keith Davis
FYE: December 31
Type: Private

Jimi Hendrix's electrified version of "The Star-Spangled Banner" shows what Fender guitars can do. Fender Musical Instruments is the world's #1 maker of stringed instruments (and the nation's #1 maker of solid-body electric guitars, including the Stratocaster and Telecaster lines that have made it a favorite of strummers). Fender also makes instruments such as acoustic guitars, electric basses, mandolins, banjos, and violins, as well as amplifiers and PA equipment. Other notable brands include Guild (acoustic and electric guitars), Rodriguez (classical guitars), Benedetto (jazz guitars), and Squier (lower-priced guitars). A management group controls the firm, which acquired KMC Music in late 2007.

FENTURA FINANCIAL, INC.
OTC: FETM

175 N. Leroy St.
Fenton, MI 48430
Phone: 810-750-8725
Fax: 810-629-3892
Web: www.fentura.com

CEO: Donald L. Grill
CFO: Douglas J. Kelley
HR: —
FYE: December 31
Type: Public

It just makes *cents* to say that Fentura Financial has its hands full. Fentura Financial is the holding company for Michigan community banks The State Bank, Davison State Bank, and West Michigan Community Bank. From about 20 branch locations, the banks provide commercial and consumer banking services and products, including checking and savings accounts and loans. Commercial loans account for some two-thirds of the bank's combined loan portfolio. The State Bank, Fentura's first subsidiary, traces its origins to 1898.

	Annual Growth	12/05	12/06	12/07	12/08	12/09
Assets ($ mil.)	(4.2%)	619.1	622.3	628.0	578.6	522.1
Net income ($ mil.)	—	5.1	5.3	(0.5)	(12.2)	(17.0)
Market value ($ mil.)	(53.8%)	67.5	73.8	49.9	15.3	3.1
Employees	(14.4%)	196	130	236	217	105

FENWAY PARTNERS, INC.

152 W. 57th St., 59th Fl.
New York, NY 10019
Phone: 212-698-9400
Fax: 212-581-1205
Web: www.fenwaypartners.com

CEO: Peter D. Lamm
CFO: Walter Wiacek
HR: —
FYE: December 31
Type: Private

No red socks here, but private equity firm Fenway Partners does boast an eclectic portfolio of midsized companies (valued between $100 million and $600 million) in the consumer products and transportation sectors. Its holdings include stakes in Easton-Bell Sports (maker of official NFL helmets), 1-800 CONTACTS, scholastic memorabilia maker Amercan Achievement, trucking concern Panther Expedited Services, and charter bus operator Coach America. Upon making its investment in a company, Fenway Partners provides management and strategy advice to boost performance. Despite its name, the company has offices in New York and Los Angeles, but not in Boston, home of baseball's Fenway Park.

	Annual Growth	12/04	12/05	12/06	12/07	12/08
Est. sales ($ mil.)	—	—	—	—	—	157.0
Employees	—	—	—	—	—	1,600

FERGUSON ENTERPRISES, INC.

12500 Jefferson Ave.
Newport News, VA 23602
Phone: 757-874-7795
Fax: 757-989-2501
Web: www.ferguson.com

CEO: Frank W. Roach
CFO: —
HR: Steven M. Roznowski
FYE: July 31
Type: Subsidiary

Ferguson Enterprises is part of the pipeline for pipes. It is one of North America's largest wholesale distributors of plumbing supplies, pipes, valves, and fittings. It also is a major distributor of heating, waterworks (water hydrants and meters), bathrooms and appliances, safety equipment, and tools to professional contractors and industry. Ferguson has more than 1,200 locations throughout the US, Puerto Rico, Mexico, and the Caribbean. Its customers include plumbing contractors, home owners, air conditioning dealers, the government, and irrigation and fire suppression equipment installers. Ferguson, which was formed in 1953, is a subsidiary of Wolseley.

	Annual Growth	7/04	7/05	7/06	7/07	7/08
Est. sales ($ mil.)	—	—	—	—	—	11,226.3
Employees	—	—	—	—	—	22,151

FERRARA PAN CANDY COMPANY

7301 W. Harrison St.
Forest Park, IL 60130
Phone: 708-366-0500
Fax: 708-366-5921
Web: www.ferrarapan.com

CEO: Salvatore (Sal) Ferrara II
CFO: James (Jim) Buffardi
HR: Angie Castejon
FYE: December 31
Type: Private

At Ferrara Pan Candy Company, a sour face is a happy face. Best known for its venerable, mouth-puckering Lemonhead candies (500 million every year), Ferrara makes such other familiar treats as Red Hots, Jaw Busters, Boston Baked Beans, and Atomic FireBalls. Panned candies, so-called because they are made in a rotating pan, are the company's specialty; but it also makes chocolate confections under the Ferrara name, also with Black Forest Gummies. Ferrara started out in business making the pastel-colored sugar-coated almonds served at Italian weddings and expanded to serve the candy appetites of not just newlyweds, but kids (of all ages).

	Annual Growth	12/04	12/05	12/06	12/07	12/08
Est. sales ($ mil.)	—	—	—	—	—	9.0
Employees	—	—	—	—	—	530

FERRARI NORTH AMERICA INC.

250 Sylvan Ave.
Englewood Cliffs, NJ 07632
Phone: 201-816-2600
Fax: 201-816-2626
Web: www.ferrariusa.com

CEO: Maurizio Parlato
CFO: Joe Marsella
HR: —
FYE: December 31
Type: Subsidiary

Few automotive brands are as synonymous with chic and speed as Ferrari. Ferrari North America is Ferrari's exclusive business arm for vehicle imports, marketing, sales, and dealerships crossing North, Central, and South America. Its exotic models, as expensive as they are fast, include the F430 Berlinetta, F430 Spider convertible, 599 GTB Fiorano, 430 Scuderia, and the 612 Scaglietti. Although coupe-size in operations compared with corporate goliaths like GM and Ford, Ferrari North America is on a roll. Even in the face of an economic slow down, demand exceeds supply. It continues to build fewer cars than ordered, yet add new dealerships, notably in Florida, its third-largest market.

FERRELLGAS PARTNERS, L.P.

NYSE: FGP

7500 College Blvd., Ste. 1000
Overland Park, KS 66210
Phone: 913-661-1500
Fax: 816-792-7985
Web: www.ferrellgas.com

CEO: Stephen L. (Steve) Wambold
CFO: J. Ryan VanWinkle
HR: —
FYE: July 31
Type: Public

Ferrellgas Partners' flame is burning brightly as the second-largest US retail marketer of propane, behind AmeriGas. The company sells about 875 million gallons of propane a year to 1 million industrial, commercial, and agricultural customers in all 50 states. It operates about 1,000 distribution locations, and its delivery fleet includes about 4,300 trucks and trailers. The Blue Rhino unit operates a propane cylinder-exchange business throughout the US. Ferrellgas also trades propane and natural gas, markets wholesale propane, provides liquid natural gas storage, and markets chemical feedstock. About 30% of the company's stock is held in trust for employees.

	Annual Growth	7/05	7/06	7/07	7/08	7/09
Sales ($ mil.)	4.2%	1,754.1	1,895.5	1,992.4	2,290.7	2,069.5
Net income ($ mil.)	(12.5%)	88.8	25.0	34.8	24.7	52.0
Market value ($ mil.)	(4.4%)	1,529.5	1,563.5	1,650.4	1,373.8	1,277.1
Employees	(0.5%)	3,704	3,669	3,564	3,508	3,637

FERRO CORPORATION

NYSE: FOE

1000 Lakeside Ave.
Cleveland, OH 44114
Phone: 216-641-8580
Fax: 216-875-7205
Web: www.ferro.com

CEO: James F. Kirsch
CFO: Sallie B. Bailey
HR: Ann E. Killian
FYE: December 31
Type: Public

Ferro is a quite colorful character. Ferro Corporation makes all kinds of colorants, including ceramic glazes, pigments, and porcelain enamels. It produces electronics, color and glass materials, and polymer and ceramic engineered materials. The company's products are used in construction and by manufacturers of appliances, cars, electronics, and household furnishings. Ferro's industrial chemicals (including stabilizers, plasticizers, and lubricants) are used by makers of fuels, foods, cosmetics, pharmaceuticals, and plastics. A global manufacturer (with 50 plants in more than 20 countries throughout the Americas, Asia, and Europe), Ferro sells to customers in more than 100 countries.

	Annual Growth	12/05	12/06	12/07	12/08	12/09
Sales ($ mil.)	(3.1%)	1,882.3	2,041.5	2,204.8	2,245.2	1,657.6
Net income ($ mil.)	—	16.3	20.1	(94.5)	(39.7)	(40.4)
Market value ($ mil.)	(18.6%)	1,615.8	1,782.0	1,785.5	607.2	709.7
Employees	(6.6%)	6,839	6,660	6,275	5,638	5,213

FERROSTAAL INCORPORATED

3201 Enterprise Pkwy., Ste. 490
Beachwood, OH 44122
Phone: 216-504-9686
Fax: 440-756-6056
Web: www.ferrostaal-usa.com

CEO: Uwe T. Schmidt
CFO: Lutz Richter
HR: —
FYE: December 31
Type: Subsidiary

Ferrostaal Incorporated is betting on the sun. The company is a subsidiary of the German industrial and heavy construction conglomerate Ferrostaal AG and provides its parent's alternative energy business in North America. It operates, with Solar Millennium, a joint venture called Solar Trust of America (STA) that concentrates on solar power generation. The International Petroleum Investment Company of Abu Dhabi bought a majority stake in Ferrostaal from MAN SE in 2009 and dropped the former parent company's brand from what had been called MAN Ferrostaal.

FERROTEC (USA) CORPORATION

33 Constitution Dr.
Bedford, NH 03110
Phone: 603-472-6800
Fax: 603-472-2511
Web: www.ferrotec.com

CEO: Akira Yamamura
CFO: Richard R. Cesati II
HR: —
FYE: June 30
Type: Subsidiary

Ferrotec USA wishes that the magnetic force be with you. A subsidiary of Japanese specialty materials maker Ferrotec, the company makes fluids that, when controlled with a magnetic force, can be used for sealing, sensing, lubrication, and heat transfer. Known as ferrofluidics, these liquids are used by makers of audio speakers and lighting — General Electric is a major customer — and in its own engineered products. Ferrotec USA's sealing devices are used for making semiconductors and in oil and chemical production. The company's US locations are in California and New Hampshire.

FFD FINANCIAL CORPORATION

NASDAQ (CM): FFDF

321 N. Wooster Ave.
Dover, OH 44622
Phone: 330-364-7777
Fax: 330-364-7779
Web: www.onlinefirstfed.com

CEO: Trent B. Troyer
CFO: Robert R. Gerber
HR: —
FYE: June 30
Type: Public

FFD Financial is the holding company for First Federal Community Bank, which serves Tuscarawas County and contiguous portions of eastern Ohio through about five branches. Founded in 1898, the bank offers a full range of retail products, including checking and savings accounts, CDs, IRAs, and credit cards. The bank mainly uses these funds to originate one- to four-family residential mortgages, nonresidential real estate loans, and land loans. First Federal Community Bank also originates business, consumer, and multifamily residential real estate loans.

	Annual Growth	6/05	6/06	6/07	6/08	6/09
Assets ($ mil.)	6.2%	148.6	161.2	173.0	181.7	189.0
Net income ($ mil.)	0.0%	1.1	1.4	1.6	1.2	1.1
Market value ($ mil.)	(5.1%)	17.2	17.2	16.1	12.8	13.9
Employees	4.9%	43	44	48	48	52

FHC HEALTH SYSTEMS, INC.

240 Corporate Blvd.
Norfolk, VA 23502
Phone: 757-459-5100
Fax: 757-459-5219
Web: www.fhchealthsystems.com

CEO: Ronald I. Dozoretz
CFO: —
HR: Larry Anderson
FYE: December 31
Type: Private

FHC Health Systems makes life just a little bit saner, providing behavioral health care services to millions of people through its operating subsidiaries. Its majority-owned subsidiary ValueOptions manages behavioral health care benefits offered by commercial and public health plans, serving some 23 million people. Through its Rx Innovations unit, the company provides institutional pharmacy services for long-term care facilities and other treatment centers. And FHC's FirstLab subsidiary offers drug testing and employment screening. FHC sold its Alternative Behavioral Services subsidiary, which offered residential psychiatric care and case management services, to Psychiatric Solutions for about $200 million.

FIBERTOWER CORPORATION

NASDAQ (GM): FTWR

185 Berry St., Ste. 4800
San Francisco, CA 94107
Phone: 415-659-3500
Fax: 415-659-0007
Web: www.fibertower.com

CEO: Kurt J. Van Wagenen
CFO: Thomas A. Scott
HR: —
FYE: December 31
Type: Public

FiberTower rises to great heights to provide wireless backhaul and access services. Its offerings include spectrum leasing, backhauling of mobile phone traffic, and the provision of broadband connectivity and extensions to fiber-optic networks. Customers include mobile, fiber, and other high-speed telecommunications carriers, large-volume enterprise users, and government agencies. The company owns wireless spectrum licenses in high-frequency 24 GHz and 39 GHz bands that cover virtually all of the US. FiberTower provides backhaul services in more than a dozen markets across the country.

	Annual Growth	12/05	12/06	12/07	12/08	12/09
Sales ($ mil.)	164.1%	1.3	13.8	27.1	49.2	63.2
Net income ($ mil.)	—	(11.3)	(57.3)	(272.1)	(249.8)	(2.1)
Market value ($ mil.)	(46.8%)	2,390.9	2,693.2	1,044.3	73.3	191.5
Employees	49.3%	29	219	221	152	144

FIBRE-CRAFT MATERIALS CORP.

6400 W. Howard St.
Niles, IL 60714
Phone: 847-647-1140
Fax: 847-647-8997
Web: www.fibrecraft.com

CEO: John J. Abens Jr.
CFO: George W. Helmsbock
HR: —
FYE: December 31
Type: Private

Fibre-Craft Materials manufactures arts and crafts components, doll and floral supplies, and decorative accessories. In addition to its Creative Hands craft brand, the company offers dolls and teddy bears through its Springfield and Bears Boulevard collections. Fibre-Craft products are sold online and through mass merchandisers and specialty retailers (such as Hobby Lobby and Office Depot) nationwide, as well as in Australia, Canada, and the UK. The company got its start making wood fiber for handcrafting artificial flowers in the 1950s.

	Annual Growth	12/04	12/05	12/06	12/07	12/08
Est. sales ($ mil.)	—	—	—	—	—	18.7
Employees	—	—	—	—	—	124

FIBROCELL SCIENCE, INC.

Pink Sheets: FCSC

405 Eagleview Blvd.
Exton, PA 19341
Phone: 484-713-6000
Fax: 484-713-6001
Web: www.fibrocellscience.com

CEO: David M. Pernock
CFO: Declan Daly
HR: —
FYE: December 31
Type: Public

No cow collagen here — Fibrocell Science (formerly Isolagen) lets you be your beautiful self, using your beautiful cells. The company's autologous cellular therapy process extracts fibroblasts (collagen-producing cells) from a small tissue sample taken from behind a patient's ear. The cells reproduce over six to eight weeks and are then injected back into the patient, giving him or her a "natural" boost. The company is hoping the technique will receive FDA approval for use on wrinkle correction, burn and acne scars, and to regenerate tissue lost from periodontal disease. The company filed for and emerged from Chapter 11 bankruptcy during 2009.

	Annual Growth	12/05	12/06	12/07	12/08	12/09
Sales ($ mil.)	(43.4%)	8.8	6.1	1.4	1.1	0.9
Net income ($ mil.)	—	(35.8)	(35.8)	(35.6)	(31.4)	60.9
Employees	(37.2%)	141	55	44	9	22

An in-depth profile of this company is available to Hoover's Online members at hoovers.com.

605

FIDELITY BANCORP, INC.

NASDAQ (GM): FSBI

1009 Perry Hwy.	CEO: Richard G. Spencer
Pittsburgh, PA 15237	CFO: Lisa L. Griffith
Phone: 412-367-3300	HR: Richard L. Barron
Fax: 412-364-6504	FYE: September 30
Web: www.fidelitybancorp-pa.com	Type: Public

Fidelity Bancorp is the holding company for Fidelity Bank, which has faithfully served the Greater Pittsburgh area since 1927. The bank caters to individuals and small business customers from about a dozen branch offices in the city and its northern suburbs in Allegheny and Butler counties. Deposit products include checking and savings accounts, CDs, IRAs, and money market accounts. Real estate loans, including single-family residential mortgages, commercial mortgages, and construction loans, make up about two-thirds of the bank's loan portfolio, which also includes consumer installment loans and business loans and leases.

	Annual Growth	9/05	9/06	9/07	9/08	9/09
Assets ($ mil.)	1.9%	677.8	730.7	726.6	727.2	730.0
Net income ($ mil.)	—	3.9	3.9	3.6	0.8	(1.7)
Market value ($ mil.)	(24.1%)	58.5	57.9	47.2	38.1	19.4
Employees	5.1%	132	160	162	158	161

FIDELITY D & D BANCORP, INC.

OTC: FDBC

Corner of Blakely and Drinker Streets	CEO: Patrick J. Dempsey
Dunmore, PA 18512	CFO: Salvatore R. DeFrancesco Jr.
Phone: 570-342-8281	HR: Theresa Ferraro
Fax: 570-346-5724	FYE: December 31
Web: www.the-fidelity.com	Type: Public

Don't worry, eight-sided dice are not needed at Fidelity D & D Bancorp. The institution is the holding company for The Fidelity Deposit and Discount Bank, serving Lackawanna and Luzerne counties in northeastern Pennsylvania through about a dozen locations. The bank attracts local individuals and business customers by offering such services as checking and savings accounts, certificates of deposit, investments, and trust services. Commercial loans, including mortgages, account for slightly more than half of the company's loan portfolio; residential real estate loans make up more than a quarter. The bank also writes consumer loans, construction loans, and direct financing leases.

	Annual Growth	12/05	12/06	12/07	12/08	12/09
Assets ($ mil.)	0.5%	544.1	562.3	587.4	575.7	556.0
Net income ($ mil.)	—	4.6	4.1	4.6	3.6	(1.4)
Market value ($ mil.)	(19.9%)	80.3	71.3	60.7	56.4	33.0
Employees	(0.1%)	186	188	188	196	185

FIDELITY NATIONAL FINANCIAL, INC.

NYSE: FNF

601 Riverside Ave.	CEO: Alan L. (Al) Stinson
Jacksonville, FL 32204	CFO: Anthony J. Park
Phone: 904-854-8100	HR: —
Fax: 904-357-1007	FYE: December 31
Web: www.fnf.com	Type: Public

To make sure that buying a dream home doesn't become a nightmare, Fidelity National Financial provides title insurance, escrow, and other services related to real estate transactions. It is now the big dog in the title insurance sector, (the next largest player is First American) and accounts for more than 45% of all title insurance policies in the US. The company operates through underwriters including Fidelity National Title Company, Chicago Title, Ticor Title, Security Union Title, and Alamo Title. It sells its products both directly and through independent agents. Fidelity National Financial's specialty lines include flood and home warranty insurance.

	Annual Growth	12/05	12/06	12/07	12/08	12/09
Assets ($ mil.)	7.7%	5,900.5	7,259.6	7,556.4	8,368.2	7,934.4
Net income ($ mil.)	(19.7%)	539.0	437.8	129.8	(179.0)	224.5
Market value ($ mil.)	(13.8%)	5,592.7	5,484.7	3,355.6	4,076.8	3,091.5
Employees	(3.1%)	19,500	17,800	15,500	13,700	17,200

FIDELITY NATIONAL INFORMATION SERVICES, INC.

NYSE: FIS

601 Riverside Ave.	CEO: Frank R. Martire
Jacksonville, FL 32204	CFO: Michael D. (Mike) Hayford
Phone: 904-854-5000	HR: Michael P. Oates
Fax: 904-357-1105	FYE: December 31
Web: www.fidelityinfoservices.com	Type: Public

Fidelity National Information Services (FIS) provides software, outsourcing, and information technology consulting for the financial services and mortgage industries. For banks and other financial institutions, the division offers software for lending, community and wholesale banking, customer relationship management, data management, and e-business. For mortgage lenders, FIS offers billing and customer care, data and service order exchange, and mortgage servicing applications. The company focuses on providing software and services for the world's largest financial institutions; FIS serves 14,000 customers in over 100 countries, including 40 of the world's 50 largest banks.

	Annual Growth	12/05	12/06	12/07	12/08	12/09
Sales ($ mil.)	35.5%	1,117.1	4,132.6	4,758.0	3,446.0	3,769.5
Net income ($ mil.)	(4.5%)	130.3	259.1	561.2	214.8	108.5
Market value ($ mil.)	0.9%	8,508.5	8,410.0	8,724.6	6,127.1	8,827.2
Employees	12.5%	19,323	24,871	31,000	26,000	31,000

⊞ FIDELITY SOUTHERN CORPORATION

NASDAQ (GS): LION

3490 Piedmont Rd. NE, Ste. 1550	CEO: James B. Miller Jr.
Atlanta, GA 30305	CFO: Stephen H. Brolly
Phone: 404-639-6500	HR: Stephanie Huckaby
Fax: 404-814-8060	FYE: December 31
Web: www.lionbank.com	Type: Public

Fidelity Southern Corporation is the holding company for Fidelity Bank, which operates about two dozen branches mostly in and around Atlanta, and another one in Jacksonville, Florida. The bank offers traditional deposit services such as checking and savings accounts, CDs, and IRAs. Indirect auto loans, which the company purchases from auto franchises and independent dealers throughout the Southeast, make up almost half of its loan portfolio. Real estate construction, commercial real estate, business, residential mortgage, and other consumer loans round out its lending activities. Subsidiary LionMark Insurance Company offers consumer credit-related insurance products.

	Annual Growth	12/05	12/06	12/07	12/08	12/09
Assets ($ mil.)	7.1%	1,405.7	1,649.2	1,686.5	1,763.1	1,851.5
Net income ($ mil.)	—	10.3	10.4	6.6	(12.2)	(3.9)
Market value ($ mil.)	(32.6%)	182.2	189.4	95.0	36.9	37.6
Employees	8.2%	356	374	406	366	488

FIELDPOINT PETROLEUM CORPORATION

NYSE Amex: FPP

1703 Edelweiss Dr., Ste. 301	CEO: Ray D. Reaves
Cedar Park, TX 78613	CFO: Ray D. Reaves
Phone: 512-250-8692	HR: —
Fax: 512-335-1294	FYE: December 31
Web: www.fppcorp.com	Type: Public

Got oil and gas? FieldPoint Petroleum can point to its oil and gas fields and its interests in 360 productive oil and gas wells in Louisiana, New Mexico, Oklahoma, Texas, and Wyoming. The independent oil and gas exploration company operates some 60 of these wells. About two-thirds of its gross productive oil wells are located in Oklahoma. FieldPoint Petroleum has proved reserves of more than 885,240 barrels of oil and 2.7 billion cu. ft. of natural gas. Chairman and CEO Ray Reaves, an oil and gas industry veteran, controls about 34% of the company.

	Annual Growth	12/05	12/06	12/07	12/08	12/09
Sales ($ mil.)	(0.6%)	4.0	4.1	4.4	6.6	3.9
Net income ($ mil.)	—	1.0	1.2	0.6	0.6	0.0
Market value ($ mil.)	(23.7%)	56.7	19.2	9.9	18.9	19.2
Employees	0.0%	4	4	4	4	4

FIESTA MART, INC.

5235 Katy Fwy.
Houston, TX 77007
Phone: 713-869-5060
Fax: 713-869-6197
Web: www.fiestamart.com

CEO: Louis Katopodis
CFO: Stacey Walker
HR: Wanda Parish
FYE: May 31
Type: Subsidiary

Fiesta Mart celebrates food every day of the year. The company runs some 55 stores in Texas that sell ethnic and conventional groceries, including items popular with its target customers: Mexican- and Asian-Americans. Its stores are located mainly in the Houston area, but Fiesta also has been adding stores in the Dallas/Fort Worth area and in Austin. Fiesta purchased three supermarkets from Winn-Dixie Stores when the grocer left Texas. At its supermarkets, Fiesta leases kiosks to vendors who offer such items as jewelry and cell phones. The company also runs some 15 Fiesta liquor stores. Fiesta Mart, founded in 1972 by Donald Bonham and O. C. Mendenhall, was acquired by wholesaler Grocers Supply Co. in 2004.

	Annual Growth	5/04	5/05	5/06	5/07	5/08
Est. sales ($ mil.)	—	—	—	—	—	1,137.7
Employees	—	—	—	—	—	5,900

FIFTH THIRD BANCORP

NASDAQ (GS): FITB

38 Fountain Sq. Plaza, Fifth Third Center
Cincinnati, OH 45263
Phone: 513-579-5300
Fax: 513-534-0629
Web: www.53.com

CEO: Kevin T. Kabat
CFO: Daniel T. (Dan) Poston
HR: Teresa J. Tanner
FYE: December 31
Type: Public

Fifth Third Bancorp wants to be first in the hearts and minds of its customers. The holding company operates more than 1,200 Fifth Third Bank branches in the Midwest and Southeast. It operates through five segments: branch banking, commercial banking, processing solutions, consumer lending, and investment advisors. It provides consumer and business banking (including deposit accounts, loans, and credit cards); investment advisory services (mutual funds, private banking, and securities brokerage); and ATM and merchant transaction processing. The company also runs the Jeanie ATM network.

	Annual Growth	12/05	12/06	12/07	12/08	12/09
Assets ($ mil.)	1.9%	105,225.0	100,669.0	110,962.0	119,764.0	113,380.0
Net income ($ mil.)	(16.9%)	1,548.0	1,184.0	1,076.0	(2,113.0)	737.0
Market value ($ mil.)	(28.7%)	29,980.5	32,531.8	19,973.7	6,565.2	7,749.5
Employees	(1.1%)	22,901	21,362	22,678	22,423	21,901

FIJI WATER COMPANY, LLC

11444 W. Olympic Blvd., Ste. 210
Los Angeles, CA 90064
Phone: 310-312-2850
Fax: 310-312-2828
Web: www.fijiwater.com

CEO: John Edward Cochran
CFO: Kim Katzenberger
HR: —
FYE: December 31
Type: Subsidiary

Even *Desperate Housewives* drink FIJI Water. Sourced and bottled on Viti Levu, the largest of the Republic of Fiji's islands, the water has garnered the attention of celebrity chefs and also made its way to the set of many popular television programs and movies, including ABC's soapy dramedy. In real life, the premium water, which comes from an artesian aquifer at the edge of a rainforest, is available at retail food merchants and in luxury hotels, spas, and restaurants worldwide. The company, which sells genuine silver sleeves for the water bottles on its Web site, also offers home delivery of its water throughout the continental US. FIJI Water is part of Roll International's holdings.

FILA USA, INC

1 Fila Way
Sparks, MD 21152
Phone: 410-773-3000
Fax: 410-773-4989
Web: www.fila.com/us/eng/corporate

CEO: Jon Epstein
CFO: Young-Chan Cho
HR: —
FYE: December 31
Type: Private

After tripping over a few hurdles, Fila USA is feeling nimble and virile again. The company markets athletic shoes and sportswear to major US retailers (Foot Locker, Kohl's). To tout its products, it signs up the talents of professional athletes such as tennis stars James Blake and Jimmy Arias and musical acts such as hip-hop headliners Nas and the Wu-Tang Clan. With a history of high design in athletic shoes and sportswear, Fila had run down its image in lieu of a hodgepodge of athletic endorsements. The ailing US entity, along with other Fila global footwear and apparel units, was acquired by Fila Korea in 2007 from Sport Brands International (SBI). Fila Korea chairman Gene Yoon holds a 20% ownership stake.

FINACITY CORPORATION

281 Tresser Blvd., Two Stamford Plaza, 11th Fl.
Stamford, CT 06901
Phone: 203-428-3500
Fax: 203-428-3904
Web: www.finacity.com

CEO: Adrian Katz
CFO: Michael Rodgers
HR: Michael Rodgers
FYE: December 31
Type: Joint venture

Finacity wants to give clients financial tenacity. The firm buys, services, and securitizes trade accounts receivable for middle market and larger companies, offering receivables purchase and funding, credit management, risk mitigation services, and receivables sales. It processes and funds some $15 billion in receivables per year for clients in North America and Europe. Finacity is a cooperative venture between ABN AMRO, Bank of America, Euler Hermes, and AMROC Investments. Kleiner Perkins Caufield & Byers, Avenue Capital, and Ecoban also own stakes in the company.

	Annual Growth	12/04	12/05	12/06	12/07	12/08
Est. sales ($ mil.)	—	—	—	—	—	1.3
Employees	—	—	—	—	—	15

FINANCIAL ENGINES, INC.

NASDAQ (GM): FNGN

1804 Embarcadero Rd.
Palo Alto, CA 94303
Phone: 650-565-4900
Fax: 650-565-4905
Web: www.financialengines.com

CEO: Jeffrey N. (Jeff) Maggioncalda
CFO: Raymond J. (Ray) Sims
HR: Deborah J. (Debbi) Behrman
FYE: December 31
Type: Public

Like the little engine that could, Financial Engines does. What it does is provide financial advice, portfolio management, and retirement assessment services. The company serves US retirement-plan participants, sponsors, and service providers across a wide range of industries that includes more than 100 *FORTUNE* 500 companies and seven *FORTUNE* 20 companies. It delivers its services online, as well as by telephone. Financial Engines has more than $500 billion in assets under management and serves some 7.6 million individual retirement-plan participants. The company went public in 2010 with an offering worth $127.2 million.

	Annual Growth	12/05	12/06	12/07	12/08	12/09
Assets ($ mil.)	17.8%	—	—	42.1	42.3	58.4
Net income ($ mil.)	—	—	(8.0)	(1.8)	(3.6)	5.7
Employees	3.1%	—	—	—	256	264

An in-depth profile of this company is available to Hoover's Online members at hoovers.com.

607

⊞ FINANCIAL FEDERAL CORPORATION

733 3rd Ave.	CEO: Paul R. Sinsheimer
New York, NY 10017	CFO: Steven F. (Steve) Groth
Phone: 212-599-8000	HR: —
Fax: 212-286-5885	FYE: July 31
Web: www.financialfederal.com	Type: Subsidiary

Has your crane been grounded, your Caterpillar lost its wiggle, or your bull-dozer become hamburger? Financial Federal may be able to help. The company provides loans, leases, and installment sales plans for heavy-duty industrial and commercial equipment such as bulldozers, buses, cement mixers, cranes, earthmovers, trucks, recycling equipment, and machine tools. Financial Federal's customers are primarily construction firms, waste-disposal firms, and trucking companies in the US that have up to $25 million in annual sales. Virtually all of its finance receivables are secured by first liens on the equipment financed. People's United Financial bought the company in 2010 for about $738 million.

	Annual Growth	7/05	7/06	7/07	7/08	7/09
Sales ($ mil.)	5.9%	126.6	162.5	191.3	188.4	159.1
Net income ($ mil.)	4.1%	36.7	43.6	50.0	50.1	43.1
Employees	(2.2%)	225	247	230	225	206

FINANCIAL GUARANTY INSURANCE COMPANY

125 Park Ave.	CEO: John S. Dubel
New York, NY 10017	CFO: Nick Santoro
Phone: 212-312-3000	HR: —
Fax: 212-312-3093	FYE: December 31
Web: www.fgic.com	Type: Private

Financial Guaranty Insurance Company (FGIC), like a superhero, secured the city . . . well, secured the city bonds, anyway, until things got really tough. The company provided credit enhancement on public finance (including transportation, state and local leases, and municipal electric utility), structured finance (asset-backed securities including mortgage and consumer loans), and global infrastructure and utility securities. FGIC has historically guaranteed the scheduled payments of principal and interest on an issuer's obligation. Founded in 1983, the company is owned by investors including mortgage guaranty insurer The PMI Group. FGIC is currently not issuing new policies or paying claims.

FINANCIAL INSTITUTIONS, INC.   NASDAQ (GS): FISI

220 Liberty St.	CEO: Peter G. Humphrey
Warsaw, NY 14569	CFO: —
Phone: 585-786-1100	HR: Bruce H. Nagle
Fax: 585-786-5254	FYE: December 31
Web: www.fiiwarsaw.com	Type: Public

Well, you certainly can't accuse Financial Institutions of wasting valuable company funds to create a snazzy name. The holding company owns Five Star Bank, which serves western and central New York through some 50 branches. Serving area businesses and consumers, it offers standard deposit products, such as checking and savings accounts, CDs, and IRAs. Subsidiary Five Star Investment Services offers brokerage and financial planning services. An area of growth for Five Star Bank, indirect consumer loans originated through agreements with local franchised car dealers account for the largest percentage of the company's loan portfolio, followed by commercial mortgages.

	Annual Growth	12/05	12/06	12/07	12/08	12/09
Assets ($ mil.)	0.5%	2,022.4	1,907.6	1,857.9	1,916.9	2,062.4
Net income ($ mil.)	60.0%	2.2	17.4	16.4	(26.2)	14.4
Market value ($ mil.)	(12.0%)	214.3	251.8	194.7	156.8	128.7
Employees	(3.0%)	700	640	621	665	620

FINDEX.COM INC.   OTC: FIND

11204 Davenport St., Ste. 100	CEO: Steven Malone
Omaha, NE 68154	CFO: Kirk R. Rowland
Phone: 402-333-1900	HR: —
Fax: 402-778-5763	FYE: December 31
Web: www.quickverse.com/shopfiles	Type: Public

For churches not blessed with financial management skills, FindEx.com is an answer to prayers. The company develops, publishes, and distributes (through a license agreement) software for churches, ministries, and other Christian organizations. Its primary product is a search application called QuickVerse, which is designed to facilitate biblical research. Other offerings include publishing software for Christian-themed printed materials, applications that assist pastors in developing sermons, children's Christian entertainment software, and language tutorials for Greek and Hebrew. Investment firm Barron Partners owns about 60% of FindEx.com.

	Annual Growth	12/05	12/06	12/07	12/08	12/09
Sales ($ mil.)	(20.7%)	5.3	3.7	3.2	2.4	2.1
Net income ($ mil.)	—	(1.6)	0.7	(0.6)	(0.4)	(0.6)
Market value ($ mil.)	(48.4%)	6.0	2.0	3.6	1.8	0.4
Employees	(18.9%)	30	23	20	14	13

FINISAR CORPORATION   NASDAQ (GS): FNSR

1389 Moffett Park Dr.	CEO: Eitan Gertel
Sunnyvale, CA 94089	CFO: Kurt Adzema
Phone: 408-548-1000	HR: Katherine Watt
Fax: 408-541-6138	FYE: April 30
Web: www.finisar.com	Type: Public

Finisar helps put the "work" in network with equipment that enables high-speed data communications over LANs or metro-area and storage-area networks (MANs/SANs). Finisar's optical components and subsystems include data links (transmitters, receivers, and transceivers) and link extenders. The company's customers include Cisco Systems (about 16% of sales), EMC, Hewlett-Packard, and IBM. Finisar gets around two-thirds of its sales from customers outside the US. In 2008 the company merged with rival Optium in a stock-swap deal valued at approximately $243 million.

	Annual Growth	4/05	4/06	4/07	4/08	4/09
Sales ($ mil.)	17.8%	280.8	364.3	418.5	440.2	541.2
Net income ($ mil.)	—	(114.1)	(24.9)	(46.6)	(76.4)	(254.8)
Market value ($ mil.)	(14.9%)	660.6	2,464.2	1,897.9	707.8	346.0
Employees	18.0%	2,580	3,688	3,908	4,476	5,004

⊞ THE FINISH LINE, INC.   NASDAQ (GS): FINL

3308 N. Mitthoeffer Rd.	CEO: Glenn S. Lyon
Indianapolis, IN 46235	CFO: Edward W. (Ed) Wilhelm
Phone: 317-899-1022	HR: Gary D. Cohen
Fax: 317-899-0237	FYE: February 28
Web: www.finishline.com	Type: Public

The Finish Line is losing ground in the race for athletic footwear and other customers. The company sells athletic and casual big-brand name (adidas, NIKE, PUMA) footwear through about 680 Finish Line stores in 47 states. The firm also peddles products through its finishline.com online store. Finish Line's brick-and-mortar stores are bigger than its competitors' and offer more apparel and accessories, including jackets, backpacks, warm-ups, sunglasses, and watches. Ailing Finish Line in July 2009 sold its Man Alive business, which offered hip-hop-inspired apparel, to focus on its primary Finish Line locations.

	Annual Growth	2/06	2/07	2/08	2/09	2/10
Sales ($ mil.)	(2.7%)	1,306.0	1,338.2	1,277.2	1,262.3	1,172.4
Net income ($ mil.)	(12.4%)	60.5	32.4	(60.8)	3.8	35.7
Market value ($ mil.)	(7.8%)	910.0	690.9	153.8	225.6	657.2
Employees	(4.2%)	13,200	13,200	13,100	12,300	11,100

FINISHMASTER, INC.

Pink Sheets: FMST

54 Monument Circle, 8th Fl.
Indianapolis, IN 46204
Phone: 317-237-3678
Fax: 317-237-2150
Web: www.finishmaster.com

CEO: John A. Lacy
CFO: Robert R. (Bob) Millard
HR: Robert (Bob) Pruim
FYE: December 31
Type: Public

Accidents are why pencils have erasers and why FinishMaster sells tons of paint. The company is a top US distributor of automotive paints, coatings, and accessories, which it sells mainly to customers in the collision repair industry. FinishMaster distributes a wide variety of brand-name products from such producers as BASF, DuPont, 3M, and PPG (its top suppliers accounting for 85% of sales). It also sells refinishing accessories under the FinishMaster private brand name. The firm's distribution network serves its customers from about 175 sales outlets in nearly 30 states. Chairman emeritus Andre Lacy controls a three-quarters stake in FinishMaster through holding company LDI, Ltd.

FINLAY ENTERPRISES, INC.

OTC: FNLY

529 5th Ave.
New York, NY 10017
Phone: 212-808-2800
Fax: 212-557-3848
Web: www.finlayenterprises.com

CEO: Arthur E. Reiner
CFO: —
HR: —
FYE: January 31
Type: Public

Finlay Enterprises used to get the most from the leased. The company operates about 100 upscale jewelry stores under the Bailey Banks & Biddle, Carlyle & Co. Jewelers, and Congress Jewelers banners. It also has about 80 licensed jewelry departments with Bon-Ton Stores. Its Finlay Fine Jewelry unit was the top operator of leased jewelry departments in the US, selling moderately priced fine jewelry such as necklaces, earrings, bracelets, rings, and watches in host department stores. Battered by the deep recession in the US, which has depressed demand for discretionary purchases such as jewelry, Finlay filed for Chapter 11 bankruptcy protection in 2009, auctioned its assets, and began closing all of its stores.

	Annual Growth	1/05	1/06	1/07	1/08	1/09
Sales ($ mil.)	(4.9%)	923.6	990.1	761.8	835.9	754.3
Net income ($ mil.)	—	16.0	(55.7)	4.4	(10.0)	(107.3)
Market value ($ mil.)	(80.3%)	158.2	86.0	85.9	18.4	0.2
Employees	12.8%	6,000	6,000	4,500	7,300	9,700

FIRED UP, INC.

7500 Rialto Blvd., Bldg. 1, Ste. 250
Austin, TX 78735
Phone: 512-263-0800
Fax: 512-263-8055
Web: www.carinos.com

CEO: Creed L. Ford III
CFO: Brian Kelly
HR: Vici Wilkerson
FYE: December 31
Type: Private

Italian cooking and casual dining are two things that excite this company. Fired Up operates and franchises more than 140 Carino's Italian Grill restaurants in more than 25 states. The full-service eateries offer pizza and freshly prepared pasta along with beef, chicken and pork dishes inspired by the cuisine of Southern Italy. The company owns about half the restaurants and franchises the rest; a handful of franchised Carino's units are located in Bahrain, Egypt, Kuwait, and United Arab Emirates. Fired Up was founded in 1997 by partners and former Brinker International executives Norman Abdallah and Creed Ford. The company is backed by private equity firm Rosewood Capital.

	Annual Growth	12/04	12/05	12/06	12/07	12/08
Est. sales ($ mil.)	—	—	—	—	—	14.7
Employees	—	—	—	—	—	415

FIREMAN'S FUND INSURANCE COMPANY

777 San Marin Dr.
Novato, CA 94998
Phone: 415-899-2000
Fax: 415-899-3600
Web: www.firemansfund.com

CEO: Michael E. (Mike) LaRocco
CFO: Jill E. Paterson
HR: Pamela Romoli
FYE: December 31
Type: Subsidiary

Firemen still appreciate Fireman's Fund Insurance. The property/casualty insurer sells commercial insurance for small and midsized businesses and personal lines focused on wealthy individuals. Its commercial products include ordinary specialty insurance such as professional liability insurance, as well as truly niche coverage to protect vineyards and wineries from crop damage and shipping mishaps. Founded in 1863, the company is named for a now-defunct arrangement that saw 10% of its profits supporting widows and orphans of firefighters. These days the Fireman's Fund Heritage program provides grants for equipment and training to fire departments. Fireman's Fund is a subsidiary of German insurer Allianz.

FIRESTONE DIVERSIFIED PRODUCTS, LLC

250 W. 96th St.
Indianapolis, IN 46260
Phone: 317-575-7000
Fax: 317-575-7100

CEO: Kenneth W. (Ken) Weaver
CFO: —
HR: Pam Kelley
FYE: December 31
Type: Subsidiary

Don't come to this Firestone looking for that spare tire. A subsidiary of tire giant Bridgestone's Bridgestone Americas, Firestone Diversified Products handles many of the non-tire aspects of Bridgestone's business, including building and roofing products, air springs (for trucks, trailers, and industrial applications), natural and synthetic rubber products, and fibers and textiles. Though it doesn't make tires itself, Firestone Diversified does supply its parent and others with both natural and synthetic rubber with which the tires are manufactured. In 2009 Bridgestone renamed the company (formerly called BFS Diversified Products) to better identify it as part of the Firestone diversified operations.

FIRST ACCEPTANCE CORPORATION

NYSE: FAC

3322 West End Ave., Ste. 1000
Nashville, TN 37203
Phone: 615-844-2800
Fax: 615-327-9957
Web: www.firstacceptancecorp.com

CEO: Stephen J. (Steve) Harrison
CFO: Kevin P. Cohn
HR: —
FYE: June 30
Type: Public

First Acceptance sells car insurance to customers wanting to stay on the right side of the law. A personal auto insurer operating in a dozen states, First Acceptance specializes in providing non-standard auto insurance — that is, insurance for drivers who have trouble getting coverage because of poor driving records or payment histories, but who must have the minimum coverage required by state laws. First Acceptance sells its policies, branded Acceptance Insurance, through some 400 retail offices staffed by its own employee agents. In the Chicago area it uses the names Yale Insurance and Insurance Plus.

	Annual Growth	6/05	6/06	6/07	6/08	6/09
Assets ($ mil.)	2.1%	330.7	434.3	498.9	473.2	359.0
Net income ($ mil.)	—	26.2	28.1	(16.7)	(17.8)	(68.3)
Market value ($ mil.)	(31.1%)	458.7	571.2	492.6	155.2	103.3
Employees	12.8%	725	1,225	1,350	1,230	1,175

FIRST ADVANTAGE BANCORP, INC.

NASDAQ (GM): FABK

1430 Madison St.	CEO: Earl O. Bradley III
Clarksville, TN 37040	CFO: Patrick C. Greenwell
Phone: 931-552-6176	HR: —
Fax: 931-920-6617	FYE: December 31
Web: www.firstfederalsb.com	Type: Public

First Advantage Bancorp is the holding company for First Federal Savings Bank, which serves northern Tennessee from about a half-dozen branch offices. Founded in 1953, the thrift offers standard retail products and services including deposit accounts and loans. One- to four-family residential and commercial mortgages account for about half of First Federal's loan portfolio; the company also writes construction and land loans and, to a lesser extent, consumer and business loans. First Advantage was established when the bank converted to the holding company structure in 2007.

	Annual Growth	12/05	12/06	12/07	12/08	12/09
Assets ($ mil.)	11.8%	220.7	213.4	253.4	338.4	344.2
Net income ($ mil.)	(48.1%)	5.5	0.6	(0.3)	(8.1)	0.4
Market value ($ mil.)	0.0%	—	—	42.4	41.0	42.4
Employees	(1.2%)	—	—	87	85	85

FIRST ADVANTAGE CORPORATION

12395 First American Way	CEO: —
Poway, CA 92064	CFO: John Lamson
Phone: 727-214-3411	HR: Anita Tefft
Fax: 727-214-3410	FYE: December 31
Web: www.fadv.com	Type: Subsidiary

I screen, you screen, we all screen with First Advantage. The company provides such risk management services as employment background screening, occupational health (especially drug testing), tenant screening (credit history, eviction actions, and rental payment history), and motor vehicle reports. Additionally it offers specialized credit reports for mortgage and auto lenders, data security breach notification services, litigation consulting, computer forensics, and investigative services for detecting corporate fraud. The company is a subsidiary of title insurance and business information giant The First American Corporation.

	Annual Growth	12/04	12/05	12/06	12/07	12/08
Sales ($ mil.)	30.8%	266.5	643.7	817.6	842.9	780.0
Net income ($ mil.)	34.4%	10.7	58.4	66.2	138.1	34.9
Employees	23.9%	1,700	3,800	4,400	4,600	4,000

⊞ THE FIRST AMERICAN FINANCIAL CORPORATION

NYSE: FAF

1 First American Way	CEO: Dennis J. Gilmore
Santa Ana, CA 92707	CFO: Anthony S. (Buddy) Piszel
Phone: 714-250-3000	HR: Karen J. Collins
Fax: —	FYE: December 31
Web: www.firstam.com	Type: Public

The First American Financial knows that when you're buying real estate you'll probably want some insurance to go along with it. Along with good old title insurance from its First American Title subsidiary, the company's financial services arm also provides specialty property/casualty insurance and home warranties through its First American Home Buyers Protection business. Its First American Trust offers banking and trust services to the escrow and real estate industries. Previously known as First American Corporation, the company spun off its real estate information services business and moved its remaining operations into its First American Financial business.

	Annual Growth	12/05	12/06	12/07	12/08	12/09
Assets ($ mil.)	3.5%	7,598.6	8,224.3	8,647.9	8,730.1	8,723.1
Net income ($ mil.)	(19.9%)	485.3	287.7	(3.1)	(26.3)	199.7
Market value ($ mil.)	(7.5%)	4,706.8	4,226.7	3,545.1	3,001.7	3,440.2
Employees	(3.4%)	35,444	39,670	37,354	31,411	30,922

FIRST AMERICAN TITLE INSURANCE COMPANY

1 First American Way	CEO: Dennis J. Gilmore
Santa Ana, CA 92707	CFO: Anthony S. (Buddy) Piszel
Phone: 714-250-3000	HR: —
Fax: 714-800-3142	FYE: December 31
Web: title.firstam.com	Type: Subsidiary

First, you find the home of your dreams, and then you make SURE that the party selling it is really entitled to sell it, and that's where First American Title Insurance steps in to help. First American Title Insurance's products protect real estate buyers and mortgage lenders with coverage against any title "defects" such as outstanding liens or other encumbrances. It is one of the largest title insurance providers in the US with offices in 47 states nationwide. Its international operations outside the US span 21 other countries on five continents worldwide. First American Title is the largest subsidiary of The First American Corporation. Parent First American plans to spin off its insurance operations (including First American Title) in 2010.

FIRST AVIATION SERVICES INC.

Pink Sheets: FAVS

15 Riverside Ave.	CEO: Aaron P. Hollander
Westport, CT 06880	CFO: James Howell
Phone: 203-291-3300	HR: —
Fax: 203-291-3330	FYE: January 31
Web: www.favs.com	Type: Public

The superstore of aerospace, First Aviation Services (FAvS) pushes parts and components that keep aircraft flying high. The company sells about 200,000 new and reconditioned parts from 170 small manufacturers and OEMs such as General Electric, Goodrich, and Parker Hannifin. Cornerstone unit Aerospace Products International (API) and subsidiaries in the Asia/Pacific region, Canada, China, and Europe tap 6,000-plus manufacturers, maintenance providers, and operators of commercial, corporate and general aviation aircraft. API also offers overhaul and repair services for brakes and starters/generators, and builds hose assemblies. In addition to parts, API offers third-party logistics and inventory management services.

	Annual Growth	1/04	1/05	1/06	1/07	*1/08
Sales ($ mil.)	4.3%	105.8	124.2	131.5	119.4	125.2
Net income ($ mil.)	—	0.0	(2.2)	1.0	(14.5)	(3.7)
Employees	2.3%	198	196	204	212	—

*Most recent year available

FIRST BANCORP.

NYSE: FBP

1519 Ponce de León Ave., Stop 23	CEO: Luis M. Beauchamp
Santurce, PR 00908	CFO: Orlando Berges
Phone: 787-729-8200	HR: Aida M. Garcia
Fax: 787-729-8205	FYE: December 31
Web: www.firstbankpr.com	Type: Public

Not to be confused with North Carolina's First Bancorp, this First BanCorp is the holding company for FirstBank Puerto Rico and FirstBank Florida. The company offers banking, mortgage, and insurance services from around 75 locations on the island, in the US, and the US and British Virgin Islands. Commercial lending, including business, construction, and mortgage loans, represents more than half of First BanCorp's loan portfolio; residential mortgages make up about another quarter. FirstBank owns Money Express La Financiera, a consumer loan company with nearly 40 offices throughout Puerto Rico, and car rental agency First Leasing and Rental, which has about 10 locations.

	Annual Growth	12/05	12/06	12/07	12/08	12/09
Assets ($ mil.)	(0.4%)	19,917.7	17,390.3	17,186.9	—	19,628.4
Net income ($ mil.)	—	114.6	84.6	68.1	—	(275.2)
Market value ($ mil.)	(34.4%)	1,148.5	881.9	674.6	—	212.8
Employees	(0.1%)	2,725	3,037	3,000	2,995	2,713

FIRST BANCORP

NASDAQ (GS): FBNC

341 N. Main St.
Troy, NC 27371
Phone: 910-576-6171
Fax: 910-576-1070
Web: www.firstbancorp.com

CEO: Jerry L. Ocheltree
CFO: Eric P. Credle
HR: —
FYE: December 31
Type: Public

First Bancorp (not to be confused with First Bancorp in Virginia or First BanCorp in Puerto Rico) is the holding company for First Bank, which operates some 100 branches in east-central North Carolina, east South Carolina, and western Virginia. The bank offers checking, savings, money market, and NOW accounts; IRAs; investments; and discount brokerage services. It focuses lending on mortgage loans, which account for some three-quarters of its loan portfolio. The company also owns in-house and third-party data processor Montgomery Data Services, as well as a property/casualty insurance agency.

THE FIRST BANCORP, INC.

NASDAQ (GS): FNLC

223 Main St.
Damariscotta, ME 04543
Phone: 207-563-3195
Fax: 207-563-6853
Web: www.the1st.com

CEO: Daniel R. Daigneault
CFO: F. Stephen Ward
HR: Susan A. Norton
FYE: December 31
Type: Public

The First Bancorp (formerly First National Lincoln) is the holding company for The First, a regional bank serving coastal Maine from about 15 branches. The bank offers traditional retail products and services, including checking and savings accounts, CDs, IRAs, and loans. Residential mortgages make up about half of the company's loan portfolio; business loans account for another third. Bank subsidiary First Advisors offers private banking and investment management services. The bank traces its roots to 1864 and has grown through acquisitions and the opening of new branches.

	Annual Growth	12/05	12/06	12/07	12/08	12/09
Assets ($ mil.)	6.3%	1,042.2	1,104.9	1,223.3	1,325.7	1,331.4
Net income ($ mil.)	0.4%	12.8	12.3	13.1	14.0	13.0
Market value ($ mil.)	(3.2%)	171.5	163.0	142.8	194.0	150.4
Employees	(0.5%)	216	212	418	213	212

FIRST BANCSHARES, INC.

NASDAQ (GM): FBSI

142 E. 1st St.
Mountain Grove, MO 65711
Phone: 417-926-5151
Fax: 417-926-4362
Web: www.firsthomesavingsbank.com

CEO: Thomas M. Sutherland
CFO: Ronald J. (Ron) Walters
HR: —
FYE: June 30
Type: Public

First Bancshares is the holding company for First Home Savings Bank, which has about a dozen locations serving south-central Missouri. First Home Savings offers a range of retail banking services, including checking and savings, as well as NOW accounts and CDs. Residential mortgages account for more than half of First Home Savings' lending portfolio; commercial real estate loans represent another quarter. First Home Savings Bank was founded in 1911 as Mountain Grove Building and Loan Association.

	Annual Growth	6/05	6/06	6/07	6/08	6/09
Assets ($ mil.)	(1.5%)	244.0	228.4	241.3	249.2	229.9
Net income ($ mil.)	—	1.3	(0.2)	0.3	0.4	(4.0)
Market value ($ mil.)	(10.7%)	28.7	25.8	25.6	21.2	18.2
Employees	8.0%	100	106	125	126	—

THE FIRST BANCSHARES, INC.

NASDAQ (CM): FBMS

6480 US Hwy. 98 West
Hattiesburg, MS 39402
Phone: 601-268-8998
Fax: 601-268-8904
Web: www.thefirstbank.com

CEO: David E. Johnson
CFO: DeeDee Lowery
HR: —
FYE: December 31
Type: Public

Hoping to be first in the hearts of its customers, The First Bancshares is the holding company for The First, a community bank with some 10 branch locations in southern Mississippi's Hattiesburg and surrounding areas. The company provides such standard deposit products as checking and savings accounts, NOW and money market accounts, and IRAs. Real estate loans account for about 80% of the bank's lending portfolio, including about equal portions of residential mortgages, commercial mortgages, and construction loans. The bank also writes business loans and consumer loans.

	Annual Growth	12/05	12/06	12/07	12/08	12/09
Assets ($ mil.)	12.9%	294.4	417.8	496.1	474.8	477.6
Net income ($ mil.)	(2.7%)	1.9	3.3	3.8	1.8	1.7
Market value ($ mil.)	(18.6%)	48.3	91.4	64.9	27.3	21.2
Employees	12.7%	98	168	184	158	158

FIRST BANKING CENTER, INC.

OTC: FBCI

400 Milwaukee Ave.
Burlington, WI 53105
Phone: 262-763-3581
Fax: 262-763-5314
Web: www.firstbankingcenter.com

CEO: Brantly (Brant) Chappell
CFO: James Schuster
HR: —
FYE: December 31
Type: Public

First Banking Center, Inc., is the holding company for First Banking Center, a community-oriented financial institution that offers deposit accounts, loans, and investments from more than 15 locations across southern Wisconsin. Serving local residents and businesses, the bank offers standard services such as checking and savings accounts and CDs. Residential mortgages account for the largest portion of the bank's loan portfolio, followed by commercial real estate loans, construction and land development loans, and farmland loans. The bank also offers investment products and services, including retirement plans, trust services, financial planning, investment management, and estate administration.

FIRST BANKS, INC.

135 N. Meramec Ave.
Clayton, MO 63105
Phone: 314-854-4600
Fax: 314-592-6840
Web: www.firstbanks.com

CEO: Terrance M. (Terry) McCarthy
CFO: Lisa K. Vansickle
HR: John D. Kitson
FYE: December 31
Type: Private

First Banks keeps it in the family. The holding company for its namesake First Bank, it is owned by chairman James Dierberg and his family; many First Bank branches and ATMs are located in Dierbergs Markets, a Missouri-based grocery chain owned by relatives of the chairman. First Bank has about 160 branches in California, Florida, Illinois, and Missouri, with a concentration in metropolitan markets. The bank offers standard services like deposit products, mortgages, and business and consumer loans. Subsidiaries and affiliates offer brokerage, insurance, trust, private banking, and institutional money management services.

FIRST BUSEY CORPORATION

NASDAQ (GS): BUSE

201 W. Main St.
Urbana, IL 61801
Phone: 217-365-4528
Fax: 217-365-4592
Web: www.busey.com

CEO: Van A. Dukeman
CFO: David B. (Dave) White
HR: Lisa A. Davis
FYE: December 31
Type: Public

First Busey Corporation sure stays busy. It's the holding company for several subsidiaries, including Busey Bank, which has nearly 50 branches, mostly in central Illinois, but also in Florida and Indiana. Another subsidiary, Busey Bank, N.A., operates about 10 offices in three southwest Florida counties. The banks provide traditional demand and savings deposit and loan products. Real estate lending accounts for more than 80% of the company's loan portfolio, which also includes agricultural, business, and consumer loans. First Busey offers trust and investment management services through Busey Wealth Management, and retail payment processing through FirsTech.

	Annual Growth	12/05	12/06	12/07	12/08	12/09
Assets ($ mil.)	13.9%	2,263.4	2,509.5	4,192.9	4,460.1	3,814.9
Net income ($ mil.)	—	26.9	28.9	31.5	(37.9)	(323.1)
Market value ($ mil.)	(34.3%)	1,386.3	1,529.6	1,317.9	1,210.4	258.1
Employees	10.7%	608	640	1,023	986	912

FIRST BUSINESS FINANCIAL SERVICES, INC.

NASDAQ (GM): FBIZ

401 Charmany Dr.
Madison, WI 53719
Phone: 608-238-8008
Fax: 608-232-5920
Web: www.fbfinancial.net

CEO: Corey A. Chambas
CFO: James F. Ropella
HR: —
FYE: December 31
Type: Public

Business comes first at First Business Financial Services, which serves business customers through First Business Bank and First Business Bank-Milwaukee. The banks offer deposit products, cash management services, equipment leases, loans, and other products from a handful of offices in Madison and southeastern Wisconsin. About 40% of its loan portfolio is dedicated to commercial mortgages; business loans and leases add another 30%. Subsidiary First Business Capital specializes in asset-based lending. First Business Equipment Finance provides commercial equipment financing. First Business Trust & Investments offers investment management and retirement services.

	Annual Growth	12/05	12/06	12/07	12/08	12/09
Assets ($ mil.)	13.7%	669.2	788.3	918.4	1,010.8	1,117.4
Net income ($ mil.)	(32.4%)	4.8	3.7	3.3	3.1	1.0
Market value ($ mil.)	(20.2%)	60.2	58.0	44.4	33.0	24.4
Employees	3.6%	119	242	142	152	137

FIRST CALIFORNIA FINANCIAL GROUP, INC.

NASDAQ (GM): FCAL

3027 Townsgate Rd., Ste. 300
Westlake Village, CA 91361
Phone: 805-322-9655
Fax: —
Web: www.fcalgroup.com

CEO: C. G. Kum
CFO: Romolo C. Santarosa
HR: —
FYE: December 31
Type: Public

First California Financial Group was formed in 2007 when it merged with FCB Bancorp and National Mercantile Bancorp. The holding company then combined its three existing banks (First California Bank, National Mercantile Bank, and South Bay Bank) to form First California Bank, which operates about 20 branches in Southern California. The bank provides standard fare for mostly local small and midsized businesses, but also individuals, including checking and savings accounts, mortgages and other loans, and investment services. The Pohlad family (which also owns Marquette Financial Companies and the Minnesota Twins) is a major investor in First California.

	Annual Growth	12/05	12/06	12/07	12/08	12/09
Assets ($ mil.)	34.3%	448.8	501.6	1,108.8	1,178.0	1,459.8
Net income ($ mil.)	—	4.7	5.6	7.1	6.4	(4.7)
Market value ($ mil.)	(35.3%)	439.4	387.5	255.0	155.6	77.2
Employees	33.3%	77	86	205	207	243

FIRST CAPITAL BANCORP, INC.

NASDAQ (CM): FCVA

4222 Cox Rd., Ste. 200
Glen Allen, VA 23060
Phone: 804-273-1160
Fax: 804-527-0195
Web: www.1capitalbank.com

CEO: John M. Presley
CFO: William W. Ranson
HR: —
FYE: December 31
Type: Public

Moolah, scratch, bread, chedda, bucks, dough, ducats, or skrilla — it all means business for First Capital Bank and its holding company, First Capital Bancorp. Founded in 1998, the bank provides general commercial banking services from more than six branches in the Richmond, Virginia, area. First Capital Bank offers the usual array of personal and business banking services including credit cards, IRAs, consumer and commercial loans, Internet banking services, and deposit accounts. It offers investment products in association with brokerage firm BI Investments. The company terminated its agreement to merge with Eastern Virginia Bankshares in 2009.

	Annual Growth	12/05	12/06	12/07	12/08	12/09
Assets ($ mil.)	26.1%	209.5	257.2	351.9	431.6	530.4
Net income ($ mil.)	(30.7%)	1.3	1.6	1.7	0.2	0.3
Market value ($ mil.)	(35.6%)	—	53.3	34.3	19.1	14.3
Employees	8.0%	—	62	69	77	78

FIRST CAPITAL, INC.

NASDAQ (GM): FCAP

220 Federal Dr. NW
Corydon, IN 47112
Phone: 812-738-2198
Fax: 812-738-2202
Web: www.firstharrison.com

CEO: William W. Harrod
CFO: Michael C. Frederick
HR: Jill Keinsley
FYE: December 31
Type: Public

First Capital is the holding company for First Harrison Bank, which operates about a dozen branches in Clark, Floyd, Harrison, and Washington counties in southern Indiana. Targeting area consumers and small to midsized businesses, the bank offers standard deposit products such as checking and savings accounts, certificates of deposit, and individual retirement accounts. Residential mortgages make up nearly half of the company's loan portfolio; consumer loans and commercial mortgages are around 20% apiece. First Harrison Bank also offers access to investments such as stocks, bonds, and mutual funds.

	Annual Growth	12/05	12/06	12/07	12/08	12/09
Assets ($ mil.)	1.0%	438.4	457.1	453.2	458.6	455.5
Net income ($ mil.)	(31.8%)	3.7	3.7	3.4	3.6	0.8
Market value ($ mil.)	(3.1%)	45.4	51.7	46.0	42.6	40.1
Employees	0.7%	144	147	149	141	148

⊞ FIRST CASH FINANCIAL SERVICES, INC.

NASDAQ (GS): FCFS

690 E. Lamar Blvd., Ste. 400
Arlington, TX 76011
Phone: 817-460-3947
Fax: 817-461-7019
Web: www.firstcash.com

CEO: Rick L. Wessel
CFO: R. Douglas (Doug) Orr
HR: Jan Hartz
FYE: December 31
Type: Public

Texas isn't just oil, land, and cattle. Since the 1980s, a new industry has found a home on the range: pawnshops. First Cash Financial Services operates nearly 540 pawnshops and cash advance stores there and in about a dozen other states, as well as in Mexico. The company lends money secured by such personal property as jewelry, electronics, tools, sporting goods, and musical equipment. Those shops also sell merchandise forfeited by borrowers. First Cash Financial Services is half-owner of Cash & Go, a partnership that operates about 40 cash advance and check-cashing kiosks inside convenience stores. First Cash Financial Services charges its pawn customers annual service charges of up to 240%.

	Annual Growth	12/05	12/06	12/07	12/08	12/09
Assets ($ mil.)	8.3%	186.0	233.8	291.5	265.3	256.3
Net income ($ mil.)	18.3%	25.4	31.7	35.3	(21.5)	49.8
Market value ($ mil.)	11.1%	439.2	779.3	442.2	574.2	668.5
Employees	16.1%	2,314	2,900	3,300	3,800	4,200

FIRST CENTURY BANKSHARES, INC.
OTC: FCBS

500 Federal St.
Bluefield, WV 24701
Phone: 304-325-8181
Fax: 304-325-3727
Web: www.firstcentury.com

CEO: Richard W. Wilkinson
CFO: J. Ronald Hypes
HR: Lisa A. Huff
FYE: December 31
Type: Public

First Century Bankshares is the holding company for First Century Bank, which serves southern West Virginia and southwestern Virginia from about a dozen branch locations. The bank provides traditional deposit services such as checking accounts, statement savings, money market accounts, CDs, and IRAs. It uses funds from deposits to write commercial and consumer loans, primarily real estate mortgages, which account for some 70% of the company's loan book. First Century Bank also offers real estate construction and development loans, agricultural loans, and check cards. Bank subsidiary First Century Financial Services provides trust, investment, and financial planning services.

	Annual Growth	12/05	12/06	12/07	12/08	12/09
Assets ($ mil.)	1.1%	390.8	410.9	433.9	425.7	408.4
Net income ($ mil.)	(47.7%)	4.0	4.5	4.7	3.7	0.3
Market value ($ mil.)	(10.4%)	44.3	53.3	48.5	29.8	28.5
Employees	(1.5%)	173	180	180	177	163

FIRST CHESTER COUNTY CORPORATION
OTC: FCEC

9 N. High St.
West Chester, PA 19380
Phone: 484-881-4000
Fax: 484-881-4130
Web: www.fnbchestercounty.com

CEO: John A. Featherman III
CFO: Sheryl S. Vittitoe
HR: Kelly A. Besack
FYE: December 31
Type: Public

First Chester County Corporation is the holding company of First National Bank of Chester County, which provides traditional banking services to individuals and businesses through about two-dozen branches in southeastern Pennsylvania. Besides checking and savings accounts, the bank also offers money markets, IRAs, CDs, and trust and asset management services. The company is primarily a commercial lender, with business loans and commercial mortgages accounting for more than two-thirds of its loan portfolio. Mortgage services are offered through its American Home Bank division. First Chester is being acquired by Tower Bancorp.

	Annual Growth	12/04	12/05	12/06	12/07	*12/08
Assets ($ mil.)	12.7%	805.5	845.1	872.1	914.8	1,300.2
Net income ($ mil.)	(3.0%)	6.2	6.5	7.3	7.7	5.5
Market value ($ mil.)	(20.1%)	155.0	120.7	132.4	108.7	63.0
Employees	20.3%	270	232	287	265	565

*Most recent year available

FIRST CITIZENS BANC CORP.
NASDAQ (CM): FCZA

100 E. Water St.
Sandusky, OH 44870
Phone: 419-625-4121
Fax: 419-627-3359
Web: www.fcza.com

CEO: James O. Miller
CFO: Todd A. Michel
HR: —
FYE: December 31
Type: Public

First Citizens Banc Corp. is the holding company for The Citizens Banking Company and its Citizens Bank and Champaign Bank divisions, which together operate more than 30 branches in northern Ohio. The banks offer such deposit products as checking and savings accounts and CDs, in addition to trust services. They concentrate on real estate lending, with residential mortgages and commercial mortgages each comprising approximately 40% of the company's loan portfolio. The Citizens Banking Company's Citizens Wealth Management division provides financial planning, brokerage, insurance, and investments through an agreement with third-party provider UVEST (part of LPL Financial).

	Annual Growth	12/05	12/06	12/07	12/08	12/09
Assets ($ mil.)	10.1%	750.9	749.0	1,119.3	1,053.6	1,102.8
Net income ($ mil.)	(29.0%)	6.7	6.2	6.9	(39.0)	1.7
Market value ($ mil.)	(30.1%)	150.3	151.8	108.4	46.2	35.8
Employees	2.2%	259	250	263	300	283

FIRST CITIZENS BANCORPORATION, INC.
OTC: FCBN

1230 Main
Columbia, SC 29201
Phone: 803-733-2020
Fax: 803-733-2763
Web: www.firstcitizensonline.com

CEO: Jim B. Apple
CFO: Craig L. Nix
HR: Annette Rollins
FYE: December 31
Type: Public

First Citizens Bancorporation is the holding company for First Citizens Bank and Trust Company, which has more than 170 branches in South Carolina and Georgia, and The Exchange Bank of South Carolina, which has four branches. In 2008 the company bought the six-branch Merchants and Farmers Bank in rural northeastern Georgia, which kept its name. The banks provide standard products and services for individuals and businesses, including checking and savings accounts, credit cards, and online banking. Residential and commercial mortgages comprise most of First Citizens Bancorporation's loan portfolio. Lease financing and construction, business, land, and consumer loans round out the banks' lending activities.

FIRST CITIZENS BANCSHARES, INC.
NASDAQ (GS): FCNCA

4300 Six Forks Rd.
Raleigh, NC 27609
Phone: 919-716-7000
Fax: 919-716-7074
Web: www.firstcitizens.com

CEO: Frank B. Holding Jr.
CFO: Kenneth A. Black
HR: Lou J. Davis
FYE: December 31
Type: Public

First Citizens BancShares knows the first thing about commercial banking in several states. The company owns First-Citizens Bank & Trust, which operates some 375 branches in North Carolina, Maryland, Tennessee, Virginia, West Virginia, California, and Washington; it also owns IronStone Bank, which has about 60 branches in metropolitan areas in about a dozen states in the Midwest, the Sun Belt, and along the West Coast. In addition to deposits and loans, the banks also offer discount brokerage, trust, insurance, and investment services. Real estate loans (including commercial, residential, and revolving mortgages, and construction and land development loans) make up most of the company's lending portfolio.

	Annual Growth	12/05	12/06	12/07	12/08	12/09
Assets ($ mil.)	6.0%	14,639.4	15,729.7	16,212.1	16,745.7	18,466.1
Net income ($ mil.)	0.7%	112.9	126.5	108.6	91.1	116.3
Market value ($ mil.)	(1.5%)	1,820.0	2,114.4	1,521.9	1,594.4	1,711.4
Employees	1.1%	4,794	4,764	4,781	4,843	5,006

FIRST CLOVER LEAF FINANCIAL CORP.
NASDAQ (CM): FCLF

6814 Goshen Rd.
Edwardsville, IL 62025
Phone: 618-656-6122
Fax: —
Web: www.cloverleafbank.com

CEO: Dennis M. Terry
CFO: Darlene F. (Dee) McDonald
HR: —
FYE: December 31
Type: Public

First Clover Leaf Financial counts itself lucky to be in the banking business in the greater St. Louis area. The company (formerly First Federal Financial Services) is the holding company for three-branch First Clover Leaf Bank. Under its former name, the company in 2006 acquired Clover Leaf Financial and merged the acquisition's Clover Leaf Bank with First Federal Savings & Loan Association of Edwardsville to form First Clover Leaf Bank. The bank serves individuals and businesses in and around Edwardsville and Glen Carbon, offering such standard services as deposit accounts, credit cards, and loans, including real estate (about 85% of its total portfolio), business, and consumer loans.

	Annual Growth	12/05	12/06	12/07	12/08	12/09
Assets ($ mil.)	43.0%	140.2	410.3	413.3	653.3	585.5
Net income ($ mil.)	—	1.9	1.8	2.4	2.7	(8.8)
Market value ($ mil.)	(13.7%)	105.2	91.3	80.6	54.5	58.3
Employees	71.7%	10	52	61	85	87

FIRST COMMONWEALTH FINANCIAL CORPORATION

NYSE: FCF

22 N. 6th St.
Indiana, PA 15701
Phone: 724-349-7220
Fax: 888-711-2329
Web: www.fcbanking.com

CEO: John J. Dolan
CFO: —
HR: —
FYE: December 31
Type: Public

First Commonwealth Financial is the holding company for First Commonwealth Bank, which operates some 115 offices in 15 central and western Pennsylvania counties. The bank offers standard deposit products such as checking and savings accounts and CDs; its loan book includes a mix of residential and commercial mortgages and business, construction, and consumer loans. Among First Commonwealth Financial's nonbanking subsidiaries are an insurance agency, a trust company, a financial planning company, a data processing firm, and a professional services organization.

	Annual Growth	12/05	12/06	12/07	12/08	12/09
Assets ($ mil.)	1.7%	6,026.3	6,043.9	5,883.6	6,425.9	6,446.3
Net income ($ mil.)	—	57.8	53.0	46.3	43.1	(20.1)
Market value ($ mil.)	(22.6%)	1,114.8	1,157.9	918.2	1,067.4	400.9
Employees	1.7%	1,598	1,579	1,649	1,693	1,709

FIRST COMMUNITY BANCSHARES, INC.

NASDAQ (GS): FCBC

1 Community Place
Bluefield, VA 24605
Phone: 276-326-9000
Fax: 276-326-9010
Web: www.fcbinc.com

CEO: John M. Mendez
CFO: David D. Brown V
HR: Melissa Ward
FYE: December 31
Type: Public

First Community Bancshares doesn't play second fiddle to other area banks. The firm is the holding company for First Community Bank, which serves communities in Virginia, West Virginia, the Carolinas, and Tennessee. Through some 60 branches, the bank provides traditional services such as checking and savings accounts, CDs, and credit cards. The bank is mainly a real estate lender, with residential mortgages accounting for nearly half of its loan portfolio and commercial real estate loans comprising about a third. With some $830 million of assets under management, it also provides wealth management services through its trust and financial services division and its Investment Planning Consultants subsidiary.

	Annual Growth	12/05	12/06	12/07	12/08	12/09
Assets ($ mil.)	3.9%	1,952.5	2,033.7	2,149.8	2,133.3	2,274.9
Net income ($ mil.)	—	26.3	28.9	29.6	3.1	(38.2)
Market value ($ mil.)	(21.1%)	554.1	703.5	567.1	620.1	214.3
Employees	(2.5%)	716	602	615	638	646

FIRST COMMUNITY BANK CORPORATION

NASDAQ (CM): FCFL

9001 Belcher Rd.
Pinellas Park, FL 33782
Phone: 727-520-0987
Fax: 727-471-0010
Web: www.efirstcommbank.com

CEO: Kenneth P. Cherven
CFO: Stan B. McClelland
HR: Anna Thrombley
FYE: December 31
Type: Public

Although not the first community bank *in* America, First Community Bank Corporation of America *is* the holding company for First Community Bank of America, which has about 10 branches in the Sunshine State's Tampa Bay area. The thrift concentrates on real estate lending, with commercial mortgages and residential mortgages representing the bulk of its activities. It also makes business and consumer installment loans. The company is eyeing growth and plans to expand through aquisitions of small banks or by opening new branches. Chairman Robert M. Menke owns 38% of First Community Bank Corporation of America; company officers and directors collectively own 51%.

	Annual Growth	12/05	12/06	12/07	12/08	12/09
Assets ($ mil.)	14.0%	324.8	390.9	436.5	501.6	547.9
Net income ($ mil.)	—	2.9	3.7	2.9	(3.6)	(4.9)
Market value ($ mil.)	(38.7%)	93.0	98.2	60.0	25.9	13.1
Employees	8.6%	74	110	109	100	103

FIRST COMMUNITY CORPORATION

NASDAQ (CM): FCCO

5455 Sunset Blvd.
Lexington, SC 29072
Phone: 803-951-2265
Fax: 803-951-1722
Web: www.firstcommunitysc.com

CEO: Michael C. (Mike) Crapps
CFO: Joseph G. Sawyer
HR: Robin D. Brown
FYE: December 31
Type: Public

Putting first things first, First Community is the holding company for First Community Bank, which serves individuals and smaller businesses in central South Carolina's Lexington, Richland, Kershaw, and Newberry counties. Through about a dozen offices, the bank offers such products and services as checking and savings accounts, money market accounts, CDs, IRAs, credit cards, insurance, and investment services. Commercial mortgages make up about 40% of First Community Bank's loan portfolio, which also includes residential mortgages and business, consumer, and construction loans. The company bought DutchFork Bancshares in 2004 and DeKalb Bankshares (parent of The Bank of Camden) in 2006.

	Annual Growth	12/05	12/06	12/07	12/08	12/09
Assets ($ mil.)	6.7%	467.5	548.1	565.6	650.2	605.8
Net income ($ mil.)	—	3.1	3.5	4.0	(6.8)	(25.2)
Market value ($ mil.)	(23.6%)	60.3	54.5	42.0	25.2	20.5
Employees	3.3%	123	137	138	148	140

⊞ FIRST DATA CORPORATION

5565 Glenridge Connector, NE
Atlanta, GA 30342
Phone: 303-967-8000
Fax: 303-967-7000
Web: www.firstdatacorp.com

CEO: Joe W. Forehand
CFO: Raymond E. (Ray) Winborne Jr.
HR: Peter W. Boucher
FYE: December 31
Type: Private

Paper, plastic, or Internet — in whatever form, First Data moves the money. The world's largest electronic payments processor, First Data provides services for more than 5 million merchants and 2,000 card issuers in some 35 countries. It provides a variety of secure funds transfer and related services including credit card payments, fraud protection and authentication, check guarantee (through subsidiary TeleCheck), and point-of-sale (POS) services. First Data operates through two primary segments — retail and alliance services and financial services. Its merchant acquiring business is its largest revenue-earner. Investment firm KKR bought the company in 2007.

	Annual Growth	12/04	12/05	12/06	12/07	12/08
Sales ($ mil.)	11.6%	—	—	7,076.4	8,051.4	8,811.3
Net income ($ mil.)	—	—	—	1,513.4	158.9	(3,764.3)
Employees	(4.2%)	—	—	29,000	27,000	26,600

FIRST DEFIANCE FINANCIAL CORP.

NASDAQ (GS): FDEF

601 Clinton St.
Defiance, OH 43512
Phone: 419-782-5015
Fax: 419-782-5145
Web: www.fdef.com

CEO: William J. Small
CFO: Donald P. Hileman
HR: —
FYE: December 31
Type: Public

Named for its hometown, not its attitude, First Defiance Financial is the holding company for First Federal Bank of the Midwest, which operates more than 35 branches serving northwestern Ohio, western Indiana, and southern Michigan. The bank offers standard deposit products including checking, savings, and money market accounts and CDs. Commercial real estate loans account for about 40% of the bank's loan portfolio; residential mortgages make up about another 20%. The company's insurance agency subsidiary, First Insurance & Investments, provides life insurance, property/casualty coverage, and investments. In 2008 First Defiance bought Pavilion Bancorp, giving the bank its first branches in Michigan.

	Annual Growth	12/05	12/06	12/07	12/08	12/09
Assets ($ mil.)	8.9%	1,461.1	1,527.9	1,609.4	1,957.4	2,057.5
Net income ($ mil.)	(12.0%)	12.0	15.6	13.9	7.4	7.2
Market value ($ mil.)	(19.7%)	219.9	245.6	178.8	62.8	91.6
Employees	3.8%	476	476	510	556	553

FIRST EAGLE INVESTMENT MANAGEMENT, LLC

1345 Avenue of the Americas, 44th Fl.
New York, NY 10105
Phone: 212-698-3300
Fax: 212-299-4360
Web: firsteagleinstitutional.com

CEO: John P. Arnhold
CFO: —
HR: —
FYE: December 31
Type: Private

First Eagle flies high in the world of investment management. The firm (formerly Arnhold and S. Bleichroeder Advisers) manages more than $37 million of assets for retail, institutional, and high-net-worth investors. It manages the First Eagle Funds, a family of five value-oriented mutual funds geared toward capital preservation. Other products include separate institutional accounts and alternative investments such as hedge funds. The company prides itself on conducting extensive research into the firms in which it invests, including visiting prospective companies, and ideally holding those investments for the long haul. First Eagle is owned by key employees and the Arnhold family.

FIRST FEDERAL BANCSHARES OF ARKANSAS

NASDAQ (GM): FFBH

1401 Hwy. 62-65 North
Harrison, AR 72601
Phone: 870-741-7641
Fax: 870-365-8369
Web: www.ffbh.com

CEO: Larry J. Brandt
CFO: Sherri R. Billings
HR: –
FYE: December 31
Type: Public

If there's gold in them thar Ozark Mountains, it's probably tucked away in First Federal Bancshares of Arkansas, Inc. Its subsidiary — First Federal Bank of Arkansas — serves commercial and individual customers through some 20 branches in north central and northwestern portions of the state. The bank offers standard retail services such as savings, checking, and money market accounts, as well as certificates of deposit. Funds generated are largely used to write single-family residential mortgages (about one-third of the company's loan portfolio), real estate construction loans (a quarter), and commercial mortgages (nearly 20%). The bank also writes business and consumer loans. It was founded in 1934.

	Annual Growth	12/05	12/06	12/07	12/08	12/09
Assets ($ mil.)	(3.8%)	852.4	852.5	792.0	795.2	731.1
Net income ($ mil.)	—	7.8	7.4	2.6	2.5	(45.5)
Market value ($ mil.)	(44.6%)	117.8	117.9	68.3	36.7	11.1
Employees	(4.8%)	333	329	329	312	274

FIRST FEDERAL OF NORTHERN MICHIGAN

NASDAQ (GM): FFNM

100 S. 2nd Ave.
Alpena, MI 49707
Phone: 989-356-9041
Fax: 989-354-8671
Web: www.first-federal.com

CEO: Martin A. Thomson
CFO: Amy E. Essex
HR: Joseph W. Gentry II
FYE: December 31
Type: Public

First Federal of Northern Michigan Bancorp, Inc., is the holding company for savings bank First Federal of Northern Michigan, serving area residents and businesses from nearly 10 locations in the northern part of the state's Lower Peninsula. Deposit services include checking, savings, and money market accounts, CDs, and IRAs. The bank's lending activities mainly consist of residential mortgages (nearly half of its loan portfolio), commercial mortgages, business loans, and home equity loans. It also offers construction loans, consumer loans, and credit cards. In 2009 First Federal sold InsuranCenter of Alpena (ICA), which provided life, property/casualty, and health insurance and investment products.

	Annual Growth	12/05	12/06	12/07	12/08	12/09
Assets ($ mil.)	(4.7%)	282.8	281.0	250.8	247.7	233.5
Net income ($ mil.)	—	0.4	0.5	(1.6)	(3.2)	(6.8)
Market value ($ mil.)	(38.9%)	25.2	26.2	21.2	3.6	3.5
Employees	(6.6%)	129	109	102	96	98

FIRST FINANCIAL BANCORP

NASDAQ (GS): FFBC

4000 Smith Rd., Ste. 400
Cincinnati, OH 45209
Phone: 513-979-5837
Fax: 513-867-3111
Web: bankatfirst.com

CEO: Claude E. Davis
CFO: J. Franklin (Frank) Hall
HR: —
FYE: December 31
Type: Public

First Financial spreads itself thick. The holding company's flagship subsidiary, First Financial Bank, operates through more than 125 branches in Ohio, Indiana, and Kentucky. Founded in 1863, the bank offers checking and savings accounts, money market accounts, CDs, credit cards, private banking, wealth management, and trust services. Commercial loans, including real estate and construction loans, make up about 70% of First Financial's total loan portfolio; the bank also offers residential mortgage and consumer loans. Another subsidiary, First Financial Capital Advisors, acts as the investment advisor to the company's proprietary mutual funds, The First Funds Group.

	Annual Growth	12/05	12/06	12/07	12/08	12/09
Assets ($ mil.)	16.0%	3,690.8	3,301.6	3,369.3	3,699.1	6,681.1
Net income ($ mil.)	59.7%	37.9	21.3	35.7	23.0	246.5
Market value ($ mil.)	(4.5%)	1,013.5	960.9	659.5	716.8	842.3
Employees	2.2%	1,604	1,283	1,159	1,127	1,748

FIRST FINANCIAL BANKSHARES, INC.

NASDAQ (GS): FFIN

400 Pine St.
Abilene, TX 79601
Phone: 325-627-7155
Fax: 325-627-7393
Web: www.ffin.com

CEO: F. Scott Dueser
CFO: J. Bruce Hildebrand
HR: Pamela (Pam) Mann
FYE: December 31
Type: Public

Texas hold 'em? Well, sort of. First Financial Bankshares is the Texas-based holding company for First Financial Bankshares of Delaware, which in turn owns 10 banks consolidated under the First Financial brand and a trust company, all of which are located in small and midsized markets in North and West Texas. Together, they have about 50 locations. The company maintains a decentralized management structure, with each of the ten subsidiary banks having their own local leadership and decision-making authority. Its trust subsidiary, First Financial Trust & Asset Management, administers retirement and employee benefit plans in addition to providing trust services.

	Annual Growth	12/05	12/06	12/07	12/08	12/09
Assets ($ mil.)	4.7%	2,733.8	2,850.2	3,070.3	3,212.4	3,279.5
Net income ($ mil.)	5.2%	44.0	46.0	49.5	53.2	53.8
Market value ($ mil.)	11.5%	730.9	872.7	784.9	1,151.0	1,130.6
Employees	(0.6%)	975	975	975	1,000	950

FIRST FINANCIAL CORPORATION

NASDAQ (GS): THFF

1 First Financial Plaza
Terre Haute, IN 47807
Phone: 812-238-6000
Fax: 812-238-6140
Web: www.first-online.com

CEO: Norman L. Lowery
CFO: Rodger McHargue
HR: Karen Stinson
FYE: December 31
Type: Public

Which came first . . . the First Financial in Indiana, Rhode Island, Tennessee, Texas, or Wisconsin? Regardless, this particular First Financial Corporation is the holding company for First Financial Bank, which operates about 50 branches in west-central Indiana and east-central Illinois. With roots dating back to 1834, the banks offer traditional deposit services such as CDs and checking and savings accounts, as well as Internet banking. Residential mortgages account for about half of the company's loan portfolio. First Financial also operates an insurance agency and two investment subsidiaries.

	Annual Growth	12/05	12/06	12/07	12/08	12/09
Assets ($ mil.)	4.2%	2,136.9	2,176.0	2,231.6	2,302.7	2,518.7
Net income ($ mil.)	(0.4%)	23.1	23.5	25.6	24.8	22.7
Market value ($ mil.)	3.1%	354.0	464.8	371.6	537.5	400.2
Employees	0.7%	808	798	798	766	830

An in-depth profile of this company is available to Hoover's Online members at hoovers.com.

615

FIRST FINANCIAL HOLDINGS, INC.

NASDAQ (GS): FFCH

34 Broad St.
Charleston, SC 29401
Phone: 843-529-5933
Fax: 843-529-5883
Web: www.firstfinancialholdings.com

CEO: R. Wayne Hall
CFO: Blaise B. Bettendorf
HR: Jerry P. Gazes
FYE: September 30
Type: Public

First Financial Holdings serves the Carolinas through thrift subsidiary First Federal Savings and Loan of Charleston. With more than 65 branches (including more than a dozen in-store locations in Wal-Mart Supercenters and Lowe's and Kroger groceries), the bank offers checking and savings accounts, retirement accounts, and credit cards. One- to four-family residential mortgages make up about 40% of the company's loan portfolio, followed by commercial mortgages and land, home equity, mobile home, and consumer loans. Subsidiaries provide insurance, trust, asset management, and securities brokerage services.

	Annual Growth	9/05	9/06	9/07	9/08	9/09
Assets ($ mil.)	8.6%	2,522.4	2,658.1	2,711.4	2,974.0	3,510.3
Net income ($ mil.)	(62.8%)	26.2	27.6	25.1	22.6	0.5
Market value ($ mil.)	(15.2%)	509.7	565.5	517.0	432.7	263.9
Employees	6.6%	791	847	873	915	1,023

FIRST FINANCIAL NORTHWEST, INC.

NASDAQ (GS): FFNW

201 Wells Ave., South
Renton, WA 98057
Phone: 425-255-4400
Fax: 425-228-7227
Web: www.fsbnw.com

CEO: Victor Karpiak
CFO: Kari Stenslie
HR: Suzie Salle
FYE: December 31
Type: Public

Searching for green in The Evergreen State, First Financial Northwest is the holding company for First Savings Bank Northwest, a small community bank that serves King, Pierce, and other counties in western Washington. Through its single branch location, the bank offers deposit services like checking and savings accounts, as well as a variety of lending services. Almost half of First Savings Bank's loan portfolio consists of one- to four-family residential loans; other real estate loans include ones for construction and land development, commercial property, and multifamily residences. Because the bank focuses almost exclusively on real estate loans, it writes very few unsecured consumer and commercial loans.

	Annual Growth	12/05	12/06	12/07	12/08	12/09
Assets ($ mil.)	10.6%	879.7	1,004.7	1,140.9	1,244.4	1,315.3
Net income ($ mil.)	—	9.1	7.1	(4.0)	4.7	(40.7)
Market value ($ mil.)	(18.4%)	—	—	185.0	175.6	123.2
Employees	14.7%	—	—	79	101	104

FIRST FINANCIAL SERVICE CORPORATION

NASDAQ (GM): FFKY

2323 Ring Rd.
Elizabethtown, KY 42701
Phone: 270-765-2131
Fax: 270-765-2135
Web: www.ffsbky.com

CEO: B. Keith Johnson
CFO: Steven M. Zagar
HR: —
FYE: December 31
Type: Public

First Financial Service Corporation is the holding company for First Federal Savings Bank of Elizabethtown, which operates about 15 branches in nine central Kentucky cities. Founded in 1923, the bank offers CDs, IRAs, and savings, NOW, and money market accounts, primarily using deposit funds to originate commercial real estate loans (about 60% of its loan portfolio) and residential mortgages (about 20%). Other loans include home equity, consumer, and business loans. First Service Corporation of Elizabethtown, a subsidiary of the bank, sells investment products to the bank's customers.

	Annual Growth	12/05	12/06	12/07	12/08	12/09
Assets ($ mil.)	12.1%	766.5	822.8	872.7	1,017.0	1,209.5
Net income ($ mil.)	—	9.1	10.3	9.4	4.8	(6.7)
Market value ($ mil.)	(21.6%)	112.9	132.1	113.2	55.7	42.7
Employees	6.2%	262	277	277	321	333

FIRST FRANKLIN CORPORATION

NASDAQ (GM): FFHS

4750 Ashwood Dr.
Cincinnati, OH 45241
Phone: 513-469-8000
Fax: 513-469-5360
Web: www.franklinsavings.com

CEO: John J. (Jack) Kuntz
CFO: Daniel T. Voelpel
HR: Robert (Rob) Snyder
FYE: December 31
Type: Public

First Franklin is the holding company for The Franklin Savings and Loan Company, which serves individuals and businesses through nearly 10 branches in and around Cincinnati. Established in 1883, Franklin Savings offers standard retail banking services such as savings, checking, and money market accounts, as well as CDs, IRAs, and credit cards. Residential mortgage loans account for more than half of the company's loan portfolio, which also includes commercial real estate, construction, and consumer loans. First Franklin also has a 51% interest in DirectTeller Systems, a provider of software for the financial industry. Former long-time CEO Thomas Siemers owns about a quarter of First Franklin.

	Annual Growth	12/05	12/06	12/07	12/08	12/09
Assets ($ mil.)	0.4%	296.7	332.0	318.9	318.8	301.7
Net income ($ mil.)	—	1.2	1.4	0.5	(1.4)	(1.5)
Market value ($ mil.)	(15.9%)	27.0	26.1	16.9	6.7	13.5
Employees	11.2%	64	64	62	58	98

FIRST HARTFORD CORPORATION

Pink Sheets: FHRT

149 Colonial Rd.
Manchester, CT 06040
Phone: 860-646-6555
Fax: 860-646-8572
Web: firsthartford.com

CEO: Neil H. Ellis
CFO: Stuart I. Greenwald
HR: —
FYE: April 30
Type: Public

First Hartford puts real estate first. The company, operating through subsidiary First Hartford Realty, invests in and develops commercial and other real estate. Its portfolio is located primarily in the Northeast and includes shopping centers, a restaurant, and a business and technology school campus. First Hartford has also built single-family homes, public housing units, government facilities, and several industrial properties. It is a preferred developer for CVS Caremark in areas of Texas, New Jersey, New York, and Lousiana. The company's largest tenants include Stop & Shop, Big Y Foods, and Kmart. Subsidiary Lead Tech provides lead and asbestos inspection and remediation services.

	Annual Growth	4/05	4/06	4/07	4/08	4/09
Sales ($ mil.)	24.1%	6.5	33.9	12.2	11.9	15.4
Net income ($ mil.)	—	(0.7)	0.7	0.0	(1.3)	(4.1)
Market value ($ mil.)	(21.5%)	12.0	5.1	6.5	6.8	4.5
Employees	25.7%	30	32	65	59	75

⊞ FIRST HEALTH GROUP CORP.

3200 Highland Ave.
Downers Grove, IL 60515
Phone: 630-737-7900
Fax: —
Web: www.firsthealth.com

CEO: George E. Bennett
CFO: R. Blaine Faulkner II
HR: —
FYE: December 31
Type: Subsidiary

First Health Group wants to have the last word on managed care. The company provides a dizzying array of services to commercial and public health plans, self-insured employers, and third-party administrators (TPAs) throughout the US and in Puerto Rico. It provides administrative services, programs such as disease management and pharmacy benefit management, and a ready-made preferred provider organization. Clients such as large multistate companies who self-insure their employees' health benefits use First Health's PPO and its other services to run their programs. The company also serves federal employee health plans and workers' compensation programs. First Health Group is a subsidiary of Coventry Health Care.

	Annual Growth	12/04	12/05	12/06	12/07	12/08
Est. sales ($ mil.)	—	—	—	—	—	327.2
Employees	—	—	—	—	—	6,000

FIRST HORIZON NATIONAL CORPORATION

NYSE: FHN

165 Madison Ave.
Memphis, TN 38103
Phone: 901-523-4444
Fax: 901-523-4266
Web: www.fhnc.com

CEO: D. Bryan Jordan
CFO: William C. (BJ) Losch III
HR: John M. Daniel
FYE: December 31
Type: Public

First Horizon would like to be the first bank people think of in the Volunteer State. The company operates about 180 First Tennessee Bank branches in its home state and neighboring markets. It provides various financial services through three primary business segments: Regional Banking, Mortgage Banking, and Capital Markets. In addition to general banking services, the company also offers trust, brokerage, financial advisory, investment, and insurance services. Subsidiary FTN Financial performs securities sales and trading, fixed-income underwriting, and other investment banking services through nearly 20 offices in more than a dozen states, as well as Hong Kong and Tokyo.

	Annual Growth	12/05	12/06	12/07	12/08	12/09
Assets ($ mil.)	(8.1%)	36,579.1	37,918.3	37,015.5	31,022.0	26,068.7
Net income ($ mil.)	—	441.1	461.6	(170.1)	(192.0)	(258.4)
Market value ($ mil.)	(20.8%)	7,576.2	8,234.5	3,577.2	2,186.5	2,980.7
Employees	(32.3%)	26,676	12,398	10,130	6,266	5,598

FIRST INDUSTRIAL REALTY TRUST, INC.

NYSE: FR

311 S. Wacker Dr., Ste. 4000
Chicago, IL 60606
Phone: 312-344-4300
Fax: 312-922-6320
Web: www.firstindustrial.com

CEO: Bruce W. Duncan
CFO: Scott A. Musil
HR: John Potempa
FYE: December 31
Type: Public

First Industrial wants to be the first and only stop for your industrial property needs. As its name suggests, the self-administered real estate investment trust (REIT) owns, manages, and develops industrial real estate. Its portfolio consists of about 730 properties in the US and Canada, with the largest concentrations in Michigan, Texas, and Colorado. The REIT's more than 60 million sq. ft. of space is weighted toward light industrial properties but also includes bulk and regional warehouses, research and development buildings, and manufacturing facilities. Its tenants include manufacturing, retail, trade, and wholesale companies. First Industrial also builds customized spaces.

	Annual Growth	12/05	12/06	12/07	12/08	12/09
Sales ($ mil.)	2.9%	367.1	396.0	434.9	526.3	412.0
Net income ($ mil.)	(56.1%)	107.8	181.6	215.7	34.0	4.0
Market value ($ mil.)	(39.3%)	2,436.3	2,967.3	2,189.5	477.8	331.0
Employees	(15.1%)	441	500	518	340	229

FIRST INSURANCE COMPANY OF HAWAII, LTD.

1100 Ward Ave.
Honolulu, HI 96814
Phone: 808-527-7777
Fax: 808-543-3200
Web: www.ficoh.com

CEO: Allen B. Uyeda
CFO: —
HR: Theresa (Terri) Stephens
FYE: December 31
Type: Joint venture

They may be living in paradise, but even the island denizens of Hawaii need protection from life's rough waters. That's just what First Insurance Company of Hawaii aims to do by providing personal and commercial property/casualty coverage. The company is the leading property/casualty insurer in the island state and has been operating since 1911. Personal products include automobile, homeowners, and dwelling fire coverage, as well as home warranty and personal umbrella insurance. Commercial lines include commercial auto, general liability, property, surety, and workers' compensation insurance. The company is jointly owned by CNA Financial and Tokio Marine and Nichido Fire Insurance, a unit of Japan's Tokio Marine Holdings.

	Annual Growth	12/04	12/05	12/06	12/07	12/08
Est. sales ($ mil.)	—	—	—	—	—	156.3
Employees	—	—	—	—	—	310

FIRST INSURANCE FUNDING CORP.

450 Skokie Blvd., Ste. 1000
Northbrook, IL 60062
Phone: 847-374-3000
Fax: 800-837-3709
Web: www.firstinsurancefunding.com

CEO: Frank J. Burke
CFO: Michelle H. Perry
HR: —
FYE: December 31
Type: Subsidiary

If premium financing is the last thing you need, don't call First Insurance Funding. Working through independent insurance agents and brokers, First Insurance Funding provides loans to businesses to finance the cost of their commercial insurance, including liability and property/casualty coverage. Clients finance their insurance premiums to preserve cash flow, consolidate insurance payments, and to potentially realize a tax deduction on the loan interest. One of the largest insurance premium finance companies in the country, First Insurance Funding is a subsidiary of Illinois-based financial holding company Wintrust Financial.

	Annual Growth	12/04	12/05	12/06	12/07	12/08
Est. sales ($ mil.)	—	—	—	—	—	41.0
Employees	—	—	—	—	—	135

FIRST INTERSTATE BANCSYSTEM, INC.

NASDAQ (CM): FIBK

401 N. 31st St.
Billings, MT 59116
Phone: 406-255-5390
Fax: 406-255-5160
Web: www.firstinterstatebank.com

CEO: Lyle R. Knight
CFO: Terrill R. Moore
HR: —
FYE: December 31
Type: Public

This Treasure State bank wants to be your treasury. First Interstate BancSystem is the holding company for First Interstate Bank, which has around 70 branches in Montana, South Dakota, and Wyoming. It offers individuals, businesses, and municipalities traditional banking services, including deposit accounts, insurance, and agricultural, consumer, commercial, and mortgage loan products. It also offers trust and wealth management services. Commercial loans, including real estate loans, make up about 50% of the bank's loan portfolio; other loans include farm and home loans. First Interstate filed to go public in 2010.

	Annual Growth	12/05	12/06	12/07	12/08	12/09
Assets ($ mil.)	11.8%	4,562.3	4,974.1	5,216.8	6,628.3	7,137.7
Net income ($ mil.)	(0.4%)	54.7	75.6	68.6	70.6	53.9
Employees	2.4%	1,576	1,608	1,858	1,771	1,730

FIRST INVESTORS CORPORATION

110 Wall St.
New York, NY 10005
Phone: 212-858-8000
Fax: 212-858-8014
Web: www.firstinvestors.com

CEO: Kathryn S. Head
CFO: William M. Lipkus
HR: Karen Nelson
FYE: December 31
Type: Private

So maybe they weren't the very first investors, but they *have* been around for a while. Founded in 1930, First Investors oversees a variety of investment and insurance operations through its subsidiaries and affiliates. The company's products and services include mutual funds, life insurance, annuities, college savings plans, and retirement planning. First Investors also runs First Investors Federal Savings Bank, which serves as custodian for its clients' IRAs. The firm has more than $7 billion in assets under management and prides itself on its personal approach to investment management. First Investors has about 50 offices in more than two-dozen states.

An in-depth profile of this company is available to Hoover's Online members at hoovers.com.

617

FIRST INVESTORS FINANCIAL SERVICES

OTC: FIFS

675 Bering Dr., Ste. 710
Houston, TX 77057
Phone: 713-977-2600
Fax: 800-528-2384
Web: www.fifsg.com

CEO: Tommy A. Moore Jr.
CFO: Bennie H. Duck
HR: Mary Dela Cruz
FYE: April 30
Type: Public

They're not the first investors in the subprime auto loan market, but they're coming on. First Investors Financial Services Group, Inc., originates subprime auto loans (made to people with blemished or nonexistent credit) indirectly through auto dealers or directly to consumers. The dealer indirect program consists of loans originated through hundreds of franchised auto dealers in nearly 30 states. First Investors Financial Services drums up business for its direct lending through direct mail campaigns in about 15 states. The company also purchases portfolios of auto loans from other lenders. It has some 40,000 customers and $600 million in receivables. Texas is its largest market.

FIRST KEYSTONE CORPORATION

OTC: FKYS

111 W. Front St.
Berwick, PA 18603
Phone: 570-752-3671
Fax: 570-752-4022
Web: www.fnbbwk.com

CEO: J. Gerald Bazewicz
CFO: Diane C. A. Rosler
HR: —
FYE: December 31
Type: Public

First Keystone Corporation is not a group of fumbling and bumbling cops. It's the holding company for First Keystone National Bank, which serves individuals and businesses from more than a dozen locations in northeastern and central Pennsylvania. The bank provides traditional deposit products including checking and savings accounts, debit cards, and CDs; it also offers trust and investment advisory services. Commercial mortgages constitute more than half of the bank's loan portfolio; residential mortgages, business loans, and consumer installment loans make up the remainder. In 2007 the company acquired Pocono Community Bank, which still operates as a division of First Keystone National Bank.

	Annual Growth	12/05	12/06	12/07	12/08	12/09
Assets ($ mil.)	10.3%	512.4	525.9	681.2	714.9	758.3
Net income ($ mil.)	3.8%	6.8	6.2	6.1	7.6	7.9
Market value ($ mil.)	(3.1%)	104.9	97.9	86.0	78.9	92.5
Employees	6.9%	144	142	178	181	188

FIRST KEYSTONE FINANCIAL, INC.

NASDAQ (GM): FKFS

22 W. State St.
Media, PA 19063
Phone: 610-565-6210
Fax: 610-892-5150
Web: www.firstkeystone.com

CEO: Hugh J. Garchinsky
CFO: David M. Takats
HR: Carol Walsh
FYE: September 30
Type: Public

First Keystone wants to be the cornerstone of its customers' financial security. It is the holding company for First Keystone Federal Savings Bank, which serves the Keystone State's southeastern corner (a market area that includes Philadelphia and nearby Wilmington, Delaware) from about 10 offices. The bank offers standard deposit products and services such as checking and savings accounts, CDs, IRAs, and money market accounts, as well as credit cards, insurance, and investments. Single-family residential mortgages and home equity loans account for more than two-thirds of the company's loan portfolio. Bryn Mawr Bank Corporation is buying First Keystone, which will be folded into Bryn Mawr Trust.

	Annual Growth	9/05	9/06	9/07	9/08	9/09
Assets ($ mil.)	0.5%	518.1	523.0	524.9	522.1	528.4
Net income ($ mil.)	—	0.6	1.0	0.5	(1.0)	(1.6)
Market value ($ mil.)	(20.4%)	53.5	48.0	32.4	21.9	21.5
Employees	(2.6%)	112	128	110	106	101

FIRST LOOK STUDIOS, INC.

Pink Sheets: FRST

2000 Avenue of the Stars, Ste. 410
Century City, CA 90067
Phone: 424-202-5000
Fax: —
Web: www.firstlookmedia.com

CEO: Trevor Short
CFO: —
HR: —
FYE: December 31
Type: Public

Turn to these guys for a first look at the latest art film or second go 'round at *Baywatch*. First Look Studios provides film development, production and distribution, and foreign sales of its extensive film and television library, which has more than 700 titles, including *Waking Ned Devine* and *Baywatch*. More recent films include *Aqua Teen Hunger Force Colon Movie Film for Theaters* and *Paris, je t'aime*. The company operates in the home entertainment market through its First Look Home Entertainment subsidiary. It is owned by a group that includes the management team of independent studio Nu Image (Avi Lerner, Trevor Short, and Danny Dimbort).

FIRST M&F CORPORATION

NASDAQ (GS): FMFC

134 W. Washington St.
Kosciusko, MS 39090
Phone: 662-289-5121
Fax: 662-289-8084
Web: www.mfbank.com

CEO: Hugh S. Potts Jr.
CFO: John G. Copeland
HR: —
FYE: December 31
Type: Public

First M&F Corporation is the holding company for Merchants and Farmers Bank of Kosciusko, which operates nearly 50 branches in Alabama, Florida, Mississippi, and Tennessee. Merchants and Farmers offers a full range of commercial and consumer services, including trust services, credit cards, loans, and a variety of deposit products. Its lending activities consist of commercial real estate loans (60% of its loan book), residential mortgages, and consumer, business, and agricultural loans. First M&F also has subsidiaries, and affiliates that offer insurance and investment products, asset-based lending, property management, and factoring services. It provides investment services through UVEST Financial.

	Annual Growth	12/05	12/06	12/07	12/08	12/09
Assets ($ mil.)	7.0%	1,267.1	1,540.3	1,653.8	1,596.9	1,663.0
Net income ($ mil.)	—	12.6	13.9	14.5	0.5	(59.8)
Market value ($ mil.)	(39.8%)	152.9	177.7	143.3	76.7	20.0
Employees	2.1%	472	570	564	543	512

THE FIRST MARBLEHEAD CORPORATION

NYSE: FMD

The Prudential Tower, 800 Boylston St., 34th Fl.
Boston, MA 02199
Phone: 617-638-2000
Fax: 617-638-2100
Web: www.firstmarblehead.com

CEO: Daniel M. (Dan) Meyers
CFO: Kenneth S. (Ken) Klipper
HR: —
FYE: June 30
Type: Public

With a Harvard education costing six figures, that government student loan just isn't going to cut it anymore. Enter First Marblehead. The company creates programs and provides services for lenders and schools who offer private (not secured by the government) student loans for undergraduate, graduate, and professional education, and to a lesser extent, continuing education and study abroad programs. First Marblehead also provides marketing, servicing, and processing services; it has processed more than 1.4 million student loans. In response to deteriorating economic conditions and a decline in loan volume, the firm eliminated some 500 jobs (more than half of its personnel) in 2008.

	Annual Growth	6/05	6/06	6/07	6/08	6/09
Assets ($ mil.)	10.1%	558.2	770.3	1,214.5	1,200.9	821.3
Net income ($ mil.)	—	159.7	236.0	371.3	(235.1)	(363.0)
Market value ($ mil.)	(45.8%)	2,340.1	3,800.4	3,868.5	257.3	202.2
Employees	(28.3%)	842	932	1,042	376	223

An in-depth profile of this company is available to Hoover's Online members at hoovers.com.

FIRST MARINER BANCORP

NASDAQ (GM): FMAR

1501 S. Clinton St.
Baltimore, MD 21224
Phone: 410-342-2600
Fax: 410-563-1594
Web: www.1stmarinerbank.com

CEO: Edwin F. Hale Sr.
CFO: Paul B. Susie
HR: Lorraine Ash
FYE: December 31
Type: Public

First Mariner Bancorp helps customers navigate banking seas (and fees). It's the holding company for First Mariner Bank, which operates more than two-dozen branches along the Baltimore/Washington, DC, corridor. Targeting individuals and businesses, First Mariner Bank offers standard deposit products such as checking, savings, and money market accounts. Lending activities consist of commercial mortgages (more than 30% of all loans), as well as consumer, residential construction and mortgage, and business loans. Subsidiary First Mariner Mortgage originates mortgages for sale to secondary markets. First Mariner Bancorp sold consumer finance subsidiary Mariner Finance in 2009.

	Annual Growth	12/05	12/06	12/07	12/08	12/09
Assets ($ mil.)	0.4%	1,362.5	1,263.3	1,246.8	1,307.5	1,384.6
Net income ($ mil.)	—	7.8	1.9	(10.1)	(15.1)	(22.3)
Market value ($ mil.)	(51.7%)	309.3	327.9	100.2	12.7	16.8
Employees	6.8%	730	1,000	1,000	975	950

FIRST MERCHANTS CORPORATION

NASDAQ (GS): FRME

200 E. Jackson St.
Muncie, IN 47305
Phone: 765-747-1500
Fax: 765-747-1473
Web: www.firstmerchants.com

CEO: Michael C. (Mike) Rechin
CFO: Mark K. Hardwick
HR: Kimberly J. (Kim) Ellington
FYE: December 31
Type: Public

First Merchants makes community banking its first priority. The company owns First Merchants Bank, which operates some 80 branches in Indiana and western Ohio. The bank provides standard consumer and commercial banking services, including checking and savings accounts, CDs, and check cards. Loans secured by commercial real estate and farmland account for the largest portion of the company's loan portfolio (more than a third), followed by residential mortgages and business loans. First Merchants Corporation also owns First Merchants Trust Company, which provides trust and asset management services, and First Merchants Insurance Services, which sells personal, property/casualty, and employee benefit coverage.

	Annual Growth	12/05	12/06	12/07	12/08	12/09
Assets ($ mil.)	8.5%	3,237.1	3,554.9	3,782.1	4,784.2	4,481.0
Net income ($ mil.)	—	30.2	30.2	31.6	20.6	(40.8)
Market value ($ mil.)	(30.9%)	663.6	694.0	557.4	566.9	151.6
Employees	2.1%	1,109	1,131	1,121	1,367	1,207

FIRST MERCURY FINANCIAL CORPORATION

NYSE: FMR

29110 Inkster Rd., Ste. 100
Southfield, MI 48034
Phone: 248-358-4010
Fax: 248-358-2459
Web: www.firstmercury.com

CEO: Richard H. Smith
CFO: John A. Marazza
HR: —
FYE: December 31
Type: Public

First Mercury Financial Corporation (FMFC) would like to take after its namesake, the Roman god of commerce and profit, by capitalizing on its expertise in niche insurance markets. Through its CoverX and FM Emerald wholesale brokerages the company provides general and professional liability policies for businesses, with a special focus on the security industry — private investigators, security guards, armored car units, and the like. Its special general liability unit insures small to midsized building contractors, oil and gas contractors, and construction contractors. The company also provides professional liability coverage to the hospitality, outdoor recreation, and other industries.

	Annual Growth	12/05	12/06	12/07	12/08	12/09
Assets ($ mil.)	33.4%	365.6	512.9	747.3	943.7	1,157.6
Net income ($ mil.)	18.1%	22.8	21.9	41.7	40.8	44.4
Market value ($ mil.)	(16.5%)	—	416.8	432.4	252.7	243.0
Employees	27.7%	136	148	195	338	362

FIRST MID-ILLINOIS BANCSHARES, INC.

OTC: FMBH

1515 Charleston Ave.
Mattoon, IL 61938
Phone: 217-234-7454
Fax: 217-258-0426
Web: www.firstmid.com

CEO: William S. Rowland
CFO: Michael L. Taylor
HR: Kelly A. Downs
FYE: December 31
Type: Public

Money doesn't grow on trees, so when farmers in central Illinois need a little cash, they turn to First Mid-Illinois Bank & Trust. The primary subsidiary of First Mid-Illinois Bancshares is a major supplier of farm credit (including real estate, machinery, and production loans; inventory financing; and lines of credit) in its market area. In addition to agricultural loans, the bank also offers commercial, consumer, and real estate lending. It also provides deposit products such as savings and checking accounts, plus trust and investment services through a partnership with Raymond James. First Mid-Illinois, which has more than 25 branches, is buying about 10 more in northern Illinois from First Banks.

	Annual Growth	12/05	12/06	12/07	12/08	12/09
Assets ($ mil.)	6.5%	850.6	980.6	1,016.3	1,049.7	1,095.2
Net income ($ mil.)	(4.4%)	9.8	10.0	10.2	10.5	8.2
Market value ($ mil.)	(10.3%)	165.0	166.1	159.0	135.5	106.8
Employees	2.2%	318	347	346	343	347

FIRST MIDWEST BANCORP, INC.

NASDAQ (GS): FMBI

1 Pierce Place, Ste. 1500
Itasca, IL 60143
Phone: 630-875-7450
Fax: 630-875-7369
Web: www.firstmidwest.com

CEO: Michael L. Scudder
CFO: Paul F. Clemens
HR: —
FYE: December 31
Type: Public

There's a lot of cabbage in corn country. Just ask First Midwest Bancorp, holding company for First Midwest Bank. Through about 100 branches, the bank mainly serves suburban Chicago, though its market extends into central and western Illinois and neighboring portions of Iowa and Indiana. Focusing on area small to midsized businesses, it offers deposit products, loans, wealth management, and retirement plan services; it has approximately $3.5 billion of client trust and investment assets under management. Commercial real estate loans account for more than half of the company's portfolio; commercial and industrial loans are around 30%.

	Annual Growth	12/05	12/06	12/07	12/08	12/09
Assets ($ mil.)	1.7%	7,210.2	8,441.5	8,091.5	8,528.3	7,710.7
Net income ($ mil.)	—	101.4	117.2	80.2	49.3	(25.8)
Market value ($ mil.)	(25.3%)	2,596.2	2,864.2	2,265.9	1,478.8	806.4
Employees	2.1%	1,625	1,892	1,845	1,794	1,766

FIRST NATIONAL BANCSHARES, INC.

NASDAQ (GM): FNSC

215 N. Pine St.
Spartanburg, SC 29302
Phone: 864-948-9001
Fax: 864-281-0830
Web: www.firstnational-online.com

CEO: Jerry L. Calvert
CFO: Kitty B. Payne
HR: —
FYE: December 31
Type: Public

First National Bancshares is the holding company for First National Bank of the South. Also known as First National Bank of Spartanburg, the bank operates more than a half-dozen offices in South Carolina, offering checking, savings, and money market accounts, as well as trust and investment management services. Commercial real estate loans make up more than half of the bank's loan portfolio. First National Bancshares also operates a small business lending division, First National Business Capital. The company added four branches when it acquired Carolina National Corporation and its Carolina National Bank subsidiary in 2008.

	Annual Growth	12/05	12/06	12/07	12/08	12/09
Assets ($ mil.)	21.6%	328.7	465.4	586.5	812.7	717.7
Net income ($ mil.)	—	2.8	4.1	4.1	(44.8)	(43.7)
Market value ($ mil.)	(55.8%)	144.1	122.5	107.6	16.9	5.5
Employees	15.7%	77	102	136	156	138

An in-depth profile of this company is available to Hoover's Online members at hoovers.com.

FIRST NATIONAL BANK ALASKA
OTC: FBAK

101 W. 36th Ave.
Anchorage, AK 99503
Phone: 907-777-4362
Fax: 907-777-4569
Web: www.fnbalaska.com

CEO: Daniel H. Cuddy
CFO: Jason L. Roth
HR: —
FYE: December 31
Type: Public

First National Bank Alaska is a financial anchor in Anchorage. Founded in 1922, the bank (formerly The First National Bank of Anchorage) is one of the state's oldest and largest financial institutions. With about 30 branches throughout The Last Frontier (and about 20 ATMs in rural communities), the bank offers traditional deposit products such as checking, savings, and money market accounts; credit cards; and trust and escrow services. Commercial mortgages represent more than 35% of the bank's loan portfolio; commercial and industrial loans account for about another 25%. The family of longtime president Daniel Cuddy owns a majority of the company.

FIRST NATIONAL OF NEBRASKA, INC.
Pink Sheets: FINN

1620 Dodge St.
Omaha, NE 68197
Phone: 402-341-0500
Fax: 402-342-4332
Web: www.fnni.com

CEO: Bruce R. Lauritzen
CFO: Michael A. Summers
HR: —
FYE: December 31
Type: Public

It's not corny to say that First National of Nebraska is one of the largest community bank holding companies west of the Mississippi. It is the parent of about 10 western and midwestern banks, including First National Bank Omaha, First National Bank of Colorado, First National Bank South Dakota, First National Bank Southwest in Texas, and Illinois-based Castle Bank. All told, the company has more than 90 banking locations that offer deposits, loans, credit cards, and other traditional banking services for individuals and businesses alike, with an emphasis on agricultural lending. First National of Nebraska also owns several non-banking financial services subsidiaries operating throughout the US.

FIRST NATIONAL COMMUNITY BANCORP, INC.
OTC: FNCB

102 E. Drinker St.
Dunmore, PA 18512
Phone: 570-346-7667
Fax: 570-348-6426
Web: www.fncb.com

CEO: Gerard A. (Jerry) Champi
CFO: Eugene T. Sobol
HR: Robert J. Mancuso
FYE: December 31
Type: Public

First National Community Bancorp is the holding company for First National Community Bank, which has about 20 offices in Lackawanna, Luzerne, Wayne, and Monroe counties in northeastern Pennsylvania. The bank offers standard retail services such as checking and savings accounts, credit cards, mortgages, and other loans. Real estate loans account for approximately 65% of its loan portfolio, while commercial and industrial loans make up another 20%. Executives and directors of First National Community Bancorp collectively own nearly 30% of the company.

	Annual Growth	12/05	12/06	12/07	12/08	12/09
Assets ($ mil.)	8.5%	1,008.1	1,184.8	1,296.2	1,313.8	1,395.4
Net income ($ mil.)	—	11.2	13.5	14.7	15.1	(11.3)
Market value ($ mil.)	(25.4%)	317.3	377.6	309.7	176.9	98.0
Employees	5.8%	260	345	302	310	326

FIRST NIAGARA FINANCIAL GROUP, INC.
NASDAQ (GS): FNFG

726 Exchange St., Ste. 618
Buffalo, NY 14210
Phone: 716-625-7500
Fax: 716-625-8405
Web: www.fnfg.com

CEO: John R. Koelmel
CFO: Michael W. Harrington
HR: Elizabeth A. (Beth) Bauman
FYE: December 31
Type: Public

A lot of water and a few barrels have gone over Niagara Falls since First Niagara Bank was founded. Tracing its roots to 1870, the flagship subsidiary of acquisitive First Niagara Financial Group operates more than 250 branches across upstate New York and Pennsylvania, offering deposit and loan products, insurance, and investments. Commercial real estate loans and residential mortgages account for most of the bank's loan portfolio. Subsidiary First Niagara Commercial Bank accepts municipal deposits. First Niagara Financial entered the Pennsylvania market in a big way. It acquired more than 50 branches from PNC Financial in 2009; the following year it acquired bank holding company Harleysville National.

	Annual Growth	12/05	12/06	12/07	12/08	12/09
Assets ($ mil.)	16.0%	8,064.8	7,945.5	8,096.2	9,331.4	14,584.8
Net income ($ mil.)	(3.8%)	92.9	91.9	84.1	88.4	79.4
Market value ($ mil.)	(1.0%)	3,024.6	3,106.1	2,516.6	3,379.9	2,907.5
Employees	10.9%	1,984	1,922	1,824	1,909	3,000

FIRST NATIONAL CORPORATION
Pink Sheets: FXNC

112 W. King St.
Strasburg, VA 22657
Phone: 540-465-9121
Fax: 540-465-5946
Web: www.firstbank-va.com

CEO: Harry S. Smith
CFO: M. Shane Bell
HR: —
FYE: December 31
Type: Public

First National Corporation knows that being number one is always good. The financial institution is the holding company for First Bank, which has about a dozen branches in northern Virginia's Shenandoah Valley. The bank provides community-oriented deposit products and services, including checking and savings accounts, IRAs, money market accounts, CDs, and NOW accounts. Mortgages account for about 60% of the company's loan portfolio; it also provides business, construction, and consumer loans. Additionally, First Bank provides trust and asset management services.

	Annual Growth	12/05	12/06	12/07	12/08	12/09
Assets ($ mil.)	3.9%	475.0	527.9	541.6	548.2	552.7
Net income ($ mil.)	(21.0%)	5.4	5.8	5.7	4.2	2.1
Market value ($ mil.)	(22.0%)	79.4	79.3	66.1	47.7	29.4
Employees	5.8%	130	151	172	160	163

FIRST NORTHERN COMMUNITY BANCORP
OTC: FNRN

195 N. First St.
Dixon, CA 95620
Phone: 707-678-3041
Fax: 707-678-9734
Web: www.thatsmybank.com

CEO: Owen J. (John) Onsum
CFO: Louise A. Walker
HR: Larry Miller
FYE: December 31
Type: Public

First Northern Community Bancorp is the holding company for First Northern Bank, which operates about 10 branches in the northern California counties of El Dorado, Placer, Sacramento, Solano, and Yolo. Founded in 1910, the bank offers community-oriented services such as checking, savings, and money market accounts, and certificates of deposit. It also offers electronic check depositing. Its loan products include real estate mortgages (which account for about half of the bank's portfolio), commercial and construction loans, and agricultural and installment loans. Investment products and services are available to customers via a pact with Raymond James Financial.

	Annual Growth	12/05	12/06	12/07	12/08	12/09
Assets ($ mil.)	3.1%	660.6	685.2	709.9	670.8	747.6
Net income ($ mil.)	—	8.7	8.8	7.3	(1.4)	(1.1)
Market value ($ mil.)	(29.6%)	179.3	176.5	129.5	52.3	44.0
Employees	(0.5%)	236	242	243	228	231

THE FIRST OF LONG ISLAND CORPORATION

NASDAQ (CM): FLIC

10 Glen Head Rd.	CEO: Michael N. Vittorio
Glen Head, NY 11545	CFO: Mark D. Curtis
Phone: 516-671-4900	HR: —
Fax: 516-676-7900	FYE: December 31
Web: www.fnbli.com	Type: Public

When it comes to banking, The First of Long Island wants to be the first thing on Long Islanders' minds. The company owns The First National Bank of Long Island, which offers a variety of lending, investment, and deposit services through about two dozen branches on New York's Long Island and in Manhattan. Loans secured by real estate, including residential and commercial mortgages, home equity loans, and construction loans, make up more than 85% of the bank's loan portfolio. To a lesser extent, the bank also writes business and consumer loans. Other services include checking and savings accounts, IRAs, CDs, and credit cards. Subsidiary The First of Long Island Agency sells mutual funds and annuities.

	Annual Growth	12/05	12/06	12/07	12/08	12/09
Assets ($ mil.)	15.4%	944.2	954.2	1,069.0	1,261.6	1,675.2
Net income ($ mil.)	2.4%	12.3	11.2	11.5	13.0	13.5
Market value ($ mil.)	4.6%	153.2	159.4	134.6	172.3	183.2
Employees	4.3%	203	214	215	213	240

FIRST PACTRUST BANCORP, INC.

NASDAQ (GM): FPTB

610 Bay Blvd.	CEO: Hans R. Ganz
Chula Vista, CA 91910	CFO: Regan J. Lauer
Phone: 619-691-1519	HR: Lisa Moss
Fax: 619-691-1350	FYE: December 31
Web: www.firstpactrustbancorp.com	Type: Public

First PacTrust Bancorp is the holding company for Pacific Trust Bank, which operates about 10 branches in Southern California's Riverside and San Diego counties. The community bank offers standard services such as deposit accounts and real estate loans, with mortgages secured by one- to four-family residences accounting for nearly 60% of its loan portfolio. Multifamily residential and commercial mortgages and business, construction, and consumer loans round out its lending activities. The bank was founded in 1941 as Rohr Employees Federal Credit Union; a handful of former Rohr executives remain on First PacTrust's board of directors.

	Annual Growth	12/05	12/06	12/07	12/08	12/09
Assets ($ mil.)	4.3%	755.2	808.3	774.7	876.5	893.9
Net income ($ mil.)	—	4.8	4.7	3.0	(0.5)	(1.0)
Market value ($ mil.)	(33.4%)	148.2	150.9	99.2	52.5	29.1
Employees	(3.7%)	114	116	107	107	98

FIRST PHYSICIANS CAPITAL GROUP, INC.

OTC: TISG

433 N. Camden Dr. #810	CEO: David Hirschhorn
Beverly Hills, CA 90210	CFO: Donald C. (Donnie) Parkerson
Phone: 310-860-2501	HR: —
Fax: —	FYE: September 30
Web: www.firstphysicianscapitalgroup.com	Type: Public

First Physicians Capital Group (formerly Tri-Isthmus Group or TIGroup) is an investment and financing firm with an eye toward the health care industry. The group invests in and manages health care facilities, primarily rural critical access hospitals and ambulatory surgical centers. It owns or holds stakes in about a half-dozen medical facilities in Southern California and Oklahoma. In 2009 First Physicians Capital signed a letter of intent to acquire the assets of a hospital in southeastern Texas and to develop a new community hospital in the region. Oklahoma-based investor Carol Schuster owns more than 40% of the company's common stock. Director David Hirschhorn holds about 20%.

	Annual Growth	1/05	1/06	1/07	*9/08	9/09
Sales ($ mil.)	647.4%	—	—	0.7	29.6	39.1
Net income ($ mil.)	—	—	—	(1.6)	(4.2)	(10.1)
Market value ($ mil.)	30.9%	—	—	5.3	5.4	9.0
Employees	1,356.0%	—	—	2	3	424
					*Fiscal year change	

FIRST PLACE FINANCIAL CORP.

NASDAQ (GS): FPFC

185 E. Market St.	CEO: Steven R. Lewis
Warren, OH 44481	CFO: David W. Gifford
Phone: 330-373-1221	HR: Robert J. Kowalski
Fax: 330-393-5578	FYE: June 30
Web: www.firstplace.net	Type: Public

First Place Financial is the holding company for First Place Bank, which serves businesses and consumers through about 45 branch offices in the Midwest. First Place Bank has offices in northern and central Ohio, and its Franklin Bank division operates in Michigan. First Place Financial also operates some 20 loan production offices in Ohio, Michigan, North Carolina, and Indiana. Other subsidiaries include property management firms, insurance and title insurance agencies, real estate brokerage firms, and a wealth management firm. Commercial loans — primarily mortgages — make up about half of First Place Financial's loan portfolio; residential mortgages account for another third of loans.

	Annual Growth	6/05	6/06	6/07	6/08	6/09
Assets ($ mil.)	8.0%	2,498.9	3,113.2	3,226.2	3,341.0	3,404.5
Net income ($ mil.)	—	18.9	23.0	25.6	10.8	(110.4)
Market value ($ mil.)	(37.3%)	341.0	390.6	358.1	159.5	52.8
Employees	4.5%	774	868	870	938	924

FIRST POTOMAC REALTY TRUST

NYSE: FPO

7600 Wisconsin Ave., 11th Fl.	CEO: Douglas J. (Doug) Donatelli
Bethesda, MD 20814	CFO: Barry H. Bass
Phone: 301-986-9200	HR: —
Fax: 301-986-5554	FYE: December 31
Web: www.first-potomac.com	Type: Public

Will First Potomac Realty Trust build a portfolio as mighty as its namesake? The self-managed real estate investment trust (REIT) owns and manages more than 160 industrial properties and business parks in the Mid-Atlantic region, covering Washington, DC, Maryland, and Virginia. Its portfolio totals more than 11 million sq. ft. of space. As with many real estate firms located in the area, the REIT's largest tenant is the US government, which accounts for about 7% of its rental revenues; manufacturers account for about 25%. First Potomac Realty Trust generally purchases generous warehouse spaces and adds offices to add property value and increase revenue.

	Annual Growth	12/05	12/06	12/07	12/08	12/09
Sales ($ mil.)	14.6%	77.6	104.5	124.6	124.3	133.9
Net income ($ mil.)	30.8%	1.4	10.0	0.5	22.8	4.1
Market value ($ mil.)	(17.1%)	985.5	1,078.5	640.6	344.6	465.7
Employees	9.0%	99	119	131	137	140

FIRST QUALITY ENTERPRISES, INC.

80 Cuttermill Rd., Ste. 500	CEO: Kambiz Damaghi
Great Neck, NY 11021	CFO: —
Phone: 516-829-3030	HR: —
Fax: 516-829-4949	FYE: December 31
Web: www.firstquality.com	Type: Private

Typically, products that prevail are top in their class. First Quality Enterprises (FQE) is a group of companies that manufactures adult incontinence products under the Prevail brand name, Femtex and Opal brand tampons, and diapers, training pants, baby wipes, adult washcloths, and consumer paper products (bath tissue and paper towels). The consumer products maker distributes its sanitary goods to institutions, including long-term care and assisted living facilities, businesses, and retailers in the US and abroad. In addition to its branded products, FQE manufactures private-label goods for others. The firm, established in 1988, is managed and owned by several generations of the founding Damaghi family.

	Annual Growth	12/04	12/05	12/06	12/07	12/08
Est. sales ($ mil.)	—	—	—	—	—	37.8
Employees	—	—	—	—	—	300

An in-depth profile of this company is available to Hoover's Online members at hoovers.com.

621

FIRST REPUBLIC BANK

111 Pine St.
San Francisco, CA 94111
Phone: 415-392-1400
Fax: 415-392-1413
Web: www.firstrepublic.com

CEO: James H. Herbert II
CFO: Willis H. Newton Jr.
HR: —
FYE: December 31
Type: Subsidiary

First Republic Bank offers private banking, wealth management, trust, and brokerage services for businesses and high-net-worth clients though about 50 branches. About half are in Northern California, around the San Francisco Bay area, Silicon Valley, and the wine country; the rest are in Southern California, the Northeast, the Pacific Northwest, and Las Vegas. The bank's lending focuses on commercial and residential real estate and personal loans, including vacation home mortgages and aircraft and yacht financing. Bank of America, which assumed ownership of First Republic as part of its 2009 acquisition of Merrill Lynch, is selling the bank to an investor group led by General Atlantic and Colony Capital.

FIRST REPUBLIC PREFERRED CAPITAL CORPORATION   OTC: FRCCO

111 Pine St., 2nd Fl.
San Francisco, CA 94111
Phone: 415-392-1400
Fax: 415-392-1413

CEO: James J. Baumberger
CFO: Willis H. Newton Jr.
HR: —
FYE: December 31
Type: Public

First Republic Preferred Capital prefers mortgages to almost any other type of investment. The company is a real estate investment trust (REIT) that invests in conforming and nonconforming single-family residential mortgages originated by affiliate First Republic Bank and other lenders. Its portfolio of multifamily mortgages consists mainly of loans secured by urban properties in San Francisco and Los Angeles. California accounts for about 80% of its total portfolio. The company is also open to investing in commercial mortgages. Merrill Lynch, which acquired First Republic Preferred Capital and First Republic Bank in 2007, was bought by Bank of America in 2009.

FIRST RESERVE CORPORATION

1 Lafayette Place
Greenwich, CT 06830
Phone: 203-661-6601
Fax: 203-661-6729
Web: www.frcorp.com

CEO: William E. (Bill) Macaulay
CFO: Jennifer C. Zarrilli
HR: Maria Bliss
FYE: December 31
Type: Private

First Reserve Corporation fuels the companies that help fuel the world. The private equity firm invests in middle-market energy companies involved in such sectors as oilfield services, equipment and manufacturing, energy infrastructure and reserves, renewable and alternative energy, and energy-related insurance and financial products. First Reserve's investor base is primarily composed of corporations, endowments, foundations, governments, and public retirement funds. The company's current portfolio includes stakes in more than 30 firms, including Brand Energy & Infrastructure Services and Dresser.

FIRST REVENUE ASSURANCE CORPORATION

4500 Cherry Creek Dr. South, Ste. 450
Denver, CO 80246
Phone: 303-595-4400
Fax: 303-388-1372
Web: www.firstrevenue.com

CEO: Watse Krol
CFO: Tracy Norman
HR: Chris Barta
FYE: December 31
Type: Subsidiary

Revenue comes first with First Revenue Assurance. The debt collection agency provides accounts receivable management services, including skip tracing, debt collection, and call center support. It allows debtors to set up payment plans, make payments, and record disputes and bankruptcies from its website. First Revenue Assurance, which was established in 1997, was acquired by UK outsourcing firm Vertex (a subsidiary of Oak Hill Capital Partners) in 2004. First Revenue Assurance primarily serves clients in the telecommunications, financials services, and retail sectors. It collects between $4 million and $6 million monthly.

FIRST ROBINSON FINANCIAL CORPORATION   OTC: FRFC

501 E. Main St.
Robinson, IL 62454
Phone: 618-544-8621
Fax: 618-544-7506
Web: www.frsb.net

CEO: Rick L. Catt
CFO: Jamie E. McReynolds
HR: —
FYE: March 31
Type: Public

If heaven holds a place for those who pay, hey, hey, hey, then here's to you, First Robinson! First Robinson Financial is the holding company for First Robinson Savings Bank, which provides traditional banking services to individuals and businesses through four locations in eastern Illinois' Crawford County. In 2008 the bank opened a division in Vincennes, Indiana, called First Vincennes Savings Bank. The banks' services include savings, checking, and NOW accounts; IRAs; and CDs. They use funds from deposits primarily to originate one- to four-family real estate loans (accounting for about half of the company's loan portfolio), and to a lesser extent, consumer, business, agricultural, and municipal loans.

	Annual Growth	3/05	3/06	3/07	3/08	3/09
Assets ($ mil.)	10.2%	111.4	109.4	112.3	133.8	164.4
Net income ($ mil.)	(2.9%)	0.9	1.0	1.0	1.0	0.8
Market value ($ mil.)	9.3%	10.6	10.9	14.9	15.5	15.2
Employees	1.5%	49	45	42	48	52

FIRST SAVINGS FINANCIAL GROUP, INC.   NASDAQ (CM): FSFG

501 E. Lewis and Clark Pkwy.
Clarksville, IN 47129
Phone: 812-283-0724
Fax: 812-288-2558
Web: www.fsbbank.net

CEO: Larry W. Myers
CFO: Anthony A. (Tony) Schoen
HR: —
FYE: September 30
Type: Public

First Savings Financial Group was formed in 2008 to be the holding company for First Savings Bank, a community bank serving consumers and small businesses in southern Indiana. Through more than a dozen branches, the bank offers standard deposit services like savings, checking, and retirement accounts, as well as a variety of lending services. One- to four- family residential loans make up about 60% of First Savings Bank's loan portfolio; other loans in the bank's portfolio include commercial real estate, construction, consumer, and commercial business. In 2009 the company bought Community First Bank, which kept its name after the acquisition and now operates as a division of First Savings Bank.

	Annual Growth	9/05	9/06	9/07	9/08	9/09
Assets ($ mil.)	23.6%	205.8	206.4	203.3	228.9	480.8
Net income ($ mil.)	—	1.2	0.4	0.8	(0.2)	0.0
Market value ($ mil.)	—	—	—	—	—	25.8
Employees	37.1%	—	—	84	80	158

FIRST SECURITY GROUP, INC.

NASDAQ (GS): FSGI

531 Broad St.
Chattanooga, TN 37402
Phone: 423-266-2000
Fax: 423-267-3383
Web: www.fsgbank.com

CEO: Rodger B. Holley
CFO: William L. (Chip) Lusk Jr.
HR: —
FYE: December 31
Type: Public

Pardon me boy, as Glenn Miller would say, but if you've got your fare and a trifle to spare, you might want to turn to First Security Group. The holding company for FSGBank operates about 40 branches in eastern and middle Tennessee (including Chattanooga) and northern Georgia; in addition to the FSGBank brand, the company also operates certain locations under the Dalton Whitfield Bank, Jackson Bank & Trust, and Primer Banco Seguro names. The bank offers standard deposit and lending services, including checking and savings accounts and CDs. Real estate loans and mortgages make up about three-quarters of First Security's loan portfolio, which also includes business, agricultural, and consumer loans.

	Annual Growth	12/05	12/06	12/07	12/08	12/09
Assets ($ mil.)	6.8%	1,040.7	1,129.8	1,212.0	1,276.2	1,353.8
Net income ($ mil.)	—	7.4	11.1	11.4	1.4	(33.0)
Market value ($ mil.)	(29.7%)	159.9	189.3	147.4	75.9	39.1
Employees	(0.7%)	366	376	355	372	356

FIRST SOLAR, INC.

NASDAQ (GS): FSLR

350 W. Washington St., Ste. 600
Tempe, AZ 85281
Phone: 602-414-9300
Fax: 602-414-9400
Web: www.firstsolar.com

CEO: Robert J. (Rob) Gillette
CFO: Jens Meyerhoff
HR: Carol Campbell
FYE: December 31
Type: Public

Like the ancient Egyptians who worshiped Ra, First Solar looks to the sun for rising fortunes. The company manufactures photovoltaic (PV) modules for converting sunlight into electricity. Using a thin-film semiconductor process, a piece of glass is transformed into a complete solar module in less than three hours. The technology is cheaper and produces more electricity under real-world conditions than conventional solar panels with similar power ratings. Founded in Ohio, more than 90% of its sales come from outside of the US, primarily from solar project developers and system integrators in Germany, France, Italy, and Spain. First Solar also provides solar power plant project development services.

	Annual Growth	12/05	12/06	12/07	12/08	12/09
Sales ($ mil.)	156.0%	48.1	135.0	504.0	1,246.3	2,066.2
Net income ($ mil.)	—	(6.6)	4.0	158.4	348.3	640.1
Market value ($ mil.)	65.6%	—	2,545.1	22,784.7	11,766.8	11,548.4
Employees	65.0%	634	723	1,462	3,524	4,700

FIRST SOUTH BANCORP, INC.

NASDAQ (GS): FSBK

1311 Carolina Ave.
Washington, NC 27889
Phone: 252-946-4178
Fax: 252-946-3873
Web: www.firstsouthnc.com

CEO: Thomas A. Vann
CFO: William L. (Bill) Wall
HR: —
FYE: December 31
Type: Public

First South Bancorp (not to be confused with the South Carolina company of the same name) is the holding company for First South Bank. Founded in 1902, the bank has about 30 offices throughout the eastern half of North Carolina. Its deposit products include checking, savings, and money market accounts; CDs; and IRAs; these are used to fund a variety of loans. Commercial real estate loans comprise more than half of the bank's loan portfolio, which is rounded out by construction loans (more than 20%), residential mortgages, home equity loans, and business and consumer loans. Retail investment services are offered through a pact with UVEST; bank subsidiary First South Leasing provides equipment lease financing.

	Annual Growth	12/05	12/06	12/07	12/08	12/09
Assets ($ mil.)	(0.1%)	833.1	910.5	909.3	—	829.9
Net income ($ mil.)	(16.1%)	14.1	17.2	17.0	—	7.0
Market value ($ mil.)	(18.7%)	229.4	310.7	216.2	—	100.4
Employees	2.5%	252	294	287	303	278

FIRST STATE BANCORPORATION

NASDAQ (GS): FSNM

7900 Jefferson NE
Albuquerque, NM 87109
Phone: 505-241-7500
Fax: 505-241-7572
Web: www.fsbnm.com

CEO: H. Patrick Dee
CFO: Christopher C. Spencer
HR: —
FYE: December 31
Type: Public

First State Bancorporation is the holding company for First Community Bank, which operates about 40 branches in New Mexico and Arizona. Founded as First State Bank in 1922, First Community Bank provides retail services such as checking and savings accounts, money market accounts, CDs, and credit cards. The bank's lending activities are focused on residential real estate and construction, which together account for about three-fourths of the loan portfolio. First State Bancorporation has grown by acquiring other, smaller financial companies in the area; it expanded into Arizona in 2006 and into Colorado the following year. To raise capital, the company sold its Colorado branches and exited the market in 2009.

	Annual Growth	12/05	12/06	12/07	12/08	12/09
Assets ($ mil.)	6.2%	2,157.6	2,801.6	3,424.2	3,415.0	2,744.4
Net income ($ mil.)	—	21.4	22.8	24.8	(153.6)	(110.5)
Market value ($ mil.)	(64.1%)	499.1	514.9	289.2	34.3	8.3
Employees	(4.9%)	663	864	903	813	542

FIRST STUDENT INC.

705 Central Ave., Ste. 300
Cincinnati, OH 45202
Phone: 513-241-2200
Fax: 513-381-0149
Web: www.firststudentinc.com

CEO: Linda Burtwistle
CFO: Dean Suhre
HR: —
FYE: March 31
Type: Subsidiary

School bus operator First Student knows that a student's first assignment is to get to school. Together, First Student and sister company FirstCanada transports about 4 million students to and from their classrooms every day via a fleet of about 60,000 buses. Combined, the companies represent North America's #1 school bus business. They operate from a network of more than 650 locations, spanning 40 states in the US and about 10 provinces in Canada. First Student is a subsidiary of FirstGroup America, which in turn is a unit of UK-based bus and train operator FirstGroup.

FIRST TRUST BANK

OTC: NCFT

1420 E. Third St.
Charlotte, NC 28204
Phone: 704-377-3936
Fax: 704-377-8869
Web: www.firsttrustnc.com

CEO: Jim Bolt
CFO: Jean Galloway
HR: —
FYE: December 31
Type: Public

Tar Heels might put their trust in First Trust Bank. It provides retail and commercial banking services through five locations in the North Carolina communities of Charlotte, Concord, Monroe, and Mooresville. The bank provides standard deposit services and products, including checking and savings accounts, IRAs, CDs, and debit cards. Commercial mortgages make up approximately half of First Trust Bank's loan portfolio, followed by construction and land development loans (more than a quarter) and commercial and industrial loans (about 15%). Residential mortgages, farmland loans, and personal loans round out the bank's lending activities.

FIRST UNITED CORPORATION

NASDAQ (GM): FUNC

19 S. 2nd St.
Oakland, MD 21550
Phone: 301-334-9471
Fax: 301-334-2318
Web: www.mybankfirstunited.com

CEO: William B. Grant
CFO: Carissa L. Rodeheaver
HR: Jeannette R. Fitzwater
FYE: December 31
Type: Public

First United is the holding company for First United Bank & Trust and other financial services subsidiaries. Founded in 1900, the bank operates about 25 branches in the panhandles of western Maryland and eastern West Virginia, as well as the Morgantown, West Virginia, area. The bank provides standard services such as checking and savings accounts, money market accounts, and CDs, as well as retirement and trust services. Commercial loans make up the largest portion of the company's loan portfolio (more than 45%), followed by real estate mortgages (more than 35%), consumer installment loans, and construction loans.

	Annual Growth	12/05	12/06	12/07	12/08	12/09
Assets ($ mil.)	7.4%	1,311.0	1,349.3	1,478.9	1,639.1	1,743.7
Net income ($ mil.)	—	12.2	12.6	12.8	8.9	(11.3)
Market value ($ mil.)	(27.1%)	130.5	134.6	123.0	82.8	36.9
Employees	2.1%	449	463	472	485	487

FIRST WEST VIRGINIA BANCORP, INC.

NYSE Amex: FWV

1701 Warwood Ave.
Wheeling, WV 26003
Phone: 304-277-1100
Fax: 304-277-4705
Web: www.progbank.com

CEO: Sylvan J. Dlesk
CFO: Francie P. Reppy
HR: Stephanie A. LaFlam
FYE: December 31
Type: Public

First, West Virginia, and then the world! First West Virginia Bancorp is the holding company for Progressive Bank, which operates about ten branches in the upper Ohio River Valley of the Mountaineer State and neighboring parts of eastern Ohio. Targeting individuals and local businesses, the bank offers standard retail products like checking and savings accounts, certificates of deposit, and individual retirement accounts. Lending activities consist primarily of commercial and residential real estate mortgages (which together account for approximately two-thirds of the company's loan portfolio), but Progressive Bank also originates business, consumer, and municipal loans.

	Annual Growth	12/05	12/06	12/07	12/08	12/09
Assets ($ mil.)	0.5%	266.2	254.4	253.2	258.2	271.1
Net income ($ mil.)	0.0%	2.3	2.1	2.0	2.2	2.3
Market value ($ mil.)	(10.4%)	29.6	30.2	22.6	20.8	19.1
Employees	0.2%	111	125	106	108	112

FIRSTBANK CORPORATION

NASDAQ (GS): FBMI

311 Woodworth Ave.
Alma, MI 48801
Phone: 989-463-3131
Fax: 989-466-2042
Web: www.firstbankmi.com

CEO: Thomas R. (Tom) Sullivan
CFO: Samuel G. Stone
HR: David L. Miller
FYE: December 31
Type: Public

Firstbank Corporation is the holding company for six separately chartered subsidiary banks offering services under the Firstbank banner; it also owns Keystone Community Bank, which it acquired in 2005. Through more than 50 branches in Michigan's Lower Peninsula, the banks attract deposits from area residents and businesses by providing standard services such as checking and savings accounts and CDs. The company also owns subsidiaries that provide real estate appraisal services, armored car services, and title insurance. Firstbank bought another Michigan-based bank holding company, ICNB Financial, parent of Ionia County Community Bank (now Firstbank – West Michigan), in 2007.

	Annual Growth	12/05	12/06	12/07	12/08	12/09
Assets ($ mil.)	8.7%	1,061.1	1,095.1	1,365.7	1,425.3	1,482.4
Net income ($ mil.)	(28.1%)	10.1	10.2	8.4	0.7	2.7
Market value ($ mil.)	(21.4%)	171.5	165.0	107.2	62.5	65.3
Employees	3.6%	405	405	492	483	466

FIRSTCITY FINANCIAL CORPORATION

NASDAQ (GS): FCFC

6400 Imperial Dr.
Waco, TX 76712
Phone: 254-761-2800
Fax: —
Web: www.fcfc.com

CEO: James T. Sartain
CFO: J. Bryan Baker
HR: —
FYE: December 31
Type: Public

FirstCity Financial helps loans deal with performance issues. Through operating subsidiaries, FirstCity Financial buys, manages, and sells primarily non-performing loans from financial institutions, government agencies, and other lenders. It buys typically buys nonperforming loans at a deep discount but buys performing loans, as well. The company or one of its affiliates services the loans it acquires. FirstCity Financial manages a portfolio worth approximately $11 billion. In addition to buying loans, the company invests in special situations such as restructurings, turnarounds, and executive buyouts through its majority-owned FirstCity Denver subsidiary.

	Annual Growth	12/05	12/06	12/07	12/08	12/09
Sales ($ mil.)	24.9%	36.1	42.6	54.6	45.4	87.9
Net income ($ mil.)	22.9%	8.2	9.8	2.2	(46.7)	18.7
Market value ($ mil.)	(10.3%)	115.4	110.9	81.4	19.9	74.9
Employees	14.3%	214	208	241	265	365

⊞ FIRSTENERGY CORP.

NYSE: FE

76 S. Main St.
Akron, OH 44308
Phone: 800-633-4766
Fax: 330-384-3866
Web: www.firstenergycorp.com

CEO: Anthony J. Alexander
CFO: Mark T. Clark
HR: Dennis L. Dabney
FYE: December 31
Type: Public

FirstEnergy's first goal is to deliver power, but its second goal is to survive deregulation. Its utilities provide electricity to 4.5 million customers in Ohio, Pennsylvania, and New Jersey, three states that are ushering in power-industry competition. The company's domestic power plants have a total generating capacity of more than 14,000 MW, most generated by coal-fired plants. Subsidiary FirstEnergy Solutions trades energy commodities in deregulated US markets, and has more than 120,000 accounts. FirstEnergy's other nonregulated operations include electrical and mechanical contracting and energy planning and procurement. In 2010 the company agreed to acquire Allegheny Energy in a $8.5 billion deal.

	Annual Growth	12/05	12/06	12/07	12/08	12/09
Sales ($ mil.)	2.0%	11,989.0	11,501.0	12,802.0	13,627.0	12,967.0
Net income ($ mil.)	3.1%	891.0	1,254.0	1,309.0	1,342.0	1,006.0
Market value ($ mil.)	(1.3%)	14,933.9	18,381.6	22,051.8	14,808.9	14,159.6
Employees	(2.1%)	14,586	13,739	14,534	14,698	13,379

FIRSTGROUP AMERICA, INC

600 Vine St., Ste. 1400
Cincinnati, OH 45202
Phone: 513-241-2200
Fax: 513-419-3242
Web: www.firstgroupamerica.com

CEO: Michael C. (Mike) Murray
CFO: Mark Lawton
HR: Brad Jokovich
FYE: March 31
Type: Subsidiary

If the trip is by bus, FirstGroup America aims to be the first option. Its First Student unit and sister company FirstCanada provide school bus services under contracts with districts throughout the US and Canada. FirstGroup America's First Transit unit manages bus systems for transit agencies and private companies in the US and Puerto Rico, and First Services provides maintenance and asset management for vehicle fleet operators. The company's Greyhound unit is North America's leading intercity bus company. Overall FirstGroup America has a fleet of about 70,000 buses. The company is a subsidiary of FirstGroup plc, a leading UK bus and train operator.

	Annual Growth	3/05	3/06	3/07	3/08	3/09
Sales ($ mil.)	26.1%	1,250.8	1,437.3	1,575.5	6,618.4	3,160.2
Employees	—	—	—	—	—	—

An in-depth profile of this company is available to Hoover's Online members at hoovers.com. ⊞

FIRSTMERIT CORPORATION

NASDAQ (GS): FMER

3 Cascade Plaza, 7th Fl.
Akron, OH 44308
Phone: 330-996-6300
Fax: —
Web: www.firstmerit.com

CEO: Paul G. Greig
CFO: Terrence E. Bichsel
HR: Christopher J. Maurer
FYE: December 31
Type: Public

FirstMerit Corporation is the holding company for FirstMerit Bank, which provides retail and commercial banking services through more than 150 branches in Ohio and western Pennsylvania, and about another 50 in the Chicago area. Serving local consumers and small to midsized businesses, it provides standard services such as deposit accounts, credit and debit cards, and loans. The bank and its subsidiaries also offer wealth management, securities brokerage, equipment lease financing, insurance, and trust services. FirstMerit entered the Chicago market in early 2010 by buying some two-dozen branches there from First Banks. It had already acquired most of that company's asset-based lending portfolio.

	Annual Growth	12/05	12/06	12/07	12/08	12/09
Assets ($ mil.)	0.9%	10,161.3	10,252.6	10,400.7	11,100.0	10,539.9
Net income ($ mil.)	(10.9%)	130.5	94.9	123.0	119.5	82.2
Market value ($ mil.)	(5.8%)	2,329.1	2,170.0	1,798.7	1,850.9	1,836.5
Employees	(4.9%)	3,050	2,755	2,755	2,575	2,495

FIRSTPOINT, INC

225 Commerce Pl.
Greensboro, NC 27401
Phone: 336-378-6270
Fax: —
Web: www.firstpointresources.com

CEO: Michael F. Bumpass
CFO: Dan Barbour
HR: —
FYE: December 31
Type: Holding company

FirstPoint is happy being first to point the finger. The financial and credit services holding company offers accounts receivable management and collection services through a family of companies including FirstPoint Collection Resources, Equifax, and Checkfax, which offers check warranty, verification, and collection. Other divisions include Insight (pre-employment screening), Rentfacts (tenant screening), and Customer 1st (mystery shopping service). FirstPoint also offers association management and residential mortgage reports. The divisions previously operated independently under separate business names but were united in 2001 under the FirstPoint umbrella.

	Annual Growth	12/04	12/05	12/06	12/07	12/08
Est. sales ($ mil.)	—	—	—	—	—	8.2
Employees	—	—	—	—	—	200

FIRSTWAVE TECHNOLOGIES, INC.

Pink Sheets: FSTW

7000 Central Pkwy., Ste. 330
Atlanta, GA 30328
Phone: 678-672-3100
Fax: 678-672-3130
Web: www.firstwave.com

CEO: Richard T. Brock
CFO: —
HR: —
FYE: December 31
Type: Public

Firstwave Technologies doesn't want you using second-hand, antiquated methods of managing customers and relationships. The company provides customer relationship management (CRM) software that helps marketing, sales, and customer service personnel generate sales leads, manage marketing campaigns, collect customer information, and share account information securely over the Web. Firstwave also offers industry-specific versions of its products. The company was founded in 1984 and services customers in industries including communications, financial services, manufacturing, and retail.

FISERV, INC.

NASDAQ (GS): FISV

255 Fiserv Dr.
Brookfield, WI 53045
Phone: 262-879-5000
Fax: 262-879-5013
Web: www.fiserv.com

CEO: Jeffery W. (Jeff) Yabuki
CFO: Thomas J. Hirsch
HR: Lance F. Drummond
FYE: December 31
Type: Public

It's 10:30, America. Do you know where your money is? Fiserv does. The company provides information management and electronic commerce services including transaction processing, electronic billing and payments, and business process outsourcing. Its clients include banks, lenders, credit unions, insurance firms, merchants, government agencies, and leasing companies. Fiserv operates in two primary business segments — financial institution services and payments and industry products (via its CheckFree business, acquired in 2007). It sold the bulk of its insurance services business in 2009. The company primarily operates in the US but has offices in about 20 other countries.

	Annual Growth	12/05	12/06	12/07	12/08	12/09
Sales ($ mil.)	0.1%	4,059.5	4,544.2	3,922.0	4,739.0	4,077.0
Net income ($ mil.)	(2.0%)	516.4	449.9	439.0	569.0	476.0
Market value ($ mil.)	2.9%	6,603.4	7,999.8	8,468.3	5,550.4	7,398.5
Employees	(2.4%)	22,000	23,000	25,000	20,000	20,000

FISHER COMMUNICATIONS, INC.

NASDAQ (GM): FSCI

100 4th Ave. North, Ste. 510
Seattle, WA 98109
Phone: 206-404-7000
Fax: 206-404-6037
Web: www.fsci.com

CEO: Colleen B. Brown
CFO: Joseph L. (Joe) Lovejoy
HR: Karen L. Aliabadi
FYE: December 31
Type: Public

Fisher Communications not only broadcasts to the sleepless in Seattle, but also Oregon and Idaho. The company owns and operates more than a dozen full-power television stations serving markets in California, Idaho, Oregon, and Washington, including the Seattle metropolitan area. Its stations are mostly affiliated with broadcast networks ABC and CBS, as well as Hispanic networks TeleFutura and Univision (both owned by Univision Communications). In addition to its portfolio of TV stations, Fisher operates almost 10 radio stations serving listeners in Great Falls, Montana, and Seattle. It also owns and operates Fisher Plaza, a high-tech office park located near downtown Seattle.

	Annual Growth	12/05	12/06	12/07	12/08	12/09
Sales ($ mil.)	(2.7%)	149.3	154.7	160.4	173.8	133.7
Net income ($ mil.)	—	(5.1)	16.8	31.9	44.7	(9.3)
Market value ($ mil.)	(20.9%)	363.8	388.2	333.3	181.3	142.7
Employees	(2.6%)	931	812	882	776	837

FISHER CONTROLS INTERNATIONAL LLC

301 S. 1st Ave.
Marshalltown, IA 50158
Phone: 641-754-3011
Fax: 641-754-2830
Web: www.emersonprocess.com/Fisher

CEO: Terry Buzbee
CFO: —
HR: —
FYE: September 30
Type: Subsidiary

Fisher Controls International has control issues, all around the world. The subsidiary of Emerson's Process Management segment manufactures control valves and regulators for the chemical, food & beverage, oil & gas, life sciences, LNG, power, pulp & paper, refining, and water & wastewater industries. Its products include valve positioners, steam conditioning equipment, ball valves, regulators, oil and gas control equipment, and sliding stem valves and actuators. It maintains operations in the US as well as in Asia and Europe. Fisher Controls dates back to the late 19th century and was family-controlled until sold to Monsanto in 1969; the company became a part of Emerson in 1992.

	Annual Growth	9/04	9/05	9/06	9/07	9/08
Est. sales ($ mil.)	—	—	—	—	—	794.6
Employees	—	—	—	—	—	7,400

FISHER INVESTMENTS

13100 Skyline Blvd.
Woodside, CA 94062
Phone: 800-587-5512
Fax: 650-529-1341
Web: www.fi.com

CEO: Kenneth L. (Ken) Fisher
CFO: —
HR: —
FYE: December 31
Type: Private

Established in 1979, Fisher Investments is a private money management firm serving *Fortune* 500 companies, foundations, and endowments, as well as wealthy individuals with at least $500,000 to invest. The firm is active in the US and in the UK, where it operates through subsidiary Fisher Wealth Management. In Germany, Fisher does business through its joint-venture affiliate, Grüner Fisher Investments. At the helm of Fisher Investments is founder, CEO, and chief investment officer Ken Fisher, who has authored several books on investing and has written the "Portfolio Strategy" column for *Forbes* magazine for more than 20 years.

	Annual Growth	12/04	12/05	12/06	12/07	12/08
Est. sales ($ mil.)	—	—	—	—	—	26.1
Employees	—	—	—	—	—	182

FISK UNIVERSITY

1000 17th Ave. North
Nashville, TN 37208
Phone: 615-329-8500
Fax: —
Web: www.fisk.edu

CEO: Hazel R. O'Leary
CFO: Spence Maners
HR: Marie Lang
FYE: June 30
Type: School

Fisk University is a predominantly African-American liberal arts university with an enrollment of around 1,000 students. Notable alumni include W. E. B. Du Bois and Booker T. Washington, as well as poets James Weldon Johnson and Nikki Giovanni (now a professor at Virginia Tech). It has 25 majors and pre-professional certification programs. The oldest university in Nashville, Fisk was founded in 1866 as an institution of higher learning committed to educating the country's newly freed slaves. It is affiliated with the United Church of Christ.

FISKARS BRANDS, INC.

2537 Daniels St.
Madison, WI 53718
Phone: 608-259-1649
Fax: 608-294-4790
Web: www.fiskarsbrands.com

CEO: Kari Kauniskangas
CFO: —
HR: —
FYE: December 31
Type: Subsidiary

Fiskars Brands is fairly frisky in its old age. It is a subsidiary of the Finnish company Fiskars Corporation — the second-oldest incorporated firm in the world, having celebrated some 350 anniversaries. Fiskars Brands caters to the craft, garden, housewares, and outdoor recreation markets through its portfolio of products. While orange-handled scissors are a signature product of its top-selling Fiskars brand, the company also manufactures cutting tools under the Leborgne and Montana brands; gardening products under Ebert and Werga; camping and recreation supplies under the Brunton and Gerber names; and sewing gadgets by Gingher.

FITCH

585 S. Front St., Ste. 50
Columbus, OH 43065
Phone: 614-885-3453
Fax: 614-885-4289
Web: www.fitch.com

CEO: Rodney Fitch
CFO: —
HR: Kay Levelle
FYE: December 31
Type: Subsidiary

This firm helps market its clients through all the senses. Not to be confused with the credit rating agency, Fitch is a leading brand development and communications agency that specializes in creating unique consumer experiences for its mostly retail clients. It offers creative services for corporate identity and communications collateral, as well as product and packaging design. Fitch also provides architectural services for interior and exterior store designs, and it develops events and displays that allow customers to experience brands first-hand. The firm offers digital and interactive marketing services. Working from offices in a dozen countries, it is a unit of UK-based advertising conglomerate WPP Group.

	Annual Growth	12/04	12/05	12/06	12/07	12/08
Est. sales ($ mil.)	—	—	—	—	—	0.2
Employees	—	—	—	—	—	1

FITCH RATINGS INC.

1 State Street Plaza
New York, NY 10004
Phone: 212-908-0500
Fax: 212-480-4435
Web: www.fitchratings.com

CEO: Stephen W. Joynt
CFO: David Kennedy
HR: —
FYE: December 31
Type: Subsidiary

Because governments can have lousy credit, too. Fitch Ratings, one of the top three credit rating agencies in the world (alongside Moody's and Standard & Poor's), issues ratings for thousands of banks, financial institutions, insurance companies, corporations, and governments. With dual headquarters in New York and London and about 50 offices worldwide, Fitch Ratings engages in the politically charged business of rating the debt of nations; it covers companies and governments in more than 90 nations. French holding company Fimalac owns 60% of Fitch Ratings; The Hearst Corporation owns the rest. Financial statistician John Knowles Fitch founded the company in 1913.

FITNESS QUEST INC.

1400 Raff Rd. SW
Canton, OH 44750
Phone: 330-478-0755
Fax: 330-479-5075
Web: www.fitnessquest.com

CEO: Robert R. (Bob) Schnabel Jr.
CFO: —
HR: —
FYE: December 31
Type: Private

Fitness Quest wants to provide the tools for customers on a quest for improved fitness. The company manufactures and sells its exercise bikes, ellipticals, gliders, treadmills, rowers, and other fitness equipment under such brand names as Total Gym, Ab Lounge, Eclipse, and Easy Shaper. The company's products are sold at retail stores like Target and Sears, through catalogs like Spiegel, and on home shopping TV channels, including QVC and HSN, as well as the Fitness Quest website. The company's products are most notably seen through its infomercials: Tony Little's Gazelle Freestyle machine. Fitness Quest was founded by president and CEO Bob Schnabel Jr.

	Annual Growth	12/04	12/05	12/06	12/07	12/08
Est. sales ($ mil.)	—	—	—	—	—	22.8
Employees	—	—	—	—	—	147

FIVE STAR COOPERATIVE

1949 N. Linn Ave.
New Hampton, IA 50659
Phone: 641-394-3052
Fax: 641-394-2920
Web: www.fivestarcoop.com

CEO: Ron Pumphrey
CFO: Robert Lynch
HR: —
FYE: December 31
Type: Cooperative

If Old MacDonald actually *had* a farm, he'd *want* to be a member of the Five Star Cooperative. Operating in north-central and northeast Iowa, Five Star has operations in more than 15 small to midsized towns in the Hawkeye State. The cooperative is divided into five divisions, according to the products and services offered — agronomy, petroleum (diesel fuel and home heating oil), feed (for beef cattle and swine), grain, and hardware — it operates a True Value hardware store in New Hampton that offers all the usual hardware products and services. Established in 1916, Five Star Cooperative provides a full complement for its member/farmers.

	Annual Growth	12/04	12/05	12/06	12/07	12/08
Est. sales ($ mil.)	—	—	—	—	—	289.7
Employees	—	—	—	—	—	75

FIVE STAR QUALITY CARE, INC.

NYSE Amex: FVE

400 Centre St.
Newton, MA 02458
Phone: 617-796-8387
Fax: 617-796-8385
Web: www.fivestarqualitycare.com

CEO: Bruce J. Mackey Jr.
CFO: Paul V. Hoagland
HR: Maryann Hughes
FYE: December 31
Type: Public

Five Star Quality Care aims to become the long-term care industry's Five Star provider. Operating in about 30 states, Five Star Quality Care runs some 210 senior living facilities with around 22,000 living units. Five Star's facilities consist of independent living apartments, assisted living suites, and nursing homes. Services include rehabilitation, occupational therapy, nutritional support, and social and recreational services, as well as skilled nursing care. In addition, Five Star Quality Care operates a handful of pharmacies and two rehabilitation hospitals, as well as over a dozen affiliated rehabilitation clinics.

	Annual Growth	12/05	12/06	12/07	12/08	12/09
Sales ($ mil.)	12.0%	757.5	827.3	972.9	1,104.2	1,192.6
Net income ($ mil.)	—	(84.2)	(116.7)	23.3	(4.5)	38.3
Market value ($ mil.)	(18.5%)	281.1	396.3	296.1	54.6	123.8
Employees	29.4%	7,852	17,018	18,301	21,062	22,000

FLAGSTAR BANCORP, INC.

NYSE: FBC

5151 Corporate Dr.
Troy, MI 48098
Phone: 248-312-2000
Fax: —
Web: www.flagstar.com

CEO: Joseph P. (Joe) Campanelli
CFO: Paul D. Borja
HR: —
FYE: December 31
Type: Public

This bank's flag flies high. Flagstar Bancorp is the holding company for Flagstar Bank, which operates some 165 branches (some of which are in retail stores) in Michigan, Indiana, and Georgia. Home loans are a major focus for Flagstar. It originates, purchases, and services residential mortgage loans in all 50 states through a network of loan offices. It also originates mortgages online though its website. More than 90% of the company's revenues are linked to mortgage lending. However, Flagstar would like to see its revenue mix become more diverse by playing up its standard retail banking services offered to individuals and small business customers.

	Annual Growth	12/05	12/06	12/07	12/08	12/09
Assets ($ mil.)	(1.8%)	15,075.4	15,497.2	15,792.7	14,203.7	14,013.3
Net income ($ mil.)	—	79.9	75.2	(39.2)	(275.4)	(496.7)
Market value ($ mil.)	(54.8%)	22,073.6	22,748.1	10,684.2	1,088.4	919.7
Employees	9.1%	2,405	2,510	3,960	3,920	3,411

FLANDERS CORPORATION

NASDAQ (GS): FLDR

2399 26th Ave. N.
St. Petersburg, FL 33734
Phone: 727-822-4411
Fax: 727-823-5510
Web: www.flanderscorp.com

CEO: Harry L. Smith Jr.
CFO: John Oakley
HR: Brenda Davis
FYE: December 31
Type: Public

This Flanders handles flecks, fleas, flies, fluff, and other airborne flotsam. The company makes air filters under such brand names as Air Seal, Eco-Air, and Precisionaire. Its products include high-efficiency particulate air (HEPA) filters used in industrial cleanrooms, as well as standard residential and commercial heating, ventilation, and air-conditioning filters. The company makes most of its sales from aftermarket replacement filters that it sells directly to wholesalers, distributors, and retail outlets. Flanders' customers include The Home Depot, Motorola, Texas Instruments, and Wal-Mart. Chairman Robert Amerson owns 26% of the company.

	Annual Growth	12/05	12/06	12/07	12/08	12/09
Sales ($ mil.)	(0.8%)	229.3	238.4	244.9	217.3	222.4
Net income ($ mil.)	(13.5%)	12.5	5.5	(19.9)	(13.2)	7.0
Market value ($ mil.)	(22.2%)	317.8	258.7	146.6	122.6	116.6
Employees	(6.0%)	2,743	3,067	2,800	2,090	2,139

FLANIGAN'S ENTERPRISES, INC.

NYSE Amex: BDL

5059 NE 18th Ave.
Fort Lauderdale, FL 33334
Phone: 954-377-1961
Fax: 954-351-1245
Web: www.flanigans.net

CEO: James G. Flanigan II
CFO: Jeffrey D. Kastner
HR: —
FYE: September 30
Type: Public

Seafood and sauce are the catch of the day at Flanigan's Enterprises. The company operates and manages about 15 restaurants that do business as Flanigan's Seafood Bar and Grill, along with a chain of eight package liquor stores called Big Daddy's Liquors. (Four properties have combination liquor store/restaurant operations.) Six of its restaurants are franchised and owned primarily by family members of company executives. All the company's lounges and liquor stores are located in Florida. In addition, Flanigan's owns the Mardi Gras adult entertainment club in Atlanta, which is operated by a third party. The family of former chairman and CEO Joseph "Big Daddy" Flanigan owns more than 50% of the company.

	Annual Growth	9/05	9/06	9/07	9/08	9/09
Sales ($ mil.)	8.2%	49.0	55.0	61.1	64.2	67.1
Net income ($ mil.)	6.2%	1.1	1.3	1.3	1.1	1.4
Market value ($ mil.)	(12.2%)	17.9	16.8	16.4	11.3	10.6
Employees	6.9%	691	927	950	1,003	903

FLATBUSH FEDERAL BANCORP, INC.

OTC: FLTB

2146 Nostrand Ave.
Brooklyn, NY 11210
Phone: 718-859-6800
Fax: 718-421-3210
Web: www.flatbush.com

CEO: Jesus R. Adia
CFO: John S. Lotardo
HR: —
FYE: December 31
Type: Public

Flatbush residents looking to finance a new flat might turn to Flatbush Federal Bancorp, the holding company for Flatbush Federal Savings and Loan. The thrift has been serving the Flatbush neighborhood of Brooklyn, New York, since 1883. Through three branches, the bank offers checking and savings accounts, CDs, IRAs, credit cards, and a variety of loans. One- to four-family real estate mortgages account for about three-quarters of the company's loan portfolio. The bank also writes commercial mortgages, construction loans, consumer loans, and a small number of Small Business Administration loans. Mutual holding company Flatbush Federal Bancorp, MHC, owns a majority of Flatbush Federal Bancorp.

	Annual Growth	12/05	12/06	12/07	12/08	12/09
Assets ($ mil.)	2.0%	144.0	154.4	148.8	149.7	156.0
Net income ($ mil.)	(15.9%)	0.4	0.2	0.1	0.1	0.2
Market value ($ mil.)	(15.5%)	21.5	20.8	16.4	9.6	10.9
Employees	(8.3%)	51	48	37	38	36

FLATIRON CONSTRUCTION CORP.

10090 I-25 Frontage Rd.
Longmont, CO 80504
Phone: 303-485-4050
Fax: 303-485-3922
Web: www.flatironcorp.com

CEO: Thomas J. (Tom) Rademacher
CFO: Paul R. Driscoll
HR: Jerry Hartbarger
FYE: December 31
Type: Subsidiary

There's not a *Bridge Too Far* for Flatiron Construction (as long as it's in North America). The company, which has regional offices throughout the US and western Canada, provides transportation construction and civil engineering services for major bridge, highway and rail projects. The company's Terno division concentrates on electrical work (traffic signaling, ramp metering, highway lighting) for civil construction projects. Flatiron has worked on such projects as California's Carquinez Suspension Bridge, the John James Audubon Bridge in Louisiana, and the San Francisco/Oakland Bay Bridge. Founded in 1947, the company was acquired by Germany's HOCHTIEF in 2007.

FLEETCOR TECHNOLOGIES, INC.

655 Engineering Dr., Ste. 300
Norcross, GA 30092
Phone: 770-449-0479
Fax: 770-449-3471
Web: www.fleetcor.com

CEO: Ronald F. (Ron) Clarke
CFO: Eric R. Dey
HR: —
FYE: December 31
Type: Private

You might say this company urges motor pool fleets to pay with plastic. FleetCor is a leading provider of fleet cards and payment processing services aimed at commercial fleets. When a fleet card is used by a driver, FleetCor tracks fuel, maintenance work, and state-specific taxes that are needed for company tax purposes. The company serves more than 530,000 accounts across almost 20 countries; its cards are accepted at about 83,000 locations in Europe and North America. FleetCor also manages fleet services for major oil companies, including BP and Chevron. Controlled by private equity firms Advent International, Bain Capital, and Summit Partners, the company plans to go public through an IPO.

	Annual Growth	12/04	12/05	12/06	12/07	12/08
Est. sales ($ mil.)	—	—	—	—	—	291.6
Employees	—	—	—	—	—	875

🔲 FLEETWOOD ENTERPRISES, INC.
OTC: FLTWQ

3125 Myers St.
Riverside, CA 92503
Phone: 951-351-3500
Fax: 951-351-3312
Web: www.fleetwood.com

CEO: Elden L. Smith
CFO: Andrew M. (Andy) Griffiths
HR: Michael B. Shearin
FYE: April 30
Type: Public

Fleetwood Enterprises is a leading maker of manufactured housing. The company's manufactured homes feature vaulted ceilings, walk-in closets, and porches. Fleetwood operates about a dozen plants located in nine states, and it has a dealer network throughout Canada and the US. After filing for Chapter 11 protection from creditors in 2009, the company closed its unprofitable travel trailer division and sold the assets of its recreational vehicle (RV) business. Fleetwood blamed its bankruptcy filing on the recessionary conditions in the RV and travel trailer markets. Cavco Industries is buying the company's manufactured housing assets; Fleetwood is seeking buyers for the rest of its operations.

	Annual Growth	4/04	4/05	4/06	4/07	*4/08
Sales ($ mil.)	(10.7%)	2,608.0	2,374.7	2,432.4	2,007.9	1,660.0
Net income ($ mil.)	—	(22.3)	(161.5)	(28.4)	(90.0)	(1.0)
Market value ($ mil.)	(30.2%)	3,033.8	1,598.5	1,966.8	1,742.9	721.8
Employees	(17.5%)	13,800	12,700	11,500	9,300	6,400

*Most recent year available

FLEISCHMANN'S YEAST

1350 Timberlake Manor Pkwy., Ste. 550
Chesterfield, MO 63017
Phone: 636-349-8800
Fax: 636-349-8825
Web: www.fleischmannsyeast.com

CEO: Andrew Armstrong
CFO: Christopher (Chris) Bohnert
HR: —
FYE: September 30
Type: Business segment

Fleischmann's Yeast manages to get a rise out of most folks — it is, after all, a leading maker of baker's yeast. The company offers fresh yeast cakes, and traditional active dried and quick-rise yeasts for use by the baking industry and home bakers alike. Fleischmann's also makes specially designed yeasts for use in bread machines. The company was acquired by Associated British Foods in 2004. ABF stirred Fleischmann's into its ACH Food Companies group of US businesses along with Mazola corn oil, Karo syrup, Argo cornstarch, and Tone spices. Fleischmann's baking products are available in the US and Canada.

	Annual Growth	9/04	9/05	9/06	9/07	9/08
Est. sales ($ mil.)	—	—	—	—	—	27.5
Employees	—	—	—	—	—	300

FLEISHMAN-HILLARD INC.

200 N. Broadway
St. Louis, MO 63102
Phone: 314-982-1700
Fax: 314-231-2313
Web: www.fleishman.com

CEO: David (Dave) Senay
CFO: Fred Rohlfing
HR: —
FYE: December 31
Type: Subsidiary

Communication is everything at Fleishman-Hillard. One of the leading public relations firms in the US, the company specializes in about 30 different practice groups and offers services ranging from public relations to marketing to reputation management. Conducting business in more than 20 languages, its expertise includes graphic design, media training, market research, and story placement. Fleishman-Hillard, which is a division of advertising conglomerate Omnicom, has about 80 offices across the globe. The firm's clients have included such heavy hitters as Procter & Gamble, Dell, Nortel, and Wal-Mart. Fleishman-Hillard was founded in 1946 by Al Fleishman and Bob Hillard; it was acquired by Omnicom in 1997.

FLEX-N-GATE CORPORATION

1306 E. University Ave.
Urbana, IL 61802
Phone: 217-278-2600
Fax: 217-278-2616
Web: www.flex-n-gate.com

CEO: Shahid Khan
CFO: —
HR: Grace Clapper
FYE: June 30
Type: Private

Flex-N-Gate makes metal and plastic automotive components and assemblies, such as bumpers, grilles, hinges, interior panels and pillars, latches, pedal systems, parking brakes, and running boards. The company also offers prototyping, mechanical assembly, and sequencing services. The company makes products for a wide range of car platforms; customers have included BMW, Chrysler, Ford, Honda, General Motors, Toyota, and Volvo. The company has more than 50 manufacturing and engineering facilities in Argentina, Canada, Mexico, Spain, and the US. Founded in 1956, president Shahid Khan has owned Flex-N-Gate since 1980.

FLEXSTEEL INDUSTRIES, INC.

NASDAQ (GM): FLXS

3400 Jackson St.
Dubuque, IA 52004
Phone: 563-556-7730
Fax: 563-556-8345
Web: www.flexsteel.com

CEO: Ronald J. Klosterman
CFO: Timothy E. Hall
HR: —
FYE: June 30
Type: Public

Are you sitting down for this? If not, Flexsteel Industries might ask why. It's not as if the firm hasn't given you plenty of options. Flexsteel makes wood and upholstered furniture for every room in the home as well as for the recreational vehicle and commercial markets. Most of its upholstered products — including recliners, rockers, and sofas — incorporate a unique drop-in spring for which the company is named. Crafting its goods mostly in the US, Flexsteel distributes to furniture retailers, department stores, catalog companies, RV manufacturers, hotels, and health care facilities. The company's DMI Furniture subsidiary produces furnishings for the home and office. Flexsteel was incorporated in 1929.

	Annual Growth	6/05	6/06	6/07	6/08	6/09
Sales ($ mil.)	(5.7%)	410.0	426.4	425.4	405.7	324.2
Net income ($ mil.)	—	6.0	4.7	9.3	4.2	(1.5)
Market value ($ mil.)	(12.5%)	95.0	86.4	96.3	74.7	55.7
Employees	(12.6%)	2,400	2,400	2,250	2,000	1,400

FLIGHT OPTIONS, LLC

26180 Curtiss Wright Pkwy.
Cleveland, OH 44143
Phone: 216-261-3500
Fax: 216-261-3595
Web: www.flightoptions.com

CEO: Michael J. (Mike) Silvestro
CFO: Michael Rossi
HR: Robert Sullivan
FYE: December 31
Type: Private

When you want the comfort and privacy of a private jet, you have options. Flight Options provides fractional jet ownership services, in which customers share ownership and are guaranteed access to a particular type of aircraft operated by the company. Its fleet of about 110 aircraft includes Beechjet, Hawker, Cessna Citation, and Embraer Legacy jets. Its primary service area spans the continental US and locations within 200 miles of its borders. Besides fractional ownership, Flight Options offers aircraft leasing and management and a membership program, JetPASS, that gives customers access to various aircraft. Investment firms Directional Capital and Resilience Capital own a majority stake in Flight Options.

FLINT TELECOM GROUP, INC.

OTC: FLTT

375 N. Stephanie St., Ste. 1411
Henderson, NV 89014
Phone: 561-394-2748
Fax: —
Web: www.flinttel.com

CEO: Vincent Browne
CFO: Vincent Browne
HR: —
FYE: June 30
Type: Public

Flint Telecom Group fans the flame of advanced communications. Through eight subsidiaries, the holding company provides a host of products and technologies to US and international communications service providers, including cable companies, ISPs, and telcos. It distributes advanced broadband, hosted digital phone, voice and data, and wireless products, as well as prepaid cellular and calling card products. The company's Digital Phone Solutions subsidiary offers VoIP services to independent cable companies, a niche that is showing strong market growth, particularly in the US.

	Annual Growth	3/05	3/06	3/07	3/08	*6/09
Sales ($ mil.)	108.9%	1.8	2.4	1.6	1.0	34.3
Net income ($ mil.)	—	(0.7)	(1.4)	(2.1)	(2.1)	(14.6)
Market value ($ mil.)	(48.8%)	835.4	438.6	229.7	26.1	57.4
Employees	(2.2%)	23	26	19	14	21

*Fiscal year change

FLIR SYSTEMS, INC.

NASDAQ (GS): FLIR

27700A SW Parkway Ave.
Wilsonville, OR 97070
Phone: 503-498-3547
Fax: 503-498-3904
Web: www.flir.com

CEO: Earl R. Lewis
CFO: Anthony L. Trunzo
HR: Paul T. Zaninovich
FYE: December 31
Type: Public

You can run, but you cannot hide from FLIR Systems. The company's thermal imaging and obscurant-proof camera systems detect heat and radiation, thus allowing operators to see objects through fog, darkness, or smoke. FLIR's imaging products enhance vision for military and commercial applications, such as search and rescue, drug interdiction, border patrol, surveillance, navigation, and broadcast newsgathering. Industrial customers use FLIR's thermography products, which employ infrared cameras to measure temperatures from a distance, for equipment monitoring, process control, product development, and other applications. US government agencies collectively account for about 43% of FLIR's sales.

	Annual Growth	12/05	12/06	12/07	12/08	12/09
Sales ($ mil.)	22.5%	508.6	575.0	779.4	1,077.0	1,147.1
Net income ($ mil.)	26.2%	90.8	100.9	136.7	203.7	230.2
Market value ($ mil.)	30.8%	1,712.1	2,440.4	4,799.6	4,704.5	5,018.9
Employees	12.0%	1,320	1,419	1,743	1,943	2,079

FLORIDA CRYSTALS CORPORATION

1 N. Clematis St., Ste. 200
West Palm Beach, FL 33401
Phone: 561-366-5100
Fax: 561-366-5158
Web: www.floridacrystals.com

CEO: Alfonso (Alfy) Fanjul Jr.
CFO: Luis J. Fernandez
HR: Jose A. Perez
FYE: March 31
Type: Private

Florida Crystals leans heavily on its cane. Producing more than 4 million tons of sugar ever year, the company is one of the top sugar producers in the US. The company, a unit of Flo-Sun, grows sugar cane and rice on its 180,000 acres. It operates two sugar mills, a rice mill, a refinery, a packaging and distribution center, and a renewable energy facility. The company's sugar products include granulated, baking, powdered, and large- and fine-grain, organic, and regular sugars under the C&H, Florida Crystals, Redpath, and Jack Frost brand names. With the Sugar Cane Growers Cooperative of Florida (SCGC), Florida Crystals jointly owns American Sugar Refining, the owner and producer of the Domino brand sugar.

FLORIDA DEPARTMENT OF THE LOTTERY

250 Marriott Dr.
Tallahassee, FL 32399
Phone: 850-487-7777
Fax: 850-487-4541
Web: www.flalottery.com

CEO: Leo DiBenigno
CFO: Marcy Jackson
HR: Karen Boulding
FYE: June 30
Type: Government agency

The State of Florida Department of the Lottery runs instant-play scratch tickets and lotto games, including Florida Lotto, Mega Money, Fantasy 5, and Cash 3. In addition to its own games, Florida is part of the Multi-State Lottery Association, which operates the popular Powerball drawing. Proceeds from the games are contributed to Florida's Educational Enhancement Trust Fund, which provides funding for a variety of education programs from pre-kindergarten up to the state university level. The lottery has returned more than $19 billion to the state since starting in 1988.

FLORIDA GAMING CORPORATION

OTC: FGMG

3500 NW 37th Ave.
Miami, FL 33142
Phone: 305-633-6400
Fax: 305-638-1330
Web: www.fla-gaming.com

CEO: W. Bennett Collett
CFO: Kimberly R. (Kim) Tharp
HR: Yolande Coleman
FYE: December 31
Type: Public

Jai-alai is the high life for this company. Florida Gaming Corporation owns and operates two jai-alai frontons in Miami and Ft. Pierce, Florida, that feature live jai-alai competition with wagering. The gaming centers offer wagering on simulcast jai-alai from other locations, as well as simulcast horse racing and dog racing. In addition, its Miami location features a card room for poker. Florida Gaming also owns Tara Club Estates, a real estate development project near Atlanta. Chairman W. Bennett Collett owns more than 45% of the company, partially through his holding company Freedom Financial.

	Annual Growth	12/05	12/06	12/07	12/08	12/09
Sales ($ mil.)	1.1%	13.4	17.4	15.8	14.0	14.0
Net income ($ mil.)	—	(2.8)	(0.6)	(6.7)	(0.1)	(4.9)
Market value ($ mil.)	(25.4%)	56.4	51.5	83.6	8.0	17.5
Employees	25.9%	142	50	53	375	357

FLORIDA GAS TRANSMISSION COMPANY, LLC

1331 Lamar St., Ste. 650
Houston, TX 77010
Phone: 713-853-0300
Fax: —
Web: www.panhandleenergy.com/comp_fld.asp

CEO: Robert O. (Rob) Bond
CFO: Richard N. (Rick) Marshall
HR: John Moore
FYE: December 31
Type: Joint venture

Florida Gas Transmission gasses up the Gulf Coast. The company transports natural gas to cogeneration facilities, electric utilities, independent power producers, municipal generators, and local distribution companies through a 5,000-mile natural gas pipeline extending from south Texas to south Florida. It delivers 2.3 billion cu. ft. of natural gas a day to more than 250 delivery points consisting of more than 50 natural gas-fired electric generation facilities. Florida Gas Transmission is operated by Citrus Corp., which is a joint venture of Southern Union and El Paso Corp.

FLORIDA HOUSING FINANCE CORPORATION

227 N. Bronough St., Ste. 5000
Tallahassee, FL 32301
Phone: 850-488-4197
Fax: 850-488-9809
Web: www.floridahousing.org

CEO: Stephen P. Auger
CFO: Barb Goltz
HR: Donna Light
FYE: June 30
Type: Government-owned

Owning a home in Florida is just a bit easier thanks to Florida Housing Finance Corporation. Established in 1997 by the Florida Legislature as a public corporation, Florida Housing's mission is to help Floridians obtain safe, decent housing that might otherwise be unavailable to them. Florida Housing pursues its mission through a number of programs that provide financial assistance for first time homebuyers, and for developers of multifamily dwellings that serve elderly and low income Floridians. Florida Housing partners with various local, state, and federal agencies, as well as developers, and not-for-profit organizations to achieve its goals.

	Annual Growth	6/04	6/05	6/06	6/07	6/08
Est. sales ($ mil.)	—	—	—	—	—	336.2
Employees	—	—	—	—	—	130

FLORIDA INTERNATIONAL UNIVERSITY

11200 SW 8th St.
Miami, FL 33199
Phone: 305-348-2000
Fax: 305-348-6476
Web: www.fiu.edu

CEO: Mark B. Rosenberg
CFO: Kenneth A. Jessell
HR: Jaffus Hardrick
FYE: June 30
Type: School

For the people in South Florida who don't want to party, there's Florida International University (FIU). The university has an enrollment of more than 38,000 students from throughout the US and more than 130 foreign countries at two primary campuses in Miami-Dade County, as well as a research center and one smaller site in Broward County. FIU offers bachelor's, master's, and doctoral degree programs in more than 200 majors at more than 20 colleges and schools. FIU is a member of the State University System of Florida. It held its first classes in 1972.

	Annual Growth	6/04	6/05	6/06	6/07	6/08
Est. sales ($ mil.)	—	—	—	—	—	307.5
Employees	—	—	—	—	—	4,000

FLORIDA POWER & LIGHT COMPANY

700 Universe Blvd.
Juno Beach, FL 33408
Phone: 561-694-4000
Fax: —
Web: www.fpl.com

CEO: Armando J. Olivera
CFO: Armando Pimentel Jr.
HR: James W. Poppell Sr.
FYE: December 31
Type: Subsidiary

Florida Power & Light (FPL) sheds extra light onto the Sunshine State. The company, a subsidiary of utility holding company NextEra Energy, serves some 4.5 million electricity customers in eastern and southern Florida. FPL has about 73,650 miles of transmission and distribution lines, as well as interests in fossil-fueled and nuclear power plants that give it a generating capacity of about 26,700 MW. FPL's Energy Marketing and Trading unit purchases and sells energy commodities (including electricity, natural gas, and oil) to wholesale customers.

	Annual Growth	12/04	12/05	12/06	12/07	12/08
Est. sales ($ mil.)	—	—	—	—	—	11,649.0
Employees	—	—	—	—	—	10,499

FLORIDA POWER CORPORATION

299 1st Ave. North
St. Petersburg, FL 33701
Phone: 727-820-5151
Fax: 727-384-7865
Web: www.progress-energy.com

CEO: Vincent M. (Vinny) Dolan
CFO: Mark F. Mulhern
HR: Anne M. Huffman
FYE: December 31
Type: Subsidiary

Sometimes the sunshine state just isn't bright enough, and that's when Florida Power really shines. The utility transmits and distributes electricity to 1.6 million customers and oversees about 9,360 MW of generating capacity from interests in nuclear and coal-, oil-, and gas-fired power plants. Additionally, Florida Power purchases about 20% of the energy it provides. The utility, a subsidiary of holding company Progress Energy, also sells wholesale power to other utilities and marketers. The company is interconnected with 22 municipal power systemsn and with nine rural electric cooperative systems.

THE FLORIDA STATE UNIVERSITY

600 W. College Ave.	CEO: Eric J. Barron
Tallahassee, FL 32306	CFO: John R. Carnaghi
Phone: 850-644-3420	HR: Joyce A. Ingram
Fax: 850-644-4447	FYE: —
Web: www.fsu.edu	Type: School

Home to the Florida State Seminoles, Florida State University offers more than 300 undergraduate, graduate, and professional programs, including M.D. (medicine) and J.D. (law) programs. It has 16 colleges dedicated to academic fields ranging from liberal arts, music, visual arts, and education, to criminology, engineering, social work, and information. The research institution is also home to the National High Magnetic Field Laboratory, or "Mag Lab," the only national lab in Florida and the only such high magnetic facility in the US. Florida State was founded in 1851 and is part of the ten-school Florida State University System.

FLORIDA'S NATURAL GROWERS

20205 US Hwy. 27 North	CEO: Stephen Caruso
Lake Wales, FL 33853	CFO: William (Chip) Hendry
Phone: 863-676-1411	HR: Susan Langley
Fax: —	FYE: August 31
Web: floridanatural.com	Type: Cooperative

Florida's Natural Growers is known for squeezing out profits. The cooperative is one of the largest citrus juice sellers in the US, ranking right up there with the country's two giant brand names: PepsiCo's Tropicana and Coca-Cola's Minute Maid. Some 1,000 farmer/members harvest more than 60,000 acres of citrus groves for the co-op's products — frozen concentrated and not-from-concentrate juices (orange, grapefruit, lemonade, apple, and fruit blends). The co-op provides juice to customers in the foodservice, retail food, and vending industries. Its brands include Florida's Natural, Growers Pride, Bluebird, Donald Duck, Vintage, and Adams.

FLOTEK INDUSTRIES, INC.

	NYSE: FTK
2930 W. Sam Houston Pkwy. North, Ste. 300	CEO: John W. Chisholm
Houston, TX 77043	CFO: —
Phone: 713-849-9911	HR: —
Fax: 713-896-4511	FYE: December 31
Web: www.flotekind.com	Type: Public

Flotek Industries works to keep oil and gas flowing. The company gets about half of its sales from chemicals used in the cementing and stimulation of oil and gas wells. (Cementing holds well casings in place; stimulation opens up cracks in the earth to allow for the easier flow of oil.) Flotek also makes the equipment used in cementing and stimulation, as well as Petrovalve downhole pump valves (used to pump off the liquids in gas wells) and Turbeco casing centralizers (used to center pipe). The company markets its products throughout the US and is expanding into international markets.

	Annual Growth	12/05	12/06	12/07	12/08	12/09
Sales ($ mil.)	20.8%	52.9	100.6	158.0	226.1	112.6
Net income ($ mil.)	—	7.7	11.4	16.7	(31.9)	(50.7)
Market value ($ mil.)	(38.4%)	280.6	422.0	1,084.5	75.8	40.3
Employees	19.5%	157	253	448	500	320

🔲 FLOW INTERNATIONAL CORPORATION

	NASDAQ (GM): FLOW
23500 64th Ave. South	CEO: Charles M. (Charley) Brown
Kent, WA 98032	CFO: Allen M. Hsieh
Phone: 253-850-3500	HR: Theresa S. Treat
Fax: 253-813-9377	FYE: April 30
Web: www.flowcorp.com	Type: Public

Don't use Flow International's products to wash the car or your dog — unless you want them in the next county. The company makes waterjet cutting and industrial cleaning systems with ultrahigh pressure (up to 87,000 pounds per square inch). Its machines are used to cut metallic and non-metallic materials in the aerospace, automotive, and steel and stonecutting industries; they are also used to cut food and paper. Flow International manufactures robotics and automated assembly equipment, isostatic and flexform press systems, and consumable waterjet system parts, such as seals, garnet, and orifices. The US accounts for over half of the company's sales.

	Annual Growth	4/05	4/06	4/07	4/08	4/09
Sales ($ mil.)	(1.1%)	219.4	203.3	217.3	244.3	210.1
Net income ($ mil.)	—	(10.8)	5.3	3.7	22.4	(23.8)
Market value ($ mil.)	(25.5%)	277.5	634.8	545.7	470.2	85.3
Employees	(5.3%)	806	732	756	759	649

🔲 FLOWERS FOODS, INC.

	NYSE: FLO
1919 Flowers Cir.	CEO: George E. Deese
Thomasville, GA 31757	CFO: R. Steve Kinsey
Phone: 229-226-9110	HR: Donald A. Thriffiley Jr.
Fax: 229-225-3806	FYE: December 31
Web: www.flowersfoods.com	Type: Public

Look for Flowers Foods in your breadbox, not your garden — the company is one of the largest wholesale bakeries in the US. It produces, markets, and distributes fresh breads, buns, rolls, corn and flour tortillas, and sweet bakery goodies to retail food and foodservice customers throughout the southeastern, southwestern, and mid-Atlantic sections of the US, as well as in selected areas of California and Nevada. The company's brand names include BlueBird, Cobblestone Mill, and Nature's Own. Flowers Foods makes snack cakes, pastry, donuts, and frozen bread products for retail, vending, and co-pack customers nationwide. It also rolls out hamburger buns for large national fast-food restaurant chains.

	Annual Growth	12/05	12/06	12/07	12/08	12/09
Sales ($ mil.)	11.0%	1,715.9	1,888.7	2,036.7	2,414.9	2,600.8
Net income ($ mil.)	20.8%	61.2	81.6	94.6	119.2	130.3
Market value ($ mil.)	6.6%	1,685.6	1,650.8	2,147.7	2,234.9	2,179.8
Employees	4.1%	7,500	7,800	7,800	8,800	8,800

FLOWSERVE CORPORATION

	NYSE: FLS
5215 N. O'Connor Blvd., Ste. 2300	CEO: Mark A. Blinn
Irving, TX 75039	CFO: Richard J. (Dick) Guiltinan Jr.
Phone: 972-443-6500	HR: —
Fax: 972-443-6800	FYE: December 31
Web: www.flowserve.com	Type: Public

Flowserve is pumped about flow control equipment. After its reorganization in 2010 the company operates through two divisions. Flow Control division (FCD) makes valves and actuators that control the flow of liquids and gases. Flow Solutions Group (FSG) manufactures industrial pumps, valves, and mechanical seals for the chemical, oil and gas, power generation, and water management industries. It also makes nuclear pumps, submersible motors, and thrusters, as well as provides mechanical seals, sealing systems, and repair services to OEMs that make pumps, compressors, and mixers. The company offers its products and services to customers in more than 50 countries around the globe.

	Annual Growth	12/05	12/06	12/07	12/08	12/09
Sales ($ mil.)	12.8%	2,695.3	3,061.1	3,762.7	4,473.5	4,365.3
Net income ($ mil.)	145.4%	11.8	115.0	255.8	442.4	427.9
Market value ($ mil.)	24.3%	2,217.9	2,829.5	5,393.3	2,887.3	5,299.7
Employees	3.6%	13,000	14,000	15,000	15,000	15,000

🔲 An in-depth profile of this company is available to Hoover's Online members at hoovers.com.

631

FLSMIDTH CENTRY

9020 S. Sandy Pkwy.	CEO: Randall (Randy) Harmsen
Sandy, UT 84070	CFO: —
Phone: 801-582-2002	HR: —
Fax: 801-584-1440	FYE: December 31
Web: www.flsmidth.com	Type: Subsidiary

FLSmidth CEntry (formerly CEntry Constructors & Engineers) is on the look-out for new construction projects. The company offers industrial construction and engineering services to the oil and gas, mining, metals, minerals, sulfur recovery, and hazardous waste incineration sectors. It specializes in industrial plant construction, upgrades, expansion, and maintenance. FLSmidth CEntry got its new name after CEntry was sold by the The Layton Companies (which had acquired it in 2000) to Danish cement and minerals firm FLSmidth & Co in 2008. The company is active primarily in the Western US.

FLUIDIGM CORPORATION

7000 Shoreline Ct., Ste. 100	CEO: Gajus V. Worthington
South San Francisco, CA 94080	CFO: Vikram Jog
Phone: 650-266-6000	HR: —
Fax: 650-871-7152	FYE: December 31
Web: www.fluidigm.com	Type: Private

When Fluidigm develops microfluidic systems and measures volume by the *nanoliter*, it's not using itty bitty Erlenmeyer flasks. Based on the fabrication technology that brought forth semiconductors, Fluidigm develops integrated fluidic circuits (IFCs) and strings them together as systems to automate certain tasks in drug development and other life sciences research. Its Topaz System uses chips, reagents, hardware, and software that allow researchers to efficiently screen crystalized proteins. Fluidigm's BioMark and Fluidigm EP1 systems are designed to be used for genetic analysis. The company's customers range across the pharmaceutical development and life sciences research industries.

FLUKE CORPORATION

6920 Seaway Blvd.	CEO: Barbara B. Hulit
Everett, WA 98203	CFO: Monti Ackerman
Phone: 425-347-6100	HR: Kurt Loring
Fax: 425-446-5116	FYE: December 31
Web: www.fluke.com	Type: Subsidiary

These products are really hip (pocket-sized, that is). Fluke, a subsidiary of Danaher (maker of Craftsman tools), makes handheld electronic test tools used by electricians, HVAC technicians, and plant engineers to install, maintain, and service electrical and electronic equipment. The company's multimeters, oscilloscopes, and other devices measure current, voltage resistance, frequency, temperature, and pressure. It also makes calibrators and calibration software, waveform generators, and power harmonics meters. Its process tools are used in control applications in the chemicals, food, petroleum, and wastewater management industries. Fluke has production facilities in the US, the UK, Asia, and the Netherlands.

FLUKE NETWORKS, INC.

6920 Seaway Blvd.	CEO: David Coffin
Everett, WA 98203	CFO: —
Phone: 425-446-4519	HR: —
Fax: 425-446-5043	FYE: December 31
Web: www.flukenetworks.com	Type: Subsidiary

Fluke Networks doesn't want the flawless functioning of your local or wide area network to be just a happy accident. A business entity of Danaher, Fluke Networks makes hardware and software for installation, certification, monitoring, and maintenance of LAN/WAN environments and their underlying fiber, copper, and wireless networks. Fluke Networks' products include handheld network testing devices, hardware and software network analyzers, and cable analyzers. Fluke Networks' partners include CA, Concord Communications, Extreme Networks, Microsoft, and Verizon. Fluke Networks distributes its products to network operators in more than 50 countries and gets around 45% of revenues from outside of the US.

FLUOR CORPORATION

	NYSE: FLR
6700 Las Colinas Blvd.	CEO: Alan L. Boeckmann
Irving, TX 75039	CFO: D. Michael (Mike) Steuert
Phone: 469-398-7000	HR: Glenn C. Gilkey
Fax: 469-398-7255	FYE: December 31
Web: www.fluor.com	Type: Public

Fluor Corporation is one of the world's largest international design, engineering, and contracting firms. The company provides engineering, procurement, construction, maintenance, and project management services for a variety of industrial sectors around the world. Its projects include manufacturing facilities, refineries, pharmaceutical facilities, health care buildings, power plants, and telecommunications and transportation infrastructure. The oil and gas industry accounts for more than half of Fluor's sales. The company also provides operations and maintenance services for its projects, as well as administrative and support services to the US government.

	Annual Growth	12/05	12/06	12/07	12/08	12/09
Sales ($ mil.)	13.7%	13,161.1	14,078.5	16,691.0	22,325.9	21,990.3
Net income ($ mil.)	31.8%	227.3	263.5	533.3	720.5	684.9
Market value ($ mil.)	3.9%	6,904.6	7,296.9	13,022.7	8,019.9	8,050.3
Employees	0.9%	34,836	37,560	41,260	42,119	36,152

FLUSHING FINANCIAL CORPORATION

	NASDAQ (GS): FFIC
1979 Marcus Ave., Ste. E140	CEO: John R. Buran
Lake Success, NY 11042	CFO: David W. Fry
Phone: 718-961-5400	HR: Ruth E. Filiberto
Fax: —	FYE: December 31
Web: www.flushingsavings.com	Type: Public

Flush with cash? You could keep it at Flushing Financial. The holding company's Flushing Savings Bank operates about 15 branches in the Brooklyn, Manhattan, and Queens boroughs of New York City and in nearby Nassau County. Deposit products include CDs and checking, savings, passbook, money market, and NOW accounts. Multifamily residential and mixed-use real estate mortgage loans account for the majority of the bank's loan portfolio; other offerings include commercial mortgages and one- to four-family mortgages, construction loans, and SBA loans.

	Annual Growth	12/05	12/06	12/07	12/08	12/09
Assets ($ mil.)	15.2%	2,353.2	2,836.5	3,354.5	3,949.5	4,143.2
Net income ($ mil.)	2.2%	23.5	21.6	20.2	22.3	25.6
Market value ($ mil.)	(7.8%)	485.1	531.9	500.1	372.6	350.8
Employees	7.8%	264	324	269	343	356

FLYING J INC.

1104 Country Hills Dr.
Ogden, UT 84403
Phone: 801-624-1000
Fax: 801-624-1587
Web: www.flyingj.com

CEO: Crystal C. Maggelet
CFO: Robert L. Inkley
HR: —
FYE: January 31
Type: Private

Flying J puts out a welcome mat for truckers in North America. From its beginnings in 1968 with four locations, the firm has become a leading diesel-fuel distributor and truck-stop operator in the US — with more than 270 amenity-loaded Flying J Travel Plazas and fuel stops in some 40 US states and six Canadian provinces. Flying J goes beyond the usual truck-stop fare (food, fuel, showers) by offering extra services, including banking, bulk-fuel programs, wireless Internet connections, fuel-cost analysis, and truck-fleet sales. Flying J's travel center business is being acquired out of bankruptcy by Pilot Travel Centers. The firm has put its other businesses, including refineries, up for sale.

	Annual Growth	1/04	1/05	1/06	1/07	1/08
Sales ($ mil.)	30.5%	5,585.7	5,910.0	9,450.0	11,350.0	16,200.0
Employees	7.5%	12,000	13,000	14,600	16,300	16,000

FMC CORPORATION

NYSE: FMC

1735 Market St.
Philadelphia, PA 19103
Phone: 215-299-6000
Fax: 215-299-5998
Web: www.fmc.com

CEO: Pierre Brondeau
CFO: W. Kim Foster
HR: Kenneth R. Garrett
FYE: December 31
Type: Public

E may $= mc^2$, but FMC = chemicals. Once in areas as diverse as oil field equipment and food machinery, FMC Corporation now focuses on industrial, specialty, and agricultural chemicals. The company's industrial chemicals include soda ash (it's one of the largest producers), hydrogen peroxide, and phosphorus chemicals. The rest of its sales come from agricultural products (insecticides, herbicides, and fungicides) and specialty chemicals (food and pharmaceutical additives). FMC's equation lately has improved after a few years' effort to increase its efficiency, profitability, and credit rating. The company cut costs across the board, including closing plants, refocusing on growth areas like specialty chemicals.

	Annual Growth	12/05	12/06	12/07	12/08	12/09
Sales ($ mil.)	7.1%	2,150.2	2,347.0	2,632.9	3,115.3	2,826.2
Net income ($ mil.)	19.5%	117.1	132.0	132.4	304.6	238.8
Market value ($ mil.)	20.3%	1,932.7	2,782.6	3,965.8	3,251.9	4,053.7
Employees	(1.0%)	5,000	5,000	5,000	5,000	4,800

FMC TECHNOLOGIES, INC.

NYSE: FTI

1803 Gears Rd.
Houston, TX 77067
Phone: 281-591-4000
Fax: 281-591-4102
Web: www.fmctechnologies.com

CEO: Peter D. Kinnear
CFO: William H. (Bill) Schumann III
HR: —
FYE: December 31
Type: Public

FMC Technologies is named after food machinery, but this company's bread and butter is oil and gas. Through its energy production systems unit, FMC Technologies offers subsea drilling and production systems for the exploration and production of oil and gas. Its energy processing systems segment makes fluid control, measurement, loading, separation, material handling, and blending systems. FMC Technologies operates about 20 manufacturing centers in 15 countries. It spun off its industrial food equipment and airport systems unit into a separate company called John Bean Technologies in 2008. FMC Technologies was formed as subsidiary of FMC Corporation in 2000 and went public as an independent unit the next year.

	Annual Growth	12/05	12/06	12/07	12/08	12/09
Sales ($ mil.)	8.1%	3,226.7	3,790.7	4,615.4	4,550.9	4,405.4
Net income ($ mil.)	36.0%	106.1	276.3	302.8	361.3	363.3
Market value ($ mil.)	29.8%	2,477.1	3,556.9	6,544.7	2,897.5	7,032.9
Employees	1.0%	10,000	11,000	13,000	9,800	10,400

FMR LLC

82 Devonshire St.
Boston, MA 02109
Phone: 617-563-7000
Fax: 617-476-6150
Web: www.fidelity.com

CEO: Edward C. (Ned) Johnson III
CFO: Robert J. (Bob) Chersi
HR: Stuart Grief
FYE: December 31
Type: Private

FMR is *semper fidelis* (ever faithful) to its core business. The financial services conglomerate, better known as Fidelity Investments, is one of the world's largest mutual fund firms. Serving more than 20 million individual and institutional clients, Fidelity manages almost 500 funds and has more than $1.5 trillion of assets under management. It also operates a leading online discount brokerage and has more than 100 investor centers in the US and Canada, as well as locations in Europe and Asia. The founding Johnson family controls FMR; Abigail Johnson, CEO Ned Johnson's daughter and perhaps his successor (not to mention one of the richest women in America), is the company's largest single shareholder.

	Annual Growth	12/04	12/05	12/06	12/07	12/08
Sales ($ mil.)	0.3%	—	—	12,870.0	14,900.0	12,937.3
Employees	(2.3%)	—	—	41,900	46,400	40,000

FNB BANCORP

OTC: FNBG

975 El Camino Real
South San Francisco, CA 94080
Phone: 650-588-6800
Fax: 650-588-9695
Web: www.fnbnorcal.com

CEO: Thomas C. (Tom) McGraw
CFO: David A. (Dave) Curtis
HR: —
FYE: December 31
Type: Public

To be or not to FNB? If that's your question, you might want to look into FNB Bancorp. It's the holding company for First National Bank of Northern California, which serves consumers and small to midsized businesses in San Mateo and San Francisco counties. Through about a dozen branches, the bank offers traditional products such as checking and savings accounts, IRAs, CDs, and credit cards. Real estate loans, including commercial and residential mortgages, account for approximately 70% of the company's loan portfolio. The bank also originates business, consumer, and construction loans.

	Annual Growth	12/05	12/06	12/07	12/08	12/09
Assets ($ mil.)	5.6%	569.1	581.3	644.5	661.0	708.3
Net income ($ mil.)	(43.0%)	5.7	7.6	6.7	4.0	0.6
Market value ($ mil.)	(28.1%)	93.4	93.8	65.9	34.7	24.9
Employees	1.3%	176	183	187	180	185

F.N.B. CORPORATION

NYSE: FNB

1 F.N.B. Blvd.
Hermitage, PA 16148
Phone: 724-981-6000
Fax: 724-983-4873
Web: www.fnbcorporation.com

CEO: Stephen J. (Steve) Gurgovits
CFO: Vincent J. Calabrese
HR: Brian F. Lilly
FYE: December 31
Type: Public

F.N.B. Corporation is the holding company for First National Bank of Pennsylvania, which operates more than 225 bank branches in Pennsylvania and northeastern Ohio. The company also has more than 50 consumer finance offices in those states and Tennessee, plus a handful of loan production offices in Florida. It operates in four segments, providing community banking, wealth management, insurance, and consumer finance products and services to retail clients and small businesses. Commercial loans make up about half of the company's loan portfolio. F.N.B. Corporation bought Pennsylvania-based banks Omega Financial and Iron and Glass Bancorp in 2008.

	Annual Growth	12/05	12/06	12/07	12/08	12/09
Assets ($ mil.)	11.7%	5,590.3	6,007.6	6,088.0	8,364.8	8,709.1
Net income ($ mil.)	(7.2%)	55.3	67.6	69.7	35.6	41.1
Market value ($ mil.)	(20.9%)	1,986.1	2,090.2	1,681.8	1,510.1	776.8
Employees	8.9%	1,793	1,844	1,893	2,497	2,525

An in-depth profile of this company is available to Hoover's Online members at hoovers.com.

633

FNB UNITED CORP.

NASDAQ (GS): FNBN

150 South Fayetteville St.
Asheboro, NC 27203
Phone: 336-626-8300
Fax: 336-625-2452
Web: www.myyesbank.com

CEO: R. Larry Campbell
CFO: Mark A. Severson
HR: Deborah B. Auman
FYE: December 31
Type: Public

FNB United is the holding company for CommunityONE Bank (formerly First National Bank and Trust), which has about 45 branches in North Carolina. The bank's offerings include checking, savings, and money market accounts, CDs, IRAs, credit cards, and trust services. It concentrates on real estate lending: Commercial mortgages account for more than 35% of the company's loan portfolio, while residential mortgages and construction loans are about 25% apiece. The bank also makes business and consumer loans. Subsidiary Dover Mortgage Company originates mortgages for sale into the secondary market through about five loan production offices in its home state.

	Annual Growth	12/05	12/06	12/07	12/08	12/09
Assets ($ mil.)	17.5%	1,102.1	1,814.9	1,906.5	2,044.4	2,101.3
Net income ($ mil.)	—	9.9	12.2	12.4	(59.8)	(101.7)
Market value ($ mil.)	(48.9%)	217.1	209.6	138.9	35.9	14.9
Employees	12.2%	350	584	490	492	554

FNBH BANCORP, INC.

OTC: FNHM

101 E. Grand River
Howell, MI 48843
Phone: 517-546-3150
Fax: 517-546-6275
Web: www.fnbsite.com

CEO: Ronald L. Long
CFO: —
HR: Nancy Morgan
FYE: December 31
Type: Public

If Thurston III and Lovey ever did get off that island, they might've stashed their fortune here. FNBH Bancorp is the holding company for First National Bank of Howell, which serves individuals and local businesses through nearly ten branches in Livingston County, Michigan, west of Detroit. The bank offers traditional deposit products such as checking and savings accounts, in addition to trust, investment, and wealth management services. Commercial loans, including loans for land development, new home construction, and business leasing, comprise about 85% of the company's loan portfolio. Founded in 1934, the bank has traditionally served rural communities, but has seen its market become increasingly suburban.

	Annual Growth	12/05	12/06	12/07	12/08	12/09
Assets ($ mil.)	(8.6%)	477.2	473.9	432.9	388.8	332.4
Net income ($ mil.)	—	6.5	5.6	(6.6)	(13.4)	(13.7)
Market value ($ mil.)	(78.4%)	79.8	83.7	42.7	13.9	0.2
Employees	(8.7%)	134	120	104	102	93

FOCUS BRANDS INC.

200 Glenridge Point Pkwy., Ste. 200
Atlanta, GA 30342
Phone: 404-255-3250
Fax: 404-255-4978
Web: www.focusbrands.com

CEO: Russell V. (Russ) Umphenour Jr.
CFO: Lenore L. Krentz
HR: Jean Boland
FYE: December 31
Type: Private

The focus of this company is on sweets, spicy food, and sandwiches. FOCUS Brands is a leading multi-concept restaurant franchisor with more than 2,200 locations in the US and about 35 other countries. Its brands include Carvel, a leading chain of more than 550 ice cream stores operating primarily in the Northeast, and Cinnabon, a popular sweet snacks chain with more than 750 units found in shopping malls and other high-traffic locations. Through subsidiary MSWG, FOCUS Brands franchises more than 400 quick-casual Mexican outlets under the Moe's Southwest Grill banner. It also owns sandwich chain Schlotzsky's. FOCUS Brands was formed in 2004 by private equity firm Roark Capital Group.

FOCUS ENHANCEMENTS, INC.

Pink Sheets: FCSEQ

1370 Dell Ave.
Campbell, CA 95008
Phone: 408-866-8300
Fax: 408-866-4859
Web: www.focusinfo.com

CEO: Brett A. Moyer
CFO: Gary L. Williams
HR: Elizabeth Fisher
FYE: December 31
Type: Public

FOCUS Enhancements is all about a clear picture. The company offers products and services for the video production, media asset management, and media delivery markets as well as designing and manufacturing video encoder chips, video scan converters, and other wireless media products. FOCUS' converters are used for business presentations, videoconferencing, classroom activities, and gaming. The company also makes PC-to-TV video co-processor chips and digital video mixers. Customers located in the US account for about 60% of sales. FOCUS Enhancements filed for Chapter 11 protection from creditors in September 2008.

FOCUS RECEIVABLES MANAGEMENT, LLC

1130 Northchase Pkwy., Ste. 150
Marietta, GA 30067
Phone: 678-228-0000
Fax: 678-228-0019
Web: www.focusrm.com

CEO: Gregory E. (Greg) Schubert
CFO: Tom Palmer
HR: Terence Cheatham
FYE: December 31
Type: Private

Focus Receivables Management has debtors in its sights. The company handles pre- and post-charge-off collection services of delinquent commercial and individual accounts. Offerings include pre-collection letters, skip tracing, asset location, and customized reports. The company specializes in the financial, telecommunications, auto, consumer services, and student loan industries. Focus Receivables Management has offices in Georgia and New Mexico. Company executives and board members Bill Strong, Greg Schubert, and Peter Hendricks founded Focus Receivables Management in 2001.

	Annual Growth	12/04	12/05	12/06	12/07	12/08
Est. sales ($ mil.)	—	—	—	—	—	17.0
Employees	—	—	—	—	—	275

FOCUSFRAME

2880 Stevens Creek Blvd., Ste. 101
San Jose, CA 95128
Phone: 408-296-3900
Fax: 408-296-3909
Web: www.focusframe.com

CEO: Vaughn Paladin
CFO: Kari Gothie
HR: Kari Gothie
FYE: December 31
Type: Business segment

FocusFrame can help you build a platform for technological success. The company provides a variety of IT services, such as implementation, systems integration, network design, application development, support, training, and consulting from offices in Mexico, the Netherlands, the UK, and the US. It also specializes in software applications from Hewlett-Packard, Oracle, and SAP, among other vendors. It is focusing on growing its offshore sales. FocusFrame's clients include aerospace, automotive, financial services, health care, manufacturing, retail, and technology firms. The company is a subsidiary of Hexaware Technologies.

	Annual Growth	12/04	12/05	12/06	12/07	12/08
Est. sales ($ mil.)	—	—	—	—	—	10.6
Employees	—	—	—	—	—	125

FOG CUTTER CAPITAL GROUP INC.

OTC: FCCG

301 Arizona Ave., Ste. 200
Santa Monica, CA 90401
Phone: 310-319-1850
Fax: 310-319-1863
Web: www.fccgi.com

CEO: Andrew A. (Andy) Wiederhorn
CFO: R. Scott Stevenson
HR: —
FYE: December 31
Type: Public

This company's beacon shines brightest on the fast-food business. Fog Cutter Capital Group has investments in a variety of enterprises, but its primary operating business is Fatburger. The 82%-owned hamburger chain, with more than 90 restaurants, is popular for its gourmet burgers and retro-themed diner interiors. Fatburger has locations in more than a dozen states, primarily in California; more than 60 of the fast food eateries are franchised. In addition, Fog Cutter owns an industrial manufacturing business (DAC International) and has a number of real estate holdings.

	Annual Growth	12/04	12/05	12/06	12/07	*12/08
Sales ($ mil.)	1.0%	47.7	42.5	49.6	43.6	49.7
Net income ($ mil.)	—	(3.9)	(6.9)	(10.1)	(10.2)	(12.2)
Market value ($ mil.)	(49.6%)	24.7	29.4	9.5	8.0	1.6
Employees	9.9%	599	659	676	724	875

*Most recent year available

FOLEY & LARDNER LLP

777 E. Wisconsin Ave.
Milwaukee, WI 53202
Phone: 414-271-2400
Fax: 414-297-4900
Web: www.foley.com

CEO: Ralf-Reinhard (Ralf) Böer
CFO: Tom L. Budde
HR: Stanley S. (Stan) Jaspan
FYE: January 31
Type: Partnership

Though most famous for its cheese, Wisconsin has another thing going for it: lawyers. Foley & Lardner, the largest and oldest law firm in Wisconsin, has nearly 1,000 lawyers and has expanded far beyond its Milwaukee base, with offices in more than 15 other US cities (including four in Florida and six in California). In addition, Foley & Lardner has international offices in Brussels, Shanghai, and Tokyo. The firm, founded in 1842, has one of the nation's leading health law practices and an increased focus on its intellectual property practice; other areas of expertise include business law, litigation, regulatory issues, and tax planning.

	Annual Growth	1/04	1/05	1/06	1/07	1/08
Sales ($ mil.)	8.3%	523.0	542.5	610.5	668.0	720.4
Employees	4.4%	—	2,305	2,405	2,527	2,621

FOLLETT CORPORATION

2233 West St.
River Grove, IL 60171
Phone: 708-583-2000
Fax: 708-452-9347
Web: www.follett.com

CEO: Charles R. (Chuck) Follett Jr.
CFO: Kathryn A. Stanton
HR: Richard A. Ellspermann
FYE: March 31
Type: Private

Not all kids like to read, but (fortunately for Follett) by the time they reach college, they don't have a choice. Follett is the #1 operator of college bookstores, with more than 850 campus bookshops (vs. about 635 for Barnes & Noble) across the US, as well as Canada. The company's business groups, which reach about 60 countries, also provide books and audiovisual materials to grade school and public libraries, library automation and management software, textbook reconditioning, and other services. Follett acquired its smaller online rival Varsity Group in 2008, complementing its own efollett.com website that sells college textbooks. The Follett family has owned and managed the company for four generations.

	Annual Growth	3/04	3/05	3/06	3/07	3/08
Sales ($ mil.)	7.1%	1,899.0	2,000.0	2,370.0	2,520.0	2,500.0
Employees	0.0%	10,000	10,000	8,300	8,000	10,000

FONAR CORPORATION

NASDAQ (CM): FONR

110 Marcus Dr.
Melville, NY 11747
Phone: 631-694-2929
Fax: 631-753-5150
Web: www.fonar.com

CEO: Raymond V. Damadian
CFO: Raymond V. Damadian
HR: —
FYE: June 30
Type: Public

SONAR finds objects hidden under the water using sound waves; FONAR uses magnetic resonance imaging (MRI) to find disease or injury hidden inside the body. The company was the first to market a commercial MRI scanner in 1980, and it is trying to stay at the forefront of the field with its Upright MRI, which scans patients in sitting, standing, or bending positions. FONAR also makes the FONAR 360, a room-sized MRI that does away with the claustrophobia-producing enclosed tubes of traditional machines. Additionally, FONAR's Health Management Corporation of America (HMCA) subsidiary provides management services to about 10 diagnostic imaging centers, primarily in Florida and New York.

	Annual Growth	6/05	6/06	6/07	6/08	6/09
Sales ($ mil.)	(21.6%)	104.9	33.1	33.2	35.6	39.7
Net income ($ mil.)	2.4%	1.0	(30.0)	(25.5)	(13.5)	1.1
Market value ($ mil.)	(49.8%)	160.7	73.7	26.8	12.1	10.2
Employees	(12.3%)	494	409	370	268	292

FONIX CORPORATION

OTC: FNIX

387 S. 520 West, Ste. 110
Linton, UT 84042
Phone: 801-553-6600
Fax: 801-553-6707
Web: www.fonix.com

CEO: Roger D. Dudley
CFO: Roger D. Dudley
HR: —
FYE: December 31
Type: Public

Fonix hopes to get speech down pat. The company develops text-to-speech and automated speech recognition applications that are integrated into a variety of products, enabling such services as voice-activated telephone menus. Marketing its products primarily to software developers, consumer electronics manufacturers, video game developers, and others who embed the software in their own products, Fonix also offers applications targeted to consumers.

	Annual Growth	12/04	12/05	12/06	12/07	*12/08
Sales ($ mil.)	(45.7%)	14.9	16.2	1.3	1.8	1.3
Net income ($ mil.)	—	(15.1)	(22.6)	(10.7)	15.0	(6.2)
Market value ($ mil.)	(88.0%)	62,546.7	6,481.5	907.4	64.8	13.0
Employees	1.2%	61	61	61	61	64

*Most recent year available

FOOD LION, LLC

2110 Executive Dr.
Salisbury, NC 28145
Phone: 704-633-8250
Fax: 704-636-5024
Web: www.foodlion.com

CEO: Cathy D. Green
CFO: —
HR: —
FYE: December 31
Type: Subsidiary

Food Lion is a king among grocery chains in the Southeast and Mid-Atlantic regions where it operates about 1,330 supermarkets under the Food Lion, Bloom, Bottom Dollar, and Harveys banners. About half of the company's stores are in the Carolinas, but it also has outlets in nine other states, including Virginia, Georgia, and Tennessee. Food Lion, which prides itself on extra low prices, has taken a beating from low-cost competitors, most notably Wal-Mart Supercenters, and a weak economy. The company's private-label Food Lion brand products accounts for about 20% of sales. Founded in 1957 as Food Town, Food Lion is the largest US subsidiary of Delhaize America, a subsidiary of Brussels-based grocer Delhaize.

An in-depth profile of this company is available to Hoover's Online members at hoovers.com.

635

FOOD TECHNOLOGY SERVICE, INC.

NASDAQ (CM): VIFL

502 Prairie Mine Rd.
Mulberry, FL 33860
Phone: 863-425-0039
Fax: 863-425-5526
Web: www.foodtechservice.com

CEO: Richard G. Hunter
CFO: Richard G. Hunter
HR: —
FYE: December 31
Type: Public

Food Technology Service operates a facility in Mulberry, Florida, that irradiates foods using gamma irradiation to kill insects and pathogens and to extend the shelf-life of foods by retarding spoilage. The company provides contract sterilization services to the food, medical-device, and consumer-goods industries, and also irradiates packaging, cosmetic ingredients, and horticultural items. Given that only three customers account for 67% of its sales, Food Technology has sought to diversify its customer base, mainly by emphasizing its medical sterilization services, which now account for 80% of its sales. Canada-based MDS Inc., a life-science services company, owns about 31% of Food Technology Service.

	Annual Growth	12/05	12/06	12/07	12/08	12/09
Sales ($ mil.)	10.1%	1.7	1.8	2.1	2.5	2.5
Net income ($ mil.)	49.5%	0.1	0.7	0.2	0.8	0.5
Market value ($ mil.)	(15.3%)	9.3	6.9	7.6	2.6	4.8
Employees	6.8%	10	12	13	13	13

FOODARAMA SUPERMARKETS, INC.

922 Hwy. 33, Bldg. 6, Ste. 1
Freehold, NJ 07728
Phone: 732-462-4700
Fax: 732-294-2322

CEO: Richard J. Saker
CFO: Thomas H. Flynn
HR: —
FYE: October 31
Type: Private

Foodarama Supermarkets thinks its customers deserve world-class grocery stores. A member of the Wakefern Food purchasing and distribution cooperative, the company operates about 25 ShopRite supermarkets in central New Jersey. The majority of Foodarama's stores are classified by the company as World Class, meaning they are larger than 50,000 sq. ft. and offer amenities such as international foods, in-store bakeries, kosher sections, snack bars, and pharmacies. Foodarama also operates two liquor stores, a garden center, a food processing facility (which supplies its stores with meat and prepared foods), and a bakery. The founding Saker family took the company private in 2006.

FOODBUY LLC

1105 Lakewood Pkwy., Ste. 400
Alpharetta, GA 30009
Phone: 678-256-8000
Fax: 678-256-8100
Web: www.foodbuy.com

CEO: Tony Shearer
CFO: —
HR: —
FYE: September 30
Type: Subsidiary

Restaurants can turn to this company when they need to buy some food. Foodbuy is a group purchasing organization (GPO) that serves as the in-house purchasing operation for the contract foodservice operations of Compass Group USA, a division of UK-based foodservice provider Compass Group. It sources food and non-food goods from more than 400 manufacturers for more than 12,000 dining locations, managing about $5 billion in purchases each year. Foodbuy also serves third-party customers, including restaurant chains, hotels, and other multi-unit foodservice operators.

FOOT LOCKER, INC.

NYSE: FL

112 W. 34th St.
New York, NY 10120
Phone: 212-720-3700
Fax: 212-720-4397
Web: www.footlocker-inc.com

CEO: Kenneth C. (Ken) Hicks
CFO: Robert W. McHugh
HR: Laurie J. Petrucci
FYE: January 31
Type: Public

Foot Locker leads the pack in the race to capture the biggest share of the athletic footwear market. The company is a leading retailer of athletic shoes and apparel, with about 3,500 specialty stores in more than 20 countries in North America and Europe, as well as Australia and New Zealand. Its 1,900-plus-store namesake Foot Locker chain is the #1 seller of name-brand (NIKE) athletic footwear in the US. The company also operates stores under the Lady Foot Locker, Kids Foot Locker, Footaction, Champs Sports, and CCS banners. In addition to its bricks-and-mortar business, Foot Locker markets sports gear through its direct-to-customer unit, which consists of catalog retailer Eastbay and Footlocker.com.

	Annual Growth	1/06	1/07	1/08	1/09	1/10
Sales ($ mil.)	(3.7%)	5,653.0	5,750.0	5,437.0	5,237.0	4,854.0
Net income ($ mil.)	(34.7%)	264.0	250.0	51.0	(80.0)	48.0
Market value ($ mil.)	(16.0%)	3,558.0	3,514.1	2,143.9	1,152.6	1,768.0
Employees	(3.3%)	44,276	45,406	44,415	39,758	38,764

FORBES INC.

60 5th Ave.
New York, NY 10011
Phone: 212-620-2200
Fax: 212-620-2245
Web: www.forbesinc.com

CEO: Malcolm S. (Steve) Forbes Jr.
CFO: Sean P. Hegarty
HR: Sharon Jautz
FYE: December 31
Type: Private

Repeat after Forbes: Capitalism is good! The family-owned company publishes the biweekly business magazine Forbes, long promoted as the "Capitalist Tool." It also publishes a handful of other magazines, including ForbesWoman and ForbesLife, a lifestyle magazine for business leaders. Its Forbes Digital includes websites such as Forbes.com, Investopedia.com, and RealClearPolitics.com. In addition, the company produces business-related conferences and publishes newsletters and custom magazines. Scottish immigrant and journalist B.C. Forbes launched Forbes in 1917. CEO Malcolm "Steve" Forbes (B.C.'s grandson) became known as a self-funded Republican presidential candidate in 1996 and 2000.

FORCE PROTECTION, INC.

NASDAQ (CM): FRPT

9801 Hwy. 78, Bldg. 1
Ladson, SC 29456
Phone: 843-574-7000
Fax: 843-329-0380
Web: www.forceprotectioninc.com

CEO: Michael Moody
CFO: Charles Mathis
HR: David R. (Dave) Hudson
FYE: December 31
Type: Public

Force Protection's vehicles protect military forces from blast forces. The company makes armored land vehicles designed to protect troops from landmines, bombs, and hostile fire. Force Protection's products include the 22-ton Buffalo, which is designed for mine-clearing operations, and the Cougar, a lighter-weight vehicle with similar armoring that can be used for route clearance support, urban patrol, and other activities. The Cheetah is the smallest of the company's offerings. It is used for reconnaissance and other urban operations. While the US Marine Corps is Force Protection's largest single customer, the US Army and friendly foreign governments also purchase military vehicles from the company.

	Annual Growth	12/05	12/06	12/07	12/08	12/09
Sales ($ mil.)	110.6%	49.7	196.0	890.7	1,326.3	977.1
Net income ($ mil.)	—	(16.6)	18.2	7.7	46.9	29.5
Market value ($ mil.)	60.8%	54.8	1,223.5	328.9	420.2	366.1
Employees	37.3%	329	658	1,300	1,170	1,170

FORCE10 NETWORKS, INC.

350 Holger Way	CEO: Henry Wasik
San Jose, CA 95134	CFO: William (Bill) Zerella
Phone: 408-571-3500	HR: Mary B. Cole
Fax: 408-571-3550	FYE: September 30
Web: www.force10networks.com	Type: Private

Force10 Networks develops communications networking equipment to be reckoned with. The company provides wireless backhaul equipment, Ethernet routing and switching systems, and metro and converged access equipment. Serving both the enterprise data center and communication network operator markets, Force10 sells to wireline and wireless service providers and large enterprises; other customers include educational institutions and research labs. It has such clients as data center and Internet exchange provider Equinix, NYSE Euronext, SEGA, and Yahoo! The company gets about three-quarters of its sales in the US. As the IPO market showed signs of coming to life again, Force10 filed to go public in 2010.

FORD FOUNDATION

320 E. 43rd St.	CEO: Luis A. Ubiñas
New York, NY 10017	CFO: Nicholas M. Gabriel
Phone: 212-573-5000	HR: —
Fax: 212-351-3677	FYE: September 30
Web: www.fordfound.org	Type: Foundation

As one of the US's largest philanthropic organizations, the Ford Foundation can afford to be generous. The foundation offers grants to individuals and institutions around the world that work to meet its goals of strengthening democratic values, reducing poverty and injustice, promoting international cooperation, and advancing human achievement. The Ford Foundation's charitable giving has run the gamut from A (Association for Asian Studies) to Z (Zanzibar International Film Festival). The foundation has an endowment of about $10 billion. Established in 1936 by Edsel Ford, whose father founded the Ford Motor Company, the foundation no longer owns stock in the automaker or has ties to the founding family.

FORD MOTOR COMPANY   NYSE: F

1 American Rd.	CEO: Alan R. Mulally
Dearborn, MI 48126	CFO: Lewis W.K. Booth
Phone: 313-322-3000	HR: Felicia J. Fields
Fax: 313-845-6073	FYE: December 31
Web: www.ford.com	Type: Public

Ford Motor began a manufacturing revolution with mass production assembly lines in the early 20th century. One of the world's largest auto makers, Ford brands include Ford, Lincoln, and Mercury — the latter to be dropped in late 2010. Among its successes are the redesigned Ford Mustang, the F-Series pickup, and the fuel-efficient Focus. Finance unit Ford Motor Credit is one of the US's leading auto finance companies. Ford owns a small stake in Mazda and controls the Volvo nameplate; the automaker has agreed to sell Volvo to Zhejiang Geely Holding, parent of Geely Automobile, for about $1.8 billion. Though it operates about 90 plants worldwide, Ford Motor gets more than half of its sales from North America.

	Annual Growth	12/05	12/06	12/07	12/08	12/09
Sales ($ mil.)	(9.6%)	177,089.0	160,123.0	172,455.0	146,277.0	118,308.0
Net income ($ mil.)	6.8%	2,275.0	(12,613.0)	(2,723.0)	(14,672.0)	2,962.0
Market value ($ mil.)	6.7%	26,298.8	25,583.4	22,926.3	7,801.1	34,065.8
Employees	(9.9%)	300,000	283,000	246,000	213,000	198,000

FORD MOTOR CREDIT COMPANY LLC

One American Rd.	CEO: Michael E. (Mike) Bannister
Dearborn, MI 48126	CFO: Kenneth R. Kent
Phone: 313-322-3000	HR: —
Fax: 313-323-2959	FYE: December 31
Web: www.fordcredit.com	Type: Subsidiary

Seems its trucks aren't the only things built Ford tough. The automaker's subsidiary, Ford Motor Credit, is proving to be pretty resilient, too. One of the world's largest auto financing companies, it funds autos for and through Ford, Lincoln, Mercury, and Volvo dealerships in some 70 countries. It finances new, used, and leased vehicles, and provides wholesale financing, mortgages, and capital loans for dealers. The company also offers business fleet financing and insurance. It had provided funding for Jaguar, Land Rover, and Mazda vehicles, but Ford sold or reduced its interests in those name-plates through separate transactions. The carmaker has arranged to sell Volvo, as well.

FOREMOST FARMS USA, COOPERATIVE

E10889 Penny Ln.	CEO: David E. (Dave) Fuhrmann
Baraboo, WI 53913	CFO: Michael Doyle
Phone: 608-355-8700	HR: Mike McDonald
Fax: 608-355-8699	FYE: December 31
Web: www.foremostfarms.com	Type: Cooperative

No jokes about "herd mentality," please. Foremost Farms USA (owned by some 2,300 dairy farmers in its founding state of Wisconsin and six other upper-Midwestern states) is a major US dairy cooperative. The co-op's member/farmers' herds supply some 5 billion pounds of milk per year, which Foremost turns into dairy products for its customers. Taking the "America's Dairyland" motto of its home state seriously, the cooperative also makes cheese, butter, and dairy-based ingredients. To reduce its dependence on the always fluctuating prices of commodity products, Foremost manufactures non-dairy value-added items, such as pharmaceutical-grade lactose and whey-based ingredients. Its products are sold worldwide.

	Annual Growth	12/04	12/05	12/06	12/07	12/08
Sales ($ mil.)	4.1%	—	1,419.2	1,245.8	1,600.0	1,600.0
Employees	(3.8%)	—	1,540	1,523	1,400	1,370

FOREST CITY ENTERPRISES, INC.   NYSE: FCEA

1100 Terminal Tower, 50 Public Sq.	CEO: Charles A. Ratner
Cleveland, OH 44113	CFO: Robert G. O'Brien
Phone: 216-621-6060	HR: Elena S. Iracane
Fax: —	FYE: January 31
Web: www.forestcity.net	Type: Public

Forest City Enterprises has gone from treeline to skyline. Founded in 1920 as a lumber dealer, the company now focuses on commercial and residential real estate development in metropolitan areas across the US. Its commercial group develops and manages 100 retail and office properties, hotels, life science buildings, and nearly 20 regional malls in about 15 states. The residential group owns and manages some 120 upscale and middle-market apartments, condominiums, senior citizen, and military housing units. Forest City also owns some 10,500 acres of land, some held for sale and some held for future development. The interrelated Ratner, Miller, and Shafran families control Forest City.

	Annual Growth	1/06	1/07	1/08	1/09	1/10
Sales ($ mil.)	1.2%	1,200.8	1,168.8	1,295.6	1,290.4	1,257.2
Net income ($ mil.)	—	83.5	177.3	52.4	(112.2)	(24.0)
Market value ($ mil.)	(26.1%)	5,927.7	9,465.8	6,253.0	1,087.2	1,770.6
Employees	(8.4%)	4,279	4,484	3,957	3,237	3,019

An in-depth profile of this company is available to Hoover's Online members at hoovers.com.

FOREST LABORATORIES, INC.

NYSE: FRX

909 3rd Ave.	CEO: Howard Solomon
New York, NY 10022	CFO: Francis I. Perier Jr.
Phone: 212-421-7850	HR: Bernard J. McGovern
Fax: 212-750-9152	FYE: March 31
Web: www.frx.com	Type: Public

Forest Laboratories doesn't just blend in with the trees. The company develops and manufactures name-brand as well as generic prescription and over-the-counter pharmaceutical products. The company's central nervous system (CNS) pharmaceutical line includes antidepressants Celexa and Lexapro, as well as Namenda, which treats Alzheimer's disease. Other products include treatments for thyroid disease, hypertension, respiratory ailments, and pain. Forest Laboratories markets directly to doctors, hospitals, drugstore chains, managed care organizations, and distributors through its own sales force in the US; it also has affiliated and independent sales representatives in the UK and Ireland.

	Annual Growth	3/05	3/06	3/07	3/08	3/09
Sales ($ mil.)	5.6%	3,159.6	2,912.1	3,441.8	3,836.3	3,922.8
Net income ($ mil.)	(2.2%)	838.8	708.5	454.1	967.9	767.7
Market value ($ mil.)	(12.2%)	11,172.6	13,494.8	15,554.0	12,097.9	6,640.1
Employees	0.4%	5,136	5,050	5,126	5,211	5,225

FOREST OIL CORPORATION

NYSE: FST

707 17th St., Ste. 3600	CEO: H. Craig Clark
Denver, CO 80202	CFO: Michael N. Kennedy
Phone: 303-812-1400	HR: Paul J. Dusha
Fax: 303-812-1602	FYE: December 31
Web: www.forestoil.com	Type: Public

Forest Oil hasn't gotten lost among the big trees of the oil and gas business as it squeezes hydrocarbons from old forests buried deep underground. The independent exploration and production company explores primarily in Arkansas, Louisiana, Texas, and western Canada and is focusing on building additional reserves in these core areas. It holds substantial acreage in Canada (11% of total reserves). Forest Oil also holds exploration acreage in Italy and South Africa. In 2008 the company reported estimated proved reserves of about 2.7 trillion cu. ft. of natural gas equivalent, of which 75% is natural gas.

	Annual Growth	12/05	12/06	12/07	12/08	12/09
Sales ($ mil.)	(8.0%)	1,072.0	820.0	1,083.9	1,647.2	768.5
Net income ($ mil.)	—	151.6	168.5	169.3	(1,026.3)	(923.1)
Market value ($ mil.)	(7.6%)	3,432.1	3,674.8	5,716.8	1,854.3	2,502.0
Employees	8.6%	506	585	728	814	705

FOREST PHARMACEUTICALS, INC.

13600 Shoreline Dr.	CEO: William B. (Bill) Sparks Jr.
St. Louis, MO 63045	CFO: C. Douglas Glidewell
Phone: 314-493-7000	HR: Joan Williams
Fax: —	FYE: March 31
Web: www.forestpharm.com	Type: Subsidiary

Forest Pharmaceuticals manufactures and distributes the drugs developed by its parent, Forest Laboratories. Its production lines crank out prescription tablets, capsules, and liquids at facilities in Ohio. It then packages the products at facilities in Missouri, New York, and Ohio. The company's facilities in Missouri serve as Forest Laboratories' national distribution hub, taking in products manufactured at other facilities, and shipping them out to customers throughout the US and Puerto Rico. Forest Pharmaceuticals also maintains customer support services to provide product information to prescribing physicians and patients.

FORESTAR GROUP INC.

NYSE: FOR

1300 S. MoPac Expwy., Ste. 3 South	CEO: James M. (Jim) DeCosmo
Austin, TX 78746	CFO: Christopher L. Nines
Phone: 512-433-5200	HR: —
Fax: 512-433-5204	FYE: December 31
Web: www.forestargroup.com	Type: Public

Forestar Group (formerly Forestar Real Estate Group) wants to succeed by going south. The company, which operates in the southern US, operates through three segments: real estate, mineral resources, and fiber resources. Its primary activity is developing residential and mixed-use communities; it has two-dozen entitlement projects, mostly in Texas and in the Atlanta area. Forestar owns more than 250,000 acres of real estate, mostly undeveloped land. The group also holds some 625,000 net acres of oil and gas mineral interests. The fiber resources segment encompasses the sale of wood fiber taken from the company's land holdings. Forestar was spun off from paper products manufacturer Temple-Inland in late 2007.

	Annual Growth	12/05	12/06	12/07	12/08	12/09
Sales ($ mil.)	(1.5%)	155.5	225.6	178.0	159.7	146.3
Net income ($ mil.)	14.1%	34.9	51.8	24.8	12.0	59.1
Market value ($ mil.)	(3.5%)	—	—	859.1	346.7	800.4
Employees	4.3%	—	82	88	93	93

FOREVER 21, INC.

2001 S. Alameda St.	CEO: Do Won (Don) Chang
Los Angeles, CA 90058	CFO: —
Phone: 213-741-5100	HR: —
Fax: 213-741-5161	FYE: December 31
Web: www.forever21.com	Type: Private

You don't have to be 21 or older to shop at Forever 21 stores — you just need your wallet. The fast-growing retailer operates more than 450 stores under the Forever 21, XXI Forever, ForLove 21, and Heritage 1981 banners in the US, Canada, and a dozen Asian countries, as well as an e-commerce site. The chain, which helped to pioneer fast fashion, offers cheap and chic apparel and accessories for women, men, teens, and kids. It also carries women's footwear, lingerie, and cosmetics. Most of Forever 21's trendy wares are private label and made in Southern California. CEO Don Chang and his wife founded the company as Fashion 21 in 1984.

	Annual Growth	12/04	12/05	12/06	12/07	12/08
Sales ($ mil.)	27.2%	—	—	1,050.0	1,300.0	1,700.0
Employees	—	—	—	—	—	—

FOREVER LIVING PRODUCTS INTERNATIONAL, INC.

7501 E. McCormick Pkwy.	CEO: Rex Gene Maughan
Scottsdale, AZ 85258	CFO: Rjay Lloyd
Phone: 480-998-8888	HR: —
Fax: 800-455-3503	FYE: December 31
Web: www.foreverliving.com	Type: Private

Forever Living Products might not lead you to immortality, but its aloe-vera-based health care products are intended to improve your well-being. The company sells aloe vera drinks, as well as aloe-vera-based aromatherapy products, cosmetics, dietary and nutritional supplements, lotion, soap, and tooth gel products. Owner and billionaire Rex Maughan also owns aloe vera plantations in the Dominican Republic, Mexico, and Texas; Aloe Vera of America, a processing plant; and Forever Resorts' US resorts and marinas, including Dallas-area Southfork Ranch (of *Dallas* TV show fame). Forever Living Products, founded in 1978, sells its goods through a global network of more than 9.3 million independent distributors.

FOREVERGREEN WORLDWIDE CORPORATION — OTC: FVRG

972 N. 1430 West
Orem, UT 84057
Phone: 801-655-5500
Fax: 801-655-5505
Web: www.forevergreen.org

CEO: Ronald K. (Ron) Williams
CFO: Paul T. Frampton
HR: —
FYE: December 31
Type: Public

ForeverGreen Worldwide wants to give customers a piece of its mind, naturally. The company offers 100% natural foods and personal-care products via a network of independent distributors. Its chemical-free goodies include salsas, snack packs (mixes of seeds, nuts, fruits, and grains), body oils, creams, lotions, cleansers, and shampoos. Its major brands include Pulse snack bars, FrequenSea drink, and 24 Karat Chocolate. Company board member George H. Brimhall II owns 45% of ForeverGreen; chairman and CEO Ronald Williams owns approximately 15%; and board member John S. Clayton owns some 11%.

	Annual Growth	12/05	12/06	12/07	12/08	12/09
Sales ($ mil.)	33.6%	3.8	3.5	22.7	21.7	12.1
Net income ($ mil.)	—	(2.0)	(1.2)	0.0	(1.1)	(1.2)
Market value ($ mil.)	(46.8%)	26.9	25.1	18.4	10.0	2.2
Employees	15.0%	20	50	62	56	35

FORGENT NETWORKS, INC. — NASDAQ (CM): ASUR

108 Wild Basin Dr.
Austin, TX 78746
Phone: 512-437-2700
Fax: 512-437-2365
Web: www.forgentnetworks.com

CEO: Pat Goepel
CFO: —
HR: —
FYE: July 31
Type: Public

Forgent Networks (dba Asure Software) can assure a more organized workplace. The company provides Web-based software through its NetSimplicity and iEmployee divisions. NetSimplicity's offerings include Meeting Room Manager, which lets users reserve meeting rooms and schedule equipment and resources. NetSimplicity also provides an asset management tool called Visual Asset Manager that tracks and manages fixed and mobile IT assets. The company's iEmployee division offers tools for managing time and attendance, benefits, payroll, and expense information. Forgent primarily sells its products directly, but it utilizes resellers for customers outside the US and federal government sales.

	Annual Growth	7/05	7/06	7/07	7/08	7/09
Sales ($ mil.)	0.3%	9.9	14.9	40.4	10.2	10.0
Net income ($ mil.)	—	(6.6)	(3.6)	12.2	(12.7)	(9.7)
Market value ($ mil.)	(43.6%)	48.7	12.6	25.9	8.9	4.9
Employees	22.8%	33	37	189	103	75

FORMFACTOR, INC. — NASDAQ (GS): FORM

7005 Southfront Rd.
Livermore, CA 94551
Phone: 925-290-4000
Fax: 925-290-4010
Web: www.formfactor.com

CEO: G. Carl Everett Jr.
CFO: Richard DeLateur
HR: Henry I. Feir
FYE: December 31
Type: Public

Welcome to *FormFactor*! On tonight's show, contestants must dive off a high platform, retrieve a silicon wafer at the bottom of the water tank, and then run tests on the semiconductors! Using its interconnect technology called MicroSpring, FormFactor makes wafer probe cards that test semiconductor circuits (especially memory chips) while they are still part of semiconductor wafers — before the wafers are cut into individual chips. FormFactor touts the process for its cost-effectiveness, since it allows testing of many chips at once across a range of scales and temperatures. Elpida Memory represents nearly half of sales. The company gets about three-fourths of revenues from the Asia/Pacific region.

	Annual Growth	12/05	12/06	12/07	12/08	12/09
Sales ($ mil.)	(13.1%)	237.5	369.2	462.2	210.2	135.3
Net income ($ mil.)	—	30.2	60.8	72.9	(80.6)	(155.7)
Market value ($ mil.)	(2.8%)	1,221.6	1,862.6	1,655.1	730.0	1,088.6
Employees	5.5%	653	936	1,124	940	808

FORMICA CORPORATION

10155 Reading Rd.
Cincinnati, OH 45241
Phone: 513-786-3400
Fax: 513-786-3566
Web: www.formica.com

CEO: Mark Adamson
CFO: —
HR: Linda Farfsing
FYE: December 31
Type: Subsidiary

Where would the modern kitchen be without it? Formica Corporation designs, makes, and distributes its eponymous high-pressure laminate used for countertop, table, floor, and other surfaces. Other products include fire-rated wall panels, sinks, doors, and toilet partitions. It also makes metal, stone, and wood veneer surface materials. In addition to residential kitchens, Formica's products are used in commercial buildings, including restaurants, stores, offices, and hospitals. The company sells its products in more than 100 countries in North America, South America, Europe, and Asia. Formica was acquired by New Zealand materials company Fletcher Building in 2007.

FORMOSA PLASTICS CORPORATION, U.S.A.

9 Peach Tree Hill Rd.
Livingston, NJ 07039
Phone: 973-992-2090
Fax: 973-992-9627
Web: www.fpcusa.com

CEO: Chih-Tsun Lee
CFO: D. Lin
HR: Martin Hass
FYE: December 31
Type: Subsidiary

Formosa Plastics Corp., U.S.A., is the prince of PVC. Affiliated with Taiwan's Formosa Plastics Corporation (one of the world's largest PVC suppliers), the company produces all manner of petrochemicals and plastic resins. Its product roster includes polyethylene, polypropylene, vinyl, and chlor alkali products like caustic soda. The company also produces suspension and specialty PVC resins, the former for pipe and fencing, the latter for flooring and insect screening. Other Formosa products are used for packaging and chemical processing. The fully vertically integrated company operates three manufacturing locations that are fed raw materials by oil and gas-producing and transportation subsidiaries.

FORRESTER RESEARCH, INC. — NASDAQ (GS): FORR

400 Technology Sq.
Cambridge, MA 02139
Phone: 617-613-6000
Fax: 617-613-5000
Web: www.forrester.com

CEO: George F. Colony
CFO: Michael A. Doyle
HR: Elizabeth Lemons
FYE: December 31
Type: Public

Can't see the tech forest for the trees? Maybe a Forrester ranger can guide you through the technological timber. One of the leading market research firms focused on the Internet and technology, Forrester Research supplies reports and briefs to more than 2,600 corporate clients, providing insight into market forces, industry trends, and consumer behavior. Forrester also offers custom research and consulting services to give its clients additional understanding of the technology market. In addition, the company produces a number of events where its clients can network with each other as well as with players in the technology industry.

	Annual Growth	12/05	12/06	12/07	12/08	12/09
Sales ($ mil.)	11.1%	153.2	181.5	212.1	240.9	233.4
Net income ($ mil.)	13.7%	11.3	17.8	18.9	29.2	18.9
Market value ($ mil.)	8.5%	422.6	611.1	631.6	635.9	584.9
Employees	8.1%	693	779	903	1,048	947

An in-depth profile of this company is available to Hoover's Online members at hoovers.com.

FORSTMANN LITTLE & CO.

767 5th Ave., Ste. 44
New York, NY 10153
Phone: 212-355-5656
Fax: 212-759-9059

CEO: Theodore J. (Ted) Forstmann
CFO: Winston W. Hutchins
HR: —
FYE: December 31
Type: Private

Don't let the "Little" fool you. Buyout firm Forstmann Little & Co. has been home to some big names. The company, which specializes in telecommunications, technology, education, and health care investments, counts among its former advisory board members Donald Rumsfeld, Colin Powell, George Shultz, and Henry Kissinger. Since its founding in 1978, Forstmann Little has invested in about 30 companies, including former holdings Gulfstream Aerospace, General Instrument, Dr Pepper, and Revlon. Current holdings include IMG and 24 Hour Fitness. It is led by the surviving founding group member, Ted Forstmann.

	Annual Growth	12/04	12/05	12/06	12/07	12/08
Est. sales ($ mil.)	—	—	—	—	—	1,681.0
Employees	—	—	—	—	—	17,034

FORSYTHE TECHNOLOGY, INC.

7770 Frontage Rd.
Skokie, IL 60077
Phone: 847-213-7000
Fax: 847-213-7922
Web: www.forsythe.com

CEO: William P. (Bill) Brennan
CFO: Albert L. (Al) Weiss
HR: Julie F. Nagle
FYE: December 31
Type: Private

Forsythe Technology believes it has the foresight to provide valuable business and information technology consulting services. The company helps businesses and government agencies manage their IT infrastructure, providing services ranging from strategy to implementation and support. It also provides leasing and other financial services. Serving clients from offices throughout the US and western Canada, the company works with vendors such as Cisco Systems and Oracle. Forsythe Technology customers have included Aflac and TriZetto. Chairman Richard Forsythe founded the company in 1971 as Forsythe McArthur Associates. Today the employee-owned company operates from about 50 offices in North America.

	Annual Growth	12/04	12/05	12/06	12/07	12/08
Sales ($ mil.)	11.7%	449.3	517.6	604.1	628.9	700.0
Employees	8.6%	639	619	718	808	890

FORT ORANGE FINANCIAL CORP.

OTC: FOFC

1375 Washington Ave.
Albany, NY 12206
Phone: 518-434-1212
Fax: 518-434-1242
Web: www.capitalbank.com

CEO: Peter D. Cureau
CFO: Steven J. Owens
HR: Victoria A. Harkins
FYE: December 31
Type: Public

Small businesses might find a veritable fortress in this orange. Fort Orange Financial was formed in 2006 to be the holding company for community-oriented Capital Bank, which operates three branch offices in and around Albany, New York. Capital Bank specializes in business banking, but also serves the general public. It offers checking and savings accounts, debit cards, IRAs, and CDs, among other traditional banking services. About half of the bank's lending portfolio is devoted to commercial mortgages, followed by business loans (one-third of loans), single- to four-family residential mortgages, construction loans, and multifamily mortgages.

FORTINET, INC.

NASDAQ (GM): FTNT

1090 Kifer Rd.
Sunnyvale, CA 94086
Phone: 408-235-7700
Fax: 408-235-7737
Web: www.fortinet.com

CEO: Ken Xie
CFO: Kenneth A. (Ken) Goldman
HR: Sherry Pulvers
FYE: December 31
Type: Public

Fortinet bravely tackles a host of security issues. The company develops and markets security appliances (sold under its FortiGate line) that integrate antivirus, firewall, content filtering, VPN, intrusion prevention systems (IPS), antispam and traffic shaping to detect and eliminate computer viruses, worms, intrusions, and inappropriate Web content. Continuous updates against all new threats are delivered by Fortinet's FortiGuard subscription services to provide real-time network protection. The company also offers complementary products that include its FortiMail e-mail security system and FortiAnalyzer logging, reporting and analysis systems. The company completed an IPO in 2009.

	Annual Growth	12/05	12/06	12/07	12/08	12/09
Sales ($ mil.)	26.0%	100.0	123.5	155.4	211.8	252.1
Net income ($ mil.)	—	—	(5.3)	(21.8)	7.4	60.2
Market value ($ mil.)	—	—	—	—	—	1,185.0
Employees	15.0%	700	—	1,000	1,151	1,223

FORTRESS INTERNATIONAL GROUP, INC.

Pink Sheets: FIGI

7226 Lee DeForest Dr.
Columbia, MD 21046
Phone: 410-423-7423
Fax: 410-423-7437
Web: www.thefigi.com

CEO: Thomas P. (Tom) Rosato
CFO: Timothy C. Dec
HR: —
FYE: December 31
Type: Public

Fortress International Group, Inc. (FIGI) is a bastion of security. FIGI companies design, build, and maintain secure, temperature-controlled data centers and IT storage facilities for private companies and government agencies. FIGI offers its start-to-finish service by operating through subsidiaries that specialize in a certain function, such as IT consulting or construction. Projects are either built from scratch or upgraded through renovations. While most of its customers are top secret, FIGI has worked with Digital Realty Trust and Internap Network Services, and is cleared to work at Department of Defense and US Army Corps of Engineers properties. CEO Tom Rosato controls about 20% of the company.

	Annual Growth	12/05	12/06	12/07	12/08	12/09
Sales ($ mil.)	(2.4%)	—	—	50.5	102.5	48.1
Net income ($ mil.)	—	—	—	(7.4)	(32.9)	(18.8)
Market value ($ mil.)	(64.0%)	—	—	68.9	13.5	9.0
Employees	(21.6%)	—	—	184	156	113

FORTRESS INVESTMENT GROUP LLC

NYSE: FIG

1345 Avenue of the Americas
New York, NY 10105
Phone: 212-798-6100
Fax: —
Web: www.fortressinv.com

CEO: Daniel H. (Dan) Mudd
CFO: Daniel N. Bass
HR: —
FYE: December 31
Type: Public

Who gives a fig about finance? Fortress (trading symbol FIG) certainly does. The global alternative investment firm manages private equity and hedge funds for institutional investors, wealthy individuals, and on its own behalf. Its private equity arm buys long-term, controlling stakes in undervalued companies; it also manages real estate investors Newcastle Investment and Eurocastle Investment. The hedge fund arm invests in liquid and hybrid hedge funds. Fortress has also begun offering a more traditional investment line. The group earns management fees, incentive revenues based on fund performance, and investment income on its own capital investments. The firm has some $40 billion in assets under management.

	Annual Growth	12/05	12/06	12/07	12/08	12/09
Sales ($ mil.)	(12.7%)	1,004.9	1,521.3	1,236.0	731.8	584.1
Net income ($ mil.)	—	192.7	442.9	(59.8)	(322.3)	(909.1)
Market value ($ mil.)	(46.6%)	—	—	7,152.9	459.1	2,043.0
Employees	19.6%	400	550	699	850	819

FORTUNE BRANDS, INC.   NYSE: FO

520 Lake Cook Rd.   CEO: Bruce A. Carbonari
Deerfield, IL 60015   CFO: Craig P. Omtvedt
Phone: 847-484-4400   HR: Elizabeth R. Lane
Fax: 847-478-0073   FYE: December 31
Web: www.fortunebrands.com   Type: Public

Execs at Fortune Brands have good reason to meet over a game of golf and a glass of bourbon. The holding company is a leading US producer and distributor of distilled spirits such as Jim Beam, Sauza, DeKuyper, Canadian Club, and Maker's Mark. Its golf equipment company, Acushnet, manufactures and markets brands such as Titleist, FootJoy, and Pinnacle. However, Fortune's largest segment is home products and hardware, where its holdings include Moen faucets, MasterBrand Cabinets, Master Lock padlocks, and Therma-Tru doors. All of Fortune Brands' products are sold primarily in Europe, Australia, and throughout North America.

	Annual Growth	12/05	12/06	12/07	12/08	12/09
Sales ($ mil.)	(0.1%)	6,734.7	8,255.0	8,052.2	7,608.9	6,694.7
Net income ($ mil.)	(20.9%)	621.1	830.1	762.6	311.1	242.8
Market value ($ mil.)	(13.7%)	11,884.3	13,006.9	11,022.1	6,287.9	6,580.4
Employees	(5.4%)	30,298	36,251	31,027	27,100	24,248

FORTUNE INDUSTRIES, INC.   NYSE Amex: FFI

6402 Corporate Dr.   CEO: Tena Mayberry
Indianapolis, IN 46278   CFO: Randy Butler
Phone: 317-532-1374   HR: —
Fax: 317-235-1011   FYE: August 31
Web: www.fdvi.net   Type: Public

Once a holding company owning several diversified businesses, Fortune Industries now seeks its fortune as a PEO. As a professional employer organization (PEO), Fortune Industries provides outsourced human resource services to small and midsized businesses (1 to 1,000 employees) in such areas as HR management, payroll, benefits, and tax processing. In order to focus solely on its PEO operations, in late 2008 the company divested subsidiary J.H. Drew, which made roadway guardrails and structural steel for commercial buildings, and a wireless infrastructure unit that catered to the telecommunications industry. In conjunction with the refocus, the company is changing its name to Fortune Employer Solutions.

	Annual Growth	8/04	8/05	8/06	8/07	*8/08
Sales ($ mil.)	24.0%	66.9	113.1	157.1	158.3	158.4
Net income ($ mil.)	—	2.4	(2.3)	2.2	(7.3)	(19.0)
Market value ($ mil.)	(39.5%)	105.1	77.0	53.2	29.3	14.1
Employees	5.6%	373	524	580	503	464

*Most recent year available

FORWARD AIR CORPORATION   NASDAQ (GS): FWRD

430 Airport Rd.   CEO: Bruce A. Campbell
Greeneville, TN 37745   CFO: Rodney L. Bell
Phone: 423-636-7000   HR: —
Fax: 423-636-7279   FYE: December 31
Web: www.forwardair.com   Type: Public

When it's time to haul freight, Forward Air never looks back. The company transports deferred airfreight — cargo that requires specific-time delivery but is less time-sensitive than airfreight. Forward Air typically receives freight that has been transported by plane, sends it to a sorting facility, then dispatches it by truck to a terminal near its destination. The company has about 2,300 trailers and 490 trailers and straight trucks in its fleet. It operates from about 85 terminals at or near airports in the US and Canada, including about a dozen regional hubs. Forward Air contracts with owner-operator truckers for cargo hauling. It also provides services such as warehousing and local pick-up and delivery.

	Annual Growth	12/05	12/06	12/07	12/08	12/09
Sales ($ mil.)	6.8%	320.9	352.8	392.7	474.4	417.4
Net income ($ mil.)	(31.6%)	44.9	48.9	44.9	42.5	9.8
Market value ($ mil.)	(9.1%)	1,062.1	838.4	903.3	703.3	725.3
Employees	24.8%	1,134	1,225	2,637	2,021	2,755

FORWARD INDUSTRIES, INC.   NASDAQ (CM): FORD

1801 Green Rd., Ste. E   CEO: Douglas W. Sabra
Pompano Beach, FL 33064   CFO: James O. McKenna
Phone: 954-419-9544   HR: —
Fax: 954-419-9735   FYE: September 30
Web: www.forwardindustries.com   Type: Public

Forward Industries helps keep the gadget guy and gal on the go. The company designs and markets custom carrying cases, bags, clips, hand straps, and related accessories made of leather, nylon, vinyl, plastic, PVC, and other synthetic fibers. It sells its goods to makers of portable products such as cellular telephones, laptop computers, MP3 players, and cameras. Three-quarters of Forward's sales come from medical monitoring and diagnostic kit carrying cases sold to just three customers — Abbott, Johnson & Johnson's Lifescan, and Roche — for use by diabetics (a growing population) and others. Contractors in China manufacture most of the company's products.

	Annual Growth	9/05	9/06	9/07	9/08	9/09
Sales ($ mil.)	(23.9%)	51.9	30.6	22.2	20.0	17.4
Net income ($ mil.)	—	9.4	1.5	(0.6)	(0.9)	(1.4)
Market value ($ mil.)	(48.0%)	186.9	40.8	24.5	16.3	13.6
Employees	(19.4%)	71	49	49	53	30

FOSSIL, INC.   NASDAQ (GS): FOSL

2280 N. Greenville Ave.   CEO: Kosta N. Kartsotis
Richardson, TX 75082   CFO: Mike L. Kovar
Phone: 972-234-2525   HR: Dean Carter
Fax: 972-234-4669   FYE: December 31
Web: www.fossil.com   Type: Public

Fossil digs the watch business while unearthing a place in the accessories and apparel niches. A leading mid-priced watchmaker in the US, it generates most of its sales from watches. Brands include its Fossil and Relic watches, as well as licensed names Armani, Michael Kors, adidas, Burberry, and Marc Jacobs, and private-label watches for Target and Wal-Mart. Fossil also distributes fashion accessories, such as leather goods, sunglasses, and apparel. The firm sells through department stores and specialty shops in more than 100 countries and in the US through some 200 company-owned stores, as well as through its own catalog and website. Its products are also sold in gift shops on cruise ships and in airports.

	Annual Growth	12/05	12/06	12/07	12/08	12/09
Sales ($ mil.)	10.4%	1,040.5	1,214.0	1,433.0	1,583.2	1,548.1
Net income ($ mil.)	15.5%	78.1	77.6	123.3	138.1	139.2
Market value ($ mil.)	11.8%	1,449.3	1,521.4	2,828.5	1,125.2	2,261.2
Employees	2.5%	7,160	7,400	6,000	7,355	7,900

FOSTER POULTRY FARMS

1000 Davis St.   CEO: Ron Foster
Livingston, CA 95334   CFO: John Landis
Phone: 209-357-1121   HR: Tim Walsh
Fax: 209-394-6342   FYE: December 31
Web: www.fosterfarms.com   Type: Private

It doesn't matter if Henny Penny is having hot flashes, Foster Poultry Farms never uses hormones (nor does it inject salt water into its birds to plump them up). The company is one of the leading poultry processors in the US with vertically integrated operations, taking chickens and turkeys from the incubator to grocers' meat cases, delis, and freezers. It sells poultry products mostly under the Foster Farms brand. In addition to the retail market, Foster Poultry Farms supplies customers in the foodservice industry, including restaurant and other hospitality operators. The family-owned company was started in 1939 by Max and Verda Foster. The Fosters also own and operate sister company Foster Dairy Farms.

	Annual Growth	12/04	12/05	12/06	12/07	12/08
Est. sales ($ mil.)	4.8%	1,660.0	1,730.0	1,800.0	1,890.0	2,000.0
Employees	0.0%	10,000	10,000	10,500	10,000	10,000

⊞ FOSTER'S AMERICAS

610 Airpark Rd.
Napa, CA 94558
Phone: 707-259-4500
Fax: 707-259-4542
Web: www.fosters.com.au/about/companies.htm

CEO: Stephen Brauer
CFO: James Collins
HR: Lisa Hailey
FYE: June 30
Type: Subsidiary

A name, give me a name. According to the Way Back Machine, this company was once called Beringer Blass Wine Estates but was given its first Foster moniker (Foster's Wine Estates) after Australia's Foster's Group bought it from Texas Pacific Group in 2001 and combined it with Mildara Blass. It was renamed again in 2006, when its parent combined it with its Southcorp Wines Americas group. Foster's Americas (the name now seems permanent) offers premium wines; its brands include Beringer, Lindemans, Penfolds, Rosemount Estate, and Wolf Blass. It also distributes Foster's Lager in the US, Canada, and Central and South America. The company sells some 6 million cases of beer and 20 million cases of wine per year.

	Annual Growth	6/04	6/05	6/06	6/07	6/08
Est. sales ($ mil.)	—	—	—	—	—	69.3
Employees	—	—	—	—	—	900

FOUR OAKS FINCORP, INC.

OTC: FOFN

6114 US 301 South
Four Oaks, NC 27524
Phone: 919-963-2177
Fax: 919-963-4169
Web: portal.fxfn.com/zfobtnc

CEO: Ayden R. Lee Jr.
CFO: Nancy S. Wise
HR: —
FYE: December 31
Type: Public

There's no need to knock on wood when trusting your money to Four Oaks Fincorp. It's the holding company for Four Oaks Bank & Trust, which (with the 2008 acquisition of LongLeaf Community Bank) operates about 20 branches in central and eastern North Carolina. The bank offers standard retail products and services, including checking and savings accounts, CDs, IRAs, and money market accounts. It originates mostly real estate loans, which account for nearly 90% of loans. It also writes business, consumer, and farm loans. Four Oaks Bank also offers insurance and investment services. The company in 2009 acquired Nuestro Banco, a single-branch bank serving Hispanic customers in Raleigh.

	Annual Growth	12/05	12/06	12/07	12/08	12/09
Assets ($ mil.)	16.9%	522.4	608.1	708.3	924.8	976.8
Net income ($ mil.)	—	5.3	7.0	5.7	4.2	(2.1)
Market value ($ mil.)	(24.8%)	123.1	182.0	117.9	51.6	39.3
Employees	11.1%	135	156	177	208	206

FOX & HOUND RESTAURANT GROUP

1551 N. Waterfront Pkwy., Ste. 310
Wichita, KS 67206
Phone: 316-634-0505
Fax: 316-634-6060
Web: www.tentcorp.com

CEO: Stephen M. Johnson
CFO: James K. (Jim) Zielke
HR: Jennifer Kurth
FYE: December 31
Type: Private

You might say sports fans can really dig in at this bar and grill chain. Fox & Hound Restaurant Group operates about 85 sports bars and pubs in 25 states under the banners Fox & Hound Pub & Grille and Bailey's Pub & Grille. Popular for watching sports on TV while enjoying a menu heavy on burgers and other carnivorous cravings, the locations also offer a wide selection of beer, billiards, darts, and other entertainments. Most of the pubs are found in Texas, North Carolina, and Tennessee. Restaurateur Jamie Coulter started the Fox & Hound chain in 1997. The company is owned by F & H Acquisition Corp., an investment group led by Dallas-based Newcastle Partners that also owns the Champps family entertainment chain.

FOX CHASE BANCORP, INC.

NASDAQ (CM): FXCB

4390 Davisville Rd.
Hatboro, PA 19040
Phone: 215-682-7400
Fax: 215-682-4147
Web: www.foxchasebank.com

CEO: Thomas M. Petro
CFO: Roger Deacon
HR: Mary Regnery
FYE: December 31
Type: Public

Fox Chase Bancorp is the holding company for Fox Chase Bank, which has served individuals and businesses in the Philadelphia area since 1867. The bank operates about a dozen offices in southeastern Pennsylvania and southern New Jersey; it offers standard products and services including checking and savings accounts, CDs, and money market accounts. Residential mortgages make up about half of the bank's loan portfolio; home equity loans add another 15%. Other offerings include commercial loans and automobile loans. Mutual holding company Fox Chase MHC owns 60% of Fox Chase Bancorp, but the bank plans to convert to a stock holding company structure.

	Annual Growth	12/05	12/06	12/07	12/08	12/09
Assets ($ mil.)	10.7%	781.3	757.0	812.9	931.3	1,173.8
Net income ($ mil.)	—	6.0	3.6	1.9	1.2	(1.0)
Market value ($ mil.)	(11.0%)	—	183.7	155.1	149.7	129.6
Employees	1.2%	145	151	153	151	152

⊞ FOX ENTERTAINMENT GROUP, INC.

10201 W. Pico Blvd., Bldg. 100, Ste. 3220
Los Angeles, CA 90035
Phone: 310-369-1000
Fax: 310-969-3300
Web: www.fox.com

CEO: Chase Carey
CFO: David F. DeVoe
HR: Mitsy Wilson
FYE: June 30
Type: Subsidiary

This Fox has cunning ways to keep TV and movie fans entertained. Fox Entertainment Group (FEG) oversees a broad collection of film and TV entertainment assets owned by media giant News Corporation. Its Fox Filmed Entertainment (FFE) division is a leading producer of movies for theatrical and home entertainment release through such studios as Fox 2000, Fox Searchlight, and its flagship Twentieth Century Fox imprint. FEG also oversees the FOX television network, the upstart MyNetworkTV, and more than 25 company-owned TV broadcasting stations. In addition, it runs a portfolio of cable channels, including FOX News, FX, and the regional sports networks of Fox Sports Net.

FOX NEWS NETWORK, LLC

1211 Avenue of the Americas
New York, NY 10036
Phone: 212-301-3000
Fax: 212-301-8588
Web: www.foxnews.com

CEO: Roger Ailes
CFO: Mark Kranz
HR: —
FYE: June 30
Type: Subsidiary

This news channel reports and people have decided to watch. FOX News Network operates the FOX News Channel, the leading 24-hour cable news station that reaches more than 95 million US homes. It provides round-the-clock news coverage and commentary, including such top rated programs as *The O'Reilly Factor*, featuring commentator Bill O'Reilly, and *Hannity* with Sean Hannity. FOX News also produces content distributed to TV affiliates of the FOX network and publishes news online; its FOX News Radio Network syndicates news to radio stations around the country. Launched by Rupert Murdoch's News Corporation in 1996, the channel's less than tacit support of conservative politics has stirred both passion and criticism.

FOX RACING, INC.

18400 Sutter Blvd.
Morgan Hill, CA 95037
Phone: 408-776-8633
Fax: 408-776-8610
Web: www.foxracing.com

CEO: Peter Fox
CFO: —
HR: —
FYE: December 31
Type: Private

Fox Racing caters to those who are crazy like a Fox Head. Fox Racing sells motocross apparel including motocross pants, jerseys, gloves, boots, and helmets emblazoned with its iconic fox head graphic. The company also makes BMX and mountain bike apparel, T-shirts, hats, jeans, sweaters, sweatshirts, and jackets. Fox Racing, which now sells eyewear and footwear, sells its products through sporting goods and cycle shops nationwide; it also operates a store in Santa Clara, California. Fox Racing is branching out into surfwear and sells its products in surf shops. In 1974, Geoff Fox founded the company, which is still family-owned and -operated.

	Annual Growth	12/04	12/05	12/06	12/07	12/08
Est. sales ($ mil.)	—	—	—	—	—	244.0
Employees	—	—	—	—	—	420

FPB BANCORP, INC.

NASDAQ (GM): FPBI

1301 SE Port St. Lucie Blvd.
Port St. Lucie, FL 34952
Phone: 772-398-1388
Fax: 772-398-1399
Web: www.1stpeoplesbank.com

CEO: David W. (Dave) Skiles
CFO: Nancy E. Aumack
HR: —
FYE: December 31
Type: Public

FPB Bancorp is for the birds. Snow birds, that is. It's the holding company for First Peoples Bank, which targets retired winter visitors, as well as year-round residents and small to midsized businesses in southeastern Florida. The six-branch bank operates in Fort Pierce, Palm City, Port St. Lucie, Stuart, and Vero Beach, offering such standard deposit products as CDs and checking, savings, and money market accounts. Commercial real estate and business loans together account for about 85% of its loan portfolio; consumer loans make up most of the rest. The bank sells into the secondary market all of the fixed-rate residential mortgages that it writes. First Peoples Bank opened two new branches in 2008.

	Annual Growth	12/05	12/06	12/07	12/08	12/09
Assets ($ mil.)	18.2%	127.3	153.4	196.8	239.2	248.2
Net income ($ mil.)	—	0.8	0.6	0.2	(3.0)	(9.2)
Market value ($ mil.)	(48.1%)	32.7	34.3	20.2	4.1	2.4
Employees	7.2%	56	71	81	73	74

FPIC INSURANCE GROUP, INC.

NASDAQ (GS): FPIC

225 Water St., Ste. 1400
Jacksonville, FL 32202
Phone: 904-354-2482
Fax: 904-475-1159
Web: www.fpic.com

CEO: John R. Byers
CFO: Charles Divita III
HR: —
FYE: December 31
Type: Public

Pulled the wrong tooth or read an X-ray backwards? FPIC Insurance Group knows that these things happen. Through its First Professionals Insurance subsidiary, the company sells medical professional liability (including medical error and malpractice) insurance to more than 13,000 physicians and dentists. Its Anesthesiologists Professional Assurance Company subsidiary serves that specialty market. Although the company is licensed in nearly 30 states, Florida accounts for more than 80% of its premiums written. FPIC's subsidiaries sell its policies through independent agents and First Professionals Insurance is an endorsed carrier for several local medical associations.

	Annual Growth	12/05	12/06	12/07	12/08	12/09
Assets ($ mil.)	(5.8%)	1,308.5	1,219.1	1,077.0	998.0	1,031.5
Net income ($ mil.)	(0.7%)	35.0	51.6	50.9	32.1	34.0
Market value ($ mil.)	2.7%	226.0	253.8	280.0	285.2	251.6
Employees	(23.1%)	472	160	143	140	165

FRAGRANCENET.COM, INC.

Pink Sheets: FGNT

104 Parkway Dr. South
Hauppauge, NY 11788
Phone: 631-582-5204
Fax: 631-582-8433
Web: www.fragrancenet.com

CEO: Dennis M. Apfel
CFO: Dennis M. Apfel
HR: —
FYE: March 31
Type: Public

FragranceNet.com has set its sights on the sweet smell of success through its fragrance site. Customers can buy — but not sample — more than 10,000 discounted brand-name fragrances, hair and skin care products, aromatherapy items, and scented candles at FragranceNet.com. The company carries products under designer names Ralph Lauren, Christian Dior, Hermes, Nicole Miller, Yves Saint Laurent, Oscar de la Renta, Fendi, and others. In addition to the website, the fragrance firm operates a wholesale business called FragranceNet Wholesales. FragranceNet.com got its start in 1995 by selling fragrances via an 800 number.

FRANK CONSOLIDATED ENTERPRISES, INC.

666 Garland Place
Des Plaines, IL 60016
Phone: 847-699-7000
Fax: 847-699-6494
Web: www.wheels.com

CEO: James S. (Jim) Frank
CFO: Mary Ann O'Dwyer
HR: Joan Richards
FYE: August 31
Type: Private

Frank Consolidated Enterprises believes that where there's a "Wheels," there's a way — to make money. Frank Consolidated is a holding company for Wheels, which pioneered the auto leasing concept and provides fleet management services (including administrative, management, and financing assistance) to help clients maintain their vehicle fleets. The company operates in the US as Wheels and does business in other countries through Fleet Synergy International, an alliance of fleet management and leasing firms. Overall, Wheels manages about 300,000 vehicles. It also purchases and remarkets some 120,000 vehicles annually. Wheels was established in 1939, and is owned and led by the family of founder Zollie Frank.

	Annual Growth	8/04	8/05	8/06	8/07	8/08
Sales ($ mil.)	5.7%	1,600.0	1,733.0	1,890.0	2,000.0	2,000.0
Employees	2.2%	550	551	602	600	600

⊞ FRANKLIN COVEY CO.

NYSE: FC

2200 W. Parkway Blvd.
Salt Lake City, UT 84119
Phone: 801-817-1776
Fax: 801-817-8069
Web: www.franklincovey.com

CEO: Robert A. (Bob) Whitman
CFO: Stephen D. (Steve) Young
HR: Todd Davis
FYE: August 31
Type: Public

Franklin Covey knows a few habits that will help you. The publisher of *The 7 Habits of Highly Effective People* offers clients productivity and time-management seminars, training and consulting in practice areas such as leadership, strategy execution, customer loyalty, trust, sales performance, and individual effectiveness. Clients have included companies, government entities, and educational institutions, mostly in the US. The company sold its Consumer Solutions unit (which sold audio- and videotapes, binders, books, planners, and software) in 2008 to focus on consulting and training. Franklin Covey was formed in 1997 when Franklin Quest acquired the company created by productivity guru Stephen Covey.

	Annual Growth	8/05	8/06	8/07	8/08	8/09
Sales ($ mil.)	(17.7%)	283.5	278.6	284.1	260.1	130.1
Net income ($ mil.)	—	10.2	28.6	7.6	5.8	(10.8)
Market value ($ mil.)	(5.7%)	118.8	97.5	127.1	151.8	94.0
Employees	(18.1%)	1,333	1,237	1,425	600	600

An in-depth profile of this company is available to Hoover's Online members at hoovers.com.

643

FRANKLIN CREDIT HOLDING CORPORATION

Pink Sheets: FCMC

101 Hudson St.
Jersey City, NJ 07302
Phone: 201-604-1800
Fax: 201-604-4400
Web: www.franklincredit.com

CEO: Thomas J. (Tom) Axon
CFO: Paul D. Colasono
HR: —
FYE: December 31
Type: Public

Franklin Credit Holding is the holding company of mortgage servicer Franklin Credit Management. Franklin Credit Management bought discounted subprime mortgage assets (sometimes referred to as "scratch and dent" loans) in the secondary market, while subsidiary Tribeca Lending issued subprime residential mortgage loans to borrowers with poor or limited credit histories. However, like many others, the company was hamstrung by the mortgage mess and ceased originating and acquiring loans under terms of restructuring agreements with creditors in 2007. After a dismal 2008, the company entered into a major restructuring agreement with its lender that transferred most of its bad loans off the books.

	Annual Growth	12/05	12/06	12/07	12/08	12/09
Sales ($ mil.)	—	121.4	163.8	169.3	109.9	(244.8)
Net income ($ mil.)	—	7.9	(1.8)	(8.6)	(476.3)	(358.1)
Market value ($ mil.)	(41.9%)	63.4	37.8	6.8	2.8	7.2
Employees	(8.1%)	216	232	207	220	154

FRANKLIN ELECTRIC CO., INC.

NASDAQ (GS): FELE

400 E. Spring St.
Bluffton, IN 46714
Phone: 260-824-2900
Fax: 260-824-2909
Web: www.franklinelect.com

CEO: R. Scott Trumbull
CFO: John J. Haines
HR: Gary D. Ward
FYE: December 31
Type: Public

Franklin Electric would do Old Ben proud. The company keeps things flowing by making and distributing submersible and specialty electric motors, electronic drives and controls, and related items. Franklin Electric's fueling system products include electronic tank monitoring equipment, fittings, flexible piping, nozzles, and vapor recovery systems. Its products are used primarily by OEMs that incorporate them in freshwater or underground petroleum pumping systems, sewage pumps, and vacuum pumping systems. The US makes up more than half of sales. Major customers include ITT Corp. and Pentair.

	Annual Growth	12/05	12/06	12/07	12/08	12/09
Sales ($ mil.)	9.2%	439.6	557.9	602.0	745.6	626.0
Net income ($ mil.)	(13.3%)	46.0	57.0	28.7	44.1	26.0
Market value ($ mil.)	(7.4%)	919.7	1,195.3	890.1	653.8	675.7
Employees	5.7%	2,800	3,100	3,200	3,500	3,500

⊞ FRANKLIN ELECTRONIC PUBLISHERS, INCORPORATED

1 Franklin Plaza
Burlington, NJ 08016
Phone: 609-386-2500
Fax: 609-387-1787
Web: www.franklin.com

CEO: Barry J. Lipsky
CFO: Frank A. Musto
HR: —
FYE: March 31
Type: Private

Like to read but hate turning those pesky pages? Franklin Electronic Publishers may have a solution for you. The company markets handheld, electronic devices (which are made by third parties) that display the text of reference and entertainment publications. It owns or licenses more than 115,000 electronic titles in sixteen languages. Those titles run the gamut from *Merriam-Webster's Collegiate Dictionary*, to popular fiction, to the *Holy Bible*, and can be downloaded to Franklin's own handheld devices and those of other electronics manufacturers using Windows, Palm, Pocket PC, Windows CE/Smartphone, and Symbian operating systems. In addition, Franklin owns linguistic software maker Proximity Technology.

	Annual Growth	3/05	3/06	3/07	3/08	3/09
Sales ($ mil.)	(6.8%)	62.1	59.6	52.2	60.6	46.8
Net income ($ mil.)	—	2.4	2.0	(3.2)	2.5	(7.1)
Employees	(9.7%)	200	185	177	174	133

FRANKLIN FINANCIAL SERVICES CORPORATION

OTC: FRAF

20 S. Main St.
Chambersburg, PA 17201
Phone: 717-264-6116
Fax: 717-261-3545
Web: www.fmtrustonline.com

CEO: William E. Snell Jr.
CFO: Mark R. Hollar
HR: Karen C. Carmack
FYE: December 31
Type: Public

Ben Franklin said, "A penny saved is a penny earned," but Franklin Financial might be able to convert those pennies into dollars. It's the holding company for Farmers and Merchants Trust Company (F&M Trust), a community bank serving south-central Pennsylvania from more than 20 locations. Established in 1906, F&M Trust offers standard deposit products, including checking and savings accounts, IRAs, and CDs. It also provides discount brokerage, insurance, retirement planning, and other investment services. More than half of the company's lending portfolio is devoted to commercial, industrial, and agricultural loans; the bank also makes consumer, construction, and residential mortgage loans.

	Annual Growth	12/05	12/06	12/07	12/08	12/09
Assets ($ mil.)	12.0%	621.4	799.3	820.4	902.5	979.4
Net income ($ mil.)	2.0%	6.1	7.6	9.3	8.6	6.6
Market value ($ mil.)	(10.3%)	97.9	105.8	96.7	70.7	63.3
Employees	5.6%	204	230	254	261	254

FRANKLIN PRECISION INDUSTRY, INC.

3220 Bowling Green Rd.
Franklin, KY 42134
Phone: 270-586-4450
Fax: 270-586-0180
Web: www.fpik.com

CEO: Kenji Kasamatsu
CFO: —
HR: Mari Beth Barnes
FYE: March 31
Type: Subsidiary

When it comes to helping vehicles meet emission requirements, Franklin Precision Industry (FPI) is, in a word, precise. As a QS-9000 and ISO-14000 registered supplier of air-induction and emission components, FPI makes throttle bodies, carbon canisters, fuel pumps modules, and other parts for auto makers. The company uses POKAYOKE (mistake-proof) devices in its manufacturing process, as well as the Toyota Production System and the KAIZEN continuous improvement program to increase efficiency on a company-wide level. Major customers include Toyota, Nissan, and Denso. A subsidiary of Aisan Industry, FPI was founded in 1991.

⊞ FRANKLIN RESOURCES, INC.

NYSE: BEN

1 Franklin Pkwy., Bldg. 970, 1st Fl.
San Mateo, CA 94403
Phone: 650-312-2000
Fax: 650-312-5606
Web: www.franklintempleton.com

CEO: Gregory E. (Greg) Johnson
CFO: Kenneth A. Lewis
HR: Penelope S. Alexander
FYE: September 30
Type: Public

Franklin Resources believes a penny saved is a penny lost — if it's not wisely invested. Operating as Franklin Templeton Investments, the firm manages a family of more than 300 mutual funds that invest in international and domestic stocks; taxable and tax-exempt money market instruments; and corporate, municipal, and US government bonds. The investment products are sold under the Franklin, Templeton, Mutual Series, Bissett, Darby, and Fiduciary banners. Franklin Resources also offers separately managed accounts and insurance product funds. The company has more than $520 billion in assets under management and 21 million shareholder accounts.

	Annual Growth	9/05	9/06	9/07	9/08	9/09
Assets ($ mil.)	1.6%	8,893.9	9,499.9	9,943.3	9,176.5	9,468.5
Net income ($ mil.)	(4.0%)	1,057.6	1,267.6	1,772.9	1,588.2	896.8
Market value ($ mil.)	4.6%	19,087.4	24,041.1	28,985.7	20,035.4	22,870.3
Employees	1.7%	7,200	8,000	8,700	8,800	7,700

FRANKLIN STREET PROPERTIES CORP.

NYSE Amex: FSP

401 Edgewater Place, Ste. 200	CEO: George J. Carter
Wakefield, MA 01880	CFO: John G. Demeritt
Phone: 781-557-1300	HR: —
Fax: 781-246-2807	FYE: December 31
Web: www.franklinstreetproperties.com	Type: Public

A real estate investment trust (REIT), Franklin Street Properties acquires, finances, leases, and manages office properties in about 15 states throughout the US. It owns some 30 properties located mainly in suburban areas and manages about a dozen others; Dallas, Denver, Houston, and Washington, DC, are its largest markets. The company's FSP Investment unit is an investment bank and brokerage that organizes REITs that invest in single properties and raises equity for them through private placements. Another subsidiary, FSP Management, manages properties for Franklin Street, as well as for some of the REITs sponsored by FSP Investment.

	Annual Growth	12/05	12/06	12/07	12/08	12/09
Sales ($ mil.)	6.6%	99.4	118.2	128.9	123.8	128.5
Net income ($ mil.)	(11.1%)	44.6	49.5	37.3	32.0	27.9
Market value ($ mil.)	(8.6%)	1,669.3	1,677.3	1,179.3	1,175.3	1,164.1
Employees	2.5%	39	38	38	40	43

FRANKLIN WIRELESS CORP.

OTC: FKWL

9853 Pacific Heights Blvd., Ste. J	CEO: O. C. Kim
San Diego, CA 92121	CFO: O. C. Kim
Phone: 858-623-0000	HR: —
Fax: 858-623-0050	FYE: June 30
Web: www.fklt.com	Type: Public

Franklin Wireless is a founding father of the mobile nation. The company makes connectivity products for wireless devices. Its products include USB, embedded, and standalone modems, as well as PC cards. Customers use its products to connect their mobile computers to wireless broadband networks. The company sells directly to wireless operators and through distributors. Its customers include consumer electronics makers, cellular operators, and end users. Franklin generated about three quarters of its revenues from customers in Caribbean and South American countries in fiscal 2008.

	Annual Growth	6/05	6/06	6/07	6/08	6/09
Sales ($ mil.)	199.1%	0.3	1.0	10.4	34.7	24.0
Net income ($ mil.)	—	(0.7)	(0.3)	1.3	3.9	3.6
Market value ($ mil.)	(4.5%)	11.6	8.2	20.3	27.4	9.6
Employees	41.4%	5	8	9	13	20

⊞ FRED MEYER STORES, INC.

3800 SE 22nd Ave.	CEO: Michael L. (Mike) Ellis
Portland, OR 97202	CFO: David W. Deatherage
Phone: 503-232-8844	HR: Carl Wojciechowski
Fax: 503-797-5609	FYE: January 31
Web: www.fredmeyer.com	Type: Subsidiary

Fred Meyer Stores went out for groceries and wound up in Kroger's cart. The chain — known as Freddy's — is a supercenter pioneer providing food and general merchandise to cost-conscious consumers in the Pacific Northwest and Alaska. One of the largest supercenter operators in the US (along with Wal-Mart and Costco Wholesale), Fred Meyer's 130-odd multidepartment stores (averaging 155,000 sq. ft.) offer everything from apparel and home goods to groceries, consumer electronics, fuel, and jewelry. Its Web store delivers to the Alaska Bush. Kroger has leveraged Fred Meyer's general merchandising expertise as defense against Wal-Mart, which has overtaken Kroger as the largest seller of groceries in the US.

FREDERICK'S OF HOLLYWOOD GROUP INC.

NYSE Amex: FOH

1115 Broadway	CEO: Thomas J. Lynch
New York, NY 10010	CFO: Thomas Rende
Phone: 212-798-4000	HR: —
Fax: 212-684-3295	FYE: July 31
Web: www.fohgroup.com	Type: Public

Frederick's of Hollywood Group is making big business out of little somethings. Through the 2008 merger of Frederick's of Hollywood and Movie Star, the group pairs two of the top intimates makers and retailers. The group boasts US retail operations and wholesales in the US and Canada. Its Frederick's of Hollywood subsidiary peddles intimates, as well as wigs, hosiery, and dresses, through its catalog, e-commerce site, and more than 130 namesake stores. The group's Movie Star unit designs intimate apparel, sleepwear, leisurewear, and loungewear under brands Movie Star, Cinema Etoile, and others. Movie Star sells to discount, specialty, mass merchandise, and department stores and to catalog merchants.

	Annual Growth	6/05	6/06	6/07	*7/08	7/09
Sales ($ mil.)	31.8%	58.5	51.6	63.5	182.2	176.3
Net income ($ mil.)	—	(3.1)	(1.0)	0.1	(15.4)	(34.0)
Market value ($ mil.)	(14.0%)	45.5	40.2	137.4	25.9	24.8
Employees	57.5%	289	304	312	1,922	1,779

*Fiscal year change

⊞ FREDERICK'S OF HOLLYWOOD, INC.

6255 W. Sunset Blvd., Ste. 600	CEO: Linda LoRe
Hollywood, CA 90028	CFO: Thomas Rende
Phone: 323-466-5151	HR: Khybrette Neal
Fax: 323-464-5149	FYE: July 31
Web: www.fredericks.com	Type: Subsidiary

Even in a town not known for modesty, Frederick's of Hollywood is an eye-opener. Operating about 130 women's intimate apparel shops in the US (primarily in malls), it sells lingerie, bras, panties, foundations, dresses, wigs, costumes, fragrances, and hosiery under the Frederick's of Hollywood brand name. Frederick's pioneered the push-up bra and other dainties designed from a man's point of view, but has extended its reach by adding ready-to-wear items, jewelry, and perfume. It operates a mail-order catalog unit in the US and Canada and an online shopping site. In 2008 Frederick's merged with Movie Star — which now trades as Frederick's of Hollywood Group — and became the retail arm for its new parent.

	Annual Growth	7/05	7/06	7/07	7/08	7/09
Sales ($ mil.)	(4.4%)	—	—	155.0	153.7	141.8
Employees	—	—	—	—	—	1,000

FRED'S, INC.

NASDAQ (GS): FRED

4300 New Getwell Rd.	CEO: Bruce Efird
Memphis, TN 38118	CFO: Jerry A. Shore
Phone: 901-365-8880	HR: —
Fax: 901-328-0354	FYE: January 31
Web: www.fredsinc.com	Type: Public

Those whose greenbacks feature George and Abe rather than Andrew and Ulysses may very well shop at Fred's. Generally serving customers with modest incomes, Fred's operates about 640 discount stores in 15 states, primarily in small towns in the Southeast. The stores carry more than 12,000 brand-name, off-brand, and private-label products, including pharmaceuticals, household goods, clothing and linens, food and tobacco items, health and beauty aids, and paper and cleaning supplies. About 45% of its stores have full-service pharmacies; it also fills mail-order prescriptions. The company also provides goods and services to some two dozen franchised Fred's stores. Fred's was founded in 1947.

	Annual Growth	1/06	1/07	1/08	1/09	1/10
Sales ($ mil.)	3.0%	1,589.3	1,767.2	1,780.9	1,798.8	1,788.1
Net income ($ mil.)	(2.5%)	26.1	26.7	10.7	16.6	23.6
Market value ($ mil.)	(10.9%)	626.1	530.3	371.8	404.5	395.4
Employees	(2.7%)	10,370	10,010	10,150	9,979	9,304

⊞ An in-depth profile of this company is available to Hoover's Online members at hoovers.com.

645

FREEDOM COMMUNICATIONS, INC.

17666 Fitch Ave.
Irvine, CA 92614
Phone: 949-253-2300
Fax: 949-474-7675
Web: www.freedom.com

CEO: Burl Osborne
CFO: Mark A. McEachen
HR: Marcy E. Bruskin
FYE: December 31
Type: Private

You might say this company really believes in freedom of the press. Freedom Communications is a leading newspaper publisher with more than 30 daily papers mostly in California, North Carolina, and Texas. Its portfolio includes *The Orange County Register* in California, which boasts a circulation of about 195,000. The company also publishes more than 60 weekly community papers and it owns nearly 10 TV stations, mostly affiliated with CBS and ABC, serving markets in a half dozen states. Freedom Communications, which emerged from bankruptcy in 2010, was founded by R. C. Hoiles. It is controlled by an investment group that includes Angelo Gordon & Co., Alden Global Capital, and Luxor Capital Group.

FREEDOM RESOURCES ENTERPRISES, INC.

OTC: FRDR

901 E. 7800 South
Midvale, UT 84047
Phone: 801-566-5931
Fax: —

CEO: Neil Christiansen
CFO: —
HR: —
FYE: December 31
Type: Public

Freedom Resources Enterprises is a development stage company. It developed a series of eight self-help, self-improvement workshops. Each self-taught workshop consisted of an audio tape and a workbook, which Freedom Resources marketed over the Internet. The company's workshops did not generated expected revenue, and Freedom Resources has announced plans to pursue other business opportunities.

	Annual Growth	12/05	12/06	12/07	12/08	12/09
Sales ($ mil.)	—	—	—	—	0.0	0.0
Net income ($ mil.)	—	—	—	—	0.0	0.0
Market value ($ mil.)	0.0%	—	—	—	0.3	0.3
Employees	—	—	—	—	—	—

FREEDOMROADS, L.L.C.

250 Parkway Dr., Ste. 270
Lincolnshire, IL 60069
Phone: 847-808-3000
Fax: 847-808-7015
Web: www.campingworld.com

CEO: Marcus A. Lemonis
CFO: Roger Nuttall
HR: Gene Schrecengost
FYE: December 31
Type: Private

"Home, home on the road, where the semis and the SUVs play . . . " That's how FreedomRoads would sing it. The company sells and rents new and used recreational vehicles and travel products through more than 40 dealerships nationwide. Its locations feature Camping World stores, which offer some 8,000 RV-specific items not usually carried by general merchandise retailers, including bedding, furniture, replacement hardware, and sanitation systems. FreedomRoads dealers provide maintenance and repair services as well as financing. Chairman and CEO Marcus Lemonis founded the company in 2003. It is owned indirectly by Steve Adams, chairman of RV products company Affinity Group.

FREEMAN DECORATING SERVICES, INC.

1600 Viceroy, Ste. 100
Dallas, TX 75266
Phone: 214-445-1000
Fax: 214-445-0200
Web: www.freemanco.com

CEO: Joseph V. (Joe) Popolo Jr.
CFO: —
HR: —
FYE: June 30
Type: Private

Freeman Decorating Services knows there's no business like the trade show business. Doing business simply as Freeman, the firm stages thousands of conventions, corporate meetings, expositions, and trade shows every year and prepares exhibits for its clients. Its operations include event design and production, Party Time Rentals (equipment rental for events in Canada), and Stage Rigging (theatrical rigging). The company's Freeman Audio Visual unit specializes in providing audio and visual technology and equipment used for meetings and events. Freeman was founded by D.S. "Buck" Freeman in 1927; the company is owned by the Freeman family (including chairman Donald Freeman) and company employees.

	Annual Growth	6/05	6/06	6/07	6/08	6/09
Sales ($ mil.)	0.6%	1,173.0	1,270.0	1,300.0	1,377.0	1,202.0
Employees	(0.8%)	—	32,000	32,000	32,200	31,200

FREEPORT-MCMORAN COPPER & GOLD INC.

NYSE: FCX

333 N. Central Ave.
Phoenix, AZ 85004
Phone: 602-366-8100
Fax: —
Web: www.fcx.com

CEO: Richard C. Adkerson
CFO: Kathleen L. Quirk
HR: —
FYE: December 31
Type: Public

Freeport-McMoRan Copper & Gold (FCX) really digs its profits. Its 91%-owned subsidiary, PT Freeport Indonesia (PT-FI), operates the vast open-pit Grasberg gold, copper, and silver mine in Indonesia, whose government owns the other 9%. FCX controls proved and probable reserves of about 100 billion pounds of copper, 47 million ounces of gold, and 2.5 billion pounds of molybdenum. Copper, in the form of concentrates and in refined products such as cathodes and anodes, accounts for most of FCX's sales. It's the world's #2 copper company behind Codelco. FCX is also engaged in smelting and refining through PT-FI's 25% stake in PT Smelting, which operates a copper smelter and refinery in Indonesia.

	Annual Growth	12/05	12/06	12/07	12/08	12/09
Sales ($ mil.)	37.7%	4,179.1	5,790.5	16,939.0	17,796.0	15,040.0
Net income ($ mil.)	37.3%	995.1	1,456.5	2,977.0	(11,067.0)	3,534.0
Market value ($ mil.)	10.5%	23,276.5	24,111.5	44,320.4	10,573.9	34,737.3
Employees	1.3%	26,938	7,000	25,400	29,300	28,400

FREESCALE SEMICONDUCTOR, INC.

6501 W. William Cannon Dr.
Austin, TX 78735
Phone: 512-895-2000
Fax: —
Web: www.freescale.com

CEO: Richard M. (Rich) Beyer
CFO: Alan Campbell
HR: Michel C. Cadieux
FYE: December 31
Type: Private

Freescale Semiconductor just wants to be free. Freescale, once Motorola's Semiconductor Products Sector, is one of the oldest and most diverse makers of microchips in the world. It produces many different kinds of chips for use in automobiles, computers, industrial equipment, wireless communications and networking equipment, and other applications. The company's global client roster includes such blue-chip companies as Alcatel-Lucent, Bosch, Cisco Systems, Fujitsu, Hewlett-Packard, QUALCOMM, and Siemens, as well as former parent Motorola. Freescale nets about half of its sales from the Asia/Pacific region. The company is owned by The Blackstone Group, The Carlyle Group, Permira Advisers, and TPG Capital.

	Annual Growth	12/04	12/05	12/06	12/07	12/08
Sales ($ mil.)	(9.4%)	—	—	6,363.0	5,722.0	5,226.0
Net income ($ mil.)	—	—	—	—	(1,607.0)	(7,913.0)
Employees	(2.3%)	—	—	24,000	23,200	22,900

FREIGHTCAR AMERICA, INC.

NASDAQ (GS): RAIL

2 N. Riverside Plaza, Ste. 1250
Chicago, IL 60606
Phone: 312-928-0850
Fax: 312-928-0890
Web: www.freightcaramerica.com

CEO: Edward J. Whalen
CFO: Christopher L. (Chris) Nagel
HR: Tom McCarthy
FYE: December 31
Type: Public

Coal keeps FreightCar America in the black. The company designs and makes railroad cars, close to 70% of which are aluminum-bodied coal-carrying ones. FreightCar America claims the top spot as North America's manufacturer of both aluminum-bodied and coal-carrying railcars. Other products include coil steel cars, flatcars, intermodal cars, mill gondola cars, and motor vehicle carriers. FreightCar America also refurbishes and rebuilds railcars and supplies forged, cast, and fabricated parts for its railcars and ones made by other companies. Customers include leasing companies, railroads, and utilities; Norfolk Southern, CSX Transportation, and First Union Rail account for 22%, 21%, and 10% of sales, respectively.

	Annual Growth	12/05	12/06	12/07	12/08	12/09
Sales ($ mil.)	(28.0%)	927.2	1,444.8	817.0	746.4	248.5
Net income ($ mil.)	(42.8%)	45.7	128.7	26.5	4.6	4.9
Market value ($ mil.)	(19.9%)	573.7	661.7	417.6	218.0	236.6
Employees	(38.2%)	1,289	1,429	576	875	188

FREQUENCY ELECTRONICS, INC.

NASDAQ (GM): FEIM

55 Charles Lindbergh Blvd.
Mitchel Field, NY 11553
Phone: 516-794-4500
Fax: 516-794-4340
Web: www.freqelec.com

CEO: Martin B. Bloch
CFO: Alan L. Miller
HR: —
FYE: April 30
Type: Public

Frequency Electronics, Inc. (FEI) lets the good times roll. The company makes quartz-, rubidium-, and cesium-based time and frequency control products, such as oscillators and amplifiers, used by commercial customers to synchronize voice, data, and video transmissions in satellite and wireless communications. The US military uses its products for navigation, communications, surveillance, and timing systems in aircraft, satellites, and missiles. While FEI was once primarily a military contractor, it has diversified and gets around three-quarters of its sales from commercial clients. Customers located in the US make up about two-thirds of sales.

	Annual Growth	4/05	4/06	4/07	4/08	4/09
Sales ($ mil.)	(1.2%)	55.2	52.8	56.2	64.4	52.7
Net income ($ mil.)	—	5.0	4.8	(0.3)	0.9	(11.0)
Market value ($ mil.)	(26.7%)	94.0	113.4	88.7	54.3	27.2
Employees	1.6%	375	425	500	500	400

FRESENIUS MEDICAL CARE NORTH AMERICA

920 Winter St.
Waltham, MA 02451
Phone: 781-699-9000
Fax: —
Web: www.fmcna.com

CEO: Rice Powell
CFO: —
HR: —
FYE: December 31
Type: Subsidiary

Fresenius Medical Care North America (FMCNA) operates a network of more than 1,700 dialysis clinics located throughout the US. One of the largest providers of kidney dialysis services, FMCNA offers outpatient and in-home hemodialysis treatments for chronic kidney disease, as well as nutritional counseling and other patient services through its UltraCare business segment. Through its other operating businesses, the company markets and sells dialysis machines and related equipment to physicians and companies, and it offers renal research and laboratory services. FMCNA was established in 1996.

	Annual Growth	12/04	12/05	12/06	12/07	12/08
Est. sales ($ mil.)	—	—	—	—	—	6,000.0
Employees	—	—	—	—	—	700

FRESH DEL MONTE PRODUCE INC.

NYSE: FDP

241 Sevilla Ave.
Coral Gables, FL 33134
Phone: 305-520-8400
Fax: 305-567-0320
Web: www.freshdelmonte.com

CEO: Mohammad Abu-Ghazaleh
CFO: Richard Contreras
HR: Marissa R. Tenazas
FYE: December 31
Type: Public

Fresh Del Monte Produce expects to be squeezed and sniffed. Sniff and squeeze away — the success of the company's Del Monte Gold Extra Sweet-branded pineapples have made it one of the world's largest fresh pineapple producers and marketers; it is also one of the world's top banana producers, and offers a full array of vegetables and other fruits. Fresh Del Monte's brand names include Del Monte, Rosy, and UTC. Its prepared and freshly cut foods include potato salad, cole slaw, bagged sliced products, and fruit juices and fruit drinks; it also makes industrial fruit products (purees, pulps, and concentrates) for food manufacturing companies. Fresh Del Monte sells its fruit and vegetables in more than 90 countries.

	Annual Growth	12/05	12/06	12/07	12/08	12/09
Sales ($ mil.)	1.8%	3,259.7	3,214.3	3,365.5	3,531.0	3,496.4
Net income ($ mil.)	7.8%	106.6	(145.1)	179.8	157.7	143.9
Market value ($ mil.)	(0.7%)	1,413.7	925.7	2,084.8	1,392.0	1,372.1
Employees	4.4%	37,000	37,500	35,000	40,000	44,000

FRESH DIRECT HOLDINGS, LLC

23-30 Borden Ave.
Long Island City, NY 11101
Phone: 718-928-1000
Fax: 718-433-0648
Web: www.freshdirect.com

CEO: Richard S. (Rick) Braddock
CFO: Jason Ackerman
HR: —
FYE: September 30
Type: Private

The emphasis is on fresh at online grocer FreshDirect. The Internet grocery shopping service delivers to many New York City neighborhoods in Manhattan, Brooklyn, Queens, and some parts of Staten Island. It has also expanded to serve parts of Connecticut, Long Island, New Jersey, and Westchester County. The company sells more than 3,000 fresh food and grocery items, as well as kosher and organic products to more than 250,000 customers. With a business model similar to computer maker Dell, FreshDirect deals directly with producers and makes food to order, which undercuts its rivals. Jason Ackerman founded the company in 1999; it has filled more than 10 million orders since its delivery service launched.

	Annual Growth	9/04	9/05	9/06	9/07	9/08
Est. sales ($ mil.)	10.0%	—	—	—	200.0	220.0
Employees	0.0%	—	—	—	1,800	1,800

FRESH ENTERPRISES, INC.

5900A Katella Ave., Ste. 101
Cypress, CA 90630
Phone: 562-391-2400
Fax: —
Web: www.bajafresh.com

CEO: David Kim
CFO: —
HR: —
FYE: December 31
Type: Private

This company thinks it has a fresh take on Mexican food. Fresh Enterprises operates and franchises more than 250 Baja Fresh Mexican Grill fast-casual restaurants mostly in California and about 20 other states. The chain's menu features made-to-order burritos and tacos, as well as quesadillas, nachos, and salads. Founded in 1990, Baja Fresh is known for using fresh ingredients without fillers and eschewing freezers and microwaves. In addition to its flagship chain, Fresh Enterprises oversees the La Salsa Fresh Mexican Grill chain. An investment group led by David Kim owns the company.

FRESH INC.

495 Harrison Ave, Ste. 1
Boston, MA 02118
Phone: 617-482-9411
Fax: 617-482-3734
Web: www.fresh.com

CEO: Jean Marc Plisson
CFO: Francois Bonin
HR: Joanna Gillo
FYE: December 31
Type: Subsidiary

There was a time when being fresh spurred a slap to the face. For personal care products firm Fresh, it is a "uniquely gratifying multi-sensory experience." Using natural ingredients like sugar, milk, and soy, the company makes cosmetics, fragrances, soaps, candles, and skin care and hair care products. Its goods are sold through more than 15 namesake boutiques and online, and are carried by upscale retailers and specialty beauty stores worldwide, including Neiman Marcus, Saks Fifth Avenue, and Sephora. Fresh was founded in 1991 by husband-and-wife team Lev Glazman and Alina Roytberg. Luxury brands giant LVMH added Fresh to its portfolio in 2000.

THE FRESH MARKET, INC.

628 Green Valley Rd., Ste. 500
Greensboro, NC 27408
Phone: 336-272-1338
Fax: —
Web: www.thefreshmarket.com

CEO: Craig Carlock
CFO: Lisa K. Klinger
HR: —
FYE: December 31
Type: Private

When it comes to food, it's good to get fresh. The Fresh Market operates about 95 full-service upscale specialty grocery stores in some 20 US states, from Florida to Wisconsin. As the name suggests, the chain specializes in perishable goods, including fruits and vegetables, meat, and seafood. The stores average 21,000 sq. ft., about a third to half the size of a conventional supermarket. However, customers won't find the nonfood items sold in most grocery stores these days, such as cleaning and cooking supplies. Founded by husband-and-wife team Ray and Beverly Berry who opened their first store in 1982, The Fresh Market filed an initial public offering in 2010.

FREUDENBERG-NOK GENERAL PARTNERSHIP

47690 E. Anchor Ct.
Plymouth, MI 48170
Phone: 734-451-0020
Fax: 734-451-2547
Web: www.freudenberg-nok.com

CEO: Mohsen M. Sohi
CFO: Ralf Krieger
HR: Sarah A. O'Hare
FYE: December 31
Type: Joint venture

Freudenberg-NOK, the Americas joint venture of Freudenberg & Co. (Germany) and NOK Corporation (Japan), is a maker of rubber and sealing products used primarily in the automotive industry. Freudenberg-NOK's operations include such brand names as Corteco (automotive aftermarket sealing and gasket products), Dichtomatik (seals and o-rings), Flexitech (automotive hose assemblies), Simrit (industrial and medical seals and o-rings), TransTec (transmission and power steering seals), and Vibracoustic (noise and vibration control). Other markets include aerospace, oil and gas, marine, and chemical processing. Founded in 1989, Freudenberg-NOK has operations in the US, Canada, Brazil, Malaysia, and Mexico.

	Annual Growth	12/04	12/05	12/06	12/07	12/08
Est. sales ($ mil.)	—	—	—	—	—	1,364.1
Employees	—	—	—	—	—	6,232

🏛 FRIEDMAN INDUSTRIES, INCORPORATED

NYSE Amex: FRD

4001 Homestead Rd.
Houston, TX 77028
Phone: 713-672-9433
Fax: 713-672-7043
Web: www.friedmanindustries.com

CEO: William E. (Bill) Crow
CFO: Benny B. (Ben) Harper
HR: —
FYE: March 31
Type: Public

Steel processor Friedman Industries operates in two business segments: coil products and tubular products. The company's Texas Tubular Products unit, the larger of Friedman's segments, buys pipe and coil material and processes it for use in pipelines, oil and gas drilling, and piling and structural applications. Friedman Industries' coil products unit purchases hot-rolled steel coils and processes them into sheet and plate products. The company's XSCP unit sells Nucor's surplus prime, secondary, and transition steel coils. Friedman Industries' processing facilities are located near mills operated by U.S. Steel and Nucor.

	Annual Growth	3/05	3/06	3/07	3/08	3/09
Sales ($ mil.)	2.7%	188.0	181.9	199.7	178.8	208.8
Net income ($ mil.)	21.9%	6.2	6.5	7.0	4.5	13.7
Market value ($ mil.)	(7.9%)	46.4	63.2	62.8	34.9	33.5
Employees	(1.8%)	140	140	150	130	130

🏛 FRIENDFINDER NETWORKS INC.

6800 Broken Sound Pkwy., Ste. 100
Boca Raton, FL 33487
Phone: 561-912-7000
Fax: 561-912-7038
Web: www.ffn.com

CEO: Marc H. Bell
CFO: Ezra Shashoua
HR: Carmela Monti
FYE: December 31
Type: Private

If you're looking for friendship, try knocking on some doors below the penthouse. FriendFinder Networks (formerly Penthouse Media Group) owns and operates a variety of social networking websites, including FriendFinder.com, AdultFriendFinder.com, Amigos.com, and AsiaFriendFinder.com. All total, its sites are offered to some 245 million members in some 170 countries. The company also publishes the venerable adult magazine *PENTHOUSE*, and produces adult video content and images. It began focusing on the Web when it acquired Various (doing business as FriendFinder) in 2007. The following year the company changed its name from Penthouse Media Group to FriendFinder Networks. In 2010 it cancelled plans to go public.

	Annual Growth	12/04	12/05	12/06	12/07	12/08
Sales ($ mil.)	120.2%	—	31.0	30.0	48.1	331.0
Net income ($ mil.)	—	—	(16.9)	(49.9)	(29.9)	(46.0)
Employees	(2.3%)	—	—	—	426	416

🏛 FRIENDLY ICE CREAM CORPORATION

1855 Boston Rd.
Wilbraham, MA 01095
Phone: 413-731-4000
Fax: 413-731-4471
Web: www.friendlys.com

CEO: Ned R. Lidvall
CFO: Steve Sanchioni
HR: Garrett J. Ulrich
FYE: December 31
Type: Private

Screaming ice cream lovers can soothe their pipes at Friendly's. Friendly Ice Cream operates a chain of more than 500 family-style restaurants in more than 15 states that specialize in frozen dairy treats. Among fan favorites are Friendly's Fribble shakes, the Royal Banana Split Sundae, and Chocolate Covered Berry Patch desserts. In addition to ice cream, the restaurants serve breakfast, lunch, and dinner — mostly traditional American fare such as sandwiches and burgers. Most of the chain's locations are company-operated. Friendly's also distributes ice cream and other frozen desserts through some 4,000 supermarkets and other retail sites. The company is owned by private equity firm Sun Capital Partners.

FRIENDSTER, INC.

800 W. El Camino Real, Ste. 170	CEO: Richard B. Kimber
Mountain View, CA 94040	CFO: Nimesh Shah
Phone: 650-964-4966	HR: Karin Visnick
Fax: —	FYE: December 31
Web: www.friendster.com	Type: Private

Is everyone on Friendster connected to Kevin Bacon? Friendster hosts social networks of friends through Friendster.com, where members create profiles, trade messages, view each other's tastes and preferences, and write testimonials about friends. It also features a blogging service powered by software firm Six Apart. Friendster has about 75 million registered users. Founded in 2002 by Jonathan Abrams, the service received considerable buzz early on, but the hype has since fizzled in the US. The company has a renewed focus that emphasises business in Asia, as well as a younger audience. Online payments provider MOL Global owns Friendster.

	Annual Growth	12/04	12/05	12/06	12/07	12/08
Est. sales ($ mil.)	—	—	—	—	—	2.4
Employees	—	—	—	—	—	50

FRISCH'S RESTAURANTS, INC.
NYSE Amex: FRS

2800 Gilbert Ave.	CEO: Craig F. Maier
Cincinnati, OH 45206	CFO: Donald H. (Don) Walker
Phone: 513-961-2660	HR: Michael E. (Mike) Conner Sr.
Fax: 513-559-5160	FYE: May 31
Web: www.frischs.com	Type: Public

Buddie Boy, Big Boy, Super Big Boy, Brawny Lad — Frisch's burger menu reads like an arm-wrestling contest marquee. Frisch's Restaurants operates and licenses about 115 Frisch's Big Boy family-style restaurants in Indiana, Kentucky, and Ohio. Famous for its double-decker hamburgers, the Big Boy chain also offers chicken, roast beef, pasta, and seafood dinners, as well as a breakfast bar that converts to a soup and salad bar at lunch. More than 25 locations are operated by licensees. In addition, Frisch's operates about 35 buffet-style Golden Corral steak houses in many of the same areas. The family of president and CEO Craig Maier owns more than 55% of the company.

	Annual Growth	5/05	5/06	5/07	5/08	5/09
Sales ($ mil.)	1.6%	279.2	291.0	289.9	299.6	297.9
Net income ($ mil.)	(7.5%)	14.6	9.2	9.3	5.9	10.7
Market value ($ mil.)	3.7%	125.6	127.1	161.4	139.7	145.6
Employees	2.6%	7,500	9,000	8,800	8,300	8,300

FRITO-LAY NORTH AMERICA, INC.

7701 Legacy Dr.	CEO: Albert P. (Al) Carey
Plano, TX 75024	CFO: Nancy S. Loewe
Phone: 972-334-7000	HR: Michele R. Thatcher
Fax: 972-334-2019	FYE: December 31
Web: www.fritolay.com	Type: Subsidiary

Frito-Lay is the undisputed chip champ of North America. The company makes some of the best-known and top-selling snack foods around, including Cheetos, Doritos, Lay's, Ruffles, and Tostitos. Frito-Lay also makes Grandma's cookies, Funyuns onion-flavored rings, Cracker Jack candy-coated popcorn, and Smartfood popcorn. It also offers a light line of chips made with the fat substitute, Olestra. Owned by PepsiCo, Frito-Lay North America (i.e., the US and Canada) accounts for about one-third of the soda maker's sales. Frito-Lay's Mexican sales are reported within Pepsi's Latin America Foods segment.

FRONTIER AIRLINES, INC.

7001 Tower Rd.	CEO: Bryan K. Bedford
Denver, CO 80249	CFO: —
Phone: 720-374-4200	HR: —
Fax: 720-374-4375	FYE: March 31
Web: www.frontierairlines.com	Type: Subsidiary

Faster by far than covered wagons, Frontier Airlines' planes part the clouds and fly the skies from the Mile High City. The company's primary subsidiary, Frontier Airlines, operates as a budget carrier from its hub at Denver International Airport. The airline maintains a fleet of about 50 Airbus 319 and 318 jets with onboard amenities that include satellite TV. With subsidiary Lynx Aviation, it serves about 50 cities, primarily in the US west of the Mississippi but also in Mexico and Costa Rica. In April 2008, Frontier Airlines entered Chapter 11 bankruptcy protection. It emerged in October 2009 after it was acquired by Republic Airways for about $109 million.

	Annual Growth	3/05	3/06	3/07	3/08	3/09
Sales ($ mil.)	11.5%	833.6	994.3	1,170.9	1,399.0	1,289.4
Net income ($ mil.)	—	(23.4)	(14.0)	(20.4)	(60.3)	(248.2)
Employees	3.9%	4,526	4,770	5,265	6,170	5,283

FRONTIER COMMUNICATIONS CORPORATION
NYSE: FTR

3 High Ridge Park	CEO: Mary Agnes (Maggie) Wilderotter
Stamford, CT 06905	CFO: Donald R. (Don) Shassian
Phone: 203-614-5600	HR: Cecilia K. McKenney
Fax: 203-614-4602	FYE: December 31
Web: www.frontier.com	Type: Public

Serving city dwellers and country folk alike, Frontier Communications provides local, long-distance, and digital phone services, as well as Internet access to about 3 million primarily residential subscribers in 24 states. The company, formerly known as Citizens Communication, is active mostly in rural and small to midsized markets, where it is the incumbent local-exchange carrier (ILEC) operating under the Frontier Residential brand. Other offerings include satellite television services (enable through a partnership with DISH Network), as well as data, Internet, and telephone packages and equipment for business clients. Frontier, which had been the company's brand for years, was adopted as the corporate name in 2008.

	Annual Growth	12/05	12/06	12/07	12/08	12/09
Sales ($ mil.)	(0.5%)	2,162.5	2,025.4	2,288.0	2,237.0	2,117.9
Net income ($ mil.)	(12.1%)	202.4	344.6	214.7	182.7	120.8
Market value ($ mil.)	(10.6%)	3,832.8	4,503.4	3,989.5	2,739.0	2,447.6
Employees	(3.0%)	6,103	5,446	5,900	5,671	5,400

FRONTIER OIL CORPORATION
NYSE: FTO

10000 Memorial Dr., Ste. 600	CEO: Michael C. (Mike) Jennings
Houston, TX 77024	CFO: Douglas S. (Doug) Aron
Phone: 713-688-9600	HR: —
Fax: 713-688-0616	FYE: December 31
Web: www.frontieroil.com	Type: Public

Frontier Oil's marketing territory covers the old frontier of the Rocky Mountains and the Great Plains. The company refines crude oil and markets petroleum products. Frontier's Cheyenne, Wyoming, refinery can handle 52,000 barrels of heavy crude oil per day, and it processes 130,000 barrels of oil per day at its refinery in El Dorado, Kansas. Both refineries, which produce diesel, gasoline, and other petroleum products, have the advantage of being able to refine heavier, sulfur rich, less expensive forms of crude. They also produce asphalt. The firm also owns Ethanol Management Company, which operates a terminal and blending plant near Denver that processes about 25,000 barrels of petroleum products a day.

	Annual Growth	12/05	12/06	12/07	12/08	12/09
Sales ($ mil.)	1.4%	4,001.2	4,796.0	5,188.7	6,498.8	4,237.2
Net income ($ mil.)	—	275.0	379.3	499.1	80.2	(83.8)
Market value ($ mil.)	(10.5%)	1,985.3	3,040.6	4,293.3	1,336.2	1,273.8
Employees	3.8%	727	747	800	860	843

An in-depth profile of this company is available to Hoover's Online members at hoovers.com.

649

FROST & SULLIVAN

7550 W. Interstate 10, Ste. 400	CEO: Krishna Srinivasan
San Antonio, TX 78229	CFO: —
Phone: 210-348-1000	HR: —
Fax: 888-690-3329	FYE: December 31
Web: www.frost.com	Type: Private

Research and consulting firm Frost & Sullivan provides market intelligence and strategic advice through a subscription program to help its clients grow. From about 40 offices worldwide, the firm performs research on regional and national economic trends, customer segments, emerging technologies, and best practices, among other things. It also offers public workshops and on-site training in project management, customer service, sales, professional development, and cross-cultural interactions. Frost & Sullivan serves clients in a number of market sectors, including aerospace and defense, chemicals, energy, environmental, health care, information technology, and transportation. The firm was founded in 1961.

FROZEN FOOD EXPRESS INDUSTRIES, INC.   NASDAQ (GS): FFEX

1145 Empire Central Pl.	CEO: Stoney M. (Mit) Stubbs Jr.
Dallas, TX 75247	CFO: John McManama
Phone: 214-630-8090	HR: Donna Mecom
Fax: 214-819-5559	FYE: December 31
Web: www.ffeinc.com	Type: Public

The frozen assets of other companies mean big business for Frozen Food Express Industries, one of the largest temperature-controlled trucking companies in the US. Through its subsidiaries, which include FFE Transportation Services and Lisa Motor Lines, the company transports truckload and less-than-truckload (LTL) shipments in the US, Canada, and Mexico. Hauling temperature-sensitive cargo accounts for most of the company's sales. Frozen Food Express Industries also hauls dry freight, under the American Eagle Lines brand, and offers logistics services. Overall, the company maintains a fleet of about 2,000 tractors and 4,000 trailers. FFE traces its roots to 1946.

	Annual Growth	12/05	12/06	12/07	12/08	12/09
Sales ($ mil.)	(8.1%)	524.1	483.7	452.2	490.5	373.1
Net income ($ mil.)	—	20.4	11.2	(7.7)	0.6	(16.4)
Market value ($ mil.)	(26.0%)	189.8	148.0	101.5	97.7	56.8
Employees	(7.3%)	2,956	2,691	2,477	2,587	2,187

FROZEN SPECIALTIES, INC.

1465 Timber Wolf Dr.	CEO: Rick Alavarez
Holland, OH 43528	CFO: Gary Swartzbeck
Phone: 419-446-6500	HR: Paula Gleckler
Fax: 419-867-2054	FYE: June 30
Web: www.frozenspecialties.com	Type: Private

Frozen Specialties' specialty arena lies in frozen pizza pies. The company makes private-label frozen pizzas (in value-priced, lean, and microwaveable variations) and a frozen pizza-flavored snack called Pizza Bites for the North American convenience and grocery store markets. Its pizzas are primarily sold under store-brand names at major grocery chains. Frozen Specialties, Inc., (also known as FSI) is a top player in the frozen pizza industry and produces more than 100 million pizzas every year. Investment firm Swander Pace Capital is the majority owner of Frozen Specialties.

	Annual Growth	6/04	6/05	6/06	6/07	6/08
Est. sales ($ mil.)	—	—	—	—	—	23.1
Employees	—	—	—	—	—	255

FRU-CON CONSTRUCTION CORPORATION

15933 Clayton Rd.	CEO: Clement V. (Clem) Mitchell
Ballwin, MO 63022	CFO: Ralf-Rainer Fuchs
Phone: 636-391-6700	HR: Charles R. Weeks
Fax: 636-391-4513	FYE: December 31
Web: www.frucon.com	Type: Subsidiary

Fru-Con Construction has a *con do* attitude when it comes to large construction projects. The company, with offices in St. Louis and Washington, DC, is an engineering and construction firm that offers services from design through procurement, construction, startup, and maintenance. The group targets the environmental, heavy industrial, and government and institutional facilities markets. Customers have included TriHealth Fitness, Florida Rock Industries, Bibbs & Associates, and MEMC Electronic Materials. A wholly owned subsidiary of Germany-based Bilfinger Berger since 1984, Fru-Con Construction was founded in 1872 by Jeremiah Fruin.

FRUIT OF THE LOOM, INC.

1 Fruit of the Loom Dr.	CEO: John B. Holland
Bowling Green, KY 42103	CFO: G. William Newton
Phone: 270-781-6400	HR: —
Fax: 270-781-6588	FYE: December 31
Web: www.fruit.com	Type: Subsidiary

Fruit of the Loom wants to be in your drawers. In addition to its mainstay basics — underwear made under the BVD, Fruit of the Loom, and Lofteez names — its products include activewear, casual wear, and children's underwear sold under names such as Russell, Funpals, Fungals, and Underoos (which feature licensed characters). Fruit of the Loom's products are sold primarily in North America through discount and mass merchandisers as well as in department stores, wholesale clubs, and screen printers. Fruit of the Loom boasts the largest market share for branded men's and boy's underwear; its Russell Athletic leads in team uniforms. Warren Buffett's Berkshire Hathaway owns the company.

FRY'S ELECTRONICS, INC.

600 E. Brokaw Rd.	CEO: John Fry
San Jose, CA 95112	CFO: Chris Scheiber
Phone: 408-487-4500	HR: —
Fax: 408-487-4741	FYE: December 31
Web: www.frys.com	Type: Private

Trying to catalog all the things this superstore carries could fry your brain. Fry's Electronics is a leading big-box retailer of computers, consumer electronics, and appliances with some 35 stores in about 10 states. The retail chain's extensive inventory includes computer software and components, industry magazines, movies and music, refrigerators, washers and dryers, small appliances, stereo equipment, and televisions. Each store also typically stocks a variety of snacks and other impulse items. The technogeek's dream store began in 1985 as the brainchild of CEO John Fry (with brothers Randy and Dave) and VP Kathy Kolder. The Fry brothers, who got their start at Fry's Food Stores, still own the company.

	Annual Growth	12/04	12/05	12/06	12/07	12/08
Est. sales ($ mil.)	1.6%	2,250.0	2,340.0	2,610.0	2,350.0	2,400.0
Employees	21.1%	6,500	12,000	12,000	14,000	14,000

FRY'S FOOD AND DRUG STORES

500 S. 99th Ave.
Tolleson, AZ 85353
Phone: 623-936-2100
Fax: 623-907-1910
Web: www.frysfood.com

CEO: Jon C. Flora
CFO: —
HR: —
FYE: January 31
Type: Subsidiary

Fry's Food and Drug Stores operates about 100 supermarkets under the Fry's Food & Drug banner, mostly in Phoenix but also in Tucson, Arizona. In addition to traditional supermarket fare, many Fry's stores have in-store pharmacies, and a third of its supermarkets offer full-service banking in partnership with Bank One. Fry's also operates about 20 Fry's Marketplace stores, large (up to 120,000 sq. ft.) multi-department stores that offer full-service grocery and pharmacy departments, as well as expanded general merchandise, electronics, home goods, and toy sections. Fry's Food and Drug Stores is owned by The Kroger Co., the #1 pure grocery chain in the US.

FSI INTERNATIONAL, INC.

NASDAQ (GM): FSII

3455 Lyman Blvd.
Chaska, MN 55318
Phone: 952-448-5440
Fax: 952-448-2825
Web: www.fsi-intl.com

CEO: Donald S. (Don) Mitchell
CFO: Patricia M. (Pat) Hollister
HR: —
FYE: August 31
Type: Public

FSI International stays focused on semiconductor wafers all around the world. The company's surface conditioning equipment performs key cleaning, etching, and stripping functions that remove contaminants from silicon wafers and prepare them for subsequent production steps. FSI's equipment is used by electronics manufacturers worldwide, such as Intel, Samsung Electronics (about one-third of sales), STMicroelectronics, and Texas Instruments, as well as by other high-tech organizations, including Sandia National Laboratories. Customers outside the US account for almost three-quarters of sales.

	Annual Growth	8/05	8/06	8/07	8/08	8/09
Sales ($ mil.)	(12.6%)	86.4	113.2	116.2	78.3	50.5
Net income ($ mil.)	—	(3.3)	(7.3)	(14.6)	(13.6)	(17.6)
Market value ($ mil.)	(31.7%)	128.7	186.6	83.6	36.7	28.0
Employees	(14.9%)	486	560	429	408	255

FTD GROUP, INC.

3113 Woodcreek Dr.
Downers Grove, IL 60515
Phone: 630-719-7800
Fax: 630-719-6170
Web: www.ftd.com

CEO: Mark R. Goldston
CFO: Becky A. Sheehan
HR: —
FYE: December 31
Type: Subsidiary

Mercury, the Roman god of speed and commerce with winged feet (and an icon for megaflorist FTD), comes bearing flowers. FTD Group (formerly Mercury Man Holdings) is the holding company for operating subsidiaries FTD.COM and FTD, Inc., which was established in 1910. Flowers, plants, gourmet foods, and gift baskets loaded with all of the above find their way to about 45,000 florist shops in North America, the UK, and Ireland. FTD Group was formed in 2003 when Green Equity Investors, a business unit of Leonard Green & Partners, acquired the company for about $420 million. It went public in early 2005. FTD Group was later acquired by Internet company United Online in 2008, in a deal valued at about $441 million.

FTD, INC.

3113 Woodcreek Dr.
Downers Grove, IL 60515
Phone: 630-719-7800
Fax: 630-719-6170
Web: www.ftd.com

CEO: Mark R. Goldston
CFO: Becky A. Sheehan
HR: Mark Monitello
FYE: June 30
Type: Subsidiary

The world's well-known floral delivery service, FTD links about 16,000 North American florists and some 45,000 additional florists in about 155 countries through its largest subsidiary, Florists' Transworld Delivery, Inc. (FTDI). FTD provides technology for FTDI, handling billing, and marketing. It also operates a direct-to-consumer business through FTD.COM and 1-800-SEND-FTD, offering more than 400 floral arrangements and 800-plus specialty products delivered next day throughout most of the US. FTD, formed in 1910, offered the first flowers-by-wire service. It is owned by holding company FTD Group (formerly Mercury Man Holdings), which was acquired in 2008 by Internet service provider United Online.

	Annual Growth	6/04	6/05	6/06	6/07	6/08
Est. sales ($ mil.)	—	—	—	—	—	613.0
Employees	—	—	—	—	—	725

FTI CONSULTING, INC.

NYSE: FCN

777 S. Flagler Dr., Ste. 1500, West Tower
West Palm Beach, FL 33401
Phone: 561-515-1900
Fax: —
Web: www.fticonsulting.com

CEO: Jack B. Dunn IV
CFO: David G. Bannister
HR: Roger D. Carlile
FYE: December 31
Type: Public

When someone has been cooking the books, FTI Consulting has a recipe for recovery. Established in 1982, the company is one of the leading providers of forensic accounting and litigation support services in the US. Its experts offer investigative services to companies confronted with problems such as fraud in order to assist them in their legal defense or pursuit of recoveries. FTI also provides consulting services related to corporate finance and restructuring (through FD International and other units). Other consulting service areas include economics, strategic and financial communications, and technology. FTI's main clients are large business enterprises and major law firms.

	Annual Growth	12/05	12/06	12/07	12/08	12/09
Sales ($ mil.)	26.9%	539.5	707.9	1,001.3	1,293.1	1,399.9
Net income ($ mil.)	26.2%	56.4	42.0	92.1	125.4	143.0
Market value ($ mil.)	14.5%	1,288.9	1,310.0	2,895.3	2,098.7	2,215.2
Employees	26.9%	1,338	2,079	2,549	3,378	3,472

FUBU THE COLLECTION, LLC

350 5th Ave., Ste. 6617
New York, NY 10118
Phone: 212-273-3300
Fax: 212-273-3333
Web: www.fubu.com

CEO: Daymond John
CFO: —
HR: —
FYE: December 31
Type: Private

Urban youth and youthful are down with FUBU's hip-hop inspired sportswear. Besides making sportswear, FUBU (an acronym for "for us, by us") also licenses its name for men's, women's, and children's wear, as well as footwear and accessories such as watches, eyewear, caps, and bags. The company also offers a line of suits, athletic shoes, tuxedos, and housewares (sheets and pillows in university colors). Its collections are named FUBU and Platinum FUBU, which includes the Fat Albert and Harlem Globetrotters clothing lines. The apparel maker, which is expanding rapidly in Asia, boasts about 100 franchised stores worldwide. Founders Daymond John, Alexander Martin, Carl Brown, and Keith Perrin own FUBU.

An in-depth profile of this company is available to Hoover's Online members at hoovers.com.

651

FUCHS LUBRICANTS CO.

17050 Lathrop Ave.
Harvey, IL 60426
Phone: 708-333-8900
Fax: 708-333-9180
Web: www.fuchs.com

CEO: L. Frank Kleinman
CFO: Pamela (Pam) Watson
HR: Cindy Hall
FYE: December 31
Type: Subsidiary

Squeaky wheels should direct their requests toward Fuchs Lubricants, the US subsidiary of Germany's Fuchs Petrolub, one of the world's top manufacturers of specialty lubricants and greases. Its products, including heavy-duty greases, hydraulic fluids, industrial grease and maintenance lubricants, and metal working fluids, are used by customers in the food processing, industrial equipment, metals and mining, and pharmaceutical industries. Fuchs Lubricants also provides chemical process management services, including process control, usage reduction, and waste minimization services. The company also has units to produce lubricants for the steel industry and for mining companies.

	Annual Growth	12/04	12/05	12/06	12/07	12/08
Est. sales ($ mil.)	—	—	—	—	—	211.7
Employees	—	—	—	—	—	465

FUEL SYSTEMS SOLUTIONS, INC.

NASDAQ (GM): FSYS

780 3rd Ave., 25th Fl.
New York, NY 10017
Phone: 646-502-7170
Fax: —
Web: www.fuelsystemssolutions.com

CEO: Mariano Costamagna
CFO: Matthew Beale
HR: —
FYE: December 31
Type: Public

Fuel Systems Solutions was green before green was hip. Operating through two primary subsidiaries, the holding company (formerly IMPCO Technologies, Inc.) manufactures and supplies equipment that allows internal combustion engines to run cleaner by using alternative fuels. Subsidiary IMPCO Technologies makes fuel systems that allow engines to burn gaseous fuels such as natural gas, propane, or biogas. IMPCO serves the heavy-duty, power generation, stationary power, and industrial markets. Italy-based BRC Gas Equipment subsidiary serves the transportation market by making fuel conversion systems for vehicles so they can meet official government emission standards. Fuel Systems was formed in 1957 as IMPCO.

	Annual Growth	12/05	12/06	12/07	12/08	12/09
Sales ($ mil.)	26.9%	174.5	220.8	265.3	382.7	452.3
Net income ($ mil.)	—	(10.6)	6.9	5.9	23.1	49.8
Market value ($ mil.)	41.4%	181.8	388.9	251.7	577.0	726.4
Employees	26.3%	694	845	1,002	1,448	1,767

FUEL TECH, INC.

NASDAQ (GS): FTEK

27601 Bella Vista Pkwy.
Warrenville, IL 60555
Phone: 630-845-4500
Fax: 630-845-4502
Web: www.ftek.com

CEO: Douglas G. (Doug) Bailey
CFO: Ellen T. Albrecht
HR: Michael (Mike) Petrak
FYE: December 31
Type: Public

Thanks in part to the Clean Air Act, Fuel Tech is batting in the clean-up position. The company sells its NOxOUT brand of products, equipped with a retro-fittable system, for the reduction of nitrogen oxide in boilers, incinerators, furnaces, and other combustion sources. Fuel Tech's NOx reduction technologies are installed worldwide on more than 450 combustion units, including utility, industrial and municipal solid waste applications. The air pollution control company also makes FUEL CHEM to reduce slag formation and corrosion in boilers and furnaces. Chairman Ralph Bailey and son Douglas Bailey, a director, together own almost 25% of Fuel Tech.

	Annual Growth	12/05	12/06	12/07	12/08	12/09
Sales ($ mil.)	7.8%	52.9	75.1	80.3	81.1	71.4
Net income ($ mil.)	—	7.6	6.8	7.2	3.6	(2.3)
Market value ($ mil.)	(2.6%)	219.6	596.6	548.4	256.4	197.8
Employees	12.7%	104	137	178	196	168

FUELCELL ENERGY, INC.

NASDAQ (GM): FCEL

3 Great Pasture Rd.
Danbury, CT 06813
Phone: 203-825-6000
Fax: 203-825-6100
Web: www.fuelcellenergy.com

CEO: R. Daniel Brdar
CFO: Joseph G. Mahler
HR: Joseph G. Mahler
FYE: October 31
Type: Public

FuelCell Energy engages in fuelish pursuits. Founded in 1969 the company develops electrochemical technologies, such as carbonate and planar oxide fuel cells and electrochemical engines, which generate electricity without combustion. The company's commercial products include Direct FuelCell (DFC), which does not need an external hydrogen supply and can be fed fuel directly without an external reactor; the equipment can be fired up with biogas, coal gas, coal-mine methane, diesel, methanol, natural gas, or propane. FuelCell Energy operates more than 50 branded DFC Power Plants for government, industrial, and utility customers around the world. The US market accounts for about 35% of company sales.

	Annual Growth	10/05	10/06	10/07	10/08	10/09
Sales ($ mil.)	30.4%	30.4	33.3	48.2	100.7	88.0
Net income ($ mil.)	—	(68.2)	(76.1)	(68.7)	(93.4)	(68.7)
Market value ($ mil.)	(21.5%)	739.9	560.0	849.7	403.7	281.3
Employees	8.9%	335	384	443	534	472

FUJIFILM MEDICAL SYSTEMS USA, INC.

419 West Ave.
Stamford, CT 06902
Phone: 203-324-2000
Fax: 203-327-6485
Web: www.fujimed.com

CEO: Naohiro Fujitani
CFO: John Weber
HR: —
FYE: March 31
Type: Subsidiary

FUJIFILM Medical Systems USA wants to take snapshots of your heart. A division of Japanese camera and film company FUJIFILM, the company markets and sells FUJIFILM's imaging equipment and software in the US, Puerto Rico, and the Caribbean. It is one of the largest providers of machines utilizing digital X-ray technology (known as Computed Radiography, or CR). The company also makes picture archiving software (branded Synapse) and heads up Fuji's R&D operations for such software technology. Other products include conventional X-ray equipment, imaging printers, and mammography systems.

FUJIFILM U.S.A., INC.

200 Summit Lake Dr., 2nd Fl.
Valhalla, NY 10595
Phone: 914-789-8100
Fax: 914-789-8295
Web: www.fujifilmusa.com/gateway/usa

CEO: Ryutaro Hosoda
CFO: —
HR: —
FYE: March 31
Type: Subsidiary

Smile, you've been captured on FUJIFILM U.S.A. The company is the sales and marketing subsidiary of Tokyo-based FUJIFILM Holdings. It also makes digital cameras and photographic products (such as film, printers, and disposable cameras), as well as offers printing and sharing services for digital pictures. FUJIFILM U.S.A. operates through an imaging division, electronic imaging division, and a motion picture unit. Clients include consumers, professional photographers, cinematographers, and retail photofinishers and processing labs. The company's operations span several states, such as California, Georgia, Illinois, New Jersey, New York, and Texas.

FUJIMI CORPORATION

11200 SW Leveton Dr.	CEO: Masayuki (Mike) Nagaoka
Tualatin, OR 97062	CFO: —
Phone: 503-682-7822	HR: —
Fax: 503-612-9721	FYE: March 31
Web: www.fujimico.com	Type: Subsidiary

Fujimi Corporation is in the fine powder business. And it's perfectly legal. A subsidiary of Japan's Fujimi Incorporated, the company supplies ultra fine, precision graded abrasives and polishing compounds to semiconductor manufacturers and makers of glass, ceramic, and metal products. Fujimi claims a significant share of the global market for silicon wafer lapping powders used to manufacture substrates. The company also makes nickel plated and CMP (chemical-mechanical planarization) polishes, which use abrasives and corrosive slurries to create a flat surface. It also sells wheels and pads used with its products. Fujimi has two plants in the US that make products for North American and global markets.

	Annual Growth	3/04	3/05	3/06	3/07	3/08
Est. sales ($ mil.)	—	—	—	—	—	67.2
Employees	—	—	—	—	—	105

FUJITEC AMERICA, INC.

7258 Innovation Way	CEO: Vic Harada
Mason, OH 45040	CFO: Louis Mattina
Phone: 513-932-8000	HR: —
Fax: 513-933-5539	FYE: March 31
Web: www.fujitecamerica.com	Type: Subsidiary

When you're up, you're up, and when you're down, you're down; Fujitec America offers you the somewhere in between. A subsidiary of Fujitec Co., Ltd., the company designs, develops, manufactures, markets, installs, maintains, and modernizes elevators, escalators, moving walks, vertical parking equipment, and new transportation systems. Projects include the installation of transit escalators in the subway systems of Los Angeles, San Francisco, and Washington, DC. The company operates over 10 manufacturing facilities, four R&D centers, and about 50 sales and service offices throughout the world. Fujitec America was established in 1977.

FUJITSU AMERICA, INC.

1250 E. Arques Ave.	CEO: Farhat Ali
Sunnyvale, CA 94085	CFO: Ari Hovsepyan
Phone: 408-746-6200	HR: Andy Montrose
Fax: 408-746-5060	FYE: March 31
Web: solutions.us.fujitsu.com	Type: Subsidiary

Fujitsu America believes in the power of information and technology. A subsidiary of Fujitsu, the company offers a broad portfolio of IT products and services. Its offerings include PCs, data storage systems, servers, and point-of-sale systems, as well as consulting, managed services, systems integration, and professional services. In 2008 Fujitsu reorganized its North American business, bringing three of its subsidiaries — Fujitsu Computer Systems, Fujitsu Consulting, and Fujitsu Transaction Solutions — under the umbrella of a company called Fujitsu North America Holdings. In 2009 the subsidiaries were integrated and Fujitsu North America Holdings was renamed Fujitsu America.

FUJITSU COMPUTER PRODUCTS OF AMERICA, INC.

1255 E. Arques Ave.	CEO: Etsuro Sato
Sunnyvale, CA 94085	CFO: Takeshi Moriguchi
Phone: 408-746-7000	HR: —
Fax: —	FYE: March 31
Web: www.fcpa.fujitsu.com	Type: Subsidiary

Fujitsu Computer Products of America (FCPA) sells Fujitsu computer products in — you guessed it — America. The company, a subsidiary of Japanese technology titan Fujitsu Limited, provides data storage systems and software, notebook and tablet PCs, high-definition video encoder/decoder hardware, servers, and workgroup image scanners to customers in the US. The company's other products include Ethernet switches and biometric authentication systems, as well as degaussers (data disposal systems). FCPA markets to the education, financial services, government, health care, and insurance industries.

FUJITSU MICROELECTRONICS AMERICA, INC.

1250 E. Arques Ave.	CEO: Shinichi (James) Machida
Sunnyvale, CA 94085	CFO: —
Phone: 408-737-5600	HR: —
Fax: 408-737-5999	FYE: March 31
Web: www.fujitsumicro.com	Type: Subsidiary

Fujitsu Microelectronics America (FMA) is the US semiconductor arm of Japanese electronics giant Fujitsu. It offers many types of semiconductors, including application-specific integrated circuits, ferroelectric random-access memories, biometric sensors, and microcontrollers. It also sells LCD modules and other display components. The company markets its products in North and South America to customers in the automotive, communications, consumer, industrial, networking, and security markets. Fujitsu Microelectronics America was founded in 1979. In 2008 Fujitsu created a new parent company for FMA, Fujitsu Microelectronics.

FUJITSU NETWORK COMMUNICATIONS, INC.

2801 Telecom Pkwy.	CEO: Satoshi Ikeuchi
Richardson, TX 75082	CFO: Hirofuma Shimmura
Phone: 972-690-6000	HR: Joe Snayd
Fax: 972-479-4647	FYE: March 31
Web: www.fujitsu.com/us/services/telecom	Type: Subsidiary

Fujitsu Network Communications designs, manufactures, and maintains a variety of broadband transmission systems. The company supplies optical transport equipment and network management software to telecommunications carriers and cable television service providers. Its products include multiplexers, switches, and transponders. The company also provides network design, deployment, maintenance, and testing services. Its customers include AT&T, Qwest Communications, and Verizon Communications. Fujitsu Network Communications is a subsidiary of the Japan-based electronics and computer systems giant Fujitsu Limited.

	Annual Growth	3/04	3/05	3/06	3/07	3/08
Est. sales ($ mil.)	—	—	—	—	—	800.0
Employees	—	—	—	—	—	1,400

An in-depth profile of this company is available to Hoover's Online members at hoovers.com.

653

FULL HOUSE RESORTS, INC.

NYSE Amex: FLL

4670 S. Fort Apache Rd., Ste. 190
Las Vegas, NV 89147
Phone: 702-221-7800
Fax: 702-221-8101
Web: www.fullhouseresorts.com

CEO: Andre M. Hilliou
CFO: Mark J. Miller
HR: —
FYE: December 31
Type: Public

When it comes to gaming outside of Sin City, nothing beats a Full House. Full House Resorts owns 50% of Harrington Raceway and Casino (formerly called Midway Slots and Simulcast) in Delaware. Harrington offers more than 2,100 slot machines and gaming devices, a 450-seat buffet, a 50-seat diner, and an entertainment lounge area. The company also owns Stockman's Casino in Fallon, Nevada, featuring 280 slot and gaming machines, four table games, and keno. In addition, Full House has collaborated with a Native American tribe in Battle Creek, Michigan to manage the FireKeepers Casino. The property has 2,680 slot machines, nearly 80 table games, and 12 poker tables along with with five restaurants and lounges.

	Annual Growth	12/05	12/06	12/07	12/08	12/09
Sales ($ mil.)	50.5%	3.7	3.9	9.6	9.7	19.0
Net income ($ mil.)	62.7%	0.8	0.6	0.9	1.6	5.6
Market value ($ mil.)	2.6%	55.8	68.4	50.4	20.2	61.9
Employees	295.9%	8	9	10	630	1,965

FULLER THEOLOGICAL SEMINARY

135 N. Oakland Ave.
Pasadena, CA 91182
Phone: 626-584-5200
Fax: 626-584-5449
Web: www.fuller.edu

CEO: Richard J. Mouw
CFO: H. Lee Merritt
HR: Teresa A. Lewis
FYE: June 30
Type: School

Looking for a fuller life experience? Fuller Theological Seminary offers just that through its schools of theology, psychology, and intercultural studies. It offers about 25 master's and doctoral degree programs and seven certificate programs to more than 4,000 students from some 70 countries. In addition to its main campus in Pasadena, California, the seminary operates six regional campuses (in Arizona, California, Colorado, Texas, and Washington) as well as online classes. It also offers degree programs in Spanish and Korean. Fuller Theological Seminary was founded in 1947 by radio evangelist Charles E. Fuller and pastor Harold John Ockenga.

	Annual Growth	6/04	6/05	6/06	6/07	6/08
Est. sales ($ mil.)	—	—	—	—	—	78.4
Employees	—	—	—	—	—	700

FULLNET COMMUNICATIONS, INC.

OTC: FULO

201 Robert S. Kerr Ave., Ste. 210
Oklahoma City, OK 73102
Phone: 405-236-8200
Fax: 405-236-8201
Web: web.fullnet.net

CEO: Timothy J. (Tim) Kilkenny
CFO: Roger P. Baresel
HR: —
FYE: December 31
Type: Public

FullNet Communications is trying to net as many Oklahoma Internet users as possible. Established in 1995, the company provides dial-up Internet access to the state's consumers and small to midsized businesses. It sells connectivity on a retail or wholesale basis, allowing other Internet service providers to resell the service under their own brand names. FullNet's wholly owned FullTel subsidiary is a competitive local-exchange carrier (CLEC) that provides the company with the local phone numbers necessary to offer dial-up service.

	Annual Growth	12/05	12/06	12/07	12/08	12/09
Sales ($ mil.)	(6.9%)	2.4	1.8	1.9	1.9	1.8
Net income ($ mil.)	—	0.1	(0.5)	(0.3)	(0.4)	(0.2)
Market value ($ mil.)	(24.0%)	0.7	0.2	0.3	0.2	0.2
Employees	(5.1%)	16	13	13	13	13

FULTON FINANCIAL CORPORATION

NASDAQ (GS): FULT

1 Penn Sq.
Lancaster, PA 17604
Phone: 717-291-2411
Fax: 717-295-4792
Web: www.fult.com

CEO: R. Scott Smith Jr.
CFO: Charles J. Nugent
HR: Craig H. Hill
FYE: December 31
Type: Public

Fulton Financial is simply full of banks. The multibank holding company owns 10 community banks, which together operate about 270 branches in Delaware, Maryland, New Jersey, Pennsylvania, and Virginia. Most of its banks maintain a local identity. Their products include checking and savings accounts, credit cards, consumer loans, and equipment leasing. Commercial loans and mortgages account for nearly two-thirds of the company's loan portfolio. Home loans are available through Fulton Mortgage Company. Other nonbank subsidiaries and divisons provide trust, brokerage, investment management and advisory, life insurance, and international payment processing services.

	Annual Growth	12/05	12/06	12/07	12/08	12/09
Assets ($ mil.)	7.6%	12,401.6	14,919.0	15,923.1	16,185.1	16,635.6
Net income ($ mil.)	(18.3%)	166.1	185.5	152.7	(5.6)	73.9
Market value ($ mil.)	(15.1%)	2,960.3	2,949.3	1,981.5	1,698.9	1,540.0
Employees	5.3%	2,900	4,400	3,680	3,630	3,560

FURMAN UNIVERSITY

3300 Poinsett Hwy.
Greenville, SC 29613
Phone: 864-294-2000
Fax: 864-294-3479
Web: www.furman.edu

CEO: David E. Shi
CFO: Mary Lou Merkt
HR: —
FYE: June 30
Type: School

This school's slogan could be, "Go Further than Furman." More than 70% of Furman University's graduates go on to law, medical, or other forms of graduate school. The private school offers an undergraduate liberal arts curriculum and a graduate program focused on teaching and education. Some 3,000 graduate and undergraduate students from 46 states and 31 foreign countries attend Furman. Its campus — with features including lake, bell tower, amphitheater, and rose and Japanese gardens, is regarded as one of the most beautiful college campuses in the US. Furman was founded in 1826.

	Annual Growth	6/04	6/05	6/06	6/07	6/08
Est. sales ($ mil.)	—	—	—	—	—	142.8
Employees	—	—	—	—	—	759

FURMANITE CORPORATION

NYSE: FRM

2435 N. Central Expwy.
Richardson, TX 75080
Phone: 972-699-4000
Fax: 972-644-3524
Web: www.furmanite.com

CEO: Charles R. Cox
CFO: Robert S. Muff
HR: —
FYE: December 31
Type: Public

Furmanite hopes its products stick. The specialty contractor provides on-site leak sealing, heat treating, and valve testing and repair primarily to the energy and power generation industries around the globe. Furmanite has 70 field offices on five continents. Formerly called Xanser, Furmanite spun off its oil pipeline operations and wholesale fuel marketing services businesses to focus on its technical services. Customers include petroleum refineries, chemical plants, steel mills, nuclear power stations, pulp and paper mills, and food processing plants. Subsidiary Xtria also provides information technology services through contracts with state and federal government agencies.

	Annual Growth	12/05	12/06	12/07	12/08	12/09
Sales ($ mil.)	15.7%	153.9	246.4	290.3	320.9	275.9
Net income ($ mil.)	—	(4.3)	(3.4)	12.5	21.9	(2.8)
Market value ($ mil.)	6.7%	108.0	178.5	433.5	198.0	140.0
Employees	13.5%	1,047	1,647	1,805	1,925	1,737

田 FURNITURE BRANDS INTERNATIONAL, INC.   NYSE: FBN

101 S. Hanley Rd.   CEO: Ralph P. Scozzafava
St. Louis, MO 63105   CFO: Steven G. (Steve) Rolls
Phone: 314-863-1100   HR: Mary E. Sweetman
Fax: 314-863-5306   FYE: December 31
Web: www.furniturebrands.com   Type: Public

Furniture Brands International runs a furniture-making empire. The company ranks as one of the top US makers of residential furniture. Furniture Brands' subsidiaries offer a line-up of nationally recognized brands, including Broyhill, Lane, Thomasville, and Drexel Heritage, among others. Broyhill makes mid-priced furniture for the bedroom and dining room, as well as other home furnishings. Laneventure (outdoor wicker and teak collections) and Henredon (wood and upholstered pieces) target the premium-priced furniture market. Furniture Brands distributes its products through a network of furniture centers, independent dealers, national and local chains, and department stores.

	Annual Growth	12/05	12/06	12/07	12/08	12/09
Sales ($ mil.)	(15.4%)	2,386.8	2,418.2	2,082.1	1,743.2	1,224.4
Net income ($ mil.)	—	61.4	55.1	(45.6)	(385.9)	(108.7)
Market value ($ mil.)	(29.7%)	1,082.4	786.7	487.6	107.1	264.7
Employees	(13.5%)	15,150	13,800	11,900	8,100	8,500

FUSION TELECOMMUNICATIONS INTERNATIONAL   NYSE Amex: FSN

420 Lexington Ave., Ste. 1718   CEO: Matthew D. Rosen
New York, NY 10170   CFO: —
Phone: 212-201-2400   HR: —
Fax: 212-972-7884   FYE: December 31
Web: www.fusiontel.com   Type: Public

Fusion Telecommunications International, Inc., understands that modern communications is a blend of old and familiar processes with new technologies. Fusion provides VoIP (Voice over Internet Protocol) telephone and other Internet services primarily to other US communciations carriers. Fusion offers such services as voice calling and broadband Internet access. Top clients include communications services providers Qwest (40% of sales) and Telco Group (10%). The company also serves consumers through its Mobilink brand and offers ISP and hosted PBX services among others to enterprise customers.

	Annual Growth	12/05	12/06	12/07	12/08	12/09
Sales ($ mil.)	(4.6%)	49.4	47.1	55.0	50.6	40.9
Net income ($ mil.)	—	(9.4)	(13.4)	(12.7)	(15.6)	(9.6)
Market value ($ mil.)	(53.1%)	267.3	116.7	33.9	19.9	13.0
Employees	(12.1%)	92	86	68	71	55

FUTABA CORPORATION OF AMERICA

711 State Pkwy.   CEO: Hiroshi Sakurada
Schaumburg, IL 60173   CFO: —
Phone: 847-884-1444   HR: —
Fax: 847-884-1635   FYE: March 31
Web: www.futaba.com   Type: Subsidiary

Futaba Corporation of America likes to show off and take off. The company, a subsidiary of Japan-based Futaba Corporation, makes vacuum fluorescent display modules used in factory automation and fabricating machines, jigs, and tools used to enable industrial processes like press-die setting and plastic injection molding. Futaba also manufactures radio controllers for the hobby and industrial markets. Its radio control products are used to steer battery-powered cars and airplanes for fun, as well as to maneuver heavy-duty cranes and agricultural machinery. In the US, Futaba has operations in Alabama, Illinois, and Michigan.

	Annual Growth	3/04	3/05	3/06	3/07	3/08
Est. sales ($ mil.)	—	—	—	—	—	147.4
Employees	—	—	—	—	—	98

FUTURE US, INC.

4000 Shoreline Ct., Ste. 400   CEO: John E. Marcom Jr.
South San Francisco, CA 94080   CFO: John Sutton
Phone: 650-872-1642   HR: Nancy Durlester DuBois
Fax: 650-238-2312   FYE: December 31
Web: www.futureus-inc.com   Type: Subsidiary

Plenty of young men share this company's vision of a future full of computers, video games, and wailing guitars. Future US (formerly Future Network USA) is a magazine publisher primarily targeting computers users, video game players, and guitar enthusiasts. Titles include *Guitar World*, *Maximum PC*, and *PC Gamer*. The company also produces niche titles for specific game platforms; these include *PlayStation: The Official Magazine* and *Official Xbox Magazine*. The subsidiary of UK-based publisher Future plc also operates companion websites for its print magazines.

FUTUREFUEL CORP.   OTC: FTFL

8235 Forsyth Blvd., 4th Fl.   CEO: Lee E. Mikles
Clayton, MO 63105   CFO: —
Phone: 805-565-9800   HR: —
Fax: 805-565-0800   FYE: December 31
Web: www.futurefuelcorporation.com   Type: Public

FutureFuel may fire on biofuel, but it gets its pep from chemicals. The company is a manufacturer of biodiesel and other biofuels; however, its core business is specialty chemicals, which includes such chemicals as herbicides, detergent additives, colorants, photographic and imaging chemicals, and food additives. Selling its products primarily in North America, the company's customers include industrial and consumer goods manufacturers, as well as pharmaceutical companies and agribusinesses. It manufactures both its biofuel and chemical products at a single plant located in Arkansas. FutureFuel was formed in 2005 for the purpose of acquiring FutureFuel Chemical Co., which remains its main operating subsidiary.

	Annual Growth	12/04	12/05	12/06	12/07	*12/08
Sales ($ mil.)	—	—	—	—	—	198.3
Employees	—	—	—	—	—	460

*Most recent year available

FX ENERGY, INC.   NASDAQ (GM): FXEN

3006 Highland Dr., Ste. 206   CEO: David N. Pierce
Salt Lake City, UT 84106   CFO: Clay Newton
Phone: 801-486-5555   HR: —
Fax: 801-486-5575   FYE: December 31
Web: www.fxenergy.com   Type: Public

FX Energy is not exactly fixated on energy in Poland, but it is in western Poland's Permian Basin where it is hoping to make its big breakthrough. In 2008 the independent exploration and production company reported proved reserves of 45.9 billion cu. ft. of natural gas equivalent in Poland, and 45,000 barrels of oil equivalent in the US (from properties in Montana and Nevada). Partners include state-owned Polish Oil and Gas and CalEnergy Gas, which have served as operators for exploration wells in Poland. FX Energy holds about 5.4 million net acres in western Poland.

	Annual Growth	12/05	12/06	12/07	12/08	12/09
Sales ($ mil.)	25.6%	5.9	8.2	18.0	17.8	14.7
Net income ($ mil.)	—	(11.4)	(13.8)	(11.7)	(54.7)	(0.5)
Market value ($ mil.)	(22.7%)	345.2	266.5	245.7	120.7	123.3
Employees	5.9%	39	42	40	47	49

FXI-FOAMEX INNOVATIONS

1400 N. Providence Rd., Ste. 2000
Media, PA 19063
Phone: 610-744-2300
Fax: —
Web: www.fxi.com

CEO: John G. (Jack) Johnson Jr.
CFO: Harold J. Earley
HR: John G. (Jack) Johnson Jr.
FYE: December 31
Type: Private

Foam, sweet foam. FXI-Foamex International (formerly Foamex International) is one of North America's largest makers of flexible polyurethane and polymer foams for carpets and furniture. Products include mattresses, couches, car interior trim, and carpet cushions. Computer cabinets, industrial filters, and gaskets are a few of the uses for the products made by FXI's technical products division. FXI's customers include auto supplier Johnson Controls, as well as other major automobile and bedding manufacturers. The company emerged from Chapter 11 bankruptcy protection in 2007, after filing in 2005. Still beset by a heavy debt load, FXI entered Chapter 11 again in early 2009 and emerged in June of that year.

G2 DIRECT & DIGITAL

200 Fifth Ave.
New York, NY 10010
Phone: 212-537-3700
Fax: 212-537-3737
Web: www.g2directanddigital.com

CEO: Wendy Lurrie
CFO: John Payne
HR: Eric Raff
FYE: December 31
Type: Subsidiary

Not to be too forward, but G2 Direct & Digital (formerly Grey Direct) is a leading direct marketing agency. The firm helps develop and implement direct mail, response television, and other marketing campaigns. It offers creative and production services, as well as planning, data analytics, and database marketing services to such clients as GlaxoSmithKline, Procter & Gamble, and Pfizer. In addition, the agency provides services for interactive and e-mail marketing campaigns. G2 Direct & Digital operates through 45 offices in more than 30 countries. It is a subsidiary of Grey Group, which in turn is a unit of UK-based advertising and marketing services conglomerate WPP Group.

G-III APPAREL GROUP, LTD.

512 7th Ave.
New York, NY 10018
Phone: 212-403-0500
Fax: 212-403-0551
Web: www.g-iii.com

NASDAQ (GM): GIII
CEO: Morris Goldfarb
CFO: Neal S. Nackman
HR: —
FYE: January 31
Type: Public

G-III Apparel Group has the leather part of Stevie Nicks' leather and lace wrapped up. It's best known for making leather jackets under the names G-III, Marvin Richards, Black Rivet, Winlit, Siena Studio, La Nouvelle Renaissance, and other labels (such as Andrew Marc), as well as under licensed names. It also makes leather and other pants, skirts, and sportswear. More than 60% of its sales are generated from licensed apparel it makes for the NFL, NBA, NHL, and MLB teams, as well as for Jones New York, Nine West, and Kenneth Cole. Its customers include department stores such as Macy's and mass merchants like Wal-Mart. Father and son team Aron and Morris Goldfarb own some 20% of G-III Apparel.

	Annual Growth	1/06	1/07	1/08	1/09	1/10
Sales ($ mil.)	25.4%	324.1	427.0	518.9	711.1	800.9
Net income ($ mil.)	45.4%	7.1	13.2	17.5	(14.0)	31.7
Market value ($ mil.)	16.2%	182.1	414.6	255.4	105.0	332.5
Employees	38.6%	510	510	573	1,245	1,880

GABRIEL BROTHERS, INC.

55 Scott Ave.
Morgantown, WV 26508
Phone: 304-292-6965
Fax: 304-292-3874
Web: www.gabrielbrothers.com

CEO: Arthur (Art) Gabriel Sr.
CFO: —
HR: Don Mancini
FYE: January 31
Type: Private

Gabriel, blow your horn! Your magical, mystical discount horn, that is. Gabriel Brothers sells discounted brand-name clothing through about 100 stores, under the Gabriel Brothers (commonly called "Gabes") and Rugged Wearhouse banners. Stores are located in about a dozen East Coast and Mid-Atlantic states. The company's offerings include men's, women's, and children's apparel and footwear, as well as housewares, with markdowns as high as 70% off of their original retail prices. It carries such brands as Anne Klein, Kenneth Cole, and Liz Claiborne. The family-run company was established in 1961 by James and Arthur Gabriel.

	Annual Growth	1/04	1/05	1/06	1/07	1/08
Est. sales ($ mil.)	—	—	—	—	—	379.0
Employees	—	—	—	—	—	3,500

THE GAGE GROUP INC.

14724 Ventura Blvd., Ste. 505
Sherman Oaks, CA 91403
Phone: 818-905-3800
Fax: 818-905-3322

CEO: Martin Gage
CFO: —
HR: —
FYE: December 31
Type: Private

It's the job of The Gage Group to gauge whether the prospective client a) has talent and b) is commercially marketable. The organization is a theatrical and literary agency founded in 1973 by talent agent Martin Gage. The firm operates offices in Los Angeles and New York City, enabling it to serve both coasts. Gage Group represents actors for all areas of the entertainment industry. It represents adult actors only, not infants or children. The firm's clients have included Benjamin McKenzie (of *The OC*), Robert Pastorelli (of *Murphy Brown*), and Ric Young (of *Indiana Jones and the Temple of Doom*, *The Last Emperor*, and *Seven Years in Tibet*).

	Annual Growth	12/04	12/05	12/06	12/07	12/08
Est. sales ($ mil.)	—	—	—	—	—	0.4
Employees	—	—	—	—	—	8

GAIAM, INC.

360 Interlocken Blvd.
Broomfield, CO 80021
Phone: 303-222-3600
Fax: 303-222-3700
Web: www.gaiam.com

NASDAQ (GM): GAIA
CEO: Lynn Powers
CFO: —
HR: Jackie Abraham
FYE: December 31
Type: Public

If you're into living a healthy, sustainable lifestyle, Gaiam is your kind of company. The name Gaiam (pronounced "guy-um") is a combination of Gaia (the Earth goddess) and "I am." The company's more than 12,000 products (some 8,000 are proprietary items) include environmentally friendly apparel, organic foods, fair-trade crafts, alternative health care products, and at-home fitness programs. Its offerings are marketed through catalogs, its e-commerce site, and major retailers (including Barnes & Noble, Target, and Whole Foods). Gaiam also runs the Gaia community website and Gaiam Travel eco-tourism site. The company owns about a 55% stake in Real Goods Solar, which went public in 2008.

	Annual Growth	12/05	12/06	12/07	12/08	12/09
Sales ($ mil.)	18.2%	142.5	219.5	262.9	257.2	278.5
Net income ($ mil.)	(30.7%)	1.3	5.6	8.5	(35.6)	0.3
Market value ($ mil.)	(13.1%)	313.9	317.9	689.7	107.4	178.7
Employees	9.0%	367	363	454	526	519

GAINSCO, INC.

NYSE Amex: GAN

3333 Lee Pkwy., Ste. 1200
Dallas, TX 75219
Phone: 972-629-4301
Fax: 972-629-4302
Web: www.gainsco.com

CEO: Glenn W. Anderson
CFO: Daniel J. Coots
HR: Richard M. Buxton
FYE: December 31
Type: Public

Although at times it might be more appropriate, you wouldn't call an insurance company LOSSCO, would you? Through its MGA Insurance subsidiary, GAINSCO sells personal nonstandard auto insurance. The company does a majority of its business in Florida but has laid the groundwork for sales growth in Arizona, California, Georgia, Nevada, New Mexico, South Carolina, and Texas. Its products are sold through more than 4,000 independent agencies. GAINSCO aims its marketing efforts at Hispanics, its core customer market, and most of the company's customer service staff is bilingual. A handful of GAINSCO executives and directors collectively own more than 70% of the company.

	Annual Growth	12/05	12/06	12/07	12/08	12/09
Assets ($ mil.)	3.3%	212.2	289.3	245.3	239.5	241.9
Net income ($ mil.)	(9.1%)	6.0	9.6	(18.6)	(3.5)	4.1
Market value ($ mil.)	(30.0%)	181.5	190.1	96.8	33.7	43.5
Employees	7.6%	295	391	368	342	395

GALARDI GROUP, INC.

7700 Irvine Center Dr., Ste. 550
Irvine, CA 92618
Phone: 949-892-2699
Fax: —
Web: www.wienerschnitzel.com

CEO: John N. Galardi
CFO: —
HR: —
FYE: December 31
Type: Private

It's not Oscar Mayer, but Galardi Group is focused on serving wieners. The company operates and franchises about 350 Wienerschnitzel quick-service restaurants in California and a dozen other mostly Western states. One of the largest hot dog chains, the restaurants offer a variety of toppings for its wieners, such as chili, cheese, and barbecued bacon, as well as alternative menu items including chicken sandwiches, corn dogs, and hamburgers. About 90% of Wienerschnitzel locations are operated by franchisees. Galardi Group also owns Tastee Freez, a chain of ice cream stands, and The Original Hamburger Stand. Owner, founder, and CEO John Galardi opened his first hot dog stand, called Der Wienerschnitzel, in 1961.

	Annual Growth	12/04	12/05	12/06	12/07	12/08
Est. sales ($ mil.)	—	—	—	—	—	40.0
Employees	—	—	—	—	—	50

GALDERMA LABORATORIES, L.P.

14501 North Fwy.
Fort Worth, TX 76177
Phone: 817-961-5000
Fax: 817-961-0041
Web: www.galdermausa.com

CEO: Albert Draaijer
CFO: —
HR: Robin Clayton
FYE: December 31
Type: Private

Galderma Laboratories can't soothe all of the irritations of the world, but it can help with itchy, spotty, and sensitive skin. The company is the North American operation of Swiss firm Galderma, a joint venture between L'Oréal and Nestlé founded in 1981. The company focuses exclusively on developing over-the-counter and prescription dermatology products. In addition to such consumer brands as Cetaphil, the company offers treatments for skin conditions such as acne, rosacea, atopic dermatitis (eczema), psoriasis, and melasma. Galderma Laboratories operates research and development facilities in France, Japan, and the US.

	Annual Growth	12/04	12/05	12/06	12/07	12/08
Est. sales ($ mil.)	—	—	—	—	—	530.5
Employees	—	—	—	—	—	499

GALE

27500 Drake Rd.
Farmington Hills, MI 48331
Phone: 248-699-4253
Fax: 800-414-5043
Web: gale.cengage.com

CEO: Patrick C. Sommers
CFO: —
HR: —
FYE: December 31
Type: Subsidiary

Gale, part of Cengage Learning, publishes educational and reference material for schools, libraries, and businesses. The company creates and maintains some 600 databases that are available in a variety of formats, including online, eBooks, print, and microfilm. Imprints include Macmillan Reference USA for reference titles, Lucent Books for the K-12 education market, and Thorndike Press for large print editions of popular titles. The company also owns online reference service HighBeam Research. Gale has offices in Australia, Germany, Switzerland, Malaysia, the UK, and the US.

THE GALE COMPANY

4 Becker Farm Rd.
Roseland, NJ 07068
Phone: 973-577-2500
Fax: 973-422-9520
Web: www.thegalecompany.com

CEO: Stanley C. (Stan) Gale
CFO: Ron Gentile
HR: Philip Boffa
FYE: December 31
Type: Subsidiary

Real estate is a breeze for The Gale Company. The construction and development arm of commercial real estate investment trust (REIT) Mack-Cali Realty, Gale provides construction and related services for office and other commercial properties, primarily in the Northeast US. Activities include asset management, property and facility management, and land development services. The company has developed more than 50 projects comprising some 3,500 acres of land. Its property portfolio is centered mainly in the *Fortune 500* mecca of New Jersey. Gale was formed in 1993 and acquired by Mack-Cali in 2006.

GALLATIN STEEL COMPANY

4831 US Hwy. 42 West
Ghent, KY 41045
Phone: 859-567-3100
Fax: 859-567-3165
Web: www.gallatinsteel.com

CEO: Tobin Pospisil
CFO: —
HR: —
FYE: December 31
Type: Joint venture

A more beautiful America is just one by-product of Gallatin Steel's manufacturing process. Gallatin Steel, a joint venture between ArcelorMittal and Gerdau AmeriSteel, manufactures more than a million tons of coils using recycled metal each year. The company uses about 1.5 million tons of scrap metal each year to manufacture its products, which are designed to customers' specifications. Gallatin's recycling operation removes some 4,000 tons of scrap metal from US landscapes and junkyards every day. The company, which operates a compact strip production facility in central Kentucky, began operations in 1995.

GALLAUDET UNIVERSITY

800 Florida Ave., NE
Washington, DC 20002
Phone: 202-651-5000
Fax: 202-651-5508
Web: www.gallaudet.edu

CEO: T. Alan Hurwitz
CFO: Paul Kelly
HR: Eileen Matthews
FYE: September 30
Type: School

Gallaudet University (GU) gives deaf and hard-of-hearing students the chance to be in the majority. Designed to accomodate hearing impaired students, GU offers undergraduate and graduate degrees in more than 40 majors to some 2,000 students annually. The bilingual university uses both American Sign Language (ASL) and English; GU admits a small number of hearing, ASL-proficient students to each incoming freshman class. Through the Laurent Clerc National Deaf Education Center, GU provides training and support for teachers and parents of hearing impaired children; it operates demonstration schools on its campus. GU was founded in 1864; it was named for Thomas Hopkins Gallaudet, a pioneer in education for the deaf.

GALLERY OF HISTORY, INC.

3601 W. Sahara Ave., Promenade Ste.
Las Vegas, NV 89102
Phone: 702-364-1000
Fax: 702-364-1285
Web: www.galleryofhistory.com

CEO: Todd M. Axelrod
CFO: Rod R. Lynam
HR: —
FYE: September 30
Type: Private

Those who don't know the Gallery of History are doomed to buy their memorabilia from another auction house. The company auctions autographs, memorabilia, and manuscripts from artists, authors, athletes, entertainers, politicians, and scientists, among other notable figures. Its inventory of about 190,000 items have included baseballs autographed by Hank Aaron, letters written by Albert Einstein, and signed photos from Cecil B. De Mille. Although the Internet is its primary sales channel, the company also offers autographs and manuscripts through a retail gallery, located at its headquarters. The Gallery of History was incorporated in 1981. Founder, chairman, and CEO Todd Axelrod owns about 90% of the company.

	Annual Growth	9/05	9/06	9/07	9/08	9/09
Sales ($ mil.)	(22.3%)	1.1	0.7	0.6	0.5	0.4
Net income ($ mil.)	—	(0.8)	(0.5)	(0.4)	(0.5)	(0.6)
Employees	(5.4%)	10	5	7	8	8

THE GALLUP ORGANIZATION

901 F St. NW
Washington, DC 20004
Phone: 202-715-3030
Fax: 202-715-3041
Web: www.gallup.com

CEO: Jim Clifton
CFO: James (Jim) Krieger
HR: Matt Mosser
FYE: December 31
Type: Private

More than a pollster, The Gallup Organization draws from its research and behavioral studies to offer consulting services related to performance management. Other specialties include branding, marketing, and recruiting. The company delivers its services on the Web, through its Gallup University campuses, and through more than 40 global offices. It draws customers from a variety of industries, including automotive, business services, health care, hospitality, and retail. Despite its diversified business offerings, the company is still most famous for its Gallup Poll surveys. The company was founded in 1935 by Dr. George Gallup, a pioneer in the science of polling. It is owned by its employees.

	Annual Growth	12/04	12/05	12/06	12/07	12/08
Est. sales ($ mil.)	—	—	—	—	—	300.6
Employees	—	—	—	—	—	2,000

⊞ GAMCO INVESTORS, INC.

NYSE: GBL

1 Corporate Center
Rye, NY 10580
Phone: 914-921-5100
Fax: 914-921-5392
Web: www.gabelli.com

CEO: Mario J. Gabelli
CFO: Jeffrey M. (Jeff) Farber
HR: —
FYE: December 31
Type: Public

Investments are anything but a game for "Super Mario" Gabelli, founder and CEO of GAMCO Investors (formerly Gabelli Asset Management). The company oversees the mutual fund- and securities-related portion of Gabelli's financial empire. GAMCO provides advisory services to more than 20 mutual funds under the Gabelli, GAMCO, and Comstock brands, as well as to separate accounts for wealthy individuals and, to a lesser extent, pension plans, trusts, and profit-sharing plans. Despite the renown of its founder, the company adopted the GAMCO Investors name from one of its subsidiaries, which changed its name to GAMCO Asset Management. Gabelli controls the company.

	Annual Growth	12/05	12/06	12/07	12/08	12/09
Assets ($ mil.)	(0.5%)	721.1	837.2	757.6	697.6	707.8
Net income ($ mil.)	(3.3%)	63.4	69.5	79.6	24.9	55.5
Market value ($ mil.)	2.6%	1,192.5	1,053.6	1,895.7	748.4	1,322.9
Employees	(0.8%)	200	200	214	214	194

⊞ GAMESTOP CORP.

NYSE: GME

625 Westport Pkwy.
Grapevine, TX 76051
Phone: 817-424-2000
Fax: 817-424-2002
Web: www.gamestop.com

CEO: J. Paul (Paul) Raines
CFO: Robert A. (Rob) Lloyd
HR: —
FYE: January 31
Type: Public

GameStop holds the top score in the video game retailing industry. The company is the largest retailer of new and used games, hardware, entertainment software, and accessories. GameStop boasts more than 6,400 stores located in the US, Canada, Australia, and Europe. A majority of the company's revenue is generated by sales of new and used video games. Stores branded as GameStop and EB Games carry an average of 1,000 new titles and 3,500 used ones. The company also operates e-commerce websites (GameStop.com, ebgames.com); publishes *Game Informer*, a video game magazine that reaches some 4 million subscribers; and offers GameStop TV in many of its locations.

	Annual Growth	1/06	1/07	1/08	1/09	1/10
Sales ($ mil.)	30.9%	3,091.8	5,318.9	7,094.0	8,805.9	9,078.0
Net income ($ mil.)	39.1%	100.8	158.3	288.3	398.3	377.3
Market value ($ mil.)	(0.5%)	3,080.2	4,082.7	7,879.6	3,787.0	3,021.3
Employees	8.9%	42,000	32,000	43,000	41,000	59,000

GAMETECH INTERNATIONAL, INC.

NASDAQ (GM): GMTC

900 Sandhill Rd.
Reno, NV 89521
Phone: 775-850-6000
Fax: 775-850-6090
Web: www.gametech-inc.com

CEO: Floyd W. (Bud) Glisson
CFO: Marcia R. Martin
HR: Ellen Droog
FYE: October 31
Type: Public

Name an old-fashioned parlor game that could benefit from a high-tech makeover. Bingo! GameTech International designs and sells electronic handheld and fixed-base bingo systems that allow contestants to play up to 2,000 bingo cards at once. Its bingo systems are used by commercial, charity, and Native American bingo halls in about 40 states. The company also markets video lottery terminals and systems used by casinos, taverns, and truck stops in 15 states. GameTech generates revenue from the sale of software and equipment, as well as from maintenance and upgrade services.

	Annual Growth	10/05	10/06	10/07	10/08	10/09
Sales ($ mil.)	(1.0%)	49.7	49.3	58.8	55.4	47.8
Net income ($ mil.)	—	1.3	4.4	4.7	(11.2)	(10.5)
Market value ($ mil.)	(24.0%)	46.8	116.8	102.0	27.7	15.6
Employees	(1.3%)	200	200	233	208	190

GAMING PARTNERS INTERNATIONAL

NASDAQ (GM): GPIC

1700 Industrial Rd.
Las Vegas, NV 89102
Phone: 702-384-2425
Fax: 702-384-1965
Web: www.gpigaming.com

CEO: Gregory Gronau
CFO: David W. Grimes
HR: Cynthia Allen
FYE: December 31
Type: Public

This company doesn't care if gamblers win or crap out, as long as they do it using its products. Gaming Partners International Corporation is a leading manufacturer of casino gaming products, including dealing shoes, dice, gaming chips, playing cards, and roulette wheels. It also supplies table furniture and layouts for blackjack, poker, baccarat, craps, and other casino games. With manufacturing facilities in the US, Mexico, and France, the company markets its products under the brands Bourgogne et Grasset, Bud Jones, and Paulson to casino operators around the world. French holding company Holding Wilson owns almost 50% of Gaming Partners International.

	Annual Growth	12/05	12/06	12/07	12/08	12/09
Sales ($ mil.)	(3.5%)	57.1	74.0	58.8	60.5	49.5
Net income ($ mil.)	(30.6%)	4.3	5.1	0.2	4.5	1.0
Market value ($ mil.)	(15.8%)	91.7	147.5	57.6	42.9	46.0
Employees	(7.2%)	870	760	720	685	645

GANDER MOUNTAIN COMPANY

180 E. 5th St., Ste. 1300
St. Paul, MN 55101
Phone: 651-325-4300
Fax: 651-325-2003
Web: www.gandermountain.com

CEO: David C. Pratt
CFO: Robert J. (Bob) Vold
HR: —
FYE: January 31
Type: Private

Gander Mountain has got the gear to get you out of the office and up the mountain. The company operates about 120 outdoor sporting goods stores focused on a variety of outdoor activities, such as hunting, camping, and fishing, in some two dozen states. In addition to outdoor equipment and related accessories, the stores also sell apparel and footwear. While Gander Mountain has sold fishing and pontoon boats since 2007 through an arrangement with Tracker Marine Group, a unit of Bass Pro Shops, the retailer exited its all terrain vehicle (ATV) and boat categories in late 2009. Founded in 1960 as an outdoor catalog operation, Gander Mountain went private in early 2010.

	Annual Growth	1/05	1/06	1/07	1/08	1/09
Sales ($ mil.)	13.5%	642.1	804.5	911.4	969.4	1,064.6
Net income ($ mil.)	—	1.6	(13.3)	(13.2)	(31.8)	(15.5)
Employees	2.9%	5,000	5,600	6,000	6,238	5,605

G & J PEPSI-COLA BOTTLERS, INC.

9435 Waterstone Blvd., Ste. 390
Cincinnati, OH 45249
Phone: 513-785-6060
Fax: 513-683-9467

CEO: Timothy (Tim) Hardig
CFO: Dale Watkins
HR: —
FYE: December 31
Type: Private

Cincinnati-based G & J Pepsi-Cola Bottlers delivers. And it has done so for the more than 40 years that it has distributed Pepsi products in Ohio and Kentucky. The company is one of the larger Pepsi bottlers in the US, shipping the leading PepsiCo brands, including Pepsi-Cola, Mountain Dew, Gatorade, Slice, SoBe, and Aquafina to its beverage retailing customers. The bottler also offers Dr Pepper products, Dole and Tropicana juices, Lipton teas, and Starbucks' Frappuccino. G & J operates distribution centers in Cheshire, Chillicothe, and Hillsboro, Ohio, as well as in Winchester and Harrodsburg, Kentucky.

G&K SERVICES, INC.

NASDAQ (GS): GKSR

5995 Opus Pkwy., Ste. 500
Minnetonka, MN 55343
Phone: 952-912-5500
Fax: 952-912-5999
Web: www.gkservices.com

CEO: Douglas A. (Doug) Milroy
CFO: Jeffrey L. (Jeff) Wright
HR: Jacqueline T. (Jackie) Punch
FYE: June 30
Type: Public

G&K Services likes uniformity. The company is the third-largest uniform rental agency (behind #1 Cintas and #2 ARAMARK). G&K makes and supplies uniforms for more than 175,000 customers in the automotive, manufacturing, hospitality, and technology industries, among others, from about 170 locations in the US, Canada, Ireland, and the Dominican Republic. Along with rentals and sales, the company provides cleaning, repair, and replacement services for all of its uniforms. G&K also carries clean room garments used by the semiconductor industry. In addition, the company offers facility services, providing restroom supplies and renting items such as dust mops, floor mats, and towels. G&K was founded in 1902.

	Annual Growth	6/05	6/06	6/07	6/08	6/09
Sales ($ mil.)	4.4%	788.8	880.8	929.5	1,002.4	936.0
Net income ($ mil.)	—	39.9	41.9	43.2	46.1	(72.5)
Market value ($ mil.)	(13.5%)	700.5	636.9	732.9	565.6	392.7
Employees	2.4%	7,743	9,685	7,720	7,800	8,500

GANNETT CO., INC.

NYSE: GCI

7950 Jones Branch Dr.
McLean, VA 22107
Phone: 703-854-6000
Fax: 703-854-2053
Web: www.gannett.com

CEO: Craig A. Dubow
CFO: Gracia C. Martore
HR: Roxanne V. Horning
FYE: December 31
Type: Public

Gannett satisfies news junkies with a stash of daily US papers. The company is the top newspaper publisher in the US with about 85 daily papers boasting a total circulation of about 5.7 million. Its flagship *USA TODAY*, with a circulation of 1.8 million, is the nation's second-largest newspaper (behind the *Wall Street Journal*). Other papers in Gannett's holdings include *The Arizona Republic* and the *Detroit Free Press*. The company also owns about 650 non-daily publications, as well as more than 200 papers in the UK through Newsquest. In addition, Gannett owns 23 television stations in about 20 markets, publishes periodicals and inserts (including *USA WEEKEND*), and operates websites for many of its papers.

	Annual Growth	12/05	12/06	12/07	12/08	12/09
Sales ($ mil.)	(7.3%)	7,598.9	8,033.4	7,439.5	6,767.6	5,613.0
Net income ($ mil.)	(26.6%)	1,225.9	1,160.8	981.8	(6,647.6)	355.3
Market value ($ mil.)	(29.6%)	14,426.1	14,399.9	9,288.7	1,905.4	3,536.9
Employees	(9.7%)	52,600	49,675	46,100	41,500	35,000

GANNETT FLEMING, INC.

207 Senate Ave.
Camp Hill, PA 17011
Phone: 717-763-7211
Fax: 717-763-8150
Web: www.gannettfleming.com

CEO: William M. Stout
CFO: —
HR: —
FYE: December 31
Type: Holding company

Engineering firm Gannett Fleming has waded through water, waste, and sludge for nearly a century. Founded in 1915, the company focuses on serving the transportation, water and wastewater, facilities, technology, and environmental industries. Gannett Fleming operates through about a dozen subsidiaries that offer a variety of services that range from design/build, construction management, ground testing and soil strengthening, site remediation, structural rehabilitation, electrical and mechanical installation, geophysical mapping and surveying, and 3D visualization. The company works on projects around the world and has more than 55 offices throughout the US and Canada.

	Annual Growth	12/04	12/05	12/06	12/07	12/08
Est. sales ($ mil.)	—	—	—	—	—	250.5
Employees	—	—	—	—	—	800

THE GAP, INC.   NYSE: GPS

2 Folsom St.	CEO: Glenn K. Murphy
San Francisco, CA 94105	CFO: Sabrina Simmons
Phone: 650-952-4400	HR: Eva Sage-Gavin
Fax: —	FYE: January 31
Web: www.gap.com	Type: Public

The ubiquitous clothing retailer Gap has been filling closets with jeans and khakis, T-shirts, and poplin since the Woodstock era. The firm, which operates about 3,100 stores worldwide, built its iconic casual brand on basics for men, women, and children, but over the years has expanded through the urban chic chain Banana Republic and budgeteer Old Navy, launched in 1994. Other brand extensions include GapBody, GapKids, and babyGap; each also has its own online incarnation. All Gap clothing is private-label merchandise made exclusively for the company. From the design board to store displays, Gap controls all aspects of its trademark casual look. Gap was founded by Doris and the late Don Fisher in 1969.

	Annual Growth	1/06	1/07	1/08	1/09	1/10
Sales ($ mil.)	(3.0%)	16,023.0	15,943.0	15,763.0	14,526.0	14,197.0
Net income ($ mil.)	(0.2%)	1,113.0	778.0	833.0	967.0	1,102.0
Market value ($ mil.)	1.3%	11,769.2	12,471.9	12,419.8	7,338.7	12,413.3
Employees	(3.1%)	153,000	154,000	150,000	134,000	135,000

GARAN, INCORPORATED

350 Fifth Ave.	CEO: Seymour Lichtenstein
New York, NY 10118	CFO: —
Phone: 212-563-2000	HR: —
Fax: 212-971-2250	FYE: December 31
Web: www.garanimals.com	Type: Subsidiary

If you've ever enlisted the help of a monkey to match your shirt and shorts, you're likely to be familiar with Garan. The company designs, manufactures, and distributes coordinated apparel for infants, toddlers, and children. Products are sold under its customers' private labels, as well as its own brand, Garanimals. Characters like Charley Chimp help young children dress themselves with coordinated hang-tags. Most of Garan's products are sold through distribution centers in the US to major national chains, such as Wal-Mart, department stores, and specialty stores. Founded in 1941, Garan is a subsidiary of Warren Buffett's Berkshire Hathaway.

GARDA CASH LOGISTICS

301 N. Lake Ave., Ste. 600	CEO: Richard A. Drutman
Pasadena, CA 91101	CFO: Hugues Trottier
Phone: 626-564-4284	HR: —
Fax: 626-564-4293	FYE: January 31
Web: www.gardacashlogistics.com	Type: Subsidiary

When it comes to cash, Garda Cash Logistics (formerly AT Systems) can count it, transport it, and deposit it in the bank. The company is a leading provider of secure cash transportation, offering armored vehicles and cash management services, as well as ATM services and cash vault services for banks, credit unions, financial service companies, and other businesses in need of secure transportation pickup and delivery. It additionally sells, installs, and maintains a range of safes and locks. Garda Cash Logistics is particularly strong in Canada and the US Midwest. The company is a subsidiary of Garda World Security.

	Annual Growth	1/04	1/05	1/06	1/07	1/08
Sales ($ mil.)	343.6%	—	—	—	120.6	535.0
Employees	—	—	—	—	—	12,000

GARDEN RIDGE CORPORATION

19411 Atrium Place, Ste. 170	CEO: Tom Kibarian
Houston, TX 77084	CFO: —
Phone: 832-391-7201	HR: —
Fax: —	FYE: January 31
Web: www.gardenridge.com	Type: Private

Megastore retailer Garden Ridge Corporation offers decorating accessories for more than just the garden. The company operates about 40 stores, each covering almost three acres and located off major highways in more than 15 states Florida to Michigan. (Texas has 15 stores). Its stores sell baskets, candles, crafts, home accents, home textiles, housewares, mirrors, party supplies, patio furniture, pictures and frames, pottery, seasonal items, and silk and dried flowers. Garden Ridge, which started as a single store outside of San Antonio in 1979, is owned by a group of investors led by the New York-based private equity firm Three Cities Research.

GARDNER DENVER, INC.   NYSE: GDI

1800 Gardner Expwy.	CEO: Barry L. Pennypacker
Quincy, IL 62305	CFO: Helen W. Cornell
Phone: 217-222-5400	HR: Armando L. Castorena
Fax: 217-228-8247	FYE: December 31
Web: www.gardnerdenver.com	Type: Public

Gardner Denver doesn't grow flowers in the Mile High City. The company makes blowers, petroleum pumps, and a variety of compressors, such as reciprocating, rotary screw, and sliding vane compressors, as well as positive displacement and centrifugal blowers. Manufacturing plants and industrial facilities use the compressors to produce durable goods, process petroleum and pharmaceuticals, and treat wastewater. Compressed air products are its principal offering. Gardner Denver also makes vacuum products, fluid-transfer products, and well-servicing pumps for oil and natural gas companies, and it is adding new lines, such as water-jetting products. About two-thirds of the company's sales come from outside the US.

	Annual Growth	12/05	12/06	12/07	12/08	12/09
Sales ($ mil.)	10.0%	1,214.6	1,669.2	1,868.8	2,018.3	1,778.1
Net income ($ mil.)	—	67.0	132.9	205.1	166.0	(165.2)
Market value ($ mil.)	14.6%	1,291.9	1,955.4	1,729.5	1,223.3	2,230.1
Employees	1.2%	6,200	6,000	6,200	7,700	6,500

GARELLI WONG & ASSOCIATES, INC.

200 S. Michigan Ave., Ste. 1220	CEO: James F. (Jim) Wong
Chicago, IL 60604	CFO: —
Phone: 312-583-9264	HR: —
Fax: 312-583-9268	FYE: December 31
Web: www.garelliwong.com	Type: Subsidiary

Garelli Wong finds the right people to keep the books at Chicago-area businesses. The recruiting firm specializes in finance and accounting staffing, filling positions ranging from accounting clerk to CFO. Clients include startups and not-for-profit companies, as well as large corporations. The company's Jackson Wabash division helps place temporary and contract professionals in finance and accounting jobs. The group was founded by Jim Wong and Mike Garelli. It works closely with another accounting staffing firm, Accounting Principals. Garelli Wong was part of MPS Group, which was acquired by global staffing rival Adecco in 2010.

	Annual Growth	12/04	12/05	12/06	12/07	12/08
Est. sales ($ mil.)	—	—	—	—	—	30.0
Employees	—	—	—	—	—	40

GARMIN LTD.

NASDAQ (GS): GRMN

1200 E. 151st St.	CEO: Min H. Kao
Olathe, KS 66062	CFO: Kevin S. Rauckman
Phone: 913-397-8200	HR: Laurie Minard
Fax: 913-397-8282	FYE: December 31
Web: www.garmin.com	Type: Public

You may not know where you're headed, but Garmin can tell you where you are. The company manufactures navigation products that use Global Positioning System (GPS) technology to wirelessly deliver geographic location data through satellite communications. Its portable products incorporate electronic maps and navigational charts. Garmin also makes communications devices that combine cellular and GPS technology. Boat maker Ranger and Piper Aircraft incorporate Garmin equipment into their products. The company sells its consumer products through retailers including Bass Pro Shops, Best Buy (about 13% of sales), and Wal-Mart. Garmin gets around two-thirds of its sales in North America.

	Annual Growth	12/05	12/06	12/07	12/08	12/09
Sales ($ mil.)	30.1%	1,027.8	1,774.0	3,180.3	3,494.1	2,946.4
Net income ($ mil.)	22.6%	311.2	514.1	855.0	732.8	704.0
Market value ($ mil.)	(1.9%)	6,607.5	11,085.9	19,319.7	3,818.1	6,114.6
Employees	29.0%	3,043	4,751	8,434	8,919	8,437

GARTNER, INC.

NYSE: IT

56 Top Gallant Rd.	CEO: Eugene A. (Gene) Hall
Stamford, CT 06902	CFO: Christopher J. (Chris) Lafond
Phone: 203-964-0096	HR: Robin B. Kranich
Fax: 203-316-6488	FYE: December 31
Web: www.gartner.com	Type: Public

You might not know IT, but Gartner does. The company helps clients understand the information technology (IT) industry and make informed decisions about IT products. It provides more than 10,000 client organizations with competitive analysis reports, industry overviews, market trend data, and product evaluation reports. Its GartnerG2, Gartner Dataquest, and other research services are made available through subscriptions, primarily to CIOs and other IT professionals. Gartner also offers technology and management consulting services, and it produces a number of conferences, seminars, and other events aimed at the technology sector. The company operates in more than 80 countries.

	Annual Growth	12/05	12/06	12/07	12/08	12/09
Sales ($ mil.)	3.6%	989.0	1,060.3	1,189.2	1,279.1	1,139.8
Net income ($ mil.)	—	(2.4)	58.2	73.6	103.9	83.0
Market value ($ mil.)	8.7%	1,240.8	1,903.5	1,689.0	1,715.0	1,735.2
Employees	4.4%	3,622	3,784	4,006	4,198	4,305

GAS TRANSMISSION NORTHWEST CORPORATION

1400 SW 5th Ave., Ste. 900	CEO: Jeff R. Rush
Portland, OR 97201	CFO: —
Phone: 503-833-4000	HR: Kelly Zwicker
Fax: 403-527-7706	FYE: December 31
Web: www.gastransmissionnw.com	Type: Subsidiary

Gas Transmission Northwest (formerly PG&E Gas Transmission, Northwest) takes the phrase "pipe down" literally. The company pumps nearly 3 billion cubic feet of gas a day through more than 610 miles of pipeline running from Western Canada to the pacific Northwest, California, and Nevada. Gas Transmission Northwest, a unit of TransCanada, provides firm and interruptible transportation services to more than 100 customers, including gas producers, marketers, and electric and gas utilities. Through Gas Transmission Northwest's pipeline, customers can also store, borrow, or sell their excess capacity.

	Annual Growth	12/04	12/05	12/06	12/07	12/08
Est. sales ($ mil.)	—	—	—	—	—	110.1
Employees	—	—	—	—	—	205

GASCO ENERGY, INC.

NYSE Amex: GSX

8 Inverness Dr. East, Ste. 100	CEO: Charles B. Crowell
Englewood, CO 80112	CFO: W. King Grant
Phone: 303-483-0044	HR: —
Fax: 303-483-0011	FYE: December 31
Web: www.gascoenergy.com	Type: Public

Gasco Energy is not your local gas company or energy provider. The exploration and production independent develops and explores for natural gas and crude petroleum primarily in the Rocky Mountains. The company's exploration activities are focused on Utah's Uinta Basin and Wyoming's Green River Basin. At the end of 2008, Gasco Energy's proved reserves stood at 53.1 billion cu. ft. of natural gas equivalent. It had working interests in 330,923 gross acres (214,483 net acres) located in California, Nevada, Utah, and Wyoming. That year it had stakes in 126 gross producing wells (77 net).

	Annual Growth	12/05	12/06	12/07	12/08	12/09
Sales ($ mil.)	5.7%	16.9	25.7	22.2	41.9	21.1
Net income ($ mil.)	—	0.0	(55.8)	(104.4)	14.5	(50.2)
Market value ($ mil.)	(46.6%)	703.5	263.9	214.4	42.0	57.1
Employees	13.3%	17	21	34	37	28

GASTAR EXPLORATION LTD.

NYSE Amex: GST

1331 Lamar St., Ste. 1080	CEO: J. Russell Porter
Houston, TX 77010	CFO: Michael A. Gerlich
Phone: 713-739-1800	HR: —
Fax: 713-739-0458	FYE: December 31
Web: www.gastar.com	Type: Public

Gastar Exploration has hitched its star to exploring for natural gas in the US. Its primary areas of exploration and production are Deep Bossier (in East Texas), the Powder River Basin, and the Appalachian Basin. Once active in Australia, Gastar Exploration is now focusing on lucrative US properties, including Wyoming's Powder River Basin, one of the most active coalbed methane plays in the US. It also is exploring the Marcellus Shale play in northern West Virginia and southwestern Pennsylvania. The company has proved reserves of 63.7 billion cu. ft. of natural gas and 12,000 barrels of oil. Chesapeake Energy owns 16% of the company.

	Annual Growth	12/05	12/06	12/07	12/08	12/09
Sales ($ mil.)	4.7%	27.4	26.8	34.6	63.2	32.9
Net income ($ mil.)	—	(25.7)	(84.8)	(30.5)	(5.4)	48.8
Market value ($ mil.)	(23.6%)	—	541.8	315.0	84.2	241.4
Employees	12.5%	15	19	23	22	24

GATE GOURMET, INC.

11710 Plaza America Dr., Ste. 800	CEO: Guy Dubois
Reston, VA 20190	CFO: Thomas Bucher
Phone: 703-964-2300	HR: Richard Wells
Fax: 703-964-2399	FYE: December 31
Web: www.gategourmet.com	Type: Subsidiary

Dining at 30,000 feet is no problem when the plane is loaded with food from Gate Gourmet. The foodservice company is one of the world's largest in-flight caterers, alongside rival LSG Sky Chefs. Gate Gourmet prepares more than 200 million meals a year for travelers from its 100 flight kitchens in more than 25 countries. The company contracts for about 250 airlines, including American Airlines, Delta Air Lines, and Thai Airways. Gate Gourmet also offers consulting on menu and service design, cost monitoring, and logistics. Gate Gourmet began in 1992 as the catering arm of Swissair; it is now part of the publicly traded gategroup.

An in-depth profile of this company is available to Hoover's Online members at hoovers.com.

661

GATE PETROLEUM COMPANY

9540 San Jose Blvd.
Jacksonville, FL 32257
Phone: 904-737-7220
Fax: 904-732-7660
Web: www.gatepetro.com

CEO: Herbert H. (Herb) Peyton
CFO: P. Jeremy Smith
HR: Mary Ann Bright
FYE: June 30
Type: Private

Gate Petroleum swings many ways. The company runs a chain of 225 Gate Food Post stores in Florida, Georgia, Kentucky, Louisiana, North Carolina, South Carolina, and Virginia that sell gas and groceries and offer fleet management services. The firm is also a wholesale fuel distributor to customers throughout the Southeast. The company is also active in the real estate and construction materials businesses. In Florida Gate owns several private clubs, office buildings, and business parks. Subsidiary Gate Concrete has plants in about half a dozen states that make and sell concrete and building materials. CEO Herbert Peyton, who founded the company in 1960, owns the majority of Gate Petroleum.

GATEHOUSE MEDIA, INC.

Pink Sheets: GHSE

350 Willowbrook Office Park
Fairport, NY 14450
Phone: 585-598-0030
Fax: 585-248-2631
Web: gatehousemedia.com

CEO: Michael E. (Mike) Reed
CFO: Melinda A. Janik
HR: Amy V. Kahn
FYE: December 31
Type: Public

GateHouse Media lets the local news flow freely. The company is a leading community newspaper publisher with more than 500 publications in about 20 states. Its portfolio includes nearly 100 daily newspapers, along with many more weeklies and shoppers that reach about 10 million readers. GateHouse generates revenue primarily through advertising; its papers serve ads from more than 230,000 business advertisers. In conjunction with its print publications, the company operates some 250 websites. GateHouse also produces a half dozen yellow page directories and it offers commercial printing services. Private equity firm Fortress Investment Group owns more than 40% of the company.

	Annual Growth	12/05	12/06	12/07	12/08	12/09
Sales ($ mil.)	48.7%	119.5	314.9	588.9	683.1	585.0
Net income ($ mil.)	—	9.6	(1.6)	(231.4)	(673.3)	(530.6)
Market value ($ mil.)	(77.9%)	—	1,078.3	510.1	2.3	11.6
Employees	8.7%	4,100	4,000	7,212	6,538	5,720

GATES CORPORATION

1551 Wewatta St.
Denver, CO 80202
Phone: 303-744-1911
Fax: 303-744-4443
Web: www.gates.com

CEO: Jim Nicol
CFO: John Zimmerman
HR: Cynthia Brabander
FYE: April 30
Type: Subsidiary

Success is no stretch for Gates Corp. Formerly The Gates Rubber Co., the company has evolved to rival the largest manufacturers of automotive and industrial belts and hoses. Gates drives three worldwide product groups: auto hoses, hydraulic and industrial hose and connectors, and power transmission. Its lines include specialty products for auto racing, marine, off-road, snowmobiles, as well as lawn and garden equipment applications. These are peddled to major auto and industrial OEM markets across the Americas, Europe, Asia, Australia, and the Middle East, directly and through a distributor network. Part of the UK Tomkins plc family of industrial and automotive operations, Gates branches to some 25 countries.

GATEWAY ENERGY CORPORATION

OTC: GNRG

500 Dallas St., Ste. 2615
Houston, TX 77002
Phone: 713-336-0844
Fax: 713-336-0855
Web: www.gatewayenergy.com

CEO: Frederick M. (Fred) Pevow Jr.
CFO: Jill Marlatt
HR: —
FYE: December 31
Type: Public

The door swings both ways for Gateway Energy, which serves as a go-between for natural gas producers and customers. It owns natural gas gathering, transportation, and distribution systems (totaling 280 miles of pipeline) in Texas, and in the Gulf of Mexico. Gateway Offshore Pipeline Company owns pipelines, a related operating platform, and an onshore terminal facility (the Crystal Beach facility) that services producers in Texas and Louisiana offshore waters and Galveston Bay. Gateway Energy owns two active onshore pipeline systems, in Texas. The company gathers gas at the wellhead and transports it to distribution companies or its own processing facilities.

	Annual Growth	12/05	12/06	12/07	12/08	12/09
Sales ($ mil.)	(10.6%)	10.5	10.2	11.5	15.0	6.7
Net income ($ mil.)	—	1.8	0.3	2.4	0.8	(0.2)
Market value ($ mil.)	(2.2%)	6.8	9.1	14.6	7.8	6.2
Employees	(19.1%)	14	14	7	7	6

GATEWAY, INC.

7565 Irvine Center Dr.
Irvine, CA 92618
Phone: 949-471-7000
Fax: 949-471-7041
Web: www.gateway.com

CEO: Rudi Schmidleithner
CFO: Ming Wang
HR: Lenny Pollak
FYE: December 31
Type: Subsidiary

Gateway opens doors to the world of computers. The company provides desktop and portable PCs, displays, and computer accessories. It also offers support services for its products, as well as for electronics products by other manufacturers. The company sells its products through retailers (Best Buy, Office Depot, Wal-Mart), e-tailers (Newegg), and various additional channel partners. Gateway was acquired by Acer for $710 million in 2007. Acer also markets the eMachines and Packard Bell brands. The Taiwanese company has overtaken Dell to become the second-largest PC manufacturer in the world, trailing only Hewlett-Packard.

GATEWAY TRAVEL MANAGEMENT INC.

1501 Ardmored Blvd., Ste. 400
Pittsburgh, PA 15221
Phone: 412-244-3740
Fax: 412-731-1785
Web: www.gtmtravel.com

CEO: James M. Pekins
CFO: Jim Harris
HR: Joy Betler
FYE: December 31
Type: Subsidiary

Gateway Travel Management (GTM) opens the, well, gate for corporate travel. The company provides airfare, hotel, rental car, and travel package arrangements to more than 300 corporate clients, which are primarily based in the Midwest and Mid-Atlantic. It also operates a corporate meetings division that plans executive retreats, seminars, conventions, and incentive trips for groups of 10 to 4,000 participants. Formed in 1984, the company operates from two offices in Pennsylvania. In 2010 GTM was acquired by Paris-based Carlson Wagonlit Travel (CWT), a leading business travel firm whose operations span more than 150 countries and territories. The purchase strengthens CWT's eastern US operations.

THE GATORADE COMPANY

555 W. Monroe St.
Chicago, IL 60661
Phone: 312-821-1000
Fax: —
Web: www.gatorade.com

CEO: Rich Beck
CFO: —
HR: —
FYE: December 31
Type: Subsidiary

There's a reason why the product's name is Gatorade. The beverage was invented during the 1960s by University of Florida doctors in order to hydrate the university's football team (The Gators). Officially called Gatorade Thirst Quencher, the lemon-lime-flavored rehydrating drink has grown to become the leading sports drink in the US. Knowing that one product wouldn't keep it in business forever, the company has continued to create new beverages, including its vitamin-enhanced Propel Fitness Water; its Thirst Quencher series with names like Rain, Frost, and Fierce; and its Performance series, sold under the brand name Endurance.

GC SERVICES LIMITED PARTNERSHIP

6330 Gulfton St.
Houston, TX 77081
Phone: 713-777-4441
Fax: 713-777-6619
Web: www.gcserv.com

CEO: J. B. Katz
CFO: —
HR: —
FYE: December 31
Type: Private

GC Services considers it a Good Call when it Gets Cash. The company, one of the nation's top collection agencies, provides a wide range of services, including customer relations and receivables management, to clients throughout North America from about 35 US call centers. Its teleservices division provides inbound and outbound call center management services, including general reception and operator services, billing and payment assistance, and back-office processing of accounts. Its receivables management division provides debt collection, data management, and other services. The company has the capacity to take operator-assisted calls in some 20 languages and handles about one million calls daily.

⊞ GATX CORPORATION

NYSE: GMT

222 W. Adams St.
Chicago, IL 60606
Phone: 312-621-6200
Fax: 312-621-6648
Web: www.gatx.com

CEO: Brian A. Kenney
CFO: Robert C. Lyons
HR: Mary K. Lawler
FYE: December 31
Type: Public

GATX never tried to unite Georgia and Texas, but the holding company does bring together some diverse businesses. Short for General American Transportation Corporation, GATX operates three business segments. Rail, with its over 165,000 railcars (mostly tank and freight, plus 700 locomotives), is the company's biggest unit, handling tank, freight car, and locomotive leasing in the US and Europe. Its Specialty segment handles leases, affiliate investments, and loans for the marine, shipping, aerospace, construction and mining, and industrial equipment industries. The American Steamship Company (ASC) business is a shipping company with a fleet of self-unloading ships operating on the Great Lakes.

	Annual Growth	12/05	12/06	12/07	12/08	12/09
Sales ($ mil.)	(0.2%)	1,134.6	1,229.1	1,346.0	1,443.1	1,124.9
Net income ($ mil.)	—	(14.3)	111.7	203.7	196.0	81.4
Market value ($ mil.)	(5.5%)	1,670.5	2,006.2	1,698.3	1,433.9	1,331.1
Employees	0.8%	1,870	2,340	2,094	2,119	1,929

GDF SUEZ ENERGY NORTH AMERICA, INC.

1990 Post Oak Blvd., Ste. 1900
Houston, TX 77056
Phone: 713-636-0000
Fax: 713-636-1364
Web: www.suezenergyna.com

CEO: Zin Smati
CFO: Geert Peeters
HR: Mike Thompson
FYE: December 31
Type: Subsidiary

GDF SUEZ Energy North America (GDF-SENA) manages GDF Suez Energy International's energy business in Canada, Mexico, and the US. The company develops and operates electricity and cogeneration facilities, markets and sells energy products and services, and imports and distributes natural gas and liquefied natural gas (LNG). It serves both commercial and industrial customers. (GDF-SENA)'s primary unit (GDF SUEZ Energy Generation NA) owns and operates 60 power, cogeneration, steam, and chilled-water facilities, including those in construction, representing a capacity of 7,500 MW of electricity generation, 6 million pounds per hour of steam, and 42,000 tons per hour of chilled water.

⊞ GAYLORD ENTERTAINMENT COMPANY

NYSE: GET

1 Gaylord Dr.
Nashville, TN 37214
Phone: 615-316-6000
Fax: 615-316-6555
Web: www.gaylordentertainment.com

CEO: Colin V. Reed
CFO: Mark Fioravanti
HR: Gara Pryor
FYE: December 31
Type: Public

Gaylord Entertainment may be hollerin' for attention in the hospitality game, but it's no corporate hayseed. Its properties consist of resort hotels tethered closely to attractions that appeal to the meetings and conventions market. They include The Radisson Hotel at Opryland and the Gaylord Opryland Resort & Convention Center (home to the Gaylord Springs golf course), both in Nashville; the Gaylord Palms Resort in Florida (close to Disney World); and the Gaylord Texan Resort near Dallas. It also owns the Gaylord National Resort and Convention Center in the Washington, DC, area. Other holdings include the famous Grand Ole Opry and related attractions, the Ryman Auditorium, and the General Jackson Showboat.

	Annual Growth	12/05	12/06	12/07	12/08	12/09
Sales ($ mil.)	0.3%	868.8	947.9	747.7	930.9	879.1
Net income ($ mil.)	—	(34.0)	(79.4)	111.9	4.4	0.0
Market value ($ mil.)	(18.0%)	2,053.1	2,398.8	1,906.1	510.6	930.2
Employees	(6.5%)	12,178	12,031	9,013	10,555	9,307

GDF SUEZ ENERGY RESOURCES NA

1990 Post Oak Blvd., Ste. 1900
Houston, TX 77056
Phone: 713-636-0000
Fax: 713-599-2601
Web: www.suezenergyresources.com

CEO: Geert Peeters
CFO: —
HR: —
FYE: December 31
Type: Subsidiary

GDF SUEZ Energy Resources (formerly SUEZ Energy Resources) helps companies get on track with their energy needs. The firm provides retail electricity supply solutions to more than 12,000 commercial and industrial clients in 10 deregulated US states and Washington, DC. It is working toward expanding its offerings into additional states and plans to enter the retail natural gas market. The company manages budgeting, price structure, and risk management issues involved with corporate energy purchases. Its customers include retail and manufacturing firms, real estate properties, educational facilities, and municipal authorities. GCF SUEZ Energy Resources is the retail subsisidary of GDF SUEZ Energy North America.

⊞ An in-depth profile of this company is available to Hoover's Online members at hoovers.com.

663

GE AVIATION SYSTEMS LLC

1 Neumann Way	CEO: David L. Joyce
Cincinnati, OH 45215	CFO: Shane M. Wright
Phone: 513-243-2000	HR: Raghu Krishnamoorthy
Fax: 513-243-1568	FYE: December 31
Web: www.geae.com	Type: Subsidiary

Once a sky-baby next to Pratt & Whitney and Rolls-Royce, GE Aviation now rules the runway as the world's largest producer of engines for commercial and military planes. This division of General Electric's Infrastructure segment makes jet, turboprop, and turboshaft engines that power aircraft from cargo, executive, and passenger jets to bombers and helicopters. GE Aviation also makes aircraft engine derivatives for marine propulsion and industrial power sources. For service after the sale, GE Aviation's GE Engine Services unit offers maintenance, service, and spare parts. It operates in more than 50 locations worldwide.

GE CAPITAL REAL ESTATE

901 Main Ave.	CEO: Ronald R. (Ron) Pressman
Norwalk, CT 06851	CFO: Stewart B. Koenigsberg
Phone: 203-750-2900	HR: Bernard M. Garrigues
Fax: —	FYE: December 31
Web: www.gecapital.com	Type: Business segment

Whether you need a partner, financier, or manager, GE Capital Real Estate has the commercial real estate market covered. A unit of conglomerate General Electric, GE Capital Real Estate owns, manages, and provides financing for retail, industrial, multifamily, hospitality, and office properties. The unit also performs loan servicing and property management services. It operates through joint ventures, direct investment, and debt financings and has some $84 billion in assets under management. GE Capital Real Estate operates globally and maintains more than 40 offices in 31 markets in North America, Europe, and Asia.

GE CAPITAL SOLUTIONS FLEET SERVICES

3 Capital Dr.	CEO: Clarence Nunn
Eden Prairie, MN 55344	CFO: Christina Selby
Phone: 952-828-1000	HR: —
Fax: —	FYE: December 31
Web: www.gefleet.com	Type: Subsidiary

GE Capital Solutions Fleet Services helps to keep businesses' eyes on the road and hands on the wheel. Better known as GE Fleet Services, the General Electric unit is a leading corporate vehicle fleet manager. The company has nearly 2 million cars and trucks under lease and service management contracts in North America, Europe, and the Asia/Pacific region. Along with vehicle financing and acquisition, GE Fleet Services offers maintenance and fuel purchasing programs. Its website helps to streamline the ordering process, allowing customers to analyze manufacturer specifics and pricing.

GE COMMERCIAL AVIATION SERVICES LLC

201 High Ridge Rd.	CEO: Norman C. T. Liu
Stamford, CT 06927	CFO: —
Phone: 203-357-3776	HR: —
Fax: 203-316-7865	FYE: December 31
Web: www.gecas.com	Type: Business segment

Everyone who owns a car has heard about car leases; what a lot of people *don't* realize is that many airlines lease some or all of their aircraft. GE Commercial Aviation Services (GECAS), the business aircraft finance unit of GE Capital Corporation (GECC), has the largest fleet of planes for leasing in the world — about 1,500 aircraft including widebodies, narrowbodies, freight planes, and regional jets. GECAS also leases and offers financing to customers that wish to buy aircraft, engines, and spare parts. To top it off, the unit also provides pilot training services. GECAS counts more than 200 airline customers in some 75 countries.

GE ENGINE SERVICES, INC.

1 Neumann Way M/D G58	CEO: David L. Joyce
Cincinnati, OH 45215	CFO: Stephen J. (Steve) Sedita Jr.
Phone: 513-243-2000	HR: Jack Ryan
Fax: —	FYE: December 31
Web: www.geae.com/services	Type: Subsidiary

General Electric is the world's largest maker of jet engines, so if you've ever been to an airport, you've doubtless heard the whine of GE jet engines. Keeping all those engines functioning is the task of GE Engine Services. The company provides engine maintenance, repair, overhaul services, and technology upgrades, as well as engine exchange. It supplies customers with new and used engine parts; leases engines and provides financing for engine customers; and inspects, analyzes, and diagnoses engines. Not only does it work on its own engines, but it also works on its competitors' engines, including those made by Rolls-Royce and Pratt & Whitney.

GE FRANCHISE FINANCE

8377 E. Hartford Dr., Ste. 200	CEO: Darren Kowalske
Scottsdale, AZ 85255	CFO: —
Phone: 480-585-4500	HR: —
Fax: 480-585-2225	FYE: December 31
Web: www.gefranchisefinance.com	Type: Subsidiary

Entrepreneurs who want to put a tiger in their customers' tanks, give them the Midas touch, or help them make a run for the border are saying, "Oh, thank heaven for GE Franchise Finance." The General Electric Capital subsidiary provides real estate and other financing for more than 6,000 franchise operators at some 21,000 locations in the US and Canada. The firm finances restaurants, hotels and other hospitality providers, and auto service and parts retailers. It also offers credit for buying equipment or acquiring new or expanding locations.

GE GLOBAL RESEARCH

1 Research Circle	CEO: Mark M. Little
Niskayuna, NY 12309	CFO: —
Phone: 518-387-5000	HR: —
Fax: 518-387-6696	FYE: December 31
Web: www.ge.com/research	Type: Business segment

This business segment of behemoth General Electric helps its parent bring good things to life. GE Global Research develops new materials and technologies in a variety of fields, including specialty chemicals, health care, security, imaging, energy, nanotechnology, and computing. Its research is conducted by a staff of about 2,800 scientists, and GE Global Research obtains hundreds of patents each year. The company, founded in 1900 in scientist Charles Steinmetz's backyard barn, operates from facilities in Bangalore, India; Munich, Germany; Niskayuna, New York; and Shanghai, China.

GE HONDA AERO ENGINES LLC

134 Merchant St., Ste. 240, Mail Drop U121	CEO: William J. Dwyer
Cincinnati, OH 45246	CFO: —
Phone: 513-552-3332	HR: —
Fax: —	FYE: —
Web: www.gehonda.com	Type: Joint venture

Singularly, GE is the world's #1 maker of jet airplane engines; while Honda is primarily known for automobiles; together, the two giants have revved up to build engines for small jets. Their joint venture, GE Honda Aero Engines (50%-owned by GE Aircraft Engines and 50%-owned by Honda Aero) was formed in 2004 to produce engines for 4-8 seat business jets. In particular, the company began producing Honda's HF118 engine for the light business jet market in 2005 and is currently in the midst of producing the HF120, a 2,000-pound thrust turbofan engine.

GE INFRASTRUCTURE

4636 Somerton Rd.	CEO: John G. Rice
Trevose, PA 19053	CFO: —
Phone: 215-355-3300	HR: —
Fax: —	FYE: December 31
	Type: Subsidiary

What would a GE business be without constant reorganization? What was GE Infrastructure was divided into GE Energy Infrastructure and GE Technology Infrastructure, representing about half of the conglomerate's sales. The segments of General Electric oversee the operations of GE's aircraft engines, water technologies, and energy businesses, among others. GE Aviation is the world's largest maker of engines for commercial and military aircraft. GE Water and Process Technologies makes water treatment chemicals, pumps, and filters. GE Energy designs, builds, installs, and provides maintenance for power generation plants of all stripes: coal, natural gas, nuclear, solar, steam, and wind.

GE SECURITY, INC.

8985 Town Center Pkwy.	CEO: Dean S. Seavers
Bradenton, FL 34202	CFO: —
Phone: 941-739-4200	HR: —
Fax: —	FYE: December 31
Web: www.gesecurity.com	Type: Subsidiary

GE Security seems the logical choice to protect your home from burglars or fire. The company provides security systems for residential and commercial use, including intrusion and fire protection systems. GE Security also distributes products for access and building control, video surveillance, explosive and drug detection, key management, and structured wiring. In addition to targeting residential and consumer clients, the company provides services for commercial markets, and the government and military. GE Security has operations in more than 30 countries. United Technologies Corporation (UTC), a diversified provider of technology and services to building systems and aerospace markets, owns GE Security.

GE SENSING

The Boston Center, 1100 Technology Dr.	CEO: Tim Povall
Billerica, MA 01821	CFO: Roger Owen
Phone: 978-437-1000	HR: —
Fax: —	FYE: December 31
Web: www.gesensing.com	Type: Business segment

GE Sensing products are more sensible than sensual; they monitor pressure, flow, temperature, gas, moisture, humidity, fluid levels, and electrical signals. The company specializes in precision measuring and testing equipment, including pressure sensors, calibration standards, portable calibration equipment, and aviation ground support systems. It provides recertification, repair, and calibration services, as well as a rental program. Established as Druck in 1972, GE Sensing was acquired by General Electric in 2002. It serves the aerospace, automotive, building facilities, biotechnology, defense, industrial, medical, meteorology, petrochemical, pharmaceutical, power generation, and transportation industries.

	Annual Growth	12/04	12/05	12/06	12/07	12/08
Est. sales ($ mil.)	—	—	—	—	—	128.4
Employees	—	—	—	—	—	639

GE TRAILER FLEET SERVICES

530 E. Swedesford Rd.	CEO: Joe Artuso
Wayne, PA 19087	CFO: Shila Ray
Phone: 484-254-0100	HR: Sunil Bijali
Fax: —	FYE: December 31
Web: www.trailerservices.com	Type: Business segment

With all due respect to rockers Deep Purple, GE Trailer Fleet Services (formerly Transport International Pool or TIP) wants to be a "highway star." The company, a division of General Electric's Equipment Services business, rents, leases, sells, and remarkets over-the-road transport trailers. The company also offers mobile maintenance and vehicle protection plan services. GE Trailer Fleet Services has a fleet of more than 135,000 units and more than 100 branches throughout Canada, Mexico, and the US. GE Trailer Fleet Services also keeps a fleet of some 25,000 used trailers for sale. The company was founded in 1957 as Container Leasing, Inc.

An in-depth profile of this company is available to Hoover's Online members at hoovers.com.

665

GEEKNET, INC.

NASDAQ (GM): LNUX

650 Castro St., Ste. 450
Mountain View, CA 94041
Phone: 650-694-2100
Fax: 650-694-2111
Web: geek.net

CEO: Scott L. Kauffman
CFO: Patricia S. Morris
HR: —
FYE: December 31
Type: Public

This company is fanning the flames of the open source software movement. Geeknet (formerly SourceForge) produces websites aimed primarily at open source software developers and other technology enthusiasts. The company's websites include SourceForge.net (an online collaborative development site), Slashdot.org (peer-produced and -moderated technology news), Ohloh (a free public directory of open source software), and freshmeat.net (catering to Linux users). It also operates ThinkGeek, an online shop for apparel, books, and tech gadgets. The company sold its enterprise software business in 2007. Founded by former chairman Larry Augustin in 1993, the business adopted the Geeknet name in late 2009.

	Annual Growth	7/05	7/06	7/07	7/08	*12/09
Sales ($ mil.)	18.8%	32.9	43.6	45.6	55.3	65.6
Net income ($ mil.)	—	(4.7)	11.0	8.7	(4.3)	(14.0)
Market value ($ mil.)	(8.8%)	104.3	240.8	225.0	84.3	72.2
Employees	0.0%	127	121	101	120	127
						*Fiscal year change

GEHL COMPANY

143 Water St.
West Bend, WI 53095
Phone: 262-334-9461
Fax: 262-338-7517
Web: www.gehl.com

CEO: Malcolm F. (Mac) Moore
CFO: —
HR: Brian L. Pearlman
FYE: December 31
Type: Subsidiary

Gehl Company asks the question, "Can you dig it?" The company manufactures light-construction equipment bearing the Gehl and Mustang brand names primarily used by building contractors. Products include mini-excavators, mini-loaders, and skid steer loaders for material handling; telescopic loaders; and asphalt pavers for building sidewalks, parking lots, trails, and driveways. It has about 750 independent dealers around the globe, but most are located in North America. Gehl also offers financing to its dealers and their customers. In 2006 the company exited the agricultural machinery business. France-based MANITOU BF, previously one of Gehl's largest shareholders, acquired the company in 2008.

	Annual Growth	12/04	12/05	12/06	12/07	12/08
Est. sales ($ mil.)	—	—	—	—	—	457.6
Employees	—	—	—	—	—	848

GEISINGER HEALTH SYSTEM

100 N. Academy Ave.
Danville, PA 17822
Phone: 570-271-6211
Fax: 570-271-7498
Web: www.geisinger.org

CEO: Glenn D. Steele Jr.
CFO: —
HR: —
FYE: June 30
Type: Not-for-profit

Geisinger Health System provides health care to a large section of the Keystone State, serving residents of about 40 counties in the central and northeastern portions of Pennsylvania. Founded in 1915, the system's flagship facility is Geisinger Medical Center, a 400-bed medical-surgical hospital in Danville that includes the Janet Weis Children's Hospital. With joint venture partner HealthSouth, the organization runs a rehabilitation hospital in Danville. The system also includes the 240-bed Geisinger Wyoming Valley Medical Center and numerous outpatient facilities and doctors' offices throughout the region. Additionally, Geisinger runs the Geisinger Health Plan, a not-for-profit HMO with some 220,000 members.

GENCO DISTRIBUTION SYSTEM, INC.

100 Papercraft Park
Pittsburgh, PA 15238
Phone: 412-820-3700
Fax: 412-820-3689
Web: www.genco.com

CEO: Herbert S. (Herb) Shear
CFO: Rick Roadarmel
HR: Mark Boyer
FYE: December 31
Type: Private

GENCO Distribution System, which does business as GENCO Supply Chain Solutions, provides third-party logistics services. Among the company's offerings are warehousing and distribution services, reverse logistics (processing of returned goods), product liquidation, supply chain analysis, transportation management (including parcel management), and damage research (analyzing causes of damage to customers' unsaleable products). The company maintains about 37 million sq. ft. of warehouse space at about 130 locations in the US and Canada. Customers include manufacturers, retailers, and government agencies. CEO Herb Shear owns the company, which was founded in 1898 by his grandfather Hyman Shear.

GENCO SHIPPING & TRADING LIMITED

NYSE: GNK

299 Park Ave., 20th Fl.
New York, NY 10171
Phone: 646-443-8550
Fax: 646-443-8551
Web: gencoshipping.com

CEO: Robert Gerald Buchanan
CFO: John C. Wobensmith
HR: —
FYE: December 31
Type: Public

Marine transportation company Genco Shipping & Trading transports dry cargo in a wet environment. The company maintains a fleet of about 30 oceangoing dry bulk carriers, which it charters mainly on long-term contracts to shippers of bulk commodities and marine transportation companies. Its fleet has an overall capacity of about 2.4 million deadweight tons (DWT). Genco Shipping's vessels transport cargo such as coal, grain, iron ore, and steel products. About 90% of its vessels on time-charter contracts. Customers have included BHP Billiton, Cargill, Lauritzen Bulkers and NYK. Pacific Basin Chartering and Cargill make up about 10% of the company's revenues. Genco Shipping & Trading was founded in 2004.

	Annual Growth	12/05	12/06	12/07	12/08	12/09
Sales ($ mil.)	34.2%	116.9	133.2	185.4	405.4	379.5
Net income ($ mil.)	28.5%	54.5	63.5	106.8	86.6	148.6
Market value ($ mil.)	6.4%	556.6	891.8	1,747.8	472.4	714.3
Employees	18.0%	408	475	617	701	791

GENCOR INDUSTRIES, INC.

NASDAQ (GM): GENC

5201 N. Orange Blossom Trail
Orlando, FL 32810
Phone: 407-290-6000
Fax: 407-578-0577
Web: www.gencor.com

CEO: E. J. (Mike) Elliott
CFO: L. Ray Adams
HR: —
FYE: September 30
Type: Public

Gencor Industries loves the smell of asphalt in the morning. The company makes industrial process equipment, such as machinery that makes hot-mix asphalt and other highway construction materials. Gencor's products include asphalt plants, combustion systems (large burners that transform various fuels into usable energy), and fluid heat transfer systems under the Hy-Way and Beverley names. It also produces soil decontamination machines and combustion systems for dryers, kilns, boilers, and tank heaters. Gencor Industries makes most of its sales in the US.

	Annual Growth	9/05	9/06	9/07	9/08	9/09
Sales ($ mil.)	4.2%	48.1	67.1	75.3	88.3	56.8
Net income ($ mil.)	—	31.3	11.6	18.5	15.2	(2.6)
Market value ($ mil.)	1.4%	78.3	88.9	95.2	77.7	82.7
Employees	(1.0%)	294	346	434	461	282

GENCORP INC.

NYSE: GY

Hwy. 50 and Aerojet Rd.
Rancho Cordova, CA 95742
Phone: 916-355-4000
Fax: 916-351-8668
Web: www.gencorp.com

CEO: Scott J. Seymour
CFO: Kathleen E. Redd
HR: Elizabeth Zacharias
FYE: November 30
Type: Public

Rocket men have GenCorp to thank for their timeless flight and their yearning for earth. The company's core subsidiary, Aerojet-General, manufactures propulsion systems for defense and space applications. Its propulsion products are used in missiles, maneuvering systems, launch vehicles, spacecraft, and satellites. Aerojet is the only domestic supplier of all four propulsion types: solid, liquid, air-breathing, and electric. Customers include the US Department of Defense, NASA, Raytheon, Lockheed Martin, and Boeing. GenCorp's other business segment deals in real estate, the sale and leasing of excess land held in California. Sales to the US government and its prime contractors represent nearly 90% of revenues.

	Annual Growth	11/05	11/06	11/07	11/08	11/09
Sales ($ mil.)	6.3%	624.0	621.1	745.4	742.3	795.4
Net income ($ mil.)	—	(230.0)	(36.6)	69.0	1.5	59.3
Market value ($ mil.)	(19.1%)	1,068.2	807.9	707.9	167.3	456.9
Employees	(0.2%)	3,101	3,144	3,252	3,057	3,071

GENELINK, INC.

OTC: GNLK

317 Wekiva Springs Rd., Ste. 200
Longwood, FL 32779
Phone: 407-772-7160
Fax: 407-772-7193
Web: www.genelinkbio.com

CEO: Gary J. Beeman
CFO: —
HR: —
FYE: December 31
Type: Public

GeneLink has taken the science of molecular genetics and turned it into a way to sell face cream and vitamins. Operating through its GeneWize subsidiary, the company creates customized nutritional supplements based upon a genetic assessment obtained from a cheek swab. Its products are sold direct to consumers through a multilevel marketing structure under the LifeMap Nutrition brand. Other products in development include customized skin care products to be marketed under the Dermagenetics brand. It is also developing consumer products to predict how an individual's skin will age, or if an individual has a significant risk of developing cardiovascular disease or osteopenia.

	Annual Growth	12/05	12/06	12/07	12/08	12/09
Sales ($ mil.)	115.3%	0.4	0.2	0.1	6.4	8.6
Net income ($ mil.)	—	(1.1)	(0.6)	(1.6)	(2.6)	(2.7)
Market value ($ mil.)	7.5%	10.6	6.5	14.1	16.5	14.1
Employees	10.9%	11	14	15	15	—

GENENCOR INTERNATIONAL, INC.

925 Page Mill Rd.
Palo Alto, CA 94304
Phone: 650-846-7500
Fax: 650-845-6500
Web: www.genencor.com

CEO: Tjerk de Ruiter
CFO: Andrew (Andy) Ashworth
HR: Jim Sjoerdsma
FYE: December 31
Type: Subsidiary

If you've got the money, honey, Genencor International's got the 'zyme. Genencor manufactures genetically modified enzymes for the industrial, agricultural, and consumer products markets. Using its biotechnology know-how, the company discovers useful enzymes (naturally occurring protein catalysts) and develops them for mass production; the enzymes are used in myriad ways, including as additives in animal feed and detergents, as a method of converting starch into ethanol, and in the production of textiles and paper. Genencor International is a division of food ingredient company Danisco.

GENENTECH, INC.

1 DNA Way
South San Francisco, CA 94080
Phone: 650-225-1000
Fax: 650-225-6000
Web: www.gene.com

CEO: Ian T. Clark
CFO: Steve Krognes
HR: Denise Smith-Hams
FYE: December 31
Type: Subsidiary

"The few, the proud, the profitable" could be Genentech's motto. One of the world's oldest and most successful biotechs (in an industry full of money-losers), the firm has a number of blockbuster cancer therapies based on its antibody (protein) technologies: Rituxan, which fights non-Hodgkin's lymphoma; Avastin, a treatment for colorectal, breast, and lung cancers; and Herceptin for breast cancer. Lung cancer drug Tarceva rounds out its oncology portfolio. Genentech's other marketed drugs include age-related macular degeneration treatment Lucentis, human growth hormone Nutropin, cystic fibrosis drug Pulmozyme, and asthma drug Xolair. The company is a wholly owned subsidiary of Swiss drugmaker Roche.

	Annual Growth	12/04	12/05	12/06	12/07	12/08
Est. sales ($ mil.)	—	—	—	—	—	13,418.0
Employees	—	—	—	—	—	11,174

GENEON ENTERTAINMENT (USA) INC.

2001 Wilshire Blvd., Ste. 600
Santa Monica, CA 90403
Phone: 310-586-5700
Fax: —
Web: www.geneonanimation.com

CEO: Yushin Soga
CFO: —
HR: —
FYE: March 31
Type: Subsidiary

Geneon Entertainment (formerly Pioneer Entertainment) produces film, music, animation, and television shows on VHS, DVD, and CD. The company also licenses and distributes a variety of popular Japanese programming, including *Sailor Moon, Pokémon,* and *Dragon Ball Z.* The Geneon/Pioneer Classics music label features artists such as Judy Garland, Ringo Starr, Miles Davis, and Ray Charles, among others. Geneon was previously part of the Pioneer North American Group, a subsidiary of Pioneer Corporation, before Tokyo-based ad giant Dentsu purchased the company in 2003. The company's name is derived from combining the words "generate" and "eon."

GENERAC HOLDINGS INC.

NYSE: GNRC

S45 W29290 Hwy. 59
Waukesha, WI 53187
Phone: 262-544-4811
Fax: 262-968-3791
Web: www.generac.com

CEO: Aaron Jagdfeld
CFO: York A. Ragen
HR: —
FYE: December 31
Type: Public

Perfect storms make good business for Generac Power Systems. That's because the company manufactures engine-driven standby and portable generators for homes, businesses, hospitals, and recreational vehicles. The company also makes industrial power generation equipment, automatic transfer switches, switch gear and controls, and remote monitoring software. Generac sells its products through retailers, such as Home Depot, and wholesale distributors. The US and Canada represent over 99% of company sales. Established in 1959, Generac was purchased by private equity firm CCMP Capital Advisors in 2006. Generac went public in 2010.

	Annual Growth	12/05	12/06	12/07	12/08	12/09
Sales ($ mil.)	(4.7%)	—	680.4	555.7	574.2	588.2
Net income ($ mil.)	—	—	(3.2)	(9.7)	(556.0)	43.1
Employees	(10.0%)	—	—	—	1,504	1,354

An in-depth profile of this company is available to Hoover's Online members at hoovers.com.

667

GENERAL ATLANTIC LLC

Three Pickwick Plaza
Greenwich, CT 06830
Phone: 203-629-8600
Fax: 203-622-8818
Web: www.generalatlantic.com

CEO: William E. (Bill) Ford
CFO: Thomas (Tom) Murphy
HR: —
FYE: December 31
Type: Private

General Atlantic helps little fish become bigger fish in the big pond called business. The private equity firm provides both capital and strategic support to public and private growth companies. With about $13 billion in capital under management, General Atlantic focuses its investments on such sectors as energy, financial services, health care, media, and technology. Typical investments range from $50 million to $500 million, and its average investment period lasts from five to seven years. Established in 1980, General Atlantic has stakes in about 40 firms. Portfolio companies include AKQA, Lenovo Group, and ZAGAT Survey.

GENERAL ATOMICS

3550 General Atomics Ct.
San Diego, CA 92121
Phone: 858-455-3000
Fax: 858-455-3621
Web: www.ga.com

CEO: James N. (Neal) Blue
CFO: Anthony G. Navarra
HR: Karin Yates
FYE: December 31
Type: Private

General Atomics has more than nuclear energy these days. The company, which was founded in 1955 to research atomic energy, continues to develop and operate nuclear power reactor systems, but may be finding more demand for its research and engineering expertise in areas such as unmanned military aircraft, airborne sensors, hazardous waste, superconducting magnets, and information technology. Through several divisions and subsidiaries, the company commercializes and develops its technology to customers worldwide. Customers have included the US Department of Defense, the US Department of Energy, and National Science Foundation. General Atomics was originally a division of defense titan General Dynamics.

GENERAL ATOMICS AERONAUTICAL SYSTEMS, INC.

16761 Via Del Campo Ct.
San Diego, CA 92127
Phone: 858-455-2810
Fax: 858-455-4247
Web: www.ga-asi.com

CEO: James N. (Neal) Blue
CFO: Alan Adelman
HR: Shannon McGhee
FYE: December 31
Type: Subsidiary

"It's a bird, it's a plane — it's a Predator with a Hellfire missile! RUN!" General Atomics Aeronautical Systems' Predator unmanned aerial vehicle (UAV) gained fame when it became the first UAV ever to identify *and* attack a target (an al Qaeda convoy). The four-cylinder, 90mph Predator, which can carry 450 pounds and remain over a target for about 24 hours at heights up to 25,000 feet, has video cameras, GPS, and an infrared system. The Predator B flies at 50,000 feet and can carry 800 pounds. Lesser-known General Atomics Aeronautical Systems UAVs include the GNAT (endurance) and the Mariner (maritime surveillance). The company is a subsidiary of General Atomics.

GENERAL BEARING CORPORATION

Pink Sheets: GNRL

44 High St.
West Nyack, NY 10994
Phone: 845-358-6000
Fax: 845-358-6277
Web: www.generalbearing.com

CEO: David L. Gussack
CFO: Rocky Cambrea
HR: Fran Garner-Laino
FYE: December 31
Type: Public

General Bearing's business generally just keeps on a rollin'. The company manufactures and distributes a line of bearings under the The General and Hyatt brands. Its products include ball bearings, tapered roller bearings, spherical roller bearings, and cylindrical roller bearings and components. The line caters to US and Canadian OEMs of trains, trucks, trailers, office equipment, and appliances, and industrial aftermarket distributors. Through joint ventures, General Bearing makes its bearing products in China, and engineers and sells them from the US. Founder and chairman Seymour Gussack, son and CEO David Gussack, daughter Nina Gussack, and son-in-law Robert Baruc collectively hold over half of the company.

⊞ GENERAL CABLE CORPORATION

NYSE: BGC

4 Tesseneer Dr.
Highland Heights, KY 41076
Phone: 859-572-8000
Fax: 859-572-8458
Web: www.generalcable.com

CEO: Gregory B. Kenny
CFO: Brian J. Robinson
HR: Peter J. Olmsted
FYE: December 31
Type: Public

With General Cable, you can keep the lights on and call if the power goes out. The company makes a comprehensive line of aluminum, copper, and fiber-optic wire and cable products, primarily sold to OEMs and distributors in the communications, construction, electric utility, and electrical infrastructure markets. Commercial and industrial applications include electrical distribution and transmission, voice and data communications, and power generation. Brand names include BICC, Carol, and NextGen. The company also makes flexible cords for temporary power and custom wire harnesses for any industry using wires and connectors. General Cable has about 44 manufacturing facilities in more than 20 countries.

	Annual Growth	12/05	12/06	12/07	12/08	12/09
Sales ($ mil.)	16.5%	2,380.8	3,665.1	4,614.8	6,230.1	4,385.2
Net income ($ mil.)	29.0%	39.2	135.3	208.6	217.2	108.7
Market value ($ mil.)	10.5%	1,026.3	2,277.1	3,817.5	921.6	1,532.6
Employees	11.5%	7,300	7,700	11,800	13,000	11,300

GENERAL CHEMICAL INDUSTRIAL PRODUCTS INC.

120 Eagle Rock Ave.
East Hanover, NJ 07936
Phone: 973-599-5500
Fax: —
Web: www.genchem.com

CEO: DeLyle W. Bloomquist
CFO: —
HR: —
FYE: December 31
Type: Subsidiary

General Chemical Industrial Products makes soda, but don't be tempted to take a drink. The company produces soda ash, which is a raw ingredient in the manufacture of everything from glass to soap and detergent to textiles. General Chemical's lone production facility and mine are located in Wyoming; the company owns 75% of the facility, with glass container manufacturer Owens-Illinois owning the rest. In 2008 General Chemical acquired the mica production assets of Zemex. Soon after that deal, Tata Chemicals bought the company for about $1 billion, at which point Zemex was spun off to General Chemical's shareholders. The company sold its electronic chemicals unit to KMG Chemicals for $26 million in 2010.

GENERAL CHEMICAL PERFORMANCE PRODUCTS LLC

90 E. Halsey Rd.	CEO: William E. Redmond Jr.
Parsippany, NJ 07054	CFO: Thomas B. Testa
Phone: 973-515-3221	HR: Robert D. (Rob) Novo
Fax: 973-515-3229	FYE: December 31
Web: www.generalchemical.com	Type: Private

General Chemical Performance Products can be found in your water pipes, in your refrigerator, and inside your medicine cabinet. General Chemical manufactures performance chemicals for such industries as food additives and pharmaceuticals (active ingredients for drugs), environmental services (water treatment), high technology (chemicals for semiconductor manufacturing), and chemicals processing. In 2009 private equity group American Securities paid $675 million including debt to buy General Chemical's parent company, GenTek. It also then spun off another GenTek segment, which makes valve actuation products such as automotive valve-train components, as GT Technologies.

	Annual Growth	12/04	12/05	12/06	12/07	12/08
Sales ($ mil.)	(7.9%)	843.9	920.0	611.4	608.2	608.0
Net income ($ mil.)	—	195.3	(0.8)	(2.1)	29.8	(109.0)
Employees	(36.9%)	7,000	6,500	1,525	1,475	1,110

⊞ GENERAL CIGAR CO., INC.

7300 Beaufont Springs Dr., Ste. 400	CEO: Dan Carr
Richmond, VA 23225	CFO: —
Phone: 804-302-1700	HR: —
Fax: 804-302-1760	FYE: December 31
Web: www.cigarworld.com	Type: Subsidiary

It may be true that sometimes a cigar is just a cigar, but for General Cigar a cigar is money. The company produces Macanudo, the #1 premium cigar in the US, and other brands, such as Cohiba and Bolivar, which are distributed for sale through tobacco retailers nationwide. The Macanudo brand consists of Macanudo, Macanudo Robust, Macanudo Maduro, and Macanudo Vintage Cabinet Selection. The firm operates the Club Macanudo cigar bar in New York City and grows, cures, ages, and processes wrapper tobacco in Connecticut through its Culbro Tobacco unit. Swedish Match, the world's leading producer of matches, acquired the cigar maker in 2005. General Cigar sells about 30% of the cigars consumed in the US.

GENERAL COMMUNICATION, INC.

NASDAQ (GS): GNCMA

2550 Denali St., Ste. 1000	CEO: Ronald A. (Ron) Duncan
Anchorage, AK 99503	CFO: John M. Lowber
Phone: 907-868-5600	HR: —
Fax: 907-868-5676	FYE: December 31
Web: www.gci.com	Type: Public

Customers don't turn to General Communication, Inc. (GCI) for its catchy name, but through its operating subsidiaries, the company provides them with facilities-based phone services to about 90,000 long-distance customers and 80,000 local callers in Anchorage, Fairbanks, and Juneau, Alaska. The competitive local-exchange carrier is also Alaska's leading cable TV provider, with more than 132,000 basic cable subscribers; it provides wireless services to 100,000-plus customers through a partnership with AT&T Mobility. Other services include dial-up and cable Internet access.

	Annual Growth	12/05	12/06	12/07	12/08	12/09
Sales ($ mil.)	7.7%	443.0	477.5	520.3	575.4	595.8
Net income ($ mil.)	(36.0%)	20.8	18.5	13.5	(1.9)	3.5
Market value ($ mil.)	(11.3%)	569.2	866.7	482.1	445.7	351.5
Employees	6.7%	1,262	1,264	1,295	1,628	1,635

THE GENERAL COUNCIL OF THE ASSEMBLIES OF GOD

1445 N. Boonville Ave.	CEO: George O. Wood
Springfield, MO 65802	CFO: George O. Wood
Phone: 417-862-2781	HR: —
Fax: 417-862-8558	FYE: March 31
Web: ag.org	Type: Private

The General Council of the Assemblies of God oversees the US activities of one of the world's largest Pentecostal churches. In the US, the Assemblies of God includes more than 12,300 churches that have about 3 million constituents. In addition, the group has some 60 million constituents around the world. Its US-based Gospel Publishing House arm prints, sells, and distributes Bibles and other religious resources. (Every day the unit prints more than 12 tons of literature.) The Assemblies of God traces its roots to a religious revival that swept across the world during the late 1900s. The General Council of the Assemblies of God was founded in Hot Springs, Arkansas, in 1914.

GENERAL DYNAMICS C4 SYSTEMS, INC.

8201 E. McDowell Rd.	CEO: Christopher (Chris) Marzilli
Scottsdale, AZ 85257	CFO: —
Phone: 480-441-3033	HR: Craig Hadges
Fax: 877-449-0599	FYE: December 31
Web: www.gdc4s.com	Type: Subsidiary

General Dynamics C4 Systems (GDC4S), a wholly owned subsidiary of General Dynamics, helps fight the "fog of war." The "C4" stands for command, control, communications networking, and computing; in short, the unit makes communications and information systems for military and business customers. Products include battlefield communications systems, combat search and rescue systems, ruggedized computers and displays, and encryption systems. Applications include air traffic control, radio and television broadcasts, and wireless communications. The US government is a major customer; C4 also works for the militaries of Australia, Canada, Germany, and the UK, as well as NATO.

⊞ GENERAL DYNAMICS CORPORATION

NYSE: GD

2941 Fairview Park Dr., Ste. 100	CEO: Jay L. Johnson
Falls Church, VA 22042	CFO: L. Hugh Redd
Phone: 703-876-3000	HR: Walter M. Oliver
Fax: 703-876-3125	FYE: December 31
Web: www.gendyn.com	Type: Public

General Dynamics brings it on — by land, air, and sea. The company is a prime military contractor to the Pentagon (the US government accounts for over 70% of sales). General Dynamics' military operations include Information Systems & Technology (information technology and collection, and command control systems); Marine Systems (warships, commercial tankers, and nuclear submarines); and Combat Systems (tanks, amphibious assault vehicles, munitions, ammunition/ordnance, and chemical/biohazard detection products). Its Aerospace unit, which is comprised of Gulfstream Aerospace, Jet Aviation, and General Dynamics Aviation Services, designs/manufactures/refurbishes business jets primarily for civilian customers.

	Annual Growth	12/05	12/06	12/07	12/08	12/09
Sales ($ mil.)	10.8%	21,244.0	24,063.0	27,240.0	29,300.0	31,981.0
Net income ($ mil.)	13.1%	1,461.0	1,856.0	2,072.0	2,459.0	2,394.0
Market value ($ mil.)	4.6%	21,996.2	28,678.9	34,326.0	22,214.1	26,295.1
Employees	6.2%	72,200	81,000	83,500	92,300	91,700

⊞ An in-depth profile of this company is available to Hoover's Online members at hoovers.com.

669

GENERAL DYNAMICS INFORMATION TECHNOLOGY, INC.

3211 Jermantown Rd.
Fairfax, VA 22030
Phone: 703-246-0200
Fax: 703-246-0682
Web: www.gdit.com

CEO: S. Daniel (Dan) Johnson
CFO: Michael (Mike) Garrity
HR: David Breen
FYE: December 31
Type: Subsidiary

General Dynamics Information Technology puts boots on the ground in the US government's struggle to manage data. The company, a subsidiary of leading defense contractor General Dynamics, provides systems integration and data networking services primarily to the Department of Defense and other national security agencies. It specializes in systems design and implementation and network operations management, as well as business process consulting, database development, and software engineering. The company primarily operates from facilities in the eastern US, but it has field offices in California and Arizona. General Dynamics Information Technology is a part of its parent company's Government Systems business.

GENERAL DYNAMICS LAND SYSTEMS INC.

38500 Mound Rd.
Sterling Heights, MI 48310
Phone: 586-825-4000
Fax: 586-825-4013
Web: www.gdls.com

CEO: Mark C. Roualet
CFO: —
HR: —
FYE: December 31
Type: Subsidiary

Patton and Rommel would love General Dynamics Land Systems' (GDLS) products. A subsidiary of General Dynamics, the company makes tracked and wheeled armored vehicles and amphibious combat vehicles for the US military and international allies. Its big gun is the M1A1/M1A2 Abrams main battle tank — the only main battle tank in the US military. GDLS's other vehicles include the Nuclear Biological Chemical Reconnaissance System (NBCRS), the Stryker wheeled infantry combat vehicle, the Marines' Expeditionary Fighting Vehicle (EFV), and the Wolverine Heavy Assault Bridge. Applications include personnel transport, medical evacuation, fire support, anti-tank missions, combat engineering, and reconnaissance.

GENERAL ELECTRIC CAPITAL CORPORATION

901 Main Ave.
Norwalk, CT 06828
Phone: 203-840-6300
Fax: —
Web: www.gecapital.com

CEO: Michael A. (Mike) Neal
CFO: Jeffrey S. (Jeff) Bornstein
HR: Jack Ryan
FYE: December 31
Type: Subsidiary

General Electric Capital (GE Capital) encompasses the financing operations of sprawling conglomerate General Electric. GE Capital provides mid-market and small businesses with mortgages and loans, as well as loans and leases for premises and equipment. One unit, GE Capital Commercial Aviation Services, specializes in leasing airplanes and helicopters. Commercial lending accounts for nearly 40% of sales. Its energy financial services arm provides project funding for customers in the energy industry. GE Capital's consumer finance business offers private-label credit card and sales financing. GE Capital and its divisions are active in more than 50 countries, mostly in North America, Asia, and Europe.

	Annual Growth	12/04	12/05	12/06	12/07	12/08
Est. sales ($ mil.)	—	—	—	—	—	67,994.0
Employees	—	—	—	—	—	80,500

⊞ GENERAL ELECTRIC COMPANY

NYSE: GE

3135 Easton Tpke.
Fairfield, CT 06828
Phone: 203-373-2211
Fax: 203-373-3131
Web: www.ge.com

CEO: Jeffrey R. (Jeff) Immelt
CFO: Keith S. Sherin
HR: Deborah (Deb) Elam
FYE: December 31
Type: Public

From turbines to TV, from household appliances to power plants, General Electric (GE) is plugged in to businesses that have shaped the modern world. The company produces — take a deep breath — aircraft engines, locomotives and other transportation equipment, kitchen and laundry appliances, lighting, electric distribution and control equipment, generators and turbines, and medical imaging equipment. GE is also one of the US's pre-eminent financial services providers. GE Capital, comprising commercial finance, commercial aircraft leasing, real estate, and energy financial services, is its largest segment. GE's other segments are Energy, Technology Infrastructure, NBC Universal, and GE Home & Business Solutions.

	Annual Growth	12/05	12/06	12/07	12/08	12/09
Assets ($ mil.)	3.8%	673,342.0	697,239.0	795,337.0	797,769.0	781,818.0
Net income ($ mil.)	(8.9%)	16,353.0	20,829.0	22,208.0	17,410.0	11,241.0
Market value ($ mil.)	(18.9%)	374,211.9	397,273.2	395,778.5	172,959.6	161,535.7
Employees	(1.0%)	316,000	319,000	327,000	323,000	304,000

⊞ GENERAL EMPLOYMENT ENTERPRISES, INC.

NYSE Amex: JOB

1 Tower Ln., Ste. 2200
Oakbrook Terrace, IL 60181
Phone: 630-954-0400
Fax: 630-954-0447
Web: www.generalemployment.com

CEO: Salvatore J. Zizza
CFO: —
HR: —
FYE: September 30
Type: Public

Who's got jobs for information technology, engineering, and accounting professionals? General Employment Enterprises specializes in finding this group permanent and temporary employment. Most offices operate under the General Employment name and provide both full-time employee placement and contract staffing (other brand names include Triad Personnel Services, Business Management Personnel, Generation Technologies, and Omni One). The firm places permanent employees for a fee based on a percentage of their salaries. Contract workers remain employees of the company, which bills clients hourly for their services. In mid-2009 the company was acquired by PSQ, LLC, a newly formed limited liability company.

	Annual Growth	9/05	9/06	9/07	9/08	9/09
Sales ($ mil.)	(15.4%)	20.3	20.1	19.7	15.2	10.4
Net income ($ mil.)	—	0.7	1.0	0.9	(1.8)	(4.2)
Market value ($ mil.)	(23.0%)	27.8	22.6	21.5	6.0	9.8
Employees	(15.3%)	330	320	280	250	170

GENERAL FINANCE CORPORATION

NASDAQ (GM): GFN

39 E. Union St.
Pasadena, CA 91103
Phone: 626-584-9722
Fax: 626-795-8090
Web: www.generalfinance.com

CEO: Ronald F. Valenta
CFO: Charles E. Barrantes
HR: —
FYE: June 30
Type: Public

General Finance Corporation wants to help you get your hands on some equipment. The investment company is building up a portfolio of specialty financing and equipment leasing companies in North America, Europe, and the Asia/Pacific. It made its first acquisition of RWA Holdings and its subsidiaries (collectively known as Royal Wolf) in 2007. Royal Wolf leases and sells portable storage containers, portable buildings, and freight containers to customers in the defense, mining, moving and storage, and road and rail markets in Australia. General Finance acquired Pac-Van, a provider of modular buildings and mobile offices, in 2008.

	Annual Growth	6/05	6/06	6/07	6/08	6/09
Sales ($ mil.)	—	—	—	0.0	95.6	146.5
Net income ($ mil.)	—	—	—	0.3	4.1	(3.7)
Market value ($ mil.)	(70.0%)	—	—	—	98.0	29.4
Employees	653.3%	—	—	4	250	227

GENERAL GROWTH PROPERTIES, INC.

NYSE: GGP

110 N. Wacker Dr.
Chicago, IL 60606
Phone: 312-960-5000
Fax: 312-960-5475
Web: www.generalgrowth.com

CEO: Adam S. Metz
CFO: Edmund Hoyt
HR: —
FYE: December 31
Type: Public

General Growth Properties has an idea for an economic stimulus plan: Let's all hang out at the mall! With more than shopping malls throughout the US, General Growth is the country's #2 mall operator, behind Simon Property Group. A real estate investment trust (REIT), the company's retail portfolio includes some 200 million sq. ft. of space leased to tenants including J. C. Penney, Sears, and Old Navy. A subsidiary manages its properties, as well as properties owned by third parties. The REIT also owns stakes in master-planned community developments and commercial properties. After struggling to handle debt levels of more than $25 billion, General Growth filed for Chapter 11 bankruptcy protection in early 2009.

	Annual Growth	12/05	12/06	12/07	12/08	12/09
Sales ($ mil.)	0.5%	3,073.4	3,256.3	3,261.8	3,361.5	3,135.8
Net income ($ mil.)	—	75.6	59.3	288.0	26.3	(1,304.8)
Market value ($ mil.)	(29.6%)	14,911.1	16,573.9	13,067.4	409.3	3,668.3
Employees	(9.2%)	4,700	4,700	4,200	3,500	3,200

GENERAL MARITIME CORPORATION

NYSE: GMR

299 Park Ave.
New York, NY 10171
Phone: 212-763-5600
Fax: 212-763-5602
Web: www.generalmaritimecorp.com

CEO: John P. Tavlarios
CFO: Jeffrey D. Pribor
HR: —
FYE: December 31
Type: Public

Black gold on the deep blue brings in the green for General Maritime. A leading operator of midsized tankers, General Maritime transports crude oil, primarily in the Atlantic Basin but also in the Black Sea. The company's fleet of about 30 double-hull tankers includes Aframax and Suezmax vessels and has an overall capacity of about 3.9 million deadweight tons (DWT). General Maritime deploys its vessels both on the spot market (voyage by voyage) and under longer-term charter contracts. Customers have included major oil companies such as Chevron, CITGO, Exxon Mobil, Hess, and Shell. Chairman Peter Georgiopoulos founded the company in 1997.

	Annual Growth	12/05	12/06	12/07	12/08	12/09
Sales ($ mil.)	(11.4%)	567.9	326.0	255.0	326.1	350.5
Net income ($ mil.)	—	212.4	156.8	44.5	29.8	(12.0)
Market value ($ mil.)	(34.1%)	2,157.5	2,049.8	1,424.2	629.1	407.2
Employees	34.2%	349	530	573	1,128	1,132

GENERAL MILLS, INC.

NYSE: GIS

1 General Mills Blvd.
Minneapolis, MN 55426
Phone: 763-764-7600
Fax: 763-764-7384
Web: www.generalmills.com

CEO: Kendall J. (Ken) Powell
CFO: Donal Leo (Don) Mulligan
HR: Michael A. (Mike) Peel
FYE: May 31
Type: Public

General Mills gets its Kix trying to grab the spotlight as the US's #1 breakfast cereal maker (wrangling for the top spot every year with *über*-rival Kellogg). But #1 or not, the company has supermarket-aisles-full of kid-friendly products. Its Big G Cereals include the well-known brands Cheerios, Chex, and Wheaties. Its products are manufactured in 15 countries and available in more than 100. General Mills operates 70 production facilities (down from 79 in 2008, the closures were a cost-controlling measure) — 44 in the US, 11 in the Asia/Pacific region, three in Canada, seven in Europe, four in Latin America and Mexico, and one in South Africa.

	Annual Growth	5/05	5/06	5/07	5/08	5/09
Sales ($ mil.)	6.9%	11,244.0	11,640.0	12,442.0	13,652.1	14,691.3
Net income ($ mil.)	1.3%	1,240.0	1,090.0	1,144.0	1,294.7	1,304.4
Market value ($ mil.)	0.8%	16,422.9	17,215.9	20,318.0	20,968.3	16,980.3
Employees	1.9%	27,800	28,100	28,500	29,500	30,000

GENERAL MOLY, INC.

NYSE Amex: GMO

1726 Cole Blvd., Ste. 115
Lakewood, CO 80401
Phone: 303-928-8599
Fax: 303-928-8598
Web: www.generalmoly.com

CEO: Bruce D. Hansen
CFO: David A. Chaput
HR: —
FYE: December 31
Type: Public

General Moly, reporting for molybdenum duty. The mineral development, exploration, and mining company (formerly Idaho General Mines) finds and exploits molybdenum oxide (moly), a mineral used primarily as an alloy in steel production. Steel makers create moly-enhanced pipes valued by the construction, aircraft manufacturing, and desalination industries for their strength and resistance to heat and corrosion. Refiners use the pipes and employ the mineral to remove sulfur from diesel fuel and crude oil. General Moly owns two properties in Nevada, one in an 80/20 joint venture with Korean steel company POSCO and one outright. It plans to have both mines producing nearly 50 million pounds annually by 2010.

	Annual Growth	12/05	12/06	12/07	12/08	12/09
Sales ($ mil.)	—	—	—	—	—	0.0
Net income ($ mil.)	—	—	—	—	—	(10.2)
Market value ($ mil.)	—	—	—	—	—	150.9
Employees	—	—	—	—	—	34

GENERAL MOTORS COMPANY

300 Renaissance Center
Detroit, MI 48265
Phone: 313-556-5000
Fax: —
Web: www.gm.com

CEO: Edward E. (Ed) Whitacre Jr.
CFO: Christopher P. (Chris) Liddell
HR: Diana D. Tremblay
FYE: December 31
Type: Private

General Motors (GM) makes a wide portfolio of cars and trucks, with brands such as Buick, Cadillac, Chevrolet, and GMC. GM also produces cars through its GM Daewoo, Opel, Vauxhall, and Holden units. Financing and insurance business is primarily conducted by Ally Financial (formerly known as GMAC), of which GM owns about a 10% stake. The century-old GM is experiencing historic financial challenges that threaten the company's longevity. The company received billions of dollars in loans from the Canadian and US governments as it restructured, negotiating concessions with its labor unions and jettisoning brands. The giant automotive manufacturer went through a brief Chapter 11 bankruptcy reorganization in 2009.

	Annual Growth	12/05	12/06	12/07	12/08	12/09
Sales ($ mil.)	(14.2%)	192,604.0	207,349.0	181,122.0	148,979.0	104,589.0
Net income ($ mil.)	—	(10,458.0)	(1,978.0)	(38,732.0)	(30,860.0)	104,821.0
Employees	(10.3%)	335,000	280,000	266,000	243,000	217,000

GENERAL PARTS, INC.

2635 E. Millbrook Rd.
Raleigh, NC 27604
Phone: 919-573-3000
Fax: 919-573-3551

CEO: O. Temple Sloan Jr.
CFO: John Gardner
HR: John Dibenedetto
FYE: December 31
Type: Private

Feel free to salute General Parts, distributor of replacement automotive parts, supplies, and tools for every make and model of foreign and domestic car, truck, bus, and farm or industrial vehicle. The firm operates the CARQUEST auto parts distribution network of some 40 distribution centers, and owns about 1,400 of CARQUEST's 3,400 auto parts stores across the US, Canada, and Mexico. The company sells its parts to DIY mechanics, professional installers, body shops, farmers, and fleet owners (commercial customers account for most sales). General Parts has traditionally grown through acquisitions. The company, founded in 1961 by college student Temple Sloan, owns CARQUEST Canada.

	Annual Growth	12/04	12/05	12/06	12/07	12/08
Est. sales ($ mil.)	9.8%	2,000.0	2,250.0	2,400.0	2,870.0	2,910.0
Employees	(4.3%)	20,000	23,000	24,500	18,000	16,800

GENERAL RE CORPORATION

695 E. Main St.
Stamford, CT 06904
Phone: 203-328-5000
Fax: 203-328-6423
Web: www.genre.com

CEO: Franklin (Tad) Montross IV
CFO: William G. Gasdaska Jr.
HR: Sandra Bell
FYE: December 31
Type: Subsidiary

General Re, or Gen Re to its friends, is a subsidiary of Berkshire Hathaway and a leading property/casualty and life reinsurance player. The company's main subsidiary, General Reinsurance, is one of the biggest reinsurers in the US. Its second-largest operating company is Germany's Kölnische Rückver-sicherungs-Gesellschaft (Cologne Re), the world's oldest reinsurer and a major force in international reinsurance. In addition to insurance, Gen Re has nearly a dozen subsidiaries offering investment and risk management services to reinsurers and accident and disability case management. Its London market Faraday subsidiary offers reinsurance in the UK while USAU offers aviation and aerospace insurance in the US.

GENERAL REVENUE CORPORATION

11501 Northlake Dr.
Cincinnati, OH 45249
Phone: 513-469-1472
Fax: 800-234-5035
Web: www.generalrevenue.com

CEO: James A. (Alex) Reed
CFO: —
HR: Julia Pfirrman
FYE: December 31
Type: Subsidiary

Go on, take the money and run. Then expect to hear from General Revenue Corporation (GRC). The company, a subsidiary of education lender SLM (better known as Sallie Mae), specializes in the recovery of education-related receivables. It also serves government, telecommunications, utility, retail, and other clients. One of the nation's largest university-focused collection agencies, GRC performs collections for more than 1,200 clients, many of which are higher education institutions located throughout the US. GRC operates offices in Cincinnati; Horseheads, New York; Indianapolis; and Muncie, Indiana. It also has smaller sales offices throughout the country.

GENERAL SHALE BRICK, INC.

3015 Bristol Hwy.
Johnson City, TN 37601
Phone: 423-282-4661
Fax: 423-952-4103
Web: www.generalshale.com

CEO: Richard L. (Dick) Green
CFO: Bruno Geissmann
HR: Ken Parham
FYE: December 31
Type: Subsidiary

Brick walls don't have to be bland. Just ask Johnny Hagerman and other sculptors at General Shale Brick, who shape them into three-dimensional works of art. The company also manufactures more than 250 types of brick, as well as landscaping materials and concrete masonry units. Its production facilities make more than 1 billion bricks per year for use in public buildings and private residences primarily in the eastern US and Canada. General Shale Brick's corporate office is also home to a museum showcasing a collection of ancient brick specimens. Founded in 1928, the company is the North American subsidiary of Wienerberger AG.

GENERAL SUPPLY & SERVICES, INC.

2 Corporate Dr., 10th Fl.
Shelton, CT 06484
Phone: 203-944-3000
Fax: —
Web: www.gexpro.com

CEO: Mitch Williams
CFO: Mark Testa
HR: —
FYE: December 31
Type: Subsidiary

When working with electricity, Gexpro feels quite at ohm with watt industry needs. The company, once a unit of General Electric, is a global distributor of electrical, voice, and data products. Its inventory of products — from GE and more than 200 other manufacturers — includes such items as cable and wire, conduits, industrial controls, electrical distribution equipment, lighting products, motors, and power conditioning devices. Gexpro also provides ordering and technical support services. The unit has operations on three continents. In 2006 Rexel acquired GE Supply for $725 million in cash and changed the unit's name to Gexpro the following year. Gexpro continues to operate as a stand-alone organization.

GENESCO INC.

NYSE: GCO

Genesco Park, 1415 Murfreesboro Rd.
Nashville, TN 37217
Phone: 615-367-7000
Fax: 615-367-8278
Web: www.genesco.com

CEO: Robert J. (Bob) Dennis
CFO: James S. Gulmi
HR: —
FYE: January 31
Type: Public

Genesco's sole concern is nicely capped off, to boot (so to speak). It sells casual and dress shoes and headgear — primarily for men and boys — through some 2,240 department, discount, and specialty stores in the US, Puerto Rico, and Canada. Genesco operates through four footwear segments and one for head-wear. Shoe operations include Journeys, Underground Station (with Jarman, targeting young urban men), Johnston & Murphy, and Licensed Brands (Levi Strauss' Dockers footwear). Its Hat World unit consists of Lids, Hat Shack, Hat Zone, Head Quarters, Cap Connection, and Lids Kids. Genesco and rival Finish Line, which offered to acquire the firm for about $1.5 billion in 2007, terminated the deal in 2008.

	Annual Growth	1/06	1/07	1/08	1/09	1/10
Sales ($ mil.)	5.2%	1,283.9	1,460.5	1,502.1	1,551.6	1,574.4
Net income ($ mil.)	(17.7%)	62.7	67.6	6.9	152.6	28.8
Market value ($ mil.)	(11.8%)	936.8	947.3	802.3	370.4	567.1
Employees	5.8%	11,100	12,750	13,950	14,125	13,900

GENESEE & WYOMING INC.

NYSE: GWR

66 Field Point Rd.
Greenwich, CT 06830
Phone: 203-629-3722
Fax: 203-661-4106
Web: www.gwrr.com

CEO: John C. Hellmann
CFO: Timothy J. Gallagher
HR: Matthew C. Brush
FYE: December 31
Type: Public

Genesee & Wyoming (GWI) once relied on the salt of the earth — hauling salt on a 14-mile railroad for one customer. Now the company owns stakes in more than 60 short-line and regional freight railroads that operate over a total of about 10,700 miles of track, including about 6,800 miles of track owned and leased by the company and another 3,100 miles belonging to other railroads. Freight transported by GWI railroads includes coal, forest products, and pulp and paper. Outside the US and Canada, the company has operations in Australia and the Netherlands and a minority stake in a railroad in Bolivia.

	Annual Growth	12/05	12/06	12/07	12/08	12/09
Sales ($ mil.)	9.0%	385.4	478.8	516.2	602.0	544.9
Net income ($ mil.)	5.3%	50.1	134.0	55.2	72.2	61.5
Market value ($ mil.)	6.9%	1,032.4	1,082.2	996.8	1,257.9	1,346.1
Employees	(8.3%)	3,513	2,677	2,307	2,647	2,481

GENESIS ENERGY, L.P.

NYSE Amex: GEL

500 Dallas St., Ste. 2500
Houston, TX 77002
Phone: 713-860-2500
Fax: 713-860-2640
Web: www.genesiscrudeoil.com

CEO: Grant E. Sims
CFO: Robert V. (Bob) Deere
HR: Joe Mueller
FYE: December 31
Type: Public

In the beginning was the oil. And on the third day (or thereabouts) there was oil gathering and marketing and related activities. Genesis Energy purchases and aggregates crude oil at the wellhead and makes bulk buys at pipeline and terminal facilities for resale. The company transports crude oil through three common carrier pipeline systems (totaling 500 miles) along the US Gulf Coast. Genesis Energy also has a storage capacity of more than 1 million barrels, and has a fleet of 270 tractor-trailers that carry oil from the wellhead to end users. The company also provides sulfur-related refinery services to eight refineries, and is engaged in wholesale carbon dioxide and other industrial gas marketing.

	Annual Growth	12/05	12/06	12/07	12/08	12/09
Sales ($ mil.)	7.4%	1,078.7	918.4	1,199.7	2,141.7	1,435.4
Net income ($ mil.)	19.3%	4.0	8.4	(13.6)	26.1	8.1
Market value ($ mil.)	12.9%	461.2	771.1	930.3	343.9	748.2
Employees	38.3%	185	190	655	610	676

GENESIS HEALTHCARE CORPORATION

101 E. State St.
Kennett Square, PA 19348
Phone: 610-444-6350
Fax: 610-925-4000
Web: www.genesishcc.com

CEO: George V. Hager Jr.
CFO: Tom DiVittorio
HR: —
FYE: September 30
Type: Private

Genesis HealthCare Corporation cares for people when care is what counts. The company operates about 200 assisted living and skilled nursing facilities in more than a dozen states throughout the eastern US. Its facilities have some 25,000 beds total. Genesis HealthCare's rehabilitation division provides speech, physical, and occupational therapy services through contracts with health care providers. The company also offers respiratory therapy, adult day care, Alzheimer's care, dialysis, and home and hospice care. Genesis HealthCare is owned by a group of private equity investors from Formation Capital and the private equity arm of real estate investment firm J. E. Roberts.

GENESYS TELECOMMUNICATIONS LABORATORIES INC.

2001 Junipero Serra Blvd.
Daly City, CA 94014
Phone: 650-466-1100
Fax: 650-466-1260
Web: www.genesyslab.com

CEO: Paul Segre
CFO: Bill Behrend
HR: Susan Deady
FYE: December 31
Type: Subsidiary

Genesys Telecommunications Laboratories believes the beginning of a beautiful customer relationship starts with the right contact center software. The company, a subsidiary of French telecom equipment giant Alcatel-Lucent, makes computer telephony integration software that brings together phones, computers, databases, and the Internet for customer contact centers and other call centers. Its software platforms identify callers, route calls and e-mail, and report caller statistics. Companies also use its voice portal system to offer self-service resources over the phone.

GENEX SERVICES, INC.

440 E. Swedesford Rd., Ste. 1000
Wayne, PA 19087
Phone: 610-964-5100
Fax: 610-964-1919
Web: www.genexservices.com

CEO: Peter C. Madeja
CFO: John D. Keohane
HR: Debbi Bromley
FYE: December 31
Type: Subsidiary

This GENEX isn't a bunch of disaffected slackers. The company provides health care cost-containment and disability management services, mostly in the worker's compensation market, to more than 1,200 employer groups, insurance and managed care providers, and benefit administrators. Services include workplace injury management, vocational rehabilitation, catastrophic case management, medical bill auditing, and Social Security disability claim representation. GENEX also offers information management services to help pre-identify high-risk claimants. GENEX is controlled by Stone Point Capital.

GENIO GROUP, INC.

OTC: GNOI

400 Garden City Plaza
Garden City, NY 11530
Phone: 516-873-2000
Fax: —

CEO: Steven A. Horowitz
CFO: Steven A. Horowitz
HR: —
FYE: September 30
Type: Public

Genio Group has decided that playing cards just isn't in the cards. Until 2005 the company designed and marketed entertainment products including the Genio Cards card collection, which consisted of 360 cards spanning 30 different educational categories, such as endangered animals, man-made landmarks, and space travel. The game-playing cards used popular Marvel super heroes to promote learning. Citing lack of sufficient funding, Genio Group exited that business. Steven Horowitz succeeded Matthew Cohen as CEO in mid-2006. The firm is currently searching for new operations.

	Annual Growth	9/05	9/06	9/07	9/08	9/09
Sales ($ mil.)	—	—	—	—	—	0.0
Net income ($ mil.)	—	—	—	—	—	(0.8)
Market value ($ mil.)	—	—	—	—	—	117.8
Employees	—	—	—	—	—	

GENIUS PRODUCTS, INC.

Pink Sheets: GNPR

3301 Exposition Blvd., Ste. 100
Santa Monica, CA 90404
Phone: 310-453-1222
Fax: —
Web: www.geniusproducts.com

CEO: Trevor J. Drinkwater
CFO: Ed Byrnes
HR: —
FYE: December 31
Type: Public

Genius Products isn't just for geniuses. The company is active in content production and management in categories such as children's, lifestyle, sports, and independent cinema. In 2009 Vivendi Entertainment, a division of Universal Music Group Distribution, acquired the rights to distribute the bulk of Genius' catalog and future releases, which include some 3,550 feature films and documentaries, and 4,000 hours of TV programming. Brands include titles from companies such as Sesame Workshop, World Wrestling Entertainment, The Weinstein Company, and Classic Media. Genius Products, Inc. does business through its Genius Products, LLC subsidiary, which is 60%-owned by affiliates of Quadrant Management.

An in-depth profile of this company is available to Hoover's Online members at hoovers.com.

673

GENOMIC HEALTH, INC.

NASDAQ (GM): GHDX

301 Penobscot Dr.
Redwood City, CA 94063
Phone: 650-556-9300
Fax: 650-556-1132
Web: www.genomichealth.com

CEO: Kimberly J. (Kim) Popovits
CFO: G. Bradley (Brad) Cole
HR: Tricia Tomlinson
FYE: December 31
Type: Public

Genomic Health believes the genome is key to good health. The company conducts genomic research to develop molecular diagnostics and assays that can predict the likelihood of disease recurrence and response to therapy and treatments. Genomic Health's Onco*type* DX assay predicts the likelihood of chemotherapy effectiveness and breast cancer recurrence in women with newly diagnosed, early stage invasive breast cancer. Genomic Health's research efforts are targeted at providing a wider base of cancer-related tests, and in 2010 it launched a new Onco*type* DX test to predict recurrence rates for stage II colon cancer patients. The company markets its products directly to oncologists and pathologists.

	Annual Growth	12/05	12/06	12/07	12/08	12/09
Sales ($ mil.)	131.6%	5.2	29.2	64.0	110.6	149.5
Net income ($ mil.)	—	(31.4)	(28.9)	(27.3)	(16.1)	(9.4)
Market value ($ mil.)	21.0%	262.2	535.3	651.6	560.6	562.9
Employees	38.3%	124	191	288	387	453

GENOPTIX, INC.

NASDAQ (GM): GXDX

2110 Rutherford Rd.
Carlsbad, CA 92008
Phone: 760-268-6200
Fax: 760-268-6201
Web: www.genoptix.com

CEO: Tina S. Nova
CFO: Douglas A. Schuling
HR: Cheri Caviness
FYE: December 31
Type: Public

Genoptix is promoting optimal cancer diagnostics. The biotechnology company is a specialized laboratory service provider founded in 1999. It analyzes blood and tissue samples in order to diagnose and monitor diseases such as leukemia, and markets those services to community-based hematologists and oncologists treating malignancies of the blood and bone marrow, as well as other types of cancer. Its key service offerings are COMPASS (short for Comprehensive Assessment) and CHART (a condition monitoring service). Genoptix was started by Dr. Tina Nova, who also co-founded San Diego-based life science companies Ligand Pharmaceuticals and Nanogen.

	Annual Growth	12/05	12/06	12/07	12/08	12/09
Sales ($ mil.)	144.0%	5.2	24.0	59.3	116.2	184.4
Net income ($ mil.)	—	(9.2)	(3.8)	13.4	31.4	30.6
Market value ($ mil.)	7.6%	—	—	537.8	597.0	622.4
Employees	38.4%	120	113	155	307	440

GEN-PROBE INCORPORATED

NASDAQ (GS): GPRO

10210 Genetic Center Dr.
San Diego, CA 92121
Phone: 858-410-8000
Fax: 858-410-8625
Web: www.gen-probe.com

CEO: Carl W. Hull
CFO: Herm Rosenman
HR: Diana De Walt
FYE: December 31
Type: Public

Gen-Probe knows the answer is flowing through your veins. The company is a leading provider of diagnostic tests and instruments to detect HIV, chlamydia, and other sexually transmitted diseases. Gen-Probe also makes diagnostics to detect a host of infectious, disease-causing bacteria and fungi, including those behind tuberculosis, strep throat and influenza. In addition, the company makes products that screen donated blood for these diseases. Gen-Probe's products are designed to provide results within hours, while traditional cultured tests can take days. Major blood suppliers, including The American Red Cross and America's Blood Centers, use its products to screen much of the US blood supply.

	Annual Growth	12/05	12/06	12/07	12/08	12/09
Sales ($ mil.)	13.0%	306.0	354.8	403.0	472.7	498.3
Net income ($ mil.)	11.2%	60.1	59.5	86.1	107.0	91.8
Market value ($ mil.)	(3.2%)	2,420.5	2,598.1	3,122.0	2,125.3	2,129.3
Employees	9.6%	866	925	1,049	1,037	1,250

GENTA INCORPORATED

OTC: GNTA

200 Connell Dr.
Berkeley Heights, NJ 07922
Phone: 908-286-9800
Fax: 908-464-1701
Web: www.genta.com

CEO: Raymond P. Warrell Jr.
CFO: Gary Siegel
HR: —
FYE: December 31
Type: Public

Genta plays rough with cancer. The firm develops drugs, including DNA/RNA medicines and more traditional small molecule drugs, for cancer and other diseases. Lead candidate Genasense blocks production of a protein that can cause resistance to cancer treatments. The company is hoping for marketing approval of Genasense to be used in conjunction with chemotherapy by patients with lymphocytic leukemia and malignant melanoma. Genasense is also in clinical trials for treatment of other diseases, such as prostate and colon cancer. Its small molecule program yielded Ganite, an FDA-approved treatment for hypercalcemia (a potentially fatal side effect of cancer); but the company does not actively market the drug.

	Annual Growth	12/05	12/06	12/07	12/08	12/09
Sales ($ mil.)	(70.6%)	26.6	0.7	0.6	0.4	0.2
Net income ($ mil.)	—	(2.2)	(56.8)	(23.3)	(505.8)	(86.3)
Market value ($ mil.)	(88.1%)	330,348.6	100,122.8	19,609.7	101.8	65.6
Employees	(27.8%)	59	55	47	25	16

⊞ GENTEX CORPORATION

NASDAQ (GS): GNTX

600 N. Centennial St.
Zeeland, MI 49464
Phone: 616-772-1800
Fax: 616-772-7348
Web: www.gentex.com

CEO: Fred T. Bauer
CFO: Steve Dykman
HR: Bruce Los
FYE: December 31
Type: Public

To find competitors in the race for market share, Gentex can just check its rearview mirror. The company manufactures interior and exterior automotive mirrors based on electrochromic technology, which uses electricity to darken a mirror's surface. Its Night Vision Safety (NVS) automatic-dimming car mirrors are featured as standard or optional equipment on more than 200 vehicle models. Automotive products account for most of the company's sales; major customers include BMW, Daimler, General Motors, Toyota, and Volkswagen. Gentex also manufactures more than 60 models of smoke detectors and 160 kinds of fire alarms and signaling devices. The company gets about two-thirds of sales outside the US.

	Annual Growth	12/05	12/06	12/07	12/08	12/09
Sales ($ mil.)	0.4%	536.5	572.3	653.9	623.8	544.5
Net income ($ mil.)	(12.4%)	109.5	108.8	122.1	62.1	64.6
Market value ($ mil.)	(2.2%)	2,719.7	2,170.2	2,478.4	1,231.5	2,489.6
Employees	1.2%	2,264	2,393	2,718	2,279	2,371

GENTIVA HEALTH SERVICES, INC.

NASDAQ (GS): GTIV

3350 Riverwood Pkwy., Ste. 1400
Atlanta, GA 30339
Phone: 770-951-6450
Fax: —
Web: www.gentiva.com

CEO: H. Anthony (Tony) Strange
CFO: Eric R. Slusser
HR: —
FYE: December 31
Type: Public

Gentiva Health Services is a gentle giant. As one of the nation's largest home health care services firms, the company provides home nursing care through a network of more than 300 agency locations in about 40 states. Gentiva's home care nurses provide services ranging from acute-care treatment to housekeeping for the elderly or disabled. The home health firm also provides hospice care services in the southeast portion of the US. The company also offers consulting services to the homecare industry to help with regulatory and reimbursement issues. Gentiva was formed a decade ago when staffing firm Olsten spun off its health services unit after being acquired by Adecco.

	Annual Growth	12/05	12/06	12/07	12/08	12/09
Sales ($ mil.)	7.3%	868.8	1,106.6	1,229.3	1,300.4	1,152.5
Net income ($ mil.)	26.1%	23.4	20.8	32.8	153.4	59.2
Market value ($ mil.)	16.3%	438.7	567.3	566.7	870.8	803.9
Employees	(20.7%)	13,935	7,600	15,450	4,200	5,500

GENUARDI'S FAMILY MARKETS, INC.

805 E. Germantown Pike
Norristown, PA 19401
Phone: 610-277-6000
Fax: 610-277-7783
Web: www.genuardis.com

CEO: Steve Neibergall
CFO: —
HR: John Vuotto
FYE: December 31
Type: Subsidiary

Gaspare Genuardi put the horse before the cart in 1920, selling produce from a horse-drawn wagon. He founded Genuardi's Family Markets in Philadelphia, which was family owned and operated for three generations before it was acquired by one of the nation's top supermarket chains, Safeway, in 2001. Today, there are about 40 Genuardi's Family Market stores located primarily in Pennsylvania, but also in nearby Delaware, and New Jersey. As part of Safeway's Eastern Division Genuardi's has struggled and lost market share to competitors including Acme Markets and ShopRite.

GENUINE PARTS COMPANY
NYSE: GPC

2999 Circle 75 Pkwy.
Atlanta, GA 30339
Phone: 770-953-1700
Fax: 770-956-2211
Web: www.genpt.com

CEO: Thomas C. (Tom) Gallagher
CFO: Jerry W. Nix
HR: R. Bruce Clayton
FYE: December 31
Type: Public

What do spark plugs, hydraulic hoses, note pads, and magnet wire have in common? They're all Genuine Parts. The diversified company is the largest member and majority owner of National Automotive Parts Association (NAPA), a voluntary trade association that distributes auto parts nationwide. Genuine Parts Company (GPC) operates about 1,100 NAPA Auto Parts stores in more than 40 US states. North of the border, NAPA Canada runs some 600 auto parts and TRACTION stores, supplied by UAP. GPC's Auto Todo unit runs four auto parts stores and four tire centers in Mexico. Other subsidiaries include auto parts distributor Balkamp, industrial parts supplier Motion Industries, and office products distributor S.P. Richards.

	Annual Growth	12/05	12/06	12/07	12/08	12/09
Sales ($ mil.)	0.7%	9,783.0	10,457.9	10,843.2	11,015.3	10,057.5
Net income ($ mil.)	(2.2%)	437.4	475.4	506.3	475.4	399.6
Market value ($ mil.)	(3.6%)	6,974.2	7,531.5	7,352.1	6,011.9	6,027.8
Employees	(2.2%)	31,700	32,000	32,000	30,300	29,000

GENVEC, INC.
NASDAQ (GM): GNVC

65 W. Watkins Mill Rd.
Gaithersburg, MD 20878
Phone: 240-632-0740
Fax: 240-632-0735
Web: www.genvec.com

CEO: Paul H. Fischer
CFO: Douglas J. Swirsky
HR: Margaret M. (Marge) Meyer
FYE: December 31
Type: Public

GenVec is all over the medical map. The clinical-stage biopharmaceutical firm develops gene-based drugs and vaccines for everything from cancer to HIV. Its lead candidate, TNFerade, may boost the effectiveness of chemotherapy used to treat pancreatic and other types of cancer. Another drug candidate, AdPEDF, is in early clinical testing to treat age-related macular degeneration, a leading cause of blindness. GenVec is also developing multiple vaccines for contagious diseases, such as HIV, malaria, and foot-and-mouth, through grants from and collaborations with several federal agencies: National Institute of Allergy and Infectious Diseases, US Department of Homeland Security, and US Department of Agriculture.

	Annual Growth	12/05	12/06	12/07	12/08	12/09
Sales ($ mil.)	(15.0%)	26.6	18.9	14.0	15.1	13.9
Net income ($ mil.)	—	(14.0)	(19.3)	(18.7)	(26.1)	(18.4)
Market value ($ mil.)	(7.7%)	212.7	309.4	189.5	55.4	154.7
Employees	(4.7%)	109	109	119	98	90

GENWORTH FINANCIAL, INC.
NYSE: GNW

6620 W. Broad St.
Richmond, VA 23230
Phone: 804-281-6000
Fax: 804-662-2414
Web: www.genworth.com

CEO: Michael D. (Mike) Fraizer
CFO: Patrick B. (Pat) Kelleher
HR: Michael S. Laming
FYE: December 31
Type: Public

What's a Genworth? Insurance and investment specialist Genworth might ask what your life or your nest egg is worth. Genworth specializes in long-term care insurance, as well as life insurance, retirement investments, and supplemental health insurance. Internationally the company offers mortgage insurance and other payment protection products. Genworth also provides private residential mortgage insurance in the US. Genworth focuses its retirement investment products, including individual and group annuities and mutual funds, on affluent individuals. Genworth serves over 15 million customers in 25 countries; its products are sold through independent distributors and financial advisors.

	Annual Growth	12/05	12/06	12/07	12/08	12/09
Assets ($ mil.)	0.7%	105,292.0	110,871.0	114,315.0	107,389.0	108,187.0
Net income ($ mil.)	—	1,221.0	1,324.0	1,220.0	(572.0)	(399.0)
Market value ($ mil.)	(24.3%)	16,912.4	16,731.4	12,447.1	1,384.1	5,551.1
Employees	(3.4%)	6,900	7,200	7,000	6,000	6,000

GENWORTH MORTGAGE INSURANCE CORPORATION

6601 Six Forks Rd.
Raleigh, NC 27615
Phone: 919-846-4100
Fax: 919-846-3188
Web: mortgageinsurance.genworth.com

CEO: Kevin D. Schneider
CFO: Georgette Nichols
HR: Elizabeth Cole
FYE: December 31
Type: Subsidiary

Movin' on up but don't want to put too much down? Adding Genworth Mortgage Insurance to your home-buying plans may help you. One of the biggest private mortgage insurers in the US, Genworth Mortgage Insurance allows customers to buy homes with a low down payment (less than 20%) and reduces financial risk for lenders and investors by protecting them against borrower default. Committed to doing business on the Internet, about 90% of the company's products are now available online. In addition to straight mortgage insurance, the company also offers homebuyer education classes and job-loss mortgage insurance. The mortgage insurer is a subsidiary of Genworth Financial.

GENWOVE U.S. LTD.

100 Pyler Rd.
Indian Trail, NC 28079
Phone: 704-821-7628
Fax: 704-821-6559
Web: www.gwv.com

CEO: Marcel Elefant
CFO: Satish Chawla
HR: —
FYE: December 31
Type: Subsidiary

Genwove U.S. manufactures hardwood veneer and lumber products. A subsidiary of Quebec-based General Woods & Veneers (GWV), Genwove produces and markets its veneer and lumber products by utilizing GWV's extensive source holdings. The company primarily processes oak, ash, cherry, walnut and other hardwood species. Hardwood veneer accounts for the majority of the company's production. Its products can be found in office furniture, panels, doors, and more. Genwove was formed as a result of GWV's purchase of Atlantic Lumber in North Carolina in the late 1970s.

	Annual Growth	12/04	12/05	12/06	12/07	12/08
Est. sales ($ mil.)	—	—	—	—	—	14.7
Employees	—	—	—	—	—	210

GENZYME CORPORATION

NASDAQ (GS): GENZ

500 Kendall St.
Cambridge, MA 02142
Phone: 617-252-7500
Fax: 617-252-7600
Web: www.genzyme.com

CEO: Henri A. Termeer
CFO: Michael S. Wyzga
HR: Zoltan A. Csimma
FYE: December 31
Type: Public

Genzyme makes big money off uncommon diseases. The company's product portfolio focuses on treatments for rare genetic disorders, as well as kidney disease and cancer. One of its main products, Cerezyme, is a leading (and pricey) treatment for Gaucher disease, a rare enzyme-deficiency condition. Founded in 1981, Genzyme also is involved in drug development, genetic testing, and other services. In addition, the company develops gene-based cancer diagnosis and treatment products, renal care and immunological therapies, and orthopedic biosurgery products. Genzyme's products are sold to health care professionals in some 100 countries through a specialized marketing force and wholesale distributors.

	Annual Growth	12/05	12/06	12/07	12/08	12/09
Sales ($ mil.)	13.4%	2,734.8	3,187.0	3,813.5	4,605.0	4,515.5
Net income ($ mil.)	(1.1%)	441.5	(16.8)	480.2	421.1	422.3
Market value ($ mil.)	(8.8%)	18,889.0	16,433.8	19,865.7	17,712.1	13,079.2
Employees	10.0%	8,200	9,000	10,000	11,000	12,000

THE GEO GROUP, INC.

NYSE: GEO

1 Park Place, 621 NW 53rd St., Ste. 700
Boca Raton, FL 33487
Phone: 561-893-0101
Fax: 561-999-7635
Web: www.thegeogroupinc.com

CEO: George C. Zoley
CFO: Brian R. Evans
HR: Stephen V. (Steve) Fuller
FYE: December 31
Type: Public

The GEO Group sticks to its convictions, and it relies on them to generate business. The company, one of the largest operators of private correctional facilities in the US (along with Corrections Corporation of America), operates about 60 correctional, detention, and mental health facilities with some 60,000 beds. Besides incarceration, GEO offers educational, rehabilitative, and vocational training programs at its facilities. The firm offers mental health and residential treatment services through its GEO Care subsidiary. Most of the company's facilities are in the US; it also has operations in Australia, Canada, Cuba (Guantanamo Bay), South Africa, and the UK.

	Annual Growth	12/05	12/06	12/07	12/08	12/09
Sales ($ mil.)	16.8%	612.9	860.9	1,024.8	1,043.0	1,141.1
Net income ($ mil.)	75.2%	7.0	30.2	41.8	58.9	66.0
Market value ($ mil.)	30.1%	376.0	922.9	1,377.5	887.0	1,076.4
Employees	11.4%	8,463	10,253	11,037	12,378	13,026

GEOBIO ENERGY, INC.

OTC: GBOE

601 Union St., Ste. 4500
Seattle, WA 98121
Phone: 206-838-9715
Fax: —
Web: www.geobioenergy.com

CEO: Kenneth R. (Ken) Bennett
CFO: Al Perron
HR: —
FYE: September 30
Type: Public

GeoBio Energy used to think biodiesel was the way of the future, but lately it's decided that the oil and gas industry isn't going anywhere anytime soon. Though in 2008 it acquired GeoAlgae Technologies, which develops low-cost, renewable feedstock used for the production of biodiesel, GeoBio Energy has since switched directions. In 2009 it agreed to buy H&M Precision Products, which makes chemicals used in the drilling of oil and gas wells. In 2010 it also agreed to acquire a Colorado-based oil field site preparation and maintenance company.

GEOEYE, INC.

NASDAQ (GM): GEOY

21700 Atlantic Blvd.
Dulles, VA 20166
Phone: 703-480-7500
Fax: 703-450-9570
Web: www.geoeye.com

CEO: Matthew M. O'Connell
CFO: Joseph F. Greeves
HR: —
FYE: December 31
Type: Public

GeoEye provides satellite-collected Earth imagery and geospatial information for commercial and government organizations. It operates high-resolution imaging satellites that collect detailed land, sea, and atmospheric images, which the company processes and distributes. The company's imagery and information is used for a variety of applications, including mapping, environmental monitoring, urban planning, resource management, homeland defense, national security, and emergency preparedness. GeoEye also offers advanced image processing and production software and services. The company gets more than half of its sales in the US.

	Annual Growth	12/05	12/06	12/07	12/08	12/09
Sales ($ mil.)	60.7%	40.7	151.2	183.8	146.7	271.1
Net income ($ mil.)	—	(24.3)	23.4	42.4	26.6	32.1
Market value ($ mil.)	26.3%	241.6	427.0	742.5	424.3	615.2
Employees	16.0%	295	318	410	484	534

GEOMET, INC.

NASDAQ (GM): GMET

909 Fannin, Ste. 1850
Houston, TX 77010
Phone: 713-659-3855
Fax: 713-571-6394
Web: www.geometinc.com

CEO: J. Darby Seré
CFO: William C. Rankin
HR: —
FYE: December 31
Type: Public

Hoping for the day when high gas prices will result in geometric financial growth, GeoMet is engaged in the exploration and production of natural gas from coalbed methane properties in Alabama, Virginia, West Virginia, and Canada. The methane gas explorer is developing the Gurnee field in the Cahaba Basin and the Garden City and White Oak Creek field (all in Alabama), and the Pond Creek and Lasher fields in the Appalachian Basin. It also has holdings in the Peace River field in British Columbia. GeoMet controls a total of 213,000 net acres of coalbed methane assets. In 2008 the company reported proved reserves of 319.5 billion cu. ft. of natural gas equivalent.

	Annual Growth	12/05	12/06	12/07	12/08	12/09
Sales ($ mil.)	(7.3%)	42.0	58.1	51.0	69.1	31.0
Net income ($ mil.)	—	(1.6)	17.3	5.2	(22.5)	(167.1)
Market value ($ mil.)	(48.0%)	—	409.8	204.9	67.8	57.5
Employees	4.1%	63	77	86	89	74

GEOPETRO RESOURCES COMPANY

NYSE Amex: GPR

1 Maritime Plaza, Ste. 700
San Francisco, CA 94111
Phone: 415-398-8186
Fax: 415-398-9227
Web: www.geopetro.com

CEO: Stuart J. Doshi
CFO: Paul D. Maniscalco
HR: —
FYE: December 31
Type: Public

You have to drill down deep to figure out exactly what GeoPetro Resources does. It's an oil and natural gas exploration and production company with projects in Canada, Indonesia, and the US. These sites cover about 1 million gross acres consisting of mineral leases, production sharing contracts, and exploration permits. GeoPetro operates one cash-generating property in the Madisonville Project in Texas; almost all of the revenue from this project has been derived from natural gas sales to two clients: Luminant Energy and ETC Katy Pipeline. GeoPetro Resources also has put together a geographically diverse portfolio of exploratory and appraisal prospects with the potential for oil and natural gas reserves.

	Annual Growth	12/05	12/06	12/07	12/08	12/09
Sales ($ mil.)	(15.4%)	8.0	6.7	6.9	6.2	4.1
Net income ($ mil.)	—	2.6	(0.5)	(1.6)	(0.2)	(25.8)
Market value ($ mil.)	(36.9%)	—	99.4	120.3	25.0	25.0
Employees	22.1%	9	10	10	20	20

An in-depth profile of this company is available to Hoover's Online members at hoovers.com.

GEOPHARMA, INC.

Pink Sheets: GORX

6950 Bryan Dairy Rd.
Largo, FL 33777
Phone: 727-544-8866
Fax: 727-999-8765
Web: www.geopharmainc.com

CEO: Mihir K. Taneja
CFO: Carol Dore-Falcone
HR: —
FYE: March 31
Type: Public

Working under several names, GeoPharma hopes to create a world of pharmaceuticals. Its Innovative Health Products subsidiary has the capacity to provide contract manufacturing of nutritional supplements. GeoPharma's Belcher Pharmaceuticals manufactures and markets skin care products and vitamins. Its American Antibiotics subsidiary is preparing to develop and manufacture oral and injectable generic antibiotics. The company's sole pharmaceutical product is Vetprofen, a generic version of a non-steroidal anti-inflammatory drug for veterinary use. Chairman Jugal Taneja, his son, CEO Mihir Taneja, and their families hold some 30% of the company's shares.

	Annual Growth	3/05	3/06	3/07	3/08	3/09
Sales ($ mil.)	22.3%	28.2	49.7	59.8	55.0	63.0
Net income ($ mil.)	—	(0.9)	1.8	2.5	(7.0)	(26.1)
Market value ($ mil.)	(37.0%)	71.4	101.6	103.0	58.5	11.2
Employees	27.4%	103	150	180	342	271

GEORESOURCES, INC.

NASDAQ (GM): GEOI

110 Cypress Station Dr., Ste. 220
Houston, TX 77090
Phone: 281-537-9920
Fax: 281-537-8324
Web: www.georesourcesinc.com

CEO: Frank A. Lodzinski
CFO: Howard E. Ehler
HR: —
FYE: December 31
Type: Public

GeoResources has been expanding geographically to increase its oil and gas resources. The company, once a regional explorer in Montana and North Dakota only, has grown to incorporate exploration acreage in the Southwest, the Gulf Coast, and the Williston Basin. In 2009 GeoResources reported proved reserves of 141.4 billion cu. ft. of natural gas equivalent. That year it reported a portfolio of about 484,000 gross acres and 234,000 net acres. Its Southern Bay Energy unit operates out of Houston, while G3 Operating is based in Denver.

	Annual Growth	12/05	12/06	12/07	12/08	12/09
Sales ($ mil.)	78.0%	8.0	8.9	40.1	94.6	80.4
Net income ($ mil.)	45.3%	2.2	1.7	3.1	13.5	9.8
Market value ($ mil.)	13.9%	160.0	126.6	177.5	171.4	269.4
Employees	40.0%	13	13	61	52	50

GEORGE P. JOHNSON COMPANY

3600 Giddings Rd.
Auburn Hills, MI 48326
Phone: 248-475-2500
Fax: 248-475-2325
Web: www.gpjco.com

CEO: Robert G. Vallee Jr.
CFO: David Drews
HR: Eva-Katerine Miller
FYE: December 31
Type: Private

The George P. Johnson Company (GPJ) is a leading event marketing firm that helps businesses strut their stuff at some 5,000 events each year. The company produces and markets the entire experience — from architectural engineering, graphic design, and lighting to scripting, storyboarding, and audience acquisition. It also handles digital marketing campaigns. Clients have included such big names as IBM, Cisco Systems, Toyota, and Bayer MaterialScience. Operating more than 25 offices worldwide, the company was founded by George P. Johnson in 1914 as a flag and decoration business.

GEORGE RISK INDUSTRIES, INC.

OTC: RISKA

GRI Plaza, 802 S. Elm St.
Kimball, NE 69145
Phone: 308-235-4645
Fax: 308-235-2609
Web: www.grisk.com

CEO: Ken R. Risk
CFO: Stephanie Risk
HR: —
FYE: April 30
Type: Public

George Risk Industries (GRI) wants customers to be able to manage risks. The company makes burglar alarm components and systems, including panic buttons (for direct access to alarm monitoring centers). In addition to security products, GRI manufactures pool alarms, which are designed to sound alerts when a pool or spa area has been entered. The company also makes thermostats, specialty computer keyboards and keypads, custom-engraved key caps, and push-button switches. Chairman and president Ken Risk, a son of founder George Risk, owns more than half of the company.

	Annual Growth	4/05	4/06	4/07	4/08	4/09
Sales ($ mil.)	(9.5%)	13.1	14.3	13.4	11.4	8.8
Net income ($ mil.)	(33.1%)	2.5	2.7	3.0	2.3	0.5
Market value ($ mil.)	(11.4%)	28.4	41.0	36.7	30.4	17.5
Employees	(7.5%)	205	275	225	175	150

GEORGE S. MAY INTERNATIONAL COMPANY

303 S. Northwest Hwy.
Park Ridge, IL 60068
Phone: 847-825-8806
Fax: 847-825-7937
Web: www.georgesmay.com

CEO: Israel Kushnir
CFO: Michael J. (Mike) Hanrahan
HR: Teri Cole
FYE: December 31
Type: Private

One of the oldest management consulting firms in the US, George S. May International offers its services to mostly small and midsized clients in industries such as construction, health care, manufacturing, and retail. Over the years it has served more than 500,000 clients in some 3,000 industry classifications. The company aims to help clients increase productivity and profits; its areas of expertise include customer relations, human capital management, productivity training, quality management, and strategic planning. It maintains offices in the US and Canada. George S. May founded the family-owned firm in 1925.

	Annual Growth	12/04	12/05	12/06	12/07	12/08
Est. sales ($ mil.)	—	—	—	—	—	5.0
Employees	—	—	—	—	—	1,000

GEORGE WESTON BAKERIES INC.

55 Paradise Ln.
Bay Shore, NY 11706
Phone: 800-355-1260
Fax: 973-785-0009
Web: www.gwbakeries.com

CEO: Gary J. Prince
CFO: Stephen J. (Steve) Mollick
HR: Louis A. (Lou) Minella
FYE: December 31
Type: Subsidiary

The folks at George Weston Bakeries want you to lay it on. What you should "lay on" is butter, jam, or any other yummy topping of your choice. What you should "lay it on" is one of Weston's many well-known brands of bagels, breads, English muffins, pitas, and pizza crusts. The company makes such branded baked-goods labels as Arnold, Boboli, Brownberry, Entenmann's, Freihofer's, Stroehmann, and Thomas'. George Weston Bakeries was subsidiary of Canadian grocery giant George Weston Limited until 2008, when it was sold to Mexican baking company, Grupo Bimbo.

An in-depth profile of this company is available to Hoover's Online members at hoovers.com.

677

GEORGETOWN UNIVERSITY

37th and O Streets NW	CEO: John J. (Jack) DeGioia
Washington, DC 20057	CFO: Christopher L. (Chris) Augostini
Phone: 202-687-0100	HR: Mary Anne Mahin
Fax: 202-687-5595	FYE: June 30
Web: www.georgetown.edu	Type: School

Founded in 1789 by John Carroll, the nation's first Catholic bishop, Georgetown University is the oldest Catholic university in the US. Its more than 14,000 students (about half are undergraduates) are instructed by some 1,800 faculty members in eight schools ranging from the university's renowned Law Center to the Edmund A. Walsh School of Foreign Service and Georgetown's School of Medicine. The university is also home to the Georgetown University Medical Center, and has forged numerous ties with its neighbors in the Washington, DC, community. Among its alumni are President Bill Clinton, basketball great Patrick Ewing, and former US Surgeon General Antonia Novello.

	Annual Growth	6/04	6/05	6/06	6/07	6/08
Est. sales ($ mil.)	—	—	—	—	—	809.3
Employees	—	—	—	—	—	9,700

GEORGIA CROWN DISTRIBUTING CO.

100 Georgia Crown Dr.	CEO: Donald M. Leebern Jr.
McDonough, GA 30253	CFO: —
Phone: 770-302-3000	HR: —
Fax: 770-302-3080	FYE: July 31
Web: www.georgiacrown.com	Type: Private

Georgia Crown Distributing wears its royal headgear proudly. The family-owned and -operated company offers a full range of domestic and imported libations, including beer, wine, champagne, liquor, bottled water, juices, and other soft drinks to beverage retailers throughout Georgia and Alabama. It serves Tennessee as well, stocking the Volunteer State with domestic and imported beers, soda, and soft drinks. The company's Melwood Springs division offers Melwood Springs, Poland Springs, Deer Park, and Perrier brand home and office water sales. Third-generation CEO Donald Leebern Jr. and fourth-generation president Don Leebern III are the current crop of Leeberns to own and manage the company.

	Annual Growth	7/04	7/05	7/06	7/07	7/08
Est. sales ($ mil.)	—	—	—	—	—	154.8
Employees	—	—	—	—	—	475

GEORGIA FARM BUREAU MUTUAL INSURANCE COMPANY

1620 Bass Rd.	CEO: Vincent (Zippy) Duvall
Macon, GA 31209	CFO: Wayne Daniel
Phone: 478-474-8411	HR: —
Fax: 478-474-8869	FYE: December 31
Web: www.gfb.org/insurance	Type: Mutual company

You don't have to be a farmer to get insurance coverage here, but it helps. Georgia Farm Bureau Mutual Insurance and its affiliates provide a variety of commercial and individual property/casualty products to members of the Georgia Farm Bureau. Its offerings include automobile, farm, marine, homeowners, business owners, and personal liability insurance. The company specializes in writing lower-cost, preferred risk policies (policies for customers that are less likely to file claims). A network of more than 550 company agents and representatives market Georgia Farm Bureau Mutual's products. A part of the Georgia Farm Bureau, the company was founded in 1959.

	Annual Growth	12/04	12/05	12/06	12/07	12/08
Est. sales ($ mil.)	—	—	—	—	—	548.1
Employees	—	—	—	—	—	1,210

GEORGIA GULF CORPORATION

NYSE: GGC

115 Perimeter Center Place, Ste. 460	CEO: Paul D. Carrico
Atlanta, GA 30346	CFO: Gregory C. (Greg) Thompson
Phone: 770-395-4500	HR: James L. Worrell
Fax: 770-395-4529	FYE: December 31
Web: www.ggc.com	Type: Public

It doesn't take an old sweet song to tell you what Georgia Gulf Corporation does. The company makes chlorovinyls and aromatics used by the construction and housing, plastics, pulp and paper, and pharmaceutical industries. Its primary chlorovinyl products are PVC (polyvinyl chloride), caustic soda, and chlorine; this segment also makes vinyl chloride monomer (VCM), used by Georgia Gulf to manufacture PVC resins. Aromatics include phenol (for makers of wood adhesives and engineered plastics), acetone (for makers of acrylic resins), and cumene (used to make phenol and acetone). Much of Georgia Gulf's sales are to the construction market; though it sells globally, Georgia Gulf does most of its business in the US.

	Annual Growth	12/05	12/06	12/07	12/08	12/09
Sales ($ mil.)	(3.3%)	2,273.7	2,427.8	3,157.3	2,916.5	1,990.1
Net income ($ mil.)	11.2%	95.5	48.5	(266.0)	(257.6)	145.8
Market value ($ mil.)	(61.1%)	25,645.7	16,279.4	5,581.0	902.1	586.1
Employees	32.8%	1,123	6,654	5,249	4,463	3,489

GEORGIA INSTITUTE OF TECHNOLOGY

225 North Ave. NW	CEO: G. P. (Bud) Peterson
Atlanta, GA 30332	CFO: Steven G. (Steve) Swant
Phone: 404-894-2000	HR: Chuck Donbaugh
Fax: 404-894-1277	FYE: June 30
Web: www.gatech.edu	Type: School

The Georgia Institute of Technology, commonly known as Georgia Tech, is one of the country's top engineering schools for both graduate and undergraduate students. The university also offers degrees in the Colleges of Architecture, Sciences, Computing, and Management, and the Ivan Allen College of Liberal Arts. It has an enrollment of more than 16,000 students. The school is also renowned for its scientific and technological research, receiving more than $355 million in research awards annually. Georgia Tech was founded in 1885 as the Georgia School of Technology.

GEORGIA LOTTERY CORPORATION

250 Williams St., Ste. 3000	CEO: Margaret R. DeFrancisco
Atlanta, GA 30303	CFO: Joan Schoubert
Phone: 404-215-5000	HR: Douglas Parker
Fax: 404-215-8983	FYE: June 30
Web: www.galottery.com	Type: Government-owned

You might say these games of chance are just peachy. The Georgia Lottery operates a number of instant-win ticket and lotto style games, including Cash 3, Fantasy 5, and Win for Life. It also takes part in the multi-state Mega Millions drawing game. Tickets are sold through more than 7,500 retailers throughout the state. Since it was established in 1993, the lottery has contributed more than $10 billion in proceeds to state education programs, including the HOPE Scholarship Program and Georgia's Prekindergarten Program.

	Annual Growth	6/04	6/05	6/06	6/07	6/08
Sales ($ mil.)	6.8%	2,710.0	2,922.0	2,960.2	3,421.7	3,519.3
Employees	3.6%	—	—	260	266	279

GEORGIA POWER COMPANY

241 Ralph McGill Blvd. NE
Atlanta, GA 30308
Phone: 404-506-6526
Fax: 404-506-3771
Web: www.georgiapower.com

CEO: Michael D. (Mike) Garrett
CFO: Ronnie R. Labrato
HR: —
FYE: December 31
Type: Subsidiary

Bigger than a giant peach, Georgia Power is the largest subsidiary of US utility holding company Southern Company. The regulated utility provides electricity to more than 2.3 million residential, commercial, and industrial customers throughout most of Georgia. It has interests in 14 fossil-fueled, 2 nuclear, and 20 hydroelectric power plants that give it about 16,000 MW of generating capacity. When necessary the company purchases excess power from nine small power producers. Georgia Power sells wholesale electricity to several cooperatives and municipalities in the region. The utility also offers energy efficiency, surge protection, and outdoor lighting products and services.

	Annual Growth	12/04	12/05	12/06	12/07	12/08
Est. sales ($ mil.)	—	—	—	—	—	8,411.6
Employees	—	—	—	—	—	9,337

GEORGIA-CAROLINA BANCSHARES, INC.

3527 Wheeler Rd.
Augusta, GA 30909
Phone: 706-731-6600
Fax: 706-731-6601
Web: www.firstbankofga.com

CEO: Remer Y. Brinson III
CFO: Thomas J. (Tom) Flournoy
HR: Amy M. Sykes
FYE: December 31
Type: Public

Georgia-Carolina Bancshares is holding the line on banking in and around Augusta, Georgia. The holding company owns First Bank of Georgia, which has about a half-dozen branches along the eastern edge of the Peach State. The company also owns First Bank Mortgage, which originates residential loans and other mortgage products through offices in Georgia and Florida. The bank focuses on real estate lending, in addition to providing standard deposit products such as checking and savings accounts. Other lending activities include business and consumer loans. The bank's FB Financial Services division offers financial planning and investment services through an agreement with LPL Financial.

	Annual Growth	12/05	12/06	12/07	12/08	12/09
Assets ($ mil.)	8.5%	349.5	417.5	447.9	460.8	484.0
Net income ($ mil.)	2.1%	3.5	2.9	2.9	2.8	3.8
Market value ($ mil.)	(15.7%)	50.0	49.1	38.6	35.1	25.3
Employees	0.3%	170	166	160	167	172

⊞ GEORGIA-PACIFIC LLC

133 Peachtree St. NE
Atlanta, GA 30303
Phone: 404-652-4000
Fax: 404-749-2454
Web: www.gp.com

CEO: James (Jim) Hannan
CFO: Tyler L. Woolson
HR: Julie Brehm
FYE: December 31
Type: Subsidiary

What's on Georgia-Pacific's mind? A whole lotta different products, that's what. Georgia-Pacific (GP) is the world's largest tissue products producer and the force behind such household items as Brawny paper towels and Quilted Northern bath tissues. Not one to be pigeonholed, the company makes a wide variety of other products including cardboard packaging, plywood and lumber, related chemicals, fertilizers, recycled paper fibers, Dixie-brand paper cups, touchless towel dispensers, and office paper. GP is the second-largest US forest products manufacturer (behind International Paper). A subsidiary of diversified group Koch Industries, GP has more than 300 manufacturing facilities in the Americas and Europe.

THE GEPPETTO GROUP

95 Morton St.
New York, NY 10014
Phone: 212-462-8140
Fax: 212-462-8197
Web: www.geppettogroup.com

CEO: Julie Halpin
CFO: —
HR: —
FYE: December 31
Type: Subsidiary

This agency can pull a few strings when it comes to youth marketing. The Geppetto Group is a leading advertising firm specializing in creating ad campaigns that appeal to kids and teens. It offers creative development services for both broadcast and print advertising, as well as campaign planning and management services. Geppetto Group is part of UK-based advertising services conglomerate WPP Group.

	Annual Growth	12/04	12/05	12/06	12/07	12/08
Est. sales ($ mil.)	—	—	—	—	—	4.8
Employees	—	—	—	—	—	19

GERBER PRODUCTS COMPANY

12 Vreeland Rd.
Florham Park, NJ 07932
Phone: 973-593-7500
Fax: 973-593-7663
Web: www.gerber.com

CEO: Kurt T. Schmidt
CFO: David Nieto
HR: Carrie Kifner
FYE: December 31
Type: Subsidiary

Gerber Products Company doesn't strain to make money. But it does strain to make its products. Gerber's more than 200 baby offerings include the almost ubiquitous glass jars of baby food. The company, which had its beginnings in 1927 in Dorothy Gerber's kitchen, also makes baby cereal, juices, and toddler food, along with baby bath and skin care products, bottles, teethers, pacifiers, breastfeeding accessories, spill-proof cups, and infant toys. Its Gerber Life Insurance Company offers various whole and term life products. Gerber feeds, soothes, and amuses babies worldwide. In 2007 Nestlé acquired the company from Novartis.

⊞ GERBER SCIENTIFIC, INC.

NYSE: GRB

83 Gerber Rd. West
South Windsor, CT 06074
Phone: 860-644-1551
Fax: 860-643-7039
Web: www.gerberscientific.com

CEO: Marc T. Giles
CFO: Michael R. Elia
HR: —
FYE: April 30
Type: Public

Gerber Scientific began with baby steps. Now the company is an industry leader in making products for the specialty graphics, ophthalmic lens processing, and apparel and flexible materials industries. The company produces automated manufacturing systems for sign-making, industrial manufacturing, and eyeglass lens production. Its signage subsidiaries, Gerber Scientific Products and Spandex, make digital imaging systems, materials, cutting systems, and software. The company's Gerber Technology subsidiary provides CAD/CAM pattern-making and cutting systems for apparel, automotive, composite, furniture, and technical textile companies. Gerber Coburn Optical makes eyeglass lens manufacturing equipment.

	Annual Growth	4/05	4/06	4/07	4/08	4/09
Sales ($ mil.)	1.7%	517.3	530.4	574.8	640.0	552.8
Net income ($ mil.)	—	(5.6)	3.0	13.5	14.5	2.2
Market value ($ mil.)	(13.6%)	178.1	260.9	251.8	233.2	99.4
Employees	2.2%	2,000	2,022	2,190	2,200	2,179

⊞ An in-depth profile of this company is available to Hoover's Online members at hoovers.com.

679

⊞ GERDAU AMERISTEEL CORPORATION

NYSE: GNA

4221 W. Boy Scout Blvd., Ste. 600
Tampa, FL 33607
Phone: 813-286-8383
Fax: 813-207-2355
Web: www.gerdauameristeel.com

CEO: Mario Longhi
CFO: Barbara R. Smith
HR: Jim Paull
FYE: December 31
Type: Public

Gerdau Ameristeel is putting its stamp on the steel business in the US. The company is one of the largest minimill steelmakers in North America, producing about 4.2 million tons of finished steel annually. Through about 20 mills, Gerdau Ameristeel sells to the eastern two-thirds of North America. The company also operates scrap recycling operations, specialty processing centers, and rebar fabricating and coating plants. Its minimills produce beams, flat-rolled steel, merchant bar, rebar, and wire rod primarily used in the automotive, appliance, construction, machinery, and equipment industries. Brazilian steelmaker Gerdau owns approximately two-thirds of the company, and in 2010, made an offer to buy the rest.

	Annual Growth	12/05	12/06	12/07	12/08	12/09
Sales ($ mil.)	1.9%	3,897.1	4,464.2	5,806.6	8,528.5	4,195.7
Net income ($ mil.)	—	295.5	378.6	537.9	(587.4)	(161.7)
Market value ($ mil.)	10.0%	2,444.9	3,866.8	6,164.3	2,627.0	3,576.3
Employees	2.9%	7,000	10,140	10,140	10,951	7,850

GERMAN AMERICAN BANCORP

NASDAQ (GS): GABC

711 Main St.
Jasper, IN 47546
Phone: 812-482-1314
Fax: 812-482-0721
Web: www.germanamericanbancorp.com

CEO: Mark A. Schroeder
CFO: Bradley M. Rust
HR: —
FYE: December 31
Type: Public

German American Bancorp is the holding company for German American Bank, which operates some 30 branches in 10 southwestern Indiana counties and offers such standard retail products as checking and savings accounts, certificates of deposit, and IRAs. German American Bank was founded in 1910. Commercial and industrial loans make up about half of the bank's loan portfolio; agricultural loans account for about 20%. Other offerings include residential mortgages and consumer loans. German American Bancorp also operates insurance and trust, financial planning, and brokerage subsidiaries.

	Annual Growth	12/05	12/06	12/07	12/08	12/09
Assets ($ mil.)	7.1%	946.5	1,093.4	1,131.7	1,190.8	1,243.0
Net income ($ mil.)	5.9%	9.7	10.2	9.4	12.8	12.2
Market value ($ mil.)	5.4%	146.1	159.6	141.4	126.4	180.4
Employees	(4.5%)	402	395	365	342	335

GERON CORPORATION

NASDAQ (GM): GERN

230 Constitution Dr.
Menlo Park, CA 94025
Phone: 650-473-7700
Fax: 650-473-7750
Web: www.geron.com

CEO: Thomas B. Okarma
CFO: David L. Greenwood
HR: —
FYE: December 31
Type: Public

Not far from the center of the controversy over human embryonic stem cell (hESC) research is Geron. The company hopes to parlay its work into viable therapies for various diseases and conditions. One of the company's lead products is an hESC therapy called GRNOPC1 for spinal cord injury, which was approved to enter the world's first hESC human clinical trials until the FDA put a hold on the trials while the agency reviewed new data. Geron is also focused on anticancer drug candidate GRN163L, which inhibits telomerase, an enzyme that may prolong cellular life and prevents apoptosis (programmed cell death). Geron has been in business since 1992 and has subsidiaries in Scotland and Hong Kong.

	Annual Growth	12/05	12/06	12/07	12/08	12/09
Sales ($ mil.)	54.3%	0.3	3.3	7.6	2.8	1.7
Net income ($ mil.)	—	(33.5)	(31.4)	(36.7)	(62.0)	(70.2)
Market value ($ mil.)	(10.4%)	845.3	862.0	557.7	458.5	544.9
Employees	17.6%	90	103	140	159	172

GERRESHEIMER GLASS INC.

537 Crystal Ave.
Vineland, NJ 08360
Phone: 856-692-3600
Fax: —
Web: www.gerresheimer.com

CEO: Uwe Röhrhoff
CFO: —
HR: Richard Hasenauer
FYE: November 30
Type: Subsidiary

Scientists rely on Gerresheimer Glass for their laboratory research as much as they do on specimens. The company, a subsidiary of German glass maker Gerresheimer Glas, manufactures glassware for use as pharmaceutical, scientific, and laboratory equipment. Products include injection vials, ampoules, screw-cap bottles, dropper bottles, flasks, check sets, pharmaceutical packaging, and disposable specimen containers. The tubular division manufactures tubing and rods. The company operates in China, Europe, Latin America, and the US. Founded as Kimble Glass in 1901 by Col. E. Kimble, the company became a part of the Gerresheimer Glas portfolio of companies in 1994.

THE GERSH AGENCY

232 N. Canon Dr., Ste. 201
Beverly Hills, CA 90210
Phone: 310-274-6611
Fax: 310-278-6232
Web: www.gershagency.com

CEO: David Gersh
CFO: Stephen M. Kravit
HR: Kisha Settle
FYE: July 31
Type: Private

Have you heard this one? "A man walks into a talent agency's office in Los Angeles . . . ." The Gersh Agency is a talent agency with a flair for representing comics (including Arsenio Hall, Drew Carey, Bobcat Goldthwait, Jamie Foxx, Nick Cannon, Norm Macdonald, Bill Bellamy, Dave Chappelle, and Dave Foley). With offices in Beverly Hills and New York, the talent agency maintains departments devoted to talent, feature literary, TV literary, theater, comedy, and below-the-line talent (cinematographers, production designers, costume, etc.). The Gersh Agency has also formed its own sports division. The agency's Comedy Department is based in Los Angeles. The company opened a New York office in 1992.

GERSON LEHRMAN GROUP, INC.

850 3rd Ave., 9th Fl.
New York, NY 10022
Phone: 212-984-8500
Fax: 212-984-8538
Web: www.glgroup.com

CEO: Alexander Saint-Amand
CFO: Michael Blumstein
HR: —
FYE: December 31
Type: Private

Gerson Lehrman Group (GLG) is the expert who experts turn to when *they* need advice. The research firm connects investors with industry experts from a range of sectors, including health care, telecom, insurance, financial services, and energy. GLG has a network of more than 200,000 consultants consisting of executives, physicians, scientists, engineers, attorneys, and other professionals. The company offers clients a Web-based application for its custom research projects. Unlike other research firms, it doesn't publish reports or make recommendations. Gerson Lehrman Group was founded in 1998 by Yale Law School alum Mark Gerson and former hedge fund manager Thomas Lehrman.

GETINGE USA, INC.

1777 E. Henrietta Rd.	CEO: Andrew Ray
Rochester, NY 14623	CFO: —
Phone: 585-475-9040	HR: Shelly Knapp
Fax: 585-272-5033	FYE: December 31
Web: www.getingeusa.com	Type: Subsidiary

In the world of cleaning, there's clean, really clean, and Grandma's-visiting-clean. Getinge USA will just get things to surgical-room-clean and you're on your own from there. The company manufactures and distributes sterilization and surgical equipment under the Arjo, Getinge, and Maquet brands. Its products include autoclaves, detergents and cleaners, surgical tables and lighting systems, scrub sinks, and washing equipment. Its clients are the health care and life science industries, including hospitals and pharmaceutical researchers. The company also provides consulting, training, and maintenance services. Getinge USA is a subsidiary of Sweden-based Getinge AB.

GETTY IMAGES, INC.

601 N. 34th St.	CEO: Jonathan D. Klein
Seattle, WA 98103	CFO: Jeff Dunn
Phone: 206-925-5000	HR: Lisa Calvert
Fax: 206-925-5001	FYE: December 31
Web: www.gettyimages.com	Type: Private

With an eye out for the big picture, visual content provider Getty Images is a major supplier of creative (stock) and editorial still and moving images and illustrations, as well as music. It also offers photo services for corporate clients. The company targets four main markets: advertising and graphic design firms; editorial organizations, such as newspapers, magazines, and online publishers; corporate communications departments; and film and broadcast producers. Getty Images, which distributes its products online, has customers in more than 100 countries around the world; most of its sales come from outside the US. In mid-2008, Getty Images was acquired by private equity firm Hellman & Friedman.

GETTY PETROLEUM MARKETING INC.

1500 Hempstead Tpke.	CEO: Vadim Gluzman
East Meadow, NY 11554	CFO: Michael K. Hantman
Phone: 516-542-4900	HR: —
Fax: 516-832-8272	FYE: December 31
Web: www.getty.com	Type: Subsidiary

A remnant of J. Paul Getty's oil empire, Getty Petroleum Marketing distributes gasoline and heating fuels. The company, a subsidiary of Russian oil giant LUKOIL, has more than 2,000 gas stations (some of which maintain convenience stores, auto repair centers, or car washes) in 13 northeastern and mid-Atlantic US states. It sells more than 2 billion gallons of gasoline a year. The company sells heating oil through its KOSCO subsidiary. It also has six petroleum terminals and 170 delivery vehicles. Getty Petroleum Marketing is converting its stations to the LUKOIL brand as LUKOIL tries to build the brand awareness and customer loyalty that the Getty brand has long enjoyed in the US.

GETTY REALTY CORP.

NYSE: GTY

125 Jericho Tpke., Ste. 103	CEO: David B. Driscoll
Jericho, NY 11753	CFO: Thomas J. Stirnweis
Phone: 516-478-5400	HR: —
Fax: 516-478-5476	FYE: December 31
Web: www.gettyrealty.com	Type: Public

Some black gold is sold on property owned by Getty Realty Corp. The self-administered real estate investment trust (REIT) owns and leases about 1,100 gas service stations, adjacent convenience stores, and petroleum distribution terminals primarily in the Northeast and Mid-Atlantic. One-third of its properties reside in New York; about 80% of its properties are leased to one tenant, Getty Petroleum Marketing Inc., which is responsible for operating and maintaining its property, as well as the remediation of any environmental contamination it causes. Getty Realty was formed in 1997 when it spun off Getty Petroleum Marketing and sold its heating oil distribution business.

	Annual Growth	12/05	12/06	12/07	12/08	12/09
Sales ($ mil.)	4.3%	71.4	72.4	78.5	81.2	84.5
Net income ($ mil.)	0.9%	45.4	42.7	33.9	41.8	47.0
Market value ($ mil.)	(2.7%)	651.1	765.3	660.8	521.6	582.8
Employees	0.0%	16	16	16	16	16

GFI GROUP INC.

NASDAQ (GS): GFIG

100 Wall St.	CEO: Michael A. (Mickey) Gooch
New York, NY 10005	CFO: James A. Peers
Phone: 212-968-4100	HR: Karen Aflalo
Fax: 212-968-4124	FYE: December 31
Web: www.gfigroup.com	Type: Public

A financial matchmaker, GFI Group is an inter-dealer hybrid brokerage that acts as an intermediary for more than 2,000 institutional clients such as banks, large corporations, insurance companies, and hedge funds. The firm deals primarily in over-the-counter derivatives, which tend to be less liquid and thus harder to trade than other assets. It also offers market data and analysis on credit, equity, commodity, and currency derivatives, and other financial instruments. Other products include foreign exchange options, freight, and energy derivatives including electric power, coal, and carbon emissions options. GFI has about 20 offices in North and South America, Europe, and Australasia.

	Annual Growth	12/05	12/06	12/07	12/08	12/09
Sales ($ mil.)	11.3%	533.6	747.2	970.5	1,015.5	818.7
Net income ($ mil.)	(23.7%)	48.1	61.1	94.9	53.1	16.3
Market value ($ mil.)	(21.3%)	1,418.2	1,861.7	2,862.2	423.4	544.2
Employees	11.3%	1,151	1,438	1,599	1,740	1,768

GFK CUSTOM RESEARCH NORTH AMERICA

75 9th Ave., 5th Fl.	CEO: Debra A. Pruent
New York, NY 10011	CFO: —
Phone: 212-240-5300	HR: —
Fax: 212-240-5353	FYE: December 31
Web: www.gfkamerica.com	Type: Business segment

GfK Custom Research North America is a flagship division for GfK Group, one of the world's largest market research companies. The company offers statistical sampling and methodology services, marketing sciences, online strategy consulting, and other related research services. It primarily targets the automotive, consumer, financial services, media and communications, and technology sectors. GfK Custom Research operates out of about 15 offices in the US and Canada; it also taps into its parent company's vast global network of subsidiaries and office locations which expands its customer reach across 70 countries.

GFK HEALTHCARE, LP

587 Skippack Pike
Blue Bell, PA 19422
Phone: 215-283-3200
Fax: 215-283-3201
Web: www.gfkhc.com

CEO: Richard B. (Dick) Vanderveer
CFO: —
HR: Sandra White
FYE: December 31
Type: Business segment

GfK Healthcare provides market research and strategic consulting services to pharmaceutical, biotech, and medical diagnostics companies. Its market research services include qualitative, quantitative, product positioning, project management, and market landscape research. Clients have included Pfizer, Novartis, and GlaxoSmithKline. The company is a segment of German market research conglomerate GfK Group. It utilizes its parent company's resources in order to reach more than 115 offices across 100 countries. GfK Healthcare was formerly made up of three separate companies (GfK Market Measures, GfK Strategic Marketing, and GfK V2) until early 2009, when GfK combined them under the GfK Healthcare banner.

GFK MEDIAMARK RESEARCH & INTELLIGENCE, LLC

75 9th Ave., 5th Fl.
New York, NY 10011
Phone: 212-884-9200
Fax: 212-884-9339
Web: www.gfkmri.com

CEO: Kathleen D. (Kathi) Love
CFO: Steve Goodreds
HR: Steve Goodreds
FYE: December 31
Type: Business segment

Advertisers turn to this company to make sure their ads will hit their intended mark. GfK Mediamark Research & Intelligence (GfK MRI) provides audience demographic data covering all forms of media, including radio, television, print, and the Internet. Its reports allow advertisers and advertising agencies to target ad placement for maximum exposure to their intended demographic. Media owners also use its information to better sell ad time or ad space. (Its *Survey of the American Consumer* is a notable source of audience data for the US consumer magazine industry.) GfK MRI collects its data through more than 26,000 interviews with consumers throughout the country. It is a unit of leading research firm GfK Group.

GGNSC HOLDINGS LLC

1000 Fianna Way
Fort Smith, AR 72919
Phone: 479-201-2000
Fax: 479-201-1101
Web: www.goldenliving.com

CEO: Neil M. Kurtz
CFO: Darlene Burch
HR: Michael Karicher
FYE: December 31
Type: Private

GGNSC Holdings puts the "Golden" in "Golden Years." The holding company does business as Golden Living and operates more than 300 skilled nursing homes and some 40 assisted living facilities nationwide. Golden Living's subsidiaries operate under a range of names including Aegis Therapies for rehabilitation therapy, AseraCare hospice and home health care, 360 Healthcare Staffing, and Ceres, a buying cooperative for health care products such as disposable gloves, sanitary products, and wheelchairs. Previously named Beverly Enterprises, GGNSC is owned by private equity firm Fillmore Capital Partners.

	Annual Growth	12/04	12/05	12/06	12/07	12/08
Sales ($ mil.)	1.6%	—	—	2,500.0	2,490.0	2,580.0
Employees	1.2%	—	—	40,000	41,000	41,000

GHIRARDELLI CHOCOLATE COMPANY

1111 139th Ave.
San Leandro, CA 94578
Phone: 510-483-6970
Fax: 510-297-2649
Web: www.ghirardelli.com

CEO: Andreas Pfluger
CFO: Beat Hermann
HR: Leslie Yewell
FYE: December 31
Type: Subsidiary

With boxes, bars, and business gifts, Ghirardelli Chocolate speaks to American chocolate lovers on many levels. The company makes premium chocolate products such as its signature chocolate squares, baking chocolate, and chocolate beverage mixes, controlling the entire manufacturing process. It distributes its products nationwide. Ghirardelli's chocolate products are available at retail outlets including grocery, drug, mass-merchandise, department, and specialty stores. It also sells foodservice products including chocolate beverage mixes, sauces, and frappe mixes, as well as specialty ingredients for other food manufacturers. Ghirardelli is a subsidiary of Switzerland's Chocoladefabriken Lindt & Sprüngli.

G-I HOLDINGS INC.

1361 Alps Rd.
Wayne, NJ 07470
Phone: 973-628-3000
Fax: —

CEO: John F. Rebele
CFO: John F. Rebele
HR: Gary Schneid
FYE: December 31
Type: Private

G-I Holdings isn't your average Joe in the roofing materials business. Formerly GAF Corporation, G-I Holdings and its subsidiary Building Materials Corporation of America manufacture flashing, vents, and complete roofing systems. Products include residential shingles and commercial asphalt roofing under such brands as Everguard, Ruberoid, and Timberline. Other products include natural stone, ornamental ironwork, and ducting. G-I Holdings has been operating under Chapter 11 bankruptcy protection since 2001; it filed due to asbestos liability claims. The family of the late chairman Samuel Heyman owns the company.

GIANT CEMENT HOLDING, INC.

320-D Midland Pkwy.
Summerville, SC 29485
Phone: 843-851-9898
Fax: 843-851-9881
Web: www.gchi.com

CEO: Manuel Llop
CFO: Bratton Fennell
HR: Jerry Geier
FYE: December 31
Type: Subsidiary

Giant Cement Holding thinks big. A subsidiary of Spain's Cementos Portland Valderrivas, the holding company produces Portland and masonry cements through Giant Cement Company in South Carolina, Keystone Cement in Pennsylvania, and Dragon Cement in Maine. Its products, which are sold throughout the eastern US, are used in the construction of buildings, bridges, and highways. Giant Cement Holdings' Giant Resource Recovery unit processes industrial waste for use as fuel for the company's cement kilns. Coastal Cement, an affiliate of Dragon Cement, maintains two deep-water shipping terminals in New England.

GIANT EAGLE, INC.

101 Kappa Dr.
Pittsburgh, PA 15238
Phone: 412-963-6200
Fax: 412-968-1617
Web: www.gianteagle.com

CEO: David S. (Dave) Shapira
CFO: Mary Winston
HR: Michele M. Reuss
FYE: June 30
Type: Private

Giant Eagle has its talons firmly wrapped around parts of Pennsylvania and Ohio. The grocery chain, a market leader in Pittsburgh and eastern Ohio, operates about 160 company-owned stores and some 60 franchised supermarkets, as well as about 150 GetGo convenience stores (which feature fresh foods and sell gas at discounted prices through the fuelperks! program). Many Giant Eagle stores feature video rental, banking, photo processing, dry cleaning services, and ready-to-eat meals. Giant Eagle is also a wholesaler to licensed stores and sells groceries to other retail chains. CEO David Shapira is the grandson of one of the men who founded the company in 1931. The founders' families own Giant Eagle.

GIANT FOOD INC.

8301 Professional Place, Ste. 115
Landover, MD 20785
Phone: 301-341-4100
Fax: 301-618-4998
Web: www.giantfood.com

CEO: Carl Schlicker
CFO: Paula A. Price
HR: Paula Labian
FYE: December 31
Type: Subsidiary

A monster among mid-Atlantic grocers, Giant Food (dba Giant-Landover) operates about 180 Giant Food and Super G supermarkets. It's #1 in the Baltimore and Washington, DC, markets; it also operates in the most populous areas of Delaware, Maryland, and Virginia. Most of its supermarkets house full-service pharmacies and some have Toys "R" Us toy departments. The company also operates its own dairy, beverage bottling, and ice cream plants. Founded in 1936, Giant was acquired in 1998 by Ahold USA, which owns more than 700 supermarkets in the US, including the New England-based Stop & Shop chain, Giant Food's sister company. Ahold USA is the US arm of Dutch grocer Royal Ahold.

GIANT FOOD STORES, LLC

1149 Harrisburg Pike
Carlisle, PA 17013
Phone: 717-249-4000
Fax: 717-960-1327
Web: www.giantpa.com

CEO: Rick Herring
CFO: —
HR: John Bussenger
FYE: December 31
Type: Subsidiary

Giant Food Stores (aka Giant-Carlisle) operates more than 175 supermarkets under the Giant and Martin's Food Markets banners in Pennsylvania, and in Maryland, Virginia, and West Virginia. Not to be confused with its Landover, Maryland-based sister company Giant Food, both firms are divisions of Ahold USA, which operates some 725 supermarkets in the eastern US. Giant Food Stores was founded in 1923 in Carlisle, Pennsylvania, and acquired by Amsterdam-based Royal Ahold in 1981. As a result of the latest reorganization of its US operations, the grocery company's Dutch parent has positioned Giant Food Stores for growth by separating its support functions from those of its other US chains.

GIBRALTAR INDUSTRIES, INC.

NASDAQ (GS): ROCK

3556 Lake Shore Rd.
Buffalo, NY 14219
Phone: 716-826-6500
Fax: 716-826-1589
Web: www.gibraltar1.com

CEO: Brian J. Lipke
CFO: Kenneth W. (Ken) Smith
HR: Paul M. Murray
FYE: December 31
Type: Public

When it comes to metal products, Gibraltar Industries is rock solid. The company makes building and industrial products such as metal roofing, vents, gutters, steel framing, and hardware. It's one of the leading mailbox makers in the US. Through its AIMCO subsidiary the company manufactures metal bar grating, perforated metal, fiberglass grating, and vinyl bead accessories. Gibraltar has been adjusting its business mix by selling off non-core operations and acquiring others that are a better strategic fit. The company operates 59 facilities in 26 US states, Canada, England, Germany, and Poland.

	Annual Growth	12/05	12/06	12/07	12/08	12/09
Sales ($ mil.)	(8.3%)	1,178.2	1,303.4	1,311.8	1,232.3	834.2
Net income ($ mil.)	—	43.5	57.3	13.2	24.1	(52.0)
Market value ($ mil.)	(9.0%)	694.1	711.4	466.6	361.3	476.0
Employees	(13.9%)	4,450	3,460	3,950	3,270	2,450

GIBSON, DUNN & CRUTCHER LLP

333 S. Grand Ave.
Los Angeles, CA 90071
Phone: 213-229-7000
Fax: 213-229-7520
Web: www.gibsondunn.com

CEO: Kenneth M. (Ken) Doran
CFO: Lawrence J. Ulman
HR: Leslie Ripley
FYE: October 31
Type: Partnership

One of the top US-based corporate transactions law firms, Gibson, Dunn & Crutcher also practices in such areas as labor and employment, crisis management, litigation, public policy, real estate, tax, and white collar defense and investigations. The firm has 1,000 lawyers in about 15 offices, not only in California but also elsewhere in the US and in Europe and the Middle East. It has a significant presence in Washington, DC. Along with multinational companies, Gibson Dunn clients include commercial and investment banks, government entities, individuals, and startups. The firm was founded in 1890.

GIBSON GUITAR CORP.

309 Plus Park Blvd.
Nashville, TN 37217
Phone: 615-871-4500
Fax: 615-889-5509
Web: www.gibson.com

CEO: Henry E. Juszkiewicz
CFO: —
HR: Leah McGreary
FYE: December 31
Type: Private

Real pickers put Gibson Guitar on a pedestal. Though it trails top guitar maker Fender, Gibson builds instruments that are held in unparalleled esteem by many guitarists, including top professional musicians. The company's most popular guitar is the legendary Les Paul. Gibson also makes guitars under such brands as Epiphone, Kramer, and Steinberger. In addition to guitars, the company manufactures pianos through its Baldwin unit, Slingerland drums, Tobias bass, Wurlitzer vending machines and jukeboxes, and Echoplex amplifiers, as well as many accessory items. Company namesake Orville Gibson began making mandolins in the late 1890s. Gibson Guitar is owned by executives Henry Juszkiewicz and David Berryman.

An in-depth profile of this company is available to Hoover's Online members at hoovers.com.

683

GIGA-TRONICS INCORPORATED

NASDAQ (CM): GIGA

4650 Norris Canyon Rd.
San Ramon, CA 94583
Phone: 925-328-4650
Fax: 925-328-4700
Web: www.gigatronics.com

CEO: John R. Regazzi
CFO: Patrick J. Lawlor
HR: —
FYE: March 31
Type: Public

Giga-tronics has a cool gig in electronics. Its three units — Giga-tronics Instruments, Microsource, and ASCOR — make test, measurement, and control equipment for both commercial and military customers. The units make synthesizers and power measurement instruments used in electronic warfare, radar, satellite, and telecommunications devices; switching systems for aircraft and automated test equipment; and oscillators and filters used in microwave instruments. Top customers include the US Department of Defense and its prime contractors (62% of sales). More than three-fifths of the company's sales are to customers located in the US.

	Annual Growth	3/06	3/07	3/08	3/09	3/10
Sales ($ mil.)	(1.9%)	20.6	18.0	18.3	17.4	19.1
Net income ($ mil.)	—	(1.0)	(1.9)	(0.2)	(0.3)	1.3
Market value ($ mil.)	(3.0%)	12.8	9.7	7.3	5.4	11.3
Employees	(5.2%)	120	117	93	97	97

GIGOPTIX, INC.

OTC: GGOX

2400 Geng Rd., Ste. 100
Palo Alto, CA 94303
Phone: 650-424-1937
Fax: 650-424-1938
Web: www.gigoptix.com

CEO: Avi Katz
CFO: Ronald K. (Ron) Shelton
HR: —
FYE: December 31
Type: Public

GigOptix (formerly Lumera) hopes its light shines bright in an optical universe. The company develops polymer materials and products for use in wireless and optical communications networks. Products include optical and radio-frequency (RF) amplifiers, compact panel wireless antennas, and electro-optic modulators and optical interconnects for use in telecommunications. In late 2008 Lumera Corp. merged with GigOptix LLC, a California-based supplier of optical modulator drivers and receivers, in a stock-swap transaction. The combined company offers a broader portfolio of optical components for fiber-optic communications networks and for connections to electronic equipment.

	Annual Growth	12/05	12/06	12/07	12/08	12/09
Sales ($ mil.)	86.0%	—	2.3	3.2	9.7	14.8
Net income ($ mil.)	—	—	(10.3)	(6.4)	(7.7)	(10.0)
Market value ($ mil.)	110.0%	—	—	—	9.3	19.6
Employees	20.5%	—	56	65	67	98

GILBANE, INC.

7 Jackson Walkway
Providence, RI 02903
Phone: 401-456-5800
Fax: 401-456-5936
Web: www.gilbaneco.com

CEO: Thomas F. (Tom) Gilbane Jr.
CFO: Robert C. Zerbe
HR: —
FYE: December 31
Type: Private

Family-owned Gilbane has been the bane of its rivals for four generations, with a fifth generation on the way. Subsidiary Gilbane Building provides construction management, contracting, and design and build services to construct office buildings, manufacturing plants, schools, prisons, and more for the firm's governmental, commercial, and industrial clients. Landmark projects include work on the National Air and Space Museum, Baltimore's Inner Harbor project, and the World War II memorial and Capitol Visitors Center in Washington, DC. Another subsidiary, Gilbane Development Company, develops and finances public and private projects and acts as a property manager. William Gilbane founded the firm in 1873.

	Annual Growth	12/04	12/05	12/06	12/07	12/08
Sales ($ mil.)	5.6%	2,580.0	2,832.0	2,790.0	2,970.0	3,210.0
Employees	6.0%	1,757	1,800	2,024	2,180	2,216

GILBARCO INC.

NASDAQ (CM): GIGA

7300 W. Friendly Ave.
Greensboro, NC 27410
Phone: 336-547-5000
Fax: 336-547-5299
Web: www.gilbarco.com

CEO: Martin Gafinowitz
CFO: —
HR: —
FYE: December 31
Type: Subsidiary

Gilbarco (which does business as Gilbarco Veeder-Root) is all about giving you gas. The company supplies the fuel industry with retail POS (point-of-sale) computer systems, including fuel dispensing, tank monitoring, and credit card processing equipment. The company makes sales through a network of distributors and affiliates in about 100 countries worldwide. Customers include car rental companies, local governments, convenience stores, fuel retailers, and truck fleet operators. The company is also a leading rebuilder of fuel dispensing equipment. Gilbarco is a subsidiary of Danaher, which also owns fuel management systems maker Veeder-Root, as well as petroleum dispensing system vendor Gasboy.

GILEAD SCIENCES, INC.

NASDAQ (GS): GILD

333 Lakeside Dr.
Foster City, CA 94404
Phone: 650-574-3000
Fax: 650-578-9264
Web: www.gilead.com

CEO: John C. Martin
CFO: Robin L. Washington
HR: Kristen M. Metza
FYE: December 31
Type: Public

Gilead Sciences has biotech balms for infectious diseases, including hepatitis, HIV, and infections related to AIDS. The company's HIV franchise includes blockbuster Truvada, a combination of two of its other drugs, Viread and Emtriva. It co-promotes another HIV treatment, called Atripla, in the US and Europe with Bristol-Myers Squibb. Other products on the market include AmBisome, used to treat systemic fungal infections such as those that accompany AIDS; Vistide, for AIDS-related eye infections; and hepatitis B antiviral Hepsera. Outside of the infectious disease realm, Gilead markets Letairis, a treatment for pulmonary arterial hypertension (PAH), or high pulmonary blood pressure.

	Annual Growth	12/05	12/06	12/07	12/08	12/09
Sales ($ mil.)	36.4%	2,028.4	3,026.1	4,230.0	5,335.8	7,011.4
Net income ($ mil.)	34.1%	813.9	(1,190.0)	1,615.3	2,011.2	2,635.8
Market value ($ mil.)	13.3%	23,391.4	28,891.1	40,945.0	45,510.3	38,506.6
Employees	19.3%	1,900	2,515	2,979	3,441	3,852

GILMAN CIOCIA, INC.

OTC: GTAX

11 Raymond Ave.
Poughkeepsie, NY 12603
Phone: 845-486-0900
Fax: 845-483-9332
Web: www.gtax.com

CEO: Michael P. Ryan
CFO: Karen Fisher
HR: Jamie Darrion
FYE: June 30
Type: Public

Gilman Ciocia (formerly Gilman + Ciocia) helps make the most of your dollars + cents. The firm provides financial planning and accounting services, primarily for middle- and upper-income clients. Financial planning offerings (about 90% of revenue) include fee-based investment advisory services and securities, insurance, and mortgage brokerage. The firm also provides commercial accounting services and prepares federal, state, and local tax returns. (Most financial planning customers initially come to Gilman Ciocia for its tax return preparation services.) The company owns and operates about 30 offices in New York, New Jersey, and Florida and licenses more than 50 independently owned offices in a dozen states.

	Annual Growth	6/05	6/06	6/07	6/08	6/09
Assets ($ mil.)	(2.7%)	17.1	16.6	16.5	16.7	15.3
Net income ($ mil.)	—	(1.8)	(2.6)	0.8	3.7	(1.8)
Market value ($ mil.)	(38.9%)	41.4	19.3	4.8	11.6	5.8
Employees	0.0%	—	205	227	218	205

GIORGIO ARMANI CORPORATION

114 5th Ave., 17th Fl.
New York, NY 10011
Phone: 212-366-9720
Fax: 212-366-1685
Web: www.armani.com

CEO: Bruno Laguardia
CFO: —
HR: —
FYE: December 31
Type: Subsidiary

Oh, Gio! Giorgio Armani Corporation is the American arm of Italian fashion house Giorgio Armani S.p.A. The US operation, which generates about a quarter of its parent's revenue, makes and retails upscale apparel for men, women, juniors, and babies. It boasts a retail network of about 50 Armani Exchange stores, a dozen Giorgio Armani boutiques, and a pair each of Armani/Casa and Armani/Café outlets. The firm also has a dozen Emporio Armani shops and is expanding the banner in Hawaii. Giorgio Armani licenses its name to manufacturers of perfume, cosmetics, watches, eyewear, jewelry, and accessories. Its Giorgio Armani Cosmetics unit operates within its own stores, as well as through Nordstrom and Saks.

GIRL SCOUTS OF THE UNITED STATES OF AMERICA

420 5th Ave.
New York, NY 10018
Phone: 212-852-8000
Fax: 212-852-6514
Web: www.girlscouts.org

CEO: Kathy Cloninger
CFO: Florence Corsello
HR: Jaclyn E. Libowitz
FYE: September 30
Type: Not-for-profit

For the Girl Scouts of the United States of America, the calendar includes one month of cookie sales and 12 months of character-building. One of the largest groups devoted to girls, it boasts about 2.7 million girl members, plus some 928,000 adult volunteers. Girl Scouts of the USA, founded in 1912, is open to girls between ages 5 and 17 and strives to develop character and leadership skills through projects involving technology, sports, the environment, literacy, the arts, and the sciences. The US organization is part of the World Association of Girl Guides and Girl Scouts, which encompasses some 10 million girls and adults in about 145 countries.

	Annual Growth	9/04	9/05	9/06	9/07	9/08
Est. sales ($ mil.)	—	—	—	—	—	123.0
Employees	—	—	—	—	—	500

GKN AEROSPACE CHEM-TRONICS INC.

1150 W. Bradley Ave.
El Cajon, CA 92020
Phone: 619-448-2320
Fax: 619-258-5279
Web: www.chem-tronics.com

CEO: James Legler
CFO: —
HR: —
FYE: December 31
Type: Subsidiary

Allied to aluminum and totally committed to titanium, GKN Aerospace Chem-tronics fabricates components (such as doors, ducts, enclosures, exhaust nozzles, keels, and bulkheads) for commercial and military aircraft, and spacecraft. The company, a subsidiary of GKN, specializes in lightweight chemically milled titanium and aluminum alloy parts for engines, airframe structures, and launch vehicles. GKN Aerospace Chem-tronics makes components for Aerojet, Allison, Boeing, General Electric, Lockheed Martin, Pratt & Whitney, Rocketdyne, Rolls-Royce, and other aerospace companies. Additional products include complex welds, cases, modules, pressure vessels, and rings. The company was founded in 1953.

GKN DRIVELINE NORTH AMERICA INC.

3300 University Dr.
Auburn Hills, MI 48326
Phone: 248-377-1200
Fax: 248-377-1370
Web: www.gkndriveline.com

CEO: Max Owen
CFO: John Giannangeli
HR: —
FYE: December 31
Type: Business segment

GKN Driveline North America primarily oversees the US business of UK's GKN plc. Through its various facilities, the company manufactures automotive driveline components, constant velocity (CV) joints, propshafts, and torque management devices. GKN's CV joints are used by almost every major carmaker in the world. GKN Driveline North America's other products include power takeoff shafts and wheels for off-highway vehicles including agriculture, forestry, construction, and mining equipment. GKN Driveline North America also includes one manufacturing facility in Mexico, where it makes CV joints as well.

GKN SINTER METALS, INC.

3300 University Dr.
Auburn Hills, MI 48326
Phone: 248-371-0800
Fax: 248-371-0809
Web: www.gknsintermetals.com

CEO: Andrew Reynolds Smith
CFO: Chris Granger
HR: —
FYE: December 31
Type: Subsidiary

GKN Sinter Metals makes precision pressed-powder metal components for use principally in the automotive, lawn and garden, power tool, and home appliance industries. The company uses a process known as powder metallurgy to make intricate and complex parts with performance attributes comparable with components produced through such processes as forging and casting. Its metal components include gears, bearings, and pulleys, primarily for use in engines, transmissions, and other drive mechanisms. Customers include Deere, Volkswagen, and Volvo. GKN Sinter Metals is a subsidiary of UK-based automotive components and aerospace concern GKN plc.

GLACIER BANCORP, INC.

49 Commons Loop
Kalispell, MT 59901
Phone: 406-756-4200
Fax: —
Web: www.glacierbancorp.com

NASDAQ (GS): GBCI

CEO: Michael J. (Mick) Blodnick
CFO: Ronald J. (Ron) Copher
HR: Robin S. Roush
FYE: December 31
Type: Public

Glacier Bancorp is on a Rocky Mountain High. The multibank holding company owns about a dozen community banks in Montana, Idaho, Utah, Washington, Colorado, and Wyoming. Serving individuals, small to midsized businesses, not-for-profits, and public entities, the banks operate a total of about 100 branches. Glacier Bancorp offers traditional deposit products and credit cards, in addition to retail brokerage and investment services through agreements with third-party providers. Its lending activities consist of commercial real estate loans (almost half of the company's loan portfolio), as well as residential mortgages, business loans, and consumer loans.

	Annual Growth	12/05	12/06	12/07	12/08	12/09
Assets ($ mil.)	13.7%	3,706.3	4,467.7	4,817.3	5,554.0	6,191.8
Net income ($ mil.)	(10.0%)	52.4	61.1	68.6	65.7	34.4
Market value ($ mil.)	(9.0%)	1,440.7	1,757.5	1,347.6	1,367.8	986.6
Employees	11.5%	1,125	1,356	1,480	1,571	1,739

An in-depth profile of this company is available to Hoover's Online members at hoovers.com.

685

GLACIER WATER SERVICES, INC.

Pink Sheets: GWSV

1385 Park Center Dr.
Vista, CA 92081
Phone: 760-560-1111
Fax: 760-560-3333
Web: www.glacierwater.com

CEO: Brian H. McInerney
CFO: Steve Stringer
HR: Luz E. Gonzales
FYE: December 31
Type: Public

Glacier Water Services serves those who shun the tap. The company operates more than 16,000 self-service vending machines that dispense filtered drinking water, making it a leading brand in vended water. Its machines are in 43 US states and Canada. The machines are connected to municipal water sources and are designed to reduce impurities in the water through processes such as micron filtration, reverse osmosis, carbon absorption, and ultraviolet disinfection. Glacier Water's machines are placed outside supermarkets and other stores; it uses indoor models in colder climates.

GLADSTONE CAPITAL CORPORATION

NASDAQ (GS): GLAD

1521 Westbranch Dr., Ste. 200
McLean, VA 22102
Phone: 703-287-5800
Fax: 703-287-5801
Web: www.gladstonecapital.com

CEO: David J. Gladstone
CFO: Gresford Gray
HR: Paula Novara
FYE: September 30
Type: Public

If your fledgling company shows promise, Gladstone Capital might be glad to provide some capital. The business development company (BDC) provides loans, generally between $3 million and $15 million, to small and medium-sized family-owned companies or firms backed by leveraged buyout funds or venture capital outfits. Gladstone Capital particularly targets firms undergoing ownership transitions. The firm then shepherds its portfolio companies towards merger or acquisition transactions or initial public offerings. Company affiliate Gladstone Management Corporation provides management services to the firm's portfolio companies. Subsidiary Gladstone Business Loan holds the loan investment portfolio.

	Annual Growth	9/05	9/06	9/07	9/08	9/09
Sales ($ mil.)	(0.6%)	22.2	34.0	29.4	45.7	21.7
Net income ($ mil.)	(29.6%)	15.5	24.4	15.0	(21.3)	3.8
Market value ($ mil.)	(20.7%)	474.4	463.1	410.7	320.6	187.9
Employees	—	0	0	0	35	0

GLADSTONE COMMERCIAL CORPORATION

NASDAQ (GM): GOOD

1521 Westbranch Dr., Ste. 200
McLean, VA 22102
Phone: 703-287-5800
Fax: 703-287-5801
Web: www.gladstonecommercial.com

CEO: David J. Gladstone
CFO: Danielle Jones
HR: Paula Novara
FYE: December 31
Type: Public

Gladstone Commercial will gladly buy your commercial property, or lease you some if you need a business home. A real estate investment trust (REIT), Gladstone invests in commercial and industrial real estate properties and long-term commercial mortgages. The company owns more than 50 properties across the US with assets that include office buildings, warehouses, retail, and manufacturing facilities. Gladstone predominantly leases to small and midsized businesses; most properties carry triple-net leases. The firm is closely affiliated with management investment firm Gladstone Capital, which is also headed by chairman and CEO David Gladstone.

	Annual Growth	12/05	12/06	12/07	12/08	12/09
Sales ($ mil.)	33.3%	13.5	25.9	32.8	40.9	42.6
Net income ($ mil.)	6.3%	3.6	4.4	6.1	4.9	4.6
Market value ($ mil.)	(5.1%)	141.0	172.1	149.9	72.6	114.6
Employees	—	33	45	0	0	—

GLAXOSMITHKLINE RESEARCH & DEVELOPMENT

5 Moore Dr.
Research Triangle Park, NC 27709
Phone: 919-483-2100
Fax: 919-549-7459
Web: www.gsk.com/research

CEO: Jean-Pierre (JP) Garnier
CFO: Julian Heslop
HR: —
FYE: —
Type: Business segment

GlaxoSmithKline Research & Development is the actual pipeline filled with products in various stages of completion for pharmaceutical giant GlaxoSmithKline. With multiple locations in the US, across Europe, and Japan, the company has treatments in the works for infectious diseases, neuroscientific requirements, cardiovascular ailments, oncology, and respiratory needs. It has approximately 150 pharmaceutical products in clinical trial stages. The organization's facilities are grouped into Molecular Discovery Research (preclinical), Centres of Excellence for Drug Discovery (early stage clinical), and Medicine Development Centres (late-stage clinical).

GLAZER'S WHOLESALE DRUG COMPANY, INC.

14911 Quorum Dr., Ste. 400
Dallas, TX 75254
Phone: 972-392-8200
Fax: 972-702-8508
Web: www.glazers.com

CEO: Bennett J. Glazer
CFO: Cary Rossel
HR: Kristin Snyder
FYE: December 31
Type: Private

Glazer's Wholesale Drug, named during Prohibition when only drugstores and drug wholesalers could deal in liquor, is a wholesale distributor of alcoholic beverages. In Texas it is the largest company of its kind and one of the largest wine and spirits distributors in the US. The company distributes Budweiser Beer, Robert Mondavi wines, Brown-Forman and Bacardi spirits, and Diageo products. CEO Bennett Glazer and his family own Glazer's. The company's origins date back to the early 1900s when the Glazer family sold flavored soda water, which it distributed using horse-drawn wagons. Today Glazer owns and operates 43 offices in 11 US states.

	Annual Growth	12/04	12/05	12/06	12/07	12/08
Est. sales ($ mil.)	1.7%	2,800.0	2,900.0	3,000.0	3,150.0	3,000.0
Employees	(1.3%)	5,800	5,800	5,800	5,900	5,500

GLEACHER & COMPANY, INC.

NASDAQ (GM): GLCH

1290 Avenue of the Americas, 4th and 5th Fl.
New York, NY 10017
Phone: 212-273-7100
Fax: —
Web: www.gleacher.com

CEO: Eric J. Gleacher
CFO: Jeffrey H. Kugler
HR: —
FYE: December 31
Type: Public

Gleacher & Company (formerly Broadpoint Gleacher Securities Group) provides investment banking, debt capital markets services, and equity research to institutional clients in the US and Europe. Subsidiary DESCAP sells and trades mortgage-related and asset-backed securities. FA Technology Ventures provides venture capital to high-tech US firms. In 2009 Broadpoint Securities acquired Gleacher Partners, a firm best known for its M&A advisory practice, and added Gleacher to its name. The company officially changed its name to Gleacher & Company the following year.

	Annual Growth	12/05	12/06	12/07	12/08	12/09
Sales ($ mil.)	18.9%	179.0	130.7	47.1	145.0	357.4
Net income ($ mil.)	—	(10.2)	(44.4)	(19.5)	(17.4)	54.9
Market value ($ mil.)	(10.5%)	895.5	298.9	152.0	382.7	574.7
Employees	(3.1%)	388	284	211	255	342

An in-depth profile of this company is available to Hoover's Online members at hoovers.com.

GLEASON CORPORATION

1000 University Ave.
Rochester, NY 14692
Phone: 585-473-1000
Fax: 585-461-4348
Web: www.gleason.com

CEO: John J. Perrotti
CFO: John W. Pysnack
HR: Nanci Malin-Peck
FYE: December 31
Type: Private

If you love the v-v-vrooom, 0-to-60-in-seconds experience, then you can thank Gleason Corporation. The company designs, manufactures, and sells the machines that make, test, and finish the gears used in drive shafts. Gleason sells to makers of aircraft, boats, buses, cars, recreational vehicles, SUVs, and trucks, as well as agricultural and construction machinery. The company also provides replacement parts for the aftermarket, and inspection software and training programs for its customers. Gleason, founded in 1865, was taken private in 2000 and is owned by members of the Gleason family, the Gleason Foundation, senior executives of the company, and Vestar Capital Partners.

GLEN BURNIE BANCORP

NASDAQ (CM): GLBZ

101 Crain Hwy. SE
Glen Burnie, MD 21061
Phone: 410-766-3300
Fax: 410-787-8581
Web: www.thebankofglenburnie.com

CEO: Michael G. Livingston
CFO: John E. Porter
HR: —
FYE: December 31
Type: Public

Glen Burnie Bancorp has an interest in the Old Line State. The institution is the holding company for Bank of Glen Burnie, which has about 10 branches in central Maryland's Anne Arundel County, south of Baltimore. The bank offers such services as checking and savings accounts, money market and individual retirement accounts, CDs, and remote banking services. It focuses on real estate lending, with residential and commercial mortgages accounting for the largest portions of its loan portfolio. The bank also writes indirect automobile loans, which are originated through a network of about 50 area car dealers. Bank of Glen Burnie was founded in 1949.

	Annual Growth	12/05	12/06	12/07	12/08	12/09
Assets ($ mil.)	3.6%	306.6	317.7	307.3	332.5	353.4
Net income ($ mil.)	(17.5%)	2.8	2.7	2.8	0.4	1.3
Market value ($ mil.)	(11.4%)	40.1	38.2	34.8	29.4	24.7
Employees	(1.9%)	125	119	118	114	116

GLEN ROSE PETROLEUM CORPORATION

OTC: GLRP

1 Energy Sq., Ste. 200, 4925 Greenville Ave.
Dallas, TX 75206
Phone: 214-800-2663
Fax: —
Web: www.glenrosepetroleum.com

CEO: Joseph Tovey
CFO: Joseph Tovey
HR: —
FYE: March 31
Type: Public

Glen Rose Petroleum is developing oil and gas prospects in South Texas. In 2006 the company, then known as United Heritage Corporation, was acquired by its largest shareholder, Lothian Oil, which holds a 71% stake. However, Lothian Oil filed for bankruptcy in 2007. In order to raise cash the company sold its New Mexico properties that year. Its remaining assets are two lease-holds in the Wardlaw Field in Edwards County, Texas. In 2008 United Heritage changed its name to Glen Rose Petroleum.

	Annual Growth	3/05	3/06	3/07	3/08	3/09
Sales ($ mil.)	(33.1%)	0.5	0.6	1.0	0.1	0.1
Net income ($ mil.)	—	(0.8)	(17.4)	(11.4)	(3.3)	(2.2)
Market value ($ mil.)	(45.1%)	27.0	36.8	12.7	11.6	2.5
Employees	2.7%	9	7	5	5	10

GLG PARTNERS, INC.

NYSE: GLG

390 Park Ave., 20th Fl.
New York, NY 10022
Phone: 212-224-7200
Fax: —
Web: www.glgpartners.com

CEO: Emmanuel Roman
CFO: Jeffrey Rojek
HR: —
FYE: December 31
Type: Public

For private investors looking for a place to put their money, GLG Partners may be able to offer an alternative. As one of Europe's largest alternative investment managers, GLG offers a range of investment products and account management services to clients in the UK and other European markets. The company manages a portfolio of about 40 funds that contains a mix of alternative funds (such as hedge, mixed-asset long-short, arbitrage, convertible bond) and long-only funds (non-hedged), and serves both wealthy individuals and institutional clients. UK-based Man Group is acquiring GLG for some $1.6 billion. The deal will create a hedge fund giant with approximately $63 billion of assets under management.

	Annual Growth	12/05	12/06	12/07	12/08	12/09
Assets ($ mil.)	(28.7%)	—	—	984.1	489.7	500.8
Net income ($ mil.)	—	—	—	92.6	(629.7)	(319.0)
Market value ($ mil.)	(51.3%)	—	—	3,416.9	570.3	809.0
Employees	(0.4%)	—	—	349	346	346

GLIMCHER REALTY TRUST

NYSE: GRT

150 E. Broad St.
Columbus, OH 43215
Phone: 614-621-9000
Fax: 614-621-9321
Web: www.glimcher.com

CEO: Michael P. Glimcher
CFO: Mark E. Yale
HR: —
FYE: December 31
Type: Public

In Glimcher's ideal world, we'd all be glimmering and glamourous shopaholics. A self-administered and self-managed real estate investment trust (REIT), Glimcher acquires, develops, and manages retail real estate. Its portfolio includes some 23 enclosed shopping malls (a couple owned through a joint venture) and four strip shopping centers for a total of some 21.7 million sq. ft. of space. Properties are located in about 15 states, primarily in the East and Midwest. Major tenants include Limited Brands, The Gap, and Foot Locker. Glimcher has spent several years divesting its shopping centers so it can focus on its mall properties.

	Annual Growth	12/05	12/06	12/07	12/08	12/09
Sales ($ mil.)	(1.8%)	335.2	311.2	303.9	319.6	311.4
Net income ($ mil.)	(34.7%)	20.9	(77.2)	38.4	16.8	3.8
Market value ($ mil.)	(42.3%)	1,676.1	1,840.9	984.9	193.7	186.1
Employees	(2.1%)	1,128	1,168	1,042	1,054	1,038

GLOBAL AXCESS CORP

OTC: GAXC

7800 Belfort Pkwy., Ste. 165
Jacksonville, FL 32256
Phone: 904-280-3950
Fax: 904-280-8588
Web: www.glxs.biz

CEO: George A. McQuain
CFO: Michael J. Loiacono
HR: —
FYE: December 31
Type: Public

Global Axcess has no ax to grind, just a bunch of ATMs to manage. Through subsidiaries, the company provides products, software, and services for about 4,500 ATMs it owns or operates in more than 40 states across the country. Through subsidiary Nationwide Money Services, the company provides full-service management of its ATM network. Global Axcess ATMs are placed in areas with high pedestrian traffic, including grocery and convenience stores, major retailers, malls, colleges, and sports arenas. Its network is concentrated in the South (Georgia has more of its ATMs than any other state) and on the East Coast.

	Annual Growth	12/05	12/06	12/07	12/08	12/09
Sales ($ mil.)	2.3%	19.6	21.4	21.8	22.2	21.5
Net income ($ mil.)	—	(0.7)	(4.9)	0.4	1.2	2.8
Market value ($ mil.)	(7.0%)	26.1	8.1	7.5	2.9	19.5
Employees	(7.7%)	66	51	47	45	48

An in-depth profile of this company is available to Hoover's Online members at hoovers.com.

687

GLOBAL CASH ACCESS HOLDINGS, INC.

NYSE: GCA

3525 E. Post Rd., Ste. 120
Las Vegas, NV 89120
Phone: 702-855-3000
Fax: 866-672-4371
Web: www.globalcashaccess.com

CEO: Scott H. Betts
CFO: —
HR: —
FYE: December 31
Type: Public

If you're losing your shirt at the casino tables, Global Cash Access can get you more money on the spot. The company provides such services as ATM cash withdrawals, credit- and debit-card advances, and check guarantee to the gaming industry in the US, Asia, Canada, Latin America, South Africa, and Europe. Altogether the company provides services to more than 1,000 casinos including Harrah's and MGM Mirage. Global Cash Access also has developed cashless gaming systems including special ticket vouchers and systems that allow players to access funds without leaving their gaming machines. Other services include casino marketing and patron credit information through its QuikReports and CentralCredit database.

	Annual Growth	12/05	12/06	12/07	12/08	12/09
Sales ($ mil.)	10.1%	454.1	548.1	600.9	671.6	667.7
Net income ($ mil.)	10.4%	22.6	26.6	23.7	26.0	33.6
Market value ($ mil.)	(15.4%)	960.5	1,068.4	398.9	146.1	493.1
Employees	14.6%	279	354	354	626	481

GLOBAL CASINOS, INC.

OTC: GBCS

5455 Spine Rd., Ste. C
Boulder, CO 80301
Phone: 303-527-2903
Fax: 303-527-2916

CEO: Clifford L. Neuman
CFO: Todd Huss
HR: —
FYE: June 30
Type: Public

Global Casinos owns and operates two casinos in Colorado. Its Bull Durham Saloon & Casino in Black Hawk, Colorado, boasts more than 180 slot machines and offers limited food services along with other customer amenities. Its customer base consists primarily of day visitors from Denver. The company also owns a second property, the Doc Holliday Casino, in Central City, Colorado, with about 200 slot machines. Both casinos offer charter services to bring groups of patrons from Denver. Company president Clifford Neuman owns nearly 10% of Global Casinos.

	Annual Growth	6/05	6/06	6/07	6/08	6/09
Sales ($ mil.)	13.2%	3.9	4.0	3.6	4.4	6.4
Net income ($ mil.)	—	0.9	0.1	0.1	0.1	0.0
Market value ($ mil.)	(18.3%)	7.2	5.8	6.1	4.5	3.2
Employees	(0.8%)	32	34	31	36	31

⊞ GLOBAL CROSSING LIMITED

NASDAQ (GS): GLBC

200 Park Ave., Ste. 300
Florham Park, NJ 07932
Phone: 973-937-0100
Fax: 973-360-0148
Web: www.globalcrossing.com

CEO: John J. Legere
CFO: John A. Kritzmacher
HR: Laurinda Pang
FYE: December 31
Type: Public

Born to bridge the seas, Global Crossing surfs the bandwidth wave. The global Internet protocol (IP)-based telecommunications carrier operates an integrated global system of data networks that reaches about 700 cities in 60 countries. It connects the Americas and Europe, and links to Asia through submarine fiber-cable networks. This fiber stream supports a wide range of services, including Internet access and other data services, for multinational corporations, government agencies, and other telecom service providers. Global Crossing also provides voice calling services over its network. The company operates from offices and facilities throughout Asia, Europe, Latin America, and North America.

	Annual Growth	12/05	12/06	12/07	12/08	12/09
Sales ($ mil.)	6.5%	1,968.0	1,871.0	2,261.0	2,592.0	2,536.0
Net income ($ mil.)	—	(354.0)	(324.0)	(306.0)	(277.0)	(141.0)
Market value ($ mil.)	(2.9%)	968.7	1,483.5	1,332.4	479.8	861.1
Employees	11.4%	3,400	3,700	4,936	5,219	5,235

GLOBAL DEFENSE TECHNOLOGY & SYSTEMS

NASDAQ (GM): GTEC

1501 Farm Credit Dr., Ste. 2300
McLean, VA 22102
Phone: 703-738-2840
Fax: 703-883-4037
Web: www.globalgroup.us.com

CEO: John F. Hillen III
CFO: James P. (Jim) Allen
HR: Lisa Broome
FYE: December 31
Type: Public

Military intelligence is no joking matter to the folks at Global Defense Technology & Systems, Inc. The holding company operates mainly through subsidiary Global Strategies Group (North America). It provides software, system engineering, and technology development to help the Department of Defense, the CIA, Homeland Security, and other government agencies fight terrorism. Global Defense Technology's Technology and Intelligence Services (TIS) focuses on counter-terrorism and communications systems, while its Force Mobility and Modernization Systems (FMMS) designs highly mobile computer systems to support military missions. The company, which filed its IPO in 2009, is part of British firm Global Strategies Group.

	Annual Growth	12/05	12/06	12/07	12/08	12/09
Sales ($ mil.)	20.0%	—	123.1	134.8	189.4	212.8
Net income ($ mil.)	—	—	(0.8)	(4.1)	1.1	1.3
Market value ($ mil.)	—	—	—	—	—	149.3
Employees	3.0%	—	—	—	675	695

GLOBAL DIVERSIFIED INDUSTRIES, INC.

OTC: GDIV

1200 Airport Dr.
Chowchilla, CA 93610
Phone: 559-665-5800
Fax: 559-665-5700
Web: www.gdvi.net

CEO: Phillip (Phil) Hamilton
CFO: Adam N. DeBard
HR: —
FYE: April 30
Type: Public

Global Diversified Industries is the new mod squad. Through its Global Modular subsidiary, the company makes pre-fabricated portable modular buildings, mainly for use as classrooms. It also constructs permanent one- and two-story structures. Clients include public and private schools, universities, child-care facilities, and municipalities. The company is active throughout California. Global Diversified divested its MBS Construction subsidiary, which provided construction site management services, in 2006. Company president Phil Hamilton has voting control of more than 20% of Global Diversified's stock.

	Annual Growth	4/05	4/06	4/07	4/08	4/09
Sales ($ mil.)	(13.3%)	9.2	14.9	6.6	5.7	5.2
Net income ($ mil.)	—	0.5	0.6	(1.3)	(8.4)	(1.5)
Market value ($ mil.)	(66.4%)	30.1	23.1	4.6	1.8	0.4
Employees	(30.5%)	150	145	100	30	35

GLOBAL EARTH ENERGY, INC.

OTC: GLER

534 Delaware Ave., Ste. 412
Buffalo, NY 14202
Phone: 716-332-7150
Fax: 716-332-7170
Web: www.globalearthenergy.com

CEO: Sydney A. Harland
CFO: Edmund J. Gorman
HR: —
FYE: August 31
Type: Public

Global Earth Energy (formerly Global Wataire) believes strongly that the global earth energy to exploit is biodiesel. The company plans to build on the growing momentum for using biodiesel as way to decrease US dependency on foreign crude oil and limit carbon emissions by establishing a 1 million-gallon-per-year biodiesel production plant in North Carolina. It is also planning to move into the even greener energy sources of solar and wind power generation. Formerly operating as water purification firm Global Wataire, the company, which had struggled to achieve profitability, changed its name and industry focus in 2008. Chairman Betty-Ann Harland owns 25% of Global Earth Energy.

	Annual Growth	8/05	8/06	8/07	8/08	8/09
Sales ($ mil.)	—	—	—	—	—	0.0
Net income ($ mil.)	—	—	—	—	—	(1.0)
Market value ($ mil.)	—	—	—	—	—	0.8
Employees	—	—	—	—	—	3

GLOBAL ENERGY HOLDINGS GROUP, INC.

NYSE Amex: GNH

3348 Peachtree Rd., Ste. 250, Tower Place 200
Atlanta, GA 30326
Phone: 404-814-2500
Fax: 404-848-2879
Web: www.gnhgroup.com

CEO: Jimmy L. Bobo
CFO: Steven Paulik
HR: —
FYE: December 31
Type: Public

Global Energy Holdings (formerly Xethanol) is trying to make a buck through developing diverse and renewable energy sources. Global Energy Systems develops renewable energy projects, including biomass gasification and landfill-gas-to-energy projects. It also coordinates and manages energy efficiency projects for third parties, including government agencies and the US armed forces. The company ran into major liquidity problems and in 2009 it ceased the activities of its Global Energy Ventures unit (which invests in early-stage energy companies developing future power sources). Global Energy Holdings was forced to file for Chapter 11 bankruptcy protection in November 2009.

	Annual Growth	6/04	*12/05	12/06	12/07	†12/08
Sales ($ mil.)	—	0.0	4.3	11.0	11.0	3.8
Net income ($ mil.)	—	0.0	(11.4)	(20.2)	(31.3)	(13.3)
Market value ($ mil.)	(69.2%)	—	119.7	65.7	17.4	3.5
Employees	(8.0%)	—	27	34	30	21

*Fiscal year change †Most recent year available

GLOBAL ENTERTAINMENT CORPORATION

NYSE Amex: GEE

1600 N. Desert Dr., Ste. 301
Tempe, AZ 85281
Phone: 480-994-0772
Fax: 480-994-0759
Web: www.globalentertainment2000.com

CEO: Richard (Rick) Kozuback
CFO: James C. Yeager
HR: —
FYE: May 31
Type: Public

Global Entertainment Corporation is helping to bring sports to the hinterlands. The company, through its subsidiaries, offers project management services to small communities looking to develop event centers and sports facilities. It also offers facilities management services, as well as sponsorship and marketing consulting. Through its WPHL (Western Professional Hockey League) subsidiary, Global Entertainment manages the Central Hockey League, a development league affiliated with the National Hockey League. WPHL Holdings, which is affiliated with chairman James Treliving and his son Brad Treliving, controls more than 40% of the company.

	Annual Growth	5/05	5/06	5/07	5/08	5/09
Sales ($ mil.)	(0.6%)	13.5	14.3	26.4	12.4	13.2
Net income ($ mil.)	—	0.4	0.2	(4.1)	(4.0)	0.0
Market value ($ mil.)	(37.2%)	34.2	45.9	32.6	12.3	5.3
Employees	14.6%	110	453	628	295	190

GLOBAL GEOPHYSICAL SERVICES, INC.

NYSE: GGS

13927 S. Gessner Rd.
Missouri City, TX 77489
Phone: 713-972-9200
Fax: 713-972-1008
Web: www.globalgeophysical.com

CEO: Richard A. Degner
CFO: P. Mathew Verghese
HR: —
FYE: December 31
Type: Public

Global Geophysical builds its business from the ground down. The company provides seismic data acquisition services to the oil and gas industry for locating potential reservoirs and studying known reserves. Global Geophysical transmits sound waves below the earth's surface to create two- and three-dimensional images of the existing subsurface geology. The firm's seismic crews work in a wide variety of terrains, including deserts, jungles, mountains, and swamps, and have completed projects in more than 100 countries, including Algeria, Argentina, Chile, Colombia, Georgia, India, Iraq, Mexico, Oman, Peru, and Uganda. In 2010 the company went public.

	Annual Growth	12/05	12/06	12/07	12/08	12/09
Sales ($ mil.)	88.6%	24.7	83.6	225.7	376.3	312.8
Net income ($ mil.)	(20.5%)	1.0	1.9	2.4	(8.0)	0.4
Employees	22.4%	365	376	1,041	1,300	818

GLOBAL HEALTHCARE EXCHANGE, LLC

1315 W. Century Dr.
Louisville, CO 80027
Phone: 720-887-7000
Fax: 720-887-7200
Web: www.ghx.com

CEO: Bruce Johnson
CFO: Rob Gillespie
HR: Wendi Welton
FYE: December 31
Type: Private

Global Healthcare Exchange (GHX) provides an electronic trading exchange designed for health care providers, suppliers, and manufacturers to buy and sell supplies online. GHX aims to lower supply chain costs for its users by allowing them to perform transactions with multiple parties through one electronic platform, as well as by automating the purchasing process and reducing purchase order errors. The firm was founded in 2000 by a group of five health care manufacturers: Abbott Labs, Baxter International, GE Medical Systems, Johnson & Johnson, and Medtronic. It is now owned by the original five plus a slew of other distributors, hospitals, group purchasing organizations, and manufacturers.

GLOBAL IMAGING SYSTEMS, INC.

3820 Northdale Blvd., Ste. 200A
Tampa, FL 33624
Phone: 813-960-5508
Fax: 813-264-7877
Web: www.global-imaging.com

CEO: Michael E. (Mike) Shea Jr.
CFO: Ed Bass
HR: Barb Brooslin
FYE: March 31
Type: Subsidiary

Global Imaging Systems (GIS) is consolidating the fragmented office equipment industry one acquisition at a time. The company sells and services products such as copiers, fax machines, printers, projectors, and conferencing equipment under such brands as Canon, Hewlett-Packard, InFocus, Konica, and Sharp. It also provides its customers — principally businesses with fewer than 1,000 employees — with network integration services and systems (network design, software, hardware). GIS operates from more than 180 locations in about 35 states and the District of Columbia. In 2007 the acquisitive firm was purchased itself by Xerox for about $1.5 billion and became a subsidiary of the technology products giant.

GLOBAL INDUSTRIES, LTD.

NASDAQ (GS): GLBL

8000 Global Dr.
Carlyss, LA 70665
Phone: 337-583-5000
Fax: 337-583-5100
Web: www.globalind.com

CEO: John B. Reed Jr.
CFO: C. Andrew (Andy) Smith
HR: David R. Sheil Jr.
FYE: December 31
Type: Public

Global Industries industriously provides global offshore construction and support services including pipeline construction, platform installation and removal, and diving services to the oil and gas industry in the all of the world's major offshore oil patches. Global's services include pipeline installation pipelay, simultaneous multiple pipeline laying, pipeline burial, and pipeline maintenance and repair. Global installs pipelines, insulated pipe-in-pipe, and bundled flowlines. Its barge fleet provides derrick services and heavy-lift capabilities for installation and removal of offshore platforms, and drilling and workover rigs. Petróleos Mexicanos (PEMEX) accounted for 10% of the company's revenue in 2008.

	Annual Growth	12/05	12/06	12/07	12/08	12/09
Sales ($ mil.)	7.3%	688.6	1,234.8	992.5	1,071.0	914.3
Net income ($ mil.)	20.6%	34.8	199.7	160.0	(117.4)	73.7
Market value ($ mil.)	(11.0%)	1,304.1	1,498.3	2,461.2	401.0	819.3
Employees	(2.0%)	3,024	3,279	3,009	3,863	2,793

An in-depth profile of this company is available to Hoover's Online members at hoovers.com.

GLOBAL KNOWLEDGE TRAINING LLC

9000 Regency Pkwy., Ste. 500
Cary, NC 27518
Phone: 919-461-8600
Fax: 919-461-8646
Web: www.globalknowledge.com

CEO: Brian K. Branson
CFO: Robert A. (Bob) Kalainikas
HR: Donna B. Peffley
FYE: December 31
Type: Private

Companies keep employee skills up-to-date with Global Knowledge. The company provides technical training services to the employees of clients such as travel reservations firm Sabre, ACTS Retirement-Life Communities, and the Netherlands Ministry of Defence. Specializing in networking systems and telecommunications, Global Knowledge offers more than 700 vendor-authorized and proprietary courses covering the products of specific manufacturers, including Microsoft and Cisco Systems. The company also provides custom integration and training services and outsourced education management services. Global Knowledge operates in about two-dozen countries around the world.

	Annual Growth	12/04	12/05	12/06	12/07	12/08
Est. sales ($ mil.)	—	—	—	—	—	49.0
Employees	—	—	—	—	—	1,050

GLOBAL MED TECHNOLOGIES, INC.

12600 W. Colfax Ave., Ste. C-420
Lakewood, CO 80215
Phone: 303-238-2000
Fax: 303-238-3368
Web: www.globalmedtech.com

CEO: Michael I. Ruxin
CFO: Darren P. Craig
HR: —
FYE: March 31*
Type: Subsidiary

Global Med Technologies doesn't shrink from the sight of blood. Through subsidiary Wyndgate Technologies, the company develops information management software that tracks blood donations and manages information for blood banks, transfusion centers, hospitals, clinics, and other health care facilities. Global Med's SafeTrace software keeps track of blood products from donor recruitment through shipment and includes transfusion management information systems. PeopleMed.com, an 83%-owned subsidiary of Global Med, offers Internet-based applications that help provide disease management for patients with chronic diseases. In 2010 Haemonetics acquired Global Med for about $60 million in cash.

	Annual Growth	12/05	12/06	12/07	12/08	12/09
Sales ($ mil.)	29.8%	11.2	12.6	16.1	23.4	31.8
Net income ($ mil.)	—	(10.8)	1.4	2.0	(0.4)	1.5
Employees	27.9%	74	83	90	186	198
						*Fiscal year-end change

GLOBAL NUCLEAR FUEL - AMERICAS, LLC

3901 Castle Hayne Rd.
Wilmington, NC 28402
Phone: 910-675-5000
Fax: 910-675-6666
Web: www.gepower.com

CEO: Lisa Price
CFO: —
HR: —
FYE: December 31
Type: Joint venture

Global Nuclear Fuel Americas is powered by three giants: GE Energy, Toshiba, and Hitachi. As part of the Global Nuclear Fuel joint venture formed in 2001, it combines the design, manufacturing, and marketing operations of its parent companies to manufacture light-water nuclear reactor fuel. It serves customers in Europe, Mexico, Taiwan, and the US. Global Nuclear Fuel Americas operates a plant in Wilmington, North Carolina. The company works with affiliate Global Nuclear Fuel — Japan, and they both work with GE-Hitachi Nuclear Energy, which designs nuclear reactors.

GLOBAL PARTNERS LP

NYSE: GLP

800 South St.
Waltham, MA 02454
Phone: 781-894-8800
Fax: 781-398-4160
Web: www.globalp.com

CEO: Eric Slifka
CFO: Thomas J. (Tom) Hollister
HR: Barbara E. Rosenbloom
FYE: December 31
Type: Public

Global Partners (formerly Global Companies) imports petroleum products from global sources, but its marketing is strictly regional. The company wholesales heating oil, residual fuel oil, diesel oil, kerosene, and gasoline to commercial, retail, and wholesale customers in New England. A major player in the regional home heating oil wholesale market, Global Partners operates storage facilities at about 20 bulk terminals with a total storage capacity of 8 million barrels. Global Partners was founded in 1933 as a one-truck heating oil retailer by current CEO Eric Slifka's grandfather, Abraham Slifka. The Slifka family controls about 43% of the company.

	Annual Growth	12/05	12/06	12/07	12/08	12/09
Sales ($ mil.)	46.9%	1,248.9	4,472.4	6,757.8	9,019.1	5,818.4
Net income ($ mil.)	37.2%	9.4	33.5	47.0	21.1	33.3
Market value ($ mil.)	5.3%	317.5	443.0	442.3	191.9	389.9
Employees	9.8%	172	180	230	220	250

GLOBAL PAYMENT TECHNOLOGIES, INC.

Pink Sheets: GPTX

170 Wilbur Place
Bohemia, NY 11716
Phone: 631-563-2500
Fax: 631-563-2630
Web: www.gptx.com

CEO: Andre Soussa
CFO: William McMahon
HR: —
FYE: September 30
Type: Public

GPT's advice: Don't take any wooden nickels (or counterfeit dollar bills). Global Payment Technologies (GPT) makes systems that detect counterfeit paper currency. The gaming industry accounts for most of GPT's sales, but the company also makes products for vending machines, beverage dispensers, and other devices. GPT's basic currency validators accept, count, and store legal tender. Its advanced Generation II and Argus systems recognize coins and paper denominations from more than 50 countries, and incorporate bar-code readers, security sensors, and other features.

GLOBAL PAYMENTS INC.

NYSE: GPN

10 Glenlake Pkwy. NE, North Tower
Atlanta, GA 30328
Phone: 770-829-8000
Fax: 770-829-8224
Web: www.globalpaymentsinc.com

CEO: Paul R. Garcia
CFO: David E. Mangum
HR: —
FYE: May 31
Type: Public

Charge! And when you do, there's a good chance that Global Payments will be right there ensuring a smooth transaction. Global Payments provides credit and debit card processing, check authorization, and other electronic payment processing services for merchants, financial institutions, governments, gaming institutions, and multinational corporations. The company operates throughout North America and in Europe and the Asia/Pacific region. Global Payments also offers electronic tax payment and benefits transfer processing. The company sold noncore international transfer businesses DolEx Dollar Express and Europhil for $85 million to Palladium Equity Partners in 2010.

	Annual Growth	5/05	5/06	5/07	5/08	5/09
Sales ($ mil.)	19.5%	784.3	908.1	1,061.5	1,274.2	1,601.5
Net income ($ mil.)	(20.5%)	92.9	125.5	143.0	162.8	37.2
Market value ($ mil.)	0.9%	2,827.7	3,801.2	3,267.5	3,853.5	2,934.6
Employees	10.6%	3,900	4,277	4,680	4,899	5,844

An in-depth profile of this company is available to Hoover's Online members at hoovers.com.

GLOBAL POWER EQUIPMENT GROUP INC.

Pink Sheets: GLPW

6120 S. Yale St., Ste. 1480
Tulsa, OK 74136
Phone: 918-488-0828
Fax: 918-488-8389
Web: www.globalpower.com

CEO: David L. (Dave) Keller
CFO: David Willis
HR: —
FYE: December 31
Type: Public

Global Power Equipment Group (GPEG) doesn't let global power go to its head, but to its bottom line. The company operates through several manufacturing and design businesses, supplying heat recovery and auxiliary power equipment to OEMs, as well as engineering and construction, and power generation and process industries. A service segment offers upgrades and maintenance services to utility and industrial companies. Auxiliary parts for natural-gas-fired turbines are made under the Braden Manufacturing and Consolidated Fabricators brands, and heat recovery boilers under Deltak. Williams Industrial Services assists in nuclear and hydroelectric power plant maintenance. North America represents 90% of GPEG's sales.

GLOBAL RAILWAY INDUSTRIES LTD.

Toronto: GBI

1160K Pittsford-Victor Rd.
Pittsford, NY 14534
Phone: 585-419-9720
Fax: —
Web: www.globalrailway.com

CEO: Terry R. McManaman
CFO: Brian McMullan
HR: —
FYE: December 31
Type: Public

Global Railway Industries is signalling a plan to keep it on track. The company operates through subsidiaries such as Bach-Simpson (vehicle monitoring systems and event recorders), CAD Railway Services (locomotive and railcar repair), G&B Specialties (switch machine components, electric locks, signal products, railgear equipment that allows motor vehicles to travel on rail tracks), and Prime Railway Services (rail car doors and replacement parts). Global Railway is looking to sell one or more of its subsidiaries as part of an agreement with lenders. Customers include Bombardier, GE, and ALSTOM. Global Railway Industries was founded in 1997.

	Annual Growth	12/05	12/06	12/07	12/08	12/09
Sales ($ mil.)	25.4%	25.6	27.3	37.5	50.5	63.4
Net income ($ mil.)	—	(3.2)	2.7	3.4	(1.4)	(6.5)
Market value ($ mil.)	(11.6%)	24.3	41.2	75.9	9.3	14.8
Employees	24.3%	164	193	193	200	392

GLOBAL TELECOM & TECHNOLOGY, INC.

OTC: GTLT

8484 Westpark Dr., Ste. 720
McLean, VA 22102
Phone: 703-442-5500
Fax: 703-442-5501
Web: www.gt-t.net

CEO: Richard D. (Rick) Calder Jr.
CFO: Eric A. Swank
HR: —
FYE: December 31
Type: Public

Global Telecom & Technology offers businesses a choice of ways to phone home. The company provides data and telecommunications network design and integration, network monitoring, and support services to customers in about 50 countries. It also provides consulting, network security evaluation, and project management services. The company has distribution partnerships with technology suppliers, including iPass. Global Telecom & Technology serves customers in such industries as banking, industrial manufacturing, and wireless communications. Clients include Airbus, Comsat, and Equant.

	Annual Growth	12/05	12/06	12/07	12/08	12/09
Sales ($ mil.)	82.9%	—	10.5	57.6	67.0	64.2
Net income ($ mil.)	—	—	(1.8)	(4.3)	(42.4)	0.5
Market value ($ mil.)	(29.9%)	—	59.9	18.1	6.0	20.7
Employees	246.2%	—	2	78	65	83

GLOBAL TRAFFIC NETWORK, INC.

NASDAQ (GM): GNET

800 2nd Ave., 5th Fl.
New York, NY 10017
Phone: 212-896-1255
Fax: —
Web: www.globaltrafficnetwork.com

CEO: William L. Yde III
CFO: Scott E. Cody
HR: —
FYE: June 30
Type: Public

Great, just what we need: more traffic. Global Traffic Network (GTN) provides customized traffic reports to some 70 radio stations in nearly 20 markets in Australia. In exchange for its content, GTN receives commercial airtime from the stations, which the company sells to advertisers. In addition, the firm produces radio and TV news reports in Australia. GTN also does business in the US through a deal with Metro Networks. It provides traffic reports in Canada through an agreement with Corus Entertainment, and provides news, weather, sports, and business reports in Canada through subsidiary Wise Broadcasting Network. GTN additionally provides radio traffic reporting services to more than 10 stations in the UK.

	Annual Growth	6/05	6/06	6/07	6/08	6/09
Sales ($ mil.)	45.7%	—	19.5	31.7	51.0	60.3
Net income ($ mil.)	—	—	(3.0)	(2.0)	1.7	(1.1)
Market value ($ mil.)	(11.7%)	—	101.3	126.8	164.6	69.8
Employees	(62.6%)	—	115	158	190	6

GLOBAL WATER RESOURCES, INC.

21410 N. 19th Ave., Ste. 201
Phoenix, AZ 85027
Phone: 623-580-9600
Fax: 623-518-4100
Web: www.gwresources.com

CEO: Trevor T. Hill
CFO: Cindy M. Liles
HR: —
FYE: December 31
Type: Private

Global Water Resources took the phrase "Think globally, act locally" to heart. The company provides water, wastewater, and recycled water utility services to 14 utilities and more than 60,000 people in its service area around Phoenix. Its recycled water is treated and purified wastewater used for non-potable and outdoor purposes, sent through a separate system of pipes than drinking water. Global Water says its reclaimed water project saves up to 40% of drought-prone Phoenix's scarce groundwater. The private utility also extends water and wastewater infrastructure financing to regional developers and builders. Global Water formed in 2003.

GLOBALFOUNDRIES INC.

1050 E. Arques Ave.
Sunnyvale, CA 94085
Phone: 408-749-4000
Fax: —
Web: www.globalfoundries.com

CEO: Doug Grose
CFO: Bruce McDougall
HR: —
FYE: December 31
Type: Joint venture

GLOBALFOUNDRIES makes chips so AMD doesn't have to worry about expensive manufacturing issues. In 2009 the company was spun off by AMD as a joint venture with Abu-Dhabi-based Advanced Technology Investment Company (ATIC) to handle semiconductor production. Wafer fabrication facilities (or fabs) are multibillion-dollar facilities to build and maintain; many semiconductor companies are chip design firms that contract out their manufacturing to silicon foundries, chip makers that provide wafer fabrication services. GLOBALFOUNDRIES offers manufacturing services to AMD, as well as QUALCOMM, STMicro, and IBM. The company absorbed Chartered Semiconductor in 2010, making it a global leader in the industry.

	Annual Growth	12/04	12/05	12/06	12/07	12/08
Est. sales ($ mil.)	—	—	—	—	—	0.2
Employees	—	—	—	—	—	3

An in-depth profile of this company is available to Hoover's Online members at hoovers.com.

691

GLOBALOPTIONS GROUP, INC.
NASDAQ (CM): GLOI

75 Rockefeller Plaza, 27th Fl.
New York, NY 10019
Phone: 212-445-6262
Fax: —
Web: www.globaloptionsgroup.com

CEO: Harvey Schiller
CFO: Jeff Nyweide
HR: —
FYE: December 31
Type: Public

GlobalOptions likes to think of itself as the secure choice. The firm provides security consulting and investigation services through more than 10 offices in the US. Other offerings include risk mitigation, decision support, emergency management, litigation support, anti-fraud solutions, business intelligence, and related security services. The company provides services to government entities, corporations, and high net-worth and high-profile individuals throughout the world. The company also owns security firm Secure Source. GlobalOptions was founded in 1999.

	Annual Growth	12/05	12/06	12/07	12/08	12/09
Sales ($ mil.)	83.5%	9.0	61.9	87.1	104.2	102.1
Net income ($ mil.)	—	(3.6)	(17.8)	(27.9)	(8.0)	(5.3)
Market value ($ mil.)	(48.4%)	333.4	172.4	64.7	28.6	23.7
Employees	45.8%	169	435	567	611	764

GLOBALSCAPE, INC.
NYSE Amex: GSB

4500 Lockhill-Selma Rd., Ste. 150
San Antonio, TX 78249
Phone: 210-308-8267
Fax: 210-293-8003
Web: www.globalscape.com

CEO: James R. (Jim) Morris
CFO: Mendy Marsh
HR: Andrea Farmer
FYE: December 31
Type: Public

GlobalSCAPE is pretty cute, for a software company. With packages like CuteFTP and CuteSITE Builder, GlobalSCAPE provides content management, file management, and Web site development tools for businesses and individuals. GlobalSCAPE's software can be downloaded from its Web site, and the company sells CD-ROM versions in Fry's and other retail stores. Its CuteFTP and CuteFTP Pro products, which enable file transfers via the Internet and other networks, account for a majority of sales. Formed in 1996 as the Internet subsidiary of ATSI Communications, GlobalSCAPE became independent in 2002, when investors Thomas Brown and David Mann (who collectively own 45% of the company) acquired a controlling interest.

	Annual Growth	12/05	12/06	12/07	12/08	12/09
Sales ($ mil.)	24.8%	6.8	11.0	18.4	15.8	16.5
Net income ($ mil.)	(1.7%)	1.5	2.0	3.9	(7.7)	1.4
Market value ($ mil.)	(19.6%)	—	51.5	97.3	14.9	26.7
Employees	17.8%	41	56	66	72	79

⊞ GLOBALSTAR, INC.
NASDAQ (GM): GSAT

461 S. Milpitas Blvd.
Milpitas, CA 95035
Phone: 408-933-4000
Fax: 408-933-4100
Web: www.globalstar.com

CEO: Peter J. Dalton
CFO: Fuad Ahmad
HR: —
FYE: December 31
Type: Public

Globalstar provides satellite voice and data services, targeting areas underserved by traditional wireless and wireline services. It utilizes digital CDMA (code division multiple access) technology developed by Globalstar co-founder QUALCOMM. The company's satellites bounce calls from special mobile phones back to ground-based gateways connected with traditional phone networks. Its network of satellites and ground stations provides service to about 340,000 customers in 120 countries. Customers include companies in the energy and maritime industries. Half of its ground stations are operated by independent companies that buy Globalstar's services on a wholesale basis. North America is the company's biggest market.

	Annual Growth	12/05	12/06	12/07	12/08	12/09
Sales ($ mil.)	(15.7%)	127.1	136.7	98.4	86.1	64.3
Net income ($ mil.)	—	18.7	23.6	(27.9)	(68.0)	(74.9)
Market value ($ mil.)	(60.3%)	—	4,159.4	2,395.6	59.9	260.5
Employees	1.0%	322	349	335	419	335

GLOBE SPECIALTY METALS, INC.
NASDAQ (GS): GSM

1 Penn Plaza, Ste. 2514, 250 W. 34th St.
New York, NY 10119
Phone: 212-798-8122
Fax: 212-798-8185
Web: www.glbsm.com

CEO: Jeff Bradley
CFO: Malcolm Applebaum
HR: —
FYE: June 30
Type: Public

Globe Specialty Metals is an apt name for a company that peddles its metals around the world. The specialty metals manufacturer sells silicon metal and silicon-based alloys to customers in the Americas, Asia, and Europe from facilities in the US, Argentina, China, and Poland. Its silicon metal and alloys are used to make a variety of industrial products, from aluminum and automotive parts to steel and semiconductors. It holds about one-fifth of the western market share for magnesium ferrosilicon. Globe also recycles by-products such as silica fume, a dust-like material known as microsilica that is collected in air filtration systems, which it sells for use as a concrete additive.

	Annual Growth	6/05	6/06	6/07	6/08	6/09
Sales ($ mil.)	38.6%	—	—	221.9	452.6	426.3
Net income ($ mil.)	—	—	—	11.1	36.5	(42.0)
Market value ($ mil.)	—	—	—	—	—	520.3
Employees	(11.8%)	—	—	1,064	1,373	828

GLOBECOMM SYSTEMS INC.
NASDAQ (GS): GCOM

45 Oser Ave.
Hauppauge, NY 11788
Phone: 631-231-9800
Fax: 631-231-1557
Web: www.globecommsystems.com

CEO: David E. Hershberg
CFO: Andrew C. Melfi
HR: Paul Eterno
FYE: June 30
Type: Public

Globecomm Systems sends data flying. The company designs, assembles, and installs satellite earth stations, complete uplink centers, and media broadcast centers. It also builds Internet protocol-based communications networks. Its Globecomm Network Services subsidiary provides broadband satellite-delivered Internet and intranet access, Web hosting, video broadcasting, and network management services. Globecomm markets to communications carriers, government agencies, equipment makers, content providers, and broadcasters. The company serves agencies of the US government as well as commercial clients, which have included CBS and Reuters.

	Annual Growth	6/05	6/06	6/07	6/08	6/09
Sales ($ mil.)	11.6%	109.6	126.0	150.7	196.5	170.2
Net income ($ mil.)	(8.9%)	4.8	4.5	8.3	27.0	3.3
Market value ($ mil.)	4.5%	129.3	159.8	312.2	177.1	154.2
Employees	20.8%	163	192	282	316	347

GLOWPOINT, INC.
OTC: GLOW

225 Long Ave.
Hillside, NJ 07205
Phone: 973-282-2000
Fax: 973-391-1901
Web: www.glowpoint.com

CEO: Joseph (Joe) Laezza
CFO: Edwin F. Heinen
HR: —
FYE: December 31
Type: Public

Glowpoint adds a little light to virtual meeting rooms, providing subscription-based video-conferencing services that enable businesses, government offices, educational institutions, and other customers to engage in video communications over an Internet protocol-based network. The company also offers Webcasting services, streaming live and recorded video via standard video-conferencing systems. Glowpoint operates 11 network points of presence (POPs) around the globe. The company counts government agencies, corporations, and not-for-profits among its customers.

	Annual Growth	12/05	12/06	12/07	12/08	12/09
Sales ($ mil.)	10.6%	17.7	19.5	22.8	24.5	26.5
Net income ($ mil.)	—	(16.4)	(10.8)	(5.5)	(7.3)	(0.5)
Market value ($ mil.)	0.7%	54.8	31.1	39.2	24.5	56.4
Employees	4.1%	85	59	65	82	100

GLU MOBILE INC.

NASDAQ (GM): GLUU

2207 Bridgepointe Pkwy., Ste. 250	CEO: Niccolo M. de Masi
San Mateo, CA 94404	CFO: Eric R. Ludwig
Phone: 650-532-2400	HR: —
Fax: 650-532-2500	FYE: December 31
Web: www.glu.com	Type: Public

Glu Mobile hopes to get your phone stuck permanently to your hand. The company develops and publishes video games for wireless devices. Glu Mobile's portfolio includes more than 100 games, including original titles, as well as applications based on licensed, third-party brands such as *Sonic the Hedgehog*. It also produces ringtones and wallpapers for mobile phones. Glu Mobile brings its applications to the mobile masses through wireless service providers, such as Sprint Nextel, T-Mobile USA, Verizon Wireless, and Vodaphone. The company gets more than half of its sales outside the US.

	Annual Growth	12/05	12/06	12/07	12/08	12/09
Sales ($ mil.)	32.5%	25.7	46.2	66.9	89.8	79.3
Net income ($ mil.)	—	(17.6)	(12.3)	(3.3)	(106.7)	(18.2)
Market value ($ mil.)	(53.1%)	—	—	159.8	15.3	35.2
Employees	25.4%	—	243	417	550	479

GLYCOTEX, INC.

2275 Research Blvd., Ste. 500	CEO: Reinhard Koenig
Rockville, MD 20850	CFO: David R. Seaton
Phone: 301-670-2825	HR: —
Fax: 301-576-5633	FYE: June 30
Web: www.glycotexinc.com	Type: Subsidiary

Glycotex wants to see such creatures as ulcers, bed sores, and sunburns put on the Australian endangered species list. The biopharmaceutical company researches and develops products based on molecular glucan receptors that trigger the healing process. Connective tissue repair, skin ulcers, and bone fractures are primary recovery fields for its glucan receptor products. Glycotex's lead product candidate, MG3601, is a topical treatment for ulcers, and it has completed Phase II clinical trials. Other therapeutic candidates include Glucocol and Glucoprime, active ingredients designed to treat tendon regeneration and topical needs, respectively. Its parent company, Novogen, owns 84% of Glycotex.

GMAC MORTGAGE, LLC

1100 Virginia Dr.	CEO: Michael A. (Mike) Carpenter
Fort Washington, PA 19034	CFO: —
Phone: 215-734-8899	HR: —
Fax: —	FYE: December 31
Web: www.gmacmortgage.com	Type: Subsidiary

GMAC Mortgage is one of the largest residential mortgage servicing companies in the US. The company offers consumers purchasing and refinancing, FHA loans, and flexible down payment options. Its ditech.com arm provides online mortgage brokerage services. GMAC Mortgage is part of the Residential Capital (ResCap) mortgage arm of Ally Financial, the financing arm of General Motors. The US government owns 56% of Ally Financial after providing the group with a series of financial bailouts. GMAC Mortgage was created in 1985 when Ally Financial (then GMAC) acquired mortgage operations of Colonial Mortgage Service and Norwest Mortgage.

GMR MARKETING LLC

5000 S. Towne Dr.	CEO: Gary Reynolds
New Berlin, WI 53151	CFO: Lisa Cieslak
Phone: 262-786-5600	HR: Heather Gaecke
Fax: 262-786-0697	FYE: December 31
Web: www.gmrlive.com	Type: Subsidiary

GMR Marketing brings products to the people. The company produces product promotions at shopping malls, temporary retail locations, concerts, sports, and lifestyle events such as car shows and Spring Break — as well as "virtual" events tied in with video games and online spaces. It provides all-inclusive services — from concept and design to construction and site management. GMR productions have included the Microsoft Xbox Odyssey, the Kraft Food and Family Show, and the Miller Lite Racing Garage. CEO Gary M. Reynolds founded the company in 1979. It is a part of The Radiate Group, a unit of advertising giant Omnicom. GMR owns seven offices in the US and five in Beijing, London, Paris, Toronto, and Vancouver.

GMX RESOURCES INC.

NASDAQ (GM): GMXR

9400 N. Broadway, Ste. 600	CEO: Ken L. Kenworthy Jr.
Oklahoma City, OK 73114	CFO: James A. (Jim) Merrill
Phone: 405-600-0711	HR: Pam Scott
Fax: 405-600-0600	FYE: December 31
Web: www.gmxresources.com	Type: Public

Natural resources in productive, hydrocarbon-rich geological basins are the target for GMX Resources. The Oklahoma-based independent oil and natural gas company explores on more than 28,800 net developed acres located in the Cotton Valley in East Texas. GMX Resources also has property assets in Louisiana and New Mexico. In 2007 the company reported proved reserves of 434.5 billion cu. ft. of natural gas equivalent and 930 net well locations. It has a large inventory of drilling and recompletion projects and operates gas gathering systems at its production sites. GMX Resources also owns and operates three drilling rigs. Ken L. Kenworthy Jr. and Ken L. Kenworthy Sr. each own about 5% of the company.

	Annual Growth	12/05	12/06	12/07	12/08	12/09
Sales ($ mil.)	48.9%	19.2	32.0	68.1	125.7	94.3
Net income ($ mil.)	—	7.2	9.0	16.9	(81.7)	(180.6)
Market value ($ mil.)	(21.4%)	1,108.4	1,093.0	993.9	779.6	423.1
Employees	56.1%	16	99	115	149	95

GN HELLO DIRECT, INC.

75 Northeastern Blvd.	CEO: Phyllis McCullagh
Nashua, NH 03062	CFO: —
Phone: 603-598-1100	HR: —
Fax: 800-456-2566	FYE: December 31
Web: www.hello-direct.com	Type: Subsidiary

Ah, the poetic justice GN Hello Direct delivers. The company sells telephones and accessories (including headsets and amplifiers) to small and mid-sized businesses and the very telemarketers who ring you just when dinner is served. It also sells the phones that screen those annoying telemarketer calls as well as recording, distance-conferencing, mobile navigation, and VoIP products. More than 50 major brands are represented in the firm's inventory, including AT&T, Panasonic, and Motorola, as well as its own Hello Direct and GN Netcom labels. Products are sold through GN Hello Direct's catalog and website. The company was acquired in 2000 by GN Netcom, a Denmark-based maker of hands-free telecom equipment.

	Annual Growth	12/04	12/05	12/06	12/07	12/08
Est. sales ($ mil.)	—	—	—	—	—	28.7
Employees	—	—	—	—	—	300

An in-depth profile of this company is available to Hoover's Online members at hoovers.com.

693

GNC CORPORATION

300 6th Ave.
Pittsburgh, PA 15222
Phone: 412-288-4600
Fax: 412-288-4764
Web: www.gnc.com

CEO: Joseph (Joe) Fortunato
CFO: Michael M. Nuzzo
HR: Robert M. (Bob) Chessen
FYE: December 31
Type: Private

What's good for the customer is good for GNC Corporation (formerly General Nutrition Centers). With more than 6,900 stores throughout the US and Canada (including more than 900 franchises and some 1,870 stores within Rite Aid drugstores) as well as franchise operations in about 45 foreign markets, GNC is the leading nutritional-supplements retail chain devoted solely to items such as vitamins and dietary products. The company also makes Rite Aid private-label products. GNC sells its products online, as well, through a partnership with drugstore.com. In 2007 Apollo Advisors sold GNC to Ontario Teachers' Pension Plan and Ares Management, a US private-equity firm, for about $1.6 billion.

	Annual Growth	12/04	12/05	12/06	12/07	12/08
Sales ($ mil.)	5.4%	1,344.7	1,317.7	1,487.1	1,552.8	1,656.7
Net income ($ mil.)	7.1%	41.7	18.4	37.4	(32.3)	54.8
Employees	(1.4%)	13,618	12,415	12,707	13,239	12,862

THE GO DADDY GROUP, INC.

14455 N. Hayden Rd., Ste. 219
Scottsdale, AZ 85260
Phone: 480-505-8800
Fax: 480-505-8844
Web: www.godaddy.com

CEO: Robert R. (Bob) Parsons
CFO: Michael J. Zimmerman
HR: —
FYE: December 31
Type: Private

Go Daddy, go! Go Daddy provides individuals and businesses with such Internet services as domain name registration and website hosting through its affiliates. It also offers related services and software for functions including e-mail, e-commerce, and website creation. Touting discounted pricing on domain names and hosting services, Go Daddy has become the largest domain registrar accredited by ICANN (the international regulatory body for the public Internet) in the world, with more than 30 million domain names. The company has affiliates that address market niches in site registration and hosting, including Domains By Proxy and Wild West Domains. CEO Bob Parsons owns the company, which he founded in 1997.

GODFATHER'S PIZZA, INC.

2808 N. 108th St.
Omaha, NE 68114
Phone: 402-391-1452
Fax: 402-255-2687
Web: www.godfathers.com

CEO: Ronald B. (Ron) Gartlan
CFO: Annette M. Sneckenberg
HR: Kathleen M. (Kathy) Johnson
FYE: May 31
Type: Private

Maybe the head of this family is named Don Pizzeria. Godfather's Pizza operates a leading quick-service restaurant chain with more than 600 family-oriented pizza joints in more than 40 states, mostly in the Upper Midwest. The parlors offer a crew of pizzas and a mob of topping choices, as well as appetizers, salads, and sandwiches. The company's locations typically offer dine-in, delivery, and carry-out service. More than 100 restaurants are company-owned while the rest are franchised. Founded by Nebraska native Willy Theisen in 1973, the business is owned by a group led by CEO Ron Gartlan.

GODIVA CHOCOLATIER, INC.

355 Lexington Ave., 16th Fl.
New York, NY 10017
Phone: 212-984-5900
Fax: 212-984-5901
Web: www.godiva.com

CEO: James A. (Jim) Goldman
CFO: David S. Marberger
HR: Kris Breuer
FYE: December 31
Type: Subsidiary

Riding into the hearts and tummies of chocolate aficionados everywhere, Godiva Chocolatier makes and sells premium chocolate concoctions, including bonbons, truffles, flavored coffee, cocoa mixes, cookies, ice cream, and liqueurs. Godiva's chocolate products are available worldwide at its 450 boutique stores, in department and specialty stores, through mail order, and from its website. The company began operations in North America in 1966 as an importer and distributor of Godiva chocolates from Belgium. Godiva is owned by Turkish confectioner Ülker Bisküvi Sanayi, which acquired Godiva from Campbell Soup in 2008.

GOJO INDUSTRIES

1 GOJO Plaza, Ste. 500
Akron, OH 44311
Phone: 330-255-6000
Fax: 330-255-6119
Web: www.gojo.com

CEO: Joe Kanfer
CFO: —
HR: —
FYE: December 31
Type: Private

GOJO Industries wants to go where other forms of good hygiene haven't. The company makes hand cleaners for professional and consumer use for clients such as automotive, foodservice, education, government, and health care facilities. Its product dispensers are seen in many public restrooms. GOJO also offers a line of health care products under the PROVON brand. Its waterless hand sanitizer PURELL, marketed under license with Johnson & Johnson, is sold through retail channels. GOJO, which sells its products worldwide, boasts offices in Brazil, Japan, the UK, and the US. The company is named after its heavy-duty hand cleaner, which was formulated by GOJO founder, Jerome Lippman.

	Annual Growth	12/04	12/05	12/06	12/07	12/08
Est. sales ($ mil.)	—	—	—	—	—	83.3
Employees	—	—	—	—	—	700

GOLD RESERVE INC.

NYSE Amex: GRZ

926 W. Sprague Ave., Ste. 200
Spokane, WA 99201
Phone: 509-623-1500
Fax: 509-623-1634
Web: www.goldreserveinc.com

CEO: Rockne J. Timm
CFO: Robert A. McGuinness
HR: Mary E. Smith
FYE: December 31
Type: Public

Gold Reserve's primary asset was the Brisas project in Venezuela, which contains estimated reserves of about 10 million ounces of gold and 1.4 billion pounds of copper. Gold Reserve had been developing Brisas since 1992. However, all activity on the mine ceased in late 2009 when the Venezuelan government canceled Gold Reserve's permits and seized the assets of the Brisas project. The company is pursuing an arbitration claim through the World Bank against the Venezuelan government in an effort to recoup its investment in the Brisas project. The company is actively pursuing other mining opportunities while it appeals the Venezuelan actions, though it was not engaged in any commercial production in mid-2010.

	Annual Growth	12/05	12/06	12/07	12/08	12/09
Sales ($ mil.)	23.0%	1.4	8.3	6.5	2.4	3.2
Net income ($ mil.)	—	(9.0)	(7.0)	(12.4)	(19.7)	(165.4)
Market value ($ mil.)	(21.9%)	169.3	272.7	300.5	54.1	63.0
Employees	21.3%	65	8	8	116	—

GOLD SUMMIT CORPORATION

TSX Venture: GSM

970 Caughlin Crossing, Ste. 100
Reno, NV 89509
Phone: 775-284-7200
Fax: 775-284-7202
Web: www.goldsummitcorp.com

CEO: Anthony P. Taylor
CFO: —
HR: —
FYE: April 30
Type: Public

The top of the gold heap is where Gold Summit aims to be. The company explores for and develops gold and silver prospect properties in the eastern and western US. Gold Summit focuses on explorations at several properties across Nevada, including Monte Cristo, Gold Basin, and Blue Sphinx. The company, with partner Astral Mining, is also developing properties in North and South Carolina (Saluda and Bear Creek) where miners have not explored underground since the mid-1800s.

	Annual Growth	4/05	4/06	4/07	4/08	4/09
Sales ($ mil.)	—	—	—	—	—	0.1
Net income ($ mil.)	—	—	—	—	—	(0.3)
Market value ($ mil.)	—	—	—	—	—	1.2
Employees	—	—	—	—	—	—

GOLDEN CORRAL CORPORATION

5151 Glenwood Ave., Ste. 300
Raleigh, NC 27612
Phone: 919-781-9310
Fax: 919-881-4686
Web: www.goldencorral.net

CEO: Theodore M. (Ted) Fowler
CFO: Lamar Bell
HR: Judith (Judy) Irwin
FYE: December 31
Type: Private

If you're so hungry you could eat a horse, ride into the Golden Corral. The company operates and franchises more than 480 steak buffet restaurants in 40 states, primarily in the Southeast. The family dining locations serve a variety of steak, chicken, and pork entrees along with an expansive buffet offering both hot and cold food items. Golden Corral units also feature a Brass Bell Bakery serving fresh-baked breads, rolls, cookies, and brownies, as well as a Dessert Café. More than 100 of the restaurants are company-owned, while the rest are franchised. Chairman James Maynard, who controls Golden Corral through his holding company, Investors Management Corp., founded the chain with partner Bill Carl in 1973.

	Annual Growth	12/04	12/05	12/06	12/07	12/08
Est. sales ($ mil.)	—	—	—	—	—	195.1
Employees	—	—	—	—	—	9,000

GOLDEN EAGLE INTERNATIONAL, INC.

OTC: MYNG

9661 S. 700 East
Salt Lake City, UT 84070
Phone: 801-619-9320
Fax: 801-619-1747
Web: www.geii.com

CEO: Terry C. Turner
CFO: Tracy A. Madsen
HR: —
FYE: December 31
Type: Public

In search of gold and copper, Golden Eagle International has spread its wings in Bolivia. The company is exploring prospects in the Tipuani-Cangalli area north of La Paz and in the Precambrian Shield area in eastern Bolivia. Gold production on the company's Cangalli claims was halted in 2004 because of a farmers' strike and has not yet re-started; the company has yet to produce minerals on its other properties. Golden Eagle has generated no revenue since late 2004.

	Annual Growth	12/04	12/05	12/06	12/07	*12/08
Sales ($ mil.)	—	—	—	—	—	0.6
Net income ($ mil.)	—	—	—	—	—	(1.7)
Market value ($ mil.)	—	—	—	—	—	3.5
Employees	—	—	—	—	—	31

*Most recent year available

GOLDEN ENTERPRISES, INC.

NASDAQ (GM): GLDC

1 Golden Flake Dr.
Birmingham, AL 35205
Phone: 205-458-7316
Fax: 205-458-7327
Web: www.goldenflake.com

CEO: Mark W. McCutcheon
CFO: Patty Townsend
HR: David Jones
FYE: May 31
Type: Public

Golden Enterprises is a source for true "suth'n" snacks — goodies such as pork rinds and vinegar-and-salt-flavored potato chips. Doing business as Golden Flake Snack Foods, the company makes and distributes salty snacks in 12 states throughout the southern US. Its crunchy lineup includes regular and Cajun hot potato chips, fried pork skins, corn chips, onion rings, and popcorn. Golden Enterprises also sells Golden Flake-branded snack cakes and cookies, canned dips, dried meat products, pretzels, and nuts packaged by other manufacturers. The family of the late Sloan Y. Bashinsky, controls 54% of the company.

	Annual Growth	5/05	5/06	5/07	5/08	5/09
Sales ($ mil.)	4.3%	103.1	106.5	110.8	113.4	122.2
Net income ($ mil.)	—	0.0	0.3	1.2	1.1	2.0
Market value ($ mil.)	(10.4%)	43.5	33.2	36.6	28.0	28.0
Employees	(5.6%)	1,032	991	970	991	818

GOLDEN GATE CAPITAL LP

One Embarcadero Center, 39th Fl.
San Francisco, CA 94111
Phone: 415-983-2700
Fax: 415-983-2701
Web: www.goldengatecap.com

CEO: David Dominik
CFO: —
HR: —
FYE: December 31
Type: Private

The California gold rush is alive and well at Golden Gate Capital. The private equity firm specializes in leveraged buyouts, public-to-private transactions, recapitalizations, industry consolidation, and companies in bankruptcy. It invests in a number of sectors: software and information technology services, semiconductors, electronics, consumer products and retail, financial and business services, security, and media. Golden Gate has some $9 billion under management. Portfolio holdings include interests in Orchard Brands and Herbalife. The company acquired women's clothing retailer J. Jill for some $75 million from The Talbots in 2009.

	Annual Growth	12/04	12/05	12/06	12/07	12/08
Est. sales ($ mil.)	—	—	—	—	—	100.0
Employees	—	—	—	—	—	21,180

GOLDEN PEANUT COMPANY, LLC

100 N. Point Center East, Ste. 400
Alpharetta, GA 30022
Phone: 770-752-8205
Fax: 770-752-8306
Web: www.goldenpeanut.com

CEO: James W. (Jimmy) Dorsett
CFO: Fritz Holzgrefe
HR: Rhonda Starling
FYE: December 31
Type: Private

Golden Peanut Company (GPC) shells and processes peanuts for retail and commercial distribution to customers worldwide. Its products include raw shelled and in-shell peanuts, as well as peanut flour, oil, extract, and peanut seed. After processing, GPC's peanut products are sold to snack-food makers, industrial food manufacturers, and animal-food makers. Its seeds are sold to commercial farmers and to home gardeners. The company also processes other farmers' peanut crops. GPC serves growers in both the southeastern and southwestern US and in Argentina.

	Annual Growth	12/04	12/05	12/06	12/07	12/08
Est. sales ($ mil.)	—	—	—	—	—	550.0
Employees	—	—	—	—	—	1,250

GOLDEN STAR RESOURCES LTD.

NYSE Amex: GSS

10901 W. Toller Dr., Ste. 300	CEO: Thomas G. (Tom) Mair
Littleton, CO 80127	CFO: John A. Labate
Phone: 303-830-9000	HR: —
Fax: 303-830-9094	FYE: December 31
Web: www.gsr.com	Type: Public

Gold gets top billing at Golden Star Resources. The company's producing assets — the Bogoso and Wassa properties — are in Ghana, in West Africa's Ashanti gold belt. (The Ghanaian government owns 10% of each of those properties.) The company has proved and probable reserves of about 3 million ounces of gold and produces about 300,000 ounces annually. It also explores other mineral properties elsewhere in West Africa and South America.

	Annual Growth	12/05	12/06	12/07	12/08	12/09
Sales ($ mil.)	43.1%	95.5	128.7	175.6	257.4	400.7
Net income ($ mil.)	—	(13.5)	64.7	(36.4)	(135.3)	16.5
Market value ($ mil.)	4.3%	680.7	760.6	814.8	257.8	804.5
Employees	10.0%	1,500	1,800	2,150	2,800	2,200

GOLDEN STATE FOODS CORP.

18301 Von Karman Ave., Ste. 1100	CEO: Mark S. Wetterau
Irvine, CA 92612	CFO: —
Phone: 949-252-2000	HR: Steve Becker
Fax: 949-252-2080	FYE: December 31
Web: www.goldenstatefoods.com	Type: Private

You might say this company helps make the Golden Arches shine. Golden State Foods is a leading foodservice supplier that primarily supplies McDonald's restaurants with more than 130 products, including beef patties, Big Mac sauce (which it helped formulate), buns, ketchup, and mayonnaise. It distributes goods to more than 20,000 quick-service eateries from 15 US distribution centers. In addition, the company runs the GSF Foundation, a not-for-profit organization that supports local charities focused on helping children and families. Founded in 1947 by the late William Moore, Golden State Foods is controlled by Wetterau Associates, an investment group led by CEO Mark Wetterau.

	Annual Growth	12/04	12/05	12/06	12/07	12/08
Sales ($ mil.)	16.1%	2,200.0	2,375.0	2,600.0	3,000.0	4,000.0
Employees	4.7%	2,500	2,500	2,800	3,000	3,000

THE GOLDFIELD CORPORATION

NYSE Amex: GV

1684 W. Hibiscus Blvd.	CEO: John H. Sottile
Melbourne, FL 32901	CFO: Stephen R. Wherry
Phone: 321-724-1700	HR: —
Fax: 321-724-1163	FYE: December 31
Web: www.goldfieldcorp.com	Type: Public

The Goldfield Corporation earns more laying cable now than it used to digging for mother lodes. Through subsidiary Southeast Power, Goldfield builds and maintains electrical facilities in the Southeast, West, and Mid-Atlantic regions for utilities and industrial customers, including Florida Power & Light Company and Duke Energy. The unit also installs transmission lines and fiber-optic cable. Goldfield's Bayswater Development subsidiary maintains real estate operations in Florida, specializing in developing waterfront condominiums for retirees. The company, which had been in the mining industry since 1906, divested those operations in 2002 after deciding that it had become economically unfeasible.

	Annual Growth	12/05	12/06	12/07	12/08	12/09
Sales ($ mil.)	(7.2%)	39.3	47.5	27.3	31.4	29.2
Net income ($ mil.)	—	2.3	3.0	(2.3)	(5.4)	(1.9)
Market value ($ mil.)	(14.9%)	21.9	30.3	18.3	9.7	11.5
Employees	0.4%	123	120	119	121	125

THE GOLDMAN SACHS GROUP, INC.

NYSE: GS

85 Broad St.	CEO: Lloyd C. Blankfein
New York, NY 10004	CFO: David A. Viniar
Phone: 212-902-1000	HR: Edith Hunt
Fax: 212-902-3000	FYE: December 31
Web: www.goldmansachs.com	Type: Public

Goldman Sachs has traditionally possessed the Midas touch in the investment banking world. A global leader in mergers and acquisitions advice and securities underwriting, Goldman offers a gamut of investment banking and asset management services to corporate and government clients worldwide, as well as institutional and individual investors. It owns Goldman Sachs Execution & Clearing, one of the largest market makers on the NYSE and a leading market maker for fixed income products, currencies, and commodities. Through affiliates GS Capital Partners, GS Mezzanine Partners, and others, Goldman Sachs is also one of the largest private equity investors in the world.

	Annual Growth	11/05	11/06	11/07	11/08	*12/09
Sales ($ mil.)	4.5%	43,391.0	69,353.0	87,968.0	53,579.0	51,673.0
Net income ($ mil.)	24.2%	5,626.0	9,537.0	11,599.0	2,322.0	13,385.0
Market value ($ mil.)	7.0%	66,387.2	100,280.9	116,671.7	40,663.2	86,916.9
Employees	1.2%	31,005	26,467	30,522	30,067	32,500

*Fiscal year change

GOLD'S GYM INTERNATIONAL, INC.

125 E. John Carpenter Fwy., Ste. 1300	CEO: James A. Snow
Irving, TX 75062	CFO: Aaron Watkins
Phone: 214-574-4653	HR: Becky Copeland
Fax: 214-296-5000	FYE: February 28
Web: www.goldsgym.com	Type: Private

The site of America's most famous muscle beach is the birth place of one of the world's best-known muscle makers. Gold's Gym, which first opened in Venice Beach, California in 1965, franchises more than 600 gyms in 30 countries, with franchises accounting for most of its locations. The chain boasts more than 3 million members. In addition to opening franchises, the firm buys smaller regional health clubs and converts them to Gold's Gyms. The company also licenses the Gold's Gym name for products such as fitness equipment and accessories, luggage, t-shirts, and men's and women's sportswear. Gold's Gym is owned by TRT Holdings, the umbrella company for Dallas-based investor Robert Rowling's holdings.

GOLF GALAXY, INC.

300 Industry Dr., RIDC Park West	CEO: Joseph H. (Joe) Schmidt
Pittsburgh, PA 15275	CFO: —
Phone: 724-273-3400	HR: —
Fax: 724-227-1904	FYE: January 31
Web: www.golfgalaxy.com	Type: Subsidiary

Let Golf Galaxy help with your galactic battle to break par. It operates about 90 golf superstores in some 30 states. Its stores offer *Everything for the Game,* including equipment, apparel and shoes, gifts, accessories, books, and videos. Golf Galaxy also sells pre-owned clubs and has a trade-in program. In-store amenities include computer video swing analysis, on-site certified club technicians, indoor driving bays, full-sized putting greens, and advice on equipment from a staff that includes PGA and LPGA professionals. Golf Galaxy also operates a Web site (golfgalaxy.com) and catalog. Founded in 1997 by former CEO Randy Zanatta and Greg Maanum, the firm was acquired by Dick's Sporting Goods in 2007.

GOLFSMITH INTERNATIONAL HOLDINGS, INC.   NASDAQ (GM): GOLF

11000 N. IH-35	CEO: Martin E. (Marty) Hanaka
Austin, TX 78753	CFO: Sue E. Gove
Phone: 512-837-8810	HR: Sue E. Gove
Fax: 512-837-1245	FYE: December 31
Web: www.golfsmith.com	Type: Public

You might not be so quick to wrap that 5 iron around a tree if you'd made it yourself. Golfsmith International was founded in 1967 as a mail-order seller of custom-made golf clubs, and it still teaches golfers how to assemble their own irons, woods, and putters. The company sells its products through its catalogs, Web site, and more than 70 golf superstores in about 20 states. The company's stores — averaging about 20,000 sq. ft. — sell private-label and brand-name golf equipment, apparel, and accessories, and offer such services as swing analysis. Golfsmith also operates the Harvey Penick Golf Academy, an instructional school for golfers.

	Annual Growth	12/05	12/06	12/07	12/08	12/09
Sales ($ mil.)	1.1%	323.8	357.9	388.2	378.8	338.0
Net income ($ mil.)	—	3.0	(7.0)	(40.8)	(0.5)	(3.5)
Market value ($ mil.)	(38.5%)	—	152.2	60.7	11.0	35.5
Employees	4.7%	1,330	1,540	1,665	1,585	1,599

THE GOLUB CORPORATION

501 Duanesburg Rd.	CEO: Neil M. Golub
Schenectady, NY 12306	CFO: John J. Endres
Phone: 518-355-5000	HR: Wesley (Wes) Holloway
Fax: 518-379-3536	FYE: April 30
Web: www.pricechopper.com	Type: Private

Supermarket operator The Golub Corporation offers tasty come-ons such as table-ready meals, gift certificates, automatic discount cards, and a hotline where cooks answer food-related queries. Golub operates about 120 Price Chopper supermarkets in Connecticut, Massachusetts, New Hampshire, upstate New York, northeastern Pennsylvania, and Vermont. It also runs Mini Chopper service stations and convenience stores. Golub discontinued its HouseCalls home delivery service in 2001 but is giving home delivery another try. Brothers Bill and Ben Golub founded the company in 1932. Today the Golub family runs the company and owns 45% of the regional grocery chain; employees own slightly more than 50%.

GO-MART, INC.

915 Riverside Dr.	CEO: John D. Heater
Gassaway, WV 26624	CFO: —
Phone: 304-364-8000	HR: —
Fax: 304-364-4690	FYE: December 31
	Type: Private

Go-Mart helps drivers stay on the go with convenient gas and food. The company operates about 100 Go-Mart branded combination convenience stores and gas stations in Kentucky, Ohio, Virginia, and West Virginia. Customers can find coffee, fresh food, and drinks while filling up on gasoline or diesel fuel. Owned by the Heater family, Go-Mart was founded in 1914 as the Heater Oil Co. by Frank Heater. Today the regional chain is led by president John Heater.

GOMEMBERS, INC.

1315 W. 22nd St., Ste. 407	CEO: Paul Plaia III
Oak Brook, IL 60523	CFO: —
Phone: 630-756-0186	HR: —
Fax: 630-574-4870	FYE: December 31
Web: www.gomembers.com	Type: Subsidiary

If you have a lot of active members on the go, look no further than gomembers. The company develops software designed to help organizations such as bar associations, cultural institutions, health care networks, and labor unions put their members in contact with each other. It offers data management applications for tasks such as accounting, financial management, member communications, relationship management, and transaction processing. Customers include the American Heart Association, Caterpillar, CIGNA, DIRECTV, and Duke University. The company was founded in 1982 by chairman and CEO Paul Plaia. In 2009 CDC Software acquired gomembers, adding to its software-as-a-service (SaaS) portfolio.

GOMEZ, INC.

10 Maguire Rd., Ste. 330	CEO: Jaime W. Ellertson
Lexington, MA 02421	CFO: Richard M. (Rick) Darer
Phone: 781-778-2700	HR: —
Fax: 781-778-2799	FYE: December 31
Web: www.gomez.com	Type: Subsidiary

Performance is the true measure of a Web site, according to Gomez. The company provides Web site testing and management services primarily to companies in the financial services, retail, and travel industries. Its offerings help companies measure Web application performance, perform load testing, and analyze the performance of Web sites and applications. The company serves more than 2,500 customers worldwide, including clients such as Google, Expedia, Facebook, and Home Depot. Founded in 1997, Gomez filed for an IPO in 2008. Before completing its IPO, Gomez was acquired in 2009 by Compuware for $295 million in cash.

GONZAGA UNIVERSITY

502 E. Boone Ave.	CEO: Thayne M. McCulloh
Spokane, WA 99258	CFO: Charles J. Murphy
Phone: 509-328-4220	HR: —
Fax: —	FYE: May 31
Web: www.gonzaga.edu	Type: School

Gonzaga University provides instruction to more than 7,500 undergraduate, graduate, doctoral, and law students. The school offers about 75 undergraduate majors, more than two dozen master's degree programs, and a doctoral program in leadership studies. The university offers a Juris Doctor degree at its School of Law, one of three in Washington State. The Roman Catholic university is run by the Society of Jesus — the Jesuits — and is named after a sixteenth-century Italian Jesuit, Aloysius Gonzaga, the patron saint of youth. The university was founded in 1887. In addition to its main campus in Spokane, Washington, Gonzaga University has a campus in Florence, Italy, where Aloysius Gonzaga lived as a student.

	Annual Growth	5/04	5/05	5/06	5/07	5/08
Est. sales ($ mil.)	—	—	—	—	—	155.3
Employees	—	—	—	—	—	650

GOOD TECHNOLOGY, INC.

101 Redwood Shores Pkwy., Ste. 400
Redwood City, CA 94065
Phone: 650-486-6000
Fax: 650-622-9591
Web: www.good.com

CEO: Brian A. Bogosian
CFO: Stephen (Steve) Anderson
HR: —
FYE: December 31
Type: Private

Good Technology is key to getting your message across. The company (formerly Visto) develops desktop, server, and mobile device software that provides handset users with access to e-mail, calendar, social networking, contacts, and other data. Its software works with a wide range of cell phones and smartphones based on various operating systems. The company's technology partners include Microsoft, Palm, and Symbian. It markets to the consumer, enterprise, and government sectors. Looking to expand its client base, Visto acquired fellow mobile e-mail software developer Good Technology from Motorola in 2009; the combined companies adopted the Good Technology name.

GOOD TIMES RESTAURANTS INC.

NASDAQ (CM): GTIM

601 Corporate Cir.
Golden, CO 80401
Phone: 303-384-1400
Fax: 303-273-0177
Web: www.goodtimesburgers.com

CEO: Boyd E. Hoback
CFO: Susan M. Knutson
HR: Gary Staton
FYE: September 30
Type: Public

Good Times Restaurants operates and franchises more than 50 Good Times Drive Thru fast-food eateries, located primarily in the Denver area. The hamburger chain is made up mostly of double drive-through and walk-up eateries that feature a menu of burgers, fries, and frozen custard. A limited number of Good Times outlets also offer dine-in seating. More than 20 of the locations are operated by franchisees, while the rest are co-owned and co-operated under joint venture agreements. The family of director Geoffrey Bailey owns almost 30% of the company.

	Annual Growth	9/05	9/06	9/07	9/08	9/09
Sales ($ mil.)	8.7%	17.0	20.9	25.0	25.9	23.7
Net income ($ mil.)	—	(0.4)	0.0	0.0	(1.1)	(1.6)
Market value ($ mil.)	(32.1%)	22.1	24.2	21.3	8.8	4.7
Employees	3.9%	394	475	551	536	459

THE GOODHEART-WILLCOX CO., INC.

Pink Sheets: GWOX

18604 W. Creek Dr.
Tinley Park, IL 60477
Phone: 708-687-5000
Fax: 708-687-0315
Web: www.g-w.com

CEO: John F. Flanagan
CFO: —
HR: —
FYE: April 30
Type: Public

Goodheart-Willcox's educational textbooks run more toward HVAC than Homer. The company publishes textbooks, workbooks, computer software supplements, and instructor's guides for junior and senior high schools, vocational schools, technical and private trade schools, and colleges. Its titles cover industrial and technical topics (AutoCAD, drafting) and family and consumer topics (child care, nutrition). Apprentice trainers, educators, and do-it-yourselfers also use the company's books. Goodheart-Willcox hires authors and designs, edits, illustrates, and sells its books directly to schools or through bookstores. The company was founded in 1921.

GOODMAN GLOBAL, INC.

5151 San Felipe, Ste. 500
Houston, TX 77056
Phone: 713-861-2500
Fax: 713-861-3207
Web: www.goodmanglobal.com

CEO: David L. (Dave) Swift
CFO: Lawrence M. Blackburn
HR: Donald R. King
FYE: December 31
Type: Private

While a good man may be hard to find, *this* Goodman makes it easy to find comfort with its residential and light-commercial HVAC products. The company manufactures heating, ventilation, and air conditioning (HVAC) equipment, including split-system air conditioners and heat pumps, gas furnaces, packaged units, air handlers, and evaporator coils. Goodman operates seven plants in Texas, Tennessee, Arizona, Pennsylvania, and Florida. It sells products under the Goodman, Amana, and Quietflex brands through some 135 company-operated distribution centers and about 700 independent distributor locations throughout North America. Investment firm Hellman & Friedman bought the company in 2008.

	Annual Growth	12/04	12/05	12/06	12/07	12/08
Sales ($ mil.)	9.3%	1,317.6	1,565.4	1,794.8	1,935.7	1,877.4
Net income ($ mil.)	—	47.7	24.9	57.5	101.4	(39.7)
Employees	(2.2%)	4,816	—	—	—	4,401

GOODRICH CORPORATION

NYSE: GR

Four Coliseum Centre, 2730 W. Tyvola Rd.
Charlotte, NC 28217
Phone: 704-423-7000
Fax: 704-423-7002
Web: www.goodrich.com

CEO: Marshall O. Larsen
CFO: Scott E. Kuechle
HR: Terrence G. (Terry) Linnert
FYE: December 31
Type: Public

Goodrich is a tireless leader in aerospace systems. The company serves regional/business aircraft, original equipment and aftermarket, helicopters, military, and space markets through its three aerospace divisions. Goodrich's largest unit, Actuation and Landing Systems, makes fuel systems, aircraft wheels, brakes, landing gear, and flight control systems. Nacelles and Interior Systems offers MRO services and makes aerostructures (pylons and thrust reversers), as well as aircraft seats, and cargo and lighting systems. Finally, the Electronic Systems division makes fuel and engine controls, flight management systems, and reconnaissance and surveillance systems. Goodrich makes about half of its sales in the US.

	Annual Growth	12/05	12/06	12/07	12/08	12/09
Sales ($ mil.)	5.5%	5,396.5	5,878.3	6,392.2	7,061.7	6,685.6
Net income ($ mil.)	23.4%	263.6	481.5	482.6	681.2	610.8
Market value ($ mil.)	11.8%	5,144.8	5,701.9	8,838.9	4,634.1	8,042.7
Employees	1.5%	22,600	23,400	23,400	25,000	24,000

GOODRICH PETROLEUM CORPORATION

NYSE: GDP

801 Louisiana St., Ste. 700
Houston, TX 77002
Phone: 713-780-9494
Fax: 713-780-9254
Web: www.goodrichpetroleum.com

CEO: Walter G. (Gil) Goodrich
CFO: Jan L. Schott
HR: —
FYE: December 31
Type: Public

From deep in the good, rich hydrocarbon-impregnated rocks of ancient Mother Earth, Goodrich Petroleum brings forth oil and gas. The independent exploration and production company delves into formations in the Hayneville Shale play in Texas and Louisiana. The company also operates in the Cotton Valley trend (also in Texas and Louisiana), and it leases acreage in Michigan. Goodrich Petroleum owns interests in more than 460 active oil and gas wells in six states and reported estimated proved reserves of 420.6 billion cu. ft. of natural gas equivalent at the end of 2009.

	Annual Growth	12/05	12/06	12/07	12/08	12/09
Sales ($ mil.)	12.8%	68.3	116.2	111.3	216.1	110.4
Net income ($ mil.)	—	(17.5)	1.6	(45.0)	136.2	(251.0)
Market value ($ mil.)	(0.8%)	944.6	1,358.8	849.5	1,124.8	914.5
Employees	18.2%	64	84	93	116	125

An in-depth profile of this company is available to Hoover's Online members at hoovers.com.

GOODWILL INDUSTRIES INTERNATIONAL, INC.

15810 Indianola Dr.   CEO: Jim Gibbons
Rockville, MD 20855   CFO: —
Phone: 301-530-6500   HR: —
Fax: 301-530-1516   FYE: December 31
Web: www.goodwill.org   Type: Not-for-profit

Goodwill Industries International supports the operations of about 200 independent Goodwill chapters worldwide. Though most well known for its 2,250
thrift stores, the group focuses on providing rehabilitation, job training, placement, and employment services for people with disabilities and others. Goodwill is one of the world's largest providers of such services, as well as one of
the world's largest employers of the physically, mentally, and emotionally disabled. Support for the organization's programs is generated primarily from
sales of donated goods, both at the retail stores and through an online auction
site, as well as from contract work and from government grants. Goodwill was
founded in 1902.

	Annual Growth	12/04	12/05	12/06	12/07	12/08
Sales ($ mil.)	(66.1%)	2,390.0	2,650.0	2,903.2	3,163.5	31.7
Employees	1.8%	80,142	82,185	86,375	87,444	86,000

GOODWIN PROCTER LLP

Exchange Place, 53 State St.   CEO: Regina M. Pisa
Boston, MA 02109   CFO: Michael P. Kiskinis
Phone: 617-570-1000   HR: Allison V. Friend
Fax: 617-523-1231   FYE: September 30
Web: www.goodwinprocter.com   Type: Partnership

One of the largest law firms in Beantown, Goodwin Procter has branched
beyond its Boston roots to establish offices on the East and West Coasts of the
US. Its more than 700 lawyers practice in a variety of areas including corporate, real estate, environmental, litigation, tax, and estate planning. (It assisted
with more than 450 private equity and venture capital transactions in 2008
alone.) It has offices in Boston, London, Hong Kong, Los Angeles, New York
City, San Diego, San Francisco, and Washington, DC. Robert Goodwin and
Joseph Procter founded the firm in 1912.

GOODY PRODUCTS, INC.

3 Glenlake Pkwy.   CEO: A.J. Ross
Atlanta, GA 30328   CFO: Natalie Poteran
Phone: 770-418-7300   HR: Andréa Carter
Fax: 770-615-4740   FYE: December 31
Web: www.goody.com   Type: Subsidiary

Goody has the tools to help even the Bride of Frankenstein have a good hair
day. Goody Products manufactures hair care accessories, brushes, combs, and
travel storage products and sells them through food, drug, and discount
stores, such as Target, Wal-Mart and Walgreen. The firm makes products
under the Goody, Ace, Stayput, Ouchless, TherapySolutions, Styling Therapy,
ColourCollection, and StylingSolutions trademarks. The Goody brand set root
in 1907 when Henry Goodman and his son, Abraham, began selling
rhinestone-studded hair combs off a pushcart in New York City. Since 1993 it
has been owned by Newell Rubbermaid. Goody Products is a subsidiary in its
parent's home-and-family segment.

GOODYEAR DUNLOP TIRES NORTH AMERICA LTD.

200 John James Audubon Pky.   CEO: Joseph Rosen
Amherst, NY 14228   CFO: —
Phone: 716-639-5200   HR: Sheree Schmidt
Fax: 716-639-5017   FYE: December 31
Web: www.dunloptire.com   Type: Subsidiary

You could say that Goodyear Dunlop Tires North America knows its way
around the tire industry. The company, a part of The Goodyear Tire & Rubber
Company, makes tires bearing the Dunlop brand name. Other product offerings include tires for all terrain vehicles (ATVs), commercial trucks, competition go-carts (karts), and motorcycles. As legend has it, the late John Boyd
Dunlop patented his design for the modern tire after watching his son ride a
tricycle with solid rubber wheels. The Dunlop brand is a sponsor for many
racing and other high-performance automotive events.

⊞ THE GOODYEAR TIRE & RUBBER COMPANY   NYSE: GT

1144 E. Market St.   CEO: Richard J. (Rich) Kramer
Akron, OH 44316   CFO: Darren R. Wells
Phone: 330-796-2121   HR: Joseph B. (Joe) Ruocco
Fax: 330-796-2222   FYE: December 31
Web: www.goodyear.com   Type: Public

With a worldwide alliance with Sumitomo Rubber Industries designed to dominate the tire industry, The Goodyear Tire & Rubber Company remains a leading
tire maker, trailing rivals Bridgestone and Michelin. The company primarily
sells tires under the Goodyear, Dunlop, Kelly, Fulda, Debica, and Sava brands for
the replacement market as well as to the world's automakers. In addition to its
own brand of tires, Goodyear makes Dunlop tires for sale in North America and
Europe through its alliance with Japan's Sumitomo. The company operates
about 57 plants worldwide, and has around 1,500 retail tire and auto repair centers. More than 60% of sales come from outside the US.

	Annual Growth	12/05	12/06	12/07	12/08	12/09
Sales ($ mil.)	(4.7%)	19,723.0	20,258.0	19,644.0	19,488.0	16,301.0
Net income ($ mil.)	—	239.0	(330.0)	602.0	(77.0)	(364.0)
Market value ($ mil.)	(5.1%)	4,221.9	5,098.9	6,855.2	1,450.2	3,425.2
Employees	(3.6%)	80,000	77,000	72,000	74,700	69,000

⊞ GOOGLE INC.   NASDAQ (GS): GOOG

1600 Amphitheatre Pkwy.   CEO: Eric E. Schmidt
Mountain View, CA 94043   CFO: Patrick Pichette
Phone: 650-253-0000   HR: Laszlo Bock
Fax: 650-253-0001   FYE: December 31
Web: www.google.com   Type: Public

If you've never Googled, you probably aren't finding what you want online.
Google operates the leading Internet search engine, offering targeted search
results from billions of Web pages. Results are based on a proprietary algorithm — Google's technology for ranking Web pages is called PageRank. The
company generates nearly all of its revenue through ad sales. Advertisers can
deliver relevant ads targeted to search queries or Web content. The Google
Network is a network of third-party customers that use Google's ad programs
to deliver relevant ads to their own websites. Google subsidiaries include
YouTube and DoubleClick. Founders Sergey Brin and Larry Page each have
nearly 30% voting control of the firm.

	Annual Growth	12/05	12/06	12/07	12/08	12/09
Sales ($ mil.)	40.1%	6,138.6	10,604.9	16,594.0	21,795.6	23,650.6
Net income ($ mil.)	45.2%	1,465.4	3,077.4	4,203.7	4,226.9	6,520.4
Market value ($ mil.)	10.6%	132,127.3	146,656.7	220,227.0	97,982.4	197,455.3
Employees	36.7%	5,680	10,674	16,805	20,222	19,835

⊞ An in-depth profile of this company is available to Hoover's Online members at hoovers.com.

GORDON BROTHERS GROUP, LLC

101 Huntington Ave., 10th Fl.
Boston, MA 02199
Phone: 617-426-3233
Fax: 617-422-6222
Web: www.gordonbrothers.com

CEO: Michael G. Frieze
CFO: Robert L. (Bob) Paglia
HR: —
FYE: December 31
Type: Private

Gordon Brothers Group organizes the sale of assets, including retail inventories, equipment, real estate, accounts receivable, intellectual property, and other assets. The company, which prides itself on discretion and speed, also facilitates mergers and acquisitions and manages closings of underperforming stores for top retailers. Its GB Merchant Partners affiliate provides debt financing to, and takes equity positions in, middle-market retail and consumer products firms for growth, acquisitions, or turnarounds; its holdings include stakes in Deb Shops, Laura Secord, and Things Remembered. Gordon Brothers Group has about 15 offices in the US, Japan, and Europe.

GORDON FOOD SERVICE, INC.

333 50th St. SW
Grand Rapids, MI 49501
Phone: 616-530-7000
Fax: 616-717-7600
Web: www.gfs.com

CEO: Dan Gordon
CFO: Jeff Maddox
HR: —
FYE: October 31
Type: Private

This company delivers the goods that feed hungry restaurant patrons. Gordon Food Service (GFS) is a leading foodservice supplier in North America with more than 20 distribution centers in the US and Canada. It distributes food items, ingredients, and beverages to restaurant operators, schools, health care facilities, and institutional foodservice operators in parts of 15 states and all across Canada. In addition to its distribution operation, GFS operates more than 130 GFS Marketplace wholesale stores that are open to the general public. Isaac Van Westenbrugge started the family-owned business in 1897.

THE GORES GROUP, LLC

10877 Wilshire Blvd., 18th Fl.
Los Angeles, CA 90024
Phone: 310-209-3010
Fax: 310-209-3310
Web: www.gores.com

CEO: Alec E. Gores
CFO: —
HR: Jeremy D. Rossen
FYE: December 31
Type: Private

Gores Group is engorged with technology (software, hardware, technology services) and telecommunications companies. The private investment company buys and manages mature and growing businesses mostly in the tech and industrial sectors. The firm, which has offices in North America and Europe, does its own due diligence, usually takes full ownership, and sets its experts to work to turn around the company. Since its founding by chairman Alec Gores in 1987, it has bought more than 60 companies around the world. Typical targets have revenues between $30 million and more than $1 billion and are often spinoffs of noncore operations from large corporate parents.

THE GORMAN-RUPP COMPANY

NYSE Amex: GRC

305 Bowman St.
Mansfield, OH 44903
Phone: 419-755-1011
Fax: 419-755-1233
Web: www.gormanrupp.com

CEO: Jeffrey S. Gorman
CFO: Wayne L. Knabel
HR: Lee A. Wilkins
FYE: December 31
Type: Public

Gorman-Rupp keeps pumping out pumps. The company, founded in 1933 by engineers J.C. Gorman and H.E. Rupp, makes a myriad of pumps and fluid controls used in construction, sewage treatment, petroleum refining, agriculture, and fire fighting, as well as for HVAC and military applications. Gorman-Rupp's pumps range in size from 1/4-in. (one gallon per minute) to 84-in. (500,000 gallons per minute). Smaller pumps are used for dispensing soft drinks and making ice cubes, while large pumps are central to refueling aircraft and boosting low water pressure in municipal fresh water markets. Gorman-Rupp sells its products through 1,000 distributors, OEM representatives, distributor catalogs, and direct sales.

	Annual Growth	12/05	12/06	12/07	12/08	12/09
Sales ($ mil.)	3.6%	231.2	270.9	305.6	330.6	266.2
Net income ($ mil.)	13.8%	10.9	19.1	22.9	27.2	18.3
Market value ($ mil.)	18.2%	236.5	494.2	521.4	520.0	461.9
Employees	(1.6%)	1,021	1,049	1,065	1,093	957

GORTON'S INC.

128 Rogers St.
Gloucester, MA 01930
Phone: 978-283-3000
Fax: 978-281-8295
Web: www.gortons.com

CEO: Judson Reis
CFO: —
HR: —
FYE: March 31
Type: Subsidiary

As a leader in the US branded frozen seafood sector, Gorton's has lots of fish to fry. And freeze. And sell to food retailers and foodservice suppliers across the country. The company's products include breaded, frozen popcorn fish and shrimp; fish sticks and fillets; and fish tenders (for dipping). Other Gorton products include battered fish products. Its Canadian unit, BlueWater Seafoods, produces one of Canada's leading seafood brands. Gorton's was founded in 1849 in Gloucester, Massachusetts. A former Unilever subsidiary, Gorton's was acquired by Japanese seafood giant Nippon Suisan Kaisha in 2001 and became a wholly owned subsidiary of Nippon Suisan (USA).

	Annual Growth	3/04	3/05	3/06	3/07	3/08
Est. sales ($ mil.)	—	—	—	—	—	99.3
Employees	—	—	—	—	—	975

GOSS INTERNATIONAL CORPORATION

3 Territorial Ct.
Bolingbrook, IL 60440
Phone: 630-755-9300
Fax: 630-755-9301
Web: www.gossinternational.com

CEO: Jochen Meissner
CFO: Torben Rasmussen
HR: —
FYE: December 31
Type: Private

Goss International always has some pressing news. The company manufactures web-offset printing presses and finishing systems for newspapers, commercial printers, and other high-volume print applications. Distribution of Goss presses, related parts, and services is driven through sales offices and plants in North America, Europe, and Asia. The company courts newspaper publishers in more than 120 countries, including *The Asahi Shimbun* (Japan), *The People's Daily* (China), the Moscow Newspaper Printing Plant (which prints *MK*, *Pravda*, and other Russian publications), and *The Financial Times* (UK). Investment firm Matlin Patterson Global Opportunities Partners and Shanghai Electric (Group) Corp. control the company.

	Annual Growth	12/04	12/05	12/06	12/07	12/08
Est. sales ($ mil.)	(3.1%)	—	1,100.0	1,140.0	1,110.0	1,000.0
Employees	(1.2%)	—	4,100	4,100	4,000	—

THE GOTHAM GROUP, INC.

150 E. 42nd St., 12th Fl.	CEO: Peter McGuinness
New York, NY 10017	CFO: —
Phone: 212-414-7000	HR: Barbara Jewell
Fax: 212-414-7107	FYE: December 31
Web: www.gothaminc.com	Type: Subsidiary

The residents of this Gotham are mad about marketing. One of New York City's leading advertising agencies, The Gotham Group — known better as Gotham — provides creative development and campaign management services aimed at building and promoting consumer brands. In addition to traditional ad work, the firm offers targeted retail marketing and allied communications services, as well as product and packaging design services. The agency has developed advertisements for Credit Suisse, Lufthansa, and IMS Health. The Interpublic Group established Gotham in 1994, and it continues to operate as an independent agency of the global marketing services holding company.

GOULD ELECTRONICS INC.

2555 West Fairview St., Ste. 103	CEO: John P. Callahan
Chandler, AZ 85224	CFO: Thomas N. (Tom) Rich
Phone: 480-223-0870	HR: —
Fax: 480-821-9003	FYE: March 31
Web: www.gould.com	Type: Subsidiary

Gould Electronics manufactures a variety of copper foils used to make printed circuit boards (PCBs) — commonly used in computers, home entertainment systems, mobile phones, and other electronics. Products include its JTC-brand electrodeposited copper foil, TCR-brand resistor foil, and special application foils. The company is based in Germany and distributes its products globally through a network of independent distributors. Founded in 1884, the company is now a division of Nikko Materials (a Nippon Mining subsidiary).

	Annual Growth	3/04	3/05	3/06	3/07	3/08
Est. sales ($ mil.)	—	—	—	—	—	5.9
Employees	—	—	—	—	—	64

GOULD PAPER CORPORATION

11 Madison Ave.	CEO: Harry E. Gould Jr.
New York, NY 10010	CFO: Carl Matthews
Phone: 212-301-0000	HR: Barbara O'Grady
Fax: 212-481-0067	FYE: December 31
Web: www.gouldpaper.com	Type: Private

Paper is as good as gold for Gould Paper, one of the largest privately owned distributors of printing and fine papers in North America. The company distributes and sells paper to multiple markets, including fine paper, commercial printing, lithography, newsprint, direct-mail, catalog, envelope, and specialty paper companies. Gould supplies paperboard, which is used in packaging material for consumer and industrial products. It also operates paper-converting operations. Touting sales of 2 million tons of paper products annually, the company represents most major domestic and offshore mills. In 2010 Japan Pulp & Paper acquired a majority stake in Gould.

	Annual Growth	12/04	12/05	12/06	12/07	12/08
Sales ($ mil.)	(4.7%)	1,210.0	1,240.0	1,150.0	1,160.0	1,000.0
Employees	1.7%	410	374	464	431	—

GOULDS PUMPS, INCORPORATED

240 Fall St.	CEO: Ken Napolitano
Seneca Falls, NY 13148	CFO: Tom Wu
Phone: 315-568-2811	HR: Ron Golumbeck
Fax: 315-568-2418	FYE: December 31
Web: www.gouldspumps.com	Type: Subsidiary

When it comes to energy and maintenance issues, Goulds Pumps has a fluid answer that folks listen to. The company manufactures water utility, irrigation, and industrial pumping products. For more than 150 years Goulds Pumps has been producing pumps; it boasts more than a million of its centrifugal and turbine pumps installed worldwide. Goulds Pumps also offers replacement parts and repair services for its lineup. Its products are sold under brands including Goulds, A-C Pump, PumpSmart, and ProServices. The company's industrial pumps cater to the chemical, pulp and paper, power generation, oil refining, and mining industries. Goulds Pumps operates as a part of ITT Fluid Technology, a subsidiary of ITT.

GOUVERNEUR BANCORP, INC.

NYSE Amex: GOV

42 Church St.	CEO: Charles C. VanVleet
Gouverneur, NY 13642	CFO: —
Phone: 315-287-2600	HR: —
Fax: 315-287-3340	FYE: September 30
Web: www.gouverneurbank.com	Type: Public

Gouverneur Bancorp is the holding company for Gouverneur Savings and Loan, which serves upstate New York through two branches. Chartered in 1892, the thrift offers deposit products such as checking and savings accounts, NOW accounts, CDs, and money market accounts. Gouverneur Savings and Loan primarily uses funds from deposits to originate residential mortgages, which account for approximately 80% of its loan portfolio. It also offers commercial mortgages, business loans, and consumer loans (mostly automobile loans). Cambray Mutual Holding Company owns a majority of Gouverneur Bancorp.

⊞ GOVERNMENT EMPLOYEES INSURANCE COMPANY

1 GEICO Plaza	CEO: Olza M. (Tony) Nicely
Washington, DC 20076	CFO: Mike Campbell
Phone: 301-986-3000	HR: Jan Stewart
Fax: —	FYE: December 31
Web: www.geico.com	Type: Subsidiary

The Government Employees Insurance Company, widely known as GEICO, has found that driving down costs brings drivers by the droves into its fold. GEICO has traditionally provided auto and other insurance to preferred low-risk demographic groups (such as government and military employees) but has also begun to sell to nonstandard (high-risk) drivers. In addition to auto coverage, the company's offerings include motorcycle insurance and emergency road service. GEICO eschews agents in favor of direct marketing through such vehicles as direct mail, TV, radio, and the Internet. Its gecko mascot is one of the most recognized marketing icons. The company is a subsidiary of Warren Buffett's Berkshire Hathaway.

⊞ An in-depth profile of this company is available to Hoover's Online members at hoovers.com.

701

GOVERNMENT NATIONAL MORTGAGE ASSOCIATION

Potomac Center South, 550 12th St. SW, 3rd Fl.
Washington, DC 20024
Phone: 202-708-1535
Fax: 202-708-0490
Web: www.ginniemae.gov

CEO: Thomas R. Weakland
CFO: Michael J. (Mike) Najjum Jr.
HR: —
FYE: September 30
Type: Government-owned

Ginnie Mae is government-owned corporation operating within the US Department of Housing and Urban Development (HUD). More formally known as the Government National Mortgage Association, Ginnie Mae doesn't buy or sell loans or issue mortgage-backed securities. Rather, it manages the mortgage-backed securities program, providing liquidity, allowing lenders to obtain better prices for their loans on the secondary market, and lowering costs for homebuyers and renters throughout the nation, particularly low- to moderate-income Americans. Since its creation in 1968, Ginnie Mae has guaranteed more than $2.5 trillion in mortgage-backed securities and helped more than 34 million Americans secure affordable housing.

GOVERNMENT PROPERTIES INCOME TRUST   NYSE: GOV

400 Centre St.
Newton, MA 02458
Phone: 617-219-1440
Fax: —
Web: www.govreit.com

CEO: Barry M. Portnoy
CFO: David M. Blackman
HR: —
FYE: December 31
Type: Public

If Government Properties Income Trust had one request of Uncle Sam it would be this: "I want you to lease our properties." As a real estate investment trust (REIT), Government Properties Income Trust invests in properties that are leased to government tenants. It owns 3.3 million sq. ft. of leasing space at its 29 properties, many of which are located in the Washington, DC, area and 14 other states. The company leases mostly to federal agencies (such as the FBI, IRS, and FDA), but it does lease to some state-run agencies as well. Government Properties Income Trust went public in 2009. Former majority owner HRPT Properties Trust owns 49.9% of the company following the IPO.

	Annual Growth	12/05	12/06	12/07	12/08	12/09
Sales ($ mil.)	4.0%	—	—	73.1	75.4	79.0
Net income ($ mil.)	(10.0%)	—	—	32.1	31.8	26.0
Market value ($ mil.)	—	—	—	—	—	718.3
Employees	—	—	—	—	570	—

☐ GOYA FOODS, INC.

100 Seaview Dr.
Secaucus, NJ 07096
Phone: 201-348-4900
Fax: 201-348-6609
Web: www.goya.com

CEO: Robert I. (Bob) Unanue
CFO: Miguel Lugo
HR: Tony Rico
FYE: December 31
Type: Private

Whether you call 'em *frijoles* or *habichuelas*, beans are beans, and Goya's got 'em, and lots more. Goya Foods produces approximately 1,600 Hispanic and Caribbean grocery items, including canned and dried beans, canned meats, fruit nectars, oils, olives, rice, seasonings and sauces, plantain and yucca chips, and frozen entrees. It sells many different types of rice and some 38 types of beans and peas. The company's brands include Goya and Canilla. It also sells beverages such as tropical fruit nectars and juices, tropical sodas, and coffee. Goya is owned and operated by one of the richest Hispanic *familias* in the US, the Unanues, who founded the company in 1936.

	Annual Growth	5/04	5/05	*12/06	12/07	12/08
Est. sales ($ mil.)	11.2%	850.0	750.0	1,190.0	1,260.0	1,300.0
Employees	4.7%	2,500	2,500	3,000	3,000	3,000
						*Fiscal year change

GP STRATEGIES CORPORATION   NYSE: GPX

6095 Marshalee Dr., Ste. 300
Elkridge, MD 21075
Phone: 410-379-3600
Fax: 410-540-5302
Web: www.gpstrategies.com

CEO: Scott N. Greenberg
CFO: Sharon Esposito-Mayer
HR: —
FYE: December 31
Type: Public

GP Strategies, through its General Physics subsidiary, offers a broad range of consulting, engineering, staffing, and training services. The company divides its offerings into four main business segments: manufacturing and business process outsourcing (BPO), which accounts for 45% of its total sales; process and government; energy (which offers engineering services to electric power utilities and clients in the power generation industry); and training and marketing (comprised primarily of its Sandy unit). General Physics has more than 500 clients, including auto manufacturers, electric utilities, government agencies and contractors, and technology companies.

	Annual Growth	12/05	12/06	12/07	12/08	12/09
Sales ($ mil.)	5.7%	175.6	178.8	248.4	267.9	219.2
Net income ($ mil.)	—	7.2	6.6	9.7	7.8	(1.2)
Market value ($ mil.)	(2.0%)	151.9	154.5	198.2	83.9	140.2
Employees	3.0%	1,580	1,205	1,747	1,777	1,780

GRACENOTE, INC.

2000 Powell St., Ste. 1380
Emeryville, CA 94608
Phone: 510-547-9680
Fax: 510-547-9681
Web: www.gracenote.com

CEO: Craig Palmer
CFO: James A. (Jim) Doehrman
HR: —
FYE: December 31
Type: Subsidiary

Whether your taste in music tends toward Graceland or the Blue Note Café, Gracenote will send you the songs you seek. The company (formerly CDDB) provides music recognition technologies that compare digital music files to a worldwide database of music information, enabling digital audio devices to identify the songs. The company licenses its technologies to developers of consumer electronics devices and online media players, who integrate the technologies into media players, home and car stereos, and digital music devices. Offerings include the CDDB music identification service and the MusicID universal identification system. Gracenote was acquired by Sony for $260 million in 2008.

GRACO CHILDREN'S PRODUCTS, INC.

150 Oaklands Blvd.
Exton, PA 19341
Phone: 610-884-8000
Fax: 610-884-8730
Web: www.gracobaby.com

CEO: Jay D. Gould
CFO: —
HR: —
FYE: December 31
Type: Subsidiary

Dogs might be man's best friend, but Graco is mom's and dad's best buddy. The company is a unit of Newell Rubbermaid and part of its Home & Family segment. Graco has built a business making and marketing a variety of accoutrements that make life as a parent more enriching. While Graco has expertise in swing-making, its products portfolio has grown to include highchairs, strollers, car seats, play yards, and activity centers. It also makes potty training items to help Junior say goodbye to diapers for good. Graco also sells furniture through a licensing agreement. Its products are sold nationwide at major retailers, such as Babies "R" Us, via shops in more than 40 countries, and through its website.

GRACO INC.

NYSE: GGG

88 11th Ave. NE
Minneapolis, MN 55413
Phone: 612-623-6000
Fax: 612-378-3505
Web: www.graco.com

CEO: Patrick J. McHale
CFO: James A. Graner
HR: David Ahlers
FYE: December 31
Type: Public

To state the obvious: Graco has fluid management skills. The company, which was founded in 1926 as Gray Company, manufactures fluid handling equipment designed to move, measure, control, dispense, and apply fluid materials. Products include pumps, applicators, spray guns, pressure washers, filters, valves, and accessories; these goods are used in industrial and commercial applications to handle paints, adhesives, sealants, and lubricants. In addition to painting contractors, Graco's customers include automotive, construction equipment, and vehicle lubrication companies. Graco sells its products through independent distributors, with approximately 30,000 outlets worldwide.

	Annual Growth	12/05	12/06	12/07	12/08	12/09
Sales ($ mil.)	(5.7%)	731.7	816.5	841.3	817.3	579.2
Net income ($ mil.)	(21.0%)	125.9	149.8	152.8	120.9	49.0
Market value ($ mil.)	(5.9%)	2,210.8	2,401.1	2,258.1	1,438.1	1,731.5
Employees	(0.6%)	2,100	2,300	2,200	2,400	2,050

GRAEBEL COMPANIES, INC.

16346 E. Airport Cir.
Aurora, CO 80011
Phone: 303-214-6683
Fax: 303-214-2156
Web: www.graebel.com

CEO: William (Bill) Graebel
CFO: Brad Siler
HR: Mary Dymond
FYE: December 31
Type: Private

Graebel Companies grapples for market share in the moving business. The company provides household and commercial relocation services in the US and internationally. Most of Graebel's business comes from companies needing to arrange the transfers of their employees, but it also provides individual household moving services and storage and freight forwarding. Graebel operates from service centers throughout the US and from international forwarding offices at major US ports. It provides transportation services in Europe, the Middle East, and Africa through a hub in Prague and elsewhere in the world via a network of partners. The family-run company was founded by chairman Dave Graebel in 1950.

	Annual Growth	12/04	12/05	12/06	12/07	12/08
Est. sales ($ mil.)	—	—	—	—	—	334.2
Employees	—	—	—	—	—	1,771

GRAFTECH INTERNATIONAL LTD.

NYSE: GTI

12900 Snow Rd.
Parma, OH 44130
Phone: 216-676-2000
Fax: 216-676-2526
Web: www.graftech.com

CEO: Craig S. Shular
CFO: Mark R. Widmar
HR: —
FYE: December 31
Type: Public

If GrafTech International were a bard, it could wax poetic in an ode to the electrode. The company is a leading maker in the US of graphite electrodes, which are essential to the production of electric arc furnaces. GrafTech also manufactures advanced carbon materials, flexible graphite products, flow field plates, gas diffusion layers, and carbon electrodes and refractories for the aeronautics, construction, energy, fire protection, marine, and transportation industries. Customers include Arcelor Mittal, BaoSteel, Elkem, Griffin Wheel (railroad wheels), Samsung Electronics, and ThyssenKrupp Steel. GrafTech gets more than 80% of sales outside the US.

	Annual Growth	12/05	12/06	12/07	12/08	12/09
Sales ($ mil.)	(7.2%)	886.7	855.4	1,004.8	1,190.2	659.0
Net income ($ mil.)	—	(125.2)	91.3	153.7	210.3	12.6
Market value ($ mil.)	25.7%	774.2	861.4	2,209.4	1,035.6	1,935.6
Employees	(13.6%)	3,851	2,757	2,554	2,511	2,147

GRAHAM CORPORATION

NYSE Amex: GHM

20 Florence Ave.
Batavia, NY 14020
Phone: 585-343-2216
Fax: 585-343-1097
Web: www.graham-mfg.com

CEO: James R. Lines
CFO: Jeffrey F. (Jeff) Glajch
HR: —
FYE: March 31
Type: Public

You're not crackers if you know that Graham Corporation takes the biscuit when it comes to helping companies make beer, soap, and other products. The company makes vacuum systems, pumps, compressors, and heat exchangers designed to create vacuums, condense steam, or produce heat. Graham sells its equipment to manufacturers in the petroleum, plastics, chemicals, food processing, and other industries, where its gear is used in processes ranging from power generation to brewing beer and making soap. The company sells its products directly and through independent sales representatives worldwide.

	Annual Growth	3/05	3/06	3/07	3/08	3/09
Sales ($ mil.)	25.1%	41.3	55.2	65.8	86.4	101.1
Net income ($ mil.)	—	(2.9)	3.6	5.8	15.0	17.5
Market value ($ mil.)	27.0%	34.0	76.8	65.1	175.3	88.3
Employees	2.7%	243	250	265	281	270

GRAHAM PACKAGING COMPANY INC.

NYSE: GRM

2401 Pleasant Valley Rd.
York, PA 17402
Phone: 717-849-8500
Fax: 717-848-4836
Web: www.grahampackaging.com

CEO: Mark S. Burgess
CFO: David W. Bullock
HR: —
FYE: December 31
Type: Public

Grocery stockers to mechanics can't keep their hands off Graham Packaging. No cookie-cutter, the company designs, manufactures, and sells blow-molded plastic containers for a diversity of branded consumer goods, including food and beverages, automotive lubricants, and household and personal care items. Graham Packaging's 80-plus manufacturing plants, which dot North and South America, and Europe, supply blue-chip customers Clorox, Danone, Heinz, and PepsiCo. About one-third of plant operations are set onsite at customers' production facilities; the top 20 customers represent nearly 70% of sales. Blackstone Group and affiliates hold a 64% stake in the company. Graham Packaging completed an IPO in February 2010.

	Annual Growth	12/05	12/06	12/07	12/08	12/09
Sales ($ mil.)	(2.1%)	2,473.4	2,500.4	2,470.9	2,559.0	2,271.0
Net income ($ mil.)	—	(52.6)	(120.4)	(207.4)	(57.9)	14.3
Employees	(5.2%)	8,900	8,400	7,800	7,400	7,200

GRAMERCY CAPITAL CORP.

NYSE: GKK

420 Lexington Ave.
New York, NY 10170
Phone: 212-297-1000
Fax: 212-297-1090
Web: www.gramercycapitalcorp.com

CEO: Roger M. Cozzi
CFO: Jon W. Clark
HR: —
FYE: December 31
Type: Public

Gramercy Capital, a real estate investment trust (REIT), invests in commercial real estate and real estate loans secured by commercial properties throughout the US. The company's portfolio includes mezzanine financing, bridge loans, interests in whole loans, preferred equity, private equity investments, and mortgage-backed securities. In 2008 Gramercy Capital acquired American Financial Realty Trust, which invested in real estate leased to banks and other financial institutions. The merger expanded the REIT's business beyond investments in financial structures into investments in real brick-and-mortar structures.

	Annual Growth	12/05	12/06	12/07	12/08	12/09
Sales ($ mil.)	71.6%	88.1	198.2	423.0	609.9	763.8
Net income ($ mil.)	—	31.4	55.9	161.6	59.3	(520.4)
Market value ($ mil.)	(41.9%)	1,136.9	1,541.6	1,213.2	63.9	129.3
Employees	—	0	—	—	71	131

An in-depth profile of this company is available to Hoover's Online members at hoovers.com.

GRAND CANYON EDUCATION, INC.

NASDAQ (GM): LOPE

3300 W. Camelback Rd.	CEO: Brian E. Mueller
Phoenix, AZ 85017	CFO: Daniel E. Bachus
Phone: 602-639-7500	HR: —
Fax: 602-589-2717	FYE: December 31
Web: www.gcu.edu	Type: Public

Like its geological namesake, Grand Canyon Education (aka Grand Canyon University) wants to expand your horizons. The regionally accredited Christian institution offers online graduate and undergraduate programs in education, business, and health care through the Ken Blanchard College of Business, College of Education, College of Nursing and Health Sciences, and College of Humanities and Social Sciences. It also offers programs at its brick-and-mortar campus in Phoenix and onsite at the facilities of employers. Grand Canyon enrolls roughly 15,000 students annually; approximately 85% are enrolled in online programs, and more than half are pursuing master's degrees. The university filed to go public in 2008.

	Annual Growth	12/05	12/06	12/07	12/08	12/09
Sales ($ mil.)	50.0%	51.8	72.1	99.3	161.3	261.9
Net income ($ mil.)	—	(4.3)	0.6	1.5	6.7	27.3
Market value ($ mil.)	1.2%	—	—	—	858.3	868.8
Employees	64.5%	—	—	702	1,365	1,899

GRAND RIVER DAM AUTHORITY

226 W. Dwain Willis Ave.	CEO: Kevin A. Easley
Vinita, OK 74301	CFO: Carolyn Dougherty
Phone: 918-256-5545	HR: —
Fax: 918-256-5289	FYE: December 31
Web: www.grda.com	Type: Government-owned

It took the dam authority of the State of Oklahoma to create the body that would dam the Grand River. The resulting power provider, the Grand River Dam Authority, is responsible for supplying wholesale electricity to municipal and cooperative utilities and industrial customers in its service territory, which encompasses 24 counties in northeastern Oklahoma. The state-owned utility has 1,480 MW of generating capacity from hydroelectric and fossil-fueled power plants and operates a 2,000-mile transmission system. Grand River Dam Authority also manages two lakes.

	Annual Growth	12/04	12/05	12/06	12/07	12/08
Est. sales ($ mil.)	—	—	—	—	—	323.7
Employees	—	—	—	—	—	500

GRANDE COMMUNICATIONS HOLDINGS, INC.

401 Carlson Cir.	CEO: Roy H. Chestnutt
San Marcos, TX 78666	CFO: Michael L. (Mike) Wilfley
Phone: 512-878-4000	HR: Kay Stroman
Fax: 512-878-4010	FYE: December 31
Web: www.grandecom.com	Type: Private

Grande Communications' grand vision is to become a key player in Texas telecommunications. Through operating subsidiary Grande Communications Networks, the company provides bundled telephone services, Internet access, and cable television to more than 100,000 residential and business customers over its own fiber-optic network. It also provides wholesale communications services to other telecoms and ISPs through its Grande Networks division. While its core central Texas service area includes Austin, San Marcos, and San Antonio, it also provides service in Corpus Christi, Dallas, Midland, Odessa, and Waco. Grande Communications is controlled by Boston-based private equity firm ABRY Partners.

	Annual Growth	12/04	12/05	12/06	12/07	12/08
Sales ($ mil.)	3.5%	179.0	194.7	189.9	197.1	205.3
Net income ($ mil.)	—	(55.0)	(89.8)	(141.6)	(50.5)	(50.4)
Employees	(2.6%)	873	835	810	831	785

GRANGE MUTUAL CASUALTY COMPANY

650 S. Front St.	CEO: Robert V. James
Columbus, OH 43206	CFO: Thomas H. (Tom) Welch
Phone: 614-445-2900	HR: Robert C. Rissmeyer
Fax: 614-445-2337	FYE: December 31
Web: www.grangeinsurance.com	Type: Mutual company

Grange Mutual Casualty offers many breeds of insurance and financial products to grangers and others in the Midwest. Founded in 1935, the company (also known as Grange Insurance) offers auto, commercial, farm, homeowners, and life insurance coverage to customers in about a dozen US states, mostly in the farm belt. The company targets small to midsized businesses for its commercial policies; offerings include workers' compensation, commercial auto, and umbrella insurance. Grange Mutual and its subsidiaries (including Grange Life, Grange Indemnity, and Grange Property and Casualty) sell their products through a network of some 15,000 independent agents.

GRANITE CITY FOOD & BREWERY LTD.

NASDAQ (CM): GCFB

5402 Parkdale Dr., Ste. 101	CEO: Steven J. (Steve) Wagenheim
Minneapolis, MN 55416	CFO: James G. (Jim) Gilbertson
Phone: 952-215-0660	HR: Liz Severance
Fax: 952-525-2021	FYE: December 31
Web: www.gcfb.net	Type: Public

Drinking and dining form the bedrock of this small restaurant chain. Granite City Food & Brewery owns and operates more than 25 casual dining brewpubs in about a dozen Midwestern states, mostly in Minnesota, Kansas, Illinois, Indiana, and Iowa. The restaurants offer a variety of handcrafted beers that are brewed on-site, including such varieties as Broad Axe Stout, Duke of Wellington (English ale), and Northern Light Lager. Granite City's food menu features chicken, steak, and seafood entrees, along with appetizers, burgers and other sandwiches, and salads.

	Annual Growth	12/05	12/06	12/07	12/08	12/09
Sales ($ mil.)	24.1%	36.2	58.3	75.9	96.3	85.8
Net income ($ mil.)	—	(3.7)	(5.5)	(9.6)	(15.8)	(9.6)
Market value ($ mil.)	(50.3%)	209.5	229.8	117.6	14.5	12.8
Employees	2.6%	1,955	2,150	3,270	2,462	2,168

GRANITE CONSTRUCTION INCORPORATED

NYSE: GVA

585 W. Beach St.	CEO: James H. Roberts
Watsonville, CA 95076	CFO: Laurel J. Krzeminski
Phone: 831-724-1011	HR: Margaret B. (Peg) Wynn
Fax: 831-722-9657	FYE: December 31
Web: www.graniteconstruction.com	Type: Public

Granite Construction is building its way from coast to coast. The holding company operates through its main subsidiary, Granite Construction Company, a transportation and heavy construction contractor that works on public infrastructure projects ranging from airports, bridges, and dams to highways, mass transit systems, and tunnels. For private-sector firms, it performs site preparation for residential and commercial development. The company is aligned geographically into two divisions: Granite West and Granite East. One of its biggest customers is the California Department of Transportation, which accounts for 12% of revenues. Granite also is involved in real estate development and services.

	Annual Growth	12/05	12/06	12/07	12/08	12/09
Sales ($ mil.)	(7.1%)	2,641.4	2,969.6	2,737.9	2,674.2	1,963.5
Net income ($ mil.)	(3.1%)	83.2	80.5	112.1	122.4	73.5
Market value ($ mil.)	(1.6%)	1,393.4	1,952.6	1,403.9	1,704.6	1,306.1
Employees	(15.1%)	5,200	5,200	4,200	3,500	2,700

GRANT THORNTON INTERNATIONAL LTD

175 W. Jackson Blvd., 20th Fl.
Chicago, IL 60604
Phone: 312-856-0200
Fax: 312-602-8099
Web: www.gti.org

CEO: Edward E. (Ed) Nusbaum
CFO: —
HR: Mike Starr
FYE: September 30
Type: Not-for-profit

Grant Thornton International is a kid brother to the Big Four. The umbrella organization consists of nearly 100 independent member firms, which offer accounting and management consulting to public companies and private entities. Member firms (including Grant Thornton LLP) operate from 500 offices in more than 110 countries, making it one of the top second-tier companies that trail behind the big guys (Deloitte Touche Tohmatsu, Ernst & Young Global, KPMG International, and PricewaterhouseCoopers). Services include assurance, tax, business risk, corporate advisory, and other services. By virtue of the consolidation in the industry, Grant Thornton is the longest-lived, same-name network in the world.

	Annual Growth	9/04	9/05	9/06	9/07	9/08
Sales ($ mil.)	17.3%	2,092.0	2,454.0	2,772.0	3,461.0	3,956.0
Employees	10.6%	20,486	22,066	24,577	27,861	30,662

GRANT THORNTON LLP

175 W. Jackson Blvd., 20th Fl.
Chicago, IL 60604
Phone: 312-856-0200
Fax: 312-602-8099
Web: www.grantthornton.com

CEO: Stephen Chipman
CFO: Fred K. Walz
HR: —
FYE: December 31
Type: Partnership

Grant Thornton grants accounting wishes to US clients. The firm encompasses the US operations of Grant Thornton International, one of the largest accountancies outside of the Big Four (Deloitte Touche Tohmatsu, Ernst & Young, KPMG, and PricewaterhouseCoopers). The firm has some 50 US offices. In addition to auditing, Grant Thornton provides its customers with such services as Sarbanes-Oxley expertise, mergers and acquisitions advice, tax services, and business valuations. Target industries include construction, consumer goods, financial services, health care, and technology. Founded as Alexander Richardson in 1924, the firm took its current name in 1986 when it joined with the UK firm Thornton Baker.

	Annual Growth	12/05	12/06	12/07	12/08	12/09
Sales ($ mil.)	—	—	—	—	—	1,210.3
Employees	—	—	—	—	—	5,840

GRAPHIC PACKAGING HOLDING COMPANY

NYSE: GPK

814 Livingston Ct.
Marietta, GA 30067
Phone: 770-644-3000
Fax: 770-644-2962
Web: www.graphicpkg.com

CEO: David W. Scheible
CFO: Daniel J. (Dan) Blount
HR: Cynthia A. Baerman
FYE: December 31
Type: Public

If you've ever toted a 12-pack home, you can appreciate Graphic Packaging's work. The company, operating through subsidiary Graphic Packaging International, is a leading maker of cartons for beverages, food, and consumer products. Most of the company's sales come from its paperboard unit, which makes paperboard at its mills and then converts it into laminated, coated, and printed packaging such as beverage carriers, cereal boxes, and detergent cartons. Customers include such widely recognized companies as Kraft Foods, Anheuser-Busch, Molson Coors Brewing, General Mills, SABMiller, and various Coca-Cola and Pepsi bottlers. In 2008 Graphic Packaging merged with Altivity Packaging in a $1.75 billion deal.

	Annual Growth	12/05	12/06	12/07	12/08	12/09
Sales ($ mil.)	14.5%	2,384.0	2,413.0	2,421.2	4,079.4	4,095.8
Net income ($ mil.)	—	(91.1)	(100.5)	(74.6)	(99.7)	56.4
Market value ($ mil.)	11.1%	782.6	1,486.3	1,266.6	391.3	1,191.1
Employees	13.8%	7,800	7,700	7,400	14,400	13,100

GRAPHON CORPORATION

OTC: GOJO

5400 Soquel Ave., Ste. A2
Santa Cruz, CA 95062
Phone: 603-225-3525
Fax: 831-475-3017
Web: www.graphon.com

CEO: Robert P. (Bob) Dilworth
CFO: William (Bill) Swain
HR: —
FYE: December 31
Type: Public

GraphOn keeps its thin clients on a diet. The company provides business connectivity software that delivers applications to PCs and workstations from a host computer. The company's products enable clients to relocate desktop software to centralized servers and deploy and manage applications when needed, thus conserving computing resources. GraphOn's software can be used to provide access to applications through Linux, UNIX, and Windows platforms. The company serves clients in a variety of industries, including telecommunications, software development, manufacturing, financial services, and electronics.

	Annual Growth	12/05	12/06	12/07	12/08	12/09
Sales ($ mil.)	11.7%	5.2	5.2	11.5	6.7	8.1
Net income ($ mil.)	—	(1.1)	(3.0)	0.2	(2.6)	(1.8)
Market value ($ mil.)	(18.2%)	8.7	6.9	18.4	3.2	3.9
Employees	6.9%	26	34	31	34	34

GRAY TELEVISION, INC.

NYSE: GTN

4370 Peachtree Rd. NE
Atlanta, GA 30319
Phone: 404-504-9828
Fax: 404-261-9607
Web: www.graycommunications.com

CEO: Hilton H. Howell Jr.
CFO: James C. (Jim) Ryan
HR: —
FYE: December 31
Type: Public

Gray Television has The Eye for local television markets. The company is the largest independent operator of TV stations affiliated with the CBS network, with 17 stations in more than a dozen states. In total the company operates more than 35 stations in 30 midsized and smaller markets mostly in the Midwest and South. Its other stations are affiliated with ABC, NBC, and FOX. In addition to traditional analog signals, Gray Television broadcasts an additional 40 digital channels mostly carrying programming from The CW and MyNetworkTV. Former CEO J. Mack Robinson and his family control more than 35% of the company.

	Annual Growth	12/05	12/06	12/07	12/08	12/09
Sales ($ mil.)	0.8%	261.6	332.1	307.3	327.2	270.4
Net income ($ mil.)	—	3.4	11.7	(23.2)	(202.0)	(23.0)
Market value ($ mil.)	(35.4%)	490.8	418.8	458.2	22.9	85.7
Employees	1.1%	2,113	2,117	2,138	1,988	2,208

GRAYBAR ELECTRIC COMPANY, INC.

34 N. Meramec Ave.
St. Louis, MO 63105
Phone: 314-573-9200
Fax: 314-573-9455
Web: www.graybar.com

CEO: Robert A. Reynolds Jr.
CFO: D. Beatty D'Alessandro
HR: Beverly L. Propst
FYE: December 31
Type: Private

There's no gray area when it comes to Graybar Electric: it's one of the largest distributors of electrical products in the US. The employee-owned company pushes more than 1 million electrical, communications, and networking tools through 230-plus distribution facilities. Its diversified lineup nets a myriad of wire, cable, and lighting products from thousands of manufacturers and suppliers, as well as a slate of supply chain management and logistics services. Affiliate Graybar Financial Services offers equipment leasing and financing. Graybar Electric caters to construction contractors, industrial plants, power utilities, and telecommunications providers, primarily in the US.

	Annual Growth	12/04	12/05	12/06	12/07	12/08
Sales ($ mil.)	7.3%	4,079.6	4,288.0	5,009.1	5,258.3	5,400.2
Net income ($ mil.)	58.1%	14.0	16.8	57.4	83.4	87.4
Employees	1.3%	7,700	7,800	8,400	8,600	8,100

An in-depth profile of this company is available to Hoover's Online members at hoovers.com.

GRAYMARK HEALTHCARE, INC.

NASDAQ (CM): GRMH

210 Park Ave., Ste. 1350   CEO: Stanton Nelson
Oklahoma City, OK 73102   CFO: Grant Christianson
Phone: 405-601-5300   HR: —
Fax: 405-601-4550   FYE: December 31
Web: www.graymarkhealthcare.com   Type: Public

Graymark Healthcare wants its businesses to help remedy the ills of small-town Americans. Through its operating subsidiaries, Graymark Healthcare acquires and operates independent pharmacies and sleep diagnostic centers, many of which are located in smaller US markets. Its ApothecaryRx subsidiary manages about 20 pharmacies doing business in a handful of central US states, and the company's Sleep Disorder Centers (SDC) subsidiary manages about 10 sleep diagnostics businesses in the South and Midwest. Formerly Graymark Productions (a film production firm), Graymark changed its name in 2008 following the acquisitions of ApothecaryRx and SDC. In 2009 it added two Kansas-based sleep disorder centers to its network.

	Annual Growth	12/05	12/06	12/07	12/08	12/09
Sales ($ mil.)	304.6%	0.4	0.4	50.3	96.6	107.2
Net income ($ mil.)	—	(0.6)	(2.2)	0.3	0.7	(5.3)
Market value ($ mil.)	13.6%	—	—	—	44.6	50.7
Employees	269.5%	3	2	207	342	559

GREAT AMERICAN FINANCIAL RESOURCES, INC.

525 Vine St.   CEO: S. Craig Lindner
Cincinnati, OH 45202   CFO: Christopher P. Miliano
Phone: 513-333-5300   HR: —
Fax: 513-412-3777   FYE: December 31
Web: www.gafri.com   Type: Subsidiary

Great American Financial Resources (GAFRI) flies the patriotic banners of retirement products and insurance. Its principal subsidiary, Great American Life Insurance Company (GALIC), has marketed insurance products since 1959. The company sells retirement products, primarily fixed and variable annuities. It also offers supplemental health and life insurance through its Loyal American Life Insurance and United Teacher Associates Insurance subsidiaries. Both independent agents and captive agents sell GAFRI's products to its core customers: teachers, government employees, and folks working in the not-for-profit sector. GAFRI is owned by chairman Carl Lindner's American Financial Group.

	Annual Growth	12/04	12/05	12/06	12/07	12/08
Est. sales ($ mil.)	—	—	—	—	—	1,044.0
Employees	—	—	—	—	—	1,422

GREAT AMERICAN INSURANCE COMPANY

580 Walnut St.   CEO: Carl H. Lindner III
Cincinnati, OH 45202   CFO: David J. Witzgall
Phone: 513-369-5000   HR: Spencer Stooksbury
Fax: —   FYE: December 31
Web: www.greatamericaninsurance.com   Type: Subsidiary

Great American Insurance Company is the flagship company of the Great American Insurance Group and is a subsidiary of American Financial Group (AFG). As a niche player in a number of specialty commercial property/casualty markets, the company provides insurance coverage to customers ranging from cattle ranches to adult day care providers to long-haul truckers. It also provides risk management and surety insurance products to lenders, banks, construction contractors, and vehicle leasers. Other products include crop insurance, professional liability coverage, pollution liability, trucking and cargo insurance, excess liability insurance, and alternative risk services.

THE GREAT ATLANTIC & PACIFIC TEA COMPANY

NYSE: GAP

2 Paragon Dr.   CEO: Ron Marshall
Montvale, NJ 07645   CFO: Brenda M. Galgano
Phone: 201-573-9700   HR: —
Fax: 201-505-3054   FYE: February 28
Web: www.aptea.com   Type: Public

Once the biggest baggers of groceries in the US, The Great Atlantic & Pacific Tea Company, Inc. (A&P), had been reduced to a handful of regional grocery chains, but is moving toward filling up its cart again. It runs more than 430 supermarkets in eight eastern states and the District of Columbia. In addition to its mainstay A&P chain, the firm now operates seven others, including Super Fresh along the East Coast from New Jersey to Virginia and The Food Emporium and Waldbaum chains in the New York and New Jersey area. A&P acquired its longtime rival in the Northeast, Pathmark Stores, for about $1.4 billion in 2007, reversing years of decline at the grocery company. Germany's Tengelmann Group owns about 40% of A&P.

	Annual Growth	2/06	2/07	2/08	2/09	2/10
Sales ($ mil.)	0.2%	8,740.3	6,850.3	6,401.1	9,516.2	8,813.6
Net income ($ mil.)	—	392.6	26.9	(160.7)	(139.9)	(876.5)
Market value ($ mil.)	(31.1%)	1,802.4	1,776.7	1,513.0	227.4	406.2
Employees	4.3%	38,000	38,000	51,000	48,000	45,000

GREAT DANE LIMITED PARTNERSHIP

2555 S. Blue Island Ave.   CEO: Phillip (Phill) Pines
Chicago, IL 60608   CFO: John J. Sobota
Phone: 773-254-5533   HR: —
Fax: —   FYE: December 31
Web: www.greatdanetrailers.com   Type: Partnership

Some Great Danes have an all-American heritage. Great Dane Trailers is one of the largest manufacturers of truck trailers in North America. The company makes standard dry freight trailers, refrigerated trailers (reefers), and platform (or flatbed) trailers. Great Dane has manufacturing plants in six US states, with sales, parts, and service centers across North America and South America. Due to the economic downturn and the need for more efficient manufacturing, Great Dane in 2009 closed its original plant in Savannah, Georgia, transferring reefer production to plants in Indiana and Nebraska. Great Dane is a unit of Chicago-based investment group CC Industries, which is controlled by Henry Crown and Company.

	Annual Growth	12/04	12/05	12/06	12/07	12/08
Est. sales ($ mil.)	—	—	—	—	—	422.8
Employees	—	—	—	—	—	3,892

GREAT FLORIDA BANK

NASDAQ (GM): GFLB

15050 NW 79th Ct., Ste. 200   CEO: M. Mehdi Ghomeshi
Miami Lakes, FL 33016   CFO: Gary J. Laurash
Phone: 305-514-6900   HR: Deborah Winkles
Fax: 305-557-4313   FYE: December 31
Web: www.greatfloridabank.com   Type: Public

Great Florida Bank hopes to be the next great Florida bank. Established in 2004, the bank serves Miami-Dade, Broward, and Palm Beach counties through about 30 branches. Serving both individuals and businesses, it offers the usual compliment of products and services, such as checking and savings accounts, CDs, and loans and lines of credit, as well as online money management and banking tools. The bank is mainly a real estate lender: Single-family and multifamily residential mortgages account for about half of its loan portfolio; commercial mortgages and construction and land development loans make up most of the rest. Great Florida Bank also writes business loans and, to a much lesser extent, consumer loans.

	Annual Growth	12/04	12/05	12/06	12/07	*12/08
Assets ($ mil.)	52.4%	341.9	1,006.2	1,536.0	1,809.4	1,843.9
Net income ($ mil.)	—	(7.7)	(3.4)	6.1	0.9	(19.2)
Employees	28.3%	99	134	218	228	268

*Most recent year available

GREAT LAKES AVIATION, LTD.

OTC: GLUX

1022 Airport Pkwy.	CEO: Charles R. Howell IV
Cheyenne, WY 82001	CFO: Michael O. Matthews
Phone: 307-432-7000	HR: Christine Gervais
Fax: 307-432-7001	FYE: December 31
Web: www.flygreatlakes.com	Type: Public

Great Lakes Aviation goes to great lengths to get people where they need to be, even if it's far from the big city. Flying as Great Lakes Airlines, the regional carrier transports passengers to more than 60 destinations in the western and midwestern US, mainly from Denver but also from markets such as Phoenix, Kansas City, and Ontario, California. It maintains code-sharing agreements with Frontier Airlines and United Airlines. (Code-sharing enables carriers to sell tickets on one another's flights and thus extend their networks.) Great Lakes operates a fleet of about 40 turboprop aircraft, consisting mostly of 19-passenger Beechcraft 1900Ds but also including 30-passenger Embraer Brasilia 120s.

	Annual Growth	12/05	12/06	12/07	12/08	12/09
Sales ($ mil.)	12.4%	76.4	87.6	98.2	116.2	121.8
Net income ($ mil.)	48.3%	1.2	15.7	19.2	1.9	5.8
Market value ($ mil.)	8.8%	14.3	32.4	32.9	21.4	20.0
Employees	9.2%	826	845	929	929	1,175

GREAT LAKES CHEESE COMPANY, INC.

17825 Great Lakes Pkwy.	CEO: Gary Vanic
Hiram, OH 44234	CFO: Russell (Russ) Mullins
Phone: 440-834-2500	HR: Beth Wendell
Fax: 440-834-1002	FYE: December 31
Web: www.greatlakescheese.com	Type: Private

Great Lakes Cheese understands the power of provolone, the charm of cheddar, and the goodness of gruyere. Based in Ohio, the firm manufactures and distributes natural and processed cheeses and cheese spreads, including varieties such as cheddar, Colby, Swiss, mozzarella, and provolone. It also makes the premium Adams Reserve New York Cheddar. Great Lakes packages shredded, chunked, and sliced cheese for deli, bulk, and foodservice sale under the Great Lakes, Adams Reserve, and private-label brands. With seven manufacturing plants, Great Lakes Cheese distributes its products, which are sold in deli and dairy cases, throughout the US.

	Annual Growth	12/04	12/05	12/06	12/07	12/08
Sales ($ mil.)	11.8%	1,375.0	1,375.0	1,700.0	1,700.0	2,150.0
Employees	0.0%	1,700	1,700	1,700	1,700	—

GREAT LAKES DREDGE & DOCK CORPORATION

NASDAQ (GS): GLDD

2122 York Rd.	CEO: Douglas B. (Doug) Mackie
Oak Brook, IL 60523	CFO: Deborah A. Wensel
Phone: 630-574-3000	HR: —
Fax: 630-574-2909	FYE: December 31
Web: www.gldd.com	Type: Public

Dig this: Great Lakes Dredge & Dock (GLDD) provides dredging services around the world. The company's services include beach improvement or renourishment, rock dredging, harbor excavation, land reclamation, demolition, and restoration of aquatic and wetland habitats. Among GLDD's projects are maintenance dredging at the Miami Harbor, nourishing San Diego beaches, and expanding Pier J in Long Beach, California. GLDD also owns an 85% stake in North American Site Developers, a commercial/industrial demolition firm. The company was founded in 1890 as the partnership of William A. Lydon & Fred C. Drews.

	Annual Growth	12/05	12/06	12/07	12/08	12/09
Sales ($ mil.)	13.5%	—	426.0	515.8	586.9	622.2
Net income ($ mil.)	99.6%	—	2.2	7.1	5.0	17.5
Market value ($ mil.)	0.2%	—	377.7	510.6	243.0	379.5
Employees	21.6%	—	943	1,491	317	1,694

GREAT NORTHERN IRON ORE PROPERTIES

NYSE: GNI

W-1290 First National Bank Bldg., 332 Minnesota St.	CEO: Joseph S. Micallef
St. Paul, MN 55101	CFO: Thomas A. Janochoski
Phone: 651-224-2385	HR: Thomas A. Janochoski
Fax: 651-224-2387	FYE: December 31
Web: www.gniop.com	Type: Public

Great Northern Iron Ore Properties is the landlord of one big iron formation. The trust gets income from royalties on iron ore minerals (principally taconite) taken from its more than 67,000 acres on the Mesabi Iron Formation in Minnesota. The trust was formed in 1906 to own the properties of an affiliate of Burlington Northern Santa Fe (BNSF, formerly Great Northern Railway). The trust's beneficiaries were the heirs of railroad founder James Hill; however, the last survivor, his grandson Louis Hill, died in 1995. In 2015 (20 years after Louis Hill's death) the land will be transferred to a unit of ConocoPhillips, which acquired the BNSF assets in 2005.

	Annual Growth	12/05	12/06	12/07	12/08	12/09
Sales ($ mil.)	(5.3%)	18.4	17.6	17.2	20.8	14.8
Net income ($ mil.)	(7.7%)	15.7	14.8	14.5	17.6	11.4
Market value ($ mil.)	(9.4%)	208.9	179.2	191.6	107.3	141.0
Employees	0.0%	10	10	10	10	—

GREAT PLAINS ENERGY INCORPORATED

NYSE: GXP

1201 Walnut St.	CEO: Michael J. (Mike) Chesser
Kansas City, MO 64106	CFO: James C. Shay
Phone: 816-556-2200	HR: Heather Humphrey
Fax: 816-556-2992	FYE: December 31
Web: www.greatplainsenergy.com	Type: Public

Great Plains Energy is sweeping the fruited plains with electric light. The holding company serves more than 820,000 electricity customers in Missouri and eastern Kansas through regulated utility Kansas City Power & Light (KCP&L) and KCP&L Greater Missouri Operations Company (which serves customers in Missouri through Missouri Public Service and St. Joseph Light & Power). The utility company has more than 6,000 MW of primarily coal-fired generating capacity. Great Plains Energy has exited most of its deregulated businesses in order to focus on its utility operations.

	Annual Growth	12/05	12/06	12/07	12/08	12/09
Sales ($ mil.)	(6.8%)	2,604.9	2,675.3	3,267.1	1,670.1	1,965.0
Net income ($ mil.)	(1.9%)	162.3	127.6	159.2	154.5	150.4
Market value ($ mil.)	(8.7%)	3,789.7	4,310.2	3,974.1	2,620.0	2,628.1
Employees	7.6%	2,382	2,470	2,504	3,259	3,197

GREAT SOUTHERN BANCORP, INC.

NASDAQ (GS): GSBC

1451 E. Battlefield	CEO: Joseph W. (Joe) Turner
Springfield, MO 65804	CFO: —
Phone: 417-887-4400	HR: Matt Snyder
Fax: —	FYE: December 31
Web: www.greatsouthernbank.com	Type: Public

What do Elvis Presley, Rosa Parks, William Faulkner, and a bank have in common? They're all great southerners. Great Southern Bancorp is the holding company for Great Southern Bank, which operates about 50 branches in Missouri, plus another 20 in Iowa, Kansas, and Nebraska. Founded in 1923, the bank offers checking and savings accounts, CDs, IRAs, and credit cards. Its lending activities include commercial and industrial revenue bonds (about 25% of its loan portfolio), commercial construction loans (another 25%), and residential construction loans (20%). It also writes consumer loans and residential mortgages.

	Annual Growth	12/05	12/06	12/07	12/08	12/09
Assets ($ mil.)	15.0%	2,081.2	2,240.3	2,431.7	2,659.9	3,641.1
Net income ($ mil.)	30.1%	22.7	30.7	29.3	(4.4)	65.0
Market value ($ mil.)	(6.2%)	370.8	396.3	294.9	153.6	286.9
Employees	11.4%	681	725	775	741	1,047

An in-depth profile of this company is available to Hoover's Online members at hoovers.com.

GREAT WEST CASUALTY COMPANY

1100 W. 29th St.
South Sioux City, NE 68776
Phone: 402-494-2411
Fax: 402-494-7480
Web: ssl.gwccnet.com

CEO: Jim Jensen
CFO: Gaylen TenHulzen
HR: —
FYE: December 31
Type: Subsidiary

Great West Casualty Company keeps truckers truckin' across the US. The company, a subsidiary of Chicago-based Old Republic International, specializes in providing insurance and various services for the transportation industry. It offers several kinds of coverage — including auto liability, cargo, garagekeepers, downtime, and inland marine — with trucking companies and owner-operators in mind. Through Great West and Joe Morten & Sons offices, the company serves customers in more than 40 states. Great West Casualty also offers insurance products such as general liability, umbrella, and workers' compensation, and it provides equipment financing through Old Republic Financial Acceptance Corporation.

	Annual Growth	12/04	12/05	12/06	12/07	12/08
Est. sales ($ mil.)	—	—	—	—	—	147.7
Employees	—	—	—	—	—	607

GREAT WESTERN BANCORPORATION, INC.

100 N. Phillips Ave., Ste. 100
Sioux Falls, SD 57104
Phone: 605-334-2548
Fax: —
Web: www.greatwesternbank.com

CEO: Jeffory A. Erickson
CFO: Kevin Roadnight
HR: Colleen Stratton
FYE: June 30
Type: Subsidiary

Great Western Bank operates more than 200 branches in Iowa, Kansas, Missouri, Nebraska, and South Dakota, as well as Arizona and Colorado. Founded in 1907, the bank offers standard services including checking and savings accounts, CDs, and IRAs. Commercial mortgages, construction and land loans, business loans, farm loans, and residential mortgages make up the bulk of the bank's loan portfolio. The bank also offers wealth management, trust, investment, and private banking services. Great Western is owned by National Australia Bank, which acquired the firm in 2008.

GREAT WOLF RESORTS, INC.

NASDAQ (GM): WOLF

122 W. Washington Ave.
Madison, WI 53703
Phone: 608-661-4700
Fax: 608-661-4701
Web: greatwolfresorts.com

CEO: Kimberly K. (Kim) Schaefer
CFO: James A. (Jim) Calder
HR: —
FYE: December 31
Type: Public

Great Wolf Resorts has its customers muttering "Great Scott!" as they pull up to the company's drive-to family resorts. Great Wolf owns and operates a handful of resorts under the Great Wolf Lodge name in mostly midwestern US states. It also operates the Blue Harbor Resort, which features a conference center with a nautical theme. Great Wolf's properties are open year-round and include lodging, indoor water parks, themed restaurants, and other diversions such as arcades, spas, and organized children's activities. The company is growing quickly and plans to open at least two new resorts each year. Great Wolf was formed in 2004 to succeed the properties' previous owner, The Great Lakes Companies.

	Annual Growth	12/05	12/06	12/07	12/08	12/09
Sales ($ mil.)	17.3%	139.4	148.6	187.6	245.5	264.0
Net income ($ mil.)	—	(24.4)	(49.3)	(9.6)	(40.7)	(58.5)
Market value ($ mil.)	(30.8%)	333.2	451.2	317.1	49.8	76.6
Employees	17.0%	2,560	3,600	4,200	4,300	4,800

GREATBATCH, INC.

NYSE: GB

10000 Wehrle Dr.
Clarence, NY 14031
Phone: 716-759-5600
Fax: 716-759-5660
Web: www.greatbatch.com

CEO: Thomas J. Hook
CFO: Thomas J. Mazza
HR: Barbara Davis
FYE: December 31
Type: Public

Greatbatch likes to keep its business close to the heart. The company is a leading maker of batteries used in implantable medical devices such as pacemakers and implantable cardioverter defibrillators (ICDs). Other medical components include electrodes, capacitors, and feedthroughs (used to deliver electrical signals from an implantable medical device to an electrode). Greatbatch also makes batteries for demanding industrial applications, such as oil and gas exploration, and supplies power sources for the Space Shuttle. Boston Scientific, Medtronic, and St. Jude Medical are the company's top customers; together, they account for about 44% of sales. Greatbatch gets nearly half of its sales from US clients.

	Annual Growth	12/05	12/06	12/07	12/08	12/09
Sales ($ mil.)	21.3%	241.1	271.1	318.7	546.6	521.8
Net income ($ mil.)	—	10.1	16.1	15.1	18.6	(9.0)
Market value ($ mil.)	(7.3%)	604.1	625.2	464.3	614.5	446.6
Employees	23.0%	1,338	1,835	2,445	3,283	3,061

GREAT-WEST LIFE & ANNUITY INSURANCE COMPANY

8515 E. Orchard Rd.
Greenwood Village, CO 80111
Phone: 303-737-3000
Fax: 303-737-4861
Web: www.greatwest.com

CEO: Mitchell T. G. Graye
CFO: James L. McCallen
HR: —
FYE: December 31
Type: Subsidiary

Great-West Life & Annuity Insurance is the southern arm of a northern parent. The company, a subsidiary of Canada's Great-West Lifeco and a member of the Power Financial family, represents the Great-West group's primary US operations. The company's Financial Services segment offers life insurance and annuities to individuals and, under the Great-West Retirement Services brand, administers employer-sponsored retirement products, including defined-benefit and 401(k) plans. In 2008 the company sold its Healthcare division to CIGNA for $1.5 billion; the segment offered group life and medical insurance products to US businesses, with an emphasis on self-funded programs for small and midsized employers.

	Annual Growth	12/04	12/05	12/06	12/07	12/08
Est. sales ($ mil.)	—	—	—	—	—	2,011.1
Employees	—	—	—	—	—	6,600

GREATWIDE LOGISTICS SERVICES, LLC

12404 Park Central Dr., Ste. 300S
Dallas, TX 75251
Phone: 972-228-7300
Fax: 972-228-7328
Web: www.greatwide.com

CEO: Leo H. Suggs
CFO: Robert C. (Bob) LaRose
HR: Kyle Killingsworth
FYE: December 31
Type: Private

Greatwide Logistics Services brings together a world of freight transportation and logistics companies. The third-party logistics provider offers dedicated transportation, in which drivers and equipment are assigned to a customer long-term; distribution logistics; truckload freight brokerage; and truckload freight transportation, largely via a network of more than 20,000 independent owner-operators. Greatwide calls upon a fleet of some 5,000 trucks and has 3 million sq. ft. of warehouse space in the US. Clients have included such heavy hitters as Target, Wal-Mart, and IBM. In March 2009 Greatwide emerged from Chapter 11 bankruptcy protection after being acquired by an investor group.

	Annual Growth	12/04	12/05	12/06	12/07	12/08
Sales ($ mil.)	3.4%	—	1,087.0	1,200.0	1,140.0	1,200.0
Employees	3.5%	—	2,800	3,000	3,000	—

An in-depth profile of this company is available to Hoover's Online members at hoovers.com.

GREEN BANKSHARES, INC
NASDAQ (GS): GRNB

100 N. Main St.
Greeneville, TN 37743
Phone: 423-639-5111
Fax: 423-787-1235
Web: www.mybankconnection.com

CEO: Stephen M. Rownd
CFO: James E. Adams
HR: Steve D. Ottinger
FYE: December 31
Type: Public

The color of money is Green Bankshares' favorite hue. The holding company owns GreenBank, which operates more than 60 branches, mostly in central and eastern and Tennessee. It also has single branches in North Carolina and Virginia. The bank focuses on real estate lending, with commercial mortgages making up approximately 60% of its loan portfolio and residential mortgages adding almost another 20%. Its deposit products include checking and savings accounts and CDs. Money management is offered through its GreenWealth division. Subsidiaries include consumer finance firm Superior Financial Services, subprime auto lending firm GCB Acceptance Corporation, and title insurance company Fairway Title.

	Annual Growth	12/05	12/06	12/07	12/08	12/09
Assets ($ mil.)	12.8%	1,620.0	1,772.7	2,947.7	2,944.7	2,619.1
Net income ($ mil.)	—	14.2	21.3	24.4	(5.4)	(150.7)
Market value ($ mil.)	(39.8%)	357.6	519.3	251.0	178.6	46.8
Employees	6.3%	561	609	789	737	716

GREEN BAY PACKAGING INC.

1700 N. Webster Ct.
Green Bay, WI 54307
Phone: 920-433-5111
Fax: 920-433-5471
Web: www.gbp.com

CEO: William F. (Will) Kress
CFO: Joseph Baemmert
HR: —
FYE: December 31
Type: Private

Green Bay Packaging is the other Green Bay packers' enterprise. The integrated and diversified paperboard packaging manufacturer operates through 30 divisions in 15 states. In addition to corrugated containers, the company makes pressure-sensitive label stock, folding cartons, linerboard, and lumber products. Its Fiber Resources division in Arkansas manages more than 210,000 acres of company-owned forests and produces lumber, woodchips, recycled paper, and wood fuel. Green Bay Packaging also offers fiber procurement, wastepaper brokerage, and paper-slitting services. The company is owned by the family of its founder, George Kress.

THE GREEN BAY PACKERS, INC.

Lambeau Field Atrium, 1265 Lombardi Ave.
Green Bay, WI 54304
Phone: 920-569-7500
Fax: 920-569-7301
Web: www.packers.com

CEO: Mark H. Murphy
CFO: Paul Baniel
HR: Autumn Thomas-Beenenga
FYE: March 31
Type: Not-for-profit

On the frozen tundra of Lambeau Field, the Green Bay Packers battle for pride in the National Football League. The not-for-profit corporation owns and operates the storied Packers football franchise, which was founded in 1919 by Earl "Curly" Lambeau and joined the NFL in 1921. Home to such icons as Bart Starr, Ray Nitschke, and legendary coach Vince Lombardi, Green Bay boasts a record 12 championship titles, including three Super Bowl victories (its last in Super Bowl XXXI after the 1996 season). The team is also the only community-owned franchise in American professional sports with more than 112,000 shareholders. The shares do not increase in value nor pay dividends, and can only be sold back to the team.

	Annual Growth	3/05	3/06	3/07	3/08	3/09
Sales ($ mil.)	5.5%	200.0	208.4	218.1	241.0	247.9
Employees	15.6%	150	150	200	189	268

GREEN MOUNTAIN COFFEE ROASTERS, INC.
NASDAQ (GS): GMCR

33 Coffee Ln.
Waterbury, VT 05676
Phone: 802-244-5621
Fax: 802-244-5436
Web: www.greenmountaincoffee.com

CEO: Lawrence J. (Larry) Blanford
CFO: Frances G. (Fran) Rathke
HR: Kathryn S. (Kathy) Brooks
FYE: September 30
Type: Public

Green Mountain Coffee Roasters' business amounts to more than a hill of beans. The company offers more than 200 varieties of coffee, cocoa, and tea, which it sells to wholesale customers such as supermarkets, convenience stores, resorts, and office-delivery services. Its client list has included ExxonMobil convenience stores and McDonald's restaurants. The firm's coffee is sold under the Newman's Own Organics, Tully's, and its namesake Green Mountain Coffee labels. In addition, Green Mountain sells the K-Cup single-cup brewing systems for office and home use made by its subsidiary Keurig. Following a string of acquisitions in 2009, the firm bought California-based Diedrich Coffee in 2010.

	Annual Growth	9/05	9/06	9/07	9/08	9/09
Sales ($ mil.)	49.3%	161.5	225.3	341.7	500.3	803.0
Net income ($ mil.)	57.9%	9.0	8.4	12.8	22.3	55.9
Market value ($ mil.)	75.8%	339.0	358.7	970.4	1,150.3	3,238.5
Employees	22.4%	676	849	995	1,220	1,517

GREEN MOUNTAIN ENERGY COMPANY

300 W 6th St., Ste. 900
Austin, TX 78701
Phone: 512-691-6100
Fax: 512-691-6151
Web: www.greenmountain.com

CEO: Paul D. Thomas
CFO: Bryan M. DeCordova
HR: —
FYE: December 31
Type: Private

The power is always greener on this side of the mountain. Green Mountain Energy buys and resells green power generated from hydroelectric, solar, wind, geothermal, and natural and landfill gas facilities. It has helped develop about 40 wind and solar renewable facilities around the US (which along with other green energy initiatives has led to the delivery of more than 33 million MWh of cleaner energy into the US power market). The renewable energy facilities have been responsible for avoiding the use of more than 674,340 tons of carbon dioxide, a greenhouse gas that is a primary contributor to global warming. Dutch utility Nuon and oil giant BP have invested heavily in the firm.

GREEN PLAINS RENEWABLE ENERGY, INC.
NASDAQ (CM): GPRE

105 N. 31st Ave., Ste. 103
Omaha, NE 68131
Phone: 402-884-8700
Fax: 402-884-8776
Web: www.gpreinc.com

CEO: Todd A. Becker
CFO: Jerry L. Peters
HR: —
FYE: December 31
Type: Public

It's plain to Green Plains Renewable Energy that, with stratospheric oil prices, there is green to be made in ethanol production. Formed in 2004, the company operates six ethanol facilities in Indiana, Iowa, Nebraska, and Tennessee. A combination of plants it has constructed itself and others Green Plains Renewable has bought, the company produces about 480 million gallons of ethanol annually. It also sells ethanol produced by others, bringing the company's total to almost 800 million gallons. In addition, Green Plains Renewable Energy's plants, when operating at full capacity, produce 1.5 million tons of animal feed known as distillers grains, the primary by-product of ethanol production.

	Annual Growth	11/05	11/06	11/07	*12/08	12/09
Sales ($ mil.)	634.1%	—	—	24.2	188.8	1,304.2
Net income ($ mil.)	—	—	—	(7.1)	(6.9)	19.8
Market value ($ mil.)	21.9%	—	—	313.5	57.7	466.2
Employees	196.0%	—	—	50	308	438

*Fiscal year change

An in-depth profile of this company is available to Hoover's Online members at hoovers.com.

GREEN ST. ENERGY, INC.

Pink Sheets: GSTY

123 Green St.
Tehachapi, CA 93561
Phone: 310-556-9688
Fax: 310-277-1278
Web: greenstenergy.com

CEO: Anthony J. (Tony) Cataldo
CFO: Jeffrey Figelwicz
HR: —
FYE: December 31
Type: Public

Green St. Energy (formerly known as M~Wave) got bored with boards and got into alternative energy. The company in early 2009 signed an agreement to purchase 160 acres of land in California that will be developed as a wind farm. Green St. Energy is negotiating to purchase another 4,840 acres of land in the same location. Senior executives of the company in 2008 offered to buy M~Wave's assets for $500,000 and the assumption of all operating liabilities; the transaction was completed in early 2009. M~Wave then changed its name to Green St. Energy.

	Annual Growth	12/04	12/05	12/06	12/07	*12/08
Sales ($ mil.)	—	17.5	16.6	9.8	11.6	0.0
Net income ($ mil.)	—	(0.3)	(5.4)	(3.2)	(1.5)	(1.4)
Market value ($ mil.)	(68.8%)	37.9	16.4	16.4	11.1	0.4
Employees	(39.9%)	23	20	21	21	3

*Most recent year available

GREENBERG TRAURIG, LLP

1221 Brickell Ave.
Miami, FL 33131
Phone: 305-579-0500
Fax: 305-579-0717
Web: www.gtlaw.com

CEO: Richard A. Rosenbaum
CFO: Larry Harris
HR: Carol Allen
FYE: December 31
Type: Partnership

Greenberg Traurig is known for its entertainment practice, but show business isn't the firm's only legal business. Its 1,800-plus lawyers maintain a wide range of practices, including corporate and securities, intellectual property, labor and employment, litigation, and real estate. Clients have included Delta Air Lines, Lorimar Pictures, and Metromedia Company. The firm has about 30 offices, mainly in the US but also in Europe and the Asia/Pacific region. It extends its network in Europe and Asia via strategic alliances. Greenberg Traurig was founded in 1967 by Mel Greenberg.

	Annual Growth	12/04	12/05	12/06	12/07	12/08
Sales ($ mil.)	0.3%	—	—	—	1,200.0	1,204.0
Employees	—	—	—	—	—	—

THE GREENBRIER COMPANIES, INC.

NYSE: GBX

1 Centerpointe Dr., Ste. 200
Lake Oswego, OR 97035
Phone: 503-684-7000
Fax: 503-684-7553
Web: www.gbrx.com

CEO: William A. (Bill) Furman
CFO: Mark J. Rittenbaum
HR: —
FYE: August 31
Type: Public

Greenbrier has been working for the railroads all the livelong day. The company manufactures, repairs, and refurbishes railcars. Its railcar line includes 100-ton-capacity boxcars, intermodal railcars, tank cars, and conventional railcars such as gondolas, center-partition cars, and flat cars. The company maintains manufacturing facilities in North America and Europe. Greenbrier's leasing unit owns and manages a fleet of about 9,000 railcars and manages another 226,000 railcars on behalf of railroads and other transportation and leasing companies in North America. Greenbrier also makes marine vessels, primarily ocean-going barges. The company gets more than 80% of its sales within the US.

	Annual Growth	8/05	8/06	8/07	8/08	8/09
Sales ($ mil.)	(0.1%)	1,024.2	953.8	1,223.8	1,290.1	1,018.1
Net income ($ mil.)	—	29.8	39.6	22.0	19.5	(54.1)
Market value ($ mil.)	(18.3%)	494.4	476.0	503.4	343.6	220.5
Employees	(1.8%)	3,972	3,661	4,239	4,174	3,693

GREENE COUNTY BANCORP, INC.

NASDAQ (CM): GCBC

302 Main St.
Catskill, NY 12414
Phone: 518-943-2600
Fax: 518-943-4431
Web: www.thebankofgreenecounty.com

CEO: Donald E. Gibson
CFO: Michelle M. Plummer
HR: Rebecca R. Main
FYE: June 30
Type: Public

This company helps put the "green" in Greene. Greene County Bancorp is the holding company for The Bank of Greene County, serving upstate New York's Catskill Mountains region from about 10 branches. Founded in 1889 as a building and loan association, the bank offers traditional retail products such as savings, NOW, checking, and money market accounts; IRAs; and CDs. Real estate loans make up nearly 85% of the bank's lending activities; it also writes business and consumer loans. Through affiliations with Fenimore Asset Management and Essex Corp., Greene County Bancorp offers investment products to existing customers. Subsidiary Greene County Commercial Bank is a state-chartered limited purpose commercial bank.

	Annual Growth	6/05	6/06	6/07	6/08	6/09
Assets ($ mil.)	11.8%	294.7	307.6	325.8	379.6	460.5
Net income ($ mil.)	9.0%	2.9	2.2	2.3	2.7	4.1
Market value ($ mil.)	(5.0%)	73.4	61.0	56.0	56.2	59.7
Employees	4.0%	106	101	118	122	124

GREENHILL & CO, INC.

NYSE: GHL

300 Park Ave., 23rd Fl.
New York, NY 10022
Phone: 212-389-1500
Fax: 212-389-1700
Web: www.greenhill-co.com

CEO: Scott L. Bok
CFO: Richard J. Lieb
HR: —
FYE: December 31
Type: Public

It's no secret what the favorite color is around the offices of Greenhill & Co. The investment bank specializes in mergers and acquisitions, corporate restructurings, venture capital, and merchant banking for clients worldwide. Merchant banking activities are conducted through the firm's Greenhill Capital Partners unit, which makes private equity investments typically in the $10 million to $75 million range. Its Barrow Street Capital unit invests in real estate funds. Greenhill's high-profile transactions have included advising on the acquisition of Northwest Airlines by Delta Air Lines and Nikko Cordial's share exchange with Citigroup.

	Annual Growth	12/05	12/06	12/07	12/08	12/09
Sales ($ mil.)	7.8%	221.2	290.6	400.4	221.9	298.6
Net income ($ mil.)	6.4%	55.5	75.7	115.3	49.0	71.2
Market value ($ mil.)	9.3%	1,654.1	2,173.7	1,958.1	2,055.0	2,363.4
Employees	17.7%	151	201	214	234	290

GREENLIGHT CAPITAL, INC.

2 Grand Central Tower, 140 E. 45th St., 24th Fl.
New York, NY 10017
Phone: 212-973-1900
Fax: 212-973-9219
Web: www.greenlightcapital.com

CEO: David M. Einhorn
CFO: Harry Brandler
HR: —
FYE: December 31
Type: Private

Red means stop, and green means . . . more capital? Greenlight Capital is a hedge fund firm that invests primarily in publicly traded North American corporate debt offerings and equities. Founded in 1996, the $6 billion Greenlight Capital also manages a fund of funds and a private equity fund through its affiliates, Greenlight Masters and Greenlight Private Equity Partners. It also operates Greenlight Capital Re, a property/casualty reinsurer. The company is led by activist investor David Einhorn, who has made a name for himself both in the boardroom and at the card table (as a finalist in the World Series of Poker).

	Annual Growth	12/04	12/05	12/06	12/07	12/08
Est. sales ($ mil.)	—	—	—	—	—	0.7
Employees	—	—	—	—	—	8

GREENMAN TECHNOLOGIES, INC.

OTC: GMTI

12498 Wyoming Ave. South
Savage, MN 55378
Phone: 781-224-2411
Fax: 781-224-0114
Web: www.greenman.biz

CEO: Lyle E. Jensen
CFO: Charles E. (Chuck) Coppa
HR: —
FYE: September 30
Type: Public

GreenMan Technologies grew tired of collecting old tires and is betting on alternative fuel systems and recycled materials as the primary sources of its future revenues. The company had collected and shredded the equivalent of about 13 million passenger tires a year for use in landfills, roads, and septic fields. In mid-2009 it sold this low-margin business, acquired American Power Group (APG), and announced plans to commercialize APG's proprietary dual-fuel energy technology. These external fuel systems allow for the easy conversion of diesel engines to dual-fuel use, such as diesel and compressed natural gas. GreenMan's GreenTech Products uses granulated, recycled rubber to make playground turf.

	Annual Growth	9/05	9/06	9/07	9/08	9/09
Sales ($ mil.)	(38.3%)	22.1	17.6	20.2	26.7	3.2
Net income ($ mil.)	—	(15.2)	(3.7)	0.3	7.9	8.0
Market value ($ mil.)	24.9%	7.6	10.9	11.6	12.9	18.5
Employees	(31.5%)	159	79	77	88	35

GREENSHIFT CORPORATION

OTC: GERS

1 Penn Plaza, Ste. 1612
New York, NY 10119
Phone: 212-994-5374
Fax: 646-572-6336
Web: www.greenshift.com

CEO: Kevin E. Kreisler
CFO: Edward R. Carroll
HR: —
FYE: December 31
Type: Public

In a case of modern alchemy, GreenShift (formerly GS CleanTech) is working overtime to turn organic material into biodiesel. The company's proprietary technologies are used to produce biomass-derived end products, and at reduced cost and risk by extracting and refining raw materials that other producers cannot access or process. GreenShift owns and operates four proprietary corn oil extraction facilities, one biodiesel production facility, and one vegetable oilseed crushing plant. GreenShift claims that its technologies have the capability of extracting more than 6.5 million gallons of crude corn oil for every 100 million gallons of corn ethanol produced. The company also produces culinary oil.

	Annual Growth	12/0	12/06	12/07	12/08	12/09
Sales ($ mil.)	—	—	—	—	—	3.9
Employees	—	—	—	—	—	75

GREIF, INC.

NYSE: GEF

425 Winter Rd.
Delaware, OH 43015
Phone: 740-549-6000
Fax: 740-549-6100
Web: www.greif.com

CEO: Michael J. Gasser
CFO: Donald S. (Don) Huml
HR: Karen P. Lane
FYE: October 31
Type: Public

Unlike a box of chocolates, with Greif (rhymes with "life") you know what you're going to get. The company produces containers and containerboard, mainly for bulk shippers in chemical, food, petroleum, and pharmaceutical industries. Greif's lineup includes shipping drums and drum closure systems, as well as water bottles. It also makes containerboard, corrugated sheets and containers, and multiwall packaging for specialized markets. Greif's multiwall bag products are used to ship industrial and consumer products, from chemicals to flour, pet foods, seed, and sugar. Greif manages timber properties in the US and Canada, too. Manufacturing plants dot 45-plus countries, largely supporting sales in North America.

	Annual Growth	10/05	10/06	10/07	10/08	10/09
Sales ($ mil.)	3.6%	2,424.3	2,628.5	3,322.3	3,776.8	2,792.2
Net income ($ mil.)	6.0%	104.7	142.1	156.4	234.4	132.4
Market value ($ mil.)	15.2%	1,431.8	2,206.5	2,995.0	1,911.0	2,520.3
Employees	(2.6%)	9,100	9,025	10,300	9,600	8,200

GREY GLOBAL GROUP INC.

200 5th Ave.
New York, NY 10010
Phone: 212-546-2020
Fax: 212-546-2001
Web: www.grey.com

CEO: James R. (Jim) Heekin III
CFO: —
HR: Natalia Schultz
FYE: December 31
Type: Subsidiary

Advertising expertise is certainly not gray area for this company. A unit of UK-based conglomerate WPP Group, Grey Global Group provides advertising and marketing services through about 430 offices in more than 95 countries. Its flagship agency network, Grey Worldwide, offers creative ad development and campaign management services along with a variety of other marketing disciplines. The company also offers specialized public relations and communications services through Grey Healthcare. Its G2 Worldwide unit is a leading brand development agency, while G2 Direct & Digital offers direct marketing services. It was originally founded in 1917 as Grey Advertising.

GREYHOUND LINES, INC.

600 Vine Street, Ste. 1400
Cincinnati, OH 45202
Phone: 513-241-2200
Fax: 513-419-3394
Web: www.greyhound.com

CEO: Dave Leach
CFO: Andrew Kaplinsky
HR: Rhonda Piar MacAndrew
FYE: December 31
Type: Subsidiary

If you're going by bus, the old gray dog is likely to be the only one on the track. The only US bus company with a regular nationwide intercity schedule, Greyhound Lines carries some 22 million passengers yearly to more than 3,100 destinations, mainly in the US but also in Canada and Mexico. Some markets are served via partnerships with regional bus lines. The company's fleet includes about 1,250 buses. In conjunction with its intercity passenger service, Greyhound offers express package delivery. It also provides charter bus services. Greyhound is a unit of FirstGroup America.

GREYSTONE LOGISTICS, INC.

OTC: GLGI

1613 E. 15th St.
Tulsa, OK 74120
Phone: 918-583-7441
Fax: 918-583-7442
Web: www.greystonelogistics-glgi.com

CEO: Warren F. Kruger
CFO: —
HR: —
FYE: May 31
Type: Public

If you need plastic pallets, then Greystone Logistics is the logical choice for you. The company manufactures and sells plastic pallets for various commercial applications. Its products include the Greystone Beverage Pallet, Hawker Series fire-retardant plastic pallets, Tank picture frame pallets, and the Granada Series (including nestable and flat-deck plastic pallets). Greystone Logistics also offers multi-station plastic injection molding systems. The company uses a proprietary recycled resin mix and manufacturing process to produce its plastics. It serves customers in the pharmaceutical, beverage, and other industries, primarily in the US.

	Annual Growth	5/05	5/06	5/07	5/08	5/09
Sales ($ mil.)	15.8%	9.3	16.0	12.5	21.1	16.7
Net income ($ mil.)	—	(10.4)	(2.3)	(2.6)	0.9	0.8
Market value ($ mil.)	(3.6%)	7.6	2.6	5.2	5.7	6.5
Employees	(4.1%)	84	75	85	85	71

An in-depth profile of this company is available to Hoover's Online members at hoovers.com.

GREYSTONE POWER CORPORATION

4040 Bankhead Hwy.
Douglasville, GA 30134
Phone: 770-942-6576
Fax: 770-489-0940
Web: www.greystonepower.com

CEO: Gary A. Miller
CFO: Kara Pearson
HR: Marcita Scharnhorst
FYE: December 31
Type: Cooperative

By the power of GreyStone, customers in northwestern Georgia are not in peril of darkness. GreyStone Power is an electric membership cooperative that provides transmission and distribution services to more than 101,000 residential, commercial, and industrial customers in eight counties west of Atlanta (Bartow, Carroll, Cobb, Coweta, Douglas, Fayette, Fulton, and Paulding). The utility operates more than 6,400 miles of power lines. GreyStone Power offers natural gas services through a partnership with Gas South and also offers banking, residential and commercial security, and surge protection operations.

	Annual Growth	12/04	12/05	12/06	12/07	12/08
Est. sales ($ mil.)	—	—	—	—	—	218.9
Employees	—	—	—	—	—	268

GRIFFIN INDUSTRIES, INC.

4221 Alexandria Pike
Cold Spring, KY 41076
Phone: 859-781-2010
Fax: 859-572-2575
Web: www.griffinind.com

CEO: Robert A. Griffin
CFO: Anthony Griffin
HR: Nancy Cooper
FYE: December 31
Type: Private

Griffin Industries takes what no one else wants to deal with and renders it useful. The company gathers up the inedible scraps and waste from meat-processing plants and grocery stores, used cooking oils and waste from restaurants and bakeries, and even just plain old dead farm animals. It then turns these into animal feed, fertilizer, tanned leather, solvents, industrial oils and fats, and alternative fuel for vehicles. (Its biodiesel is created from spent cooking oil, so exhaust from vehicles using the fuel can smell like french fries.) Griffin's products are sold around the world. Griffin Industries is owned and operated by the five sons of John and Rosellen Griffin, who founded the company in 1943.

	Annual Growth	12/04	12/05	12/06	12/07	12/08
Est. sales ($ mil.)	—	—	—	—	—	103.6
Employees	—	—	—	—	—	1,000

GRIFFIN LAND & NURSERIES, INC.

NASDAQ (GM): GRIF

1 Rockefeller Plaza
New York, NY 10020
Phone: 212-218-7910
Fax: 212-218-7917
Web: www.imperialnurseries.com

CEO: Frederick M. Danziger
CFO: Anthony J. Galici
HR: —
FYE: November 30
Type: Public

Griffin Land & Nurseries aims to reshape the suburban landscape. Through subsidiary Imperial Nurseries, it grows and distributes container-based plants, mostly broadleaf evergreens such as rhododendrons, to garden center operators and the garden departments of retail chain stores. Griffin also has real estate operations, including land holdings in Connecticut and Massachusetts for industrial, commercial, and residential development. Griffin owns small percentages of a nursery distributor and a business magazine publisher. The Cullman and Ernst families together own more than 50% of Griffin.

	Annual Growth	11/05	11/06	11/07	11/08	11/09
Sales ($ mil.)	(1.7%)	41.9	53.2	59.4	44.5	39.2
Net income ($ mil.)	—	(1.4)	(0.2)	8.3	(8.3)	(5.5)
Market value ($ mil.)	4.0%	120.9	160.2	187.0	163.3	141.5
Employees	(14.9%)	223	206	205	174	117

GRIFFITH LABORATORIES INTERNATIONAL, INC.

1 Griffith Center
Alsip, IL 60803
Phone: 708-371-0900
Fax: 708-597-3294
Web: www.griffithlaboratories.com

CEO: Hervé de la Vauvre
CFO: Joseph (Joe) Maslick
HR: Stephen (Steve) Lee
FYE: September 30
Type: Private

A little pinch here, a little pinch there, pretty soon you have a business. Griffith Laboratories is a food-ingredient manufacturer with operations and customers worldwide. The company's clients include food manufacturers; foodservice operators, such as restaurants, hotels, and cruise lines; and food retailers and wholesalers. Its products include seasonings, sauce and soup mixes, condiments, texturizers, and bakery blends. Griffith's subsidiaries include Custom Culinary (food bases and mixes) and Innova (meat and savory flavors). The company also offers customized ingredient services. Griffith has operations in the Americas, Asia, Europe, India, Africa, and the Middle East.

	Annual Growth	9/04	9/05	9/06	9/07	9/08
Est. sales ($ mil.)	—	—	—	—	—	635.0
Employees	—	—	—	—	—	2,500

⊞ GRIFFON CORPORATION

NYSE: GFF

712 Fifth Ave., 18th Fl.
New York, NY 10019
Phone: 212-957-5000
Fax: —
Web: www.griffoncorp.com

CEO: Ronald J. Kramer
CFO: Douglas J. (Doug) Wetmore
HR: —
FYE: September 30
Type: Public

Griffon has its fingers in a number of pies — a wide variety of pies, in fact. Its largest division is Clopay Plastic Products, which develops and makes specialty plastic films for use in disposable diapers, adult incontinence products, medical garments, and surgical drapes. Clopay Building Products makes residential and commercial garage doors. (Both Clopay units are part of subsidiary Clopay Corporation.) Finally, Telephonics makes advanced information and communications products used in radar, air-traffic control, and defense systems. The US government accounts for most of Telephonics' sales, but the firm also serves commercial and foreign clients. The US accounts for about 70% of Griffon's overall sales.

	Annual Growth	9/05	9/06	9/07	9/08	9/09
Sales ($ mil.)	(3.9%)	1,402.0	1,636.6	1,616.6	1,269.3	1,194.1
Net income ($ mil.)	(17.3%)	48.8	51.8	22.1	(40.5)	22.8
Market value ($ mil.)	(20.0%)	1,466.8	1,423.3	900.4	537.8	600.5
Employees	(9.1%)	5,700	5,700	5,300	4,100	3,900

GRIFOLS, INC.

2410 Lillyvale Ave.
Los Angeles, CA 90032
Phone: 800-421-0008
Fax: 323-227-7616
Web: www.grifolsusa.com/divisions.html

CEO: Gregory Gene (Greg) Rich
CFO: Alfredo Arroyo Guerra
HR: Mateo Borrás
FYE: December 31
Type: Private

Grifols has a good grip on the health care industry. The company provides products and services through three primary divisions: bioscience, diagnostic, and hospital. The bioscience division processes plasma from the company's collection centers into therapeutic derivative products such as coagulation factors and liver dialysis products. Its diagnostic division makes reagents and testing devices and instruments for laboratories, including blood bags, separators, incubators, and refrigerators. Grifols provides equipment, software, nutritional products, and IV preparations for hospitals and pharmacies through its hospital division. The company operates nationwide and is a subsidiary of Spain-based Grifols, S.A.

THE GROCERS SUPPLY CO., INC.

3131 E. Holcombe Blvd.
Houston, TX 77021
Phone: 713-747-5000
Fax: 713-746-5611
Web: www.grocerssupply.com

CEO: Max S. Levit
CFO: Vicki Baum
HR: Cindy Bradley
FYE: December 31
Type: Private

Need crackers in Caracas or vanilla in Manila? Grocers Supply Co. distributes groceries near and far. The company (not to be confused with fellow Texas distributor GSC Enterprises) supplies food, health and beauty items, household products, and school and office supplies to nearly 2,000 convenience stores and grocery retailers, as well as some 200 schools, within a 350-mile radius of Houston. The company's international division, meanwhile, ships supplies to oil company operations, US embassies, and other customers around the world. It also owns Fiesta Mart, a chain of ethnic food stores. Grocers Supply was founded by Joe Levit in 1923; his family, led by president Max Levit, continues to own the company.

	Annual Growth	12/04	12/05	12/06	12/07	12/08
Est. sales ($ mil.)	15.8%	—	1,900.0	2,510.0	2,720.0	2,950.0
Employees	68.4%	—	2,000	8,800	8,900	9,550

GROEN BROTHERS AVIATION, INC.

Pink Sheets: GNBA

2640 W. California Ave.
Salt Lake City, UT 84104
Phone: 801-973-0177
Fax: 801-973-4027
Web: www.groenbros.com

CEO: David L. Groen
CFO: David L. Groen
HR: —
FYE: June 30
Type: Public

A centaur is part man, part horse; a griffin is part eagle, part lion; and a gyroplane is part helicopter, part airplane. Through its subsidiaries Groen Brothers Aviation develops and manufactures gyroplane and gyrodyne rotor-wing aircraft. Its Hawk series gyroplane is designed to be safer in low and slow flight than either an airplane or a helicopter. Gyroplanes, also known as autogyros or gyrocopters, derive lift from rotary blades and thrust from a propeller. Potential applications for the Hawk series include commercial surveying, fire patrol, law enforcement, and military surveillance.

	Annual Growth	6/04	6/05	6/06	6/07	*6/08
Sales ($ mil.)	85.3%	0.5	0.9	3.1	3.4	5.9
Net income ($ mil.)	—	(12.5)	(13.4)	(20.1)	(25.4)	(19.8)
Market value ($ mil.)	(28.4%)	32.6	32.6	27.4	27.4	8.6
Employees	(68.8%)	—	—	72	92	7

*Most recent year available

GROENDYKE TRANSPORT, INC.

2510 Rock Island Blvd.
Enid, OK 73701
Phone: 580-234-4663
Fax: 580-234-1216
Web: www.groendyke.com

CEO: John D. Groendyke
CFO: —
HR: Robert J. (Rob) Fries
FYE: December 31
Type: Private

Using a fleet of about 1,050 tractors and 1,700 trailers, Groendyke Transport hauls bulk cargo throughout North America. The company operates from a network of more than 30 terminals, primarily in the southwestern and midwestern US. Among the commodities moved by Groendyke Transport are chemicals, petroleum, and grain products. Customers have included ADM, BASF, Dow Chemical, Eastman Chemical, and Koch Industries. Founded by Harold Groendyke in 1932, Groendyke Transport is owned by the Groendyke family, including chairman and CEO John Groendyke, Harold's son.

GROUP 1 AUTOMOTIVE, INC.

NYSE: GPI

950 Echo Ln., Ste. 100
Houston, TX 77024
Phone: 713-647-5700
Fax: 713-647-5858
Web: www.group1auto.com

CEO: Earl J. Hesterberg
CFO: John C. Rickel
HR: J. Brooks O'Hara
FYE: December 31
Type: Public

Group 1 Automotive is only one in a group of firms (AutoNation and Penske Automotive Group are the largest) striving to consolidate US auto sales. The company owns and operates about 125 franchises at about 95 dealerships, as well as about 20 collision service centers in about 15 US states. More than half of Group 1's dealerships are located in Texas, Oklahoma, and California. Group 1 Automotive also has several dealerships in the UK. The company's dealerships offer new (about 55% of sales) and used cars and light trucks under more than 30 different brands. It also offers financing, provides maintenance and repair services, and sells replacement parts.

	Annual Growth	12/05	12/06	12/07	12/08	12/09
Sales ($ mil.)	(6.7%)	5,969.6	6,083.5	6,393.0	5,654.1	4,525.7
Net income ($ mil.)	(16.1%)	70.3	88.4	68.0	(31.5)	34.8
Market value ($ mil.)	(2.5%)	771.2	1,269.0	582.8	264.3	695.6
Employees	(4.5%)	8,400	8,785	8,932	7,687	6,990

GROUP HEALTH COOPERATIVE

521 Wall St.
Seattle, WA 98121
Phone: 206-448-5600
Fax: 206-448-4010
Web: www.ghc.org

CEO: Scott Armstrong
CFO: Richard (Ric) Magnuson
HR: —
FYE: December 31
Type: Cooperative

Group Health Cooperative gives new meaning to the term "consumer-driven health care." The organization is a not-for-profit managed health care group serving more than a half a million residents of Washington and Idaho. Governed by a board that its members elect, the co-op offers health insurance through its Group Health Options and KPS Health Plans subsidiaries, and it also provides medical care at its own facilities. It maintains a partnership with Group Health Permanente, a multispecialty medical group that provides care in those facilities. The co-op also partners with Kaiser Permanente to market its services, share knowledge, and offer reciprocal membership benefits.

	Annual Growth	12/04	12/05	12/06	12/07	12/08
Est. sales ($ mil.)	—	—	—	—	—	2,665.3
Employees	—	—	—	—	—	6,000

GROUP HEALTH INCORPORATED

441 9th Ave.
New York, NY 10001
Phone: 212-615-0000
Fax: 212-563-8561
Web: www.ghi.com

CEO: Frank J. Branchini
CFO: Michael (Mike) Palmateer
HR: Thomas Nemeth
FYE: December 31
Type: Subsidiary

Group Health Incorporated (GHI) is a not-for-profit health benefits company that provides managed health care coverage and related services to some 2.1 million members in New York State. Established in 1937, the company offers a wide range of medical, dental, and prescription drug plans to individuals, businesses, and government agencies. For businesses, it provides fully insured coverage or administrative services for self-insured employers. The firm also provides Medicare Advantage plans and manages care for recipients of Medicaid and other state-sponsored programs in some counties. Along with affiliate Health Insurance Plan of Greater New York (HIP), GHI is part of EmblemHealth.

An in-depth profile of this company is available to Hoover's Online members at hoovers.com.

GROWMARK, INC.

1701 Towanda Ave.	CEO: William (Bill) Davisson
Bloomington, IL 61701	CFO: Jeff Solberg
Phone: 309-557-6000	HR: —
Fax: 309-829-8532	FYE: August 31
Web: www.growmark.com	Type: Cooperative

Retail farm-supply and grain-marketing cooperative GROWMARK can mark its growth by the grain. A member-owed agricultural co-op, GROWMARK serves farmers in the midwestern US and Ontario, Canada. Founded in 1980, it has more than 250,000 members. Under the FAST STOP name, the co-op runs more than 300 fuel stations and convenience stores in the Midwest. Its Seedway subsidiary sells commercial vegetable seed and farm seed for turf, and grains including alfalfa, corn, wheat, and soybeans. GROWMARK also offers fertilizer, seeds, ethanol, biodiesel, and farm financing. Its MID-CO COMMODITIES subsidiary trades grain and offers advice regarding futures and options.

GRUBB & ELLIS COMPANY
NYSE: GBE

1551 N. Tustin Ave., Ste. 300	CEO: Thomas P. (Tom) D'Arcy
Santa Ana, CA 92705	CFO: Matthew A. (Matt) Engel
Phone: 714-667-8252	HR: —
Fax: 877-888-7348	FYE: December 31
Web: www.grubb-ellis.com	Type: Public

Want to swap that dingy old office building for a shiny glass skyscraper? Call Grubb & Ellis. Through a network of nearly 130 owned and affiliated offices, the company provides commercial real estate services to property owners, institutional investors, and tenants. Its 1,800 brokers and some 6,000 affiliated real estate professionals offer advisory and brokerage, property management, construction consultation, and other services. The company, founded in 1958, operates in three segments: transaction services, which comprise its brokerage operations; management services, including facilities and project management; and investment management.

	Annual Growth	6/06	6/07	*12/07	12/08	12/09
Sales ($ mil.)	2.2%	490.1	513.3	231.4	611.8	535.6
Net income ($ mil.)	—	4.9	3.5	20.8	(330.9)	(80.5)
Market value ($ mil.)	(39.0%)	642.3	805.5	445.1	86.1	88.9
Employees	0.0%	5,000	5,100	4,700	5,000	5,000

*Fiscal year change

GRUMA CORPORATION

1159 Cottonwood Ln., Ste. 200	CEO: Roberto González Barrera
Irving, TX 75038	CFO: Raúl A. Peláez Cano
Phone: 972-232-5000	HR: Valina Ussery
Fax: 972-232-5176	FYE: December 31
Web: www.gruma.com	Type: Subsidiary

Gruma Corporation has it all wrapped up. With operations in the US and Europe, the company manufactures and distributes more than 20 varieties of corn flour, corn tortillas, and related products, such as tortilla chips. Gruma's brand name offerings include Mission and Guerrero tortillas and Maseca corn flour. The company is a wholly owned subsidiary of Mexican food company Gruma, S.A.B. de C.V. and accounts for the majority of its parent's revenue. It produces about 1.3 million tons of corn flour and tortillas every year, and its products are available in some 30,000 US stores. In 2008, Gruma Corporation saw sales dip slightly for the first time in years.

GS CAPITAL PARTNERS, L.P.

85 Broad St.	CEO: Joseph H. Gleberman
New York, NY 10004	CFO: —
Phone: 212-902-1000	HR: —
Fax: 212-902-3000	FYE: November 30
Web: www.goldmansachs.com	Type: Partnership

GS Capital Partners makes private equity investments on behalf of Goldman Sachs and others. It participates in a range of transaction types, including leveraged buyouts, recapitalizations, acquisitions, and build-outs. An active investor that partners with its portfolio companies, GS Capital Partners typically invests between $200 million to $800 million per transaction in middle-market or large firms in a variety of industries. In 2007 GS Capital Partners closed its latest fund, GS Capital Partners VI, which raised some $20 billion, including more than $7 billion from Goldman Sachs; it is one of the largest private equity funds ever.

GS FINANCIAL CORP.
NASDAQ (GM): GSLA

3798 Veterans Blvd.	CEO: Stephen E. Wessel
Metairie, LA 70002	CFO: Stephen F. Theriot
Phone: 504-457-6220	HR: Bruce A. Scott
Fax: 504-457-6227	FYE: December 31
Web: www.gsfinancialcorp.com	Type: Public

GS Financial wants to make banking easy in The Big Easy. It's the holding company for Guaranty Savings Bank, which operates about five branches in and around New Orleans. Founded in 1937, the bank mainly serves small business owners and retail customers, offering such traditional services as checking and savings accounts, individual retirement accounts, certificates of deposit, and debit and credit cards. Its lending activities consist mainly of one-to four-family residential mortgages, as well as commercial mortgages and construction loans. More than half of GS Financial's stock is beneficially owned by its officers, directors, and employees, and passive institutional investors.

	Annual Growth	12/05	12/06	12/07	12/08	12/09
Assets ($ mil.)	11.2%	177.6	168.4	186.5	221.9	271.6
Net income ($ mil.)	—	(3.7)	2.1	0.7	0.0	0.9
Market value ($ mil.)	(0.0%)	18.9	24.9	23.8	15.7	18.9
Employees	10.7%	38	43	46	42	57

GSC ENTERPRISES, INC.

130 Hillcrest Dr.	CEO: Michael J. Bain
Sulphur Springs, TX 75482	CFO: Kerry Law
Phone: 903-885-7621	HR: Janet Price
Fax: 903-885-6240	FYE: December 31
Web: www.grocerysupply.com	Type: Private

GSC Enterprises brings the groceries to the grocery store. Doing business as Grocery Supply Company (not to be confused with Grocers Supply Co.), the wholesale distributor supplies more than 4,500 independent convenience stores, grocers, discounters, and other retailers and wholesalers with some 12,000 items. It distributes such goods as beverages, dry goods, and prepared foods to customers in about 15 states, mostly in the South and Southeast. In addition, GSC's Fidelity Express division supplies equipment and services to allow smaller retailers to process money orders. Ken McKenzie, Curtis McKenzie, and Woodrow Brittain started the family-owned business in 1947.

GSE SYSTEMS, INC.

NYSE Amex: GVP

1332 Londontown Blvd., Ste. 200
Sykesville, MD 21784
Phone: 410-970-7800
Fax: 410-970-7997
Web: www.gses.com

CEO: John V. Moran
CFO: Jeffery G. Hough
HR: —
FYE: December 31
Type: Public

GSE Systems is into power and control. The company provides simulation software to train power plant operators, engineers, and managers. Its systems, used primarily for the nuclear power, fossil energy, and chemical industries, can also be used to test new plant systems before they are installed. GSE Systems also offers training services through a partnership with General Physics. Customers have included Archer Daniels Midland Company, BASF Corporation, Cargill Incorporated, and Merck. The company has interational facilities in China and Sweden.

	Annual Growth	12/05	12/06	12/07	12/08	12/09
Sales ($ mil.)	16.2%	22.0	27.5	31.9	29.0	40.1
Net income ($ mil.)	—	(4.8)	(0.3)	1.2	(0.7)	(0.8)
Market value ($ mil.)	45.0%	23.5	125.9	193.9	111.7	103.8
Employees	13.1%	123	135	153	178	201

GSI COMMERCE, INC.

NASDAQ (GS): GSIC

935 1st Ave.
King of Prussia, PA 19406
Phone: 610-491-7000
Fax: —
Web: www.gsicommerce.com

CEO: Michael G. Rubin
CFO: Michael R. Conn
HR: James (Jim) Flanagan
FYE: December 31
Type: Public

If you're not feeling generally secure in your e-commerce initiatives, GSI Commerce aims to help. The company provides e-commerce services such as website development and maintenance, order fulfillment, and customer service. Its interactive marketing offerings include brand development and e-mail marketing services. GSI also operates a business segment called "consumer engagement," which runs websites such as RueLaLa.com (online private sales business) and SmartBargains.com (a marketplace for discounted merchandise). All told, the company serves about 500 companies and brands in markets such as retail, consumer goods manufacturing, and media. Clients include Dell, Polo Ralph Lauren, and Expedia.

	Annual Growth	12/05	12/06	12/07	12/08	12/09
Sales ($ mil.)	22.9%	440.4	609.6	750.0	966.9	1,004.2
Net income ($ mil.)	—	2.7	53.4	3.0	(16.9)	(11.0)
Market value ($ mil.)	13.9%	937.3	1,164.6	1,211.2	653.4	1,577.1
Employees	33.5%	1,729	2,521	4,679	4,470	5,500

GSI GROUP INC.

Pink Sheets: GSIGQ

39 Manning Rd.
Billerica, MA 01821
Phone: 978-439-5511
Fax: 978-663-0131
Web: www.gsig.com

CEO: Michael E. Katzenstein
CFO: Glenn E. Davis
HR: Anthony J. (Tony) Bellantuoni
FYE: December 31
Type: Public

GSI Group has its laser sights set on manufacturing. The global company makes components for precision motion and motion control products for niche markets, and laser-based manufacturing systems primarily for the semiconductor, telecommunications, and electronics industries. Laser functions include marking, tuning, drilling, placement, and inspection, and are also used in lithography, industrial processing, medical, and military applications. Manufacturing facilities are located in the US, China, and the UK; products are sold directly or through distributors to OEMs. Customers in the Asia/Pacific region account for more than half of the company's sales. The company filed for Chapter 11 bankruptcy in November 2009.

	Annual Growth	12/04	12/05	12/06	12/07	*12/08
Sales ($ mil.)	(3.3%)	330.0	260.8	313.6	317.8	288.5
Net income ($ mil.)	—	41.5	9.7	21.7	19.0	(203.8)
Market value ($ mil.)	(52.8%)	549.9	520.2	464.2	442.6	27.4
Employees	2.5%	1,175	1,167	1,347	1,363	1,297

*Most recent year available

GSI TECHNOLOGY, INC.

NASDAQ (GM): GSIT

2360 Owen St.
Santa Clara, CA 95054
Phone: 408-980-8388
Fax: 408-980-8377
Web: www.gsitechnology.com

CEO: Lee-Lean Shu
CFO: Douglas Schirle
HR: —
FYE: March 31
Type: Public

Gee whiz, GSI provides some fast chips. GSI Technology designs and markets specialized SRAM (static random-access memory) integrated circuits used in high-speed networking equipment. Its chips allow routers, switches, and other gear from the likes of Alcatel-Lucent and Cisco Systems to retrieve data at the speeds needed for broadband transmission. The fabless semiconductor company does most of its business through contract electronics manufacturers, such as Celestica, and through distributors, including Avnet (about 29% of sales) and Nu Horizons. Other top customers include SMART Modular Technologies (around 28% of sales), which buys memory chips for products it makes on behalf of Cisco.

	Annual Growth	3/06	3/07	3/08	3/09	3/10
Sales ($ mil.)	11.9%	43.1	58.2	53.2	62.1	67.6
Net income ($ mil.)	25.4%	4.2	7.4	6.8	9.3	10.4
Market value ($ mil.)	(3.6%)	—	144.2	73.5	70.4	129.2
Employees	6.2%	100	100	103	108	127

GT SOLAR INTERNATIONAL, INC.

NASDAQ (GS): SOLR

243 Daniel Webster Hwy.
Merrimack, NH 03054
Phone: 603-883-5200
Fax: 603-595-6993
Web: www.gtsolar.com

CEO: Thomas (Tom) Gutierrez
CFO: Richard J. Gaynor
HR: Brian Logue
FYE: March 31
Type: Public

GT Solar International is a beacon along the path of the solar power supply chain. The company manufactures equipment used in the production of silicon wafers, solar cells, and other products destined for use in solar power generation systems. Its key products include photovoltaic wafer fabrication machinery, silicon furnaces, and optical scanning systems. The company also provides solar module assembly services. GT Solar does most of its business in Asia, primarily in China. Top clients include such global solar products suppliers as BP Solar, LDK Solar (20% of sales), Schott Solar, SolarWorld, Suntech Power, and Yingli Green Energy.

	Annual Growth	3/06	3/07	3/08	3/09	3/10
Sales ($ mil.)	84.7%	46.8	60.1	244.1	541.0	544.2
Net income ($ mil.)	—	(21.8)	(18.4)	36.1	88.0	87.3
Market value ($ mil.)	(21.2%)	—	—	—	956.0	753.0
Employees	32.9%	123	248	305	332	384

GTC BIOTHERAPEUTICS, INC.

OTC: GTCB

175 Crossing Blvd., Ste. 410
Framingham, MA 01702
Phone: 508-620-9700
Fax: 508-370-3797
Web: www.gtc-bio.com

CEO: Geoffrey F. Cox
CFO: John B. Green
HR: Patricia (Pat) Nagle
FYE: December 31
Type: Public

Transgenic manipulation is the name of the game at GTC Biotherapeutics. The firm makes its products by inserting human DNA into animals who then produce the protein in their milk; the proteins are purified from the milk and used for human treatments. This process of creating what are known as recombinant proteins makes it easier and cheaper to produce large quantities of certain therapeutic proteins. The company's lead candidate ATryn received European regulatory approval in 2006 and FDA approval in 2009; the product is a recombinant human antithrombin, which has anticoagulant and anti-inflammatory properties that help prevent blood clots. French firm LFB Biotechnologies owns about 20% of GTC.

	Annual Growth	12/05	12/06	12/07	12/08	12/09
Sales ($ mil.)	(9.6%)	4.2	6.1	13.9	16.7	2.8
Net income ($ mil.)	—	(30.1)	(35.3)	(36.3)	(22.7)	(27.0)
Market value ($ mil.)	(53.8%)	499.0	337.8	264.7	97.4	22.8
Employees	(4.3%)	130	153	178	159	109

An in-depth profile of this company is available to Hoover's Online members at hoovers.com.

GTE SOUTHWEST, INC.

600 Hidden Ridge
Irving, TX 75038
Phone: 972-718-5000
Fax: 972-719-0079
Web: www22.verizon.com/about/community/tx

CEO: Carl E. Erhart
CFO: —
HR: —
FYE: December 31
Type: Subsidiary

GTE Southwest, which does business as Verizon Southwest, provides residential and business wireline and wireless communications services in the southwestern US. Based in its core service area of Texas (where it has about 3 million subscribers), the company also serves customers in Arkansas, New Mexico, and Oklahoma. It is a subsidiary of New York City-based Verizon Communications, a leading provider with about 90 million subscribers nationwide. Verizon Southwest provides telecom services including local telephone exchange access, long-distance calling, and Internet services, as well as corporate data services, IT systems integration, and billing and collections. Top clients have included Texas A&M University.

	Annual Growth	12/04	12/05	12/06	12/07	12/08
Est. sales ($ mil.)	—	—	—	—	—	892.3
Employees	—	—	—	—	—	6,948

GTECH CORPORATION

GTECH Center, 10 Memorial Blvd.
Providence, RI 02903
Phone: 401-392-1000
Fax: 401-392-1234
Web: www.gtech.com

CEO: Jaymin B. Patel
CFO: Stefano Bortoli
HR: Sheri Southern
FYE: February 28
Type: Subsidiary

GTECH will make you happy when your number comes up — lottery number, that is. One of the world's leading operators of lottery systems, the company supplies or operates lotteries for customers in more than 50 countries. It designs, installs, operates, and maintains lottery and instant ticket systems and furnishes the hardware and software to keep lotteries humming. It also develops and operates online and video lottery systems, as well as other online and casino gaming systems primarily through such units as Atronic, Boss Media, and Finsoft. GTECH is a subsidiary of Italian lottery giant Lottomatica.

GTSI CORP.

NASDAQ (GM): GTSI

2553 Dulles View Dr., Ste. 100
Herndon, VA 20171
Phone: 703-502-2000
Fax: 703-222-5204
Web: www.gtsi.com

CEO: Scott W. Friedlander
CFO: Peter Whitfield
HR: Bridget Atkinson
FYE: December 31
Type: Public

GTSI supplies the goods when the government goes shopping. The company resells computers, software, and networking products to federal, state, and local governments in the US. It offers products from vendors including Cisco Systems, Hewlett-Packard, IBM, Microsoft, and Panasonic. Founded in 1983, GTSI also provides asset management, consulting, design, integration, maintenance, procurement, and support services. The company offers financing through its GTSI Financial Services subsidiary. It also has a unit devoted to logistics services. Direct business with the federal government accounts for about 70% of GTSI's sales; it also sells to prime government contractors.

	Annual Growth	12/05	12/06	12/07	12/08	12/09
Sales ($ mil.)	(3.7%)	886.3	850.2	723.5	821.2	761.9
Net income ($ mil.)	—	(16.0)	(3.0)	(1.8)	7.8	5.5
Market value ($ mil.)	(8.3%)	67.3	88.7	94.7	57.7	47.7
Employees	(4.3%)	732	719	679	643	615

GTX, INC.

NASDAQ (GM): GTXI

3 N. Dunlap St., Van Vleet Bldg.
Memphis, TN 38163
Phone: 901-523-9700
Fax: 901-523-9772
Web: www.gtxinc.com

CEO: Mitchell S. Steiner
CFO: Mark E. Mosteller
HR: —
FYE: December 31
Type: Public

GTx knows hormones are just as important to men as they are to women. The company develops therapies targeting estrogens and androgens for prostate cancer and other diseases in the arena of men's health. GTx's lead drug candidate, Acapodene, could prevent men who have been identified with certain precancerous conditions from developing prostate cancer. The drug may also be useful in treating osteoporosis, hot flashes, and other side effects of androgen-deprivation therapy (a treatment for advanced prostate cancer). To fund its work, GTx sells Fareston, a drug for metastatic breast cancer. Chairman J.R. Hyde owns nearly one-third of the company.

	Annual Growth	12/05	12/06	12/07	12/08	12/09
Sales ($ mil.)	40.2%	3.8	7.5	7.1	13.5	14.7
Net income ($ mil.)	—	(36.8)	(35.5)	(40.4)	(51.8)	(46.3)
Market value ($ mil.)	(13.7%)	275.3	649.7	522.6	613.3	153.0
Employees	9.3%	84	91	111	147	120

GUARANTY BANCORP

NASDAQ (GS): GBNK

1331 17th St., Ste. 300
Denver, CO 80202
Phone: 303-293-5563
Fax: —
Web: www.gbnk.com

CEO: Daniel M. (Dan) Quinn
CFO: Paul W. Taylor
HR: Paul W. Taylor
FYE: December 31
Type: Public

Guaranty Bancorp (formerly Centennial Bank Holdings) knows a thing or two about dollars and cents. After all, it's the holding company for Colorado's Guaranty Bank and Trust. The bank operates about 35 branches, primarily in the metropolitan Denver and North Front Range areas. Guaranty Bank and Trust offers traditional checking, savings, money market, and NOW accounts as well as IRAs. Real estate mortgages and business loans each make up more than one-third of a loan portfolio that also includes construction and other types of consumer and business loans. In 2008 the company merged subsidiary Centennial Bank of the West into Guaranty Bank and Trust and, following suit, changed its own name.

	Annual Growth	12/05	12/06	12/07	12/08	12/09
Assets ($ mil.)	(8.1%)	2,980.8	2,720.6	2,371.7	2,102.7	2,127.6
Net income ($ mil.)	—	14.7	24.4	(138.1)	(256.7)	(29.2)
Market value ($ mil.)	(42.8%)	653.4	499.7	305.3	105.6	69.7
Employees	(11.8%)	617	518	476	387	373

GUARANTY FEDERAL BANCSHARES, INC.

NASDAQ (GM): GFED

1341 W. Battlefield
Springfield, MO 65807
Phone: 417-520-4333
Fax: 417-520-3607
Web: www.gfed.com

CEO: Shaun A. Burke
CFO: Carter M. Peters
HR: Melissa Carr
FYE: December 31
Type: Public

Like the Simpsons, Guaranty Bank calls Springfield home. The flagship subsidiary of Guaranty Federal Bancshares has six branches in Springfield, Missouri, and two more, including a branch inside a Wal-Mart, in nearby Nixa. The bank offers CDs and checking, savings, money market, and retirement accounts, mainly using deposit funds to originate commercial mortgages (more than 30% of the company's loan portfolio) and business loans (around 20%), as well as residential mortgages, consumer loans, and construction loans. Guaranty Bank also invests in mortgage-backed, US government, and other securities.

	Annual Growth	12/05	12/06	12/07	12/08	12/09
Assets ($ mil.)	11.3%	481.0	524.8	565.8	675.7	737.8
Net income ($ mil.)	—	5.9	6.5	6.1	(5.4)	(2.3)
Market value ($ mil.)	(34.7%)	73.7	75.8	75.9	14.0	13.4
Employees	13.0%	105	158	169	174	171

GUARDIAN BUILDING PRODUCTS DISTRIBUTION, INC.

979 Batesville Rd.
Greer, SC 29651
Phone: 864-297-6101
Fax: 864-281-3498
Web: www.guardianbp.com

CEO: Duane Faulkner
CFO: Cara Hamilton
HR: Amy Hennes
FYE: December 31
Type: Subsidiary

Despite the popularity of music CDs, Guardian Building Products Distribution (GBPD) still releases some of its product on vinyl. The company offers building supplies through more than 90 distribution centers across the US and Canada. GBPD sells roofing, millwork, insulation, vinyl siding, and other materials. It also provides capital equipment and other business services. The company's base of some 30,000 customers includes builders, building materials dealers, contractors, cooperatives, and warehouse chains, such as The Home Depot and Lowe's. GBPD is part of Guardian Building Products' group of companies, owned by Guardian Industries, one of the world's largest glassmakers.

GUARDIAN INDUSTRIES CORP.

2300 Harmon Rd.
Auburn Hills, MI 48326
Phone: 248-340-1800
Fax: 248-340-9988
Web: www.guardian.com

CEO: Jeffrey A. Knight
CFO: Jeffrey A. Knight
HR: —
FYE: December 31
Type: Private

Giving its customers a break would never occur to Guardian Industries, one of the world's largest glassmakers. With more than 60 facilities on five continents, Guardian primarily produces float glass and fabricated glass products for the automobile and construction markets. It also makes architectural glass (mirrors), fiberglass, and automotive trim parts. Through its Guardian Building Products, the company operates one of largest building supply distribution centers in North America. Former president and CEO William Davidson took Guardian Industries public in 1968, buying it back in 1985. Ownership of the privately held company remains with the Davidson family.

	Annual Growth	12/04	12/05	12/06	12/07	12/08
Est. sales ($ mil.)	3.8%	—	5,000.0	5,330.0	5,470.0	5,600.0
Employees	0.0%	—	19,000	19,000	19,000	19,000

THE GUARDIAN LIFE INSURANCE COMPANY OF AMERICA

7 Hanover Sq.
New York, NY 10004
Phone: 212-598-8000
Fax: 212-919-2170
Web: www.guardianlife.com

CEO: Dennis J. Manning
CFO: Robert E. Broatch
HR: John P. McCarthy
FYE: December 31
Type: Mutual company

When your guardian angel fails you, there's Guardian Life Insurance Company of America. The mutual company, owned by its policy holders, offers life insurance, disability income insurance, and — more recently — retirement programs to individuals and businesses. Guardian's employee health indemnity plans provide HMO, PPO, and dental and vision plans, as well as disability plans. In the retirement area, the company's Guardian Insurance & Annuity subsidiary offers mutual funds and annuity products, which are managed by its Guardian Investor Services. Guardian also offers estate planning and education savings programs.

	Annual Growth	12/05	12/06	12/07	12/08	12/09
Assets ($ mil.)	5.6%	24,807.0	26,719.0	28,328.0	28,973.0	30,895.0
Net income ($ mil.)	(47.7%)	375.0	376.0	292.0	437.0	28.0
Employees	1.9%	5,000	5,000	5,000	5,400	5,400

GUARDIAN TECHNOLOGIES INTERNATIONAL, INC.

OTC: GDTI

516 Herndon Pkwy., Ste. A
Herndon, VA 20170
Phone: 703-464-5495
Fax: 703-464-8530
Web: www.guardiantechintl.com

CEO: Michael W. Trudnak
CFO: Gregory E. Hare
HR: —
FYE: December 31
Type: Public

Guardian Technologies (formerly RJL Marketing Services) might consider itself a protector of sorts. The company provides software to help medical personnel identify health threats and airport security workers to detect explosives. Guardian's FlowPoint products are used by hospitals, radiology centers, and clinics to create and archive diagnostic images. Its PinPoint Threat Identification software is used in aviation security to help screen baggage.

	Annual Growth	12/05	12/06	12/07	12/08	12/09
Sales ($ mil.)	(29.3%)	0.4	0.5	0.3	0.1	0.1
Net income ($ mil.)	—	(13.1)	(10.1)	(10.5)	(8.7)	(8.5)
Market value ($ mil.)	(48.8%)	151.6	54.9	32.0	13.1	10.5
Employees	(14.3%)	39	33	24	23	21

GUARDSMARK, LLC

10 Rockefeller Plaza
New York, NY 10020
Phone: 212-765-8226
Fax: 212-603-3854
Web: www.guardsmark.com

CEO: Ira A. Lipman
CFO: Jeffrey B. Westcott
HR: —
FYE: June 30
Type: Private

When FBI agents leave Quantico, they go to Guardsmark. The company, a leading employer of former FBI agents (as well as former agents of the Secret Service, the DEA, state and local police forces, and the military), provides security services to companies in the financial, health care, transportation, and utility industries. Guardsmark offers security guards, private investigation, and drug testing services. The company also conducts background checks (employment, education, and criminal history) and consults with architects and builders to design security programs. Chairman and president Ira Lipman owns the company, which he founded in 1963.

	Annual Growth	6/04	6/05	6/06	6/07	6/08
Est. sales ($ mil.)	—	—	—	—	—	460.1
Employees	—	—	—	—	—	18,000

GUESS?, INC.

NYSE: GES

1444 S. Alameda St.
Los Angeles, CA 90021
Phone: 213-765-3100
Fax: 213-744-7838
Web: www.guess.com

CEO: Paul Marciano
CFO: Dennis R. Secor
HR: Susan Tenney
FYE: January 31
Type: Public

Guess? wants you to get in its pants. Founded as a designer jeans maker, the company makes trendy, upscale apparel and accessories for men, women, and children under brand names GUESS, GUESS Kids, Baby GUESS, and GUESS by MARCIANO, among others. Its trademark sexy ads, featuring the likes of Claudia Schiffer and Drew Barrymore, are designed in-house. Guess? sells its lines through a website, some 430 retail locations in the US and Canada, and about 140 stores in Europe, Asia, and Mexico. Guess? licenses its name for accessories (eyewear, footwear, jewelry, watches). Chairman Maurice Marciano and his brother Paul (CEO) run the company founded by their father. Together they own more than a third of its shares.

	Annual Growth	12/06	*1/07	1/08	1/09	1/10
Sales ($ mil.)	15.8%	1,185.2	1,749.9	1,749.9	2,093.4	2,128.5
Net income ($ mil.)	18.5%	123.2	186.5	186.5	213.6	242.8
Market value ($ mil.)	5.8%	2,946.2	3,349.4	3,466.0	1,494.7	3,688.9
Employees	9.6%	8,800	9,900	9,900	10,800	12,700

*Fiscal year change

An in-depth profile of this company is available to Hoover's Online members at hoovers.com.

717

GUIDANCE SOFTWARE, INC.

NASDAQ (GM): GUID

215 N. Marengo Ave., 2nd Fl.
Pasadena, CA 91101
Phone: 626-229-9191
Fax: 626-229-9199
Web: www.guidancesoftware.com

CEO: Victor Limongelli
CFO: Barry J. Plaga
HR: Sandy Gyenes
FYE: December 31
Type: Public

Guidance Software leads investigators down the right path. The company provides applications that government authorities, police agencies, and corporate investigators use for functions such as digital forensic investigations, information auditing, and information technology threat assessment and response. The company's EnCase software is a forensics platform that helps organizations respond quickly to threats and analyze information, including court-validated forensics tools for government and corporate investigations. Clients outside the US account for 21% of sales.

	Annual Growth	12/05	12/06	12/07	12/08	12/09
Sales ($ mil.)	17.3%	39.5	55.9	78.9	91.5	74.9
Net income ($ mil.)	—	1.6	(3.1)	(2.9)	(10.6)	(13.9)
Market value ($ mil.)	(30.4%)	—	377.9	338.8	99.0	127.2
Employees	3.5%	305	346	350	415	350

GUIDED THERAPEUTICS, INC.

Pink Sheets: GTHP

4955 Avalon Ridge Pkwy., Ste. 300
Norcross, GA 30071
Phone: 770-242-8723
Fax: 770-242-8639
Web: www.guidedtherapeutics.com

CEO: Mark L. Faupel
CFO: —
HR: —
FYE: December 31
Type: Public

Guided Therapeutics (formerly SpectRx) can shed some light on your condition. The firm is developing diagnostic products, including a cervical cancer detection device, using its proprietary biophotonic technology known as LightTouch. The technology uses optics and spectroscopy to provide doctors with non-invasive diagnostic methods for finding cancer. In order to zero in on its diagnostic business, the company in 2007 sold its SimpleChoice line of insulin pumps, which diabetics use to control blood glucose levels, to ICU Medical; it changed its name to Guided Therapeutics the following year to reflect its new focus.

	Annual Growth	12/05	12/06	12/07	12/08	12/09
Sales ($ mil.)	10.7%	1.0	1.0	1.0	1.3	1.5
Net income ($ mil.)	—	(2.1)	(4.9)	3.0	(4.8)	(6.2)
Market value ($ mil.)	45.5%	10.4	12.5	7.9	8.3	46.7
Employees	(13.3%)	39	26	26	20	22

⊞ GUITAR CENTER, INC.

5795 Lindero Canyon Rd.
Westlake Village, CA 91362
Phone: 818-735-8800
Fax: 818-735-8822
Web: www.guitarcenter.com

CEO: Marty P. Albertson
CFO: Erick Mason
HR: Dennis Haffeman
FYE: December 31
Type: Private

What AutoZone is to the garage, Guitar Center is to the garage band. The #1 US retailer of guitars, amps, keyboards, and pro-audio equipment operates more than 210 stores in 40 states. Major brands include Fender, Gibson, and Roland, as well as Guitar Center's own Laguna, Raven, and Harbinger labels. Stores also offer used and vintage instruments, computer hardware and software, and musician services (such as CD duplication and digital distribution). In addition to Guitar Center, the firm runs about 100 Music & Arts Center locations that sell and rent band and orchestral instruments. Its Musician's Friend unit markets musical gear online. Guitar Center has been owned by investment firm Bain Capital since 2007.

	Annual Growth	12/04	12/05	12/06	12/07	12/08
Est. sales ($ mil.)	0.0%	—	—	—	2,300.0	2,300.0
Employees	0.0%	—	—	—	9,540	9,540

GULF ISLAND FABRICATION, INC.

NASDAQ (GS): GIFI

583 Thompson Rd.
Houma, LA 70363
Phone: 985-872-2100
Fax: 985-872-2129
Web: www.gulfisland.com

CEO: Kerry J. Chauvin
CFO: Robin A. Seibert
HR: —
FYE: December 31
Type: Public

Through its subsidiaries, holding company Gulf Island Fabrication makes islands in the stream — the Gulf Stream, that is. Its subsidiaries make offshore drilling and production platforms for use mainly in the Gulf of Mexico. Products include jackets and deck sections of fixed production platforms, hull and deck sections of floating production platforms, piles, subsea templates, wellhead protectors, and various production, compressor, and utility modules. Gulf Island also produces and repairs pressure vessels and refurbishes existing platforms. St. Denis J. Villere & Company, L.L.C., owns 13% of the company.

	Annual Growth	12/05	12/06	12/07	12/08	12/09
Sales ($ mil.)	13.4%	188.5	312.2	472.7	420.5	311.5
Net income ($ mil.)	12.5%	13.0	21.3	31.2	29.0	20.8
Market value ($ mil.)	(3.6%)	348.0	528.2	453.9	206.3	301.0
Employees	5.0%	1,150	1,800	1,850	2,030	1,400

GULF POWER COMPANY

1 Energy Place
Pensacola, FL 32520
Phone: 850-444-6111
Fax: 850-444-6448
Web: www.gulfpower.com

CEO: Susan N. Story
CFO: Philip C. Raymond
HR: —
FYE: December 31
Type: Subsidiary

Pensacola power patrons presently put Gulf Power to work. The regulated utility, a subsidiary of Southern Company, transmits and distributes electricity to more than 429,900 customers in northwestern Florida. Gulf Power generates 2,659 MW of capacity from its fossil-fueled power plants, and it operates 1,600 miles of transmission lines and about 7,600 miles of distribution lines in its service territory. The utility also provides wholesale electricity to two distributors in Florida, and it offers conservation, outdoor lighting, surge protection, and other energy-related products and services.

	Annual Growth	12/04	12/05	12/06	12/07	12/08
Est. sales ($ mil.)	—	—	—	—	—	1,387.2
Employees	—	—	—	—	—	1,324

GULF SOUTH PIPELINE COMPANY, LP

9 Greenway Plaza, Ste. 2800
Houston, TX 77046
Phone: 713-479-8000
Fax: —
Web: www.gulfsouthpl.com

CEO: Rolf A. Gafvert
CFO: —
HR: —
FYE: December 31
Type: Subsidiary

Although natural gas is known to rise, this company likes to keep it underground and flowing horizontally in the south. Gulf South Pipeline, a subsidiary of Boardwalk Pipeline Partners (itself a subsidiary of Loews), operates an interstate natural gas pipeline system that transports products from southern Texas to western Florida. Its system consists of about 7,700 miles of natural gas gathering systems and pipeline and about 40 compressor stations. The company also owns two natural gas storage fields in Louisiana and Mississippi capable (together) of holding approximately 131 billion cu. ft. of natural gas.

GULF STATES TOYOTA, INC.

7701 Wilshire Place Dr.
Houston, TX 77040
Phone: 713-580-3300
Fax: 713-580-3332

CEO: Toby N. Hynes
CFO: Frank Gruen
HR: Dominic Gallo
FYE: December 31
Type: Private

Even good ol' boys buy foreign cars from Gulf States Toyota (GST). One of only two US Toyota distributors not owned by Toyota Motor Sales (the other is JM Family Enterprises' Southeast Toyota Distributors), GST distributes Toyota, Lexus, and Scion brand cars, trucks, and sport utility vehicles in Arkansas, Louisiana, Mississippi, Oklahoma, and Texas. GST has expanded its vehicle processing center in Houston to handle Toyota Tundra pickup trucks built in nearby San Antonio. Founded in 1969 by its Chairman Thomas Friedkin, GST distributes new Toyotas, parts, and accessories to around 145 dealers in Texas and other states in the region. GST plans to move to a new headquarters in west Houston.

	Annual Growth	12/04	12/05	12/06	12/07	12/08
Est. sales ($ mil.)	6.3%	4,000.0	4,600.0	4,600.0	5,700.0	5,100.0
Employees	(23.5%)	3,500	1,200	1,200	1,275	1,200

GULFMARK OFFSHORE, INC.

NYSE: GLF

10111 Richmond Ave., Ste. 340
Houston, TX 77042
Phone: 713-963-9522
Fax: 713-963-9796
Web: www.gulfmark.com

CEO: Bruce A. Streeter
CFO: Quintin V. Kneen
HR: David Darling
FYE: December 31
Type: Public

GulfMark Offshore makes its mark on the high seas. The company offers support services for the construction, positioning, and operation of offshore oil and natural gas rigs and platforms. At the end of 2009 it owned, managed, or chartered vessels in the North Sea (38), the Americas (Brazil, Mexico and Trinidad, 37), and Southeast Asia (13). Marine services include anchor handling; cargo, supply, and crew transportation; towing; and emergency services. Some of its ships conduct seismic data gathering and provide diving support. GulfMark Offshore serves both oil majors and smaller independents.

	Annual Growth	12/05	12/06	12/07	12/08	12/09
Sales ($ mil.)	17.5%	204.0	250.9	306.0	411.7	388.9
Net income ($ mil.)	7.1%	38.4	89.7	99.0	183.8	50.6
Market value ($ mil.)	(1.1%)	775.6	979.6	1,225.2	622.9	741.3
Employees	7.2%	1,212	1,243	1,300	1,800	1,600

GULFPORT ENERGY CORPORATION

NASDAQ (GS): GPOR

14313 N. May Ave., Ste. 100
Oklahoma City, OK 73134
Phone: 405-848-8807
Fax: 405-848-8816
Web: www.gulfportenergy.com

CEO: James D. (Jim) Palm
CFO: Michael G. (Mike) Moore
HR: Kit Coffin
FYE: December 31
Type: Public

Gulfport Energy puts most of its eggs into just a couple of baskets. It operates off the Gulf Coast of Louisiana, with a heavy concentration in two areas: the West Cote Blanche Bay and Hackberry Fields. It also operates in the Permian Basin of West Texas. In 2008 Gulfport had about 160 net producing wells and reported proved reserves of 25.5 million barrels of oil equivalent. That year the exploration and production company sold 87% of its oil to Shell and 60% of its gas to Chevron. It also has non-operating minority stakes in a handful of other assets, including oil sands in Alberta, the Bakken Shale in the Williston Basin, and the Phu Horm gas field in Thailand.

	Annual Growth	12/05	12/06	12/07	12/08	12/09
Sales ($ mil.)	32.6%	27.6	60.4	106.2	141.2	85.3
Net income ($ mil.)	21.3%	10.9	27.8	37.8	(184.5)	23.6
Market value ($ mil.)	(1.3%)	514.7	580.4	779.9	168.7	489.0
Employees	(10.7%)	63	151	70	37	40

GULFSTREAM AEROSPACE CORPORATION

500 Gulfstream Rd.
Savannah, GA 31407
Phone: 912-965-3000
Fax: 912-965-3084
Web: www.gulfstream.com

CEO: Joseph T. (Joe) Lombardo
CFO: Dan Clare
HR: Jennifer Giffen
FYE: December 31
Type: Subsidiary

Prom-goers may prefer limos, but grownups who have really made it — executives, celebrities, and heads of state — arrive in jets (and rarely rent tuxes). Gulfstream Aerospace, a General Dynamics subsidiary, is the largest maker of private jets in the world, ahead of Bombardier. The company's smallest plane, the G150, seats up to eight and has a range of 2,950 nautical miles (nm); its largest, the G650, seats up to 18, and cruises at Mach 0.925, with a range of up to 6,750nm. Gulfstream arranges financing through its Financial Services unit; it sells pre-owned aircraft, and provides maintenance, repair, and overhaul (MRO) services to its customers. Gulfstream accounts for about 16% of its parent's revenues.

	Annual Growth	12/04	12/05	12/06	12/07	12/08
Sales ($ mil.)	15.7%	—	—	4,116.0	4,828.0	5,512.0
Employees	10.8%	—	—	7,900	9,100	9,700

GULFSTREAM INTERNATIONAL GROUP, INC.

NYSE Amex: GIA

3201 Griffin Rd., 4th Fl.
Fort Lauderdale, FL 33312
Phone: 954-985-1500
Fax: 954-985-5245
Web: www.gulfstreamair.com

CEO: David F. Hackett
CFO: Robert M. Brown
HR: —
FYE: December 31
Type: Public

Going to the Bahamas on a Gulfstream isn't just for the jet set. Gulfstream International Group, through its Gulfstream International Airlines subsidiary, provides service between Florida and the Bahamas with a fleet of about 35 turboprop aircraft. It serves about two dozen destinations overall. The regional airline, no relation to high-end business jet manufacturer Gulfstream Aerospace, flies primarily under the Continental Connection brand on behalf of Continental Airlines. It also operates as a code-sharing partner of carriers such as United and Copa Airlines and provides charter services. In addition to its airline operations, Gulfstream International Group runs a pilot-training school.

	Annual Growth	12/05	12/06	12/07	12/08	12/09
Sales ($ mil.)	(1.3%)	92.0	105.1	112.3	105.3	87.3
Net income ($ mil.)	—	0.7	1.2	(3.1)	(14.8)	(7.6)
Market value ($ mil.)	(60.8%)	—	—	33.4	5.7	5.1
Employees	(1.3%)	—	629	707	554	604

GULFSTREAM NATURAL GAS SYSTEM, L.L.C.

2701 Rocky Point Dr., Ste. 1050
Tampa, FL 33607
Phone: 941-723-7100
Fax: —
Web: www.gulfstreamgas.com

CEO: Phillip D. (Phil) Wright
CFO: David (Dave) Shammo
HR: —
FYE: December 31
Type: Joint venture

In the case of Gulfstream Natural Gas, the name says it all. The natural gas transportation and storage company delivers approximately 1.25 billion cu. ft. of natural gas per day from source areas on the Gulf Coast (in East Louisiana and Mississippi) to customers in Central and Southern Florida. Its system consists of some 745 miles of pipeline (including 294 miles of pipeline in Florida and 419 miles offshore). The company boasts the largest pipeline in the Gulf of Mexico. Gulfstream Natural Gas is a joint venture between The Williams Companies and Spectra Energy.

An in-depth profile of this company is available to Hoover's Online members at hoovers.com.

719

GUTHY-RENKER LLC

41-550 Eclectic St., Ste. 200 — CEO: Kevin Knee
Palm Desert, CA 92260 — CFO: Kevin Knee
Phone: 760-773-9022 — HR: —
Fax: 760-733-9016 — FYE: December 31
Web: www.guthy-renker.com — Type: Private

What do Kathie Lee Gifford, Cindy Crawford, Victoria Principal, and Tony Robbins have in common? Each has starred in a program produced by Guthy-Renker, one of the largest infomercial producers in the US. With distribution in some 60 countries, the electronic retailing company pursues marketing opportunities through direct TV, cable and satellite, mail, and telemarketing. Its pitch people hawk a variety of goods and services, including skin care products and cosmetics such as Proactiv Solution (the company's primary category), fitness equipment, and motivational tapes. Guthy-Renker was founded in 1988 by Bill Guthy and Greg Renker, after being spun off from Guthy's Cassette Productions Unlimited (CPU).

	Annual Growth	12/04	12/05	12/06	12/07	12/08
Est. sales ($ mil.)	0.0%	—	1,500.0	1,500.0	1,800.0	1,500.0
Employees	0.0%	—	825	825	—	—

GXS, INC.

9711 Washingtonian Blvd. — CEO: Bob Segert
Gaithersburg, MD 20878 — CFO: John Duvall
Phone: 301-340-4000 — HR: Ann Addison
Fax: 301-340-5299 — FYE: December 31
Web: www.gxs.com — Type: Private

Global eXchange Services (GXS) wants the world to transact. The company operates one of the world's largest business-to-business (B2B) e-commerce networks, connecting 29,000 trading partners and managing more than a billion transactions each year. It also offers electronic data interchange (EDI) software and services, helping trading partners exchange electronic documents that are essential for business transactions. Other applications address shipping and labeling, product information management, order management, and logistics functions. In 2010 GXS merged with competitor Inovis, forming a B2B e-commerce leader with some 2,400 employees.

🔲 THE GYMBOREE CORPORATION — NASDAQ (GS): GYMB

500 Howard St. — CEO: Matthew K. (Matt) McCauley
San Francisco, CA 94105 — CFO: Jeffrey P. Harris
Phone: 415-278-7000 — HR: Marina Armstrong
Fax: 707-678-1315 — FYE: January 31
Web: www.gymboree.com — Type: Public

Despite being more than a quarter-of-a-century old, The Gymboree Corporation is still a retail toddler, stumbling periodically, learning quickly, and growing fast. The company sells clothes and accessories for kids in the US, Canada, and Puerto Rico at about 630 Gymboree stores that carry colorful, fashionable playsuits and rompers for kids up to 12 years old. It also operates 120 Janie and Jack (better newborn and toddler apparel) and about 140 Gymboree Outlet stores and corresponding e-commerce sites. The firm also provides parent-child play programs (designed to enhance child development) at some 640 franchised and eight company-operated Gymboree Play & Music centers in the US and 30 other countries.

	Annual Growth	1/06	1/07	1/08	1/09	1/10
Sales ($ mil.)	10.6%	678.5	791.6	920.8	1,000.7	1,014.9
Net income ($ mil.)	31.9%	33.7	60.3	80.3	93.5	101.9
Market value ($ mil.)	12.2%	725.7	1,275.1	1,125.7	721.6	1,149.0
Employees	6.6%	9,600	9,500	10,400	11,500	12,400

GYRODYNE COMPANY OF AMERICA, INC. — NASDAQ (CM): GYRO

1 Flowerfield, Ste. 24 — CEO: Stephen V. Maroney
St. James, NY 11780 — CFO: Gary J. Fitlin
Phone: 631-584-5400 — HR: —
Fax: 631-584-7075 — FYE: December 31
Web: www.gyrodyne.com — Type: Public

This Gyro has the wrap on real estate. Gyrodyne is a self-managed and self-administered real estate investment trust (REIT) that buys, owns, and manages a variety of property types. Its portfolio includes medical office parks and industrial properties, as well as undeveloped land. Gyrodyne began as a helicopter maker working from its 68-acre Flowerfield site on Long Island, New York, but switched to real estate development as its helicopter business declined in the 1970s. Since then, it has been converting its Flowerfield property for commercial, industrial, and residential use. The REIT has also acquired medical properties in Virginia and owns a minority stake in a planned development in Florida.

	Annual Growth	4/05	4/06	*12/07	12/08	12/09
Sales ($ mil.)	24.5%	2.0	1.6	1.9	3.1	4.8
Net income ($ mil.)	—	(0.1)	13.1	(1.6)	1.5	1.5
Market value ($ mil.)	(0.1%)	52.6	61.1	59.3	32.2	52.3
Employees	4.7%	10	8	7	10	12

*Fiscal year change

GYRUS ACMI, LLC

136 Turnpike Rd. — CEO: Brian L. Steer
Southborough, MA 01772 — CFO: Simon Shaw
Phone: 508-804-2600 — HR: Julie Seurer
Fax: 508-804-2624 — FYE: December 31
Web: www.gyrusgroup.com — Type: Subsidiary

Gyrus Group will cut you, but not anymore than it absolutely has to. Operating as Gyrus ACMI in the US, where it does most of its business, the UK-based company specializes in equipment for minimally invasive surgical procedures. It makes Invisio visualization tools (i.e. camera systems) and endoscopes that let doctors see what they're doing during gynecological and urological procedures. Its radiofrequency surgery systems, using its proprietary PK technology, can be used for minimally invasive hysterectomies and enlarged prostate procedures, as well as laparoscopic and traditional "open" surgeries. Gyrus Group is owned by Olympus Corporation.

	Annual Growth	12/04	12/05	12/06	12/07	12/08
Est. sales ($ mil.)	—	—	—	—	—	466.7
Employees	—	—	—	—	—	30

H GROUP HOLDING, INC.

71 S. Wacker Dr. — CEO: John Stellato
Chicago, IL 60606 — CFO: —
Phone: 312-873-4900 — HR: —
Fax: 312-873-4983 — FYE: December 31
— Type: Private

Owned and operated by Chicago's wealthy Pritzker family, H Group Holding is the investment holding company for a number of glamorous assets. It owns 85% of luxury hotel operator Hyatt, which has more than 400 owned and franchised hotels around the world as well as some 20 Classic Residence senior living communities in the US. Other holdings include credit reporting agency TransUnion, property investor Pritzker Realty, and a stake in the Royal Caribbean cruise ship line. Since the death of Jay Pritzker in 1999, family squabbles over its vast (estimated $20 billion) fortune have led the Pritzkers to break up the empire. Hyatt filed an IPO in 2009.

	Annual Growth	12/04	12/05	12/06	12/07	12/08
Est. sales ($ mil.)	—	—	—	—	—	4,921.0
Employees	—	—	—	—	—	42,000

H. MUEHLSTEIN & CO., INC.

800 Connecticut Ave.	CEO: John K. Donohue
Norwalk, CT 06854	CFO: Ronald (Ron) Nardozzi
Phone: 203-855-6000	HR: —
Fax: 203-855-6221	FYE: December 31
Web: www.muehlstein.com	Type: Private

H. Muehlstein & Co. has been bouncing around the plastic and rubber distribution business since the early 20th century. The company distributes polymers manufactured by the likes of Dow, Exxon Mobil, and BP. Its products include engineering resins, polyethylene, polypropylene, and polystyrene. Muehlstein sells 3 billion pounds of plastic and rubber products to about 6,500 manufacturers in 75 countries. It also operates through subsidiaries Muehlstein International, Channel Prime Alliance, and Pegasus Polymers. The company has been a part of European chemical and plastics distributor the Ravago Group since 2006.

	Annual Growth	12/04	12/05	12/06	12/07	12/08
Est. sales ($ mil.)	—	—	—	—	—	100.0
Employees	—	—	—	—	—	500

HAAS AUTOMATION, INC.

2800 Sturgis Rd.	CEO: Gene F. Haas
Oxnard, CA 93030	CFO: John Gwynn
Phone: 805-278-1800	HR: —
Fax: 805-278-2255	FYE: —
Web: www.haascnc.com	Type: Private

If you said they're a bunch of cutups at Haas Automation, they wouldn't be laughing — they'd be cutting serious metal. Haas makes and distributes such machine tools as computer numerical controlled (CNC) vertical and horizontal machining centers, which can cut cast iron, alloy and stainless steels, and high-nickel and aluminum alloys. Other products include lathes, collet indexers, rotary tables, and axis machines. The company's primary markets include the aerospace, heavy equipment, and automotive industries. The company sells its products through a worldwide network of about 500 distributors. President Gene Haas, who founded the company in 1983, owns the business.

HABER, INC.

	Pink Sheets: HABE
58 Medford St.	CEO: Albert B. (Al) Conti
Arlington, MA 02474	CFO: Peter R. (Pete) D'Angelo
Phone: 781-643-2727	HR: —
Fax: 781-643-6164	FYE: May 31
Web: www.haberscience.com	Type: Public

All that glitters may not be gold, but Haber makes the shiny stuff that really is gold a little easier to get. The company's Haber Gold Process is used to extract gold much the same way as cyanide does, but without the toxic side effects. It licenses its technology to gold exploration companies. Haber's other operations include the development of electromolecular propulsion (EMP), an electrochemical process used to evaluate and identify biological stains. The company, along with joint venture partner Etruscan Resources, owns a gold exploration concession in Ghana and has properties in the US it owns with exploration company Gold City.

HABERSHAM BANCORP

	NASDAQ (GM): HABC
282 Historic Hwy. 441 North	CEO: David D. Stovall
Cornelia, GA 30531	CFO: Annette Banks
Phone: 706-778-1000	HR: —
Fax: 706-778-6886	FYE: December 31
Web: www.habcorp.com	Type: Public

Habersham Bancorp is the holding company for Habersham Bank, which serves northern Georgia from about a dozen branches. The bank offers checking and savings accounts, IRAs, CDs, and NOW accounts, as well as trust services, credit cards, and asset management. Construction and land development loans account for nearly half of the company's loan portfolio; residential and commercial mortgages are around 40%. Bank subsidiary Advantage Insurers sells property/casualty, life, and business insurance. Habersham Bancorp is active in Forsyth, Cherokee, Gwinnett, Habersham, Hall, Stephens, Warren, and White counties. Chairman Thomas Arrendale III and his family own more than a third of the company.

	Annual Growth	12/05	12/06	12/07	12/08	12/09
Assets ($ mil.)	(1.2%)	478.4	555.7	514.2	494.9	456.0
Net income ($ mil.)	—	3.8	5.3	2.9	(14.8)	(26.1)
Market value ($ mil.)	(57.5%)	64.7	67.6	44.0	6.8	2.1
Employees	(10.5%)	162	180	180	161	104

HABITAT FOR HUMANITY INTERNATIONAL, INC.

121 Habitat St.	CEO: Jonathan T. M. Reckford
Americus, GA 31709	CFO: Ed Quibell
Phone: 800-422-4828	HR: Connie Steward
Fax: 229-928-8811	FYE: June 30
Web: www.habitat.org	Type: Not-for-profit

Thanks to Habitat for Humanity, more than 1.7 million people worldwide know there's no place like home. The mission of the not-for-profit, ecumenical Christian organization is to provide adequate and affordable shelter. It has built more than 350,000 houses at cost for families who demonstrate a need and are willing to invest "sweat equity" during construction. Homeowners make payments on no-interest mortgages; Habitat funnels the funds back into the construction of homes for others. The group operates in all 50 states, the District of Columbia, Guam, and Puerto Rico, in addition to affiliates in more than 90 countries. Habitat for Humanity was founded in 1976 by Linda Fuller and her late husband Millard.

	Annual Growth	6/05	6/06	6/07	6/08	6/09
Sales ($ mil.)	6.6%	197.6	357.2	363.5	249.4	254.7
Net income ($ mil.)	(10.9%)	—	131.7	62.4	—	93.3
Employees	—	—	—	—	—	—

HACHETTE BOOK GROUP

237 Park Ave.	CEO: David Young
New York, NY 10017	CFO: Thomas (Tom) Maciag
Phone: 212-364-1200	HR: Andrea Weinzimer
Fax: 212-364-0930	FYE: December 31
Web: www.hachettebookgroup.com	Type: Subsidiary

Hachette Book Group goes by the book. The division of Hachette Livre is home to book publisher Little, Brown and hardcover, mass market, and trade paperback publisher Grand Central Publishing (formerly Warner Books). Other imprints include FaithWords (religious books) and Center Street (for readers in America's heartland). The company's best sellers have included books by Malcolm Gladwell (*The Tipping Point*), Stephenie Meyer (*Twilight*), and Jon Stewart and the *Daily Show* writers (*America*). The current iteration of the company was formed in 2006 when French media firm Lagardère acquired Time Warner Book Group from Time Warner's Time Inc. unit. Time Warner Book Group subsequently became Hachette Book Group.

An in-depth profile of this company is available to Hoover's Online members at hoovers.com.

HACHETTE FILIPACCHI MEDIA U.S., INC.

1633 Broadway
New York, NY 10019
Phone: 212-767-6000
Fax: 212-767-5600
Web: www.hfmus.com

CEO: Alain Lemarchand
CFO: Philippe Perthuis
HR: —
FYE: December 31
Type: Subsidiary

Every day is *Woman's Day* at Hachette Filipacchi Media U.S. (HFM U.S.) The subsidiary of Lagardère Active publishes about a dozen magazines in five areas: automotive (*Car and Driver, Road & Track*); fashion (*ELLE*); shelter (*ELLE Decor*); women's interest (*Woman's Day*) and enthusiast (*Cycle World*). Its magazines reach about 60 million readers every month. HFM U.S. also publishes the magazines' websites, as well as three stand-alone sites: ELLEgirl.com, Premiere.com, and PointClickHome.com. With a circulation of 1 million, *ELLE* is HFM U.S.'s second-most popular title, behind *Woman's Day*, which has a readership of 3.8 million.

HACKENSACK UNIVERSITY MEDICAL CENTER

30 Prospect Ave.
Hackensack, NJ 07601
Phone: 201-996-2000
Fax: 201-489-1766
Web: www.humed.com

CEO: Robert C. Garrett
CFO: Robert L. (Bob) Glenning
HR: Nancy R. Corcoran
FYE: December 31
Type: Not-for-profit

If you sprain an ankle playing hacky sack, head to Hackensack! Hackensack University Medical Center, that is. The acute care hospital has nearly 800 beds and serves the residents of northern New Jersey and parts of New York. The acute care facility provides general medical and surgical care, as well as a full spectrum of specialty care. The medical center provides treatment for sick kids through its Joseph M. Sanzari Children's Hospital and the Tomorrow's Children's Institute (specializing in cancer and blood disorders). It is also affiliated with the University of Medicine and Dentistry of New Jersey. Founded in 1888, Hackensack University Medical Center has more than 1,400 physicians and dentists on staff.

	Annual Growth	12/04	12/05	12/06	12/07	12/08
Est. sales ($ mil.)	—	—	—	—	—	1,183.9
Employees	—	—	—	—	—	7,200

THE HACKETT GROUP, INC.

1001 Brickell Bay Dr., Ste. 3000
Miami, FL 33131
Phone: 305-375-8005
Fax: 305-379-8810
Web: www.thehackettgroup.com

NASDAQ (GM): HCKT

CEO: Ted A. Fernandez
CFO: Robert A. Ramirez
HR: —
FYE: December 31
Type: Public

The Hackett Group makes sure its clients can hack it in the business world. The business and technology consultancy provides corporations with advisory programs, benchmarking, business transformation services, and working capital management. Its services span such functions as IT, human resources, accounting, and customer service. The Hackett Group also provides services related to best practice research with a focus on sales, general and administrative functions, and supply chain services. The company provides business applications consulting through its Hackett Technology Solutions (HTS) unit, which specializes in software from Oracle and SAP. Its clients have included ABIOMED, Exelon, and Waste Management.

	Annual Growth	12/05	12/06	12/07	12/08	12/09
Sales ($ mil.)	(3.3%)	163.3	180.6	177.0	192.1	142.7
Net income ($ mil.)	—	1.6	(5.0)	9.0	17.9	(6.8)
Market value ($ mil.)	(10.1%)	174.9	126.8	199.2	120.2	114.4
Employees	(3.3%)	800	800	721	724	—

HADDON HOUSE FOOD PRODUCTS, INC.

250 Old Marlton Pike
Medford, NJ 08055
Phone: 609-654-7901
Fax: 609-654-8533
Web: www.haddonhouse.com

CEO: David H. Anderson
CFO: —
HR: —
FYE: December 31
Type: Private

Haddon House Food Products is a wholesale grocery distributor that specializes in ethnic food, gourmet ingredients, and organic products. It supplies more than 15,000 items encompassing several different brands, including such in-house names as Asian Gourmet, Jane's Krazy Mixed-Up Seasonings, Medford Farms, and Twin Tree Gardens. Haddon House serves specialty food retailers and other retail grocers nationwide.

	Annual Growth	12/04	12/05	12/06	12/07	12/08
Est. sales ($ mil.)	—	—	—	—	—	137.1
Employees	—	—	—	—	—	700

⊞ HAEMONETICS CORPORATION

NYSE: HAE

400 Wood Rd.
Braintree, MA 02184
Phone: 781-848-7100
Fax: 781-356-3558
Web: www.haemonetics.com

CEO: Brian Concannon
CFO: Christopher J. (Chris) Lindop
HR: Joseph J. Forish
FYE: March 31
Type: Public

Haemonetics helps health care providers hold on to blood. The company develops and produces blood recovery systems that automate the collection of blood products from donors. Its donor systems allow blood banks to collect and process whole blood, taking only the components (such as plasma or red blood cells) that they might need. Haemonetics also makes systems that collect and re-infuse a patient's own blood during surgery; these surgical blood salvage systems are sold under the OrthoPAT, cardioPAT, and Cell Saver brand names by its patient division. Additionally, the company sells information management software and provides consulting services to blood banks and hospitals.

	Annual Growth	3/05	3/06	3/07	3/08	3/09
Sales ($ mil.)	11.7%	383.6	419.7	449.6	516.4	597.9
Net income ($ mil.)	10.6%	39.6	69.1	49.1	52.0	59.3
Market value ($ mil.)	6.9%	1,059.2	1,275.5	1,174.5	1,496.8	1,383.8
Employees	6.9%	1,546	1,661	1,826	1,875	2,016

HAGEMEYER NORTH AMERICA, INC.

1460 Tobias Gadson Blvd.
Charleston, SC 29407
Phone: 843-745-2400
Fax: 843-745-6942
Web: www.hagemeyerna.com

CEO: David G. (Dave) Gabriel
CFO: Andros Neocleous
HR: Dawn McCoy
FYE: December 31
Type: Subsidiary

Hagemeyer North America (HNA) gets a charge out of spreading things around. The company distributes electrical, industrial, safety and other maintenance, repair, and operations (MRO) products from more than 300 locations across North America. It also performs instrumentation repair and calibration, hydrostatic testing, and air sampling, as well as other services including inspection, cleaning, and installation of safety equipment and logistics. Customers include 3M, DuPont, Philips, Cardiac Science, Cummins Engine, Philips Lighting, and other government, defense, transportation, aviation, petrochemical, and utility entities. HNA became a subsidiary of French distribution giant Sonepar's US subsidiary in 2008.

HAGGAR CLOTHING CO.

11511 Luna Rd.
Dallas, TX 75234
Phone: 214-352-8481
Fax: —
Web: www.haggar.com

CEO: Paul M. Buxbaum
CFO: —
HR: —
FYE: September 30
Type: Private

Haggar is hooked on classics. A leading maker and marketer of men's casual and dress apparel, the company's products include pants, sport coats, suits, shirts, and shorts. Haggar's clothes (including its "wrinkle-free" shirts and tab-waist expandable pants) are sold through about 10,000 stores in the US, Canada, Mexico, and the UK. Its Haggar brand is sold in department stores, such as J. C. Penney, Kohl's, and Sears, and at more than 70 Haggar outlet stores. The company makes lower-priced brands for mass merchandisers and offers private-label clothing. Founded in 1926, Haggar was publicly held until it was sold to the private investment firm Infinity Associates LLC in 2005.

HAGGEN, INC.

2211 Rimland Dr.
Bellingham, WA 98226
Phone: 360-733-8720
Fax: 360-650-8235
Web: www.haggen.com

CEO: James L. (Jim) Donald
CFO: Tom Kenney
HR: Derrick Anderson
FYE: December 31
Type: Private

Haggen showers shoppers in the Pacific Northwest with salmon, coffee, and other essentials. The area's largest independent grocer, Haggen operates 30-plus combination supermarkets throughout Washington and Oregon. Most upscale Haggen Food & Pharmacy stores feature specialty departments, while the TOP Food & Drug outlets emphasize savings; however, both may offer such amenities as Starbucks coffee shops, Blockbuster video outlets, or childcare centers. To keep up with the Joneses of supermarket fame and fortune, Haggen partnered with ShopEaze.com (an e-commerce service provider), which failed, leaving Haggen without an online store. Brothers and co-chairmen Don and Rick Haggen own the chain.

	Annual Growth	12/04	12/05	12/06	12/07	12/08
Est. sales ($ mil.)	—	—	—	—	—	787.8
Employees	—	—	—	—	—	3,900

HAHL INC.

126 Glassmaster Rd.
Lexington, SC 29072
Phone: 803-359-0706
Fax: —
Web: www.lenzing.com/plastics/en

CEO: Johann Huber
CFO: Mark Hartig
HR: —
FYE: August 31
Type: Subsidiary

Fishermen, seamstresses, and landscapers are among those who can put Hahl's products to use. The company, the US subsidiary of Lenzing's plastics unit, makes extruded monofilaments, made from nylon, polyester, and other engineered resins, that have varied uses such as fishing line, lawn-trimmer line, and sewing thread. Hahl's manufacturing facility is located in South Carolina. Austrian plastics and fibers company Lenzing acquired the company, formerly called Glassmaster, out of Chapter 11 bankruptcy protection in 2007. Hahl now operates as a much-stripped-down company, forgoing many of its former operations that included automation controls and composite materials.

HAIER AMERICA TRADING LLC

1356 Broadway
New York, NY 10018
Phone: 212-594-3330
Fax: 212-594-9667
Web: www.haieramerica.com

CEO: Sharif Kan
CFO: Tony Chung
HR: —
FYE: December 31
Type: Subsidiary

Haier America is the US sales and marketing arm of Chinese home appliance and consumer electronics giant Haier Group. Haier Group makes refrigerators, freezers, air conditioners, dishwashers, laundry machines, and small appliances, as well as mobile phones, Wi-Fi media players, and plasma and flat-screen televisions. Its more recent product additions include freestanding and built-in wine refrigerators, beverage centers, and beer dispensers to cater to the trend of home media rooms, gamerooms, and outdoor kitchens. Haier's products are sold through retailers such as Wal-Mart, Bed Bath & Beyond, Home Depot, Lowe's, and Target. The division was founded in 1999 and has operations in New York and South Carolina.

	Annual Growth	12/04	12/05	12/06	12/07	12/08
Est. sales ($ mil.)	—	—	—	—	—	17.8
Employees	—	—	—	—	—	240

HAIGHTS CROSS COMMUNICATIONS, INC.

10 New King St., Ste. 102
White Plains, NY 10604
Phone: 914-289-9400
Fax: 914-289-9401
Web: www.haightscross.com

CEO: Ronald H. Schlosser
CFO: Paul J. Crecca
HR: —
FYE: December 31
Type: Private

Haights Cross Communications helps students buckle down on their studies. The company offers test preparation materials for the K-12 Education and library markets. Its imprints include Buckle Down and Triumph Learning. It additionally publishes skills assessment products for math and reading students under the Options Publishing imprint. Haights Cross also publishes audio books for public libraries and schools through its Recorded Books business. Customers include educators and school systems, public and school libraries, and consumers. Saddled with debt, the company filed for Chapter 11 in early 2010; about a month later, it emerged from bankruptcy.

	Annual Growth	12/04	12/05	12/06	12/07	12/08
Sales ($ mil.)	0.0%	170.9	210.5	222.0	231.9	171.1
Net income ($ mil.)	—	(26.4)	(44.4)	(72.9)	63.5	(38.0)
Employees	(6.2%)	700	822	821	855	542

THE HAIN CELESTIAL GROUP, INC.

58 S. Service Rd.
Melville, NY 11747
Phone: 631-730-2200
Fax: 631-730-2550
Web: www.hain-celestial.com

CEO: Irwin D. Simon
CFO: Ira J. Lamel
HR: Mary Celeste Anthes
FYE: June 30
Type: Public

The Hain Celestial Group serves up guiltless eating. It sells specialty foods and beverages (coffee and tea) in the kosher, low-cal, sugar-free and low-salt, natural and organic, snack, and weight-management categories. The company's products are mainstays in natural foods stores and are increasingly available in mainstream supermarkets; club, mass-market, and drug stores; and through foodservice channels. Hain is also a player in the personal care products sector, offering disposable diapers and shampoo; its JĀSÖN Natural Products makes grooming products for adults, such as skin- and hair-care items. Hain's products are sold throughout the US and in some 50 other countries.

	Annual Growth	6/05	6/06	6/07	6/08	6/09
Sales ($ mil.)	16.3%	620.0	738.6	900.4	1,056.4	1,135.3
Net income ($ mil.)	—	21.9	37.1	47.5	41.2	(24.7)
Market value ($ mil.)	(5.4%)	798.5	1,054.9	1,111.4	961.5	639.2
Employees	8.0%	1,487	2,074	2,131	2,986	2,022

HAJOCA CORPORATION

127 Coulter Ave.
Ardmore, PA 19003
Phone: 610-649-1430
Fax: 610-649-1798
Web: www.hajoca.com

CEO: Richard Klau
CFO: —
HR: —
FYE: December 31
Type: Private

Sinks from Hajoca wash off grease from Philly cheese steaks, just as well as sauce from Texas barbecue. One of the nation's leading plumbing and heating wholesalers, Hajoca operates through more than 260 locations, primarily in California, Florida, Pennsylvania, and Texas, but also in about 30 other states. Hajoca wholesales plumbing, HVAC, swimming pool, and industrial supplies for commercial and residential customers. The company has expanded through acquisitions of other distributors that continue to operate under their original names. Founded in 1858, the company takes its current name from the cable address for Haines, Jones, & Cadbury Exports.

HAL LEONARD CORPORATION

7777 W. Bluemound Rd.
Milwaukee, WI 53213
Phone: 414-774-3630
Fax: 414-774-3259
Web: www.halleonard.com

CEO: Keith Mardak
CFO: Dan Bauer
HR: —
FYE: December 31
Type: Private

From Mozart to McCartney, Debussy to Disney, Hal Leonard Corporation knows music. The company publishes sheet music, songbooks, and musical method books for instruments and voice. It also offers accompaniment CDs and related items. Hal Leonard's products are sold in more than 65 countries through a network of distributors. Domestically, the company markets its product to more than 7,500 music stores in the US and Canada. Hal Leonard started in 1947 as a music store. The company was founded by Harold "Hal" Edstrom, his brother Everett "Leonard" Edstrom, and their friend Roger Busdicker. In 1985, Hal Leonard was purchased from the original founders by an internal management team led by CEO Keith Mardak.

HALF PRICE BOOKS, RECORDS, MAGAZINES, INCORPORATED

5803 E. Northwest Hwy.
Dallas, TX 75231
Phone: 214-360-0833
Fax: 214-379-8010
Web: www.halfpricebooks.com

CEO: Sharon Anderson Wright
CFO: Laura Beverly
HR: Tim Jernigan
FYE: June 30
Type: Private

Half Price Books tries to live up to its name and its hippie roots. The bookstore chain sells used and new books, magazines, videos, DVDs, and music. Only about half of the merchandise it sells is new. Its more than 100 stores are located in about 15 states, primarily in Texas. Its wholesale catalog division, Texas Bookman, reprints classics and other public domain works. Half Price Books has grown slowly but steadily; its stores keep a small-company look with secondhand and employee-made furnishings. The company was started by Ken Gjemre and Pat Anderson (late mom of president and CEO Sharon Anderson Wright) in 1972 to save trees by recycling unwanted books. The Anderson family owns most of the company.

	Annual Growth	6/04	6/05	6/06	6/07	6/08
Est. sales ($ mil.)	—	—	—	—	—	136.1
Employees	—	—	—	—	—	1,740

HALIFAX CORPORATION OF VIRGINIA

5250 Cherokee Ave.
Alexandria, VA 22312
Phone: 703-750-2202
Fax: 703-658-2478
Web: www.hxcorp.com

CEO: Charles L. McNew
CFO: Robert W. (Rob) Drennen
HR: —
FYE: March 31
Type: Private

Halifax Corporation of Virginia, which does business as simply Halifax, provides IT services to businesses and government agencies across the US. The company's Enterprise Maintenance Solutions (EMS) division offers technology support services, including maintenance and repair of computers, printers, networking equipment, and storage systems from such vendors as Hewlett-Packard, IBM, and Oracle. Its Enterprise Logistics Solutions (ELS) unit helps customers manage customer support, fulfillment, inventory, on-site repairs, and warranties. In 2010 an affiliate of Global Equity Capital acquired Halifax for about $4 million in cash, taking the company private.

	Annual Growth	3/05	3/06	3/07	3/08	3/09
Sales ($ mil.)	(13.9%)	62.0	54.9	50.7	43.9	34.0
Net income ($ mil.)	—	(1.4)	1.5	(2.8)	(2.5)	0.9
Employees	(13.1%)	581	520	517	408	331

HALLADOR PETROLEUM COMPANY

OTC: HPCO

1660 Lincoln St., Ste. 2700
Denver, CO 80264
Phone: 303-839-5504
Fax: 303-832-3013

CEO: Victor P. Stabio
CFO: William A. (Andy) Bishop
HR: —
FYE: December 31
Type: Public

Despite its *Harry Potter*-like name, Hallador Petroleum could find no magic in oil and natural gas exploration and production — just a lot of hard and dirty work. It therefore decided to focus on its coal operations. Hallador sells coal from its Carlisle Mine in Indiana to three utilities in the Midwest. First commercial production began at the mine in 2007. That year it sold 972,500 tons at an average price of $28 per ton. Hallador has recoverable coal reserves of 36 million tons. It is exploring the possibility of other contracts with a number of coal purchasers.

	Annual Growth	12/05	12/06	12/07	12/08	12/09
Sales ($ mil.)	192.0%	1.6	2.5	27.2	70.7	116.3
Net income ($ mil.)	217.0%	0.2	(0.8)	(2.4)	8.9	20.2
Market value ($ mil.)	24.7%	90.3	83.3	97.2	83.3	218.1
Employees	165.9%	6	90	148	6	300

HALLIBURTON COMPANY

NYSE: HAL

3000 N. Sam Houston Parkway E.
Houston, TX 77032
Phone: 281-575-3000
Fax: —
Web: www.halliburton.com

CEO: David J. (Dave) Lesar
CFO: Mark A. McCollum
HR: Lawrence J. Pope
FYE: December 31
Type: Public

One of the largest oilfield services companies in the world, Halliburton serves the upstream oil and gas industry with a complete range of services, from the location of hydrocarbons to the production of oil and gas. It operates in two segments: Drilling and Evaluation and Completion and Production. Services include providing production optimization, drilling evaluation, fluid services, and oilfield drilling software and consulting. It combines tried-and-true well drilling and optimization techniques with high-tech analysis and modeling software and services. Halliburton works in established oilfields from the North Sea to the Middle East as well as in newer sites in Southeast Asia and Africa.

	Annual Growth	12/05	12/06	12/07	12/08	12/09
Sales ($ mil.)	(8.6%)	21,007.0	22,504.0	15,264.0	18,279.0	14,675.0
Net income ($ mil.)	(16.3%)	2,358.0	2,348.0	3,499.0	1,778.0	1,155.0
Market value ($ mil.)	(0.7%)	28,045.4	28,108.8	34,319.0	16,457.9	27,239.7
Employees	(16.7%)	106,000	104,000	51,000	57,000	51,000

HALLMARK CARDS, INCORPORATED

2501 McGee Trafficway
Kansas City, MO 64108
Phone: 816-274-5111
Fax: 816-274-5061
Web: www.hallmark.com

CEO: Donald J. (Don) Hall Jr.
CFO: Jeff McMillen
HR: —
FYE: December 31
Type: Private

As the #1 producer of warm fuzzies, Hallmark Cards is the Goliath of greeting cards. The company's cards are sold under brand names such as Hallmark, Shoebox, and Ambassador and can be found in more than 41,000 US retail stores. (About 3,300 stores bear the Hallmark Gold Crown name; the majority of these stores are independently owned.) Hallmark also offers electronic greeting cards, gifts, and flowers through its website. In addition to greeting cards, the company owns crayon manufacturer Crayola (formerly Binney & Smith), a majority of cable broadcaster Crown Media, and Kansas City's Crown Center real estate development firm. Members of the founding Hall family own two-thirds of Hallmark.

	Annual Growth	12/05	12/06	12/07	12/08	12/09
Sales ($ mil.)	(1.2%)	4,200.0	4,100.0	4,400.0	4,300.0	4,000.0
Employees	(7.1%)	18,000	16,000	15,900	15,500	13,400

HALLMARK FINANCIAL SERVICES, INC.

NASDAQ (GM): HALL

777 Main St., Ste. 1000
Fort Worth, TX 76102
Phone: 817-348-1600
Fax: 817-348-1815
Web: www.hallmarkgrp.com

CEO: Mark J. Morrison
CFO: Jeffrey R. Passmore
HR: —
FYE: December 31
Type: Public

Personal or commercial, on the ground or in the air, Hallmark Financial sells insurance to cover risks both general and exceptional. Its Hallmark General Agency unit provides general commercial property/casualty insurance while its Texas General Agency sells specialty property/casualty coverage to businesses that don't fit into standard coverage. Its Aerospace unit provides general and specialty aviation insurance to both commercial and private pilots and small airports. Hallmark's Phoenix unit writes higher-risk non-standard personal auto insurance to folks in the southwestern and northwestern US. Chairman Mark Schwarz owns about 70% of the company, primarily through his investment firm, Newcastle Partners.

	Annual Growth	12/05	12/06	12/07	12/08	12/09
Assets ($ mil.)	31.7%	208.9	416.0	606.3	538.4	628.9
Net income ($ mil.)	27.9%	9.2	9.2	27.4	12.9	24.6
Market value ($ mil.)	(0.6%)	164.2	199.4	319.2	176.5	160.2
Employees	18.1%	165	347	361	329	321

THE HALLWOOD GROUP INCORPORATED

NYSE Amex: HWG

3710 Rawlins St., Ste. 1500
Dallas, TX 75219
Phone: 214-528-5588
Fax: 214-522-9254
Web: www.hallwood.com

CEO: Anthony J. Gumbiner
CFO: Richard Kelley
HR: —
FYE: December 31
Type: Public

The Hallwood Group spawns fabric for everyday life. The Group is a holding company of Brookwood Companies, a producer of high-tech fabric for the outdoor and sportswear industries, and one of the largest suppliers of coated nylon fabric in the US. Brookwood dyes, finishes, coats, and prints a slew of woven synthetics, used in products such as consumer apparel, luggage, and sailcloth. A laminating arm processes fabrics for military uniforms and camouflage equipment, industrial applications, and waterproof gear. Roughly 70% of sales are made to manufacturers of military goods, such as Tennier Industries and ORC Industries. Hallwood's former interest in Hallwood Energy ended in 2009 following the energy company's reorganization.

	Annual Growth	12/05	12/06	12/07	12/08	12/09
Sales ($ mil.)	7.5%	134.6	112.2	132.5	162.2	179.6
Net income ($ mil.)	(10.2%)	26.3	(6.7)	(32.8)	1.4	17.1
Market value ($ mil.)	(16.0%)	118.8	186.8	119.0	50.3	59.2
Employees	0.9%	462	447	467	460	478

HALOZYME THERAPEUTICS, INC.

NASDAQ (GM): HALO

11388 Sorrento Valley Rd.
San Diego, CA 92121
Phone: 858-794-8889
Fax: 858-704-8311
Web: www.halozyme.com

CEO: Jonathan E. Lim
CFO: Kurt A. Gustafson
HR: —
FYE: December 31
Type: Public

Halozyme Therapeutics makes enzymes for therapeutic and drug delivery applications. The company's products are based on recombinant human PH20, a human synthetic enzyme it hopes will offer safety benefits over animal-derived versions. The firm's first commercial product, Cumulase, is used for in-vitro fertilization. Another product, Hylenex, is used as an adjuvant for drug and fluid infusions. Products under development include drug delivery agents using the company's Enhanze technology, as well as therapeutic enzymes for cancer, metabolism, and dermatology applications. Halozyme's development partners include Roche and Baxter International.

	Annual Growth	12/05	12/06	12/07	12/08	12/09
Sales ($ mil.)	242.1%	0.1	1.0	3.8	8.8	13.7
Net income ($ mil.)	—	(13.3)	(14.8)	(23.9)	(48.7)	(58.4)
Market value ($ mil.)	34.0%	167.2	739.7	653.3	514.6	539.4
Employees	42.2%	34	40	92	129	139

HAMAMATSU CORPORATION

360 Foothill Rd.
Bridgewater, NJ 08807
Phone: 908-231-0960
Fax: 908-231-1218
Web: usa.hamamatsu.com

CEO: Akira Hiruma
CFO: Marvin Mofsowitz
HR: —
FYE: September 30
Type: Subsidiary

Hamamatsu sells electronic components and assemblies, such as infrared detectors, fiber-optic plates, photodiodes, and optical oscilloscopes. The company also makes light sources, such as light-emitting diodes (LEDs), metal halide lamps, and xenon lamps. For the semiconductor industry, Hamamatsu makes equipment for failure analysis and for process monitoring and control. The parent company, Hamamatsu Photonics, was established in 1953. The American subsidiary was incorporated in 1969.

HAMILTON BEACH BRANDS, INC.

4421 Waterfront Dr.
Glen Allen, VA 23060
Phone: 804-273-9777
Fax: 804-527-7142
Web: www.hamiltonbeach.com

CEO: Gregory H. Trepp
CFO: James H. Taylor
HR: —
FYE: December 31
Type: Subsidiary

Hamilton Beach Brands peddles the products that blend strawberry daiquiris and brew the piping hot coffee that's necessary the morning after. It's a leading marketer of small electric household appliances (blenders, coffeemakers, air purifiers, food processors, humidifiers, irons, and toasters) under the Hamilton Beach, Proctor-Silex, Eclectrics, and TrueAir brands. It also offers General Electric-branded appliances for Wal-Mart and caters to the foodservice and hospitality markets with drink mixers, glass washers, and hair dryers. Citing unfavorable market conditions, parent NACCO Industries reversed its decision to spin off Hamilton Beach Brands (HBB). It replaced its president and CEO in 2010, as well.

An in-depth profile of this company is available to Hoover's Online members at hoovers.com.

725

HAMILTON SUNDSTRAND CORPORATION

1 Hamilton Rd.	CEO: Alain M. Bellemare
Windsor Locks, CT 06095	CFO: Peter F. Longo
Phone: 860-654-6000	HR: Tatsuo Shirane
Fax: —	FYE: December 31
Web: www.hamiltonsundstrandcorp.com	Type: Subsidiary

Out in space, yet down-to-earth, Hamilton Sundstrand manufactures systems for space, land, and sea. A unit of United Technologies (UTC), the company's energy, space, and defense business provides systems and components for power generation, engine and control, and flight. It also makes products for homeland security (chemical/biological detection), solar power, underwater propulsion, and missile and satellite applications. Customers include NASA, commercial airlines, and the US military. Its industrial division's companies — Milton Roy, Sullair, and Sundyne — manufacture air compressors, fluid handling equipment, and metering pumps. The company accounts for a little more than 10% of UTC's sales.

	Annual Growth	12/04	12/05	12/06	12/07	12/08
Sales ($ mil.)	14.6%	3,600.0	4,300.0	5,000.0	5,636.0	6,207.0
Employees	3.4%	16,000	16,500	17,000	18,600	18,300

HAMMACHER SCHLEMMER & CO., INC.

9307 N. Milwaukee Ave.	CEO: Richard (Rich) Tinberg
Niles, IL 60714	CFO: Barry Orr
Phone: 847-581-8600	HR: Ken Gustin
Fax: 847-581-8616	FYE: December 31
Web: www.hammacher.com	Type: Private

Its name may not roll off the tongue, but Hammacher Schlemmer has been spoken for more than 160 years. Founded as a New York hardware store, it's one of the nation's most seasoned retailers, producing the longest continually published catalog in the US. Offering a pricey lineup it calls "the Best, the Only and the Unexpected," the retailer sells innovative, upscale gifts, gadgets, and housewares. It has been the first to sell a number of cutting-edge products, including the pop-up toaster (1930), steam iron (1948), microwave oven (1968), portable DVD player (1998), and robotic lawnmower (2000). It operates a flagship store in New York City and a website. Heirs of J. Roderick MacArthur own the company.

	Annual Growth	12/04	12/05	12/06	12/07	12/08
Est. sales ($ mil.)	—	—	—	—	—	34.1
Employees	—	—	—	—	—	200

HAMPDEN BANCORP, INC.

NASDAQ (GM): HBNK

19 Harrison Ave.	CEO: Thomas R. Burton
Springfield, MA 01103	CFO: Robert A. Massey
Phone: 413-736-1812	HR: Lynn Stevens Bunce
Fax: 413-294-1099	FYE: June 30
Web: www.hampdenbank.com	Type: Public

Despite its name, Hampden Bancorp's (the holding company for Hampden Bank) services extend beyond Massachusetts's Hampden County. Serving a handful of cities and towns in western Massachusetts, Hampden Bank offers savings and checking deposit services, as well as a variety of lending services, to its consumer and business customers. The bank's primary loan products include one-to-four-family residential loans and commercial real estate loans, each of which make up about a third of the bank's total loan portfolio. Loans for construction, businesses, and consumers make up the rest. Hampden Bancorp operates through more than a half-dozen branches.

	Annual Growth	6/05	6/06	6/07	6/08	6/09
Assets ($ mil.)	7.9%	419.6	468.8	523.9	543.8	567.7
Net income ($ mil.)	(36.1%)	1.8	1.0	(1.5)	1.2	0.3
Market value ($ mil.)	(6.2%)	—	—	80.5	71.7	70.8
Employees	0.6%	—	107	107	105	109

HAMPSHIRE GROUP, LIMITED

Pink Sheets: HAMP

1924 Pearman Dairy Rd.	CEO: Heath L. Golden
Anderson, SC 29625	CFO: Jonathan W. Norwood
Phone: 864-231-1200	HR: Diane Votteler
Fax: 864-231-1201	FYE: December 31
Web: www.hamp.com	Type: Public

The Hampshire Group has warmed to the sweater business. It's a holding company that operates through several wholly owned subsidiaries including Hampshire Designers and Item-Eyes. As one of the largest US makers and marketers of sweaters, Hampshire peddles its Designers Originals-brand sweaters to department stores (Kohl's, Macy's, J. C. Penney) and makes private-label items as well. The firm is licensed to manufacture men's sweaters by Geoffrey Beene, Dockers, and Joseph Abboud. Its Item-Eyes unit makes women's woven and knit separates under the Requirements and Nouveaux labels, among others. In April 2009 the company terminated a takeover agreement with a private equity firm it had entered into in February.

	Annual Growth	12/05	12/06	12/07	12/08	12/09
Sales ($ mil.)	(15.5%)	324.0	347.9	310.8	240.9	165.2
Net income ($ mil.)	—	12.8	2.5	0.0	(29.9)	(6.0)
Market value ($ mil.)	(36.0%)	150.3	104.6	88.4	25.3	25.2
Employees	(20.3%)	370	413	420	301	149

HAMPTON ROADS BANKSHARES, INC.

NASDAQ (GS): HMPR

999 Waterside Dr., Ste. 200	CEO: John A. B. (Andy) Davies
Norfolk, VA 23510	CFO: Lorelle L. Fritsch
Phone: 757-217-1000	HR: —
Fax: 757-217-3656	FYE: December 31
Web: www.bankofhamptonroads.com	Type: Public

Hampton Roads Bankshares is the holding company for the Bank of Hampton Roads and Shore Bank, which together have about 40 offices in southeastern Virginia and eastern Maryland. Gateway Bank & Trust, a division of Bank of Hampton Roads, has about 25 locations in Virginia and North Carolina. Serving area consumers and businesses, the banks offer standard services such as checking and savings accounts, CDs, retirement accounts, and loans. Through other affiliates, the banks also offer insurance, investment, and mortgage banking services. Hampton Roads Bankshares acquired Shore Financial and Gateway Financial Holdings in 2008.

	Annual Growth	12/05	12/06	12/07	12/08	12/09
Assets ($ mil.)	64.2%	409.5	476.3	563.8	3,085.7	2,975.6
Net income ($ mil.)	—	5.5	6.0	6.8	7.2	(145.5)
Market value ($ mil.)	(36.6%)	235.9	265.9	278.3	193.4	38.1
Employees	41.4%	175	176	182	721	699

HANA BIOSCIENCES, INC.

NASDAQ (GM): HNAB

7000 Shoreline Ct., Ste. 370	CEO: Steven R. Deitcher
South San Francisco, CA 94080	CFO: Craig W. Carlson
Phone: 650-588-6404	HR: —
Fax: 650-588-2787	FYE: December 31
Web: www.hanabiosciences.com	Type: Public

Hana Biosciences is fighting the good fight against the big "C." The development stage pharmaceutical company is looking to acquire and develop new drugs with a focus on cancer treatments. Hana Biosciences' lead product candidate, Marqibo, is a unique formulation of an existing cancer drug targeting forms of leukemia and melanoma. The company has other oncology pharmaceuticals in its pipeline, including therapies to treat solid tumor cancers (including lung and ovarian) and drugs to counteract side effects of cancer treatments.

	Annual Growth	12/05	12/06	12/07	12/08	12/09
Sales ($ mil.)	—	—	—	1.1	0.0	0.0
Net income ($ mil.)	—	—	—	(26.0)	(22.2)	(24.1)
Market value ($ mil.)	(57.7%)	—	—	84.6	19.1	15.2
Employees	(3.8%)	—	—	27	33	25

HANCOCK FABRICS, INC.

Pink Sheets: HKFI

1 Fashion Way	CEO: Jane F. Aggers
Baldwyn, MS 38824	CFO: Robert W. Driskell
Phone: 662-365-6000	HR: James Britz
Fax: —	FYE: January 31
Web: www.hancockfabrics.com	Type: Public

Through careful piecing and pinning, Hancock Fabrics has become a leading nationwide fabric chain (far behind Jo-Ann Stores). The company caters to customers who sew by offering fabrics, crafts, sewing machines, and accessories through some 265 stores (down from nearly 450 in 2004) in more than 35 states. To compensate for the waning popularity of sewing clothes, the company has expanded its selection of home decorating products, including drapery and upholstery fabrics and home accent pieces. Slumping sales led Hancock Fabrics to file for Chapter 11 bankruptcy protection in 2007. It emerged from bankruptcy in mid-2008. Investment firm Aspen Advisors LLC owns about 28% of the company's shares.

	Annual Growth	1/06	1/07	1/08	1/09	1/10
Sales ($ mil.)	(9.2%)	403.2	376.2	276.2	276.4	274.1
Net income ($ mil.)	—	(30.3)	(46.4)	(28.0)	(12.4)	1.8
Market value ($ mil.)	(7.7%)	90.8	79.7	15.9	8.0	65.9
Employees	(8.5%)	6,000	5,200	3,700	3,800	4,200

HANCOCK HOLDING COMPANY

NASDAQ (GS): HBHC

1 Hancock Plaza, 2510 14th St.	CEO: John M. Hairston
Gulfport, MS 39501	CFO: Michael M. Achary
Phone: 228-868-4000	HR: —
Fax: 228-563-5673	FYE: December 31
Web: www.hancockbank.com	Type: Public

Hancock Holding holds its own as a Gulf Coast financial force. It is the holding company of the Mississippi-based Hancock Bank, Hancock Bank of Louisiana, Hancock Bank of Florida, and Hancock Bank of Alabama, which together operate more than 180 branch offices. The community-oriented banks offer traditional products and services, including deposit accounts; trust services; residential mortgages; and business, consumer, and construction loans. Hancock Holding also has subsidiaries or business units offering insurance, discount brokerage services, mutual funds, and consumer financing.

	Annual Growth	12/05	12/06	12/07	12/08	12/09
Assets ($ mil.)	10.0%	5,950.2	5,964.6	6,056.0	7,167.3	8,697.1
Net income ($ mil.)	8.5%	54.0	101.8	73.9	65.4	74.8
Market value ($ mil.)	3.8%	1,394.3	1,948.5	1,408.7	1,676.4	1,615.5
Employees	6.6%	1,735	1,848	1,888	1,952	2,240

HANDANGO, INC.

5615 High Point Dr., Ste. 700	CEO: Alex Bloom
Irving, TX 75038	CFO: —
Phone: 972-894-0999	HR: —
Fax: —	FYE: December 31
Web: www.handango.com	Type: Private

Handango can lend a hand when it comes to software applications on the go. The company is a leading publisher and platform provider for mobile software, marketing applications and digital media titles, with more than 140,000 products for download. Its Handango AMPP (application management and provisioning platform) is used by a variety of customers for software delivery. The company also offers worldwide distribution, marketing support, and e-commerce services to its partners. Handango's customers include consumers, software developers, mobile operators, and OEMs. In 2010 the company was acquired by PocketGear, Inc., creating one of the largest independent applications stores in the world.

	Annual Growth	12/04	12/05	12/06	12/07	12/08
Est. sales ($ mil.)	—	—	—	—	—	7.7
Employees	—	—	—	—	—	70

H&E EQUIPMENT SERVICES, INC.

NASDAQ (GS): HEES

11100 Mead Rd., Ste. 200	CEO: John M. Engquist
Baton Rouge, LA 70816	CFO: Leslie S. Magee
Phone: 225-298-5200	HR: —
Fax: 225-298-5308	FYE: December 31
Web: www.he-equipment.com	Type: Public

Whether you're a he or a she, if you have a project that requires heavy lifting, H&E Equipment Services can help. The company sells and rents new and used equipment for construction, earthmoving, and material handling. H&E Equipment offers services such as planned maintenance, mobile service, repair, fleet management, and crane remanufacturing, as well as parts for aerial platform equipment and industrial lift trucks, among others. The company markets its products and services throughout the US and represents lift, crane, and truck manufacturers such as JLG, Bobcat, and Komatsu. President, CEO, and director John Engquist owns about 13% of the company.

	Annual Growth	12/05	12/06	12/07	12/08	12/09
Sales ($ mil.)	3.2%	600.2	804.4	1,003.1	1,069.0	679.7
Net income ($ mil.)	—	28.2	32.7	64.6	43.3	(11.9)
Market value ($ mil.)	(24.9%)	—	864.4	658.9	269.1	366.4
Employees	2.0%	1,448	1,677	2,095	1,871	1,568

H&M COMPANY, INC.

50 Security Dr.	CEO: Richard L. Fite
Jackson, TN 38305	CFO: Michael A. (Mike) Farris
Phone: 731-664-6300	HR: Connie McBee
Fax: 731-668-6841	FYE: December 31
Web: www.hmcompany.com	Type: Private

H&M Company = a provider of heavy industrial and manufacturing facility construction services. The group provides architectural, engineering, and construction services for manufacturing, distribution, and heavy industrial facilities. It also offers construction management for educational and institutional projects, and is one of the top US school builders. H&M Company is consistently ranked among the nation's top design/build firms. In 1957 Charles "Chicken" Fite and Frank Warmath established the company, which became one of the first US contractors to use design/build project delivery. Chairman David Fite, his brother Richard Fite (CEO), and president and COO Jim Campbell own the company.

	Annual Growth	12/04	12/05	12/06	12/07	12/08
Est. sales ($ mil.)	—	—	—	—	—	283.6
Employees	—	—	—	—	—	300

H&R BLOCK, INC.

NYSE: HRB

1 H&R Block Way	CEO: Russell P. (Russ) Smyth
Kansas City, MO 64105	CFO: Jeffrey T. (Jeff) Brown
Phone: 816-854-3000	HR: Tammy S. Serati
Fax: 816-854-8500	FYE: April 30
Web: www.hrblock.com	Type: Public

Only two things are certain in this life, and H&R Block has a stranglehold on one. The company, which boasts some 23 million tax customers worldwide, is the leading tax return preparer in the US with a network of some 13,000 retail offices; it also prepares tax returns in Canada and Australia (it exited the UK in 2007) through some 1,500 offices. Many of its offices are franchised. H&R Block also operates more than 1,500 shared locations in Wal-Mart and Sears. Average fee per client is $196. In addition to its ubiquitous tax-preparation services, the company provides a number of other products and services such as tax-preparation software and insurance, as well as retail banking through H&R Block Bank.

	Annual Growth	4/05	4/06	4/07	4/08	4/09
Sales ($ mil.)	(2.0%)	4,420.0	4,872.8	4,021.3	4,403.9	4,083.6
Net income ($ mil.)	(6.5%)	635.9	490.4	(433.7)	(308.6)	485.7
Market value ($ mil.)	(11.7%)	8,199.6	7,516.4	7,444.0	7,200.3	4,984.6
Employees	(0.0%)	133,800	134,500	136,600	137,200	133,700

An in-depth profile of this company is available to Hoover's Online members at hoovers.com.

HANES COMPANIES, INC.

500 N. McLin Creek Rd.
Conover, NC 28613
Phone: 828-464-4673
Fax: 828-464-0459
Web: www.hanesindustries.com

CEO: Jerry W. Greene Jr.
CFO: Shannon Marshall
HR: Samantha Howell
FYE: December 31
Type: Subsidiary

When the job calls for specialty threads, look no further than Hanes Companies. Part of Leggett & Platt since 1993, the group makes, converts, and distributes woven and non-woven textiles and knits for coveralls, scrubs, and school uniforms, as well as construction fabrics for furniture including dust covers and webbing, and bedding such as filler cloths, flame-retardant barriers, and water-resistant liners. Its lineup taps landscape and geotechnical uses for weed control, ground cover, and soil stabilization, as well as filtration solutions, and automotive headliners, acoustic panel materials, and seat fabrics. The label reaches to building products, too, like roof fabrics and driveway underlayment.

HANESBRANDS INC.

NYSE: HBI

1000 E. Hanes Mill Rd.
Winston-Salem, NC 27105
Phone: 336-519-8080
Fax: —
Web: www.hanesbrands.com

CEO: Richard A. (Rich) Noll
CFO: E. Lee Wyatt Jr.
HR: Kevin W. Oliver
FYE: December 31
Type: Public

Hanesbrands can't wait until it gets its Hanes on you. The company makes bras, boxers, hosiery, socks, and other unmentionables under top brand names, including Bali, Champion, Barely There, Just My Size, Hanes, L'eggs, Playtex, and Wonderbra. Its bras are tops in the US; its underwear, legwear, and activewear units are leaders, as well. Hanesbrands, which sells its products through stores such as Wal-Mart, Target, and Kohl's, also makes legwear under license for Donna Karan and underwear for Polo Ralph Lauren. Former parent Sara Lee spun off the division in September 2006. During the years since the spinoff, Hanesbrands has been shuttering plants and eliminating up to 5,300 jobs or some 10% of its workforce.

	Annual Growth	6/05	6/06	*12/07	12/08	12/09
Sales ($ mil.)	(4.5%)	4,683.7	4,472.8	4,474.5	4,248.8	3,891.3
Net income ($ mil.)	(30.4%)	218.5	322.5	126.1	127.2	51.3
Market value ($ mil.)	(5.8%)	—	—	2,597.2	1,218.8	2,304.7
Employees	(1.3%)	50,000	49,000	47,600	45,200	47,400
				*Fiscal year change		

HANGER ORTHOPEDIC GROUP, INC.

NYSE: HGR

2 Bethesda Metro Center, Ste. 1200
Bethesda, MD 20814
Phone: 301-986-0701
Fax: 301-986-0702
Web: www.hanger.com

CEO: Thomas F. Kirk
CFO: George E. McHenry
HR: Brian A. Wheeler
FYE: December 31
Type: Public

No hanger-on here. Hanger Orthopedic Group is one of the US's leading operators of orthotic and prosthetic (O&P) rehabilitation centers, with some 670 facilities nationwide. The company's Southern Prosthetic Supply procures and distributes standard and customized braces and prosthetic devices to affiliated and independent O&P centers. Its Innovative Neurotronics (IN) subsidiary makes neuromuscular stimulation products for patients with a loss of mobility. The company also has programs to manage patient care for health insurance providers through subsidiary Linkia. Hanger Orthopedic Group has distribution, custom-fabrication, and corporate facilities across the US.

	Annual Growth	12/05	12/06	12/07	12/08	12/09
Sales ($ mil.)	7.1%	578.2	598.8	637.3	703.1	760.1
Net income ($ mil.)	19.3%	17.8	3.4	19.3	26.7	36.1
Market value ($ mil.)	24.8%	182.6	240.8	352.1	464.0	442.3
Employees	2.5%	3,290	3,303	3,364	3,211	3,636

HANMI FINANCIAL CORPORATION

NASDAQ (GS): HAFC

3660 Wilshire Blvd., Penthouse Ste. A
Los Angeles, CA 90010
Phone: 213-382-2200
Fax: 213-384-0990
Web: www.hanmifinancial.com

CEO: Jay S. Yoo
CFO: Brian E. Cho
HR: —
FYE: December 31
Type: Public

No hand-me-down operation, Hanmi Financial is headquartered in a penthouse suite along Los Angeles' Wilshire Boulevard. The company owns Hanmi Bank, which serves California's Korean-American communities in the Los Angeles, San Diego, San Francisco Bay, and Silicon Valley areas. Hanmi Bank offers retail and small business banking, with an emphasis on the latter, from some 20 California branches and another handful of loan offices throughout the US. Commercial and industrial loans, including SBA and international trade finance loans, account for about two-thirds of its loan portfolio; real estate loans make up most of the rest. Korean bank Woori Finance plans to buy Hanmi Financial to expand its US operations.

	Annual Growth	12/05	12/06	12/07	12/08	12/09
Assets ($ mil.)	(1.9%)	3,414.3	3,725.2	3,983.7	3,875.8	3,162.7
Net income ($ mil.)	—	58.2	65.6	(60.5)	(102.1)	(122.3)
Market value ($ mil.)	(49.1%)	914.1	1,153.1	441.2	105.4	61.4
Employees	(2.0%)	552	589	659	528	509

HANNAFORD BROS. CO.

145 Pleasant Hill Rd.
Scarborough, ME 04074
Phone: 207-883-2911
Fax: 207-885-2859
Web: www.hannaford.com

CEO: Beth M. Newlands-Campbell
CFO: Greg Amoroso
HR: Bradford A. (Brad) Wise
FYE: December 31
Type: Subsidiary

Hannaford Bros. may have started as a fruit and vegetable stand in 1883, but it has expanded from its Maine roots to become an upscale grocer with more than 170 stores under the Hannaford Supermarkets banner throughout Maine, Massachusetts, New Hampshire, upstate New York, and Vermont. Still, produce continues to be a major focus at the Hannaford supermarkets, as are expansive meat selections and natural food products. More than 75% of the Hannaford stores are combination grocery stores and pharmacies. The stores average about 48,500 sq. ft. Maine's largest supermarket chain, Hannaford Bros. is owned by Delhaize America (parent of Food Lion), which in turn is owned by Belgium's Delhaize Group.

	Annual Growth	12/04	12/05	12/06	12/07	12/08
Est. sales ($ mil.)	—	—	—	—	—	2,820.8
Employees	—	—	—	—	—	26,000

HANOVER DIRECT, INC.

1500 Harbor Blvd.
Weehawken, NJ 07086
Phone: 201-863-7300
Fax: 201-272-3280
Web: www.hanoverdirect.com

CEO: Wayne P. Garten
CFO: —
HR: Jordan Vargas
FYE: December 31
Type: Private

If catalogs are junk mail, then Hanover Direct is one big junkyard dog. Mailing more than 180 million catalogs a year, the company sells home fashions (*The Company Store, Domestications*), as well as men's and women's apparel (*International Male, Silhouettes,* and *Undergear*). Each catalog has a corresponding e-commerce site. In addition to its own websites, Hanover Direct also sells its products through affiliated third-party websites, such as Amazon.com. The company makes Scandia Down comforters and pillows for sale in its catalogs, on its websites, and at its three retail outlet stores. Majority stockholder Chelsey Direct, controlled by Hanover director Stuart Feldman, took the company private in 2007.

HANOVER FOODS CORPORATION

1486 York St.
Hanover, PA 17331
Phone: 717-632-6000
Fax: 717-637-2890
Web: hanoverfoods.com

CEO: John A. Warehime
CFO: Gary T. Knisely
HR: Patty Townsend
FYE: May 31
Type: Private

Hanover Foods manufactures foods hand over fist — it makes some 40 million cases of prepared food a year. The company's retail products include canned and frozen vegetables and canned soups, baked beans, and bean salads; its foodservice items offer the same, as well as a full line of salty snacks, canned tomato products, creamed chipped beef, and frozen soft pretzels. Hanover's customers consist of businesses in the retail-food, foodservice, private-label, military, club-store, and food manufacturing sectors throughout the US. Its brands include Hanover, Meyers, Mitchell's, and Superfine. The company also owns two factory outlet stores in Pennsylvania, one in Hanover and the other in York.

THE HANOVER INSURANCE GROUP, INC.

NYSE: THG

440 Lincoln St.
Worcester, MA 01653
Phone: 508-855-1000
Fax: 508-853-6332
Web: www.hanover.com

CEO: Frederick H. (Fred) Eppinger
CFO: Steven J. (Steve) Bensinger
HR: Bryan D. Allen
FYE: December 31
Type: Public

The Hanover Insurance Group is an all-around property/casualty insurance holding company. Through its Hanover Insurance Company, it provides personal and commercial automobile, homeowners, workers' compensation, and commercial multiple-peril insurance and professional liability coverage. In Michigan, it operates as Citizens Insurance Company. The group sells its products through a network of 2,000 independent agents in the midwestern, northeastern, and southeastern US, but Michigan and Massachusetts account for more than a third of its business. Its Opus Investment Management subsidiary provides institutional investment management services.

	Annual Growth	12/05	12/06	12/07	12/08	12/09
Assets ($ mil.)	(6.7%)	10,634.0	9,856.6	9,815.6	9,230.2	8,042.7
Net income ($ mil.)	—	(325.2)	169.7	253.1	20.6	197.2
Market value ($ mil.)	1.6%	1,873.2	2,188.4	2,053.9	1,927.0	1,992.4
Employees	0.0%	4,100	4,000	3,900	4,000	4,100

HANSEN CORPORATION

901 S. 1st St.
Princeton, IN 47670
Phone: 812-385-3415
Fax: 812-385-3013
Web: www.hansen-motor.com

CEO: William K. Poyner
CFO: W. Michael Hollars
HR: —
FYE: March 31
Type: Subsidiary

For more than a century, Hansen has kept motors ticking. The company manufactures a broad array of precision electric motors, from synchronous motors, to DC motors, stepper motors, damper actuators, and AC clock movements. The lineup is sold worldwide, one at a time or in volume, as well as by custom built design, directly by Hansen's sales force. Customers are predominantly in the automotive industry, followed by HVAC system, instrumentation, office, and medical equipment industries. Hansen operates as a subsidiary of Tokyo-based machinery and components maker Minebea.

HANSEN MEDICAL, INC.

NASDAQ (GM): HNSN

308 N. Bernardo Ave.
Mountain View, CA 94043
Phone: 650-404-5800
Fax: 650-404-5901
Web: www.hansenmedical.com

CEO: Frederic H. Moll
CFO: Peter Osborne
HR: —
FYE: December 31
Type: Public

Hansen Medical helps doctors maneuver catheters within tricky parts of the heart. The company's portable Sensei system incorporates advanced robotics to assist in guiding the movement of flexible catheters in such places as the atria and ventricles. The system is designed to work along with its Artisan control catheters. Sensei has received FDA and European regulatory approval for the manipulation, positioning, and control of mapping catheters in electrophysiology procedures (designed to diagnose irregular electrical impulses in the heart). The product is awaiting clearance for use in more highly sensitive ablation procedures in the treatment of cardiac arrhythmia.

	Annual Growth	12/05	12/06	12/07	12/08	12/09
Sales ($ mil.)	48.3%	—	—	10.1	30.2	22.2
Net income ($ mil.)	—	—	—	(50.4)	(53.4)	(52.4)
Market value ($ mil.)	(68.2%)	—	—	1,606.2	387.3	162.6
Employees	(5.8%)	—	—	195	208	173

HANSEN NATURAL CORPORATION

NASDAQ (GS): HANS

550 Monica Circle, Ste. 201
Corona, CA 92880
Phone: 951-739-6200
Fax: 951-739-6220
Web: www.hansens.com

CEO: Rodney C. Sacks
CFO: Hilton H. Schlosberg
HR: Linda Lopez
FYE: December 31
Type: Public

No matter the weather, Hansen Natural always has the energy to reach higher than the blue sky. Adding to its Blue Sky energy drink, the company has expanded its stable of "alternative" sodas, juices, and teas to include a variety of energy beverages, such as the popular Monster brand. Other products made by Hansen include fruit juice, smoothies, and dry juice mixes. The company sells its products to grocery chains, wholesale clubs, distributors, and foodservice operators mainly in the US and Canada. Through Branded Limited Partnership, Hansen chairman and CEO Rodney Sacks and vice chairman and president Hilton Schlosberg own approximately 19% of the company.

	Annual Growth	12/05	12/06	12/07	12/08	12/09
Sales ($ mil.)	34.5%	348.9	605.8	904.5	1,033.8	1,143.3
Net income ($ mil.)	35.0%	62.8	97.9	149.4	108.0	208.7
Market value ($ mil.)	18.2%	1,748.9	2,989.7	3,931.5	2,976.4	3,408.7
Employees	40.9%	363	748	713	1,270	1,430

HANSON BRICK EAST, LLC

15720 John J. Delaney Dr., Ste. 555
Charlotte, NC 28277
Phone: 704-341-8750
Fax: 704-341-8735
Web: www.hansonbrick.com

CEO: Bob Christensen
CFO: —
HR: —
FYE: December 31
Type: Subsidiary

Brick by brick, Hanson Brick has risen up as North America's biggest brick maker. It has capacity to churn out 1.7 billion bricks annually from plants in the US and Canada. Over 1,000 styles in five regional brick lines are offered. Its clay brick and concrete roof tiles are touted for their "green" building durability. Hanson Brick and five sister companies operate as divisions of Hanson Building Products North America. Often sold in conjunction with brick, Hanson Roof Tile makes concrete roof tile for residential and commercial projects, and its Hardscapes makes pavers, tiles, and retaining walls. Hanson companies are part of HeidelbergCement Group, a global cement, concrete, and heavy building products giant.

An in-depth profile of this company is available to Hoover's Online members at hoovers.com.

729

HARBINGER GROUP INC.

NYSE: HRG

100 Meridian Centre, Ste. 350	CEO: Philip Falcone
Rochester, NY 14618	CFO: Francis T. (Frank) McCarron
Phone: 585-242-2000	HR: —
Fax: 585-242-8677	FYE: December 31
Web: www.zapatacorp.com	Type: Public

Harbinger Group (formerly Zapata Corporation) zapped its former image as an oil and gas company and is on the lookout for new acquisitions. The holding company has more than $150 million to make investments. Former US President George H. W. Bush co-founded the company as Zapata in 1953. It sold its energy businesses in the 1990s and became a producer of marine protein through its holdings in Omega Protein. Omega's facilities suffered major hurricane damage in 2005, and Zapata sold Omega the next year. Hedge fund Harbinger Capital Partners acquired a controlling stake in Harbinger Group in 2009.

	Annual Growth	12/05	12/06	12/07	12/08	12/09
Sales ($ mil.)	—	—	—	—	—	0.0
Net income ($ mil.)	—	—	—	—	—	(13.3)
Market value ($ mil.)	—	—	—	—	—	135.4
Employees	—	—	—	—	—	8

HARBOR BIOSCIENCES, INC.

NASDAQ (GM): HRBR

4435 Eastgate Mall, Ste. 400	CEO: James M. Frincke
San Diego, CA 92121	CFO: Robert W. Weber
Phone: 858-587-9333	HR: —
Fax: 858-558-6470	FYE: December 31
Web: www.harborbiosciences.com	Type: Public

Adrenal steroids do the heavy lifting in the body's natural defense and metabolic systems, and Harbor Biosciences (formerly Hollis-Eden Pharmaceuticals) hopes to harness their power. The company focuses on developing adrenal steroid hormones and hormone analogs, which may reduce inflammation, regulate immunity, and stimulate cell growth. Natural levels of adrenal steroid hormones can decline as a result of aging or stress, leaving the body less able to fend off illnesses. Harbor Biosciences' TRIOLEX candidate is being tested as a possible treatment for type 2 diabetes, rheumatoid arthritis, and ulcerative colitis. Its APOPTONE candidate is being investigated as a therapy for prostate and breast cancer.

	Annual Growth	12/05	12/06	12/07	12/08	12/09
Sales ($ mil.)	—	0.1	0.4	0.6	0.0	0.0
Net income ($ mil.)	—	(29.4)	(30.2)	(23.1)	(21.6)	(15.6)
Market value ($ mil.)	(42.5%)	142.7	155.1	46.3	20.0	15.6
Employees	(26.2%)	64	66	56	42	19

HARBOR DISTRIBUTING L.L.C.

1625 S. Lewis St.	CEO: Thomas A. (Tom) Reyes
Anaheim, CA 92805	CFO: Greg Geane
Phone: 714-712-2400	HR: —
Fax: 714-935-0720	FYE: December 31
Web: www.reyesholdings.com/harbor_dist.html	Type: Subsidiary

This company helps satisfy Southern California's thirst for frosty cold beverages. Harbor Distributing is a leading beer distributor in the Golden State, with operations in Anaheim, Gardena, and Santa Ana. It supplies more than 6,000 customers with more than 20 million cases of beer, including both domestic (Coors, Miller, and Pabst) and import (Beck's, Heineken) labels. It also distributes some craft beer brands (Samuel Adams, Sierra Nevada). Harbor Distributing is part of Reyes Beverage Group, a division of Illinois-based Reyes Holdings.

HARD ROCK CAFE INTERNATIONAL, INC.

6100 Old Park Ln.	CEO: Hamish Dodds
Orlando, FL 32835	CFO: Thomas (Tom) Gispanski
Phone: 407-445-7625	HR: Kim Creighton
Fax: 407-445-9709	FYE: December 31
Web: www.hardrock.com	Type: Subsidiary

You can rock hard, eat hard, buy merchandise hard, even sleep hard with Hard Rock Cafe International. The company operates the Hard Rock Cafe chain of theme restaurants, which serve up typical American fare, as well as rock-music memorabilia and plenty of Hard Rock-branded merchandise. The chain has more than 125 company-owned and franchised locations in more than 45 countries. The company also has about 10 branded hotels and hotel casinos operated by third-parties, as well as four concert venues in the US and Mexico. Its collection of rock n' roll memorabilia boasts more than 70,000 items. The Hard Rock chain is owned by the Seminole Tribe of Florida.

HARDINGE INC.

NASDAQ (GS): HDNG

1 Hardinge Dr.	CEO: Richard L. Simons
Elmira, NY 14902	CFO: Edward J. Gaio
Phone: 607-734-2281	HR: —
Fax: 607-732-4925	FYE: December 31
Web: www.hardinge.com	Type: Public

Hardinge just keeps on turning. The company makes industrial machine tools for small and midsized shops that turn out machined parts for the aerospace, automotive, construction, medical equipment, and farm equipment industries. The company's precision turning and grinding machine tools shape metal, composites, and plastics. Its computer-controlled machines cut either horizontally or vertically and can be connected to automatic material feeders for unattended machining. Hardinge also offers a line of work- and tool-holding devices. The company gets almost 70% of its sales outside of North America, predominantly in Western Europe. Hardinge has manufacturing facilities in China, Switzerland, Taiwan, and the US.

	Annual Growth	12/05	12/06	12/07	12/08	12/09
Sales ($ mil.)	(7.3%)	289.9	326.6	356.3	345.0	214.1
Net income ($ mil.)	—	7.0	13.9	14.9	(34.3)	(33.3)
Market value ($ mil.)	(24.9%)	201.1	174.9	194.8	46.9	63.9
Employees	(5.5%)	1,429	1,457	1,519	1,427	1,138

HARLAND CLARKE CORP.

10931 Laureate Dr.	CEO: Charles T. (Chuck) Dawson
San Antonio, TX 78249	CFO: Peter A. Fera Jr.
Phone: 210-697-8888	HR: —
Fax: 210-696-1676	FYE: December 31
Web: www.harlandclarke.com	Type: Subsidiary

Check it out: Harland Clarke Holdings produces billions of checks and deposit slips annually. The company's products are sold through financial institutions and also directly to consumers and businesses under brands such as B≈Direct, Checks In The Mail, Clarke American, and Harland. Subsidiary Alcott Routon provides direct marketing services to businesses. Overall, Harland Clarke maintains about 20 manufacturing facilities and contact centers throughout the US and Puerto Rico. The company took its current form in May 2007 when holding company M & F Worldwide, the owner of Clarke American Checks, bought rival printer John H. Harland and combined the companies' check-related operations.

	Annual Growth	12/04	12/05	12/06	12/07	12/08
Est. sales ($ mil.)	—	—	—	—	—	1,369.9
Employees	—	—	—	—	—	7,000

HARLAND FINANCIAL SOLUTIONS, INC.

605 Crescent Executive Ct., Ste. 600
Lake Mary, FL 32746
Phone: 407-804-6600
Fax: 407-829-6702
Web: www.harlandfs.com

CEO: Raju M. (Raj) Shivdasani
CFO: —
HR: —
FYE: December 31
Type: Subsidiary

Harland Financial Solutions supplies software and services for financial institutions. The company's software offerings include applications for lending and account origination, customer relationship management, business intelligence, bank and credit union core processing systems, teller and call center platforms, mortgage lending and servicing, and regulatory compliance training. Harland Financial Solutions also offers a service bureau for outsourced core processing, as well as document imaging and electronic statement processing services.

HARLEY-DAVIDSON, INC.

NYSE: HOG

3700 W. Juneau Ave.
Milwaukee, WI 53208
Phone: 414-342-4680
Fax: 414-343-8230
Web: www.harley-davidson.com

CEO: Keith E. Wandell
CFO: John A. Olin
HR: —
FYE: December 31
Type: Public

"Put your a** on some class," reads one (not necessarily official) Harley-Davidson T-shirt. Harley-Davidson is a major US maker of motorcycles and the nation's #1 seller of heavyweight cruisers. The company offers over 30 models of touring and custom Harleys through a worldwide network of more than 1,500 dealers. Harley models include the Electra Glide, the Sportster, and the Fat Boy. The company also makes motorcycles under the MV Agusta and Cagiva nameplates. Harley-Davidson sells attitude with its brand-name products, which include a line of clothing and accessories (MotorClothes). Harley-Davidson Financial Services offers financing to dealers and consumers in the US and Canada.

	Annual Growth	12/05	12/06	12/07	12/08	12/09
Sales ($ mil.)	(2.7%)	5,342.2	6,185.6	5,726.8	5,594.3	4,781.9
Net income ($ mil.)	—	959.6	1,043.2	933.8	654.7	(55.1)
Market value ($ mil.)	(16.4%)	12,123.4	16,592.3	10,998.0	3,995.6	5,933.4
Employees	(6.9%)	9,700	9,704	9,775	10,100	7,300

HARLEYSVILLE GROUP INC.

NASDAQ (GS): HGIC

355 Maple Ave.
Harleysville, PA 19438
Phone: 215-256-5000
Fax: 215-256-5799
Web: www.harleysvillegroup.com

CEO: Michael L. Browne
CFO: Arthur E. (Art) Chandler
HR: Beth A. Friel
FYE: December 31
Type: Public

The reckless, the accident-prone, or the just plain apprehensive take heed: Harleysville Group (also known as Harleysville Insurance) hopes to extend a safety net for all of you. A regional insurance holding company, Harleysville Group sells a broad line of personal and commercial property/casualty insurance policies. The company offers coverage for homeowners, auto, commercial multi-peril, and workers' compensation. Harleysville provides services throughout the eastern and midwestern US. It has regional offices in about a dozen states, and its products are marketed through some 1,400 independent agencies in more than 30 states. Harleysville Mutual Insurance Company owns a majority stake in Harleysville Group.

	Annual Growth	12/05	12/06	12/07	12/08	12/09
Assets ($ mil.)	3.3%	2,905.3	2,991.0	3,072.4	3,155.3	3,302.0
Net income ($ mil.)	8.9%	61.4	110.1	100.1	42.3	86.3
Market value ($ mil.)	4.7%	730.1	959.3	974.7	956.8	875.8
Employees	(4.1%)	2,029	1,898	1,800	1,729	1,713

HARLEYSVILLE SAVINGS FINANCIAL

NASDAQ (GM): HARL

271 Main St.
Harleysville, PA 19438
Phone: 215-256-8828
Fax: 215-513-9393
Web: www.harleysvillesavings.com

CEO: Ronald B. Geib
CFO: Brendan J. McGill
HR: —
FYE: September 30
Type: Public

Get your moola runnin'! Harleysville Savings Financial Corporation is the holding company of Harleysville Savings Bank, which operates about a half-dozen branches in southeastern Pennsylvania's Montgomery County. The bank offers standard deposit products such as checking and savings accounts, CDs, and IRAs. Its lending activities consist primarily of single-family residential mortgages, which account for more than two-thirds of the company's loan portfolio; home equity loans account for nearly 15%. To a lesser extent, Harleysville Savings Bank also originates commercial mortgages, residential construction loans, and consumer lines of credit.

	Annual Growth	9/05	9/06	9/07	9/08	9/09
Assets ($ mil.)	2.0%	767.0	775.6	773.5	825.7	830.0
Net income ($ mil.)	(1.5%)	5.0	4.2	3.2	4.4	4.7
Market value ($ mil.)	(5.4%)	62.8	61.9	50.2	46.1	50.2
Employees	4.3%	98	104	117	117	116

HARMAN INTERNATIONAL INDUSTRIES

NYSE: HAR

400 Atlantic St., 15th Fl.
Stamford, CT 06901
Phone: 203-328-3500
Fax: —
Web: www.harman.com

CEO: Dinesh C. Paliwal
CFO: Herbert K. Parker
HR: John Stacey
FYE: June 30
Type: Public

Harman International Industries, Incorporated, is loud and clear. It makes high-end stereo and audio equipment for consumer and professional markets. Its consumer group makes loudspeakers, CD and DVD players, CD recorders, and amplifiers under brands such as Harman/Kardon, Infinity, Becker, Logic 7, JBL, Mark Levinson, and others. Harman's auto unit sells branded audio systems through several carmakers, including Toyota and General Motors. Its professional unit makes audio equipment, such as monitors, amplifiers, microphones, and mixing consoles for recording studios, cinemas, touring performers, and others. In addition, Harman offers computer software and development tools to the automotive, energy, medical, and telecom industries.

	Annual Growth	6/05	6/06	6/07	6/08	6/09
Sales ($ mil.)	(1.2%)	3,030.9	3,247.9	3,551.1	4,112.5	2,891.0
Net income ($ mil.)	—	232.8	255.3	314.0	107.8	(422.6)
Market value ($ mil.)	(30.7%)	5,656.8	5,935.6	8,120.9	2,877.8	1,307.1
Employees	(3.3%)	10,845	11,246	11,688	11,694	9,482

HARMONIC INC.

NASDAQ (GM): HLIT

549 Baltic Way
Sunnyvale, CA 94089
Phone: 408-542-2500
Fax: 408-542-2511
Web: www.harmonicinc.com

CEO: Patrick J. Harshman
CFO: Carolyn V. Aver
HR: Peter E. (Pete) Hilliard
FYE: December 31
Type: Public

Harmonic answers the demand for advanced television features. The company provides fiber-optic and wireless network transmission products used to enable video-on-demand services. Its video transmission equipment includes digital headend systems, digital signal encoders, and complete provider-to-subscriber delivery systems. Harmonic also supplies multiplexers, optical nodes, transmitters, optical amplifiers, and other broadband network access equipment. The company sells directly and through distributors and systems integrators, primarily to cable and satellite TV providers. Its customers include Cablevision, Charter Communications, Comcast, and Time Warner Cable. It makes nearly half of sales outside the US.

	Annual Growth	12/05	12/06	12/07	12/08	12/09
Sales ($ mil.)	5.6%	257.4	247.7	311.2	365.0	319.6
Net income ($ mil.)	—	(5.7)	1.0	23.4	64.0	(24.1)
Market value ($ mil.)	6.8%	470.1	704.6	1,015.7	543.7	612.5
Employees	8.0%	618	639	658	698	840

An in-depth profile of this company is available to Hoover's Online members at hoovers.com.

731

HARPERCOLLINS PUBLISHERS, INC.

10 E. 53rd St.
New York, NY 10022
Phone: 212-207-7000
Fax: 212-207-7145
Web: www.harpercollins.com

CEO: Brian Murray
CFO: Janet Gervasio
HR: Diane Bailey
FYE: June 30
Type: Subsidiary

HarperCollins Publishers has a real page-turner on its hands. The book-publishing subsidiary of Rupert Murdoch's News Corp., HarperCollins is the publisher of best-sellers including *Coraline* by Neil Gaiman, *Super-Freakanomics* by Steven Levitt and Stephen Dubner, and Scott Adams' *Dilbert* books. The company's publishing groups include HarperCollins General Books (imprints such as Avon and Eos), HarperCollins Children's Book Group, HarperCollins UK, HarperCollins Canada, and HarperCollins Australia/New Zealand. Its Zondervan unit publishes Bibles and Christian books. The company also sells e-books from its website and through other online retailers. HarperCollins provides about 5% of parent News Corp.'s sales.

	Annual Growth	6/04	6/05	6/06	6/07	6/08
Est. sales ($ mil.)	—	—	—	—	—	1,300.0
Employees	—	—	—	—	—	1,425

HARPO, INC.

110 N. Carpenter St.
Chicago, IL 60607
Phone: 312-633-1000
Fax: 312-633-1976
Web: www.oprah.com

CEO: Oprah G. Winfrey
CFO: Douglas J. (Doug) Pattison
HR: —
FYE: December 31
Type: Private

You might say this company puts the "O" in Oprah. Harpo controls the entertainment and media interests of talk show host/actress/producer Oprah Winfrey. Its flagship *The Oprah Winfrey Show* is the highest-rated TV talk show in history and is seen in almost every US market and in 145 countries. Harpo also owns 50% of The Oprah Winfrey Network, a joint venture with Discovery Communications that will operate startup cable channel OWN: The Oprah Winfrey Network. In addition to TV, Winfrey's *O, The Oprah Magazine*, published with Hearst Magazines, boasts a circulation of about 2.4 million. Other activities include a SIRIUS XM Radio program and feature film production. Oprah started her production company in 1986.

HARPS FOOD STORES, INC.

918 S. Gutensohn Rd.
Springdale, AR 72762
Phone: 479-751-7601
Fax: 479-751-3625
Web: www.harpsfood.com

CEO: Roger Collins
CFO: Jim Antz
HR: Frank Ray
FYE: December 31
Type: Private

It's tough to survive in the face of Arkansas giant Wal-Mart, but Harps Food Stores (founded when Sam Walton was 12 years old) is putting up a fight. The company, which got its start when Floy and Harvard Harp put down $500 cash and opened the first Harp's Cash Grocery in 1930, operates more than 60 grocery stores, mostly in Arkansas but also in Missouri and Oklahoma. Its stores, operating under the Harps Food Stores and Price Cutter Food Warehouse banners, range in size from 13,000 to 63,000 sq. ft. and often feature bakeries, pharmacies, and meat departments. Harps operated as a family-run chain until 2001 when it became an employee-owned business.

	Annual Growth	12/04	12/05	12/06	12/07	12/08
Sales ($ mil.)	10.0%	—	—	—	400.0	440.0
Employees	—	—	—	—	—	3,200

HARRAH'S ENTERTAINMENT, INC.

1 Caesars Palace Dr.
Las Vegas, NV 89109
Phone: 702-407-6000
Fax: 702-407-6037
Web: www.harrahs.com

CEO: Gary W. Loveman
CFO: Jonathan S. Halkyard
HR: Mary H. Thomas
FYE: December 31
Type: Private

Harrah's Entertainment likes to spread its bets. The world's largest gaming company, Harrah's owns, operates, and/or manages about 50 casinos (under such names as Harrah's, Bally's, Caesars, Horseshoe, and Rio), primarily in the US and the UK. Operations include casino hotels, dockside and riverboat casinos, and Native American gaming establishments. Among Harrah's plethora of locations on the Las Vegas strip is the Planet Hollywood Resort & Casino (which operates separately from Planet Hollywood International). Harrah's became the world's #1 gaming company when it acquired rival Caesars Entertainment for $9.4 billion in 2005. The company is owned by private equity firms Apollo Advisors and TPG Capital.

	Annual Growth	12/04	12/05	12/06	12/07	12/08
Sales ($ mil.)	(6.4%)	—	—	—	10,825.2	10,127.0
Net income ($ mil.)	—	—	—	—	619.4	(5,197.2)
Employees	(8.0%)	—	—	—	87,000	80,000

HARRINGTON WEST FINANCIAL GROUP, INC.

OTC: HWFG

610 Alamo Pintado Rd.
Solvang, CA 93463
Phone: 805-688-6644
Fax: 805-688-4959
Web: www.hwfg.com

CEO: Craig J. Cerny
CFO: Kerril K. (Kerry) Steele
HR: —
FYE: December 31
Type: Public

This is not your father's bank. It's Los Padres Bank, the flagship subsidiary of Harrington West Financial Group. Los Padres has about a dozen branches along California's central coast, as well as the Phoenix metropolitan area. The bank serves individuals and small businesses, offering standard services such as deposit products and loans. Commercial mortgages make up about a third of its portfolio. Other loans include business loans, residential mortgages, and construction loans. The bank's Harrington Wealth Management unit provides trust and investment services. In 2009 Harrington West Financial sold its Kansas-based Harrington Bank subsidiary to Arvest Bank in order to focus on its core markets.

	Annual Growth	12/04	12/05	12/06	12/07	*12/08
Assets ($ mil.)	2.5%	1,081.3	1,140.2	1,154.5	1,223.4	1,195.6
Net income ($ mil.)	—	8.2	8.3	8.2	4.2	(10.8)
Market value ($ mil.)	(42.9%)	138.8	122.2	127.0	82.8	14.7
Employees	2.5%	177	186	189	198	195

*Most recent year available

HARRIS & HARRIS GROUP, INC.

NASDAQ (GM): TINY

111 W. 57th St., Ste. 1100
New York, NY 10019
Phone: 212-582-0900
Fax: 212-582-9563
Web: www.tinytechvc.com

CEO: Douglas W. Jamison
CFO: Daniel B. Wolfe
HR: Sandra M. Forman
FYE: December 31
Type: Public

Harris & Harris Group likes to think small. The business development company (BDC) invests mostly in startup firms developing so-called "tiny technology" — microsystems, microelectromechanical systems, and nanotechnology used in applications in such sectors as electronics, medical devices, pharmaceuticals, semiconductors, telecommunications, and clean technology. The company seeks out small, thinly capitalized firms lacking operating history or experienced management. Harris & Harris has made more than 80 venture capital investments since 1983; its current portfolio consists of interests in some 30 firms, including Molecular Imprints, Nanosys, and NeoPhotonics.

	Annual Growth	12/05	12/06	12/07	12/08	12/09
Sales ($ mil.)	—	—	—	—	(36.5)	8.9
Net income ($ mil.)	—	—	—	—	(49.2)	(0.1)
Market value ($ mil.)	15.7%	—	—	—	121.9	141.1
Employees	0.0%	—	—	—	11	11

An in-depth profile of this company is available to Hoover's Online members at hoovers.com.

HARRIS BANKCORP, INC.

111 W. Monroe St.
Chicago, IL 60603
Phone: 312-461-6298
Fax: 312-461-7869
Web: www.harrisbank.com

CEO: Ellen M. Costello
CFO: Pamela C. (Pam) Piarowski
HR: Deirdre Drake
FYE: October 31
Type: Subsidiary

The US banking arm of Bank of Montreal (BMO), Harris Bankcorp offers personal and commercial banking and other financial services through Harris Bank and other subsidiaries. The company has more than 300 bank branches in the Chicago area, Indiana, and Wisconsin; it also has locations in Arizona, Florida, New York, and a handful of other states. In addition to Harris Bank, the company owns Harris Investment Management, middle-market investment bank BMO Capital Markets, and private bank and wealth management unit Harris Private Bank. Harris Bank added more than 50 branches in the Midwest when it acquired the failed AMCORE Bank in an FDIC-assisted deal in 2010.

	Annual Growth	10/04	10/05	10/06	10/07	10/08
Est. sales ($ mil.)	—	—	—	—	—	2,361.9
Employees	—	—	—	—	—	6,600

HARRIS CORPORATION

NYSE: HRS

1025 W. NASA Blvd.
Melbourne, FL 32919
Phone: 321-727-9100
Fax: 321-674-4740
Web: www.harris.com

CEO: Howard L. Lance
CFO: Gary L. McArthur
HR: Jeffrey S. (Jeff) Shuman
FYE: June 30
Type: Public

Hail Harris for a high-flying, high-tech hookup. The company, which develops communications products for government and commercial customers worldwide, makes microwave, satellite, and other wireless network transmission equipment; air traffic control systems; mobile radio systems; and digital network broadcasting and management systems. Among its largest customers are the US government, prime contractors, and foreign militaries, which together account for more than three-quarters of sales. Harris' commercial clients are construction companies, oil producers, radio and TV broadcasters, and utilities, including Clear Channel Communications, Lockheed Martin, and Sony. Harris gets most of its sales in the US.

	Annual Growth	6/05	6/06	6/07	6/08	6/09
Sales ($ mil.)	13.6%	3,000.6	3,474.8	4,243.0	5,311.0	5,005.0
Net income ($ mil.)	(34.2%)	202.2	237.9	480.4	444.2	37.9
Market value ($ mil.)	(1.0%)	3,836.0	5,101.9	6,704.6	6,205.6	3,682.1
Employees	5.1%	12,600	13,900	16,000	16,500	15,400

HARRIS INTERACTIVE INC.

NASDAQ (GS): HPOL

161 6th Ave.
New York, NY 10013
Phone: 585-272-8400
Fax: 585-272-8680
Web: www.harrisinteractive.com

CEO: Kimberly Till
CFO: Eric W. Narowski
HR: Patti B. Hoffman
FYE: June 30
Type: Public

Harris Interactive has a high opinion of polling data. The company is a leading market research and opinion polling firm best known for its *Harris Poll*, which takes the pulse of public opinion on various topics each week. Harris conducts its market research and polling primarily through an Internet panel consisting of millions of people from around the world. It offers research services to about 1,800 companies in such industries as consumer goods, health care, transportation, and technology; its Harris Interactive Service Bureau provides market research services to other market research firms. Harris traces its roots back to 1956, with the founding of Louis Harris & Associates.

	Annual Growth	6/05	6/06	6/07	6/08	6/09
Sales ($ mil.)	(1.7%)	197.0	216.0	211.8	238.7	184.3
Net income ($ mil.)	—	1.6	9.5	9.1	(84.6)	(75.3)
Market value ($ mil.)	(46.1%)	264.7	309.8	290.2	109.2	22.3
Employees	(11.9%)	1,763	1,283	1,015	1,350	1,064

HARRIS MORAN SEED COMPANY

555 Codoni Ave.
Modesto, CA 95352
Phone: 209-579-7333
Fax: 209-527-5312
Web: www.harrismoran.com

CEO: Matthew Johnston
CFO: —
HR: —
FYE: June 30
Type: Subsidiary

When mothers intone "eat your veggies," it's music to the ears of Harris Moran. Harris Moran Seed Company, a unit of French seed giant cooperative Groupe Limagrain, serves up an array of vegetable seeds for markets in about 65 countries. The company's seeds are destined for fresh-food and processed-food end uses. With operations in the US and Mexico, the company researches, breeds, and wholesales seeds for such mom-pleasers as beans, broccoli, cabbage, cauliflower, corn, lettuce, melons, peppers, pumpkins, squash, and tomatoes. Harris Moran, which was acquired by Limagrain in 1996, traces its roots back more than 140 years. In 2010 the company acquired Mesa Maize, a sweet corn company in Olathe, Colorado.

HARRIS PUBLICATIONS, INC.

1115 Broadway
New York, NY 10010
Phone: 212-807-7100
Fax: 212-924-2352
Web: www.harris-pub.com

CEO: Stanley R. Harris
CFO: Warren Sherman
HR: —
FYE: December 31
Type: Private

Content is king at Harris Publications. The company publishes a variety of niche magazines, including *King* (a men's magazine aimed at African-Americans, dubbed by some as the "black *Maxim*"), *XXL* (a hip-hop music magazine), *Rides* (all about cars), and *Antenna* (consumer products). Publications in its Harris Tactical Group are focused on weaponry, with titles such as *Tactical Knives* and *Combat Handguns*. In contrast to its testosterone-laden titles, the eclectic Harris Publications also publishes content for women, including craft magazine *Quilt*, as well as *Cottage Style* and *Romantic Country*. Other holdings include *Dog News* (often called the bible of the dog show world) and the comic book *Vampirella*.

	Annual Growth	12/04	12/05	12/06	12/07	12/08
Est. sales ($ mil.)	—	—	—	—	—	15.7
Employees	—	—	—	—	—	125

HARRIS TEETER, INC.

701 Crestdale Rd.
Matthews, NC 28105
Phone: 704-844-3100
Fax: 704-844-3138
Web: www.harristeeter.com

CEO: Frederick J. (Fred) Morganthall II
CFO: Jeff D. Sherman
HR: C. Douglas Rhodes
FYE: September 30
Type: Subsidiary

Harris Teeter operates about 190 supermarkets, mostly in North Carolina, but also in about a half-dozen other southeastern states and the District of Columbia. Most of the regional chain's grocery stores feature niceties such as sushi bars, gourmet delis, cafes, and wine departments. About 120 of the stores house pharmacies. Harris Teeter is accelerating its growth in Maryland, northern Virginia, and the competitive Washington, D.C., market and nearby suburbs. Formed by the combination of Harris Super Markets and Teeter's Food Marts in 1960, Harris Teeter was acquired by Ruddick in 1969. Harris Teeter accounts for about 95% of parent company Ruddick's sales.

An in-depth profile of this company is available to Hoover's Online members at hoovers.com.

HARRY & DAVID HOLDINGS, INC.

2500 S. Pacific Hwy.
Medford, OR 97501
Phone: 541-864-2362
Fax: 541-864-2742
Web: www.hndcorp.com

CEO: Steven J. (Steve) Heyer
CFO: Edward F. (Ed) Dunlap
HR: —
FYE: June 30
Type: Private

Harry & David Holdings (HDH) wants customers to enjoy the fruits — and flowers — of its labors. Its Harry and David Direct Marketing catalogs and Internet unit offers gift baskets filled with gourmet foods, most notably its Royal Riviera pears, Moose Munch popcorn snacks, and Tower of Treats gifts. It also runs the Fruit-of-the-Month Club. Harry and David Stores sell fruit and flowers at 135-plus factory outlet and specialty shops in more than 35 US states. The specialty food and gift retailer expanded its menu with the acquisition of the Wolferman's and Cushman brands in 2008. HDH is owned by the New York investment firm Wasserstein Partners, which in 2008 withdrew an offering to take the company public.

	Annual Growth	6/04	6/05	6/06	6/07	6/08
Est. sales ($ mil.)	—	—	—	—	—	545.1
Employees	—	—	—	—	—	1,321

HARRY WINSTON INC.

718 5th Ave.
New York, NY 10019
Phone: 212-245-2000
Fax: 212-765-8809
Web: www.harrywinston.com

CEO: Frédéric de Narp
CFO: Alan S. Mayne
HR: Beth Bandler
FYE: August 31
Type: Subsidiary

Diamonds are Harry Winston's best friend. The retail arm of Canada's Harry Winston Diamond Corp. (formerly Aber Diamond Corp.), Harry Winston company buys, designs, and sells diamonds and gems. With about a dozen salons in locales, including Beijing, London, New York, and Paris, the company's clientele includes sultans, starlets, and other affluent types who can afford the average $100,000 price tag for a Winston bauble. The company also sells its timepieces through more than 150 locations worldwide and online. The House of Harry Winston was established in 1932 by Harry Winston, the son of a New York jeweler. Harry's son Ronald retired as an executive of the company in 2008.

	Annual Growth	8/04	8/05	8/06	8/07	8/08
Est. sales ($ mil.)	—	—	—	—	—	16.9
Employees	—	—	—	—	—	200

HARSCO CORPORATION

NYSE: HSC

350 Poplar Church Rd.
Camp Hill, PA 17011
Phone: 717-763-7064
Fax: 717-763-6424
Web: www.harsco.com

CEO: Salvatore D. Fazzolari
CFO: Stephen J. Schnoor
HR: Gerald F. (Gerry) Vinci
FYE: December 31
Type: Public

If you're a metal producer or a construction company, Harsco is at your service. Its metals segment offers metal reclamation, slag processing, scrap management, and other services for steel and nonferrous metals producers. This segment's units act as an on-site service partner at approximately 170 locations in 35 countries. Harsco's Infrastructure Services businesses, SGB Group, Hünnebeck Group, and Patent Construction Systems, rent and sell concrete-forming equipment, scaffolding, and bridge-decking products, primarily to companies in the industrial maintenance and nonresidential construction industries. Other Harsco units make railway track, industrial grating, and heat exchangers.

	Annual Growth	12/05	12/06	12/07	12/08	12/09
Sales ($ mil.)	2.0%	2,766.2	3,423.3	3,688.2	3,967.8	2,990.6
Net income ($ mil.)	(5.3%)	156.7	196.4	299.5	240.9	125.8
Market value ($ mil.)	(1.1%)	2,717.7	3,063.5	5,158.5	2,228.6	2,594.9
Employees	(1.7%)	21,000	21,500	21,500	21,500	19,600

HART & COOLEY, INC.

5030 Corporate Exchange Blvd.
Grand Rapids, MI 49512
Phone: 616-656-8200
Fax: 800-223-8461
Web: www.hartandcooley.com

CEO: Bernard Roy
CFO: Dave Martin
HR: —
FYE: December 31
Type: Subsidiary

Hart & Cooley ensures that air and exhaust gases go where they're supposed to go. Products include residential and commercial HVAC grilles, diffusers, and registers; decorative brass and hardwood floor and wall registers; all-fuel chimneys; gas vents and chimney liners; flexible duct systems; and duct system components such as fire dampers, ceiling radiation dampers, and access doors. The company, which sells its products through wholesalers and distributors, has operations in seven US states and Mexico. Founded in 1901, Hart & Cooley was acquired by UK-based Tomkins in 2000. In 2008 Hart & Cooley's operations were consolidated with sister company Selkirk.

HARTE-HANKS, INC.

NYSE: HHS

200 Concord Plaza Dr., Ste. 800
San Antonio, TX 78216
Phone: 210-829-9000
Fax: 210-829-9403
Web: www.harte-hanks.com

CEO: Larry D. Franklin
CFO: Douglas (Doug) Shepard
HR: —
FYE: December 31
Type: Public

Harte-Hanks has the scoop on direct marketing services. The former newspaper company is also one of the largest producers of shoppers (advertising circulars sent by mail) in the US. The company provides integrated direct-marketing services in the US and internationally, including market research and analytics, building contact databases and tracking leads, and telephone, e-mail, and printing and mailing services designed to connect customers with their potential clients. Customers include major retailers and companies from the financial services, health care, and technology industries. The company's shopper division boasts a weekly circulation of more than 11.5 million in key markets in California and Florida.

	Annual Growth	12/05	12/06	12/07	12/08	12/09
Sales ($ mil.)	(6.7%)	1,135.0	1,184.7	1,162.9	1,082.8	860.1
Net income ($ mil.)	(19.7%)	114.5	111.8	92.6	62.7	47.7
Market value ($ mil.)	(20.1%)	1,678.8	1,762.7	1,100.5	397.0	685.8
Employees	(3.9%)	7,106	6,338	7,026	6,300	—

THE HARTFORD FINANCIAL SERVICES GROUP, INC.

NYSE: HIG

One Hartford Plaza
Hartford, CT 06155
Phone: 860-547-5000
Fax: 860-547-2680
Web: www.thehartford.com

CEO: Liam E. McGee
CFO: Christopher J. Swift
HR: Eileen G. Whelley
FYE: December 31
Type: Public

Despite its name, at its heart The Hartford Financial Services Group is an insurer with a range of personal and commercial life and property/casualty products. Through its Hartford Life subsidiary, the company offers individual and group life insurance and annuities, as well as the financial services mentioned in its name (asset management, retirement plans, and mutual funds). Its property/casualty operations include both personal (homeowners, auto) and business coverage (workers' compensation) and specialty commercial coverage for large companies. The Hartford, in business since 1810, sells its products through about 11,000 independent agencies and more than 100,000 registered broker-dealers.

	Annual Growth	12/05	12/06	12/07	12/08	12/09
Assets ($ mil.)	1.9%	285,557.0	326,710.0	360,361.0	287,583.0	307,717.0
Net income ($ mil.)	—	2,274.0	2,745.0	2,949.0	(2,749.0)	(887.0)
Market value ($ mil.)	(27.9%)	38,144.0	41,439.2	38,721.3	7,292.2	10,329.8
Employees	(1.7%)	30,000	31,000	31,000	31,000	28,000

HARTFORD LIFE, INC.

200 Hopmeadow St.
Simsbury, CT 06089
Phone: 860-547-5000
Fax: 860-843-3528
Web: www.hartfordinvestor.com

CEO: John C. Walters
CFO: Glenn D. Lammey
HR: Jennifer Geisler
FYE: December 31
Type: Subsidiary

When choosing life insurance, you might find yourself having a heart-to-hart conversation with Hartford Life. As the life insurance arm of The Hartford Financial Services Group, Hartford Life provides retail and institutional investment opportunities including annuities, mutual funds, and private placement life insurance. It also provides life insurance for wealth protection, accumulation, and transfer, and offers group benefits, as well as fixed and variable annuity retirement and savings products. Subsidiary PLANCO Financial Services distributes the company's wares to brokerages, dealers, and representatives. Hartford Life has operations in the US, Canada, Japan, Ireland, Brazil, and the UK.

HARTVILLE GROUP, INC.

OTC: HVLL

3840 Greentree Ave. SW
Canton, OH 44706
Phone: 330-484-8080
Fax: 330-484-8081
Web: www.hartvillegroup.com

CEO: Dennis C. Rushovich
CFO: Christopher R. Sachs
HR: —
FYE: December 31
Type: Public

Whether your heart belongs to a Fluffy or a Duke, Hartville can serve your pet insurance needs. Its Petsmarketing Insurance.com Agency subsidiary markets and sells health coverage for household pets across the US on behalf of insurance underwriters. Another unit, Hartville Re, provides reinsurance for pet health policies. Petsmarketing's products cover only cats and dogs, but range from the basic (illnesses, injuries, and neutering) to the deluxe (long-term and chronic illnesses, dental cleanings, and vaccinations). Proving itself no mere runt, Hartville insures over 60,000 pets and has been in business since 1997. The company sells its products by telephone and online.

THE HARTZ MOUNTAIN CORPORATION

400 Plaza Dr.
Secaucus, NJ 07094
Phone: 201-271-4800
Fax: 201-271-0164
Web: www.hartz.com

CEO: William D. (Bill) Ecker
CFO: —
HR: —
FYE: March 31
Type: Subsidiary

Hartz Mountain offers a mountain of products for pets of all sizes. The company makes more than 1,500 pet care products, including nutritional items for small pets, birds, and fish; over-the-counter animal health products; and toys and accessories for dogs, cats, and birds. The company also caters to ferrets, guinea pigs, hamsters, and rabbits. Products are sold through about 40,000 retailers in the US and Canada, as well as online. German immigrant Max Stern began making pet supplies under the Hartz name in 1932. His family operated the company for more than 75 years under the Hartz Group umbrella along with the family's real estate operations. Today Hartz is owned by Japan's general trading giant Sumitomo.

HARVARD BIOSCIENCE, INC.

NASDAQ (GM): HBIO

84 October Hill Rd., Ste. 7
Holliston, MA 01746
Phone: 508-893-8999
Fax: 508-429-5732
Web: www.harvardbioscience.com

CEO: Chane Graziano
CFO: Thomas McNaughton
HR: —
FYE: December 31
Type: Public

Toss a Harvard Bioscience catalog to a bioscience researcher and it will keep him busy for hours. The company develops, manufactures, and markets the scientific gizmos and instruments used in pharmaceutical, biotechnology, academic, and government labs around the world. Its 11,000-item-strong product line is focused on molecular biology and ADMET (absorption, distribution, metabolism, elimination, and toxicology); Harvard Bioscience sells tests to screen drug candidates for these qualities. Other products include spectrophotometers, analyzers, ventilators, and protein calculators. Customers can shop directly online, from its printed *Harvard Apparatus* catalog, or through distributors.

	Annual Growth	12/05	12/06	12/07	12/08	12/09
Sales ($ mil.)	6.2%	67.4	76.2	83.4	88.0	85.8
Net income ($ mil.)	—	(31.9)	(2.3)	(1.4)	1.7	7.2
Market value ($ mil.)	(5.4%)	131.7	152.7	135.5	78.4	105.7
Employees	6.6%	269	299	334	315	348

HARVARD PILGRIM HEALTH CARE, INC.

93 Worcester St.
Wellesley, MA 02481
Phone: 617-509-1000
Fax: 617-509-7590
Web: www.harvardpilgrim.org

CEO: Eric H. Schultz
CFO: James M. DuCharme
HR: Vicki Coates
FYE: December 31
Type: Not-for-profit

If Harvard Pilgrim Health Care were any more New England-centric, it would have to be located on Plymouth Rock. A leading provider of health benefits in Massachusetts, the not-for-profit organization also offers plans to residents of New Hampshire and Maine. It has more than 1 million members enrolled in its HMO, PPO, point-of-service, and government plans. Those members have access to regional and nationwide networks of hospitals and doctors. Harvard Pilgrim Health Care also targets multi-state employers with its Choice Plus and Options PPO plans, offered through a partnership with UnitedHealth. The Harvard Pilgrim Foundation provides community health and wellness programs.

	Annual Growth	12/04	12/05	12/06	12/07	12/08
Sales ($ mil.)	3.0%	2,300.0	2,200.0	2,488.1	2,498.3	2,591.0
Net income ($ mil.)	5.7%	38.6	74.1	70.5	45.6	48.1
Employees	—	—	—	—	—	—

HARVARD UNIVERSITY

Massachusetts Hall
Cambridge, MA 02138
Phone: 617-495-1000
Fax: 617-495-0754
Web: www.harvard.edu

CEO: Drew Gilpin Faust
CFO: Dan Shore
HR: Marilyn M. Hausammann
FYE: June 30
Type: School

Many parents dream of sending their children to Harvard — and at more than $45,000 a year (undergraduate), some even dream of being able to afford it. Harvard, the oldest institution of higher learning in the US, is home to Harvard College (undergraduate studies) and 10 graduate schools including the Harvard Business, Law, and Medical schools. The Radcliffe Institute for Advanced Study at Harvard was created when Radcliffe College and Harvard University merged in 1999. Harvard has about 20,000 students, more than half of whom are enrolled in graduate or professional programs. Harvard's endowment of approximately $37 billion is the largest of any university in the world. (Yale ranks #2.)

	Annual Growth	6/04	6/05	6/06	6/07	6/08
Sales ($ mil.)	7.6%	2,597.7	2,800.9	2,999.6	3,210.5	3,482.3
Employees	0.5%	15,000	18,000	13,000	14,865	15,302

An in-depth profile of this company is available to Hoover's Online members at hoovers.com.

735

HARVEST NATURAL RESOURCES, INC.

NYSE: HNR

1177 Enclave Pkwy., Ste. 300
Houston, TX 77077
Phone: 281-899-5700
Fax: 281-899-5702
Web: www.harvestnr.com

CEO: James A. Edmiston
CFO: Stephen C. Haynes
HR: Paul White
FYE: December 31
Type: Public

Harvest Natural Resources is keen to harvest the natural resources of oil and gas. The independent's main exploration and production work takes place in Venezuela, where it operates through its 80%-owned subsidiary, Harvest Vinccler. Harvest's operations hit a snag in 2005, due to Venezuela's difficult political climate, which has restricted the company's contracts and production activities. In 2008 it acquired a 50% stake in the Dussafu Marin exploration- and production-sharing contract located offshore Gabon from South African synthetic fuels firm Sasol.

	Annual Growth	12/05	12/06	12/07	12/08	12/09
Sales ($ mil.)	—	—	—	—	—	0.2
Net income ($ mil.)	—	—	—	—	—	(3.1)
Market value ($ mil.)	—	—	—	—	—	175.9
Employees	—	—	—	—	—	23

HARVEY INDUSTRIES, INC.

1400 Main St.
Waltham, MA 02451
Phone: 781-899-3500
Fax: 781-398-7715
Web: www.harveyind.com

CEO: Thomas (Tom) Bigony
CFO: Frances E. (Frank) Martel
HR: —
FYE: February 28
Type: Private

At Harvey Industries the window of opportunity is always open. The company, also known as Harvey Building Products, designs and manufactures its own line of vinyl and wood windows, as well as storm windows, doors, and patio enclosures. It also distributes brand-name exterior building products (including vinyl siding and roofing materials) from such makers as CertainTeed, Alcoa Home Exteriors, and James Hardie. Harvey Industries operates about a dozen showrooms and some 30 warehouses in the Northeast that mainly serve professional contractors and builders. Co-founders Fred Bigony and Bob Morrison control the company, which was incorporated in 1961.

	Annual Growth	2/04	2/05	2/06	2/07	2/08
Est. sales ($ mil.)	—	—	—	—	—	425.1
Employees	—	—	—	—	—	2,000

⊞ HASBRO, INC.

NYSE: HAS

1027 Newport Ave.
Pawtucket, RI 02862
Phone: 401-431-8697
Fax: 401-431-8535
Web: www.hasbro.com

CEO: Brian Goldner
CFO: Deborah (Deb) Thomas
HR: Dolph Johnson
FYE: December 31
Type: Public

It's all fun and games at Hasbro, the #2 toy maker in the US (after Mattel) and the producer of such childhood favorites as G.I. Joe, Play-Doh, Tonka toys, Nerf balls, and My Little Pony. Besides toys, Hasbro makes board games under its Milton Bradley (*Scrabble, Candy Land*), Cranium, and Parker Brothers (*Monopoly, Trivial Pursuit*) brands, as well as trading cards such as *Magic: The Gathering* (through its Wizards of the Coast unit) and *Dungeons & Dragons*. Hasbro also makes *Star Wars* action figures; the company's the licensee of action figures and games for the prequels. Besides Disney and Disney's Marvel Entertainment, Hasbro licenses popular names and characters for toys and games.

	Annual Growth	12/05	12/06	12/07	12/08	12/09
Sales ($ mil.)	7.1%	3,087.6	3,151.5	3,837.6	4,021.5	4,067.9
Net income ($ mil.)	15.3%	212.1	230.1	333.0	306.8	374.9
Market value ($ mil.)	12.3%	2,935.2	3,963.6	3,720.7	4,242.8	4,663.2
Employees	(0.4%)	5,900	5,800	5,900	5,900	5,800

⊞ HASTINGS ENTERTAINMENT, INC.

NASDAQ (GM): HAST

3601 Plains Blvd.
Amarillo, TX 79102
Phone: 806-351-2300
Fax: 806-467-8330
Web: www.gohastings.com

CEO: John H. Marmaduke
CFO: Dan Crow
HR: —
FYE: January 31
Type: Public

Hastings Entertainment has it all for a small-town Saturday night. The company operates some 150 multimedia stores in about 20 midwestern and western US states, mostly in small and midsized towns. Its stores and website sell new and used CDs, DVDs, books, periodicals, and video games, in addition to related electronics, such as video game consoles and DVD players. The retailer's online store also offers ringtone and music downloads. Hastings' locations average about 20,000 sq. ft. and offer such amenities as music listening stations, reading chairs, coffee bars, snacks, and children's play areas. The founding Marmaduke family, including CEO John and director Stephen, owns about 40% of Hastings.

	Annual Growth	1/06	1/07	1/08	1/09	1/10
Sales ($ mil.)	(0.3%)	537.9	548.3	547.7	538.7	531.3
Net income ($ mil.)	4.9%	5.7	5.0	10.2	4.1	6.9
Market value ($ mil.)	(5.6%)	49.8	54.9	81.3	23.5	39.5
Employees	(2.6%)	6,344	5,962	6,080	5,774	5,704

HASTINGS MANUFACTURING COMPANY, LLC

Pink Sheets: HGMG

325 N. Hanover St.
Hastings, MI 49058
Phone: 269-945-2491
Fax: 269-945-4667
Web: www.hastingsmanufacturing.com

CEO: Fredrick A (Fred) Cook
CFO: Richard L. (Rick) Zwiernikowski Jr.
HR: —
FYE: December 31
Type: Public

Hastings Manufacturing is one of the automotive industry's ring leaders. The company's core business is making piston rings for the automotive aftermarket. Customers include engine rebuilders, retailers, and warehouse distributors. Hastings also makes piston rings for OEM giants, such as Chrysler, as well as motorcycle, snowmobile, and all-terrain vehicle builders, Harley-Davidson and Polaris, and for smaller uses, such as lawn and garden, and marine gasoline engines. Hastings distributes its products, including top compression rings, oil control rings, and all steel nitride racing rings, throughout the US and Canada. The firm was founded in 1915; it is owned by Michigan-based investment company Anderson Group.

HAT WORLD CORPORATION

7555 Woodland Dr.
Indianapolis, IN 46278
Phone: 317-334-9428
Fax: 317-337-1428
Web: www.hatworld.com

CEO: Kenneth J. (Ken) Kocher
CFO: Richard E. (Rich) Cramer
HR: Carla Rodecap
FYE: January 31
Type: Subsidiary

Hat World tells its customers to put a lid on it. The largely mall-based retailer specializes in caps featuring licensed logos of pro (MLB, NBA, NFL and NHL) and college sports teams. The company operates some 885 stores under the name Hat World and about half a dozen other banners in the US, Puerto Rico, and Canada. It opened its first store in 1995; six years later, Hat World bought bankrupt rival Lids and tripled in size. Stores and websites operate under both names and stock caps with regional team favorites. Hat World was acquired by footwear retailer Genesco in 2004 for $165 million; the company also signed a licensing agreement with industry big-head Mainland Headwear Holdings.

HATCH MOTT MACDONALD GROUP, INC.

27 Bleeker St.
Millburn, NJ 07041
Phone: 973-379-3400
Fax: 973-376-1072
Web: www.hatchmott.com

CEO: Larry Sullivan
CFO: —
HR: —
FYE: December 31
Type: Subsidiary

Hatch Mott MacDonald builds North America's underlying framework. The engineering firm, which is a subsidiary of Mott MacDonald, offers planning, project development, analysis, design, construction management, facility maintenance, and asset management for all types of infrastructure projects. It specializes in tunnels, wastewater systems, pipelines, rail and transit systems, buildings, and utilities. Customers are both private companies and municipalities. The company was formed in 1996 after Hatch Associates of Canada merged with Mott MacDonald. The company has more than doubled in size since the merger and often acquires smaller engineering firms. It now includes some 55 offices throughout North America.

	Annual Growth	12/04	12/05	12/06	12/07	12/08
Est. sales ($ mil.)	—	—	—	—	—	321.2
Employees	—	—	—	—	—	1,600

HATTERAS FINANCIAL CORP.

NYSE: HTS

110 Oakwood Dr., Ste. 340
Winston-Salem, NC 27103
Phone: 336-760-9331
Fax: —
Web: hatfin.com

CEO: Michael R. Hough
CFO: Kenneth A. Steele
HR: —
FYE: December 31
Type: Public

Hatteras Financial hopes for smooth sailing on the sometimes tumultuous seas of mortgage investing. The company is a real estate investment trust (REIT) that invests in adjustable-rate and hybrid adjustable-rate single-family residential mortgages guaranteed by a US government agency or a government-backed company such as Ginnie Mae, Fannie Mae, or Freddie Mac. Hatteras Financial's investment portfolio, valued at some $7 billion, consists mostly of hybrid adjustable-rate loans with terms of three to five years. Hatteras Financial is externally managed by Atlantic Capital Advisors.

	Annual Growth	12/05	12/06	12/07	12/08	12/09
Sales ($ mil.)	522.7%	—	—	7.3	192.3	283.1
Net income ($ mil.)	1,105.5%	—	—	1.2	79.1	174.4
Market value ($ mil.)	5.1%	—	—	—	970.1	1,019.8
Employees	22.5%	—	—	6	8	9

⊞ HAUPPAUGE DIGITAL, INC.

NASDAQ (GM): HAUP

91 Cabot Ct.
Hauppauge, NY 11788
Phone: 631-434-1600
Fax: 631-434-3198
Web: www.hauppauge.com

CEO: Kenneth H. (Ken) Plotkin
CFO: Gerald (Jerry) Tucciarone
HR: Cheryl Willins
FYE: September 30
Type: Public

Wanna watch TV at work? Hauppauge Digital's WinTV analog and digital video boards let viewers videoconference, watch TV, and view input from VCRs and camcorders in a resizable window on a PC monitor. Hauppauge (pronounced "HAW-pog") also offers boards that accommodate radio and Internet broadcasts, and makes a line of PC video editing boards. The company outsources its manufacturing to companies in Europe and Asia. The company sells its products to contract electronics manufacturers, including ASUSTeK Computer and Hon Hai Precision Industry (Foxconn), and partners with companies such as Intel and Microsoft. Customers outside the US make up more than half of sales.

	Annual Growth	9/05	9/06	9/07	9/08	9/09
Sales ($ mil.)	(6.8%)	78.5	97.7	110.9	89.7	59.3
Net income ($ mil.)	—	1.4	2.4	5.3	(3.1)	(7.1)
Market value ($ mil.)	(23.5%)	34.1	54.3	44.2	12.4	11.7
Employees	5.2%	138	141	145	158	169

HAVERTY FURNITURE COMPANIES, INC.

NYSE: HVT

780 Johnson Ferry Rd. NE, Ste. 800
Atlanta, GA 30342
Phone: 404-443-2900
Fax: 404-443-4180
Web: www.havertys.com

CEO: Clarence H. Smith
CFO: Dennis L. Fink
HR: Allan J. DeNiro
FYE: December 31
Type: Public

A table for dining, a chair to recline in — Haverty Furniture Companies fills the bill. Better known as Havertys, the company sells its own brand of furniture (launched 2000) as well as name-brand home furnishings and accessories in the middle to upper-middle price range. Private-label Havertys Collections and Havertys Premium Collections carry higher margins. The furniture seller has about 120 stores in 80 cities in more than 15 southern and central US states. Havertys is growing by enlarging or replacing smaller stores in high-growth markets. The retailer also sells bedding products in its showrooms from Sealy, Serta, and Tempur-Pedic. Furniture accounts for about 80% of the company's sales.

	Annual Growth	12/05	12/06	12/07	12/08	12/09
Sales ($ mil.)	(8.2%)	827.7	859.1	784.6	691.1	588.3
Net income ($ mil.)	—	15.1	16.0	1.8	(12.1)	(4.2)
Market value ($ mil.)	1.6%	278.7	320.0	194.4	201.7	296.9
Employees	(9.1%)	4,400	4,500	4,200	3,560	3,000

HAWAIIAN ELECTRIC INDUSTRIES, INC.

NYSE: HE

900 Richards St.
Honolulu, HI 96813
Phone: 808-543-5662
Fax: 808-543-7602
Web: www.hei.com

CEO: Constance H. (Connie) Lau
CFO: James A. (Jim) Ajello
HR: —
FYE: December 31
Type: Public

When the luau bonfires go out, Hawaiian Electric Industries (HEI) keeps the islands lit up. HEI is the holding company for Hawaiian Electric Company (HECO) and some nonutility businesses. HECO (along with its utility subsidiaries Maui Electric and Hawaii Electric Light) serves more than 440,000 customers as the sole public electricity provider on the islands of Hawaii, Lanai, Maui, Molokai, and Oahu. The utilities account for the bulk of HEI's sales and have a generating capacity of about 1,670 MW. Nonutility businesses include American Savings Bank (with more than 60 retail branches in the state), investment firms, and energy-related services providers.

	Annual Growth	12/05	12/06	12/07	12/08	12/09
Sales ($ mil.)	1.0%	2,215.6	2,460.9	2,536.4	3,218.9	2,309.6
Net income ($ mil.)	(10.0%)	126.7	108.0	84.8	90.3	83.0
Market value ($ mil.)	(5.2%)	2,413.2	2,529.7	2,121.6	2,062.9	1,947.3
Employees	0.5%	3,383	3,447	3,520	3,560	3,451

⊞ HAWAIIAN HOLDINGS, INC.

NASDAQ (GM): HA

3375 Koapaka St., Ste. G-350
Honolulu, HI 96819
Phone: 808-835-3700
Fax: 808-835-3690
Web: www.hawaiianair.com

CEO: Mark B. Dunkerley
CFO: Peter R. Ingram
HR: Barbara D. Falvey
FYE: December 31
Type: Public

Luaus, leis, and lazing in the sun — Hawaiian Holdings knows how to get you there. The company's main subsidiary, Hawaiian Airlines, transports passengers and cargo between Honolulu and 10 major cities in the western US. Transpacific routes account for most of the carrier's revenue. Hawaiian Airlines also serves four of the six main Hawaiian Islands and destinations in the South Pacific such as American Samoa, Australia, the Philippines, and Tahiti. It operates a fleet of about 30 Boeing aircraft. In addition to its scheduled passenger and cargo operations, Hawaiian Airlines provides charter services.

	Annual Growth	12/05	12/06	12/07	12/08	12/09
Sales ($ mil.)	23.8%	504.3	888.0	982.6	1,210.9	1,183.3
Net income ($ mil.)	—	(12.4)	(40.5)	7.1	28.6	116.7
Market value ($ mil.)	15.1%	206.5	253.6	264.0	330.3	362.3
Employees	3.8%	3,317	3,454	3,415	3,707	3,844

⊞ An in-depth profile of this company is available to Hoover's Online members at hoovers.com.

737

HAWAIIAN TELCOM HOLDCO, INC.

1177 Bishop St.
Honolulu, HI 96813
Phone: 808-546-4511
Fax: 808-546-6194
Web: hawaiiantel.com

CEO: Eric K. Yeaman
CFO: Robert F. (Bob) Reich
HR: William (Bill) Chung
FYE: December 31
Type: Private

No "coconut telegraph," Hawaiian Telcom, through its operating subsidiaries, provides modern telecommunications services to residential and business customers in the island state. Hawaiian Telcom serves Hawaii's main island with about 500,000 local access lines in service. The company also provides long-distance lines and broadband Internet access over digital subscriber line (DSL) connections. It resells wireless communications services through an agreement with Sprint Nextel. Hawaiian Telcom, the state's incumbent local exchange carrier, has been in operation since 1883. In late 2008 the company filed for Chapter 11 bankruptcy, citing increased competition and economic volatility.

	Annual Growth	12/04	12/05	12/06	12/07	12/08
Est. sales ($ mil.)	—	—	—	—	—	483.7
Employees	—	—	—	—	—	1,504

HAWK CORPORATION

NYSE Amex: HWK

200 Public Sq., Ste. 1500
Cleveland, OH 44114
Phone: 216-861-3553
Fax: 216-861-4546
Web: www.hawkcorp.com

CEO: Ronald E. Weinberg
CFO: John T. Bronstrup
HR: —
FYE: December 31
Type: Public

Whether you're flying an airplane or driving a tractor, Hawk wants to help you stop. The company makes friction products used in brakes, clutches, and transmissions for construction and farm equipment, trucks, and motorcycles, along with brake parts for commercial and general aircraft landing systems. It also makes components used to make phosphoric acid fuel cells for the stationary fuel cell market. In 2008 Hawk sold its performance racing division, which made race car clutches, transmissions, and driveline systems, in order to focus on friction products. Hawk has manufacturing facilities in the US, Italy, Canada, and China. The company gets nearly three-quarters of its sales in the US.

	Annual Growth	12/05	12/06	12/07	12/08	12/09
Sales ($ mil.)	(10.2%)	265.4	212.1	228.7	269.6	172.4
Net income ($ mil.)	—	(1.3)	3.0	17.3	20.8	6.4
Market value ($ mil.)	4.7%	114.7	93.6	140.8	129.7	137.6
Employees	(14.7%)	1,800	1,115	1,150	1,110	953

HAWKER BEECHCRAFT CORPORATION

10511 E. Central Ave.
Wichita, KS 67206
Phone: 316-676-7111
Fax: 316-676-6614
Web: www.hawkerbeechcraft.com

CEO: William W. (Bill) Boisture Jr.
CFO: Sidney E. Anderson
HR: Sharad (Rich) Jiwanlal
FYE: December 31
Type: Private

Hawker Beechcraft prefers its business to be up in the air. The company manufactures passenger planes and offers service and support for aircraft. Its product line includes business jets, turboprops, and piston-powered aircraft. The company has service centers in 30 countries that provide parts, maintenance, and flight support services. While Hawker Beechcraft is best known for its commercial planes, the company also makes military training aircraft for the US Air Force and the US Navy. The US government accounts for more than a quarter of sales, primarily for Beechcraft T-6A trainer aircraft. More than half of the company's sales come from the US (which includes sales to foreign militaries).

	Annual Growth	12/05	12/06	12/07	12/08	12/09
Sales ($ mil.)	(3.9%)	—	—	3,464.2	3,546.5	3,198.5
Net income ($ mil.)	—	—	—	11.0	(139.9)	(451.3)
Employees	(12.0%)	—	—	9,300	9,800	7,200

HAWKER PACIFIC AEROSPACE

11240 Sherman Way
Sun Valley, CA 91352
Phone: 818-765-6201
Fax: 818-765-5759
Web: www.hawker.com

CEO: Klaus Klesfer
CFO: Dennis Jacobs
HR: Victoria Lewis
FYE: December 31
Type: Subsidiary

Hawker Pacific Aerospace has made it through the turbulence of the aviation industry on a fixed wing and a repair. A subsidiary of Lufthansa Technik and part of that firm's Landing Gear Division, Hawker provides overhaul and repair services for aircraft landing gear, hydromechanical components, wheels, and brake systems from locations in London and California. It has smaller operations in Germany and China operated with Ameco, a joint venture controlled by Lufthansa and Air China. Hawker Pacific also sells aftermarket parts for the fixed-wing aircraft and helicopters of about 80 manufacturers. Customers include commercial airlines, cargo carriers, and the US government.

HAWKINS, INC.

NASDAQ (GM): HWKN

3100 E. Hennepin Ave.
Minneapolis, MN 55413
Phone: 612-331-6910
Fax: 612-331-5304
Web: www.hawkinschemical.com

CEO: John R. Hawkins
CFO: Kathleen P. Pepski
HR: —
FYE: March 31
Type: Public

Hawkins processes and distributes bulk specialty chemicals. Its industrial chemicals segment stores and distributes caustic soda, phosphoric acid, and aqua ammonia, among many others. The segment also makes bleach (sodium hypochlorite), repackages liquid chlorine, and custom-blends other chemicals. Hawkins' water treatment group distributes products and equipment used to treat drinking water, municipal and industrial wastewater, and public swimming pools. It also distributes laboratory-grade chemicals for the pharmaceutical industry. Through its fleet of trucks and tankers, the company operates facilities and serves customers throughout the midwestern US.

	Annual Growth	3/06	3/07	3/08	3/09	3/10
Sales ($ mil.)	15.7%	143.3	160.4	196.4	284.4	257.1
Net income ($ mil.)	27.9%	8.9	8.1	9.1	23.8	23.8
Market value ($ mil.)	14.5%	144.7	151.8	156.6	158.7	248.8
Employees	3.3%	235	243	265	281	268

▣ HAWORTH, INC.

1 Haworth Center
Holland, MI 49423
Phone: 616-393-3000
Fax: 616-393-1570
Web: www.haworth.com

CEO: Franco Bianchi
CFO: John Mooney
HR: Ann M. Harten
FYE: December 31
Type: Private

Designers at Haworth sit at their cubicles and think about . . . more cubicles. The company is one of the top office furniture manufacturers in the US, competing with top rivals Steelcase and HNI. Known for innovative design, it offers a full range of furniture, including partitions, desks, chairs, tables, and storage products. Brands include Monaco, Patterns, PLACES, and X99. The company operates about 60 showrooms worldwide and sells its products through more than 600 dealers. Dilbert and other long-suffering office drones have Haworth to thank for inventing the prewired partitions that make today's cubicled workplace possible. Haworth is owned by the family of Gerrard Haworth, who founded the company in 1948.

	Annual Growth	12/04	12/05	12/06	12/07	12/08
Sales ($ mil.)	7.0%	1,260.0	1,400.0	1,480.0	1,660.0	1,650.0
Employees	0.0%	7,500	7,500	8,000	8,000	7,500

HAWTHORN BANCSHARES, INC.
NASDAQ (GM): HWBK

300 SW Longview Blvd.
Lee's Summit, MO 64081
Phone: 816-347-8100
Fax: 816-268-6318
Web: www.exchangebancshares.com

CEO: James E. Smith
CFO: Richard G. Rose
HR: —
FYE: December 31
Type: Public

Hawthorn Bancshares keeps a hawk eye on its customers' money. It is the indirect holding company for Hawthorn Bank, which operates some two-dozen branches in central and west-central Missouri. Originally founded in 1932, the bank offers traditional commercial banking services including deposit accounts, CDs, and lending. Its loan portfolio includes commercial and industrial loans, consumer installment loans, and commercial and residential mortgages. The bank also offers trust and brokerage services. Hawthorn Bancshares owns Hawthorn Bank through subsidiary Union State Bancshares.

	Annual Growth	12/05	12/06	12/07	12/08	12/09
Assets ($ mil.)	2.4%	1,126.5	1,142.7	1,195.8	1,279.7	1,236.5
Net income ($ mil.)	(15.7%)	9.9	10.9	7.8	(30.6)	5.0
Market value ($ mil.)	(23.9%)	122.1	130.3	103.4	71.3	41.0
Employees	(2.0%)	377	389	378	344	348

HAY GROUP, INC.

100 Penn Sq. East
Philadelphia, PA 19107
Phone: 215-861-2000
Fax: 215-861-2111
Web: www.haygroup.com

CEO: Chris Matthews
CFO: Stephen Kaye
HR: Mary M Fontaine
FYE: December 31
Type: Private

Hay Group offers organizational and human resources consulting services to companies around the world. The firm helps its clients design organizational structures that are in line with business strategy, clarify roles and responsibilities, develop and retain talented leaders, measure the value of various kinds of work, and set up effective performance management processes. It also performs employee attitude surveys, leadership assessments, and compensation and benefits benchmarking studies. Hay Group operates from about 85 offices in more than 45 countries around the world. The firm was founded in 1943 as Edward N. Hay and Associates.

	Annual Growth	12/04	12/05	12/06	12/07	12/08
Est. sales ($ mil.)	—	—	—	—	—	97.0
Employees	—	—	—	—	—	432

⊞ HAYES LEMMERZ INTERNATIONAL, INC.

15300 Centennial Dr.
Northville, MI 48168
Phone: 734-737-5000
Fax: 734-737-2198
Web: www.hayes-lemmerz.com

CEO: Curtis J. Clawson
CFO: Mark A. Brebberman
HR: Tim Welcer
FYE: January 31
Type: Private

Steel Wheels is more than a Stones' album — it's a living for Hayes Lemmerz. The company rolls along as the world's #1 manufacturer of fabricated steel and cast aluminum wheels for passenger cars and light trucks, and steel wheels primarily for commercial trucks and sport utility vehicles. The company operates through two reportable segments: automotive wheels and other products. It has, however, eliminated most of its components and intercompany activities comprising automotive brakes, suspensions, and powertrain parts. Customers are major car and truck OEMs in North America, Europe, and Japan, including GM, Ford, Honda, Nissan, and Toyota. Hayes Lemmerz emerged from Chapter 11 reorganization in late 2009.

	Annual Growth	1/05	1/06	1/07	1/08	1/09
Sales ($ mil.)	(4.0%)	2,244.5	2,277.2	2,056.2	2,126.7	1,904.3
Net income ($ mil.)	—	(64.9)	(457.5)	(166.9)	(196.6)	(370.2)
Employees	(12.7%)	11,000	10,500	8,500	8,900	6,400

HAYNES INTERNATIONAL, INC.
NASDAQ (GS): HAYN

1020 W. Park Ave.
Kokomo, IN 46904
Phone: 765-456-6000
Fax: 765-456-6905
Web: www.haynesintl.com

CEO: Mark M. Comerford
CFO: Marcel Martin
HR: —
FYE: September 30
Type: Public

Haynes International is an ally of companies that use alloys. Haynes develops and manufactures nickel- and cobalt-based alloys. The company specializes in high-temperature alloys (HTAs) able to withstand extreme temperatures and corrosion-resistant alloys (CRAs) that stand up to corrosive substances and processes. HTAs are used in jet engines, gas turbines used for power generation, and waste incinerators, while CRAs have applications in chemical processing, power plant emissions control, and hazardous waste treatment. HTAs account for about three-quarters of the company's sales. The aerospace industry is the biggest market for Haynes, accounting for more than a third of its business.

	Annual Growth	9/05	9/06	9/07	9/08	9/09
Sales ($ mil.)	7.8%	325.0	434.4	559.8	637.0	438.6
Net income ($ mil.)	—	(4.1)	35.5	66.1	62.8	(52.3)
Market value ($ mil.)	6.2%	303.6	473.6	1,036.7	568.7	386.4
Employees	(3.0%)	1,060	1,072	1,084	1,138	940

HAYWARD BAKER INC.

1130 Annapolis Rd., Ste. 202
Odenton, MD 21113
Phone: 410-551-8200
Fax: 410-551-1900
Web: www.haywardbaker.com

CEO: George R. Grisham
CFO: Daniel E. Jordan
HR: Linda Kosmicky
FYE: December 31
Type: Subsidiary

Hayward Baker is well grounded. The company provides ground modification services used to prepare soil foundations prior to commercial and infrastructure building construction. Its services include soil stabilization, underpinning, excavation support, foundation rehabilitation, and groundwater and settlement control. The company has worked on projects including the Wickiup Dam in Oregon, the Merchant RR Bridge across the Mississippi River in St. Louis, tunnel improvements in Los Angeles, and improvements to the Queretaro Bus Terminal in Queretaro, Mexico. Hayward Baker is a subsidiary of UK-based Keller Group and operates from offices in the US, Canada, and Latin America.

	Annual Growth	12/04	12/05	12/06	12/07	12/08
Est. sales ($ mil.)	—	—	—	—	—	421.0
Employees	—	—	—	—	—	1,100

HAYWARD INDUSTRIES, INC.

620 Division St.
Elizabeth, NJ 07207
Phone: 908-351-5400
Fax: 908-351-5675
Web: www.haywardnet.com

CEO: Robert Davis
CFO: Andrew Diamond
HR: —
FYE: December 31
Type: Private

Hayward Industries wants everyone to take the plunge! Hayward makes fluid-control and related equipment for the pool and spa market. Hayward Pool Products is a leader in its industry, and manufactures automatic cleaning systems, filters, heaters, pool pumps, and other pool-related accessories and equipment such as pool safety products (barriers and vacuum release systems). The company also distributes fiber-optic lighting designed to illuminate pools and backyards. Hayward has operations in North America, Europe, and Australia. Chairman Oscar Davis owns Hayward, which traces its roots to a company founded in 1923.

	Annual Growth	12/04	12/05	12/06	12/07	12/08
Est. sales ($ mil.)	—	—	—	—	—	199.5
Employees	—	—	—	—	—	1,600

⊞ An in-depth profile of this company is available to Hoover's Online members at hoovers.com.

739

HAZEN AND SAWYER, P.C.

498 Seventh Ave., 11th Fl.
New York, NY 10018
Phone: 212-777-8400
Fax: 212-228-8369
Web: www.hazenandsawyer.com

CEO: James W. (Jim) Fagan
CFO: William Crayon
HR: Cheryl Courchaine
FYE: December 31
Type: Private

Hazen and Sawyer, P.C. is very PC when it comes to solid waste and water — make it clean and keep it clean. One of the top environmental engineering firms, the company provides services to public and private clients for solid waste, water, and wastewater collection and treatment systems. Specific areas of expertise include architectural design, aquatic sciences, biosolids management, buried infrastructure, odor control, resource economics, risk management, utility management services, and wastewater collection. The employee-owned firm operates from some 25 offices throughout the eastern US and two international branch offices in South America.

	Annual Growth	12/04	12/05	12/06	12/07	12/08
Est. sales ($ mil.)	—	—	—	—	—	131.4
Employees	—	—	—	—	—	775

⊞ H.B. FULLER COMPANY

NYSE: FUL

1200 Willow Lake Blvd.
St. Paul, MN 55110
Phone: 651-236-5900
Fax: 651-236-5426
Web: www.hbfuller.com

CEO: Michele Volpi
CFO: James R. (Jim) Giertz
HR: Ann B. Parriott
FYE: November 30
Type: Public

H.B. Fuller has stuck with glue for more than a century. Long known for making adhesives, the company also makes sealants, powder coatings for metals (office furniture, appliances), and liquid paints (in Latin America). Its industrial and performance adhesives customers include companies in the packaging, graphic arts, automotive, woodworking, and nonwoven textiles industries. Adhesives account for more than three-quarters of sales. In addition to metal coatings and paints, non-adhesive products include construction materials, principally ceramic tile installation products (TEC specialty products) and HVAC insulating coatings (through Foster products). Fuller owns manufacturing facilities in about 15 countries.

	Annual Growth	11/05	11/06	11/07	11/08	11/09
Sales ($ mil.)	(4.9%)	1,512.2	1,472.4	1,400.3	1,391.6	1,234.7
Net income ($ mil.)	8.0%	61.6	135.0	102.2	18.9	83.7
Market value ($ mil.)	7.1%	757.9	1,275.6	1,237.5	868.0	996.2
Employees	(6.2%)	4,000	3,700	3,200	3,100	3,100

H.C. BRILL COMPANY, INC.

1912 Montreal Rd.
Tucker, GA 30084
Phone: 770-938-3823
Fax: 770-939-2934
Web: www.hcbrill.com

CEO: Troy Hendricks
CFO: —
HR: —
FYE: December 31
Type: Subsidiary

If you love ooey-gooey-good baked goods, H.C. Brill has found your thrill. The company, a subsidiary of global ingredients giant CSM, makes a wide variety of commercial bakery products, including frozen doughs and batters, icings and glazes, powdered and liquid fillings, whipped toppings, and frozen cakes. It also makes consumer products such as prepared mixes for bread, brownies, cakes, and puddings, as well as fruit-based glazes and fillings. Its products are available in some 25 countries. Brill took its present form in 2005 when CSM combined its three bakery-ingredient businesses — H.C. Brill (which CSM had acquired in 2003), Baker & Baker, and Henry & Henry.

H.C. STARCK INC.

45 Industrial Place
Newton, MA 02461
Phone: 617-630-5800
Fax: 617-630-5879
Web: www.hcstarck.com

CEO: Richard P. McCorry
CFO: Peter A. Weiss
HR: —
FYE: December 31
Type: Private

The kind of powders produced by H.C. Starck have nothing to do with ski slopes or *Miami Vice* busts. The company (the US unit of German-based H.C. Starck GmnH, AKA H. C. Starck Group) manufactures metal powders, thermal spray powders, metal products, and specialty chemicals. Its powders go into everything from concrete to sporting goods, from pigments and plastics to medical and dental supplies. Starck also makes electroconductive polymers and colloidal silica for the electronics industry. H. C. Starck Group has more than a dozen plants located in Europe, North America, and Asia. It is owned by private investors Advent International and The Carlyle Group.

HCA-HEALTHONE, LLC

4900 S. Monaco St., Ste. 380
Denver, CO 80237
Phone: 303-788-2500
Fax: 303-779-4993
Web: www.healthonecares.com

CEO: Jeffrey (Jeff) Dorsey
CFO: Greg D'Argonne
HR: Roger Smith
FYE: December 31
Type: Joint venture

HCA-HealthONE wants to be #1 in the lives of Denverites. A joint venture between HCA and The Colorado Health Foundation, the health care network provides residents of Denver and surrounding communities with a range of health care services through seven hospitals with more than 2,250 beds, about a dozen ambulatory surgery centers, and 35 outpatient facilities. Its hospitals include The Medical Center of Aurora, North Suburban Medical Center, Presbyterian/St. Luke's Medical Center, Rose Medical Center, Swedish Medical Center, Sky Ridge Medical Center, and Spalding Rehabilitation Hospital.

	Annual Growth	12/04	12/05	12/06	12/07	12/08
Est. sales ($ mil.)	—	—	—	—	—	211.6
Employees	—	—	—	—	—	4,500

⊞ HCA INC.

1 Park Plaza
Nashville, TN 37203
Phone: 615-344-9551
Fax: 615-344-2266
Web: www.hcahealthcare.com

CEO: Richard M. Bracken
CFO: R. Milton Johnson
HR: John M. Steele
FYE: December 31
Type: Private

As the largest for-profit hospital operator in the US, "HCA" could stand for Health Care for America. HCA (AKA Hospital Corporation of America) operates roughly 170 acute care, psychiatric, and rehabilitation hospitals in the US and England. It also runs about 100 ambulatory surgery centers, as well as cancer treatment and outpatient rehab centers that form health care networks in many of the communities it serves. HCA has facilities in 20 states; about three-quarters of its hospitals are in the southern US (approximately 70 are in Florida and Texas). The hospital giant's HCA International operates its hospitals and clinics in the UK. HCA is planning to go public through a $4.6 billion initial public offering.

	Annual Growth	12/05	12/06	12/07	12/08	12/09
Sales ($ mil.)	5.7%	—	25,477.0	26,858.0	28,374.0	30,052.0
Net income ($ mil.)	0.6%	—	1,036.0	874.0	673.0	1,054.0
Employees	1.1%	—	186,000	186,000	191,000	192,000

HCC INSURANCE HOLDINGS, INC.

NYSE: HCC

13403 Northwest Fwy.
Houston, TX 77040
Phone: 713-690-7300
Fax: 713-462-2401
Web: www.hcch.com

CEO: John N. Molbeck Jr.
CFO: William T. (Tobin) Whamond
HR: Lisa A. Moore
FYE: December 31
Type: Public

From skyway to waterway, HCC Insurance Holdings sells specialized property/casualty insurance, underwrites for its own and other insurance companies, and provides related services for commercial and individual customers. Its largest subsidiary is Houston Casualty Corporation. The company's products include direct and reinsurance policies for the aviation, marine, and offshore energy industries; property/casualty and health policies; medical stop-loss; directors' and officers' liability coverage, and workers' compensation and occupational accident insurance. HCC Insurance Holdings' subsidiaries also offer surety and life coverage. The company operates in Bermuda, Ireland, Spain, the UK, and the US.

	Annual Growth	12/05	12/06	12/07	12/08	12/09
Assets ($ mil.)	5.9%	7,026.1	7,630.1	8,074.6	8,332.4	8,834.4
Net income ($ mil.)	15.9%	195.9	342.3	395.4	304.8	353.9
Market value ($ mil.)	(1.5%)	3,413.2	3,690.4	3,298.2	3,076.3	3,216.5
Employees	6.5%	1,448	1,660	1,682	1,864	1,864

HCP, INC.

NYSE: HCP

3760 Kilroy Airport Way, Ste. 300
Long Beach, CA 90806
Phone: 562-733-5100
Fax: 562-733-5200
Web: www.hcpi.com

CEO: James F. (Jay) Flaherty III
CFO: Thomas M. (Tom) Herzog
HR: William J. Budzinski
FYE: December 31
Type: Public

Old age isn't for sissies, but as far as HCP (formerly Health Care Property Investors) is concerned, it is for making money. HCP is a self-administered real estate investment trust (REIT) that invests in, develops, and manages real estate that it leases to health care facilities, including senior living and skilled nursing facilities, hospitals, medical office buildings, and biotech and pharmaceutical laboratories. It has interests in about 700 properties in more than 40 states and Mexico, though nearly half of its holdings are in California and Texas. The company also provides mortgages and other financing to health care providers.

	Annual Growth	12/05	12/06	12/07	12/08	12/09
Sales ($ mil.)	24.8%	477.3	619.1	982.5	1,025.8	1,157.0
Net income ($ mil.)	(4.1%)	173.1	417.5	589.0	448.5	146.2
Market value ($ mil.)	4.6%	7,513.6	10,823.6	10,223.9	8,163.3	8,977.6
Employees	14.4%	83	165	151	144	142

HCSB FINANCIAL CORPORATION

OTC: HCFB

5201 Broad St.
Loris, SC 29569
Phone: 843-756-6333
Fax: 843-716-6136
Web: www.horrycountystatebank.com

CEO: James R. Clarkson
CFO: Edward L. Loehr Jr.
HR: Denise Floyd
FYE: December 31
Type: Public

HCSB Financial has erased the state lines in the Carolinas. The institution is the holding company for Horry County State Bank, which operates more than a dozen branches that serve Horry and Marion counties in South Carolina, and Columbus and Brunswick counties in North Carolina. Horry County State Bank offers traditional deposit products such as checking and savings accounts, CDs, money market accounts, and IRAs. The bank originates primarily real estate loans (more than half of its loan portfolio), followed by business loans, construction and development loans, consumer loans, and agricultural loans. The bank also offers investment services.

	Annual Growth	12/05	12/06	12/07	12/08	12/09
Assets ($ mil.)	23.0%	331.7	359.5	438.4	644.3	759.6
Net income ($ mil.)	—	2.4	2.8	2.0	2.2	(1.3)
Market value ($ mil.)	(6.2%)	53.7	66.0	78.5	98.4	41.7
Employees	8.7%	113	132	154	159	158

HD SUPPLY DISTRIBUTION SERVICES, LLC

26940 Aliso Viejo Pkwy.
Aliso Viejo, CA 92656
Phone: 949-643-4700
Fax: 949-643-4130
Web: www.crownbolt.com

CEO: Jon Michael Adinolfi
CFO: Brian Steele
HR: Debbie Brogdon
FYE: January 31
Type: Subsidiary

Because handymen aren't available 24/7, HD Supply Distribution Services is. The company distributes rope, fasteners, threaded rod, anchors, chain, and related builder's hardware products worldwide. It also offers storage containers for small hardware pieces. Carrying 10,000-plus standard parts, the company distributes from four facilities in the US. In addition, HD Supply Distribution Services sets up an online ordering program at Pro Desk aisles in Home Depot stores, its largest customer. Formerly operating under the Crown Bolt brand, the company evolved as a member of the HD Supply family of companies created by Home Depot. It was acquired in 2007 by Bain Capital, Carlyle Group, and Clayton, Dubilier & Rice.

	Annual Growth	1/04	1/05	1/06	1/07	1/08
Sales ($ mil.)	25.5%	—	—	—	255.0	320.0
Employees	—	—	—	—	—	900

HD SUPPLY, INC.

3100 Cumberland Blvd., Ste. 1700
Atlanta, GA 30339
Phone: 770-852-9000
Fax: —
Web: www.hdsupply.com

CEO: Joseph J. (Joe) DeAngelo
CFO: Mark T. Jamieson
HR: Meg Newman
FYE: January 31
Type: Holding company

Do-it-yourselfers shop Home Depot or Lowe's, but the pros do business at HD Supply. Formerly the professional services division of Home Depot, HD Supply operates about 800 locations throughout North America that distribute building materials and tools and provide installation services to professionals in the construction, maintenance and repair, and energy and infrastructure markets. The company also operates about a dozen business units, including its Canadian arm HD Supply Canada. HD Supply was formed in 1997 when big-box retailer Home Depot bought Maintenance Warehouse. It has been controlled by Bain Capital, The Carlyle Group, and Clayton Dubilier & Rice since 2007, when Home Depot sold the business.

HDR, INC.

8404 Indian Hills Dr.
Omaha, NE 68114
Phone: 402-399-1000
Fax: 402-399-1238
Web: www.hdrinc.com

CEO: Richard R. (Dick) Bell
CFO: Terrence C. (Terry) Cox
HR: Judy Webster
FYE: December 31
Type: Private

From restoring the Pentagon and the Everglades to the Hoover Dam Bypass project, HDR has left its mark on the US. HDR is an architecture, engineering, and consulting firm that specializes in projects including bridges, water- and wastewater-treatment plants, and hospitals. HDR also provides mechanical and plumbing services, construction and project management, and utilities planning. The group has completed projects throughout the US and in some 60 countries abroad and has more than 185 locations around the world. The employee-owned company was founded as Henningson Engineering in 1917 to build municipal plants in the rural Midwest.

An in-depth profile of this company is available to Hoover's Online members at hoovers.com.

741

H. E. BUTT GROCERY COMPANY

646 S. Main Ave.
San Antonio, TX 78204
Phone: 210-938-8000
Fax: 210-938-8169
Web: www.heb.com

CEO: Charles C. Butt
CFO: Martin Otto
HR: Tina James
FYE: October 31
Type: Private

The Muzak bounces between Tejano and country, and the warm tortillas and marinated fajita meat are big sellers at H. E. Butt Grocery (H-E-B). Texas' largest private company and the #1 food retailer in South and Central Texas, H-E-B owns more than 315 supermarkets, including a growing number of large (70,000 sq. ft.) gourmet Central Market stores in major metropolitan areas and 80-plus smaller (24,000-30,000 sq. ft.) H-E-B-Pantry stores, often in more rural areas. H-E-B also has about 30 upscale and discount stores in Mexico. H-E-B processes some of its own bread, dairy products, meat, and tortillas. The 100-year-old company is owned by the Butt family, which founded H-E-B in Kerrville, Texas, in 1905.

	Annual Growth	10/04	10/05	10/06	10/07	10/08
Sales ($ mil.)	9.3%	10,500.0	11,500.0	12,400.0	13,500.0	15,000.0
Employees	3.2%	60,000	60,000	60,000	63,000	68,000

HEADWATERS INCORPORATED

NYSE: HW

10653 S. River Front Pkwy., Ste. 300
South Jordan, UT 84095
Phone: 801-984-9400
Fax: 801-984-9410
Web: www.headwaters.com

CEO: Kirk A. Benson
CFO: Steven G. (Steve) Stewart
HR: Harvey North
FYE: September 30
Type: Public

Headwaters is a modern-day alchemist, turning stone and coal into money. Through subsidiaries, it provides building materials and coal combustion products (CCP) and reclaims waste coal in North America. Its light building products segment (its largest segment) makes stone products and siding accessories under such brands as FlexCrete Building Systems, Eldorado Stone, and Tapco. The heavy construction materials segment sells residuals from the coal combustion process (such as fly ash), which can be used as a substitute for Portland cement in building materials. Headwaters' energy technology segment owns and operates coal-cleaning facilities and licenses coal conversion and heavy oil upgrading technology.

	Annual Growth	9/05	9/06	9/07	9/08	9/09
Sales ($ mil.)	(11.0%)	1,064.6	1,121.4	1,207.8	886.4	666.7
Net income ($ mil.)	—	121.3	102.1	20.1	(169.7)	(415.5)
Market value ($ mil.)	(43.3%)	2,260.5	1,411.3	899.4	806.9	233.9
Employees	(11.7%)	4,500	4,300	3,900	3,400	2,740

HEADWAY TECHNOLOGIES, INC.

678 S. Hillview Dr.
Milpitas, CA 95035
Phone: 408-934-5300
Fax: 408-934-5475
Web: www.headway.com

CEO: Mao-Min Chen
CFO: Gary Pester
HR: —
FYE: March 31
Type: Subsidiary

Headway Technologies is making progress in the disk drive market. The company designs and manufactures recording heads for computer disk drives, including giant magnetoresistive heads, the industry's current standard. Headway's products are used in disk drives for PCs, portable computers, and computer servers. They are sold in the form of sliced wafer rows (sliders), sliders attached to steel suspensions (head gimbal assemblies), and ceramic wafers. Headway's customers include disk drive manufacturers Fujitsu, Hitachi, Seagate, and Toshiba. The company is a subsidiary of TDK.

HEALTH CARE REIT, INC.

NYSE: HCN

1 SeaGate, Ste. 1500
Toledo, OH 43603
Phone: 419-247-2800
Fax: 419-247-2826
Web: www.hcreit.com

CEO: George L. Chapman
CFO: Scott A. Estes
HR: —
FYE: December 31
Type: Public

Health Care REIT is a real estate investment trust (REIT) that invests in senior living and health care facilities, primarily skilled nursing and assisted-living facilities designed for older people needing help with everyday living. The trust also has investments in independent living facilities, medical office buildings, and specialty care facilities. It owns some 600 properties leased to health care operators in about 40 states. Additionally, the company develops new build-to-suit properties through its HCN Development Services Group subsidiary. It also invests in mortgage loans and provides construction financing for its existing properties.

	Annual Growth	12/05	12/06	12/07	12/08	12/09
Sales ($ mil.)	19.2%	281.8	322.8	486.0	551.2	569.0
Net income ($ mil.)	23.0%	84.3	102.8	141.4	288.1	192.9
Market value ($ mil.)	6.9%	4,207.4	5,339.3	5,546.6	5,237.5	5,500.6
Employees	50.8%	42	113	198	203	217

HEALTH CARE SERVICE CORPORATION

300 E. Randolph St.
Chicago, IL 60601
Phone: 312-653-6000
Fax: 312-819-1220
Web: www.hcsc.com

CEO: Patricia A. (Pat) Hemingway Hall
CFO: Denise A. Bujack
HR: David D. Jones
FYE: December 31
Type: Mutual company

Health Care Service Corporation (HCSC) has the Blues in Chicago and the Southwest. A licensee of the Blue Cross and Blue Shield Association, HCSC consists of four regional Blue health plans: Blue Cross Blue Shield of Illinois, Blue Cross and Blue Shield of Texas, Blue Cross and Blue Shield of New Mexico, and Blue Cross Blue Shield of Oklahoma. The mutually owned company provides group and individual health plans — including traditional indemnity plans, managed care programs, and Medicare supplemental coverage — to more than 12 million members, a majority of them in Illinois and Texas. Through some non-Blue subsidiaries, HCSC sells life, disability, and property/casualty insurance.

	Annual Growth	12/04	12/05	12/06	12/07	12/08
Sales ($ mil.)	13.1%	9,809.2	11,713.9	12,971.6	14,348.4	16,024.6
Net income ($ mil.)	(7.0%)	994.7	1,145.6	1,115.4	865.7	742.6
Employees	7.7%	—	14,000	16,500	16,500	17,500

HEALTH DIALOG SERVICES CORPORATION

60 State St., Ste. 1100
Boston, MA 02109
Phone: 617-406-5200
Fax: 617-406-5201
Web: www.healthdialog.com

CEO: Patrick Flynn
CFO: Mark Hampton
HR: Simon Trussler
FYE: December 31
Type: Subsidiary

Health Dialog Services wants to improve health care for both consumers and providers in the US and UK. The company provides health management coaching to patients and families. It also offers analytic services through its Health Dialog Analytic Solutions, which enable health plans, provider groups, government programs, and large employers to find and eliminate inefficiencies in their offerings while still providing quality care. Analytic solutions include patient profiling, opportunity analysis, predictive modeling and provider performance. Health Dialog Services was founded in 1997; the UK's private health insurer BUPA paid $640 million to acquire Health Dialog Services in late 2007.

HEALTH FIRST, INC.

6450 US Hwy. 1
Rockledge, FL 32955
Phone: 321-434-4300
Fax: 321-434-4272
Web: www.health-first.org

CEO: Michael D. Means
CFO: Robert C. Galloway
HR: Robert W. Suttles
FYE: December 31
Type: Not-for-profit

Health First works to keep Florida's Space Coast denizens in tip-top shape. The not-for-profit health system operates three hospitals in Brevard County, with a fourth under construction. Health First's biggest hospital is Holmes Regional Medical Center in Melbourne, with more than 500 beds. Its Cape Canaveral Hospital and Palm Bay Community Hospital have 150 and 60 beds, respectively. The system also runs outpatient clinics, a home health service, and a physicians group. Its for-profit subsidiary Health First Health Plans is the county's largest insurer, with about 30,000 commercial members and just over 22,000 Medicare members.

	Annual Growth	12/04	12/05	12/06	12/07	12/08
Est. sales ($ mil.)	—	—	—	—	—	869.0
Employees	—	—	—	—	—	6,000

HEALTH GRADES, INC.

NASDAQ (CM): HGRD

500 Golden Ridge Rd., Ste. 100
Golden, CO 80401
Phone: 303-716-0041
Fax: 303-716-1298
Web: www.healthgrades.com

CEO: Kerry R. Hicks
CFO: Allen Dodge
HR: Caroline Petty
FYE: December 31
Type: Public

Health Grades (which does business as HealthGrades) takes the health care industry to school. The company offers report cards on hospitals, physicians, nursing homes, home health agencies, hospice programs, and other health care providers. It sells the quality and patient safety information to a number of constituencies, including consumers, health plans, employers, and liability insurance companies. Hospitals themselves represent its biggest customer base; however, providers can license HealthGrades' ratings and trademarks (its Distinguished Hospital Award, for instance) to use in their marketing campaigns. They also come to the company for quality improvement consulting.

	Annual Growth	12/05	12/06	12/07	12/08	12/09
Sales ($ mil.)	26.0%	20.8	27.8	36.2	39.7	52.5
Net income ($ mil.)	14.7%	4.1	3.2	6.7	4.7	7.1
Market value ($ mil.)	(9.2%)	188.5	133.9	177.5	61.4	127.9
Employees	18.5%	106	123	142	184	209

HEALTH INSURANCE PLAN OF GREATER NEW YORK

55 Water St.
New York, NY 10041
Phone: 646-447-5000
Fax: 646-447-3011
Web: www.hipusa.com

CEO: Anthony L. Watson
CFO: Michael D. Fullwood
HR: Fred Blickman
FYE: December 31
Type: Subsidiary

HIP is hip to be square on health care. Health Insurance Plan of Greater New York (HIP) is a not-for-profit HMO founded in 1947 to provide low-cost health care to New York City employees. HIP now boasts some 1.2 million members and is one of the largest HMOs in the New York metro area, as well as one of New York state's biggest Medicare providers. It also offers PPO, point-of-service, and consumer-driven (high-deductible) plan options. The organization also provides access to medical, lab, and pharmacy services through some 43,000 physicians and more than 72,000 locations in New York, Connecticut, and Massachusetts. Along with Group Health Incorporated (GHI), HIP is a part of EmblemHealth.

HEALTH MANAGEMENT ASSOCIATES, INC.

NYSE: HMA

5811 Pelican Bay Blvd., Ste. 500
Naples, FL 34108
Phone: 239-598-3131
Fax: 239-598-2705
Web: www.hma-corp.com

CEO: Gary D. Newsome
CFO: Kelly E. Curry
HR: Frederick L. Drow
FYE: December 31
Type: Public

William Schoen, chairman of Health Management Associates (HMA) once described his company as the "Wal-Mart of the hospital business" because, like Sam Walton's empire, HMA thrives in small-town America. The company operates a network of about 60 acute care and psychiatric hospitals in 15 mainly southern states (although it also has facilities in Washington and Pennsylvania). Combined, the facilities have about 8,000 beds. HMA's hospitals provide general medical and surgical care, along with outpatient and emergency room services and specialty care in some areas such as cancer care and obstetrics. It also operates about a dozen rural health clinics and outpatient surgery centers.

	Annual Growth	9/05	*12/06	12/07	12/08	12/09
Sales ($ mil.)	6.5%	3,588.8	4,056.6	4,392.1	4,451.6	4,617.1
Net income ($ mil.)	(17.5%)	353.1	182.7	119.9	167.2	163.9
Market value ($ mil.)	(25.4%)	5,875.4	5,284.6	1,497.0	448.1	1,819.9
Employees	2.1%	31,000	34,500	35,645	32,700	33,700

*Fiscal year change

HEALTH MANAGEMENT SYSTEMS, INC.

401 Park Ave. South
New York, NY 10016
Phone: 212-725-7965
Fax: 212-857-5973
Web: www.hmsy.com

CEO: William C. (Bill) Lucia
CFO: Walter D. Hosp
HR: David Schmid
FYE: December 31
Type: Subsidiary

Health Management Systems (HMS) specializes in squeezing pennies for Uncle Sam's health insurers. The company supplies information management services and software used by government health agencies and government-sponsored managed care firms to recover money from health care providers that were either overpaid or paid in error. The company's services include retroactive insurance claims reprocessing and third-party liability recovery, as well as pharmacy recovery services for the overpayment of pharmaceuticals. HMS operates nationwide out of more than two-dozen regional offices. Health Management Systems is a subsidiary of HMS Holdings Corp.

HEALTH NET, INC.

NYSE: HNT

21650 Oxnard St.
Woodland Hills, CA 91367
Phone: 818-676-6000
Fax: 818-676-8591
Web: www.healthnet.com

CEO: Jay M. Gellert
CFO: Joseph C. Capezza
HR: Karin D. Mayhew
FYE: December 31
Type: Public

Health Net is not another website trying to give you health advice, but it is a web of health services. The company provides managed health care medical coverage to millions of members across the US. The company's health plan services unit offers HMO, PPO, Medicare, and Medicaid plans, as well as vision, dental care, and pharmacy benefit programs. The Managed Health Network subsidiary provides behavioral health and employee assistance to about 7 million individuals, including traditional health plan customers. Health Net's products are marketed to commercial clients through its sales force and external brokers; individual plans are sold mostly through independent agents.

	Annual Growth	12/05	12/06	12/07	12/08	12/09
Sales ($ mil.)	7.1%	11,940.5	12,908.3	14,108.3	15,366.6	15,713.2
Net income ($ mil.)	—	229.8	329.3	193.7	95.0	(49.0)
Market value ($ mil.)	(18.0%)	5,123.4	4,836.2	4,800.4	1,082.3	2,314.7
Employees	(1.0%)	9,286	10,068	9,910	9,646	8,922

An in-depth profile of this company is available to Hoover's Online members at hoovers.com.

HEALTHCARE OF TODAY, INC.

2219 W. Olive Ave., Ste. 266
Burbank, CA 91506
Phone: 866-963-2417
Fax: 310-362-8657
Web: www.healthcareoftoday.com

CEO: Henry L. Jan
CFO: Robert J. Hipple
HR: —
FYE: September 30
Type: Holding company

Healthcare of Today hopes it can meet your health care needs today, tomorrow, and for years to come. The holding company acquires, owns, and develops businesses primarily within the health care industry. Its subsidiaries are a diverse group that deal in health care staff training and education, home care and adult daycare services, health care IT, insurance, medical supplies, nurse staffing, real estate brokerage, and senior living facilities operation. It also owns a private chef network for assisted living facilities and a full-service maintenance and office cleaning provider.

HEALTHCARE REALTY TRUST INCORPORATED   NYSE: HR

3310 West End Ave., Ste. 700
Nashville, TN 37203
Phone: 615-269-8175
Fax: 615-269-8461
Web: www.healthcarerealty.com

CEO: David R. Emery
CFO: Scott W. Holmes
HR: Rebecca T. Oberlander
FYE: December 31
Type: Public

Healthcare Realty Trust has the prescription for health care providers. The self-managed and self-administered real estate investment trust (REIT) invests in, develops, and manages medical office buildings, physician clinics, and inpatient and outpatient health care facilities. It owns about 200 properties with more than 12 million sq. ft. of space in some two-dozen states. Healthcare Realty Trust also invests in mortgages backed by health care properties and provides property management services for about 140 health care facilities. The REIT's largest tenant is HealthSouth, which accounts for more than 10% of the company's revenues.

	Annual Growth	12/05	12/06	12/07	12/08	12/09
Sales ($ mil.)	0.3%	254.5	264.9	212.6	220.8	257.2
Net income ($ mil.)	(0.8%)	52.7	39.7	60.1	41.7	51.1
Market value ($ mil.)	(10.4%)	2,072.5	2,463.1	1,581.7	1,462.7	1,336.8
Employees	1.6%	215	201	208	223	229

HEALTHCARE SERVICES GROUP, INC.   NASDAQ (GS): HCSG

3220 Tillman Dr., Ste. 300
Bensalem, PA 19020
Phone: 215-639-4274
Fax: 215-639-2152
Web: www.hcsgcorp.com

CEO: Daniel P. McCartney
CFO: Richard W. Hudson
HR: Nicholas R. (Nick) Marino
FYE: December 31
Type: Public

Healthcare Services Group gets swept up in its work every day. The company provides housekeeping, laundry and linen, food, and maintenance services to hospitals, nursing homes, rehabilitation centers, and retirement facilities. It tidies up more than 2,100 long-term care facilities in Canada and almost every state in the US. Housekeeping and laundry and linen services are the company's top revenue generators. The company's food services division prepares food for residents and monitors nutritional needs in more than 275 facilities. Healthcare Services Group was established in 1977.

	Annual Growth	12/05	12/06	12/07	12/08	12/09
Sales ($ mil.)	10.4%	466.3	511.6	577.7	602.7	692.7
Net income ($ mil.)	12.2%	19.1	25.5	29.6	26.6	30.3
Market value ($ mil.)	11.7%	604.4	845.2	927.2	697.4	939.5
Employees	(30.0%)	20,400	23,600	23,850	24,200	4,900

HEALTHFIRST

25 Broadway
New York, NY 10004
Phone: 212-801-6000
Fax: 212-801-3245
Web: www.healthfirstny.com

CEO: Patricia (Pat) Wang
CFO: Marybeth Tita
HR: Andrea Forino
FYE: December 31
Type: Not-for-profit

Healthfirst is a hospital-owned, not-for-profit health care management organization that serves some 480,000 members throughout New York City and Long Island, as well as northern New Jersey. The company offers a variety of government-sponsored health insurance programs, including Medicaid, Medicare, Family Health Plus, and Child Health Plus plans, to low-income and special needs clients. It also offers commercial HMO and point-of-service plans to individuals and small employer groups. The company was formed in 1993 and is owned by 39 New York-area hospitals, and it offers access to a wider network of some 19,000 medical care providers. Its plans are administered by HF Management Services.

HEALTHMARKETS, INC.

9151 Boulevard 26
North Richland Hills, TX 76180
Phone: 817-255-5200
Fax: 817-255-5390
Web: www.healthmarkets.com

CEO: Phillip J. (Phil) Hildebrand
CFO: Steven P. (Steve) Erwin
HR: Vicki A. Cansler
FYE: December 31
Type: Private

HealthMarkets lets the self-employed shop for better insurance. The company offers health insurance through its MEGA Life and Health Insurance, Chesapeake Life Insurance Company, and Mid-West National Life Insurance Company of Tennessee to mostly self-employed individuals in about 45 states. It provides dental, vision, accident, and worker's compensation insurance; health care options include health spending accounts (HSAs) and high-deductible health plans (HDHPs). Other services include third-party administrative and distribution services for health care providers and reinsurance through the company's Zon Re subsidiary. A consortium led by the Blackstone Group owns HealthMarkets.

	Annual Growth	12/04	12/05	12/06	12/07	12/08
Sales ($ mil.)	(12.6%)	—	2,121.0	2,146.6	1,595.3	1,416.9
Net income ($ mil.)	—	—	—	237.7	70.2	(53.5)
Employees	(18.7%)	—	2,700	1,800	2,000	1,450

HEALTHNOW NEW YORK, INC.

1901 Main St.
Buffalo, NY 14240
Phone: 716-887-6900
Fax: 716-887-8981
Web: www.healthnowny.com

CEO: Alphonso O'Neil-White
CFO: Stephen T. Swift
HR: Thomas A. Fentner
FYE: December 31
Type: Not-for-profit

HealthNow New York provides health insurance and related services to about 1 million members in more than 50 counties in New York state. The company offers a wide range of Blue Cross and Blue Shield-branded products, including PPO, HMO, POS, and traditional indemnity health plans, primarily through its Blue Cross Blue Shield of Western New York and BlueShield of Northeastern New York subsidiaries. HealthNow also provides resources to help its members maintain and improve their health and avoid the pitfalls associated with unhealthy lifestyles. The company serves businesses large and small as well as individuals.

	Annual Growth	12/04	12/05	12/06	12/07	12/08
Est. sales ($ mil.)	—	—	—	—	—	2,271.1
Employees	—	—	—	—	—	2,200

HEALTHPORT, INC.

925 North Point Pkwy., Ste. 350
Alpharetta, GA 30005
Phone: 770-670-2150
Fax: —
Web: www.healthport.com

CEO: Michael J. (Mike) Labedz
CFO: Brian M. Grazzini
HR: —
FYE: December 31
Type: Private

HealthPort offers safe port in a sea of patient information. The company provides practice management, electronic medical records, and claims management software applications, as well as offerings such as outsourced release-of-information services, electronic data interchange, network design and implementation, training programs, consulting, online diagnostics support, and technical support. HealthPort maintains technology partnerships with vendors including Hewlett-Packard, IBM, Sybase, and Toshiba America. HealthPort serves nearly 2,000 hospitals and health systems, as well as about 8,000 independent physician clinics. The company filed for an IPO in 2009, but later postponed plans to go public.

HEALTHSOUTH CORPORATION

NYSE: HLS

3660 Grandview Pkwy., Ste. 200
Birmingham, AL 35243
Phone: 205-967-7116
Fax: 205-969-3543
Web: www.healthsouth.com

CEO: Jay Grinney
CFO: Douglas E. (Doug) Coltharp
HR: Cheryl Levy
FYE: December 31
Type: Public

Don't let the name fool you, HealthSouth doesn't just operate down south, it is one of the nation's largest rehabilitation services providers. Its facilities include rehabilitation hospitals, outpatient centers, home health, and long-term acute care facilities that provide nursing and therapy to patients who have experienced significant disabilities as a result of stroke, spinal cord injury, neuromuscular disease, or other conditions. Operating in more than two-dozen states and Puerto Rico, HealthSouth owns or leases about 100 facilities with roughly 6,500 beds. Most of HealthSouth's income is derived from its inpatient operations, which are concentrated in Texas, Pennsylvania, and Florida.

	Annual Growth	12/05	12/06	12/07	12/08	12/09
Sales ($ mil.)	(12.1%)	3,207.7	3,000.1	1,752.5	1,842.4	1,911.1
Net income ($ mil.)	—	(446.0)	(625.0)	653.4	252.4	128.8
Market value ($ mil.)	(6.4%)	2,292.3	2,119.2	1,964.8	1,025.5	1,756.2
Employees	(15.9%)	37,000	33,000	22,000	22,000	—

HEALTHSPORT, INC.

OTC: HSPO

10130 Mallard Creek, Ste. 331
Charlotte, NC 28262
Phone: 866-225-7548
Fax: —
Web: www.healthsportinc.com

CEO: Kevin Taheri
CFO: Thomas A. Beckett
HR: —
FYE: December 31
Type: Public

When swigging a liquid is too complicated, HealthSport hopes you'll slip its products in your mouth. The company has developed a dissolving edible thin-strip product containing electrolytes equivalent to one fluid ounce of most recognized sports drinks. Its products, sold under the Enlyten Sport Strips brand, are designed to replenish the body's stores of electrolytes. HealthSport has developed other edible strips to replace electrolytes in sick kids (PediaStrips) and hung-over adults (Fix Strips). Additionally, it is working on products for the US military and for the treatment of coughs and colds. In 2010 HealthSport announced plans to merge with affiliate Supplemental Manufacturing and Ingredients (SMI).

	Annual Growth	12/05	12/06	12/07	12/08	12/09
Sales ($ mil.)	—	—	0.0	0.4	1.5	2.6
Net income ($ mil.)	—	—	(1.4)	(9.8)	(9.0)	(19.0)
Market value ($ mil.)	(62.4%)	—	275.8	63.7	71.1	14.7
Employees	48.1%	—	4	46	43	13

HEALTHSPRING, INC.

NYSE: HS

9009 Carothers Pkwy., Ste. 501
Franklin, TN 37067
Phone: 615-291-7000
Fax: 615-401-4566
Web: www.myhealthspring.com

CEO: Herbert A. (Herb) Fritch
CFO: J. Lankford Wade
HR: —
FYE: December 31
Type: Public

Looking to keep a spring in Grandma's step, HealthSpring provides Medicare Advantage plans in seven US states. The company has about 190,000 members in Alabama, Florida, Georgia, Illinois, Mississippi, Tennessee, and Texas. Its Medicare Advantage plans offer the support of Medicare with additional benefits such as Medicare Part D prescription benefits, vision and hearing benefits, and transportation programs. In addition, HealthSpring runs a nationwide prescription drug plan with more than 310,000 members, and offers management services to independent physician associations in Alabama, Tennessee, and Texas.

	Annual Growth	12/05	12/06	12/07	12/08	12/09
Sales ($ mil.)	37.9%	737.4	1,309.0	1,574.8	2,188.3	2,666.0
Net income ($ mil.)	49.8%	26.5	80.8	86.5	119.0	133.6
Market value ($ mil.)	(4.7%)	—	1,179.1	1,103.8	1,157.1	1,020.4
Employees	18.9%	900	1,200	1,320	1,728	1,800

HEALTHSTREAM, INC.

NASDAQ (GM): HSTM

209 10th Ave. South, Ste. 450
Nashville, TN 37203
Phone: 615-301-3100
Fax: 615-301-3200
Web: www.healthstream.com

CEO: Robert A. Frist Jr.
CFO: Gerard M. (Gerry) Hayden Jr.
HR: Alfred E. Newman
FYE: December 31
Type: Public

HealthStream replenishes the well of knowledge for medical workers. The company offers Internet-based educational and training content for health care professionals. Courses train employees on new equipment, introduce new pharmaceuticals, provide continuing education credits, and disseminate regulatory information. The company's flagship HealthStream Learning Center has nearly 2 million subscribers. It generates sales from subscription fees based on the number of users and type of content provided. Clients include health care organizations, pharmaceutical companies, and medical device firms. The company also provides data management and research products through its HealthStream Research division.

	Annual Growth	12/05	12/06	12/07	12/08	12/09
Sales ($ mil.)	20.3%	27.4	31.8	43.9	51.6	57.4
Net income ($ mil.)	64.8%	1.9	2.5	4.1	2.9	14.0
Market value ($ mil.)	14.1%	50.7	85.9	76.1	50.7	85.9
Employees	25.5%	160	160	420	400	397

HEALTHTRONICS, INC.

NASDAQ (GS): HTRN

1301 Capital of Texas Hwy., Ste. 200B
Austin, TX 78746
Phone: 512-328-2892
Fax: 512-328-8510
Web: www.healthtronics.com

CEO: James S. B. Whittenburg
CFO: Richard A. Rusk
HR: —
FYE: December 31
Type: Public

HealthTronics' cup runneth over with urological health care services and equipment. The company makes and sells such equipment as lasers and lithotripters, which use shock waves to break up kidney and gall-bladder stones. HealthTronics contracts with medical facilities to provide lithotripsy services including the provision of equipment, scheduling, training, and clinical technicians. It also offers other urology-related services, including urological pathology testing and cryosurgical (freezing of tissue) treatments for enlarged prostate and prostate cancer. In addition, HealthTronics supplies equipment such as patient tables and X-ray imaging systems. The company is being acquired by Endo Pharmaceuticals.

	Annual Growth	12/05	12/06	12/07	12/08	12/09
Sales ($ mil.)	(8.8%)	267.7	142.9	140.4	165.9	185.3
Net income ($ mil.)	54.0%	9.2	8.7	(14.6)	(128.7)	51.8
Market value ($ mil.)	(23.4%)	348.6	304.0	209.2	102.5	120.3
Employees	(8.3%)	930	310	419	580	658

An in-depth profile of this company is available to Hoover's Online members at hoovers.com.

745

HEALTHWAREHOUSE.COM, INC.

OTC: IONN

100 Commerce Blvd.
Cincinnati, OH 45140
Phone: 513-618-0911
Fax: —
Web: www.healthwarehouse.com

CEO: Lalit P. Dhadphale
CFO: Patrick E. Delaney
HR: —
FYE: December 31
Type: Public

HealthWarehouse.com sells over-the-counter in more than one way. The online pharmacy sells prescription and over-the-counter drugs to more than 30,000 customers. It sources its products from suppliers including Masters Pharmaceutical and The Harvard Drug Group. HealthWarehouse went public through a reverse merger with OTC-traded Clacendix in 2009. Clacendix provided products that protected enterprise data and networks from security threats. Faced with declining sales and mounting losses, Clacendix sold its assets to network security specialist Cryptek for $3.2 million in early 2008. The following year Clacendix merged with HealthWarehouse and changed its name.

	Annual Growth	12/05	12/06	12/07	12/08	12/09
Sales ($ mil.)	(4.7%)	4.6	3.4	3.3	0.0	3.8
Net income ($ mil.)	—	0.2	(0.8)	0.1	(0.7)	(2.4)
Market value ($ mil.)	(14.7%)	33.8	19.9	11.9	5.0	17.9
Employees	(10.1%)	26	20	2	2	17

HEALTHWAYS, INC.

NASDAQ (GS): HWAY

701 Cool Springs Blvd.
Franklin, TN 37067
Phone: 615-614-4929
Fax: —
Web: www.healthways.com

CEO: Ben R. Leedle Jr.
CFO: Mary A. Chaput
HR: Christopher (Chris) Cigarran
FYE: December 31
Type: Public

For health insurers, healthy plan members are cheap plan members; that's where Healthways comes in. The health services company provides disease management and wellness programs to managed care companies, self-insured employers, governments, and hospitals, with the ultimate goals of improving members' health and lowering health care costs. Its disease management programs help members manage chronic illnesses like diabetes and emphysema, making sure they keep up with treatment plans and maintain healthy behaviors. Healthways' wellness offerings, including its SilverSneakers program for seniors, encourage fitness and other good lifestyle choices.

	Annual Growth	8/06	8/07	8/08	*12/08	12/09
Sales ($ mil.)	14.9%	412.3	615.6	736.2	244.7	717.4
Net income ($ mil.)	(27.3%)	37.2	45.1	54.8	734.0	10.4
Market value ($ mil.)	(22.8%)	1,760.6	1,698.5	649.7	—	625.5
Employees	1.2%	2,855	3,800	3,500	—	3,000

*Fiscal year change

HEALTHY FAST FOOD, INC.

Pink Sheets: HFFI

1075 American Pacific, Ste. C
Henderson, NV 89074
Phone: 702-448-5301
Fax: —

CEO: Henry E. (Hank) Cartwright
CFO: —
HR: —
FYE: December 31
Type: Public

This company hopes to have customers circling its frozen yogurt shops. Healthy Fast Food operates and franchises a small number of U-SWIRL Frozen Yogurt outlets. The chain offers non-fat frozen yogurt treats available with more than 40 different toppings. U-SWIRL locations operate primarily in Nevada. In addition to its yogurt franchising business, Healthy Fast Food operates two franchised hamburger outlets under the EVOS banner. The quick-service eateries offer healthy burgers and fries along with wraps and salads.

	Annual Growth	12/05	12/06	12/07	12/08	12/09
Sales ($ mil.)	135.1%	—	0.1	1.0	0.7	1.3
Net income ($ mil.)	—	—	(0.3)	(0.7)	(1.6)	(1.1)
Market value ($ mil.)	154.5%	—	—	—	1.5	3.9
Employees	8.9%	—	31	32	40	40

THE HEARST CORPORATION

300 W. 57th St.
New York, NY 10019
Phone: 212-649-2000
Fax: 212-649-2108
Web: www.hearst.com

CEO: Frank A. Bennack Jr.
CFO: Mitchell Scherzer
HR: Scherri Roberts
FYE: December 31
Type: Private

Like founder William Randolph Hearst's castle, The Hearst Corporation is sprawling. Through Hearst Newspapers, the company owns some 15 daily newspapers (such as the *San Francisco Chronicle* and the *Houston Chronicle*) and 50 weekly newspapers. Its Hearst Magazines publishes some 15 US consumer magazines (*Cosmopolitan*, *Esquire*) with nearly 200 international editions. Hearst has broadcasting operations through its Hearst Television subsidiary. Its Hearst Entertainment & Syndication unit includes syndication service King Features, newspaper production service Reed Brennan, and stakes in cable networks (A&E, ESPN). The Hearst Corporation is owned by the Hearst family, but managed by a board of trustees.

	Annual Growth	12/04	12/05	12/06	12/07	12/08
Est. sales ($ mil.)	4.7%	4,000.0	4,550.0	4,520.0	4,380.0	4,810.0
Employees	4.7%	16,667	17,016	17,062	17,070	20,000

HEARST ENTERTAINMENT & SYNDICATION

300 W. 57th St., 15th Fl.
New York, NY 10019
Phone: 212-969-7553
Fax: 646-280-1553
Web: www.hearst.com/entertainment

CEO: Scott M. Sassa
CFO: —
HR: —
FYE: —
Type: Subsidiary

Hearst knows how to entertain. Hearst Entertainment & Syndication (HES), one of the main operating units of The Hearst Corporation, includes Hearst's stakes in various cable TV holdings, such as cable network ESPN and A&E Television Networks (AETN, operator of Lifetime, A&E, and The History Channel). The unit also has television programming activities, producing documentary and reality shows such as The History Channel's *Modern Marvels* series. In addition, HES houses King Features Syndicate, a distributor of comics, columns, and puzzles to newspapers, and Reed Brennan Media Associates, a provider of production support and editing services for newspapers. HES also features a library of more than 250 films.

HEARST NEWSPAPERS

959 8th Ave.
New York, NY 10019
Phone: 212-649-2000
Fax: 212-649-2108
Web: www.hearst.com/newspapers

CEO: Steven R. Swartz
CFO: John M. (Jack) Condon
HR: —
FYE: December 31
Type: Subsidiary

Working against a deadline is routine for this business. A division of media giant Hearst Corporation, Hearst Newspapers publishes about a dozen daily newspapers in major markets, including the *Houston Chronicle*, the *San Antonio Express-News*, and the *San Francisco Chronicle*. It also owns a small portfolio of weekly papers serving small markets, and it operates a newswire service that distributes news and features to some 600 subscribing publications. In addition to traditional publishing, Hearst Newspapers publishes news online through companion websites for its daily papers. It also publishes telephone directories through White Directory Publishers and Associated Publishing Company.

HEARTLAND EXPRESS, INC.

NASDAQ (GS): HTLD

901 N. Kansas Ave.
North Liberty, IA 52317
Phone: 319-626-3600
Fax: 319-626-3619
Web: www.heartlandexpress.com

CEO: Russell A. Gerdin
CFO: John P. Cosaert
HR: —
FYE: December 31
Type: Public

Home is where the heart is, and Heartland Express stays close to home as a short- to medium-haul truckload carrier — its average trip is about 514 miles. The company mainly operates east of the Rockies; it also offers service in the southwestern US. Although most of its loads go directly from origin to destination, Heartland also operates from regional distribution hubs, which are located near major customers. The regional hubs focus on short-haul freight movements (less than 400 miles). Heartland transports general commodities, including appliances, auto parts, consumer products, food, and paper products.

	Annual Growth	12/05	12/06	12/07	12/08	12/09
Sales ($ mil.)	(3.2%)	523.8	571.9	591.9	625.6	459.5
Net income ($ mil.)	(5.7%)	71.9	87.2	76.2	70.0	56.9
Market value ($ mil.)	0.1%	1,380.1	1,362.1	1,286.0	1,429.3	1,384.8
Employees	(2.1%)	3,029	3,317	3,291	3,279	2,781

HEARTLAND FINANCIAL USA, INC.

NASDAQ (GS): HTLF

1398 Central Ave.
Dubuque, IA 52001
Phone: 563-589-2100
Fax: 563-589-2011
Web: www.htlf.com

CEO: Lynn B. Fuller
CFO: John K. Schmidt
HR: Nancy Wilson
FYE: December 31
Type: Public

Heartland Financial USA's heart is in the right place. The multibank holding company owns flagship subsidiary Dubuque Bank & Trust and nine other banks that together operate about 60 branches in the Midwest and Southwest. It also owns consumer lender Citizens Finance, which has offices in Illinois, Iowa, and Wisconsin. Approximately 70% of Heartland Financial's loan portfolio comes from commercial loans, but, in keeping with the bank's midwestern identity, it also makes agricultural, residential mortgage, and consumer loans, each around 10% of its loan book. The banks also offer retirement, wealth management, trust, and investment services, including socially responsible investing.

	Annual Growth	12/05	12/06	12/07	12/08	12/09
Assets ($ mil.)	9.2%	2,818.3	3,058.2	3,264.1	3,630.3	4,013.0
Net income ($ mil.)	(27.1%)	22.7	25.1	25.6	11.3	6.4
Market value ($ mil.)	(9.8%)	355.0	472.0	303.8	336.8	234.8
Employees	2.4%	909	959	982	1,028	1,001

HEARTLAND INDUSTRIAL PARTNERS LP

177 Broad St., 10th Fl.
Stamford, CT 06901
Phone: 203-327-1202
Fax: 203-327-1201
Web: www.heartlandpartners.com

CEO: Daniel P. Tredwell
CFO: Steve Lamb
HR: —
FYE: December 31
Type: Private

Heartland Industrial Partners is an investment firm that primarily targets industrial and auto parts companies. The company's holdings include a more than 40% stake in vehicle component maker TriMas. It sold auto parts maker Metaldyne to an affiliate of Ripplewood Holdings in early 2007. David Stockman, who co-founded Heartland Industrial Partners in 1999, is a former Michigan congressman and was director of the Office of Management and Budget during the Reagan administration. He was also chairman and CEO of one of Heartland Industrial's former portfolio companies, auto fabrics company Collins & Aikman, but was ousted in 2005.

HEARTLAND PAYMENT SYSTEMS, INC.

NYSE: HPY

90 Nassau St.
Princeton, NJ 08542
Phone: 609-683-3831
Fax: 609-683-3815
Web: www.heartlandpaymentsystems.com

CEO: Robert O. (Bob) Carr
CFO: Robert H. B. (Bob) Baldwin Jr.
HR: —
FYE: December 31
Type: Public

If you're using your card to charge throughout the heartland, Heartland Payment Systems makes sure the transactions don't get lost along the way. The company provides credit card, debit card, and payroll processing services to large national clients, and more than 170,000 small and midsized merchants in the US and Canada, including retailers, convenience stores, and restaurants. (The latter account for more than half of Heartland's processing volume.) The company, which handles some 4 billion transactions a year, also processes merchant-issued gift cards and sells and rents point-of-sale card processing equipment as well as provides electronic check processing services.

	Annual Growth	12/05	12/06	12/07	12/08	12/09
Sales ($ mil.)	18.6%	834.6	1,097.0	1,313.8	1,544.9	1,652.1
Net income ($ mil.)	—	19.1	28.5	35.9	41.8	(51.8)
Market value ($ mil.)	(11.8%)	819.4	1,068.8	1,013.9	662.1	496.7
Employees	17.3%	1,616	2,026	2,406	2,979	3,055

HEARUSA, INC.

NYSE Amex: EAR

1250 Northpoint Pkwy.
West Palm Beach, FL 33407
Phone: 561-478-8770
Fax: 561-478-9603
Web: www.hearx.com

CEO: Stephen J. Hansbrough
CFO: Francisco V. (Frank) Puñal
HR: —
FYE: December 31
Type: Public

Have you heard of HearUSA? The company operates a network of hearing care centers that offer hearing aids, testing, diagnosis, and rehabilitation services for the hearing impaired. More than 185 centers operate under names such as HearUSA, HEARx, and National Ear Care Plan, with centers located in about nine states. HearUSA caters primarily to managed care and health insurance providers, but the company also markets to the general public. In addition, it offers products and services nationwide through affiliated providers, and it has a network of about 1,900 contracted audiologists across the US.

	Annual Growth	12/05	12/06	12/07	12/08	12/09
Sales ($ mil.)	3.8%	76.7	88.8	102.8	112.0	88.9
Net income ($ mil.)	—	(1.1)	(3.2)	(3.3)	(3.2)	2.1
Market value ($ mil.)	2.3%	61.0	60.1	60.6	23.8	66.9
Employees	7.6%	422	654	618	607	565

HECLA MINING COMPANY

NYSE: HL

6500 N. Mineral Dr., Ste. 200
Coeur d'Alene, ID 83815
Phone: 208-769-4100
Fax: 208-769-7612
Web: www.hecla-mining.com

CEO: Phillips S. Baker Jr.
CFO: James A. (Jim) Sabala
HR: —
FYE: December 31
Type: Public

Not all that glitters at Hecla Mining is gold — in fact, most of it is silver. Hecla explores for and mines gold, silver, lead, and zinc. It produces about 9 million ounces of silver and 75,000 ounces of gold annually; silver accounts for more than half of the company's sales. Hecla operates mines in the US (Alaska and Idaho) and Mexico. Half of the company's sales are to Teck Resources, which processes the minerals at its smelter in British Columbia. The company's Greens Creek gold/silver/zinc/lead mine in Alaska had been a joint venture with Rio Tinto until Hecla bought it outright in 2008. Hecla sold properties in Venezuela to help pay for its acquisition of the Greens Creek property that year.

	Annual Growth	12/05	12/06	12/07	12/08	12/09
Sales ($ mil.)	29.8%	110.2	217.4	222.6	192.7	312.5
Net income ($ mil.)	—	(25.4)	69.1	53.2	(54.5)	67.8
Market value ($ mil.)	11.1%	997.7	1,882.3	2,297.6	688.1	1,518.7
Employees	(13.9%)	1,191	1,163	871	742	656

An in-depth profile of this company is available to Hoover's Online members at hoovers.com.

747

HEELYS, INC.

NASDAQ (GM): HLYS

3200 Belmeade Dr., Ste. 100
Carrollton, TX 75006
Phone: 214-390-1831
Fax: 214-390-1661
Web: www.heelys.com

CEO: Thomas C. (Tom) Hansen
CFO: Craig D. Storey
HR: —
FYE: December 31
Type: Public

Heelys can't touch Elvis as The King of Rock 'n' Roll, but the company has made a name for itself with those who walk and roll. Its flagship product, HEELYS footwear, includes a wheel in the heel that enables the user to transition from walking to skating. It also sells helmets and other protective gear, as well as replacement wheels. Founded in 2000, Heelys has been on a roll since and sells its products at big-box and specialty retailers nationwide, including Academy, Journeys, and Sports Authority, as well as online through the likes of Zappos.com. It sells excess inventory through discounter Ross. Heelys also has independent distributors in Japan, South Korea, China, and Southeast Asia.

	Annual Growth	12/05	12/06	12/07	12/08	12/09
Sales ($ mil.)	(0.1%)	44.0	188.2	183.5	70.7	43.8
Net income ($ mil.)	—	4.3	29.2	22.3	(5.9)	(5.1)
Market value ($ mil.)	(59.4%)	—	899.6	191.9	62.6	60.1
Employees	7.6%	38	41	55	63	51

HEERY INTERNATIONAL, INC.

999 Peachtree St. NE
Atlanta, GA 30309
Phone: 404-881-9880
Fax: 404-892-8479
Web: www.heery.com

CEO: James J. (Jim) Moynihan
CFO: Theodore E. (Ted) Sak
HR: Daniel P. (Dan) Wise
FYE: December 31
Type: Subsidiary

Engineering and architectural group Heery International is known as much for its program management as for the schools and stadiums it designs. Architect George Heery, who helped found the firm in 1952, was an early practitioner of program management, which involves consulting and client representation for complex projects at each phase of construction. A subsidiary of UK engineering giant Balfour Beatty, Heery also offers facilities and construction management and interior design services. Government projects make up most of the firm's billings, and markets include educational, medical, correctional, and justice facilities.

	Annual Growth	12/04	12/05	12/06	12/07	12/08
Est. sales ($ mil.)	—	—	—	—	—	541.9
Employees	—	—	—	—	—	1,651

HEI, INC.

Pink Sheets: HEII

1495 Steiger Lake Ln.
Victoria, MN 55386
Phone: 952-443-2500
Fax: 952-443-2668
Web: www.heii.com

CEO: Mark B. Thomas
CFO: Mark B. Thomas
HR: Nina A. Anderson
FYE: December 31
Type: Public

For HEI, it's a small world after all. The company manufactures ultraminiature microelectronic components and products that use those components, for the communications, medical, and wireless markets. HEI offers other services common to contract electronics manufacturers, including chip packaging, assembly, and testing, as well as high-density interconnect design and fabrication. The company's tiny products are found in such devices as hearing aids, implantable defibrillators, and mobile phones. HEI is highly dependent on the hearing aid and medical instrument markets. Customers include Animas, Cochlear, GE Medical Systems, and Siemens.

HEICO CORPORATION

NYSE: HEI

3000 Taft St.
Hollywood, FL 33021
Phone: 954-987-4000
Fax: 954-987-8228
Web: www.heico.com

CEO: Laurans A. Mendelson
CFO: Thomas S. Irwin
HR: —
FYE: October 31
Type: Public

Here's a HEICO haiku: HEICO companies/ Providing for jet engines/ In flight or on land. Its Flight Support Group makes FAA-approved replacement parts for jet engines that can be substituted for original parts, including airfoils, bearings, combustion chambers, and compressor blades. Flight Support operations, which include repair and overhaul services, account for about three-quarters of HEICO's sales. Its Electronic Technologies Group makes a variety of electro-optical, electronic, and microwave products, including power supplies, receivers, simulation systems, and interconnection devices. HEICO, which gets about two-thirds of its sales from the US, also has facilities in Canada, India, Singapore, and the UK.

	Annual Growth	10/05	10/06	10/07	10/08	10/09
Sales ($ mil.)	18.9%	269.6	392.2	507.9	582.3	538.3
Net income ($ mil.)	18.3%	22.8	31.9	39.0	48.5	44.6
Market value ($ mil.)	14.4%	580.4	949.8	1,425.2	1,007.1	995.6
Employees	7.8%	1,556	1,843	2,185	2,328	2,100

HEIDELBERG USA, INC.

1000 Gutenberg Dr.
Kennesaw, GA 30144
Phone: 770-419-6600
Fax: 770-419-6550
Web: www.us.heidelberg.com

CEO: James P. Dunn
CFO: Thomas Topp
HR: Susan P. Nofi
FYE: March 31
Type: Subsidiary

Heidelberg USA is a manufacturer of sheetfed printing presses and prepress, printing, and binding equipment for customers in the print media industry. The company also sells such consumables as plates and film and resells products made by other manufacturers, including Kodak. Through its Print Media Academy program, Heidelberg USA offers product training at locations in Canada and the US. The company is the main US subsidiary of German printing giant Heidelberger Druckmaschinen (known as Heidelberg), along with Baumfolder Corporation, Heidelberg Digital LLC, and Heidelberg Print Finance Americas, Inc.

	Annual Growth	3/04	3/05	3/06	3/07	3/08
Est. sales ($ mil.)	—	—	—	—	—	154.1
Employees	—	—	—	—	—	1,000

HEIDRICK & STRUGGLES INTERNATIONAL

NASDAQ (GS): HSII

233 S. Wacker Dr., Ste. 4200
Chicago, IL 60606
Phone: 312-496-1200
Fax: 312-496-1290
Web: www.heidrick.com

CEO: L. Kevin Kelly
CFO: Scott J. Krenz
HR: Richard J. (Dick) Caldera
FYE: December 31
Type: Public

Finding top dogs for clients in many industries, Heidrick & Struggles International, Inc., is one of the largest global recruiting firms. The company has about 350 headhunters spanning 70 offices in 40 countries filling CEO, CFO, director, and other high-level positions for companies that range from start-up ventures to established *FORTUNE* 500 firms. It's divided into search groups that specialize by industry, such as financial services and industrial, which together account for half of sales. The company's fees are generally equal to one-third of a hired executive's first-year compensation. Heidrick & Struggles also provides temporary placement, management assessment, and professional development services.

	Annual Growth	12/05	12/06	12/07	12/08	12/09
Sales ($ mil.)	(1.1%)	432.9	502.0	648.3	644.9	414.7
Net income ($ mil.)	—	39.2	34.2	56.5	39.1	(20.9)
Market value ($ mil.)	(0.6%)	559.9	740.0	648.2	376.3	545.7
Employees	2.1%	1,286	1,550	1,647	1,751	1,400

An in-depth profile of this company is available to Hoover's Online members at hoovers.com.

HEINEKEN USA INC.

360 Hamilton Ave., Ste. 1103
White Plains, NY 10601
Phone: 914-681-4100
Fax: 914-681-1900
Web: www.heinekenusa.com

CEO: Dolf van den Brink
CFO: Daniel Sullivan
HR: —
FYE: December 31
Type: Subsidiary

Americans love their green Heinies. Heineken USA is a subsidiary of Netherlands-based Heineken. The US operation offers Heineken, Amstel Light (one of the US's best-selling imported light beers), Buckler (non-alcoholic), Murphy's Irish Stout, and Irish Amber. As a result of its parent's 2008 acquisition (along with Carlsberg) of the former Scottish & Newcastle, Heineken owns the import rights for Newcastle Brown Ale. It is also the sole US importer and seller of Mexico's FEMSA Cerveza's beer brands, including Tecate, Dos Equis, Sol, Carta Blanca, and Bohemia. For teetotalers, the company sells Buckler, a nonalcoholic beer. Heineken was first imported into the US in 1880.

HELICOS BIOSCIENCES CORPORATION

NASDAQ (GM): HLCS

1 Kendall Sq., Bldg. 700
Cambridge, MA 02139
Phone: 617-264-1800
Fax: —
Web: www.helicosbio.com

CEO: Ronald A. (Ron) Lowy
CFO: Jeffrey R. Moore
HR: Jo Norton
FYE: December 31
Type: Public

Helicos BioSciences is in the business of developing genetic analysis technologies. Its True Single Molecule Sequencing (tSMS) platform allows for the direct analysis of DNA and RNA samples without amplification, cloning, or other time-consuming preparation techniques. The company serves the research, clinical diagnostic, and drug discovery markets and aims to provide customers with the ability to compare thousands of samples. Its HeliScope genetic analysis system can be integrated into existing laboratories and consists of a computer-controlled instrument and related supplies and reagents.

	Annual Growth	12/05	12/06	12/07	12/08	12/09
Sales ($ mil.)	146.6%	—	0.2	0.6	0.8	3.0
Net income ($ mil.)	—	—	(20.6)	(36.8)	(45.7)	(28.0)
Market value ($ mil.)	(68.6%)	—	—	834.4	31.2	82.3
Employees	0.4%	—	79	114	71	80

HELEN OF TROY LIMITED

NASDAQ (GS): HELE

1 Helen of Troy Plaza
El Paso, TX 79912
Phone: 915-225-8000
Fax: 915-225-8004
Web: www.helenoftroyusa.com

CEO: Gerald J. Rubin
CFO: Thomas J. (Tom) Benson
HR: —
FYE: February 28
Type: Public

Need help battling your hair? You might call on those warriors who sailed in search of Helen of Troy. The firm, Helen of Troy, sells licensed personal care products and accessories under the Vidal Sassoon and Revlon brand names, as well as its own brands (Helen of Troy, Karina, Wigo). Its products include appliances (hair dryers, curling irons, shavers, massagers), personal care products (liquid hair styling products, liquid and powdered skin care products), and hair accessories. The company has made inroads into the housewares market with its OXO International purchase. Helen of Troy boosted its grooming, skin care, and hair care segment in the US through acquisitions.

	Annual Growth	2/06	2/07	2/08	2/09	2/10
Sales ($ mil.)	2.4%	589.7	634.9	652.5	622.7	647.6
Net income ($ mil.)	9.9%	49.3	50.1	61.5	(56.8)	71.8
Market value ($ mil.)	4.8%	613.3	709.9	484.0	307.7	740.8
Employees	2.2%	804	901	931	924	877

HELIOS & MATHESON NORTH AMERICA INC.

NASDAQ (CM): HMNA

200 Park Ave. South, Ste. 901
New York, NY 10003
Phone: 212-979-8228
Fax: 212-979-8003
Web: www.tact.com

CEO: Salvatore M. (Sal) Quadrino
CFO: Salvatore M. (Sal) Quadrino
HR: —
FYE: December 31
Type: Public

Helios & Matheson North America is a source (or outsource) of IT services. The company provides database management, project management, network design and implementation, application development, and Web enablement and related e-business services. The company also markets and distributes third-party software products. HMNA primarily serves global corporations and larger organizations in the automotive, banking, insurance, and pharmaceutical industries. BMW (nearly one-quarter of sales) and Merrill Lynch (10%) are Helios & Matheson's leading customers. Other top customers include MetLife and Pfizer. Nearly all of its clients are in the US.

	Annual Growth	12/05	12/06	12/07	12/08	12/09
Sales ($ mil.)	(13.3%)	26.4	24.9	20.8	19.7	14.9
Net income ($ mil.)	—	(0.5)	0.9	(0.8)	(2.9)	(2.1)
Market value ($ mil.)	(37.3%)	14.1	9.8	5.9	1.4	2.2
Employees	8.1%	90	98	106	92	123

HELENA CHEMICAL COMPANY

225 Schilling Blvd., Ste. 300
Collierville, TN 38017
Phone: 901-761-0050
Fax: 901-761-5754
Web: www.helenachemical.com

CEO: Mike McCarty
CFO: Troy D. Traxler Jr.
HR: —
FYE: March 31
Type: Subsidiary

Kind of like cops for crops, Helena Chemical's mission is to protect and serve. The product line of the company — the agricultural products division of Japanese business group Marubeni's US trading arm — is split into two units: Crop Protection and Crop Production. It produces agricultural chemicals, seeds, and fertilizers. Helena Chemical has four toll manufacturing sites — in Arkansas, California, Georgia, and Iowa — and sales, marketing, and distribution locations throughout the US. Ancillary product lines and services include forestry, aquatic, and vegetation management. Helena sells to Asia, Australia, Latin America, the Middle East, and Western Europe.

	Annual Growth	3/04	3/05	3/06	3/07	3/08
Est. sales ($ mil.)	—	—	—	—	—	2,632.5
Employees	—	—	—	—	—	1,000

HELIX BIOMEDIX, INC.

OTC: HXBM

22122 20th Ave. SE, Ste. 204
Bothell, WA 98021
Phone: 425-402-8400
Fax: 425-806-2999
Web: www.helixbiomedix.com

CEO: R. Stephen Beatty
CFO: R. Stephen Beatty
HR: —
FYE: December 31
Type: Public

Helix BioMedix wants to remove wrinkles and acne without leaving red, itchy skin. The company has a library of bioactive peptides with antimicrobial properties it hopes to exploit as it works to formulate wrinkle- and acne-fighting creams, along with topical treatments for skin and wound infections. The firm also hopes to use its peptides to develop a treatment that will speed the healing of wounds with minimal scarring, as well as to prevent drug resistant staph infections. Helix is looking to partner with large, better-funded drugmakers to develop some of its product candidates. The company also licenses its peptides to consumer products makers.

	Annual Growth	12/05	12/06	12/07	12/08	12/09
Sales ($ mil.)	41.4%	0.1	0.1	0.5	0.6	0.4
Net income ($ mil.)	—	(3.3)	(3.8)	(3.4)	(4.5)	(3.8)
Market value ($ mil.)	(18.7%)	20.0	22.3	12.8	9.0	8.7
Employees	(6.1%)	9	8	8	6	7

An in-depth profile of this company is available to Hoover's Online members at hoovers.com.

749

HELIX ENERGY SOLUTIONS GROUP, INC.

NYSE: HLX

400 N. Sam Houston Pkwy. East, Ste. 400
Houston, TX 77060
Phone: 281-618-0400
Fax: 281-618-0501
Web: www.helixesg.com

CEO: Owen E. Kratz
CFO: Anthony (Tony) Tripodo
HR: —
FYE: December 31
Type: Public

Helix Energy Solutions is in the energy services mix as a top marine shallow and deepwater contractor and operator of offshore oil and gas properties and production facilities. Its Contracting Deepwater unit primarily works in water depths greater than 1,000 feet, using dynamically positioned and remotely operated vehicles that offer a range of engineering, repair, maintenance, and pipe and cable burial services in global offshore markets. Subsidiary Energy Resource Technology buys and operates mature fields, primarily in the Gulf of Mexico, and in 2008 reported proved reserves of 665 billion cu. ft. of natural gas equivalent.

	Annual Growth	12/05	12/06	12/07	12/08	12/09
Sales ($ mil.)	16.3%	799.5	1,366.9	1,767.4	2,148.3	1,461.7
Net income ($ mil.)	3.6%	152.6	347.4	320.5	(630.8)	175.8
Market value ($ mil.)	(24.4%)	3,752.7	3,280.1	4,339.3	757.0	1,228.6
Employees	(3.7%)	1,800	2,300	3,370	3,600	1,550

HELLA NORTH AMERICA, INC.

43811 Plymouth Oaks Blvd.
Plymouth, MI 48170
Phone: 734-414-0900
Fax: 734-414-5098
Web: www.hellausa.com

CEO: Martin Fischer
CFO: —
HR: —
FYE: May 31
Type: Subsidiary

A subsidiary of Hella KGaA Hueck & Co., Hella North America offers a helluva selection when it comes to aftermarket and OEM automotive lighting products. Hella North America's aftermarket lighting products include auxiliary lighting such as fog lamps, replacement headlamps, work lamps, LED lighting, warning lights, and bulbs. In addition to lighting products, Hella North America makes OEM automotive electronics and vehicle modules. In 2005 Hella North America was split into three operating groups: Hella Lighting North America, Hella Electronics North America, and Hella North American Aftermarket and Special Equipment.

HELLMAN & FRIEDMAN LLC

1 Maritime Plaza, 12th Fl.
San Francisco, CA 94111
Phone: 415-788-5111
Fax: 415-788-0176
Web: www.hf.com

CEO: Philip U. Hammarskjold
CFO: Georgia Lee
HR: —
FYE: December 31
Type: Private

Hellman & Friedman has no trouble finding businesses to invest in. The private equity investment firm, which has raised and managed more than $16 billion in capital and invested in more than 50 companies since its 1984 founding, focuses on the financial services, professional services, information services, software, and media sectors in the US and Europe. Despite the range of industries, the company isn't loose with its money; it targets established companies with predictable revenue, and invests in only about five per year. It typically puts up between $300 million to $1 billion per transaction in buyouts, restructurings, and majority and minority investments.

HELLMANN WORLDWIDE LOGISTICS, INC.

10450 Doral Blvd.
Doral, FL 33178
Phone: 305-406-4500
Fax: 305-406-4519
Web: www.hellmann.net

CEO: Frank Scheibner
CFO: Julian M. Riches
HR: Kenneth Finneran
FYE: December 31
Type: Private

Hellmann Worldwide Logistics, the US branch of a German logistics company with the same name, can arrange the transportation of freight by air or sea. As a freight forwarder, Hellmann buys transportation capacity from carriers and resells it to shippers. Related services include customs brokerage, supply chain management, and warehousing. The company's US network of 25 offices includes facilities in major trade gateways such as Atlanta, Chicago, Houston, New York, Los Angeles, and Miami. Overall, Hellmann operates almost 440 offices in more than 150 countries. Carl Heinrich Hellmann founded the parent company in 1871; the Hellmann family still owns the company.

HELM U.S. CORPORATION

1110 Centennial Ave.
Piscataway, NJ 08854
Phone: 732-981-1116
Fax: 732-981-0528
Web: www.helmusa.com

CEO: Andreas Weimann
CFO: Bill Van Fossen
HR: Andreas Weimann
FYE: December 31
Type: Subsidiary

Chemical distributor HELM U.S. (a subsidiary of Germany-based HELM Aktiengesellschaft) distributes specialty and industrial chemicals from chemical producers to industrial customers in the Americas. Founded in 1976, the company specializes in distributing raw materials for producers of thermoset resins and coatings. Typical products include both liquid (acetone, acrylates, methanol, propylenes, xylenes) and solid (borax, fumaric acid, melamine, titanium dioxide) chemicals. The company also offers logistics services such as chemical tanker chartering, documentation, and import and export regulatory assistance.

	Annual Growth	12/04	12/05	12/06	12/07	12/08
Est. sales ($ mil.)	—	—	—	—	—	135.0
Employees	—	—	—	—	—	20

⊞ HELMERICH & PAYNE, INC.

NYSE: HP

1437 S. Boulder Ave.
Tulsa, OK 74119
Phone: 918-742-5531
Fax: 918-742-0237
Web: www.hpinc.com

CEO: Hans Helmerich
CFO: Juan P. Tardio
HR: —
FYE: September 30
Type: Public

In the oil and gas industry, Helmerich & Payne knows the drill: The contract driller operates 244 land and nine offshore platform rigs, mostly for industry giants such as BPOccidental Petroleum, and Devon Energy. Its US contract drilling operations are conducted mainly in Louisiana, Oklahoma, Texas, and Wyoming, as well as offshore California, in the Gulf of Mexico, in South America, and in North and West Africa. Helmerich & Payne operates 140 FlexRigs (drilling rigs equipped with new technologies, environmental and safety design, and the capability of simultaneous crew activity). The company also has real estate operations, including a shopping center and office buildings in Tulsa.

	Annual Growth	9/05	9/06	9/07	9/08	9/09
Sales ($ mil.)	24.0%	800.7	1,224.8	1,629.7	2,036.5	1,894.0
Net income ($ mil.)	29.0%	127.6	293.9	449.3	461.7	353.5
Market value ($ mil.)	7.0%	3,192.6	2,435.0	3,471.2	4,566.5	4,179.6
Employees	8.9%	4,801	5,705	6,456	6,198	—

HELMSMAN MANAGEMENT SERVICES, LLC

175 Berkeley St.
Boston, MA 02117
Phone: 617-357-9500
Fax: —
Web: www.libertymutual.com/helmsman

CEO: Edmond (Ted) Kelly
CFO: Dennis Langwell
HR: —
FYE: December 31
Type: Subsidiary

Helmsman Management Services helps businesses steer clear of risk. The third-party administrator provides risk management programs in the alternative risk marketplace for more than 300 clients across the US. The company's services, which are provided on a state, regional, or national basis, include claims management, litigation management, loss prevention, managed care and occupational health services, medical bill review, and utilization review. Helmsman Management Services is part of the Boston-based Liberty Mutual Insurance group. It utilizes Liberty Mutual's national network of claims and loss prevention specialists.

	Annual Growth	12/04	12/05	12/06	12/07	12/08
Est. sales ($ mil.)	—	—	—	—	—	90.0
Employees	—	—	—	—	—	400

HELZBERG DIAMONDS

1825 Swift Ave.
North Kansas City, MO 64116
Phone: 816-842-7780
Fax: 816-480-0294
Web: www.helzberg.com

CEO: Beryl B. Raff
CFO: Lonnie Lawton
HR: J. Kevin Fitzpatrick
FYE: December 31
Type: Subsidiary

Helzberg Diamonds is into hard rocks. The company sells a wide selection of diamonds and precious gems — mostly set into rings, but also set into other jewelry; Helzberg Diamonds also sells men's and women's watches. One of the largest national jewelry chains, the company operates more than 230 stores nationwide. The mall-based chain also sells jewelry online. Helzberg Diamonds was founded in 1915 by Morris Helzberg and remained in his family until 1995, when it was acquired by investment guru Warren Buffett's Berkshire Hathaway (owner of jewelry chains Ben Bridge Jeweler and Borsheim's). Helzberg Diamonds offers a 60-day return or exchange option and free jewelry repairs for 12 months after purchase.

	Annual Growth	12/04	12/05	12/06	12/07	12/08
Est. sales ($ mil.)	—	—	—	—	—	479.7
Employees	—	—	—	—	—	2,500

HEMACARE CORPORATION

OTC: HEMA

15350 Sherman Way, Ste. 350
Van Nuys, CA 91406
Phone: 818-226-1968
Fax: 818-251-5300
Web: www.hemacare.com

CEO: Peter van der Wal
CFO: Peter van der Wal
HR: Lois Coburn
FYE: December 31
Type: Public

HemaCare Corporation is a supplier of blood products and services to hospitals and researchers. The company collects whole blood from donors at donor centers and mobile donor vehicles and processes it into red blood cells, plasma, and other products used by hospitals for blood transfusion. HemaCare has blood collection centers in California and Maine; it operates under the name Coral Blood Services at its East Coast facilities. The company also provides therapeutic apheresis, a kind of blood treatment used for patients with autoimmune and other conditions, for hospitals in California and some mid-Atlantic states, including New York.

	Annual Growth	12/05	12/06	12/07	12/08	12/09
Sales ($ mil.)	3.9%	31.2	36.5	34.2	37.6	36.4
Net income ($ mil.)	(14.7%)	1.7	1.9	(7.8)	1.0	0.9
Market value ($ mil.)	(20.9%)	15.4	28.1	3.9	3.5	6.0
Employees	0.7%	244	271	239	254	251

HEMAGEN DIAGNOSTICS, INC.

OTC: HMGN

9033 Red Branch Rd.
Columbia, MD 21045
Phone: 443-367-5500
Fax: 443-367-5527
Web: www.hemagen.com

CEO: William P. Hales
CFO: Catherine M. Davidson
HR: —
FYE: September 30
Type: Public

Hemagen Diagnostics lets no disease go undetected. The company makes diagnostic kits and related components. Its Virgo product line is used to identify infectious and autoimmune diseases such as rheumatoid arthritis, lupus, measles, and syphilis. Physicians and veterinarians use its Analyst reagent system and related components to test blood for substances like cholesterol, glucose, and triglycerides. Hemagen sells products internationally primarily through distributors; its Brazilian subsidiary markets its products in South America.

	Annual Growth	9/05	9/06	9/07	9/08	9/09
Sales ($ mil.)	(8.2%)	7.6	7.3	4.5	6.4	5.4
Net income ($ mil.)	—	(1.3)	0.3	(0.8)	0.4	(0.8)
Market value ($ mil.)	(24.8%)	3.9	4.6	2.5	1.9	1.2
Employees	(14.6%)	47	46	33	34	25

HEMISPHERX BIOPHARMA, INC.

NYSE Amex: HEB

1 Penn Center, 1617 JFK Blvd., 6th Fl.
Philadelphia, PA 19103
Phone: 215-988-0080
Fax: 215-988-1739
Web: www.hemispherx.net

CEO: William A. Carter
CFO: Charles T. Bernhardt
HR: —
FYE: December 31
Type: Public

Targeting chronic viral diseases and immune disorders, Hemispherx Biopharma hopes to do a world of good with its RNA (ribonucleic acid) and other drugs. The company has acquired the rights to Alferon N, an FDA-approved drug for genital warts that the company is developing to fight other viral diseases, such as West Nile virus. Hemispherx also is developing Ampligen, an intravenously administered RNA drug that is in clinical trials to treat HIV and chronic fatigue syndrome (CFS). Ampligen is also being tested as an adjuvant for vaccines conditions including seasonal flu and bird flu. The compound has received orphan status from the FDA for kidney cancer, melanoma, CFS, and HIV.

	Annual Growth	12/05	12/06	12/07	12/08	12/09
Sales ($ mil.)	(45.1%)	1.1	0.9	1.1	0.3	0.1
Net income ($ mil.)	—	(13.2)	(19.4)	(18.1)	(12.2)	(13.4)
Market value ($ mil.)	(28.7%)	288.3	292.3	101.0	47.8	74.4
Employees	0.6%	43	71	48	46	44

HEMIWEDGE INDUSTRIES, INC.

Pink Sheets: HWEG

1011 Beach Airport Rd.
Conroe, TX 77301
Phone: 936-539-5770
Fax: 936-539-9396
Web: www.hemiwedge.com

CEO: Kenton (Ken) Chickering III
CFO: Matthew C. (Matt) Flemming
HR: —
FYE: December 31
Type: Public

Hemiwedge Industries (formerly Shumate Industries) is a maker of oil and gas services machinery products. Following the sale of its Shumate Machine Works subsidiary in late 2008, the company is focusing on another subsidiary, Hemiwedge Valve Corporation (HVC), which makes a quarter-turn valve designed to outperform traditional ball, butterfly, and gate valves. Customers include Baker Hughes, Smith International, and Halliburton Energy Services. Shumate Industries renamed itself Hemiwedge Industries in early 2009, its second name change in three years.

	Annual Growth	12/04	12/05	12/06	12/07	*12/08
Sales ($ mil.)	(4.7%)	3.4	5.0	7.7	9.0	2.8
Net income ($ mil.)	—	1.2	2.0	(1.3)	(7.2)	(0.8)
Market value ($ mil.)	(19.1%)	8.4	19.0	31.9	19.2	3.6
Employees	(7.4%)	38	54	83	—	28

*Most recent year available

An in-depth profile of this company is available to Hoover's Online members at hoovers.com.

751

HEMLOCK SEMICONDUCTOR CORPORATION

12334 Geddes Rd.	CEO: Rick Doornbos
Hemlock, MI 48626	CFO: Aaron Howald
Phone: 989-301-5000	HR: Kevin Burke
Fax: 989-301-5564	FYE: —
Web: www.hscpoly.com	Type: Joint venture

Hemlock Semiconductor looks to the earth for quartz, not poisonous plants. The company manufactures polycrystalline silicon (polysilicon) from quartz rock, a key component used to make semiconductors and solar cells. Hemlock Semiconductor produces almost 20,000 tons of polysilicon every year; in fact, it's responsible for about one-third of the world's silicon supply used for solar panels and electronic devices. Its polysilicon is available as rods, chunks, chips, or powder. Hemlock Semiconductor is more than 60% owned by Dow Corning. Two of Japan's largest single-crystal wafer manufacturers, Shin-Etsu Handotai and Mitsubishi Materials, control the remainder.

HENDRICK AUTOMOTIVE GROUP

6000 Monroe Rd., Ste. 100	CEO: James F. (Jim) Huzl
Charlotte, NC 28212	CFO: Edward J. (Ed) Brown III
Phone: 704-568-5550	HR: Tim Taylor
Fax: 704-566-3295	FYE: December 31
Web: www.hendrickauto.com	Type: Private

For megadealer Hendrick Automotive Group, variety is the spice of life. The second-largest privately owned dealership group in the US, Hendrick Automotive sells new and used cars and light trucks under more than 20 makes, from Acura to Volvo. It has a network of about 70 dealerships in 10 states from the Carolinas to California. The company also offers financing, as well as automobile parts, accessories, maintenance, and body repair services. Founder and chairman Rick Hendrick owns the company, which began in 1976 as a single dealership in Bennettsville, South Carolina. He also founded Hendrick Motorsports, a major force in NASCAR Sprint Cup auto racing.

HENKEL CORPORATION

1001 Trout Brook Crossing	CEO: Jeffrey C. (Jeff) Piccolomini
Rocky Hill, CT 06067	CFO: —
Phone: 860-571-5100	HR: —
Fax: 860-571-5465	FYE: December 31
Web: www.henkelcorp.com	Type: Subsidiary

The US subsidiary of German giant Henkel KGaA, Henkel Corporation helps consumers stick to it in many parts of their lives and projects. The company operates through three business sectors: laundry and home care, cosmetics and toiletries, and adhesives technologies. Some of its well-known brands are Dial soap, Loctite and Pattex adhesives, Sista sealants, Thomsit flooring adhesives, Right Guard antiperspirant, LA LOOKS hair gel, Soft Scrub cleaner, and Purex laundry detergent. Henkel manufactures and markets industrial and engineering adhesives and surface technologies, as well. The founding Henkel family controls the company.

HENKELS & MCCOY, INC.

985 Jolly Rd.	CEO: Kenneth L. Rose
Blue Bell, PA 19422	CFO: Robert J. Delark
Phone: 215-283-7600	HR: —
Fax: 215-283-7659	FYE: September 30
Web: www.henkels.com	Type: Private

When utilities, communications companies, or governments need the real McCoy to install or repair their transmission networks, they can call on specialty contractor Henkels & McCoy (H&M). The firm provides engineering, construction, and network development services globally. H&M also installs aerial and underground electrical distribution systems, gas transmission lines, and fiber-optic networks on electric transmission towers or along railroad rights-of-way. It has some 80 offices throughout the US, as well as Canada and Mexico. John Henkels Jr. and John McCoy founded H&M in Philadelphia in 1923 as a tree-trimming and landscaping firm. Employees and the Henkels family own H&M.

HENRY BROS. ELECTRONICS, INC.

NASDAQ (CM): HBE

17-01 Pollitt Dr.	CEO: James E. (Jim) Henry
Fair Lawn, NJ 07410	CFO: John P. Hopkins
Phone: 201-794-6500	HR: T. Robert (Bob) Hodgson
Fax: 201-794-8341	FYE: December 31
Web: www.hbe-inc.com	Type: Public

Security systems integrator Henry Bros. Electronics (formerly Diversified Security Solutions) designs, installs, and maintains closed-circuit television (CCTV) and access control systems. The company also installs system components such as CCTVs, intercoms, alarm monitors, video recorders, and card access controls. Henry Bros. Electronics markets its services to large and midsized businesses and to government agencies. Revenues from the government represent about 40% of the company's sales. New York, New Jersey, and California account for two-thirds of business.

	Annual Growth	12/05	12/06	12/07	12/08	12/09
Sales ($ mil.)	6.9%	42.2	42.1	57.9	62.4	55.1
Net income ($ mil.)	—	1.1	(2.3)	(0.3)	1.6	(0.8)
Market value ($ mil.)	(1.0%)	27.0	22.9	26.7	36.2	26.0
Employees	4.5%	172	198	205	246	205

HENRY COMPANY

909 N. Sepulveda Blvd., Ste. 650	CEO: Warner W. Henry
El Segundo, CA 90245	CFO: —
Phone: 310-955-9200	HR: George Priggins
Fax: 310-640-7663	FYE: December 31
Web: www.henry.com	Type: Private

Henry Company can put a roof over your head and pavement under your feet. It operates in the US through three divisions. The Henry Building Products arm offers roof coatings and systems, driveway maintenance products, and air and vapor barriers. The Bakor division sells commercial envelope and waterproofing systems, and residential roofing and driveway maintenance products. Henry's Resin Technology Company deals in polyurethane foam roof systems and other insulation products. Specialty products include undercoating for mobile homes, rust-proofing products for the auto industry, green roof systems, and protective coatings for industrial and commercial applications.

	Annual Growth	12/04	12/05	12/06	12/07	12/08
Est. sales ($ mil.)	—	—	—	—	—	84.0
Employees	—	—	—	—	—	560

HENRY CROWN AND COMPANY

222 N. LaSalle St.
Chicago, IL 60601
Phone: 312-236-6300
Fax: 312-899-5039

CEO: James S. Crown
CFO: —
HR: John Merritt
FYE: December 31
Type: Private

The jewels of Henry Crown and Company shine on like crazy diamonds. Controlled by Chicago's prominent Crown family, Henry Crown and Company is an investment firm that owns or has interests in a variety of business assets. These holdings include stakes in sports teams (the Chicago Bulls and the New York Yankees), leisure (Aspen Skiing Company), banking (JPMorgan Chase), and real estate (Rockefeller Center). The company also has a stake in General Dynamics; after once controlling the company outright, it still has a seat on the board. Affiliate CC Industries holds and manages some of the Crown family's investments.

HENRY FORD HEALTH SYSTEM

1 Ford Place
Detroit, MI 48202
Phone: 313-876-8700
Fax: 313-876-9243
Web: www.henryfordhealth.org

CEO: Nancy M. Schlichting
CFO: David E. Mazurkiewicz
HR: Kathleen M. (Kathy) Oswald
FYE: December 31
Type: Not-for-profit

In 1915 automaker Henry Ford founded the hospital that forms the cornerstone of southeastern Michigan's not-for-profit Henry Ford Health System (HFHS), a hospital network that is also involved in medical research and education. The system's half-dozen hospitals — including the flagship Henry Ford Hospital, as well as Henry Ford Wyandotte Hospital and mental health facility Kingswood Hospital — hold more than 2,300 beds. HFHS also operates a 1,000-doctor-strong medical group, as well as nursing homes, hospice, and a home health care network. The system's Health Alliance Plan of Michigan provides managed care and health insurance to about 500,000 members.

	Annual Growth	12/04	12/05	12/06	12/07	12/08
Sales ($ mil.)	6.7%	2,846.3	3,049.1	3,250.0	3,470.0	3,690.0
Net income ($ mil.)	(14.6%)	16.0	112.0	134.9	105.8	8.5
Employees	13.4%	13,000	14,900	16,000	17,489	21,500

HENRY MODELL & COMPANY, INC.

498 7th Ave., 20th Fl.
New York, NY 10018
Phone: 212-822-1000
Fax: 212-822-1025
Web: www.modells.com

CEO: Mitchell B. (Mitch) Modell
CFO: Eric J. Spiel
HR: Thomas Tilley
FYE: January 31
Type: Private

Modell's colors change from city to city. Henry Modell & Company sells sporting goods, fitness equipment, apparel (including local team apparel), and brand-name athletic footwear at about 140 Modell's Sporting Goods stores in 10 northeastern states, the District of Columbia, and online. Best known for offering branded products at reasonable prices, Modell has stores in malls, regional shopping centers, and busy urban areas, including Manhattan. Founded in 1889 by Hungarian immigrant Morris Modell (who first sold menswear from a Lower East Side pushcart in New York City), the chain is the oldest family-owned and -operated sports retailer in the country; it is in its fourth generation of Modell management.

	Annual Growth	1/04	1/05	1/06	1/07	1/08
Est. sales ($ mil.)	—	—	—	—	—	636.5
Employees	—	—	—	—	—	5,430

HENRY SCHEIN, INC.

135 Duryea Rd.
Melville, NY 11747
Phone: 631-843-5500
Fax: 631-843-5658
Web: www.henryschein.com

NASDAQ (GS): HSIC

CEO: Stanley M. Bergman
CFO: Steven Paladino
HR: —
FYE: December 31
Type: Public

Whether you're in Poughkeepsie or Prague, Henry Schein will help your dentist get those sparkly whites to shine. The company is a leading global distributor of dental supplies and equipment, with operations in North America, Europe, and Australia. Henry Schein provides such items as impression materials, X-ray equipment, and anesthetics. But the company isn't only interested in teeth: It also supplies doctors' offices, veterinarians, and other office-based health care providers with diagnostic kits, surgical tools, drugs, vaccines, and animal health products. Additionally, its technology division offers practice management software and other services to dental, medical, and veterinary offices.

	Annual Growth	12/05	12/06	12/07	12/08	12/09
Sales ($ mil.)	9.0%	4,635.9	5,153.1	5,920.2	6,394.9	6,538.3
Net income ($ mil.)	21.8%	151.3	163.8	215.2	243.1	333.2
Market value ($ mil.)	4.8%	3,987.6	4,475.6	5,610.5	3,352.6	4,806.4
Employees	3.2%	11,000	11,000	12,000	12,500	12,500

HENSEL PHELPS CONSTRUCTION CO.

420 6th Ave.
Greeley, CO 80632
Phone: 970-352-6565
Fax: 970-352-9311
Web: www.henselphelps.com

CEO: Jerry L. Morgensen
CFO: Stephen J. (Steve) Carrico
HR: —
FYE: December 31
Type: Private

Hensel Phelps Construction builds it all, from the courthouse to the big house. The employee-owned general contractor provides a full range of development, preconstruction, and construction services for commercial, institutional, and government projects throughout the US and abroad. Its project portfolio includes prisons, airports, arenas, laboratories, government complexes, offices, and more. Major clients have included the US Army Corps of Engineers, IBM, United Airlines, The University of Texas, NASA, and Whole Foods. Hensel Phelps founded the eponymous company as a homebuilder in 1937.

	Annual Growth	5/04	5/05	*12/06	12/07	12/08
Sales ($ mil.)	16.7%	1,800.0	1,728.0	2,130.0	2,520.0	3,337.0
Employees	1.0%	2,500	2,324	2,534	2,727	2,600
						*Fiscal year change

HENSLEY & COMPANY

4201 N. 45th Ave.
Phoenix, AZ 85031
Phone: 602-264-1635
Fax: 623-247-7094
Web: www.hensley.com

CEO: Robert M. (Bob) Delgado
CFO: Andrew K. (Andy) McCain
HR: Barbara L. Sahr
FYE: December 31
Type: Private

Their Bud is for you. Hensley & Company has become one of the largest companies in Arizona by selling brands of Anheuser-Busch beer. The enterprise, which primarily serves Phoenix and its surrounding areas, maintains its own fleet of sales and delivery vehicles. It is one of the top A-B wholesalers/distributors in the US. All is not Bud, however. The company carries more than 200 different brands of beer and other beverages. It is chaired by Cindy McCain, daughter of company founder, the late Jim Hensley, and wife of US Senator, John McCain.

An in-depth profile of this company is available to Hoover's Online members at hoovers.com.

753

HERAEUS PRECIOUS METALS MANAGEMENT, INC.

540 Madison Ave.
New York, NY 10022
Phone: 212-752-2180
Fax: 212-752-7141
Web: www.heraeuspm.com

CEO: Uve Kupka
CFO: Artin Janian
HR: —
FYE: December 31
Type: Subsidiary

Heraeus wants the business side of metal to be a little less heavy for its customers. Heraeus Precious Metals Management (HPM) sells precious metals and offers metal trading and hedging services to its customers. The company deals in precious metals such as gold, silver, platinum, and palladium, in physical forms from grains to ingots and bars. It also operates a refining division for scrap precious metals (i.e., jewelry and dental filling scraps) and other materials such as petroleum, photographic films and papers, and other chemical catalysts containing metals. Heraeus Precious Metals is the North American trading unit of Heraeus Holding.

HERBALIFE LTD.

NYSE: HLF

800 W. Olympic Blvd.
Los Angeles, CA 90015
Phone: 310-410-9600
Fax: 310-258-7019
Web: www.herbalife.com

CEO: Michael O. Johnson
CFO: John DeSimone
HR: —
FYE: December 31
Type: Public

Is it a weight-loss supplement or a way of life? Only Herbalife Ltd. knows for sure. Formerly known as WH Holdings (Cayman Islands), this holding company operates through Herbalife International, which manufactures and distributes weight control products including meal replacements, snacks and "enhancers." It also offers nutritional supplements, energy drinks, and skin care products. The company has international subsidiaries in 70 countries. Herbalife's multilevel marketing program involves some 2 million independent distributors throughout the world.

	Annual Growth	12/05	12/06	12/07	12/08	12/09
Sales ($ mil.)	10.4%	1,566.8	1,885.5	2,145.8	2,359.2	2,324.6
Net income ($ mil.)	21.6%	93.1	143.1	191.5	221.2	203.3
Market value ($ mil.)	5.7%	1,949.6	2,407.6	2,414.8	1,299.7	2,432.2
Employees	2.0%	3,788	3,644	3,600	4,000	4,100

HERCULES OFFSHORE, INC.

NASDAQ (GS): HERO

9 Greenway Plaza, Ste. 2200
Houston, TX 77046
Phone: 713-350-5100
Fax: 713-350-5105
Web: www.herculesoffshore.com

CEO: John T. Rynd
CFO: Stephen M. Butz
HR: Lisa W. Rodriguez
FYE: December 31
Type: Public

"With the strength of 10, ordinary men . . . " Hercules Offshore, through its subsidiaries, provides shallow-water drilling and liftboat services to major integrated energy companies and independent oil and natural gas exploration and production companies. It owns and operates a fleet of 20 jackup rigs and three submersible rigs in the Gulf of Mexico; 11 jackup rigs and one platform rig outside the Gulf; and six conventional and 11 posted barge rigs that operate inland, as well as 45 self-propelled, self-elevating liftboats. Its Delta Towing business operates a fleet of 30 inland tugs, 16 offshore tugs, 34 crew boats, 46 deck barges, 17 shale barges, and four spud barges.

	Annual Growth	12/05	12/06	12/07	12/08	12/09
Sales ($ mil.)	46.5%	161.3	344.3	766.8	1,111.8	742.9
Net income ($ mil.)	—	27.5	119.1	136.5	(1,070.9)	(91.7)
Market value ($ mil.)	(36.0%)	3,260.2	3,316.5	2,728.9	545.1	548.5
Employees	30.9%	750	920	3,300	3,100	2,200

HERCULES TECHNOLOGY GROWTH CAPITAL

NASDAQ (GM): HTGC

400 Hamilton Ave., Ste. 310
Palo Alto, CA 94301
Phone: 650-289-3060
Fax: 650-473-9194
Web: www.herculestech.com

CEO: Manuel A. Henriquez
CFO: David M. Lund
HR: —
FYE: December 31
Type: Public

Hercules Technology Growth Capital, Inc. (HTGC), performs its feats of strength with money. The closed-end investment firm offers financing vehicles to companies in the technology and life sciences sectors. HTGC provides primarily private companies (as well as some public ones) with such products as mezzanine loans, senior secured loans, and select private-equity investments. Loans typically range from $1 million to $30 million. HTGC's portfolio includes around 125 companies; about half are communications, information services, or biopharmaceuticals companies. Portfolio holdings include data network provider IKANO Communications and software company Talisma. CEO Manuel Henriquez co-founded HTGC in 2003.

	Annual Growth	12/05	12/06	12/07	12/08	12/09
Sales ($ mil.)	59.4%	11.5	30.4	63.9	78.5	74.3
Net income ($ mil.)	59.5%	2.1	11.4	42.4	21.0	13.6
Market value ($ mil.)	(3.5%)	434.6	516.5	450.2	287.1	376.6
Employees	24.1%	19	26	38	45	45

HERFF JONES, INC.

4501 W. 62nd St.
Indianapolis, IN 46268
Phone: 317-297-3740
Fax: 317-329-3308
Web: www.herff-jones.com

CEO: Joe Slaughter
CFO: Michael (Mike) Parrett
HR: —
FYE: June 30
Type: Private

Herff Jones Company wants its products to play an integral part in all noteworthy achievements, ceremonies, and traditions. It makes commemorative items for educational and athletic institutions, including caps, gowns, diplomas, awards, rings, medals, and yearbooks. The firm, founded in 1920, also makes and markets robes to religious and judicial entities, including those for the Supreme Court. Its education division, Nystrom, makes and publishes classroom materials for history and social studies classes, including globes, maps, atlases, and other items. As part of the same educational unit, It's About Time publishes programs for math and science study that are supported by the National Science Foundation.

	Annual Growth	6/04	6/05	6/06	6/07	6/08
Est. sales ($ mil.)	—	—	—	—	—	532.9
Employees	—	—	—	—	—	3,500

HERITAGE BANKSHARES, INC.

OTC: HBKS

150 Granby St.
Norfolk, VA 23510
Phone: 757-648-1700
Fax: 757-626-0064
Web: www.heritagenorfolk.com

CEO: Michael S. (Mike) Ives
CFO: John O. Guthrie
HR: —
FYE: December 31
Type: Public

Heritage Bankshares comes from a long line of money. Heritage Bankshares is the holding company for Heritage Bank & Trust, a community-based institution in Virginia with about half a dozen branches in Chesapeake, Norfolk, and Virginia Beach. The bank, which opened in the mid-1970s, offers standard banking products and services, including checking and savings accounts, debit cards, CDs, and IRAs. Real estate loans, primarily mortgages, account for the largest portion of its loan portfolio; the bank also originates loans for businesses, individuals, and municipalities. The bank offers insurance and investment services through its subsidiary, Sentinel Financial.

	Annual Growth	12/05	12/06	12/07	12/08	12/09
Assets ($ mil.)	7.6%	204.6	222.9	221.2	265.5	274.6
Net income ($ mil.)	8.3%	0.8	0.2	0.9	0.7	1.1
Market value ($ mil.)	(10.3%)	33.7	36.8	25.6	18.4	21.8
Employees	(7.9%)	82	74	71	63	59

HERITAGE COMMERCE CORP
NASDAQ (GS): HTBK

150 Almaden Blvd.
San Jose, CA 95113
Phone: 408-947-6900
Fax: 408-947-6910
Web: www.heritagecommercecorp.com

CEO: Walter T. (Walt) Kaczmarek
CFO: Lawrence D. McGovern
HR: —
FYE: December 31
Type: Public

If you know the way to San Jose, you may also know the way to Heritage Commerce. It is the holding company for Heritage Bank of Commerce, which operates about a dozen branches in the South Bay region of the San Francisco area. Serving consumers and small to midsized businesses and their owners and managers, the bank offers savings and checking accounts, money market and retirement accounts, and CDs, as well as cash management services and loans. Commercial, construction, land, and mortgage loans make up most of the company's loan portfolio, which is rounded out by home equity and consumer loans.

	Annual Growth	12/05	12/06	12/07	12/08	12/09
Assets ($ mil.)	4.8%	1,130.5	1,037.1	1,347.5	1,499.2	1,363.9
Net income ($ mil.)	—	14.4	17.3	14.1	1.8	(12.0)
Market value ($ mil.)	(34.2%)	254.1	314.9	217.4	132.9	47.5
Employees	2.3%	188	196	225	225	206

HERITAGE FINANCIAL CORPORATION
NASDAQ (GS): HFWA

201 5th Ave. SW
Olympia, WA 98501
Phone: 360-943-1500
Fax: 360-943-8046
Web: www.heritagebankwa.com

CEO: Brian L. Vance
CFO: Donald J. Hinson
HR: Sabrina Robisson
FYE: December 31
Type: Public

Heritage Financial is the bank holding company for Heritage Bank and Central Valley Bank, which together operate some 20 branches in Washington in the southern Puget Sound area and the central part of the state, respectively. The banks offer a full range of consumer deposit services such as CDs, IRAs, and checking, savings, NOW, and money market accounts. Commercial loans account for more than half of Heritage Financial's loan portfolio, while mortgages secured by multifamily real estate comprise about 20%. The banks also write single-family mortgages, construction loans, and consumer loans.

	Annual Growth	12/05	12/06	12/07	12/08	12/09
Assets ($ mil.)	7.8%	751.2	852.9	886.1	946.1	1,014.9
Net income ($ mil.)	(51.1%)	10.5	10.5	10.7	6.4	0.6
Market value ($ mil.)	(13.3%)	270.5	275.0	220.5	135.8	152.7
Employees	1.3%	211	233	224	217	222

HERITAGE FINANCIAL GROUP
NASDAQ (GM): HBOS

721 North Westover Blvd.
Albany, GA 31707
Phone: 229-420-0000
Fax: 229-878-2054
Web: www.eheritagebank.com

CEO: O. Leonard (Len) Dorminey
CFO: T. Heath Fountain
HR: —
FYE: December 31
Type: Public

Chartered in the 1950s as a credit union to serve its hometown Marine base, HeritageBank of the South has remained "always faithful" to its local customers. The flagship subsidiary of Heritage Financial Group operates some 15 branches that provide traditional deposit and loan products and services to individuals and small to midsized businesses in southwestern Georgia and Ocala, Florida. Consumer loans and residential mortgages each account for about a quarter of the company's loan portfolio, which also includes business loans and commercial property loans. The bank also offers investment and insurance products and services. Mutual holding company Heritage MHC owns more than 70% of Heritage Financial.

	Annual Growth	12/05	12/06	12/07	12/08	12/09
Assets ($ mil.)	12.0%	363.8	413.3	468.7	502.1	571.9
Net income ($ mil.)	—	3.0	2.4	2.9	(0.3)	(1.7)
Market value ($ mil.)	(10.9%)	119.8	173.2	116.9	93.6	75.4
Employees	2.4%	122	128	125	120	134

HERITAGE OAKS BANCORP
NASDAQ (CM): HEOP

545 12th St.
Paso Robles, CA 93446
Phone: 805-239-5200
Fax: 805-238-6257
Web: www.heritageoaksbancorp.com

CEO: Lawrence P. Ward
CFO: Margaret A. Torres
HR: Joni Watson
FYE: December 31
Type: Public

Stash your acorns at Heritage Oaks Bancorp. It's the holding company for Heritage Oaks Bank, which serves retail customers, farmers, and small to midsized businesses in Central California's San Luis Obispo and Santa Barbara counties. Through about a dozen offices, the bank offers standard products such as checking, savings, and money market accounts, CDs, IRAs, and credit cards. Commercial real estate loans account for over 40% of its loan portfolio; business loans make up nearly 25%. Land loans are the third-largest segment of its portfolio. In 2007 Heritage Oaks Bancorp acquired Business First National Bank (now simply Business First), which operates as a division of Heritage Oaks Bank with two locations.

	Annual Growth	12/05	12/06	12/07	12/08	12/09
Assets ($ mil.)	17.9%	488.5	541.8	745.6	805.6	945.2
Net income ($ mil.)	—	6.6	6.7	6.9	1.6	(7.0)
Market value ($ mil.)	(28.9%)	152.0	127.4	93.4	39.1	38.9
Employees	8.7%	190	212	242	223	265

HERITAGE-CRYSTAL CLEAN, INC.
NASDAQ (GM): HCCI

2175 Point Blvd., Ste. 375
Elgin, IL 60123
Phone: 847-836-5670
Fax: 847-836-5677
Web: www.crystal-clean.com

CEO: Joseph Chalhoub
CFO: Gregory (Greg) Ray
HR: —
FYE: December 31
Type: Public

It's a dirty job, but somebody's gotta do it . . . and that "somebody" might be Heritage-Crystal Clean. The company helps US businesses clean parts and dispose of highly-regulated waste materials, such as cleaning solvents, used oil, and paint, that can't be discarded through municipal trash systems or standard drains. Customers are primarily small to midsized companies and include car dealerships, auto repair shops, trucking firms, and manufacturers, such as metal fabricators. Heritage-Crystal Clean regularly services more than 40,000 client sites from some 50 branches in nearly 40 states. President and CEO Joseph Chalhoub founded Heritage-Crystal Clean in 1999.

	Annual Growth	12/05	12/06	12/07	12/08	12/09
Sales ($ mil.)	13.5%	59.2	73.7	89.7	108.1	98.4
Net income ($ mil.)	(2.6%)	2.0	4.3	7.1	(0.8)	1.8
Market value ($ mil.)	(9.8%)	—	—	—	124.3	112.1
Employees	6.8%	—	423	465	525	516

HERLEY INDUSTRIES, INC.
NASDAQ (GM): HRLY

3061 Industry Dr., Ste. 200
Lancaster, PA 17603
Phone: 717-397-2777
Fax: 717-397-9503
Web: www.herley.com

CEO: Richard F. (Rich) Poirier
CFO: Anello C. (Neil) Garefino
HR: John A. Carroll
FYE: July 31
Type: Public

Herley Industries makes microwave products for aerospace, commercial, and military customers. Aerospace and military offerings include flight instruments, navigation system components, missile guidance systems, unmanned vehicle command-and-control systems, and flight-termination receivers (used to trigger explosives to destroy a craft if something goes wrong). The company sells its products to military agencies and contractors. Herley's commercial products include amplifiers for nuclear magnetic resonance systems (used by researchers and scientists) and amplifiers and components used in medical magnetic resonance imaging (MRI) systems. Most sales are in the US.

	Annual Growth	7/05	7/06	7/07	7/08	7/09
Sales ($ mil.)	1.4%	151.4	176.3	163.1	152.5	160.1
Net income ($ mil.)	—	10.8	10.4	3.1	(10.3)	(41.2)
Market value ($ mil.)	(11.1%)	267.4	146.8	194.4	217.0	166.7
Employees	(0.1%)	1,026	1,014	926	903	1,022

An in-depth profile of this company is available to Hoover's Online members at hoovers.com.

HERMAN MILLER, INC.

NASDAQ (GS): MLHR

855 E. Main Ave.
Zeeland, MI 49464
Phone: 616-654-3000
Fax: 616-654-5234
Web: www.hermanmiller.com

CEO: Brian C. Walker
CFO: Gregory J. (Greg) Bylsma
HR: Andrew J. (Andy) Lock
FYE: May 31
Type: Public

Desk jockeys can ride Herman Miller's products all the way up the corporate ladder and home again. A top US maker of office furniture, it's known for developing designs for corporate, government, home office, leisure, and health care environments. Herman Miller's products include ergonomic devices, filing and storage systems, free-standing furniture, lighting, seating, textiles, and wooden casegoods. It makes products in the UK and the US and sells them worldwide through its sales staff and dealer network, as well as through independent dealers and the Internet. Columbia Wanger Asset Management and Ariel Capital Management each own about a 10% stake in the firm.

	Annual Growth	5/05	5/06	5/07	5/08	5/09
Sales ($ mil.)	1.8%	1,515.6	1,737.2	1,918.9	2,012.1	1,630.0
Net income ($ mil.)	0.0%	68.0	99.2	129.1	152.3	68.0
Market value ($ mil.)	(16.4%)	1,658.1	1,664.3	2,050.5	1,412.6	810.5
Employees	(4.3%)	6,234	6,242	6,574	6,478	5,229

HERR FOODS INC.

20 Herr Dr.
Nottingham, PA 19362
Phone: 610-932-9330
Fax: 610-932-2137
Web: www.herrs.com

CEO: James M. Herr
CFO: Edwin H. (Ed) Herr
HR: Richard White
FYE: August 31
Type: Private

Herr Foods is your best friend when you've got a case of the munchies. The snack food manufacturer, in business since 1946, makes about 340 different kinds of snack foods (all sold under the Herr's brand name) including potato chips, pretzels, tortilla chips, cheese curls, corn chips, pita chips, popcorn, crackers, nuts, pork rinds, onion rings, and meat sticks. The company distributes its food items to retail food outlets in the US (primarily east of the Mississippi River), as well as in Canada. Herr Foods is run by chairman and CEO James M. Herr, son of company founder, James Stauffer Herr.

HERSHA HOSPITALITY TRUST

NYSE: HT

44 Hersha Dr.
Harrisburg, PA 17102
Phone: 717-236-4400
Fax: 717-774-7383
Web: www.hersha.com

CEO: Jay H. Shah
CFO: Ashish R. Parikh
HR: —
FYE: December 31
Type: Public

Hersha Hospitality Trust's fortune is in hotels, not chocolate. The self-advised real estate investment trust (REIT) invests in hotel properties, primarily midscale, upscale, and extended-stay properties in metropolitan markets. It owns or co-owns about 70 hotels containing a total of more than 9,200 rooms, most of them in the Northeast, from Boston to Washington, DC, and in the western US. The properties are operated under such brand names as Courtyard by Marriott, Hampton Inn, Holiday Inn Express, Residence Inn, and Hyatt Summerfield Suites. Hersha Hospitality Trust leases its wholly owned hotels to subsidiary 44 New England Management Company.

	Annual Growth	12/05	12/06	12/07	12/08	12/09
Sales ($ mil.)	28.5%	80.9	147.9	242.1	264.8	220.5
Net income ($ mil.)	—	3.3	5.1	17.8	(8.8)	(58.5)
Market value ($ mil.)	(23.2%)	1,246.4	1,568.7	1,314.2	415.0	434.4
Employees	16.6%	13	21	20	24	24

THE HERSHEY COMPANY

NYSE: HSY

100 Crystal A Dr.
Hershey, PA 17033
Phone: 717-534-4200
Fax: —
Web: www.thehersheycompany.com

CEO: David J. (Dave) West
CFO: Humberto P. (Bert) Alfonso
HR: Charlene H. Binder
FYE: December 31
Type: Public

The Hershey Company will cover you in Kisses and bring you Almond Joy. The company makes such well-known chocolate and candy brands as Hershey's Kisses, Reese's peanut butter cups, Swizzles licorice, Mounds, York Peppermint Patty, and Kit Kat (licensed from Nestlé). Hershey also makes grocery goods such as baking chocolate, ice-cream toppings, chocolate syrup, cocoa mix, cookies, snack nuts, hard candies, and lollipops. Its products are sold throughout North America and exported overseas. The Hershey Trust — which benefits the Milton Hershey School for disadvantaged children — controls 80% of Hershey's voting power.

	Annual Growth	12/05	12/06	12/07	12/08	12/09
Sales ($ mil.)	2.3%	4,836.0	4,944.2	4,946.7	5,132.8	5,298.7
Net income ($ mil.)	(3.0%)	493.2	559.1	214.2	311.4	436.0
Market value ($ mil.)	(10.3%)	12,554.7	11,316.3	8,953.0	7,894.1	8,132.7
Employees	(0.1%)	13,750	15,000	12,800	14,400	13,700

HERSHEY ENTERTAINMENT & RESORTS COMPANY

27 W. Chocolate Ave.
Hershey, PA 17033
Phone: 717-534-3131
Fax: 717-534-3887
Web: www.hersheypark.com

CEO: Theodore J. (Ted) Kleisner
CFO: Dave Lavery
HR: —
FYE: December 31
Type: Private

Life is sweet for Hershey Entertainment & Resorts. The company owns the many chocolate-related entertainment destinations in Hershey, Pennsylvania. Its holdings include Hersheypark, one of the US's top amusement parks with more than 60 rides and attractions; Hersheypark Arena; ZooAmerica wildlife park; the Hotel Hershey; and the Hershey Lodge. Hershey Entertainment's other holdings include the Giant Center arena in Hershey, as well as the Dutch Wonderland Family Amusement Park in nearby Lancaster. The company is fully owned by the Hershey Trust, which controls a majority voting stake in candy firm Hershey Foods. The Hershey Trust also acts as trustee for the Milton Hershey School.

	Annual Growth	12/04	12/05	12/06	12/07	12/08
Est. sales ($ mil.)	—	—	—	—	—	274.0
Employees	—	—	—	—	—	7,100

HERTZ GLOBAL HOLDINGS, INC.

NYSE: HTZ

225 Brae Blvd.
Park Ridge, NJ 07656
Phone: 201-307-2000
Fax: 201-307-2644
Web: www.hertz.com

CEO: Mark P. Frissora
CFO: Elyse Douglas
HR: LeighAnne G. Baker
FYE: December 31
Type: Public

If you've ever said, "Don't worry about it, it's just a rental," guess who hurts: Hertz, a world leader in car rental. On its own and through agents and licensees, Hertz operates some 8,100 rental locations in more than 145 countries worldwide, including about 500 at US airports. Its fleet includes approximately 444,000 cars from Ford, General Motors, Toyota, and other manufacturers. Car rental accounts for more than 80% of its sales. Hertz also rents a variety of heavy equipment through 322 locations in North America, Europe, and China. In 2010 Hertz agreed to acquire Dollar Thrifty Automotive Group.

	Annual Growth	12/05	12/06	12/07	12/08	12/09
Sales ($ mil.)	(1.3%)	7,469.2	8,058.4	8,685.6	8,525.1	7,101.5
Net income ($ mil.)	—	350.0	115.9	264.6	(1,206.7)	(126.0)
Market value ($ mil.)	(11.8%)	—	7,159.8	6,542.3	2,087.4	4,907.7
Employees	(8.0%)	32,200	31,500	29,350	24,900	23,050

HESKA CORPORATION

NASDAQ (CM): HSKA

3760 Rocky Mountain Ave.
Loveland, CO 80538
Phone: 970-493-7272
Fax: 970-619-3003
Web: www.heska.com

CEO: Robert B. Grieve
CFO: Jason A. Napolitano
HR: Mark D. Cicotello
FYE: December 31
Type: Public

If you lie down with dogs, Heska makes sure you don't get up with fleas. The company makes diagnostic products, vaccines, and pharmaceuticals for domestic animals, primarily cats and dogs. Products on the market and in development include diagnostics and treatments for allergies, arthritis, cancer, fleas, heartworms, skin problems, thyroid problems, and viral infections. The company also operates a diagnostic lab and makes veterinary diagnostic and monitoring devices. Subsidiary Diamond Animal Health manufactures vaccines for cattle, small mammals, and fish. Heska's products are sold worldwide through direct representatives and independent distributors.

	Annual Growth	12/05	12/06	12/07	12/08	12/09
Sales ($ mil.)	2.2%	69.4	75.1	82.3	81.7	75.7
Net income ($ mil.)	64.6%	0.3	1.8	34.8	(0.9)	2.2
Market value ($ mil.)	(20.5%)	68.9	87.6	95.5	13.0	27.5
Employees	(0.9%)	286	299	311	312	276

HESS CORPORATION

NYSE: HES

1185 Avenue of the Americas
New York, NY 10036
Phone: 212-997-8500
Fax: 212-536-8593
Web: www.hess.com

CEO: John B. Hess
CFO: John P. Rielly
HR: —
FYE: December 31
Type: Public

Hess Corporation (formerly Amerada Hess) has what it takes. The integrated oil and gas company conducts exploration and production primarily in Algeria, Australia, Azerbaijan, Brazil, Denmark, Egypt, Equatorial Guinea, Gabon, Ghana, Indonesia, Libya, Malaysia, Norway, Peru, Russia, Thailand, the UK, and the US. In 2009 Hess reported proved reserves totaling more than 1.4 billion barrels of oil equivalent. It operates a 50%-owned refinery (HOVENSA) in the US Virgin Islands and a smaller one in New Jersey, and it markets gasoline through about 1,360 HESS gas stations in 16 US states, chiefly in the eastern US. It also provides power to customers in the Northeast and Mid-Atlantic.

	Annual Growth	12/05	12/06	12/07	12/08	12/09
Sales ($ mil.)	6.2%	23,255.0	28,067.0	31,647.0	41,165.0	29,569.0
Net income ($ mil.)	(12.1%)	1,242.0	1,916.0	1,832.0	2,360.0	740.0
Market value ($ mil.)	9.4%	13,880.0	16,275.8	33,116.3	17,612.1	19,864.5
Employees	3.5%	11,610	13,700	13,300	13,500	13,300

HEWITT ASSOCIATES, INC.

NYSE: HEW

100 Half Day Rd.
Lincolnshire, IL 60069
Phone: 847-295-5000
Fax: 847-295-7634
Web: www.hewittassociates.com

CEO: Russell P. (Russ) Fradin
CFO: Robert A. (Rob) Schriesheim
HR: Andres Tapia
FYE: September 30
Type: Public

If any of a company's resources are human, chances are it'll need the assistance of Hewitt Associates. As one of the primary leaders in its industry, the company provides a variety of HR-related services including payroll, organizational change management, talent and reward consulting, and the largest portion of the company's business — benefits outsourcing. Hewitt Associates administers medical, 401(k), and pension plans on an outsourced basis for larger companies with complex benefit programs. The company also provides consulting for the design, implementation, and operation of many of the same human resources programs. Hewitt Associates was founded by Ted Hewitt in 1940 and has about 105 offices worldwide.

	Annual Growth	9/05	9/06	9/07	9/08	9/09
Sales ($ mil.)	1.5%	2,898.4	2,857.2	2,990.3	3,227.6	3,073.6
Net income ($ mil.)	18.4%	134.7	(115.9)	(175.1)	188.1	265.1
Market value ($ mil.)	7.5%	2,538.8	2,257.7	3,261.9	3,391.2	3,390.3
Employees	1.1%	22,000	24,000	23,000	23,000	23,000

HEWLETT-PACKARD COMPANY

NYSE: HPQ

3000 Hanover St.
Palo Alto, CA 94304
Phone: 650-857-1501
Fax: 650-857-5518
Web: www.hp.com

CEO: Mark V. Hurd
CFO: Catherine A. (Cathie) Lesjak
HR: Marcela Perez de Alonso
FYE: October 31
Type: Public

HP wants to be "it" when it comes to IT. Hewlett-Packard provides one of the tech world's most comprehensive portfolios of hardware, software, and services. Its products include PCs, servers, storage devices, printers, and networking equipment. The company's services unit provides IT and business process outsourcing, application development and management, consulting, systems integration, and other technology services. HP's software products include enterprise IT management, information management, business intelligence, and carrier-grade communications applications. The company markets to consumers, businesses, government agencies, and schools in more than 170 countries.

	Annual Growth	10/05	10/06	10/07	10/08	10/09
Sales ($ mil.)	7.2%	86,696.0	91,658.0	104,286.0	118,364.0	114,552.0
Net income ($ mil.)	33.7%	2,398.0	6,198.0	7,264.0	8,329.0	7,660.0
Market value ($ mil.)	14.1%	65,756.4	90,848.9	121,194.4	89,770.2	111,298.1
Employees	19.3%	150,000	156,000	172,000	321,000	304,000

HEXCEL CORPORATION

NYSE: HXL

281 Tresser Blvd., 2 Stamford Plaza, 16th Fl.
Stamford, CT 06901
Phone: 203-969-0666
Fax: 203-358-3977
Web: www.hexcel.com

CEO: David E. Berges
CFO: Wayne C. Pensky
HR: Robert G. Hennemuth
FYE: December 31
Type: Public

The first footprints on the moon didn't come from Neil Armstrong, but from Hexcel, a maker of composite materials. Back then Hexcel made the footpads on the Apollo 11 lunar module; today the company makes advanced structural materials used in everything from aircraft components to wind turbine blades. Its composite materials include structural adhesives and honeycomb panels used in products like satellites, auto parts, golf clubs, and even window blinds. Commercial aerospace companies account for half of Hexcel's sales; military and other governmental space and defense sales add up to almost 30%. Markets for Hexcel industrial products include wind energy, recreational equipment, and transportation.

	Annual Growth	12/05	12/06	12/07	12/08	12/09
Sales ($ mil.)	(1.2%)	1,161.4	1,193.1	1,171.1	1,324.9	1,108.3
Net income ($ mil.)	(20.6%)	141.3	65.9	61.3	111.2	56.3
Market value ($ mil.)	(7.9%)	1,751.4	1,689.3	2,355.9	717.1	1,259.5
Employees	(4.3%)	4,460	4,459	4,081	4,275	3,734

HEXION SPECIALTY CHEMICALS, INC.

180 E. Broad St.
Columbus, OH 43215
Phone: 614-225-4000
Fax: —
Web: www.hexionchem.com

CEO: Craig O. Morrison
CFO: William H. (Bill) Carter
HR: Judith A. (Judy) Sonnett
FYE: December 31
Type: Private

Hexion Specialty Chemicals is the world's largest thermosetting resins (or thermosets) maker, ahead of competitor Georgia-Pacific. Thermosets add a desired quality (heat resistance, gloss, adhesion, etc.) to a number of different paints and adhesives. Hexion also is among the largest makers of formaldehyde and other forest product resins, epoxy resins, and raw materials for coatings and inks. The company has four operating divisions, including Epoxy and Phenolic Resins, Formaldehyde and Forest Products Resins, Coatings and Inks, and Performance Products. Apollo Management controls more than 90% of Hexion.

	Annual Growth	12/04	12/05	12/06	12/07	12/08
Sales ($ mil.)	31.8%	2,019.0	4,470.0	5,205.0	5,810.0	6,093.0
Net income ($ mil.)	—	(114.0)	(87.0)	(109.0)	(65.0)	(1,190.0)
Employees	(0.4%)	6,900	7,000	6,900	6,400	6,800

An in-depth profile of this company is available to Hoover's Online members at hoovers.com.

757

HF FINANCIAL CORP.

NASDAQ (GM): HFFC

225 S. Main Ave.
Sioux Falls, SD 57104
Phone: 605-333-7556
Fax: 605-333-7621
Web: www.homefederal.com

CEO: Curtis L. Hage
CFO: Darrel L. Posegate
HR: Mary F. Hitzemann
FYE: June 30
Type: Public

Those in South Dakota who want their finances to go north might turn to HF Financial. It's the holding company for Home Federal Bank, which serves consumers and businesses through more than 30 branches in eastern and central South Dakota and a single branch in southwestern Minnesota. Deposit products include checking and savings accounts and CDs. Commercial mortgages and loans account for about 40% of HF Financial's loan portfolio. Residential, multifamily, and agricultural real estate loans account for another 30% of loans. Bank subsidiary Hometown Insurors sells insurance and annuities; Mid America Capital provides equipment financing. Home Federal Bank was founded in 1929.

	Annual Growth	6/05	6/06	6/07	6/08	6/09
Assets ($ mil.)	7.0%	897.9	961.3	1,001.5	1,103.5	1,176.8
Net income ($ mil.)	10.7%	5.2	4.5	5.4	5.8	7.8
Market value ($ mil.)	(12.2%)	137.8	118.6	121.6	113.1	82.0
Employees	1.1%	309	312	315	307	323

HFF, INC.

NYSE: HF

One Oxford Centre, 301 Grant St., Ste. 600
Pittsburgh, PA 15219
Phone: 412-281-8714
Fax: 412-281-2792
Web: www.hfflp.com

CEO: John H. Pelusi Jr.
CFO: Gregory R. Conley
HR: —
FYE: December 31
Type: Public

Don't huff and puff — HFF will help you finance that high-rise! HFF, also known as Holliday Fenoglio Fowler, provides capital markets services including lending and transaction brokerage, loan servicing, investment sales, and debt placement. Subsidiary HFF Securities provides advisory services, seeks private and joint venture equity capital, places private listings, and provides institutional marketing for commercial property investments. The company operates about 20 offices throughout the US. CEO John Pelusi controls HFF through majority-owner HFF Holdings.

	Annual Growth	12/05	12/06	12/07	12/08	12/09
Sales ($ mil.)	(21.7%)	205.8	229.7	255.7	131.7	77.5
Net income ($ mil.)	—	46.8	49.7	12.5	0.2	(0.8)
Market value ($ mil.)	(10.1%)	—	—	148.7	47.1	120.1
Employees	1.4%	355	400	130	433	376

H.H. BROWN SHOE COMPANY, INC.

124 W. Putnam Ave.
Greenwich, CT 06830
Phone: 203-661-2424
Fax: —
Web: www.hhbrown.com

CEO: James E. (Jim) Issler
CFO: Scott Bohling
HR: —
FYE: December 31
Type: Subsidiary

This Brown is no Buster, but it does make shoes. H.H. Brown manufactures and distributes casual, work, and dress shoes and boots under more than a dozen brands, including Bøc, Børn, Brunswick, Carolina, Corcoran, Dexter, Double-H, Kork-Ease, Matterhorn, Nurse Mates, Söfft, and Softspots. Founded in 1883, H.H. Brown is named after Massachusetts shoemaker Henry H. Brown and is a subsidiary of Berkshire Hathaway. The company owns and sells through two websites (shoeline.com and supershoes.com); more than 50 of its own H.H. Brown SuperShoes stores; and retailers such as Bergdorf Goodman, Macy's, Neiman Marcus, Payless ShoeSource, and REI.

HHGREGG, INC.

NYSE: HGG

4151 E. 96th St.
Indianapolis, IN 46240
Phone: 317-848-8710
Fax: 317-848-8723
Web: www.hhgregg.com

CEO: Dennis L. May
CFO: Jeremy J. Aguilar
HR: Charles B. Young
FYE: March 31
Type: Public

hhgregg has evolved from black-and-white to digital. The appliance and electronics retailer began as a small storefront selling washing machines, refrigerators, and black-and-white TVs. Today the fast-growing firm sells name-brand products at about 125 hhgregg and Fine Lines stores in about 10 mostly southern states and online. Its offerings include TV and video products (LED TVs, Blu-ray disc players) as well as home and car audio (CD players, home theater systems), appliances (air conditioners, refrigerators, washers and dryers), notebook computers, gaming consoles, digital cameras, GPS navigators, and even mattresses. Founded in 1955, hhgregg went public in 2007.

	Annual Growth	3/06	3/07	3/08	3/09	3/10
Sales ($ mil.)	14.3%	900.4	1,059.4	1,256.7	1,396.7	1,534.3
Net income ($ mil.)	15.3%	22.2	21.4	21.4	36.5	39.2
Market value ($ mil.)	49.8%	—	—	434.2	546.1	974.1
Employees	11.5%	3,171	3,171	3,808	3,500	4,900

HIBBETT SPORTS, INC.

NASDAQ (GS): HIBB

451 Industrial Ln.
Birmingham, AL 35211
Phone: 205-942-4292
Fax: 205-912-7290
Web: www.hibbett.com

CEO: Jeffry O. Rosenthal
CFO: Gary A. Smith
HR: M. Scott Myers
FYE: January 31
Type: Public

Small-town southern sports fans are the bread and butter for Hibbett Sports. The company sells sports equipment, athletic apparel, and footwear in small to midsized markets in more than 20 states, mainly in the Southeast. Its flagship Hibbett Sports chain is composed of more than 745 locations, and stores are primarily found in malls and strip centers anchored by a Wal-Mart. Hibbett also operates four Sports & Co. superstores, which are larger format and feature in-store putting greens, basketball hoops, and appearances by athletes. On a smaller scale, it runs about 15 mall-based Sports Additions shoe shops, most of which are situated near Hibbett Sports stores. The company also operates an e-commerce site.

	Annual Growth	1/06	1/07	1/08	1/09	1/10
Sales ($ mil.)	7.8%	440.3	512.1	520.7	564.2	593.5
Net income ($ mil.)	(0.8%)	33.6	38.1	30.3	29.4	32.5
Market value ($ mil.)	(8.8%)	881.1	923.0	534.4	391.2	610.0
Employees	7.0%	4,500	5,200	5,400	5,500	5,900

HICKOK INCORPORATED

OTC: HICKA

10514 Dupont Ave.
Cleveland, OH 44108
Phone: 216-541-8060
Fax: 216-761-9879
Web: www.hickok-inc.com

CEO: Robert L. Bauman
CFO: Gregory M. Zoloty
HR: Carmelita Gerome
FYE: September 30
Type: Public

Like "Wild Bill" of Wild West lore, Hickok is quite comfortable shooting it out with competitors on its own measured road to success. The company manufactures testing equipment used by automotive technicians to repair cars. Hickok also makes instruments, indicators, and gauges for manufacturers of aircraft and locomotives. While Ford and General Motors traditionally were the company's largest customers, its biggest customer now is Environmental Systems Products (ESP), at 53% of sales. Hickok sells products primarily in the US. President and CEO Robert Bauman and the three daughters of founder Robert D. Hickok, including chairman Janet Slade, control the company.

	Annual Growth	9/05	9/06	9/07	9/08	9/09
Sales ($ mil.)	(10.9%)	9.7	15.9	12.5	12.1	6.1
Net income ($ mil.)	—	(1.6)	0.8	(0.6)	(0.8)	(3.7)
Market value ($ mil.)	1.1%	6.0	7.4	15.9	11.2	6.3
Employees	(13.8%)	147	145	160	118	81

An in-depth profile of this company is available to Hoover's Online members at hoovers.com.

HICKORY FARMS, INC.

1505 Holland Rd.
Maumee, OH 43537
Phone: 419-893-7611
Fax: 419-893-0164
Web: www.hickoryfarms.com

CEO: Mark S. Rodriguez
CFO: Marc Mucci
HR: —
FYE: January 31
Type: Private

Before your relationship goes to hell in a *gift* basket, try delighting your honey with a ham from Hickory Farms. The gift-food company sells high-end beef and cheese, chocolates, desserts, fresh fruits and nuts, seafood, and other delectables. Prices range from about $10 to more than $200. Gift-givers may order through catalogs and the company's website. In addition, Hickory Farms sells direct through about 700 shopping-mall kiosks during the holiday season, and it retails at discount merchandisers and grocers (such as Target and Safeway). Founded in 1951, Hickory Farms is owned by private investment firm Sun Capital Partners.

HICKORY TECH CORPORATION

NASDAQ (GS): HTCO

221 E. Hickory St.
Mankato, MN 56002
Phone: 507-387-3355
Fax: 507-625-9191
Web: www.hickorytech.com

CEO: John W. Finke
CFO: David A. Christensen
HR: Mary T. Jacobs
FYE: December 31
Type: Public

Its name sounds like a Division II college, but Hickory Tech's field of play is telecommunications. Hickory Tech operates two business segments: Telecom and Enventis (Internet protocol-based voice and data services). Through its subsidiaries, the company provides 55,000 residential and business customers with access lines in Iowa and Minnesota. It also offers long-distance services to 36,000 customers, broadband Internet access services to 19,000 customers, and digital television service to about 10,000 customers. Its National Independent Billing unit, which is part of the Telecom segment, provides data processing services to other telecommunications companies.

	Annual Growth	12/05	12/06	12/07	12/08	12/09
Sales ($ mil.)	10.7%	92.5	132.9	156.6	153.2	139.1
Net income ($ mil.)	7.4%	8.5	2.3	8.6	8.0	11.3
Market value ($ mil.)	2.9%	104.4	94.7	123.4	72.0	116.9
Employees	(0.7%)	460	400	400	433	448

HICKS SPORTS GROUP HOLDINGS LLC

1000 Ballpark Way, Ste. 400
Arlington, TX 76011
Phone: 817-273-5222
Fax: 817-273-5174
Web: www.hickssportsgroup.com

CEO: Thomas O. (Tom) Hicks
CFO: Robert Hutson
HR: —
FYE: December 31
Type: Holding company

Football might reign supreme in Texas, but there's plenty of other Lone Star state sports teams to go around. Hicks Sports Group Holdings is the holding company formed by Texas billionaire Thomas Hicks to oversee his interests in the Texas Rangers professional baseball team (which it is selling) and the Dallas Stars hockey team. The company also owns a 50% stake in Center Operating Company, a joint venture with Dallas Mavericks owner Mark Cuban that runs the American Airlines Center in Dallas. Other interests include a chain of ice-skating rinks operating under the Dr. Pepper StarCenter name, real estate developments, and Hicks Sports Marketing.

	Annual Growth	12/04	12/05	12/06	12/07	12/08
Est. sales ($ mil.)	—	—	—	—	—	13.1
Employees	—	—	—	—	—	370

HID GLOBAL CORPORATION

15370 Barranca Pkwy.
Irvine, CA 92618
Phone: 949-732-2000
Fax: 949-732-2120
Web: www.hidcorp.com

CEO: Denis Hébert
CFO: Will West
HR: Michelle DeWitt
FYE: December 31
Type: Subsidiary

HID Global Corporation doesn't have to keep things hidden — instead it keeps things under restricted access. The company makes contactless cards and readers for access control systems. HID uses radio-frequency identification (RFID) technology in electronic locks, alarms, biometric devices, and other systems that use encrypted access control. HID Global also makes parking area and vehicle access control systems. Its card and reader technologies are also used for network log-on security and biometric verification. With locations worldwide, the company serves retail, industrial, commercial, governmental, and institutional customers. HID is a subsidiary of the world's largest lock maker, Sweden's ASSA ABLOY.

H.I.G. CAPITAL MANAGEMENT INC.

1001 Brickell Bay Dr., Fl. 27
Miami, FL 33131
Phone: 305-379-2322
Fax: 305-379-2013
Web: www.higcapital.com

CEO: Sami W. Mnaymneh
CFO: —
HR: —
FYE: December 31
Type: Private

H.I.G. Capital keeps an eye out for good deals. The investment firm specializes in management buyouts or recapitalizations, with a focus on small and mid-sized companies in the US and Europe. An active investor with around $7.5 billion capital under management, the company typically works alongside management of its portfolio companies, which represent a wide range of industries. Other operations include distressed debt financing through Bayside Capital and stock investments through Brightpoint Capital. Its H.I.G. Ventures division funds information technology, life sciences, service industry startups, while Cronus Capital invests in US real estate.

HIGH END SYSTEMS, INC.

2105 Gracy Farms Ln.
Austin, TX 78758
Phone: 512-836-2242
Fax: 512-837-5290
Web: www.highend.com

CEO: Merritt Belisle
CFO: —
HR: Becky Koester
FYE: June 30
Type: Subsidiary

There's nothing low end about this company's light. High End Systems makes and markets lights and lighting systems for television and stage productions, as well as for restaurants, shopping malls, cruise ships, trade shows, theme parks, and churches. The company offers digital lighting, automated luminaries, lighting consoles, and effects such as fog and optical design. High End has worked on events such as concerts from Ani di Franco and ZZ Top, Super Bowl half-time shows, and the Olympic ceremonies. Headquartered in Austin, Texas, the company has additional offices in Los Angeles and London. High End Systems is a subsidiary of Barco nv, a designer and developer of visualization products.

An in-depth profile of this company is available to Hoover's Online members at hoovers.com.

759

HIGH INDUSTRIES, INC.

1853 William Penn Way
Lancaster, PA 17605
Phone: 717-293-4444
Fax: 717-293-4416
Web: www.high.net

CEO: Jeffrey D. Smith
CFO: Michael W. Van Belle
HR: Larry Brown
FYE: December 31
Type: Private

High Industries is at the top of its game, and that game is steel and construction. The company's largest division, High Steel Structures, is one of the largest steel bridge fabricators in North America. Other members of the High Industries' stable of companies include High Steel Service Center (metal processing and distribution), High Concrete Group (precast concrete components), and High Safety Consulting Services (air quality and safety). Affiliates of High Industries, such as High Hotels, are active in the real estate business. High Industries, which mostly does business along the East Coast, traces its roots to a welding shop founded by Sanford High in 1931. The company is controlled by the High family.

	Annual Growth	12/04	12/05	12/06	12/07	12/08
Sales ($ mil.)	—	—	—	—	—	429.5
Employees	—	—	—	—	—	2,479

HIGHMARK INC.

Fifth Avenue Place, 120 5th Ave.
Pittsburgh, PA 15222
Phone: 412-544-7000
Fax: 412-544-8368
Web: www.highmark.com/hmk2

CEO: Kenneth R. (Ken) Melani
CFO: Nanette P. (Nan) DeTurk
HR: —
FYE: December 31
Type: Not-for-profit

Highmark has staked its claim as the largest health insurer in the Keystone state. A licensee of the Blue Cross and Blue Shield Association, the not-for-profit firm covers some 4 million people in central and western Pennsylvania, as well as the Lehigh Valley. It serves another 800,000 customers in West Virginia and other areas of Pennsylvania through affiliations and partnerships with other insurers, and it provides administrative and network-access services nationally. In addition, Highmark sells Medicare Advantage and prescription drug plans to seniors in both states. Other subsidiaries (not operating under the BCBS license) provide dental insurance, vision care, and other products and services nationwide.

	Annual Growth	12/04	12/05	12/06	12/07	12/08
Sales ($ mil.)	9.3%	9,118.4	9,847.3	11,083.8	12,352.6	13,002.0
Net income ($ mil.)	(25.8%)	310.5	341.6	398.3	375.4	94.1
Employees	14.6%	11,000	12,000	18,500	18,500	19,000

HIGHWOODS PROPERTIES, INC.

NYSE: HIW

3100 Smoketree Ct., Ste. 600
Raleigh, NC 27604
Phone: 919-872-4924
Fax: —
Web: www.highwoods.com

CEO: Edward J. (Ed) Fritsch
CFO: Terry L. Stevens
HR: Bob Albert
FYE: December 31
Type: Public

When it comes to office space, Highwoods Properties takes the road most traveled, especially if it runs through the Southeast. A self-administered real estate investment trust (REIT), Highwoods Properties owns and manages commercial property. Its holdings include suburban office, industrial, and retail properties, focused on about a dozen core markets from Florida to the Midwest. The REIT, which was founded in 1978, owns or partially owns some 380 commercial properties (some 35 million sq. ft.). The company's stronghold is office properties, which bring in more than 80% of its revenues. Highwoods also has residential apartment holdings and owns 580 acres of undeveloped land.

	Annual Growth	12/05	12/06	12/07	12/08	12/09
Sales ($ mil.)	2.5%	410.7	416.8	437.1	461.0	454.0
Net income ($ mil.)	(0.3%)	62.5	53.7	90.7	32.0	61.7
Market value ($ mil.)	4.1%	2,036.8	2,918.1	2,103.4	1,958.8	2,387.6
Employees	(4.7%)	494	476	461	437	407

HIL TECHNOLOGY INC.

94 Hutchins Dr.
Portland, ME 04102
Phone: 207-756-6200
Fax: 207-756-6212
Web: www.hydro-international.biz/us/index_us.php

CEO: Stephen P. Hides
CFO: Brian Harrell
HR: —
FYE: December 31
Type: Subsidiary

Understanding HIL Technology is similar to drinking out of a fire hydrant. A US subsidiary of UK-based Hydro International, HIL makes and distributes stormwater management, and water and wastewater treatment equipment. Its stormwater products control and treat runoff, managing quantity and rate of flow of excess rainwater, remove sand and grit, and collect and filter water, largely for existing urban sites, and new commercial and residential projects. Water and wastewater products treat water and wastewater at municipal sewage and drinking water plants, and industrial discharge. HIL also offers rainwater harvesting systems to capture runoff for re-use. The company operates under the Hydro International name.

	Annual Growth	12/04	12/05	12/06	12/07	12/08
Est. sales ($ mil.)	—	—	—	—	—	10.9
Employees	—	—	—	—	—	40

HILAND DAIRY FOODS COMPANY, LLC

1133 E. Kearney St.
Springfield, MO 65803
Phone: 417-862-9311
Fax: 417-837-1106
Web: www.hilanddairy.com

CEO: Gary L. Aggus
CFO: Harold Mabus
HR: Randy Hyde
FYE: September 30
Type: Joint venture

They're all part of the herd: Hiland Dairy Foods is a joint venture between Prairie Farms Dairy and Dairy Farmers of America. Hiland's happy cows produce the raw material for butter, ice cream, fluid milk, cheese, yogurt, and other dairy products, all without artificial growth hormones. They are distributed in Arkansas, Colorado, Kansas, Missouri, Oklahoma, and Texas. The company also distributes dips, juice, and to-go dairy drinks. It features limited-run specialty items, such as peanut butter s'mores ice cream. The company, which has been in business since 1938, operates eight manufacturing plants located in Arkansas, Kansas, Missouri, Nebraska, and Oklahoma.

	Annual Growth	9/04	9/05	9/06	9/07	9/08
Est. sales ($ mil.)	—	—	—	—	—	632.5
Employees	—	—	—	—	—	1,300

HILAND PARTNERS, LP

NASDAQ (GS): HLND

205 W. Maple, Ste. 1100
Enid, OK 73701
Phone: 580-242-6040
Fax: 580-548-5188
Web: www.hilandpartners.com

CEO: Joseph L. (Joe) Griffin
CFO: Matthew S. (Matt) Harrison
HR: Vanessa Gainer
FYE: December 31
Type: Public

Hiland Partners is looking for the higher ground of increased profits. The company was formed through the combination of Hiland Partners LLC and Continental Gas, a former subsidiary of Continental Resources. Hiland provides natural gas gathering and processing services to customers in the Mid-Continent and Rocky Mountain regions of the US through 14 gas gathering systems with 2,024 miles of pipeline, five natural gas processing plants, seven natural gas treating facilities, and three NGL fractionation plants. It also provides air compression and water injection services for oil and gas recovery operations in North Dakota. Chairman Harold Hamm owns 61% of the company, but has made a bid for total ownership.

	Annual Growth	12/04	12/05	12/06	12/07	*12/08
Sales ($ mil.)	36.8%	110.7	166.6	219.7	278.0	388.0
Net income ($ mil.)	27.2%	7.8	10.3	14.7	10.8	20.4
Market value ($ mil.)	(48.2%)	—	344.6	512.0	473.2	48.0
Employees	24.1%	51	67	95	108	121

*Most recent year available

An in-depth profile of this company is available to Hoover's Online members at hoovers.com.

HILCORP ENERGY COMPANY

1201 Louisiana St., Ste. 1400
Houston, TX 77002
Phone: 713-209-2400
Fax: 713-209-2640
Web: www.hilcorp.com

CEO: Jeffrey Hildebrand
CFO: —
HR: —
FYE: —
Type: Private

"Come and listen to a story 'bout a man named Jed . . . " Ok, his name is Jeff but the story still ends with oil, black gold, Texas tea. And first thing you know, ol' Jeff's a *billion*aire. Hilcorp Energy, an oil and natural gas producer founded in 1989 by Jeffrey Hildebrand, is one of the nation's largest privately held energy companies. It employs the latest technology to extract oil and gas from mature fields that have been abandoned by other operators. The company pumps about 25 million barrels of oil and natural gas equivalent annually and has proved reserves of 120 million barrels. A former Exxon Mobil geologist, Hildebrand started the company with former partner Thomas Hook.

HILL & KNOWLTON, INC.

825 3rd Ave.
New York, NY 10022
Phone: 212-885-0300
Fax: 212-885-0570
Web: www.hillandknowlton.com

CEO: Paul Taaffe
CFO: Mark Thorne
HR: Ruth Clark
FYE: December 31
Type: Subsidiary

Public relations firm Hill & Knowlton has ridden its reputation as a straight-shooter straight to the top. The company (whose founder John W. Hill emphasized the importance of dealing honestly and openly with the press) is one of the largest PR firms in the US and a part of advertising conglomerate WPP Group. Hill & Knowlton's services range from marketing communications to corporate reputation management to political lobbying. With almost 80 offices spanning some 45 countries, it caters to the technology and health industries; clients have included Microsoft and Intel. Lobbying firm Wexler & Walker Public Policy Associates and Finnish unit Hill and Knowlton Finland Oy act as subsidiaries for Hill & Knowlton.

HILL, HOLLIDAY, CONNORS, COSMOPULOS, INC.

53 State St.
Boston, MA 02109
Phone: 617-366-4000
Fax: 617-366-8405
Web: www.hhcc.com

CEO: Michael J. (Mike) Sheehan
CFO: —
HR: James F. (Jim) French
FYE: December 31
Type: Subsidiary

These hills are alive with the sound of advertising. Hill, Holliday, Connors, Cosmopulos — which does business as Hill Holliday — is a full-service advertising agency operating through offices in Boston, New York City, and Greenville, South Carolina. It offers creative development and campaign management services along with media planning, brand promotion, direct marketing, customer relationship management, and corporate communications. In addition, the firm offers expertise in Hispanic marketing strategies. Clients have included Dunkin' Donuts, CVS, Chili's Grill & Bar, and Liberty Mutual. Founded in 1968, the agency is part of advertising services giant Interpublic Group.

HILL INTERNATIONAL, INC.

NYSE: HIL

303 Lippincott Centre
Marlton, NJ 08053
Phone: 856-810-6200
Fax: 856-810-1309
Web: www.hillintl.com

CEO: Irvin E. Richter
CFO: John Fanelli III
HR: Gregg D. Metzinger
FYE: December 31
Type: Public

Hill International, a leader in the construction advice business, is far from over the hill. The company offers project management and construction claims consulting services worldwide. It manages all aspects of the construction process, from pre-design through completion — even troubled project turnaround. Construction claims services include expert witness testimony and litigation support. The company provides its services for such clients as the Arizona Diamondbacks, Consolidated Edison, Kimpton Hotel & Restaurant Group, and Walt Disney. It also counts US government agencies and international governments among its clients. Hill International operates out of 80 offices in more than 30 countries.

	Annual Growth	12/05	12/06	12/07	12/08	12/09
Sales ($ mil.)	28.8%	—	197.5	290.3	380.5	421.8
Net income ($ mil.)	31.4%	—	8.6	14.1	17.7	19.5
Market value ($ mil.)	(4.4%)	—	288.6	572.0	284.2	251.9
Employees	18.2%	—	1,426	1,800	2,342	2,356

HILL PHOENIX, INC.

1003 Sigman Rd.
Conyers, GA 30013
Phone: 770-285-3264
Fax: 770-285-3224
Web: www.hillphoenix.com

CEO: William (Bill) Johnson
CFO: Al Alden
HR: —
FYE: December 31
Type: Subsidiary

Hill Phoenix has been keepin' it cool since 1887, when a New Jersey grocer developed the first cold case. The company engineers, manufactures, and markets industrial walk-in coolers, freezers, and refrigerated display cases. It also makes electrical distribution units featuring switchboards, load centers, and lighting control panels. Aside from the expected supermarkets, other customers of Hill Phoenix include big-box retailers, commercial and industrial refrigeration companies, and convenience stores. In 2009 the subsidiary of Dover Corporation mushroomed; Hill Phoenix acquired the assets and IP of Tyler Refrigeration, formerly a unit of Carrier Commercial Refrigeration.

HILLENBRAND, INC.

NYSE: HI

1 Batesville Blvd.
Batesville, IN 47006
Phone: 812-934-7000
Fax: 812-934-7613
Web: www.hillenbrandinc.com

CEO: Kenneth A. Camp
CFO: Cynthia L. (Cindy) Lucchese
HR: P. Douglas (Doug) Wilson
FYE: September 30
Type: Public

Hillenbrand knows a thing or two about life and death. As the holding company for Batesville Casket Company, Hillenbrand sits on top of the death care industry, supplying nearly half the coffins used in the US. Batesville makes a variety of caskets in materials ranging from wood to stainless steel. It also produces urns and other cremation products. Beyond its death care business, Hillenbrand supplies industrial manufacturing equipment through K-Tron International, which it acquired in early 2010. Hillenbrand added K-Tron to its portfolio following its spinoff from former parent Hill-Rom Holdings (formerly Hillenbrand Industries, hospital bed maker) in March 2008.

	Annual Growth	9/05	9/06	9/07	9/08	9/09
Sales ($ mil.)	(0.4%)	659.4	1,962.9	667.2	678.1	649.1
Net income ($ mil.)	(0.1%)	102.8	221.2	99.5	93.2	102.3
Market value ($ mil.)	1.0%	—	—	—	1,255.3	1,268.4
Employees	(29.6%)	—	9,300	3,380	3,400	3,250

HILLERICH & BRADSBY CO.

800 W. Main St.	CEO: John A. Hillerich IV
Louisville, KY 40202	CFO: Allan Klimusko
Phone: 502-585-5226	HR: Nancy Martin
Fax: 502-585-1179	FYE: June 30
Web: www.slugger.com	Type: Private

Hillerich & Bradsby (H&B) is batty for baseball. Maker of the venerable Louisville Slugger, the company has been a bane to pitchers for more than a century: Honus Wagner, Ty Cobb, Babe Ruth, Ted Williams, and Ken Griffey Jr. are among the tens of thousands of players who've wielded the company's baseball bats. In the 1970s and 1980s, little leaguers, softballers, and colleges began using newfangled, more durable metal bats; H&B was slow to adjust and nearly went out of business. Today metal bats are H&B's biggest moneymaker. The company also sells Bionic baseball and softball gloves, hockey equipment, and PowerBilt golf equipment. The Hillerich family and H&B employees own the company.

THE HILLMAN COMPANIES, INC.

10590 Hamilton Ave.	CEO: Max W. Hillman Jr.
Cincinnati, OH 45231	CFO: James P. Waters
Phone: 513-851-4900	HR: —
Fax: 513-851-4997	FYE: December 31
Web: www.hillmangroup.com	Type: Private

If you were to *label* it, the *key* to success — according to The Hillman Cos. — is doing things by the *numbers*. Operating through subsidiary The Hillman Group, it distributes thousands of small hardware items, such as fasteners, keys, signs, letters, numbers, and engraved tags to home centers, as well as hardware, pet, and grocery stores. Hillman sells to about 20,000 retail customers in nearly 60 countries. It also makes and markets key duplication and engraving systems. Services range from design and installation of merchandising systems to maintenance of store inventory. Customers include Wal-Mart, Home Depot, Lowe's, Sears, and PetSmart. Investment firm Oak Hill Capital Partners owns Hillman.

	Annual Growth	12/04	12/05	12/06	12/07	12/08
Sales ($ mil.)	8.2%	351.6	382.5	423.9	445.6	481.9
Net income ($ mil.)	—	(18.7)	(3.7)	(7.6)	(9.8)	(3.0)
Employees	2.7%	1,794	1,853	1,897	2,055	1,996

THE HILLMAN COMPANY

330 Grant St., Ste. 1900	CEO: Joseph Manzinger
Pittsburgh, PA 15219	CFO: Eric C. (Rick) Johnson
Phone: 412-281-2620	HR: Vicky J. Brilmyer
Fax: 412-338-3520	FYE: December 31
	Type: Private

Shhh! The Hillman Company is making money. Founded in 1951, the publicity-shy venture capital and investment firm quietly has holdings primarily in real estate, as well as in medical technology, information technology, and other high-tech enterprises. It was an early backer of investment firm Kohlberg Kravis Roberts (KKR). Billionaire philanthropist Henry Hillman (who once told *FORTUNE* magazine that "a whale is harpooned only when it spouts" when asked why he eschews interviews) stepped down as chairman of The Hillman Company in 2004, but continues to steer the firm's executive committee and charitable activities.

HILL-ROM CO., INC.

1069 State Rte. 46 East	CEO: John J. Greisch
Batesville, IN 47006	CFO: Gregory N. Miller
Phone: 812-934-7777	HR: John K. Dickey
Fax: 812-934-8189	FYE: September 30
Web: www.hill-rom.com	Type: Subsidiary

Hill-Rom's bottom line rests on hospital beds and other items for patient care and comfort. The company makes hospital beds, including beds for specific departments such as the ICU and OR, and other furnishings for patient rooms and home health use. It also provides non-invasive devices that improve circulation and treat bed sores — both problems common to those confined to their beds. Hill-Rom sells its beds worldwide through a direct sales force and distributors; much of its revenue comes through deals with group purchasing organizations and government entities. The sole operating subsidiary of Hill-Rom Holdings, Hill-Rom also rents medical equipment, such as infusion pumps and ventilators.

⊞ HILL-ROM HOLDINGS, INC.   NYSE: HRC

1069 State Rte. 46 East	CEO: John J. Greisch
Batesville, IN 47006	CFO: Gregory N. Miller
Phone: 812-934-7777	HR: John H. Dickey
Fax: 812-934-8189	FYE: September 30
Web: www.hill-rom.com/usa	Type: Public

Hill-Rom Holdings holds Hill-Rom, which, in turn, holds hospital patients safe and secure. Hill-Rom makes, sells, and rents hospital beds and other patient-room furniture and equipment, along with stretchers, surgical table accessories, and other equipment for lifting and transporting patients. The company also sells non-invasive therapeutic products and surfaces for the care of pulmonary, bariatric, and circulatory conditions and wounds. Hill-Rom also provides information technology products, namely communication and software used in health care settings. Its primary customers are acute and long-term care facilities around the world.

	Annual Growth	9/05	9/06	9/07	9/08	9/09
Sales ($ mil.)	(8.0%)	1,938.0	1,962.9	2,023.7	1,507.7	1,386.9
Net income ($ mil.)	—	(94.0)	221.2	190.6	115.8	(405.0)
Market value ($ mil.)	(3.7%)	1,596.7	1,933.7	1,867.1	1,913.1	1,374.7
Employees	(9.8%)	9,800	9,300	9,900	6,800	6,500

HILL'S PET NUTRITION, INC.

400 SW 8th St.	CEO: Neil Thompson
Topeka, KS 66603	CFO: —
Phone: 785-354-8523	HR: —
Fax: 785-368-5786	FYE: December 31
Web: www.hillspet.com	Type: Subsidiary

Hill's Pet Nutrition is barking up the right tree as one of the leading producers of premium pet food worldwide. The company's Science Diet pet food is available through pet supply stores and veterinary professionals while its Prescription Diet products are sold only through veterinarians. The firm's cat and dog foods are produced in varieties geared to a pet's dietary requirements, medical condition, and age. Hill's also makes animal treats. Its products are sold in the US, Japan, and more than 90 other countries worldwide. This subsidiary of Colgate-Palmolive was founded in 1948, after a veterinarian cooked up a special food to treat a guide dog's kidney problems.

HILLSTONE RESTAURANT GROUP, INC.

147 S. Beverly Dr.	CEO: George Williams Biel
Los Angeles, CA 90212	CFO: R. Scott Ashby
Phone: 310-385-7343	HR: Jeff Bell
Fax: 310-385-7119	FYE: December 31
Web: www.hillstone.com	Type: Private

Thanks to this company, you don't have to travel to Texas to get some Houston flavor. Hillstone Restaurant Group operates a small portfolio of about 50 upscale casual-dining restaurants, including its flagship Houston's chain. With more than 30 locations mostly in big city markets around the country, Houston's offers a menu of classic American foods, including burgers, ribs, and seafood dishes. The restaurants are distinct from one another by utilizing different exterior and interior designs. Hillstone also operates about a dozen other eateries under such names as Bandera, Café R+D, Gulfstream, and Rutherford Grill. CEO George Biel opened the first Houston's in 1977.

HILLTOP HOLDINGS INC.

NYSE: HTH

200 Crescent Ct., Ste. 1330	CEO: Jeremy B. Ford
Dallas, TX 75201	CFO: Darren Parmenter
Phone: 214-855-2177	HR: —
Fax: —	FYE: December 31
Web: www.hilltop-holdings.com	Type: Public

Manufactured housing communities by any other name are no longer called trailer parks, and Hilltop Holdings is no longer Affordable Residential Communities (ARC). In 2007 Farallon Capital Management and partners acquired the majority of Hilltop's business, which comprised 275 residential communities with more than 57,000 home sites in some two-dozen states. What's left? Hilltop Holdings is a property and casualty insurance provider that offers coverage for low-value homes through its NLASCO subsidiary. It sells its insurance through some 6,600 independent agents in more than 20 states. NLASCO operates primarily in the southern US through subsidiaries National Lloyds Insurance and American Summit Insurance.

	Annual Growth	12/05	12/06	12/07	12/08	12/09
Assets ($ mil.)	(11.9%)	1,728.5	1,542.7	1,085.5	1,048.8	1,040.8
Net income ($ mil.)	—	(184.9)	(17.4)	293.2	(22.6)	(2.1)
Market value ($ mil.)	5.1%	538.4	658.1	616.9	550.2	657.6
Employees	(38.9%)	960	901	146	135	134

HILTI, INC.

5400 S. 122nd East Ave.	CEO: Cary R. Evert
Tulsa, OK 74146	CFO: Eugene Hodel
Phone: 918-252-6000	HR: Marcus Oden
Fax: 800-879-7000	FYE: December 31
Web: www.us.hilti.com	Type: Subsidiary

Hilti makes drills that cut through brick like butta. A subsidiary of Liechtenstein-based Hilti Corporation, the company manufactures and markets tools and related items, including adhesives, blades, compressors, drills, fastening systems, foam, screws, and studs for the construction and building-maintenance industries. It operates throughout North America. For contractors who frequent big-box retailers, Hilti runs some 300 Pro Shops inside Home Depot stores. Hilti Tool Fleet Management provides maintenance, repair, and replacement services for the construction industry. As its parent invests in R&D, Hilti has been rolling out new products. In 2010 it acquired Unirac, a maker of solar-panel mounting products.

HILTON WORLDWIDE

7930 Jones Branch Dr., Ste. 1100	CEO: Christopher J. (Chris) Nassetta
McLean, VA 22102	CFO: Thomas C. (Tom) Kennedy
Phone: 703-883-1000	HR: Dottie Brienza
Fax: —	FYE: December 31
Web: www.hiltonworldwide.com	Type: Private

If you need a bed for the night, Hilton Worldwide (formerly Hilton Hotels) has a few hundred thousand of them. The company is one of the world's largest hoteliers with a lodging empire that includes about 3,500 hotels and resorts in nearly 80 countries operating under such names as Doubletree, Embassy Suites, and Hampton, as well as its flagship Hilton brand. Many of its hotels serve the mid-market segment, though its Hilton and Conrad hotels offer full-service, upscale lodging. In addition, its Homewood Suites chain offers extended-stay services. The company franchises many of its hotels; it owns the Waldorf-Astoria and the New York Hilton. Hilton is owned by private equity firm The Blackstone Group.

	Annual Growth	12/04	12/05	12/06	12/07	12/08
Est. sales ($ mil.)	(4.0%)	—	—	—	8,090.0	7,770.0
Employees	(3.7%)	—	—	—	135,000	130,000

HINES INTERESTS LIMITED PARTNERSHIP

Williams Tower, 2800 Post Oak Blvd.	CEO: Jeffery C. (Jeff) Hines
Houston, TX 77056	CFO: C. Hastings (Hasty) Johnson
Phone: 713-621-8000	HR: Stephanie Fore
Fax: 713-966-2053	FYE: December 31
Web: www.hines.com	Type: Private

Hines has many interests, but none of them involve ketchup. Hines Interests invests in, develops, renovates, manages, and finances commercial real estate including office buildings, industrial parks, medical facilities, mixed-use developments, and master-planned residential communities. Its portfolio includes more than 1,100 properties completed, under development, managed, or invested in around the world. Hines has collaborated with such world-renowned architects as I. M. Pei, Philip Johnson, and Frank Gehry. Management services include marketing, tenant relations, and contract negotiations. Chairman Gerald Hines founded the family-controlled company in 1957.

HINGHAM INSTITUTION FOR SAVINGS

NASDAQ (GM): HIFS

55 Main St.	CEO: Robert H. Gaughen Jr.
Hingham, MA 02043	CFO: Deborah J. Jackson
Phone: 781-749-2200	HR: —
Fax: 781-749-7835	FYE: December 31
Web: www.hinghamsavings.com	Type: Public

The Hingham Institution for Savings is a haven for wayward cash. The company has about 10 branches in Boston's south shore communities, operating in Boston, Cohasset, Hingham, Hull, Norwell, Scituate, South Hingham, and South Weymouth, Massachusetts. Founded in 1834, the bank offers traditional deposit products such as checking and savings accounts, NOW accounts, IRAs, and certificates of deposit. Its loan portfolio is roughly split between commercial mortgages and residential mortgages (including home equity loans). To a far lesser extent, the bank also originates construction, business, and consumer loans.

	Annual Growth	12/05	12/06	12/07	12/08	12/09
Assets ($ mil.)	10.2%	628.3	691.7	744.6	806.2	925.6
Net income ($ mil.)	6.6%	6.2	4.6	4.5	6.3	8.0
Market value ($ mil.)	(5.7%)	82.4	72.8	63.0	53.3	65.2
Employees	7.6%	81	80	—	101	—

An in-depth profile of this company is available to Hoover's Online members at hoovers.com.

763

HIRERIGHT, INC.

5151 California Ave.
Irvine, CA 92617
Phone: 949-428-5800
Fax: 949-428-5801
Web: www.hireright.com

CEO: Michael A. (Mike) Petrullo
CFO: Mark Mayo
HR: Janet R. Randolph
FYE: December 31
Type: Subsidiary

Because it would just be plain silly to hire wrong. HireRight provides pre-employment screening services for human resources and security professionals. The company helps businesses perform background verification, drug screening, and skills and behavioral assessment for prospective new hires. HireRight calls its main product offering on-demand because it's available via the Web. It offers its products and services in more than 200 countries around the globe; overall, it serves more than 2,000 customers. HireRight is a subsidiary of employment screening provider Altegrity (formerly US Investigations Services), which acquired the company in August 2008.

HIRSCH ELECTRONICS LLC

1900-B Carnegie Ave.
Santa Ana, CA 92705
Phone: 949-250-8888
Fax: 949-250-7372
Web: www.hirschelectronics.com

CEO: Lawrence W. Midland
CFO: Diana Midland
HR: Carol Schumacher
FYE: December 31
Type: Subsidiary

Feeling insecure about your facilities? Hirsch Electronics could help reassure you. The company's catalog includes a number of products for controlling access to buildings, from its ScramblePad keypad (which keeps onlookers from learning access codes) to its DIGI*TRAC controllers. Hirsch's Velocity Security Management System software not only supervises facility security systems; it allows remote monitoring and control of facility temperatures, identifies problems and emergencies, and can turn the lights on and off, thanks to XML-based Web services capabilities. Hirsch Electronics was started in 1981 by Steven Hirsch, who left the business in 1987. SCM Microsystems acquired the company in 2009.

⊞ HIRSCH INTERNATIONAL CORP.

50 Engineers Rd.
Hauppauge, NY 11788
Phone: 631-436-7100
Fax: 631-436-7054
Web: www.tajima-hirsch.com

CEO: Paul Gallagher
CFO: —
HR: —
FYE: December 31
Type: Private

Hirsch International happily keeps the apparel industry in stitches. The company supplies single- and multi-head embroidery machines, embroidery supplies, machine parts, and software, as well as digital printers and textile lasers. Hirsch is the exclusive US distributor of Tajima Industries equipment (multiple-head embroidery machines), MHM screen printing equipment, SEIT textile bridge lasers, and other industry tech brands. Tajima-built equipment accounts for about 50% of sales. Core customers are manufacturers that produce thread, appliqué, and rhinestone-decorative apparel and accessories, uniforms, or sportswear, as well as apparel screenprinters and retailers. In 2009 CEO Paul Gallagher took the company private.

	Annual Growth	1/04	1/05	1/06	*12/07	12/08
Sales ($ mil.)	(3.0%)	48.1	43.6	51.1	52.6	42.5
Net income ($ mil.)	—	0.4	(1.8)	0.5	2.1	(6.9)
Market value ($ mil.)	(41.4%)	22.6	10.0	12.5	17.7	2.7
Employees	3.6%	120	97	98	113	138

*Fiscal year change

HI-SHEAR TECHNOLOGY CORPORATION

24225 Garnier St.
Torrance, CA 90505
Phone: 310-784-2100
Fax: 310-325-5354
Web: www.hstc.com

CEO: George W. Trahan
CFO: Jan L. Hauhe
HR: Linda A. Nespole
FYE: May 31
Type: Subsidiary

Hi-Shear Technology cuts loose with a slew of electronic, pyrotechnic, and mechanical devices used by the defense and aerospace industry. Hi-Shear's power cartridges and separation devices provide command-release for structures designed to hold together under rigorous conditions. The devices are used in rockets and satellites, such as the Space Shuttle and the Patriot missile, and in airplane ejector seats. Major customers include the US Government, Boeing, and Lockheed Martin. Hi-Shear also makes pyrotechnic-powered LifeShear cutters that slice through steel and other materials to free trapped victims. In late 2009 British defense contractor Chemring Group acquired the company for about $132 million.

	Annual Growth	5/05	5/06	5/07	5/08	5/09
Sales ($ mil.)	12.6%	16.1	21.1	21.1	27.6	25.9
Net income ($ mil.)	140.6%	0.2	2.3	3.4	3.5	6.7
Employees	(0.3%)	87	100	100	117	86

HISPANIC TELESERVICES

5615 Kirby Dr., Ste. 820
Houston, TX 77005
Phone: 713-225-5482
Fax: 713-807-1639
Web: www.htc.to

CEO: Alejandro Jaime
CFO: Rodolfo Gloria
HR: Francisco Ramirez
FYE: December 31
Type: Business segment

Hispanic Teleservices offers bilingual customer service, technical support, and other telemarketing services serving the US Hispanic market. The company helps its clients connect with Spanish speakers by providing inbound sales, order taking, product registration, and customer satisfaction surveys. Headquartered in Houston, Texas, the company provides its outsourced contact services from centers in Monterrey and Guadalajara, Mexico. Founded in 1999, Hispanic Teleservices is a unit of Teleperformance S.A., one of the largest call center operators in the world.

HITACHI AMERICA, LTD.

50 Prospect Ave.
Tarrytown, NY 10591
Phone: 914-332-5800
Fax: 914-332-5555
Web: www.hitachi.us

CEO: Chiaki Fujiwara
CFO: —
HR: —
FYE: March 31
Type: Subsidiary

Hitachi America supplies North America with a broad range of high-tech products for the consumer and for business applications. The wholly owned subsidiary of the Hitachi Ltd. conglomerate makes and sells a broad range of automotive systems, electronic devices, computer systems and components, information systems, telecom equipment, and power and industrial equipment. The company's home electronics offerings include TVs, camcorders, and DVD players; its computer-related products range from data storage systems to semiconductor manufacturing equipment; and its industrial products include such diverse lines as automotive systems and components, power tools, and nuclear steam turbines.

HITACHI AUTOMOTIVE PRODUCTS (USA) INC.

955 Warwick Rd.
Harrodsburg, KY 40330
Phone: 859-734-9451
Fax: 859-734-5309
Web: www.hap.com

CEO: Masaaki (Mark) Fujisawa
CFO: —
HR: David Edwards
FYE: December 31
Type: Subsidiary

Hitachi Automotive Products (USA) likes to get things started in the automotive industry. The company, a subsidiary of Hitachi America (which is a subsidiary of Hitachi, Ltd.), manufactures electrical and electronic automotive components including alternators, starters, solenoid valves, fuel injectors, drivetrains, and gas and airflow sensors. The company also makes components (starters, generators, and oil pump motors) for hybrid-electric vehicles. In addition to its headquarters in Kentucky, Hitachi Automotive Products (USA) has sales and technical centers in California and Michigan.

	Annual Growth	12/04	12/05	12/06	12/07	12/08
Est. sales ($ mil.)	—	—	—	—	—	400.0
Employees	—	—	—	—	—	900

HITACHI CONSULTING CORPORATION

2001 Bryan St., Ste. 3600
Dallas, TX 75201
Phone: 214-665-7000
Fax: 214-665-7010
Web: www.hitachiconsulting.com

CEO: Philip R. Parr
CFO: Barry D. Honea
HR: Barry D. Honea
FYE: March 31
Type: Subsidiary

Hitachi Consulting, a unit of Japanese technology giant Hitachi, provides business management and information technology consulting services. It groups its offerings into four main areas: business intelligence and performance management; corporate management; customer and channel; and supply chain. The firm, which operates from more than 15 offices in the US, Europe, and the Asia/Pacific region, practices in a variety of industries, ranging from aerospace and defense to consumer goods to utilities. Clients have included Coldwater Creek, Raytheon Aircraft, and Toyota. Hitachi Consulting was founded in 2000 when Hitachi bought a consulting arm of accounting firm Grant Thornton.

HITACHI DATA SYSTEMS CORPORATION

750 Central Expwy.
Santa Clara, CA 95050
Phone: 408-970-1000
Fax: 408-727-8036
Web: www.hds.com

CEO: Jack Domme
CFO: Susan Lynch
HR: Nancy Long
FYE: March 31
Type: Subsidiary

Hitachi Data Systems (HDS) is mounting a raid on the data storage market. A wholly owned subsidiary of Hitachi, HDS contends with the likes of EMC and IBM in the market for high-end RAID (redundant array of independent disks) storage devices and software. Its storage systems range in size from PC-sized units to massive cabinets that can manage more than 30 petabytes of data. The company also sells network-attached storage (NAS) servers, and its software portfolio encompasses backup and recovery, content archiving, replication, and storage resource management applications. HDS, which does business in 170 countries, offers training, support, and financing services.

	Annual Growth	3/04	3/05	3/06	3/07	3/08
Sales ($ mil.)	—	—	—	—	—	2,500.0
Employees	—	—	—	—	—	3,800

HITACHI GLOBAL STORAGE TECHNOLOGIES, INC.

3403 Yerba Buena Rd.
San Jose, CA 95135
Phone: 408-717-6000
Fax: —
Web: www.hitachigst.com

CEO: Stephen D. (Steve) Milligan
CFO: Michael A. (Mick) Murray
HR: John R. Viera
FYE: December 31
Type: Subsidiary

Hitachi Global Storage Technologies (HGST) manufactures hard-disk drives and components for PCs, servers, and electronic devices such as handheld computers and digital cameras. Its data storage product portfolio ranges from 3.5-inch computer drives to miniature drives used in digital music players. The company also provides consulting and hard drive integration services to consumer electronics manufacturers through five design studios. HGST sells through distributors such as Bell Microproducts and Ingram Micro. The company operates multiple development and manufacturing operations in Asia and North America. Hitachi Global Storage Technologies is a wholly owned subsidiary of Hitachi.

HITACHI MEDICAL SYSTEMS AMERICA, INC.

1959 Summit Commerce Park
Twinsburg, OH 44087
Phone: 330-425-1313
Fax: 330-425-1410
Web: www.hitachimed.com

CEO: Donald Broomfield
CFO: Richard Kurz
HR: —
FYE: March 31
Type: Subsidiary

Hitachi Medical Systems America (HMSA) handles the North American distribution of Hitachi Medical Corporation's diagnostic imaging equipment, including 360-degree X-ray machines, magnetic resonance imaging systems, and ultrasound products. The company is one of the leading distributors of open MRIs in the US; its parent company's Altaire brand was developed specifically for the US market. Other MRI systems are sold under the Echelon and AIRIS brands. HMSA also conducts workshops and provides customer support programs. The company also distributes PET, computed tomography, 3D dental imaging, and ultrasound systems. HMSA was founded in 1989 to increase the profile of Hitachi's medical imaging products in the US.

HITACHI METALS AMERICA, LTD.

2 Manhattanville Rd., Ste. 301
Purchase, NY 10577
Phone: 914-694-9200
Fax: 914-694-9279
Web: www.hitachimetals.com

CEO: Kazuyuki Konishi
CFO: —
HR: Michelle Hays
FYE: March 31
Type: Subsidiary

Hitachi Metals America (HMA) has been rocking out in the States since 1965. The international subsidiary of Hitachi Metals makes castings, electronic materials, magnetic products, and steel-related parts for customers in automotive, computer, consumer goods, steel, and telecommunications markets. The company employs about 2,000 people, with plants in Illinois, North and South Carolina, Ohio, and Pennsylvania. Its Metglas Inc. subsidiary, an amorphous metal maker, touts steel for making transformers that spur efficient energy generation and reduced emissions. Despite the downturn in the auto industry eroding HMA's profitability, HMA has kept its supplier status with the reinvented Chrysler, led by Fiat.

An in-depth profile of this company is available to Hoover's Online members at hoovers.com.

765

HITCO CARBON COMPOSITES, INC.

1600 W. 135th St.
Gardena, CA 90249
Phone: 310-527-0700
Fax: 310-516-5714
Web: www.hitco.com

CEO: Peter Hoffman
CFO: Steve Bower
HR: —
FYE: December 31
Type: Subsidiary

HITCO hits the heights with its complex aerospace composites. A subsidiary of SGL CARBON AG, the company manufactures composite aerostructure assemblies and a variety of fiberglass, carbon, and graphite composite products, which are combined with insulation components and temperature-resistant fabrics (nonwovens and metal foils) to meet the elevated temperatures required by the related industries. HITCO serves the aerospace and defense, automotive, chemical processing, electronics, power generating, chemical processing, and transportation industries. Its market "hits" include brake components, jet engine flaps and seals, solid rocket motor nozzles, thermal shields, and specialty fabrication techniques.

HI-TECH DURAVENT

400 E. Main St.
Georgetown, MA 01833
Phone: 978-352-2077
Fax: 978-352-2487
Web: www.hitechduravent.com

CEO: William (Bill) Mack
CFO: Douglas (Doug) Tilley
HR: —
FYE: December 31
Type: Subsidiary

Hi-Tech Duravent looks at the world through hose-colored glasses. The company, a unit of Smiths Group plc's Flexible Technologies division, manufactures flexible hose as small as 10 mm and as large as 36 inches in diameter and up to 100 feet in length. Typical uses for Hi-Tech Duravent hoses range from ducting for HVAC systems to landfill ventilation. It maintains a 60,000 sq. ft. plant in Massachusetts. The company's products are also used in medical laboratories.

🔲 HI-TECH PHARMACAL CO., INC.

NASDAQ (GS): HITK

369 Bayview Ave.
Amityville, NY 11701
Phone: 631-789-8228
Fax: 631-789-8429
Web: www.hitechpharm.com

CEO: David S. Seltzer
CFO: William Peters
HR: —
FYE: April 30
Type: Public

Hi-Tech Pharmacal combines imitation with innovation, making and distributing dozens of liquid and semi-solid prescription, over-the-counter (OTC), and nutritional products. The company primarily produces generic forms of prescription drugs, including off-brand versions of antibiotic Bactrim (made by Roche) and allergy medicine Flonase (from GlaxoSmithKline), as well as prescription skin creams, mouthwashes, and pediatric multivitamins. Hi-Tech also makes branded over-the-counter products, including a line of products for diabetes patients and the Zostrix line of pain and arthritis medications. In addition, the company has a handful of branded prescription products.

	Annual Growth	4/05	4/06	4/07	4/08	4/09
Sales ($ mil.)	12.6%	67.7	78.0	58.9	62.0	108.7
Net income ($ mil.)	4.2%	8.3	11.5	(2.0)	(5.1)	9.8
Market value ($ mil.)	(16.5%)	192.6	302.0	163.8	108.3	93.4
Employees	12.8%	232	246	262	288	375

HITTITE MICROWAVE CORPORATION

NASDAQ (GS): HITT

20 Alpha Rd.
Chelmsford, MA 01824
Phone: 978-250-3343
Fax: 978-250-3373
Web: www.hittite.com

CEO: Stephen G. Daly
CFO: William W. Boecke
HR: —
FYE: December 31
Type: Public

And lo, the Hittites did rise up out of their land, and they sacked Babylon. Actually, these Hittites rise up out of the Commonwealth of Massachusetts, and they're out to sell semiconductors. Hittite Microwave designs and develops microwave, millimeter-wave, and radio-frequency (RF) chips for aerospace, broadband, cellular, and military applications. In addition to amplifiers, frequency multipliers, mixers, modulators, switches, and other components, the company provides custom RF integrated circuits (ICs). Boeing and Motorola are among Hittite's hundreds of customers. The company gets more than half of its sales outside the US.

	Annual Growth	12/05	12/06	12/07	12/08	12/09
Sales ($ mil.)	19.2%	80.7	130.3	156.4	180.3	163.0
Net income ($ mil.)	21.6%	21.1	42.7	51.2	53.8	46.2
Market value ($ mil.)	15.2%	704.7	984.3	1,454.6	897.2	1,241.7
Employees	12.2%	220	267	315	332	349

🔲 H. J. HEINZ COMPANY

NYSE: HNZ

1 PPG Place, Ste. 3100
Pittsburgh, PA 15222
Phone: 412-456-5700
Fax: 412-456-6128
Web: www.heinz.com

CEO: William R. (Bill) Johnson
CFO: Arthur B. (Art) Winkleblack
HR: Steve Clark
FYE: April 30
Type: Public

Forget those original 57 varieties. H. J. Heinz now has thousands of products. One of the world's largest food companies, Heinz produces ketchup and other condiments, soups, sauces, frozen foods, beans, pasta meals, infant food, and other processed food products. Its flagship product is ketchup, of course, and the company dominates the US ketchup market. The company's customers include food retailers, the foodservice industry, and the US military. Its leading brands include the aforementioned ketchup, Lea & Perrins Worcestershire sauce, Classico pasta sauces, Ore-Ida frozen potatoes, and its Boston Market, T.G.I. Friday's, and Weight Watchers frozen foods.

	Annual Growth	4/05	4/06	4/07	4/08	4/09
Sales ($ mil.)	3.3%	8,912.3	8,643.4	9,001.6	10,070.8	10,148.1
Net income ($ mil.)	5.2%	752.7	645.6	785.7	844.9	923.1
Market value ($ mil.)	(1.7%)	11,653.3	13,127.0	14,897.9	14,872.6	10,884.9
Employees	(5.6%)	41,000	36,000	33,000	32,500	32,500

HK SYSTEMS, INC.

2855 S. James Dr.
New Berlin, WI 53151
Phone: 262-860-7000
Fax: 262-860-7010
Web: www.hksystems.com

CEO: Michael L. (Mike) Gonzalez
CFO: James Purko
HR: Kathleen Bennett
FYE: December 31
Type: Private

HK Systems is all about going with the flow of things. The company makes material-handling systems and equipment, including automated guided vehicles, conveyors, palletizers (product binding machines), storage and retrieval machinery, and sortation tools to manage warehouse items. HK also provides customer support, consulting, aftermarket, and even outsourcing services to maintain its systems. A suite of supply chain management software is hosted, too. With over 1,000 material-handling systems in operation, the privately held company has served industries of all types, from auto and transportation to food and beverage, pharmaceuticals, and paper and publishing. Top customers are FedEx, MillerCoors, and Nike.

HKN, INC.

NYSE Amex: HKN

180 State St., Ste. 200
Southlake, TX 76092
Phone: 817-424-2424
Fax: —
Web: www.harkenenergy.com

CEO: Mikel D. Faulkner
CFO: Anna M. Williams
HR: —
FYE: December 31
Type: Public

HKN (formerly Harken Energy) harkens back to the days when a certain President George W. Bush was an oil man. HKN, which bought Bush's small oil company more than a decade ago, explores for and produces oil and gas primarily in the US, where it has interests in oil and gas wells in the Gulf Coast region of Texas and Louisiana, and holds coalbed methane assets in the Midwest. Internationally, it has stakes in exploration and production assets in South America (Global Energy Development, 34%) and in Canada (Spitfire Energy, 27%). In 2008 HKN reported proved reserves (all in the US) of 4.2 billion cu. ft. of gas and 1.5 million barrels of oil. Lyford Investments Enterprises owns 36% of the voting stock of HKN.

	Annual Growth	12/05	12/06	12/07	12/08	12/09
Sales ($ mil.)	(25.4%)	40.1	29.0	21.1	19.5	12.4
Net income ($ mil.)	—	43.0	0.0	3.2	(26.7)	(3.3)
Market value ($ mil.)	(26.8%)	122.0	109.2	76.9	28.4	35.1
Employees	(23.2%)	46	22	17	15	16

🏠 HM CAPITAL PARTNERS LLC

200 Crescent Ct., Ste. 1600
Dallas, TX 75201
Phone: 214-740-7300
Fax: 214-720-7888
Web: www.hmcapital.com

CEO: John R. Muse
CFO: David (Dave) Knickel
HR: —
FYE: December 31
Type: Private

Private equity firm HM Capital (formerly Hicks, Muse, Tate & Furst) seeks out controlling stakes in underperforming enterprises in the energy, food, and media sectors. After acquiring a company, HM Capital provides strategic guidance such as installing new management, assisting in the development of new products, investing in infrastructure, improving efficiency, and making acquisitions or divestures. It exits its investments via a sale or IPO once its strategic goals are met. The company's current portfolio holdings include LIN TV, wholesale insurance brokerage Swett & Crawford, and oil and gas extraction and production outfits BlackBrush, TriDimension, and SunTerra.

HMG/COURTLAND PROPERTIES, INC.

NYSE Amex: HMG

1870 S. Bayshore Dr.
Coconut Grove, FL 33133
Phone: 305-854-6803
Fax: 305-856-7342

CEO: Maurice Wiener
CFO: Carlos Camarotti
HR: —
FYE: December 31
Type: Public

Sun, sea, and sand are key parts of the business mix for HMG/Courtland Properties, a real estate investment trust (REIT) that owns and manages commercial properties in the Miami area. The company owns the posh Grove Isle — a Coconut Grove-area luxury resort, which includes a hotel, restaurant, spa, and marina. The property, managed by Grand Heritage Hotel Group, accounts for about 70% of HMG/Courtland's rental income. The REIT also holds a 50% interest in a 16,000 sq. ft. seafood restaurant at the marina, in addition to a 5,000 sq. ft. corporate office building. HMG/Courtland has two properties held for development in Rhode Island and Vermont and has equity interests in other commercial real estate operations.

	Annual Growth	12/05	12/06	12/07	12/08	12/09
Sales ($ mil.)	1.8%	9.6	11.3	10.3	10.9	10.3
Net income ($ mil.)	—	(0.4)	(0.7)	(0.4)	(1.6)	(0.1)
Market value ($ mil.)	(25.1%)	10.7	14.5	10.4	3.4	3.4
Employees	213.8%	1	—	0	97	97

HMN FINANCIAL, INC.

NASDAQ (GM): HMNF

1016 Civic Center Dr. NW
Rochester, MN 55901
Phone: 507-535-1200
Fax: 507-535-1300
Web: www.justcallhome.com

CEO: Bradley C. Krehbiel
CFO: Jon J. Eberle
HR: —
FYE: December 31
Type: Public

HMN Financial is the holding company for Home Federal Savings Bank, which operates about a dozen branches in southern Minnesota and central Iowa. Serving individuals and local businesses, the bank offers such deposit products as checking and savings accounts, CDs, and IRAs. Its lending activities include commercial mortgages (more than 30% of the company's loan portfolio), business loans (about 25%), residential mortgages, and construction, development, and consumer loans. The bank provides financial planning, investment management, and investment products through its Osterud Insurance Agency subsidiary and Home Federal Investment Management.

	Annual Growth	12/05	12/06	12/07	12/08	12/09
Assets ($ mil.)	1.1%	991.2	977.8	1,117.1	1,145.5	1,036.2
Net income ($ mil.)	—	11.1	8.4	11.3	(10.1)	(10.8)
Market value ($ mil.)	(38.6%)	127.3	149.0	106.0	18.0	18.1
Employees	0.1%	224	223	221	219	225

HMS HOLDINGS CORP.

NASDAQ (GS): HMSY

401 Park Ave. South
New York, NY 10016
Phone: 212-857-5000
Fax: 212-857-5973
Web: www.hms.com

CEO: William C. (Bill) Lucia
CFO: Walter D. Hosp
HR: John D. Schmid
FYE: December 31
Type: Public

HMS Holdings makes sure government health providers are paying only as much as they have to. Through its Health Management Systems subsidiary, the company specializes in helping public programs identify and recover costs that should have been paid by a third party, or that were paid in error. It serves Medicaid programs in some 40 states, as well as Medicaid managed care plans, state Childrens' Health Insurance Programs (SCHIP), and federal agencies including Centers for Medicare & Medicaid Services and Veterans Health Administration. The company also provides services to commercial insurers, employer groups, pharmacies, and other health care providers. HMS Holdings has operations throughout the US.

	Annual Growth	12/05	12/06	12/07	12/08	12/09
Sales ($ mil.)	39.8%	60.0	87.9	146.7	184.5	229.2
Net income ($ mil.)	39.2%	8.0	5.3	15.0	21.4	30.0
Market value ($ mil.)	58.8%	207.7	411.3	901.7	855.8	1,322.0
Employees	40.9%	331	578	760	922	1,306

🏠 HNI CORPORATION

NYSE: HNI

408 E. 2nd St.
Muscatine, IA 52761
Phone: 563-272-7400
Fax: 563-272-7655
Web: www.hnicorp.com

CEO: Stanley A. (Stan) Askren
CFO: Kurt Tjaden
HR: —
FYE: December 31
Type: Public

Tired of your office furniture? HNI Corporation can supply you with replacements, along with a fireplace to burn the old set. HNI is a leading US manufacturer of office furniture, and more than 80% of the firm's sales come from this division. It sells primarily to furniture dealers, wholesalers, and retail superstores (OfficeMax, Office Depot, and Staples). The company's Hearth & Home Technologies unit is one of the largest US makers of wood- and gas-burning fireplaces for the home. HNI has distribution partners in more than 50 countries, but the majority of its products are sold in Canada and the US. State Farm Insurance Companies owns more than 15% of the company.

	Annual Growth	12/05	12/06	12/07	12/08	12/09
Sales ($ mil.)	(9.3%)	2,450.6	2,679.8	2,570.5	2,477.6	1,656.3
Net income ($ mil.)	—	137.4	123.4	120.4	45.5	(6.3)
Market value ($ mil.)	(15.8%)	2,483.8	2,008.1	1,585.3	716.2	1,249.4
Employees	(6.3%)	11,304	14,200	13,300	12,200	8,700

🏠 An in-depth profile of this company is available to Hoover's Online members at hoovers.com.

767

HNTB COMPANIES

715 Kirk Dr.
Kansas City, MO 64105
Phone: 816-472-1201
Fax: 816-472-4060
Web: www.hntb.com

CEO: Paul A. Yarossi
CFO: Terry M. Campbell
HR: Richard Cybulski
FYE: December 31
Type: Private

HNTB knows the ABCs of A/E. The company ranks among the pack of "pure designers," firms that derive most of their revenues from architecture, engineering, or environmental design operations. HNTB Companies' operations are carried out by three firms — HNTB Corporation (transportation infrastructure), HNTB Architecture, and HNTB Federal Services (government contracts). The company is best-known for its highway and transit system design (New Jersey Turnpike) as well as airports (Midway) and sports arenas (Invesco Field). HNTB has about 60 locations in the US. Employee-owned HNTB (which once stood for Howard Needles Tammen & Berendoff) traces its roots to 1914.

HOBART CORPORATION

701 S. Ridge Ave.
Troy, OH 45374
Phone: 937-332-3000
Fax: 937-332-2852
Web: www.hobartcorp.com

CEO: John T. McDonough
CFO: —
HR: —
FYE: December 31
Type: Subsidiary

Cooks in commercial kitchens would be lost without the products manufactured by Hobart. The company makes a variety of commercial foodservice equipment including mixers, fryers, food warmers, refrigerators (under the Traulsen brand), and dishwashers for the foodservice and retail industries. It also offers Baxter brand baking equipment and Mannhart vegetable cutters and salad dryers. Hobart's retail products include ovens, ranges, toasters, and slicers sold to grocery stores and specialty shops. Its service unit provides installation, maintenance, and repair for all of its own equipment. As a subsidiary of Illinois Tool Works, Hobart also will service the equipment of sister companies including Vulcan.

HOBBY LOBBY STORES, INC.

7707 SW 44th St.
Oklahoma City, OK 73179
Phone: 405-745-1100
Fax: 405-745-1547
Web: www.hobbylobby.com

CEO: David Green
CFO: John Cargill
HR: Bill Owens
FYE: December 31
Type: Private

If something wicker this way comes, Hobby Lobby Stores may be the source. The firm operates about 435 stores in some 35 states and sells arts and crafts supplies, baskets, beads, candles, frames, home-decorating accessories, and silk flowers. It also has operations in China, Hong Kong, and the Philippines, and it is the #3 craft and fabric retailer (behind Michaels Stores and Jo-Ann Stores). Sister companies, Crafts, Etc! and Hemispheres, supply Hobby Lobby stores with merchandise, received from its Oklahoma distribution facility. CEO David Green, who owns the company with his wife Barbara, founded Hobby Lobby in 1972 and operates it according to biblical principles, including closing stores on Sunday.

	Annual Growth	12/04	12/05	12/06	12/07	12/08
Sales ($ mil.)	6.5%	1,400.0	1,500.0	1,620.0	1,800.0	1,800.0
Employees	3.0%	16,000	17,000	17,500	18,000	18,000

HO-CHUNK, INC.

1 Mission Dr.
Winnebago, NE 68071
Phone: 402-878-2809
Fax: 402-878-2560
Web: www.hochunkinc.com

CEO: Lance Morgan
CFO: Dennis Johnson
HR: Sarah Snake
FYE: December 31
Type: Holding company

Ho-Chunk, Inc. (HCI) the economic development corporation run by the Winnebago Tribe of Nebraska, manages about 18 subsidiaries in the fields of communications, construction, distribution, gasoline and convenience store retail (under the Heritage Express banner in Iowa and Nebraska), government contracting, lodging (The WinnaVegas Inn), marketing, used-vehicle sales, and more. The profits from these businesses are in turn managed by the Ho-Chunk Community Development Corporation, a not-for-profit organization that directs commercial growth and community infrastructure development for the tribe. "Ho-Chunk" is a modernized form of Hochungra, the Winnebago tribe's traditional name.

	Annual Growth	12/04	12/05	12/06	12/07	12/08
Est. sales ($ mil.)	—	—	—	—	—	121.4
Employees	—	—	—	—	—	350

HOEGANAES CORPORATION

1001 Taylors Ln.
Cinnaminson, NJ 08077
Phone: 856-829-2220
Fax: 856-829-7156
Web: www.hoeganaes.com

CEO: David J. Kasputis
CFO: Norman Mackey
HR: —
FYE: December 31
Type: Subsidiary

Hoeganaes (pronounced HEY-gun-ess) keeps its powder dry and turns it into money. The company produces powdered ferrous metals (atomized steel and sponge iron) for use by auto parts makers and other manufacturers. The steel and iron powders are used to make structural parts, filters, and bearings, as well as in friction applications such as brake pads and linings. Hoeganaes products also are used in chemical and welding applications. Outside the US, the company has operations in Germany, and is planning to open a plant in China in 2010. Hoeganaes was founded in 1953. It is part of the automotive business segment of UK-based GKN.

HOFFMAN CORPORATION

805 SW Broadway, Ste. 2100
Portland, OR 97205
Phone: 503-221-8811
Fax: 503-221-8934
Web: www.hoffmancorp.com

CEO: Wayne A. Drinkward
CFO: Scott W. Fredricks
HR: Sheri Sundstrom
FYE: December 31
Type: Private

Hoffman cherishes a challenge — such as building the nation's deepest subway station in Portland, Oregon, or the snake-like, metal-clad Experience Music Project in Seattle. Through several subsidiaries, including flagship Hoffman Construction, the general contractor and construction manager builds civic, commercial, and industrial facilities, primarily in the northwestern US. A leading builder of semiconductor facilities, the group also serves such sectors as education, health care, hospitality, sports, transportation, industrial, and government. It provides electrical, mechanical, surveying, and other services, as well. Employees own Hoffman Corporation, which was founded in 1922.

	Annual Growth	12/04	12/05	12/06	12/07	12/08
Sales ($ mil.)	(13.1%)	—	—	1,600.0	1,190.0	1,209.3
Employees	5.5%	—	—	920	971	

HOFFMANN-LA ROCHE INC.

340 Kingsland St.
Nutley, NJ 07110
Phone: 973-235-5000
Fax: 973-777-3327
Web: www.roche-nutley.com

CEO: Ivor MacLeod
CFO: Ivor MacLeod
HR: —
FYE: December 31
Type: Subsidiary

Hoffmann-La Roche, also known as Roche Nutley, conducts drug research in the suburban community of Nutley, New Jersey. The company is part of Roche USA and is one of the primary US research facilities for its parent, Swiss drug giant Roche Holdings. It serves as a lead location for Roche's oncology, inflammatory disease, virology, and metabolism R&D programs, developing drugs to treat conditions including tumorous cancers, asthma, rheumatoid arthritis, diabetes, and heart disease. Hoffmann-La Roche also has extensive programs in gene-based and protein-based biotechnology research.

HOFSTRA UNIVERSITY

1000 Fulton Ave.
Hempstead, NY 11549
Phone: 516-463-6600
Fax: 516-463-5100
Web: www.hofstra.edu

CEO: Stuart Rabinowitz
CFO: Catherine Hennessy
HR: —
FYE: August 31
Type: School

With some 500 annual cultural events, Hofstra University is happening. The private, four-year university has an annual enrollment of some 12,500 full- and part-time students and offers more than 140 undergraduate programs and approximately 150 graduate programs in liberal arts and sciences, allied human services, business, communications, education, law, and medicine. It also has an honors college. Hofstra University was founded in 1935 by trustees of the estate of William Hofstra, who made his fortune in the lumber, wood pulp, and newsprint businesses.

	Annual Growth	8/04	8/05	8/06	8/07	8/08
Est. sales ($ mil.)	—	—	—	—	—	324.5
Employees	—	—	—	—	—	2,000

THE HOGUE CELLARS, LTD.

2800 Lee Rd.
Prosser, WA 99350
Phone: 509-786-4557
Fax: 509-786-4580
Web: www.hoguecellars.com

CEO: Gary Hogue
CFO: —
HR: —
FYE: March 31
Type: Subsidiary

The Hogue family has lived off the land for more than 50 years, growing a wide assortment of crops durng that time, but Mike Hogue's experiment with grapes in 1979 marked the beginning of The Hogue Cellars. Today, the Washington State winery produces some 500,000 cases of wine per year under the Hogue, Genesis, and Reserve labels. Its offerings include cabernet sauvignon, chardonnay, gewürztraminer, merlot, pinot grigio, and syrah. They are available in the US as well as abroad. Vincor purchased The Hogue Cellars in 2001. In 2006 Vincor and its subsidiaries, including Hogue, were acquired by Constellation Brands.

	Annual Growth	3/04	3/05	3/06	3/07	3/08
Est. sales ($ mil.)	—	—	—	—	—	6.2
Employees	—	—	—	—	—	60

HOHNER, INC.

1000 Technology Park Dr.
Glen Allen, VA 23059
Phone: 804-515-1900
Fax: 804-515-0840
Web: www.hohnerusa.com

CEO: Clayman Edwards
CFO: —
HR: —
FYE: March 31
Type: Subsidiary

Hohner has made a big business of selling little harmonicas. The company (AKA Hohner HSS) is the US marketing and distribution arm of German instrument maker, Matth. Hohner. Established in the US in 1986, the company distributes Hohner harmonicas as well as accordions, recorders, melodicas, fretted instruments, HSS bags and cases, Sonor drums and percussion items, Lanikai ukuleles, and Rockwood drums and guitars. Hohner also makes music stands and accessories and has a separate line of musical instruments and toys for children (Hohner Kids) that includes shakers, whistles, finger castanets, and drums. Matthias Hohner founded the parent company in 1857 at age 24, to mass produce harmonicas.

	Annual Growth	3/04	3/05	3/06	3/07	3/08
Est. sales ($ mil.)	—	—	—	—	—	32.0
Employees	—	—	—	—	—	60

HOK GROUP, INC.

211 N. Broadway, Ste. 700
St. Louis, MO 63102
Phone: 314-421-2000
Fax: 314-421-6073
Web: www.hok.com

CEO: Patrick MacLeamy
CFO: Robert M. (Bob) Pratzel
HR: Susan Mitchell-Ketzes
FYE: December 31
Type: Private

HOK has designs on your project, but in this case that's a good thing. The global architectural company provides planning, design, and delivery services for a wide variety of sectors including aviation, entertainment/media, health care, and government. HOK tackles all aspects of a project's life cycle, from pre-planning and engineering to landscape architecture and facilities management. Notable projects include the Priory Chapel in St. Louis; the National Air and Space Museum in Washington, DC; and King Saud University in Saudi Arabia. The firm has offices in two-dozen countries in North America, Europe, and Asia. St. Louis architects George Hellmuth, Gyo Obata, and George Kassabum founded HOK Group in 1955.

	Annual Growth	12/04	12/05	12/06	12/07	12/08
Est. sales ($ mil.)	—	—	—	—	—	132.6
Employees	—	—	—	—	—	1,839

HOKU CORPORATION

NASDAQ (GM): HOKU

1075 Opakapaka St.
Kapolei, HI 96707
Phone: 808-682-7800
Fax: 808-682-7807
Web: www.hokuscientific.com

CEO: Scott B. Paul
CFO: Darryl S. Nakamoto
HR: —
FYE: March 31
Type: Public

Hoku Corporation (formerly Hoku Scientific) doesn't fight the power — it wants to provide the power. The company is riding the wave of alternative energy technologies on a variety of fronts. Hoku originally developed fuel cells using membrane electrode assemblies, or MEAs. The company is winding down its activities in that technology, however, and moving into manufacturing polysilicon and reselling photovoltaic solar modules made by other companies. The US Navy's Naval Air Warfare Center Weapons Division, Hawaii's Paradise Beverages, and Resco, Inc. are leading customers.

	Annual Growth	3/05	3/06	3/07	3/08	3/09
Sales ($ mil.)	14.6%	2.9	5.5	5.4	3.2	5.0
Net income ($ mil.)	—	(0.7)	1.3	(2.8)	(4.3)	(3.0)
Market value ($ mil.)	(26.4%)	—	351.2	322.1	445.6	139.9
Employees	8.8%	20	27	17	21	28

An in-depth profile of this company is available to Hoover's Online members at hoovers.com.

769

HOLCIM (US) INC.

201 Jones Rd.
Waltham, MA 02451
Phone: 781-647-2501
Fax: 781-647-2516
Web: www.holcim.com/USA

CEO: Bernard Terver
CFO: Thomas Aebischer
HR: Gaétan Jacques
FYE: December 31
Type: Subsidiary

There's nothing abstract about the concrete made by Holcim (US). The US arm of Swiss building products giant Holcim Ltd., the company produces, imports, and sells cement, ready-mix concrete, asphalt, and aggregates to manufacturers and dealers around the nation. Holcim (US) operates about 15 manufacturing facilities and has an annual production capacity of 15 million metric tons; it also imports products from overseas affiliates. The company has more than 75 distribution terminals in a dozen sales regions; customers include manufacturers of concrete products and building materials dealers.

HOLLAND & KNIGHT LLP

195 Broadway, 24th Fl.
New York, NY 10007
Phone: 212-513-3200
Fax: 212-385-9010
Web: www.hklaw.com

CEO: Steven Sonberg
CFO: Mia Stutzman
HR: Paul Thomas
FYE: December 31
Type: Partnership

Your legal knight in shining armor might be just around the corner. Holland & Knight maintains almost 20 offices throughout the US, plus another half-dozen in other countries, including representative offices. It has more than 1,100 lawyers overall. The firm maintains about 150 practice areas and draws clients from a wide range of industries; it has been recognized for its work in such areas as corporate transactions, litigation, maritime law, and real estate. Holland & Knight traces its roots to a law office opened by Peter Knight in Florida in 1889; it took its current shape in 1968 when Knight's firm was combined with one led by US Sen. Spessard Holland.

HOLIDAY COMPANIES

4567 American Blvd., West
Bloomington, MN 55437
Phone: 952-830-8700
Fax: 952-830-8864
Web: holidaystationstores.com

CEO: Ronald A. (Ron) Erickson
CFO: —
HR: Robert S. (Bob) Nye
FYE: December 31
Type: Private

If your holiday involves a road trip across the central or western US, chances are you'll encounter a Holiday Stationstore. Holiday Companies operates about 400 convenience stores (about 100 of which are franchised) in a dozen states, from Michigan to Washington and Alaska under the Holiday Stationstores banner. The shops sell the company's own brand of Blue Planet gasoline (low-sulfur fuel available in Minnesota, South Dakota, and Wisconsin). The firm exited sporting goods retailing when its Gander Mountain chain (acquired in 1997) went public in 2004. Holiday Companies was founded in 1928 as a general store in a small Wisconsin town by two Erickson brothers, whose descendants still own and run the company.

	Annual Growth	12/04	12/05	12/06	12/07	12/08
Est. sales ($ mil.)	11.2%	1,310.0	1,742.0	1,820.0	2,000.0	2,000.0
Employees	3.6%	4,000	4,200	4,410	4,600	4,600

THE HOLLAND, INC.

109 W. 17th St.
Vancouver, WA 98660
Phone: 360-694-1521
Fax: 360-694-9114
Web: www.hollandinc.com

CEO: Jeffrey R. (Jeff) Harvey
CFO: Kyle Dean
HR: —
FYE: May 31
Type: Private

Wooden shoes are not required attire at these eateries. The Holland is a leading fast-food operator in the Northwest, with about 40 Burgerville quick-service restaurants in Oregon and Washington. The chain's menu offers several varieties of burgers, along with other sandwiches, salads, and sides. The Holland also owns Beaches, a bar and restaurant in Vancouver, Washington, offering pizza, seafood, and pasta dishes, along with happy hour drinks. The family-owned company was founded as The Holland Creamery by Jacob Propstra in 1926 and opened its first Burgerville in 1961.

HOLLAND AMERICA LINE INC.

300 Elliott Ave. West
Seattle, WA 98119
Phone: 206-281-3535
Fax: 206-281-7110
Web: www.hollandamerica.com

CEO: Stein Kruse
CFO: Larry D. Calkins
HR: Brendan J. Vierra
FYE: November 30
Type: Subsidiary

Not content to sail on any old barge? Holland America Line might have the berth for you. The subsidiary of #1 cruise ship company Carnival operates nearly 15 luxury cruise ships with a passenger capacity of more than 21,000 and sails to more than 320 destinations in the US along the West Coast, in New England, and Alaska. It also offers service to Asia, Europe, and the Caribbean, as well as round-the-world cruises. In addition to seafaring adventure, its Holland America Tours operates almost a dozen hotels, motorcoaches and rail service in Alaska and Canada's Yukon Territory. Holland America was founded in 1873 as the Netherlands-America Steamship Company.

HOLLISTER INCORPORATED

2000 Hollister Dr.
Libertyville, IL 60048
Phone: 847-680-1000
Fax: 847-680-2123
Web: www.hollister.com

CEO: Alan F. Herbert
CFO: Samuel P. (Sam) Brilliant
HR: —
FYE: December 31
Type: Private

Hollister manufactures a variety of specialty medical products which are distributed to more than 90 countries. The employee-owned company concentrates on products for wound care, continence care, bowel management, patient tube fastening, and ostomy care. Its products include catheters, collection devices, and wound dressings, among other items. The company has two US manufacturing centers located in Missouri and Virginia, and two European manufacturing facilities in Denmark and Ireland. John Dickinson Schneider founded Hollister in 1921 as JDS Printer Craftsman, and first specialized in printing birth certificates.

	Annual Growth	12/04	12/05	12/06	12/07	12/08
Est. sales ($ mil.)	—	—	—	—	—	183.3
Employees	—	—	—	—	—	2,400

HOLLY CORPORATION

NYSE: HOC

100 Crescent Ct., Ste. 1600	CEO: Matthew P. (Matt) Clifton
Dallas, TX 75201	CFO: Bruce R. Shaw
Phone: 214-871-3555	HR: Nancy F. Hartmann
Fax: 214-871-3560	FYE: December 31
Web: www.hollycorp.com	Type: Public

Holly Corporation refines crude oil to produce gasoline, diesel fuel, and jet fuel, which it sells in the southwestern US, northern Mexico, and Montana. Subsidiary Navajo Refining (New Mexico) has a refining capacity of 100,000 barrels a day; Holly's Woods Cross refinery in Utah, 31,000 barrels; and its Tulsa refinery, 125,000 barrels. It owns a 34% stake in Holly Energy Partners, which has 960 miles of crude oil pipelines located primarily in West Texas and New Mexico, and 2,500 miles of petroleum product pipelines. Holly also owns and operates Holly Asphalt Company, which manufactures and markets asphalt products from various terminals in Arizona and New Mexico.

	Annual Growth	12/05	12/06	12/07	12/08	12/09
Sales ($ mil.)	10.8%	3,212.7	4,023.2	4,791.7	5,867.7	4,834.3
Net income ($ mil.)	(24.8%)	167.0	266.6	334.1	120.6	53.3
Market value ($ mil.)	(3.4%)	1,565.8	2,734.2	2,707.1	969.8	1,363.4
Employees	16.7%	881	859	909	978	1,632

HOLLY ENERGY PARTNERS, L.P.

NYSE: HEP

100 Crescent Ct., Ste. 1600	CEO: Matthew P. (Matt) Clifton
Dallas, TX 75201	CFO: Bruce R. Shaw
Phone: 214-871-3555	HR: Nancy F. Hartmann
Fax: 214-871-3560	FYE: December 31
Web: www.hollyenergy.com	Type: Public

Holly Energy Partners is having a jolly good time piping petroleum. The company transports refined petroleum products and crude oil from Holly Corporation's Navajo refinery in New Mexico, Woods Cross refinery in Utah, and Alon USA's Big Spring refinery in Texas, to customers in the southwestern US. It operates 1,330 miles of refined petroleum pipelines (including 340 miles of leased pipelines), 11 distribution terminals, one jet fuel terminal, and two truck-loading facilities used to transport gasoline, diesel, and jet fuel. Holly Corporation, the parent of the company's general partner (Holly Logistics), holds a 34% stake in Holly Energy Partners.

	Annual Growth	12/05	12/06	12/07	12/08	12/09
Sales ($ mil.)	16.3%	80.1	89.2	105.4	118.1	146.6
Net income ($ mil.)	25.3%	26.8	27.5	39.3	25.4	66.0
Market value ($ mil.)	1.9%	779.9	850.9	924.9	451.4	842.3
Employees	14.3%	82	89	106	121	140

HOLLY HUNT LTD.

801 W. Adams St.	CEO: Holly A. Hunt
Chicago, IL 60607	CFO: —
Phone: 312-329-5999	HR: —
Fax: 312-993-0331	FYE: December 31
Web: www.hollyhunt.com	Type: Private

Holly wants to facilitate your hunt for fancy furniture pieces. Holly Hunt is an upscale design house that makes and markets home and office furnishings, lighting fixtures, rugs, and textiles. The company has showrooms in Chicago, Miami, Minneapolis, New York, Los Angeles, and Washington, DC. It also shows its products in other selected furniture stores. Founder Holly Hunt's introduction of French designer Christian Liaigre helped to secure the company's position in the furniture-with-flair niche. Other showcased furniture designers include Alison Berger, John Hutton, and Studio H. Texan Holly Hunt founded the design firm as a single store in 1984.

	Annual Growth	12/04	12/05	12/06	12/07	12/08
Est. sales ($ mil.)	—	—	—	—	—	141.0
Employees	—	—	—	—	—	225

HOLLYWOOD ENTERTAINMENT CORPORATION

9275 SW Peyton Ln.	CEO: Sherif J. Mityas
Wilsonville, OR 97070	CFO: Lucinda M. (Cindy) Baier
Phone: 503-570-1600	HR: —
Fax: 503-570-1680	FYE: December 31
Web: www.hollywoodvideo.com	Type: Subsidiary

Hollywood Entertainment hopes you'll skip the theaters and go straight to video. A subsidiary of struggling Movie Gallery, the #2 US video chain behind Blockbuster, the company operates video rental stores under the Hollywood Video banner. (Hollywood Entertainment was acquired by Movie Gallery for $1 billion following a battle with Blockbuster.) The stores also rent video games and game players, VCRs, and DVD players. In-store video game department Game Crazy buys, sells, and trades used and new game software, hardware, and accessories. The stores are primarily located in strip malls or other high-traffic locales. Movie Gallery filed for Chapter 11 bankruptcy protection in 2010 and is liquidating.

HOLLYWOOD MEDIA CORP.

NASDAQ (GM): HOLL

2255 Glades Rd., Ste. 221 A	CEO: Mitchell (Mitch) Rubenstein
Boca Raton, FL 33431	CFO: Scott A. Gomez
Phone: 561-998-8000	HR: —
Fax: 561-998-2974	FYE: December 31
Web: www.hollywoodmedia.com	Type: Public

This company helps get people to the theatre and the local multiplex. Hollywood Media Corp. is a leading provider of live theater tickets, including Broadway and off-Broadway productions, as well as performances in London's West End district through Broadway.com, Theatre.com, and its 1-800-BROADWAY phone service. Its Theatre Direct International subsidiary provides wholesale tickets to groups and travel agents. The company additionally has a 26% stake in MovieTickets.com, and owns an intellectual property business, as well as CinemasOnline, which offers website maintenance for cinemas and live theaters in the UK. At the close of 2009 Hollywood Media announced plans to sell Broadway.com and Theatre Direct.

	Annual Growth	12/05	12/06	12/07	12/08	12/09
Sales ($ mil.)	2.0%	95.6	115.9	123.9	117.1	103.4
Net income ($ mil.)	—	(8.9)	9.5	1.7	(16.9)	(5.6)
Market value ($ mil.)	(24.5%)	134.4	131.0	90.4	31.2	43.7
Employees	(18.1%)	271	230	184	130	122

HOLLYWOOD PRESBYTERIAN MEDICAL CENTER, INC.

1300 N. Vermont Ave.	CEO: Jeff A. Nelson
Los Angeles, CA 90027	CFO: Galen Gorman
Phone: 213-413-3000	HR: Norma Braun
Fax: 323-644-7613	FYE: December 31
Web: www.hollywoodpresbyterian.com	Type: Not-for-profit

It's everything one might expect from a hospital in Hollywood. In addition to nurses and doctors, the staff at Hollywood Presbyterian Medical Center (HPMC) includes bellmen, concierges, and parking valets. Aiming to blur the lines between acute care hospital and hotel, HPMC cares for the oft-pampered community of Hollywood, California. Its health care services include a cancer treatment center; physical, speech, and occupational therapy; and the Institute of Maternal Fetal Health which performs fetal surgeries. Other services include community health outreach programs and The Chalet, a skilled nursing facility. The 430-bed hospital is part of CHA Health Systems, headed by fertility specialist Dr. Kwang Yul Cha.

An in-depth profile of this company is available to Hoover's Online members at hoovers.com.

771

HOLMAN ENTERPRISES

7411 Maple Ave.
Pennsauken, NJ 08109
Phone: 856-663-5200
Fax: 856-665-3444
Web: www.holmanenterprises.com

CEO: Melinda (Mindy) Holman
CFO: Robert Campbell
HR: —
FYE: December 31
Type: Private

Holman sells a whole lot of cars. Family-owned Holman Enterprises owns a dozen car and truck dealerships in southern New Jersey and about 10 more in South Florida. The company sells Audi, BMW, Ford, Infiniti, Jaguar, Lincoln, Rolls-Royce, and Toyota cars, as well as Ford and Sterling trucks. Holman also offers collision repair and sunroof installation services and operates a pair of leasing companies. Its Automotive Resources International unit is one of the largest independently owned fleet leasing groups in the world. Holman's Reconditioned Motors and Parts business distributes small parts and engines authorized by Ford.

	Annual Growth	12/04	12/05	12/06	12/07	12/08
Est. sales ($ mil.)	—	—	—	—	—	915.3
Employees	—	—	—	—	—	2,751

HOLOGIC, INC.

NASDAQ (GS): HOLX

35 Crosby Dr.
Bedford, MA 01730
Phone: 781-999-7300
Fax: 781-280-0669
Web: www.hologic.com

CEO: Robert A. (Rob) Cascella
CFO: Glenn P. Muir
HR: David J. Brady
FYE: September 30
Type: Public

With its mammography and breast biopsy systems, Hologic puts the squeeze on women to help save their lives. Its mammography products include film-based and digital systems, as well as the workstations and computer-aided detection systems that interpret the images. Additional products include X-ray and ultrasound bone densitometers, which detect and monitor osteoporosis, and breast biopsy collection systems (branded ATEC) sold by its Suros division. The buy a few years ago of women's health firm Cytyc, gave Hologic several other product lines, including tests to screen for cervical cancer. The company markets its products to hospitals and clinical labs worldwide through distributors and a direct sales force.

	Annual Growth	9/05	9/06	9/07	9/08	9/09
Sales ($ mil.)	54.4%	287.7	462.7	738.4	1,674.5	1,637.1
Net income ($ mil.)	—	28.3	27.4	94.6	(385.6)	(2,176.2)
Market value ($ mil.)	3.1%	3,740.6	5,637.8	7,902.2	5,008.2	4,233.5
Employees	46.1%	870	1,617	3,580	3,933	3,959

HOLTZBRINCK PUBLISHING HOLDINGS LIMITED PARTNERSHIP

175 5th Ave.
New York, NY 10010
Phone: 212-674-5151
Fax: 212-420-9314
Web: us.macmillan.com

CEO: John Sargent
CFO: —
HR: —
FYE: December 31
Type: Subsidiary

Holtzbrinck Publishing Holdings keeps its readers' headiness at the ready. The company is the US subsidiary of German media and publishing company Verlagsgruppe Georg von Holtzbrinck, and includes American imprints such as St. Martin's Press, Henry Holt & Company, and Farrar, Straus & Giroux. The company also publishes *Scientific American* magazine, a periodical created in 1845 and devoted to developments in science and technology. Holtzbrinck Publishing does business alongside the US operations of Verlagsgruppe Georg von Holtzbrinck's Macmillan Publishers. (The US activities of Macmillan and Holtzbrinck operate together under the Holtzbrinck Publishers umbrella.)

HOME BANCORP, INC.

NASDAQ (GM): HBCP

503 Kaliste Saloom Rd.
Lafayette, LA 70508
Phone: 337-237-1960
Fax: 337-264-9280
Web: www.home24bank.com

CEO: John W. Bordelon
CFO: Joseph B. Zanco
HR: —
FYE: December 31
Type: Public

Making its home in Cajun Country, Home Bancorp is the holding company for Home Bank, a community bank which offers deposit and loan services to consumers and small to midsized businesses in southern Louisiana. Through about 20 branches, the bank offers standard savings and checking accounts, as well as lending services like mortgages, consumer loans, and credit cards. One- to four-family residential mortgage loans represent the bank's largest loan segment (about 40%), followed by commercial real estate loans (approximately 20%). Home Bank expanded in 2010 when it acquired the six Lousiana branches of Statewide Bank, which failed and had been seized by regulators.

	Annual Growth	12/05	12/06	12/07	12/08	12/09
Assets ($ mil.)	9.4%	—	400.5	422.4	528.4	524.6
Net income ($ mil.)	7.6%	3.5	4.0	3.3	2.7	4.7
Market value ($ mil.)	25.0%	—	—	—	84.7	105.8
Employees	0.0%	—	—	143	143	143

HOME BANCSHARES, INC.

NASDAQ (GS): HOMB

719 Harkrider, Ste. 100
Conway, AR 72032
Phone: 501-328-4715
Fax: 501-328-4679
Web: www.homebancshares.com

CEO: C. Randall (Randy) Sims
CFO: Randy E. Mayor
HR: —
FYE: December 31
Type: Public

At this Home, you don't have to stash your cash under the mattress. Home BancShares is the holding company for Centennial Bank, which operates more than 65 branches in Arkansas and Florida. The bank offers traditional services such as checking, savings, and money market accounts, IRAs, and CDs. It focuses on commercial real estate lending, including construction, land development, and agricultural loans, which make up more than 60% of its lending portfolio. The bank also writes residential mortgage, business, and consumer loans. Nonbank subsidiaries offer trust and insurance services. Investments are available to customers through an agreement with third-party provider LPL Financial.

	Annual Growth	12/05	12/06	12/07	12/08	12/09
Assets ($ mil.)	8.9%	1,911.5	2,190.6	2,291.6	2,580.1	2,684.9
Net income ($ mil.)	23.8%	11.4	15.9	20.4	10.1	26.8
Market value ($ mil.)	2.7%	—	572.4	499.5	693.3	619.2
Employees	2.7%	544	562	595	594	605

HOME BOX OFFICE, INC.

1100 Avenue of the Americas
New York, NY 10036
Phone: 212-512-1000
Fax: 212-512-1182
Web: www.hbo.com

CEO: Bill Nelson
CFO: Robert (Rob) Roth
HR: Shelley Fischel
FYE: December 31
Type: Subsidiary

The theater might be in your living room, but you still have to pay this company to see the movies. Home Box Office is a leading pay-TV operator with more than 40 million subscribers to its HBO and Cinemax cable television services. The channels offer a variety of Hollywood movies and foreign films, along with original series programming including *Big Love, Curb Your Enthusiasm,* and *Entourage.* Subscribers also receive sports events, concerts, and other specialty programming. Internationally, HBO reaches more than 50 countries in Asia, Europe, and Latin America. In addition to its movie channels, Home Box Office produces films and TV programming through HBO Films. The company is a subsidiary of Time Warner.

HOME CITY ICE COMPANY, INC.

6045 Bridgetown Rd.
Cincinnati, OH 45248
Phone: 513-574-1800
Fax: 513-574-5409
Web: www.homecityice.com

CEO: Robyn Little
CFO: —
HR: Nancy Faillace
FYE: December 31
Type: Private

Home City Ice has its business down cold. The company manufactures more than 4,400 tons of ice per day in its 28 ice-manufacturing plants. It operates a distribution network made up of 36 centers and a fleet of more than 500 trucks. The network delivers the company's frozen product to individual customers and company-owned ice merchandising machines located throughout Ohio, Indiana, Illinois, Kentucky, and West Virginia, as well as in parts of Michigan, Pennsylvania, Tennessee, New York, and Maryland. The company dates back to 1896 and is owned by the Sedler family, which began its association with the company in the 1920s.

	Annual Growth	12/04	12/05	12/06	12/07	12/08
Est. sales ($ mil.)	—	—	—	—	—	80.0
Employees	—	—	—	—	—	1,200

THE HOME DEPOT, INC.

NYSE: HD

2455 Paces Ferry Rd. NW
Atlanta, GA 30339
Phone: 770-433-8211
Fax: 770-384-2356
Web: www.homedepot.com

CEO: Francis S. (Frank) Blake
CFO: Carol B. Tomé
HR: Timothy M. (Tim) Crow
FYE: January 31
Type: Public

When embarking on household projects, many start their journey at The Home Depot. As the world's largest home improvement chain and second-largest US retailer after Wal-Mart, the firm operates about 2,200 stores across North America, Puerto Rico, and China, as well as an e-commerce site. It targets the do-it-yourself and professional markets with its selection of some 40,000 items, including lumber, flooring, plumbing supplies, garden products, tools, paint, and appliances. Home Depot also offers installation services for carpeting, cabinetry, and other products. Since shuttering its unprofitable EXPO, THD Design Center, and Yardbirds stores in 2009, the retailer has focused on boosting its revenue.

	Annual Growth	1/06	1/07	1/08	1/09	1/10
Sales ($ mil.)	(5.1%)	81,511.0	90,837.0	77,349.0	71,288.0	66,176.0
Net income ($ mil.)	(17.8%)	5,838.0	5,761.0	4,395.0	2,260.0	2,661.0
Market value ($ mil.)	(8.8%)	68,138.3	68,457.6	51,486.0	36,178.0	47,066.7
Employees	(2.1%)	345,000	364,000	331,000	322,000	317,000

HOME DIAGNOSTICS, INC.

2400 NW 55th Ct.
Fort Lauderdale, FL 33309
Phone: 954-677-9201
Fax: 954-739-8506
Web: www.homediagnostics.com

CEO: Joseph H. (Joe) Capper
CFO: Ronald L. (Ron) Rubin
HR: Kim Zeltwanger
FYE: December 31
Type: Private

Whether home or abroad, Nipro Diagnostics (formerly Home Diagnostics) makes sure diabetics are kept healthy with the help of a little Sidekick. The company makes blood glucose monitoring systems and disposable supplies for diabetics, which it sells through retail pharmacies, mass merchandisers, managed care companies, mail service providers, and distributors around the globe. Nipro Diagnostics markets its testing systems and blood monitors through those distribution channels in two ways, under its own brand names — including Sidekick, TrueTrack Smart System, TRUEread, and Prestige IQ — and through co-branded partnerships. The company is a wholly owned subsidiary of Japanese medical device maker Nipro.

	Annual Growth	12/04	12/05	12/06	12/07	12/08
Sales ($ mil.)	9.8%	85.1	100.2	112.6	115.6	123.6
Net income ($ mil.)	48.0%	2.0	5.9	10.3	9.6	9.6
Employees	5.2%	—	491	500	543	571

HOME FEDERAL BANCORP, INC.

NASDAQ (GS): HOME

500 12th Ave. South
Nampa, ID 83651
Phone: 208-468-5189
Fax: 208-468-5001
Web: www.myhomefed.com

CEO: Len E. Williams
CFO: Eric S. Nadeau
HR: Denis J. Trom
FYE: September 30
Type: Public

Home Federal Bancorp's location provides it with a treasure trove of opportunity. Its subsidiary, Home Federal Bank (formerly Home Federal Savings and Loan Association of Nampa), serves the Treasure Valley region of southwestern Idaho, which includes Ada, Canyon, Elmore, and Gem counties (where nearly 40% of the state's population resides). Home Federal has 15 branches (three in Wal-Mart stores) and a loan center in Idaho, as well as seven branches in central Oregon. It also offers banking through an ATM network, and on the Internet. Its primary business is attracting deposits and using them to originate loans. In 2007 Home Federal converted from a mutual holding company to a stock ownership company.

	Annual Growth	9/05	9/06	9/07	9/08	9/09
Assets ($ mil.)	4.7%	689.6	761.3	710.0	725.1	827.9
Net income ($ mil.)	—	5.3	6.2	5.3	4.0	(7.2)
Market value ($ mil.)	0.5%	186.6	228.4	195.5	212.8	190.6
Employees	2.6%	240	249	223	201	266

HOME PRODUCTS INTERNATIONAL, INC.

4501 W. 47th St.
Chicago, IL 60632
Phone: 773-890-1010
Fax: 773-890-0523
Web: www.hpii.com

CEO: George Hamilton
CFO: Dennis Doheny
HR: John Pugh Jr.
FYE: December 31
Type: Private

Home Products International (HPI) helps folks get organized. The company makes an array of plastic storage containers, including carts, crates, bins, totes, and tubs, some with more than 60 gallons of stowing space. It also produces closet organizers, clothing hampers, ironing boards, shower caddies, hangers, and hooks. HPI's products are marketed under the HOMZ brand and sold through major retailers in North and South America, including Wal-Mart, Target, ALCO, Staples, and Bed Bath & Beyond. The company also markets its products to hotels and other clients in the hospitality industry. HPI is majority owned by Third Avenue Management.

HOME PROPERTIES, INC.

NYSE: HME

850 Clinton Square
Rochester, NY 14604
Phone: 585-546-4900
Fax: 585-546-5433
Web: www.homeproperties.com

CEO: Edward J. (Ed) Pettinella
CFO: David P. Gardner
HR: Lisa M. Critchley
FYE: December 31
Type: Public

Even homes need facelifts from time to time. Home Properties provides that proverbial Botox shot by renovating and rehabilitating multifamily apartments that are in need of both interior and exterior maintenance: from new flooring and bathroom repair to roofing and landscaping. Formerly Home Properties of New York, the real estate investment trust (REIT) focuses on suburban areas in metropolitan markets in the Northeast, Mid-Atlantic, and Southeast Florida regions. Home Properties owns and manages a portfolio of about 110 apartment communities with nearly 40,000 units. FMR LLC owns 12% of Home Properties.

	Annual Growth	12/05	12/06	12/07	12/08	12/09
Sales ($ mil.)	3.2%	443.8	454.0	505.2	510.0	503.6
Net income ($ mil.)	(12.8%)	81.5	110.5	61.5	69.7	47.1
Market value ($ mil.)	4.0%	1,482.5	2,153.6	1,629.7	1,475.2	1,733.6
Employees	(7.5%)	1,500	1,200	1,200	1,150	1,100

An in-depth profile of this company is available to Hoover's Online members at hoovers.com.

773

HOMEFED CORPORATION

OTC: HOFD

1903 Wright Place, Ste. 220
Carlsbad, CA 92008
Phone: 760-918-8200
Fax: 760-918-8210

CEO: Paul J. Borden
CFO: Erin N. Ruhe
HR: —
FYE: December 31
Type: Public

HomeFed won't provide you with room and board, but it can help you get a home. The company earns *its* keep by investing in and developing residential real estate in California. Through subsidiaries, HomeFed is developing a master-planned community in San Diego County called San Elijo Hills, which contains approximately 3,500 residences, as well as commercial space and a town center. The company is responsible for design engineering; infrastructure such as streets, utilities, and public facilities; and the completion of individual lots. It owns a 68% stake in the development.

	Annual Growth	12/05	12/06	12/07	12/08	12/09
Sales ($ mil.)	(39.0%)	107.9	69.4	23.7	10.4	14.9
Net income ($ mil.)	(45.5%)	31.8	17.2	6.8	(9.9)	2.8
Market value ($ mil.)	(22.2%)	527.9	520.0	488.5	130.0	193.0
Employees	(15.1%)	25	23	24	13	13

HOMELAND SECURITY CAPITAL CORPORATION

OTC: HOMS

1005 N. Globe Rd., Ste. 550
Arlington, VA 22201
Phone: 703-528-7073
Fax: —
Web: www.hscapcorp.com

CEO: C. Thomas McMillen
CFO: Michael T. (Mike) Brigante
HR: —
FYE: December 31
Type: Public

Homeland Security Capital stakes its financial security on the nation's security. The investment firm acquires, consolidates, and provides management assistance for companies that offer homeland security services and products. It hopes to capitalize on the highly fragmented nature of the young industry, which brings potential customers in the government and private sectors. Its leading earner is Safety & Ecology Holdings, which provides emergency response, environmental remediation, and construction services, specializing in the nuclear industry. Homeland Security also owns Nexus Technologies Group, which designs, builds, and installs closed-circuit security systems in the Mid-Atlantic.

	Annual Growth	12/04	12/05	12/06	12/07	12/09
Sales ($ mil.)	202.3%	—	—	8.7	12.6	79.5
Net income ($ mil.)	—	—	—	(5.8)	(3.0)	(9.5)
Market value ($ mil.)	17.9%	—	—	4.0	3.4	5.6
Employees	194.2%	—	—	58	27	502

HOMELAND STORES, INC.

28 E. 33rd St.
Edmond, OK 73013
Phone: 800-522-5658
Fax: —
Web: www.homelandstores.com

CEO: Darryl Fitzgerald
CFO: Deborah A. (Debbie) Brown
HR: Jim Kern
FYE: December 31
Type: Subsidiary

Shoppers who call Oklahoma home shop at Homeland Stores' supermarkets. The regional grocery chain, a division of grocery distributor Associated Wholesale Grocers (AWG), operates more than 45 stores throughout Oklahoma and a single store in Kansas. AWG operates Homeland stores through its Associated Retail Grocers subsidiary and supplies the majority of the products sold in Homeland stores. The stores sell groceries and general merchandise; most have delicatessens, pharmacies, and some have specialty departments (ethnic foods, floral services, seafood). Homeland still has struggled as a result of stiff competition from Wal-Mart and other rival chains.

HOMEOWNERS CHOICE, INC.

NASDAQ (GM): HCII

2340 Drew St., Ste. 200
Clearwater, FL 33765
Phone: 727-213-3600
Fax: 727-388-4172
Web: www.hcpci.com

CEO: Francis X. McCahill III
CFO: Richard R. Allen
HR: —
FYE: December 31
Type: Public

Floridian homeowners are picking Homeowners Choice for their insurance needs — by default. Founded in 2006, Homeowners Choice began providing property and casualty insurance for Floridians just as large national insurers began exiting the hurricane-prone market to reduce exposure. The majority of the company's insurance policies have been assumed from Citizens Property Insurance Corporation, a state-supported insurer. Although Homeowners Choice has assumed more than 50,000 property and casualty insurance policies from Citizens, the company has done so selectively, assuming policies based on its own underwriting criteria. The company also sells policies through a network of more than 1,300 independent agents.

	Annual Growth	12/05	12/06	12/07	12/08	12/09
Assets ($ mil.)	85.7%	—	—	40.0	132.0	137.9
Net income ($ mil.)	—	—	(0.1)	1.0	12.7	10.9
Market value ($ mil.)	45.5%	—	—	—	32.9	47.9
Employees	87.9%	—	—	17	35	60

HOMETOWN AMERICA L.L.C.

150 N. Wacker Dr., Ste. 2800
Chicago, IL 60606
Phone: 312-604-7500
Fax: 312-604-7501
Web: www.hometownamerica.com

CEO: Richard G. (Rich) Cline Jr.
CFO: Thomas (Tom) Curatolo
HR: Patricia Madden
FYE: December 31
Type: Private

There's no place like home for Hometown America. The company invests in and manages manufactured home parks throughout the US. It owns approximately 130 communities (many of which feature recreational facilities such as swimming pools, clubhouses, and basketball courts) consisting of more than 45,000 home sites in some 20 states. About a third of its properties — carrying the Providence brand — are targeted towards active seniors; most are located in Florida. The company also offers home financing and insurance through agreements with third-party providers. Hometown America was founded in 1997.

	Annual Growth	12/04	12/05	12/06	12/07	12/08
Est. sales ($ mil.)	—	—	—	—	—	360.7
Employees	—	—	—	—	—	1,000

HONDA AERO, INC.

2989 Tucker St.
Burlington, NC 27215
Phone: 336-226-2376
Fax: 336-227-6596
Web: world.honda.com/HondaAero

CEO: Atsukuni Waragai
CFO: —
HR: —
FYE: December 31
Type: Subsidiary

Honda is turning its eyes to the sky as Honda Aero leaves the runway for the wild blue yonder. A subsidiary of Honda Motor Co., Honda Aero specializes in developing a variety of aircraft engines. The subsidiary was founded in 2004 and holds a 50% stake in GE Honda Aero Engines, a joint venture with General Electric that produces jet engines in the 1,000 lb.–3,500 lb. thrust class. GE Honda Aero Engines' HF120 compact turbofan engine weighs less than 400 lbs. and will power the new lightweight HondaJet, as well as other business jets. The engine will be produced at Honda Aero's new 102,400-sq.-ft. production facility and headquarters located in Burlington, North Carolina.

	Annual Growth	12/04	12/05	12/06	12/07	12/08
Est. sales ($ mil.)	—	—	—	—	—	0.3
Employees	—	—	—	—	—	28

HONDA NORTH AMERICA, INC.

700 Van Ness Ave.
Torrance, CA 90501
Phone: 310-781-4000
Fax: 310-781-4142
Web: www.honda.com

CEO: Tetsuo Iwamura
CFO: Narutoshi Wakiyama
HR: Gary Kessler
FYE: March 31
Type: Subsidiary

Its cars might not be as American as apple pie, but Honda North America keeps the US appetite for Hondas sated. The subsidiary of Honda Motor coordinates the operations in North America that make, market, and distribute Accord, Civic, and Acura cars, and Gold Wing, Shadow, and Valkyrie motorcycles. Honda North America's best-selling cars include the Odyssey minivan and the CR-V SUV. Honda North America also markets hybrid versions of its Accord and Civic sedans. In 2009 Honda started selling its Insight hybrid sedan in the US, giving lower-priced competition to the Toyota Prius. North America is Honda Motor's largest market, representing nearly half of the carmaker's sales.

HONDA OF AMERICA MFG., INC.

24000 Honda Pkwy.
Marysville, OH 43040
Phone: 937-642-5000
Fax: 937-644-6575
Web: www.ohio.honda.com

CEO: Hidenobu Iwata
CFO: —
HR: —
FYE: March 31
Type: Subsidiary

Honda of America Mfg. operates four Ohio plants where Honda automobiles, engines, SUVs, and transmissions are manufactured for the North American market and other regions. The company's Marysville Auto Plant builds up to 440,000 vehicles per year, and was the first US auto plant to manufacture both right- and left-hand drive cars on the same assembly line. Honda of America Mfg.'s other plants build cars, engines, and transmissions. Vehicles made by Honda of America Mfg. include the Accord coupe and sedan, the Acura TL and RDX, the Civic Sedan, CR-V, and the Element. The vehicles built at Honda's Ohio plants are sold in more than 100 countries worldwide.

HONDA OF SOUTH CAROLINA MFG., INC.

1111 Honda Way
Timmonsville, SC 29161
Phone: 843-346-8000
Fax: —
Web: world.honda.com/HondaSouthCarolinaMfg

CEO: Takanobu Ito
CFO: —
HR: —
FYE: March 31
Type: Subsidiary

Honda of South Carolina Mfg. (HSC) is among several major automotive OEM transplants to the South. A subsidiary of Honda Motor Co., the company manufactures about a half-dozen models of Honda All-Terrain Vehicles (ATVs) for the North American market as well as markets in Australia, New Zealand, and the UK. Up until 2009 HSC also manufactured personal watercrafts (PWCs); their assembly was curbed due to reduced demand. It produces ATV components (engines, fuel tanks, and differentials) for Honda's Ohio plant, as well. Honda opened the $30 million Timmonsville plant in 1998. HSC is one of about a dozen Honda facilities in North America. Honda garners about a one-third share of the US ATV market.

HONEYWELL INTERNATIONAL INC.

NYSE: HON

101 Columbia Rd.
Morristown, NJ 07962
Phone: 973-455-2000
Fax: 973-455-4807
Web: www.honeywell.com

CEO: David M. (Dave) Cote
CFO: David J. (Dave) Anderson
HR: Mark R. James
FYE: December 31
Type: Public

Jet engines and thermostats seem worlds apart, but they're Honeywell International's bread and butter. More than a century old, the company is a diverse industrial conglomerate, with four segments; the largest include Automation and Control (HVAC and manufacturing process products) and Aerospace (turbo engines, and flight safety and landing systems). Additional segments include Honeywell Specialty Materials (thermal interconnects, fibers, and chemicals) and Transportation Systems (engine boosting systems, brake materials, car care products). Sales to the US government account for about 14% of its revenues (primarily in Aerospace). Honeywell makes more than 60% of its sales in the US; 25% come from Europe.

	Annual Growth	12/05	12/06	12/07	12/08	12/09
Sales ($ mil.)	2.8%	27,653.0	31,367.0	34,589.0	36,556.0	30,908.0
Net income ($ mil.)	6.5%	1,676.0	2,083.0	2,444.0	2,792.0	2,153.0
Market value ($ mil.)	1.3%	28,540.3	34,662.1	47,173.8	25,153.8	30,034.3
Employees	1.3%	116,000	118,000	122,000	128,000	122,000

HONEYWELL TECHNOLOGY SOLUTIONS INC.

7000 Columbia Gateway Dr.
Columbia, MD 21046
Phone: 410-964-7000
Fax: —
Web: www.honeywell.com

CEO: Mark Neas
CFO: Robert Topolski
HR: Mark Fisher
FYE: December 31
Type: Subsidiary

The world is Honeywell Technology Solutions' (HTSI) sweet spot. Operating as a subsidiary of Honeywell International, HTSI offers a breadth of services for aerospace and military efforts, domestic and foreign. Its work straddles six areas: space systems (satellite flight control and mission operations); logistics and sustainment (expeditionary logistics, depot-level maintenance, systems engineering and integration); IT and communication (security and information assurance); technical and engineering (system installation, testing, maintenance, and repair); programs (safety performance tracking, quality inspection and auditing, risk management); and metrology (lab support). HTSI's largest and oldest customer is NASA.

	Annual Growth	12/04	12/05	12/06	12/07	12/08
Est. sales ($ mil.)	—	—	—	—	—	938.0
Employees	—	—	—	—	—	6,000

HOOKER FURNITURE CORPORATION

NASDAQ (CM): HOFT

440 E. Commonwealth Blvd.
Martinsville, VA 24112
Phone: 276-632-0459
Fax: 276-632-0026
Web: www.hookerfurniture.com

CEO: Paul B. Toms Jr.
CFO: E. Larry Ryder
HR: Anne Jacobsen
FYE: January 31
Type: Public

Hooker Furniture wants to sell you the pieces that will turn your house into a home. It offers hardwood and metal furniture, including wall units, home office items, home theater cabinets, living and dining room tables, bedroom furniture, and accent pieces. Youth furniture is sold under the Opus Designs by Hooker label. Its Bradington-Young line of residential upholstered furniture features leather reclining chairs and sofas. Hooker Furniture's Sam Moore unit makes upscale chairs. Its products are sold through specialty shops (Star Furniture, Nebraska Furniture Mart) and department stores (Dillard's). Hooker Furniture executives hold more than 14% of the company.

	Annual Growth	11/05	11/06	*1/08	1/09	1/10
Sales ($ mil.)	(12.2%)	341.8	350.0	316.8	261.2	203.3
Net income ($ mil.)	(30.0%)	12.5	14.1	19.7	6.9	3.0
Market value ($ mil.)	(4.9%)	167.2	160.1	236.4	87.1	136.9
Employees	(13.9%)	1,400	1,050	950	814	768

*Fiscal year change

HOOPER HOLMES, INC.

NYSE Amex: HH

170 Mount Airy Rd.
Basking Ridge, NJ 07920
Phone: 908-766-5000
Fax: 908-953-6304
Web: www.hooperholmes.com

CEO: Roy H. Bubbs
CFO: Michael J. Shea
HR: —
FYE: December 31
Type: Public

Talk about a high-pressure exam. Paramedical examination company Hooper Holmes arranges physical examinations of life insurance applicants for insurance carriers nationwide. The company also performs phone interviews to collect medical histories, conducts wellness screenings for health management companies (including health plans), and tests blood and urine samples. Hooper Holmes conducts business through its Portamedic, Heritage Labs, Health & Wellness, and Hooper Holmes Services divisions. All of Hooper Holmes' businesses operate under the company's Health Information Division (HID). The company has about 250 locations with more than 9,000 examiners, and underwrites about 300,000 cases each year.

	Annual Growth	12/05	12/06	12/07	12/08	12/09
Sales ($ mil.)	(13.1%)	320.3	293.9	237.7	198.2	182.4
Net income ($ mil.)	—	(96.6)	(85.2)	(7.3)	(1.9)	0.0
Market value ($ mil.)	(20.1%)	177.4	230.9	119.6	17.4	72.3
Employees	(13.1%)	3,275	3,150	2,275	2,150	1,870

HOOTERS OF AMERICA, INC.

1815 The Exchange
Atlanta, GA 30339
Phone: 770-951-2040
Fax: 770-618-7032
Web: www.hooters.com

CEO: Coby G. Brooks
CFO: Jim Tessmer
HR: Doug White
FYE: December 31
Type: Private

The chicken wings aren't the only spicy items at Hooters. Hooters of America operates and franchises more than 450 Hooters restaurants in about 45 states and more than 25 other countries. The beach-themed bar-and-grills cater to sports fans and are known for their spicy chicken wings as well as their hostesses, who dress in the chain's trademark bright orange short shorts and tight T-shirts. Hooters also serves chili, sandwiches, and beer. The company operates more than 120 locations and franchises the rest. Hooters of America is controlled by CEO Coby Brooks, the son of the late Robert Brooks who built the chain. Six friends, none of whom had any restaurant experience, opened the first Hooters in 1983.

HOOVER PRECISION PRODUCTS INC.

2200 Pendley Rd.
Cumming, GA 30041
Phone: 770-889-9223
Fax: 770-889-0828
Web: www.hooverprecision.com

CEO: Eric Sturdy
CFO: —
HR: —
FYE: March 31
Type: Subsidiary

Hoover is having a ball asking, "How are balls made?" Its answer: "heading, flashing, heat treating, grinding, lapping, and polishing." Hoover Precision Products manufactures a range of ball bearings (ceramic, metal, and plastic) and cylindrical roller bearings (chrome, carbon, and steel). The company's products are used by customers in such industries as automotive, bearing, medical equipment, and furniture manufacturing. Hoover Precision Products was founded in 1913 as Hoover Steel Ball Company. The company operates from eight divisions in the Asia/Pacific region, Europe, Mexico, and the US. Hoover Precision Products was acquired in 1990 by Tsubaki Nakashima, of which the company is now a wholly owned subsidiary.

HOOVER'S, INC.

5800 Airport Blvd.
Austin, TX 78752
Phone: 512-374-4500
Fax: 512-374-4501
Web: www.hoovers.com

CEO: Hyune Hand
CFO: —
HR: Robin H. Pfahler
FYE: December 31
Type: Subsidiary

If you're reading this sentence, you know where to go for company data. Hoover's, the publisher of this profile, offers proprietary business information through the Internet, data feeds, wireless devices, and co-branding agreements with other online services. The Hoover's website features a database of information on more than 65 million corporations and organizations, and more than 85 million people. Offering both free and for-pay content, the firm focuses on selling subscriptions (the majority of its revenues) to marketing, sales, and business development professionals. Hoover's also publishes its information in reference books. The company is a subsidiary of Dun & Bradstreet (D&B).

	Annual Growth	12/05	12/06	12/07	12/08	12/09
Sales ($ mil.)	13.3%	70.0	90.0	107.5	124.9	115.3
Employees	—	—	—	—	—	—

HOPFED BANCORP, INC.

NASDAQ (GM): HFBC

4155 Lafayette Rd.
Hopkinsville, KY 42240
Phone: 270-885-1171
Fax: 270-889-0313
Web: www.bankwithheritage.com

CEO: John E. Peck
CFO: Billy C. Duvall
HR: —
FYE: December 31
Type: Public

HopFed Bancorp is the holding company for Heritage Bank (formerly Hopkinsville Federal Savings Bank), which started operations in 1879 as a building and loan association. The bank has about a dozen branches in southwestern Kentucky, with its market area extending into northwestern Tennessee. It offers standard products like checking, savings, money market, and NOW accounts, as well as CDs, IRAs, property/casualty insurance, and annuities. One- to four-family residential mortgages account for about 40% of its loan portfolio. To a lesser extent, Heritage Bank also writes multifamily residential, construction, commercial, and consumer loans. Directors and executives control 12% of the bank.

	Annual Growth	12/05	12/06	12/07	12/08	12/09
Assets ($ mil.)	12.6%	639.6	770.9	808.4	967.6	1,029.9
Net income ($ mil.)	(16.4%)	4.1	3.9	4.1	4.6	2.0
Market value ($ mil.)	(12.4%)	57.1	58.0	53.1	36.0	33.6
Employees	17.5%	126	217	242	233	240

HORACE MANN EDUCATORS CORPORATION

NYSE: HMN

1 Horace Mann Plaza
Springfield, IL 62715
Phone: 217-789-2500
Fax: 217-788-5161
Web: www.horacemann.com

CEO: Louis G. (Lou) Lower II
CFO: Peter H. (Pete) Heckman
HR: —
FYE: December 31
Type: Public

Naming itself in honor of Horace Mann, considered the father of public education, Horace Mann Educators is an insurance holding company that targets K-12 school teachers and other public school employees throughout the US. The company and its subsidiaries offer homeowners, auto, and individual and group life insurance, as well as retirement annuities. Horace Mann employs some 670 agents, many of whom are former teachers themselves. Writing business in 49 states and Washington DC, the company derives a third of its premiums from five states — California, Florida, North Carolina, Minnesota, and Texas.

	Annual Growth	12/05	12/06	12/07	12/08	12/09
Assets ($ mil.)	2.1%	5,840.6	6,329.7	6,259.3	5,507.7	6,343.1
Net income ($ mil.)	(1.3%)	77.3	98.7	82.8	10.9	73.5
Market value ($ mil.)	(9.9%)	743.7	792.3	742.9	360.5	490.3
Employees	(6.1%)	2,400	2,400	2,300	2,200	1,866

HORIZON BANCORP

NASDAQ (GM): HBNC

515 Franklin Sq.
Michigan City, IN 46360
Phone: 219-879-0211
Fax: 219-874-9305
Web: www.accesshorizon.com

CEO: Craig M. Dwight
CFO: Mark E. Secor
HR: —
FYE: December 31
Type: Public

Despite its name, Horizon Bancorp is on the up-and-up. It's the holding company for Horizon Bank, which serves northwest Indiana and southwest Michigan through more than 20 branches. It provides local individuals and businesses such standard services as checking and savings accounts, IRAs, CDs, and credit cards. Commercial, financial, and agricultural loans make up the largest segment of Horizon's loan portfolio, which also includes mortgage warehouse loans (loans earmarked for sale into the secondary market), consumer installment loans, and residential mortgages. Through subsidiaries, the bank offers trust and investment management services, life and health insurance, property/casualty coverage, and annuities.

	Annual Growth	12/05	12/06	12/07	12/08	12/09
Assets ($ mil.)	5.3%	1,127.9	1,222.4	1,258.9	1,306.9	1,387.0
Net income ($ mil.)	6.4%	7.1	7.5	8.1	9.0	9.1
Market value ($ mil.)	(11.3%)	86.4	90.5	84.6	41.2	53.5
Employees	1.0%	283	277	265	285	294

HORIZON BAY MANAGEMENT, L.L.C

5102 W. Laurel St., Ste. 700
Tampa, FL 33607
Phone: 813-287-3900
Fax: 813-287-3914
Web: www.horizonbay.com

CEO: Thilo D. Best
CFO: Jon A. DeLuca
HR: —
FYE: December 31
Type: Private

Horizon Bay Management operates a spread of senior housing communities in the US. Operating as Horizon Bay Retirement Living, the company manages independent- and assisted-living residential facilities, primarily targeting the higher-end market. It operates about 80 senior housing communities, which are located in 15 primarily southern and midwestern states and have a total of about 14,000 living units. The company's LiveWell! program, which promotes health and well-being among residents, offers educational classes and activities. Chartwell Seniors Housing REIT, a real estate investment trust that owns most of Horizon's managed properties, owns a controlling stake in Horizon Bay, which was founded in 2001.

HORIZON GROUP PROPERTIES, INC.

Pink Sheets: HGPI

5000 Hakes Dr., Ste. 500
Muskegon, MI 49441
Phone: 231-798-9100
Fax: 231-798-5100
Web: www.horizongroup.com

CEO: Gary J. Skoien
CFO: David R. Tinkham
HR: —
FYE: December 31
Type: Public

Horizon Group Properties owns, develops, renovates, and operates shopping properties. The company's portfolio includes a handful of factory outlet shopping centers in a number of states throughout the US. Horizon's centers are occupied by tenants such as clothing retailers Polo Ralph Lauren, Tommy Hilfiger, and The Gap. Horizon Group Properties is also developing a master-planned community in suburban Chicago. The company is the product of a spinoff of properties left over from the 1998 merger of Prime Retail and Horizon Group.

HORIZON HEALTHCARE SERVICES, INC.

3 Penn Plaza East
Newark, NJ 07105
Phone: 973-466-4000
Fax: 973-466-4317
Web: www.horizon-bcbsnj.com

CEO: William J. Marino
CFO: Robert J. Pures
HR: Margaret Coons
FYE: December 31
Type: Not-for-profit

Horizon Healthcare Services is growing good health for Garden Staters. The company, dba Horizon Blue Cross Blue Shield of New Jersey, is New Jersey's top health insurance provider, serving about 3.6 million members. The not-for-profit company, a licensee of the Blue Cross and Blue Shield Association, offers traditional indemnity and managed care plans, including HMO, PPO, POS, and Medicare Advantage plans. It also provides dental and behavioral health coverage and manages workers' compensation claims through Horizon Casualty Services. Horizon Healthcare — which is led by CEO William Marino — is in the process of converting to a for-profit corporation.

	Annual Growth	12/04	12/05	12/06	12/07	12/08
Sales ($ mil.)	9.7%	5,504.2	6,025.3	6,730.3	7,526.5	7,963.0
Net income ($ mil.)	—	172.8	213.8	180.1	161.0	(45.0)
Employees	4.3%	4,400	4,400	4,700	5,200	5,200

HORIZON LINES, INC.

NYSE: HRZ

4064 Colony Rd., Ste. 200
Charlotte, NC 28211
Phone: 704-973-7000
Fax: 704-973-7075
Web: www.horizonlines.com

CEO: Charles G. (Chuck) Raymond
CFO: Michael T. (Mike) Avara
HR: —
FYE: December 31
Type: Public

Horizon Lines rides the waves to connect the mainland US with its far-flung states and territories. The container shipping company transports cargo such as building materials, consumer goods, and food to and from the continental US and Alaska, Hawaii, Guam, and Puerto Rico. It maintains a fleet of about 20 containerships and about 18,500 cargo containers. Besides marine transportation, the company offers logistics software and services through Horizon Logistics, LLC. The majority of Horizon Lines' revenue (85%) comes from operations subject to the Jones Act, which restricts marine shipping between US ports to US-owned companies operating US-built vessels.

	Annual Growth	12/05	12/06	12/07	12/08	12/09
Sales ($ mil.)	1.4%	1,096.2	1,156.9	1,206.5	1,304.3	1,158.5
Net income ($ mil.)	—	(23.4)	72.4	28.9	3.1	(31.3)
Market value ($ mil.)	(17.7%)	369.3	820.8	567.5	106.3	169.6
Employees	0.2%	1,881	1,878	2,162	2,151	1,895

HORIZON MEDIA, INC.

630 3rd Ave.
New York, NY 10017
Phone: 212-916-8600
Fax: 212-916-8653
Web: www.horizonmedia.com

CEO: William A. (Bill) Koenigsberg
CFO: Vinnie O'Toole
HR: Eileen Benwitt
FYE: December 31
Type: Private

Anxious to boost your media's magnitude? Horizon Media, one of the larger independent media buying shops, plans, coordinates, and negotiates deals across the media spectrum (television, radio, newspapers, billboards, and digital). The company's Eurizon subsidiary provides media services to European clients through offices in Amsterdam, and its membership in Columbus Media International extends its reach worldwide. Horizon Media's client list has included NBC, Harrah's Entertainment Group, Panasonic, and Telemundo. The company has offices in California and New York. CEO and President Bill Koenigsberg founded Horizon Media in 1989.

	Annual Growth	12/04	12/05	12/06	12/07	12/08
Est. sales ($ mil.)	11.1%	—	—	—	1,800.0	2,000.0
Employees	—	—	—	—	—	475

An in-depth profile of this company is available to Hoover's Online members at hoovers.com.

777

HORIZON MILLING, LLC

15407 McGinty Rd. West
Wayzata, MN 55391
Phone: 952-742-2373
Fax: 952-742-4050
Web: www.horizonmilling.com

CEO: Guy R. Shoemaker
CFO: —
HR: —
FYE: December 31
Type: Joint venture

Horizon Milling is a leading producer of durum and semolina wheat flours with about 20 production facilities throughout the US and in Canada. It makes bakery flours and other specialty products primarily for food manufacturers and foodservice operators, as well as private-label flours for the retail market. In addition to customers in North America, Horizon Milling exports flour worldwide. The company was formed in 2002 as a joint venture between diversified food and agricultural products giant Cargill and grain marketer CHS (which owns about 25% of the business).

	Annual Growth	12/04	12/05	12/06	12/07	12/08
Est. sales ($ mil.)	—	—	—	—	—	189.4
Employees	—	—	—	—	—	980

HORIZON NATIONAL CONTRACT SERVICES, LLC

151 Bodman Place
Red Bank, NJ 07701
Phone: 732-945-1600
Fax: 732-945-1800
Web: www.horizon-ns.com

CEO: Michael Sullivan
CFO: —
HR: Debra Finn
FYE: —
Type: Subsidiary

Someone's gotta buff all those linoleum floors. Horizon National Contract Services offers commercial cleaning services for financial, health care, and retail facilities. The firm provides janitorial, floor care, and window cleaning services, as well as construction clean-up, landscape maintenance, and porter services. Clients have included Dollar Tree, KinderCare, Office Max, and Target. In December 2007 Horizon was acquired by Transfield Services Limited, an Australia-based provider of diversified management services.

⊞ HORMEL FOODS CORPORATION

NYSE: HRL

1 Hormel Place
Austin, MN 55912
Phone: 507-437-5611
Fax: 507-437-5129
Web: www.hormelfoods.com

CEO: Jeffrey M. Ettinger
CFO: Jody H. Feragen
HR: David P. Juhlke
FYE: October 31
Type: Public

Now that Hormel Foods has stocked its pantry with ethnic convenience foods, can we look forward to SPAM soufflé, SPAM enchiladas, or SPAM curry? Along with its famous canned "spiced ham," SPAM, the company has branched out into convenience, ethnic, and frozen foods, offering brands such as Chi-Chi's Mexican, Marrakesh Express, and House of Tsang Asian products. Its other offerings include canned Stagg chili and Dinty Moore beef stews. In addition, Hormel is a top US turkey processor and a major pork processor, making Jennie-O turkey products, Cure 81 hams, and Always Tender fresh pork. Thirty-four Hormel brands are ranked #1 or #2 in their respective markets.

	Annual Growth	10/05	10/06	10/07	10/08	10/09
Sales ($ mil.)	4.8%	5,414.0	5,745.5	6,193.0	6,754.9	6,533.7
Net income ($ mil.)	7.8%	253.5	286.1	301.9	285.5	342.8
Market value ($ mil.)	3.5%	4,250.0	4,826.0	4,875.5	3,776.9	4,872.8
Employees	1.4%	17,600	18,100	18,500	19,100	18,600

HORNBECK OFFSHORE SERVICES, INC.

NYSE: HOS

103 Northpark Blvd., Ste. 300
Covington, LA 70433
Phone: 985-727-2000
Fax: 985-727-2006
Web: www.hornbeckoffshore.com

CEO: Todd M. Hornbeck
CFO: James O. Harp Jr.
HR: Kimberly S. Patterson
FYE: December 31
Type: Public

At the beck and call of oil companies, Hornbeck Offshore Services provides marine transportation of oil field equipment and supplies and petroleum products. The company operates offshore supply vessels (OSVs) that support offshore oil and gas drilling and production in the deepwater regions of the Gulf of Mexico. The company's fleet of about 45 OSVs transports cargo such as pipe and drilling mud, as well as rig crew members. Hornbeck also operates ocean-going tug and tank barge units that transport crude and refined petroleum products in the northeastern US, Great Lakes, and Puerto Rico as well as Mexico, Trinidad, Brazil, and Qatar. Its fleet includes about 15 tugs and 20 barges.

	Annual Growth	12/05	12/06	12/07	12/08	12/09
Sales ($ mil.)	20.6%	182.6	274.6	339.0	432.1	385.9
Net income ($ mil.)	7.7%	37.4	75.7	94.8	117.1	50.4
Market value ($ mil.)	(8.1%)	862.8	942.0	1,186.1	431.2	614.3
Employees	11.8%	657	742	1,092	1,113	1,025

HORNE INTERNATIONAL, INC.

OTC: HNIN

2677 Prosperity Ave., Ste. 300
Fairfax, VA 22031
Phone: 703-641-1100
Fax: 703-641-0440
Web: www.horne.com

CEO: Darryl K. Horne
CFO: Paige Shannon
HR: —
FYE: December 31
Type: Public

At the nexus where government agencies, national security, and environmental sustainability meet, you'll find Horne International. Through its primary operating subsidiary, Horne Engineering Services, the company offers military base and homeland security, missile defense, ecosystems management and restoration, and business process engineering services. It also offers public outreach services, including the organization of public meetings and drafting Congressional testimony. Not surprisingly, the US government's departments of Homeland Security, Defense, and Transportation are Horne's primary customers. Horne, which has struggled in the recession, owes nearly 90% of sales to its three largest customers.

	Annual Growth	12/05	12/06	12/07	12/08	12/09
Sales ($ mil.)	(45.6%)	53.7	28.3	17.7	4.9	4.7
Net income ($ mil.)	—	(4.0)	(8.6)	(19.1)	(6.1)	(0.3)
Market value ($ mil.)	(38.9%)	30.3	20.1	7.7	1.3	4.2
Employees	(17.9%)	88	100	50	40	40

⊞ HORNELL BREWING CO., INC.

644 Linn St., Ste. 318
Cincinnati, OH 45203
Phone: 516-812-0300
Fax: 516-326-4988
Web: www.arizonabev.com

CEO: Richard (Rick) Adonailo
CFO: Richard (Rick) Adonailo
HR: —
FYE: December 31
Type: Private

At Hornell Brewing (which does business as Ferolito, Vultaggio & Sons) image is everything. Colorful, arty bottle and can designs distinguish the company's beverages — including AriZona iced teas, energy drinks, and fruit drinks — from the competition. The company's beverages are top sellers in the ready-to-drink iced tea sector in the US. Flavors include Green Tea with Ginseng, Pomegranate Green Tea, and Blueberry White Tea. Its other products include energy and sports drinks, juice, and smoothies. In addition to tea, Hornell Brewing makes and sells malt liquor and beer (Crazy Stallion, Mississippi Mud) and bottled water. Co-founders John Ferolito and Don Vultaggio own and run the company.

HORSEHEAD HOLDING CORP.

NASDAQ (GM): ZINC

300 Frankfort Rd.
Monaca, PA 15061
Phone: 724-774-1020
Fax: 724-774-4348
Web: www.horseheadcorp.com

CEO: James M. Hensler
CFO: Robert D. (Bob) Scherich
HR: Daryl K. Fox
FYE: December 31
Type: Public

Bearing out the adage that one person's trash is another's treasure, Horsehead turns zinc-containing dust into zinc and value-added zinc products. (Yes, "value-added zinc products.") Key raw materials for the company include dust from the electric-arc furnaces used at steel minimills and residue from the galvanizing of metals. Besides zinc metal (used in galvanizing and alloying), Horsehead's products include zinc oxide (used in the agricultural, chemical, and pharmaceutical industries) and zinc dust (used in corrosion-resistant coatings). The company operates from facilities in Illinois, Oklahoma, Pennsylvania, Tennessee, and Texas.

	Annual Growth	12/05	12/06	12/07	12/08	12/09
Sales ($ mil.)	(5.7%)	273.8	496.4	545.6	445.9	216.5
Net income ($ mil.)	—	3.1	54.5	90.7	39.4	(27.5)
Market value ($ mil.)	(13.3%)	—	—	735.4	203.7	552.5
Employees	(3.0%)	1,033	1,023	1,060	1,010	915

HOSHINO (U.S.A.) INC.

1726 Winchester Rd.
Bensalem, PA 19020
Phone: 215-638-8670
Fax: 215-245-8583
Web: www.hoshinousa.com

CEO: Bill Reim
CFO: —
HR: —
FYE: August 31
Type: Subsidiary

If you've heard of Ibanez and Tama — major names in guitars and drums — then you've indirectly heard of Hoshino (U.S.A.) and its Japanese parent, Hoshino Gakki. The company serves as the wholesale and distribution arm to countries outside of Japan. It also works with its parent's Ibanez and Tama units to design prototypes and custom musical instruments. Ibanez products include guitars, basses, and electronics. Tama-branded items include drums and related gear (pedals, stands, racks). Originally named Elger when it was acquired in 1971, the company changed its name to Hoshino (U.S.A.) in 1980.

HOSPIRA, INC.

NYSE: HSP

275 N. Field Dr.
Lake Forest, IL 60045
Phone: 224-212-2000
Fax: 224-212-3350
Web: www.hospira.com

CEO: Christopher B. Begley
CFO: Thomas E. Werner
HR: Kenneth F. (Ken) Meyers
FYE: December 31
Type: Public

Hospira helps hospitals help the hurting. The company, a spinoff of drug manufacturer Abbott Laboratories, makes specialty injectable pharmaceuticals (primarily generics) and drug delivery equipment. Its medication delivery systems include drug pumps, infusion therapy devices, and related medication management software. Its injectable drugs include cardiovascular, anesthesia, and anti-infective therapies. In addition, Hospira provides contract manufacturing services for injectable pharmaceuticals.A good portion of Hospira's sales are to group purchasing organizations (GPOs), including Broadlane, Novation, and Premier.

	Annual Growth	12/05	12/06	12/07	12/08	12/09
Sales ($ mil.)	10.2%	2,626.7	2,688.5	3,436.2	3,629.5	3,879.3
Net income ($ mil.)	14.4%	235.6	237.7	136.8	320.9	403.9
Market value ($ mil.)	4.5%	7,096.5	5,570.4	7,073.3	4,449.0	8,460.1
Employees	(0.9%)	14,000	13,000	14,000	14,500	13,500

⊞ HOSPITALITY PROPERTIES TRUST

NYSE: HPT

400 Centre St.
Newton, MA 02458
Phone: 617-964-8389
Fax: 617-969-5730
Web: www.hptreit.com

CEO: John G. Murray
CFO: Mark L. Kleifges
HR: —
FYE: December 31
Type: Public

Hospitality Properties Trust (HPT) rolls out the welcome mat for the road-weary. The real estate investment trust (REIT) owns nearly 300 hotels throughout the US and in Canada and Puerto Rico, as well as 185 full-service truck stops operating as TravelCenters of America and Petro Stopping Centers. Unlike other hospitality REITs, HPT invests in hotels but not does control the operations of those properties. Rather, it leases them to operating companies (usually former owners). Its hotels target different markets, from upscale (Crowne Plaza Hotels & Resorts) to business and family travelers (Residence Inn by Marriott). Also unlike some hospitality REITs, HPT is not affiliated with any one branded hotel company.

	Annual Growth	12/05	12/06	12/07	12/08	12/09
Sales ($ mil.)	5.6%	834.4	1,039.4	1,280.6	1,252.7	1,037.2
Net income ($ mil.)	10.4%	129.9	169.0	331.0	134.0	193.3
Market value ($ mil.)	(10.9%)	4,644.7	5,505.3	3,975.6	1,834.8	2,925.6
Employees	13.5%	400	450	500	585	—

⊞ HOST HOTELS & RESORTS, INC.

NYSE: HST

6903 Rockledge Dr., Ste. 1500
Bethesda, MD 20817
Phone: 240-744-1000
Fax: 240-744-5125
Web: hosthotels.com

CEO: W. Edward (Ed) Walter
CFO: Larry K. Harvey
HR: —
FYE: December 31
Type: Public

Host Hotels & Resorts will leave the chandelier on for you. The largest hotel real estate investment trust (REIT) in the US, Host Hotels owns some 120 luxury and upscale hotels in North America, South America, and Europe. Most of its hotels operate under the Marriott and Ritz-Carlton brands and are managed by sister firm Marriott International. Other brands include Four Seasons and Hyatt. To maintain its REIT status, the company operates through majority-owned Host Hotels & Resorts LP. All properties are leased to management firms. Host Hotels holds interests in several partnerships, including a 49% stake in Tiburon Golf Ventures, which operates a golf course in Florida.

	Annual Growth	12/05	12/06	12/07	12/08	12/09
Sales ($ mil.)	1.1%	3,984.0	4,935.0	5,480.0	5,311.0	4,158.0
Net income ($ mil.)	—	166.0	738.0	727.0	427.0	(258.0)
Market value ($ mil.)	(10.9%)	12,205.1	15,811.8	10,974.9	4,875.6	7,681.2
Employees	(2.4%)	205	229	243	215	186

⊞ HOSTESS BRANDS, INC.

6031 Connection Dr.
Irving, TX 75039
Phone: 972-532-4500
Fax: 972-892-7694
Web: www.hostessbrands.com

CEO: Craig D. Jung
CFO: J. Randall Vance
HR: Warren N. Richards
FYE: May 31
Type: Private

It's no Wonder that a Hostess would show her Home Pride by serving breads and sweet goods made by Hostess Brands (formerly Interstate Bakeries Corporation). As one of the nation's largest wholesale bakers, it operates 39 bakeries and some 700 bakery outlet stores, delivering baked goods to US supermarkets, mass marketers, and convenience stores. The company's national and regional bread brands include Wonder, Home Pride, and Beefsteak. It sells snackcakes, donuts, and sweet baked goods. Its brands include Hostess Fruit Pies, Ho-Hos, and Twinkies, it also produces croutons and stuffing under the Mrs. Cubbison's and Marie Callender's names. The company filed for bankruptcy protection in 2004 and emerged in 2009.

	Annual Growth	5/05	5/06	5/07	5/08	5/09
Est. sales ($ mil.)	—	—	—	—	—	2,700.0
Employees	—	—	—	—	—	21,000

⊞ An in-depth profile of this company is available to Hoover's Online members at hoovers.com.

779

HOT TOPIC, INC.

NASDAQ (GS): HOTT

18305 E. San Jose Ave.
City of Industry, CA 91748
Phone: 626-839-4681
Fax: 626-839-4686
Web: www.hottopic.com

CEO: Elizabeth M. (Betsy) McLaughlin
CFO: James J. (Jim) McGinty
HR: Robin L. Elledge
FYE: January 31
Type: Public

What's the Hot Topic? "Everything About the Music," according to this teen-focused retailer. Hot Topic's 680 mall-based stores in the US and Puerto Rico sell rock-inspired clothing and accessories in settings resembling the industrial clubs where kids (ages 12 to 22) rock out. The retailer also runs some 155 Torrid shops offering apparel and accessories for plus-sized females (as old as 29!). Though focused on selling licensed concert apparel from current and classic rockers including AFI, Slipknot, Nirvana, and Metallica, Hot Topic also sells tees celebrating pop culture and trendy apparel that appeals to various musical subcultures. Hot Topic was founded in 1989 to fill the music-licensed apparel niche.

	Annual Growth	1/06	1/07	1/08	1/09	1/10
Sales ($ mil.)	0.4%	725.1	751.6	728.1	761.1	736.7
Net income ($ mil.)	(14.6%)	22.4	13.6	16.0	19.7	11.9
Market value ($ mil.)	(20.5%)	639.1	463.3	247.0	380.1	255.9
Employees	(1.5%)	9,871	9,794	9,448	9,200	9,300

HOTELS.COM, L.P.

10440 N. Central Expwy., Ste. 400
Dallas, TX 75231
Phone: 214-361-7311
Fax: 214-361-7299
Web: www.hotels.com

CEO: David Roche
CFO: —
HR: —
FYE: December 31
Type: Subsidiary

Hotels.com (formerly Hotel Reservations Network) wants to transform the Internet into the inn-ternet. The company books rooms at more than 99,000 properties in markets throughout Asia, North America, Europe, the Middle East, and South Africa through several websites. It also accepts reservations through its toll-free call centers. Through Internet and call center affiliates, Hotels.com offers rooms at discounts of up to 70%. Hotels.com includes 360-degree virtual tours, property descriptions, rate calendars, maps, and more than 1 million guest reviews. The company has room supply agreements with hotel chains such as Hilton Worldwide, Best Western, Radisson, and Sheraton. Hotels.com is a subsidiary of Expedia.

HOUCHENS INDUSTRIES, INC.

700 Church St.
Bowling Green, KY 42102
Phone: 270-843-3252
Fax: 270-780-2877
Web: www.houchensindustries.com

CEO: James (Jimmie) Gipson
CFO: Gordon Minter
HR: Sharon Grooms
FYE: September 30
Type: Private

Houchens Industries is a supermarket of businesses as well as an operator of supermarkets. The diversified company runs about 170 grocery stores under the Houchens, Food Giant, IGA, Piggly Wiggly, and Buy Low banners. Its 215 Save-A-Lot discount grocery stores in a dozen states offer limited selections and cover 15,000 sq. ft. or less. Houchens also owns about 85 convenience stores and two dozen Tobacco Shoppe discount cigarette outlets, mostly in Kentucky and Tennessee. It sold cigarette maker Commonwealth Brands in 2007. Other businesses include construction, financial services, real estate, and recycling. Founded as BG Wholesale in 1917 by Ervin Houchens, the firm is 100%-owned by its employees.

	Annual Growth	9/04	9/05	9/06	9/07	9/08
Sales ($ mil.)	5.7%	2,005.0	2,360.0	1,890.0	2,000.0	2,500.0
Employees	16.2%	9,229	11,487	10,500	12,000	16,826

HOUGHTON INTERNATIONAL INC.

Madison and Van Buren Aves.
Valley Forge, PA 19482
Phone: 610-666-4000
Fax: 610-666-1376
Web: www.houghtonintl.com

CEO: Paul DeVivo
CFO: David H. Hays
HR: Wesley D. (Wes) Warner
FYE: December 31
Type: Private

It wouldn't have been called the Rust Belt if they'd used Houghton International's products more often. Houghton manufactures oils and specialty chemicals for lubrication in most of the big midwestern industries: metalworking, automotive, and steel as well as offshore deep-water oil drilling. Its products range from aluminum and steel rolling lubricants to rust preventatives to fire-resistant hydraulic fluids. Its Fluidcare system helps manufacturers reduce costs through chemical management and recycling. Based in Pennsylvania, Houghton maintains sales and manufacturing facilities throughout the world. The company was founded in 1865, and, in 2008, AEA Investors bought Houghton.

	Annual Growth	12/04	12/05	12/06	12/07	12/08
Est. sales ($ mil.)	—	—	—	—	—	467.1
Employees	—	—	—	—	—	1,600

HOUGHTON MIFFLIN HARCOURT PUBLISHING COMPANY

222 Berkeley St.
Boston, MA 02116
Phone: 617-351-5000
Fax: 617-351-1125
Web: www.hmco.com

CEO: Barry O'Callaghan
CFO: Michael Muldowney
HR: Ciara Smyth
FYE: December 31
Type: Private

Houghton Mifflin Harcourt Publishing Company would like to thank all the professional students out there. The firm is a top publisher of educational material, covering areas from pre-K through grade 12, as well as adult learners. It publishes textbooks and printed materials, and provides digital content on the Web and via CD-ROM. The company additionally publishes fiction and nonfiction titles and reference materials, and offers professional resources and educational services to teachers. The company has origins dating back to 1832, and is owned by Irish holding company Education Media Publishing Group.

HOULIHAN, LOKEY, HOWARD & ZUKIN, INC.

1930 Century Park West
Los Angeles, CA 90067
Phone: 310-553-8871
Fax: 310-553-2173
Web: www.hl.com

CEO: Jeffrey (Jeff) Werbalowsky
CFO: Gary E. Meek
HR: Cynthia Bush
FYE: December 31
Type: Subsidiary

Investment bank Houlihan Lokey Howard & Zukin soldiers on for mergers on the economic front. Operating as Houlihan Lokey, the firm provides advisory services for primarily mid-market companies involved in M&A deals and corporate restructurings, including the sale of distressed assets and other turnaround situations. Houlihan Lokey also raises private and public equity for midsized private and small-cap public companies. The company is among the top M&A advisors in the US, especially for deals valued at less than $1 billion. Houlihan Lokey operates about 15 offices in the US, Europe, and Asia. Japanese financial services company ORIX acquired control of the company in 2007.

HOULIHAN'S RESTAURANTS, INC.

8700 State Line Rd., Ste. 100
Leawood, KS 66206
Phone: 913-901-2500
Fax: 913-901-2666
Web: www.houlihans.com

CEO: Robert M. (Bob) Hartnett
CFO: Robert (Rob) Ellis
HR: Thuan Nguyen
FYE: December 31
Type: Private

Casual dining has been on Houlihan's menu for more than 30 years. Houlihan's Restaurants operates and franchises about 100 casual eateries in more than 20 states, mostly in the Eastern part of the US. Operating primarily under the Houlihan's Restaurant & Bar name, the restaurants offer a variety of main dishes, including burgers, pasta, and steaks, as well as appetizers and salads. About 60 Houlihan's locations are franchised. In addition to its flagship chain, the company operates a small number of other dining concepts, including Bristol Seafood Grill and J. Gilbert's Wood-Fired Steaks. Restaurant firm Gilbert-Robinson opened the first Houlihan's restaurant in 1972. A management group owns 51% of the company.

	Annual Growth	12/04	12/05	12/06	12/07	12/08
Est. sales ($ mil.)	—	—	—	—	—	150.0
Employees	—	—	—	—	—	4,200

HOUSTON AMERICAN ENERGY CORP.

NASDAQ (GM): HUSA

801 Travis St., Ste. 1425
Houston, TX 77002
Phone: 713-222-6966
Fax: 713-222-6440
Web: www.houstonamericanenergy.com

CEO: John F. Terwilliger
CFO: James J. (Jay) Jacobs
HR: —
FYE: December 31
Type: Public

Houston-based, with North and South American properties, and energy focused, Houston American Energy explores for and produces oil and natural gas, primarily in Colombia, but also along the US Gulf Coast. In 2008 the company reported proved reserves of 18.8 million cu. ft. of natural gas and about 213,000 barrels of oil. Of its 5,360 gross acres of proved developed leasehold, about 30% is in Colombia. The bulk of the balance is in Louisiana and Texas, although the oil and gas independent also holds some acreage in Oklahoma. President and CEO John Terwilliger owns 31% of Houston American Energy; director Orrie Tawes, 12%.

	Annual Growth	12/05	12/06	12/07	12/08	12/09
Sales ($ mil.)	29.3%	2.9	3.2	5.0	10.6	8.1
Net income ($ mil.)	—	(0.5)	(0.5)	0.5	0.5	(0.7)
Market value ($ mil.)	18.3%	97.9	228.8	94.8	105.1	191.5
Employees	31.6%	1	2	2	3	3

HOUSTON WIRE & CABLE COMPANY

NASDAQ (GM): HWCC

10201 North Loop East
Houston, TX 77029
Phone: 713-609-2100
Fax: 713-609-2101
Web: www.houwire.com

CEO: Charles A. Sorrentino
CFO: Nicol G. (Nic) Graham
HR: Carol M. Sims
FYE: December 31
Type: Public

Houston Wire & Cable (HWC) may have a Texas name, but it can keep customers wired from Seattle to Tampa. The company is a conduit between cable manufacturers and electrical distributors and their customers. It distributes specialty (electrical and electronic) wire and cable products, such as cable terminators, fiber-optic cables, and bare copper and building wire, as well as voice, data, and premise wire. It also provides cable management services (a custom program designed for wire and cable requirements) and an asset-management program (for the development and management of inventory). HWC operates 11 regional distribution centers in 10 states and sells primarily to electrical distributors.

	Annual Growth	12/05	12/06	12/07	12/08	12/09
Sales ($ mil.)	4.5%	214.0	323.5	359.1	360.9	254.8
Net income ($ mil.)	(10.6%)	12.5	30.7	30.2	23.7	8.0
Market value ($ mil.)	(17.1%)	—	370.6	250.8	165.1	211.0
Employees	(0.6%)	274	293	304	317	268

HOVENSA, L.L.C.

1 Estate Hope
Christiansted, St. Croix, VI 00820
Phone: 340-692-3000
Fax: 340-692-3521
Web: www.hovensa.com

CEO: Lawrence J. (Larry) Kupfer
CFO: Mike Fennessey
HR: —
FYE: December 31
Type: Joint venture

HOVENSA brings together US and Latin American know-how and operations to develop the oil industry in the US Virgin Islands. HOVENSA is a joint venture of Hess and Venezuelan oil giant PDVSA. The largest private employer in the US Virgin Islands, the company operates a 500,000-barrels-per-day crude oil refinery on St. Croix. This refinery operates two specialized oil processing complexes, a 150,000-barrels-per-day fluid catalytic cracking unit, and a 58,000-barrels-per-day delayed coker unit. In addition, Hess owns and operates a 70,000-barrels-per-day fluid catalytic cracking unit in Port Reading, New Jersey, to supply Hess-branded retail outlets in the Northeast.

	Annual Growth	12/04	12/05	12/06	12/07	12/08
Est. sales ($ mil.)	—	—	—	—	—	13,396.0
Employees	—	—	—	—	—	1,200

HOVIONE LLC

40 Lake Dr.
East Windsor, NJ 08520
Phone: 609-918-2600
Fax: 609-918-2615
Web: www.hovione.com

CEO: Guy Villax
CFO: Miguel Calado
HR: —
FYE: December 31
Type: Subsidiary

Hovione is the US home of Hovione FarmaCiencia, a pharmaceutical ingredient (API) maker based in Portugal. APIs are used by pharmaceutical companies to develop new drugs. Hovione serves as its parent's US base and technology transfer center (TTC) where products made at its parent are stored, packaged, and re-distributed. The TTC is integrated into its parent company's global network so it's able to offer customers real-time data and regulatory support for production at the manufacturing plants. The site also has a research lab and a facility where smaller quantities of APIs are developed and shipped to customers before larger batches are ordered from the company's facilities in Europe and Asia.

HOVNANIAN ENTERPRISES, INC.

NYSE: HOV

110 W. Front St.
Red Bank, NJ 07701
Phone: 732-747-7800
Fax: 732-747-6835
Web: www.khov.com

CEO: Ara K. Hovnanian
CFO: J. Larry Sorsby
HR: Robyn T. Mingle
FYE: October 31
Type: Public

Gimme shelter. Hovnanian Enterprises designs, builds, and markets single-family detached homes, condominiums, and townhomes for first-time, move-up, and luxury buyers as well as for empty-nesters and active adults. Hovnanian delivered over 5,300 homes in fiscal 2009 (down from more than 20,000 in 2006), with base prices ranging from $36,000 to $1.8 million and averaging about $280,000. The company operates in some 180 communities in about 20 states, primarily operating along the East Coast and in the Midwest, California, and Texas. Its K. Hovnanian American Mortgage unit offers mortgage financing and title services. Members of the Hovnanian family control more than 90% of Hovnanian Enterprises.

	Annual Growth	10/05	10/06	10/07	10/08	10/09
Sales ($ mil.)	(26.1%)	5,348.4	6,148.2	4,798.9	3,308.1	1,596.3
Net income ($ mil.)	—	471.8	149.5	(627.1)	(1,124.6)	(716.7)
Market value ($ mil.)	(45.7%)	3,487.4	2,391.3	881.3	332.5	303.1
Employees	(26.8%)	6,084	6,239	4,318	2,816	1,750

An in-depth profile of this company is available to Hoover's Online members at hoovers.com.

781

HOWDEN BUFFALO INC.

2029 W. DeKalb St.
Camden, SC 29020
Phone: 803-713-2200
Fax: 803-713-2222
Web: www.howdenbuffalo.com

CEO: Dave McDowell
CFO: David Donnell
HR: —
FYE: December 31
Type: Subsidiary

Howden Buffalo provides a variety of air movement equipment, including axial and centrifugal fans, blowers, compressors, cooling systems, hydraulic drives, and rotary heat exchangers. The company's products are used for such applications as emission control; highway, tunnel, and mine ventilation; waste water treatment; wind tunnels; and a variety of other industrial processes. Its brand names include American Blower, Buffalo Forge, Canadian Blower & Forge, and G˝rol. Howden Buffalo is the North American operating unit of Howden Air and Gas, which is a subsidiary of Charter International. The company has facilities in Michigan, New York, Ohio, South Carolina, and also in Mexico City.

HOWROYD-WRIGHT EMPLOYMENT AGENCY, INC.

327 W. Broadway
Glendale, CA 91209
Phone: 818-240-8688
Fax: —
Web: www.appleone.com

CEO: Bernard Howroyd
CFO: Michael Hoyal
HR: Deborah Guzman
FYE: December 31
Type: Private

An apple a day keeps the unemployment lines away. The Howroyd-Wright Employment Agency, doing business as AppleOne, is one of the nation's largest privately held employment agencies, with more than 200 offices across the US and Canada. It places job seekers in a variety of temporary and full-time positions in accounting, customer service, law, and information technology, among other fields. The company also offers its corporate clients human resources services, such as payroll and tax filing, continuing education, and outplacement. President Bernard Howroyd, who founded the company in 1964 after a conversation in a bar with an unhappy temp worker, controls AppleOne.

⊞ HP ENTERPRISE SERVICES, LLC

5400 Legacy Dr.
Plano, TX 75024
Phone: 972-604-6000
Fax: 972-605-6033
Web: h10134.www1.hp.com

CEO: Thomas J. (Tom) Iannotti
CFO: —
HR: Tina M. Sivinski
FYE: December 31
Type: Subsidiary

They started it! HP Enterprise Services, formerly Electronic Data Systems (EDS), pioneered the computer outsourcing business. The company delivers such services as systems integration, network and systems operations, data center management, application development, and outsourcing. It is one of the largest federal government contractors, but it also serves commercial customers in a wide range of industries, including energy, entertainment, health care, manufacturing, media, and transportation. Top clients include the US Navy and former parent General Motors. HP Enterprise Services is a subsidiary of Hewlett-Packard and operates as part of the HP Enterprise Business segment.

HP HOOD LLC

6 Kimball Ln.
Lynnfield, MA 01940
Phone: 617-887-3000
Fax: 617-887-8484
Web: www.hood.com

CEO: John A. Kaneb
CFO: Gary R. Kaneb
HR: Bruce W. Bacon
FYE: December 31
Type: Private

HP Hood tries to cream its competition — with ice cream, sour cream, and whipping cream. The company, a leading US dairy producer, also makes fluid milk, cottage cheese, and juices. Its home turf is New England, where it is one of the few remaining dairies to offer home milk delivery. Hood's products are available at chain and independent food retailers and convenience stores, and to foodservice purveyors. In addition to its own brands, the company makes private-label, licensed, and franchise dairy products; Hood also owns regional dairy producers Kemps and Crowley Foods. The company operates more than 20 manufacturing plants throughout the US.

	Annual Growth	12/04	12/05	12/06	12/07	12/08
Est. sales ($ mil.)	(1.1%)	2,300.0	2,300.0	2,500.0	2,300.0	2,200.0
Employees	(1.9%)	4,850	5,000	5,400	4,500	4,500

HQ GLOBAL WORKPLACES

15305 Dallas Pkwy., Ste. 1400
Addison, TX 75001
Phone: 972-361-8100
Fax: 972-361-8005
Web: www.hq.com

CEO: Guillermo Rotman
CFO: Jeffrey (Jeff) McCall
HR: —
FYE: December 31
Type: Subsidiary

HQ Global Workplaces leases furnished and serviced office and conference space, offering flexible and short-term options to its customers. The company, which is part of the Regus Group, offers some 950 office centers and executive suites worldwide. The company provides communications and Internet services, staffing, and other business support services to its tenants. The firm was formed in 1999 when HQ Business Centers and Omni Offices merged; it was acquired by Frontline Capital Group in 2000. When HQ Global Workplaces emerged from Chapter 11 bankruptcy in late 2003, the arrangement included its separation from Frontline Capital. UK-based serviced-office provider Regus Group acquired HQ in 2004.

HSB GROUP, INC.

1 State St.
Hartford, CT 06103
Phone: 860-722-1866
Fax: 860-722-5106
Web: www.hsb.com

CEO: Douglas G. Elliot
CFO: Saul L. Basch
HR: Susan W. Ahrens
FYE: December 31
Type: Subsidiary

While its company's names might seem quaint, HSB Group is fully modernized and up to speed. The holding company for The Hartford Steam Boiler Inspection and Insurance Company, HSB Group subsidiaries provide commercial insurance and engineering consulting services. The firm specializes in insurance against equipment breakdown with specific policies for boilers, pressure vessels, computer systems, and other machinery. HSB Group augments its insurance business by offering engineering services to prevent equipment failure and providing risk management consulting. Formerly a subsidiary of American International Group (AIG), HSB Group is now owned by German reinsurer Munich Re.

HSBC CARD SERVICES INC.

1301E. Tower Rd.
Schaumburg, IL 60173
Phone: 716-841-7141
Fax: —
Web: www.hsbccreditcard.com

CEO: Niall S. K. Booker
CFO: Edgar D. Ancona
HR: Jon N. Couture
FYE: December 31
Type: Subsidiary

HSBC Card Services is the US consumer credit card segment of gigantic British bank HSBC Holdings. One of the top credit card issuers and servicers in the country, HSBC Card Services offers HSBC- and Household Bank-branded plastic from Visa, MasterCard, and American Express with a variety of annual percentage rates and rewards programs. Its Orchard Bank unit issues cards to consumers looking to establish or re-establish their credit. HSBC Card Services also offers branded cards from General Motors, Sak's Fifth Avenue, and Best Buy, among others.

[H] HSBC FINANCE CORPORATION

26525 N. Riverwoods Blvd.
Mettawa, IL 60045
Phone: 224-544-2000
Fax: —
Web: www.hsbcusa.com/hsbc_finance

CEO: Niall S. K. Booker
CFO: Edgar D. Ancona
HR: Jon N. Couture
FYE: December 31
Type: Subsidiary

Part of gigantic British bank HSBC Holdings, HSBC Finance issues credit cards to middle-class consumers in the US, with a focus on those with less-than-ideal credit. Offering Visa, MasterCard, American Express, and Discover cards, as well as private-label cards for department stores and other retailers, it has some 16 million cards in circulation. However, after HSBC Finance experienced a rash of delinquencies and defaults on subprime loans that it acquired in the secondary market, as well as on those it originated itself, the company stopped offering home mortgages and refinancing loans, car loans, and personal loans in 2009.

	Annual Growth	12/04	12/05	12/06	12/07	12/08
Est. sales ($ mil.)	—	—	—	—	—	14,989.0
Employees	—	—	—	—	—	19,020

HSBC NORTH AMERICA HOLDINGS INC.

26525 N. Riverwoods Blvd.
Mettawa, IL 60045
Phone: 224-544-2000
Fax: 224-552-4400
Web: www.us.hsbc.com

CEO: Brendan P. McDonagh
CFO: Edgar D. Ancona
HR: Jon N. Couture
FYE: December 31
Type: Subsidiary

Atlas may hold the world on his shoulders, but this company holds most of the North American continent. HSBC North America Holdings, a subsidiary of big British bank HSBC Holdings, was formed in 2004 to comprise all of HSBC's US and Canadian operations, including HSBC USA, HSBC Bank Canada, and HSBC Finance. (Ownership of HSBC Canada was transferred to HSBC Holdings in 2010.) HSBC USA has more than 450 locations, mainly in New York, that offer personal and commercial banking services, private banking, insurance, and corporate investment banking, while HSBC Finance issues Visa, MasterCard, and private-label credit cards.

HSBC USA INC.

452 5th Ave.
New York, NY 10018
Phone: 212-525-5000
Fax: —
Web: www.us.hsbc.com

CEO: Irene M. Dorner
CFO: Gerard Mattia
HR: Suzanne Brienza
FYE: December 31
Type: Subsidiary

HSBC USA, a subsidiary of British banking behemoth HSBC Holdings, operates HSBC Bank USA. With some 375 offices, the bank has one of the largest branch networks in New York State, plus more than 100 additional locations in about a dozen other states and Washington, DC; California, New Jersey, and Florida are its next largest markets. The bank offers personal, commercial, and mortgage banking services, with a loan portfolio dominated by residential mortgages, commercial loans, and credit card loans. HSBC Bank USA's personal financial services segment also provides mutual funds, investments, and insurance. The bank offers investment banking, private banking, brokerage, and trust services as well.

	Annual Growth	12/05	12/06	12/07	12/08	12/09
Assets ($ mil.)	(4.7%)	—	—	188,373.0	185,569.0	171,079.0
Net income ($ mil.)	—	—	—	138.0	(1,689.0)	(142.0)
Employees	0.0%	—	—	12,000	11,731	12,000

[H] HSN, INC.

NASDAQ (GS): HSNI

1 HSN Dr.
St. Petersburg, FL 33729
Phone: 727-872-1000
Fax: —
Web: www.hsn.com

CEO: Mindy Grossman
CFO: Judy Schmeling
HR: Lisa Letizio
FYE: December 31
Type: Public

There's no need to worry about normal business hours when shopping from this retailer. HSN (known to night owls and from-the-couch shoppers as Home Shopping Network) operates a home shopping television network, which reaches more than 91 million US homes, and a related website HSN.com. HSN sells apparel and accessories, jewelry, computers, electronics, housewares, health, beauty, and fitness products, and more. Its Cornerstone Brands business is a catalog and Internet retailer. Titles include Garnet Hill, Smith+Noble, and TravelSmith, among others. It also operates about 25 retail outlets. Founded in 1977, HSN was a subsidiary of Barry Diller's IAC/InterActiveCorp until 2008, when it was spun off.

	Annual Growth	12/05	12/06	12/07	12/08	12/09
Sales ($ mil.)	0.7%	2,671.0	2,878.0	2,908.2	2,823.6	2,749.6
Net income ($ mil.)	(24.5%)	223.2	122.8	164.8	(2,390.9)	72.5
Market value ($ mil.)	177.7%	—	—	—	417.0	1,158.1
Employees	(6.2%)	—	—	6,600	5,973	5,807

HSW INTERNATIONAL, INC.

NASDAQ (GM): HSWI

One Capital City Plaza, 3350 Peachtree Rd., Ste. 1150
Atlanta, GA 30326
Phone: 404-760-4729
Fax: —
Web: www.hswinternational.com

CEO: Gregory M. Swayne
CFO: Shawn G. Meredith
HR: —
FYE: December 31
Type: Public

HSW International knows how stuff works, and it wants to tell the world. The online publishing firm offers translated versions of the US-based site HowStuffWorks.com to viewers in China and Brazil, two emerging markets for digital technology. The site provides information, buying guides, and informational videos on science, health, travel, consumer products, and other topics. HSW International also owns career development training and educational software businesses in China through its 2007 merger with computer software maker INTAC International. HSW International is 43%-owned by HowStuffWorks. Formerly owned by The Convex Group, HowStuffWorks was acquired by Discovery Communications in 2007.

	Annual Growth	12/05	12/06	12/07	12/08	12/09
Sales ($ mil.)	176.9%	—	—	0.3	0.5	2.3
Net income ($ mil.)	—	—	—	(39.5)	(21.9)	(11.9)
Market value ($ mil.)	(77.9%)	—	—	334.4	20.4	16.3
Employees	(20.7%)	—	—	105	70	66

H.T. HACKNEY COMPANY

502 S. Gay St.
Knoxville, TN 37901
Phone: 865-546-1291
Fax: 865-546-1501
Web: www.hthackney.com

CEO: William B. (Bill) Sansom
CFO: Mike Morton
HR: —
FYE: March 31
Type: Private

The H.T. Hackney Company is a leading wholesale distributor of food products and other retail items serving more than 20,000 convenience stores and independent grocers in more than 20 states (mostly east of the Mississippi). The company supplies more than 25,000 items, including frozen food, tobacco products, health and beauty items, and deli products. In addition, it owns bottled water producer Natural Springs Water Group, and the company is involved in furniture manufacturing through subsidiary Holland House Furniture. Founded in 1891, H.T. Hackney is owned by chairman and CEO Bill Sansom.

	Annual Growth	3/04	3/05	3/06	3/07	3/08
Sales ($ mil.)	0.4%	3,500.0	3,550.0	3,600.0	3,550.0	3,550.0
Employees	0.0%	3,600	3,600	3,450	3,570	3,600

HUB GROUP, INC.

NASDAQ (GS): HUBG

3050 Highland Pkwy., Ste. 100
Downers Grove, IL 60515
Phone: 630-271-3600
Fax: 630-964-6475
Web: www.hubgroup.com

CEO: David P. Yeager
CFO: Terri A. Pizzuto
HR: —
FYE: December 31
Type: Public

Hub Group helps its clients by handling the hubbub of freight movement throughout North America. An intermodal marketing company, Hub Group specializes in arranging the transportation of freight by a combination of rail and truck. A customer's freight is loaded into a container or trailer and transported by rail from one Hub Group operating center to another, then taken to its destination by a local trucking company, which in some cases is operated by a Hub Group unit. The company also provides truck brokerage and logistics services. It operates from about 20 main offices, each located near one or more railheads. The family of the company's late founder, Phillip Yeager, owns a controlling stake in Hub Group.

	Annual Growth	12/05	12/06	12/07	12/08	12/09
Sales ($ mil.)	(0.3%)	1,531.5	1,609.5	1,658.2	1,860.6	1,511.0
Net income ($ mil.)	1.0%	32.9	48.7	59.8	59.2	34.3
Market value ($ mil.)	11.0%	671.6	1,046.8	1,010.0	1,008.1	1,017.9
Employees	2.9%	1,184	1,513	1,412	1,420	1,329

HUB INTERNATIONAL LIMITED

55 E. Jackson Blvd.
Chicago, IL 60604
Phone: 877-402-6601
Fax: 877-402-6606
Web: www.hubinternational.com

CEO: Martin P. Hughes
CFO: Daniel (Dani) Goldsmith
HR: Deborah Deters
FYE: December 31
Type: Private

Shouldn't it be Hub North American? Hub International is an insurance broker that provides property/casualty, life and health, employee benefits, and investment products in the US and Canada. Focusing on midsized commercial clients and affluent individuals, Hub operates throughout the US and in six Canadian provinces. It operates under an organizational structure composed of a head office and more than a dozen regional brokerages called "hub" brokerages. The US accounts for more than two-thirds of Hub International's total revenues.

	Annual Growth	12/04	12/05	12/06	12/07	12/08
Est. sales ($ mil.)	—	—	—	—	—	442.6
Employees	—	—	—	—	—	3,981

HUBBARD BROADCASTING, INC.

3415 University Ave.
St. Paul, MN 55114
Phone: 651-646-5555
Fax: 651-642-4103

CEO: Stanley S. Hubbard
CFO: —
HR: Suzanne Cook
FYE: December 31
Type: Private

This company's cupboard of media assets is anything but bare. Hubbard Broadcasting is a leading television station operator with about 10 stations in Minnesota, New York, and New Mexico. Its portfolio includes ABC affiliate KSTP (Minneapolis/St. Paul) and NBC affiliate WHEC (Rochester, New York). The company also has three radio stations in the Twin Cities market; its Hubbard Radio Network subsidiary produces syndicated programming for about 20 affiliate stations in the upper Midwest. In addition, Hubbard owns cable channel ReelzChannel through Hubbard Media Group, and it has a stake in the arts and leisure channel Ovation. Stanley E. Hubbard started the family-owned broadcasting empire in 1923.

THE HUBBARD GROUP, INC.

1936 Lee Rd.
Winter Park, FL 32789
Phone: 407-645-5500
Fax: 407-623-3865
Web: www.hubbardgroup.com

CEO: Jean-Marc Vautravers
CFO: Frederick (Fred) O'Dea Jr.
HR: Jim Barontini
FYE: December 31
Type: Subsidiary

The Hubbard Group, part of the Eurovia roadbuilding unit of French construction group VINCI, operates through heavy construction subsidiaries Hubbard Construction Company (stationed in Florida) and Blythe Construction (headquartered in North Carolina). The subsidiaries pave roads and build highways, bridges, drainage systems, and building foundations, primarily in the US Southeast, in both the private and public sectors. Projects have included the Lowe's Corporate Campus and the Orlando-Orange County Expressway. The Hubbard Group also maintains a surplus of construction equipment such as dozers, excavators, trimmers, loaders, and pavers that are available for purchase.

	Annual Growth	12/04	12/05	12/06	12/07	12/08
Est. sales ($ mil.)	—	—	—	—	—	407.2
Employees	—	—	—	—	—	1,400

HUBBELL INCORPORATED

NYSE: HUB

584 Derby Milford Rd.
Orange, CT 06477
Phone: 203-799-4100
Fax: 203-799-4205
Web: www.hubbell.com

CEO: Timothy H. (Tim) Powers
CFO: David G. Nord
HR: Stephen M. Mais
FYE: December 31
Type: Public

The Hubble telescope and Hubbell Inc. both feature lots of modern electrical equipment — but you don't have to go into space to check out Hubbell's wares. The company's two operating segments — Electrical (which now includes Hubbell's former Industrial Technology segment) and Power — make electrical and electronic products for commercial, industrial, telecommunications, and utility applications. Hubbell's products include lighting fixtures, outlet boxes, enclosures and fittings, wire and cable, insulators and surge arresters, and test and measurement equipment. The company gets most of its sales in the US.

	Annual Growth	12/05	12/06	12/07	12/08	12/09
Sales ($ mil.)	2.9%	2,104.9	2,414.3	2,533.9	2,704.4	2,355.6
Net income ($ mil.)	2.2%	165.1	158.1	208.3	222.7	180.1
Market value ($ mil.)	1.2%	2,707.6	2,713.0	3,096.5	1,961.1	2,838.5
Employees	3.0%	11,300	12,000	11,500	13,000	12,700

HUBER + SUHNER, INC.

19 Thompson Dr.
Essex Junction, VT 05452
Phone: 802-878-0555
Fax: 802-878-9880
Web: www.hubersuhnerinc.com

CEO: Drew Nixon
CFO: —
HR: Yvonne Barney
FYE: December 31
Type: Subsidiary

It's in Huber + Suhner's best interest that you stay connected. The company is the North American subsidiary of Switzerland's HUBER SUHNER AG. It manufactures radio-frequency (RF) and microwave cables, connectors, assemblies, antennas, and lightning protection for the automotive, communications, industrial, instrumentation, medical equipment, military/aerospace, and transportation industries. The company also manufactures fiber-optic cables, as well as other wire and cable products. Huber + Suhner has distributors, manufacturers' representatives, and sales offices across the US, and in Canada.

	Annual Growth	12/04	12/05	12/06	12/07	12/08
Est. sales ($ mil.)	—	—	—	—	—	64.9
Employees	—	—	—	—	—	116

HUBERT COMPANY, LLC

9555 Dry Fork Rd.
Harrison, OH 45030
Phone: 513-367-8600
Fax: 513-367-8603
Web: www.hubert.com

CEO: C. Bart Kohler
CFO: J. Gregory (Greg) Ollinger
HR: —
FYE: July 31
Type: Subsidiary

Hubert Company is a leading mail-order supplier of equipment and supplies for food retailers and foodservice operators. Its inventory includes tableware, kitchen equipment and supplies, and signage, as well as display cases, packaging, and uniforms. The company also offers assistance with store openings, design and decor, and new product testing. In addition to its US office, the company has offices in Canada and Europe. Founded in 1946, Hubert Company is a unit of Franz Haniel & Cie. subsidiary TAKKT, a leading German business-to-business mail order company.

HUDDLE HOUSE, INC.

5901-B Peachtree Dunwoody Rd., NE
Atlanta, GA 30328
Phone: 770-325-1300
Fax: —
Web: www.huddlehouse.com

CEO: Philip M. (Phil) Greifeld
CFO: Tom Cossuto
HR: Claudia Levitas
FYE: —
Type: Private

Bacon and eggs, hash browns, and toast, on three. Break! Huddle House operates and franchises more than 400 family-style restaurants that are popular spots for breakfast and coffee in Georgia, South Carolina, and more than a dozen other mostly southern states. In addition to their morning menu, the classic coffee shops serve standard American fare (burgers, fried chicken, and steak) for lunch and dinner. The restaurants are mostly run by franchisees and are typically open 24 hours a day. John Sparks opened the first Huddle House in 1964. The company is owned by private equity firm Allied Capital.

HUDSON CITY BANCORP, INC.

NASDAQ (GS): HCBK

W. 80 Century Rd.
Paramus, NJ 07652
Phone: 201-967-1900
Fax: 201-967-0332
Web: www.hcsbonline.com

CEO: Ronald E. Hermance Jr.
CFO: James C. Kranz
HR: —
FYE: December 31
Type: Public

Hudson City Bancorp is the holding company for Hudson City Savings Bank. Founded in 1868, the bank has more than 125 branches in the New York City metropolitan area, including northern New Jersey, Long Island, and Fairfield County, Connecticut, as well as coastal portions of New Jersey and that state's Philadelphia suburbs. Serving middle- to high-income consumers, it originates and purchases high-quality first residential mortgages, which account for more than 98% of its loan portfolio. The bank gathers funds for its lending and investment activities by offering checking and savings accounts, CDs, and IRAs. In 2008 it began collecting deposits from customers nationwide through its online banking service.

	Annual Growth	12/05	12/06	12/07	12/08	12/09
Assets ($ mil.)	21.0%	28,075.4	35,506.6	44,424.0	54,145.3	60,267.8
Net income ($ mil.)	17.6%	276.1	288.6	295.9	445.6	527.2
Market value ($ mil.)	3.2%	6,382.3	7,309.1	7,909.4	8,404.4	7,230.1
Employees	7.8%	1,150	1,319	1,362	1,496	1,552

HUDSON GROUP

One Meadowlands Plaza
East Rutherford, NJ 07073
Phone: 201-939-5050
Fax: 201-867-0067
Web: www.hudsongroupusa.com

CEO: Joseph (Joe) DiDomizio
CFO: —
HR: Rick Yockelson
FYE: December 31
Type: Private

Hudson Group doesn't care if you're traveling to Pasadena, California, or Poughkeepsie, New York, as long as you stop over in one of its shops. The company operates about 540 newsstands, bookstores, cafes, and specialty shops in some 70 airports and other transportation terminals throughout North America. The group's flagship Hudson News format is North America's only national newsstand brand. The shops offer travelers books, magazines, apparel, souvenirs, snacks, and beverages for their journey. Other formats include Hudson Booksellers, Kids Works, and Euro Cafe. Private equity firm Advent International acquired Hudson Group in 2007 and in 2008 merged it with Swiss travel retailer Dufry AG.

HUDSON HIGHLAND GROUP, INC.

NASDAQ (GM): HHGP

560 Lexington Ave.
New York, NY 10022
Phone: 212-351-7300
Fax: 917-256-8592
Web: www.hhgroup.com

CEO: Jon F. Chait
CFO: Mary Jane Raymond
HR: —
FYE: December 31
Type: Public

Hudson Highland Group offers specialty staffing and related consulting services through the three regional businesses of Hudson Global Resources, which target the Americas, the Asia/Pacific region, and Europe. Hudson Global Resources provides temporary and contract personnel as well as permanent recruitment services. The company focuses on mid-level professionals in specialized areas such as accounting and finance, legal, and information technology. Among the company's clients are small and large businesses, government agencies, and educational institutions. Hudson Highland serves more than 8,000 clients from about 100 offices in some 20 countries.

	Annual Growth	12/05	12/06	12/07	12/08	12/09
Sales ($ mil.)	(16.6%)	1,428.3	1,373.5	1,179.1	1,080.2	691.1
Net income ($ mil.)	—	5.3	22.1	15.0	(74.3)	(40.6)
Market value ($ mil.)	(27.7%)	558.1	536.2	270.4	107.7	152.7
Employees	(13.8%)	3,800	3,600	3,600	3,100	2,100

An in-depth profile of this company is available to Hoover's Online members at hoovers.com.

785

HUDSON TECHNOLOGIES, INC.

NASDAQ (CM): HDSN

1 Blue Hill Plaza
Pearl River, NY 10965
Phone: 845-735-6000
Fax: 845-512-6070
Web: www.hudsontech.com

CEO: Kevin J. Zugibe
CFO: James R. Buscemi
HR: —
FYE: December 31
Type: Public

Hudson Technologies defends the ozone. Using proprietary reclamation technology to remove moisture and impurities from refrigeration systems, it recovers and reclaims chlorofluorocarbons (CFCs) used in commercial air-conditioning and refrigeration systems. The company sells both reclaimed and new refrigerants and also buys used refrigerants for reclamation and sale. In addition, Hudson Technologies offers on-site decontamination services, as well as services designed to improve the efficiency of customers' refrigeration systems. Customers include commercial and industrial enterprises and government entities, along with refrigerant contractors, distributors, and wholesalers and makers of refrigeration equipment.

	Annual Growth	12/05	12/06	12/07	12/08	12/09
Sales ($ mil.)	6.0%	19.2	23.5	26.9	33.2	24.2
Net income ($ mil.)	—	2.3	2.1	(2.0)	6.7	(2.5)
Market value ($ mil.)	(4.2%)	36.3	23.5	20.3	28.3	30.6
Employees	5.7%	60	72	79	100	75

HUDSON VALLEY HOLDING CORP.

OTC: HUVL

21 Scarsdale Rd.
Yonkers, NY 10707
Phone: 914-961-6100
Fax: 914-961-7378
Web: www.hudsonvalleybank.com

CEO: James J. Landy
CFO: Stephen R. Brown
HR: —
FYE: December 31
Type: Public

Hudson Valley Holding is the parent company of Hudson Valley Bank, which serves individuals, businesses, municipalities, and not-for-profit organizations from more than 35 locations throughout metropolitan New York and lower Connecticut. The bank's focus is on real estate lending, which accounts for more than 80% of the company's loan portfolio. Other products and services include savings, checking, and money market accounts; commercial and industrial loans; consumer loans; credit cards; CDs; and IRAs. Bank subsidiary A.R. Schmeidler & Co. offers money management services.

	Annual Growth	12/05	12/06	12/07	12/08	12/09
Assets ($ mil.)	7.0%	2,032.7	2,291.7	2,330.7	2,540.9	2,665.6
Net income ($ mil.)	(11.4%)	30.9	34.1	34.5	30.9	19.0
Market value ($ mil.)	(10.0%)	602.1	628.0	768.3	727.9	395.3
Employees	8.5%	359	440	421	533	498

HUF NORTH AMERICA AUTOMOTIVE PARTS MANUFACTURING, CORP.

395 T. Elmer Cox Dr.
Greeneville, TN 37743
Phone: 423-787-8500
Fax: 423-787-8537
Web: www.huf-group.com

CEO: Johannes Michalski
CFO: Leslie Carbines
HR: —
FYE: December 31
Type: Private

Huffing and puffing won't unlock the door of a car secured by Huf North America Automotive Parts Manufacturing. A subsidiary of Germany-based Huf Hülsbeck & Fürst Gmbh & Co. KG, Huf supplies mechanical and electronic automobile locks and security systems. Its lineup includes lock sets, steering locks, and remote control systems. Operating through three plants, in Tennessee, Wisconsin, and Michigan, the company develops its products in partnership with auto manufacturers such as Chrysler, General Motors, and its largest customer, Ford.

HUFFY CORPORATION

6551 Centerville Business Pkwy.
Centerville, OH 45459
Phone: 937-865-2800
Fax: 937-865-5470
Web: www.huffy.com

CEO: Michael C. Buenzow
CFO: —
HR: —
FYE: December 31
Type: Private

Huffy has built a longtime business peddling bikes and other wheeled products to children. The company is best known for its all-purpose bikes, although its Micro Scooters and Playcenters play a big role in its products portfolio. Its Huffy, Micro, and Royce Union bikes include kids' bikes and tricycles, comfort cruisers, mountain bikes, and BMX racing bikes (which are bought from makers in Asia). Products include licensed names Disney, Dora, and Thomas & Friends, among others. Most of the company's products are sold through national and regional mass marketers and specialty retailers, such as Wal-Mart, The Sports Authority, Target, AAFES, and Kmart. In 2007 the company entered the playground equipment market.

HUGHES COMMUNICATIONS, INC.

NASDAQ (GM): HUGH

11717 Exploration Ln.
Germantown, MD 20876
Phone: 301-428-5500
Fax: 301-428-1868
Web: www.hughes.com

CEO: Pradman P. Kaul
CFO: Grant A. Barber
HR: —
FYE: December 31
Type: Public

Hughes Communications keeps its principal assets even higher than visionary Howard Hughes could have imagined. Through its operating subsidiary, Hughes Network Systems, the company provides broadband satellite products and services. It uses its very small aperture terminal (VSAT) equipment and satellite network to provide consumers and businesses with broadband Internet access. The company's network also enables network applications ranging from voice services to credit authorization. In addition to its services, the company provides equipment used by fixed and mobile communication systems operators.

	Annual Growth	12/05	12/06	12/07	12/08	12/09
Sales ($ mil.)	540.5%	0.6	858.7	970.6	1,060.4	1,009.7
Net income ($ mil.)	—	68.9	(39.1)	43.5	9.0	(52.7)
Market value ($ mil.)	(17.7%)	—	1,008.4	1,181.3	344.8	563.1
Employees	4.7%	1,850	1,828	1,872	1,958	2,223

HUGHES NETWORK SYSTEMS, LLC

11717 Exploration Ln.
Germantown, MD 20876
Phone: 301-428-5500
Fax: 310-428-1868
Web: www.hughes.com

CEO: Pradman P. Kaul
CFO: Grant A. Barber
HR: —
FYE: December 31
Type: Subsidiary

Hughes Network Systems wrote the book on satellite data and Internet access network services. The pioneering company is the leading provider of broadband satellite network equipment and services to the very small aperture terminal (VSAT) business market. It is also North America's leading provider of satellite Internet access to consumers. Hughes develops communications equipment for mobile satellite-based voice and data network operators and cellular mobile network operators, as well as other users of terrestrial microwave technology. The company is a wholly owned subsidiary of Hughes Communications.

	Annual Growth	12/04	12/05	12/06	12/07	12/08
Est. sales ($ mil.)	—	—	—	—	—	1,059.9
Employees	—	—	—	—	—	1,951

HUGHES TELEMATICS, INC.

NYSE Amex: HTC

41 Perimeter Center East, Ste. 400
Atlanta, GA 30346
Phone: 770-391-6400
Fax: 770-391-6429
Web: www.hughestelematics.com

CEO: Jeffrey A. (Jeff) Leddy
CFO: Craig J. Kaufmann
HR: —
FYE: December 31
Type: Public

HUGHES Telematics wants to keep drivers and fleet managers oriented. The company provides vehicle telematics products and services like GPS navigation, emergency support, and vehicle diagnostic systems. Through its Networkfleet subsidiary, HUGHES offers fleet tracking and reporting services to companies who want to track the location of company vehicles, monitor vehicle maintenance needs, or track mileage. It also designs systems that allow drivers to access content stored in digital music players, mobile phones, and other devices while in their vehicles.

	Annual Growth	12/05	12/06	12/07	12/08	12/09
Sales ($ mil.)	—	—	—	—	—	33.0
Net income ($ mil.)	—	—	—	—	—	(163.7)
Market value ($ mil.)	—	—	—	—	—	283.0
Employees	—	—	—	—	—	276

HUGOTON ROYALTY TRUST

NYSE: HGT

901 Main St., 17th Fl.
Dallas, TX 75283
Phone: 877-228-5083
Fax: 214-209-2431
Web: www.hugotontrust.com

CEO: Nancy G. Willis
CFO: Louis G. Baldwin
HR: —
FYE: December 31
Type: Public

Hugoton Royalty Trust was formed by Cross Timbers Oil Company (now XTO Energy) to pay royalties to shareholders based on the proceeds of sales from its oil and gas holdings. Payouts depend on oil and gas prices, the volume of gas and oil produced, and production and other costs. The trust receives 80% of the net proceeds from XTO Energy's properties, located in the Hugoton fields of Kansas, Oklahoma, and Texas; the Anadarko Basin of Oklahoma; and the Green River Basin of Wyoming. In 2008 the trust reported proved reserves of 3.3 million barrels of oil and 366.3 billion cu. ft. of natural gas. XTO Energy controls the trust, which is administered through Bank of America and has no officers.

	Annual Growth	12/05	12/06	12/07	12/08	12/09
Sales ($ mil.)	(26.8%)	105.2	91.4	70.6	117.4	30.2
Net income ($ mil.)	(27.3%)	104.8	90.9	69.4	116.5	29.3
Market value ($ mil.)	(19.3%)	1,516.4	984.0	897.2	642.0	643.2
Employees	—	—	—	—	—	—

HUHTAMAKI AMERICAS, INC.

9201 Packaging Dr.
De Soto, KS 66018
Phone: 913-583-3025
Fax: 913-583-8725
Web: www.us.huhtamaki.com

CEO: Clay Dunn
CFO: John O'Dea
HR: Carl Walker
FYE: December 31
Type: Subsidiary

Huhtamaki Americas doesn't have its customers eating out of its hands, but it does make products used to serve food. The company manufactures sturdy disposable tableware and food packaging, as well as shaped paperboard, plastic, flexible, and molded fiber plates, cups, bowls, and trays for foodservice customers, and retail consumers under the Chinet brand. Huhtamaki Americas also makes packaging products for goods such as baking and snack foods, detergents, food storage, personal care, electronics, and pet foods. Product extensions include color napkins and guest towels. The company operates through 13 facilities in North and South America and is part of the Finland-based global packaging giant Huhtamäki Oyj.

	Annual Growth	12/04	12/05	12/06	12/07	12/08
Est. sales ($ mil.)	—	—	—	—	—	300.0
Employees	—	—	—	—	—	3,000

HUHTAMAKI, INC.

9201 Packaging Dr.
De Soto, KS 66018
Phone: 913-583-3025
Fax: 913-583-8781
Web: www.us.huhtamaki.com/apps/fsbu/fsbusite.nsf

CEO: Clay Dunn
CFO: —
HR: —
FYE: December 31
Type: Subsidiary

Huhtamaki Foodservice creates the perfect teacup for your tempest! The business unit of Huhtamaki Americas manufactures the top selling Chinet dinnerware, as well as a myriad of disposable foodservice products. Its lineup includes plastic and paperboard cups and containers, and molded fiber carriers, plates, and bowls, in all shapes and sizes. Instead of virgin wood fiber, the company's eco-friendly molded fiber goods, such as Chinet, use either post-industrial or post-consumer recycled fiber. These goods are compostable, too. Huhtamaki Foodservice's plants dot the US. Founded as Keyes Fibre in 1903 by Martin Fibre, Huhtamaki Americas is a subsidiary of Huhtamäki Oyj.

	Annual Growth	12/04	12/05	12/06	12/07	12/08
Est. sales ($ mil.)	—	—	—	—	—	77.8
Employees	—	—	—	—	—	1,270

HULU, LLC

12312 W. Olympic Blvd.
Los Angeles, CA 90064
Phone: 310-571-4700
Fax: 310-571-4883
Web: www.hulu.com

CEO: Jason Kilar
CFO: Tom F. Fuelling
HR: —
FYE: December 31
Type: Joint venture

When the rich and famous name their offspring, anything is possible. NBC and FOX had a digital baby — and they called it Hulu. The company operates Hulu.com, a site that features video from nearly 200 content providers. Offerings include TV shows from FOX and NBC, as well as from subsidiary cable channels such as Bravo and Syfy. Hulu also shows films from studios including Sony and MGM. Content — all total, some 1,700 TV series and movies — is streamed on demand, free of charge the day after its broadcast debut. Hulu.com was launched in 2008 as a joint venture between NBC Universal (a unit of GE) and News Corp. (the parent of FOX); the following year Disney became a shareholder and content partner.

	Annual Growth	12/04	12/05	12/06	12/07	12/08
Est. sales ($ mil.)	—	—	—	—	—	3.1
Employees	—	—	—	—	—	40

⊞ HUMAN GENOME SCIENCES, INC.

NASDAQ (GM): HGSI

14200 Shady Grove Road
Rockville, MD 20850
Phone: 301-309-8504
Fax: 301-309-8512
Web: www.hgsi.com

CEO: H. Thomas (Tom) Watkins
CFO: David P. Southwell
HR: Susan Bateson
FYE: December 31
Type: Public

Human Genome Sciences (HGS) knows that the path to good health starts at the molecular level. Using its expertise in human genetics, the firm is working on therapies for infectious and autoimmune diseases and cancer. One of its lead candidates is Albuferon, a long-acting version of protein therapy interferon alpha that it is developing with Novartis to treat hepatitis C. Monoclonal antibody LymphoStat-B is also in later stages of clinical testing; GlaxoSmithKline is HGS's partner on the drug. With funding from the US government, HGS is developing an antibody that fights anthrax infection, and it has several anticancer antibodies at earlier stages of development.

	Annual Growth	12/05	12/06	12/07	12/08	12/09
Sales ($ mil.)	94.9%	19.1	25.8	41.9	48.4	275.7
Net income ($ mil.)	—	(239.4)	(251.2)	(262.4)	(244.9)	5.7
Market value ($ mil.)	37.5%	1,603.7	2,330.6	1,955.9	397.2	5,729.1
Employees	(0.9%)	880	770	850	880	850

⊞ An in-depth profile of this company is available to Hoover's Online members at hoovers.com.

787

HUMAN PHEROMONE SCIENCES, INC.

OTC: EROX

84 W. Santa Clara St., Ste. 720
San Jose, CA 95113
Phone: 408-938-3030
Fax: 408-938-3025
Web: www.naturalattraction.com

CEO: William P. Horgan
CFO: Gregory S. Fredrick
HR: —
FYE: December 31
Type: Public

Human Pheromone Sciences (HPS) hopes its animal magnetism makes consumers hot under the collar and jonesing for its scents. HPS makes fragrances for men and women that contain a patented synthetic version of a pheromone produced by the human body to stimulate the senses. It also licenses its technology to partners in the personal care products industry. The company's products are sold through its website and through direct marketing under the Natural Attraction name. The company has granted non-exclusive rights to the Natural Attraction brand in the US, Europe, and Japan. HPS also partners with consumer products companies to license its patented technology. Renovatio Global Funds owns about 16% of the company.

	Annual Growth	12/05	12/06	12/07	12/08	12/09
Sales ($ mil.)	22.5%	0.4	1.2	1.3	1.0	0.9
Net income ($ mil.)	—	(0.9)	(0.1)	0.0	(0.2)	(0.3)
Market value ($ mil.)	(6.9%)	0.8	3.7	2.9	1.0	0.6
Employees	0.0%	3	3	3	3	3

🔲 HUMANA INC.

NYSE: HUM

500 W. Main St.
Louisville, KY 40202
Phone: 502-580-1000
Fax: 502-580-3677
Web: www.humana.com

CEO: Michael B. (Mike) McCallister
CFO: James H. (Jim) Bloem
HR: Bonita C. (Bonnie) Hathcock
FYE: December 31
Type: Public

Medicare has made Humana a big-time player in the health insurance game. One of the country's largest Medicare providers and a top health insurer, Humana provides Medicare Advantage plans and prescription drug coverage to more than 3.4 million members throughout the US. It also administers managed care plans for other government programs, including Medicaid plans in Florida and Puerto Rico and TRICARE (a program for military personnel) in 10 southern states. Additionally, Humana offers traditional health plans and some specialty products (group life and disability insurance, for example) to commercial employers and individuals. All told, it covers more than 10 million health plan members in the US.

	Annual Growth	12/05	12/06	12/07	12/08	12/09
Sales ($ mil.)	21.1%	14,418.1	21,416.5	25,290.0	28,946.4	30,960.4
Net income ($ mil.)	35.5%	308.5	487.4	833.7	647.2	1,039.7
Market value ($ mil.)	(5.2%)	9,246.8	9,413.6	12,817.6	6,345.0	7,470.0
Employees	10.7%	18,700	22,300	25,000	28,900	28,100

THE HUMANE SOCIETY OF THE UNITED STATES

2100 L St. NW
Washington, DC 20037
Phone: 202-452-1100
Fax: 202-778-6132
Web: www.hsus.org

CEO: Wayne Pacelle
CFO: G. Thomas Waite III
HR: —
FYE: December 31
Type: Not-for-profit

The Humane Society of the United States (HSUS) is a watchdog for, well, watchdogs, along with all sorts of other domestic and wild animals. A leading animal protection organization, HSUS has more than 10.5 million human members and constituents. The organization supports the work of local humane societies and implements a variety of investigative, educational, advocacy, and legislative programs to promote animal welfare. Its campaigns have addressed issues such as animal fighting, factory farming, the fur trade, and hunting practices. Most of its revenue comes from contributions and grants. An affiliate, Humane Society International, operates in other countries. HSUS was founded in 1954.

HUNT CONSOLIDATED INC.

Fountain Place, 1445 Ross at Field, Ste. 1400
Dallas, TX 75202
Phone: 214-978-8000
Fax: 214-978-8888
Web: www.huntoil.com

CEO: Ray L. Hunt
CFO: Donald (Don) Robillard
HR: Paul Hoffman
FYE: December 31
Type: Private

Hunt Consolidated is a holding company for the oil and real estate businesses of Ray Hunt, son of legendary Texas wildcatter and company founder H.L. Hunt. Founded in 1934 (reportedly with H.L.'s poker winnings), Hunt Oil is an oil and gas production and exploration company with primary interests in North and South America. Hoping to repeat huge discoveries in Yemen, Hunt Oil is exploring in Canada, Ghana, Iraq, Madagascar, and Oman. Hunt Realty handles commercial and residential real estate investment management activities. Other businesses include ranching, private equity investments and energy (refining and power interests).

	Annual Growth	12/04	12/05	12/06	12/07	12/08
Est. sales ($ mil.)	7.7%	—	2,300.0	2,130.0	2,120.0	2,870.0
Employees	0.0%	—	3,000	3,000	3,000	3,000

HUNTER DOUGLAS INC.

2 Park Way
Upper Saddle River, NJ 07458
Phone: 201-327-8200
Fax: 201-327-7938
Web: www.hunterdouglas.com

CEO: Marvin B. (Marv) Hopkins
CFO: Gordon Khan
HR: Betty Lou Smith
FYE: December 31
Type: Subsidiary

Don't move, Hunter Douglas has got you covered — well, at least it has your *windows* covered. Hunter Douglas, the North American subsidiary of Netherlands-based Hunter Douglas N.V., makes a variety of blinds, shades, and shutters. The company markets its window coverings under such names as Country Woods and Chalet Woods (wood blinds), Silhouette (shades), Palm Beach (custom shutters), Vignette (Roman shades), Luminette (privacy sheers), and Duette (honeycomb shades). In addition to its own sales outlets and specialty blind and home decor stores, Hunter Douglas sells its window products through major retailers, including Home Depot and Lowe's.

🔲 HUNTINGTON BANCSHARES

NASDAQ (GS): HBAN

Huntington Center, 41 S. High St.
Columbus, OH 43287
Phone: 614-480-8300
Fax: 614-480-5284
Web: www.huntington.com

CEO: Stephen D. (Steve) Steinour
CFO: Donald R. Kimble
HR: Shirley Graham
FYE: December 31
Type: Public

Huntington Bancshares Incorporated is the holding company for The Huntington National Bank, which operates more than 600 branches in Ohio, Michigan, Indiana, Kentucky, Pennsylvania, and West Virginia. The bank offers commercial and consumer banking, and mortgage services. The company's Auto Finance and Dealer Services Group offers auto loans and provides commercial loans to car dealerships throughout the Midwest and other states. Huntington's Private Financial and Capital Markets Group provides asset management, private banking, and brokerage services to wealthy customers. Huntington Bancshares also offers trust and insurance services and has international offices in the Cayman Islands and Hong Kong.

	Annual Growth	12/05	12/06	12/07	12/08	12/09
Assets ($ mil.)	12.0%	32,764.8	35,329.0	54,697.5	54,352.9	51,554.7
Net income ($ mil.)	—	412.1	461.2	75.2	(113.8)	(3,094.2)
Market value ($ mil.)	(37.4%)	17,018.7	17,018.7	10,576.7	5,489.0	2,615.5
Employees	7.8%	7,602	8,081	11,925	10,951	10,272

HUNTSMAN CORPORATION
NYSE: HUN

500 Huntsman Way
Salt Lake City, UT 84108
Phone: 801-584-5700
Fax: 801-584-5781
Web: www.huntsman.com

CEO: Peter R. Huntsman
CFO: J. Kimo Esplin
HR: R. Wade Rogers
FYE: December 31
Type: Public

Huntsman Corporation is stalking profits in the world's chemical marketplace. The global chemical manufacturer supplies products through five operating segments. Its products include MDI, amines, surfactants, and epoxy-based polymers, as well as polyurethanes. Huntsman's chemicals are sold in more than 100 countries to a variety of customers in the adhesives, construction products, electronics, medical, and packaging industries. The founding Huntsman family still controls more than a one-third stake in the company after US specialty chemicals company Hexion (and its majority owner, Apollo Management) failed to close a deal to buy Huntsman for more than $10.5 billion in 2008.

	Annual Growth	12/05	12/06	12/07	12/08	12/09
Sales ($ mil.)	(12.0%)	12,961.6	10,623.6	9,650.8	10,215.0	7,763.0
Net income ($ mil.)	—	(6.9)	173.9	(165.6)	595.0	106.0
Market value ($ mil.)	(10.0%)	4,116.6	4,535.0	6,143.8	822.4	2,699.0
Employees	0.5%	10,800	15,000	12,900	12,600	11,000

HURCO COMPANIES, INC.
NASDAQ (GS): HURC

1 Technology Way
Indianapolis, IN 46268
Phone: 317-293-5309
Fax: 317-328-2811
Web: www.hurco.com

CEO: Michael Doar
CFO: John G. Oblazney
HR: Judy Summers
FYE: October 31
Type: Public

Head of the class: Hurco produces PC-based industrial controls and software — the brains of metalworking machines. Its control consoles, vertical machining, and turning centers cut, bend, and mold metal components. Hurco's key product, the computerized control, is made by its 35%-owned Taiwanese company. Machines tools are assembled in Taiwan by a wholly owned subsidiary, with their housings, fittings, and screws produced by neighboring contract suppliers. The lineup is used in small-batch metal cutting processes by subcontractors that supply OEMs with parts, and to a lesser extent, by majors, such as Boeing, General Motors, and I.B.M. Europe is Hurco's largest market, generating about two-thirds of its sales.

	Annual Growth	10/05	10/06	10/07	10/08	10/09
Sales ($ mil.)	(7.7%)	125.5	148.5	188.0	224.0	91.0
Net income ($ mil.)	—	16.4	15.5	20.9	22.5	(2.3)
Market value ($ mil.)	(2.8%)	114.8	167.8	367.8	144.9	102.4
Employees	8.3%	284	320	380	430	390

HURON CONSULTING GROUP INC.
NASDAQ (GS): HURN

550 W. Van Buren St.
Chicago, IL 60607
Phone: 312-583-8700
Fax: 312-583-8701
Web: www.huronconsultinggroup.com

CEO: James H. (Jim) Roth
CFO: James K. Rojas
HR: Mary M. Sawall
FYE: December 31
Type: Public

Huron Consulting Group aims to help keep companies sailing smoothly, but the firm also will dredge through financial statements to address issues that cause businesses to sink. The firm provides a variety of financial consulting services to corporate clients that are in financial distress or involved in other legal and regulatory disputes. Its consultants offer forensic accounting and economic analysis expertise and often serve as expert witnesses. The firm's operational consulting services are delivered primarily to health care and education enterprises and to law firms. Huron Consulting operates from a network of about 20 offices, primarily in the US but also in Asia, Europe, and the Middle East.

	Annual Growth	12/05	12/06	12/07	12/08	12/09
Sales ($ mil.)	31.7%	226.0	321.9	548.0	672.2	679.5
Net income ($ mil.)	—	17.8	26.7	41.9	40.7	(32.9)
Market value ($ mil.)	(1.0%)	528.2	998.3	1,775.2	1,260.9	507.3
Employees	25.9%	773	1,035	1,600	2,129	1,945

HUSSMANN INTERNATIONAL, INC.

12999 St. Charles Rock Rd.
Bridgeton, MO 63044
Phone: 314-291-2000
Fax: 314-298-4756
Web: www.hussmann.com

CEO: John Gialouris
CFO: —
HR: —
FYE: December 31
Type: Subsidiary

Refrigeration expert Hussmann International helps supermarkets and convenience stores chill out. A part of the Ingersoll-Rand group, the company manufactures and sells refrigerated display cases and other refrigerated and non-refrigerated systems, including beverage coolers, walk-in storage coolers, and air handlers, to the commercial food industry. Hussmann sells its products to customers in about 80 countries through a network of company-operated branch facilities and through independent distributors. The company was acquired by industrial giant Ingersoll-Rand in 2000 and, along with Thermo King, forms IR's Climate Control division.

HUTCHINSON TECHNOLOGY INCORPORATED
NASDAQ (GS): HTCH

40 W. Highland Park Dr. NE
Hutchinson, MN 55350
Phone: 320-587-3797
Fax: 320-587-1404
Web: www.htch.com

CEO: Wayne M. Fortun
CFO: Steven L. (Steve) Polacek
HR: Connie L. Pautz
FYE: September 30
Type: Public

Suspensions at Hutchinson Technology have nothing to do with getting kicked out of school. The company is a top global maker of disk drive suspension assemblies. These support the read-write head above the spinning magnetic disk in hard drives, typically at a height of about a millionth of an inch — 3,000 times thinner than a piece of paper. The company's products include conventional assemblies, trace suspension assemblies, and accessories such as base plates and flexures. Customers in Asia account for nearly all of sales. Hutchinson supplies a select number of large disk drive makers; its top three customers (SAE Magnetics/TDK, Western Digital, and Seagate) provide more than 90% of sales.

	Annual Growth	9/05	9/06	9/07	9/08	9/09
Sales ($ mil.)	(10.3%)	631.6	721.5	716.1	631.6	408.0
Net income ($ mil.)	—	54.9	20.5	7.3	(117.8)	(155.6)
Market value ($ mil.)	(27.8%)	610.2	491.5	574.7	270.5	165.9
Employees	(18.2%)	5,458	5,433	4,698	4,591	2,448

HUTHWAITE INC.

901 N. Glebe Rd., Ste. 200
Arlington, VA 22203
Phone: 703-467-3800
Fax: 703-467-3801
Web: www.huthwaite.com

CEO: John Golden
CFO: Ken Thomas
HR: —
FYE: December 31
Type: Subsidiary

Huthwaite helps salespeople on the go get in the know. The company creates custom training programs and workshops for sales teams and salespeople and provides services such as coaching, consulting, and assessments of sales staff. The firm targets industries such as software, financial services, media, transportation, and pharmaceuticals. Clients include Bank of America, Boeing, Google, and IBM. Huthwaite was founded by Neil Rackham, the author of *SPIN Selling*, a book based on his research study of successful selling and sales effectiveness. Huthwaite became a division of Informa plc in 2005 after the acquisition of Huthwaite's former parent company IIR (Institute of International Research).

An in-depth profile of this company is available to Hoover's Online members at hoovers.com.

789

HUTTIG BUILDING PRODUCTS, INC.   OTC: HBPI

555 Maryville University Dr., Ste. 240
St. Louis, MO 63141
Phone: 314-216-2600
Fax: 314-216-2601
Web: www.huttig.com

CEO: Jon P. Vrabely
CFO: Philip (Phil) Keipp
HR: —
FYE: December 31
Type: Public

Hut one! Hut two! Huttig Building Products works to make buying building supplies a snap. The company is one of the US's largest distributors of millwork, building materials, and wood products. Huttig sells doors, windows, moldings, trusses, wall panels, lumber, and other supplies through about 30 distribution centers throughout the US. The centers primarily sell to building materials dealers (84 Lumber, Stock Building Supply), buying groups, home centers, and industrial users. Products typically end up in the hands of professional builders and contractors. Doors (interior, exterior, patio) account for the majority of Huttig's sales.

	Annual Growth	12/05	12/06	12/07	12/08	12/09
Sales ($ mil.)	(19.7%)	1,097.2	1,102.7	874.8	671.0	455.2
Net income ($ mil.)	—	18.4	(7.7)	(8.2)	(35.4)	(20.5)
Market value ($ mil.)	(45.3%)	193.0	121.6	80.2	10.3	17.2
Employees	(17.4%)	2,146	1,900	1,600	1,200	1,000

HVM L.L.C.

100 Dunbar St.
Spartanburg, SC 29306
Phone: 864-573-1600
Fax: 864-573-1695
Web: www.extendedstayhotels.com

CEO: Gary A. DeLapp
CFO: Joseph (Joe) Rogers
HR: Marshall L. Dildy
FYE: December 31
Type: Private

HVM's guests need not worry about wearing out their welcome. The company manages under contract more than 680 hotels throughout the US and Canada under the Extended Stay America, Extended Stay Deluxe, Homestead Studio Suites, StudioPLUS Deluxe Studios, and Crossland Economy Studios brands. A hybrid between a hotel and an apartment, its lodgings offer all-suite accommodations targeting both business and leisure travelers looking for a temporary place to call home. The rooms feature separate living and dining areas along with fully-equipped kitchens. Some properties also boast exercise centers, swimming pools, and wireless Internet access.

HY CITE CORPORATION

333 Holtzman Rd.
Madison, WI 53713
Phone: 608-273-3373
Fax: 608-273-0936
Web: www.hycite.com

CEO: Erik S. Johnson
CFO: David Zimmerman
HR: —
FYE: December 31
Type: Private

Hy Cite Corporation caters to customers who cook and clean up afterward. The company operates two divisions — Royal Prestige and OceanBlue. Royal Prestige makes and markets kitchen products and accessories, including pots and pans, flatware, dinnerware (including fine china), juice makers, kitchen knives, water filters, and other items. The unit's Health System cookware line is designed for waterless and greaseless cooking methods. Hy Cite's OceanBlue division makes a bag-free and filter-free vacuum cleaner that traps dirt in a water basin to eliminate dust or exhaust. It's also used for wet or dry vacuuming. Products are sold through a network of some 2,200 independent distributors nationwide and overseas.

⊞ HYATT HOTELS CORPORATION   NYSE: H

71 S. Wacker Dr., 12th Fl.
Chicago, IL 60606
Phone: 312-750-1234
Fax: 312-750-8550
Web: www.hyatt.com

CEO: Mark S. Hoplamazian
CFO: Harmit J. Singh
HR: Robert W. K. Webb
FYE: December 31
Type: Public

Travelers interested in luxury lodgings can check in for the Hyatt touch. The company is one of the world's top operators of full-service luxury hotels and resorts with more than 400 managed, franchised, and owned properties in some 45 countries. Its core Hyatt Regency brand offers hospitality services targeted primarily to business travelers and upscale vacationers. The firm also operates properties under the names Grand Hyatt, Park Hyatt, Hyatt Place, Hyatt Summerfield Suites, Hyatt Resorts, and Andaz. Although Hyatt Hotels was formed in 2004, the Hyatt chain traces its roots back to 1957. It is majority-owned by the wealthy Pritzker family of Chicago. In 2009 the company filed an IPO.

	Annual Growth	1/05	1/06	*12/07	12/08	12/09
Sales ($ mil.)	1.0%	3,200.0	3,471.0	3,738.0	3,837.0	3,332.0
Net income ($ mil.)	—	—	329.0	271.0	170.0	(46.0)
Market value ($ mil.)	—	—	—	—	—	5,183.4
Employees	(10.5%)	70,000	85,000	90,000	125,000	45,000

*Fiscal year change

HYDRANAUTICS

401 Jones Rd.
Oceanside, CA 92054
Phone: 760-901-2500
Fax: 760-901-2578
Web: www.hydranautics.com

CEO: Brett Andrews
CFO: —
HR: —
FYE: March 31
Type: Subsidiary

Hydranautics is a manufacturer of water purification equipment. The company's products, which are sold worldwide, use a process called membrane separation to purify water for such purposes as seawater desalination, surface water treatment, and agricultural irrigation and pharmaceutical preparation. Hydranautics serves a wide range of clients; it has supplied equipment to the Ministry of Agriculture in Cyprus for a seawater desalination plant, and the Orange County Water District for a water purification facility in Southern California, and it is marketing energy-saving membranes to the Chinese industrial water market. The company is a unit of Osaka-based industrial adhesives manufacturer Nitto Denko.

HYDRO ALUMINUM NORTH AMERICA, INC.

999 Corporate Blvd., Ste. 100
Linthicum, MD 21090
Phone: 410-487-4500
Fax: 410-487-8053
Web: www.hydro.com/en/Subsites/North-America

CEO: Fernando Simões Henriques
CFO: Frankie Winfield
HR: Sally Hobbs
FYE: December 31
Type: Business segment

Hydro Aluminum North America conducts its parent company's aluminum production throughout North America. The company divides its business into two units: Aluminum Products and Aluminum Metal. The former handles the company's extrusion operations, while the Aluminum Metal division produces aluminum billet. Its primary operations include aluminum extruded products, precision tubing, and products for the automotive industry. Norwegian metals giant Norsk Hydro is among the world's top five aluminum producers, and North America makes up a significant part of that business. The US is Norsk Hydro's largest market outside Europe, though it accounts for only about 10% of sales.

HYDROGEN LLC

1520 4th Ave., Ste. 600
Seattle, WA 98101
Phone: 206-389-9500
Fax: 206-389-4849
Web: www.hydrogenadvertising.com

CEO: Rick Peterson
CFO: —
HR: —
FYE: December 31
Type: Private

For Hydrogen (dba Hydrogen Advertising), the work is elementary. The agency provides a full spectrum of marketing services, including Web marketing, media planning, public relations, direct marketing, campaign measurement, and strategic planning (in print or for broadcast), primarily to companies on the West Coast. Hydrogen Advertising serves a variety of industries including financial services, gaming, health and fitness, technology, travel, and real estate. Clients include Aegis Living, eBay, Microsoft, and Precor. Founded in 2001, Hydrogen Advertising is a member of Worldwide Partners Inc., a global network of independent agencies.

	Annual Growth	12/04	12/05	12/06	12/07	12/08
Est. sales ($ mil.)	—	—	—	—	—	2.8
Employees	—	—	—	—	—	18

HYDROMER, INC.

OTC: HYDI

35 Industrial Pkwy.
Branchburg, NJ 08876
Phone: 908-722-5000
Fax: 908-526-3633
Web: www.hydromer.com

CEO: Manfred F. Dyck
CFO: Robert Y. Lee
HR: John Konar
FYE: June 30
Type: Public

Hydromer would say its products become lubricious when wet. Bon Jovi preferred the term "slippery," but it amounts to the same thing. The company makes lubricating and water-resistant coatings for use in medical, pharmaceutical, cosmetic, industrial, and veterinary markets. Its products include lubricated medical devices, hydro-gels for drugs, anti-fog coatings, marine hull protective coatings, barrier dips for dairy cows, and intermediaries for hair and skin care products. Services include research and development, medical device manufacturing (through subsidiary Biosearch Medical Products), and contract coating. Chairman and CEO Manfred Dyck owns a third of Hydromer.

	Annual Growth	6/05	6/06	6/07	6/08	6/09
Sales ($ mil.)	(2.1%)	8.5	7.9	8.1	8.0	7.8
Net income ($ mil.)	13.6%	0.3	(0.8)	(0.1)	0.2	0.5
Market value ($ mil.)	(7.3%)	4.2	4.7	11.0	3.8	3.1
Employees	(4.0%)	86	85	70	73	73

HYDRON TECHNOLOGIES, INC.

OTC: HTEC

4400 34th St. North, Ste. F
St. Petersburg, FL 33714
Phone: 727-342-5050
Fax: 727-344-3920
Web: www.hydron.com

CEO: Richard Banakus
CFO: —
HR: —
FYE: September 30
Type: Public

The magic is in the moisture at Hydron Technologies. The company focuses on developing skin care products that contain microbubbles of pure oxygen used in treating the epidermis and underlying tissues. Hydron Technologies also manufactures personal and oral care products that contain its moisture-attracting ingredient, the Hydron polymer. The company distributes about 40 skin, hair, and sun care products, as well as bath and body items, through its website. It also produces private-label skin care items and ships them to contract manufacturers.

	Annual Growth	12/05	12/06	*9/07	9/08	9/09
Sales ($ mil.)	—	1.5	1.5	0.9	1.1	0.0
Net income ($ mil.)	—	(0.8)	(0.6)	(0.5)	(0.7)	(0.7)
Market value ($ mil.)	(41.9%)	6.9	3.3	2.9	0.4	0.8
Employees	10.0%	15	19	17	22	22
					*Fiscal year change	

HYLAND SOFTWARE, INC.

28500 Clemens Rd.
Westlake, OH 44145
Phone: 440-788-5000
Fax: 440-788-5100
Web: www.onbase.com

CEO: Anthony J. (A.J.) Hyland
CFO: Christopher J. (Chris) Hyland
HR: Debbie Connelly
FYE: December 31
Type: Private

Hyland Software provides enterprise content management (ECM) software designed to help organizations streamline their document and content management processes and share information among employees, partners, and customers. The company's OnBase software, which electronically captures and manages everything from paper reports to Web content, is used by customers in industries ranging from financial services and government to manufacturing and health care. In addition to its core ECM product, the company also offers specific add-on modules for functions such as business process automation, digital imaging and capturing, and records management.

HYNIX SEMICONDUCTOR AMERICA INC.

3101 N. 1st St.
San Jose, CA 95134
Phone: 408-232-8000
Fax: 408-232-8103
Web: hsa.hynix.com

CEO: Jong-Kap Kim
CFO: —
HR: —
FYE: December 31
Type: Subsidiary

Hynix Semiconductor America (HSA) helps Hynix get a fix on its American markets. The company is the North American branch of Hynix Semiconductor. HSA's scope includes the development, sales, marketing, and distribution of semiconductors, as well as R&D activities that support Hynix. DRAMs, static RAMs, flash memory devices, and application-specific integrated circuits are just some of the product areas that HSA specializes in, along with embedded flash drives for MP3 players, video-game consoles, mobile phones, and other consumer electronics. Formerly part of the South Korea-based Hyundai conglomerate, Hynix is a leading maker of computer memory chips.

⊞ HYPERCOM CORPORATION

NYSE: HYC

8888 E. Raintree Dr., Ste. 300
Scottsdale, AZ 85260
Phone: 480-642-5000
Fax: 480-642-4655
Web: www.hypercom.com

CEO: Philippe Tartavull
CFO: Thomas B. (Tom) Sabol
HR: Tim Jones
FYE: December 31
Type: Public

Hypercom gets worked up over transaction processing. Businesses use the company's products to swipe credit, debit, and smart cards. In addition to card-swiping equipment, its product line includes printers, keypads, and networking gear. The company's software encompasses point-of-sale management systems, terminal operations, and systems monitoring. Hypercom also provides asset management, systems implementation, and transaction services. It sells to distributors, financial institutions, payment processors, and retail chains. The company jockeys with VeriFone and Ingenico to be the top maker of point-of-sale (POS) and payment systems. The three dominate the field, but Hypercom trails significantly in terms of revenue.

	Annual Growth	12/05	12/06	12/07	12/08	12/09
Sales ($ mil.)	13.5%	245.2	248.6	293.8	437.3	406.9
Net income ($ mil.)	—	(33.4)	7.0	(7.5)	(85.4)	(6.9)
Market value ($ mil.)	(16.1%)	349.3	347.1	272.2	59.0	173.3
Employees	(1.5%)	1,452	1,358	1,295	1,606	1,365

⊞ An in-depth profile of this company is available to Hoover's Online members at hoovers.com.

791

HYPERDYNAMICS CORPORATION

NYSE Amex: HDY

1 Sugar Creek Center Blvd., Ste. 125
Sugar Land, TX 77478
Phone: 713-353-9400
Fax: 713-353-9421
Web: www.hypd.com

CEO: Ray Leonard
CFO: Jason S. Davis
HR: —
FYE: June 30
Type: Public

Not as hyper as it was, but still dynamic, Hyperdynamics has shifted its business focus from IT consulting services to oil and gas exploration, primarily in Africa. Its SCS Corporation subsidiary concentrates on developing an oil and gas concession located offshore in the Republic of Guinea in West Africa. Hyperdynamics' HYD Resources subsidiary and gas exploration and production company focuses on low-risk shallow exploration projects in Louisiana, where in 2008 it held proved reserves of 150,435 barrels of oil. Chairman Kent Watts, who stepped down as CEO in 2009, owns 17% of Hyperdynamics.

	Annual Growth	6/05	6/06	6/07	6/08	6/09
Sales ($ mil.)	—	0.2	0.7	1.0	2.9	0.0
Net income ($ mil.)	—	(5.2)	(7.1)	(23.2)	(9.5)	(8.8)
Market value ($ mil.)	(36.5%)	268.8	218.8	327.1	176.1	43.8
Employees	(6.2%)	31	23	25	17	24

HYPERTENSION DIAGNOSTICS, INC.

OTC: HDII

2915 Waters Rd., Ste. 108
Eagan, MN 55121
Phone: 651-687-9999
Fax: 651-687-0485
Web: www.hdi-pulsewave.com

CEO: Mark N. Schwartz
CFO: —
HR: —
FYE: June 30
Type: Public

Hypertension Diagnostics can tell if your cardiovascular system is about to go snap, crackle, and pop. The company's noninvasive instruments measure the elasticity of arteries, helping physicians assess patients' risk for cardiovascular disease. Its CR-2000 Research System is marketed for research purposes to government agencies, pharmaceutical companies, academic research centers, and cardiovascular research centers worldwide; drug heavyweights AstraZeneca and Pfizer are among the system's users. The CVProfilor DO-2020 and the CVProfilor MD-3000 are intended for general physicians, cardiologists, and other health care practitioners in the US and abroad.

	Annual Growth	6/05	6/06	6/07	6/08	6/09
Sales ($ mil.)	(19.7%)	1.2	1.8	1.9	0.6	0.5
Net income ($ mil.)	—	(1.5)	(1.3)	(0.5)	(0.7)	(0.2)
Market value ($ mil.)	(37.5%)	7.0	10.8	4.8	3.7	1.1
Employees	(11.1%)	8	10	7	5	5

HYTHIAM, INC.

NASDAQ (GM): HYTM

11150 Santa Monica Blvd., Ste. 1500
Los Angeles, CA 90025
Phone: 310-444-4300
Fax: 310-444-5300
Web: www.hythiam.com

CEO: Terren S. Peizer
CFO: —
HR: —
FYE: December 31
Type: Public

Hythiam specializes in researching, developing, and licensing medical protocols for the treatment of alcohol and drug addiction. The company's PROMETA treatment programs utilize a combination of medication, nutritional supplements, and counseling to treat drug and alcohol addiction. Hythiam's PROMETA Centers are operated through management or licensing agreements with health care providers in the US. PROMETA also provides maintenance support by offering individualized care programs following medically supervised treatment. Its Catasys program offers disease management services. The company owns a controlling stake in managed behavioral health provider Comprehensive Care.

	Annual Growth	12/05	12/06	12/07	12/08	12/09
Sales ($ mil.)	5.7%	1.2	3.9	44.0	41.2	1.5
Net income ($ mil.)	—	(24.0)	(38.3)	(45.5)	(50.4)	(9.2)
Market value ($ mil.)	(48.3%)	439.3	660.0	209.3	27.9	31.4
Employees	(18.4%)	90	120	160	81	40

HYUNDAI AMERICA TECHNICAL CENTER, INC.

6800 Geddes Rd.
Superior Township, MI 48198
Phone: 734-337-9499
Fax: 734-337-3168
Web: www.hatci.com

CEO: C. K. Park
CFO: —
HR: —
FYE: December 31
Type: Subsidiary

Not willing to take a backseat to its Japanese rivals, Hyundai America Technical Center, Inc. (HATCI) also has designs on the North American market. A subsidiary of Korean carmaker Hyundai Motor Company, HATCI is Hyundai's design, engineering, technology, research and development headquarters for the North American market. HATCI's activities include design (body, chassis, electronics, and trim), evaluation and testing, quality improvement, and powertrain development. The company also serves the North American market needs of Hyundai affiliate Kia Motors. In addition to its Michigan headquarters, HATCI has operations in Alabama and California.

HYUNDAI MOTOR AMERICA

10550 Talbert Ave.
Fountain Valley, CA 92708
Phone: 714-965-3000
Fax: 714-965-3149
Web: www.hyundaiusa.com

CEO: John Krafcik
CFO: Jerry Flannery
HR: Paul Koh
FYE: December 31
Type: Subsidiary

The Accent is on US sales for Hyundai Motor America. The subsidiary of Hyundai Motor distributes Hyundai cars and SUVs in the US, serving about 800 Hyundai dealers. The company's America's Best Warranty covers Hyundai cars sold in the US. Hyundai Motor Finance provides financing for car buyers and for dealer inventory. The company operates an engineering facility in Michigan, a manufacturing facility in Alabama, and proving grounds and a research and design center in California. Hyundai Motor America plans to increase its number of dealerships to 1,000 by the end of 2010. Parent company Hyundai opened its first US auto assembly plant in 2005.

	Annual Growth	12/04	12/05	12/06	12/07	12/08
Est. sales ($ mil.)	—	—	—	—	—	8,545.7
Employees	—	—	—	—	—	879

HYUNDAI MOTOR MANUFACTURING ALABAMA, LLC

700 Hyundai Blvd.
Montgomery, AL 36105
Phone: 334-387-8000
Fax: —
Web: www.hmmausa.com

CEO: H.I. Kim
CFO: —
HR: —
FYE: December 31
Type: Subsidiary

Hyundai Motor Manufacturing Alabama (HMMA) speaks Korean with a Southern drawl. A subsidiary of South Korea's Hyundai Motor, HMMA began construction of its plant in 2002. The $1.4 billion facility turned out its first car, the Sonata sedan, in 2005. The factory includes a stamping facility, paint shop, vehicle assembly shop, and a two-mile testing track. At full capacity, HMMA will produce about 300,000 vehicles per year. Cars and SUVs built by HMMA are distributed throughout the US by sister company Hyundai Motor America, and they are sold and serviced by more than 900 US Hyundai dealerships.

HYUNDAI TRANSLEAD

8880 Rio San Diego Dr., St. 600
San Diego, CA 92108
Phone: 619-574-1500
Fax: 619-542-0301
Web: www.translead.com

CEO: Jae Il Kim
CFO: G. S. Tshin
HR: —
FYE: December 31
Type: Subsidiary

Lead, follow, or get out of the way, Hyundai Translead is on the move. The subsidiary of Hyundai Motor, Korea, manufactures refrigerated (reefer) and dry-freight van trailers and domestic containers, as well as container chassis and converter dollies. A redesigned reefer rolled out in 2009 offered improvements of reduced weight, and increased strength and airflow. Hyundai Translead containers are also produced per US EPA specifications and options for transportation customers wanting a qualified SmartWay fleet. Made in Mexico, trailers are sold both directly and through a network of dealers dotting the US, Canada, and Latin America. The company ships parts through Hyundai Motor parts distribution centers, too.

HY-VEE, INC.

5820 Westown Pkwy.
West Des Moines, IA 50266
Phone: 515-267-2800
Fax: 515-267-2817
Web: www.hy-vee.com

CEO: Richard N. (Ric) Jurgens
CFO: John C. Briggs
HR: Sheila Laing
FYE: September 30
Type: Private

Give Hy-Vee a high five for being one of the largest privately owned US supermarket chains, despite serving some modestly sized towns in the Midwest. The company runs about 225 Hy-Vee supermarkets in eight midwestern states: Illinois, Iowa, Kansas, Minnesota, Missouri, Nebraska, South Dakota, and Wisconsin. About half of its stores are in Iowa, as are most of its 25-plus Hy-Vee (formerly Drug Town) drugstores. It distributes products to its stores through several subsidiaries, including Lomar Distributing (specialty foods) and Perishable Distributors of Iowa (fresh foods). Charles Hyde and David Vredenburg founded the employee-owned firm in 1930. It takes its name from a combination of its founders' names.

	Annual Growth	9/04	9/05	9/06	9/07	9/08
Sales ($ mil.)	3.0%	—	—	5,840.0	5,600.0	6,200.0
Employees	2.8%	—	—	52,000	54,000	55,000

IA GLOBAL, INC.

101 California St., Ste. 2450
San Francisco, CA 94111
Phone: 415-946-8828
Fax: 415-946-8801
Web: www.iaglobalinc.com

NYSE Amex: IAO

CEO: Brian L. Hoekstra
CFO: Mark E. Scott
HR: —
FYE: March 31
Type: Public

IA Global has made the call to the Pacific Rim region. The holding company is focused on growing its existing businesses and making strategic acquisitions in Asia. Its primary holdings revolve around Global Hotline, a Japanese business process outsourcing (BPO) company that owns two call centers and offers telemarketing services, medical insurance, and other products to customers in Japan. IA Global also owns call center operations in the Philippines, along with parts of Japanese firms GPlus Media (online media), Slate Consulting (executive search), Taicom Securities (financial services), and Australian Secured Financial Limited (private loans and real estate investment). IA Global was formed in 1998.

	Annual Growth	12/04	12/05	12/06	12/07	*3/09
Sales ($ mil.)	15.9%	31.6	45.1	19.1	29.1	57.1
Net income ($ mil.)	—	(1.4)	(2.1)	(3.8)	(8.3)	(20.2)
Market value ($ mil.)	(38.8%)	118.2	97.0	42.4	87.9	16.6
Employees	96.4%	61	436	469	841	907
						*Fiscal year change

IAC/INTERACTIVECORP

555 West 18th St.
New York, NY 10011
Phone: 212-314-7300
Fax: —
Web: www.iac.com

NASDAQ (GS): IACI

CEO: Barry Diller
CFO: Thomas J. (Tom) McInerney
HR: —
FYE: December 31
Type: Public

IAC/InterActiveCorp (IAC) satisfies inquisitive minds who want to use the Web to explore local hot spots, meet the right partner, find a contractor, and maybe even host a party or two. The Internet conglomerate owns more than 50 brands, including search engine Ask.com, local guide Citysearch, dating site Match.com, home service provider network ServiceMagic, and online-invitation firm Evite. Other IAC holdings include shoe site Shoebuy.com, online restaurant guide Urbanspoon, current affairs Web magazine Daily Beast, and a majority stake in Connected Ventures, the parent company of racy college entertainment site CollegeHumor.com. IAC is controlled by CEO Barry Diller.

	Annual Growth	12/05	12/06	12/07	12/08	12/09
Sales ($ mil.)	(30.1%)	5,753.7	6,277.6	6,373.4	1,445.1	1,375.8
Net income ($ mil.)	—	806.0	192.6	(144.1)	(156.2)	(979.9)
Market value ($ mil.)	(4.6%)	2,739.2	3,595.5	2,604.7	1,744.2	2,270.9
Employees	(41.9%)	28,000	20,000	21,000	3,200	3,200

THE IAMS COMPANY

7250 Poe Ave.
Dayton, OH 45414
Phone: 937-898-7387
Fax: 937-264-7264
Web: www.iams.com

CEO: Dan Rajczak
CFO: Jack Lucas
HR: —
FYE: June 30
Type: Subsidiary

As Iams tells it, Old Mother Hubbard went to the cupboard to fetch her portly pooch a bag of Eukanuba Large Breed Weight Control food. The Iams Company makes Eukanuba and Iams dry and canned versions of premium dog and cat foods and sells them in pet supply stores and veterinarians' offices in more than 70 countries. However, North America accounts for the vast majority of the company's sales. Founded by Paul Iams in 1946, Iams also funds research efforts related to animal dermatology, geriatrics, allergies, and nutrition through its Paul F. Iams Technical Center. Former chairman Clayton Mathile acquired the company in 1982 and sold it to consumer products giant Procter & Gamble in 1999.

IAP WORLDWIDE SERVICES, INC.

7315 N. Atlantic Ave.
Cape Canaveral, FL 32920
Phone: 321-784-7100
Fax: 321-784-7336
Web: www.iapws.com

CEO: Steven F. (Steve) Gaffney
CFO: Charles D. Peiffer
HR: David B. Warhol
FYE: December 31
Type: Private

Wherever US troops are marching, IAP Worldwide Services is there to support them. The company provides a variety of logistics and facility support services, chiefly for the US Department of Defense and other government customers, including US states and other countries; it also undertakes work for commercial enterprises. Services include base camp facilities support, logistics planning, and temporary staffing. The company operates through three distinct segments: global operations and logistics; facilities management and base operations support; and professional and technical services. Investment firm Cerberus Capital Management owns a controlling interest in IAP, which was founded in 1989.

An in-depth profile of this company is available to Hoover's Online members at hoovers.com.

793

IASIS HEALTHCARE LLC

117 Seaboard Ln., Bldg. E
Franklin, TN 37067
Phone: 615-844-2747
Fax: 615-846-3006
Web: www.iasishealthcare.com

CEO: David R. White
CFO: John M. Doyle
HR: —
FYE: September 30
Type: Private

If you're sick in the city or have a stomach ache in the suburbs, IASIS Healthcare provides a medical oasis. The company owns and operates about 15 acute care hospitals and one behavioral health facility (more than 2,800 beds total) in Arizona, Florida, Louisiana, Nevada, Texas, and Utah. IASIS also operates several outpatient facilities and other centers providing ancillary services, such as radiation therapy, diagnostic imaging, and ambulatory surgery. Its Health Choice Arizona subsidiary is a Medicaid and Medicare managed health plan that serves about 200,000 individuals in Arizona. An investor group led by Texas Pacific Group owns the company.

	Annual Growth	9/04	9/05	9/06	9/07	9/08
Sales ($ mil.)	10.5%	1,386.6	1,523.7	1,626.0	1,850.0	2,065.5
Net income ($ mil.)	—	(32.4)	40.6	39.5	41.6	36.3
Employees	4.6%	9,000	8,800	8,877	10,826	10,775

IBASIS, INC.

20 2nd Ave.
Burlington, MA 01803
Phone: 781-505-7500
Fax: 781-505-7300
Web: www.ibasis.com

CEO: John van Vianen
CFO: Roelant Lyppens
HR: Tamah S. Rosker
FYE: December 31
Type: Subsidiary

iBasis lays a foundation for Internet telephony. The company, a subsidiary of Dutch telecommunications service provider KPN, primarily sells access to its international VoIP (voice-over-Internet protocol) network to other voice and data service carriers and resellers in about 100 countries. Its long distance services are enabled through agreements with regional providers worldwide who handle termination of calls. iBasis' clients have included China Unicom and Telefonica. While its core segment is wholesale VoIP access, the company also sells retail prepaid services through calling cards and online. iBasis has historically generated most of sales in Africa, Europe, Latin America, and the Middle East.

	Annual Growth	12/04	12/05	12/06	12/07	12/08
Sales ($ mil.)	49.7%	263.7	385.5	511.1	938.6	1,323.6
Net income ($ mil.)	—	(17.5)	(1.7)	(2.2)	16.1	(231.0)
Employees	14.6%	216	230	251	390	372

IBERDROLA RENEWABLES, INC.

1125 NW Couch, Ste. 700
Portland, OR 97209
Phone: 503-796-7000
Fax: 503-796-6901
Web: www.iberdrolarenewables.com

CEO: Ralph Currey
CFO: Pablo Canales
HR: Carl Britsch
FYE: March 31
Type: Subsidiary

IBERDROLA RENEWABLES (formerly PPM Energy) is a real power player in the energy industry. Part of IBERDROLA RENOVABLES global network, IBERDROLA RENEWABLES develops cogeneration power plants and wind farms; it has generating capacity of more than 3,100 MW in operation and more than 23,000 under construction or in the product pipeline, primarily in the Midwest and western US. IBERDROLA RENEWABLES also markets wholesale energy and offers risk and asset management services. The company's customers include public and private utilities, industrial companies, and other energy marketers. It holds the nonregulated North American operations of Scottish Power (acquired by IBERDROLA in 2007).

IBERDROLA USA, INC.

52 Farm View Dr.
New Gloucester, ME 04260
Phone: 207-688-6300
Fax: 207-688-4354
Web: www.energyeast.com

CEO: Robert D. Kump
CFO: Daniel Alcain
HR: Sheri Lamoureux
FYE: December 31
Type: Subsidiary

Iberdrola USA (formerly Energy East) is a major regional player and the leading US operating subsidiary of IBERDROLA. The utility holding company distributes electricity and natural gas in four northeastern states through Berkshire Gas, Central Maine Power, Connecticut Natural Gas, Maine Natural Gas, New York State Electric & Gas, Rochester Gas and Electric, and Southern Connecticut Gas. Iberdrola USA serves about 2 million electricity customers as well as 1 million natural gas customers. Other operations include power generation, energy marketing, gas transportation and processing, propane distribution, telecommunications, and energy infrastructure and management services.

IBERIABANK CORPORATION

NASDAQ (GS): IBKC

200 W. Congress St.
Lafayette, LA 70501
Phone: 337-521-4012
Fax: 337-364-1171
Web: www.iberiabank.com

CEO: Daryl G. Byrd
CFO: Anthony J. Restel
HR: —
FYE: December 31
Type: Public

IBERIABANK Corporation is a financial services holding company with some 200 bank branches and about 25 title insurance offices in the Southeast. It also has about 40 mortgage loan offices in nearly a dozen states. Its primary bank subsidiary, IBERIABANK, offers passbook and NOW accounts, CDs, and IRAs and uses funds from deposits mainly to make loans. Business operating loans and commercial mortgages make up approximately 60% of a portfolio that also includes consumer loans and residential mortgages (nearly 20% apiece). IBERIABANK Corporation expanded eastward from its Louisiana base by acquiring the failed CapitalSouth Bank in an FDIC-assisted transaction in 2009.

	Annual Growth	12/05	12/06	12/07	12/08	12/09
Assets ($ mil.)	35.8%	2,852.6	3,203.0	4,917.0	5,583.2	9,700.4
Net income ($ mil.)	61.9%	22.0	35.7	41.3	39.9	151.3
Market value ($ mil.)	1.3%	1,364.7	1,579.8	1,250.7	1,284.2	1,439.6
Employees	26.9%	650	754	1,319	1,356	1,685

IBW FINANCIAL CORPORATION

Pink Sheets: IBWC

4812 Georgia Ave. NW
Washington, DC 20011
Phone: 202-722-2000
Fax: 202-722-2040
Web: www.industrial-bank.com

CEO: B. Doyle Mitchell Jr.
CFO: Thomas A. Wilson Jr.
HR: —
FYE: December 31
Type: Public

IBW Financial is the holding company for Industrial Bank, one of the largest minority-owned banks in the US. Catering to the African-American community in and around Washington, DC, the bank offers standard personal and commercial services, such as checking and savings accounts, debit cards, and cash management. It primarily writes real estate loans, with residential mortgages and commercial mortgages each accounting for nearly 40% of its portfolio. Industrial Bank has about 10 branches and loan production offices in Washington, DC, and nearby parts of Maryland. The Mitchell family, including CEO B. Doyle Mitchell Jr., whose grandfather founded the bank in 1934, holds a controlling stake in IBW Financial.

	Annual Growth	12/04	12/05	12/06	12/07	*12/08
Sales ($ mil.)	—	—	—	—	—	19.4
Employees	—	—	—	—	—	126

*Most recent year available

I.C. ISAACS & COMPANY, INC.

OTC: ISAC

475 10th Ave., 9th Fl.	CEO: Robert Stephen Stec
New York, NY 10018	CFO: —
Phone: 646-459-2600	HR: —
Fax: —	FYE: December 31
Web: www.icisaacs.com	Type: Public

I.C. Isaacs & Company is putting all of its jeans in one laundry basket. A leading US licensee for French designer Girbaud, the company designs and makes jeans and sportswear targeting a young, fashionable urban market. It has otherwise cleaned out its closet to focus entirely on its Girbaud brand. (In 2001 I.C. Isaacs terminated its licenses with BOSS and Beverly Hills Polo Club and discontinued its own Urban Expedition and Isaacs lines.) The company's clothes are sold in about 1,500 specialty and department stores. The family of designers Marithé Bachellerie and François Girbaud has increased its stake in I.C. Isaacs to about 70%, making it the company's biggest shareholder.

ICAD, INC.

NASDAQ (CM): ICAD

98 Spit Brook Rd., Ste. 100	CEO: Kenneth M. (Ken) Ferry
Nashua, NH 03063	CFO: Darlene M. Deptula-Hicks
Phone: 603-882-5200	HR: —
Fax: 603-880-3843	FYE: December 31
Web: www.icadmed.com	Type: Public

Early detection is the best prevention in iCAD's eyes. The company targets the breast cancer detection market with its SecondLook computer-aided detection (CAD) systems. The systems include workstations and analytical software that help radiologists better identify potential cancers in mammography images. iCAD sells models that can be used with both film-based and digital mammography systems and offers film digitizers for radiology practices making the film-to-digital transition. SecondLook also provides image storage and patient tracking capabilities. iCAD markets its products directly and through sales partnerships with the likes of GE Healthcare, Siemens Medical Solutions, and Agfa.

	Annual Growth	12/05	12/06	12/07	12/08	12/09
Sales ($ mil.)	9.1%	19.8	19.7	26.6	37.5	28.1
Net income ($ mil.)	—	(4.8)	(6.6)	(1.5)	4.4	(2.0)
Market value ($ mil.)	6.8%	53.5	134.8	92.3	51.6	69.5
Employees	4.6%	86	91	106	115	103

ICAGEN, INC.

NASDAQ (GM): ICGN

4222 Emperor Blvd., Ste. 350	CEO: P. Kay Wagoner
Durham, NC 27703	CFO: Richard D. Katz
Phone: 919-941-5206	HR: —
Fax: 919-941-0813	FYE: December 31
Web: www.icagen.com	Type: Public

Icagen wants to set the market for ion channel modulators on fire. The development-stage biotech focuses on treatments for epilepsy, asthma, pain, and inflammation by regulating the inflow into cells of such ions as calcium, potassium, and sodium. Icagen's lead candidate, senicapoc for sickle cell disease, died in 2007 following lackluster Phase III clinical trial results. The drug was being developed in a partnership with Johnson & Johnson subsidiary McNeil Consumer & Specialty Pharmaceuticals. Shortly thereafter Icagen announced a deal collaborating with Pfizer on the development of epilepsy and pain treatments.

	Annual Growth	12/05	12/06	12/07	12/08	12/09
Sales ($ mil.)	2.2%	8.8	8.4	21.1	12.3	9.6
Net income ($ mil.)	—	(20.2)	(24.8)	(10.9)	(14.8)	(12.8)
Market value ($ mil.)	(48.5%)	307.5	48.2	80.1	25.7	21.5
Employees	(5.7%)	72	64	67	73	57

ICAHN ENTERPRISES L.P.

NYSE: IEP

767 5th Ave., Ste. 4700	CEO: Keith A. Meister
New York, NY 10153	CFO: Dominick Ragone
Phone: 212-702-4300	HR: —
Fax: 212-750-5841	FYE: December 31
Web: www.icahnenterprises.com	Type: Public

Icahn Enterprises has a can-do attitude when it comes to making money. The holding company has stakes in a variety of industries including manufacturing, real estate, food packaging, and household goods. Federal-Mogul makes automobile components, while PSC Metals is one of the US's largest scrapyard operators. Another holding, Bayswater Development, is a residential builder and developer active in Florida, Massachusetts, and New York. Icahn also owns WestPoint International, which makes and distributes bed, bath, and other home products. In 2010 the company acquired control of American Railcar Industries and Viskase from billionaire corporate raider Carl Icahn. Icahn's hedge fund owns 93% of the company.

	Annual Growth	12/05	12/06	12/07	12/08	12/09
Sales ($ mil.)	58.0%	1,262.5	1,477.9	2,487.6	5,027.0	7,865.0
Net income ($ mil.)	—	(27.0)	798.8	308.3	(43.0)	1,195.0
Market value ($ mil.)	0.9%	3,228.8	7,180.3	10,864.7	2,215.3	3,346.0
Employees	62.6%	6,060	5,340	4,500	47,423	42,368

ICC INDUSTRIES INC.

460 Park Ave.	CEO: John Oram
New York, NY 10022	CFO: Blaise Sarcone
Phone: 212-521-1700	HR: —
Fax: 212-521-1970	FYE: December 31
Web: www.iccindustries.com	Type: Private

ICC Industries is helping the world look brighter, smell better, and live healthier. The company trades basic and specialty chemicals globally. Operating through a number of subsidiaries, ICC Industries is an international maker of chemicals (Dover Chemical), plastics (Primex), and pharmaceutical products; it also distributes nutritional supplements and food ingredients. Its main subsidiary, ICC Chemical, is among the largest distributors in the US and maintains trading and marketing offices throughout the world. Other subsidiaries include Israeli flavors company Frutarom and the US plastics compounder and colorant producer O'Neil Color. The founding Farber family, including chairman John Farber, owns ICC.

ICELANDIC USA, INC.

190 Enterprise Dr.	CEO: Ævar Agnarsson
Newport News, VA 23603	CFO: Michael Thome
Phone: 757-820-4000	HR: Debra Zartman
Fax: 757-888-6250	FYE: December 31
Web: www.icelandic.com	Type: Subsidiary

Icelandic USA, a subsidiary of the Icelandic Group, processes and markets frozen fish from (where else?) the waters of Iceland (and elsewhere) for the food industry under the (what else?) Icelandic brand label. Its other brands include Packer, Samband, Seaside, and SEASTAR. The company is the largest importer of frozen ground fish for the foodservice industry in the US; its customers also include food retailers throughout the US and Canada. Icelandic's products include value-added seafood, such as frozen breaded fish fillets, crab cakes, ready-to-eat shrimp, and every kid's favorite — fish sticks.

An in-depth profile of this company is available to Hoover's Online members at hoovers.com.

ICEWEB, INC.

OTC: IWEB

45925 Maries Rd.
Dulles, VA 20166
Phone: 703-964-8000
Fax: 703-964-0160
Web: www.iceweb.com

CEO: John R. Signorello
CFO: Mark B. Lucky
HR: —
FYE: September 30
Type: Public

IceWEB helps its customers spin a security web. The company generates the majority of its revenues from its IT Solutions division, which provides network security products to local, state, and federal government agencies. Specializing in such applications as content filtering, e-mail security, intrusion detection, and network optimization, the unit implements products from partners including Blue Coat Systems, Cisco Systems, F5 Networks, McAfee, and RSA Security. The company also offers data storage products through its INLINE business unit. IceWEB's online services division provides small and midsized businesses with hosted e-mail server and security applications.

	Annual Growth	9/05	9/06	9/07	9/08	9/09
Sales ($ mil.)	(13.0%)	6.8	4.8	18.7	16.3	3.9
Net income ($ mil.)	—	(0.9)	(3.9)	(2.9)	(6.4)	(2.5)
Market value ($ mil.)	(44.6%)	97.1	48.5	64.7	11.3	9.2
Employees	(13.4%)	32	25	18	17	18

ICF CORPORATION

Pink Sheets: ICFO

4030 Pike Ln., Ste. C
Concord, CA 94520
Phone: 925-849-1400
Fax: 925-335-4002
Web: www.icf.com

CEO: Stan F. Sech
CFO: Marc Dell'Immagine
HR: —
FYE: December 31
Type: Public

ICF Corp. designs, installs, and supports local- and wide-area data and voice communication networks through its ICF Communications subsidiary. The company, which targets large enterprises, also installs customer premise wiring and distributes third-party telecommunications equipment made by the likes of Avaya, Cisco, Corning, Leviton, NEC, and Wiremold. Its customers include Bank of America and Wells Fargo. ICF has offices in California. ICF targets its services to the education, financial, health care, government, and retail markets. It distributes such products as VoIP telephones and voicemail systems.

ICF INTERNATIONAL, INC.

NASDAQ (GM): ICFI

9300 Lee Hwy.
Fairfax, VA 22031
Phone: 703-934-3000
Fax: 703-934-3740
Web: www.icfi.com

CEO: Sudhakar Kesavan
CFO: Ronald P. (Ron) Vargo
HR: Irvin Towson
FYE: December 31
Type: Public

Consultant ICF International (formerly ICF Consulting) sees opportunity in government spending. The firm advises government entities and businesses on issues related to health, human services, and social programs, as well as defense and homeland security, energy and climate change, and the environment. It groups its consulting and information technology services into three main categories: advice, implementation, and evaluation and improvement. A contract with the State of Louisiana related to the resettlement of people displaced by hurricanes has accounted for a majority of the company's sales the past few years.

	Annual Growth	12/05	12/06	12/07	12/08	12/09
Sales ($ mil.)	39.7%	177.2	331.3	727.1	697.4	674.4
Net income ($ mil.)	82.9%	2.0	11.9	40.6	28.7	22.4
Market value ($ mil.)	22.7%	—	280.7	488.2	474.9	518.0
Employees	24.4%	1,462	2,000	3,000	3,600	3,500

ICG COMMERCE, INC.

211 South Gulph Rd., Ste. 500
King of Prussia, PA 19406
Phone: 484-690-5000
Fax: 484-690-5292
Web: www.icgcommerce.com

CEO: Carl A. Guarino
CFO: Joseph F. Waterman
HR: Francesca Molinari
FYE: December 31
Type: Private

ICG Commerce wants to eliminate the extensive paperwork and never-ending phone calls that some people associate with traditional corporate buying. The company oversees the purchasing process for its customers by identifying suppliers, managing lists of preferred providers, and ensuring that items are properly shipped and paid for. ICG Commerce's customers have included oil and gas equipment manufacturer Cameron, educational materials publisher Houghton Mifflin Harcourt, aircraft component manufacturer Vought, and home appliance manufacturer Whirlpool. Investment firm Internet Capital Group owns a controlling stake in ICG Commerce, which was founded in 1992.

ICICLE SEAFOODS, INC.

4019 21st Ave. West
Seattle, WA 98199
Phone: 206-282-0988
Fax: 206-282-7222
Web: www.icicleseafoods.com

CEO: Dennis Guhlke
CFO: Brenda Morris
HR: —
FYE: December 31
Type: Private

Forget about curling up for a nice long hibernation during the winter months at this company — Icicle Seafoods is hard at work even when icicles are forming outside. The fishery and seafood-processing company catches, processes, and distributes fresh, canned, and frozen fish including cod, herring, pollock, halibut, salmon, crab, and trout. Its customers include retail food, industrial, wholesale and foodservice operations worldwide. It maintains floating seafood processing plants, shoreline plants, and other facilities in Alaska, Oregon, and Washington. Its Alaskan cannery has been in operation since 1899. The company is owned by private investment firm Paine & Partners.

	Annual Growth	12/04	12/05	12/06	12/07	12/08
Sales ($ mil.)	14.3%	—	—	—	350.0	400.0
Employees	—	—	—	—	500	—

ICL PERFORMANCE PRODUCTS LP

622 Emerson Rd., Ste. 500
St. Louis, MO 63141
Phone: 314-983-7500
Fax: 314-983-7638
Web: www.icl-pplp.com

CEO: Charles M. Weidhas
CFO: Paul M. Schlessman
HR: Michael (Mike) Bork
FYE: December 31
Type: Subsidiary

ICL Performance Products LP is phosphorific! The North American unit of the performance products segment of Israel Chemicals Limited (ICL), it produces phosphorus chemicals, phosphoric acid, and phosphate salts. The chemicals are used in foods, cleaners, water treatment, flat-panel displays, oral care products, paints and coatings, and pharmaceuticals. The company also manufactures flame retardants. ICL Performance Products operates plants in Brazil and the US (California, Kansas, Missouri, and New Jersey). It represents about a quarter of its parent's total business.

ICMA RETIREMENT CORPORATION

777 N. Capitol St., NE
Washington, DC 20002
Phone: 202-962-4600
Fax: 202-962-4601
Web: www.icmarc.org

CEO: Joan McCallen
CFO: Elizabeth Glista
HR: Catherine Leggett
FYE: December 31
Type: Not-for-profit

Because public servants need security, too. ICMA Retirement Corporation (ICMA-RC) offers financial planning and manages and administers retirement plans exclusively for public-sector employees. A not-for-profit organization, it offers products including retirement health savings plans, IRAs, 401(a)s, 401(k)s, and 457s. The company serves more than 800,000 employees of state and local governments, offering some 900 retirement savings plans in all. ICMA-RC is sponsor of the Vantagepoint and Milestone funds. The company was founded in 1972 by public-sector employers through the International City/County Management Association.

	Annual Growth	12/04	12/05	12/06	12/07	12/08
Est. sales ($ mil.)	—	—	—	—	—	132.5
Employees	—	—	—	—	—	596

ICO GLOBAL COMMUNICATIONS

NASDAQ (GM): ICOG

11700 Plaza America Dr., Ste. 1010
Reston, VA 20190
Phone: 703-964-1400
Fax: 703-964-1401
Web: www.ico.com

CEO: Benjamin G. (Ben) Wolff
CFO: Timothy Leybold
HR: —
FYE: December 31
Type: Public

When it gets off the ground, ICO Global Communications (Holdings) Limited will be a satellite-based communications system with global coverage. The company's principal operating subsidiary, DBSD North America, (formerly known as ICO North America), is authorized to operate a medium-Earth-orbit satellite service to provide mobile voice, data, and Internet services primarily in the US. In addition to telephone and messaging capabilities, its consumer-oriented service is slated to deliver mobile entertainment content such as television programming, as well as interactive navigation data to wireless computing devices and vehicle navigation systems. Debt-laden DBSD North America filed for Chapter 11 bankruptcy protection in mid-2009.

	Annual Growth	12/05	12/06	12/07	12/08	12/09
Sales ($ mil.)	—	—	—	—	—	0.0
Net income ($ mil.)	—	—	—	—	—	195.5
Market value ($ mil.)	—	—	—	—	—	273.8
Employees	—	—	—	—	—	41

ICO, INC.

NASDAQ (GM): ICOC

1811 Bering Dr., Ste. 200
Houston, TX 77057
Phone: 713-351-4100
Fax: 713-335-2201
Web: www.icopolymers.com

CEO: A. John Knapp Jr.
CFO: Bradley T. (Brad) Leuschner
HR: Keith Haddock
FYE: September 30
Type: Public

I see, oh, a bunch of paint- and plastic-producing polymers over at ICO. The company, formerly an oilfield services provider, focuses now on its global polymers processing business. That business is to grind, blend, and compound polymer resin pellets (primarily polyethylene) into powders that are used to make paint and plastic products such as toys, garbage bags, and plastic film. The company also processes resins for desired characteristics such as color and UV protection. In 2009 A. Schulman, a plastics compounder and maker of masterbatches and engineered plastics, acquired ICO in a deal that valued the company at $190 million.

	Annual Growth	9/05	9/06	9/07	9/08	9/09
Sales ($ mil.)	0.3%	296.6	324.3	417.9	446.7	300.0
Net income ($ mil.)	—	4.5	12.0	21.1	15.3	(1.2)
Market value ($ mil.)	12.4%	81.2	183.5	390.4	155.5	129.5
Employees	(0.6%)	825	831	931	910	805

ICON HEALTH & FITNESS, INC.

1500 S. 1000 West
Logan, UT 84321
Phone: 435-750-5000
Fax: 435-750-3917
Web: www.iconfitness.com

CEO: Scott R. Watterson
CFO: S. Fred Beck
HR: —
FYE: May 31
Type: Private

ICON Health & Fitness has brawn as one of the leading US makers of home fitness equipment. Its products primarily include treadmills, elliptical trainers, and weight benches. Brands include NordicTrack, HealthRider, ProForm, Reebok, and Weider. ICON also offers commercial equipment through its FreeMotion Fitness segment. The company makes most of its products in Utah, but it also has operations in Brazil, China, France, and Mexico. Products are sold through retailers (such as Sears, Wal-Mart, and Sports Authority), infomercials, and the Web. The company was founded as a housewares importer in 1977. Bain Capital, Credit Suisse, and founders Scott Watterson and Gary Stevenson collectively own ICON.

ICON PRODUCTIONS LLC

808 Wilshire Blvd., 4th Fl.
Santa Monica, CA 90401
Phone: 310-434-7300
Fax: 310-434-7377
Web: www.iconmovies.com

CEO: Mark Gooder
CFO: Vicki Christianson
HR: —
FYE: December 31
Type: Private

A passionate story helped resurrect Icon Productions. Mel Gibson's movie production company Icon Productions made a name for itself when it independently financed *The Passion of the Christ* after Fox passed on theatrically distributing the controversial surprise box office hit. Other Icon films include 2006's *Apocalypto*, released by Disney, and 2007's *Seraphim Falls*, as well as the Gibson vehicles *Braveheart*, *Payback*, and *What Women Want*. Gibson got his start with the Australian apocalyptic action film *Mad Max*, which was released in 1979. He founded his company Icon in 1989.

	Annual Growth	12/04	12/05	12/06	12/07	12/08
Est. sales ($ mil.)	—	—	—	—	—	0.7
Employees	—	—	—	—	—	15

ICONIX BRAND GROUP, INC.

NASDAQ (GS): ICON

1450 Broadway, 4th Fl.
New York, NY 10018
Phone: 212-730-0030
Fax: 212-391-2057
Web: iconixbrand.com

CEO: Neil Cole
CFO: Warren Clamen
HR: —
FYE: December 31
Type: Public

Once a shoemaker, Iconix Brand Group has stepped it up as a licensing and brand management company. Its company-owned consumer and home brands are licensed to third parties that make and sell apparel, footwear, and a variety of other fashion and home products. Consumer brands in the Iconix stable include Badgley Mischka, Danskin, Ocean Pacific, Mossimo, London Fog, Mudd, and Rocawear; among the company's home brands are Cannon, Fieldcrest, and Waverly. The firm diversified through its high-profile purchase of the Peanuts cartoon brand from E. W. Scripps in mid-2010. Along with licensing the brands, Iconix markets and promotes them through its in-house advertising and public relations services.

	Annual Growth	12/05	12/06	12/07	12/08	12/09
Sales ($ mil.)	66.5%	30.2	80.7	160.0	216.8	232.1
Net income ($ mil.)	47.4%	15.9	32.5	63.8	70.2	75.1
Market value ($ mil.)	5.6%	735.6	1,399.7	1,419.2	706.0	914.6
Employees	14.1%	39	46	94	82	66

An in-depth profile of this company is available to Hoover's Online members at hoovers.com.

797

ICOP DIGITAL, INC.

NASDAQ (CM): ICOP

16801 W. 116th St.
Lenexa, KS 66219
Phone: 913-338-5550
Fax: —
Web: icopdigital.com

CEO: David C. Owen
CFO: Mickie R. Koslofsky
HR: —
FYE: December 31
Type: Public

What happens in a police car doesn't necessarily stay in a police car — sometimes, it becomes a matter of considerable controversy. In those cases, accurate evidence is vital, and that's where ICOP Digital comes in. The company designs, engineers, and markets an in-car digital video system, including cameras and a hard disk drive, that is intended for use primarily by law enforcement agencies. Applications include portrayal of traffic stops and other contacts between police officers and the public, as well as officer performance monitoring. Chairman and CEO David Owen and president and COO Laura Owen (who are husband and wife) together own about 15% of the company.

	Annual Growth	12/05	12/06	12/07	12/08	12/09
Sales ($ mil.)	47.0%	1.8	6.6	11.8	10.9	8.4
Net income ($ mil.)	—	(2.9)	(3.5)	(5.5)	(5.9)	(5.5)
Market value ($ mil.)	(50.0%)	186.3	149.9	110.1	4.4	11.7
Employees	13.8%	31	41	53	51	52

ICROSSING, INC.

14822 N. 73rd St.
Scottsdale, AZ 85260
Phone: 480-505-5800
Fax: 480-505-5801
Web: www.icrossing.com

CEO: Don Scales
CFO: Michael J. Jackson
HR: Margaret (Maggie) Luciano-Williams
FYE: December 31
Type: Private

On the World Wide Web, success depends on being seen, and being seen depends on being found. Enter iCrossing. The digital marketing company's services include search engine optimization, paid search advertising, Web development, social media marketing, mobile marketing strategy, and custom analysis. iCrossing's clients have included such big names as Coca-Cola, Toyota, and Travelocity. The independent agency has about a dozen offices in the US and Europe. iCrossing was established in 1998. In June 2010 it agreed to be acquired by media juggernaut Hearst Corporation.

	Annual Growth	12/04	12/05	12/06	12/07	12/08
Est. sales ($ mil.)	—	—	—	—	—	231.5
Employees	—	—	—	—	—	520

ICTS USA, INC.

1 Rockefeller Plaza, Ste. 2412
New York, NY 10020
Phone: 212-218-1850
Fax: 212-218-1855

CEO: M. Albert Nissim
CFO: —
HR: —
FYE: December 31
Type: Subsidiary

This company hopes to keep America's skies clear from danger by using technologies on the ground. ICTS USA, a subsidiary of aviation security provider ICTS International, provides security technologies and services to airlines and aviation customers in the US. Its offerings include computerized passenger processing stations, documentation verification equipment, advanced passenger screening, and training services for baggage X-ray operators. The company also provides airport customs agencies with computer systems used to electronically store passport information.

	Annual Growth	12/04	12/05	12/06	12/07	12/08
Est. sales ($ mil.)	—	—	—	—	—	0.2
Employees	—	—	—	—	—	2

ICU MEDICAL, INC.

NASDAQ (GS): ICUI

951 Calle Amanecer
San Clemente, CA 92673
Phone: 949-366-2183
Fax: 949-366-8368
Web: www.icumed.com

CEO: George A. Lopez
CFO: Scott E. Lamb
HR: James J. (Jim) Reitz
FYE: December 31
Type: Public

ICU Medical sees the future of infection prevention. The company's devices protect health care workers and patients from the spread of diseases such as HIV and hepatitis. Its primary products are intravenous (IV) connection devices, called Clave needleless connectors, that reduce the risk of needle sticks and disconnections. The firm also makes custom IV sets, many of which use Clave connectors and other ICU products, for third parties. Additionally, ICU Medical makes critical care equipment, such as angiography kits and heart monitors. ICU Medical sells its products to other equipment makers and distributors throughout the US and internationally.

	Annual Growth	12/05	12/06	12/07	12/08	12/09
Sales ($ mil.)	10.1%	157.5	201.6	188.1	204.7	231.5
Net income ($ mil.)	7.0%	20.3	25.7	23.1	24.3	26.6
Market value ($ mil.)	(1.8%)	528.8	548.6	485.6	446.9	491.4
Employees	9.0%	1,373	1,819	1,796	1,829	1,936

ICX TECHNOLOGIES, INC.

NASDAQ (GM): ICXT

2100 Crystal Dr., Ste. 650
Arlington, VA 22202
Phone: 703-678-2111
Fax: 703-678-2112
Web: www.icxt.com

CEO: Colin J. Cumming
CFO: Deborah D. (Debbie) Mosier
HR: —
FYE: December 31
Type: Public

Constant vigilance may be the mantra and the mission of ICx Technologies. The firm develops high-precision products used in the detection, identification, and prevention of chemical, biological, radiation, and explosive security threats. Other products offer perimeter security and wide area surveillance. Organized in three divisions — Detection, Surveillance, and Solutions (offering integrated systems, maintenance, and training services) — ICx has a primary customer base of government agencies such as DHS and DOD. Other clients include security and defense firms that integrate ICx products into their own systems. Private equity firm Wexford Capital and its affiliates own about 65% of the company.

	Annual Growth	12/05	12/06	12/07	12/08	12/09
Sales ($ mil.)	55.5%	31.4	90.2	136.2	171.7	183.4
Net income ($ mil.)	—	(14.8)	(127.5)	(29.9)	(26.9)	(10.7)
Market value ($ mil.)	(0.5%)	—	—	335.7	276.0	332.2
Employees	(0.1%)	821	752	870	833	817

I.D. SYSTEMS, INC.

NASDAQ (GM): IDSY

1 University Plaza, 6th Fl.
Hackensack, NJ 07601
Phone: 201-996-9000
Fax: 201-996-9144
Web: www.id-systems.com

CEO: Jeffrey M. Jagid
CFO: Ned Mavrommatis
HR: —
FYE: December 31
Type: Public

I.D. Systems is trying to get its tracking business on the road. The company's products track, analyze, and control the movements of objects such as packages and vehicles. Its systems use radio-frequency identification (RFID) technology and tiny computers attached to the object to be monitored, and users can access tracking data via the Internet. The company is focused on vehicle management, rental car, package tracking, and airport ground security applications. Customers include 3M, the FAA, Ford, Hallmark Cards, Target, the US Postal Service (42% of sales), and Wal-Mart Stores (41%).

	Annual Growth	12/05	12/06	12/07	12/08	12/09
Sales ($ mil.)	(14.2%)	19.0	24.7	17.1	27.0	10.3
Net income ($ mil.)	—	0.9	(1.6)	(7.3)	(4.2)	(13.2)
Market value ($ mil.)	(39.4%)	268.4	211.8	140.2	45.6	36.1
Employees	17.2%	61	89	99	99	115

IDACORP, INC.

NYSE: IDA

1221 W. Idaho St.
Boise, ID 83702
Phone: 208-388-2200
Fax: 208-388-6955
Web: www.idacorpinc.com

CEO: J. LaMont Keen
CFO: Darrel T. Anderson
HR: Luci K. McDonald
FYE: December 31
Type: Public

Energy is more than small potatoes for IDACORP. The holding company's regulated utility, Idaho Power, distributes electricity to more than 487,900 customers in 71 cities in Idaho and nine in Oregon. The utility's generation assets include 17 hydroelectric plants, two gas-fired plants, one diesel generator and stakes in three coal-fired plants. Other IDACORP businesses include coal mining (Idaho Energy Resources, a joint venture partner of the Bridger Coal Company, which supplies coal to a power plant partly owned by IDACORP) and affordable housing investments (IDACORP Financial Services).

	Annual Growth	12/05	12/06	12/07	12/08	12/09
Sales ($ mil.)	5.1%	859.5	926.3	879.4	960.4	1,049.8
Net income ($ mil.)	18.2%	63.7	107.4	82.3	98.4	124.4
Market value ($ mil.)	2.2%	1,409.3	1,859.0	1,694.0	1,416.5	1,536.7
Employees	(0.2%)	1,993	1,976	2,044	2,057	1,979

IDAHO INDEPENDENT BANK

OTC: IIBK

1260 W. Riverstone Dr.
Coeur d'Alene, ID 83814
Phone: 208-765-3619
Fax: 208-765-6091
Web: www.theidahobank.com

CEO: Jack W. Gustavel
CFO: Paul H. Montreuil
HR: —
FYE: December 31
Type: Public

Idaho Independent Bank has about a dozen branches located throughout the state. Targeting individuals and small to midsized businesses, the bank provides such traditional products as checking and savings accounts, certificates of deposit, and credit cards. The bank also offers a variety of products and services aimed specifically at business customers, including cash management and working capital loans. Real estate loans make up more than half of the bank's loan portfolio. Idaho Independent Bank also originates business, construction, and consumer loans.

IDAHO NATIONAL LABORATORY

2525 N. Fremont Ave.
Idaho Falls, ID 83415
Phone: 208-526-0111
Fax: 208-526-4563
Web: www.inl.gov

CEO: John J. Grossenbacher
CFO: Brian Sack
HR: Mark Holubar
FYE: September 30
Type: Government-owned

Idaho National Laboratory (INL, formerly Idaho National Engineering and Environmental Laboratory) performs applied engineering research in such areas as nuclear technology, national security, and energy. The laboratory campus, which consists of nearly 570,000 acres, also serves as an environmental research park. Established in 1949, INL is funded by the US Department of Energy and operated by the Battelle Energy Alliance, a partnership of Battelle Memorial Institute, BWX Technologies, Washington Group International, MIT, and the not-for-profit Electric Power Research Institute. The Department of Energy combined the laboratory with the Idaho-based nuclear facilities of Argonne National Laboratory in 2005.

IDEA INTEGRATION CORP.

1 Independent Dr.
Jacksonville, FL 32202
Phone: 904-360-2700
Fax: 904-360-2490
Web: www.idea.com

CEO: Timothy D. (Tim) Payne
CFO: Robert P. (Bob) Crouch
HR: —
FYE: December 31
Type: Subsidiary

Idea Integration has more than a few thoughts on the subject of e-business. The company specializes in the design and development of applications for online business, but it also offers its *FORTUNE* 1000 and middle-market clients other services, including strategy consulting, creative design, and customer relationship management. The firm primarily serves the energy, government, manufacturing, education, financial, health care, and utilities sectors. Its clients have included CIGNA, Hewlett-Packard, and Microsoft. The company has offices across the US and is headquartered in Jacksonville, Florida. Idea Integration was a subsidiary of MPS Group, which was acquired by global staffing rival Adecco in 2010.

IDENIX PHARMACEUTICALS, INC.

NASDAQ (GM): IDIX

60 Hampshire St.
Cambridge, MA 02139
Phone: 617-995-9800
Fax: 617-995-9801
Web: www.idenix.com

CEO: Jean-Pierre Sommadossi
CFO: Ronald C. (Ron) Renaud Jr.
HR: Paul J. Fanning
FYE: December 31
Type: Public

Idenix Pharmaceuticals is not suffering from any identity crisis — it is clear in its focus on identifying treatments for life-threatening viruses. The biopharmaceutical firm is developing orally administered drugs to combat chronic hepatitis C (HCV) and HIV. Its lead HIV product candidate is in early clinical stages; its HCV candidates are in preclinical testing. Most are intended to be taken in combination with other therapeutic agents to improve efficacy and convenience. Under a development and commercialization agreement, Novartis has the option to license any of the product candidates developed by Idenix. Novartis owns 56% of Idenix.

	Annual Growth	12/05	12/06	12/07	12/08	12/09
Sales ($ mil.)	(33.6%)	64.7	67.4	68.0	10.0	12.6
Net income ($ mil.)	—	(50.8)	(75.1)	(82.5)	(70.2)	(53.2)
Market value ($ mil.)	(40.5%)	1,246.6	633.1	196.7	421.8	156.6
Employees	(9.8%)	218	277	219	173	144

IDEO LLC

100 Forest Ave.
Palo Alto, CA 94301
Phone: 650-289-3400
Fax: 650-289-3707
Web: www.ideo.com

CEO: Tim Brown
CFO: David (Dave) Strong
HR: John Foster
FYE: February 28
Type: Subsidiary

Ideas are IDEO's stock-in-trade. The company provides product development and branding services for a wide range of clients. It also offers packaging design, product research, and strategic consulting services. Its work has included contributions to TiVo's digital video recorder and the Palm V for Palm. In addition, IDEO (pronounced EYE-dee-oh) provides executive training and education services to help enterprises become more innovative. It operates from a network of several offices in the US, Europe, and the Asia/Pacific region. IDEO is a subsidiary of office furniture manufacturer Steelcase. Chairman David Kelley, whose design credits include the first mouse for Apple, and Bill Moggridge formed IDEO in 1991.

An in-depth profile of this company is available to Hoover's Online members at hoovers.com.

799

IDERA PHARMACEUTICALS, INC.

NASDAQ (GM): IDRA

167 Sidney St.
Cambridge, MA 02139
Phone: 617-679-5500
Fax: 617-679-5592
Web: www.iderapharma.com

CEO: Sudhir Agrawal
CFO: Louis J. (Lou) Arcudi III
HR: —
FYE: December 31
Type: Public

Idera Pharmaceuticals may try to manipulate you, but it's all for your own good. The biotech firm is developing DNA and RNA therapies that manipulate the immune system's response to disease. It is focused on Toll-Like Receptors (TLRs) — immune cell receptors that recognize and respond to viral and bacterial invaders. Some of Idera's drugs (such as treatments for infectious disease and cancer) mimic those invaders to stimulate an immune response; others (including treatments for autoimmune diseases) target TLRs to suppress the immune response. The company's lead candidate is a potential treatment for hepatitis C. Idera has partnered on some other programs with the likes of Merck & Co., Merck KGaA, and Novartis.

	Annual Growth	12/05	12/06	12/07	12/08	12/09
Sales ($ mil.)	92.7%	2.5	2.4	8.0	26.4	34.5
Net income ($ mil.)	—	(13.7)	(16.5)	(13.2)	1.5	7.5
Market value ($ mil.)	1.5%	114.6	126.6	307.7	180.4	121.4
Employees	10.3%	27	33	38	37	40

IDEX CORPORATION

NYSE: IEX

630 Dundee Rd., Ste. 400
Northbrook, IL 60062
Phone: 847-498-7070
Fax: 847-498-3940
Web: www.idexcorp.com

CEO: Lawrence D. Kingsley
CFO: Dominic A. Romeo
HR: Harold Morgan
FYE: December 31
Type: Public

The big idea at IDEX is to dispense with inefficiencies and pump up profits. The company is a major manufacturer of pumps, dispensing equipment, and other engineered industrial products. It operates through four segments. A fluid and metering segment makes pumps, meters, and injectors used in the movement and treatment of industrial chemicals, gases, and water. Its dispensing unit specializes in paint dispersal and mixing tools, sold by US and European home centers and other retailers. A health and science unit produces fluidics components for medical instruments and implantable devices. IDEX's fire and safety equipment unit manufactures clamps, firefighting pumps, and rescue tools, such as the Jaws of Life.

	Annual Growth	12/05	12/06	12/07	12/08	12/09
Sales ($ mil.)	6.3%	1,043.3	1,154.9	1,358.6	1,489.5	1,329.7
Net income ($ mil.)	0.8%	109.8	146.7	155.1	131.4	113.4
Market value ($ mil.)	3.3%	2,226.1	2,567.2	2,934.6	1,961.5	2,530.1
Employees	5.4%	4,300	4,863	5,009	5,813	5,300

IDEXX LABORATORIES, INC.

NASDAQ (GS): IDXX

1 IDEXX Dr.
Westbrook, ME 04092
Phone: 207-556-0300
Fax: 207-556-4346
Web: www.idexx.com

CEO: Jonathan W. (Jon) Ayers
CFO: Merilee Raines
HR: —
FYE: December 31
Type: Public

If IDEXX Laboratories had been on the scene, Old Yeller might have had a happier ending. A leading animal health care company, IDEXX makes diagnostic testing kits and machines and drugs for pets and livestock. Veterinarians use the company's VetTest analyzers for blood and urine chemistry and its SNAP and PetChek in-office test kits to detect heartworms, feline leukemia, and other diseases. The company also provides veterinary lab testing services and practice management software. In addition, IDEXX makes diagnostic products to detect livestock and poultry diseases (such as swine or bird flu) and to test systems for contaminants in water and antibiotics in milk. The company serves customers in 75 countries.

	Annual Growth	12/05	12/06	12/07	12/08	12/09
Sales ($ mil.)	12.8%	638.1	739.1	922.6	1,024.0	1,031.6
Net income ($ mil.)	11.8%	78.3	93.7	94.0	116.2	122.2
Market value ($ mil.)	10.4%	2,074.9	2,285.9	3,380.1	2,080.1	3,081.5
Employees	9.2%	3,300	3,900	4,700	4,700	4,700

IDS SCHEER BUSINESS PROCESS MANAGEMENT, INC.

CEO: Joerg Heistermann

1055 Westlakes Dr., Ste. 100
Berwyn, PA 19312
Phone: 610-854-6800
Fax: 610-854-7382
Web: www.ids-scheer.com/us

CEO: Joerg Heistermann
CFO: —
HR: —
FYE: December 31
Type: Subsidiary

IDS Scheer Business Process Management helps businesses get a handle on business processes and lifecycles. The company offers consulting services, and its ARIS software suite assists customers with supply chain and customer management, enterprise resource planning and application integration, and e-business. Clients range from small and midsized firms to huge global operations. The company is the North American subsidiary of German software and consulting company IDS Scheer AG, which was founded in 1984 by August-Wilhelm Scheer.

IDT CORPORATION

NYSE: IDT

520 Broad St.
Newark, NJ 07102
Phone: 973-438-1000
Fax: 973-482-3971
Web: www.idt.net

CEO: Howard S. Jonas
CFO: Bill Pereira
HR: —
FYE: July 31
Type: Public

IDT keeps a corporate finger in several pies. The company makes most of its money through IDT Telecom, which provides retail domestic and international long-distance access mainly in the US, as well as wholesale voice and data services. IDT also offers wireless service and prepaid calling cards. The company's international business consists of calling card sales to customers primarily in Europe. IDT's other operations include an energy services unit that resells natural gas and electric power in New York state and alternative energy operations in the US and Israel. The company had been involved in the debt collection business through its IDT Carmel division but sold those operations in late 2009.

	Annual Growth	7/05	7/06	7/07	7/08	7/09
Sales ($ mil.)	(11.1%)	2,468.5	2,226.4	2,012.7	1,878.0	1,538.6
Net income ($ mil.)	—	(43.8)	(178.7)	58.6	(224.3)	(155.4)
Market value ($ mil.)	(49.2%)	882.0	908.5	677.6	120.2	58.8
Employees	(30.4%)	5,951	3,000	2,360	1,850	1,400

IEC ELECTRONICS CORP.

NYSE Amex: IEC

105 Norton St.
Newark, NY 14513
Phone: 315-331-7742
Fax: 315-331-3547
Web: www.iec-electronics.com

CEO: W. Barry Gilbert
CFO: Susan E. Topel-Samek
HR: —
FYE: September 30
Type: Public

IEC makes products you may never see. Most of IEC Electronics' sales come from the contract manufacturing of printed circuit boards. The company makes a mix of boards, including models that use surface-mount technology, pin-through-hole connections, and more advanced interconnection techniques. Like many contract electronics manufacturers, IEC also offers a variety of auxiliary services, including design and prototyping, materials procurement and management, engineering, testing, packaging, and distribution. Nearly all sales are to customers located in the US.

	Annual Growth	9/05	9/06	9/07	9/08	9/09
Sales ($ mil.)	37.3%	19.1	22.6	40.9	51.1	67.8
Net income ($ mil.)	102.1%	0.3	0.2	0.9	10.5	5.0
Market value ($ mil.)	66.2%	6.7	9.8	18.1	16.9	51.0
Employees	32.9%	118	240	229	350	368

IEX CORPORATION

2425 N. Central Expy.
Richardson, TX 75080
Phone: 972-301-1300
Fax: 972-301-1321
Web: www.iex.com

CEO: Debbie May
CFO: —
HR: —
FYE: December 31
Type: Subsidiary

IEX can help you manage all sorts of operations. The company provides workforce management and call routing software that customers use to optimize and manage call center operations. More than 3,100 call centers in over 65 countries use its products to tackle tasks such as performance management, strategic planning, asset management, and scheduling. The company also offers related services such as consulting, maintenance, training, implementation, and support. IEX is a subsidiary of NICE Systems and operates out of offices in Europe, North America, and Asia.

I-FLOW CORPORATION

20202 Windrow Dr.
Lake Forest, CA 92630
Phone: 949-206-2700
Fax: 949-206-2600
Web: www.iflo.com

CEO: Joanne B. Bauer
CFO: Mark A. Buthman
HR: —
FYE: December 31
Type: Subsidiary

I-Flow lets you drift off from the pain by helping the meds flow. The company makes mobile infusion systems used in hospitals, homes, and other settings to administer non-narcotic acute pain treatments and a variety of other drugs, including antibiotics, chemotherapies, and nutrients. I-Flow's product line includes the ON-Q branded portable infusion pumps and catheters that deliver anesthetic pain medications directly to wound sites, as well as disposable products for administration of chemotherapies and antibiotics. The company's offerings are marketed through direct sales representatives and international distributors. I-Flow was acquired by Kimberly-Clark in late 2009 in a deal worth about $324 million.

	Annual Growth	12/04	12/05	12/06	12/07	12/08
Sales ($ mil.)	17.0%	71.1	100.6	93.6	116.5	133.1
Net income ($ mil.)	—	(17.1)	(8.4)	13.7	41.2	(30.5)
Employees	29.7%	389	810	990	970	1,100

IGA, INC.

8745 W. Higgins Rd., Ste. 350
Chicago, IL 60631
Phone: 773-693-4520
Fax: 773-693-4533
Web: www.iga.com

CEO: Thomas S. Haggai
CFO: John Collins
HR: —
FYE: December 31
Type: Holding company

IGA grocers are independent, but not alone. The world's largest voluntary supermarket network, IGA has 6,200 stores in more than 35 countries worldwide, including about 1,350 in the US. Collectively, its members are among North America's leaders in terms of supermarket sales. IGA (for either International or Independent Grocers Alliance, the company says) is owned by about 35 worldwide distribution companies, including SUPERVALU. Members can sell IGA-brand private-label products (over 2,300 items) and take advantage of joint operations and services, such as advertising and volume buying. Some stores in the IGA alliance, which primarily caters to smaller towns, also sell gas.

	Annual Growth	12/04	12/05	12/06	12/07	12/08
Sales ($ mil.)	0.0%	—	—	21,000.0	21,000.0	21,000.0
Employees	0.0%	—	—	92,000	92,000	92,000

IGATE CORPORATION

NASDAQ (GM): IGTE

6528 Kaiser Dr.
Fremont, CA 94555
Phone: 510-896-3000
Fax: 510-896-3010
Web: www.igatecorp.com

CEO: Phaneesh Murthy
CFO: Sujit Sircar
HR: Srinivas Kandula
FYE: December 31
Type: Public

iGate is open to all things IT. The company provides business process outsourcing (BPO) and offshore development services, including software development and maintenance outsourcing. In addition to IT-related services, iGate handles such tasks as mortgage and claims processing and call center operations. The company targets midsized and large corporations in the banking, financial services, and insurance industries. Its customers include General Electric (23% of sales), IBM, Royal Bank of Canada (nearly 27%), and TEKsystems. In addition to its US operations, iGate manages facilities in Australia, Canada, India, Malaysia, and Mexico. The company gets more than three-quarters of its revenues in North America.

	Annual Growth	12/05	12/06	12/07	12/08	12/09
Sales ($ mil.)	(8.5%)	276.0	283.6	307.3	218.8	193.1
Net income ($ mil.)	42.2%	7.0	8.7	15.6	30.9	28.6
Market value ($ mil.)	19.8%	268.7	380.4	468.3	359.9	552.9
Employees	4.1%	5,890	6,900	6,260	6,658	6,910

IGENE BIOTECHNOLOGY, INC.

Pink Sheets: IGNE

9110 Red Branch Rd.
Columbia, MD 21045
Phone: 410-997-2599
Fax: 410-730-0540
Web: www.igene.com

CEO: Stephen F. Hiu
CFO: Edward J. Weisberger
HR: —
FYE: December 31
Type: Public

Some would say IGENE Biotechnology has some ingenious ideas about the way things should be. The company manufactures biochemical products for the human and animal nutrition industry. Among its products are natural astaxanthin, a feed nutrient that is used as a coloring agent in farmed salmon, under the AstaXin brand. Other uses for astaxanthin include feed for shrimp and poultry and for coloring egg yolks. The company's proprietary fermentation of a yeast called Phaffia rhodozyma naturally extracts the nutrient, which is a potent antioxidant several times stronger than vitamin E. IGENE is trying to further develop the commercial applications of its astaxanthin as an ingredient in consumer health foods.

	Annual Growth	12/05	12/06	12/07	12/08	12/09
Sales ($ mil.)	—	—	0.0	2.3	7.6	4.0
Net income ($ mil.)	—	—	(1.2)	(1.9)	(4.0)	(0.1)
Market value ($ mil.)	(30.7%)	—	47.0	20.4	9.4	15.7
Employees	14.5%	—	12	—	18	18

IGI, INC.

NYSE Amex: IG

105 Lincoln Ave.
Buena, NJ 08310
Phone: 856-697-1441
Fax: 856-697-2259
Web: www.askigi.com

CEO: Hemanshu (Hem) Pandya
CFO: Phillip S. Forte
HR: —
FYE: December 31
Type: Public

IGI is betting big on small things. The company manufactures creams, liquids, and other topical products for drug and cosmetics companies using its microencapsulation technology. It originally licensed the technology, dubbed Novasome, from drug firm Novovax. The Novasome process entraps and protects the active ingredients of various skin care products, moisturizers, shampoos, and fragrances, allowing for greater stability during storage and a more controlled release when used. The company is examining further applications of the Novasome technology in food, personal care products, and pharmaceuticals.

	Annual Growth	12/05	12/06	12/07	12/08	12/09
Sales ($ mil.)	7.0%	2.9	2.6	4.6	4.1	3.8
Net income ($ mil.)	—	(1.3)	(1.7)	(0.3)	(1.9)	(4.9)
Market value ($ mil.)	(3.0%)	15.6	20.5	25.0	8.5	13.8
Employees	14.6%	18	19	19	23	31

An in-depth profile of this company is available to Hoover's Online members at hoovers.com.

801

IGLOO PRODUCTS CORP.

777 Igloo Rd.
Katy, TX 77494
Phone: 713-584-6800
Fax: 713-935-7763
Web: www.igloocoolers.com

CEO: James J. (Jim) Roberts
CFO: Mike Vitek
HR: Alex Hodges
FYE: December 31
Type: Private

Started in 1947 as a small metalworking shop that made metal water coolers for blue collar workers, Igloo Products is now a leading ice chest and beverage dispenser manufacturer, perhaps known best for its Playmate brand. The company's first all-plastic ice chest was introduced in 1962. Igloo makes the coolers for personal and industrial use and claims that three in every four US households owns an Igloo cooler. The company's more than 500 products (including personal, beverage, and full-sized coolers) are sold through more than 250 retailers in the US and abroad. Private investment firm Westar Capital, which purchased Igloo from Brunswick in 2001, sold the business in 2008 to J.H. Whitney & Co.

IGNITE RESTAURANT GROUP, INC.

9900 Westpark Dr., Ste. 300
Houston, TX 77063
Phone: 713-366-7500
Fax: —
Web: www.igniterestaurantgroup.com

CEO: Ray Blanchette
CFO: Jeff Rager
HR: Kevin Cottingim
FYE: December 31
Type: Private

Foodies with a burning passion for seafood might turn to this company. Formerly JCS Holdings, Ignite Restaurant Group operates Joe's Crab Shack, a leading casual dining chain with more than 110 locations in Texas, California, Florida, and about 25 other states. The eateries feature a wide variety of grilled, fried, and stuffed seafood, along with sandwiches and sides. The seafood chain is known for its fun and quirky surf-inspired atmosphere where the servers are often part of the entertainment. In addition to its flagship restaurant brand, Ignite operates a small number of Brick House Tavern + Tap locations. The company is backed by private equity group J. H. Whitney Capital Partners.

	Annual Growth	12/04	12/05	12/06	12/07	12/08
Est. sales ($ mil.)	—	—	—	—	—	216.8
Employees	—	—	—	—	—	10,000

IGO, INC.

NASDAQ (GM): IGOI

17800 N. Perimeter Dr., Ste. 200
Scottsdale, AZ 85255
Phone: 480-596-0061
Fax: 480-596-0349
Web: corporate.igo.com

CEO: Michael D. Heil
CFO: Darryl S. Baker
HR: —
FYE: December 31
Type: Public

iGo (formerly Mobility Electronics) has the power to keep electronics running. The company designs power products and chargers for portable electronics such as notebook computers, mobile phones, digital music players, handheld computers, and gaming systems. iGo's product line includes AC, DC, combination AC/DC, and battery-based universal power adapters. It sells to computer manufacturers including Dell and Lenovo, as well as distributors (D&H Distributing, Ingram Micro) and retailers (Amazon.com, RadioShack). iGo also sells directly though its website.

	Annual Growth	12/05	12/06	12/07	12/08	12/09
Sales ($ mil.)	(10.3%)	85.5	92.5	77.7	77.1	55.4
Net income ($ mil.)	—	5.0	(16.8)	(12.6)	0.5	(0.5)
Market value ($ mil.)	(40.3%)	316.0	109.6	51.0	22.9	40.2
Employees	(24.0%)	156	163	151	63	52

IHS INC.

NYSE: IHS

15 Inverness Way East
Englewood, CO 80112
Phone: 303-790-0600
Fax: 303-754-3940
Web: www.ihs.com

CEO: Jerre L. Stead
CFO: Michael J. (Mike) Sullivan
HR: Jeffrey (Jeff) Sisson
FYE: November 30
Type: Public

IHS Inc. (Information Handling Services Inc.) handles the hottest commodity around: information. A publisher of technical documents for clients in the energy, defense, aerospace, construction, electronics, and automotive industries, the company distributes its data in several electronic formats (Internet, intranet, extranet, CD-ROM). Products such as collections of technical specifications and standards, regulations, parts data, and design guides are sold through its four areas of information: Energy, Product Lifecycle, Security, and Environment. The company also offers economic-focused information and analysis through its IHS Global Insight subsidiary. IHS primarily earns revenue through subscription sales.

	Annual Growth	11/05	11/06	11/07	11/08	11/09
Sales ($ mil.)	19.4%	476.1	550.8	688.4	844.0	967.3
Net income ($ mil.)	34.1%	41.8	56.3	83.8	99.0	135.0
Market value ($ mil.)	27.1%	1,230.7	2,367.4	4,481.8	2,318.9	3,212.8
Employees	98.3%	265	2,500	3,000	3,800	4,100

IKANOS COMMUNICATIONS, INC.

NASDAQ (GM): IKAN

47669 Fremont Blvd.
Fremont, CA 94538
Phone: 510-979-0400
Fax: 510-438-5377
Web: www.ikanos.com

CEO: Diosdado P. (Dado) Banatao
CFO: Dennis Bencala
HR: Jim Murphy
FYE: December 31
Type: Public

Ikanos Communications hopes to become an icon in the field of networking semiconductors. The fabless semiconductor company designs high-speed programmable single- and multi-port chipsets that allow networks to achieve broadband transmission speeds over existing copper wires. Its SmartLeap and CleverConnect chipsets enable such high speeds over a few thousand feet of wire; this allows network access equipment makers to join multitenant units to the edge of fiber-optic networks, and enables broadband connections between neighboring buildings. In a transaction that could transform the company, Ikanos in 2009 acquired the Broadband Access product lines of Conexant Systems for $54 million in cash.

	Annual Growth	12/05	12/06	12/07	12/08	12/09
Sales ($ mil.)	11.3%	85.1	134.7	107.5	106.5	130.7
Net income ($ mil.)	—	2.7	(23.4)	(33.3)	(41.1)	(37.1)
Market value ($ mil.)	(40.3%)	799.5	471.4	291.8	68.3	101.4
Employees	34.8%	178	279	281	290	588

IKON OFFICE SOLUTIONS, INC.

70 Valley Stream Pkwy.
Malvern, PA 19355
Phone: 610-296-8000
Fax: 610-408-7025
Web: www.ikon.com

CEO: Matthew J. (Matt) Espe
CFO: Henry M. Miller Jr.
HR: Donna Venable
FYE: March 31
Type: Subsidiary

IKON Office Solutions works to ensure that when it comes to buying business equipment, customers say, "I can and I will." IKON, a subsidiary of office equipment giant Ricoh, sells and services its parent's brand of office equipment, including copiers, printers, scanners, fax machines, and more, throughout the US, Canada, and Europe. The company also offers such services as document management outsourcing, electronic file conversions, facilities management, and training. Customers are primarily large and small businesses and government agencies. IKON was acquired by Japan's Ricoh, a key supplier, in 2008 for $1.6 billion.

An in-depth profile of this company is available to Hoover's Online members at hoovers.com.

IKONICS CORPORATION

NASDAQ (CM): IKNX

4832 Grand Ave.
Duluth, MN 55807
Phone: 218-628-2217
Fax: 218-628-3245
Web: www.ikonics.com

CEO: William C. (Bill) Ulland
CFO: Jon Gerlach
HR: —
FYE: December 31
Type: Public

IKONICS makes light-sensitive coatings (emulsions) and films, used primarily by the screen printing and abrasive etching markets (to create stencil images for the one and to create architectural glass and art pieces for the other). The company also makes photoresist films and metal etching materials for sign making and ink jet receptive films for creating photopositives and photonegatives. Custom etching services and digital imaging technologies for niche industrial markets is of increasing importance to the company. IKONICS sells its products through about 200 distributors worldwide, although the US accounts for more than two-thirds of sales.

	Annual Growth	12/05	12/06	12/07	12/08	12/09
Sales ($ mil.)	1.9%	14.0	14.9	15.8	15.9	15.1
Net income ($ mil.)	—	0.9	1.1	1.2	0.8	(0.3)
Market value ($ mil.)	(0.2%)	12.5	14.8	18.3	11.3	12.4
Employees	1.1%	68	70	74	70	71

ILINC COMMUNICATIONS, INC.

Pink Sheets: ILNC

2999 N. 44th St., Ste. 650
Phoenix, AZ 85018
Phone: 602-952-1200
Fax: 602-952-0544
Web: www.ilinc.com

CEO: James M. Powers Jr.
CFO: James L. Dunn Jr.
HR: —
FYE: March 31
Type: Public

iLinc Communications provides Web-based voice and video conferencing and collaboration software and services. Companies use its products to handle meetings among co-workers at different locations, share documents, deliver corporate presentations, facilitate communications with customers, and offer remote training and education courses. iLinc Communications also offers implementation, technical support, and training services. Clients have included California Software, Cypress MicroSystems, Maximizer Software, National University, and QUALCOMM.

	Annual Growth	3/04	3/05	3/06	3/07	*3/08
Sales ($ mil.)	10.5%	5.9	10.4	12.5	14.2	8.8
Net income ($ mil.)	—	(2.0)	(5.3)	(1.2)	0.1	(2.2)
Employees	21.0%	48	92	78	88	103

*Most recent year available

ILITCH HOLDINGS, INC.

2211 Woodward Ave.
Detroit, MI 48201
Phone: 313-471-6600
Fax: 313-471-6094
Web: www.ilitchholdings.com

CEO: Christopher (Chris) Ilitch
CFO: Scott Fisher
HR: Joni C. Nelson
FYE: December 31
Type: Holding company

This holding company rules over a Caesar, tames Tigers, and takes flight on the ice. Ilitch Holdings controls the business interests of Mike and Marian Ilitch and their family, which includes the Little Caesars pizza chain, the Detroit Tigers baseball team, and the Detroit Red Wings hockey team. Subsidiary Olympia Entertainment owns Detroit's Fox Theatre and operates Comerica Park, Joe Louis Arena, and Cobo Arena. Additional holdings include Blue Line Foodservice Distribution, a leading supplier of food and equipment to restaurant operators (including Little Caesars operators), and an interest in the MotorCity Casino Hotel. The Ilitches started Little Caesars in 1959 and formed Ilitch Holdings in 1999.

	Annual Growth	12/04	12/05	12/06	12/07	12/08
Est. sales ($ mil.)	10.1%	—	1,500.0	1,480.0	1,520.0	2,000.0
Employees	19.0%	—	12,000	17,000	17,000	—

ILLINOIS LOTTERY

101 W. Jefferson St.
Springfield, IL 62702
Phone: 312-793-3026
Fax: —
Web: www.illinoislottery.com

CEO: Jodie Winnett
CFO: —
HR: —
FYE: June 30
Type: Government-owned

Just because the Cubs can't win in Illinois doesn't mean you can't. Created in 1974, the Illinois Department of the Lottery runs numbers games, including Pick 3 and Pick 4, and participates in the dozen-state Mega Millions game in which players can win jackpots starting at $12 million (odds of winning: 1 in 175 million). It also offers instant-win scratch-off games. Of the money collected from ticket sales, about 60% is paid in prizes and some 30% goes to the state's Common School Fund, which helps finance K-12 public education. The rest covers retailer commissions and expenses. The Illinois Lottery operates through more than 7,500 retail businesses. For every ticket sold, retailers receive a 5% commission.

ILLINOIS POWER COMPANY

370 S. Main St.
Decatur, IL 62523
Phone: 217-424-6600
Fax: —
Web: www.illinoispower.com

CEO: Scott A. Cisel
CFO: Martin J. Lyons Jr.
HR: —
FYE: December 31
Type: Subsidiary

Illinois Power, a unit of Ameren, lights up homes and businesses in the Land of Lincoln. The regulated utility, which operates as AmerenIP, serves 626,000 electricity customers and 427,000 natural gas customers. Illinois Power owns 40,000 circuit miles of electric transmission and distribution lines and more than 8,400 miles of gas transmission and distribution mains. To prepare for deregulation, the company has divested its fossil-fueled and nuclear power plant interests; it receives its power supply through contracts with generation companies and other utilities.

	Annual Growth	12/04	12/05	12/06	12/07	12/08
Est. sales ($ mil.)	—	—	—	—	—	1,696.0
Employees	—	—	—	—	—	1,173

[H] ILLINOIS TOOL WORKS INC.

NYSE: ITW

3600 W. Lake Ave.
Glenview, IL 60026
Phone: 847-724-7500
Fax: 847-657-4261
Web: www.itw.com

CEO: David B. Speer
CFO: Ronald D. (Ron) Kropp
HR: Sharon M. Brady
FYE: December 31
Type: Public

Don't let the name fool you — Illinois Tool Works (ITW) hammers out more than just tools, and it operates well beyond the Land of Lincoln. With 840 separate operations in 57 countries, ITW manufactures and services equipment used in the automotive, construction, electronics, food and beverage, packaging, power system, and pharmaceutical industries. The company groups its work into eight segments. The largest, transportation, plies fasteners, anchors, and other binding tools for concrete, wood, and metal applications. Second in sales, an industrial packaging arm churns out metal jacketing, stretch film, and paper and plastic products to protect shipped goods. ITW gets about half of its sales from North America.

	Annual Growth	12/05	12/06	12/07	12/08	12/09
Sales ($ mil.)	1.8%	12,921.8	14,055.0	16,170.6	15,869.4	13,877.1
Net income ($ mil.)	(10.8%)	1,494.9	1,717.7	1,869.9	1,519.0	947.0
Market value ($ mil.)	2.2%	22,106.8	23,209.8	26,903.1	17,612.1	24,114.3
Employees	4.2%	50,000	55,000	60,000	65,000	59,000

ILLUMINA, INC.

NASDAQ (GM): ILMN

9885 Towne Centre Dr.
San Diego, CA 92121
Phone: 858-202-4500
Fax: 858-202-4545
Web: www.illumina.com

CEO: Jay T. Flatley
CFO: Christian O. Henry
HR: —
FYE: December 31
Type: Public

Illumina elucidates the human genome. The firm makes tools used by life sciences and drug researchers to isolate and analyze genes. Its systems include the machinery and the software used to sequence pieces of DNA and RNA, and the means to put them through large-scale testing of genetic variation and biological function. Its proprietary BeadArray technology uses microscopic glass beads which can carry samples through the array process. The tests allow medical researchers to determine what genetic combinations are associated with various diseases, enabling faster diagnosis, better drugs, and individualized treatment. Customers include pharma and biotech companies, research centers, and academic institutions.

	Annual Growth	12/05	12/06	12/07	12/08	12/09
Sales ($ mil.)	73.5%	73.5	184.6	366.8	573.2	666.3
Net income ($ mil.)	—	(20.9)	40.0	(278.4)	50.5	72.3
Market value ($ mil.)	44.4%	858.6	2,393.8	3,608.7	3,172.7	3,736.6
Employees	47.6%	375	596	1,041	1,536	1,781

ILX RESORTS INCORPORATED

NYSE Amex: ILX

2111 E. Highland Ave., Ste. 200
Phoenix, AZ 85016
Phone: 602-957-2777
Fax: 602-957-2780
Web: www.ilxresorts.com

CEO: Joseph P. (Joe) Martori
CFO: Margaret M. Eardley
HR: —
FYE: December 31
Type: Public

ILX Resorts wants to take you away. The company develops, owns, operates, and markets timeshare resorts, primarily in the western US. Its portfolio includes about a dozen vacation resorts located near major cities or in top vacation spots in Arizona, Colorado, Indiana, Nevada, and Mexico. Resort properties are sold, fully furnished, for one-week time units. The company's Varsity Club resorts are located near major universities and offer flexible ownership packages. (Think: football season.) ILX Resorts also provides timeshare financing and markets resorts owned by other parties. Chairman and CEO Joseph Martori and his family own about 25% of ILX Resorts, which in 2009 filed for Chapter 11 bankruptcy protection.

	Annual Growth	12/05	12/06	12/07	12/08	12/09
Sales ($ mil.)	(12.3%)	56.9	54.5	48.6	27.4	33.6
Net income ($ mil.)	—	6.2	2.2	(0.7)	(8.7)	(1.8)
Market value ($ mil.)	(65.3%)	37.8	34.0	12.7	2.1	0.5
Employees	(11.3%)	840	840	720	690	520

IM FLASH TECHNOLOGIES, LLC

1550 E. 3400 North
Lehi, UT 84043
Phone: 801-767-5040
Fax: 801-767-5353
Web: imftech.com

CEO: Rodney (Rod) Morgan
CFO: —
HR: —
FYE: December 31
Type: Joint venture

IM Flash Technologies wants to jump-start success. The company makes NAND flash memory devices (removable, portable computer memory incorporated into jump drives) commonly used in mobile computing or storage applications, including wireless phones, digital still cameras and music players, game consoles, toys, GPS receivers, and mobile medical equipment. The company's flash memory is also used in flash cards, USB drives, hard drives, and printers. IM Flash operates a wafer fabrication facility (or fab) in Utah, with another under development in Singapore. The semiconductor manufacturer, which is a joint venture of Intel and Micron Technology, sells all its products to its parents.

IMAGE ENTERTAINMENT, INC.

NASDAQ (GM): DISK

20525 Nordhoff St., Ste. 200
Chatsworth, CA 91311
Phone: 818-407-9100
Fax: 818-407-9151
Web: www.image-entertainment.com

CEO: Theodore S. (Ted) Green
CFO: John Avagliano
HR: —
FYE: March 31
Type: Public

This Image has been altered to fit the format of your home entertainment center. Image Entertainment acquires rights to film and video titles and distributes them primarily in DVD format to US retailers, including Amazon.com, Wal-Mart (via Wal-Mart supplier Anderson Merchandisers), Costco, and Target. Its library contains about 3,200 DVD titles. The company also sells broadcast rights to cable and satellite channels and produces some original programming. Its Egami subsidiary acquires and distributes digital content through video on demand, streaming video, and download channels. Its newly formed theatrical distribution division is designed to bring four to six feature films to movie theaters each year.

	Annual Growth	3/05	3/06	3/07	3/08	3/09
Sales ($ mil.)	2.5%	118.4	111.9	99.8	95.8	130.7
Net income ($ mil.)	—	5.1	(0.2)	(12.6)	(23.1)	(1.8)
Market value ($ mil.)	(30.3%)	138.7	93.8	106.2	42.6	32.7
Employees	(14.8%)	205	195	160	138	108

IMAGE SENSING SYSTEMS, INC.

NASDAQ (CM): ISNS

1600 University Ave. West, 500 Spruce Tree Centre
St. Paul, MN 55104
Phone: 651-603-7700
Fax: 651-305-6402
Web: www.imagesensing.com

CEO: Kenneth R. (Ken) Aubrey
CFO: Gregory R. L. (Greg) Smith
HR: —
FYE: December 31
Type: Public

If you're stuck in traffic, you can't blame Image Sensing Systems (ISS). ISS's Autoscope vehicle detection system converts video images into digitized traffic data for traffic management. Unlike traditional embedded wire loop detectors, which are buried in the pavement, Autoscope enables wide-area detection using video cameras, a microprocessor, software, and a PC. The systems help users to design roads, manage traffic signals, and determine the environmental impact of gridlock. Royalty income from traffic management company Econolite Control Products accounts for nearly half of sales. The company gets three-quarters of its sales in North America.

	Annual Growth	12/05	12/06	12/07	12/08	12/09
Sales ($ mil.)	22.3%	11.0	13.1	15.1	26.5	24.6
Net income ($ mil.)	8.6%	2.8	3.1	0.9	5.0	3.9
Market value ($ mil.)	(3.9%)	63.9	68.6	83.3	30.5	54.6
Employees	18.6%	49	53	80	97	97

IMAGEWARE SYSTEMS, INC.

OTC: IWSY

10883 Thornmint Rd.
San Diego, CA 92127
Phone: 858-673-8600
Fax: 858-673-1770
Web: www.iwsinc.com

CEO: S. James (Jim) Miller Jr.
CFO: Wayne G. Wetherell
HR: —
FYE: December 31
Type: Public

Even if your face won't launch a thousand ships, ImageWare Systems will remember it. The company's identification products are used to manage and issue secure credentials, including national IDs, passports, driver's licenses, smart cards, and access-control credentials. Its software creates secure digital images and enables the enrollment and management of unlimited population sizes. Its digital booking products provide law enforcement with integrated mug shot, fingerprint, and investigative capabilities. The company markets its products to governments, public safety agencies, and commercial enterprises.

	Annual Growth	12/04	12/05	12/06	12/07	*12/08
Sales ($ mil.)	(11.3%)	10.5	9.5	10.2	8.5	6.5
Net income ($ mil.)	—	(9.6)	(8.4)	(5.9)	(4.7)	(5.7)
Market value ($ mil.)	(53.7%)	70.6	45.5	39.5	35.6	3.3
Employees	(8.6%)	83	93	74	72	58

*Most recent year available

IMAGINE SCHOOLS, INC.

1005 N. Glebe Rd., Ste. 610
Arlington, VA 22201
Phone: 703-527-2600
Fax: 703-527-0038
Web: www.imagineschools.com

CEO: Dennis W. Bakke
CFO: Barry J. Sharp
HR: —
FYE: June 30
Type: Not-for-profit

New solutions in education is not a stretch of the imagination for Imagine Schools. The not-for-profit company is the largest operator of charter and private schools for students in kindergarten through 12th grade in the US. The company educates some 35,000 students at more than 60 public charter and private schools in about a dozen states and Washington, DC. Imagine Schools was established in 2003 by CEO Dennis Bakke and his wife Eileen through a buyout of Chancellor Beacon Academies, the second-largest school management group in the US (behind Edison). The company, which has several new schools in development and built a 22-acre campus in Indiana, converted its business to not-for-profit status in 2006.

IMAGING DIAGNOSTIC SYSTEMS, INC.   OTC: IMDS

5307 NW 35th Court
Plantation, FL 33309
Phone: 954-581-9800
Fax: 954-581-0555
Web: www.imds.com

CEO: Linda B. Grable
CFO: Allan L. Schwartz
HR: Elizabeth Poveda
FYE: June 30
Type: Public

Imaging Diagnostic Systems is a medical technology company involved in the research and development of breast-imaging devices used for detecting cancer. Using laser-based technology, the company has created a more comfortable, radiation-free breast examination that does not require breast compression. Its CTLM (Computed Tomography Laser Mammography) system, used in conjuction with X-ray mammography, may help improve early diagnosis of cancer. The company is also researching other breast screening systems using fluorescence imaging. It had been developing laser imaging products for research with lab animals, but it has licensed the technology to Bioscan in order to focus on the women's health market.

	Annual Growth	6/05	6/06	6/07	6/08	6/09
Sales ($ mil.)	(29.3%)	0.4	0.7	0.1	0.0	0.1
Net income ($ mil.)	—	(7.3)	(7.2)	(7.2)	(4.6)	(3.9)
Market value ($ mil.)	(58.4%)	177.2	116.8	30.6	16.1	5.3
Employees	(24.5%)	43	40	28	24	14

I-MANY, INC.   NASDAQ (GM): IMNY

1735 Market St, 37th Fl.
Philadelphia, PA 19103
Phone: 215-344-1900
Fax: 215-344-1919
Web: www.imany.com

CEO: P. Kevin Kilroy
CFO: Kevin M. Harris
HR: —
FYE: December 31
Type: Public

I-many isn't afraid of dealing with the fine print found in most contracts. The company provides contract management software and services, primarily to the health care, life sciences, and pharmaceuticals industries. Its enterprise contract management software helps companies create and manage contracts, track incentive programs and rebates, verify contract compliance, negotiate terms and conditions, and handle cash collection and dispute resolution. The company also provides a price management system for health and life sciences companies, and it offers a variety of related services.

IMARX THERAPEUTICS, INC.   OTC: IMRX

12277 134th Ct. NE, Ste. 202
Redmond, WA 98052
Phone: 520-548-0062
Fax: —
Web: www.imarx.com

CEO: Richard L. Love
CFO: Greg Cobb
HR: —
FYE: December 31
Type: Public

ImaRx isn't any more. It is now a shell company, waiting for a new future. Previously, it was a pharmaceutical development company whose SonoLysis program was developing therapies for vascular disorders, such as ischemic stroke, based on a microbubble technology. Used in conjunction with ultrasound, the microbubbles were intended to break up clots and restore blood flow to oxygen-deprived tissues. After experiencing financial difficulties, ImaRx sold off its sole commercial product (urokinase for pulmonary embolism) in 2008 and then divested the SonoLysis clinical development program in 2009. In early 2010 it struck an agreement to merge with Sycamore Films, another development stage company.

	Annual Growth	12/05	12/06	12/07	12/08	12/09
Sales ($ mil.)	—	0.6	1.3	8.4	6.7	0.0
Net income ($ mil.)	—	(27.9)	(0.7)	(8.8)	(10.1)	(0.9)
Market value ($ mil.)	(91.8%)	—	—	175.7	0.9	1.2
Employees	(63.8%)	42	31	27	2	—

⊞ IMATION CORP.   NYSE: IMN

1 Imation Way
Oakdale, MN 55128
Phone: 651-704-4000
Fax: 651-704-4200
Web: www.imation.com

CEO: Mark E. Lucas
CFO: Paul R. Zeller
HR: Jacqueline A. (Jackie) Chase
FYE: December 31
Type: Public

Imation wants to start fresh with a blank disk. The company is one of the world's top makers of media used to capture, process, store, and distribute information on computers and other electronic devices. Its removable data storage media products include optical disks (CD-R, CD-RW, DVD) and magnetic storage tapes. It also offers flash memory drives. Imation sells its products directly and through distributors to customers ranging from PC owners to large corporations. Imation has used acquisitions to dramatically expand its recording media product lines. More than half of Imation's sales are to customers outside the US.

	Annual Growth	12/05	12/06	12/07	12/08	12/09
Sales ($ mil.)	7.0%	1,258.1	1,584.7	2,062.0	2,154.6	1,649.5
Net income ($ mil.)	—	87.9	76.4	(50.4)	(33.3)	(42.2)
Market value ($ mil.)	(34.0%)	1,758.5	1,772.3	801.6	518.0	332.8
Employees	(12.9%)	2,100	2,070	2,250	1,570	1,210

IMCLONE SYSTEMS INCORPORATED

180 Varick St.
New York, NY 10014
Phone: 212-645-1405
Fax: 212-645-2054
Web: www.imclone.com

CEO: John H. Johnson
CFO: —
HR: Greg Reynolds
FYE: December 31
Type: Subsidiary

ImClone Systems has one drug and it is making the most of it. The drug development company's only product on the market, Erbitux, is approved for treatment of colorectal cancer, as well as head and neck cancers. ImClone Systems co-promotes the drug with Bristol-Myers Squibb in North America and with Merck KGaA elsewhere. ImClone is continuing to develop Erbitux as a possible treatment for other kinds of cancer, including lung cancer. The company is also working on additional oncology-related antibody therapies. In 2008 ImClone was acquired by Eli Lilly for $6.5 billion, after rejecting bids from Bristol-Myers Squibb.

⊞ An in-depth profile of this company is available to Hoover's Online members at hoovers.com.

805

IMERGENT, INC.

NYSE Amex: IIG

754 E. Technology Ave.
Orem, UT 84097
Phone: 801-227-0004
Fax: 801-226-8848
Web: www.imergentinc.com

CEO: Steven G. Mihaylo
CFO: Jonathan R. (Jon) Erickson
HR: —
FYE: June 30
Type: Public

iMergent helps you cast a wide net for Internet shoppers. The company provides software and e-commerce services that enable small businesses to establish online storefronts. Its software helps merchants to create and maintain their e-commerce site and process orders. The company promotes seminars around the country to sell its products to aspiring e-commerce mavens. iMergent also offers related services such as consulting, creative design, transaction processing, data warehousing, and help desk support. Steven Mihaylo, founder and former CEO of Inter-Tel, owns about 20% of iMergent.

	Annual Growth	6/05	6/06	6/07	6/08	6/09
Sales ($ mil.)	24.7%	39.1	185.1	151.6	128.0	94.4
Net income ($ mil.)	—	(29.5)	110.6	24.0	3.1	(7.5)
Market value ($ mil.)	(9.9%)	121.4	148.8	280.0	136.7	80.1
Employees	7.0%	221	242	435	340	290

IMERYS PIGMENTS, INC.

100 Mansell Ct. East, Ste. 300
Roswell, GA 30076
Phone: 770-594-0660
Fax: 770-645-3384
Web: www.imerys-paper.com

CEO: Jens Birgersson
CFO: Eric Borne
HR: —
FYE: December 31
Type: Subsidiary

You didn't think paper just came out that brightly white, did you? Imerys Pigments for Paper develops the pigments that render that paper in front of you so very white. It produces white mineral pigments, manufacturing kaolin, ground calcium carbonate, and precipitated calcium carbonate. Paper manufacturers use those products for coating and filling applications to improve the quality of paper and paperboard. The division of French chemical company Imerys pulls in about a quarter of the parent company's annual sales and operates globally. Imerys Pigments for Paper was created in 2003.

IMG WORLDWIDE, INC.

1360 E. 9th St., Ste. 100
Cleveland, OH 44114
Phone: 216-522-1200
Fax: 216-522-1145
Web: www.imgworld.com

CEO: Theodore J. (Ted) Forstmann
CFO: Chris A. Davis
HR: Melissa Baron
FYE: December 31
Type: Subsidiary

Show me the money! Founded by the late pioneer of sports marketing Mark McCormack, IMG Worldwide (previously International Management Group) is the world's largest sports talent and marketing agency, operating in some 30 countries. The firm's clients include the hippest athletes of the day, including Annika Sorenstam and Venus Williams. In addition to sports idols, IMG represents models and other stars, such as Giselle Bundchen and Liv Tyler. IMG also represents corporate clients, acts as a literary agent, is active in real estate and golf course design, and produces sports entertainment through its IMG Media division. The company is owned by investment firm Forstmann Little & Co.

IMI CORNELIUS, INC.

101 Broadway St. West
Osseo, MN 55369
Phone: 763-488-8200
Fax: 763-488-4298
Web: www.cornelius.com

CEO: Tim Hubbard
CFO: —
HR: —
FYE: December 31
Type: Subsidiary

IMI Cornelius understands the attraction of a frosty pint on a hot day. The company is a worldwide supplier of professional beverage dispensing and cooling equipment. It specializes in such refreshing retail conveniences as draft beer dispensers, bottle coolers, cellar equipment, ice makers, and refrigerated foodservice merchandisers. In addition to producing new equipment, IMI Cornelius also remanufactures legacy beverage dispensers. The company operates a dozen manufacturing facilities, located in six countries, with direct and authorized sales distributors crisscrossing the globe. IMI Cornelius is a subsidiary of UK-based fluid control and retail food equipment manufacturer IMI plc.

IMMERSION CORPORATION

NASDAQ (GM): IMMR

801 Fox Ln.
San Jose, CA 95131
Phone: 408-467-1900
Fax: 408-467-1901
Web: www.immersion.com

CEO: Victor (Vic) Viegas
CFO: Shum Mukherjee
HR: Janice Passarello
FYE: December 31
Type: Public

Immersion isn't afraid to get touchy-feely when doing business. The company develops hardware and software for simulating tactile experiences — such as the feel of an object or the jolt of an explosion during a video game — in order to enhance on-screen events. Immersion licenses its TouchSense technology to companies such as Logitech International and Microsoft, which use TouchSense in joysticks, mice, steering wheels, and other peripherals. In addition to computing and gaming applications, Immersion provides medical and surgical procedure simulation products used for training purposes. The company's technology is also used in automotive, industrial, mobile device, and point-of-sale products.

	Annual Growth	12/05	12/06	12/07	12/08	12/09
Sales ($ mil.)	3.3%	24.3	27.9	34.7	36.5	27.7
Net income ($ mil.)	—	(13.1)	(10.4)	117.0	(47.7)	(28.3)
Market value ($ mil.)	(8.7%)	185.4	203.7	363.8	165.5	128.7
Employees	1.5%	133	145	152	186	141

IMMTECH PHARMACEUTICALS, INC.

Pink Sheets: IMMP

1 North End Ave., Ste. 1111
New York, NY 10282
Phone: 212-791-2911
Fax: 212-791-2917
Web: www.immtech-international.com

CEO: Eric L. (Rick) Sorkin
CFO: Gary C. Parks
HR: —
FYE: March 31
Type: Public

Immtech Pharmaceuticals has a vendetta against infectious diseases. The development-stage pharmaceutical company has focused its efforts on finding treatments for bacterial, viral, and fungal infections, including hepatitis C and hospital-acquired infections. Much of the company's work is in the early stages of research and development; it halted work on its clinical-stage candidate pafuramidine in 2008 because of safety issues. Immtech has licensed some of its other drug technology from academic researchers at the University of North Carolina at Chapel Hill and Georgia State University.

	Annual Growth	3/05	3/06	3/07	3/08	3/09
Sales ($ mil.)	(20.1%)	5.9	3.6	4.3	9.7	2.4
Net income ($ mil.)	—	(13.4)	(15.5)	(11.1)	(10.5)	(6.5)
Market value ($ mil.)	(63.9%)	221.2	138.0	102.4	14.6	3.7
Employees	(14.9%)	21	26	27	24	11

IMMUCELL CORPORATION

NASDAQ (CM): ICCC

56 Evergreen Dr.
Portland, ME 04103
Phone: 207-878-2770
Fax: 207-878-2117
Web: www.immucell.com

CEO: Michael F. Brigham
CFO: Michael F. Brigham
HR: —
FYE: December 31
Type: Public

Many biotech companies focus on human health but ImmuCell has udder pursuits. The company develops products to help livestock farmers maintain the health of their herds. Its animal-health products include First Defense, which prevents diarrhea in calves; MASTiK, which diagnoses bovine mammary gland inflammation; rjt, a test for highly contagious Johne's Disease in cattle; and Wipe Out Dairy Wipes, moist towelettes used to disinfect the teat area of cows prior to milking. ImmuCell makes one product for preventing disease in humans — Isolate (formerly called Crypto-Scan), a test for *cryptosporidium* in water. When present in municipal drinking water supplies, *cryptosporidium* can cause diarrheal disease in humans.

	Annual Growth	12/05	12/06	12/07	12/08	12/09
Sales ($ mil.)	(2.6%)	5.0	4.8	6.1	4.6	4.5
Net income ($ mil.)	—	0.7	0.6	0.7	(0.5)	(0.2)
Market value ($ mil.)	(8.3%)	15.6	17.7	10.5	4.9	11.0
Employees	9.4%	23	30	34	32	33

IMMUCOR, INC.

NASDAQ (GS): BLUD

3130 Gateway Dr.
Norcross, GA 30091
Phone: 770-441-2051
Fax: 770-441-3807
Web: www.immucor.com

CEO: Gioacchino (Nino) De Chirico
CFO: Richard A. (Rick) Flynt
HR: —
FYE: May 31
Type: Public

Immucor makes sure you can feel good about getting a blood transfusion. The company makes automated analyzers and reagents used by blood banks, hospitals, and clinical laboratories to test blood prior to transfusions. Its Galileo and Galileo Echo systems use its Capture proprietary reagents to perform multiple routine blood tests, including blood type and group matching, antibody detection, and infectious disease screening. Its Capture Workstation is a semi-automated instrumentation system that the company markets to smaller laboratories or as a back-up system for the Galileo analyzers. Immucor sells its systems and reagent tests primarily in North America, Western Europe, and Japan.

	Annual Growth	5/05	5/06	5/07	5/08	5/09
Sales ($ mil.)	20.0%	144.8	183.5	223.7	261.2	300.5
Net income ($ mil.)	33.6%	23.9	39.8	60.1	71.5	76.2
Market value ($ mil.)	(9.4%)	1,561.2	1,270.5	2,206.9	1,875.0	1,051.8
Employees	8.5%	526	563	610	631	729

IMMUNOGEN, INC.

NASDAQ (GM): IMGN

830 Winter St.
Waltham, MA 02451
Phone: 781-895-0600
Fax: 781-895-0611
Web: www.immunogen.com

CEO: Daniel M. (Dan) Junius
CFO: Gregory D. (Greg) Perry
HR: —
FYE: June 30
Type: Public

ImmunoGen is TAPping into cancer research. The firm's product candidates are TAPs, or tumor-activated prodrugs, that combine cancer-killing drugs with monoclonal antibodies (single-source proteins) and attach only to tumor cells. On its own, ImmunoGen is developing preclinical and clinical-stage compounds to treat conditions such as gastrointestinal and lung cancers, solid tumors, and multiple myeloma. The firm has additional candidates in clinical trials through partnerships with Genentech (part of the Roche group) and Sanofi-Aventis, and it has licensed its TAP technology to the likes of Biogen Idec and Centocor.

	Annual Growth	6/05	6/06	6/07	6/08	6/09
Sales ($ mil.)	(5.9%)	35.7	32.1	38.2	40.2	28.0
Net income ($ mil.)	—	(11.0)	(17.8)	(19.0)	(32.0)	(31.9)
Market value ($ mil.)	10.5%	332.7	179.9	318.9	175.8	495.3
Employees	5.1%	172	192	213	210	210

IMMUNOMEDICS, INC.

NASDAQ (GM): IMMU

300 American Rd.
Morris Plains, NJ 07950
Phone: 973-605-8200
Fax: 973-605-8282
Web: www.immunomedics.com

CEO: Cynthia L. Sullivan
CFO: Gerard G. (Gerry) Gorman
HR: —
FYE: June 30
Type: Public

Immunomedics is focused on developing humanized monoclonal antibodies (MAbs) to treat cancer and other serious diseases. Its lead product, epratuzumab, is in late-stage development for the treatment of lupus; biopharmaceutical firm UCB has licensed the drug for further applications in autoimmune diseases. Immunomedics is also conducting clinical trials for epratuzumab as an oncology treatment for non-Hodgkin's lymphoma and leukemia. The company has other drugs in clinical trials to treat various cancers, including veltuzumab (lymphoma) and milatuzumab (multiple myeloma). It also makes diagnostic imaging products; subsidiary IBC Pharmaceuticals develops radiotherapeutics for applications in oncology treatments.

	Annual Growth	6/05	6/06	6/07	6/08	6/09
Sales ($ mil.)	67.6%	3.8	4.4	8.5	3.7	30.0
Net income ($ mil.)	—	(26.8)	(28.8)	(16.7)	(22.9)	2.3
Market value ($ mil.)	10.4%	128.7	198.7	313.1	160.3	191.2
Employees	0.4%	118	106	108	117	120

IMPAC MORTGAGE HOLDINGS, INC.

NYSE Amex: IMPM

19500 Jamboree Rd.
Irvine, CA 92612
Phone: 949-475-3600
Fax: 949-475-3969
Web: www.impaccompanies.com

CEO: Joseph R. Tomkinson
CFO: Todd R. Taylor
HR: Sheralee Urbano
FYE: December 31
Type: Public

Impac Mortgage Holdings, which used to be a big investor in loans given to people with less-than-perfect credit, was impacted by the subprime mortgage bust of 2007 and has changed its strategy. Impac now concentrates on real estate services and asset management for the mortgage industry. It's a shift from Impac's previous strategy, in which the former real estate investment trust (REIT) primarily invested in Alt-A (one step above subprime) residential mortgages, second mortgages, and mortgage-backed securities. In an effort to remain viable, the company has rolled out a line of new fee-based services including asset management, escrow services, and financial consulting for banks and regulatory bodies.

	Annual Growth	12/05	12/06	12/07	12/08	12/09
Sales ($ mil.)	5.7%	1,472.9	1,397.9	955.3	1,519.4	1,837.3
Net income ($ mil.)	(55.3%)	270.3	(75.3)	(2,047.1)	(44.7)	10.8
Market value ($ mil.)	(56.8%)	727.2	680.1	43.3	4.6	25.4
Employees	(19.0%)	989	827	827	127	426

IMPAX LABORATORIES, INC.

NASDAQ (GM): IPXL

30831 Huntwood Ave.
Hayward, CA 94544
Phone: 510-476-2000
Fax: 510-471-3200
Web: www.impaxlabs.com

CEO: Larry Hsu
CFO: Arthur A. Koch Jr.
HR: —
FYE: December 31
Type: Public

IMPAX Laboratories hopes that its combination of generic and branded pharmaceuticals will make an impact on its financial health. The company makes specialty generic pharmaceuticals, which it markets through its Global Pharmaceuticals division and through marketing alliances with other firms, including Teva. It concentrates on controlled-release versions of branded pharmaceuticals and niche pharmaceuticals that require difficult-to-obtain raw materials or specialized expertise. The company's branded pharmaceuticals business (called IMPAX Pharmaceuticals) is developing drugs that target Parkinson's disease, epilepsy, and other central nervous system disorders.

	Annual Growth	12/05	12/06	12/07	12/08	12/09
Sales ($ mil.)	70.6%	—	—	—	210.1	358.4
Net income ($ mil.)	167.9%	—	—	—	18.7	50.1
Market value ($ mil.)	53.1%	—	—	—	551.4	844.1
Employees	4.3%	—	—	—	768	801

An in-depth profile of this company is available to Hoover's Online members at hoovers.com.

807

IMPERIAL INDUSTRIES, INC.

NASDAQ (CM): IPII

3790 Park Central Blvd. North
Pompano Beach, FL 33064
Phone: 954-917-4114
Fax: 954-970-6565
Web: www.imperialindustries.com

CEO: Howard L. Ehler Jr.
CFO: —
HR: —
FYE: December 31
Type: Public

Imperial Industries manufactures roof tile mortar, stucco and plaster, adhesive, and pool finish products through its Premix-Marbletite Manufacturing subsidiary. Its primary market is the southeastern US. Its Just-Rite Supply subsidiary, which distributed the company's products and such products as gypsum, roofing, insulation, and masonry materials made by other companies, ceased operation in mid-2009 and is selling its assets to satisfy creditors. (Just-Rite accounted for about two-thirds of Imperial Industries' sales.) Decreased demand for the company's products by the construction industry over the past several years led to the shutdown of Just-Rite. Imperial Industries was founded in 1968.

	Annual Growth	12/05	12/06	12/07	12/08	12/09
Sales ($ mil.)	(41.3%)	72.3	75.5	53.9	33.0	8.6
Net income ($ mil.)	—	3.4	2.9	(1.3)	(6.7)	(5.3)
Market value ($ mil.)	(52.7%)	33.0	20.8	10.3	0.9	1.7
Employees	(37.2%)	148	148	161	134	23

⊞ IMPERIAL SUGAR COMPANY

NASDAQ (GM): IPSU

1 Imperial Sq., 8016 Hwy. 90-A
Sugar Land, TX 77487
Phone: 281-491-9181
Fax: 281-490-9530
Web: www.imperialsugar.com

CEO: John C. Sheptor
CFO: Hal P. Mechler
HR: —
FYE: September 30
Type: Public

Imperial Sugar occupies a sweet spot in its field, manufacturing such well-known brands as Dixie Crystals, Holly, and Imperial. In addition to branded and private-label consumer products (white, brown, powdered, and organic sugars), the company sells bulk and liquid sugar to industrial and foodservice customers. Its Savannah Gold brown sugar, syrup and molasses, and specialty sugars are used by Imperial's industrial customers in confections and icings. The company also sells sugar-production by-products. It owns and operates two cane sugar refineries, one in Georgia, the other in Louisiana.

	Annual Growth	9/05	9/06	9/07	9/08	9/09
Sales ($ mil.)	(10.2%)	803.8	946.8	875.5	592.4	522.6
Net income ($ mil.)	—	(19.3)	50.1	40.2	(20.9)	(23.2)
Market value ($ mil.)	(1.7%)	164.9	378.5	317.8	164.7	154.2
Employees	(3.2%)	827	842	839	759	726

IMPLANT SCIENCES CORPORATION

NYSE Amex: IMX

600 Research Dr.
Wilmington, MA 01887
Phone: 781-246-0700
Fax: 781-246-1167
Web: www.implantsciences.com

CEO: Glenn D. Bolduc
CFO: Roger P. Deschenes
HR: —
FYE: June 30
Type: Public

Implant Sciences is giving the security industry new technologies to detect explosives. Using its ion implantation know-how, the company has developed handheld and tabletop bomb detectors for use in airports and other public places. The firm is developing a walk-through portal through a contract with the Transportation Security Administration. Originally the company applied ion implantation technology into use in medical technology and semiconductor production, but has since refocused its operations entirely into security sensors. It is building a customer base in China and the US.

	Annual Growth	6/05	6/06	6/07	6/08	6/09
Sales ($ mil.)	(8.3%)	12.3	26.4	15.4	5.2	8.7
Net income ($ mil.)	—	(7.4)	(7.1)	(10.7)	(10.7)	(12.8)
Market value ($ mil.)	(57.2%)	73.1	81.3	41.1	22.7	2.5
Employees	(24.2%)	112	150	91	95	37

IMPRESO, INC.

Pink Sheets: ZCOM

652 Southwestern Blvd.
Coppell, TX 75019
Phone: 972-462-0100
Fax: 972-462-7764
Web: www.tstimpreso.com

CEO: Marshall D. Sorokwasz
CFO: Susan M. Atkins
HR: —
FYE: August 31
Type: Public

Money is just paper to Impreso. Through its primary subsidiary TST/Impreso, the company makes and distributes specialty paper and film imaging products. Its paper products include thermal fax, copier, wide-format, continuous-feed, and special surface papers such as film transparencies. Impreso has six manufacturing plants and distributes in North America through more than 50 warehouses to dealers and other resellers. Impreso owns two other subsidiaries: Hotsheet.com (provides links to popular websites), and Alexa Springs (spring water bottling company). Impreso, under the direction of Chairman, president, and CEO Marshall Sorokwasz, suspended its SEC reporting obligations in 2006.

	Annual Growth	8/04	8/05	8/06	8/07	*8/08
Sales ($ mil.)	(9.2%)	104.0	77.7	70.3	71.6	70.8
Net income ($ mil.)	—	1.0	(2.9)	(0.8)	(0.3)	(1.0)
Employees	(35.3%)	295	191	—	—	—

*Most recent year available

⊞ IMS HEALTH INCORPORATED

901 Main Ave., Ste. 612
Norwalk, CT 06851
Phone: 203-845-5200
Fax: 203-845-5304
Web: www.imshealth.com

CEO: David R. (Dave) Carlucci
CFO: Leslye G. Katz
HR: Karla L. Packer
FYE: December 31
Type: Private

IMS Health has the dope on drugs. The company provides sales management and market research services to clients in the pharmaceutical and health care industries. It tracks not only the sale of prescription drugs and over-the-counter products but also the productivity of individual sales representatives that work for its client companies. It offers market forecasts and surveys to physicians and hospitals about drugs they are prescribing to patients. IMS Health also offers consulting and other professional services. It has clients worldwide and operates through about 100 offices in more than 100 countries. In early 2010 IMS Health was taken private by TPG Capital and CPP Investment Board.

	Annual Growth	12/05	12/06	12/07	12/08	12/09
Sales ($ mil.)	5.7%	1,754.8	1,958.6	2,192.6	2,329.5	2,189.7
Net income ($ mil.)	(2.3%)	284.1	315.5	234.0	311.3	258.5
Employees	1.2%	6,900	7,400	7,950	7,500	7,250

INCOME OPPORTUNITY REALTY INVESTORS, INC.

NYSE Amex: IOT

1755 Wittington Place, Ste. 340
Dallas, TX 75234
Phone: 972-407-8400
Fax: 972-407-8436
Web: www.incomeopp-realty.com

CEO: Daniel J. (Danny) Moos
CFO: Gene S. Bertcher
HR: —
FYE: December 31
Type: Public

When opportunity knocks, Income Opportunity Realty Investors (IORI) is there to answer. The real estate investment firm owns commercial, retail, and industrial real estate and land parcels in Texas as well as an apartment complex in Indiana. Syntek West, which oversees IORI's daily activities, owns 57% of the firm; Transcontinental Realty Investors (TRI) owns 25%. American Realty Investors shares executive officers and board members with both IORI and TRI; affiliates of Prime Income Asset Management manage IORI's properties, as well as those of TRI. In 2008 IORI sold six apartment properties in Texas (about half of its assets).

	Annual Growth	12/05	12/06	12/07	12/08	12/09
Sales ($ mil.)	(58.0%)	6.4	7.7	2.3	1.3	0.2
Net income ($ mil.)	(10.5%)	1.4	0.2	(0.7)	26.7	0.9
Market value ($ mil.)	7.5%	26.3	27.7	22.5	23.8	35.0
Employees	—	—	—	—	—	—

INCONTACT, INC.

NASDAQ (CM): SAAS

7730 S. Union Park Ave., Ste. 500
Midvale, UT 84047
Phone: 801-320-3200
Fax: 801-320-3330
Web: www.incontact.com

CEO: Paul Jarman
CFO: Gregory S. (Greg) Ayers
HR: Patricia Folts
FYE: December 31
Type: Public

inContact is breaking with its telecom tradition. Formerly called UCN, the company has long operated as a reseller of traditional phone services — including long-distance, dedicated data transmission, and calling cards — through agreements with such providers as Qwest, Global Crossing, Level 3, and Verizon. Utilizing the software-as-a-service (SaaS) model, it also offers voice and call center management services over a nationwide voice-over-Internet Protocol (VoIP) network. Its inContact software includes interactive voice response, reporting and monitoring, and call routing capabilities. inContact's traditional telecom business accounted for 75% of its sales in 2008.

	Annual Growth	12/05	12/06	12/07	12/08	12/09
Sales ($ mil.)	0.8%	81.6	82.8	79.5	79.6	84.2
Net income ($ mil.)	—	(8.1)	(7.8)	(7.5)	(10.3)	(2.9)
Market value ($ mil.)	13.4%	61.9	99.7	157.5	44.8	102.5
Employees	10.5%	196	206	266	299	292

⊞ INCYTE CORPORATION

NASDAQ (GM): INCY

Experimental Station, Route 141 & Henry Clay Rd., Bldg. E336
Wilmington, DE 19880
Phone: 302-498-6700
Fax: 302-425-2750
Web: www.incyte.com

CEO: Paul A. Friedman
CFO: David C. Hastings
HR: Paula J. Swain
FYE: December 31
Type: Public

Incyte hopes its success with inhibitors is uninhibited. The biotechnology company is focused on discovering and developing drugs that inhibit specific enzymes associated with cancer, diabetes, HIV, and inflammatory diseases. The company's lead program is its JAK kinase inhibitor program, which covers treatments for inflammatory diseases and cancers, including rheumatoid arthritis, myelofibrosis, psoriasis, multiple myeloma, and prostate cancer. Incyte has several other products in clinical trial stages, including a CCR5 antagonist designed to prevent the entry of HIV into target cells.

	Annual Growth	12/05	12/06	12/07	12/08	12/09
Sales ($ mil.)	4.5%	7.8	27.6	34.4	3.9	9.3
Net income ($ mil.)	—	(103.0)	(74.2)	(86.9)	(178.9)	(211.9)
Market value ($ mil.)	14.3%	646.9	707.4	1,217.4	459.1	1,103.5
Employees	5.7%	177	186	196	212	221

INDEPENDENCE BLUE CROSS

1901 Market St.
Philadelphia, PA 19103
Phone: 215-636-9559
Fax: 215-241-0403
Web: www.ibx.com

CEO: Joseph A. (Joe) Frick
CFO: John G. Foos
HR: Virginia P. Barakat
FYE: December 31
Type: Not-for-profit

Independence Blue Cross (IBC) provides health insurance and related services to some 3.4 million members in Philadelphia and surrounding areas. The company's plans include Personal Choice (PPO), Keystone Health Plan East (HMO and POS), and traditional indemnity options for groups, families, and individuals. It also offers supplemental Medicare, dental, vision, life, and disability insurance. Through subsidiaries AmeriHealth Administrators and FutureScripts, IBC provides third-party administration (TPA) and pharmacy benefits management (PBM) services. IBC, which was founded as the Associated Hospital Service of Philadelphia in 1938, is an independent licensee of the Blue Cross and Blue Shield Association.

INDEPENDENCE FEDERAL SAVINGS BANK

NASDAQ (CM): IFSB

1229 Connecticut Ave. NW
Washington, DC 20036
Phone: 202-628-5500
Fax: 202-626-7106
Web: www.ifsb.com

CEO: John A. Hall
CFO: Brenda Watkins Noel
HR: —
FYE: December 31
Type: Public

Founded in 1968 to provide loans to African-Americans living in Washington, DC, Independence Federal Savings Bank continues that mission today. Through three branches in the US capital and nearby Maryland, the bank offers standard deposit products such as checking and savings accounts, money market accounts, and CDs. Mortgages secured by residential or commercial real estate make up almost all of its loan portfolio; the bank ceased providing guaranteed student loans through Sallie Mae in 2008. Chairman Morton Bender owns a majority of Independence Federal. The company withdrew a plan to merge with Maryland-based Colombo Bank, after regulatory approvals were delayed indefinitely in 2010.

	Annual Growth	12/05	12/06	12/07	12/08	12/09
Assets ($ mil.)	(1.6%)	167.1	160.8	150.9	183.2	156.9
Employees	(13.3%)	53	48	35	32	30

INDEPENDENCE HOLDING COMPANY

NYSE: IHC

96 Cummings Point Rd.
Stamford, CT 06902
Phone: 203-358-8000
Fax: 203-348-3103
Web: www.ihcgroup.com

CEO: Roy T.K. Thung
CFO: Teresa A. Herbert
HR: —
FYE: December 31
Type: Public

Independence Holding wants to hold insurance policies. Through subsidiaries (including Madison National Life Insurance and Standard Security Life Insurance Company of New York), it sells and reinsures health and life insurance to groups and individuals. Instead of offering big major medical plans, the company prefers to offer niche coverage such as medical stop-loss insurance (which allows employers to limit their exposure to high health insurance claims), student health insurance, short-term medical coverage, and small-group major medical. In addition, the company provides disability products and group life insurance. The company does business throughout the US, and its protectorates.

	Annual Growth	12/05	12/06	12/07	12/08	12/09
Assets ($ mil.)	3.2%	1,150.9	1,259.7	1,308.1	1,273.9	1,304.5
Net income ($ mil.)	—	17.3	14.1	(2.3)	(23.8)	(7.1)
Market value ($ mil.)	(26.2%)	298.6	333.5	193.2	55.1	88.6
Employees	22.8%	264	652	682	624	600

INDEPENDENT BANK CORP.

NASDAQ (GS): INDB

288 Union St.
Rockland, MA 02370
Phone: 781-878-6100
Fax: 781-982-6130
Web: www.rocklandtrust.com

CEO: Christopher (Chris) Oddleifson
CFO: Denis K. Sheahan
HR: Raymond G. Fuerschbach
FYE: December 31
Type: Public

Independent Bank wants to rock your financial world. Its banking subsidiary, Rockland Trust, operates some 70 retail branches, as well as several commercial lending centers, investment management offices, and mortgage banking centers in southeastern Massachusetts and Cape Cod. Serving individuals and small to midsized businesses, the bank offers such standard deposit products as checking and savings accounts, money market accounts, and CDs. Commercial and industrial loans, including mortgages, construction loans, and business loans, account for some two-thirds of Rockland's lending portfolio. The bank also writes consumer loans and mortgages.

	Annual Growth	12/05	12/06	12/07	12/08	12/09
Assets ($ mil.)	10.2%	3,041.7	2,828.9	2,768.4	3,628.5	4,482.0
Net income ($ mil.)	(8.8%)	33.2	32.9	28.4	24.0	23.0
Market value ($ mil.)	(7.5%)	604.3	763.1	576.5	554.1	441.8
Employees	5.9%	722	708	742	827	907

⊞ An in-depth profile of this company is available to Hoover's Online members at hoovers.com.

809

INDEPENDENT BANK CORPORATION

NASDAQ (GS): IBCP

230 W. Main St.
Ionia, MI 48846
Phone: 616-527-9450
Fax: 616-527-4004
Web: www.independentbank.com

CEO: Michael M. Magee Jr.
CFO: Robert N. Shuster
HR: —
FYE: December 31
Type: Public

Independent Bank Corporation (IBC) strikes out on its own. As the holding company for Independent Bank, it serves customers in rural and suburban communities of Michigan's Lower Peninsula from about more than 100 branches and about a half-dozen loan production offices. The bank offers traditional retail products, including checking and savings accounts and certificates of deposit. The company also serves customers through several subsidiaries: IBC Financial Services (insurance), Independent Title Services, and Mepco Finance (payment plans for extended automobile warranties). Real estate loans make up about 30% of the company's loan portfolio, followed by consumer installment loans and commercial loans.

	Annual Growth	12/05	12/06	12/07	12/08	12/09
Assets ($ mil.)	(3.0%)	3,355.8	3,429.9	3,276.1	2,956.2	2,965.4
Net income ($ mil.)	—	46.9	33.2	10.4	(91.7)	(90.2)
Market value ($ mil.)	(59.2%)	623.2	607.8	228.3	51.9	17.3
Employees	4.6%	1,111	1,360	1,338	1,305	1,331

INDEPENDENT HEALTH ASSOCIATION INC.

511 Farber Lakes Dr.
Buffalo, NY 14221
Phone: 716-631-5392
Fax: 716-631-0430
Web: www.independenthealth.com

CEO: Michael W. Cropp
CFO: Mark Johnson
HR: Gord Cumming
FYE: December 31
Type: Not-for-profit

Independent Health (IH) is a not-for-profit organization that provides a range of health insurance and related products to some 365,000 members in western New York. IH's plans include HMO, PPO, indemnity, and Medicare Advantage plans. The company also provides dental and vision coverage, as well as coverage for Medicaid recipients. The firm, founded in 1980, works to keep members healthy with a variety of community-based health and fitness programs. IH's Encompass 65 offers wellness programs for seniors, including SilverSneakers, which provides for free fitness sessions. The company also works with restaurants through its Healthy Options program to offer up healthy menu items. IH is led by CEO Dr. Michael Cropp.

	Annual Growth	12/04	12/05	12/06	12/07	12/08
Est. sales ($ mil.)	—	—	—	—	—	1,280.1
Employees	—	—	—	—	—	900

INDIANA COMMUNITY BANCORP

NASDAQ (GM): INCB

501 Washington St.
Columbus, IN 47201
Phone: 812-522-1592
Fax: 812-522-1611
Web: www.myindianabank.com

CEO: John K. Keach Jr.
CFO: Mark T. Gorski
HR: Pennie Stancombe
FYE: December 31
Type: Public

Indiana Community Bancorp (formerly Home Federal Bancorp) is the holding company for Indiana Bank and Trust (the former HomeFederal Bank), which operates around 20 offices in south-central Indiana. The bank offers such standard retail services as checking and savings accounts, NOW accounts, CDs, and IRAs. Commercial and residential mortgages account for more than half of the company's loan portfolio. Indiana Bank and Trust also writes mobile home, consumer, construction, and other loans. The holding company and the bank changed their names in 2008 in honor of the bank's 100th birthday.

	Annual Growth	12/05	12/06	12/07	12/08	12/09
Assets ($ mil.)	4.4%	850.7	904.5	908.8	969.4	1,010.3
Net income ($ mil.)	—	6.1	6.4	6.1	5.0	(5.8)
Market value ($ mil.)	(25.7%)	84.0	95.6	77.0	40.3	25.5
Employees	(4.0%)	288	289	257	243	245

INDIANA PACKERS CORPORATION

Hwy 421 South, County Rd. 100 North
Delphi, IN 46923
Phone: 765-564-3680
Fax: 765-564-3684
Web: www.inpac.com

CEO: Gary L. Jacobson
CFO: Jim Miller
HR: Jim Hardison
FYE: March 31
Type: Joint venture

Don't tell Christopher Robin and Piglet or Charlotte and Wilbur, but Indiana Packers procures pigs and processes them into pork. The company's fresh pork cuts, hams, hardwood-smoked hocks, sausage, and bacon are sold under the Indiana Kitchen brand to both food retail and foodservice customers. It also offers private label products and services. Indiana Packer's products are available worldwide. The company is jointly owned by two Japanese companies: Mitsubishi Corporation and Itoham Foods. As the popularity of the "other white meat" has grown, Indiana Packers Corporation has invested some $112 million to expand its production capacity and can now accommodate (sorry, Piglet) 16,800 hogs a day.

	Annual Growth	3/04	3/05	3/06	3/07	3/08
Est. sales ($ mil.)	—	—	—	—	—	400.2
Employees	—	—	—	—	—	1,375

INDIANA STATE LOTTERY

Pan Am Plaza, Ste. 1100, 201 S. Capitol Ave.
Indianapolis, IN 46225
Phone: 317-264-4800
Fax: 317-264-4630
Web: www.in.gov/hoosierlottery

CEO: Kathryn Densborn
CFO: W. Edward (Ed) Benton
HR: Irene Lange
FYE: June 30
Type: Government-owned

The Indiana State Lottery, also known as the "Hoosier Lottery," has created more than 350 millionaires. Out of every lottery dollar earned, 30 cents goes to the State of Indiana to fund public projects. It has returned more than $3.4 billion to the state since its inception in 1989. Money is generated from the sale of both instant-win games and lotto drawings. The Hoosier Lottery also features PowerBall, a multistate lotto game that generates million-dollar jackpots. The first winning PowerBall ticket was sold in Indiana and the state leads the nation in PowerBall winners, with 36 as of January 2009.

INDIANA UNIVERSITY

107 S. Indiana Ave.
Bloomington, IN 47405
Phone: 812-855-4848
Fax: 812-855-9972
Web: www.indiana.edu

CEO: Michael A. McRobbie
CFO: Neil D. Theobald
HR: Dan Rives
FYE: June 30
Type: School

Indiana University has been schooling Hoosiers since 1820. With a total student population of some 100,000, the university offers more than 1,000 associate, baccalaureate, master's, professional, and doctoral degree programs at eight campuses: flagship institution IU-Bloomington; regional campuses in Fort Wayne, Gary, Kokomo, New Albany, Richmond, and South Bend; and an urban campus in Indianapolis that is operated jointly with Purdue University. An 1820 statute created the Indiana Seminary, the predecessor to Indiana University. In 1828 the legislature changed the name of the institution to Indiana College, and in 1838 it established Indiana University.

INDUSTRIAL DEVELOPMENTS INTERNATIONAL, INC.

1100 Peachtree St., Ste. 1100
Atlanta, GA 30309
Phone: 404-479-4000
Fax: 404-479-4162
Web: www.idi.com

CEO: Tim Gunter
CFO: Linda Booker
HR: Debbie Kvietkus
FYE: December 31
Type: Subsidiary

Industrial Developments International (IDI) develops, owns, and leases industrial properties throughout the US and Mexico. The firm has developed approximately 120 million sq. ft. of space to date, including warehouses and distribution ranging from 80,000 sq. ft. to more than 2 million sq. ft. IDI develops speculative properties as well as build-to-suit lots for clients seeking long-term leases. The company has developed properties for clients including UPS, Porsche Cars North America, and AmerisourceBergen. Property management subsidiary IDI Services Group manages some 60 million sq. ft. of space for IDI and third parties. IDI was founded in 1989 and is a subsidiary of Japanese property giant Kajima.

	Annual Growth	12/04	12/05	12/06	12/07	12/08
Est. sales ($ mil.)	—	—	—	—	—	118.7
Employees	—	—	—	—	—	218

INDUSTRIAL DISTRIBUTION GROUP, INC.

950 E. Paces Ferry Rd., Ste. 1575
Atlanta, GA 30326
Phone: 404-949-2100
Fax: 404-949-2040
Web: www.idglink.com

CEO: Charles A. Lingenfelter
CFO: James Melton
HR: Laura Wright
FYE: December 31
Type: Private

If it ain't broke, don't fix it. But if it is broke, you can call Industrial Distribution Group (IDG), a supplier of maintenance, repair, operating, and production products (including abrasives, cutting tools, hand and power tools, lubricants, and adhesives) to industrial, commercial, and institutional manufacturers. IDG has a portfolio of more than 300,000 different products drawn from more than 30,000 vendors; it sells these goods to an active customer base of 13,000 companies, including BorgWarner, Danaher, Ford, and General Electric. IDG operates dozens of distribution locations in the US, as well as in China. Luther King Capital Management acquired IDG and took it private in 2008.

INDUSTRIAL SERVICES OF AMERICA, INC.

NASDAQ (CM): IDSA

7100 Grade Ln.
Louisville, KY 40232
Phone: 502-368-1661
Fax: 502-368-1440
Web: www.isa-inc.com

CEO: Harry Kletter
CFO: Alan L. Schroering
HR: —
FYE: December 31
Type: Public

Industrial Services of America manages solid waste so its customers won't have to. Its Computerized Waste Systems (CWS) unit doesn't pick up trash but instead arranges waste disposal services for its commercial and industrial customers at 2,270 locations. CWS negotiates contracts with service providers and offers centralized billing and dispatching and invoice auditing services. Industrial Services of America's ISA Recycling unit handles ferrous and non-ferrous metals and fiber products, and the company's Waste Equipment Sales & Service (WESSCO) unit sells, leases, and services waste handling and recycling equipment. Chairman and CEO Harry Kletter owns about 36% of the company; his wife, Roberta, owns 9%.

	Annual Growth	12/05	12/06	12/07	12/08	12/09
Sales ($ mil.)	11.4%	117.4	62.1	77.0	100.0	181.1
Net income ($ mil.)	48.2%	1.1	2.2	2.6	1.5	5.3
Market value ($ mil.)	32.4%	13.3	23.5	32.4	23.5	41.1
Employees	12.5%	103	102	139	126	165

INERGY HOLDINGS, L.P.

NASDAQ (GS): NRGP

2 Brush Creek Blvd., Ste. 200
Kansas City, MO 64112
Phone: 816-842-8181
Fax: 816-842-1904
Web: www.inergypropane.com

CEO: John J. Sherman
CFO: R. Brooks Sherman Jr.
HR: —
FYE: September 30
Type: Public

Inergy Holdings is committed to putting all its energy into managing Inergy, L.P. This operating company retails about 310 million gallons of propane a year and wholesales 380 million gallons under such names as Bradley Propane, Country Gas, Direct Propane, Hoosier Propane, Independent Propane, Pro Gas, and Star Gas Propane. It serves a retail base of 800,000 customers through 300 service centers in 32 eastern states. Inergy provides wholesale services to distributors in 40 states and Canada. Also active in the midstream area, Inergy owns natural gas storage facilities, liquefied petroleum gas (LPG) and natural gas liquids (NGL) businesses, and a mining and salt production company in New York.

	Annual Growth	9/05	9/06	9/07	9/08	9/09
Sales ($ mil.)	10.6%	1,050.1	1,387.6	1,483.1	1,878.9	1,570.6
Net income ($ mil.)	16.4%	31.1	14.4	102.6	35.5	57.1
Market value ($ mil.)	8.5%	686.5	706.0	978.9	523.3	952.2
Employees	(0.4%)	2,954	3,021	2,971	3,104	2,910

INERGY, L.P.

NASDAQ (GS): NRGY

2 Brush Creek Blvd., Ste. 200
Kansas City, MO 64112
Phone: 816-842-8181
Fax: 816-842-1904
Web: www.inergypropane.com

CEO: John J. Sherman
CFO: R. Brooks Sherman Jr.
HR: —
FYE: September 30
Type: Public

Inergy's primary energy source is propane. The company retails about 310 million gallons of propane a year and wholesales about 380 million gallons to residential, commercial, industrial, and agricultural customers. It serves a retail base of 800,000 customers through 300 service centers in 32 states, and provides wholesale and logistics services to about 350 distributors in 40 states and Canada. Inergy also owns natural gas storage facilities, a liquefied petroleum gas (LPG) storage business, a salt mining company in New York, sells and leases propane equipment, and operates a natural gas liquids (NGL) supply, logistics, transportation, and wholesale marketing business for independent dealers.

	Annual Growth	9/05	9/06	9/07	9/08	9/09
Sales ($ mil.)	10.6%	1,050.1	1,387.6	1,483.1	1,878.9	1,570.6
Net income ($ mil.)	27.3%	38.6	9.8	67.0	65.1	101.4
Market value ($ mil.)	1.3%	1,862.8	1,787.0	2,082.8	1,424.7	1,961.6
Employees	0.4%	2,862	3,021	2,971	3,104	2,910

INFINERA CORPORATION

NASDAQ (GM): INFN

169 Java Dr.
Sunnyvale, CA 94089
Phone: 408-572-5200
Fax: 408-572-5343
Web: www.infinera.com

CEO: Thomas J. (Tom) Fallon
CFO: Ita Brennan
HR: Paul M. Whitney
FYE: December 31
Type: Public

To Infinera, and beyond! The buzz on this company is that it designs photonic integrated circuits (PICs) intended to replace much larger components within optical networks. It also offers networking equipment built around these chips. Infinera's chips are made from indium phosphide, a specialized compound semiconductor material that offers light-years faster performance than standard silicon. Customers include cable system operators, ISPs, and telecommunications carriers, such as Cox Communications, Deutsche Telekom, Global Crossing, Level 3 Communications (17% of sales), Qwest Communications, and XO Communications. Infinera gets more than two-thirds of its sales in the US.

	Annual Growth	12/05	12/06	12/07	12/08	12/09
Sales ($ mil.)	194.7%	4.1	58.2	245.9	519.2	309.1
Net income ($ mil.)	—	(66.0)	(89.9)	(55.3)	78.7	(86.6)
Market value ($ mil.)	(22.7%)	—	—	1,462.9	883.3	874.4
Employees	12.1%	617	605	711	937	974

An in-depth profile of this company is available to Hoover's Online members at hoovers.com.

811

INFINITE GROUP, INC.

OTC: IMCI

60 Office Park Way
Pittsford, NY 14534
Phone: 585-385-0610
Fax: 585-385-0614
Web: www.igius.com

CEO: Michael S. Smith
CFO: Michael S. Smith
HR: —
FYE: December 31
Type: Public

Infinite Group, Inc. (IGI) has endless ways to develop its customers' high technology. Once a provider of laser applications, the company has moved its focus to providing information technology (IT) services, such as systems integration, e-commerce portal development, and application implementation, as well as biometrics services to corporate as well as federal, state, and local government customers. US government contracts account for about 99% of IGI's sales.

	Annual Growth	12/05	12/06	12/07	12/08	12/09
Sales ($ mil.)	7.6%	8.5	6.4	8.5	9.9	11.4
Net income ($ mil.)	—	0.0	(1.6)	(0.7)	(0.2)	(1.0)
Market value ($ mil.)	(0.0%)	6.4	13.6	20.0	11.0	6.4
Employees	7.0%	71	75	85	83	93

INFINITE SOFTWARE CORPORATION

Pink Sheets: IFSC

20 Pacifica, Ste. 1050
Irvine, CA 92618
Phone: 949-207-7440
Fax: 866-528-1985
Web: www.infinitesoftware.com

CEO: R. Bruce Acacio
CFO: Jeremy King
HR: —
FYE: December 31
Type: Public

INFINITE Software (formerly California Software) believes in applying software to all sorts of applications. The company provides legacy extension, enterprise application integration, and business intelligence software, as well as loan production software for banks, credit unions and consumer lending institutions. Its products are used for migrating mainframe and AS/400 applications and data to newer technology platforms, including Web-based applications. Clients have included Johnson & Johnson, Caterpillar, and Fidelity Investments. The company was founded in 1975. President Carol Conway owns a majority stake in the company.

INFINITY CAPITAL GROUP, INC.

OTC: ICGP

80 Broad St., 5th Fl.
New York, NY 10004
Phone: 212-962-4400
Fax: 212-962-4422
Web: www.infinitybdc.com

CEO: Gregory H. (Greg) Laborde
CFO: Theodore A. Greenberg
HR: —
FYE: December 31
Type: Public

Infinity Capital Group is a closed-end business development company that provides early-stage or mezzanine financing and management assistance to emerging growth companies. It typically invests in companies that intend to go public through an IPO or by a reverse merger with an already public firm. It also funds small public companies that are undergoing significant change in strategy. Infinity Capital investments aren't limited to any single industry. Its largest holding is a majority stake in Satellite Organizing Solutions, of which Infinity CEO Gregory Laborde also serves as CEO. Laborde also owns 30% of Infinity Capital Group.

	Annual Growth	12/05	12/06	12/07	12/08	12/09
Sales ($ mil.)	—	0.0	0.0	0.1	0.0	0.0
Net income ($ mil.)	—	(0.8)	(0.3)	0.0	0.1	(0.9)
Market value ($ mil.)	—	—	—	—	—	0.5
Employees	—	—	—	—	—	—

INFINITY ENERGY RESOURCES, INC.

Pink Sheets: IFNY

11900 College Blvd., Ste. 204
Overland Park, KS 66210
Phone: 913-948-9512
Fax: 913-338-4458
Web: www.infinity-res.com

CEO: Stanton E. Ross
CFO: Daniel F. Hutchins
HR: —
FYE: December 31
Type: Public

Maybe nothing lasts forever, but Infinity Energy Resources hopes that US demand for fossil fuels won't go away for a long, long time. The company focuses its oil exploration and production operations in the Fort Worth Basin of Texas, in the Rocky Mountain region in the Greater Green River Basin in Wyoming, and the Sand Wash and Piceance Basins in Colorado. It is also pursuing an opportunity in offshore Nicaragua. The company has proved reserves of 7.8 billion cu. ft. of natural gas equivalent. Infinity Energy Resources has exited the oil services business.

INFINITY PHARMACEUTICALS, INC.

NASDAQ (GM): INFI

780 Memorial Dr.
Cambridge, MA 02139
Phone: 617-453-1000
Fax: 617-453-1001
Web: www.ipi.com

CEO: Adelene Q. Perkins
CFO: Steven J. Kafka
HR: Jeanette W. Kohlbrenner
FYE: December 31
Type: Public

Infinity Pharmaceuticals acts on the endless possibilities for new cancer treatments. The firm develops small-molecule anti-cancer drugs for applications in many types of cancer therapy. Its most advanced candidate is retaspimycin, which is in clinical trials for gastrointestinal, lung, and prostate cancers. Other cancer drugs in the pipeline are in discovery or early development phases. Infinity Pharmaceuticals has licensing or collaborative development partnerships with companies such as Novartis, Amgen, and Johnson & Johnson Pharmaceutical Research & Development. In 2006 Infinity merged with Discovery Partners International (DPI) in a reverse merger that made Infinity a public company.

	Annual Growth	12/05	12/06	12/07	12/08	12/09
Sales ($ mil.)	9.2%	34.8	18.5	24.5	83.4	49.5
Net income ($ mil.)	—	(14.2)	(28.4)	(16.9)	23.7	(32.5)
Market value ($ mil.)	(12.6%)	278.4	325.9	250.8	209.9	162.3
Employees	7.7%	133	115	125	161	179

INFINITY PROPERTY AND CASUALTY

NASDAQ (GS): IPCC

3700 Colonnade Pkwy.
Birmingham, AL 35243
Phone: 205-870-4000
Fax: 205-803-8231
Web: www.ipacc.com

CEO: James R. Gober
CFO: Roger Smith
HR: —
FYE: December 31
Type: Public

Infinity Property and Casualty Corporation covers all types of drivers, with emphasis on the infinitely bad ones. The insurer primarily provides personal nonstandard auto policies — Infinity is a leading writer of policies for high-risk drivers in the US. The company also offers standard and preferred personal auto, commercial nonstandard, and classic collector auto insurance. Licensed in all 50 states, the company currently focuses its business on 18 states. Personal auto insurance accounts for more than 90% of its premiums; California accounts for half of that business. The company distributes its products through more than 12,500 independent agents.

	Annual Growth	12/05	12/06	12/07	12/08	12/09
Assets ($ mil.)	(2.2%)	1,971.7	2,014.4	1,916.6	1,721.3	1,803.7
Net income ($ mil.)	(9.7%)	106.3	87.3	71.9	19.3	70.6
Market value ($ mil.)	2.2%	492.1	640.0	477.8	618.0	537.5
Employees	(4.0%)	2,100	2,100	2,100	1,860	1,780

INFOCROSSING, INC.

2 Christie Heights
Leonia, NJ 07605
Phone: 201-840-4700
Fax: 201-840-7250
Web: www.infocrossing.com

CEO: Sameer Kishore
CFO: Shivakumar Rajagopalan
HR: —
FYE: December 31
Type: Subsidiary

Infocrossing dots the i's and crosses the t's when it comes to managing your IT services. The company provides a variety of outsourced IT services, including computer facilities management, application development, remote monitoring, data center and data processing, and network management. The company also offers infrastructure management consulting, mainframe and open system outsourcing, managed hosting, and disaster recovery services. Its strategic partners include such vendors as CA, Cisco, IBM, and Microsoft. Infocrossing is a subsidiary of Wipro Technologies, one of India's largest providers of business process outsourcing (BPO) and IT services.

INFOLOGIX, INC.

NASDAQ (CM): IFLG

101 E. County Line Rd., Ste. 210
Hatboro, PA 19040
Phone: 215-604-0691
Fax: 215-604-0695
Web: www.infologix.com

CEO: David T. Gulian
CFO: John A. Roberts
HR: —
FYE: December 31
Type: Public

InfoLogix wants information to be freely available. The company provides hardware, software, and services designed to give hospitals and large companies mobile data access. Its mobile workstations connect to wireless networks and deliver patient data and enterprise information to doctors and employees. InfoLogix also provides related products such as power systems and software, as well as offering consulting, professional services, and systems integration for third-party hardware and software. Its clients are primarily health care organizations and companies with manufacturing, warehousing, and retail operations. Hercules Technology Growth Capital owns 77% of the company.

	Annual Growth	12/05	12/06	12/07	12/08	12/09
Sales ($ mil.)	11.9%	55.5	60.8	78.8	100.7	86.9
Net income ($ mil.)	—	—	(1.9)	(3.2)	(13.2)	(22.4)
Market value ($ mil.)	(63.3%)	—	480.2	205.1	48.5	23.7
Employees	260.0%	1	81	167	206	168

INFOCUS CORPORATION

13190 SW 68th Pkwy., Ste. 200
Portland, OR 97223
Phone: 503-207-4700
Fax: 503-207-1937
Web: www.infocus.com

CEO: Robert G. (Bob) O'Malley
CFO: Lisa K. Prentice
HR: —
FYE: December 31
Type: Private

InFocus helps businesses and consumers get the big picture. The company makes projectors that can present output from computers, VCRs, and DVD and laserdisc players. Its products include portable projectors, projectors for conference rooms and auditoriums, and home theater models. Larger models are used to make business presentations and double as big-screen televisions when connected to a VCR or DVD player. InFocus sells its products through distributors such as Ingram Micro and Tech Data, resellers that brand the projectors under their own labels, and directly to retailers and corporations. In 2009 the company was acquired by Image Holdings Corporation for about $39 million in cash.

INFONOW CORPORATION

Pink Sheets: INOW

1875 Lawrence St., Ste. 1100
Denver, CO 80202
Phone: 303-293-0212
Fax: 303-293-0213
Web: www.infonow.com

CEO: Mark Geene
CFO: Brandon Brancato
HR: —
FYE: December 31
Type: Public

InfoNow doesn't mean to sound impatient — it just wants sales channel partners to get the information they need. Its channel data management software tracks point-of-sale transactions and gives manufacturers detailed information on their partners and customers, enabling clients to track their products through third-party distribution and sales channels. The company also provides tools for partner analysis, sales credit assignment, and campaign generation, as well as applications to monitor and manage inventory data. InfoNow, which provides its software under the Software-as-a-Service model, markets its offerings primarily to companies in the financial services, industrial, and technology industries.

INFOGROUP INC.

NASDAQ (GS): IUSA

5711 S. 86th Circle
Omaha, NE 68127
Phone: 402-593-4500
Fax: 402-596-8902
Web: www.infogroup.com

CEO: Bill L. Fairfield
CFO: Thomas (Tom) Oberdorf
HR: —
FYE: December 31
Type: Public

Making information available keeps this collective together. Formerly infoUSA, infoGROUP is a provider of business and consumer information and research services for direct marketing, sales prospecting, and business intelligence. Its Data Group maintains databases with contact and credit information on more than 15 million businesses. Its Salesgenie.com subscription site provides access to its databases; the Data Group also includes information firm OneSource Information Services. The company additionally licenses its data to third parties, and includes a Services Group and a Marketing Research Group. Founder Vinod Gupta owns about 40% of infoGROUP, which has agreed to be acquired by CCMP Capital Advisors.

	Annual Growth	12/05	12/06	12/07	12/08	12/09
Sales ($ mil.)	6.9%	383.2	434.9	688.8	738.3	499.9
Net income ($ mil.)	—	31.5	33.3	40.9	4.8	(6.6)
Market value ($ mil.)	(7.4%)	633.5	690.3	517.6	274.7	464.8
Employees	3.9%	2,695	4,089	4,815	4,771	3,146

INFOPRINT SOLUTIONS COMPANY, LLC

6300 Diagonal Hwy.
Boulder, CO 80301
Phone: 303-924-6300
Fax: 303-924-5402
Web: www.infoprintsolutionscompany.com

CEO: Daisuke Segawa
CFO: Takashi Kawaguchi
HR: Sandy Smith
FYE: December 31
Type: Joint venture

InfoPrint Solutions' printouts come in all colors, but the dominant hue is blue. The joint venture between Ricoh and IBM markets printing hardware and software for businesses. Its hardware line ranges from multifunction office printers to high-speed production systems for mailing operations. The company's software portfolio includes print management applications, communication tools, utilities, and document design products. It also provides consulting and support services. InfoPrint was formed in 2007, when Ricoh paid $725 million in cash to acquire a 51% stake in IBM's Printing Systems Division. As part of the agreement, Ricoh is acquiring the remaining 49% over three years.

INFOR GLOBAL SOLUTIONS, INC.

13560 Morris Rd., Ste. 4100
Alpharetta, GA 30004
Phone: 678-319-8000
Fax: 678-319-8682
Web: www.infor.com

CEO: C. James (Jim) Schaper
CFO: Raghavan (Raj) Rajaji
HR: Glenn Goldberg
FYE: May 31
Type: Private

Before manufacturers and distributors get products to the shelf, Infor gets software to their computers. Infor Global Solutions supplies enterprise software — that is software used for a wide range of business purposes. Whether managing inventories, tracking shipments, or working with customers, enterprise software can link disparate functions. Infor has a history of growing and changing its global enterprise software business with acquisitions and as a result can target customers in many industries. Among these are automotive, chemicals, consumer packaged goods, food and beverage processing, metal fabrication, and pharmaceuticals. Infor has offices in more than 100 countries.

	Annual Growth	5/05	5/06	5/07	5/08	5/09
Sales ($ mil.)	(1.9%)	—	—	2,080.0	2,200.0	2,000.0
Employees	(6.7%)	—	—	9,200	9,000	8,000

INFORMA INVESTMENT SOLUTIONS, INC.

4 Gannett Dr.
White Plains, NY 10604
Phone: 914-640-0200
Fax: 914-694-6728
Web: www.informais.com

CEO: Lac An Vuong
CFO: —
HR: —
FYE: December 31
Type: Subsidiary

Keeping investors informed is what Informa Investment Solutions is all about. The company specializes in software for financial institutions, investment managers, and independent financial advisors. Informa Investment Solutions' products include PSN software for managers of separate accounts, Performer software for portfolio performance evaluation and reporting, and Wealth Management System software for financial planning. Informa Investment Solutions, which traces its roots to the founding of Effron Enterprises in 1976, took its present form in 2004 when parent Informa combined subsidiaries Effron Enterprises, Plan Sponsor Network, and netDecide into one operating unit.

INFORMATICA CORPORATION

NASDAQ (GS): INFA

100 Cardinal Way
Redwood City, CA 94063
Phone: 650-385-5000
Fax: 650-385-5500
Web: www.informatica.com

CEO: Sohaib Abbasi
CFO: Earl E. Fry
HR: —
FYE: December 31
Type: Public

Thinking about data? Think Informatica. The company provides enterprise data integration software that enables companies to access, integrate, and consolidate their data across a variety of systems and users. Informatica's PowerCenter platform consolidates, codes, and moves large data warehouses, and its PowerExchange software enables access to bulk or changed data. Other products include PowerAnalyzer, an application for improving data performance and efficiency, and SuperGlue, a metadata tool that creates data about data, integrating information from different databases to identify redundancies and analyze how the data is being used. Informatica's more than 3,400 customers include ABN AMRO, Avnet, and CVS.

	Annual Growth	12/05	12/06	12/07	12/08	12/09
Sales ($ mil.)	17.0%	267.4	324.6	391.3	455.7	500.7
Net income ($ mil.)	17.4%	33.8	36.2	54.6	56.0	64.2
Market value ($ mil.)	21.2%	1,102.0	1,121.3	1,654.8	1,260.9	2,376.7
Employees	14.8%	1,010	1,221	1,365	1,611	1,755

INFORMATION ANALYSIS INCORPORATED

OTC: IAIC

11240 Waples Mill Rd., Ste. 201
Fairfax, VA 22030
Phone: 703-383-3000
Fax: 703-293-7979
Web: www.infoa.com

CEO: Sandor Rosenberg
CFO: Richard S. (Rich) DeRose
HR: —
FYE: December 31
Type: Public

Information Analysis Incorporated (IAI) gets info across. The company's software and services help enterprises and government agencies migrate from older, mainframe-based computer systems to client-server and Web-based applications. IAI offers services such as programming, platform migration, systems analysis, staffing, and maintenance to corporate and government clients. Its customers have included Citibank, Computer Sciences Corporation, the US Department of Energy, US Army, and US Air Force. The federal government accounted for about 90% of the company's sales in 2007.

	Annual Growth	12/05	12/06	12/07	12/08	12/09
Sales ($ mil.)	(11.3%)	10.8	9.5	10.0	6.7	6.7
Net income ($ mil.)	(26.9%)	0.7	0.5	0.2	(0.4)	0.2
Market value ($ mil.)	(27.6%)	7.7	4.5	3.8	0.9	2.1
Employees	(5.9%)	42	38	39	35	33

⊞ INFORMATION BUILDERS, INC.

2 Penn Plaza, 27th Fl.
New York, NY 10121
Phone: 212-736-4433
Fax: 212-967-6406
Web: www.informationbuilders.com

CEO: Gerald D. Cohen
CFO: Harry Lerner
HR: —
FYE: December 31
Type: Private

Information Builders, Inc. (IBI) wants to help you grow your business intelligently. The company's flagship WebFOCUS software makes it easier to conduct data integration and business intelligence analysis over the Internet, intranets, and extranets. Customers use IBI's products to collect, analyze, and distribute a variety of enterprise data. The company's iWay Software subsidiary offers middleware technology that helps businesses integrate legacy systems with newer applications. Information Builders also provides consulting, training, and support services. President and CEO Gerald Cohen helped found IBI in 1975, bootstrapping the company's operations with advance payments from its first two customers.

	Annual Growth	12/04	12/05	12/06	12/07	12/08
Sales ($ mil.)	(4.2%)	—	—	—	313.0	300.0
Employees	—	—	—	—	—	1,400

INFORMATION SERVICES GROUP, INC.

NASDAQ (GM): III

Four Stamford Plaza, 107 Elm St.
Stamford, CT 06902
Phone: 203-517-3100
Fax: —
Web: www.informationsg.com

CEO: Michael P. Connors
CFO: David E. Berger
HR: —
FYE: December 31
Type: Public

True to its name, Information Services Group's (ISG) service is information. As a consulting firm, ISG provides advisory services to companies seeking to outsource their business operations. Operating through subsidiaries, the company specializes in marketing, advertising, human resources, legal, supply chain management, and other business services. It targets its advisory services to the North American, European, and Asia/Pacific markets, and serves such industries as telecom, financial services, health care, pharmaceutical, manufacturing, transportation, and utilities. Founded in 2006, the company acquired outsourcing advisory firm TPI in 2007; TPI is currently the company's primary operating subsidiary.

	Annual Growth	12/05	12/06	12/07	12/08	12/09
Sales ($ mil.)	165.0%	—	—	18.9	174.8	132.7
Net income ($ mil.)	—	—	—	4.5	(57.9)	(2.8)
Market value ($ mil.)	(32.0%)	—	—	219.0	108.7	101.4
Employees	(2.5%)	—	—	462	464	439

INFOSONICS CORPORATION

NASDAQ (GM): IFON

4350 Executive Dr., Ste. 100
San Diego, CA 92121
Phone: 858-373-1600
Fax: 858-373-1505
Web: www.infosonics.com

CEO: Joseph Ram
CFO: Roger Laungani
HR: —
FYE: December 31
Type: Public

InfoSonics answers the call for phone fulfillment. The company distributes wireless handsets and accessories from manufacturers such as LG Electronics, Novatel Wireless, and Samsung Electronics. It supplies retailers, wireless carriers, and distributors in the Americas from distribution centers in San Diego and Miami. InfoSonics' services include programming, software loading, and light assembly. Its logistics business includes outsourced supply chain services, such as inventory management and customized packaging. InfoSonics also sells its own line of phones under the verykool brand. Customers in Argentina, the company's largest market, account for 87% of its revenues.

	Annual Growth	12/05	12/06	12/07	12/08	12/09
Sales ($ mil.)	12.2%	145.8	240.9	244.7	213.2	231.3
Net income ($ mil.)	—	2.7	2.5	(1.6)	(10.4)	(1.5)
Market value ($ mil.)	(40.3%)	115.2	69.6	20.3	3.5	14.6
Employees	7.9%	28	52	54	44	38

INFOSPACE, INC.

NASDAQ (GS): INSP

601 108th Ave. NE, Ste. 1200
Bellevue, WA 98004
Phone: 425-201-6100
Fax: 425-201-6150
Web: www.infospaceinc.com

CEO: William J. (Will) Lansing
CFO: David B. Binder
HR: —
FYE: December 31
Type: Public

Why crawl the Web when others have done it for you? InfoSpace operates a portfolio of online search services that rely on metasearch search technology. Its websites, including Dogpile.com, WebFetch.com, MetaCrawler.com, and WebCrawler.com, query such leading search engines as Google, Yahoo!, and MSN, and then collates and ranks those search results. Its metasearch technology also powers third-party search services, such as Info.com. In recent years the company exited the mobile and directory businesses in order to focus on its online search services.

	Annual Growth	12/05	12/06	12/07	12/08	12/09
Sales ($ mil.)	(11.6%)	340.0	371.7	140.5	156.7	207.6
Net income ($ mil.)	(53.6%)	159.4	(15.1)	14.6	(18.7)	7.4
Market value ($ mil.)	(24.1%)	925.4	735.1	673.8	270.6	307.1
Employees	(29.1%)	620	530	170	160	157

INFOSYS CONSULTING, INC.

6607 Kaiser Dr.
Fremont, CA 94555
Phone: 510-742-3000
Fax: 510-742-3090
Web: www.infosysconsulting.com

CEO: Stephen R. (Steve) Pratt
CFO: —
HR: —
FYE: March 31
Type: Subsidiary

Infosys Consulting has a word or two of advice to offer about outsourcing. The company, a unit of India-based information technology services and business process outsourcing giant Infosys Technologies, consults with companies from a variety of industries on issues such as customer and product operations, enterprise systems, and IT strategy. Infosys Consulting aims to combine the disciplines of management consulting and IT consulting, and it works with its parent to facilitate the movement of work to countries outside the US when that makes sense for its customers. Infosys Consulting was established in 2004.

INFRASTRUX GROUP, INC.

600 University St., Ste. 600
Bellevue, WA 98101
Phone: 425-463-1010
Fax: 425-463-1011
Web: www.infrastrux.com

CEO: Michael T. Lennon
CFO: Lanny H. Michael
HR: Steven Maasch
FYE: December 31
Type: Subsidiary

InfrastruX Group brings the "X factor" to infrastructure. The company provides plant design, construction, and maintenance services for electric power and natural gas transmission companies throughout the US. It operates through a network of contractor subsidiaries which includes Hawkeye, InterCon Construction, UtilX, and B&H Maintenance. Activities include installing and maintaining overhead and underground power and transmission lines. Through its proprietary CableCURE treatments, the company restores and extends the life of water-damaged power and telecommunications cables. Parent energy investment fund Tenaska Power canceled plans to take InfrastruX public and plans to sell the company to Willbros Group .

ING BANK, FSB

1 S. Orange St.
Wilmington, DE 19801
Phone: 302-658-2200
Fax: —
Web: www.ingdirect.com

CEO: Arkadi Kuhlmann
CFO: Maria Rueda
HR: —
FYE: December 31
Type: Subsidiary

Orange you glad you can count on ING Bank? The company, better known as ING Direct, offers the Orange Savings Account, which boasts higher-than-average interest rates and one of the highest yields in the industry. Doing business in the US via the Internet, over the phone, by ATM, and by mail, ING Direct also offers certificates of deposit, individual retirement accounts, home mortgages, and paperless checking accounts. For businesses, ING Direct offers savings accounts, CDs, and 401(k) plans. The bank offers online brokerage services through its ShareBuilder subsidiary, which it acquired in 2007. ING Direct is part of Amsterdam-based ING Groep.

	Annual Growth	12/05	12/06	12/07	12/08	12/09
Assets ($ mil.)	14.2%	53,128.8	62,691.4	79,977.6	82,416.7	90,293.9
Net income ($ mil.)	—	234.2	222.0	260.3	(1,111.6)	(496.3)
Employees	17.2%	1,134	1,379	2,010	2,328	2,140

ING CLARION PARTNERS, LLC

230 Park Ave.
New York, NY 10169
Phone: 212-883-2500
Fax: 212-883-2700
Web: www.ingclarion.com

CEO: Stephen J. (Steve) Furnary
CFO: Patrick J. Tully Jr.
HR: —
FYE: December 31
Type: Subsidiary

ING Clarion Partners values properties and property values. The US arm of Dutch financial company ING Groep's real estate investment business, ING Clarion assembles and manages real estate asset portfolios for individual and institutional investors. The company acquires a variety of asset types including real property, stakes in real estate companies and trusts, and real estate-related debt. It manages assets within separate accounts as well as for pooled funds. ING Clarion oversees some $50 billion of commercial real estate including office, retail, industrial (including self-storage), multifamily, and hospitality properties. The company was founded in 1982 and became a part of ING Groep in 1998.

An in-depth profile of this company is available to Hoover's Online members at hoovers.com.

815

ING INVESTMENT MANAGEMENT AMERICAS

10 State House Sq.
Hartford, CT 06103
Phone: 860-275-3720
Fax: —
Web: www.inginvestment.com

CEO: Jeffrey T. (Jeff) Becker
CFO: —
HR: Cindy Caruso
FYE: December 31
Type: Business segment

ING Investment Management Americas is all about the Benjamins. The unit of Dutch financial services giant ING Groep administers more than $220 billion for some 500 institutional investors in the US, Canada, and Latin America. Clients include corporations, pension funds, mutual funds, health care organizations, and insurance companies. The company also manages accounts for not-for-profit organizations including endowments and foundations, and religious institutions. ING Investment Management Americas employs a variety of investment styles such as growth and value equity, core fixed income, multiasset strategies, and alternative investments including hedge funds and private equity.

ING NORTH AMERICA INSURANCE CORPORATION

5780 Powers Ferry Rd. NW
Atlanta, GA 30327
Phone: 770-980-5100
Fax: 770-980-3301
Web: www.ing-usa.com

CEO: Thomas J. (Tom) McInerney
CFO: Ewout Steenbergen
HR: Thomas P. (Tom) Waldron
FYE: December 31
Type: Subsidiary

From New York to Los Angeles, individuals to institutions, ING North America Insurance has a plan. The company offers insurance and financial products including fixed and variable annuities, life insurance, individual life reinsurance, and retirement savings plans. It also provides policy brokerage, investment planning, mutual funds, wealth management, and employee benefits administration. ING North America administers and manages the life and accident insurance policies underwritten by affiliates including ReliaStar Life Insurance, ING Life Insurance and Annuity, Midwestern United Life, and Security Life of Denver. ING North America Insurance is a subsidiary of Dutch financial services giant ING Groep.

INGENICO CORP.

6195 Shiloh Rd., Ste. D
Alpharetta, GA 30005
Phone: 678-456-1200
Fax: 678-456-1201
Web: www.ingenico-us.com

CEO: Christopher Justice
CFO: Chuck Kovach
HR: Nancy Brown
FYE: December 31
Type: Subsidiary

Ingenico Corp. wants to make a swipe across the North American electronic payment market. The company develops and sells electronic payment hardware and software for the finance, health care, hospitality, retail, and transportation industries. Its point-of-sale terminals and scanners verify check, debit, and credit payments. Other products include signature capture devices, magnetic strip readers, check readers, receipt printers, and smart cards. Ingenico Corp. is the North American subsidiary of France-based Ingenico, a leading European maker of electronic payment systems.

INGENIX, INC.

12125 Technology Dr.
Eden Prairie, MN 55344
Phone: 952-833-7100
Fax: 952-833-7079
Web: www.ingenix.com

CEO: Andrew M. (Andy) Slavitt
CFO: Gerald J. (Jerry) Knutson
HR: Dawn Kessler
FYE: December 31
Type: Subsidiary

Managed health care and drug discovery companies depend on hard numbers to stay in business and Ingenix serves them up fresh. The UnitedHealth Group subsidiary is one of the largest US health care information companies, and as such, its job is to determine exactly how long it should take you to get well, how much your doctor should be charging, and which medical codes he should be using when doing it. Ingenix's information services group provides database management, electronic health records (EHR), and a variety of consulting services to the health care and insurance industries. Its i3 group offers clinical trial management and contract research services to the pharmaceutical development industry.

INGERSOLL MACHINE TOOLS, INC.

707 Fulton Ave.
Rockford, IL 61103
Phone: 815-987-6000
Fax: 815-987-6725
Web: www.ingersoll.com

CEO: Tino Oldani
CFO: Larry Mocadlo
HR: —
FYE: December 31
Type: Subsidiary

Ingersoll Machine Tools, a unit of Italy's Camozzi Group, makes manufacturing systems, machine parts, and other related products, while also offering contract manufacturing, engineering, and other services. Products include assembly machines, crankshaft machines, drilling systems, flexible manufacturing centers, high-velocity machines, vertical turning lathes, and die machines. Prominent customers include Caterpillar and Lockheed Martin. Formerly a division of the bankrupt Ingersoll International, Ingersoll Machine Tools was resurrected in October 2003 after federal regulators approved the Camozzi Group purchase. Attilio Camozzi is the owner and founder of Camozzi Group.

	Annual Growth	12/04	12/05	12/06	12/07	12/08
Est. sales ($ mil.)	—	—	—	—	—	81.9
Employees	—	—	—	—	—	331

INGERSOLL-RAND CLIMATE CONTROL TECHNOLOGIES

12999 St. Charles Rock Rd.
Bridgeton, MO 63044
Phone: 314-291-2000
Fax: 314-298-4756
Web: www.ingersollrand.com

CEO: Didier Teirlinck
CFO: Maria Blase
HR: Ingrid Joris
FYE: December 31
Type: Business segment

Cool's the rule at Ingersoll-Rand Climate Control Technologies. The unit encompasses the climate solutions division of Ireland-based industrial giant Ingersoll-Rand (IR). The unit offers diverse refrigeration and heating, ventilation and air conditioning (HVAC) products around the world. Brands offered by the climate control division include Thermo King, which includes temperature control components used in ships, trucks, and trailers. Hussmann International provides refrigerated food-display cases found in supermarkets, restaurants, and other commercial institutions. The latest addition to the IR Climate Control lineup of brands is Trane, which serves the commercial HVAC market.

	Annual Growth	12/04	12/05	12/06	12/07	12/08
Sales ($ mil.)	—	—	—	—	—	3,356.8
Employees	—	—	—	—	—	—

INGERSOLL-RAND INDUSTRIAL TECHNOLOGIES

800-D Beaty St.
Davidson, NC 28036
Phone: 704-896-4000
Fax: 704-896-4366
Web: www.ingersollrand.com

CEO: James R. (Jim) Bolch
CFO: Edward (Ed) Schlesinger
HR: —
FYE: December 31
Type: Business segment

Folks at Ingersoll-Rand Industrial Technologies don't have to go far for a breath of fresh (compressed) air. The Industrial Technologies business segment of Ingersoll-Rand (IR) marries multiple companies that design, manufacture, sell, and service industrial and commercial products, ranging from air compressors and tools (impact wrenches) to pumps, golf cars, and microturbines. The segment straddles three arenas: Air Solutions, including compressed air systems, Productivity Solutions, offering material and fluid handling systems, and Energy Systems, featuring onsite alternative electric power and thermal energy through microturbine technology. Industrial Technologies accounts for about 20% of IR's revenue.

INGERSOLL-RAND SECURITY TECHNOLOGIES

11819 N. Pennsylvania St.
Carmel, IN 46032
Phone: 317-810-3700
Fax: —
Web: securitytechnologies.ingersollrand.com

CEO: John W. Conover IV
CFO: —
HR: —
FYE: December 31
Type: Business segment

Ingersoll-Rand Security Technologies (formerly Ingersoll-Rand Security and Safety) proves there is safety in numbers. A division of Ingersoll-Rand, the company makes a wide array of security and safety products and accessories for commercial and industrial use. Offerings include architectural hardware products, mechanical locks, and electronic and biometric access-control technologies. The division's brands include well-known lock maker Schlage (locks, keying systems), as well as Von Duprin (door hardware, exit devices), LCN (door closers, electronic security), and CISA (locks, panic exit devices, and safes).

INGLES MARKETS, INCORPORATED

NASDAQ (GM): IMKTA

2913 US Hwy. 70 West
Black Mountain, NC 28711
Phone: 828-669-2941
Fax: 828-669-3678
Web: www.ingles-markets.com

CEO: Robert P. Ingle
CFO: Ronald B. (Ron) Freeman
HR: Cynthia L. (Cindi) Brooks
FYE: September 30
Type: Public

The Ingalls family could have used an Ingles market near its little house on the prairie. Ingles Markets operates about 200 supermarkets, primarily in suburbs, small towns, and rural areas of six southeastern states. The stores largely operate under the Ingles name; about half a dozen operate as Sav-Mor. In addition to brand-name products, Ingles has Laura Lynn and Ingles Best private labels. The company also owns a dairy that sells about a third of its products to Ingles stores and the rest to other retailers and distributors. It also owns about 70 shopping centers, more than 75% of which contain an Ingles store. Descended from a long line of grocers, CEO Robert Ingle controls the company.

	Annual Growth	9/05	9/06	9/07	9/08	9/09
Sales ($ mil.)	9.3%	2,273.9	2,612.2	2,851.6	3,238.0	3,250.9
Net income ($ mil.)	2.0%	26.6	42.6	58.6	52.1	28.8
Market value ($ mil.)	0.0%	387.3	646.6	702.5	559.6	388.0
Employees	5.2%	15,200	16,100	17,000	19,000	18,600

INGRAM ENTERTAINMENT HOLDINGS INC.

2 Ingram Blvd.
La Vergne, TN 37089
Phone: 615-287-4000
Fax: 615-287-4982
Web: www.ingramentertainment.com

CEO: David B. Ingram
CFO: William D. (Donnie) Daniel
HR: —
FYE: December 31
Type: Private

Companies selling books and CDs might get the star treatment, but Ingram Entertainment doesn't mind a supporting role. The company is one of the largest independent video, DVD, and computer game distributors in the US. In addition, Ingram distributes software, audio books, electronics, and used videos and games. From some 15 sales and distribution centers, Ingram serves video stores, mass retailers, drugstores, and supermarkets. The company also operates AccessIngram.com, a business-to-business e-commerce site, and creates and maintains personalized websites for its customers through its MyVideoStore.com offering. Ingram Entertainment was spun off from Ingram Industries in 1997. David B. Ingram owns the firm.

	Annual Growth	12/04	12/05	12/06	12/07	12/08
Sales ($ mil.)	(0.3%)	—	839.0	764.0	813.0	831.0
Employees	(4.5%)	—	747	685	670	650

INGRAM INDUSTRIES INC.

1 Belle Meade Place, 4400 Harding Rd.
Nashville, TN 37205
Phone: 615-298-8200
Fax: 615-298-8242
Web: www.ingrambook.com

CEO: Orrin H. Ingram II
CFO: —
HR: —
FYE: December 31
Type: Private

Ingram Industries is big in books and boats. The company distributes books and handles digital assets through Ingram Content Group, one of its operating divisions. Ingram Content Group consists of book wholesaler Ingram Book Group, digital content distributor Ingram Digital, and on-demand book printer Lightning Source, among other units geared toward Christian bookshops and libraries. Ingram Marine Group, which operates Ingram Barge, constitutes the company's other operating division. The nation's largest inland carrier, Ingram Barge ships grain, ore, and other goods via a fleet of about 4,000 barges and some 140 towboats. The Ingram family, led by chairman Martha Ingram, owns and runs Ingram Industries.

	Annual Growth	12/04	12/05	12/06	12/07	12/08
Est. sales ($ mil.)	(1.7%)	2,310.0	2,539.0	1,810.0	2,100.0	2,160.0
Employees	(1.6%)	5,767	5,200	5,200	5,700	5,400

INGRAM MICRO INC.

NYSE: IM

1600 E. St. Andrew Place
Santa Ana, CA 92705
Phone: 714-566-1000
Fax: 714-566-7900
Web: www.ingrammicro.com

CEO: Gregory M.E. (Greg) Spierkel
CFO: William D. Humes
HR: Lynn Jolliffe
FYE: December 31
Type: Public

There's nothing micro about Ingram. Ingram Micro is the world's largest wholesale distributor of computer products. It provides thousands of products — desktop and notebook PCs, servers, storage devices, monitors, printers, and software — to more than 180,000 reseller customers around the globe. The company also provides a wide range of services for its resellers and suppliers, including contract manufacturing and warehousing, customer care, financing, logistics, outsourcing management, and enterprise network support services. Customers include resellers such as Wal-Mart.com, Staples, and Office Depot. Ingram Micro generates about 60% of its sales outside North America.

	Annual Growth	12/05	12/06	12/07	12/08	12/09
Sales ($ mil.)	0.6%	28,808.3	31,357.5	35,047.1	34,362.2	29,515.4
Net income ($ mil.)	(1.8%)	216.9	265.8	275.9	(394.9)	202.1
Market value ($ mil.)	(3.3%)	3,296.3	3,375.7	2,983.7	2,214.6	2,886.1
Employees	1.4%	13,000	13,700	15,000	14,500	13,750

An in-depth profile of this company is available to Hoover's Online members at hoovers.com.

INHIBITEX, INC.

NASDAQ (GM): INHX

9005 Westside Pkwy.
Alpharetta, GA 30004
Phone: 678-746-1100
Fax: 678-746-1299
Web: www.inhibitex.com

CEO: Russell H. Plumb
CFO: Peter Azzarello
HR: —
FYE: December 31
Type: Public

Inhibitex aims to inhibit deadly viruses. The company is pursuing the development of small-molecule antiviral compounds targeting diseases including herpes zoster (shingles), HIV, hepatitis C, and cytomegalovirus (CMV). The company was previously focused on developing anti-infectives for deadly *Staphylococcus* and other hospital-associated infections. Inhibitex continues to work on its vaccine development program targeting staph infections with Pfizer. It is also exploring diagnostics through a partnership with 3M.

	Annual Growth	12/05	12/06	12/07	12/08	12/09
Sales ($ mil.)	5.1%	0.9	0.8	2.8	3.2	1.1
Net income ($ mil.)	—	(38.6)	(31.1)	(41.5)	(13.2)	(17.6)
Market value ($ mil.)	(42.5%)	518.5	101.8	48.1	16.1	56.8
Employees	(20.5%)	80	37	32	34	32

INKSURE TECHNOLOGIES INC.

OTC: INKS

1770 NW 64th St., Ste. 350
Fort Lauderdale, FL 33309
Phone: 954-772-8507
Fax: 954-772-8509
Web: www.inksure.com

CEO: Yaron Meerfeld
CFO: Tzlil Peker
HR: —
FYE: December 31
Type: Public

InkSure Technologies markets custom security inks that are designed to prevent counterfeiting. The company also sells readers that use the company's proprietary software to identify and analyze marks printed with its inks, which can be used on a variety of paper and plastic materials and have a unique chemical code. Applications for InkSure Technologies systems include financial documents, product packaging, gift certificates, and tickets. Aviation security company ICTS International holds a 30% stake in InkSure Technologies.

	Annual Growth	12/05	12/06	12/07	12/08	12/09
Sales ($ mil.)	19.8%	1.6	2.0	2.9	2.2	3.3
Net income ($ mil.)	—	(2.2)	(3.1)	(3.1)	(3.5)	(1.5)
Market value ($ mil.)	(55.7%)	120.3	126.5	17.8	4.8	4.6
Employees	3.9%	12	15	17	12	14

INLAND REAL ESTATE CORPORATION

NYSE: IRC

2901 Butterfield Rd.
Oak Brook, IL 60523
Phone: 630-218-8000
Fax: 630-218-7350
Web: www.inlandrealestate.com

CEO: Mark E. Zalatoris
CFO: Brett A. Brown
HR: —
FYE: December 31
Type: Public

Inland Real Estate, a member of the Inland Group, buys, leases, and operates retail properties throughout the US, mainly in the Upper Midwest. The self-managed real estate investment trust (REIT) owns about 140 properties, most of which are strip shopping centers anchored by a grocery or big-box store. It also invests in single-tenant retail properties and develops properties, usually in joint ventures. The REIT's portfolio totals about 14 million sq. ft. of leasable space. Inland Real Estate primarily concentrates on the Chicago and Minneapolis/St. Paul metropolitan markets. Grocery store chain SUPERVALU is the company's largest tenant; other major clients include Dominick's Finer Foods and Roundy's.

	Annual Growth	12/05	12/06	12/07	12/08	12/09
Sales ($ mil.)	(1.7%)	182.7	178.4	189.4	191.5	170.8
Net income ($ mil.)	(34.7%)	47.3	45.2	43.8	33.3	8.6
Market value ($ mil.)	(13.8%)	1,264.2	1,600.1	1,210.3	1,109.5	696.6
Employees	7.2%	78	82	88	106	103

THE INLAND REAL ESTATE GROUP OF COMPANIES, INC.

2901 Butterfield Rd.
Oak Brook, IL 60523
Phone: 630-218-8000
Fax: 630-218-4957
Web: www.inlandgroup.com

CEO: Daniel L. (Dan) Goodwin
CFO: Alan Kremin
HR: Nora O'Conner
FYE: June 30
Type: Private

The Inland Real Estate Group lives, eats, breathes, and sleeps real estate. Through a number of affiliated firms, the group provides commercial real estate services including property investment, portfolio management, lending, brokerage, development, and property management/leasing. Through real estate investment trusts (REITs), Inland primarily invests in retail properties. Its portfolio (worth some $26 billion) includes more than 112 million sq. ft. of commercial space throughout the US. Publicly traded Inland Real Estate Corporation invests in properties in the Midwest; private REITs Inland Western and Inland American invest in the US and Canada. Inland Real Estate Brokerage is active in the Chicago area.

INNERWORKINGS, INC.

NASDAQ (GM): INWK

600 W. Chicago Ave., Ste. 850
Chicago, IL 60610
Phone: 312-642-3700
Fax: 312-642-3704
Web: www.iwprint.com

CEO: Eric D. Belcher
CFO: Joseph M. Busky
HR: —
FYE: December 31
Type: Public

Printing procurement company InnerWorkings has inserted itself into the process by which corporate customers get print jobs done. The company's proprietary software, PPM4, matches customers' jobs with printing companies' equipment and capacity. The InnerWorkings system submits a job to multiple printers, who then bid for the business. More than 7,000 suppliers participate in the company's network, which comprises 25 locations in the US and the UK. InnerWorkings' customers include companies in the advertising, consumer products, publishing, and retail industries.

	Annual Growth	12/05	12/06	12/07	12/08	12/09
Sales ($ mil.)	51.1%	76.9	160.5	288.4	419.0	400.4
Net income ($ mil.)	8.2%	4.6	8.3	22.5	16.0	6.3
Market value ($ mil.)	(28.2%)	—	728.7	788.1	299.1	269.4
Employees	44.3%	154	153	567	761	667

INNODATA ISOGEN, INC.

NASDAQ (GM): INOD

3 University Plaza
Hackensack, NJ 07601
Phone: 201-371-8000
Fax: 201-488-9099
Web: www.innodata-isogen.com

CEO: Jack S. Abuhoff
CFO: O'Neil Nalavadi
HR: —
FYE: December 31
Type: Public

Innodata Isogen handles information inundation. The company provides content management and process outsourcing services to businesses and government agencies mainly in the US and Europe. It oversees abstracting and indexing, data capture and entry, research and analysis, and technical writing. Innodata manages such tasks as digitizing paper documents into a more manageable electronic form. The company also provides consulting, technology integration and implementation services, and software and systems engineering. It primarily serves the media, publishing, and information services industries. Customers have included Alcatel-Lucent, the Defense Intelligence Agency, EBSCO, and Reed Elsevier.

	Annual Growth	12/05	12/06	12/07	12/08	12/09
Sales ($ mil.)	17.2%	42.1	41.0	67.7	75.0	79.3
Net income ($ mil.)	—	(1.7)	(7.3)	4.6	7.6	7.3
Market value ($ mil.)	12.5%	88.0	54.9	136.0	63.5	140.8
Employees	3.8%	6,087	5,476	7,768	6,745	7,060

INNOPHOS HOLDINGS, INC.

NASDAQ (GM): IPHS

259 Prospect Plains Rd.
Cranbury, NJ 08512
Phone: 609-495-2495
Fax: 609-860-0138
Web: www.innophos.com

CEO: Randolph (Randy) Gress
CFO: Neil Salmon
HR: Wilma Harris
FYE: December 31
Type: Public

Innophos Holdings adds a dash of its phosphate products to food, beverages, toothpaste, detergents, and asphalt. Innophos manufactures specialty phosphates used in consumer products, pharmaceuticals, and industrial applications. The company was formed in 2004 when Bain Capital bought Rhodia's North American specialty phosphates business. Customers use the company's phosphates to improve the quality and performance of a broad range of products, from electronics and textiles to pharmaceuticals, water, and detergents. Innophos divides its business into three segments: specialty salts and specialty acids; purified phosphoric acid; and sodium tripolyphosphate.

	Annual Growth	12/05	12/06	12/07	12/08	12/09
Sales ($ mil.)	5.6%	535.5	541.8	579.0	934.8	666.8
Net income ($ mil.)	—	(11.7)	(32.8)	(5.5)	207.2	63.1
Market value ($ mil.)	16.1%	—	314.3	318.6	424.2	492.0
Employees	(3.6%)	1,148	1,101	1,045	1,125	990

INNOSPEC INC.

NASDAQ (GM): IOSP

200 Continental Dr.
Newark, DE 19713
Phone: 302-454-8100
Fax: 302-451-1380
Web: www.innospecinc.com

CEO: Patrick S. Williams
CFO: Ian P. Cleminson
HR: Catherine (Cathy) Hessner
FYE: December 31
Type: Public

After some introspection, Octel changed its name to Innospec. In 2006 the company rebranded to align its name more closely with its growing specialty chemicals businesses. Its TEL (tetraethyl lead) product, an anti-knock gas additive sold to oil refineries worldwide, now generates less than 10% of the company's sales. Declining TEL sales after the US Clean Air Act was passed, along with similar moves by other countries, has forced the company to develop other business lines. Innospec's Fuel Specialties segment makes chemical additives that enhance fuel efficiency and engine performance, and its Active Chemicals unit makes several products used in the personal care, paper, detergent, and photographic markets.

	Annual Growth	12/05	12/06	12/07	12/08	12/09
Sales ($ mil.)	3.2%	527.7	532.1	602.4	640.5	598.5
Net income ($ mil.)	—	(123.7)	11.4	29.5	12.5	6.4
Market value ($ mil.)	5.5%	193.3	553.0	407.7	140.0	239.8
Employees	(0.4%)	802	774	769	783	790

INNOTRAC CORPORATION

NASDAQ (GM): INOC

6655 Sugarloaf Pkwy.
Duluth, GA 30097
Phone: 678-584-4000
Fax: 678-475-5840
Web: www.innotrac.com

CEO: Scott D. Dorfman
CFO: George M. Hare
HR: —
FYE: December 31
Type: Public

Behind your favorite catalog or online retailer might be a company like Innotrac, which handles customer support and fulfillment services. Innotrac takes orders through its call centers and via the Internet, and processes them through its fulfillment centers, where customers' products are stored. The company's services include inventory tracking and management, packaging, and reverse logistics (handling of returned goods). Besides retailers such as Ann Taylor and Target, Innotrac's customers include telecom giants such as AT&T and Qwest, for which the company distributes DSL modems, Caller ID units, and phones. A plan to be acquired by GSI Commerce was halted in early 2009.

	Annual Growth	12/05	12/06	12/07	12/08	12/09
Sales ($ mil.)	7.9%	73.9	82.3	121.8	131.4	100.0
Net income ($ mil.)	—	(4.7)	(5.3)	0.7	3.3	(22.7)
Market value ($ mil.)	(22.7%)	56.2	31.2	44.5	20.8	20.1
Employees	9.3%	840	1,300	1,400	1,600	1,200

IN-N-OUT BURGERS

4199 Campus Dr., 9th Fl.
Irvine, CA 92612
Phone: 949-509-6200
Fax: 949-509-6389
Web: www.in-n-out.com

CEO: Lynsi Martinez
CFO: Roger Kotch
HR: —
FYE: December 31
Type: Private

Made-to-order hamburgers are in and franchising is out at In-N-Out Burgers. The company owns and operates about 240 popular burger joints located primarily in California. The chain's menu features just four basic items — hamburgers, cheeseburgers, the Double-Double (two patties and two slices of cheese), and french fries — but patrons are free to customize how their hamburger is prepared. The chain famously does not use microwaves, heat lamps, or freezers, and it has no franchise operators. In-N-Out does offer on-site catering for parties and events with its In-N-Out Cookout Trailers. Harry and Esther Snyder started the family-owned company in 1948.

INNOVA PURE WATER, INC.

Pink Sheets: IPUR

8528 Davis Blvd., Ste. 134-210
North Richland Hills, TX 76180
Phone: 520-742-0007
Fax: 214-204-9152
Web: www.innovapurewater.com

CEO: David L. Zich
CFO: Jim R. Davisson
HR: —
FYE: June 30
Type: Public

If cleanliness is next to godliness, Innova Pure Water is set. The company makes and sells portable water filtration and water treatment products under the WaterWay and Innova brand names. Its products are sold by mass merchandisers, outdoors and sporting goods retailers, and via the company's website. Innova manufactures a sports bottle with biological and heavy metal filters. The company expanded into software in mid-2005 through its purchase of Numera Software Corporation (a proprietary software firm) and into consultant services with its acquisition of DesertView Management Services (a management consulting company). Innova was founded in 1985.

INNOVARO, INC.

NYSE Amex: INV

2109 Palm Ave.
Tampa, FL 33605
Phone: 813-754-4330
Fax: 813-754-2383
Web: www.innovaro.com

CEO: Douglas (Doug) Schaedler
CFO: Carole R. Wright
HR: —
FYE: December 31
Type: Public

Innovaro (formerly UTEK) helps turn innovations into profitable ventures. The company provides consultation services to help develop new technologies created at universities and research labs around the world, primarily in the US and UK. It works with its clients to locate new markets and develop new platforms; it also facilitates the sale of licensing deals for potential commercial use. Areas of expertise include biotechnology, energy, geology, manufacturing, and electronics. Innovaro is expanding beyond the university market into the private sector. It elected to stop operating as a business development company (BDC) in 2009, giving it greater flexibility and allowing it to work with larger clients.

	Annual Growth	12/05	12/06	12/07	12/08	12/09
Sales ($ mil.)	(16.9%)	22.7	57.0	20.3	20.2	10.8
Net income ($ mil.)	—	5.9	19.9	3.8	(8.4)	(15.3)
Market value ($ mil.)	(25.5%)	162.7	133.8	155.7	104.4	50.1
Employees	5.1%	50	48	68	115	61

An in-depth profile of this company is available to Hoover's Online members at hoovers.com.

819

INNOVATIVE CARD TECHNOLOGIES, INC.   OTC: INVC

US Bank Tower, 633 W. 5th St., Ste. 2600
Los Angeles, CA 90071
Phone: 213-223-2145
Fax: 213-223-2147
Web: www.incardtech.com

CEO: Richard J. Nathan
CFO: Richard J. Nathan
HR: —
FYE: December 31
Type: Public

Innovative Card Technologies (ICT) is almost ready to make your plastic more powerful. The company has developed power inlay technology designed for information-bearing plastic cards. The company's primary product is the ICT DisplayCard, which incorporates a battery, circuit, and display on a card the size of a credit card. The DisplayCard offers increased security by ensuring the card is physically present; at the push of a button, the card displays a one-time password that must be used in conjunction with the card for the transaction to be authorized. The DisplayCard can be configured for use as a payment card (debit or credit) or as an RFID access card serving electronic banking or data access needs.

	Annual Growth	12/05	12/06	12/07	12/08	12/09
Sales ($ mil.)	—	0.0	0.0	0.4	2.8	4.1
Net income ($ mil.)	—	(2.6)	(6.9)	(14.3)	(8.9)	(5.9)
Market value ($ mil.)	(45.5%)	76.4	134.5	77.6	2.3	6.7
Employees	6.5%	7	12	15	7	9

INNOVATIVE SOFTWARE TECHNOLOGIES, INC.   OTC: INIV

911 Ranch Rd., 620 North, Ste. 204
Austin, TX 78734
Phone: 813-387-3304
Fax: —
Web: www.istcompanies.com

CEO: Robert V. Rudman
CFO: Robert V. Rudman
HR: —
FYE: March 31
Type: Public

Innovative Software Technologies (IST) is looking for a new field to focus on. The company provided business continuity services and products, primarily to small and midsized customers. ITS' offerings included its AcXess Application Continuity Xchange, which provided Web-based access to enterprise applications. IST entered the business continuity market through its 2006 purchase of AcXess; in late 2007 the company agreed to sell the AcXess operations to the AcXess management team. IST plans to acquire a software or services company at some point in the future.

	Annual Growth	12/04	12/05	*3/07	3/08	3/09
Sales ($ mil.)	(61.0%)	17.3	0.3	0.1	0.2	0.4
Net income ($ mil.)	—	(3.2)	(2.9)	(2.9)	(1.5)	(1.0)
Market value ($ mil.)	(66.0%)	14.9	2.5	—	—	0.2
Employees	(30.7%)	—	3	5	2	1

*Fiscal year change

INNOVATIVE SOLUTIONS AND SUPPORT, INC.   NASDAQ (GS): ISSC

720 Pennsylvania Dr.
Exton, PA 19341
Phone: 610-646-9800
Fax: 610-646-0149
Web: www.innovative-ss.com

CEO: Geoffrey S. M. Hedrick
CFO: John C. Long
HR: —
FYE: September 30
Type: Public

Pilots use products made by Innovative Solutions and Support (IS&S) to gauge their success. The company makes flight information computers, electronic displays, and monitoring systems that measure flight information such as airspeed, altitude, and engine and fuel data. IS&S's reduced vertical separation minimum (RVSM) products enable planes to fly closer together vertically; engine and fuel displays help the pilot track fuel and oil levels and other engine activities. IS&S uses flat-panel displays, which take up less cockpit space than conventional displays. The company gets nearly all of its sales in the US.

	Annual Growth	9/05	9/06	9/07	9/08	9/09
Sales ($ mil.)	(12.7%)	63.3	16.7	18.3	30.5	36.7
Net income ($ mil.)	(28.0%)	18.6	(2.9)	(8.8)	(7.9)	5.0
Market value ($ mil.)	(24.6%)	260.3	243.5	318.0	91.3	84.0
Employees	(2.2%)	153	138	171	165	140

INNOVEX, INC.   Pink Sheets: INVX

3033 Campus Dr., Ste. E180
Plymouth, MN 55441
Phone: 763-383-4000
Fax: 763-383-4091
Web: www.innovexinc.com

CEO: John M. Clark III
CFO: Randy L. Acres
HR: —
FYE: September 30
Type: Public

Innovex is flexing its interconnect. The company manufactures high-density flexible circuits and interconnects used to control the flow of electrical signals within electronic products, such as hard-disk drives, notebook computers, consumer entertainment products, LCDs, semiconductor packaging, and mobile devices. Innovex targets manufacturers in need of high-end and high-volume flexible circuits, and its leading customers are TPO Displays (43% of sales), Seagate Technology (23%), and Hitachi Global Storage (22%). Other customers include Hewlett-Packard, Samsung Electronics, and TDK. Most of the company's revenues come from outside the US, primarily from manufacturers in the Pacific Rim.

	Annual Growth	9/04	9/05	9/06	9/07	*9/08
Sales ($ mil.)	(17.9%)	155.9	200.2	173.1	87.8	71.0
Net income ($ mil.)	—	(17.5)	(25.0)	(17.0)	(32.1)	(28.0)
Market value ($ mil.)	(47.5%)	79.1	82.6	40.2	24.1	6.0
Employees	(5.3%)	4,118	4,365	3,582	3,247	3,306

*Most recent year available

INNSUITES HOSPITALITY TRUST   NYSE Amex: IHT

InnSuites Hotel Centre, 1615 E. Northern Ave., Ste. 102
Phoenix, AZ 85020
Phone: 602-944-1500
Fax: 602-678-0281
Web: www.innsuitestrust.com

CEO: James F. Wirth
CFO: Anthony B. Waters
HR: —
FYE: January 31
Type: Public

This company trusts you'll have a night full of sweet dreams while staying at one of its hotels. InnSuites Hospitality Trust wholly-owns and operates five studio and two-room suite hotels in Arizona, New Mexico, and Southern California, four of which are co-branded as Best Westerns. The company also provides management services for nine hotels and trademark license services for 11 hotels. InnSuites Hospitality Trust primarily operates through the InnSuites Hotels & Suites and InnSuites Boutique Hotel Collection brands. InnSuites Hospitality Trust operates through its majority-owned affiliate RRF Limited Partnership, which in turn operates through subsidiary InnSuites Hotels.

	Annual Growth	1/06	1/07	1/08	1/09	1/10
Sales ($ mil.)	(5.5%)	21.2	21.8	22.1	20.4	16.9
Net income ($ mil.)	—	0.5	0.0	1.1	(0.6)	(1.1)
Market value ($ mil.)	0.0%	11.6	11.9	8.7	9.0	11.6
Employees	(4.8%)	446	422	450	450	366

INNUITY, INC.   OTC: INNU

8644 154th Ave. NE
Redmond, WA 98052
Phone: 425-497-9909
Fax: 425-497-0409
Web: innuity.com

CEO: John R. Wall
CFO: Linden Barney
HR: —
FYE: December 31
Type: Public

Innuity has applied some ingenuity in transforming itself from an oil and gas exploration and production firm into an Internet technology services provider. The company offers integrated Internet technology services designed to help small businesses grow their revenues, improve services to customers, and maintain daily operations. Its operations are divided into two divisions: the Commerce Division provides commerce transaction services and the Promotion Division provides a Web presence and sales and marketing tools.

INOVA HEALTH SYSTEM

2990 Telestar Ct.
Falls Church, VA 22042
Phone: 703-289-2000
Fax: 703-221-8381
Web: www.inova.org

CEO: J. Knox Singleton
CFO: Richard Magenheimer
HR: —
FYE: December 31
Type: Not-for-profit

Inova keeps NoVa (northern Virginia) healthy. Founded in 1956 in Fairfax, Virginia, Inova Health System is a not-for-profit health care provider, offering acute care, long-term care, home health care, mental health, research, and satellite family practice and emergency care services in the northern Virginia suburbs of Washington, DC. Inova's network consists of six hospitals (including a children's hospital) with some 1,800 beds, as well as nursing homes for seniors with another 400 beds. The health system has about 3,000 physicians on its medical staff. Its emergency departments receive more than 400,000 visits each year. The company is supported by the Inova Health System Foundation.

INOVA TECHNOLOGY INC.

Pink Sheets: INVA

2300 W. Sahara Ave., Ste. 800
Las Vegas, NV 89102
Phone: 800-757-9808
Fax: 866-467-7940
Web: www.inovatechnology.com

CEO: Adam Radly
CFO: Bob Bates
HR: —
FYE: April 30
Type: Public

Inova Technology has innovative ways of keeping track of things. The company provides radio frequency identification (RFID) scanners and tags through its RighTag subsidiary. Its Trakkers subsidiary offers a tracking solution that allows trade show exhibitors to scan badges of attendees to capture contact information, then store the data in a specially designated website for access from any location. Inova Technology also offers IT consulting and computer network services through its Desert Communications subsidiary. Chairman and CEO Adam Radly controls more than half of the company.

	Annual Growth	4/05	4/06	4/07	4/08	4/09
Sales ($ mil.)	81.1%	2.1	2.7	1.6	5.4	22.6
Net income ($ mil.)	—	(1.5)	0.7	0.0	(1.0)	(2.0)
Market value ($ mil.)	(43.1%)	31.1	16.1	4.5	8.0	3.3
Employees	(66.7%)	6	2	—	—	—

INOVIO BIOMEDICAL CORPORATION

NYSE Amex: INO

11494 Sorrento Valley Rd.
San Diego, CA 92121
Phone: 858-597-6006
Fax: 858-597-0451
Web: www.inovio.com

CEO: J. Joseph Kim
CFO: Peter D. Kies
HR: —
FYE: December 31
Type: Public

Inovio Biomedical is electrifying patients with its drug delivery technology. The firm focuses on electroporation, an infusion therapy that uses electrical pulses to open up cell membranes, thus optimizing the delivery of DNA vaccines and chemotherapies. The company is developing its MedPulser DNA Electroporation system (which consists of a generator and an applicator inserted into targeted tissue) to deliver chemotherapies directly into tumors. The firm is also exploring the use of the electroporation system for gene therapies and DNA vaccines, which contain large molecules that need assistance getting through cellular walls. In 2008 it agreed to merge with VGX Pharmaceuticals, a developer of DNA vaccines.

	Annual Growth	12/05	12/06	12/07	12/08	12/09
Sales ($ mil.)	13.4%	5.5	3.5	4.8	2.1	9.1
Net income ($ mil.)	—	(15.3)	(12.5)	(11.2)	(13.0)	(24.4)
Market value ($ mil.)	(15.8%)	233.3	338.1	94.5	53.4	117.2
Employees	11.7%	27	39	37	36	42

INOVIS, INC.

11720 AmberPark Dr., Ste. 400
Alpharetta, GA 30009
Phone: 404-467-3000
Fax: 404-467-3730
Web: www.inovis.com

CEO: Sean E. Feeney
CFO: Kenneth Williams
HR: Paul Trotti
FYE: December 31
Type: Subsidiary

Inovis understands that an efficient supply chain requires good communication. The company provides software that helps more than 16,000 retailers, suppliers, and other businesses standardize and manage communications. Inovis' electronic data interchange (EDI) and data translation software enables companies to use the Internet to securely exchange electronic documents, such as invoices and purchase orders. The company also offers its EDI system as a hosted service, and it provides industry-specific trading tools for the automotive, consumer packaged goods, electronics, and petrochemicals markets. In 2010 Inovis merged with rival GXS, forming a firm offering B2B integration software and B2B messaging services.

INSERRA SUPERMARKETS, INC.

20 Ridge Rd.
Mahwah, NJ 07430
Phone: 201-529-5900
Fax: 201-529-1189

CEO: Lawrence R. Inserra Jr.
CFO: —
HR: —
FYE: December 31
Type: Private

The Big Apple need never be short of apples (or oranges, for that matter), thanks to Inserra Supermarkets. Inserra owns and operates about 20 ShopRite supermarkets and superstores in northern New Jersey and southeastern New York State (most are in Westchester and Rockland counties). Inserra's superstores feature bagel bakeries, cafes, and pharmacies. The regional grocery chain also offers banking services in selected stores through agreements with Poughkeepsie Savings Bank, Statewide Savings Bank, and others. Owned by the Inserra family, the retailer is one of more than 40 members that make up cooperative Wakefern Food, the owner of the ShopRite name.

	Annual Growth	12/04	12/05	12/06	12/07	12/08
Sales ($ mil.)	0.6%	—	1,030.0	1,030.0	1,050.0	1,050.0
Employees	(6.5%)	—	4,000	4,000	3,500	

INSIGHT COMMUNICATIONS COMPANY, INC.

810 7th Ave.
New York, NY 10019
Phone: 917-286-2300
Fax: 917-286-2301
Web: www.insight-com.com

CEO: Michael S. Willner
CFO: John Abbot
HR: Jim Morgan
FYE: December 31
Type: Private

As one of the 10 largest US cable providers, Insight Communications has some inkling of what pay television and Internet subscribers want. The company's cable system serves about 700,000 consumer and business customers in the Midwest, with the bulk of its clients in Kentucky. Other key service areas include southern Indiana and Columbus, Ohio. Insight offers interactive digital video, video-on-demand, and such high-speed data services as cable Internet access and VoIP telephony services. The company has satellite offices and facilities in Indiana, Kentucky, and Ohio.

	Annual Growth	12/04	12/05	12/06	12/07	12/08
Sales ($ mil.)	(7.1%)	—	1,117.7	1,262.6	1,400.0	896.6
Employees	(10.3%)	—	3,829	4,035	2,569	2,766

An in-depth profile of this company is available to Hoover's Online members at hoovers.com.

821

INSIGHT ENTERPRISES, INC.

NASDAQ (GS): NSIT

6820 S. Harl Ave.
Tempe, AZ 85283
Phone: 480-902-1001
Fax: 480-902-1157
Web: www.insight.com

CEO: Kenneth T. (Ken) Lamneck
CFO: Glynis A. Bryan
HR: —
FYE: December 31
Type: Public

With this firm around, the end of your technology woes could be in sight. Insight Enterprises is a top distributor of computer hardware and software in North America, carrying thousands of products from major manufacturers, such as Hewlett-Packard, IBM, and Microsoft. It uses direct telesales, field sales agents, and an e-commerce site to reach clients in the public sector and at small and midsized businesses. Outside North America, the firm serves customers in about 190 countries across Europe, the Middle East, Africa, and the Asia/Pacific region. In recent years it has focused on networking and communications services, acquiring Calence (a leading Cisco provider in the US) and UK-based MINX.

	Annual Growth	12/05	12/06	12/07	12/08	12/09
Sales ($ mil.)	6.1%	3,261.1	3,817.1	4,800.4	4,825.5	4,136.9
Net income ($ mil.)	(11.7%)	55.3	76.8	77.8	(239.7)	33.6
Market value ($ mil.)	(12.6%)	906.5	872.3	843.2	319.0	527.9
Employees	5.4%	3,967	4,568	4,763	4,763	4,898

INSIGHT HEALTH SERVICES HOLDINGS CORP.

26250 Enterprise Ct., Ste. 100
Lake Forest, CA 92630
Phone: 949-282-6000
Fax: 949-462-3292
Web: www.insighthealth.com

CEO: Louis E. (Kip) Hallman III
CFO: Keith S. Kelson
HR: —
FYE: June 30
Type: Public

InSight Health Services knows what lies within the hearts, brains, and pancreases of men. The company offers diagnostic imaging services to wholesale and retail customers in some 30 states. InSight primarily provides MRI (magnetic resonance imaging) services, but also offers CT (computerized tomography) and PET (positron emission tomography) scanning, as well as conventional X-ray, mammogram, and ultrasound services. Customers include hospitals and physician practices, as well as insurance payors and Medicare or Medicaid programs. InSight primarily serves patients in western and southeastern states (including Arizona, California, Florida, and the Carolinas), as well as New England and the mid-Atlantic region.

	Annual Growth	6/05	6/06	6/07	6/08	6/09
Sales ($ mil.)	(7.8%)	316.9	306.3	286.9	242.6	229.3
Net income ($ mil.)	—	(27.2)	(210.2)	(99.0)	(169.2)	(19.8)
Market value ($ mil.)	(88.7%)	—	—	—	3.5	0.4
Employees	(9.0%)	2,270	1,806	2,148	1,435	1,560

INSIGNIA SYSTEMS, INC.

NASDAQ (CM): ISIG

6470 Sycamore Ct. North
Maple Grove, MN 55369
Phone: 763-392-6200
Fax: 763-392-6222
Web: www.insigniasystems.com

CEO: Scott F. Drill
CFO: Justin W. Shireman
HR: —
FYE: December 31
Type: Public

Insignia Systems believes all signs point to greater sales. The company's point of purchase (POP) software and services help retailers and consumer goods manufacturers create in-store advertising and promotional displays. As part of its POPSign program, Insignia Systems creates customized signs based on information from retailers and manufacturers; it generates the majority of its revenue from its POPSign program. Its Stylus software suite is used to create signs, labels, and posters. Insignia Systems also sells specialized cardstock and other printing supplies for its systems. The company's customers have included Kellogg and General Mills.

	Annual Growth	12/05	12/06	12/07	12/08	12/09
Sales ($ mil.)	10.1%	19.6	21.9	24.4	31.4	28.8
Net income ($ mil.)	—	(3.3)	2.4	2.3	(2.3)	3.7
Market value ($ mil.)	60.5%	11.1	47.3	43.5	15.2	73.9
Employees	10.8%	77	88	108	114	116

INSITE VISION INCORPORATED

OTC: INSV

965 Atlantic Ave.
Alameda, CA 94501
Phone: 510-865-8800
Fax: 510-865-5700
Web: www.insitevision.com

CEO: Louis C. (Lou) Drapeau
CFO: Louis C. (Lou) Drapeau
HR: —
FYE: December 31
Type: Public

InSite Vision provides insight into the murky realm of eye disease. The company develops ophthalmic products using its DuraSite eyedrop-based drug delivery system. Its topical anti-infective product, AzaSite, is marketed in the US by licensing partner Inspire Pharmaceuticals as a treatment for conjunctivitis (pink eye). Various other AzaSite products are in development to treat eyelid inflammation and other infections. InSite Vision has licensed rights to use azithromycin (the active ingredient in AzaSite) from Pfizer. Inspire markets AzaSite in the US and Canada, while international units are supplied by Catalent Pharma Solutions.

	Annual Growth	12/05	12/06	12/07	12/08	12/09
Sales ($ mil.)	—	0.0	0.0	23.8	13.7	9.8
Net income ($ mil.)	—	(15.2)	(16.6)	5.5	(21.3)	(14.2)
Market value ($ mil.)	(17.5%)	78.7	146.9	71.1	18.8	36.4
Employees	(24.0%)	30	44	45	36	10

INSITUFORM TECHNOLOGIES, INC.

NASDAQ (GS): INSU

17988 Edison Ave.
Chesterfield, MO 63005
Phone: 636-530-8000
Fax: 636-519-8010
Web: www.insituform.com

CEO: John J. (Joe) Burgess
CFO: David A. Martin
HR: Holly Sharp
FYE: December 31
Type: Public

Under many a city lurks a decaying infrastructure, and that's what Insituform Technologies takes care of *in situ*. The company provides trenchless technologies for rehabilitating sewers, water mains, and industrial pipes, serving municipalities and industrial plants worldwide. Its Insituform CIPP ("cured-in-place pipe") process, the company's largest revenue source, involves installing a custom-manufactured tube or liner that forms a leakproof "pipe within a pipe." The company's Tite Liner process is used to line steel pipe with corrosion-resistant polyethylene pipe. Other rehabilitation processes include the use of thermofusing resin and composite and polyethylene liners.

	Annual Growth	12/05	12/06	12/07	12/08	12/09
Sales ($ mil.)	5.1%	595.3	596.7	495.6	536.7	726.9
Net income ($ mil.)	19.9%	13.2	24.7	2.5	21.6	27.3
Market value ($ mil.)	4.1%	760.0	1,014.7	580.7	772.6	891.5
Employees	7.1%	2,281	2,000	1,600	1,550	3,000

INSMED INCORPORATED

NASDAQ (GM): INSM

8720 Stony Point Pkwy.
Richmond, VA 23235
Phone: 804-565-3000
Fax: 804-565-3500
Web: www.insmed.com

CEO: Melvin Sharoky
CFO: Kevin P. Tully
HR: —
FYE: December 31
Type: Public

Insmed is on a development path to discover drugs for neurological, muscular, and metabolic ailments. Its protein program is clinically focused on the development of lead candidate IPLEX as a potential treatment for conditions including muscular dystrophy, ALS (a neurodegenerative condition known as Lou Gehrig's disease), HARS (fat misdistribution associated with HIV), and retinopathy (abnormal growth of blood vessels in the retina). The company also has a preclinical research program for an oncology drug pipeline targeting breast, prostate, and colon cancer, among others.

	Annual Growth	12/05	12/06	12/07	12/08	12/09
Sales ($ mil.)	219.3%	0.1	1.0	7.5	11.7	10.4
Net income ($ mil.)	—	(40.9)	(56.1)	(20.0)	(15.7)	118.3
Market value ($ mil.)	(20.9%)	256.5	114.6	107.4	60.9	100.3
Employees	(35.2%)	85	157	94	97	15

INSOUND MEDICAL, INC.

39660 Eureka Dr.
Newark, CA 94560
Phone: 510-792-4000
Fax: 510-792-4050
Web: www.insoundmedical.com

CEO: David Thrower
CFO: Dan Saccani
HR: —
FYE: December 31
Type: Subsidiary

InSound Medical is actually quite sound. The company develops hearing devices made for continuous wear and that cannot be seen when used. Unlike conventional hearing aids, InSound Medical's devices are fitted into the ear by an audiology professional and worn continuously, even during sleeping or swimming. Customers buy a year's worth of devices and return every two to four months for replacement when the batteries wear out. The FDA-approved Lyric was introduced in 2008 and is marketed to younger consumers with mild to moderate hearing loss. InSound Medical was acquired by Sonova in 2010.

	Annual Growth	12/04	12/05	12/06	12/07	12/08
Est. sales ($ mil.)	—	—	—	—	—	4.6
Employees	—	—	—	—	—	31

INSPIRE PHARMACEUTICALS, INC.

NASDAQ (GM): ISPH

4222 Emperor Blvd., Ste. 200
Durham, NC 27703
Phone: 919-941-9777
Fax: 919-941-9797
Web: www.inspirepharm.com

CEO: Adrian Adams
CFO: Thomas R. (Tom) Staab II
HR: —
FYE: December 31
Type: Public

Inspire Pharmaceuticals doesn't want to leave a dry eye in the house. The company targets treatments for various respiratory and ocular diseases. Inspire Pharmaceuticals markets two eye products, Elestat for allergic conjunctivitis (red and itchy eyes) and Restasis for dry eye disease, that were developed in collaboration with Allergan. Another marketed product, AzaSite (licensed from InSite Vision), treats bacterial conjunctivitis (eye infections). The company is also working to develop new drugs for ailments such as cystic fibrosis and glaucoma.

	Annual Growth	12/05	12/06	12/07	12/08	12/09
Sales ($ mil.)	41.0%	23.3	37.1	48.7	70.5	92.2
Net income ($ mil.)	—	(31.8)	(42.1)	(63.7)	(51.6)	(40.0)
Market value ($ mil.)	2.1%	419.6	524.5	493.9	297.4	456.0
Employees	9.8%	165	170	250	250	240

INSTACARE CORP.

OTC: ISCR

2660 Townsgate Rd., Ste. 300
Westlake Village, CA 91361
Phone: 805-446-1973
Fax: 805-446-1983
Web: www.instacare.net

CEO: Keith Berman
CFO: Keith Berman
HR: —
FYE: December 31
Type: Public

instaCare (formerly CareDecision) hopes IT plus pharmaceuticals will equal success. Previously focused on wireless systems for the health care and lodging markets, in 2005 the company added a pharmaceuticals distribution unit through its purchases of CareGeneration and the Pharmaceutical Solutions unit of Kelly Company. instaCare drives customers to its pharmaceuticals business by providing wireless computing devices to doctors in clinics for the poor and uninsured; in return, doctors direct their patients to instaCare's discount mail-order prescription service. instaCare continues to sell its wireless PDA devices for the health care and lodging industries. Clearing company Cede & Co. owns 40% of instaCare.

	Annual Growth	12/05	12/06	12/07	12/08	12/09
Sales ($ mil.)	36.8%	5.6	19.2	6.3	15.0	19.6
Net income ($ mil.)	—	(4.8)	(2.8)	(1.4)	0.2	1.7
Market value ($ mil.)	(36.8%)	55.6	26.1	2.6	0.7	8.9
Employees	(3.8%)	14	9	10	9	12

INSTEEL INDUSTRIES, INC.

NASDAQ (GM): IIIN

1373 Boggs Dr.
Mount Airy, NC 27030
Phone: 336-786-2141
Fax: 336-786-2144
Web: www.insteel.com

CEO: Howard O. (H. O.) Woltz III
CFO: Michael C. Gazmarian
HR: Deborah Van Etten
FYE: September 30
Type: Public

WIRE! What is it good for? Absolutely everything — if you're Insteel Industries. The company manufactures welded wire reinforcement (WWR), used primarily to reinforce concrete pipe (pipe mesh, building mesh, engineered structural mesh, and precast manholes), driveways, and slabs. Its PC strand products are used to reinforce concrete structures such as bridges and parking garages. Insteel's customers include concrete product manufacturers, construction product distributors, and rebar fabricators. Insteel Industries operates six manufacturing facilities in the US, where the company makes most of its sales. The vast majority of its sales comes from non-residential construction.

	Annual Growth	9/05	9/06	9/07	9/08	9/09
Sales ($ mil.)	(9.7%)	345.5	329.5	297.8	353.9	230.2
Net income ($ mil.)	—	25.0	33.0	24.2	43.8	(22.1)
Market value ($ mil.)	11.8%	134.3	349.3	269.8	238.9	210.0
Employees	(9.6%)	655	621	559	523	438

INSTITUTE FOR INTERNATIONAL RESEARCH, INC.

708 3rd Ave., 4th Fl.
New York, NY 10017
Phone: 212-661-3500
Fax: 212-599-2192
Web: www.iirusa.com

CEO: Debra Chipman
CFO: Noel McDermott
HR: —
FYE: December 31
Type: Subsidiary

IIR offers up what executives want or need to know. The Institute for International Research (IIR) specializes in professional development through training, conferences, seminars, e-Learning programs, publications, and consulting. The company organizes some 200 events annually, including conferences across a number of industries such as customer service, finance, health care, pharmaceuticals, telecommunications, and marketing and new product development. The firm was established in 1973 as a newsletter company. UK-based information publisher Informa acquired IIR in 2005 for $1.4 billion, thereby gaining a foothold in the North American market.

INSULET CORPORATION

NASDAQ (GM): PODD

9 Oak Park Dr.
Bedford, MA 01730
Phone: 781-457-5000
Fax: 781-457-5011
Web: www.myomnipod.com

CEO: Duane M. DeSisto
CFO: Brian K. Roberts
HR: David Howe
FYE: December 31
Type: Public

Insulet wants to isolate an insolent disease. The medical device company manufactures an insulin pump for people with insulin-dependent diabetes. Its disposable, waterproof product, called the OmniPod Insulin Management System, weighs a mere 1.2 ounces and adheres directly to the patient's skin, making it more discrete than most insulin infusion systems that typically clip to a belt or fit in a pocket. The company markets its products to doctors, patients, and managed care companies in the US and abroad. Insulet was founded in 2000 and went public through an IPO in 2007.

	Annual Growth	12/05	12/06	12/07	12/08	12/09
Sales ($ mil.)	406.9%	0.1	3.7	13.4	36.1	66.0
Net income ($ mil.)	—	(21.6)	(36.0)	(53.5)	(92.8)	(79.5)
Market value ($ mil.)	(22.0%)	—	—	890.9	292.9	541.9
Employees	9.8%	190	190	247	294	276

An in-depth profile of this company is available to Hoover's Online members at hoovers.com.

823

⊞ INSURANCE AUTO AUCTIONS, INC.

2 Westbrook Corporate Center, Ste. 500
Westchester, IL 60154
Phone: 708-492-7000
Fax: 708-492-7078
Web: home.iaai.com

CEO: Thomas C. (Tom) O'Brien
CFO: Eric M. Loughmiller
HR: —
FYE: December 31
Type: Subsidiary

Getting something out of nothing is what this junkyard doggedly pursues. Insurance Auto Auctions (IAA) is a leading auto salvage company that auctions off vehicles declared as total losses for insurance purposes and were recovered from theft. It also offers collision-damaged rentals, dealer trade-ins, and fleet lease automobiles. IAA holds live auctions for licensed business buyers and the public at about 150 sites in the US and Canada. The company also allows buyers to place their bids online. Founded in 1982, IAA is owned by holding company KAR Auction Services, which went public in late 2009.

INSURANCE SERVICES OFFICE, INC.

Newport World Business Center, 545 Washington Blvd.
Jersey City, NJ 07310
Phone: 201-469-2000
Fax: 201-748-1472
Web: www.iso.com

CEO: Frank J. Coyne
CFO: Mark V. Anquillare
HR: —
FYE: December 31
Type: Subsidiary

All insurance coverage is based upon calculated risk — but who's doing the calculating? Insurance Services is one source for such information. Founded in 1971, Insurance Services Office (ISO) provides statistical, actuarial, and underwriting information for the property/casualty insurance and risk management industries. The company gathers premium, claim, and loss data that is filed with state regulators; the data is used to evaluate the price of insurance in each state. It's Interthinx unit provides mortgage lenders with audits, appraisals, and risk assessments to prevent fraud. ISO, a subsidiary of Verisk, has offices in Asia, Europe, and North America.

⊞ INSWEB CORPORATION

NASDAQ (GM): INSW

11290 Pyrites Way, Ste. 200
Gold River, CA 95670
Phone: 916-853-3300
Fax: 916-853-3325
Web: www.insweb.com

CEO: Hussein A. Enan
CFO: Kiran Rasaretnam
HR: —
FYE: December 31
Type: Public

It seems somehow appropriate to sell the least tangible of products — insurance coverage — via a virtual marketplace. InsWeb operates an Internet portal that allows consumers to shop for quotes on various insurance products, including automobile, term life, and homeowners insurance policies. InsWeb has alliances with more than two dozen insurance companies (including Allstate, AIG, and Liberty Mutual) which pay transaction fees to InsWeb for providing qualified customer leads. Quotes are available through the company's website at no charge to the consumer.

	Annual Growth	12/05	12/06	12/07	12/08	12/09
Sales ($ mil.)	8.9%	25.0	28.5	33.2	37.5	35.2
Net income ($ mil.)	—	(5.9)	(3.4)	2.4	(2.2)	(1.3)
Market value ($ mil.)	(0.4%)	15.9	15.4	43.4	11.5	15.7
Employees	(15.9%)	122	95	62	88	61

INTCOMEX, INC.

3505 NW 107th Ave.
Miami, FL 33178
Phone: 305-477-6230
Fax: 305-477-5694
Web: www.intcomex.com

CEO: Anthony Shalom
CFO: Russell A. Olson
HR: —
FYE: December 31
Type: Private

Intcomex is IT in Latin America and the Caribbean. The wholesaler distributes computer systems and components, peripherals, software, accessories, networking products, and digital consumer electronics to more than 40,000 customers in 40 countries. Clients are primarily third-party IT distributors, resellers, and retailers based in Latin America and the Caribbean. Intcomex offers nearly 6,000 products from about 200 manufacturers, including HP, Intel, NEC, and Seagate. Founded in 1989, the company began as a small retail store that sold computer software in South Florida. Today Intcomex operates sales offices in about a dozen countries.

	Annual Growth	12/04	12/05	12/06	12/07	12/08
Est. sales ($ mil.)	—	—	—	—	—	1,071.6
Employees	—	—	—	—	—	1,512

INTEGRA BANK CORPORATION

NASDAQ (GM): IBNK

21 SE 3rd St.
Evansville, IN 47705
Phone: 812-464-9677
Fax: 812-464-9825
Web: www.integrabank.com

CEO: Michael J. Alley
CFO: Michael B. (Mike) Carroll
HR: Cheryl Steinbacher
FYE: December 31
Type: Public

Community banking is integral to Integra Bank Corporation. Its flagship subsidiary, Integra Bank, operates more than 50 branches and loan production offices serving communities in southern Indiana and Illinois, Kentucky, and southwestern Ohio. The bank offers a variety of traditional deposit products for personal and business customers, including savings and money market accounts, CDs, and IRAs. Its lending activities mainly consist of commercial, industrial, and agricultural loans, construction and development loans, residential mortgages, home equity lines of credit, and consumer loans. In addition, Integra Bank offers annuities, insurance, credit and debit cards, and trust services.

	Annual Growth	12/05	12/06	12/07	12/08	12/09
Assets ($ mil.)	1.9%	2,708.1	2,684.5	3,350.1	3,357.1	2,921.9
Net income ($ mil.)	—	27.3	19.5	30.7	(110.9)	(191.2)
Market value ($ mil.)	(56.8%)	446.0	575.1	294.9	28.6	15.5
Employees	(3.3%)	843	802	848	870	736

INTEGRA LIFESCIENCES

NASDAQ (GS): IART

311 Enterprise Dr.
Plainsboro, NJ 08536
Phone: 609-275-0500
Fax: 609-275-5363
Web: www.integra-ls.com

CEO: Stuart M. Essig
CFO: John B. (Jack) Henneman III
HR: Richard D. Gorelick
FYE: December 31
Type: Public

Integra LifeSciences Holdings Corporation wants its products to be integral to the healing process. In fact, using its proprietary collagen matrix technology, the company makes biological implants for brain, spinal, and orthopedic surgeries that become part of a patient's body, helping it to generate new bone and tissue in place of what was damaged. In addition to its regenerative implants, grafts, and wound dressings, Integra LifeSciences makes surgical instruments, including ultrasonic surgical ablation systems and joint fixation devices, used primarily in neurosurgery and joint reconstruction. Integra LifeSciences sells products worldwide through several specialty sales forces and through distributors.

	Annual Growth	12/05	12/06	12/07	12/08	12/09
Sales ($ mil.)	25.2%	277.9	419.3	550.5	654.6	682.5
Net income ($ mil.)	8.2%	37.2	29.4	33.5	34.9	51.0
Market value ($ mil.)	1.0%	1,028.4	1,235.2	1,216.1	1,031.6	1,069.3
Employees	26.3%	1,180	2,150	2,500	2,800	3,000

An in-depth profile of this company is available to Hoover's Online members at hoovers.com. ⊞

INTEGRA TELECOM, INC.

1201 NE Lloyd Blvd., Ste. 500
Portland, OR 97232
Phone: 503-453-8000
Fax: 503-453-8221
Web: www.integratelecom.com

CEO: Dudley R. Slater
CFO: Matt Fahey
HR: Lisa Hillyer
FYE: December 31
Type: Private

Integra Telecom wants to be a key component of the US communications network. The company is a telecommunications carrier focused on small to mid-sized business customers in 11 mostly western states. The facilities-based carrier offers local access, domestic and international long-distance, and broadband Internet. Integra's other data services include Web hosting, server collocation, and virtual private networks (VPN). The company also resells and services telecom equipment from such vendors as NEC and Mitel. It serves the energy, food, broadcasting, and real estate industries, among others. Clients have included SolarWorld and the Red Cross.

	Annual Growth	12/04	12/05	12/06	12/07	12/08
Est. sales ($ mil.)	—	—	—	—	—	179.3
Employees	—	—	—	—	—	1,400

INTEGRAL SYSTEMS, INC.

NASDAQ (GS): ISYS

6721 Columbia Gateway Dr.
Columbia, MD 21046
Phone: 443-539-5008
Fax: 410-312-2705
Web: www.integ.com

CEO: Paul G. Casner Jr.
CFO: William M. Bambarger Jr.
HR: —
FYE: September 30
Type: Public

Integral Systems provides some high-flying customers with a sense of control. The company designs satellite command and control, data processing, flight simulation, integration and test, and signals analysis systems. Military agencies, commercial communication service providers, and scientific researchers use the company's EPOCH Integrated Product Suite (IPS) to monitor and control their ground systems and satellites, and to analyze the data that they gather. Integral Systems counts the US Air Force, the US Navy, the US National Oceanic and Atmospheric Administration, and China's National Space Program Office among its customers. Integral Systems gets most of its sales in the US.

	Annual Growth	9/05	9/06	9/07	9/08	9/09
Sales ($ mil.)	13.1%	97.7	116.5	128.7	160.2	159.9
Net income ($ mil.)	(35.4%)	6.3	12.3	12.8	18.2	1.1
Market value ($ mil.)	(9.6%)	180.7	273.6	188.1	363.6	120.8
Employees	9.7%	400	420	455	523	580

INTEGRAL TECHNOLOGIES, INC.

OTC: ITKG

805 W. Orchard Dr., Ste. 7
Bellingham, WA 98225
Phone: 360-752-1982
Fax: 360-752-1983
Web: www.itkg.net

CEO: William S. Robinson
CFO: William A. Ince
HR: —
FYE: June 30
Type: Public

Integral Technologies hopes to discover that technology truly is integral to everyday life. The company has developed what it calls its "ElectriPlast" product, an electrically conductive resin-based polymer that can be molded into any shape. The company's "PlasTenna" technology uses ElectriPlast for antenna design and other manufacturing processes. It can become part of the cell phone casing itself. Integral Technologies outsources its manufacturing and is marketing its products to cell phone and other wireless device manufacturers. The development stage company has yet to recognize any appreciable revenues from its products.

	Annual Growth	6/05	6/06	6/07	6/08	6/09
Sales ($ mil.)	—	—	—	—	—	0.0
Net income ($ mil.)	—	—	—	—	—	(1.6)
Market value ($ mil.)	—	—	—	—	—	15.8
Employees	—	—	—	—	—	4

INTEGRAL VISION, INC.

OTC: INVI

49113 Wixom Tech Dr.
Wixom, MI 48393
Phone: 248-668-9230
Fax: 248-668-9384
Web: www.iv-usa.com

CEO: Charles J. Drake
CFO: Mark R. Doede
HR: —
FYE: December 31
Type: Public

Integral Vision wants manufacturers to take a closer look. The company makes machine vision systems that monitor and control manufacturing processes in the small flat-panel display industry. Its systems inspect for both cosmetic and functional defects in display components used in camcorders, cell phones, digital still cameras, computer monitors, and handheld video games. Integral Vision also offers software for developing machine vision inspection applications. Customers have included Liquavista, QUALCOMM, Samsung Electronics, and Texas Instruments.

	Annual Growth	12/05	12/06	12/07	12/08	12/09
Sales ($ mil.)	26.6%	0.7	0.8	1.2	1.0	1.8
Net income ($ mil.)	—	(2.7)	(3.0)	(3.0)	(10.7)	(2.8)
Market value ($ mil.)	(58.4%)	71.4	23.2	2.5	5.7	2.1
Employees	(16.9%)	21	18	14	14	10

INTEGRAMED AMERICA, INC.

NASDAQ (GM): INMD

2 Manhattanville Rd.
Purchase, NY 10577
Phone: 914-253-8000
Fax: 914-253-8008
Web: www.integramed.com

CEO: Jay Higham
CFO: John W. Hlywak Jr.
HR: Angela Gizinski
FYE: December 31
Type: Public

IntegraMed America's specialty is identifying and entering niche medical markets throughout the US. The company operates through two segments: Fertility Services and Vein Clinics. As one might imagine, the company's fertility services include in vitro fertilization (IVF), artificial insemination, and other reproductive assistance through about 100 clinics in metropolitan markets. IntegraMed also supplies administrative and management support to its clinics through the Fertility Services division, which also helps guide potential parents through the IVF process. The second division, Vein Clinics, operates about 35 vein treatment centers throughout the US.

	Annual Growth	12/05	12/06	12/07	12/08	12/09
Sales ($ mil.)	13.9%	128.9	126.4	152.0	197.4	216.8
Net income ($ mil.)	27.6%	1.7	3.2	3.3	3.5	4.5
Market value ($ mil.)	(1.7%)	99.4	141.3	134.9	79.2	92.8
Employees	10.7%	881	949	1,182	1,202	1,322

INTEGRATED BIOPHARMA, INC.

Pink Sheets: INBP

225 Long Ave.
Hillside, NJ 07205
Phone: 973-926-0816
Fax: 973-926-1735
Web: www.healthproductscorp.us

CEO: E. Gerald Kay
CFO: Frederick Larcombe
HR: —
FYE: June 30
Type: Public

Integrated BioPharma has made nutraceuticals its business. Literally. Its only business. The company that formerly made and developed plant-derived pharmaceuticals has simplified its operations to the manufacture and distribution of organic drinks, vitamins, supplements, and the natural chemicals used to make them. Integrated BioPharma markets its products through its Manhattan Drug subsidiary. It also peddles its wares under the Vitamin Factory brand direct to consumers by mail and on the Internet and provides raw material sourcing through its IHT Health Products subsidiary. Its AgroLabs subsidiary produces health beverages extracted from pomegranates, aloe vera, and other fruits.

An in-depth profile of this company is available to Hoover's Online members at hoovers.com.

825

⊞ INTEGRATED DEVICE TECHNOLOGY, INC.

NASDAQ (GS): IDTI

6024 Silver Creek Valley Rd.
San Jose, CA 95138
Phone: 408-284-8200
Fax: 408-284-2775
Web: www.idt.com

CEO: Theodore L. (Ted) Tewksbury III
CFO: Richard D. (Rick) Crowley Jr.
HR: Roger Ervin
FYE: March 31
Type: Public

Integrated Device Technology (IDT) knows about integrating devices. The company offers hundreds of high-performance semiconductors and modules, available in thousands of configurations, primarily for computers, computer peripherals, and consumer electronics, but also for the networking and communications markets. Much of IDT's sales come from its communications and high-performance logic products, which include processors, specialized memories, logic and clock management products, and chipsets and controllers for networking gear. The company gets about three-quarters of its sales from the Asia/Pacific region.

	Annual Growth	3/05	3/06	3/07	3/08	3/09
Sales ($ mil.)	14.2%	390.6	527.8	803.6	781.5	663.2
Net income ($ mil.)	—	13.3	(81.7)	(7.6)	34.2	(1,045.2)
Market value ($ mil.)	(21.6%)	1,994.0	2,463.0	2,555.9	1,480.1	754.2
Employees	(8.1%)	2,955	2,700	2,400	2,353	2,112

INTEGRATED ELECTRICAL SERVICES, INC.

NASDAQ (GM): IESC

1800 West Loop South, Ste. 500
Houston, TX 77027
Phone: 713-860-1500
Fax: 713-860-1599
Web: www.ies-co.com

CEO: Michael J. (Mike) Caliel
CFO: Terry L. Freeman
HR: Robert B. (Bob) Callahan
FYE: September 30
Type: Public

Lights! Camera! Action! Integrated Electrical Services (IES) has a hand in all three. The company is a national provider of electrical, security, and communications systems installation to the commercial, industrial, and residential markets. In addition to installation, services for commercial buildings and homes include custom design, testing, and maintenance on low-voltage systems such as lighting, fire alarm, audio/video, and Internet cabling. On the industrial side, IES performs high- and medium-voltage systems installation and construction on power stations, oil and gas pipelines, and processing plants. The company has a network of some 90 locations serving the continental US.

	Annual Growth	9/05	9/06	9/07	9/08	9/09
Sales ($ mil.)	(11.8%)	1,102.8	419.9	892.8	818.3	666.0
Net income ($ mil.)	—	(127.8)	(8.2)	(4.4)	0.7	(11.8)
Market value ($ mil.)	(20.1%)	—	230.4	373.3	256.0	117.3
Employees	(20.8%)	8,900	7,183	5,746	4,938	3,504

INTEGRATED SECURITY SYSTEMS, INC.

OTC: IZZI

2009 Chenault Dr., Ste. 114
Carrollton, TX 75006
Phone: 972-444-8280
Fax: 972-869-3843
Web: www.integratedsecurity.com

CEO: Brooks Sherman
CFO: Sharon Doherty
HR: —
FYE: June 30
Type: Public

Integrated Security Systems might not be able to stop a train, but the company will tell you when one is coming. Subsidiary B&B ARMR builds railroad crossing safety barriers and warning gates, along with traffic control products such as crash barriers and perimeter security gates used by businesses and government agencies. B&B Roadway, a joint venture with Causey Lyon Enterprises, makes traffic control products used on roads and bridges. Integrated Security Systems' Intelli-Site unit integrates security devices from different manufacturers onto a single PC-controlled platform.

	Annual Growth	6/05	6/06	6/07	6/08	6/09
Sales ($ mil.)	(10.7%)	13.5	12.3	10.7	10.6	8.6
Net income ($ mil.)	—	(4.9)	(4.2)	(4.8)	(2.6)	5.5
Market value ($ mil.)	(43.0%)	106.5	112.2	42.1	22.4	11.2
Employees	(24.2%)	82	38	43	35	27

⊞ INTEGRATED SILICON SOLUTION, INC.

NASDAQ (GM): ISSI

1940 Zanker Rd.
San Jose, CA 95112
Phone: 408-969-6600
Fax: 408-969-7800
Web: www.issi.com

CEO: Scott D. Howarth
CFO: John M. Cobb
HR: —
FYE: September 30
Type: Public

Memories light more than the corners of ISSI's mind. Integrated Silicon Solution, Inc. (ISSI) makes static random-access memory chips (SRAMs), DRAMs, specialized read-only memories, and other devices, including voice recording chips. SRAMs, which unlike DRAMs don't need periodic refreshing from the CPU to protect data from loss, are used in cars, computers, instrumentation, and telecommunications devices. ISSI's DRAMs are used in equipment such as set-top boxes, networking equipment, and disk drives. The company's customers — either directly or through distributors and contract manufacturers — include Cisco, Garmin, Nokia, Sony, and TRW Automotive. Asian customers account for two-thirds of sales.

	Annual Growth	9/05	9/06	9/07	9/08	9/09
Sales ($ mil.)	(4.0%)	181.4	217.5	245.4	235.2	154.3
Net income ($ mil.)	—	(37.9)	(14.2)	15.4	(17.8)	(5.1)
Market value ($ mil.)	(18.2%)	217.6	144.3	163.2	59.8	97.4
Employees	3.6%	386	421	417	449	445

INTEGRATED SURGICAL SYSTEMS, INC.

Pink Sheets: ISSM

1433 N. Market Blvd., Ste. 1
Sacramento, CA 95834
Phone: 916-285-9943
Fax: 916-285-9104
Web: www.robodoc.com

CEO: Christopher A. Marlett
CFO: Gary Schuman
HR: —
FYE: December 31
Type: Public

Integrated Surgical Systems (ISS) wanted to be the hippest company around with its ROBODOC Surgical Assistant System, a computer-controlled robot used in hip and knee replacements. However, ISS ceased operations in mid-2005 because of lawsuits and lack of funding, and it sold its ROBODOC assets to Novatrix Biomedical in 2007. Using those assets, Novatrix has set up a new company called Curexo Medical to continue development of ROBODOC, which is sold in Europe, Asia, and other regions and received FDA approval in 2008. Meanwhile, ISS used the money from the asset sale to pay its debtors and is looking for acquisition opportunities.

	Annual Growth	12/05	12/06	12/07	12/08	12/09
Sales ($ mil.)	—	3.4	2.6	0.0	0.0	0.0
Net income ($ mil.)	—	2.0	1.6	5.0	(0.2)	(0.3)
Market value ($ mil.)	99.2%	0.2	2.3	2.3	2.2	2.4
Employees	—	—	10	—	—	—

INTEGRYS ENERGY GROUP, INC.

NYSE: TEG

130 E. Randolph Dr.
Chicago, IL 60601
Phone: 312-228-5400
Fax: —
Web: www.integrysgroup.com

CEO: Charles A. (Charlie) Schrock
CFO: Joseph P. (Joe) O'Leary
HR: William Laakso
FYE: December 31
Type: Public

Integrys Energy (formerly WPS Resources) provides power for the Windy City and Lake Wobegon. The energy holding company owns six regulated utilities: Michigan Gas Utilities Corporation (165,000 gas customers), Minnesota Energy Resources Corporation (211,000 gas customers), North Shore Gas Company (158,000 customers in the northern suburbs of Chicago), Peoples Gas Light and Coke Company (817,000 natural gas customers in Chicago), Wisconsin Public Service (437,000 electric customers and 317,000 natural gas customers in Wisconsin and Michigan), and Upper Peninsula Power (52,000 electricity customers). The company's nonregulated subsidiary, Integrys Energy Services, provides retail energy supply and services.

	Annual Growth	12/05	12/06	12/07	12/08	12/09
Sales ($ mil.)	1.9%	6,962.7	6,890.7	10,292.4	14,047.8	7,499.8
Net income ($ mil.)	—	162.1	158.9	254.4	129.5	(68.8)
Market value ($ mil.)	(6.7%)	4,259.8	4,161.2	3,981.0	3,310.2	3,234.0
Employees	14.3%	2,945	3,326	5,231	5,191	5,025

INTEL CORPORATION

NASDAQ (GS): INTC

2200 Mission College Blvd.
Santa Clara, CA 95054
Phone: 408-765-8080
Fax: 408-765-3804
Web: www.intel.com

CEO: Paul S. Otellini
CFO: Stacy J. Smith
HR: Patricia Murray
FYE: December 31
Type: Public

The intelligence inside your computer could very well be Intel. The company — which holds about 80% of the market share for microprocessors that go into desktop and notebook computers, and also into computer servers — is still #1 in semiconductors. Archrival AMD ate into Intel's market share for a time, but the big guy fought back with faster processors and advanced manufacturing technology. Intel also makes embedded semiconductors for the industrial, medical, and in-vehicle infotainment markets. While most computer makers use Intel processors, PC giants Dell and Hewlett-Packard are the company's largest customers. The Asia/Pacific region generates about two-thirds of Intel's revenues.

	Annual Growth	12/05	12/06	12/07	12/08	12/09
Sales ($ mil.)	(2.5%)	38,826.0	35,382.0	38,334.0	37,586.0	35,127.0
Net income ($ mil.)	(15.7%)	8,664.0	5,044.0	6,976.0	5,292.0	4,369.0
Market value ($ mil.)	(4.9%)	138,877.4	112,671.0	148,336.2	81,568.2	113,505.6
Employees	(5.5%)	99,900	94,100	86,300	83,900	79,800

INTELLICHECK MOBILISA, INC.

NYSE Amex: IDN

191 Otto St.
Port Townsend, WA 98368
Phone: 360-344-3233
Fax: 360-344-3323
Web: www.icmobil.com

CEO: Nelson Ludlow
CFO: Peter J. Mundy
HR: —
FYE: December 31
Type: Public

IntelliCheck Mobilisa will need to see some ID. The company provides handheld electronic card readers and related software for the commercial, government, and military markets. Used to secure military and federal government locations, its Defense ID System can read barcodes, magnetic stripes, optical character recognition (OCR), and radio frequency identification (RFID) codes. Its ID-Check systems are designed to verify the age and identity of customers who swipe a driver's license, military ID, or other magnetically encoded ID card. The company has installed systems in airports, bars, casinos, convenience stores, hotels, and stadiums.

	Annual Growth	12/05	12/06	12/07	12/08	12/09
Sales ($ mil.)	50.8%	2.4	3.2	3.5	10.0	12.4
Net income ($ mil.)	—	(3.2)	(2.9)	(2.7)	(33.1)	(0.5)
Market value ($ mil.)	(0.9%)	102.7	177.7	84.0	43.6	99.0
Employees	26.1%	19	21	48	48	48

INTELLIGENT SYSTEMS CORPORATION

NYSE Amex: INS

4355 Shackleford Rd.
Norcross, GA 30093
Phone: 770-381-2900
Fax: 770-381-2808
Web: www.intelsys.com

CEO: J. Leland Strange
CFO: Bonnie L. Herron
HR: —
FYE: December 31
Type: Public

Intelligent Systems Corporation doesn't want to be accused of making dumb choices. The company invests in information technology and industrial products firms, primarily in the southern US. Subsidiaries include ChemFree, which makes a non-solvent-based parts wash for automotive and industrial applications, and CoreCard, which develops software for banks and retailers to manage credit and debit card accounts. Other holdings include a stake in NKD Enterprises, dba CoreXpand, which provides software tools to manage e-commerce activities. The firm's Gwinnett Innovation Park is a small-business incubator providing office space and support systems to nascent businesses.

	Annual Growth	12/05	12/06	12/07	12/08	12/09
Sales ($ mil.)	(5.4%)	16.1	14.5	19.0	15.8	12.9
Net income ($ mil.)	—	(1.6)	4.5	(2.4)	(0.8)	(1.2)
Market value ($ mil.)	(18.6%)	19.2	28.7	30.0	9.3	8.4
Employees	(2.8%)	205	231	260	188	183

INTELLIGROUP, INC.

OTC: ITIG

499 Thornall St.
Edison, NJ 08837
Phone: 732-590-1600
Fax: 732-362-2100
Web: www.intelligroup.com

CEO: Vikram Gulati
CFO: Alok Bajpai
HR: Ramakrishna Karanam
FYE: December 31
Type: Public

Intelligroup believes that two heads are better than one. The IT consulting company provides outsourced application management and hosting services, consulting, and offshore software development to large enterprises. Intelligroup also installs complex human resources, administration, database management, and other business process software applications from software makers such as SAP and Oracle. The company's proprietary software products Pharma Express and Contractor Express — industry-specific, SAP-based systems — are also available. US-based customers account for three-quarters of sales. In 2010 NTT DATA agreed to acquire Intelligroup for about $199 million in cash.

	Annual Growth	12/05	12/06	12/07	12/08	12/09
Sales ($ mil.)	0.2%	125.3	125.3	145.1	157.1	126.5
Net income ($ mil.)	—	(6.6)	(3.7)	3.0	6.7	10.8
Market value ($ mil.)	21.2%	66.8	52.4	99.0	66.0	144.4
Employees	2.0%	1,938	2,137	2,293	2,296	2,101

INTEPLAST GROUP, LTD.

9 Peach Tree Hill Rd.
Livingston, NJ 07039
Phone: 973-994-8000
Fax: 973-994-8005
Web: www.inteplast.com

CEO: John D. Young
CFO: Benjamin Tsao
HR: Brenda Wilson
FYE: December 31
Type: Private

The Inteplast Group hopes to turn plastic into gold. Composed of three divisions, Inteplast Group makes a wide range of plastic products. Its AmTopp division makes biaxially oriented polypropylene (BOPP) film, stretch wrap, and plastic concentrates and compounds; its World-Pak unit makes fluted boards, PVC sheets and foam, and cross-laminated film; and its Integrated Bagging Systems unit makes trash can liners, produce bags, and plastic packaging. Inteplast products are used in applications including medical settings and food packaging, lamination, and shipping. Founded in 1991, Inteplast operates several plants at its 700-acre site in Texas, as well as in Massachusetts, and British Columbia.

INTER PARFUMS, INC.

NASDAQ (GS): IPAR

551 5th Ave., Ste. 1500
New York, NY 10176
Phone: 212-983-2640
Fax: 212-983-4197
Web: www.interparfumsinc.com

CEO: Jean Madar
CFO: Russell Greenberg
HR: Michelle Habert
FYE: December 31
Type: Public

Would a perfumer by any other name smell as sweet? Inter Parfums certainly hopes not. Most of the fragrance developer and manufacturer's revenue is generated by sales of prestige fragrances, including Burberry, Christian Lacroix, Lanvin, Nickel, Paul Smith, Quicksilver/Roxy, S.T. Dupont, and Van Cleef & Arpels. It also sells moderately priced perfumes, low-priced imitations of high-end perfumes, personal care products, and cosmetics, including Aziza eye makeup. The firm owns Lanvin Perfumes and the upscale men's skin care firm Nickel. Customers include department stores, mass merchandisers (Wal-Mart Stores), and drugstore chains. The company's scents are sold in more than 120 countries.

	Annual Growth	12/05	12/06	12/07	12/08	12/09
Sales ($ mil.)	10.6%	273.5	321.1	389.6	446.1	409.5
Net income ($ mil.)	10.0%	15.3	17.7	23.8	23.8	22.4
Market value ($ mil.)	0.4%	362.7	387.5	362.9	232.6	368.7
Employees	6.2%	201	235	248	245	256

INTERACTIVE BROKERS GROUP, INC.

NASDAQ (GS): IBKR

1 Pickwick Plaza
Greenwich, CT 06830
Phone: 203-618-5800
Fax: 203-618-5770
Web: www.interactivebrokers.com

CEO: Thomas Peterffy
CFO: Paul J. Brody
HR: Tammy Silby
FYE: December 31
Type: Public

Interactive Brokers Group serves investors who interact with world markets, focusing on the use of technology in securities trading. It does business through electronic market-maker Timber Hill, as well as its Interactive Brokers brokerage subsidiaries; it executes some 1 million trades daily in stocks, options, futures, foreign exchange, and corporate bonds. Customers may trade on about 80 exchanges and market centers worldwide. The company caters to experienced individual and institutional investors. Large banks and brokerages can also provide the company's interface to their customers through a white-label arrangement. Founder and chairman Thomas Peterffy controls Interactive Brokers Group.

	Annual Growth	12/05	12/06	12/07	12/08	12/09
Sales ($ mil.)	1.6%	1,099.2	1,736.8	2,023.4	2,182.1	1,169.8
Net income ($ mil.)	(49.0%)	535.5	734.2	300.5	93.0	36.2
Market value ($ mil.)	(26.0%)	—	—	1,332.1	737.4	730.4
Employees	14.6%	—	532	675	750	801

🔲 INTERACTIVE DATA CORPORATION

NYSE: IDC

32 Crosby Dr.
Bedford, MA 01730
Phone: 781-687-8500
Fax: 781-687-8005
Web: www.interactivedata.com

CEO: Raymond L. D'Arcy
CFO: Christine Sampson
HR: Lori B. Hannay
FYE: December 31
Type: Public

Interactive Data Corporation has something vital to the information superhighway — the information. The company's subscription services provide financial market data, analytics, and related services to financial institutions, active traders, and individual investors. Interactive Data Corporation conducts business through two segments: Institutional Services and Active Trader Services. Products include Interactive Data Fixed Income Analytics (fixed-income portfolio analytics for institutions), Interactive Data Pricing and Reference Data (securities information for institutions), and eSignal (real-time market data for individuals). Pearson owns about 60% of the company, and is planning to sell its stake.

	Annual Growth	12/05	12/06	12/07	12/08	12/09
Sales ($ mil.)	8.7%	542.9	612.4	689.6	750.5	757.2
Net income ($ mil.)	10.7%	93.9	93.4	126.0	142.6	141.2
Market value ($ mil.)	2.7%	2,160.4	2,286.9	3,140.2	2,345.9	2,406.7
Employees	4.5%	2,100	2,200	2,304	2,400	2,500

INTERACTIVE INTELLIGENCE, INC.

NASDAQ (GM): ININ

7601 Interactive Way
Indianapolis, IN 46278
Phone: 317-872-3000
Fax: —
Web: www.inin.com

CEO: Donald E. Brown
CFO: Stephen R. (Steve) Head
HR: —
FYE: December 31
Type: Public

Interactive Intelligence knows that managing your communications is smart business. The company's software (which is available as a hosted application that customers subscribe to on a monthly basis) helps integrate a wide array of communication systems via VoIP technology, from phone calls, voice mail, and e-mail to faxes and Web-based communications. Its applications integrate with enterprise messaging platforms such as Microsoft's Exchange and Lotus Notes and provide tools for connecting mobile workers to enterprise information systems. Interactive Intelligence also makes systems for call center operations.

	Annual Growth	12/05	12/06	12/07	12/08	12/09
Sales ($ mil.)	20.2%	62.9	83.2	109.9	121.4	131.4
Net income ($ mil.)	42.3%	2.1	10.2	17.5	4.3	8.6
Market value ($ mil.)	37.9%	89.0	391.7	459.7	111.8	321.9
Employees	13.8%	390	515	595	594	654

INTERBAKE FOODS LLC

2821 Emerywood Pkwy., Ste. 210
Richmond, VA 23294
Phone: 804-755-7107
Fax: 804-755-5901
Web: www.interbake.com

CEO: Selena Sanderson
CFO: —
HR: JoAnne Snyder
FYE: December 31
Type: Subsidiary

This is a company that a monster could love — a Cookie Monster, that is. Interbake Foods is one of the US's largest manufacturers of store-brand cookies and crackers, as well as ice cream sandwiches, cones, and other novelty ice-cream products. Dating back to 1899, the company, through its ABC Cookie Bakers division, has been a Girl Scout cookie supplier since 1939. Interbake's Norse Dairy Systems makes Interbake's novelty ice cream products. A subsidiary of Canadian food giant George Weston since 1946, Interbake has operations in the US, Canada, Mexico, and Costa Rica.

INTERBOND CORPORATION OF AMERICA

3200 SW 42nd St.
Hollywood, FL 33312
Phone: 954-797-4000
Fax: 954-797-4061
Web: www.brandsmartusa.com

CEO: Michael Perlman
CFO: Eric Beazley
HR: Janet Witczak
FYE: August 31
Type: Private

The only thing that isn't big about Interbond Corporation of America (dba BrandsMart USA) is its geographic scope. The company runs 10 BrandsMart USA stores in the South Florida and Atlanta metropolitan areas that each stock more than $8 million in merchandise. BrandsMart USA discount stores sell a wide selection of brand-name consumer electronics, including appliances, computers, TVs and home theater equipment, car stereos, mobile phones, and personal care gadgets. It also offers an array of movies, music, and games. Chairman Robert Perlman founded the company in 1977.

INTERCALL, INC.

8420 W. Bryn Mawr Ave., Ste. 400
Chicago, IL 60631
Phone: 773-399-1600
Fax: 773-399-1588
Web: www.intercall.com

CEO: J. Scott Etzler
CFO: Philip A. (Phil) Grybas
HR: Dan Veytsman
FYE: December 31
Type: Subsidiary

It's a small world after InterCall. A leading provider of conferencing services, the company provides audio, video, and Web conferencing using proprietary technology and offerings from Microsoft and WebEx Communications. It also helps customers procure conferencing equipment from manufacturers such as Polycom and TANDBERG. The company's event services consultants help customers with such tasks as investor relations conference calls, interactive training sessions, and product launches. InterCall is a subsidiary of outsourced communication services provider West Corporation.

INTERCELL USA, INC.

20 Firstfield Rd., Ste. 250	CEO: Thomas Lingelbach
Gaithersburg, MD 20878	CFO: Jeffrey R. Daniel
Phone: 301-556-4500	HR: Jin-Sook Chung
Fax: 301-556-4501	FYE: December 31
Web: www.iomai.com	Type: Subsidiary

What to do when you don't want the flu but also don't want the flu shot. Intercell USA (formerly Iomai) is developing needle-free alternatives to boost your immune system using a transcutaneous method, which delivers vaccines to cells found on the outer layers of the skin. It has a handful of product candidates in development, all in patch form, aimed at preventing seasonal flu and travelers' diarrhea (caused by E. coli, for instance). One of its patches is being funded under a contract from the US Department of Health and Human Services to aid in the treatment of pandemic flu. In 2008 the company was acquired by Austria-based vaccine maker Intercell AG.

INTERCERAMIC, INC.

2333 S. Jupiter Rd.	CEO: Víctor D. Almeida García
Garland, TX 75041	CFO: Jesús Olivas Corral
Phone: 214-503-5500	HR: —
Fax: 214-503-5555	FYE: December 31
Web: www.interceramicusa.com	Type: Subsidiary

Floors, countertops, and walls can now live in Interceramic harmony. Interceramic manufactures and distributes ceramic and natural stone floor and wall tile throughout North America. It sells its products to independent distributors as well as through the company's own wholesale branches found in the South and Southwest. Besides its own products, Interceramic Tile & Stone Gallery sells imported ceramic tile, glass, and porcelain and provides installation supplies. A subsidiary of Internacional de Cerámica, S.A.B. de C.V., Interceramic was established in Mexico in 1979 and expanded into Dallas and other Texas cities in 1988. It has eight manufacturing plants in the US and Mexico.

	Annual Growth	12/04	12/05	12/06	12/07	12/08
Est. sales ($ mil.)	—	—	—	—	—	194.6
Employees	—	—	—	—	—	650

INTER-CON SECURITY SYSTEMS, INC.

210 S. De Lacey Ave.	CEO: Enrique (Rick) Hernandez Jr.
Pasadena, CA 91105	CFO: Robins Simpson
Phone: 626-535-2200	HR: —
Fax: 626-685-9111	FYE: December 31
Web: www.icsecurity.com	Type: Private

There is no conning Inter-Con Security Systems. The company, one of the largest private security consulting firms in the US, provides custom-designed security programs for commercial, governmental, and industrial clients in North and South America, Europe, and Africa. Inter-Con's services include security consulting, investigations, and training. The company also provides security guard and fire protection services, as well as risk assessment and classified information safeguarding. The company employs more than 25,000 security personnel in some 25 countries. Inter-Con's clients have included General Motors, Kaiser Permanente, NASA, and the US Department of State. The company was founded in 1973.

INTERCONNECT DEVICES, INC.

5101 Richland Ave.	CEO: Mike Kirkman
Kansas City, KS 66106	CFO: Mark Deuel
Phone: 913-342-5544	HR: Marianne Russell
Fax: 913-342-7043	FYE: December 31
Web: www.idinet.com	Type: Subsidiary

Interconnect Devices, Inc. (IDI) makes spring-loaded contact probes used in automated test equipment (ATE), as well as semiconductor test probes and sockets. A sister company, Synergetix, makes connectors, sockets, and interfaces used by manufacturers in aerospace, ATE, automobiles, medical equipment, telecommunications, and portable electronics. Synergetix was established in 1994 and constitutes the company's brand name for IDI's test and measurement equipment. IDI was founded in 1979 and was owned by Milestone Partners, a private equity firm. In 2010 Smiths Group acquired IDI for $185 million in cash.

	Annual Growth	12/04	12/05	12/06	12/07	12/08
Est. sales ($ mil.)	—	—	—	—	—	22.4
Employees	—	—	—	—	—	230

INTERCONTINENTALEXCHANGE, INC.

NYSE: ICE

2100 RiverEdge Pkwy., Ste. 500	CEO: Jeffrey C. Sprecher
Atlanta, GA 30328	CFO: Scott A. Hill
Phone: 770-857-4700	HR: Scott A. Hill
Fax: 770-857-4755	FYE: December 31
Web: www.theice.com	Type: Public

If there were money to be made in ice futures, IntercontinentalExchange (ICE) would probably trade that as well. The company provides an online marketplace for global commodity trading, primarily of electricity, natural gas, crude oil, refined petroleum products, precious metals, and weather and emission credits. It manages two global OTC markets and three regulated futures exchanges. The company owns the ICE Futures Europe, a leading European energy futures and options platform. ICE Data provides real-time, daily, and historical market data reports. ICE is based in Atlanta and has regional offices in Calgary, Chicago, Houston, London, New York, Singapore, and Winnipeg.

	Annual Growth	12/05	12/06	12/07	12/08	12/09
Sales ($ mil.)	58.9%	155.9	313.8	574.3	813.1	994.8
Net income ($ mil.)	67.2%	40.4	143.3	240.6	301.0	316.0
Market value ($ mil.)	32.6%	2,687.9	7,978.6	14,234.3	6,096.0	8,304.0
Employees	42.0%	203	226	506	795	826

INTERCULTURAL PRESS, INC.

20 Park Plaza, Ste. 1115A	CEO: Charles (Chuck) Dresner
Boston, MA 02116	CFO: —
Phone: 617-523-3801	HR: —
Fax: 617-523-3708	FYE: December 31
Web: www.interculturalpress.com	Type: Subsidiary

If the world is your oyster, Intercultural Press has a world of information for you. The company, a unit of the UK's Nicholas Brealey Publishing, specializes in books geared toward travel, and working and studying abroad. Its more than 150 titles range from cross-cultural fiction and travel memoirs to books on intercultural issues and doing business in foreign countries. It also publishes a number of books on student exchange programs and handbooks for host families and schools. Intercultural Press welcomes authors to submit their own manuscripts for consideration.

	Annual Growth	12/04	12/05	12/06	12/07	12/08
Est. sales ($ mil.)	—	—	—	—	—	1.2
Employees	—	—	—	—	—	5

INTERDIGITAL, INC.

NASDAQ (GS): IDCC

781 3rd Ave.
King of Prussia, PA 19406
Phone: 610-878-7800
Fax: 610-992-7842
Web: www.interdigital.com

CEO: William J. Merritt
CFO: Scott A. McQuilkin
HR: Gary D. Isaacs
FYE: December 31
Type: Public

InterDigital is more than just interested in digital telecommunications. The company develops and licenses circuitry designs, software, and other technology using CDMA (code-division multiple access) and other wireless communications standards. InterDigital is also developing semiconductors and software to enable voice and data transmissions in mobile phones and portable computing devices. The company's top customers are LG Electronics (one-quarter of sales), NEC (12%), and Sharp (16%). InterDigital also licenses to Siemens and Sony Ericsson, and to many other makers of chips, software, and telecom equipment. The company gets about 80% of revenues from Asian customers.

	Annual Growth	12/05	12/06	12/07	12/08	12/09
Sales ($ mil.)	16.2%	163.1	480.5	234.2	228.5	297.4
Net income ($ mil.)	12.4%	54.7	225.2	20.0	26.2	87.3
Market value ($ mil.)	9.7%	805.5	1,475.2	1,025.8	1,209.2	1,167.8
Employees	(1.3%)	315	343	380	379	299

INTERFACE, INC.

NASDAQ (GM): IFSIA

2859 Paces Ferry Rd., Ste. 2000
Atlanta, GA 30339
Phone: 770-437-6800
Fax: 706-882-0500
Web: www.interfaceinc.com

CEO: Daniel T. Hendrix
CFO: Patrick C. Lynch
HR: —
FYE: December 31
Type: Public

Interface provides a soft place to land with its carpet lineup. The company, which puts an emphasis on environmentally friendly production, is the world's #1 producer of modular carpet used in offices and other commercial facilities. The company also offers residential carpeting and complementary floor coverings. Interface markets its modular (tiles and rolls) and broadloom carpets under such brands as Interface, Bentley Prince Street, and FLOR. It touts an antimicrobial chemical, Intersept, which it blends in its modular carpet products, as well as licenses for use in air filters. Interface manufactures carpet in North America, Europe, Asia, and Australia; it sells products in more than 110 countries.

	Annual Growth	12/05	12/06	12/07	12/08	12/09
Sales ($ mil.)	(3.4%)	985.8	1,075.8	1,081.3	1,082.3	859.9
Net income ($ mil.)	38.6%	3.2	10.0	(10.8)	(40.9)	11.8
Market value ($ mil.)	0.3%	520.5	900.4	1,033.3	293.8	526.2
Employees	(11.3%)	4,998	5,039	3,838	3,673	3,099

INTERGEN

15 Wayside Rd.
Burlington, MA 01803
Phone: 781-993-3000
Fax: 781-993-3005
Web: www.intergen.com

CEO: Neil H. Smith
CFO: Martin Rees
HR: Peter A. Capodilupo
FYE: December 31
Type: Joint venture

Independent power company InterGen is really into the power generating business as an international producer of electricity with interests in 12 power plant projects with about 8,100 MW of installed generating capacity (more than 6,250 MW net equity) in Australia, Mexico, the Netherlands, the Philippines, and the UK. All told, the company has more than 20 power plants on five continents over eight years. InterGen provides fuel procurement and project management, financing, and negotiation services. Its power is sold to utilities, energy marketers, and end-use customers. InterGen is jointly owned by Ontario Teachers' Pension Plan and GMR Infrastructure.

INTERGRAPH CORPORATION

170 Graphics Dr.
Madison, AL 35758
Phone: 256-730-2000
Fax: 256-730-2048
Web: www.intergraph.com

CEO: R. Halsey Wise
CFO: Anthony Colaluca Jr.
HR: Ed Porter
FYE: December 31
Type: Private

They like wide open spaces at Intergraph — and city streets, too. The company provides spatial information management software, which enables mapping and design functions for local, state, and federal government agencies, and for businesses in the transportation, process plant design, power, marine, public safety, and utilities industries. Its systems (a combination of software, third-party hardware, and services) are used for a wide range of functions, including plant design, ship construction, public safety dispatch, aerial photography, and geospatial mapping and analysis. In 2006 the company was acquired by the private equity firms of Texas Pacific Group and Hellman & Friedman for about $1.3 billion.

THE INTERGROUP CORPORATION

NASDAQ (CM): INTG

820 Moraga Dr.
Los Angeles, CA 90049
Phone: 310-889-2500
Fax: 310-889-2525

CEO: John V. Winfield
CFO: David T. Nguyen
HR: —
FYE: June 30
Type: Public

InterGroup buys, develops, and manages affordable housing and other projects with an eye toward social responsibility. The company owns around 20 apartment complexes, two commercial real estate properties, two single-family residences, and, through subsidiary Santa Fe Financial, majority interest in a San Francisco hotel. Its holdings are primarily concentrated in California and Texas. InterGroup also invests in securities and in real estate portfolios held by other corporations. Chairman and CEO John Winfield owns about 60% of the company. Winfield is also CEO of Santa Fe Financial and its subsidiary, Portsmouth Square.

	Annual Growth	6/05	6/06	6/07	6/08	6/09
Sales ($ mil.)	36.9%	13.0	12.0	45.0	49.1	45.6
Net income ($ mil.)		(3.1)	(1.9)	(3.6)	(0.3)	0.4
Market value ($ mil.)	(9.7%)	43.2	37.9	43.8	37.9	28.8
Employees	(37.5%)	46	11	8	7	7

INTERLAKE MECALUX, INC.

1600 N. 25th Ave.
Melrose Park, IL 60160
Phone: 708-344-9999
Fax: —
Web: www.interlake.com

CEO: Dan Wilson
CFO: —
HR: Lorene Flewellen
FYE: December 31
Type: Subsidiary

Interlake Mecalux, Inc., formerly known as United Fixtures/Interlake (UFI/Interlake) and before that, Interlake Material Handling, is still handling storage issues by manufacturing industrial storage pallet racks for distribution centers, manufacturing facilities, warehouses, and retail outlets, among other industries. The company's products and services are delivered directly and through distributors to customers including Amazon.com, The Home Depot, Nestlé, UPS, and Wal-Mart. The company filed for Chapter 11 in early 2009, but was one of several material-handling companies purchased by Spanish shelving manufacturer Mecalux and incorporated into its US division under the Interlake Mecalux, Inc., name.

INTERLEUKIN GENETICS, INC.

NYSE Amex: ILI

135 Beaver St.
Waltham, MA 02452
Phone: 781-398-0700
Fax: 781-398-0720
Web: www.ilgenetics.com

CEO: Lewis H. Bender
CFO: Eliot M. Lurier
HR: —
FYE: December 31
Type: Public

Interleukin Genetics counts on the high failure rate of crystal balls. The company develops genetic tests to identify individuals' chances of developing certain diseases. Its first commercial product, the PST, is a test for gum disease and is available in the US and Europe. The company also offers predictive tests for heart disease and general nutrition under the Gensona brand through its partnership with Alticor. Interleukin Genetics has also teamed with Alticor to develop nutritional and skin care products. Alticor subsidiary Pyxis Innovations controls 58% of the company.

	Annual Growth	12/05	12/06	12/07	12/08	12/09
Sales ($ mil.)	—	0.0	4.7	9.7	10.0	1.1
Net income ($ mil.)	—	(6.6)	(6.9)	(6.2)	(6.7)	(10.6)
Market value ($ mil.)	(36.7%)	195.2	213.5	39.8	7.3	31.4
Employees	7.1%	22	27	27	27	—

INTERLINE BRANDS, INC.

NYSE: IBI

801 W. Bay St.
Jacksonville, FL 32204
Phone: 904-421-1400
Fax: 904-358-2486
Web: www.interlinebrands.com

CEO: Michael J. Grebe
CFO: John A. Ebner
HR: Annette A. Ricciuti
FYE: December 31
Type: Public

When something breaks, bursts, or drips, you can call Interline Brands, a national distributor and direct marketer of repair and maintenance products. The company sells more than 90,000 plumbing, hardware, electrical, janitorial, and related products under private labels (including AmSan, Hardware Express, Maintenance USA, Sexauer, U.S. Lock, and Wilmar). It operates 70 regional distribution centers and some 30 showrooms serving professional contractors throughout North America. Its Florida Lighting business (acquired in 2003) distributes specialty lighting and electrical products. Interline Brands was formed in 2000 when the Wilmar, Barnett, and Sexauer companies merged. The company went public in 2004.

	Annual Growth	12/05	12/06	12/07	12/08	12/09
Sales ($ mil.)	5.6%	851.9	1,067.6	1,239.0	1,195.7	1,059.3
Net income ($ mil.)	(2.4%)	28.8	31.2	51.0	40.8	26.1
Market value ($ mil.)	(6.7%)	750.3	741.1	722.6	350.6	569.6
Employees	4.7%	2,730	3,763	3,801	3,552	3,279

INTERLINK ELECTRONICS, INC.

Pink Sheets: LINK

546 Flynn Rd.
Camarillo, CA 93012
Phone: 805-484-8855
Fax: 805-484-8989
Web: www.interlinkelec.com

CEO: Kevin J. Wiley
CFO: —
HR: Patrice R. Poleto
FYE: December 31
Type: Public

Interlink Electronics designs electronic signature capture devices and specialty interface products. The company's signature capture products include its ePad line of hardware devices and IntegriSign software. Its sensor interface components enable menu navigation, cursor control, and character input in devices such as computer mice and mobile phones. Interlink's patented force-sensing technology enables smaller, more touch-sensitive input devices. The company also provides design and integration services. Special Situations Technology Fund owns about 40% of the company.

INTERLINK-US-NETWORK, LTD.

OTC: IUSN

10390 Wilshire Blvd., Penthouse 20
Los Angeles, CA 90024
Phone: 310-777-0012
Fax: 310-777-0015

CEO: A. Frederick Greenberg
CFO: —
HR: —
FYE: December 31
Type: Public

Interlink-US-Network (formerly NuTech Digital) has found new roots. The company has shifted its emphasis away from producing and distributing music concerts on DVD in order to focus on its Jump Communications subsidiary, which manufactures a set-top box (called FRED) that delivers entertainment content and communications services to consumers through videophones, television, and Internet channels (including video on demand and high definition resolutions), voice over Internet protocol (VoIP), and the Internet. The company changed its name from NuTech Digital in 2008.

	Annual Growth	12/05	12/06	12/07	12/08	12/09
Sales ($ mil.)	(90.0%)	—	—	—	1.0	0.1
Net income ($ mil.)	—	—	—	—	(0.6)	(2.1)
Market value ($ mil.)	—	—	—	—	—	0.3
Employees	—	—	—	—	—	—

INTERMAP TECHNOLOGIES CORPORATION

Toronto: IMP

8310 South Valley Highway, Ste. 400
Englewood, CO 80112
Phone: 303-708-0955
Fax: 303-708-0952
Web: www.intermap.com

CEO: Brian L. Bullock
CFO: Brian Musfeldt
HR: —
FYE: December 31
Type: Public

Intermap Technologies is trying to put digital surveying on the map. The company, founded in 1996, provides mapping and surveying services to governmental and corporate clients using its Interferometric Synthetic Aperture Radar (IFSAR) mapping technology. Intermap's NEXTMap program has maps of entire countries in its database. Its data can be used in driver assistance, flood modeling and insurance assessment, environmental and engineering planning, and other applications that require elevation data. Customers range from governments to outdoor enthusiasts. Although the company is headquartered in Calgary, Canada, executive offices are located in Englewood, Colorado. Intermap also has offices in Asia and Europe.

	Annual Growth	12/05	12/06	12/07	12/08	12/09
Sales ($ mil.)	19.2%	15.0	21.8	33.8	37.0	30.3
Net income ($ mil.)	—	(6.5)	(11.0)	(8.9)	(13.9)	(25.8)
Market value ($ mil.)	(22.3%)	262.2	314.6	550.5	100.1	95.4
Employees	52.7%	250	250	613	891	—

INTERMATIC INCORPORATED

7777 Winn Rd.
Spring Grove, IL 60081
Phone: 815-675-2321
Fax: 815-675-7055
Web: www.intermatic.com

CEO: Michael Werner
CFO: —
HR: Linnea Ten Bruin
FYE: December 31
Type: Private

From its start in 1891 as a maker of streetcar fare registers, Intermatic has evolved to become an integrated manufacturer of energy-control products for both industrial and residential use. The company makes home timers that include pool and spa controls, portable burglar alarms, and appliance timers. It makes night-lights and portable alarms, as well as outdoor lighting systems, such as its Malibu brand of low-voltage systems. Other products include industrial surge protectors, weatherproof covers for electrical outlets, and solar-powered lights. Intermatic sells its products through retailers and wholesalers. Chairman emeritus Douglas Kinney Sr. and his family own the company.

An in-depth profile of this company is available to Hoover's Online members at hoovers.com.

831

INTERMEC, INC.

NYSE: IN

6001 36th Ave. West
Everett, WA 98203
Phone: 425-265-2400
Fax: 425-355-9551
Web: www.intermec.com

CEO: Patrick J. (Pat) Byrne
CFO: Robert J. (Bob) Driessnack
HR: Jeanne Lyon
FYE: December 31
Type: Public

Intermec keeps assets on track. The company manufactures and supports data collection and mobile computing devices. Its products include bar code scanners, RFID readers, mobile and fixed vehicle computers, printers, and label media. Intermec also sells wireless LAN equipment made by Cisco Systems. The company's products are used to automate and manage functions related to distribution, warehousing, and manufacturing. Intermec, which serves customers globally, targets industries including consumer and industrial goods, field services, health care, public sector, retail, and transportation. The company's clients have included Bally Technologies, Boeing, and PUMA.

	Annual Growth	12/05	12/06	12/07	12/08	12/09
Sales ($ mil.)	(6.9%)	875.5	850.0	849.2	890.9	658.2
Net income ($ mil.)	—	61.8	32.0	23.1	35.7	(11.8)
Market value ($ mil.)	(21.5%)	2,088.0	1,499.3	1,254.7	820.4	794.4
Employees	(8.7%)	2,497	2,407	2,308	2,070	1,734

INTERMETRO INDUSTRIES CORPORATION

651 N. Washington St.
Wilkes-Barre, PA 18705
Phone: 570-825-2741
Fax: 570-823-0250
Web: www.metro.com

CEO: John Nackley
CFO: Donald McAlonan
HR: Darrin Woodruff
FYE: September 30
Type: Subsidiary

It's a small world after all, but InterMetro Industries means to make the most of it. The company, a division of Emerson Electric, makes storage and transport systems, from shelving to carts and tables used in commercial, foodservice, consumer, and health care markets. An array of hospital general storage and medication management equipment is produced by its Flo Healthcare, Lionville Systems, and medDISPENSE businesses. Foodservice products range from wine racks to heated holding cabinets. InterMetro also touts services, such as space audits and custom product design. Company manufacturing and distribution facilities dot the US, with sales offices in Canada, Europe, Asia, the Middle East, and Latin America.

INTERMOUNTAIN HEALTH CARE, INC.

36 S. State St.
Salt Lake City, UT 84111
Phone: 801-442-2000
Fax: 801-442-3327
Web: www.ihc.com

CEO: Charles W. Sorenson
CFO: Bert R. Zimmerli
HR: —
FYE: December 31
Type: Not-for-profit

If you're whooshing down the side of one of Idaho's majestic mountains and take a nasty spill, Intermountain Health Care (IHC) will be there to save the day! From air ambulance services to urgent care clinics and general hospitals, IHC has all the tools to mend skiers (and non-skiers too) in Utah and southern Idaho. The not-for-profit health system operates some 20 hospitals, home health care agencies, dozens of physician and urgent care clinics, and rehabilitation centers. IHC was formed in 1975 when the Church of Jesus Christ of Latter Day Saints donated 15 hospitals to local communities. IHC is led by CEO Charles Sorenson, who replaced Bill Nelson when he retired after 33 years with the company.

	Annual Growth	12/04	12/05	12/06	12/07	12/08
Est. sales ($ mil.)	—	—	—	—	—	3,048.9
Employees	—	—	—	—	—	23,000

INTERMUNE, INC.

NASDAQ (GM): ITMN

3280 Bayshore Blvd.
Brisbane, CA 94005
Phone: 415-466-2200
Fax: 415-466-2300
Web: www.intermune.com

CEO: Daniel G. (Dan) Welch
CFO: John C. Hodgman
HR: Howard A. Simon
FYE: December 31
Type: Public

InterMune has found a good thing in interferon gamma. The company's sole marketed product is Actimmune (interferon gamma-1b), an FDA-approved treatment for two rare congenital disorders: chronic granulomatous disease, an immune condition; and osteopetrosis, a disease causing abnormal bone growth. Most of Actimmune's sales, however, are for off-label use of the drug to treat the deterioration of lung function from scarring caused by idiopathic pulmonary fibrosis (IPF). InterMune is developing another potential IPF treatment called pirfenidone, and it is also researching hepatitis C therapies with Roche.

	Annual Growth	12/05	12/06	12/07	12/08	12/09
Sales ($ mil.)	(18.5%)	110.5	90.8	66.7	48.2	48.7
Net income ($ mil.)	—	(5.2)	(107.2)	(89.6)	(97.7)	(116.0)
Market value ($ mil.)	(6.1%)	930.1	1,702.4	738.0	585.7	721.9
Employees	(11.0%)	193	195	132	130	121

INTERNAP NETWORK SERVICES CORPORATION

NASDAQ (GM): INAP

250 Williams St.
Atlanta, GA 30303
Phone: 404-302-9700
Fax: 404-475-0520
Web: www.internap.com

CEO: J. Eric Cooney
CFO: George E. Kilguss III
HR: —
FYE: December 31
Type: Public

Internap Network Services has a solution for CIOs losing sleep over slow network connections. The company helps businesses bypass congested public network access points (NAPs) — the crossroads where major backbone carriers connect and exchange Internet traffic — with its own private NAPs (P-NAPS). Internap has P-NAPs located in Asia, Australia, Europe, and North America. The company provides application hosting and other data center services for clients with a need to outsource the housing and management of their networks. It also offers content delivery services to enable streaming audio and video, as well as software, for clients including media companies, broadcasters, and providers of software-as-a service.

	Annual Growth	12/05	12/06	12/07	12/08	12/09
Sales ($ mil.)	13.6%	153.7	181.4	234.1	254.0	256.3
Net income ($ mil.)	—	(5.0)	3.7	(5.6)	(104.8)	(69.7)
Market value ($ mil.)	2.2%	219.1	1,011.9	424.4	127.4	239.5
Employees	4.3%	330	330	420	430	390

INTERNATIONAL AEROSPACE ENTERPRISES, INC.

OTC: LSTM

123 W. Nye Ln., Ste. 129
Carson City, NV 89706
Phone: 209-487-6449
Fax: —
Web: www.lifesteminternational.com

CEO: John M. Peck
CFO: —
HR: —
FYE: December 31
Type: Public

International Aerospace Enterprises sought a world of opportunity in a vial of blood but when that took too long, the company decided that selling military aircraft parts would be more profitable. In its previous incarnation as biotech company LifeStem International, it supplied and banked adult stem cells as well as microbiological cultures and biological data management software. However, it sold off those operations and purchased aircraft parts supplier International Aerospace Enterprises in 2008. The company now holds a warehouse full of spare aircraft parts and is ready to sell to the US military and its allies.

	Annual Growth	12/05	12/06	12/07	12/08	12/09
Sales ($ mil.)	(37.4%)	1.3	1.3	1.1	0.0	0.2
Net income ($ mil.)	—	(5.0)	0.0	0.0	(1.5)	(2.7)
Market value ($ mil.)	(96.0%)	1,476,624.8	1,954,356.3	108,575.4	34.7	3.7
Employees	(40.5%)	16	16	16	2	2

INTERNATIONAL ASSETS HOLDING

NASDAQ (CM): IAAC

220 E. Central Pkwy., Ste. 2060
Altamonte Springs, FL 32701
Phone: 407-741-5300
Fax: 407-740-0808
Web: www.intlassets.com

CEO: Sean M. O'Connor
CFO: William J. (Bill) Dunaway
HR: —
FYE: September 30
Type: Public

Going global is the name of the game for securities broker International Assets Holding Corporation and its subsidiaries. The company specializes in niche international markets, offering expertise in securities, foreign exchange, and commodities trading. Its INTL Trading subsidiary is a market-maker for some 800 foreign securities. INTL Consilium, a joint venture with Consilium Investment Capital, provides asset management services. International Assets Holding serves financial institutions, corporations, and other institutional investors in the US and abroad. In 2009 the company acquired commodities brokerage FCStone in a $130 million deal, adding commercial clients and expanding the company's international presence.

	Annual Growth	9/05	9/06	9/07	9/08	9/09
Sales ($ mil.)	36.8%	26.1	102.8	4,460.3	18,358.9	91.3
Net income ($ mil.)	36.8%	2.6	3.5	(4.5)	30.6	9.1
Market value ($ mil.)	19.1%	144.1	410.3	452.5	423.7	290.1
Employees	74.8%	67	89	170	195	625

INTERNATIONAL BALER CORP.

OTC: IBAL

5400 Rio Grande Ave.
Jacksonville, FL 32254
Phone: 904-358-3812
Fax: 904-358-7013
Web: www.intl-baler.com

CEO: D. Roger Griffin
CFO: William E. Nielsen
HR: —
FYE: October 31
Type: Public

No need to bail on International Baler. This holding company, formerly known as Waste Technology, banks on its business being in the dumps. International Baler manufactures about 50 different types of waste baling equipment. It also sells replacement parts for waste haulers. In addition, International Baler produces accessories such as conveyor belts and "rufflers," which break down refuse for better compaction. Customers include rubber and polymer makers, solid-waste recycling facilities, power generating facilities, textile and paper mills, cotton gins, and supermarkets. International Baler makes about three-quarters of its sales in the US.

	Annual Growth	10/05	10/06	10/07	10/08	10/09
Sales ($ mil.)	(2.8%)	7.4	8.1	9.6	12.8	6.6
Net income ($ mil.)	—	0.1	0.4	0.6	2.1	(0.2)
Market value ($ mil.)	(10.1%)	2.7	2.1	5.9	6.4	1.8
Employees	(10.7%)	55	65	65	62	35

INTERNATIONAL BANCSHARES CORPORATION

NASDAQ (GS): IBOC

1200 San Bernardo Ave.
Laredo, TX 78042
Phone: 956-722-7611
Fax: 956-726-6637
Web: www.iboc.com

CEO: Dennis E. Nixon
CFO: Imelda Navarro
HR: —
FYE: December 31
Type: Public

International Bancshares is leading post-NAFTA banking in South Texas. The institution's International Bank of Commerce and Commerce Bank serve residents and businesses of Texas, Oklahoma, and northern Mexico through more than 250 offices. The company facilitates trade between the US and Mexico and serves Texas' growing Hispanic population; about 30% of its deposits come from south of the border. In addition to commercial and international banking services, International Bancshares provides retail deposit services, insurance and investment products, and mortgages and consumer loans. The bulk of the company's portfolio is made up of business and construction loans.

	Annual Growth	12/05	12/06	12/07	12/08	12/09
Assets ($ mil.)	3.1%	10,391.9	10,911.5	11,167.2	12,439.3	11,762.5
Net income ($ mil.)	0.3%	140.8	117.0	121.3	132.1	142.7
Market value ($ mil.)	(8.3%)	1,817.8	1,913.7	1,426.1	1,486.7	1,287.8
Employees	2.9%	3,265	3,427	2,965	3,832	3,662

INTERNATIONAL BANK FOR RECONSTRUCTION & DEVELOPMENT

1818 H St. NW
Washington, DC 20433
Phone: 202-473-1000
Fax: 202-477-6391
Web: www.worldbank.org

CEO: Robert B. Zoellick
CFO: Vincenzo La Via
HR: Hasan Tuluy
FYE: June 30
Type: Private

Collectively known as the World Bank, the International Bank for Reconstruction & Development (IBRD) and its sister organization the International Development Association (IDA) are on a mission to improve the world. The IBRD strives to reduce poverty in creditworthy middle-income countries by promoting sustainable development through loans, guarantees, risk management products, and advisory services. The IBRD serves countries in Latin America, Asia, Africa, and Eastern Europe, funding development activities by selling bonds in international capital markets. IDA assists the world's poorest countries, helping them develop effective health care, education, and government institutions.

	Annual Growth	6/04	6/05	6/06	6/07	6/08
Est. sales ($ mil.)	—	—	—	—	—	618.8
Employees	—	—	—	—	—	10,000

INTERNATIONAL BROTHERHOOD OF TEAMSTERS

25 Louisiana Ave. NW
Washington, DC 20001
Phone: 202-624-6800
Fax: 202-624-6918
Web: www.teamster.org

CEO: James P. (Jim) Hoffa
CFO: C. Thomas (Tom) Keegel
HR: —
FYE: December 31
Type: Labor union

One of the largest and best-known labor unions in the US, the International Brotherhood of Teamsters has 1.4 million members. The Teamsters represents workers in some 20 industry sectors, including airlines, freight, parcel delivery, industrial trades, and public service. More than 200,000 of the union's members are employees of package delivery giant United Parcel Service. Besides negotiating labor contracts with employers on behalf of its members, the union oversees pension funds and serves as an advocate in legislative and regulatory arenas. The union and its affiliates have about 1,900 local chapters in the US and Canada, including about 475 Teamsters locals. The Teamsters union was founded in 1903.

	Annual Growth	12/04	12/05	12/06	12/07	12/08
Est. sales ($ mil.)	—	—	—	—	—	186.2
Employees	—	—	—	—	—	649

INTERNATIONAL BUILDING TECHNOLOGIES

OTC: INBGE

17800 Castleton St., Ste. 638
City of Industry, CA 91748
Phone: 626-581-8500
Fax: –
Web: www.ibtgi.com

CEO: Kenneth Yeung
CFO: –
HR: –
FYE: December 31
Type: Public

International Building Technologies Group, Inc., (INBG) has raced from business to business. Formerly a card game developer for casinos and a seller of racing and motorsports accessories and apparel, the company changed lanes in 2007. That's when it began a new life as a manufacturer of a specialty panel-based technology that helps buildings withstand earthquakes and hurricane-force winds. INBG also offers other services including site planning, engineering, contractor services, training, and supervision. The company plans to merge with Chinese petroleum storage company FHH Sino New Energies. The deal will allow INBG to move into yet another line of business — the energy sector.

	Annual Growth	12/05	12/06	12/07	12/08	12/09
Sales ($ mil.)	—	—	—	—	—	0.0
Net income ($ mil.)	—	—	—	—	—	(1.9)
Market value ($ mil.)	—	—	—	—	—	0.5
Employees	—	—	—	—	—	1

An in-depth profile of this company is available to Hoover's Online members at hoovers.com.

833

INTERNATIONAL BUSINESS MACHINES
NYSE: IBM

New Orchard Road
Armonk, NY 10504
Phone: 914-499-1900
Fax: 800-314-1092
Web: www.ibm.com

CEO: Samuel J. Palmisano
CFO: Mark Loughridge
HR: J. Randall (Randy) MacDonald
FYE: December 31
Type: Public

Big Blue? Try Huge Blue. International Business Machines Corporation (IBM) is the world's top provider of computer products and services. Among the leaders in almost every market in which it competes, the company focuses primarily on its growing services business, which accounts for well over half of sales. Though perhaps still best known for its hardware, its IT and business services units are among the largest in the world and serve customers across most industries. IBM is also one of the largest providers of both business software and semiconductors. The company's computing hardware legacy lives on in the form of its industry-leading enterprise server and storage products lines.

	Annual Growth	12/05	12/06	12/07	12/08	12/09
Sales ($ mil.)	1.2%	91,134.0	91,424.0	98,786.0	103,630.0	95,758.0
Net income ($ mil.)	13.9%	7,970.0	9,492.0	10,418.0	12,334.0	13,425.0
Market value ($ mil.)	12.3%	105,409.0	124,580.1	138,621.8	107,922.4	167,859.3
Employees	2.2%	366,345	355,766	426,969	398,455	399,409

INTERNATIONAL CARD ESTABLISHMENT, INC.
OTC: ICRD

555 Airport Way, Ste. A
Camarillo, CA 93010
Phone: 866-423-2491
Fax: 866-423-2492
Web: www.cardnetone.com

CEO: William J. Lopshire
CFO: Candace Mills
HR: —
FYE: December 31
Type: Public

International Card Establishment (ICE) believes that it's cool for every merchant, big or small, to have the ability to swipe your credit card. More and more customers are using electronic payments to purchase items, and ICE is there to provide businesses with the ability to accept transactions. ICE targets small businesses as its core customer base and offers a variety of credit card servicing offerings including processing systems, processing services, software, and loyalty management programs. ICE has used acquisitions to transition away from its previous business of providing Web-based event management software and services.

	Annual Growth	12/05	12/06	12/07	12/08	12/09
Sales ($ mil.)	(2.8%)	6.5	10.8	9.2	7.6	5.8
Net income ($ mil.)	—	(4.3)	(3.6)	(4.0)	0.1	(0.3)
Market value ($ mil.)	(43.8%)	7.2	8.3	4.1	1.1	0.7
Employees	(16.8%)	50	25	23	23	24

INTERNATIONAL CENTER FOR ENTREPRENEURIAL DEVELOPMENT, INC.

12715 Telge Rd.
Cypress, TX 77429
Phone: 281-256-4100
Fax: 281-373-4450
Web: www.iced.net

CEO: Stephen B. (Steve) Hammerstein
CFO: —
HR: —
FYE: December 31
Type: Holding company

The International Center for Entrepreneurial Development (ICED) is a holding company that offers several franchise opportunities. The organization specializes in the computer education, health care, and mail center and printing industries. ICED offers a number of franchise brands including Kwik Kopy, Parcel Plus, and Women's Health Boutique. Its Computer Explorers (CE) unit is a franchise group that serves some 25,000 students through about 1,000 locations worldwide. CE boasts approximately 600 educators that ensure that children in some 2,000 schools are fully engaged in learning the latest technology. Bud Hadfield founded the company in 1967 when he began franchising his Kwik Kopy centers.

	Annual Growth	12/04	12/05	12/06	12/07	12/08
Est. sales ($ mil.)	—	—	—	—	—	13.0
Employees	—	—	—	—	—	150

INTERNATIONAL COAL GROUP, INC.
NYSE: ICO

300 Corporate Centre Dr.
Scott Depot, WV 25560
Phone: 304-760-2400
Fax: —
Web: www.intlcoal.com

CEO: Bennett K. (Ben) Hatfield
CFO: Bradley W. (Brad) Harris
HR: Teresa A. Stapleton
FYE: December 31
Type: Public

International Coal Group focuses its energy on one nation, the US. The company produces coal from about a dozen mining complexes in northern and central Appalachia (Kentucky, Maryland, Virginia, and West Virginia) and from another in the Illinois Basin (in Illinois, strangely enough). International Coal Group produces low-sulfur steam coal, which is sold mainly to electric utilities, and metallurgical coal, which is sold to steelmakers. Steam coal accounts for two-thirds of the company's 1 billion tons of coal reserves. International Coal Group was formed in 2004 when investor Wilbur Ross led a group that bought many of the assets of Horizon Natural Resources in a bankruptcy auction.

	Annual Growth	12/05	12/06	12/07	12/08	12/09
Sales ($ mil.)	14.8%	647.7	891.6	849.2	1,096.7	1,125.3
Net income ($ mil.)	(9.3%)	31.8	(9.3)	(147.0)	(24.6)	21.5
Market value ($ mil.)	(20.2%)	1,935.7	1,110.5	1,092.1	468.6	786.5
Employees	13.4%	1,547	2,222	2,266	2,727	2,562

INTERNATIONAL COFFEE & TEA, LLC

1945 S. La Cienega Blvd.
Los Angeles, CA 90034
Phone: 310-237-2326
Fax: 310-815-3676
Web: www.coffeebean.com

CEO: Melvin (Mel) Elias
CFO: —
HR: Faye Moseley
FYE: December 31
Type: Private

Don't be chai; stand your grounds and espresso yourself over a cup at The Coffee Bean. International Coffee & Tea operates and franchises more than 750 coffee shops under the name The Coffee Bean & Tea Leaf. The outlets, which have about 300 shops in Arizona, California, Hawaii, Nevada, and Texas, and the rest in more than 20 foreign countries, feature a variety of fresh roasted coffees and specialty teas, along with baked goods and blended ice drinks. About 350 locations are company-owned, while the rest are franchised. The Coffee Bean & Tea Leaf also sells bagged coffee and tea at a handful of grocery stores, including Albertsons and Vons.

INTERNATIONAL CREATIVE MANAGEMENT, INC.

10250 Constellation Blvd.
Los Angeles, CA 90067
Phone: 310-550-4000
Fax: 310-550-4100
Web: www.icmtalent.com

CEO: Jeffrey S. (Jeff) Berg
CFO: Joe Friedman
HR: Karen Abrams
FYE: July 30
Type: Private

If anyone can manage creativity internationally, it's International Creative Management (ICM). The agency represents film and television actors and directors, as well as artists in theater, music, publishing, and new media. A major "tenpercentery" (along with CAA and William Morris Endeavor), ICM represents such A-list clients as Halle Berry, Rosario Dawson, Robert Duvall, Beyonce Knowles, and Chris Rock, as well as emerging performers. It has offices in Los Angeles, New York, and London. ICM was formed in 1975 by the merger of Creative Management Associates and The International Famous Agency. Private equity firm Traverse Rizvi Management and Merrill Lynch hold controlling stakes in the agency.

INTERNATIONAL DAIRY QUEEN, INC.

7505 Metro Blvd.	CEO: John Gainor
Minneapolis, MN 55439	CFO: Nathan French
Phone: 952-830-0200	HR: Angela Rud
Fax: 952-830-0273	FYE: December 31
Web: www.dairyqueen.com	Type: Subsidiary

International Dairy Queen (IDQ) has been supplying brain-freezes for more than 70 years. The company is a leading franchisor of frozen treat stores, with more than 5,600 Dairy Queen quick-service restaurants popular for their ice cream treats, including Blizzards, sundaes, and cones. Many of the stores also serve burgers, fries, and other items. A small number of units are company-owned. In addition, IDQ franchises about 400 DQ Orange Julius locations offering blended fruit drinks and a small number of Karmelkorn stands that feature popcorn snacks. IDQ franchisees operate in the US, Canada, and 20 other countries. Tracing its roots back to 1938, the company is owned by Warren Buffett's Berkshire Hathaway.

INTERNATIONAL DATA CORPORATION

5 Speen St.	CEO: Kirk S. Campbell
Framingham, MA 01701	CFO: Mark Sullivan
Phone: 508-872-8200	HR: Debra Bernardi
Fax: 508-935-4168	FYE: December 31
Web: www.idc.com	Type: Subsidiary

You can learn all about IT with the the help of IDC. International Data Corporation (IDC) is one of the world's leading providers of market research data and advisory services focused on the technology industry. It offers research in more than 110 countries on a wide array of software and hardware sectors, as well as insights on companies providing business process outsourcing, consulting, and other technology support services. IDC also offers ongoing advisory services, custom research, and consulting services. It produces a number of conferences and other events focused on information technology. As the subsidiary of publisher International Data Group, IDC has more than 60 offices worldwide.

INTERNATIONAL DATA GROUP, INC.

1 Exeter Plaza, 15th Fl.	CEO: Patrick J. (Pat) McGovern
Boston, MA 02116	CFO: Edward B. (Ted) Bloom
Phone: 617-534-1200	HR: Piper Sheer
Fax: 617-423-0240	FYE: September 30
Web: www.idg.com	Type: Private

International Data Group (IDG) is a publishing giant with digital appeal. The world's top technology publisher, IDG produces popular magazines and newspapers (including *PC World*, *Macworld*, and *CIO*) in dozens of languages for more than 200 million readers. IDG also operates 450 websites featuring technology content. In addition to publishing, IDG provides technology market research through its IDC (International Data Corporation) unit, produces more than 750 technology-focused industry events, and offers lead generation and marketing services for tech companies. All total, IDG reaches audiences in nearly 100 countries. Chairman Patrick McGovern founded the company in 1964.

INTERNATIONAL FIGHT LEAGUE, INC.   OTC: IFLI

980 N. Federal Hwy., Ste. 314	CEO: C. Leo Smith
Boca Raton, FL 33432	CFO: —
Phone: 561-367-1055	HR: —
Fax: —	FYE: December 31
	Type: Public

You might say everybody was kung fu fighting at this company. Before shuttering its operations, International Fight League (IFL) ran a mixed martial arts (MMA) league in which fighters competed in a series of bouts, including title matches to determine belt holders in various weight classes. The events were televised through a broadcasting deal with FOX Sports Net; television fees and ticket sales accounted for the majority of IFL's revenue. Citing mounting losses, IFL discontinued its operations in 2008 and became a shell company. CEO C. Leo Smith controls 90% of IFL through Insurance Marketing Solutions.

	Annual Growth	12/05	12/06	12/07	12/08	12/09
Sales ($ mil.)	—	—	—	—	—	0.0
Net income ($ mil.)	—	—	—	—	—	0.2
Market value ($ mil.)	—	—	—	—	—	0.4
Employees	—	—	—	—	—	—

INTERNATIONAL FINANCIAL GROUP, INC.

238 International Rd.	CEO: Robert D. Linton
Burlington, NC 27215	CFO: Kerry Fabor
Phone: 336-586-2500	HR: Carol Hennrikus
Fax: 336-586-2867	FYE: December 31
Web: www.burlingtoninsurance.com	Type: Holding company

International Financial Group — better known as IFG Companies — provides commercial property/casualty insurance, including general liability coverages. It also offers specialty coverage including farm, liquor, and product liability for businesses ranging from caterers to contractors. It also provides coverage for special events such as camps and concerts. IFG operates on both an admitted and non-admitted basis through its subsidiaries First Financial Insurance, Burlington Insurance, Alamance, and Guilford. Its Guilford Specialty Group specializes in larger, more complex liability risks. Most of the group's business is produced by contracted agents.

	Annual Growth	12/04	12/05	12/06	12/07	12/08
Est. sales ($ mil.)	—	—	—	—	—	18.9
Employees	—	—	—	—	—	63

INTERNATIONAL FLAVORS & FRAGRANCES INC.   NYSE: IFF

521 W. 57th St.	CEO: Douglas D. Tough
New York, NY 10019	CFO: Kevin C. Berryman
Phone: 212-765-5500	HR: Angelica T. Cantlon
Fax: 212-708-7132	FYE: December 31
Web: www.iff.com	Type: Public

If you've got a taste for the sweet and the salty, then International Flavors & Fragrances (IFF) is your kind of company. One of the world's leading creators and manufacturers of artificial and natural aromas and flavors, IFF produces fragrances used in the manufacture of perfumes, cosmetics, soaps, and other personal care and household products. The company has more than 15% of the world market. IFF sells its flavors principally to makers of prepared foods, dairy foods, beverages, confections, and pharmaceuticals. The company sells its fragrances and flavors in solid and liquid forms in amounts that range from a few pounds to several tons.

	Annual Growth	12/05	12/06	12/07	12/08	12/09
Sales ($ mil.)	3.9%	1,993.4	2,095.4	2,276.6	2,389.4	2,326.2
Net income ($ mil.)	0.3%	193.1	226.5	247.1	229.6	195.5
Market value ($ mil.)	5.3%	2,654.4	3,895.2	3,813.6	2,354.9	3,259.7
Employees	1.1%	5,160	5,087	5,315	5,300	5,400

INTERNATIONAL GAME TECHNOLOGY

NYSE: IGT

9295 Prototype Dr.
Reno, NV 89521
Phone: 775-448-7777
Fax: 775-448-0719
Web: www.igt.com

CEO: Patti S. Hart
CFO: Patrick W. (Pat) Cavanaugh
HR: Tami Corbin
FYE: September 30
Type: Public

International Game Technology (IGT) has hit the jackpot in the casino gaming business. The company is the world's largest gaming machine manufacturer, with a product portfolio that includes traditional reel slot machines, video slots and video poker, and progressive payout machines. IGT also makes casino management software systems for tracking activity on the casino floor, as well as multiplayer game software and customer relationship management (CRM) systems. It sells products mostly in North America, but it also serves international customers in about 10 other countries.

	Annual Growth	9/05	9/06	9/07	9/08	9/09
Sales ($ mil.)	(2.9%)	2,379.4	2,511.7	2,621.4	2,528.6	2,114.0
Net income ($ mil.)	(23.6%)	436.5	473.6	508.2	342.5	149.0
Market value ($ mil.)	(5.6%)	8,048.7	12,371.2	12,848.1	5,121.4	6,403.2
Employees	0.5%	5,000	5,200	5,400	5,900	5,100

INTERNATIONAL ISOTOPES INC.

OTC: INIS

4137 Commerce Circle
Idaho Falls, ID 83401
Phone: 208-524-5300
Fax: 208-524-1411
Web: www.intisoid.com

CEO: Steve T. Laflin
CFO: Laurie A. McKenzie-Carter
HR: —
FYE: December 31
Type: Public

Despite its name, International Isotopes is confined to a single US state. The firm operates primarily through subsidiary International Isotopes Idaho, where it makes calibration and measurement equipment used with nuclear imaging cameras. Most of its nuclear imaging products, including dose measurement devices and testing equipment, are made under contract with RadQual, a privately held firm that markets the devices; International Isotopes owns a minority stake in RadQual. International Isotopes also makes radioisotopes (including cobalt-60 and iodine-131) used in radiation therapy and other medical treatments. Additionally, the company processes gemstones that have been irradiated to enhance their color.

	Annual Growth	12/05	12/06	12/07	12/08	12/09
Sales ($ mil.)	19.4%	3.0	4.5	4.7	5.6	6.1
Net income ($ mil.)	—	(1.0)	(1.0)	(1.7)	(2.2)	(4.6)
Market value ($ mil.)	57.2%	26.5	32.3	235.1	61.7	161.7
Employees	4.5%	21	25	24	31	25

INTERNATIONAL LOTTERY & TOTALIZATOR SYSTEMS

OTC: ITSI

2310 Cousteau Ct.
Vista, CA 92081
Phone: 760-598-1655
Fax: —
Web: www.ilts.com

CEO: Jeffrey M. (Jeff) Johnson
CFO: T. Linh Nguyen
HR: Carla Montiel
FYE: April 30
Type: Public

Designing systems for gambling and the ballot booth, maybe this company should be called Tote & Vote. International Lottery & Totalizator Systems, Inc., (ILTS) is a leading manufacturer of computerized wagering systems used by pari-mutuel racing operators, off-track betting centers, and lottery operators. It also provides consulting and training services, along with its software and hardware. In addition to wagering, ILTS markets electronic voting systems through its Unisyn Voting Solutions subsidiary. Berjaya Lottery Management, a subsidiary of Malaysia-based Berjaya Group, owns more than 70% of ILTS.

	Annual Growth	4/05	4/06	4/07	4/08	4/09
Sales ($ mil.)	(9.5%)	9.7	3.4	11.0	13.0	6.5
Net income ($ mil.)	—	(1.8)	(2.3)	0.5	3.9	(0.9)
Market value ($ mil.)	(12.2%)	4.5	6.2	8.0	6.6	2.7
Employees	(10.9%)	57	37	35	36	36

INTERNATIONAL MINERALS CORPORATION

Toronto: IMZ

7950 E. Acoma Dr., Ste. 211
Scottsdale, AZ 85260
Phone: 480-483-9932
Fax: 480-483-9926
Web: www.intlminerals.com

CEO: Stephen J. Kay
CFO: Eric H. Edwards
HR: —
FYE: June 30
Type: Public

International Minerals is working to develop gold and silver properties in South America. The company's primary projects include the Rio Blanco, Gaby, and Cañicapa properties in Ecuador and the Antabamba and Pallancata properties in Peru. Through a 2010 purchase of Ventura Gold, International Minerals owns a 51% interest in the Peruvian Inmaculada gold/silver project. Hochschild Mining owns the remaining stake. It also bought Metallic Ventures that same year, winning a bidding contest with Solitario Exploration, to add to its Goldmine and Converse operations in Nevada. The company continues to look to acquire low-cost gold and silver mining operations in the Americas.

	Annual Growth	6/05	6/06	6/07	6/08	6/09
Sales ($ mil.)	—	—	—	—	—	0.0
Net income ($ mil.)	—	—	—	—	—	8.7
Market value ($ mil.)	—	—	—	—	—	392.9
Employees	—	—	—	—	—	—

INTERNATIONAL MONETARY SYSTEMS, LTD.

OTC: INLM

16901 W. Glendale Dr.
New Berlin, WI 53151
Phone: 800-559-8515
Fax: 262-780-3655
Web: www.internationalmonetary.com

CEO: Donald F. (Don) Mardak
CFO: David A. Powell
HR: —
FYE: December 31
Type: Public

Who says the barter system is dead? Not International Monetary Systems (IMS). IMS runs one of the world's largest trade exchanges, or barter networks, that can help businesses convert excess inventory into goods and services. Serving more than 18,000 business customers in some 50 US markets and Canada, the company operates the IMS Barter Network. Through its wholly owned subsidiaries, users can swap excess goods or services or purchase items electronically with a special trade currency called "trade dollars." Founder and CEO Donald Mardak and his family own about 30% of the company, which has grown by acquiring other trade exchanges.

	Annual Growth	12/05	12/06	12/07	12/08	12/09
Sales ($ mil.)	22.6%	6.2	8.8	14.8	14.2	14.0
Net income ($ mil.)	—	(0.2)	(0.4)	(0.4)	(0.9)	0.2
Market value ($ mil.)	(17.4%)	18.1	62.9	33.0	12.5	8.4
Employees	443.1%	4	4	118	—	—

INTERNATIONAL PACKAGING AND LOGISTICS

OTC: IPLO

7700 Irvine Center Dr., Ste. 870
Irvine, CA 92608
Phone: 949-861-3560
Fax: 949-861-3562
Web: iplgroupinc.com

CEO: Steven R. Westlund
CFO: Steven R. Westlund
HR: —
FYE: December 31
Type: Public

Moving items from point A to point B is the only thing International Packaging and Logistics Group, Inc., (formerly Kaire Holdings) seems consistent on. In 2007 the company ditched its prescription medicine delivery business and acquired H&H Glass, a glass packaging distribution business. The company's latest business focus involves importing glass packaging for such products as perfume and food condiments. It imports the products from China and Taiwan and sells them through a network of distributors located throughout the US and Canada. The recession of 2008 made for difficult business conditions for the company, which plans to expand into Australia and Europe.

An in-depth profile of this company is available to Hoover's Online members at hoovers.com.

INTERNATIONAL PAPER COMPANY

NYSE: IP

6400 Poplar Ave.
Memphis, TN 38197
Phone: 901-419-9000
Fax: 901-214-9682
Web: www.ipaper.com

CEO: John V. Faraci Jr.
CFO: Timothy S. (Tim) Nicholls
HR: Paul J. Karre
FYE: December 31
Type: Public

For International Paper (IP), business is a paper chase. It is one of the world's largest manufacturers of printing papers. Products include uncoated paper used in printers, market pulp for making towel and tissue goods, and coated paper and uncoated bristols (heavyweight art paper). In the US, IP is #1 in containerboard production, 70% of which is used in industrial corrugated boxes. A consumer packaging arm churns out board to box cosmetics and food, or print lottery tickets. IP's distribution subsidiary xpedx plies products and supply chain services to many markets in North America. IP owns forest-land in the US and Brazil, and a pulp and paper business in Russia, through a 50-50 venture with Ilim Holding.

	Annual Growth	12/05	12/06	12/07	12/08	12/09
Sales ($ mil.)	(0.8%)	24,097.0	21,995.0	21,890.0	24,829.0	23,366.0
Net income ($ mil.)	(11.3%)	1,100.0	1,050.0	1,168.0	(1,282.0)	681.0
Market value ($ mil.)	(5.5%)	14,673.9	14,887.8	14,136.9	5,151.8	11,692.0
Employees	(4.9%)	68,700	60,600	51,500	61,700	56,100

INTERNATIONAL RECTIFIER CORPORATION

NYSE: IRF

233 Kansas St.
El Segundo, CA 90245
Phone: 310-726-8000
Fax: 310-252-7903
Web: www.irf.com

CEO: Oleg Khaykin
CFO: Ilan Daskal
HR: —
FYE: June 30
Type: Public

In electronics as in politics, power tends to corrupt. International Rectifier (IR) doesn't apply itself to matters of statecraft, but it has plenty of ideas about the performance of power in electronic gear. IR is a top maker of power semi-conductors, which refine the electricity flowing into a device from a battery or a power grid, enabling more efficient operation. Its products — including MOSFETs (metal oxide semiconductor field-effect transistors), diodes, relays, and rectifiers — are used in appliances, automobiles, computers, communica-tion devices, lighting and displays, gaming consoles, industrial motors, and military equipment.

	Annual Growth	6/05	6/06	6/07	6/08	6/09
Sales ($ mil.)	(10.9%)	1,174.4	1,171.1	1,202.5	984.8	740.4
Net income ($ mil.)	—	137.5	107.2	77.7	(62.6)	(247.4)
Market value ($ mil.)	(25.4%)	3,372.4	2,761.8	2,633.2	1,356.9	1,046.6
Employees	(10.0%)	6,000	6,300	5,500	5,100	3,939

INTERNATIONAL SECURITIES EXCHANGE HOLDINGS, INC.

60 Broad St.
New York, NY 10004
Phone: 212-943-2400
Fax: 212-425-4926
Web: www.iseoptions.com

CEO: Gary Katz
CFO: Bruce Cooperman
HR: —
FYE: December 31
Type: Subsidiary

International Securities Exchange Holdings (ISE Holdings) wants you to con-sider all of your options. The company operates the ISE Options Exchange, the US's first all-electronic exchange for options trading. The exchange also offers forex (FX), exchange-traded fund (ETF), and index options. In all, ISE trades more than 2,000 products. ISE Holdings owns a minority stake of the ISE Stock Exchange, which offers both dark pool (secret pricing) and fully vis-ible markets, alternative market investments such as real estate, and market tools and trading data. ISE Holdings is a subsidiary of Eurex, a global deriva-tives exchange owned by Deutsche Börse and SIX Swiss Exchange.

INTERNATIONAL SHIPHOLDING CORPORATION

NYSE: ISH

11 N. Water St., Ste. 18290
Mobile, AL 36602
Phone: 251-243-9100
Fax: —
Web: www.intship.com

CEO: Niels M. Johnsen
CFO: Manuel G. (Manny) Estrada
HR: —
FYE: December 31
Type: Public

International Shipholding helps put the car in cargo. Most of the company's sales come from the chartering of vessels such as car and truck carriers, ships with strengthened hulls for use in polar regions, and coal and sulfur carriers. Overall, its fleet consists of more than 30 vessels. Charter customers have included Toyota, Hyundai Motor, Freeport-McMoRan's P.T. Freeport Indonesia unit, International Paper, and the US Navy's Military Sealift Command. Inter-national Shipholding's subsidiaries include Central Gulf Lines, Waterman Steamship Corporation, LCI Shipholdings, CG Railway, LMS Shipmanage-ment, and East Gulf Shipholding. The company has offices in Mobile, Alabama; New York City; and Shanghai.

	Annual Growth	12/05	12/06	12/07	12/08	12/09
Sales ($ mil.)	9.7%	262.2	274.9	197.1	238.5	380.0
Net income ($ mil.)	56.7%	7.0	17.0	17.4	39.0	42.2
Market value ($ mil.)	18.9%	115.7	100.4	162.0	188.5	231.2
Employees	(11.4%)	618	581	525	550	381

INTERNATIONAL SPECIALTY PRODUCTS, INC.

1361 Alps Rd.
Wayne, NJ 07470
Phone: 973-628-4000
Fax: 973-628-4423
Web: www.ispcorp.com

CEO: Sunil Kumar
CFO: Gregg Kam
HR: Marianne Spencer
FYE: December 31
Type: Private

If you've washed, shaved, and groomed, then you've probably shared a chemical experience with the folks at International Specialty Products (ISP). The com-pany, also called ISP Chemco, makes about 400 types of specialty chemicals, including food and pharmaceutical ingredients, personal care and fine chemi-cals, industrial chemicals (like butanediol for fibers and plastics), and minerals products. ISP also makes waterproofing agents, moisturizers, and preservatives for personal care products such as sunscreen and hair care products. The com-pany operates in 90 countries throughout the Americas, Asia, and Europe. The family of ISP's late chairman, Samuel Heyman, controls the company.

INTERNATIONAL SPEEDWAY CORPORATION

NASDAQ (GS): ISCA

1801 W. International Speedway Blvd.
Daytona Beach, FL 32114
Phone: 386-254-2700
Fax: 386-947-6816
Web: www.iscmotorsports.com

CEO: Lesa D. France Kennedy
CFO: Daniel W. (Dan) Houser
HR: Laura Jackson
FYE: November 30
Type: Public

International Speedway Corporation (ISC) doesn't believe in slow and steady. The company is the top motorsports operator in the US with more than a dozen racetracks hosting more than 100 events annually. Its race facilities include Daytona International Speedway (home of the Daytona 500), Talladega Superspeedway, and Michigan International Speedway. In addition, ISC oper-ates the Daytona 500 EXperience theme park and museum and it owns 50% of motorsports merchandiser Motorsports Authentics with rival Speedway Motor-sports. CEO James France and his family own about 70% control of the com-pany. Events sanctioned by NASCAR, also controlled by the France family, account for about 90% of sales.

	Annual Growth	11/05	11/06	11/07	11/08	11/09
Sales ($ mil.)	(1.6%)	740.1	798.4	816.6	787.3	693.2
Net income ($ mil.)	(54.6%)	159.4	116.8	86.2	134.6	6.8
Market value ($ mil.)	(16.2%)	2,639.0	2,506.5	2,060.6	1,254.9	1,304.3
Employees	(2.6%)	1,000	1,100	1,000	1,000	900

An in-depth profile of this company is available to Hoover's Online members at hoovers.com.

837

⊞ INTERNATIONAL TEXTILE GROUP, INC.

OTC: ITXN

804 Green Valley Rd., Ste. 300
Greensboro, NC 27408
Phone: 336-379-6220
Fax: 336-379-6287
Web: www.itg-global.com

CEO: Joseph L. Gorga
CFO: Willis C. (Billy) Moore III
HR: Robert (Bob) Garren
FYE: December 31
Type: Public

The totally material group — International Textile (ITG) — asks, airbags or jeans? ITG makes a range of apparel and technical fabrics, military, as well as automotive safety fabrics, upholstery, and specialty textiles. It is, plausibly, the world's #1 producer of denim fabrics, including premium denim used in retail goods, and one of North America's top makers of worsted wool, and commission prints and finishing. It operates in the US, Mexico, China, and Vietnam, regions that promise growth. Formerly Safety Components International, the company merged with an entity known as International Textile Group (comprising brands Burlington and Cone Denim) in 2006 and renamed itself International Textile Group, Inc.

	Annual Growth	12/05	12/06	12/07	12/08	12/09
Sales ($ mil.)	32.2%	220.1	720.9	1,010.9	995.1	673.1
Net income ($ mil.)	—	3.5	(50.1)	(80.2)	(241.0)	(202.7)
Market value ($ mil.)	(77.1%)	253.3	215.7	52.4	0.9	0.7
Employees	32.0%	2,900	8,700	11,900	12,000	8,800

INTERNATIONAL UNION, UAW

Solidarity House, 8000 E. Jefferson Ave.
Detroit, MI 48214
Phone: 313-926-5000
Fax: 313-926-5009
Web: www.uaw.org

CEO: Ron Gettelfinger
CFO: —
HR: —
FYE: December 31
Type: Labor union

At contract time, the International Union, UAW stands up (or sits down across the table) on behalf of some 510,000 active members and more than 575,000 retirees. The UAW (officially the United Automobile, Aerospace and Agricultural Implement Workers of America), represents workers at large and small companies, universities, and state agencies. The union has about 3,100 contracts with some 2,000 employers in the US, Canada, and Puerto Rico. Along with negotiating wages, benefits, and working conditions, the UAW provides education and training programs for its members, who belong to about 800 local unions. The organization was founded in Detroit in 1935.

	Annual Growth	12/04	12/05	12/06	12/07	12/08
Est. sales ($ mil.)	—	—	—	—	—	176.9
Employees	—	—	—	—	—	3,000

INTERNATIONAL WIRE GROUP, INC.

Pink Sheets: ITWG

12 Masonic Ave.
Camden, NY 13316
Phone: 315-245-3800
Fax: 315-245-0737
Web: itwg.client.shareholder.com

CEO: Rodney D. Kent
CFO: Glenn J. Holler
HR: —
FYE: June 30
Type: Public

International Wire Group (IWG) bares it all in the wire business. The company makes bare tin-plated and copper wire in a variety of gauges. The wire is used in audio, communications, computer, digital, and video equipment. Through acquisitions, the company has also expanded its offerings of high-performance conductors used in medical devices and aerospace equipment. IWG exited the insulated wire business to focus on its bare wire and conductors businesses. It maintains more than 15 facilities located in Europe and the US. General Cable accounts for 11% of sales. International Wire Group makes most of its sales in the US.

	Annual Growth	6/05	6/06	6/07	6/08	6/09
Sales ($ mil.)	—	—	—	—	0.0	0.0
Net income ($ mil.)	—	—	—	—	(7.8)	(6.6)
Market value ($ mil.)	31.1%	—	—	—	18.1	23.8
Employees	30.0%	—	—	—	10	13

INTERNET AMERICA, INC.

OTC: GEEK

10930 W. Sam Houston Pkwy. North, Ste. 200
Houston, TX 77064
Phone: 713-968-2500
Fax: —
Web: www.internetamerica.com

CEO: William E. (Billy) Ladin Jr.
CFO: —
HR: —
FYE: June 30
Type: Public

Internet America is changing its "lines" of business. Traditionally a provider of dial-up Internet access and, to a lesser degree, of wire-line DSL broadband Internet access to rural and suburban markets in Texas, the company is battling dwindling subscriber numbers by expanding its wireless broadband Internet business. Total subscribers number more than 30,000 with about one quarter of those connecting wirelessly. Internet America also provides installation and maintenance services from its three Texas operational centers in Corsicana, San Antonio, and Stafford (near Houston). The ISP, founded in 1995, is known regionally for its 1-800-BE-A-GEEK sign-up number.

	Annual Growth	6/05	6/06	6/07	6/08	6/09
Sales ($ mil.)	(7.4%)	10.6	9.9	8.0	8.8	7.8
Net income ($ mil.)	—	0.0	(0.6)	(0.3)	(3.0)	(2.7)
Market value ($ mil.)	(27.7%)	12.1	5.8	5.3	7.8	3.3
Employees	55.9%	10	67	66	73	59

INTERNET BRANDS, INC.

NASDAQ (GS): INET

909 N. Sepulveda Blvd., 11th Fl.
El Segundo, CA 90245
Phone: 310-280-4000
Fax: 310-280-4868
Web: www.internetbrands.com

CEO: Robert N. (Bob) Brisco
CFO: Scott A. Friedman
HR: B. Lynn Walsh
FYE: December 31
Type: Public

Looking for a car or a career change? Internet Brands can fill you in on all you need to know. The company owns and operates more than 230 websites that provide information on automobiles, careers, health issues, home-related activities, money and business, shopping, and travel and leisure. Sites feature news articles, reviews, forums, how-to's, directories, and coupons, and they generate the majority of Internet Brands' revenue through sales of online advertising. The company also licenses automotive-related technology products through its Autodata Solutions subsidiary and develops community bulletin board software through its vBulletin Solutions unit. It was founded in 1998 as CarsDirect.com.

	Annual Growth	12/05	12/06	12/07	12/08	12/09
Sales ($ mil.)	6.3%	78.1	84.8	89.9	104.0	99.8
Net income ($ mil.)	(1.9%)	13.4	93.1	0.3	11.6	12.4
Market value ($ mil.)	5.5%	—	—	324.3	268.4	361.2
Employees	3.8%	559	559	613	625	649

INTERNET CAPITAL GROUP, INC.

NASDAQ (GM): ICGE

690 Lee Rd., Ste. 310
Wayne, PA 19087
Phone: 610-727-6900
Fax: 610-727-6901
Web: www.internetcapital.com

CEO: Walter W. Buckley III
CFO: R. Kirk Morgan
HR: —
FYE: December 31
Type: Public

B2B or not B2B? That's a poignant question for Internet Capital Group (ICG). The company invests in companies involved in the business-to-business (B2B) Internet market, working with its holdings to develop strategy. It owns stakes in more than a dozen companies, including controlling interests in online marketing firm Vcommerce; Investor Force, which makes online data management software for pension managers and other financial services providers; and ICG Commerce, which offers procurement outsourcing services. Hertz and Kimberly-Clark, which are ICG Commerce's biggest customers, each account for about 17% of ICG's revenue.

	Annual Growth	12/05	12/06	12/07	12/08	12/09
Sales ($ mil.)	15.6%	50.6	64.7	52.9	71.2	90.3
Net income ($ mil.)	(20.8%)	72.5	15.6	(30.6)	(22.9)	28.5
Market value ($ mil.)	(5.2%)	299.6	373.9	427.8	198.6	242.3
Employees	5.3%	22	24	24	23	27

INTERNETARRAY, INC.

Pink Sheets: INAR

551 Fifth Ave., Ste. 1625
New York, NY 10176
Phone: 410-295-3388
Fax: —
Web: www.internetarray.com

CEO: Michael J. Black
CFO: Michael J. Black
HR: —
FYE: June 30
Type: Public

InternetArray wants to align with an assortment of online companies. The firm, formerly U.S. MedSys, offers financing and advice to early-stage Internet companies. Calling its charges "partners," InternetArray provides marketing, sales, administrative, and other back-office assistance in exchange for a share of the partner company. The company owns social media developer Noobis, which is working with social networking sites in China, the US, the UK, and Canada. Noobis' Amplify product helps not-for-profits set up fundraising networks. InternetArray also owns BidSellBuy.com, an online auction and shopping network.

INTERPHASE CORPORATION

NASDAQ (GM): INPH

2901 N. Dallas Pkwy., Ste. 200
Plano, TX 75093
Phone: 214-654-5000
Fax: 214-654-5500
Web: www.iphase.com

CEO: Gregory B. (Greg) Kalush
CFO: Thomas N. Tipton Jr.
HR: Deborah A. Shute
FYE: December 31
Type: Public

Interphase keeps acronyms connected. The company makes adapters, controllers, and other connectivity devices for storage area, local area, and wide area networks (SANs, LANs, and WANs). Its networking devices include adapters and controllers for connecting components in LANs and WANs. Interphase also offers adapters for telecom network embedded servers. Its Fibre Channel SAN systems feature utility software and adapters for connecting mass storage servers and other storage devices to networks. Interphase sells primarily through OEMs, distributors, and systems integrators. The company generates about two-thirds of its revenues outside North America.

	Annual Growth	12/05	12/06	12/07	12/08	12/09
Sales ($ mil.)	(4.6%)	30.9	33.4	30.8	26.2	25.6
Net income ($ mil.)	—	(2.3)	2.1	(1.2)	(3.0)	(5.6)
Market value ($ mil.)	(12.7%)	30.1	56.6	70.5	11.3	17.5
Employees	(0.2%)	126	132	137	124	125

⊞ THE INTERPUBLIC GROUP OF COMPANIES, INC.

NYSE: IPG

1114 Avenue of the Americas
New York, NY 10036
Phone: 212-704-1200
Fax: 212-704-1201
Web: www.interpublic.com

CEO: Michael I. Roth
CFO: Frank Mergenthaler
HR: Timothy A. Sompolski
FYE: December 31
Type: Public

Subsidiaries of this company come between brands and the general public. The Interpublic Group of Companies is one of the world's largest advertising and marketing services conglomerates, operating through offices in more than 100 countries. Its flagship creative agencies include McCann Worldgroup, DraftFCB, and Lowe & Partners, while such firms as Campbell-Ewald, Deutsch, and Hill, Holliday are leaders in the US advertising business. Interpublic also offers direct marketing, media services, and public relations through such agencies as Initiative and Weber Shandwick. Its largest clients include General Motors, Johnson & Johnson, Microsoft, and Unilever.

	Annual Growth	12/05	12/06	12/07	12/08	12/09
Sales ($ mil.)	(1.0%)	6,274.3	6,190.8	6,554.2	6,962.7	6,027.6
Net income ($ mil.)	—	(262.9)	(31.7)	167.6	295.0	121.3
Market value ($ mil.)	(6.5%)	4,721.9	5,989.2	3,968.4	1,937.7	3,611.2
Employees	(1.8%)	43,000	42,000	43,000	45,000	40,000

INTERSECTIONS INC.

NASDAQ (GM): INTX

3901 Stonecroft Blvd.
Chantilly, VA 20153
Phone: 703-488-6100
Fax: 703-488-6223
Web: www.intersections.com

CEO: Michael R. Stanfield
CFO: Madalyn C. Behneman
HR: —
FYE: December 31
Type: Public

Robert Johnson went to the crossroads to get the blues; consumers can go to Intersections to make sure they don't. Intersections provides credit management and identity-theft protection to nearly 5 million consumer subscribers in the US and the UK. Services include credit record monitoring through major reporting agencies Equifax, Experian, and Trans Union. Subsidiary Screening International provides risk management services, including pre-employment background checks and driving records. Its Intersections Insurance Services unit offers customers discounts on insurance products. Major clients, which together account for about 70% of total revenues, include Bank of America, Citibank, and Capital One.

	Annual Growth	12/05	12/06	12/07	12/08	12/09
Sales ($ mil.)	21.9%	165.2	201.1	271.7	361.6	364.6
Net income ($ mil.)	—	12.5	9.4	6.9	(16.0)	(6.4)
Market value ($ mil.)	(14.9%)	164.1	186.6	146.4	91.4	86.1
Employees	11.3%	630	933	1,022	968	968

⊞ INTERSIL CORPORATION

NASDAQ (GS): ISIL

1001 Murphy Ranch Rd., Ste. 1
Milpitas, CA 95035
Phone: 408-432-8888
Fax: 408-434-5351
Web: www.intersil.com

CEO: David B. (Dave) Bell
CFO: Jonathan A. Kennedy
HR: Vern Kelley
FYE: December 31
Type: Public

Intersil makes silicon chips that help interconnect the high-tech world. The company designs and distributes high-performance analog integrated circuits (ICs), primarily for high-end consumer electronics (such as mobile devices, DVD recorders, LCD televisions, Global Positioning System products, and MP3 players) and industrial equipment. Other leading applications are found in the communications and computing markets. The company's power management chips are used by manufacturers such as Dell and IBM in PCs, servers, and storage networking gear. The Asia/Pacific region produces about three-quarters of the company's sales.

	Annual Growth	12/05	12/06	12/07	12/08	12/09
Sales ($ mil.)	0.5%	600.3	740.6	757.0	769.7	611.4
Net income ($ mil.)	(18.1%)	85.9	151.9	140.5	(1,037.6)	38.6
Market value ($ mil.)	(11.4%)	3,077.5	2,958.8	3,028.1	1,136.8	1,897.5
Employees	3.0%	1,336	1,423	1,494	1,531	1,503

INTERSTATE BATTERY SYSTEM OF AMERICA, INC.

12770 Merit Dr., Ste. 400
Dallas, TX 75251
Phone: 972-991-1444
Fax: 972-458-8288
Web: www.ibsa.com

CEO: Carlos M. Sepulveda
CFO: Lisa Huntsberry
HR: Chris Willis
FYE: April 30
Type: Private

Interstate Battery System of America offers a battery of batteries. The company can provide the electrical juice for everything from cell phones and laptops to boats, lawn mowers, motorcycles, and RVs. It also makes replacement automobile batteries for such brands as Ford, Subaru, and Toyota. Consumers can purchase Interstate Battery's products online and at more than 200,000 retail locations, including some 340 Interstate All Battery Centers in the US, Canada, Puerto Rico, and the Dominican Republic. The company has about 300 distributors throughout North America. Interstate Battery sponsors the Joe Gibbs Racing team on the NASCAR circuit. Founded in 1952, the company is owned by chairman Norm Miller.

	Annual Growth	4/04	4/05	4/06	4/07	4/08
Sales ($ mil.)	21.0%	700.0	754.9	1,000.0	1,000.0	1,500.0
Employees	12.0%	900	1,251	1,400	1,275	1,415

⊞ An in-depth profile of this company is available to Hoover's Online members at hoovers.com.

INTERSTATE HOTELS & RESORTS, INC.

4501 N. Fairfax Dr., Ste. 500
Arlington, VA 22203
Phone: 703-387-3100
Fax: 703-543-0633
Web: www.ihrco.com

CEO: Thomas F. (Tom) Hewitt
CFO: Bruce A. Riggins
HR: Christopher L. (Chris) Bennett
FYE: December 31
Type: Private

If you're driving on the interstate and are looking for a hotel or a resort, Interstate Hotels & Resorts is your company. Interstate is the nation's largest independent hotel operator, managing more than 200 hotels in about 35 US states and Washington, D.C., and internationally in Canada, Belgium, Ireland, Mexico, and Russia. Its property portfolio boasts more than 45,000 rooms and includes locations affiliated with about 30 different hotel chains. Among its brands are Marriott, Hilton, Sheraton, Westin, Radisson, Doubletree, and Wyndham. Interstate also manages properties for some 15 independent hotels, and wholly-owns about 10 properties. Interstate was formed in 1998 as a spin-off of CapStar Hotel Company.

	Annual Growth	12/04	12/05	12/06	12/07	12/08
Sales ($ mil.)	(4.7%)	944.0	1,116.2	975.2	800.1	779.5
Net income ($ mil.)	—	(5.7)	12.9	29.8	22.8	(18.0)
Employees	(12.9%)	33,000	33,000	25,500	19,700	19,000

INTERSTATE POWER AND LIGHT COMPANY

Alliant Energy Tower, 200 1st St. SE
Cedar Rapids, IA 52401
Phone: 319-786-4411
Fax: 319-786-7633
Web: www.alliantenergy.com

CEO: William D. (Bill) Harvey
CFO: Patricia L. Kampling
HR: —
FYE: December 31
Type: Subsidiary

Interstate Power and Light (IP&L) got the bright idea of providing electricity and has hit the road to make it happen. The company, incorporated in 1925, provides energy in a tri-state portion of the Midwest. The Alliant Energy utility subsidiary serves more than 525,000 electricity customers and more than 233,800 natural gas customers. In addition, IP&L has nearly 3,000 MW of generating capacity from fossil-fueled and nuclear power plants. It also provides steam to certain customers in Cedar Rapids, and it offers other energy-related services across its service area.

THE INTERTECH GROUP, INC.

4838 Jenkins Ave.
North Charleston, SC 29405
Phone: 843-744-5174
Fax: 843-747-4092
Web: www.theintertechgroup.com

CEO: Anita Zucker
CFO: Brice Sweatt
HR: Jay Tiedemann
FYE: December 31
Type: Private

The InterTech Group likes to interweave a wide variety of technology-driven manufacturing businesses with other activities, such as business services (image marketing, financial transaction services) and entertainment. The group, a holding company with more than 100 businesses worldwide, puts its primary focus on plastics and fiber products, including industrial protective wear and fabrics used by firefighters and astronauts (through its PBI Performance Products subsidiary). InterTech's RemGrit unit makes knives, saw blades, and various handheld tools. The company was founded in 1978 by the late Jerry Zucker, who in 2006 led the acquisition of Canada's Hudson's Bay Company, and is still owned by his family.

	Annual Growth	12/04	12/05	12/06	12/07	12/08
Est. sales ($ mil.)	2.8%	—	3,500.0	3,830.0	3,450.0	3,800.0
Employees	3.3%	—	14,500	16,000	16,000	16,000

INTERVAL LEISURE GROUP, INC.

NASDAQ (GS): IILG

6262 Sunset Dr.
Miami, FL 33143
Phone: 305-666-1861
Fax: 305-667-0653
Web: www.intervalleisuregroup.com

CEO: Craig M. Nash
CFO: William L. (Bill) Harvey
HR: —
FYE: December 31
Type: Public

Your vacation time is worth something to Interval Leisure Group. The company is a leading timeshare exchange broker, offering services to nearly 2 million member-property owners. Its exchange programs allow owners to trade their timeshare intervals for accommodations at other properties in its network of more than 2,400 resorts in approximately 80 countries. In addition, its Preferred Residences is a luxury branded membership program with Preferred Hotel Group. The company generates revenue primarily through membership fees. Interval Leisure Group (formerly Interval International) was previously a subsidiary of IAC/InterActiveCorp (IAC). In 2008 IAC spun off Interval, which became a separately listed entity.

	Annual Growth	12/05	12/06	12/07	12/08	12/09
Sales ($ mil.)	11.6%	260.8	288.6	360.4	409.8	405.0
Net income ($ mil.)	(6.1%)	49.2	58.0	71.1	45.3	38.2
Market value ($ mil.)	131.4%	—	—	—	306.6	709.3
Employees	(1.8%)	—	—	2,800	2,800	2,700

INTERVEST BANCSHARES CORPORATION

NASDAQ (GS): IBCA

1 Rockefeller Plaza, Ste. 400
New York, NY 10020
Phone: 212-218-2800
Fax: 212-218-8390
Web: www.intervestnatbank.com

CEO: Lowell S. Dansker
CFO: John J. Arvonio
HR: Diane S. Rathburn
FYE: December 31
Type: Public

Intervest Bancshares is the holding company for Intervest National Bank, which operates one branch in New York City and six other branches in Pinellas County, Florida. Most of the company's lending activities are real estate-related: Commercial mortgages make up more than half of its loan portfolio, while multifamily residential mortgages account for another 40%. Some of the company's lending has historically been carried out by its Intervest Mortgage Corporation arm. However, the subsidiary drastically scaled back its lending practices as market conditions deteriorated in 2008. The family of chairman and CEO Lowell Dansker controls Intervest Bancshares.

	Annual Growth	12/05	12/06	12/07	12/08	12/09
Assets ($ mil.)	8.9%	1,706.4	1,971.8	2,021.4	2,271.8	2,401.2
Net income ($ mil.)	(35.8%)	18.2	23.5	19.4	7.3	3.1
Market value ($ mil.)	(39.7%)	204.7	284.6	142.4	33.0	27.1
Employees	1.1%	69	72	72	72	72

INTEST CORPORATION

NASDAQ (GM): INTT

7 Esterbrook Ln.
Cherry Hill, NJ 08003
Phone: 856-424-6886
Fax: 856-751-1222
Web: www.intest.com

CEO: Robert E. Matthiessen
CFO: Hugh T. Regan Jr.
HR: —
FYE: December 31
Type: Public

When semiconductor makers are testing their chips, inTEST handles the trickiest chores. The semiconductor test equipment supplier offers test head manipulators, docking hardware, and systems for managing temperatures during integrated circuit (IC) production and testing. inTEST's products facilitate testing procedures by quickly moving and connecting IC components to handling and testing equipment. The company's clients include Analog Devices, Freescale Semiconductor, Intel, Sony, STMicroelectronics, and Texas Instruments (14% of sales). inTEST built up its product line through a series of acquisitions. The company gets most of its sales in the US.

	Annual Growth	12/05	12/06	12/07	12/08	12/09
Sales ($ mil.)	(18.6%)	53.4	62.3	48.7	38.8	23.5
Net income ($ mil.)	—	(3.6)	2.9	(6.7)	(9.1)	(4.8)
Market value ($ mil.)	(15.0%)	34.1	45.1	24.2	2.6	17.8
Employees	(17.5%)	231	224	209	175	107

INTEVAC, INC.

NASDAQ (GM): IVAC

3560 Bassett St.
Santa Clara, CA 95054
Phone: 408-986-9888
Fax: 408-988-8145
Web: www.intevac.com

CEO: Kevin Fairbairn
CFO: Jeff Andreson
HR: Kimberly Burk
FYE: December 31
Type: Public

Intevac's sputtering doesn't stem from a speech impediment. The company's Equipment division manufactures sputtering systems that deposit alloy films onto hard-disk drives; the films magnetize the drives and thus enable them to record information. The Equipment division also makes sputterers used to make flat-panel displays. Intevac's Imaging division develops sensitive electro-optical devices used in high-performance digital cameras and military targeting equipment. Leading customers include Fuji Electric, Hitachi Global Storage Technologies, and Seagate. Intevac gets about two-thirds of its sales from the Asia/Pacific region.

	Annual Growth	12/05	12/06	12/07	12/08	12/09
Sales ($ mil.)	(13.2%)	137.2	259.9	215.8	110.3	78.0
Net income ($ mil.)	—	16.2	46.7	27.3	(15.3)	(10.1)
Market value ($ mil.)	(3.5%)	294.0	578.0	323.9	112.9	255.5
Employees	0.5%	362	540	480	394	370

INTRADO INC.

1601 Dry Creek Dr.
Longmont, CO 80503
Phone: 720-494-5800
Fax: 720-494-6600
Web: www.intrado.com

CEO: George K. Heinrichs
CFO: Mary Hester
HR: —
FYE: December 31
Type: Subsidiary

Dial 911 and Intrado helps to ensure that your plea for help is answered. Intrado provides 911 operations support systems services to incumbent and competitive local-exchange carriers and wireless phone companies in North America. It also offers its services directly to state and local government agencies. Intrado's National Data Services Center ensures that 911 calls are routed to the appropriate public safety agency with the caller's call-back number and location. The company also licenses its software to carriers for in-house management of 911 services.

INTRALINKS HOLDINGS, INC.

150 E. 42nd St., 8th Fl.
New York, NY 10017
Phone: 212-543-7700
Fax: 212-543-7978
Web: www.intralinks.com

CEO: J. Andrew Damico
CFO: Anthony C. Plesner
HR: Jody Tracey
FYE: December 31
Type: Private

IntraLinks wants high volumes of confidential information to travel comfortably online. The company provides its clients with secure, collaborative online digital workspaces for conducting financial transactions, discussing mergers and acquisitions, exchanging documents, and collaborating with advisers, customers, and suppliers. Intralinks sells its products to companies in the financial services, life sciences, and mergers and acquisitions markets. Customers have included DuPont, JPMorgan Chase, and Bank of America. IntraLinks claims more than 50,000 clients worldwide. IntraLinks filed for an IPO in April 2010.

	Annual Growth	12/04	12/05	12/06	12/07	12/08
Est. sales ($ mil.)	—	—	—	—	—	144.0
Employees	—	—	—	—	—	380

INTREPID POTASH, INC.

NYSE: IPI

700 17th St., Ste. 1700
Denver, CO 80202
Phone: 303-296-3006
Fax: 303-298-7502
Web: www.intrepidpotash.com

CEO: Robert P. Jornayvaz III
CFO: David W. Honeyfield
HR: James N. Whyte
FYE: December 31
Type: Public

Hungry plants turn to Intrepid Potash for their food supply. The mining company produces two potassium-containing minerals, potash and langbeinite, that are essential nutrients in plant and crop fertilizer. Intrepid culls these minerals from five mines in New Mexico and Utah, where it also operates production facilities. Potash accounts for 90% of its sales. The company sells primarily within the US to the agricultural, industrial, and feed markets; PotashCorp sells Intrepid's potash outside North America. It supplies nearly 10% of US potash consumption annually and is the country's largest producer of the stuff. (The US imports a great majority of the potash it uses.)

	Annual Growth	12/05	12/06	12/07	12/08	12/09
Sales ($ mil.)	18.5%	153.0	152.7	213.5	305.9	301.8
Net income ($ mil.)	12.5%	34.5	36.0	29.7	98.2	55.3
Market value ($ mil.)	40.4%	—	—	—	1,559.6	2,190.4
Employees	3.1%	—	710	734	776	778

INTRICON CORPORATION

NASDAQ (GM): IIN

1260 Red Fox Rd.
Arden Hills, MN 55112
Phone: 651-636-9770
Fax: 651-636-9503
Web: www.intricon.com

CEO: Mark S. Gorder
CFO: J. Scott Longval
HR: —
FYE: December 31
Type: Public

IntriCon hears its future calling, and that future is in precision microminiature components and molded plastic parts, such as volume controls and switches, primarily for use in hearing aids. Intricon's components are also used in professional audio equipment, such as headsets and microphones. The company has reshaped its product portfolio through a series of acquisitions and divestitures, including the 2010 sale of its RTI Electronics business line to Shackleton Equity Partners.

	Annual Growth	12/05	12/06	12/07	12/08	12/09
Sales ($ mil.)	3.8%	44.5	51.7	69.0	65.6	51.7
Net income ($ mil.)	—	1.5	1.2	1.9	1.0	(3.9)
Market value ($ mil.)	(6.6%)	23.2	27.2	68.3	19.7	17.7
Employees	4.9%	426	561	612	523	515

⊞ INTRUSION INC.

OTC: INTZ

1101 E. Arapaho Rd., Ste. 200
Richardson, TX 75081
Phone: 972-234-6400
Fax: 972-301-3685
Web: www.intrusion.com

CEO: G. Ward Paxton
CFO: Michael L. Paxton
HR: —
FYE: December 31
Type: Public

Think of Intrusion as a virtual police force protecting and serving your network. The security specialist sells network intrusion detection and monitoring systems. Its products include software and stand-alone security appliances that guard against misuse of classified or private information and aid law enforcement agencies in battling cyber crimes. Intrusion also provides consulting, design, installation, and technical support services. The company sells its products directly and through distributors and resellers. Intrusion markets its products to government agencies, as well as businesses ranging from health care providers to telecommunications service operators.

	Annual Growth	12/05	12/06	12/07	12/08	12/09
Sales ($ mil.)	(4.9%)	6.0	5.2	3.5	4.1	4.9
Net income ($ mil.)	—	(3.3)	(3.0)	(2.4)	(0.8)	0.2
Market value ($ mil.)	(33.9%)	24.6	5.4	2.0	4.1	4.7
Employees	(11.0%)	43	32	27	26	27

⊞ An in-depth profile of this company is available to Hoover's Online members at hoovers.com.

841

INTUIT INC.

NASDAQ (GS): INTU

2700 Coast Ave.
Mountain View, CA 94043
Phone: 650-944-6000
Fax: 650-944-3699
Web: www.intuit.com

CEO: Brad D. Smith
CFO: R. Neil Williams
HR: Sherry Whiteley
FYE: July 31
Type: Public

Intuit knows that good accounting takes more than a pocket calculator. The company is a leading provider of personal finance (Quicken), small business accounting (QuickBooks), and consumer tax preparation (TurboTax) software for consumers, accountants, and small businesses; Intuit claims more than 50 million users for its products and services. Other software offerings include industry-specific accounting and management applications for construction, real estate, retail, and wholesale distribution organizations. Intuit also provides payroll services, financial supplies, and software for professional tax preparation, as well as products and services geared toward financial institutions.

	Annual Growth	7/05	7/06	7/07	7/08	7/09
Sales ($ mil.)	11.8%	2,037.7	2,342.3	2,672.9	3,075.0	3,182.5
Net income ($ mil.)	4.0%	381.6	417.0	440.0	476.8	447.0
Market value ($ mil.)	5.5%	7,534.1	9,690.7	8,990.6	8,579.4	9,323.4
Employees	2.7%	7,000	7,500	8,200	8,200	7,800

INTUITIVE SURGICAL, INC.

NASDAQ (GS): ISRG

1266 Kifer Rd., Bldg. 101
Sunnyvale, CA 94086
Phone: 408-523-2100
Fax: 408-523-1390
Web: www.intuitivesurgical.com

CEO: Lonnie M. Smith
CFO: Marshall L. Mohr
HR: Heather Rider
FYE: December 31
Type: Public

Intuitive Surgical is haptic to meet you. Employing haptics (the science of computer-aided touch sensitivity), the firm has developed the da Vinci Surgical System, a combination of software, hardware, and optics that allows doctors to perform robotically aided surgery from a remote console. The da Vinci system reproduces the doctor's hand movements in real time, with surgery performed by tiny electromechanical arms and instruments inserted in the patient's body through small incisions. The company also makes the instruments and accessories used with its system. Intuitive Surgical sells its products in the Americas, Asia, Australia, and Europe through both a direct sales force and independent distributors.

	Annual Growth	12/05	12/06	12/07	12/08	12/09
Sales ($ mil.)	46.7%	227.3	372.7	600.8	874.9	1,052.2
Net income ($ mil.)	25.4%	94.1	72.0	144.5	204.3	232.6
Market value ($ mil.)	26.8%	4,593.0	3,756.0	12,650.6	4,973.7	11,884.2
Employees	31.8%	419	563	764	1,049	1,263

INUVO, INC.

NYSE Amex: INUV

15550 Lightwave Dr.
Clearwater, FL 33760
Phone: 727-324-0046
Fax: 727-324-0063
Web: inuvo.com

CEO: —
CFO: Wally Ruiz
HR: —
FYE: December 31
Type: Public

As consumers surf the Web, Inuvo wants to help advertisers ride the waves alongside them. Inuvo, formerly known as Think Partnership and as Kowabunga!, provides a wide range of marketing and advertising services through its Exchange and Direct operating segments. Its Inuvo platform, residing in its Exchange segment, offers affiliate marketing, search engine marketing, and lead generation services, helping customers to drive traffic and convert it into sales. Its ValidClick software acts as a pay-per-click marketplace while its MyAP platform measures and tracks browsing behavior. Inuvo's Direct segment sells direct-to-consumer membership programs, primarily targeting expectant mothers and new parents.

	Annual Growth	12/05	12/06	12/07	12/08	12/09
Sales ($ mil.)	6.4%	40.4	71.9	73.6	51.6	51.7
Net income ($ mil.)	—	0.0	0.6	(1.1)	(82.9)	(5.4)
Market value ($ mil.)	(38.3%)	198.7	273.0	128.5	5.1	28.7
Employees	(20.3%)	287	254	249	125	116

INVACARE CORPORATION

NYSE: IVC

1 Invacare Way
Elyria, OH 44036
Phone: 440-329-6000
Fax: 440-366-9008
Web: www.invacare.com

CEO: A. Malachi Mixon III
CFO: Robert K. (Rob) Gudbranson
HR: Joseph S. (Joe) Usaj
FYE: December 31
Type: Public

Invacare allows wheelchair users to set their own pace. Invacare is a leading maker of wheelchairs — including manual, powered, custom-made, and the ultra zippy chairs used by athletes. It also makes other medical equipment including crutches, bed systems, respiratory devices, and motorized scooters. It manufactures and sells its own products to home health care and medical equipment dealers in North America, Europe, and the Asia/Pacific region, as well as to government agencies and distributors. Invacare's Supply Group distributes other companies' medical equipment and disposable products, such as home diabetic and wound care items.

	Annual Growth	12/05	12/06	12/07	12/08	12/09
Sales ($ mil.)	2.6%	1,529.7	1,498.0	1,602.2	1,755.7	1,693.1
Net income ($ mil.)	(4.2%)	48.9	(317.8)	1.2	38.6	41.2
Market value ($ mil.)	(5.7%)	1,019.8	795.1	816.1	502.6	807.7
Employees	(0.8%)	6,100	6,000	5,700	6,100	5,900

INVENERGY LLC

1 S. Wacker Dr., Ste. 2020
Chicago, IL 60606
Phone: 312-224-1400
Fax: 312-224-1444
Web: www.invenergyllc.com

CEO: Michael Polsky
CFO: Jim Murphy
HR: —
FYE: December 31
Type: Private

While not quite inventing energy, Invenergy is pulling it out of thin air. The energy generation company operates about a dozen wind energy generating facilities in the US, Europe, and Canada. It builds, develops, and buys energy producing properties and has about 2,000 megawatts of wind energy capacity online. While wind is the focus, Invenergy also uses natural gas to produce 2,200 megawatts of energy from facilities in the US and Canada and has plans to enter the solar energy market as well. The company has offices in the US, Poland, and the UK. CEO and president Michael Polsky founded Invenergy in 2001.

	Annual Growth	12/04	12/05	12/06	12/07	12/08
Est. sales ($ mil.)	—	—	—	—	—	9.3
Employees	—	—	—	—	—	140

INVENTIV HEALTH, INC.

NASDAQ (GS): VTIV

500 Atrium Dr.
Somerset, NJ 08873
Phone: 732-537-4800
Fax: 732-537-4912
Web: www.ventiv.com

CEO: R. Blane Walter
CFO: David S. Bassin
HR: —
FYE: December 31
Type: Public

To sell a new drug, it may be time to get inVentiv. inVentiv Health provides commercial, clinical, communications, and patient assistance services for customers in the life sciences and pharmaceutical industries. The company's commercial services unit provides outsourced sales and marketing services, market research, data collection and management, recruitment, and training. The clinical services unit provides clinical staffing, clinical research and statistical analysis, and executive placement. It serves more than 350 clients, including Bayer Corporation, Bristol-Myers Squibb, and Noven Pharmaceuticals. In May 2010 inVentiv Health agreed to be acquired by Thomas H. Lee Partners for $1.1 billion.

	Annual Growth	12/05	12/06	12/07	12/08	12/09
Sales ($ mil.)	17.8%	556.3	766.2	977.3	1,119.8	1,072.0
Net income ($ mil.)	2.1%	43.9	51.2	47.5	(128.0)	47.7
Market value ($ mil.)	(9.0%)	800.5	1,198.0	1,049.3	391.1	548.0
Employees	11.1%	4,200	5,200	5,700	7,100	6,400

THE INVENTURE GROUP, INC.

NASDAQ (CM): SNAK

5050 N. 40th St., Ste. 300
Phoenix, AZ 85018
Phone: 623-932-6200
Fax: 602-522-2690
Web: www.inventuregroup.net

CEO: Terry McDaniel
CFO: Steve Weinberger
HR: —
FYE: December 31
Type: Public

It's always an adventure at The Inventure Group. The company — founded by Don and Jay Poore in 1986 and formerly known as Poore Brothers — makes snack chips and dips under Bob's Texas Style, Poore Brothers, Boulder Canyon Natural Foods, and Tato Skins brands. The company also makes savory snacks branded with the T.G.I. Friday's and BURGER KING names, as well as manufacturing store brands for several food chains in the southwestern US. The firm distributes its own and other companies' snack food products. Costco accounted for about 24% of the company's 2008 sales.

	Annual Growth	12/05	12/06	12/07	12/08	12/09
Sales ($ mil.)	12.6%	75.3	69.8	90.9	113.1	121.0
Net income ($ mil.)	88.7%	0.3	1.1	(1.5)	2.4	3.8
Market value ($ mil.)	(4.4%)	50.4	43.8	39.9	29.1	42.2
Employees	8.3%	270	268	361	374	372

INVERNESS CORPORATION

6 Hazel St.
Attleboro, MA 02703
Phone: 774-203-1130
Fax: 774-203-1146
Web: www.invernesscorp.com

CEO: Peter A. Indiveri
CFO: Kathleen Decroce
HR: Bill Meade
FYE: December 31
Type: Subsidiary

For its customers, Inverness Corporation is all ears. A Cookson Group subsidiary, it makes and markets the Inverness Ear Piercing System, a fully encapsulated sterile ear piercing kit. The company's piercing system is used in some 5,000 US retail outlets and is sold in about 45 countries. The system accompanies a pierced earring selection of about 200 styles. Customers have included Wal-Mart, Claire's, and Merle Norman, among others. Inverness also offers onsite training for staff. For those who like to go solo, there's a personal piercer and personal care products, such as antiseptics for ear care and body piercing care. The company boasts offices in Canada, Hong Kong, France, Japan, the UK, and the US.

	Annual Growth	12/04	12/05	12/06	12/07	12/08
Est. sales ($ mil.)	—	—	—	—	—	7.9
Employees	—	—	—	—	—	120

INVERNESS MEDICAL INNOVATIONS, INC.

NYSE: IMA

51 Sawyer Rd., Ste. 200
Waltham, MA 02453
Phone: 781-647-3900
Fax: 781-647-3939
Web: www.invernessmedical.com

CEO: Ron Zwanziger
CFO: David A. (Dave) Teitel
HR: —
FYE: December 31
Type: Public

When you really need an answer — fast — toss out the crystal ball and bring in Inverness Medical Innovations. The company offers both professional and consumer diagnostic tests as well as health management services. Its professional diagnostic products include tests for cancers, cardiovascular disease, drugs of abuse, infectious diseases, and women's health including pregnancy tests and fertility monitors. Inverness' consumer diagnostics include the First Check brand of drug testing products. The firm's health management division, Alere Medical, provides services including disease monitoring and telemedicine. The company plans to change its name to Alere and rebrand its diverse products and services.

	Annual Growth	12/05	12/06	12/07	12/08	12/09
Sales ($ mil.)	46.1%	421.9	569.5	839.5	1,671.4	1,922.6
Net income ($ mil.)	—	(19.2)	(16.8)	(241.5)	(21.8)	26.6
Market value ($ mil.)	15.0%	1,993.1	3,253.2	4,722.7	1,589.6	3,489.5
Employees	47.9%	2,360	2,561	5,153	8,300	11,300

INVESCO AIM MANAGEMENT GROUP INC.

11 Greenway Plaza, Ste. 100
Houston, TX 77046
Phone: 713-626-1919
Fax: 713-993-9890
Web: www.invescoaim.com

CEO: Philip A. (Phil) Taylor
CFO: —
HR: —
FYE: December 31
Type: Subsidiary

Ready, aim, invest! Invesco Aim Management Group is a mutual fund and investment management subsidiary of Invesco. Serving both institutional and retail investors in the US, the firm manages approximately 70 mutual funds that focus on domestic and international equities and, to a lesser extent, bonds and other fixed-income products. It also offers about 100 exchange-traded funds (under the Invesco PowerShares banner), as well as separately managed accounts, annuities, and retirement and college savings plans. Invesco Aim mainly distributes its products through third parties such as broker-dealers, financial advisors, and 401(k) plans. It has more than $60 billion of assets under management.

INVESCO LTD.

NYSE: IVZ

1555 Peachtree St., NE, Ste. 1800
Atlanta, GA 30309
Phone: 404-479-1095
Fax: 404-439-4911
Web: www.invesco.com

CEO: Martin L. (Marty) Flanagan
CFO: Loren M. Starr
HR: Washington Dender
FYE: December 31
Type: Public

Invesco (formerly AMVESCAP) is AIMing for the topmost position on the investment heap. One of the world's largest asset management companies, the firm manages investments for individuals, corporations, foundations, endowments, and government institutions under the Invesco AIM (in the US), Invesco (Europe and Asia), Invesco Perpetual (UK), and Trimark (Canada) brands. Subsidiary Atlantic Trust serves high-net-worth individuals and families. Invesco also offers managed accounts, separate accounts, and college investment plans. The company spreads its operations wide, with about 55 offices in some 20 countries. It has approximately $420 billion of assets under management.

	Annual Growth	12/05	12/06	12/07	12/08	12/09
Assets ($ mil.)	9.5%	7,577.6	9,292.0	12,925.2	9,756.9	10,909.6
Net income ($ mil.)	11.0%	212.2	490.1	673.6	481.7	322.5
Market value ($ mil.)	11.2%	6,714.4	10,754.3	13,690.5	6,299.9	10,248.2
Employees	(4.2%)	5,798	5,574	5,475	5,325	4,890

INVESCO MORTGAGE CAPITAL INC.

NYSE: IVR

1360 Peachtree St., NE
Atlanta, GA 30309
Phone: 404-892-0896
Fax: —
Web: www.invescomortgagecapital.com

CEO: Richard J. King
CFO: Donald R. Ramon
HR: —
FYE: December 31
Type: Public

At a time when many firms are fleeing mortgage securities like rats off a sinking ship, Invesco Mortgage Capital (formerly Invesco Agency Securities) is ready to weigh anchor. Backed by the deep pockets of Invesco Ltd., the real estate investment trust (REIT) plans a safe passage for investors by purchasing agency-backed mortgages secured by the likes of Fannie Mae and Freddie Mac. It is managed and advised by sibling Invesco Institutional. Invesco Mortgage Capital began operations and went public in 2009; it plans to use the proceeds from its IPO to further its strategy of acquiring agency-backed mortgages, including residential fixed- and adjustable-rate and hybrid mortgages.

	Annual Growth	12/05	12/06	12/07	12/08	12/09
Sales ($ mil.)	—	—	—	—	0.1	0.0
Net income ($ mil.)	—	—	—	—	0.0	15.1
Market value ($ mil.)	—	—	—	—	—	590.3
Employees	—	—	—	—	—	—

An in-depth profile of this company is available to Hoover's Online members at hoovers.com.

843

INVESTMENT TECHNOLOGY GROUP, INC.

NYSE: ITG

380 Madison Ave.
New York, NY 10017
Phone: 212-588-4000
Fax: 212-444-6295
Web: www.itginc.com

CEO: Robert C. (Bob) Gasser
CFO: Steven R. (Steve) Vigliotti
HR: —
FYE: December 31
Type: Public

As its name implies, Investment Technology Group (ITG) combines technology with investing. The company provides automated equity trading products and services related to order management and execution management; it serves institutional investors and brokers throughout the trading process, from analysis before the trade to post-trading evaluation. Core products include its Portfolio System for Institutional Trading (POSIT) crossing system, which lets institutional clients confidentially trade shares and stock portfolios among themselves; ITG Algorithms; and ITG Logic, for risk management. The company is active in Asia, Australia, Canada, Europe, and the US.

	Annual Growth	12/05	12/06	12/07	12/08	12/09
Sales ($ mil.)	11.6%	408.2	599.5	731.0	763.0	633.1
Net income ($ mil.)	(10.8%)	67.7	97.9	111.1	114.6	42.8
Market value ($ mil.)	(13.7%)	1,544.3	1,868.5	2,073.8	990.0	858.4
Employees	13.5%	714	1,060	1,060	1,323	1,183

INVESTORS BANCORP, INC.

NASDAQ (GS): ISBC

101 JFK Pkwy.
Short Hills, NJ 07078
Phone: 973-924-5100
Fax: 973-924-5192
Web: www.isbnj.com

CEO: Kevin Cummings
CFO: Thomas F. Splaine Jr.
HR: —
FYE: June 30
Type: Public

Apostrophe? Investors Bancorp don't need no stinking apostrophe. The firm is the holding company for Investors Savings Bank, which serves northern and eastern New Jersey from more than 60 branch offices. Founded in 1926, the bank offers such standard deposit products as savings and checking accounts, CDs, money market accounts, and IRAs. Investors Savings Bank's loan portfolio is composed almost entirely of single-family residential mortgages and home equity loans. It also offers commercial mortgages, construction loans, and consumer loans. Mutual holding company Investors Bancorp, MHC, owns 59% of Investors Bancorp.

	Annual Growth	6/05	6/06	6/07	6/08	6/09
Assets ($ mil.)	13.0%	4,992.8	5,497.2	5,601.1	6,419.1	8,136.4
Net income ($ mil.)	—	(3.1)	15.0	22.3	16.0	(64.9)
Market value ($ mil.)	(12.1%)	—	1,556.8	1,543.0	1,500.5	1,057.0
Employees	12.0%	—	502	510	571	705

INVESTORS CAPITAL HOLDINGS, LTD.

NYSE Amex: ICH

230 Broadway East
Lynnfield, MA 01940
Phone: 781-593-8565
Fax: 781-593-9464
Web: www.investorscapital.com

CEO: Timothy B. (Tim) Murphy
CFO: Kathleen L. Donnelly
HR: Andrew Effron
FYE: March 31
Type: Public

The name pretty much says it all. Investors Capital Holdings offers investment services to clients across the US through approximately 675 registered independent advisors. The company also sells through retail investment centers in Florida, Massachusetts, New Hampshire, and New Jersey. Its Investors Capital Corporation (ICC) broker-dealer subsidiary provides securities trading, research, online brokerage, and other services and generates nearly all of the company's sales. Subsidiary ICC Insurance Agency sells variable life insurance and annuities.

	Annual Growth	3/05	3/06	3/07	3/08	3/09
Sales ($ mil.)	27.8%	55.2	68.0	80.1	91.0	147.2
Net income ($ mil.)	—	0.6	0.4	(1.1)	(0.7)	(1.8)
Market value ($ mil.)	(27.7%)	32.9	21.0	36.1	31.2	9.0
Employees	(1.1%)	72	83	113	112	69

INVESTORS REAL ESTATE TRUST

NASDAQ (GS): IRET

12 S. Main St.
Minot, ND 58701
Phone: 701-837-4738
Fax: 701-838-7785
Web: www.upreits.com

CEO: Timothy P. Mihalick
CFO: Diane K. Bryantt
HR: —
FYE: April 30
Type: Public

Investors Real Estate Trust (IRET) is a self-advised umbrella partnership real estate investment trust (UPREIT) that invests in, develops, and maintains a portfolio of office, retail, and multifamily residential properties. IRET owns more than 200 properties in the Upper Midwest and Texas, including around 70 apartment communities comprising more than 9,000 individual units, more than 60 office properties, about 30 retail properties, nearly 50 medical properties (including senior housing and assisted living facilities), and about 15 industrial properties.

	Annual Growth	4/05	4/06	4/07	4/08	4/09
Sales ($ mil.)	11.3%	156.4	172.8	197.8	221.2	240.0
Net income ($ mil.)	(13.4%)	15.1	11.6	14.1	12.1	8.5
Market value ($ mil.)	0.5%	671.5	702.7	782.8	756.8	686.4
Employees	17.8%	42	42	59	69	81

INVESTORS TITLE COMPANY

NASDAQ (GM): ITIC

121 N. Columbia St.
Chapel Hill, NC 27514
Phone: 919-968-2200
Fax: 919-968-2235
Web: www.invtitle.com

CEO: J. Allen Fine
CFO: James A. Fine Jr.
HR: —
FYE: December 31
Type: Public

Investors Title insures you in case your land is, well, not completely yours. It's the holding company for Investors Title Insurance and Northeast Investors Title Insurance, which underwrite land title insurance and sell reinsurance to other title companies. (Title insurance protects those who invest in real property against loss resulting from defective titles.) Investors Title Insurance serves customers from about 30 offices in North Carolina, South Carolina, Michigan, and Nebraska, and through branches or agents in 20 additional states. Northeast Investors Title operates through an agency office in New York. Founder and CEO J. Allen Fine and his family own more than 20% of Investors Title.

	Annual Growth	12/05	12/06	12/07	12/08	12/09
Assets ($ mil.)	3.3%	128.5	143.5	149.6	139.9	146.4
Net income ($ mil.)	(22.5%)	13.3	13.2	8.4	(1.2)	4.8
Market value ($ mil.)	(7.5%)	96.4	122.1	87.7	85.4	70.6
Employees	(1.9%)	233	229	254	239	216

INVISA, INC.

OTC: INSA

290 Cocoanut Ave., Ste. 1A
Sarasota, FL 34236
Phone: 941-870-3950
Fax: 941-870-3945
Web: www.invisa.com

CEO: Edmund C. King
CFO: Edmund C. King
HR: —
FYE: December 31
Type: Public

Invisa develops and manufactures sensors used to ensure safety and security. The company's SmartGate safety sensors are used in traffic and parking control, fence and gate access, and industrial automation safety applications. The sensors are meant to keep doors and gates from closing on people or objects. Invisa's InvisaShield technology is designed to detect the presence of intruders in a monitored zone, such as the area around a museum exhibit. Customer Magnetic Automation Corp., a manufacturer of barrier gates, accounts for nearly 30% of product sales.

	Annual Growth	12/05	12/06	12/07	12/08	12/09
Sales ($ mil.)	(33.1%)	0.5	0.1	0.1	0.1	0.1
Net income ($ mil.)	—	(1.8)	(2.3)	(5.0)	0.1	(0.2)
Market value ($ mil.)	(41.9%)	4.9	1.6	0.5	0.1	0.6
Employees	(13.4%)	4	3	3	—	—

INVISTA B.V.

4123 E. 37th St. N.
Wichita, KS 67220
Phone: 316-828-1000
Fax: 316-828-1801
Web: invista.com

CEO: Jeff Gentry
CFO: Kelly Bulloch
HR: —
FYE: December 31
Type: Subsidiary

INVISTA has a fibrous outlook on life. A global leader in textile and polymer manufacturing, INVISTA is composed of four business units — Apparel, Intermediates, Performance Surfaces and Materials, and Polymers and Resins — and its portfolio includes brand names CoolMax, Dacron, Lycra, Stainmaster, and Thermolite. Its products are used in clothing, plastic packaging, automobile airbags, and pharmaceutical ingredients. A subsidiary of privately held industrial conglomerate Koch Industries, INVISTA operates in about two dozen countries worldwide.

INX INC.

NASDAQ (GM): INXI

6401 Southwest Fwy.
Houston, TX 77074
Phone: 713-795-2000
Fax: 713-795-2001
Web: www.inxi.com

CEO: James H. Long
CFO: Brian L. Fontana
HR: —
FYE: December 31
Type: Public

INX knows the IT sector. The company primarily offers Cisco-based IT infrastructure services and related hardware and software to customers in the educational, governmental, and private sectors. Its services include network design, systems integration, consulting, IP telephony implementation, network security auditing, and data center virtualization. The company also sells, installs, and integrates network storage systems from EMC and NetApp and provides virtualization products from VMWare; those three partners account for 90% of INX's product revenue.

	Annual Growth	12/04	12/05	12/06	12/07	*12/08
Sales ($ mil.)	29.2%	93.1	121.6	156.0	208.0	259.2
Net income ($ mil.)	—	1.6	(7.9)	1.2	3.7	(12.6)
Market value ($ mil.)	(13.4%)	69.0	50.1	70.9	94.3	38.8
Employees	22.2%	194	225	287	342	433

*Most recent year available

INX INTERNATIONAL INK COMPANY

150 N. Martingale Rd., Ste. 700
Schaumburg, IL 60173
Phone: 630-382-1800
Fax: 847-969-9758
Web: www.inxink.com

CEO: Richard (Rick) Clendenning
CFO: Bryce Kristo
HR: —
FYE: December 31
Type: Subsidiary

Ink-stained wretches everywhere have INX International Ink to thank (or blame) for their plight. The company, a subsidiary of Japanese ink maker Sakata, manufactures inks for digital and commercial printing applications and other coatings. INX makes inks for metal decorating; for flexible, rigid, and paper packaging; and for commercial printing. Its Triangle Digital INX subsidiary makes waterborne, UV-curable, oil-based, and solvent-based inkjet inks for wide and super-wide format digital printers. INX maintains about 30 manufacturing facilities in North America and another 20 worldwide.

	Annual Growth	12/04	12/05	12/06	12/07	12/08
Est. sales ($ mil.)	—	—	—	—	—	358.7
Employees	—	—	—	—	—	1,275

I/OMAGIC CORPORATION

OTC: IOMG

4 Marconi
Irvine, CA 92618
Phone: 949-707-4800
Fax: 949-855-3550
Web: www.iomagic.com

CEO: Tony Shahbaz
CFO: —
HR: —
FYE: December 31
Type: Public

I/OMagic has some input regarding computer peripheral output. It designs and markets optical storage products, such as CD-ROM and DVD-ROM playback and read-write devices. Other products include audio cards, digital photo frames, external hard drives, headphones, and Web cameras. The company also markets LCD-based HDTVs and home theater speakers through its Digital Research Technologies (DRT) division. I/OMagic sells to retailers such as Staples (nearly half of sales), OfficeMax, and Costco in the US and Canada. Other significant customers include distributors Tech Data (29% of sales) and D&H Distributing. The company subcontracts the manufacturing of most of its products.

	Annual Growth	12/05	12/06	12/07	12/08	12/09
Sales ($ mil.)	(27.8%)	37.8	45.9	32.1	13.4	10.3
Net income ($ mil.)	—	(1.8)	(0.3)	(4.7)	(4.3)	0.4
Employees	(12.0%)	50	50	50	30	30

IOMEGA CORPORATION

10955 Vista Sorrento Pkwy.
San Diego, CA 92130
Phone: 858-314-7000
Fax: 858-314-7001
Web: www.iomega.com

CEO: Jonathan S. Huberman
CFO: —
HR: —
FYE: December 31
Type: Subsidiary

Iomega has cleared a new space for itself in the data storage market with a slash-and-burn strategy. The company provides rewritable CD and DVD drives, desktop and portable hard drives, and floppy disk drives for the consumer market. Iomega's business products include network attached storage (NAS) equipment, and its REV line of removable hard disk drives. It also provides online storage services for the consumer and professional markets through its iStorage subsidiary. Iomega was acquired by data storage systems and software leader EMC for $213 million in 2008.

ION GEOPHYSICAL CORPORATION

NYSE: IO

2105 CityWest Blvd., Ste. 400
Houston, TX 77042
Phone: 281-933-3339
Fax: 281-879-3626
Web: www.iongeo.com

CEO: Robert P. (Bob) Peebler
CFO: R. Brian Hanson
HR: Larry Burke
FYE: December 31
Type: Public

There's a whole lotta shakin' goin' on at ION Geophysical (formerly Input/Output). The seismic data-acquisition imaging and software systems company helps worldwide petroleum exploration contractors identify and measure subsurface geological structures that could contain oil and gas. ION Geophysical's data acquisition products are capable of processing 3-D, 4-D, and multicomponent 3-C seismic data for land, marine, and transition areas (such as swamps, shoreline, marsh, and jungle). ION Geophysical also makes other products such as geophysical software, helicopter-transportable enclosures, seismic sensors, specialty cables and connectors, and radio telemetry systems.

	Annual Growth	12/05	12/06	12/07	12/08	12/09
Sales ($ mil.)	3.7%	362.7	503.6	713.1	679.5	419.8
Net income ($ mil.)	—	18.8	28.9	42.6	(221.0)	(113.6)
Market value ($ mil.)	(4.2%)	1,070.5	2,075.6	2,403.0	522.3	901.5
Employees	8.8%	804	1,015	1,201	1,413	1,128

IOWA LOTTERY

2323 Grand Ave.
Des Moines, IA 50312
Phone: 515-281-7900
Fax: 515-281-7905
Web: www.ialottery.com

CEO: Ken Brickman
CFO: Steve King
HR: —
FYE: June 30
Type: Government-owned

There is nothing corny about this heartland game. The Iowa Lottery pays out big winnings to the fortunate few, while supplementing the state general fund (education, human services, administration, justice). Offerings include instant-win scratch tickets, lotto games, and pull-tab tickets ranging in price from $1 to $20. Instant win games have been the Lottery's biggest seller since its inception in 1985. The Iowa Lottery also participates in PowerBall, which is part of the Multi-State Lottery and can produce jackpots of more than $200 million.

IOWA TELECOMMUNICATIONS SERVICES, INC.

403 W. 4th St. North
Newton, IA 50208
Phone: 641-787-2000
Fax: 641-787-2001
Web: www.iowatelecom.com

CEO: Alan L. Wells
CFO: Craig A. Knock
HR: Timothy D. Lockhart
FYE: December 31
Type: Subsidiary

Iowa Telecommunications Services (Iowa Telecom) provides a variety of communications services to residents of the Hawkeye State, as well as customers in Minnesota. It primarily provides local, long-distance, and Internet services to residential and business customers. Iowa Telecom also offers wholesale and carrier services to other telecom providers. The company operates as an incumbent local carrier in Iowa through Lakedale Telephone and Montezuma Mutual Telephone, while its competitive local exchange carrier subsidiaries are Iowa Telecom Communications and IT Communications. It operates in Minnesota through Lakedale Link and EN-TEL. The company was acquired by Windstream for about $1.2 billion in 2010.

	Annual Growth	12/05	12/06	12/07	12/08	12/09
Sales ($ mil.)	2.3%	231.6	234.1	251.4	247.0	254.1
Net income ($ mil.)	(31.0%)	46.4	34.0	29.3	23.1	10.5
Employees	6.4%	625	644	642	720	800

IPARTY CORP.

NYSE Amex: IPT

270 Bridge St., Ste. 301
Dedham, MA 02026
Phone: 781-329-3952
Fax: 781-326-7143
Web: www.iparty.com

CEO: Sal V. Perisano
CFO: David E. Robertson
HR: Rick Schnurbusch
FYE: December 31
Type: Public

What do you get when you cross a couple of investment bankers with TV's most ubiquitous florist? One rollicking party — perhaps. iParty is a little firm founded by bigwigs: former Salomon Smith Barney executive Bob Lessin, Jim McCann of 1-800-Flowers, and LBO specialist Byron Hero. It sells more than 20,000 party-related items, including balloons, invitations and greeting cards, Halloween costumes, paper party goods, gag gifts, and Hawaiian luau items from about 50 iParty retail stores in New England (about half the stores are in Massachusetts) and Florida. The company also operates an Internet site (strategic partner Taymark fulfills online orders) and offers party planning advice and information.

	Annual Growth	12/05	12/06	12/07	12/08	12/09
Sales ($ mil.)	2.0%	72.5	78.5	81.8	81.2	78.6
Net income ($ mil.)	—	(0.3)	0.4	0.6	(0.4)	1.1
Market value ($ mil.)	(10.5%)	9.1	9.1	4.9	1.4	5.8
Employees	0.4%	887	907	986	986	900

IPASS INC.

NASDAQ (GS): IPAS

3800 Bridge Pkwy.
Redwood Shores, CA 94065
Phone: 650-232-4100
Fax: 650-232-4111
Web: www.ipass.com

CEO: Evan L. Kaplan
CFO: Steven H. Gatoff
HR: —
FYE: December 31
Type: Public

On the information highway, iPass is in the passing lane. The company provides telecommuters and mobile employees with remote access to their businesses' internal networks and data. Through agreements with more than 550 carriers and ISPs, iPass' Mobile Office service encompasses a virtual network of more than 100,000 points of presence (POPs) in more than 160 countries. The network includes dial-up, Ethernet, and Wi-Fi access points. iPass was formed in 1996 when a group in Hong Kong and Canada's Sea Change developed the underpinning technology for its service. Customers of iPass include General Motors, The Hershey Company, and The Bank of New York Mellon.

	Annual Growth	12/05	12/06	12/07	12/08	12/09
Sales ($ mil.)	0.3%	169.4	182.7	191.7	191.4	171.4
Net income ($ mil.)	—	12.9	(8.4)	(34.2)	(92.0)	(13.5)
Market value ($ mil.)	(36.9%)	388.3	348.1	240.3	72.2	61.6
Employees	(1.1%)	406	575	504	508	389

IPC SYSTEMS, INC.

3 2nd St., Harborside Financial Center, Plaza 10, 15th Fl.
Jersey City, NJ 07311
Phone: 201-253-2000
Fax: 201-253-2361
Web: www.ipc.com

CEO: Lance B. Boxer
CFO: William J. McHale Jr.
HR: John McSherry
FYE: September 30
Type: Private

IPC Systems wants movers and shakers to trade up to its products. The company makes and services "turret" communications systems, also called dealerboards, that combine PBX, data switching, computer telephony, voice recording, and multimedia capabilities. Its products are used by financial institutions for voice and data transmission and routing in their trading environments. These products are designed to integrate with products from technology vendors, such as Avaya and Cisco. IPC markets its products directly and through resellers and systems integrators worldwide. Its customers include Goldman Sachs, JPMorgan Chase, and the New York Stock Exchange. IPC Systems is owned by Silver Lake Partners.

IPC THE HOSPITALIST COMPANY, INC.

NASDAQ (GM): IPCM

4605 Lankershim Blvd., Ste. 617
North Hollywood, CA 91602
Phone: 888-447-2362
Fax: 818-766-3999
Web: www.thehospitalistcompany.com

CEO: Adam D. Singer
CFO: Devra G. Shapiro
HR: Timothy Lary
FYE: December 31
Type: Public

IPC The Hospitalist Company (IPC) is on the leading edge of the growing US trend toward hospitalist specialization. The staffing firm provides more than 500 hospitalists to more than 300 hospitals and other inpatient facilities. Hospitalists are health care providers (physicians, nurses, and physicians assistants) who oversee all of a patient's treatment from the beginning to the end of their stay. They answer questions and coordinate treatment programs to improve the quality of care and reduce the length of a patient's hospital stay. In addition to providing staff, the company offers training, information management services, and risk management services for its medical professionals and clients.

	Annual Growth	12/05	12/06	12/07	12/08	12/09
Sales ($ mil.)	29.4%	110.9	148.1	190.0	251.2	310.5
Net income ($ mil.)	41.8%	4.6	1.8	(0.9)	13.6	18.6
Market value ($ mil.)	97.6%	—	—	—	273.1	539.5
Employees	18.2%	856	757	856	1,028	1,673

IPG PHOTONICS CORPORATION

NASDAQ (GM): IPGP

50 Old Webster Rd.	CEO: Valentin P. Gapontsev
Oxford, MA 01540	CFO: Timothy P. V. Mammen
Phone: 508-373-1100	HR: Coral Barry
Fax: 508-373-1103	FYE: December 31
Web: www.ipgphotonics.com	Type: Public

IPG Photonics has its name in lights. The company makes fiber-optic signal amplifiers, fiber lasers, laser diodes, and pump lasers, which are primarily used in materials processing. Its fiber lasers also have applications in medicine and in telecommunications networks to enable voice and data transmission over optical lines, among other uses. IPG has shipped more than 40,000 units to hundreds of customers around the world. The company's customers include BAE SYSTEMS, Mitsubishi Heavy Industries, and Nippon Steel. IPG Photonics gets about three-quarters of its sales outside North America.

	Annual Growth	12/05	12/06	12/07	12/08	12/09
Sales ($ mil.)	17.8%	96.4	143.2	188.7	229.1	185.9
Net income ($ mil.)	(7.6%)	7.4	29.2	29.9	36.7	5.4
Market value ($ mil.)	(11.3%)	—	1,109.1	923.8	609.1	773.2
Employees	12.3%	900	1,040	1,300	1,420	1,430

IQOR, INC.

335 Madison Ave., 27th Fl.	CEO: Vikas Kapoor
New York, NY 10017	CFO: —
Phone: 973-630-2515	HR: —
Fax: —	FYE: December 31
Web: www.iqor.com	Type: Private

When iQor comes a-ringin', you'd better come a-bringin'. One of the largest business process outsourcing companies in the world, iQor operates more than 20 call centers throughout the US, the UK, Canada, the Philippines, and India. iQor's services include third-party collections, accounts receivable management, and customer service. Its clients represent a wide swath of sectors ranging from commercial groups and financial service companies to utilities and government agencies. iQor was acquired by a group controlled by Guggenheim Investment Management in 2007.

	Annual Growth	12/04	12/05	12/06	12/07	12/08
Est. sales ($ mil.)	—	—	—	—	—	1.5
Employees	—	—	—	—	—	25

IRIDEX CORPORATION

NASDAQ (GM): IRIX

1212 Terra Bella Ave.	CEO: Theodore A. Boutacoff
Mountain View, CA 94043	CFO: James H. Mackaness
Phone: 650-940-4700	HR: —
Fax: 650-940-4710	FYE: December 31
Web: www.iridex.com	Type: Public

A meeting with IRIDEX can be an eye-opening experience. The company makes laser systems and peripheral devices used to treat three major causes of blindness: macular degeneration, glaucoma, and diabetic retinopathy. These ophthalmology products, which are sold primarily under the OcuLight name, account for about 60% of sales. IRIDEX also broadened its aesthetics business in 2007 when it acquired Laserscope from American Medical Systems, giving it a new suite of laser systems used in dermatology procedures and plastic surgery. The company markets its products through a direct sales staff and through distributors in more than 100 countries worldwide.

	Annual Growth	12/05	12/06	12/07	12/08	12/09
Sales ($ mil.)	3.9%	37.0	35.9	55.5	48.5	43.2
Net income ($ mil.)	11.2%	1.7	(5.8)	(22.3)	(7.4)	2.6
Market value ($ mil.)	(20.9%)	70.5	79.6	22.0	7.6	27.5
Employees	7.1%	114	121	151	149	150

IRIS INTERNATIONAL, INC.

NASDAQ (GM): IRIS

9172 Eton Ave.	CEO: Cesar M. García
Chatsworth, CA 91311	CFO: Martin S. McDermut
Phone: 818-709-1244	HR: —
Fax: 818-700-9661	FYE: December 31
Web: www.proiris.com	Type: Public

IRIS International provides urinalysis technology to medical institutions around the globe. IRIS International's three divisions include Iris Diagnostics, which develops imaging systems used in urinalysis and microscopic analysis, as well as related consumables (reagents and test strips) and services. Its primary product is the iQ family of microscopy analyzers, which automate the steps of routine urinalysis. Iris Sample Processing makes a variety of other small instruments and laboratory supplies, including centrifuges. The company's IRIS Molecular Diagnostics division is developing more sensitive tests based on molecular detection of specific proteins, in hopes of leading to earlier detection of diseases.

	Annual Growth	12/05	12/06	12/07	12/08	12/09
Sales ($ mil.)	10.2%	62.8	70.5	84.3	95.5	92.6
Net income ($ mil.)	0.8%	6.1	(0.2)	7.5	9.0	6.3
Market value ($ mil.)	(13.3%)	399.1	230.2	358.2	254.5	225.7
Employees	8.4%	236	274	308	318	326

IROBOT CORPORATION

NASDAQ (GM): IRBT

8 Crosby Dr.	CEO: Colin M. Angle
Bedford, MA 01730	CFO: John J. Leahy
Phone: 781-430-3000	HR: Penny Outlaw
Fax: 781-430-3001	FYE: December 31
Web: www.irobot.com	Type: Public

Fans of the old *Jetsons* episodes appreciate iRobot. The company makes robots for all sorts of applications — from government and military to home appliances. Its Roomba FloorVac and Scooba are the first of their kind to automatically clean floors; iRobot has sold 5 million of them. The firm also makes the Looj gutter-cleaning 'bot and the Seaglider unmanned underwater robot for use in oceans. iRobot also has sold more than 2,900 PackBots, which perform battlefield reconnaissance and bomb disposal for the US Army. Boasting offices in the US and Hong Kong, the company sells its products worldwide through retailers. It was founded in 1990 by robot engineers from the Massachusetts Institute of Technology.

	Annual Growth	12/05	12/06	12/07	12/08	12/09
Sales ($ mil.)	20.4%	142.0	189.0	249.1	307.6	298.6
Net income ($ mil.)	6.1%	2.6	3.6	9.1	0.8	3.3
Market value ($ mil.)	(14.8%)	839.3	454.8	455.3	227.4	443.2
Employees	18.2%	276	371	423	479	538

⊞ IRON MOUNTAIN INCORPORATED

NYSE: IRM

745 Atlantic Ave.	CEO: Robert T. (Bob) Brennan
Boston, MA 02111	CFO: Brian P. McKeon
Phone: 617-535-4766	HR: Annie Drapeau
Fax: 617-350-7881	FYE: December 31
Web: www.ironmountain.com	Type: Public

You think you have a mountain of paperwork to deal with? Iron Mountain is one of the largest records storage and information management companies in the world. The company stores paper and digital documents, computer disks, tapes, microfilm and microfiche, audio and videotapes, film, X-rays, and blueprints for more than 140,000 corporate customers. It provides such services as records filing, digital conversion, database management, packing, transportation, disaster recovery, and information destruction. Its COMAC unit stores, builds, and mails information packets for companies. Iron Mountain traces its paper trail back to when it was established — in 1951.

	Annual Growth	12/05	12/06	12/07	12/08	12/09
Sales ($ mil.)	9.7%	2,078.2	2,350.3	2,730.0	3,055.1	3,013.6
Net income ($ mil.)	17.3%	116.6	128.9	153.1	82.0	220.9
Market value ($ mil.)	(5.2%)	5,722.1	5,602.9	7,526.1	5,027.5	4,627.1
Employees	(9.7%)	15,800	18,600	20,100	21,000	10,500

⊞ An in-depth profile of this company is available to Hoover's Online members at hoovers.com.

847

IRONWOOD PHARMACEUTICALS, INC.

NASDAQ (GM): IRWD

320 Bent St.
Cambridge, MA 02141
Phone: 617-621-7722
Fax: 617-494-0908
Web: www.ironwoodpharma.com

CEO: Peter M. Hecht
CFO: Michael J. Higgins
HR: —
FYE: December 31
Type: Public

Ironwood Pharmaceuticals (formerly Microbia) is a drug developer that is busy testing the gastrointestinal drug candidates in its pipeline. The company is developing lead drug candidate linaclotide, which is undergoing trials in partnership with Forest Laboratories and other co-developers for the treatment of irritable bowel syndrome, abdominal pain, and chronic constipation. The company's Microbia biotechnology subsidiary harnesses microbes to produce specialty chemicals from renewable resources with applications the agriculture, chemical, and pharmaceutical industries. Ironwood Pharmaceuticals went public in 2010.

	Annual Growth	12/05	12/06	12/07	12/08	12/09
Sales ($ mil.)	126.7%	—	3.1	10.5	22.2	36.1
Net income ($ mil.)	—	—	(37.2)	(52.8)	(53.9)	(71.2)
Employees	(1.2%)	—	—	—	167	165

THE IRVINE COMPANY

550 Newport Center Dr.
Newport Beach, CA 92660
Phone: 949-720-2000
Fax: 949-720-2218
Web: www.irvinecompany.com

CEO: Donald L. Bren
CFO: Marc Ley
HR: —
FYE: June 30
Type: Private

At The Irvine Company, everything goes according to plan — the *master* plan. The real estate investment company plans and designs office, retail, and residential villages in Los Angeles, Orange County, San Diego, and Silicon Valley. It owns some 475 office buildings, 40 retail centers, and more than 100 apartment communities, as well as hotels, marinas, and golf clubs, not to mention Irvine Ranch, one of the largest planned communities in the US. The ranch has some 290,000 residents and covers 93,000 acres, a drop from its original 120,000 acres back in the mid-1800s, when James Irvine bought out the debts of Mexican land-grant holders. Billionaire chairman Donald Bren owns the company.

IRVINE SCIENTIFIC

2511 Daimler St.
Santa Ana, CA 92705
Phone: 949-261-7800
Fax: 949-261-6522
Web: www.irvinesci.com

CEO: Makoto Shintani
CFO: —
HR: Allison Snow
FYE: March 31
Type: Subsidiary

Corporate culture to Irvine Scientific refers to something other than "casual Friday." The culture this company thrives on is of the cellular variety; Irvine makes advanced cell culture media for the *in vitro* diagnostics and industrial bioprocessing markets, as well as others who need blood serum and non-serum media for growing cells in the laboratory. It also sells prenatal testing kits and cell culture media used for *in vitro* fertilization procedures, and provides some devices through an exclusive distribution agreement with a unit of Smiths Group. The company markets its products worldwide. Founded in 1970, Irvine Scientific is owned by Japan Energy Corporation, a subsidiary of Nippon Mining Holdings.

	Annual Growth	3/04	3/05	3/06	3/07	3/08
Est. sales ($ mil.)	—	—	—	—	—	31.0
Employees	—	—	—	—	—	103

IRVINE SENSORS CORPORATION

NASDAQ (CM): IRSN

3001 Red Hill Ave., Bldg. 4, Ste. 108
Costa Mesa, CA 92626
Phone: 714-549-8211
Fax: 714-444-8773
Web: www.irvine-sensors.com

CEO: John C. Carson
CFO: John J. Stuart Jr.
HR: —
FYE: September 30
Type: Public

Irvine Sensors puts its hopes in big returns from tiny products. Much of the company's sales comes from research and development contracts related to its minute solid-state microcircuitry technology, in which circuits are assembled in 3-D stacks (rather than flat layouts) to lower weight and boost performance. Irvine Sensors targets its lightweight components for space and aircraft applications. The US government and its military contractors account for about two-thirds of sales. The US Air Force is behind 32% of revenues. SAIC, a government contractor, and the US Army are other leading customers of Irvine Sensors.

	Annual Growth	9/05	9/06	9/07	9/08	9/09
Sales ($ mil.)	(15.9%)	23.0	30.8	35.8	16.7	11.5
Net income ($ mil.)	—	(1.8)	(8.5)	(22.1)	(21.6)	0.9
Market value ($ mil.)	(61.9%)	431.4	218.2	181.8	16.6	9.1
Employees	(9.6%)	114	165	194	84	76

IRVING OIL CORPORATION

190 Commerce Way
Portsmouth, NH 03801
Phone: 603-559-8736
Fax: 603-559-8793
Web: www.irvingoilco.com

CEO: Kenneth Irving
CFO: —
HR: Greg Bambury
FYE: December 31
Type: Private

Irving Oil Corporation, the US arm of Irving Oil Limited, is engaged in the refining and distribution of oil and natural gas; it serves wholesale, commercial, and retail customers in Eastern Canada, Quebec, and New England. The Irving Oil Canaport refinery, located in Saint John, New Brunswick, is the Western Hemisphere's first deep-water terminal, and Canada's largest refinery. The company has about 800 fueling locations, operations at 13 marine terminals, and a delivery fleet of tractor-trailers. It serves US retail customers via 300 convenience stores and gas stations, and also has home heating and wholesale operations in Maine, New Hampshire, and Vermont. The company is owned by the founding Irving family.

ISECURETRAC CORP.

OTC: ISEC

5078 S. 111th St.
Omaha, NE 68137
Phone: 402-537-0022
Fax: 402-537-9847
Web: www.isecuretrac.com

CEO: Peter A. Michel
CFO: Lincoln D. Zehr
HR: —
FYE: December 31
Type: Public

Correctional authorities that need to account for the whereabouts of parolees and probationers can look to iSECUREtrac for answers. In the company's system, offenders wear devices that use GPS (global positioning system) technology to determine their locations; data is transmitted to a central monitoring station. iSECUREtrac also offers systems that enforce house-arrest orders by verifying an offender's presence within a building. The company leases its monitoring equipment to federal, state, and local criminal justice agencies.

	Annual Growth	12/05	12/06	12/07	12/08	12/09
Sales ($ mil.)	21.7%	5.6	8.1	8.8	9.7	12.3
Net income ($ mil.)	—	(3.9)	(5.5)	(7.2)	(4.6)	(1.9)
Market value ($ mil.)	(32.7%)	18.9	11.9	6.7	2.2	3.9
Employees	1.0%	71	82	92	76	74

ISILON SYSTEMS, INC.

NASDAQ (GM): ISLN

3101 Western Ave.
Seattle, WA 98121
Phone: 206-315-7500
Fax: 206-315-7501
Web: www.isilon.com

CEO: Sujal M. Patel
CFO: William (Bill) Richter
HR: Gwen Weld
FYE: December 31
Type: Public

Isilon Systems isn't daunted by our ever-expanding digital world. The company develops clustered, disk-based storage systems. Its modular Isilon IQ nodes, which make use of the company's proprietary OneFS operating software, store and deliver large digital files, including photos, video, and audio content. The company markets its products to health care providers, media companies, oil and gas firms, and other enterprises with digital imaging and content delivery operations. Isilon sells directly and through distributors and resellers. Its customers have included ABC, Cedars-Sinai Medical Center, Eastman Kodak, Kelman Technologies, LexisNexis, MySpace.com, Pratt & Whitney, and Technicolor.

	Annual Growth	12/05	12/06	12/07	12/08	12/09
Sales ($ mil.)	55.7%	21.1	62.3	89.0	114.4	123.9
Net income ($ mil.)	—	(19.1)	(25.4)	(26.9)	(25.1)	(18.9)
Market value ($ mil.)	(37.0%)	—	1,785.6	331.4	214.6	447.5
Employees	10.2%	241	258	321	394	356

ISIS PHARMACEUTICALS, INC.

NASDAQ (GM): ISIS

1896 Rutherford Rd.
Carlsbad, CA 92008
Phone: 760-931-9200
Fax: 760-603-2700
Web: www.isispharm.com

CEO: Stanley T. Crooke
CFO: B. Lynne Parshall
HR: —
FYE: December 31
Type: Public

Isis Pharmaceuticals is trying to make sense out of antisense. The biotechnology company is developing drugs based on its antisense technology, in which drugs attach themselves to strands of RNA in order to prevent them from producing disease-causing proteins; the hoped-for end result is a therapy that fights disease without harming healthy cells. Isis Pharmaceuticals' strategy is to discover more potential drug compounds that it can develop on its own and then license them off to larger drug firms, thus producing a potential stream of revenue (in the form of milestone payments and royalties) for itself. Its lead candidate is the cholesterol-lowering drug mipomersen, which Isis has licensed to Genzyme.

	Annual Growth	12/05	12/06	12/07	12/08	12/09
Sales ($ mil.)	32.0%	40.1	24.5	69.6	107.2	121.6
Net income ($ mil.)	—	(72.4)	(45.9)	(11.0)	(12.0)	150.7
Market value ($ mil.)	20.7%	519.2	1,101.9	1,560.6	1,405.1	1,100.9
Employees	(0.8%)	258	274	300	300	250

Ⓗ ISLE OF CAPRI CASINOS, INC.

NASDAQ (GS): ISLE

600 Emerson Rd., Ste. 300
St. Louis, MO 63141
Phone: 314-813-9200
Fax: —
Web: www.isleofcapricasino.com

CEO: James B. (Jim) Perry
CFO: Dale R. Black
HR: R. Ronald (Ron) Burgess
FYE: April 30
Type: Public

Rollin' on the river takes on new meaning when you're talking about Isle of Capri Casinos. The company owns and operates about 15 dockside, riverboat, and land-based casinos in Colorado, Iowa, Louisiana, Mississippi, and Missouri. In addition, the company has a pari-mutuel harness racetrack and casino in Pompano Beach, Florida. Most of the company's casinos have hotels and feature restaurants, live entertainment, and private lounges for high-rollers. Isle of Capri is discontinuing its international operations, which include two-thirds ownership of casinos in the UK, and a casino in the Bahamas, and is restructuring its domestic operations.

	Annual Growth	4/05	4/06	4/07	4/08	4/09
Sales ($ mil.)	0.2%	1,111.6	988.0	1,001.4	1,125.4	1,118.6
Net income ($ mil.)	24.8%	18.0	19.0	(4.6)	(96.9)	43.6
Market value ($ mil.)	(18.3%)	783.9	1,012.3	793.0	218.7	348.5
Employees	(5.4%)	10,500	8,516	9,162	8,559	8,400

ISONICS CORPORATION

OTC: ISON

535 8th Ave., 3rd Fl.
New York, NY 80403
Phone: 212-356-7400
Fax: —
Web: www.isonics.com

CEO: Christopher M. (Chris) Toffales
CFO: Gregory A. (Greg) Meadows
HR: —
FYE: April 30
Type: Public

Isonics provides security systems, personnel, and investigative and security services through subsidiary Protection Plus Security Consultants. Formerly it had developed products based on stable and radioactive isotopes for biomedical research, medical imaging, and cancer therapy. In 2007, however, Isonics sold its Life Sciences division, which had conducted the isotopes business, and now concentrates on security products and services. This new focus began back in 2004 when it bought a small Washington State-based company, EnCompass Materials Group, that manufactures silicon wafers. The business now accounts for about a third of sales.

	Annual Growth	4/04	4/05	4/06	4/07	*4/08
Sales ($ mil.)	26.4%	8.7	10.1	23.7	27.7	22.2
Net income ($ mil.)	—	(4.2)	(15.2)	(32.3)	(13.2)	(11.2)
Employees	58.4%	61	457	561	481	384

*Most recent year available

ISRAEL DISCOUNT BANK OF NEW YORK

511 5th Ave.
New York, NY 10017
Phone: 212-551-8500
Fax: 212-551-8540
Web: www.idbny.com

CEO: Reuven Spiegel
CFO: Thomas Kehrer
HR: —
FYE: December 31
Type: Subsidiary

Israel Discount Bank of New York (IDB Bank) is all over the map. The institution offers personal, commercial, and private banking services in the US and abroad. Focusing on middle-market businesses, the bank provides lending services such as working capital, commercial real estate loans, construction and land development loans, asset-based lending, and factoring. It specializes in serving CPA, law, and professional services firms and not-for-profit organizations. International services include import financing, letters of credit, and foreign exchange. IDB Bank is a subsidiary of Israel Discount Bank Limited.

	Annual Growth	12/04	12/05	12/06	12/07	12/08
Est. sales ($ mil.)	—	—	—	—	—	506.2
Employees	—	—	—	—	—	789

ISRAMCO, INC.

NASDAQ (CM): ISRL

2425 West Loop South, Ste. 810
Houston, TX 77027
Phone: 713-621-5946
Fax: 713-621-3988

CEO: Haim Tsuff
CFO: Edy Francis
HR: —
FYE: December 31
Type: Public

There may be milk and honey on the other side of the River Jordan, but to date, not much oil. Because of that, in 2007 Isramco sold to I.O.C Israel Oil Company the bulk of its Israel-based activities and assets including its stake in Isramco Oil & Gas. Focusing on growing its US operations, the company is engaged (through subsidiaries Jay Petroleum and Jay Management) in oil and gas exploration, primarily in Louisiana, Oklahoma, Texas, and Wyoming. In 2007 Isramco reported proved reserves of 50.3 billion cu. ft. of gas equivalent. Chairman and CEO Haim Tsuff owns 49.8% of Isramco.

	Annual Growth	12/05	12/06	12/07	12/08	12/09
Sales ($ mil.)	42.4%	7.7	12.4	22.8	52.2	31.7
Net income ($ mil.)	—	(1.1)	3.8	(6.4)	3.2	(13.6)
Market value ($ mil.)	47.6%	41.0	79.8	129.0	84.9	194.3
Employees	22.2%	13	13	7	16	29

Ⓗ An in-depth profile of this company is available to Hoover's Online members at hoovers.com.

849

ISTA PHARMACEUTICALS, INC.

NASDAQ (GM): ISTA

15295 Alton Pkwy.
Irvine, CA 92618
Phone: 949-788-6000
Fax: 949-788-6010
Web: www.istavision.com

CEO: Vicente Anido Jr.
CFO: Lauren P. Silvernail
HR: Kathleen McGinley
FYE: December 31
Type: Public

ISTA Pharmaceuticals has set its sights on treating eye diseases. The pharmaceutical company has products in development and on the market. ISTA's marketed products include Bepreve (for allergic conjunctivitis), Istalol (a glaucoma treatment), and Xibrom (used for pain and inflammation following cataract surgery) in the US. Its drug Vitrase is a spreading agent that promotes absorption of injected drugs. The drug candidates in the company's pipeline include treatments for dry eye syndrome, ocular pain and inflammation. ISTA is also developing a once-daily version of Xibrom and is investigating the active ingredient in Bepreve for use as a nasal spray to treat allergy symptoms.

	Annual Growth	12/05	12/06	12/07	12/08	12/09
Sales ($ mil.)	79.3%	10.7	33.0	58.9	83.1	110.6
Net income ($ mil.)	—	(38.5)	(38.4)	(38.2)	(30.7)	(57.8)
Market value ($ mil.)	(8.0%)	212.4	237.5	163.7	24.0	152.3
Employees	18.3%	161	198	222	225	315

ISTAR FINANCIAL INC.

NYSE: SFI

1114 Avenue of the Americas, 39th Fl.
New York, NY 10036
Phone: 212-930-9400
Fax: 212-930-9494
Web: www.istarfinancial.com

CEO: Jay Sugarman
CFO: —
HR: —
FYE: December 31
Type: Public

iStar Financial (formerly Starwood Financial) is a real estate investment trust (REIT) that originates, acquires, and services senior and subordinate loans that are either unsecured or secured by commercial real estate located throughout the US. iStar also provides investment capital to private and corporate owners of real estate. Its corporate tenant leasing business provides capital to owners of mission-critical facilities, such as company headquarters. The REIT's loans typically range in size from $20 million to $150 million and are mainly secured by apartments or residential properties, office complexes, land, hotels, or industrial, retail, or entertainment properties.

	Annual Growth	12/05	12/06	12/07	12/08	12/09
Sales ($ mil.)	15.8%	801.5	992.6	1,455.2	1,364.1	1,440.6
Net income ($ mil.)	—	287.9	374.8	239.0	(196.8)	(769.8)
Market value ($ mil.)	(48.2%)	3,329.1	4,465.5	2,432.6	208.2	239.1
Employees	8.1%	181	214	326	270	247

ISUZU MOTORS AMERICA INC.

13340 183rd St.
Cerritos, CA 90702
Phone: 562-229-5000
Fax: 562-229-5463
Web: www.isuzu.com

CEO: J. Terry Maloney
CFO: Matt Saito
HR: —
FYE: March 31
Type: Subsidiary

Isuzu Motors America was once a real Trooper, but most of its models have seen their last Rodeo. Once a distributor of Isuzu cars, pickups, and SUVs, the subsidiary of Isuzu Motors now offers only three vehicle models (the Ascender five-passenger SUV and the i290 and i370 pickups), and it exited the light-duty vehicle market in the US altogether in early 2009. The company also makes 30 models of diesel engines that offer up to 300 horsepower; sister company Isuzu Commercial Truck of America distributes Isuzu H-series, N-series, and F-series commercial trucks. Production of the seven-passenger Ascender SUV ended in 2006, and the once-popular Trooper, Rodeo, and Axiom also were retired.

	Annual Growth	3/04	3/05	3/06	3/07	3/08
Est. sales ($ mil.)	—	—	—	—	—	198.9
Employees	—	—	—	—	—	600

ITC HOLDINGS CORP.

NYSE: ITC

27175 Energy Way
Novi, MI 48377
Phone: 248-946-3000
Fax: —
Web: www.itc-holdings.com

CEO: Joseph L. Welch
CFO: Cameron M. Bready
HR: —
FYE: December 31
Type: Public

ITC Holdings owns and operates 2,800 miles of power transmission lines in southeastern Michigan (including Detroit and Ann Arbor). Through its subsidiaries, ITC Transmission, Michigan Electric Transmission Company (METC), and ITC Midwest LLC, ITC operates regulated, high-voltage transmission systems in Michigan's Lower Peninsula and portions of Illinois, Iowa, Minnesota, and Missouri, serving a combined peak load in excess of 25,000 MW. ITC is a member of the Midwest ISO, a regional transmission organization. The company also operates as ITC Grid Development and ITC Great Plains, which invest in transmission infrastructure development in Kansas and the Great Plains region.

	Annual Growth	12/05	12/06	12/07	12/08	12/09
Sales ($ mil.)	31.9%	205.3	223.6	426.2	617.9	621.0
Net income ($ mil.)	39.4%	34.7	33.2	73.3	109.2	130.9
Market value ($ mil.)	16.7%	1,408.4	2,000.6	2,828.9	2,190.1	2,611.8
Employees	31.8%	137	223	302	392	413

ITC^DELTACOM, INC.

OTC: ITCD

7037 Old Madison Pike
Huntsville, AL 35806
Phone: 256-382-5900
Fax: 256-264-9924
Web: www.deltacom.com

CEO: Randall E. (Randy) Curran
CFO: Richard E. (Rich) Fish Jr.
HR: —
FYE: December 31
Type: Public

ITC^DeltaCom keeps businesses in the Southeast connected. The competitive local-exchange carrier (CLEC) operates in eight states — Alabama, Florida, Georgia, Louisiana, Mississippi, North Carolina, South Carolina, and Tennessee — offering integrated voice and data communications, including local and long-distance phone service and DSL Internet access, primarily to business customers. ITC^DeltaCom also wholesales transmission capacity on its fiber-optic network, which spans more than 11,000 miles, to other carriers. The company's fiber-optic network stretches from New York to Florida, and as far west as Texas.

	Annual Growth	12/05	12/06	12/07	12/08	12/09
Sales ($ mil.)	(2.6%)	520.4	487.6	492.1	497.9	469.3
Net income ($ mil.)	—	(50.8)	(53.5)	(177.0)	(22.9)	(11.0)
Market value ($ mil.)	10.1%	105.4	213.2	418.1	41.8	154.7
Employees	(8.0%)	1,950	1,975	1,800	1,565	1,398

ITERIS, INC.

NYSE Amex: ITI

1700 Carnegie Ave., Ste. 100
Santa Ana, CA 92705
Phone: 949-270-9400
Fax: 949-270-9401
Web: www.iteris.com

CEO: Abbas Mohaddes
CFO: James S. Miele
HR: —
FYE: March 31
Type: Public

Iteris helps drivers get home quickly and safely. The company manufactures vision systems used both inside and outside of vehicles. Its roadway sensors business segment includes video vehicle detection systems installed at intersections to help manage the flow of traffic and traffic data collection (Vantage). Through its automotive sensors business segment, Iteris makes a windshield-mounted video sensor that warns drivers if they drift out of their lanes (AutoVue). Iteris' transportation systems division offers engineering and consulting services and the development of transportation management and information systems. The company gets most of its revenues in the US.

	Annual Growth	3/06	3/07	3/08	3/09	3/10
Sales ($ mil.)	3.6%	50.5	58.3	65.2	69.4	58.1
Net income ($ mil.)	116.6%	0.1	2.9	12.2	10.5	2.2
Market value ($ mil.)	(6.7%)	90.6	79.0	79.3	45.0	68.7
Employees	0.2%	219	237	268	242	221

ITEX CORPORATION

OTC: ITEX

3326 160th Ave. SE, Ste. 100
Bellevue, WA 98008
Phone: 425-463-4000
Fax: 425-463-4040
Web: www.itex.com

CEO: Steven M. (Steve) White
CFO: Steven M. (Steve) White
HR: —
FYE: July 31
Type: Public

ITEX provides a business-to-business payment system for corporate members through a licensed broker network across the US and Canada. In lieu of cash, some 24,000 member businesses of the company's ITEX Marketplace barter time-sensitive, slow-moving, or surplus goods and services valued in ITEX dollars. Members represent a variety of industries including advertising, construction, dining, health care, hospitality, media, printing, and professional services. ITEX administers the trade exchange; it (or any of its 95 franchisees or licensed brokers) also acts as a record keeper for member transactions.

	Annual Growth	7/05	7/06	7/07	7/08	7/09
Sales ($ mil.)	12.2%	10.4	14.7	14.2	16.0	16.5
Net income ($ mil.)	(33.7%)	3.1	3.4	4.5	0.9	0.6
Market value ($ mil.)	13.5%	6.9	10.4	14.4	15.9	11.4
Employees	18.9%	16	19	18	31	32

ITOCHU INTERNATIONAL INC.

335 Madison Ave.
New York, NY 10017
Phone: 212-818-8000
Fax: 212-818-8543
Web: www.itochu.com

CEO: Yoshihisa Q. Suzuki
CFO: Yasuhiro Baba
HR: —
FYE: March 31
Type: Subsidiary

Doing one thing and doing it well is fine for some, but ITOCHU International is looking for some variety in its life. The North American arm of Japanese trading giant ITOCHU Corporation runs the gamut of product offerings, from aerospace components and building products to textile manufacturing and solar power systems. The company also distributes fresh produce and manufactures high-performance adhesives and sealants. Among ITOCHU's subsidiary companies are Master Halco (a maker of fencing material), PrimeSource Building Products (a distributor of nails and screws), and ITOCHU Prominent USA (a maker of men's and women's garment fabrics). The company primarily operates in Canada, Mexico, and the US.

ITRON, INC.

NASDAQ (GS): ITRI

2111 N. Molter Rd.
Liberty Lake, WA 99019
Phone: 509-924-9900
Fax: 509-891-3355
Web: www.itron.com

CEO: Malcolm Unsworth
CFO: Steven M. (Steve) Helmbrecht
HR: Jared P. Serff
FYE: December 31
Type: Public

Itron aims to make meter-reading a desk job. The company is a global supplier of wireless data acquisition and communication products for electric, gas, and water utilities. Itron makes radio- and telephone-based automatic meter-reading (AMR) systems, handheld meter-reading computers, and meter data acquisition and analysis software. Its systems are installed at more than 2,000 utilities worldwide — many using more than one Itron product. The company also provides consulting, project management, and outsourcing services. Customers include BC Hydro, Electrabel, Ford, Old Dominion Electric Cooperative, and Progress Energy. Europe is Itron's biggest market, closely followed by North America.

	Annual Growth	12/05	12/06	12/07	12/08	12/09
Sales ($ mil.)	32.2%	552.7	644.0	1,464.0	1,909.6	1,687.4
Net income ($ mil.)	—	33.1	33.8	(16.1)	28.1	(2.2)
Market value ($ mil.)	14.0%	1,613.7	2,089.3	3,867.8	2,568.9	2,723.2
Employees	45.6%	2,000	2,400	8,400	8,700	9,000

ITT CORPORATION

NYSE: ITT

1133 Westchester Ave.
White Plains, NY 10604
Phone: 914-641-2000
Fax: 914-696-2950
Web: www.itt.com

CEO: Steven R. Loranger
CFO: Denise L. Ramos
HR: Robert Ellis
FYE: December 31
Type: Public

ITT doesn't get defensive when you associate its name with fluid motion. The company has three primary segments: defense electronics & services (combat radios, night vision devices, airborne electronic warfare systems), fluid technology (pumps, mixers, heat exchangers, valves, and analytical instruments for water and wastewater systems), and fluid & motion control (connectors, boat pumps, shock absorbers, friction pads for communication and transportation applications). ITT traces its corporate roots back nearly 90 years to the old ITT phone empire; it continues to provide repair and maintenance services for the products it manufactures. The company garners about two-thirds of its sales in the US.

	Annual Growth	12/05	12/06	12/07	12/08	12/09
Sales ($ mil.)	10.1%	7,427.3	7,807.9	9,003.3	11,694.8	10,904.5
Net income ($ mil.)	15.2%	366.0	581.1	742.1	794.7	643.7
Market value ($ mil.)	(0.8%)	9,433.7	10,426.5	12,118.3	8,439.2	9,127.3
Employees	(0.4%)	40,900	37,500	39,700	40,800	40,200

ITT DEFENSE ELECTRONICS & SERVICES

1650 Tysons Blvd., Ste. 1700
McLean, VA 22102
Phone: 703-790-6300
Fax: 703-790-6360
Web: www.defense.itt.com

CEO: Lt. Gen. David F. Melcher
CFO: William T. Kansky
HR: A. John Procopio
FYE: December 31
Type: Subsidiary

When it comes to modern weaponry, high-powered equals high-tech. ITT Defense Electronics & Services (ITT Defense), which accounts for about 54% of parent ITT Corporation's sales, offers security and defense systems and technical and operational services to government agencies, commercial, and military customers. Its businesses include Space (satellite imaging, space launch), Communications (air traffic control, tactical), Sensing/Surveillance (night vision, airborne warfare), and Advanced Engineering and Sciences (homeland defense). In addition to the FAA, NASA, and the US military, customers include the governments of the UK, Saudi Arabia, and Turkey. The US represents about 90% of sales.

ITT EDUCATIONAL SERVICES, INC.

NYSE: ESI

13000 N. Meridian St.
Carmel, IN 46032
Phone: 317-706-9200
Fax: 317-706-3040
Web: www.ittesi.com

CEO: Kevin M. Modany
CFO: Daniel M. Fitzpatrick
HR: Nina F. Esbin
FYE: December 31
Type: Public

To get a mortarboard from ITT, you may need to know a little something about motherboards. One of the largest US providers of technical education, ITT Educational Services offers mainly associate and bachelor degree programs to some 65,000 students at more than 105 ITT Technical Institutes in 37 states. The company has traditionally offered a range of technology-focused degrees in areas such as computer-aided design, engineering technology, and information technology. However, ITT Educational Services also offers degrees in business, criminal justice, design, and health sciences. Some programs are offered exclusively online, while others are offered through a combination of classroom and online instruction.

	Annual Growth	12/05	12/06	12/07	12/08	12/09
Sales ($ mil.)	17.7%	688.0	757.8	869.5	1,015.3	1,319.2
Net income ($ mil.)	28.6%	109.7	118.5	151.6	203.0	300.3
Market value ($ mil.)	12.9%	2,041.5	2,292.3	2,945.0	3,280.4	3,314.2
Employees	13.0%	6,000	6,200	7,200	8,580	9,800

ITT FLUID TECHNOLOGY

10 Mountainview Rd.
Upper Saddle River, NJ 07458
Phone: 201-760-9800
Fax: 201-760-9692
Web: www.ittfluidbusiness.com

CEO: Gretchen W. McClain
CFO: Charlie Peiffer
HR: —
FYE: December 31
Type: Subsidiary

ITT Fluid is moved to pump, water and other fluids that is. A subsidiary of industrial giant ITT Corp., ITT Fluid makes fluid-handling products for water and wastewater markets worldwide. Generating almost 50% of its revenue, this segment offers submersible pumps, mixers, and treatment equipment. The company supplies industrial process markets, too, with split-case and multistage slurry pumps, ball and recycle/reject valves, and control systems for chemical, pulp and paper, and power generation. Its pumps even pair up with "watermakers" for offshore drilling and production. ITT's pumps, valves, heat exchangers, and accessories also treat residential, commercial, light industrial, and agricultural applications.

🏛 IVAX DIAGNOSTICS, INC.

NYSE Amex: IVD

2140 N. Miami Ave.
Miami, FL 33127
Phone: 305-324-2338
Fax: 305-324-2395
Web: www.ivaxdiagnostics.com

CEO: Charles R. Struby
CFO: Arthur R. Levine
HR: —
FYE: December 31
Type: Public

Its products are used for screenings, but don't confuse it with IMAX. IVAX Diagnostics operates in the US and Italy through three subsidiaries. Delta Biologicals develops scientific instrumentation, makes the Mago and Aptus lines of instruments, and distributes *in vitro* diagnostic products to hospitals and medical laboratories in Italy. Diamedix makes *in vitro* diagnostic kits and markets them to clinical and hospital labs in the US. ImmunoVision develops, makes, and markets autoimmune reagents and research products for use by clinical and research labs and other diagnostic manufacturers. Top generic drug maker Teva Pharmaceutical has sold its 72% stake in IVAX Diagnostics to a group of industry investors.

	Annual Growth	12/05	12/06	12/07	12/08	12/09
Sales ($ mil.)	(1.8%)	19.8	19.5	20.0	20.8	18.4
Net income ($ mil.)	—	(0.5)	(2.6)	(10.4)	0.2	(4.5)
Market value ($ mil.)	(38.6%)	99.5	40.9	13.5	14.4	14.1
Employees	(3.3%)	120	120	98	106	105

IVESCO, LLC

124 Country Club Rd.
Iowa Falls, IA 50126
Phone: 641-648-5123
Fax: 800-828-8934
Web: www.ivescollc.com

CEO: Randy Ingram
CFO: Randy Ingram
HR: —
FYE: September 30
Type: Private

Whether it's Barky, Bessie, Bossy, or Boots who's in need of medical attention, the folks at IVESCO (formerly Iowa Veterinary Supply) will get the correct supplies to his or her vet. The company distributes more than 25,000 products, for companion animals and livestock, including veterinary equipment and supplies, pharmaceuticals, and pesticides. It operates through six divisions — IVESCO, IVS Animal Health, WYNCO, Panhandle Veterinary Supply, Scholfield Veterinary Supply, and VMS — with about 25 locations in some 20 US states. Iowa Veterinary Supply was founded in 1945; president Tom Kruse acquired the company with partner Ken Madole (who retired in the 1980s) in 1966.

IVOICE, INC.

OTC: IVOI

750 Hwy. 34
Matawan, NJ 07747
Phone: 732-441-7700
Fax: 732-441-9895
Web: www.ivoice.com

CEO: Jerome R. (Jerry) Mahoney
CFO: Jerome R. (Jerry) Mahoney
HR: —
FYE: December 31
Type: Public

iVoice speaks the language of spinoffs and special dividends, as well as speech technology. The company has formed or acquired a variety of subsidiaries that have then been spun off to shareholders via special dividends. Spinoffs have included Trey Resources, iVoice Technology, Deep Field Technology, and SpeechSwitch. iVoice's long-term plan, however, revolves around development and licensing of proprietary speech-enabled technologies and applications for which it holds patents.

	Annual Growth	12/05	12/06	12/07	12/08	12/09
Sales ($ mil.)	—	0.0	0.3	1.3	0.2	0.1
Net income ($ mil.)	—	(1.3)	(3.1)	(3.1)	(2.6)	1.1
Market value ($ mil.)	(78.5%)	—	93.0	7.0	0.5	0.9
Employees	10.7%	2	4	3	3	3

IXIA

NASDAQ (GS): XXIA

26601 W. Agoura Rd.
Calabasas, CA 91302
Phone: 818-871-1800
Fax: 818-871-1805
Web: www.ixiacom.com

CEO: Atul Bhatnagar
CFO: Thomas B. (Tom) Miller
HR: Chris Williams
FYE: December 31
Type: Public

Ixia nixes network glitches. The company designs interface cards that transmit and analyze signals over fiber-optic and copper-line networks. Its equipment evaluates the quantity and speed of transmission of data packets, how many packets are lost during transmission, and whether the packets are received intact and in order. Ixia also designs chassis to hold the interface cards, and software to operate them. The company primarily serves network equipment manufacturers, service providers, and communications chip makers. Customers include Alcatel-Lucent, AT&T, Broadcom, Cisco (21% of sales), Ericsson, Intel, NTT, Nokia, and Texas Instruments. Ixia gets around two-thirds of its sales in the US.

	Annual Growth	12/05	12/06	12/07	12/08	12/09
Sales ($ mil.)	2.8%	159.3	180.1	174.1	175.9	178.0
Net income ($ mil.)	—	33.7	13.5	7.0	(15.9)	(44.2)
Market value ($ mil.)	(15.8%)	950.2	616.4	608.7	371.1	478.3
Employees	13.8%	640	750	756	769	1,073

🏛 IXYS CORPORATION

NASDAQ (GS): IXYS

1590 Buckeye Dr.
Milpitas, CA 95035
Phone: 408-457-9000
Fax: 408-416-0222
Web: www.ixys.com

CEO: Nathan Zommer
CFO: —
HR: John Harris
FYE: March 31
Type: Public

If you like power semiconductors — and who doesn't? — you'll like IXYS. IXYS (pronounced ike-sys) makes a variety of power semiconductors (including transistors and rectifiers) and power modules, which convert and control electric power in electronic gear. The company sells these components for use in such equipment as power supplies, motor drives, and medical electronics. IXYS also sells digital power management integrated circuits (IC), gallium arsenide field-effect transistors, and proprietary direct copper bond substrate technology. The company's 2,000-plus customers include ABB, Emerson Electric, GE, Philips, Samsung SDI, and Siemens. About 70% of its sales comes from customers outside the US.

	Annual Growth	3/05	3/06	3/07	3/08	3/09
Sales ($ mil.)	1.6%	256.6	251.5	285.9	304.5	273.6
Net income ($ mil.)	—	16.2	(6.1)	30.2	23.3	(3.3)
Market value ($ mil.)	(8.4%)	358.4	288.9	320.5	214.0	252.5
Employees	2.4%	858	965	1,018	1,049	943

J. ALEXANDER'S CORPORATION

NASDAQ (GM): JAX

3401 West End Ave.
Nashville, TN 37203
Phone: 615-269-1900
Fax: 615-269-1999
Web: www.jalexanders.com

CEO: Lonnie J. Stout II
CFO: R. Gregory Lewis
HR: J. Michael Moore
FYE: December 31
Type: Public

You might say this restaurant chain is made up of distinctive links. J. Alexander's operates more than 30 upscale casual-dining restaurants, each of which sports a different architectural design and interior. The establishments serve beef, chicken, and pasta dishes for lunch and dinner, as well as soups, sandwiches, and appetizers. Desserts and croissants are baked fresh at each location. The company has freestanding restaurants operating in more than a dozen states, primarily in Ohio, Florida, and Tennessee. Board member E. Townes Duncan owns nearly 20% of the company through his investment firm Solidus.

	Annual Growth	12/05	12/06	12/07	12/08	12/09
Sales ($ mil.)	3.3%	126.6	137.7	141.3	139.8	144.2
Net income ($ mil.)	—	3.6	4.7	4.6	0.1	(15.3)
Market value ($ mil.)	(17.5%)	47.7	53.0	62.5	14.2	22.1
Employees	0.9%	2,700	2,700	2,700	2,850	2,800

J. CREW GROUP, INC.

NYSE: JCG

770 Broadway
New York, NY 10003
Phone: 212-209-2500
Fax: 212-209-2666
Web: www.jcrew.com

CEO: Millard S. (Mickey) Drexler
CFO: James S. Scully
HR: Linda Markoe
FYE: January 31
Type: Public

The crews depicted in the polished catalogs of the J. Crew Group are far from motley. The retailer is known for its preppy fashions, including jeans, khakis, and other basic (but pricey) items sold to young professionals through its catalogs, websites, and some 320 retail and outlet stores in the US under the J. Crew, crewcuts (for kids), and Madewell banners. Madewell, launched in 2006, is a women's-only collection of hip, casual clothes. Asian contractors produce about 80% of the company's merchandise. Chief executive Millard "Mickey" Drexler, recruited in 2003 from The Gap to revive J. Crew's ailing fortunes, has led a retail renaissance at the firm, marked by taking the company public in 2006.

	Annual Growth	1/06	1/07	1/08	1/09	1/10
Sales ($ mil.)	13.4%	953.2	1,152.1	1,334.7	1,428.0	1,578.0
Net income ($ mil.)	138.7%	3.8	77.8	97.1	54.1	123.4
Market value ($ mil.)	2.6%	—	2,318.7	2,908.4	638.2	2,502.5
Employees	15.3%	6,800	7,600	8,700	10,900	12,000

THE J. JILL GROUP, INC.

4 Batterymarch Park
Quincy, MA 02169
Phone: 617-376-4300
Fax: 617-769-0177
Web: www.jjill.com

CEO: Paula Bennett
CFO: Peter S. Delahunt
HR: —
FYE: January 31
Type: Private

The J. Jill Group's fortune has been catalog fashion, and catalogs aren't so fashionable anymore. To mend its bottom line, the direct marketer turned to retail outlets and online sales, with aggressive plans to open new stores across the US; it currently operates about 205 stores nationwide. The firm targets active, affluent women ages 35 and up, and banks on its J. Jill brand. The catalog and the website offer private-label casual wear made in the US and abroad. J. Jill Group's retail operations are its fastest growing division. J. Jill was acquired in 2006 by Talbots, which amid a rapidly deteriorating retail climate for women's apparel sold the chain to Golden Gate Capital (GGC) in 2009 for $75 million.

THE J. PAUL GETTY TRUST

1200 Getty Center Dr.
Los Angeles, CA 90049
Phone: 310-440-7300
Fax: 310-440-7722
Web: www.getty.edu

CEO: James N. Wood
CFO: Patricia Woodworth
HR: —
FYE: June 30
Type: Foundation

Oilman J. Paul Getty opened a small antiquities museum in 1954. Today the Getty Trust operates the $1 billion Getty Center, a hilltop haven that focuses on art and humanities. Among the world's wealthiest art institutions, it is best known for the J. Paul Getty Museum, which primarily displays pre-20th-century works of art by Rembrandt and van Gogh, among others. The center also houses the Getty Research Institute, the Getty Conservation Institute, and institutes dedicated to art history and museum management. In addition, the trust supports the arts through grants made by the Getty Foundation. The trust received $1.2 billion from Getty's estate in 1982 and has quadrupled in recent years.

J2 GLOBAL COMMUNICATIONS, INC.

NASDAQ (GS): JCOM

6922 Hollywood Blvd., Ste. 500
Hollywood, CA 90028
Phone: 323-860-9200
Fax: —
Web: www.j2global.com

CEO: Nehemia (Hemi) Zucker
CFO: Kathleen M. (Kathy) Griggs
HR: Patty Brunton
FYE: December 31
Type: Public

Checked your messages? Customers of j2 Global Communications can retrieve e-mail, faxes, and voicemail from a single phone line. Customers receive a private phone number that can handle unlimited incoming messages. The company operates primarily under the eFax, eVoice, Electric Mail, and Onebox brands, and claims more than 11 million phone numbers for customers located in nearly 50 countries worldwide, including major US cities and international business centers such as Frankfurt, London, and Tokyo. The company counts more than 1 million paid subscribers with the balance of phone lines going to advertising-supported free subscribers. j2 Global Communications gets most of its revenues in the US.

	Annual Growth	12/05	12/06	12/07	12/08	12/09
Sales ($ mil.)	14.3%	143.9	181.1	220.7	241.5	245.6
Net income ($ mil.)	6.8%	51.3	53.1	68.5	72.6	66.8
Market value ($ mil.)	(1.2%)	965.4	1,231.1	956.4	905.3	919.3
Employees	8.6%	288	341	410	400	400

JABIL CIRCUIT, INC.

NYSE: JBL

10560 Dr. Martin Luther King Jr. St. North
St. Petersburg, FL 33716
Phone: 727-577-9749
Fax: 727-579-8529
Web: www.jabil.com

CEO: Timothy L. Main
CFO: Forbes I. J. Alexander
HR: William E. (Bill) Peters
FYE: August 31
Type: Public

Jabil Circuit takes more than a jab at contract electronics manufacturing. The company is one of the leading providers of electronics manufacturing services (EMS) in the world. Parts made by Jabil on a contract basis are used in communications products, medical instruments, computers and networking gear, and automobiles. Services range from product design and component procurement to product testing, order fulfillment, and supply chain management. Top customers include Cisco Systems, Research in Motion, Hewlett-Packard, EchoStar, and Nokia. The company, which has expanded into Asian and Eastern European markets, gets more than 80% of sales from international operations.

	Annual Growth	8/05	8/06	8/07	8/08	8/09
Sales ($ mil.)	11.6%	7,524.4	10,265.4	12,290.6	12,779.7	11,684.5
Net income ($ mil.)	—	231.8	164.5	73.2	133.9	(1,165.2)
Market value ($ mil.)	(21.9%)	6,409.0	5,840.8	4,832.8	3,670.3	2,383.8
Employees	11.1%	40,000	49,000	61,000	61,000	61,000

An in-depth profile of this company is available to Hoover's Online members at hoovers.com.

853

JACK COOPER TRANSPORT CO., INC.

2345 Grand Blvd., Ste. 400
Kansas City, MO 64108
Phone: 816-983-4000
Fax: 816-983-5000
Web: www.jackcooper.com

CEO: Greg May
CFO: Dan Theiss
HR: Terry Vasko
FYE: December 31
Type: Private

Your new car's journey from the factory to your garage might include a trip on a Jack Cooper Transport trailer. The company hauls motor vehicles from assembly plants, ports, and railway terminals to dealers and other locations across the US. Through its Jack Cooper Transport and Pacific Motor Trucking units, the company moves more than 1 million new and used vehicles each year, including cars, light trucks, and sport utility vehicles. It maintains a fleet of about 1,200 tractor-trailer pairs. The company operates primarily in the western, midwestern, and southern US. Jack Cooper Transport is owned by Thom Cooper, whose grandfather Jack Cooper founded the company in 1928.

	Annual Growth	12/04	12/05	12/06	12/07	12/08
Est. sales ($ mil.)	—	—	—	—	—	214.3
Employees	—	—	—	—	—	3,000

[H] JACK HENRY & ASSOCIATES, INC.

NASDAQ (GS): JKHY

663 W. Hwy. 60
Monett, MO 65708
Phone: 417-235-6652
Fax: 417-235-4281
Web: www.jackhenry.com

CEO: John F. (Jack) Prim
CFO: Kevin D. Williams
HR: Ann Puddister
FYE: June 30
Type: Public

Jack Henry & Associates (JHA) provides integrated in-house and outsourced computer systems to banks and credit unions. Products include core processing systems, electronic funds transfer (EFT) systems, automated teller machine networking products, digital check and document imaging and storage systems, Internet banking tools, and customer relationship management (CRM) software. The company's Symitar division offers service bureau, data processing, and other software for credit unions, while its ProfitStars brand offers revenue management products.

	Annual Growth	6/05	6/06	6/07	6/08	6/09
Sales ($ mil.)	8.6%	535.9	592.2	668.1	742.9	745.6
Net income ($ mil.)	8.1%	75.5	89.9	104.7	104.2	103.1
Market value ($ mil.)	3.2%	1,562.4	1,677.6	2,197.2	1,846.5	1,770.6
Employees	6.2%	2,989	4,299	3,583	3,824	3,808

[H] JACK IN THE BOX INC.

NASDAQ (GS): JACK

9330 Balboa Ave.
San Diego, CA 92123
Phone: 858-571-2121
Fax: 858-571-2101
Web: www.jackinthebox.com

CEO: Linda A. Lang
CFO: Jerry P. Rebel
HR: Mark H. Blankenship
FYE: September 30
Type: Public

Led by an affable "CEO" with a Ping-Pong ball for a head, Jack in the Box is among the leading quick-service restaurant businesses in the US. The company operates and franchises more than 2,200 of its flagship hamburger outlets in California, Texas, and about 15 other states. Jack in the Box offers such standard fast-food fare as burgers, fries, and soft drinks, as well as salads, tacos, and breakfast items. About 1,200 locations are company-owned, while the rest are franchised. In addition to its mainstay burger business, the company runs a chain of more than 500 Qdoba Mexican Grill fast-casual eateries through its Qdoba Restaurant subsidiary.

	Annual Growth	9/05	9/06	9/07	9/08	9/09
Sales ($ mil.)	(0.4%)	2,507.2	2,765.6	2,876.0	2,539.6	2,471.1
Net income ($ mil.)	6.7%	91.5	109.1	126.3	119.3	118.4
Market value ($ mil.)	8.2%	823.1	1,436.0	1,784.3	1,161.3	1,127.7
Employees	(5.4%)	44,600	44,300	42,500	42,700	35,700

JACK MORTON WORLDWIDE INC.

919 Third Ave., 14th Fl.
New York, NY 10022
Phone: 212-401-7000
Fax: 212-401-7010
Web: www.jackmorton.com

CEO: Josh McCall
CFO: Bill Davies
HR: Charlotte Merrell
FYE: December 31
Type: Subsidiary

Jack Morton Worldwide dramatizes marketing. The marketing firm stages more than 1,000 multimedia events, both live and virtual, to promote clients' images and brands annually. It offers creative development, planning, speaker and entertainment arrangements, video production, staffing, and logistics, among other services. Clients have included Procter & Gamble, General Motors, eBay, IBM, and NBC Universal. Jack Morton Worldwide has offices in about 10 US cities, as well as in London, Beijing, Hong Kong, and Sydney. Founded by entertainment booking agent Jack Morton, the company traces its roots back to 1939. It is a subsidiary of advertising and marketing services conglomerate Interpublic.

JACK'S FAMILY RESTAURANTS, INC.

133 W. Oxmoor Rd., Ste. 215
Birmingham, AL 35209
Phone: 205-945-8167
Fax: 205-945-9820
Web: www.eatatjacks.com

CEO: Benny M. LaRussa
CFO: Cheryl Ledbetter
HR: Guy Kirk
FYE: September 30
Type: Private

It's the hamburgers that bring the customers back to Jack's. Jack's Family Restaurants operates a chain of more than 100 burger joints across the Southeast, many of which are located in Alabama. The eateries offer a menu of hamburgers, cheeseburgers, and chicken sandwiches, along with sides, salads, and breakfast items. Most Jack's locations are company-owned; a handful of units in Alabama are franchised. The chain was started in Homewood, Alabama, in 1960 by Jack Caddell, an entrepreneur who was impressed by the early success of McDonald's. Former franchisee Benny LaRussa bought the business in 1989.

	Annual Growth	9/04	9/05	9/06	9/07	9/08
Est. sales ($ mil.)	—	—	—	—	—	49.9
Employees	—	—	—	—	—	2,300

[H] JACKSON FAMILY WINES

421 Aviation Blvd.
Santa Rosa, CA 95403
Phone: 707-544-4000
Fax: 707-569-0105
Web: www.kj.com

CEO: Jess S. Jackson Jr.
CFO: —
HR: —
FYE: June 30
Type: Private

Jackson Family Wines (JFW) plucks its success right from the vine. One of California's largest winemakers, JFW produces the top-selling chardonnay in the US: Kendall-Jackson brand Vintner's Reserve. The company's other leading (and most expensive) wine is Grand Reserve. Sold in restaurants, stores, and via the company's website (where legal), JFW's libations — in addition to its well-known chardonnay — include merlot, sauvignon blanc, pinot noir, cabernet sauvignon, and zinfandel. JFW owns and farms 14,000 acres of vineyards running along the California coast. Founder and billionaire Jess Jackson and his family own JFW.

JACKSON HEWITT TAX SERVICE INC.

NYSE: JTX

3 Sylvan Way
Parsippany, NJ 07054
Phone: 973-630-1040
Fax: 973-496-2785
Web: www.jacksonhewitt.com

CEO: Harry W. Buckley
CFO: Daniel P. (Dan) O'Brien
HR: Peter N. Karpiak
FYE: April 30
Type: Public

For Jackson Hewitt, there's no season like tax season. The #2 tax preparer in the US behind H&R Block, Jackson Hewitt prepares tax returns for low- and middle-income customers through more than 6,000 offices (primarily franchises), including locations within Wal-Mart Stores and mall kiosks. The aggressively expanding firm prepared some 2.9 million tax returns in the fiscal year ended April 2009. The firm's tax preparers use its proprietary ProFiler decision-tree software. Other Jackson Hewitt products and services include electronic filing, refund-anticipation loans, tax school, and a Visa stored-value card. Jackson Hewitt earns some 95% of revenues during the tax season of January through April.

	Annual Growth	4/05	4/06	4/07	4/08	4/09
Sales ($ mil.)	1.7%	232.5	275.4	293.2	278.5	248.3
Net income ($ mil.)	(21.0%)	50.0	58.0	65.4	32.4	19.5
Market value ($ mil.)	(28.2%)	529.9	859.6	793.4	428.9	140.7
Employees	(1.5%)	377	370	408	429	355

JACKSON NATIONAL LIFE INSURANCE COMPANY

IMG Service Center, 1 Corporate Way
Lansing, MI 48951
Phone: 517-381-5500
Fax: 517-706-5521
Web: www.jnl.com

CEO: Clark P. Manning Jr.
CFO: Andrew B. (Andy) Hopping
HR: Stephen A. (Steve) Hrapkiewicz
FYE: December 31
Type: Subsidiary

Planning for retirement with this Jackson could be as "simple as Do-Re-Me." Jackson National Life Insurance Company, a subsidiary of UK insurer Prudential plc, offers financial services (fixed, indexed, and variable annuities) and life insurance products through banks, financial planners, regional broker/dealers, and independent agents. The company also provides asset management, mutual fund, and brokerage services. Its subsidiaries include Jackson National Life Distributors (the company's wholesale distribution arm) and National Planning Holdings (broker relationship management), as well as investment consulting and account management units Curian Capital, Jackson National Asset Management, and PPM America.

	Annual Growth	12/04	12/05	12/06	12/07	12/08
Est. sales ($ mil.)	—	—	—	—	—	3,712.2
Employees	—	—	—	—	—	2,947

JACKSONVILLE BANCORP, INC.

NASDAQ (GM): JAXB

100 N. Laura St., Ste. 1000
Jacksonville, FL 32202
Phone: 904-421-3040
Fax: 904-421-3050
Web: www.jaxbank.com

CEO: Price W. Schwenck
CFO: Valerie A. Kendall
HR: Lynn Clute
FYE: December 31
Type: Public

Need to stow some greenbacks in Jax? Check out Jacksonville Bancorp, the holding company for The Jacksonville Bank, which has about five branches in Jacksonville, Florida. The community bank offers standard deposit products, including checking and savings accounts, money market accounts, CDs, and IRAs. Commercial mortgages make up some 60% of the loan portfolio; agricultural mortgages account for another 30%. The bank also offers residential mortgages and business, construction, and consumer loans. Subsidiary Fountain Financial sells insurance and investment products. Jacksonville Bancorp is unrelated to the Illinois corporation of the same name. It is, however, acquiring Atlantic BancGroup.

	Annual Growth	12/05	12/06	12/07	12/08	12/09
Sales ($ mil.)	—	—	—	—	—	26.7
Net income ($ mil.)	—	—	—	—	—	0.0
Employees	—	—	—	—	—	58

JACKSONVILLE BANCORP, INC.

NASDAQ (CM): JXSB

1211 W. Morton Ave.
Jacksonville, IL 62650
Phone: 217-245-4111
Fax: 217-245-2010
Web: www.jacksonvillesavings.com

CEO: Richard A. (Rich) Foss
CFO: Diana S. Tone
HR: John D. Eilering
FYE: December 31
Type: Public

Jacksonville Bancorp (unaffiliated with the Florida corporation of the same name) is the holding company for Jacksonville Savings Bank, which serves consumers and businesses in western Illinois through more than five offices, including its Chapin State Bank, First Midwest Savings Bank, and Litchfield Community Savings divisions. The bank is mainly a real estate lender, with residential, commercial, and agricultural mortgages accounting for more than half of its loan portfolio. Subsidiary Financial Resources Group offers investment and trust services. The company is majority-owned by mutual holding company Jacksonville Bancorp, M.H.C. but plans to convert to a stock holding company structure.

	Annual Growth	12/05	12/06	12/07	12/08	12/09
Assets ($ mil.)	3.3%	253.9	267.4	288.5	288.3	288.8
Net income ($ mil.)	11.7%	0.9	0.9	0.6	1.5	1.4
Market value ($ mil.)	(11.4%)	29.3	24.9	23.5	18.7	18.1
Employees	4.8%	98	121	118	112	118

JACKSONVILLE GREYHOUND RACING, INC.

455 Park Ave.
Orange Park, FL 32073
Phone: 904-646-0001
Fax: 904-646-0420
Web: www.jaxkennel.com

CEO: Howard Korman
CFO: Bob Kuhn
HR: Delynn Zebouni
FYE: December 31
Type: Private

Four-legged runners send this company off to the races. Jacksonville Greyhound Racing owns and operates the Orange Park Kennel Club near Jacksonville, Florida, which offers live dog racing year-round. The facility features grandstand seating for 4,000 and more than 1,100 clubhouse seats. The company also operates The "Best Bet" at St. Johns, which offers simulcast racing. In addition to dog racing, both facilities feature a poker room where players can choose from a variety of games. Jacksonville Greyhound Racing also broadcasts dog races over the Internet.

	Annual Growth	12/04	12/05	12/06	12/07	12/08
Est. sales ($ mil.)	—	—	—	—	—	15.7
Employees	—	—	—	—	—	400

JACLYN, INC.

Pink Sheets: JCLY

197 W. Spring Valley Ave.
Maywood, NJ 07607
Phone: 201-909-6000
Fax: 201-226-7801
Web: www.jaclyninc.com

CEO: Robert Chestnov
CFO: Anthony C. Christon
HR: —
FYE: June 30
Type: Public

Jaclyn wants to give a hand — or, at the very least, a handbag — to well-dressed women on the go. It designs and sells branded and private-label apparel, backpacks, handbags, cosmetic bags, sport bags, travel bags, and related accessories for men, women, and children. Its apparel lines (more than 60% of sales) include women's sleepwear, sportswear, and dresses as well as infants' and children's clothing under the Topsville, I Appel, and Smart Time labels, among others. Its apparel and accessories, made by outside contractors in Asia, are sold through general merchandise, department, and specialty stores nationwide. Wal-Mart accounts for about 40% of Jaclyn's sales; Estée Lauder contributed more than 20%.

An in-depth profile of this company is available to Hoover's Online members at hoovers.com.

855

JACO ELECTRONICS, INC.

NASDAQ (GM): JACO

145 Oser Ave.
Hauppauge, NY 11788
Phone: 631-273-5500
Fax: 631-231-1051
Web: www.jacoelectronics.com

CEO: Joel H. Girsky
CFO: Jeffrey D. Gash
HR: —
FYE: June 30
Type: Public

Jaco Electronics, doing business as Jaco Display Solutions, offers information displays for a variety of industries. In 2009 Jaco sold the assets of its electronic components distribution business to WPG Americas, Inc., a subsidiary of Taiwan-based WPG Holdings. Jaco shifted its focus to distributing displays, embedded computing products, and inverters, while providing value-added services. The components distribution business is shifting to Asia, the company noted. Jaco also offers a number of services, including inventory management and flat-panel display system configuration, but discontinued contract manufacturing services. The company still provides engineering support services for its customers.

	Annual Growth	6/04	6/05	6/06	6/07	*6/08
Sales ($ mil.)	(6.1%)	249.1	231.8	228.5	240.2	193.7
Net income ($ mil.)	—	(0.6)	(4.9)	(7.0)	0.1	(9.1)
Market value ($ mil.)	(34.3%)	38.3	18.6	23.5	14.6	7.1
Employees	(17.2%)	412	202	205	205	194

*Most recent year available

JACO OIL COMPANY

3101 State Rd.
Bakersfield, CA 93308
Phone: 661-393-7000
Fax: 661-393-8738
Web: www.fastrip.com

CEO: Thomas J. Jamieson
CFO: Brian Busacca
HR: Alissa Thome
FYE: December 31
Type: Private

Jaco Oil Company is jockeying for its piece of the convenience store pie. The company's Fastrip Food Stores subsidiary operates about 35 convenience stores and gas stations primarily in and around Bakersfield, California, but also in Arizona. The Fastrip chain offers in-store financial service centers, which provide check cashing, payday loans, wire transfer services via The Western Union Company, and other services, at many locations. Jaco Oil Company was founded in 1970.

	Annual Growth	12/04	12/05	12/06	12/07	12/08
Est. sales ($ mil.)	—	—	—	—	—	323.1
Employees	—	—	—	—	—	350

JACOBS ENGINEERING GROUP INC.

NYSE: JEC

1111 S. Arroyo Pkwy.
Pasadena, CA 91105
Phone: 626-578-3500
Fax: 626-568-7144
Web: www.jacobs.com

CEO: Craig L. Martin
CFO: John W. Prosser Jr.
HR: Patricia H. Summers
FYE: September 30
Type: Public

Jacobs climbs the ladder of success by keeping it professional. Jacobs Engineering Group provides professional, technical, and construction services for the industrial, commercial, and government sectors. It provides a wide range of services, including project design and engineering, construction, operations and maintenance, and scientific consultation. Engineering and construction projects for the chemical, petroleum, and pharmaceutical and biotech industries generate much of the group's revenues. US government contracts, chiefly for aerospace and defense, also add to Jacobs' bottom line. The company has more than 160 offices around the world, primarily in North America, Europe, Asia, and Australia.

	Annual Growth	9/05	9/06	9/07	9/08	9/09
Sales ($ mil.)	19.4%	5,635.0	7,421.3	8,474.0	11,252.2	11,467.4
Net income ($ mil.)	27.6%	151.0	196.9	287.1	420.7	399.9
Market value ($ mil.)	8.1%	4,213.1	4,671.3	9,448.9	6,789.8	5,744.6
Employees	0.2%	38,600	31,700	36,400	43,700	38,900

JACOBS ENTERTAINMENT, INC.

17301 W. Colfax Ave., Ste. 250
Golden, CO 80401
Phone: 303-215-5200
Fax: 303-215-5219
Web: www.bhwk-hr.com

CEO: Jeffrey P. Jacobs
CFO: Brett A. Kramer
HR: —
FYE: December 31
Type: Private

Jacobs Entertainment wants you to come out and play. The company operates The Lodge Casino and Gilpin Casino in Black Hawk, Colorado, and the Gold Dust West Casinos in Reno, Carson City, and Elko, Nevada. The company also has about 20 truck stop video gaming facilities throughout Louisiana; the Colonial Downs horseracing track in New Kent, Virginia; and eight satellite pari-mutuel wagering locations throughout Virginia. Chairman and CEO Jeffrey Jacobs owns 52% of the company; the Jacobs Family Economic and Control Trusts own 48%.

	Annual Growth	12/04	12/05	12/06	12/07	12/08
Sales ($ mil.)	17.6%	189.7	234.1	338.6	381.8	362.5
Net income ($ mil.)	—	5.0	(4.7)	(10.8)	5.0	(4.1)
Employees	11.4%	1,365	1,585	1,100	2,200	2,100

JACOBS FINANCIAL GROUP, INC.

OTC: JFGIE

300 Summers St., Ste. 970
Charleston, WV 25301
Phone: 304-343-8171
Fax: 304-342-9726

CEO: John M. Jacobs
CFO: John M. Jacobs
HR: —
FYE: May 31
Type: Public

If Jacob needed to bond his ladder, Jacobs Financial Group could provide the surety. Through subsidiaries, Jacobs Financial provides surety and insurance as well as investment advisory services. The company's FS Investments (FSI) is a holding company that develops surety business by creating companies engaged in the issuance of surety bonds (bonds collateralized by accounts managed by Jacobs & Co.). FSI's wholly owned subsidiary Triangle Surety Agency specializes in placing surety bonds with insurance companies, with an emphasis on clients in industries such as coal, oil, and gas. Jacobs Financial, whose background is in energy, has been expanding its insurance and surety operations through acquisitions.

	Annual Growth	5/05	5/06	5/07	5/08	5/09
Assets ($ mil.)	189.3%	0.1	4.3	4.4	5.8	7.0
Net income ($ mil.)	—	(1.1)	(1.5)	(1.3)	(1.9)	(1.4)
Market value ($ mil.)	49.5%	1.9	8.6	4.3	1.9	9.6
Employees	(3.3%)	8	8	9	9	7

JACQUES MORET, INC.

1411 Broadway, 8th Fl.
New York, NY 10018
Phone: 212-354-2400
Fax: 212-354-1052
Web: www.moret.com

CEO: Joseph (Joey) Harary
CFO: Irwin Luxembeurg
HR: —
FYE: December 31
Type: Private

Jacques Moret sounds like a French Impressionist but its business is in outfitting casual athletes rather than galleries. The company, which does business as The Moret Group, makes women's, men's, and kid's activewear and undergarments under the Jacques Moret, MoretUltra, and Jacques Moret Kids names. It also makes men's and women's undergarments marketed under the 2(X)ist and SBH Intimates monikers. Jacques Moret is the master licensee for Everlast Worldwide. The company also partners with the likes of Jockey, Mudd, DKNY, Spalding, Freestyle by Danskin, and Etonic. Jacques Moret's products are sold through department stores, mass merchandisers, and sporting goods chains nationwide.

JACUZZI BRANDS CORP.

13925 City Center Dr., Ste. 200
Chino Hills, CA 91709
Phone: 909-247-2920
Fax: —
Web: www.jacuzzibrands.com

CEO: Thomas D. Koos
CFO: David Broadbent
HR: —
FYE: September 30
Type: Private

Aaah, that feels good. Jacuzzi Brands makes the eponymous whirlpool baths, spas, and showers that soothe the aches and pains of customers in Europe, the Middle East, South America, and the US. Besides spas and baths, products include toilets and sinks, accessories such as bath pillows and heating kits, steam showers, and other Romanesque bathroom necessities. The company sells its products under brand names including Jacuzzi, Sundance, Zurn, Rainbow, and Astracast. Investment firm Apollo Management acquired Jacuzzi Brands for about $1.25 billion in 2007.

JAFCO VENTURES

505 Hamilton Ave., Ste. 310
Palo Alto, CA 94301
Phone: 650-463-8800
Fax: 650-463-8801
Web: www.jafco.com

CEO: Joe Horowitz
CFO: Yoichiro (Joe) Takami
HR: —
FYE: March 31
Type: Subsidiary

A segment of Japanese venture capital firm JAFCO Co., JAFCO Ventures focuses its attention on the US and invests venture capital in development-stage information technology companies, generally as a secondary investor. Portfolio companies include systems integrator Infinera, online security services provider Voltage Security, broadband wireless services provider Aperto Networks, wireless software designer Devicescape Software, and semiconductor designer Xambala. With the advantages of its parent company, JAFCO Ventures utilizes financial professionals and advisers in Asia to forge relationships and partnerships with potential clients as well.

	Annual Growth	3/04	3/05	3/06	3/07	3/08
Est. sales ($ mil.)	—	—	—	—	—	3.4
Employees	—	—	—	—	—	14

JAFRA COSMETICS INTERNATIONAL, INC.

2451 Townsgate Rd.
Westlake Village, CA 91361
Phone: 805-449-3000
Fax: 805-449-3254
Web: www.jafra.com

CEO: Friedrich (Fred) Kroos
CFO: —
HR: —
FYE: December 31
Type: Subsidiary

Move over, Avon; step aside, Mary Kay. There's an international sales force of money-hungry women banding together. Jafra (a combination of the first names of the company's founders, Malibu, California, couple Jan and Frank Day) sells and distributes high-end cosmetics, skin care products, and fragrances internationally through more than 500,000 independent beauty consultants in about 25 countries. Products include skin cleansers and lotions, mineral makeup, vitamin tablets, home spa sets, and nail polishes, as well as a variety of products for men, teens, and babies.

	Annual Growth	12/04	12/05	12/06	12/07	12/08
Est. sales ($ mil.)	—	—	—	—	—	82.0
Employees	—	—	—	—	—	762

JAGGED PEAK, INC.

OTC: JGPK

3000 Bayport Dr., Ste. 250
Tampa, FL 33607
Phone: 813-637-6900
Fax: 800-749-4998
Web: www.jaggedpeak.com

CEO: Paul Demirdjian
CFO: Andrew J. Norstrud
HR: —
FYE: December 31
Type: Public

Jagged Peak rises up to help customers reach the peak of supply chain management. The company's E-Business Dynamic Global Engine (EDGE) software is a ready-to-use Web-based application that captures, processes, and distributes orders from multiple sources, sending them in real-time to warehouses. With automated purchases and orders, companies can streamline their supply chain processes to improve delivery, reduce costs, and integrate inventory information. Jagged Peak took its present form in 2005, when publicly traded Absolute Glass Protection acquired the private company and adopted its name, officers, and operations.

	Annual Growth	12/05	12/06	12/07	12/08	12/09
Sales ($ mil.)	14.5%	9.7	11.5	14.4	16.6	16.7
Net income ($ mil.)	—	(0.7)	(1.4)	(0.4)	(0.2)	(0.2)
Market value ($ mil.)	(52.2%)	40.1	8.8	4.8	2.2	2.1
Employees	4.4%	80	74	105	107	95

JAGUAR MINING INC.

NYSE Arca: JAG

125 N. State St.
Concord, NH 03301
Phone: 603-224-4800
Fax: 603-228-8045
Web: www.jaguarmining.com

CEO: Daniel R. Titcomb
CFO: James M. Roller
HR: Valéria Rezende DioDato
FYE: December 31
Type: Public

Jaguar Mining is on the prowl for gold in Brazil. The company operates three gold mines in the mineral-rich state of Minas Gerais that have proved and provable reserves of almost 900,000 ounces. A fourth mining project is in development, also in Minas Gerais. Once in production, estimated to be in 2011, the Caeté mine by itself will double the company's reserves. Jaguar Mining is also exploring the northeastern state of Ceará through a partnership with Xstrata.

	Annual Growth	12/05	12/06	12/07	12/08	12/09
Sales ($ mil.)	101.7%	8.5	21.2	47.8	93.7	140.7
Net income ($ mil.)	—	(12.8)	(12.7)	(27.7)	(4.3)	(8.0)
Market value ($ mil.)	35.2%	3,945.1	6,805.6	14,070.3	6,158.0	13,175.5
Employees	22.6%	680	680	996	1,328	1,535

JAKKS PACIFIC, INC.

NASDAQ (GS): JAKK

22619 Pacific Coast Hwy.
Malibu, CA 90265
Phone: 310-456-7799
Fax: 310-317-8527
Web: www.jakkspacific.com

CEO: Stephen G. Berman
CFO: Joel M. Bennett
HR: Michael Dwyer
FYE: December 31
Type: Public

JAKKS Pacific is ready to rumble. JAKKS, one of the US's top toy companies, makes and sells action figures (including an exclusive license for World Wrestling Entertainment figures), activity sets (Flying Colors), die-cast and plastic cars (Road Champs), preschool toys (Child Guidance), pens and markers (Pentech), and fashion dolls. Its inexpensive toys are sold to US retailers such as Target, Toys "R" Us, and Wal-Mart (which together account for more than 56% of company sales); hobby stores; and other retailers. JAKKS, which has been growing by acquisitions, was founded in 1995 by the late Jack Friedman and Stephen Berman, president and CEO.

	Annual Growth	12/05	12/06	12/07	12/08	12/09
Sales ($ mil.)	5.0%	661.5	765.4	857.1	903.4	803.7
Net income ($ mil.)	—	63.5	72.4	89.0	76.1	(385.5)
Market value ($ mil.)	(12.8%)	584.2	609.4	658.7	575.6	338.2
Employees	3.3%	624	702	598	998	711

An in-depth profile of this company is available to Hoover's Online members at hoovers.com.

857

JAMBA, INC.

NASDAQ (GM): JMBA

6475 Christie Ave., Ste. 150
Emeryville, CA 94608
Phone: 510-596-0100
Fax: 510-653-0764
Web: www.jambajuice.com

CEO: James D. White
CFO: Karen L. Luey
HR: Kathy Wright
FYE: December 31
Type: Public

This company is blending up business with its fruit-filled drinks. Jamba operates the Jamba Juice chain, the leading outlet for blended fruit drinks with more than 740 smoothie stands in more than 20 states and the Bahamas. Its menu includes more than 30 varieties of custom smoothies (including Aloha Pineapple, Mango-a-go-go, and Strawberry Surf Rider) and Jamba Boosts (smoothies made with vitamin and protein supplements), along with other fruit juices and food items. Jamba Juice locations include freestanding units as well as on-site kiosks in high traffic areas, including college campuses, gyms, and airports. About 460 Jamba Juice locations are company-owned, while the rest are franchised.

	Annual Growth	12/05	12/06	12/07	12/08	12/09
Sales ($ mil.)	276.6%	1.5	23.1	317.2	342.9	301.6
Net income ($ mil.)	—	1.2	(59.0)	(113.3)	(149.2)	(23.9)
Market value ($ mil.)	(30.4%)	424.4	598.5	219.9	25.6	99.9
Employees	618.6%	3	7,500	10,000	9,000	8,000

JAMES R. GLIDEWELL, DENTAL CERAMICS, INC.

4141 MacArthur Blvd.
Newport Beach, CA 92660
Phone: 949-440-2600
Fax: 800-411-9722
Web: www.glidewelldental.com

CEO: Jim Glidewell
CFO: Glenn Sasaki
HR: Stephanie Goddard
FYE: December 31
Type: Private

Glidewell Laboratories is a household name in dental offices. The dental lab makes a wide range of restorative, reconstructive, and cosmetic dental products, such as crowns, dentures, and bridges. Its BDL Prosthetics division makes aesthetic temporary teeth (known as BioTemps) used for provisional restoration until final ceramic restorations are ready. Glidewell Laboratories and BDL employ a mail-order business model, with dentists sending in dental impressions and receiving custom restorative products via the US Postal Service or FedEx. Another division, Glidewell Direct, sells clinical and laboratory products, including impression materials, via an e-commerce site.

JAMES RIVER COAL COMPANY

NASDAQ (GM): JRCC

901 E. Byrd St., Ste. 1600
Richmond, VA 23219
Phone: 804-780-3000
Fax: 804-780-0643
Web: www.jamesrivercoal.com

CEO: Peter T. Socha
CFO: Samuel M. (Sam) Hopkins II
HR: —
FYE: December 31
Type: Public

James River Coal hopes the coal keeps flowing. The company operates about 30 mines in eastern Kentucky (in the Central Appalachian Basin) and southern Indiana (in the Illinois Basin) that produce some 10 million tons of coal annually. Though a small percentage of the coal it sells comes from independent operators and third-party producers, the vast majority of James River's coal is produced from company-operated mines. It controls approximately 275 million tons of proved and probable reserves. More than three-quarters of its coal is sold to utilities. Georgia Power and South Carolina Public Service are its biggest customers, collectively accounting for nearly half of its business.

	Annual Growth	12/05	12/06	12/07	12/08	12/09
Sales ($ mil.)	10.7%	454.0	564.8	520.6	568.5	681.6
Net income ($ mil.)	—	(12.3)	(26.2)	(54.0)	(96.0)	51.0
Market value ($ mil.)	(16.6%)	1,052.2	255.6	307.9	422.2	509.3
Employees	5.0%	1,429	1,742	1,681	1,751	1,736

J & J SNACK FOODS CORP.

NASDAQ (GS): JJSF

6000 Central Hwy.
Pennsauken, NJ 08109
Phone: 856-665-9533
Fax: 856-663-8002
Web: www.jjsnack.com

CEO: Gerald B. Shreiber
CFO: Dennis G. Moore
HR: Harry Fronjian
FYE: September 30
Type: Public

Giving you a brain-freeze and a little mustard on the corner of your mouth, J & J Snack Foods offers savory and sweet items, including SUPERPRETZEL soft pretzels and ICEE frozen beverages. It makes frozen desserts and juice treats (Luigi's, Mama Tish's), churros, and funnel cakes (Tio Pepe's). The company sells cookies under the brand name Mrs. GoodCookie and CinnaPretzels (licensed from Cinnabon). J & J is also the licensed manufacturer of Minute Maid's soft frozen lemonade and frozen juice bars. Its customers include food-service operators and retail food outlets; J & J also owns four company-owed retail shops, BAVARIAN PRETZEL BAKERY and PRETZEL GOURMET, all located in the mid-Atlantic region of the US.

	Annual Growth	9/05	9/06	9/07	9/08	9/09
Sales ($ mil.)	9.3%	457.1	514.8	568.9	629.4	653.0
Net income ($ mil.)	12.3%	26.0	29.5	32.1	27.9	41.3
Market value ($ mil.)	10.6%	532.2	572.7	641.2	624.4	795.3
Employees	3.5%	2,350	2,300	2,600	2,800	2,700

JANEL WORLD TRADE LTD.

OTC: JLWT

150-14 132nd Ave.
Jamaica, NY 11434
Phone: 718-527-3800
Fax: 718-527-1689
Web: www.janelgroup.net

CEO: James N. Jannello
CFO: Linda Bieler
HR: —
FYE: September 30
Type: Public

Janel World Trade puts it all together for customers that ship by air, land, or sea. The freight forwarding and logistics management company gets lower bulk shipping rates for its clients by consolidating cargo headed to the same destination. Janel also provides customs brokerage, warehousing and distribution, and other logistics services. The company primarily handles clothing and textiles, household appliances, machinery and machine parts, and sporting goods shipped to and from the US, Europe, and the Far East. In addition to offices in the US, Janel has franchise operations in China, Guatemala, Honduras, Hong Kong, and Thailand; the company works with agents in other parts of the world.

	Annual Growth	9/05	9/06	9/07	9/08	9/09
Sales ($ mil.)	(0.5%)	73.5	77.2	74.9	82.7	71.9
Net income ($ mil.)	—	0.4	0.1	0.3	(1.6)	(1.2)
Market value ($ mil.)	8.1%	12.1	8.5	9.2	17.5	16.5
Employees	0.4%	61	64	69	79	62

JANUS CAPITAL GROUP INC.

NYSE: JNS

151 Detroit St.
Denver, CO 80206
Phone: 303-333-3863
Fax: 303-336-7497
Web: www.janus.com

CEO: Richard M. (Dick) Weil
CFO: Gregory A. (Greg) Frost
HR: —
FYE: December 31
Type: Public

Named after the Roman god with two faces, Janus Capital Group provides investment management and advisory services for institutional and individual customers. Known for its intensive equities research, the company manages more than 30 mutual funds, including its flagship Janus Fund (formed in 1969), as well as separate accounts and sub-advised funds. Subsidiary INTECH manages institutional portfolios by utilizing investment strategies based on mathematical analysis of the stock market, while Perkins Investment Management focuses on long-term value investments. All told, Janus Capital has some $160 billion of assets under management.

	Annual Growth	12/05	12/06	12/07	12/08	12/09
Assets ($ mil.)	(8.6%)	3,628.5	3,537.9	3,564.1	3,336.7	2,530.3
Net income ($ mil.)	—	87.8	133.6	116.3	136.9	(744.1)
Market value ($ mil.)	(7.8%)	3,422.8	3,966.7	6,035.4	1,475.3	2,471.1
Employees	(6.2%)	1,457	1,518	1,213	1,164	1,126

JARDEN CORPORATION

NYSE: JAH

555 Theodore Fremd Ave., Ste. B-302
Rye, NY 10580
Phone: 914-967-9400
Fax: 914-967-9405
Web: www.jarden.com

CEO: Martin E. Franklin
CFO: Ian G. H. Ashken
HR: J. David Tolbert
FYE: December 31
Type: Public

Jarden is beaming with consumer products for inside and outside the home. It makes a diverse set of branded consumer products, including Sunbeam and Oster appliances, Coleman outdoor gear, and First Alert home safety products. It also makes Ball canning jars, Diamond matches and plastic cutlery, Loew-Cornell art supplies, K2 snowboards, and Bee and Bicycle brand playing cards. Jarden sells its products primarily to retailers, such as Wal-Mart, Dick's Sporting Goods, and Target. It also supplies copper-plated zinc penny blanks to the US Mint and the Royal Canadian Mint. To further diversify its portfolio of products, Jarden acquired the Mapa Spontex baby care and home care businesses from TOTAL in 2010.

	Annual Growth	12/05	12/06	12/07	12/08	12/09
Sales ($ mil.)	12.7%	3,189.1	3,846.3	4,660.1	5,383.3	5,152.6
Net income ($ mil.)	20.7%	60.7	106.0	28.1	(58.9)	128.7
Market value ($ mil.)	0.6%	2,779.9	3,207.7	2,176.9	1,060.3	2,850.0
Employees	3.4%	17,500	20,000	25,000	20,000	20,000

🏠 JASON INCORPORATED

411 E. Wisconsin Ave., Ste. 2120
Milwaukee, WI 53202
Phone: 414-277-9300
Fax: 414-277-9445
Web: www.jasoninc.com

CEO: David Westgate
CFO: John Hengel
HR: —
FYE: December 31
Type: Private

Whether you're making the Sturgis run or just mowing your lawn, Jason Incorporated adds cush to your tush. The company's Motor Vehicle products segment has supplied seats for Harley-Davidson motorcycles since the 1930s; it also makes seats for lawn care, construction, and agricultural equipment makers such as John Deere. This unit also makes fiber insulation for the automotive industry. The company's Industrial segment makes such products as power brushes, buffing wheels, assembly processes, and metal and wire components. Investors in Jason include the company's management team and private equity firm Saw Mill Capital. Jason has operations in the US and 12 countries.

JAVELIN PHARMACEUTICALS, INC.

NYSE Amex: JAV

125 Cambridge Park Dr.
Cambridge, MA 02140
Phone: 617-349-4500
Fax: 617-349-4505
Web: javelinpharmaceuticals.com

CEO: Martin J. (Marty) Driscoll
CFO: Stephen J. Tulipano
HR: —
FYE: December 31
Type: Public

Pain, pain, go away, don't come back another day should be Javelin Pharmaceuticals' mantra. The firm develops pain management drugs, usually by taking existing ones and making them more patient-friendly through improved formulations and modes of delivery. Javelin attempts to make products less invasive and faster acting in treating moderate to severe post-operative, post-trauma, burn, and cancer pain. Its three candidates, Dyloject, Ereska, and Rylomine (all in late-stage development), are based on already-approved prescription medications: diclofenac, ketamine, and morphine. Javelin has agreed to be acquired by specialty pharmaceutical maker Hospira.

	Annual Growth	12/05	12/06	12/07	12/08	12/09
Sales ($ mil.)	245.5%	—	—	—	1.1	3.8
Net income ($ mil.)	—	—	—	—	(43.5)	(37.6)
Market value ($ mil.)	4.0%	—	—	—	81.0	84.2
Employees	(25.7%)	—	—	—	35	26

JAVO BEVERAGE COMPANY, INC.

OTC: JAVO

1311 Specialty Dr.
Vista, CA 92081
Phone: 760-560-5286
Fax: 760-560-5287
Web: www.javobeverage.com

CEO: Stanley L. (Stan) Greanias
CFO: Richard A. Gartrell
HR: —
FYE: December 31
Type: Public

Javo puts the S-Q-U-E-E-Z-E on coffee. Javo Beverage Company makes and markets coffee and tea concentrates, drink mixes, iced and hot ready-to-drink beverages, and flavor and dispenser systems. Its national and international customers do business in the retail, health care, oil, food and beverage manufacturing, and foodservice industries. Of note is Javo's line of "bag-in-a-box" products that allows restaurants, hotels, and hospitals to offer fresh-tasting coffee without having to do any actual brewing. In business since 1987, the company has never been profitable, reporting a net loss every year, and has yet to pay dividends to its stockholders, many of whom are Javo officers and/or board members.

	Annual Growth	12/05	12/06	12/07	12/08	12/09
Sales ($ mil.)	31.8%	6.2	10.3	12.6	19.4	18.7
Net income ($ mil.)	—	(4.8)	(9.9)	(7.4)	(10.8)	(13.7)
Market value ($ mil.)	(18.5%)	88.1	418.3	221.1	35.9	38.8
Employees	19.4%	30	46	55	59	61

JAZZ PHARMACEUTICALS, INC.

NASDAQ (GM): JAZZ

3180 Porter Dr.
Palo Alto, CA 94304
Phone: 650-496-3777
Fax: 650-496-3781
Web: www.jazzpharmaceuticals.com

CEO: Bruce C. Cozadd
CFO: Kathryn E. Falberg
HR: Heather McGaughey
FYE: December 31
Type: Public

Jazz Pharmaceuticals is anything but free-form or improvisational in its development of drugs to treat psychiatric and neurological conditions. The company has two products on the market, including narcolepsy treatment Xyrem. Jazz Pharmaceuticals also markets Solvay Pharmaceuticals' Luvox CR, an FDA-approved treatment for obsessive compulsive disorder (OCD) and social anxiety disorder. The company is also conducting late-stage clinical trials on the active ingredient in Xyrem as a possible treatment for fibromyalgia. Jazz Pharmaceutical has other compounds in clinical trials for the treatment of epilepsy and restless legs syndrome.

	Annual Growth	12/05	12/06	12/07	12/08	12/09
Sales ($ mil.)	56.5%	21.4	44.9	65.3	67.5	128.4
Net income ($ mil.)	—	(85.2)	(59.4)	(138.8)	(184.3)	(6.8)
Market value ($ mil.)	(26.8%)	—	—	463.6	60.9	248.5
Employees	2.9%	203	185	409	216	228

JAZZ SEMICONDUCTOR, INC.

4321 Jamboree Rd.
Newport Beach, CA 92660
Phone: 949-435-8000
Fax: 949-435-8757
Web: www.jazzsemi.com

CEO: Russell C. Ellwanger
CFO: Susanna Bennett
HR: —
FYE: December 31
Type: Subsidiary

Making semiconductors in exotic materials and processes is the specialty of Jazz Semiconductor. The company serves as a contract manufacturer of chips, also known as a silicon foundry. Jazz also uses the ol' reliable material, plain old silicon, although most of its chips for networking and wireless applications call for fabrication in silicon germanium and other compound semiconductors. Customers in the US account for most of Jazz Semiconductor's sales. In 2008 rival foundry Tower Semiconductor acquired Jazz Technologies, the parent company of Jazz Semiconductor, for about $169 million, including the assumption of debt. Jazz and Tower integrate operations under the brand name TowerJazz.

🏠 An in-depth profile of this company is available to Hoover's Online members at hoovers.com.

859

JAZZERCISE, INC.

2460 Impala Dr.
Carlsbad, CA 92010
Phone: 760-476-1750
Fax: 760-602-7180
Web: www.jazzercise.com

CEO: Judi Sheppard Missett
CFO: Sally Baldridge
HR: —
FYE: June 30
Type: Private

Jazzercise shows people how to shake their booties toward fitness. A leading fitness instruction operator, the company has more than 7,500 franchised instructors across the US and in more than 30 countries offering some 32,000 weekly fitness classes that blend jazz dancing with an aerobic workout. Jazzercise generates revenue through franchise fees, as well as the sale of clothing, books, and other merchandise. The company's JM DigitalWorks unit produces Jazzercise workout tapes and provides video production services to other clients. Its Jazzertogs division offers fitness apparel and accessories. CEO Judi Sheppard Missett, a professional dancer, founded Jazzercise in 1969 and began franchising in 1980.

	Annual Growth	6/04	6/05	6/06	6/07	6/08
Sales ($ mil.)	—	—	—	—	—	93.0
Employees	—	—	—	—	—	161

J.B. HUNT TRANSPORT SERVICES, INC.

NASDAQ (GS): JBHT

615 J.B. Hunt Corporate Dr.
Lowell, AR 72745
Phone: 479-820-0000
Fax: 479-820-3418
Web: www.jbhunt.com

CEO: Kirk Thompson
CFO: David G. Mee
HR: —
FYE: December 31
Type: Public

When it comes to hauling freight, J.B. Hunt Transport Services is a leader of the pack. Its intermodal unit, the company's largest, maintains some 2,200 tractors and 40,000 containers and moves customers' cargo by combinations of truck and train. J.B. Hunt's dedicated contract services unit supplies customers with drivers and equipment; it operates about 4,000 company-controlled trucks. The company's truckload transportation unit, which has a fleet of about 1,700 tractors, provides dry van freight transportation service in the US, Canada, and Mexico. A fourth business segment, integrated capacity solutions (ICS), manages freight transportation via third-party carriers as well as J.B. Hunt equipment.

	Annual Growth	12/05	12/06	12/07	12/08	12/09
Sales ($ mil.)	0.6%	3,127.9	3,328.0	3,489.9	3,731.9	3,203.3
Net income ($ mil.)	(9.9%)	207.3	220.0	213.1	200.6	136.4
Market value ($ mil.)	9.3%	2,882.7	2,644.6	3,507.9	3,344.9	4,108.9
Employees	(3.5%)	16,367	5,916	15,795	14,667	14,171

J.B. POINDEXTER & CO., INC.

1100 Louisiana, Ste. 5400
Houston, TX 77002
Phone: 713-655-9800
Fax: 713-951-9038
Web: www.jbpoindexter.com

CEO: John B. Poindexter
CFO: —
HR: —
FYE: December 31
Type: Private

Got baggage issues? J.B. Poindexter can handle it. J.B. operates four units, manufacturing commercial truck bodies, multi-stop step vans, truck accessories, and specialty vehicles like limos and buses. Operating subsidiary Morgan makes van bodies for mounting on medium-duty truck chassis, used by businesses like Ryder and Penske. Morgan Olson supplies the bodies for vans often used for deliveries by UPS and Frito-Lay. Leer and LoRider branded pickup bed covers are made by a truck accessories unit. J.B.'s Specialty Manufacturing Group includes subsidiaries EFP (expandable foam plastics), Specialty Vehicle, and MIC (precision metal parts, casting, machining). Chairman and CEO John B. Poindexter owns the company.

	Annual Growth	12/04	12/05	12/06	12/07	12/08
Sales ($ mil.)	4.8%	584.9	668.1	795.4	792.2	706.4
Net income ($ mil.)	(9.0%)	9.9	5.1	8.2	(0.8)	6.8
Employees	(1.7%)	—	4,000	4,500	4,227	3,795

JBS FIVE RIVERS RANCH CATTLE FEEDING LLC

3855 Precision Dr., Ste. 160
Loveland, CO 80538
Phone: 970-612-1600
Fax: 970-612-1598
Web: www.fiveriverscattle.com

CEO: Mike Thoren
CFO: —
HR: Matt Buyers
FYE: December 31
Type: Subsidiary

JBS Five Rivers Ranch Cattle Feeding hopes to milk a profit from fattening up cows for market. One of the largest cattle feeding businesses in the US, the company operates with a capacity to feed more than 800,000 head of cattle. Five Rivers operates approximately about 10 feedlots located in Colorado, Idaho, Kansas, Oklahoma, and Texas. The company, which takes care of the health and nutrition of the steer, also offers feed financing and marketing services for its customers. Five Rivers is owned by the giant Brazilian beef processor, JBS.

JBS USA HOLDINGS, INC.

1770 Promontory Circle
Greeley, CO 80634
Phone: 970-506-8000
Fax: —
Web: www.jbsswift.com

CEO: Wesley Mendonça Batista
CFO: André Nogueira de Souza
HR: Robert Daubenspeck
FYE: December 31
Type: Subsidiary

JBS USA Holdings is big beef, prodigious pork, and lord of lamb. The company, a subsidiary of Brazil's JBS (the world's #1 beef processor and exporter), operates beef, pork, sheep, and lamb processing facilities in the US and Australia. Its holdings include JBS Swift (12 processing plants) and JBS Packerland (boxed and ground beef production), both in the US, and Australia's Tasman Group (10 beef, pork, sheep, and lamb processing facilities and five feedlots). JBS USA also owns JBS Five Rivers, which operates 11 feedlots. Other businesses include a tannery, seven distribution centers, and two grease-production facilities; JBS USA exports to 60 countries. It filed to go public in 2009.

J. C. PENNEY COMPANY, INC.

NYSE: JCP

6501 Legacy Dr.
Plano, TX 75024
Phone: 972-431-1000
Fax: 972-431-9140
Web: www.jcpenney.com

CEO: Myron E. (Mike) Ullman III
CFO: Robert B. Cavanaugh
HR: Michael T. Theilmann
FYE: January 31
Type: Public

J. C. Penney Company is the holding company for department store operator J. C. Penney Corporation, one of the largest department store, catalog, and e-commerce retailers in the US with more than 1,100 JCPenney department stores in 49 states and Puerto Rico. J. C. Penney Corporation, its only subsidiary, was founded in 1902 by James Cash Penney. In 2004 the company sold its Eckerd drugstores chain to The Jean Coutu Group and CVS for $4.5 billion in cash. In 2005 it sold its controlling stake in the 62-unit Lojas Renner chain in Brazil through a public stock offering. J. C. Penney Company was formed in 2002 and is the publicly traded entity.

	Annual Growth	1/06	1/07	1/08	1/09	1/10
Sales ($ mil.)	(1.7%)	18,781.0	19,903.0	19,860.0	18,486.0	17,556.0
Net income ($ mil.)	(30.7%)	1,088.0	1,153.0	1,111.0	572.0	251.0
Market value ($ mil.)	(18.3%)	13,181.6	19,191.2	11,185.4	3,956.8	5,865.6
Employees	0.5%	151,000	155,000	155,000	147,000	154,000

JCM PARTNERS, LLC

2151 Salvio St., Ste. 325
Concord, CA 94520
Phone: 925-676-1966
Fax: 925-676-1744
Web: www.rent-one.com

CEO: Gayle M. Ing
CFO: Robert Flaharty
HR: —
FYE: December 31
Type: Private

At the northern end of the Golden State is where you'll find JCM Partners, which invests in, renovates, manages, markets, and sells multifamily residential and commercial real estate. The company also offers furnished corporate housing. JCM Partners owns about 45 properties, including apartment communities (containing a total of about 5,000 units), one multi-tenant office/retail property, office properties, and industrial properties. Nearly half of JCM Partners' residential properties are located in Sacramento County; the remainder are in San Joaquin, Solano, Stanislaus, and Contra Costa counties. JCM runs Rent-One.com — an online apartment rental guide.

	Annual Growth	12/04	12/05	12/06	12/07	12/08
Est. sales ($ mil.)	—	—	—	—	—	5.7
Employees	—	—	—	—	—	191

JDA SOFTWARE GROUP, INC.

NASDAQ (GM): JDAS

14400 N. 87th St.
Scottsdale, AZ 85260
Phone: 480-308-3000
Fax: 480-308-3001
Web: www.jda.com

CEO: Hamish N. Brewer
CFO: Peter S. (Pete) Hathaway
HR: Brian P. Boylan
FYE: December 31
Type: Public

JDA Software Group supplies the links in the supply chain. The company's supply and demand optimization (SDO) software helps retailers and other businesses manage supply and demand chains, as well as business processes ranging from planning and forecasting to e-commerce and store operations. The company also offers point-of-sale applications to handle back-office functions, including inventory management, receipts, and returns. Other products include analytic applications for decision support and collaborative tools for maintaining product and catalog information with partners, distributors, and suppliers. JDA boasts more than 6,000 customers, including Dr Pepper Snapple Group, Kraft Foods and OfficeMax.

	Annual Growth	12/05	12/06	12/07	12/08	12/09
Sales ($ mil.)	15.6%	215.8	277.5	373.6	390.3	385.8
Net income ($ mil.)	39.2%	7.0	(0.4)	26.5	3.1	26.3
Market value ($ mil.)	10.6%	709.0	573.9	852.8	547.2	1,061.6
Employees	15.0%	1,055	1,701	1,596	1,718	1,847

JDS UNIPHASE CORPORATION

NASDAQ (GS): JDSU

430 N. McCarthy Blvd.
Milpitas, CA 95035
Phone: 408-546-5000
Fax: 408-546-4300
Web: www.jdsu.com

CEO: Thomas H. (Tom) Waechter
CFO: David W. Vellequette
HR: Brett Hooper
FYE: June 30
Type: Public

JDS Uniphase (JDSU) is drawn to the warming glow of optical networks. Its Communications Test and Measurement division makes instruments and test tools used in optical and data networks, DSL services, cable networks, and digital video broadcast equipment. Its Communications and Commercial Optical Communications unit produces optical transmission and transport products, lasers, and photovoltaic cells and receivers sold to makers of network and other equipment. Advanced Optical Technologies makes optical coating and holographic technologies to protect documents, transaction cards, and consumer electronics against counterfeiting. JDSU sells to the networking, communications, medical, aerospace, and defense markets.

	Annual Growth	6/05	6/06	6/07	6/08	6/09
Sales ($ mil.)	16.1%	712.2	1,204.3	1,396.8	1,530.1	1,294.4
Net income ($ mil.)	—	(261.3)	(151.2)	(26.3)	(21.7)	(866.4)
Market value ($ mil.)	(17.0%)	2,660.1	4,457.0	2,957.4	2,501.6	1,259.6
Employees	(5.5%)	5,022	7,099	7,000	7,100	4,000

J.E. DUNN CONSTRUCTION GROUP, INC.

1001 Locust St.
Kansas City, MO 64106
Phone: 816-474-8600
Fax: 816-391-2510
Web: www.jedunn.com

CEO: Terrence P. (Terry) Dunn
CFO: Gordon E. Lansford III
HR: Richard E. (Rick) Beyer
FYE: December 31
Type: Private

J.E. Dunn Construction Group prides itself on getting the job done. Owned by descendants of founder John E. Dunn, the firm holds a group of construction companies, including flagship J. E. Dunn Construction and Atlanta-based R.J. Griffin & Company. The group builds institutional, commercial, and industrial structures around the US. It also provides construction and program management and design/build services. J. E. Dunn Construction, which ranks among the top 10 US general builders, was one of the first contractors to offer the construction management delivery method. Major projects it has completed include an IRS facility and the world headquarters for H&R Block, both in Kansas City, Missouri.

	Annual Growth	12/04	12/05	12/06	12/07	12/08
Sales ($ mil.)	14.0%	1,633.0	2,305.0	2,563.0	2,634.0	2,760.0
Employees	7.5%	3,000	3,000	3,000	4,100	4,000

JEFFERIES GROUP, INC.

NYSE: JEF

520 Madison Ave., 10th Fl.
New York, NY 10022
Phone: 212-284-2300
Fax: 212-284-2111
Web: www.jefco.com

CEO: Richard B. Handler
CFO: Peregrine C. de M. (Peg) Broadbent
HR: —
FYE: December 31
Type: Public

Because smaller companies need hostile-takeover advice, too. Jefferies Group (along with its main subsidiary Jefferies & Company) raises capital, performs securities trading and research, and provides advisory services for small and midsized companies in the US. Serving about 2,500 institutional clients worldwide, the company also trades derivatives and commodities and makes markets for some 5,000 US and international equities. Jefferies Group also oversees more than $3 billion on behalf of investors and private clients. Jefferies made a move into the municipal business in 2009 and now serves national and local governments. The company has about 25 offices in North America, Europe, and Asia.

	Annual Growth	12/05	12/06	12/07	12/08	12/09
Sales ($ mil.)	13.4%	1,497.9	1,963.2	2,718.9	1,682.7	2,472.7
Net income ($ mil.)	15.5%	157.4	204.1	144.7	(536.1)	280.0
Market value ($ mil.)	1.4%	3,861.3	4,604.7	3,957.5	2,414.0	4,074.2
Employees	6.5%	2,045	2,254	2,568	2,270	2,628

JEFFERSON BANCSHARES, INC.

NASDAQ (GM): JFBI

120 Evans Ave.
Morristown, TN 37814
Phone: 423-586-8421
Fax: 423-587-2605
Web: www.jeffersonfederal.com

CEO: Anderson L. (Andy) Smith
CFO: Jane P. Hutton
HR: —
FYE: June 30
Type: Public

Here's a Tennessee bank that will definitely volunteer its services. Jefferson Bancshares is the holding company for Jefferson Federal Bank, which has about a dozen locations in eastern parts of the Volunteer State. Founded in 1963, the bank serves individuals and businesses in Hamblen, Knox, Sullivan, and Washington counties, offering standard services such as checking and savings accounts, CDs, and IRAs. Lending activities primarily consist of commercial real estate loans and one- to four-family residential mortgages, which together account for a majority of the company's loan portfolio. In 2008 Jefferson Bancshares acquired State of Franklin Bancshares, a community bank hurt by the national mortgage crisis.

	Annual Growth	6/05	6/06	6/07	6/08	6/09
Assets ($ mil.)	22.4%	295.0	327.1	339.7	330.3	662.7
Net income ($ mil.)	(7.2%)	3.5	2.3	1.7	1.2	2.6
Market value ($ mil.)	(16.9%)	85.5	86.5	78.1	62.2	40.7
Employees	21.6%	80	101	95	91	175

An in-depth profile of this company is available to Hoover's Online members at hoovers.com.

861

JEFFERSON HEALTH SYSTEM INC.

259 N. Radnor-Chester Rd., Ste. 290
Radnor, PA 19087
Phone: 610-225-6200
Fax: 610-225-6254
Web: www.jeffersonhealth.org

CEO: Joesph T. Sebastianelli
CFO: Kirk E. Gorman
HR: —
FYE: June 30
Type: Not-for-profit

This health care system's freedom-loving namesake might approve of its work to preserve the people's freedom of choice in health care. Jefferson Health System is a not-for-profit network that includes three health systems with hospitals, specialty clinics, and other medical facilities serving communities in the greater Philadelphia area. Members include the Thomas Jefferson University Hospital family (one of the system's founders), Main Line Health (the other founding organization), and Magee Rehabilitation. The Jefferson network has some 2,400 beds and is affiliated with Thomas Jefferson University.

	Annual Growth	6/04	6/05	6/06	6/07	6/08
Est. sales ($ mil.)	—	—	—	—	—	3,009.7
Employees	—	—	—	—	—	20,700

JEFFERSON WELLS INTERNATIONAL, INC.

200 S. Executive Dr., Ste. 440
Brookfield, WI 53005
Phone: 262-957-3400
Fax: 262-957-3401
Web: www.jeffersonwells.com

CEO: Owen J. Sullivan
CFO: Kris Best
HR: John LeBlanc
FYE: December 31
Type: Subsidiary

Jefferson Wells International can attest to the fact that it specializes in internal auditing (IA) rather than attest (independent audit) services — it lets the Big Four accounting firms handle those tasks. In addition to IA, Jefferson Wells' 50 offices (primarily in the US but also in Europe and Asia) offer related consulting services, including tax auditing and compliance services and technology risk management. It also offers temporary staffing — not suprising, considering its parent is temporary employment titan Manpower. Target sectors include government agencies and the construction business. The company serves more than half of the *FORTUNE* 500.

JEFFERSONVILLE BANCORP

NASDAQ (CM): JFBC

4864 State Rte. 52
Jeffersonville, NY 12748
Phone: 845-482-4000
Fax: 845-482-3544
Web: www.jeffbank.com

CEO: Wayne V. Zanetti
CFO: John A. Russell
HR: Claire A. Pecsi
FYE: December 31
Type: Public

Jeffersonville Bancorp is the holding company for The First National Bank of Jeffersonville. The bank serves businesses and consumers through about 10 locations in southeastern New York's Sullivan County. First National Bank of Jeffersonville offers such standard retail services as demand deposit, savings, and money market accounts; NOW accounts; CDs; and IRAs to fund a variety of loans. Nearly 40% of the bank's loan portfolio consists of residential mortgages, while commercial mortgages account for another 35%. The bank also provides home equity, business, consumer, construction, and agricultural loans.

	Annual Growth	12/05	12/06	12/07	12/08	12/09
Assets ($ mil.)	2.2%	387.3	397.3	387.4	398.6	422.7
Net income ($ mil.)	(14.1%)	5.7	4.9	4.3	2.7	3.1
Market value ($ mil.)	(20.6%)	101.5	80.3	59.3	40.7	40.3
Employees	(1.1%)	135	133	135	129	129

JELD-WEN, INC.

3250 Lakeport Blvd.
Klamath Falls, OR 97601
Phone: 541-882-3451
Fax: 541-885-7454
Web: www.jeld-wen.com

CEO: Roderick C. (Rod) Wendt
CFO: R. Neil Stuart
HR: —
FYE: December 31
Type: Private

JELD-WEN can improve your outlook by providing new windows and doors for your home or by offering accommodations at a scenic resort. A leading manufacturer of windows and doors (some designed to withstand hurricane-force winds), JELD-WEN offers aluminum, vinyl, and wood windows; interior and exterior doors; garage doors; swinging and sliding patio doors; and door frames and moldings. It sells its products mainly in North America, Europe, and Australia. The company operates more than 60 manufacturing and distribution sites. If you get tired of looking out your own doors and windows, JELD-WEN also owns several resorts in Oregon and Idaho, including Eagle Crest Resort and Silver Mountain Ski Resort.

	Annual Growth	12/04	12/05	12/06	12/07	12/08
Est. sales ($ mil.)	6.0%	2,300.0	2,600.0	3,160.0	3,160.0	2,900.0
Employees	(1.2%)	21,000	25,000	23,750	23,750	20,000

JELLY BELLY CANDY COMPANY

1 Jelly Belly Ln.
Fairfield, CA 94533
Phone: 707-428-2800
Fax: 707-423-4436
Web: www.jellybelly.com

CEO: Herman (Herm) Rowland Sr.
CFO: —
HR: Jeff Brown
FYE: March 31
Type: Private

This company has cheesecake, buttered popcorn, orange sherbet, and jalapeño on the menu — who could ask for anything more? You could and can. The Jelly Belly Candy Company makes Jelly Belly jelly beans in 50 "official" flavors, with new and sometimes startlingly flavored (and named) versions introduced periodically. (Introduced in 2009 — Chili Mango.) The company's other products include gumballs, gummies, and sour candies in Jelly Belly flavors. Its more than 100 confections also include candy corn, sour candies, jellies, novelty candy, chocolates, chocolate-covered nuts, cinnamon confections, and licorice, along with seasonal offerings. Jelly Belly's candy is exported worldwide.

JENNIE-O TURKEY STORE, INC.

2505 SW Wilmar Ave.
Wilmar, MN 56201
Phone: 320-235-2622
Fax: 320-214-2885
Web: www.jennie-o.com

CEO: Robert A. Tegt
CFO: John Court
HR: Patricia (Pat) Solheid
FYE: October 31
Type: Subsidiary

Jennie-O Turkey Store is gobbling up profits in the turkey-processing marketplace. A Hormel subsidiary since 1986, Jennie-O processes more than 1 billion pounds of turkey annually for the production of fresh, frozen, refrigerated, and deli products. Answering the convenience-food call, it also offers heat-and-serve turkey entrees named SO EASY. Jennie-O also offers a full line of foodservice products. The company's more than 1,500 different turkey products are available throughout the US, as well as in other countries. It accounted for 19% of its parent's 2008 sales. The company was formed in 2001 as a result of the merger of Jennie-O Foods and The Turkey Store Company.

JENNIFER CONVERTIBLES, INC.
OTC: JENN

419 Crossways Park Dr.
Woodbury, NY 11797
Phone: 516-496-1900
Fax: 516-496-0008
Web: www.jenniferfurniture.com

CEO: Harley J. Greenfield
CFO: Rami Abada
HR: —
FYE: August 31
Type: Public

Houseguests are likely to get a good night's sleep thanks to Jennifer Convertibles. The company owns or licenses about 160 stores in the US that sell sofa beds, loveseats, recliners, and chairs; it holds the distinction of being the largest dealer of Sealy sofa beds in the US. In addition, the firm offers a full line of leather living room furniture. It sells name-brand products, as well as the company's private-label, the Bellissimo Collection. In 2009 it bought about 12% of its products from Klaussner Furniture, which owns a 12% stake in Jennifer Convertibles. Chairman and CEO Harley Greenfield owns about 19% of the company; EVP Edward Seidner owns about 12%.

	Annual Growth	8/05	8/06	8/07	8/08	8/09
Sales ($ mil.)	(6.2%)	121.9	140.4	136.6	121.0	94.2
Net income ($ mil.)	—	(3.9)	5.2	4.0	(3.3)	(11.0)
Market value ($ mil.)	(10.1%)	16.1	43.1	30.9	9.2	10.5
Employees	0.3%	443	453	493	472	448

JENNY CRAIG, INC.

5770 Fleet St.
Carlsbad, CA 92008
Phone: 760-696-4000
Fax: 760-696-4009
Web: www.jennycraig.com

CEO: Patricia A. (Patti) Larchet
CFO: Jim Kelly
HR: Chris Guglielmo
FYE: December 31
Type: Subsidiary

Jenny Craig would like for everyone to lighten up, at least a little. The weight-control company is one of the world's two largest diet firms (along with Weight Watchers). It owns or franchises about 650 centers in the US, Canada, Australia, New Zealand, Puerto Rico, and Guam. Its Jenny's Cuisine prepared foods, along with DVDs, CDs, journals, and cookbooks, are sold to participants at its centers. The program is also available at home via telephone consultations and home delivery of food and support materials. Nestlé, the largest food and drink company in the world, acquired Jenny Craig in 2006.

JEOL USA, INC.

11 Dearborn Rd.
Peabody, MA 01960
Phone: 978-535-5900
Fax: 978-536-2205
Web: www.jeolusa.com

CEO: Robert T. Santorelli
CFO: —
HR: —
FYE: March 31
Type: Subsidiary

Science is instrumental to the work at JEOL USA. The company distributes analytical instruments, electron optics, and semiconductor production equipment. JEOL's products include electron microscopes, mass spectrometers, sample preparation equipment, and silicon wafer inspection equipment. JEOL USA was founded as the US sales arm of Japan-based scientific instrument maker JEOL Ltd. in 1962. The company provides sales and support of JEOL products throughout the Americas. Researchers at Boston College, Lawrence Berkeley National Laboratory, MIT, the University of Alberta, The University of Southern California, and Wesleyan University, among other institutions, use JEOL equipment.

	Annual Growth	3/04	3/05	3/06	3/07	3/08
Est. sales ($ mil.)	—	—	—	—	—	80.0
Employees	—	—	—	—	—	320

JEPPESEN SANDERSON, INC.

55 Inverness Dr. East
Englewood, CO 80112
Phone: 303-799-9090
Fax: 303-328-4153
Web: www.jeppesen.com

CEO: Mark Van Tine
CFO: Jepson S. Fuller
HR: Ann Bozeman
FYE: December 31
Type: Subsidiary

This company helps map the way for pilots, mariners, and railway engineers. Jeppesen Sanderson is a leading publisher of navigation charts, reference materials, and other information products for the aviation, marine, and rail transportation industries. It offers printed and electronic navigation data along with computerized tools for planning trips and making other important calculations. Jeppesen also publishes training materials and offers logistics services for the air, marine, and rail industries. Captain E.B. Jeppesen started the business in 1934, producing the first instrument flying charts in the basement of his Salt Lake City home. Boeing, the world's largest aerospace company, owns Jeppesen Sanderson.

JER INVESTORS TRUST INC.
Pink Sheets: JERT

1650 Tysons Blvd., Ste. 1600
McLean, VA 22102
Phone: 703-714-8000
Fax: 703-714-8100
Web: www.jer.com

CEO: Joseph E. Robert Jr.
CFO: J. Michael McGillis
HR: —
FYE: December 31
Type: Public

A real estate investment trust (REIT), JER Investors Trust manages a portfolio of real estate structured finance products, primarily commercial mortgage-backed securities (CMBS), commercial mortgage loans, mezzanine loans, and other real estate investments. Founded in 2004, the company is managed by an affiliate of real estate investment management firm J.E. Robert Company (JER). It went public the following year. Due to the downturn in the mortgage industry and the credit industry overall, JER Investors Trust has turned its focus on managing its portfolio credit risk and maintaining liquidity. The REIT has sold some of its real property assets and CMBS investments.

	Annual Growth	12/04	12/05	12/06	12/07	*12/08
Sales ($ mil.)	135.7%	3.5	36.4	74.0	134.6	108.1
Net income ($ mil.)	—	(5.9)	19.6	31.7	23.1	(254.2)
Market value ($ mil.)	(62.0%)	—	988.1	1,205.0	627.8	54.2
Employees	—	150	150	—	—	—

*Most recent year available

JERVIS B. WEBB COMPANY

34375 W. Twelve Mile Rd.
Farmington Hills, MI 48331
Phone: 248-553-1000
Fax: 248-553-1228
Web: www.jervisbwebb.com

CEO: Masaki Hojo
CFO: John Doychich
HR: —
FYE: December 31
Type: Subsidiary

Jervis B. Webb Company, aka Webb, has spun a global web of custom-engineered material-handling systems and maintenance support services. Through manufacturing facilities in North America, India, and China, the firm makes equipment used in multiple markets including automotive production, bulk and baggage handling, automated newsprint handling, beverage bottling, and furniture manufacturing. Products include conveyors, automatic guided vehicles, SmartCart, automated storage and retrieval systems, and loading vehicles. In 2007 Webb was acquired by the Japanese-based material-handling firm Daifuku Co., Ltd., which expanded its international growth.

An in-depth profile of this company is available to Hoover's Online members at hoovers.com.

863

JESUP & LAMONT, INC.

NYSE Amex: JLI

650 Fifth Ave., 3rd Fl.
New York, NY 10019
Phone: 212-307-2660
Fax: 212-757-7478
Web: www.jesuplamont.com

CEO: Alan Weichselbaum
CFO: William Holub
HR: —
FYE: December 31
Type: Public

Jesup & Lamont performs brokerage services for retail investors and small to midsized financial institutions (e.g., credit unions, hedge funds, and money managers) throughout the US and in Europe and Asia. Related services include investment advice, market data, and portfolio management. The company also provides administrative support for a network of independent and employee broker/advisors in some 30 independently owned offices. Jesup & Lamont plans to merge with investment and advisory firm Tri-Artisan Capital Partners in 2010. The combined firm will be named Jesup Lamont Tri-Artisan and will blend Jesup's trading and research capabilities with Tri-Artisan's merchant banking services.

	Annual Growth	12/05	12/06	12/07	12/08	12/09
Sales ($ mil.)	13.3%	22.5	35.6	50.7	38.1	37.1
Net income ($ mil.)	—	2.3	(0.2)	(10.9)	(15.8)	(7.1)
Market value ($ mil.)	(40.7%)	154.8	134.7	46.5	25.2	19.2
Employees	3.8%	222	293	181	189	258

JETBLUE AIRWAYS CORPORATION

NASDAQ (GS): JBLU

118-29 Queens Blvd.
Forest Hills, NY 11375
Phone: 718-286-7900
Fax: 718-709-3621
Web: www.jetblue.com

CEO: David (Dave) Barger
CFO: Edward (Ed) Barnes
HR: David C. Clark
FYE: December 31
Type: Public

JetBlue Airways is counting on more than low fares to make its ledgers jet-black. The carrier offers one-class service — with leather seats, satellite TV from DIRECTV, satellite radio from XM, and movies — to about 60 cities in the US, Mexico, Colombia, and the Caribbean (including Puerto Rico, the Bahamas, and the Dominican Republic). Most of its flights arrive or depart from one of five key markets: Boston; Orlando and Fort Lauderdale, Florida; Long Beach, California; and New York. JetBlue's fleet of about 150 aircraft consists mainly of Airbus A320s but also includes Embraer 190s. It owns one subsidiary, in-flight entertainment system developer LiveTV.

	Annual Growth	12/05	12/06	12/07	12/08	12/09
Sales ($ mil.)	17.9%	1,701.0	2,363.0	2,842.0	3,388.0	3,286.0
Net income ($ mil.)	—	(20.0)	(1.0)	18.0	(76.0)	58.0
Market value ($ mil.)	(22.8%)	4,499.2	4,154.0	1,726.0	2,077.0	1,594.3
Employees	7.9%	9,248	10,624	11,632	11,852	12,532

JEWETT-CAMERON TRADING COMPANY LTD.

NASDAQ (CM): JCTCF

32275 NW Hillcrest
North Plains, OR 97133
Phone: 503-647-0110
Fax: 503-647-2272
Web: www.jewettcameron.com

CEO: Donald M. (Don) Boone
CFO: Murray G. Smith
HR: Janet Strand
FYE: August 31
Type: Public

Jewett-Cameron Trading Company (JCTC) puts the lumber in lumberyards, the air in pneumatic tools, and seeds in the ground. Its Jewett-Cameron Lumber Company (JCLC) subsidiary supplies wood and other building materials to home improvement chains in the western US from distribution centers in Oregon. The MSI-PRO subsidiary imports pneumatic air tools and industrial clamps from Asia. The Jewett-Cameron Seed business distributes processed agricultural seeds and grain, along with lawn, garden, and pet supplies in the US. It also owns plywood panel maker Greenwood Products. Employees own nearly 20% of the company.

	Annual Growth	8/05	8/06	8/07	8/08	8/09
Sales ($ mil.)	(13.3%)	74.6	76.1	70.5	64.3	42.1
Net income ($ mil.)	15.5%	0.9	2.3	2.3	2.6	1.6
Market value ($ mil.)	(0.6%)	14.3	17.4	21.9	17.5	14.0
Employees	(8.5%)	67	59	92	60	47

J.F. SHEA CO., INC.

655 Brea Canyon Rd.
Walnut, CA 91789
Phone: 909-594-9500
Fax: 909-594-0917
Web: www.jfshea.com

CEO: Peter O. Shea Jr.
CFO: James G. (Jim) Shontere
HR: —
FYE: December 31
Type: Private

J.F. Shea didn't build Shea Stadium — but it could have. The real estate, engineering, and construction group provides services for civil engineering, commercial, and residential projects. Flagship division J.F. Shea Construction offers design/build services, while its civil engineering division builds tunnels and water treatment and storage facilities. Another group member, Shea Homes builds planned communities and other residences in about a half-dozen states. Shea Properties invests in and develops commercial real estate. Other divisions provide construction materials, foundation construction and machinery, and venture capital. The Shea family owns J.F. Shea, which was founded as a plumbing company in 1881.

JFC INTERNATIONAL INC.

7101 E. Slauson Ave.
Los Angeles, CA 90040
Phone: 323-721-6100
Fax: 323-721-6133
Web: www.jfc.com

CEO: Hiroyuki Enomoto
CFO: —
HR: —
FYE: March 31
Type: Subsidiary

JFC International is spreading the joy of Asian flavors to food retailers and foodservice operators in the US, Canada, and Mexico. A subsidiary of Kikkoman Corporation, the company distributes about 15,000 Asian cooking items made by Japanese food companies, including canned and dried seaweeds, frozen fruits, and vegetables; crackers and other salty snacks; oils and vinegars; teas and canned coffees; rice, flours, and beans; and soy and other sauces. In addition, JFC manufactures its own food products (rice, noodles, sauces, edible oils, panko, canned goods) under the names Dynasty, Hapi, Hime, JFC, Nishiki, and Wel·Pac. It also distributes Tanzan, Daishichi, and Tomoju sakes, along with about a dozen plum wines.

J.G. BOSWELL COMPANY

101 W. Walnut St.
Pasadena, CA 91103
Phone: 626-583-3000
Fax: 626-583-3090

CEO: James W. Boswell
CFO: —
HR: —
FYE: December 31
Type: Private

J.G. Boswell grows and mills cotton in California's San Joaquin Valley. The secretive company is the country's largest cotton producer. About one-third of its 150,000 California acres are devoted to cotton. It was once said that the company produced enough cotton in one year to produce 840,000 pairs of boxer shorts. Indeed, Boswell's customers include textile makers worldwide. The company also grows tomatoes and a lot of them. One of the nation's largest tomato growers, it produced some 1 million pounds of tomatoes in 2008. Boswell's other smaller crops include wheat, sunflowers, and safflowers. Chairman emeritus James G. Boswell II died in 2009 at the age of 86.

JIFFY LUBE INTERNATIONAL, INC.

700 Milam St.
Houston, TX 77002
Phone: 713-546-4100
Fax: —
Web: www.jiffylube.com

CEO: Rick Altizer
CFO: Simone Noordegraaf
HR: Carl Reed
FYE: December 31
Type: Subsidiary

A leading oil change provider, Jiffy Lube doesn't expect to see its customers every day — but every three months or 3,000 miles will be often enough. The company boasts more than 2,000 North American outlets, of which almost 90% are franchised; the balance of its locations are company-owned and operated. Besides oil changes, Jiffy Lube facilities provide maintenance services for air conditioning, fuel systems, and transmissions. At some of its locations, it also performs inspections and emissions testing, repairs windshields, and rotates tires. The company serves vehicle fleet operators as well as individual consumers. Jiffy Lube, which is a subsidiary of Shell Oil Company, was founded in 1979.

JIMMY JOHN'S FRANCHISE, LLC

2212 Fox Dr.
Champaign, IL 61820
Phone: 217-356-9900
Fax: 217-359-2956
Web: www.jimmyjohns.com

CEO: James John (Jimmy) Liautaud
CFO: Pam Hersch
HR: —
FYE: December 31
Type: Private

For some sandwich fans, the company with two first names is the first choice for subs. Jimmy John's Franchise operates and franchises more than 850 quick-service Jimmy John's Gourmet Sandwich Shops in more than 35 mostly midwestern states. The chain's menu features submarine-style sandwiches made with a variety of toppings and carrying such names as Big John, J.J. Gargantuan, and Vito. Jimmy John's also serves club sandwiches made with whole wheat or French bread. The company's restaurants typically offer carryout and delivery services along with some limited seating. Chairman "Jimmy" John Liautaud started the Jimmy John's chain in 1983.

	Annual Growth	12/04	12/05	12/06	12/07	12/08
Est. sales ($ mil.)	—	—	—	—	—	7.5
Employees	—	—	—	—	—	45

JLG INDUSTRIES, INC.

13224 Fountain Head Plaza
Hagerstown, MD 21742
Phone: 240-420-2661
Fax: 240-420-8719
Web: www.jlg.com

CEO: Craig E. Paylor
CFO: Frank Cholewicki
HR: —
FYE: July 31
Type: Subsidiary

Need a boost? JLG Industries' lift equipment can provide that extra reach. Since 1969 when founder John L. Grove invented the first self-propelled boom lift, the company has been providing such products as aerial work platforms, telescopic material handlers, stock pickers (to access high shelving), and power deck trailers for ground-level loading of everything from heavy construction equipment to vending machines. Products are sold under such names as JLG, SkyTrak, Lull, and Triple-L. The company supplies customers in the commercial, industrial, institutional, and government and military markets. JLG is owned by Oshkosh Corp. (formerly Oshkosh Truck).

JLL PARTNERS INC.

450 Lexington Ave., 31st Fl.
New York, NY 10017
Phone: 212-286-8600
Fax: 212-286-8626
Web: www.jllpartners.com

CEO: Michael Schwartz
CFO: Michael Schwartz
HR: —
FYE: December 31
Type: Private

Jack and JLL went up the hill, to fetch a pail of . . . portfolio companies? JLL Partners (formerly Joseph, Littlejohn & Levy) is anything but child's play. The private equity firm seeks controlling stakes in middle-market companies in a range of industries, including broadcasting, chemicals, consumer products, financial services, health care, and manufacturing. An active investor that works with its portfolio companies to foment growth, the firm specializes in leveraged buyouts, restructurings, and turnaround situations. Since its founding in 1988, JLL Partners has managed private equity funds totaling some $4 billion in committed capital from institutional investors. It has stakes in more than a dozen firms.

JLM COUTURE, INC.

Pink Sheets: JLMC

225 W. 37th St., 5th Fl.
New York, NY 10018
Phone: 212-921-7058
Fax: 212-921-7608
Web: www.jlmcouture.com

CEO: Joseph L. Murphy
CFO: Joseph L. Murphy
HR: —
FYE: October 31
Type: Public

Here comes the bride, and she might be wearing a gown from JLM Couture. The company designs, manufactures, and markets bridal and bridesmaid gowns, veils, and related items in the US and the UK. Its bridal gowns, which boast price tags of several thousand dollars, are made under the Alvina Valenta, Jim Hjelm Couture, Jim Hjelm Visions, Tara Keely, and Lazaro names. JLM Couture markets its gowns through bridal magazines, trunk shows, and catalogs. The company's bridesmaid and flower girl collections are produced under the Jim Hjelm Occasions and Lazaro Bridesmaids labels; they're peddled through bridal boutiques and bridal departments in clothing stores. Its Party by JLM is a collection of evening wear.

JM FAMILY ENTERPRISES, INC.

100 Jim Moran Blvd.
Deerfield Beach, FL 33442
Phone: 954-429-2000
Fax: 954-429-2300
Web: www.jmfamily.com

CEO: Colin Brown
CFO: Brent Burns
HR: Ken Yerves
FYE: December 31
Type: Private

JM Family Enterprises is a family affair. JM, owned by the family of founder James Moran, is a holding company (Florida's second-largest private company, in fact, after Publix Super Markets) with about a dozen automotive-related businesses, including the world's largest-volume Lexus retailer, JM Lexus, in Margate, Florida. JM's major subsidiary, Southeast Toyota Distributors, is the nation's largest independent Toyota and Scion distribution franchise, delivering Toyota cars, trucks, and SUVs to more than 170 dealers in Alabama, Florida, Georgia, Texas, and the Carolinas. The firm also offers financial services, insurance and warranties, dealer IT products, and marketing services. It was established in 1968.

	Annual Growth	12/04	12/05	12/06	12/07	12/08
Sales ($ mil.)	2.4%	—	9,400.0	11,100.0	12,200.0	10,100.0
Employees	(2.4%)	—	4,300	4,600	4,700	4,000

An in-depth profile of this company is available to Hoover's Online members at hoovers.com.

865

J.M. HUBER CORPORATION

499 Thornall St., 8th Fl.
Edison, NJ 08837
Phone: 732-549-8600
Fax: 732-549-7256
Web: www.huber.com

CEO: Michael (Mike) Marberry
CFO: Jeffrey (Jeff) Prosinski
HR: Niall Mulkeen
FYE: December 31
Type: Private

As great as toothpaste, paint, and tires may be, J.M. Huber claims to make them even better. Hard to believe, we know. Founded in 1890 by Joseph M. Huber and still owned by his heirs, the company makes specialty additives and minerals used to thicken and improve the cleaning properties of toothpaste, the brightness and gloss of paper, the strength and durability of rubber, and the flame-retardant properties of wire and cable. The diverse company also makes oriented strand board (a plywood substitute), explores for and produces oil and gas, and provides technical and financial services. Huber also makes hydrocolloids (thickeners for gums) through subsidiary CP Kelco.

	Annual Growth	12/04	12/05	12/06	12/07	12/08
Sales ($ mil.)	(4.5%)	2,400.0	2,300.0	2,220.0	2,100.0	2,000.0
Employees	(4.3%)	5,000	5,000	5,000	4,500	4,200

J-M MANUFACTURING COMPANY, INC.

5200 W. Century Blvd.
Los Angeles, CA 90045
Phone: 800-621-4404
Fax: —
Web: www.jmeagle.com

CEO: Walter W. Wang
CFO: Johnny Mai
HR: Nooshin Natha
FYE: December 31
Type: Subsidiary

Extruding PVC and HDPE is as easy as ABC for J-M Manufacturing. Doing business as JM Eagle, the company produces polyvinyl chloride (PVC) and high-density polyethylene (HDPE) pipes, fittings, and tubing products. Pipe diameters range from half an inch to 63 inches; the lineup's applications include sewer as well as water main construction, and electric and communication line projects. In mid-2007 J-M acquired PW Eagle, creating a heavyweight in the global plastic pipe manufacturing arena. JM Eagle operates 23 manufacturing facilities across the US, catering to the demands of utility, plumbing, irrigation, and electrical industries.

J M SMITH CORPORATION

101 W. St. John St., Ste. 305
Spartanburg, SC 29306
Phone: 864-542-9419
Fax: 864-582-6585
Web: www.jmsmith.com

CEO: William (Bill) Cobb
CFO: James C. Wilson Jr.
HR: Rhonda Lockhart
FYE: February 28
Type: Private

J M Smith Corporation has gone from corner drugstore to serving drugstores and more. A holding company serving pharmacies and government agencies, the company consists of Smith Drug Company, Integral Solutions Group, QS/1 Data Systems, and Smith Premier Services. Smith Drug Company provides purchasing and distribution services for independent pharmacies, while QS/1 develops computer systems for medical equipment providers, institutional pharmacies, and related businesses. Smith Premier Service offers prescription benefit management services for employers and insurance carriers. Integral Solutions serves local government agencies providing hardware, software, forms and offering data processing services.

THE J. M. SMUCKER COMPANY

NYSE: SJM

1 Strawberry Ln.
Orrville, OH 44667
Phone: 330-682-3000
Fax: 330-684-6410
Web: www.smucker.com

CEO: Timothy P. (Tim) Smucker
CFO: Mark R. Belgya
HR: Barry C. Dunaway
FYE: April 30
Type: Public

The J. M. Smucker Company is best known for the sweet and sticky fruity stuff, but hopes coffee will fatten its bottom line. The #1 US producer of jams, jellies, and preserves also makes dessert toppings, juices, and specialty fruit spreads under names such as Smucker's, Laura Scudder's, and Knott's Berry Farm. The company is home to the #1 coffee brand in the US — Folgers. Many of its brands, including Folgers, Smucker's, Jif, and Crisco, are market leaders. Smucker's roster also includes baking-goods brands Hungry Jack, Pillsbury, and Eagle and PET evaporated milk products. The company has manufacturing and processing facilities in the US and Canada.

	Annual Growth	4/05	4/06	4/07	4/08	4/09
Sales ($ mil.)	16.4%	2,043.9	2,154.7	2,148.0	2,524.8	3,757.9
Net income ($ mil.)	19.8%	129.1	143.4	157.2	170.4	266.0
Market value ($ mil.)	(5.6%)	5,910.9	4,676.8	6,649.4	5,941.8	4,693.4
Employees	6.2%	3,700	3,500	3,025	3,250	4,700

JMAR TECHNOLOGIES, INC.

Pink Sheets: JMAR

10905 Technology Place
San Diego, CA 92127
Phone: 858-946-6800
Fax: 858-946-6899
Web: www.jmar.com

CEO: Charles A. (Charlie) Dickinson
CFO: Edward C. (Ned) Hall
HR: —
FYE: December 31
Type: Public

JMAR is transitioning from blazing-fast microchips to blazing bright lasers. The company was developing highly specialized systems that employed cutting-edge X-ray lithography (which JMAR calls collimated plasma lithography) to make advanced integrated circuits; development of these systems was mostly funded by grants from the US Army. JMAR converted the technology into the diode-pumped modular solid state BriteLight laser for a variety of applications. The company is addressing the biotechnology, homeland security, nanotechnology, and water quality fields.

JMB REALTY CORP.

900 N. Michigan Ave., Ste. 1400
Chicago, IL 60611
Phone: 312-440-4800
Fax: 312-915-2310

CEO: H. Rigel Barber
CFO: Gailen J. Hull
HR: —
FYE: December 31
Type: Private

JMB Realty wants to make State Street a great street again and bring glitter back to the Steel City's Golden Triangle. A major US commercial real estate investment firm, JMB Realty is heavily involved in ambitious retail developments in Chicago's Loop and downtown Pittsburgh. It owns, develops, and manages projects throughout North America, including regional malls, hotels (the Chicago Ritz-Carlton), planned communities, and office complexes. JMB Realty was founded in 1968 by Robert Judelson, Judd Malkin, and Neil Bluhm; Judelson (the "J" of JMB) is no longer involved with the company, but Malkin remains as chairman and Bluhm is president. Bluhm also owns casino company Midwest Gaming and Entertainment.

JMP GROUP INC.

NYSE: JMP

600 Montgomery St., Ste. 1100
San Francisco, CA 94111
Phone: 415-835-8900
Fax: 415-835-8910
Web: www.jmpg.com

CEO: Joseph A. Jolson
CFO: Raymond S. Jackson
HR: —
FYE: December 31
Type: Public

JMP Group wants to get the jump on the competition. The company provides equity research, trading, and investment banking services to small and mid-sized companies. It provides brokerage services to institutional clients while its investment banking arm provides assistance with mergers and acquisitions, divestitures, restructurings, and valuations. Its research department covers some 270 public companies. The company possesses expertise in the technology, health care, consumer goods, financial services, real estate, and business services sectors, with a special focus on financial services and homebuilding. The company went public in 2007.

	Annual Growth	12/05	12/06	12/07	12/08	12/09
Sales ($ mil.)	66.3%	—	—	65.5	76.6	181.2
Net income ($ mil.)	28.9%	—	—	6.5	(10.6)	10.8
Market value ($ mil.)	7.1%	—	—	183.8	120.3	210.7
Employees	5.3%	—	—	202	191	224

JO-ANN STORES, INC.

NYSE: JAS

5555 Darrow Rd.
Hudson, OH 44236
Phone: 330-656-2600
Fax: 330-463-6675
Web: www.joann.com

CEO: Darrell D. Webb
CFO: James C. Kerr
HR: —
FYE: January 31
Type: Public

Jo-Ann Stores has sewn up the leadership of the fabric store market. The company is the #1 fabric retailer in the US (ahead of Hancock Fabrics), with about 745 Jo-Ann Fabric and Craft and Jo-Ann stores in 48 states. The stores sell fabrics and sewing supplies, craft materials, frames, home decorations, artificial floral items, and seasonal goods. Most of the company's small-format stores (about 14,700 square feet) are located in strip shopping centers and operate under the Jo-Ann Fabrics and Crafts name. The company also operates a growing number of more than 225 large-format (36,500 square feet) Jo-Ann superstores and an e-commerce site, Joann.com. The company traces its roots back to the 1940s.

	Annual Growth	1/06	1/07	1/08	1/09	1/10
Sales ($ mil.)	1.4%	1,882.8	1,850.6	1,878.8	1,901.1	1,990.7
Net income ($ mil.)	—	(23.0)	(2.9)	15.4	21.9	66.6
Market value ($ mil.)	27.8%	358.6	690.4	346.6	348.7	956.4
Employees	(3.2%)	24,060	22,280	21,707	21,708	21,135

JOCKEY INTERNATIONAL, INC.

2300 60th St.
Kenosha, WI 53141
Phone: 262-658-8111
Fax: 262-658-1812
Web: www.jockey.com

CEO: Debra S. Waller
CFO: Frank Schneider
HR: Betsy Morton
FYE: December 31
Type: Private

Jockey International has nothing to do with horses and everything to do with the classic men's brief (its invention). The more than 130-year-old company makes men's, women's, and children's underwear and loungewear. Its products are sold through thousands of department and specialty stores the likes of Bloomingdale's and JCPenney. Jockey International licenses and distributes its apparel in more than 120 countries and holds numerous licensing agreements. Chairman and CEO Debra Waller and her family own the company. Jockey International was founded by Samuel Cooper in 1876 as a hosiery company intended to relieve lumberjacks of blisters and infections resulting from shoddy wool socks.

JOE'S JEANS INC.

NASDAQ (CM): JOEZ

5901 S. Eastern Ave.
Commerce, CA 90040
Phone: 323-837-3700
Fax: 323-837-3790
Web: joesjeans.com

CEO: Marc B. Crossman
CFO: Hamish S. Sandhu
HR: —
FYE: November 30
Type: Public

Joe's Jeans has jettisoned just about everything but its jeans. Following its acquisition of the Joe's brand from JD Holdings in 2007, the private-label apparel maker changed its name from Innovo Group to Joe's Jeans and revised its business plan to focus on building the Joe's and Joe's Jeans brands of denim and denim-related products. Joe's Jeans sells its apparel online at the Joe's Jeans website, in the US and Europe through high-end retailers such as Saks and Macy's, and in specialty stores including Atrium and Fred Segal. Founded in 1987, the firm changed its name in October 2007, adopted a new ticker (JOEZ), and set out in 2010 to expand its business through non-denim items.

	Annual Growth	11/05	11/06	11/07	11/08	11/09
Sales ($ mil.)	(7.3%)	108.6	46.6	62.8	69.2	80.1
Net income ($ mil.)	—	(16.4)	(9.3)	2.3	6.1	24.5
Market value ($ mil.)	0.8%	78.7	42.8	72.4	22.7	81.3
Employees	7.4%	124	81	81	109	165

JOHN B. SANFILIPPO & SON, INC.

NASDAQ (GM): JBSS

1703 N. Randall Rd.
Elgin, IL 60123
Phone: 847-289-1800
Fax: 847-289-1843
Web: www.jbssinc.com

CEO: Jeffrey T. Sanfilippo
CFO: Michael J. Valentine
HR: Thomas J. (Tom) Fordonski
FYE: June 30
Type: Public

A bunch of nuts make money for John B. Sanfilippo & Son (JBSS). The company offers peanuts, almonds, pecans, walnuts, cashews, mixed nuts and other tree nuts. JBSS processes, packages, and sells nuts under private labels and its own brands, which include Fisher, Flavor Tree, Sunshine Country, and Texas Pride. It also produces and distributes other foods and snacks such as peanut butter, ice cream and salad toppings, trail mixes, corn snacks, and candy. JBSS's products are sold worldwide to retail, wholesale, vending, industrial, foodservice, and government customers.

	Annual Growth	6/05	6/06	6/07	6/08	6/09
Sales ($ mil.)	(1.2%)	581.7	579.6	541.4	541.8	553.8
Net income ($ mil.)	(16.9%)	14.5	(14.4)	(13.7)	(6.0)	6.9
Market value ($ mil.)	(25.4%)	245.5	141.1	117.1	93.2	76.1
Employees	(6.1%)	1,740	1,800	1,600	1,500	1,350

JOHN BEAN TECHNOLOGIES CORPORATION

NYSE: JBT

200 E. Randolph Dr.
Chicago, IL 60601
Phone: 312-861-6000
Fax: 312-861-6176
Web: www.jbtcorporation.com

CEO: Charles H. (Charlie) Cannon Jr.
CFO: Ronald D. Mambu
HR: Mark Montague
FYE: December 31
Type: Public

John Bean Technologies Corporation (dba JBT Corporation) spun off from FMC Technologies in 2008. JBT Corporation manufactures industrial equipment for the food processing and air transportation industries. Its JBT FoodTech segment makes commercial-grade refrigeration systems, freezers, ovens, canning equipment, and food processing systems for fruit, poultry, meat patties, breads, pizzas, seafood, and ready-to-eat meals. JBT AeroTech manufactures and services ground support equipment (plane de-icers, aircraft tow vehicles, and cargo loading systems), airport gate equipment (Jetway brand), and military equipment. JBT operates 16 facilities in 10 countries.

	Annual Growth	12/05	12/06	12/07	12/08	12/09
Sales ($ mil.)	0.6%	823.3	844.3	978.0	1,028.1	841.6
Net income ($ mil.)	7.6%	24.5	34.6	36.4	44.2	32.8
Market value ($ mil.)	108.2%	—	—	—	230.0	478.9
Employees	3.2%	—	—	3,100	3,400	3,300

JOHN CRANE INC.

6400 W. Oakton St.
Morton Grove, IL 60053
Phone: 847-967-2400
Fax: 847-967-2857
Web: www.johncrane.com

CEO: Philip Bowman
CFO: Robert (Bob) Wasson
HR: Tim Dee
FYE: July 31
Type: Subsidiary

John Crane seals the fate — or at least the openings — of most industrial process equipment. The company manufactures seals, bearings, power transmission couplings, and filtration systems. Its lineup connects the parts used in oil and gas pipelines, chemical plants, refrigeration systems, and more. The products are sold under such brands as Metastream, Lemco, Safematic, and Flexibox. Customers are primarily kingpin oil and gas and power generation companies, refineries, pump and compressor manufacturers, and chemical, pulp and paper, and mining industries, including BP, Dresser, Siemens, and ITT. John Crane operates as a subsidiary of UK-based Smiths Group plc, representing about 30% of its parent's sales.

JOHN D. OIL AND GAS COMPANY

OTC: JDOG

8500 Station St., Ste. 345
Mentor, OH 44060
Phone: 440-255-6325
Fax: 440-205-8680
Web: www.johndoilandgas.com

CEO: Richard M. Osborne
CFO: C. Jean Mihitsch
HR: —
FYE: December 31
Type: Public

John D. Oil and Gas (formerly Liberty Self-Stor) has shed its storage sheds in favor of oil and natural gas extraction in northeastern Ohio and the Appalachian Basin. In 2008 John D. Oil and Gas reported proved reserves of 2.1 billion cu. ft. of natural gas and 17,500 barrels of oil. That year it had 49 net productive wells. The company also owns and manages Kykuit Resources, LLC, which leases natural gas and oil rights to more than 203,840 acres in the Montana Breaks region in Montana. Chairman and CEO Richard Osborne owns 46% of John D. Oil and Gas.

	Annual Growth	12/05	12/06	12/07	12/08	12/09
Sales ($ mil.)	68.2%	0.5	1.9	3.3	4.9	4.0
Net income ($ mil.)	—	1.8	(2.0)	(0.9)	(2.2)	(2.6)
Market value ($ mil.)	(36.1%)	5.4	4.7	5.9	1.8	0.9
Employees	(8.5%)	10	12	10	11	7

⊞ JOHN HANCOCK FINANCIAL SERVICES, INC.

601 Congress St.
Boston, MA 02210
Phone: 617-663-3000
Fax: 617-572-6015
Web: www.johnhancock.com

CEO: John D. DesPrez III
CFO: Lynne Patterson
HR: Diana L. Scott
FYE: December 31
Type: Subsidiary

John Hancock, the man, was a revolutionary, but the company that bears his name is a bit less fiery. John Hancock Financial Services offers insurance, investment products, investment management, and other services. Its insurance products include variable, universal, and term life. John Hancock also provides retirement savings products — annuities, mutual funds, 401(k), and long-term care insurance. One of the US's largest investors, John Hancock offers institutional asset management services, providing clients with specialty funds in such industries as timber and agriculture. It has more than $185 billion in funds under its management. First established in 1862, John Hancock is owned by Canada's Manulife.

JOHN J. KIRLIN, LLC

515 Dover Rd., Ste. 2100
Rockville, MD 20850
Phone: 301-424-3410
Fax: 301-738-8888
Web: www.jjkllc.com

CEO: Robert W. (Rob) Bacon
CFO: —
HR: —
FYE: December 31
Type: Private

John J. Kirlin isn't just blowing hot air. The mechanical contractor specializes in large heating, air-conditioning, and plumbing construction jobs. John J. Kirlin's projects represent a wide range of sectors, from sports and entertainment complexes to correctional facilities. It also works on industrial and high density residential projects. Medical and laboratory facilities work has become one of the company's specialties and is handled through its John J. Kirlin Special Projects company. Another division installs fire protection systems. John J. Kirlin operates through divisions in Florida, Maryland, and North Carolina. The company was founded in 1960.

JOHN MORRELL & CO.

805 E. Kemper Rd.
Cincinnati, OH 45246
Phone: 513-346-3540
Fax: 513-346-7556
Web: www.johnmorrell.com

CEO: Joseph B. Sebring
CFO: —
HR: Gary Junso
FYE: April 30
Type: Subsidiary

Here's one of the top names in meat. John Morrell & Co. is a leading producer of processed-meat and fresh-pork products with about 15 processing plants around the US. It makes bacon, fresh pork, hams, and sausage, as well as cold cuts and lunch meats, hot dogs and deli meats. The company's brands include Bistro Naturals, Off The Bone, and its flagship John Morrell banner. Most of its products are sold through supermarkets and other retail grocers. John Morrell also sells meat and pork products to foodservice suppliers, restaurants, and other customers in the hospitality industry. Tracing its roots to the UK, where it was founded in 1827, John Morrell is a subsidiary of top meat producer Smithfield Foods.

JOHN PAUL MITCHELL SYSTEMS, INC.

9701 Wilshire Blvd., Ste. 1205
Beverly Hills, CA 90212
Phone: 310-248-3888
Fax: 310-248-2780
Web: www.paulmitchell.com

CEO: John Paul (J. P.) DeJoria
CFO: Rick Battaglini
HR: —
FYE: December 31
Type: Private

From pomades to pompadours, John Paul Mitchell Systems offers its best to those who do 'dos. The #1 privately owned haircare firm in the US makes more than 90 different haircare products that sell in about 90,000 hair salons worldwide. John Paul Mitchell was founded in Hawaii in 1980 by John Paul "J. P." DeJoria and the late Paul Mitchell. The firm's signature white bottles with distinctive black lettering (because the founders couldn't afford color ink) have attracted the attention of counterfeiters on more than one occasion. Its brands include Paul Mitchell, Modern Elixirs, The Tea Tree Collection, Paul Mitchell LAB, and Paul Mitchell Professional Hair Color.

	Annual Growth	12/04	12/05	12/06	12/07	12/08
Est. sales ($ mil.)	—	—	—	—	—	59.3
Employees	—	—	—	—	—	174

JOHN WILEY & SONS, INC.   NYSE: JW

111 River St., Ste. 2000	CEO: William J. (Will) Pesce
Hoboken, NJ 07030	CFO: Ellis E. Cousens
Phone: 201-748-6000	HR: William J. Arlington
Fax: 201-748-6088	FYE: April 30
Web: www.wiley.com	Type: Public

John Wiley & Sons might not adorn its books with shirtless hunks, but with such titles as *Patty's Industrial Hygiene and Toxicology,* who needs Fabio? The company publishes scientific, technical, and medical works, including journals and reference works such as *Current Protocols* and *Kirk-Othmer Encyclopedia of Chemical Technology.* All total, it publishes more than 1,500 journal titles. It also produces professional and nonfiction trade books, and is a publisher of college textbooks. The firm publishes the *For Dummies* how-to series, the travel guide brand *Frommer's,* and *CliffsNotes* study guides, as well. Wiley has publishing, marketing, and distribution centers in North America, Europe, Asia, and Australia.

	Annual Growth	4/05	4/06	4/07	4/08	4/09
Sales ($ mil.)	13.4%	974.0	1,044.2	1,234.9	1,673.7	1,611.4
Net income ($ mil.)	11.2%	83.8	110.3	99.6	147.5	128.3
Market value ($ mil.)	(1.6%)	2,145.7	2,174.2	2,222.2	2,732.6	2,011.6
Employees	10.7%	3,400	3,600	4,800	4,800	5,100

THE JOHNNY ROCKETS GROUP, INC.

25550 Commercentre Dr., Ste. 200	CEO: John Fuller
Lake Forest, CA 92630	CFO: —
Phone: 949-643-6100	HR: Terri Pattillo
Fax: 949-643-6200	FYE: April 30
Web: www.johnnyrockets.com	Type: Private

Hep cats still hang out at Johnny Rockets restaurants, where U-shaped counters, padded booths, table-top jukeboxes, and white uniforms salute the classic American diner. The Johnny Rockets Group operates and franchises about 280 restaurants in some 30 states and more than 10 other countries that specialize in such classic diner fare as hamburgers, malts, fries, and apple pie. About two-thirds of the locations are operated by franchisees. The chain was founded by Ronn Teitelbaum, who opened the first Johnny Rockets on Los Angeles' fashionable Melrose Avenue in 1986. The company is owned by RedZone Capital, an investment fund led by Washington Redskins owner Dan Snyder.

	Annual Growth	4/04	4/05	4/06	4/07	4/08
Sales ($ mil.)	12.0%	147.0	177.1	199.2	209.0	231.0
Employees	—	—	—	—	—	—

JOHNS HOPKINS HEALTH SYSTEM

600 N. Wolfe St.	CEO: Ronald R. Peterson
Baltimore, MD 21287	CFO: Ronald J. Werthman
Phone: 410-955-5000	HR: Pamela D. Paulk
Fax: 410-955-0890	FYE: June 30
Web: www.hopkinshospital.org	Type: Private

Johns Hopkins Health System, an affiliate of Johns Hopkins Medicine, provides a range of health services to residents of the Baltimore area, and visitors from all over the world. The health system includes three hospitals: Johns Hopkins Hospital, Bayview Medical Center, and Howard County General Hospital. The hospitals, affiliated with The Johns Hopkins University School of Medicine, offer an array of inpatient and outpatient health services that include general medicine, emergency/trauma care, pediatrics, maternity care, senior care, and clinics in numerous specialized areas of medicine. The system also includes an area network of primary care physicians and neighborhood clinics, and a home health agency.

	Annual Growth	6/04	6/05	6/06	6/07	6/08
Est. sales ($ mil.)	—	—	—	—	—	2,438.5
Employees	—	—	—	—	—	13,000

JOHNS HOPKINS MEDICINE

720 Rutland Ave.	CEO: Edward D. Miller Jr.
Baltimore, MD 21205	CFO: Richard A. (Rich) Grossi
Phone: 410-955-5000	HR: —
Fax: 410-955-4452	FYE: June 30
Web: www.hopkinsmedicine.org	Type: Not-for-profit

Hopping John is a recipe for black-eyed peas; Johns Hopkins Medicine is a recipe for Baltimore health care. Consisting of Johns Hopkins University School of Medicine and the Johns Hopkins Health System, Johns Hopkins Medicine fosters the education of physicians and medical scientists and facilitates biomedical research and the application of medical knowledge. The system utilizes the numerous resources offered by the hospitals and clinics in the Health System, which has an approximate 1,500-bed capacity, in addition to the academic offerings of the school.

THE JOHNS HOPKINS UNIVERSITY

3400 N. Charles St.	CEO: Ronald J. Daniels
Baltimore, MD 21218	CFO: James T. McGill
Phone: 410-516-8000	HR: Charlene Moore Hayes
Fax: 410-516-7075	FYE: June 30
Web: www.jhu.edu	Type: School

Founded in 1876 with a $7 million bequest from its namesake, The Johns Hopkins University established its reputation from the beginning by molding itself in the image of a European research institution. While renowned for its School of Medicine, the private university offers 10 academic and research divisions spanning fields of study including arts and sciences, business, engineering, and international studies. Some 20,000 students attend Johns Hopkins, which has about a half-dozen campuses in Maryland and Washington, DC, as well as international facilities in China and Italy. The affiliated Johns Hopkins Health System provides health care from its three Baltimore-area hospitals.

	Annual Growth	6/04	6/05	6/06	6/07	6/08
Est. sales ($ mil.)	—	—	—	—	—	1,500.0
Employees	—	—	—	—	—	32,000

JOHNS MANVILLE CORPORATION

717 17th St.	CEO: Todd Raba
Denver, CO 80202	CFO: Mary K. Rhinehart
Phone: 303-978-2000	HR: Scott Simmons
Fax: 303-978-2318	FYE: December 31
Web: www.jm.com	Type: Subsidiary

When you want to be insulated from the vagaries of life, turn to Johns Manville (JM). JM produces commercial and industrial roofing systems and formaldehyde-free fiberglass building insulation for the commercial and residential building industries. One of the nation's top makers of residential building insulation, JM also produces specialty insulation for the aerospace, transportation, acoustics, appliance, and HVAC industries. Other offerings include fire-protection systems, thermal and acoustical insulation, glass textile wallcoverings, and fibers and nonwoven mats used in roofing and flooring. JM operates more than 40 plants in China, Europe, and North America. Warren Buffett's Berkshire Hathaway owns JM.

JOHNSON & JOHNSON

NYSE: JNJ

1 Johnson & Johnson Plaza
New Brunswick, NJ 08933
Phone: 732-524-0400
Fax: 732-214-0332
Web: www.jnj.com

CEO: William C. (Bill) Weldon
CFO: Dominic J. Caruso
HR: Russell C. Deyo
FYE: December 31
Type: Public

It's nearly impossible to get well without Johnson & Johnson (J&J). The diversified health care giant operates in three segments through more than 250 operating companies located in some 60 countries. Its Pharmaceuticals division makes drugs for an array of ailments, such as neurological conditions, blood disorders, autoimmune diseases, and pain. Top sellers are psoriasis drug Remicade and schizophrenia medication Risperdal. J&J's Medical Devices and Diagnostics division offers surgical equipment, monitoring devices, orthopedic products, and contact lenses, among other things. Its Consumer segment makes over-the-counter drugs and products for baby, skin, and oral care, as well as first aid and women's health.

	Annual Growth	12/05	12/06	12/07	12/08	12/09
Sales ($ mil.)	5.2%	50,514.0	53,324.0	61,095.0	63,747.0	61,897.0
Net income ($ mil.)	4.2%	10,411.0	11,053.0	10,576.0	12,949.0	12,266.0
Market value ($ mil.)	1.7%	165,760.0	182,087.7	183,963.2	165,015.3	177,647.3
Employees	(0.0%)	115,600	122,200	119,200	118,700	115,500

JOHNSON & JOHNSON - MERCK CONSUMER PHARMACEUTICALS CO.

7050 Camp Hill Rd.
Fort Washington, PA 19034
Phone: 215-273-7700
Fax: 215-273-4193

CEO: Calvin Schmidt
CFO: —
HR: —
FYE: December 31
Type: Joint venture

Got a fire in your belly? Johnson & Johnson — Merck Consumer Pharmaceuticals will help put it out. The joint venture, owned equally by major drug companies Johnson & Johnson and Merck, makes and markets Pepcid over-the-counter (OTC) heartburn relief products, as well as medicine cabinet stalwart Mylanta, in North America. The Pepcid family includes Pepcid Complete, which combines the quick relief of an antacid with the long-term benefits of an acid reducer, and Pepcid AC, the OTC version of Merck's prescription ulcer drug Pepcid. Its Mylanta products include liquid, chewable tablet, and soft gel formulations. The unit also makes Mylicon, an anti-gas OTC product for babies.

JOHNSON & JOHNSON PHARMACEUTICAL RESEARCH & DEVELOPMENT

920 Rte. 202 South
Raritan, NJ 08869
Phone: 908-704-4000
Fax: 908-722-5867
Web: www.jnjpharmarnd.com

CEO: Garry Neil
CFO: —
HR: —
FYE: December 31
Type: Subsidiary

The aptly named Johnson & Johnson Pharmaceutical Research & Development, L.L.C., (J&JPRD) provides research and development support for the pharmaceutical business units of parent company Johnson & Johnson. Its main research processes are divided into three franchises: central nervous system and internal medicine; biotech, immunology, and oncology (through J&J subsidiary Centocor); and virology (through Tibotec). The subsidiary — which represents the largest segment of J&J's pharmaceutical R&D — also does research in collaboration with other pharmaceutical organizations and biotech researchers, and has partnerships with the likes of Basilea Pharmaceuticals and Entelos.

JOHNSON & WALES UNIVERSITY

8 Abbott Park Place
Providence, RI 02903
Phone: 401-598-1000
Fax: 401-598-1833
Web: www.jwu.edu

CEO: John J. Bowen
CFO: William F. McArdle
HR: Toni D. Green
FYE: June 30
Type: School

Things are a little "upside-down" at Johnson & Wales University, and that's just the way they like it. The private, not-for-profit, accredited institution provides what it calls an upside-down curriculum, allowing students to take courses in their major during the first year, so they learn right away if their career choice is right for them. At the end of two years of study, students earn an associate's degree and the opportunity to go on to earn a bachelor's degree. Founded in 1914, the school enrolls more than 16,000 students on four campuses in Colorado, Florida, North Carolina, and Rhode Island. It offers degrees in business, education, foodservice, hospitality, culinary arts, and technology.

JOHNSON CONTROLS, INC.

NYSE: JCI

5757 N. Green Bay Ave.
Milwaukee, WI 53209
Phone: 414-524-1200
Fax: 414-524-2077
Web: www.johnsoncontrols.com

CEO: Stephen A. Roell
CFO: R. Bruce McDonald
HR: Susan F. Davis
FYE: September 30
Type: Public

Johnson Controls (JCI) wants to put you in the driver's seat — an environmentally conscious one. The company makes car batteries and interior parts for passenger and hybrid electric vehicles, as well as energy-efficient HVAC systems for commercial buildings. Car interior products include seating, instrument panels, and electronics. Major OEM customers include GM, Daimler, Chrysler, and Ford. The battery unit makes car batteries for retailers such as Advance Auto, AutoZone, Pep Boys, and Wal-Mart. The building efficiency division makes, installs, and services mechanical equipment that controls HVAC, lighting, security, and fire systems in commercial buildings. The unit also offers on-site facility management.

	Annual Growth	9/05	9/06	9/07	9/08	9/09
Sales ($ mil.)	0.9%	27,479.4	32,235.0	34,624.0	38,062.0	28,497.0
Net income ($ mil.)	—	909.4	1,035.0	1,252.0	979.0	(338.0)
Market value ($ mil.)	5.4%	13,913.7	16,086.6	26,484.3	20,403.1	17,194.3
Employees	3.3%	114,000	136,000	140,000	140,000	130,000

JOHNSON MATTHEY INC.

435 Devon Park Dr., Ste. 600
Wayne, PA 19087
Phone: 610-971-3000
Fax: 610-971-3191
Web: www.jmusa.com

CEO: Neil A. P. Carson
CFO: R. J. MacLeod
HR: —
FYE: March 31
Type: Subsidiary

Johnson Matthey serves the precious metals, catalysts, coatings, and pharmaceutical businesses in the US. The company provides contract research and development for the pharmaceutical industry. Its Fine Chemicals and Catalysts unit manufactures active pharmaceutical ingredients and products for chemicals makers. The Precious Metals division sells platinum sheet, tube, and wire to jewelers in addition to refining precious metals. Johnson Matthey Fuel Cells also operates in the US. The company forms the North American unit for the UK chemicals and catalysts maker Johnson Matthey.

	Annual Growth	3/04	3/05	3/06	3/07	3/08
Est. sales ($ mil.)	—	—	—	—	—	470.7
Employees	—	—	—	—	—	1,650

JOHNSON OUTDOORS INC.

NASDAQ (GM): JOUT

555 Main St.
Racine, WI 53403
Phone: 262-631-6600
Fax: 262-631-6601
Web: www.johnsonoutdoors.com

CEO: Helen P. Johnson-Leipold
CFO: David W. Johnson
HR: Sara Vidian
FYE: September 30
Type: Public

Johnson Outdoors keeps sports buffs from staying indoors. The company makes, markets, and sells camping and outdoor equipment (such as Eureka! tents and backpacks). It also focuses on supplying equipment for water activities with its diving gear (Scubapro and Uwatec masks, fins, snorkels, and tanks), trolling motors (Minn Kota), fishfinders (Humminbird), autopilot systems (Navicontrol), and watercraft (Old Town canoes, Dimension kayaks). With GPS technologies and electric boat motors, Johnson Outdoors' marine electronics unit generates about 45% of the firm's sales. The S.C. Johnson & Son family, including CEO Helen Johnson-Leipold, owns a majority stake in the company and controls some 80% of the voting power.

	Annual Growth	9/05	9/06	9/07	9/08	9/09
Sales ($ mil.)	(1.6%)	380.7	395.8	432.1	420.8	356.5
Net income ($ mil.)	—	7.1	8.7	9.2	(71.0)	(9.7)
Market value ($ mil.)	(14.3%)	158.9	165.0	206.7	120.2	85.9
Employees	(0.4%)	1,300	1,300	1,400	1,400	1,280

JOHNSON PUBLISHING COMPANY, INC.

820 S. Michigan Ave.
Chicago, IL 60605
Phone: 312-322-9200
Fax: 312-322-0918
Web: www.johnsonpublishing.com

CEO: Linda Johnson Rice
CFO: —
HR: —
FYE: December 31
Type: Private

Snubbed by advertisers when he founded his company 60 years ago, the late John Johnson pushed his magazine company to the front of the pack. Led by flagship *EBONY* (a monthly general interest magazine for African-Americans), family-owned Johnson Publishing Company is a black-owned global publishing firm. It also publishes news magazine *JET* and operates the JPC Book Division. In addition, Johnson Publishing produces a line of cosmetics (Fashion Fair Cosmetics) marketed for African-American women. John Johnson founded the company in 1942 with the publication of *Negro Digest*, inspired by *Reader's Digest*.

JOHNSONVILLE SAUSAGE, LLC

N6928 Johnsonville Way
Sheboygan Falls, WI 53085
Phone: 920-453-6900
Fax: 920-459-7824
Web: www.johnsonville.com

CEO: Ralph C. Stayer
CFO: Kris Dirkse
HR: Leah Glaub
FYE: December 31
Type: Private

This is a company you ought to link up with. Johnsonville Sausage makes a wide array of top-selling fresh, pre-cooked, and smoked sausage products, including bratwurst, breakfast links and bulk rolls, and smoked and Italian sausage. Its link and bulk meats are sold primarily through retail grocery stores and foodservice operators, but Johnsonville also operates an online store that offers gift packs, cheeses, breads and rolls, and company ephemera in addition to sausage. Johnsonville's sausage is available in about 30 countries worldwide. In the US Johnsonville products can be found on the menu at more than 4,000 McDonald's restaurants.

JOHNSTONE SUPPLY

11632 NE Ainsworth Circle
Portland, OR 97220
Phone: 503-256-3663
Fax: 503-256-3798
Web: www.johnstonesupply.com

CEO: Gary Daniels
CFO: Rich Jansen
HR: —
FYE: —
Type: Cooperative

Johnstone Supply is the Ace Hardware of heating, ventilation, air-conditioning, refrigeration, and plumbing. The cooperative company is a leading wholesale distributor of HVAC/R, plumbing, and appliance parts and supplies to about 340 independent stores operated by member-owners throughout the US. The co-op also supports member stores in South Korea and Guam. The member-owners may order more than 30,000 products from a catalog or the cooperative's website. The cooperative also provides them with assistance in training, customer loyalty programs, and financial reporting. Johnstone Supply operates distribution centers in Florida, Oregon, Pennsylvania, and Tennessee. The cooperative was founded in 1953.

JOINT COMMISSION ON ACCREDITATION OF HEALTHCARE ORGANIZATIONS

1 Renaissance Blvd.
Oakbrook Terrace, IL 60181
Phone: 630-792-5000
Fax: 630-792-5005
Web: www.jointcommission.org

CEO: Mark R. Chassin
CFO: Paige A. Rodgers
HR: Lynn B. Dragisic
FYE: December 31
Type: Not-for-profit

Its not really about joints, per se, unless they are aching and in need of repair. The Joint Commission on Accreditation of Health Care Organizations is a nonprofit that provides accreditation and certification services to more than 17,000 health care providers in the US. Its board of commissioners includes doctors, nurses, consumers, and administrators. They evaluate hospitals, health care networks, nursing homes and other long-term care facilities, laboratories, and health-related groups. The Joint Commission's Quality Check website includes each accredited organization's quality review. The group, also known simply as The Joint Commission, was founded in 1951.

	Annual Growth	12/04	12/05	12/06	12/07	12/08
Est. sales ($ mil.)	—	—	—	—	—	103.3
Employees	—	—	—	—	—	936

JONES APPAREL GROUP, INC.

NYSE: JNY

1411 Broadway
New York, NY 10018
Phone: 212-642-3860
Fax: 215-785-1795
Web: www.jny.com

CEO: Wesley R. Card
CFO: John T. McClain
HR: Aida Tejero-DeColli
FYE: December 31
Type: Public

While some are busy keeping up with the Joneses, Jones Apparel Group is too busy taking stock in its own brand portfolio to take notice. The company provides a wide range of clothing, shoes, and accessories for men, women, and children. Its brands include Anne Klein, Jones New York, Gloria Vanderbilt, Kasper, Evan-Picone, and l.e.i., among many others. Subsidiary Nine West Group designs apparel and shoes under the names Easy Spirit, Enzo Angiolini, Bandolino, and Nine West. Through licensing agreements, Jones also supplies Givenchy jewelry, Rachel Roy designer apparel, Dockers footwear, and Jessica Simpson jeanswear. The firm operates about 940 outlet and specialty stores, as well as branded e-commerce sites.

	Annual Growth	12/05	12/06	12/07	12/08	12/09
Sales ($ mil.)	(10.0%)	5,074.2	4,742.8	3,848.5	3,616.4	3,327.4
Net income ($ mil.)	—	274.3	(146.0)	311.1	(765.4)	(86.3)
Market value ($ mil.)	(15.0%)	2,676.7	2,912.9	1,393.3	510.6	1,399.4
Employees	(11.1%)	18,430	16,485	8,450	7,925	11,535

THE JONES COMPANY

215 Pendleton St.
Waycross, GA 31501
Phone: 912-285-4011
Fax: 912-285-0811

CEO: James C. (Jimmy) Jones III
CFO: Gregory M. (Greg) Higginson
HR: —
FYE: December 31
Type: Private

After more than a quarter of a century, The Jones Company has proven it isn't just a flash in the pan. The diversified holding company operates more than 170 Flash Foods convenience stores in Georgia and north Florida. A pair of subsidiaries keep the shelves and gas tanks well stocked. Jones's Fuel South unit supplies the company's service stations with fuel. Its Distribution South unit is a wholesale grocery supplier and provides much of the merchandise sold in the stores. The firm's Jones Company Restaurants subsidiary operates restaurants and Walker-Jones is a family of auto dealerships. Founded in 1979 by J. C. Jones Jr. and his father, the company is still owned and run by the Jones family.

JONES DAY

North Point, 901 Lakeside Ave.
Cleveland, OH 44114
Phone: 216-586-3939
Fax: 216-579-0212
Web: www.jonesday.com

CEO: Stephen J. Brogan
CFO: —
HR: Gregory M. (Greg) Shumaker
FYE: December 31
Type: Partnership

Legal leviathan Jones Day ranks as one of the world's largest law firms, providing counsel to about half of the *FORTUNE* 500 companies. It has some 2,400 attorneys in about 30 offices worldwide. Outside the US, Jones Day has offices in the Asia/Pacific region and in Europe. The firm's practice areas include capital markets, government regulation, intellectual property, real estate, and tax. Jones Day has counted Bridgestone/Firestone, General Motors, IBM, RJR Nabisco, and Texas Instruments among its clients. The firm traces its roots to the Cleveland law partnership founded by Edwin Blandin and William Rice in 1893.

	Annual Growth	12/04	12/05	12/06	12/07	12/08
Sales ($ mil.)	6.2%	—	1,285.0	1,310.0	1,441.0	1,540.0
Employees	2.6%	—	4,850	4,977	—	—

⊞ THE JONES FINANCIAL COMPANIES, L.L.L.P.

12555 Manchester Rd.
Des Peres, MO 63131
Phone: 314-515-2000
Fax: 314-515-2622
Web: www.edwardjones.com

CEO: James D. (Jim) Weddle
CFO: Kevin Bastien
HR: Ken Dude
FYE: December 31
Type: Partnership

This isn't your father's broker. Well, maybe it is. The Jones Financial Companies is the parent of Edward Jones, an investment brokerage network catering to individual investors. Serving some 7 million clients, the "Wal-Mart of Wall Street" has thousands of offices (mainly in rural communities and suburbs) in all 50 states and Canada. Brokers preach a conservative buy-and-hold approach, offering relatively low-risk investment vehicles such as government bonds, blue-chip stocks, high-quality mutual funds, and annuities. The company also sells insurance and engages in investment banking, underwriting and making markets for corporate securities and municipal bonds.

	Annual Growth	12/05	12/06	12/07	12/08	12/09
Sales ($ mil.)	2.7%	3,190.4	3,517.8	4,146.9	3,859.0	3,548.0
Net income ($ mil.)	(16.0%)	330.0	390.7	508.2	311.8	164.3
Employees	5.7%	32,400	34,300	38,100	40,000	40,500

⊞ JONES LANG LASALLE INCORPORATED

NYSE: JLL

200 E. Randolph Dr.
Chicago, IL 60601
Phone: 312-782-5800
Fax: 312-782-4339
Web: www.joneslanglasalle.com

CEO: Colin Dyer
CFO: Lauralee E. Martin
HR: Nazneen Razi
FYE: December 31
Type: Public

Borders mean little to Jones Lang LaSalle. The company provides commercial real estate brokerage, management, advisory, and financing services in some 60 countries around the world. Its offerings include property management and leasing, sales and dispositions, tenant representation, valuations, development services, and real estate investment banking. The company has expertise in a wide variety of commercial real estate, including office, retail, hotel, health care, industrial, cultural, and multifamily residential properties. Jones Lang LaSalle has some $40 billion in assets under management and a total portfolio of 1.6 billion sq. ft. worldwide.

	Annual Growth	12/05	12/06	12/07	12/08	12/09
Sales ($ mil.)	16.1%	1,366.8	2,013.6	2,652.1	2,697.6	2,480.7
Net income ($ mil.)	—	103.3	175.2	257.8	84.9	(3.6)
Market value ($ mil.)	4.7%	2,116.5	3,874.4	2,991.2	1,164.4	2,538.9
Employees	13.6%	22,000	25,500	32,700	36,200	36,600

JONES SODA CO.

NASDAQ (CM): JSDA

234 9th Ave. North
Seattle, WA 98109
Phone: 206-624-3357
Fax: 206-624-6857
Web: www.jonessoda.com

CEO: William R. Meissner
CFO: Michael R. O'Brien
HR: Susan Rozewski
FYE: December 31
Type: Public

There's nothing average about Jones Soda. The company makes brightly colored beverages with wacky flavors like Fufu Berry and Blue Bubble Gum. Seasonal offerings include Turkey and Gravy for Thanksgiving and Chocolate Fudge for Valentine's Day. It regularly discontinues flavors and adds new ones. Jones also customizes its labels with photos submitted by customers. The firm sells a line of noncarbonated beverages (Jones Naturals), with added ginseng, zinc, and other ingredients; energy drinks under the WhoopAss label; and bottled tea (Jones Organics). Its sodas are distributed in the US and Canada, as well as in the UK, Australia, Japan, and the United Arab Emirates.

	Annual Growth	12/05	12/06	12/07	12/08	12/09
Sales ($ mil.)	(6.1%)	33.5	39.7	39.8	35.9	26.0
Net income ($ mil.)	—	1.3	4.6	(11.6)	(15.2)	(10.5)
Market value ($ mil.)	(46.9%)	142.7	325.1	196.6	8.5	11.4
Employees	(5.2%)	52	67	82	65	42

JORDAN INDUSTRIES, INC.

1751 Lake Cook Rd., Ste. 550
Deerfield, IL 60015
Phone: 847-945-5591
Fax: 847-945-0198
Web: www.jordanindustries.com

CEO: John W. (Jay) Jordan II
CFO: Lisa M. Ondrula
HR: —
FYE: December 31
Type: Private

Like the River Jordan that touches the lives many people, so too, Jordan Industries, Inc. (JII). JII is a private holding company that fosters a diversity of businesses. The conglomerate leverages its financing muscle to open the door to capital for expansion that would otherwise elude its businesses on their own. Among JII's subsidiaries, Beemak makes point-of-purchase plastic displays for brochures and signs. Safety reflectors for bicycles and commercial vehicles are made by Sate-Lite. Deflecto produces plastic injection-molded hardware and office supply products. Formed by private equity The Jordan Company, JII is held by David Zalaznick and chairman and CEO John W. Jordan II, each with stakes of about 20%.

	Annual Growth	12/04	12/05	12/06	12/07	12/08
Est. sales ($ mil.)	—	—	—	—	—	256.7
Employees	—	—	—	—	—	1,393

JOS. A. BANK CLOTHIERS, INC.

NASDAQ (GS): JOSB

500 Hanover Pike
Hampstead, MD 21074
Phone: 410-239-2700
Fax: 410-239-5700
Web: www.josbank.com

CEO: R. Neal Black
CFO: David E. Ullman
HR: Robert B. Hensley
FYE: January 31
Type: Public

When casual Fridays put a wrinkle in the starched selling philosophy of Jos. A. Bank Clothiers, the company dressed down. Although it is still best known for making tailored clothing for the professional man, including suits, sport coats, dress shirts, and pants, it has added casual wear suitable for those dress-down Fridays and weekends. It also debuted the David Leadbetter line of golf wear. The company sells its Jos. A. Bank clothes and a few shoe brands through its catalogs, website, and some 460 company-owned or franchised stores in about 42 states and the District of Columbia. For corporate customers, it offers a credit card that provides users with discounts. Most stores house a tailoring shop.

	Annual Growth	1/06	1/07	1/08	1/09	1/10
Sales ($ mil.)	13.5%	464.6	546.4	604.0	695.9	770.3
Net income ($ mil.)	19.2%	35.3	43.2	50.2	58.4	71.2
Market value ($ mil.)	0.5%	752.7	568.2	499.9	503.9	769.1
Employees	9.6%	2,995	3,375	4,069	4,040	4,318

JOSTENS, INC.

3601 Minnesota Dr.
Minneapolis, MN 55435
Phone: 952-830-3300
Fax: 952-830-3293
Web: www.jostens.com

CEO: Timothy M. Larson
CFO: Marjorie J. (Marge) Brown
HR: Cynthia Newsom
FYE: December 31
Type: Subsidiary

Are you *sure* you want to remember high school? If so, look to Jostens, the leading US producer of yearbooks and class rings through its memory book and scholastic business segments. Class rings are sold on school campuses and through bookstores, retail jewelers, and the Web, while Jostens' sports rings commemorate professional sports champions (it has made more than 25 Super Bowl rings). Its other graduation products include diplomas, announcements, caps, and gowns. Founded in 1897, Jostens was sold to a unit of CSFB in 2003. The next year Jostens was recapitalized and became part of a newly created publishing and marketing services company, Visant, co-owned by an affiliate of CSFB and KKR & Co.

	Annual Growth	12/04	12/05	12/06	12/07	12/08
Est. sales ($ mil.)	—	—	—	—	—	850.0
Employees	—	—	—	—	—	5,691

JOURNAL COMMUNICATIONS, INC.

NYSE: JRN

333 W. State St.
Milwaukee, WI 53201
Phone: 414-224-2000
Fax: 414-224-2469
Web: www.journalcommunications.com

CEO: Steven J. Smith
CFO: Andre J. Fernández
HR: —
FYE: December 31
Type: Public

You might say this company chronicles the news in Milwaukee. Journal Communications is a leading diversified media company with operations including newspapers, radio, and television. The company's publishing business is anchored by its flagship paper the *Milwaukee Journal Sentinel*, a leading daily newspaper with a circulation of about 185,000. Its Journal Community Publishing Group also runs about 50 community newspapers and shoppers, serving markets in Wisconsin and Florida. In addition, Journal Communications owns 35 radio stations and about a dozen TV stations in more than 10 states through its Journal Broadcast unit. It also operates several websites in conjunction with its media properties.

	Annual Growth	12/05	12/06	12/07	12/08	12/09
Sales ($ mil.)	(13.2%)	764.5	671.9	582.7	544.9	433.6
Net income ($ mil.)	(49.5%)	66.2	64.4	110.1	(224.4)	4.3
Market value ($ mil.)	(27.3%)	767.3	693.6	491.7	134.8	214.0
Employees	(12.7%)	5,500	350	4,500	4,000	3,200

JOY GLOBAL INC.

NASDAQ (GS): JOYG

100 E. Wisconsin Ave., Ste. 2780
Milwaukee, WI 53202
Phone: 414-319-8500
Fax: 414-319-8520
Web: www.joyglobal.com

CEO: Michael W. Sutherlin
CFO: Michael S. (Mike) Olsen
HR: Dennis R. Winkleman
FYE: October 31
Type: Public

Joy Global is pretty happy for a company that builds equipment destined to spend the majority of its life down in a hole. The company makes heavy equipment for the mining industry through two subsidiaries. Its Joy Mining Machinery subsidiary makes underground coal-mining equipment that includes armored face conveyors, roof supports, longwall shearers, and shuttle cars. Subsidiary P&H Mining Equipment makes electric mining shovels, rotary blasthole drills, and other equipment used in open-pit mining; it also provides parts and service through its P&H MinePro Services group. Joy Global, which operates manufacturing and service facilities worldwide, gets about half of its sales from outside the US.

	Annual Growth	10/05	10/06	10/07	10/08	10/09
Sales ($ mil.)	16.9%	1,927.5	2,401.7	2,547.3	3,418.9	3,598.3
Net income ($ mil.)	32.4%	148.0	414.9	279.8	374.3	454.6
Market value ($ mil.)	13.3%	3,147.8	4,025.9	5,976.5	2,983.1	5,189.1
Employees	9.4%	7,900	8,900	9,200	11,800	11,300

JOY MINING MACHINERY

177 Thorn Hill Rd.
Warrendale, PA 15086
Phone: 724-779-4500
Fax: 724-779-4509
Web: www.joy.com

CEO: Edward L. (Ted) Doheny II
CFO: Michael S. (Mike) Olsen
HR: —
FYE: October 31
Type: Subsidiary

Joy Mining Machinery finds happiness underground. The company manufactures and distributes underground mining equipment and bulk material conveyor systems from over 45 service locations located near major mining regions throughout the world. The foundation for Joy Mining Machinery was laid when inventor Joseph F. Joy received a patent for his mechanical gathering arm loader in 1919. Products include bolting systems (used in coal mining), haulage systems, and longwall systems (consisting of shearers, roof supports, face conveyors, stageloaders, crushers, and mobile belt tail pieces). The company is a subsidiary of Joy Global. Sister company P&H Mining Equipment produces surface mining machinery.

JOYCE LESLIE, INC.

135 W. Commercial Ave.
Moonachie, NJ 07074
Phone: 201-804-7800
Fax: 877-253-5060
Web: www.joyceslie.com

CEO: Joyce G. Segal
CFO: Hermine Gewirtz
HR: Cheryl O'Reilly
FYE: January 31
Type: Private

Club-hoppers (and high schoolers) hoping to look like Paris Hilton without spending like her do their shopping at Joyce Leslie. The northeastern retail chain specializes in trendy and inexpensive women's and junior's clothing aimed primarily at teens and tweens. It operates about 50 shops filled with high-fashion knockoffs in Connecticut, New Jersey, New York, and Pennsylvania. Joyce Leslie, named after the daughter of the company's founder Julius Gewirtz, was established in Brooklyn in 1945 and originally sold women's dresses.

	Annual Growth	1/04	1/05	1/06	1/07	1/08
Est. sales ($ mil.)	—	—	—	—	—	100.9
Employees	—	—	—	—	—	900

An in-depth profile of this company is available to Hoover's Online members at hoovers.com.

873

J.P. MORGAN SECURITIES INC.

270 Park Ave., 12th. Fl.
New York, NY 10017
Phone: 212-270-6000
Fax: 212-283-6081
Web: www.jpmorgan.com/pages/jpmorgan/investbk

CEO: James E. (Jes) Staley
CFO: —
HR: —
FYE: December 31
Type: Subsidiary

J.P. Morgan Securities is the US investment banking arm of financial services giant JPMorgan Chase. The company provides debt and equity underwriting, M&A and corporate restructuring advisory, securities dealing and brokerage, and trade execution services for large-market companies and institutional investors. Subsidiary J.P. Morgan Clearing provides clearing and settlement services. The company also provides economic and equity research services. In 2008 JPMorgan Chase acquired stricken Bear Stearns, historically one of the world's leading investment banks but one of the early victims of the global financial crisis. Its operations were merged with J.P. Morgan Securities, the bank's largest nonbanking subsidiary.

JPMORGAN ASSET MANAGEMENT HOLDINGS INC.

245 Park Ave.
New York, NY 10167
Phone: 212-483-2323
Fax: —
Web: www.jpmorgan.com/pages/jpmorgan/am

CEO: Mary C. Erdoes
CFO: —
HR: —
FYE: December 31
Type: Subsidiary

JPMorgan Asset Management is no mutt. Tracing its roots to the 19th century, the business unit of JPMorgan Chase combines the venerable investment management operations of J.P. Morgan, Chase Manhattan, and Robert Fleming Holdings. (Chase Manhattan bought Robert Fleming Holdings in 2000, then merged with J.P. Morgan the following year.) JPMorgan Asset Management serves investors around the globe, offering investments in stocks, fixed-income securities, real estate, private equity, hedge funds, mutual funds, foreign currencies, and money market instruments.

⊞ JPMORGAN CHASE & CO.

NYSE: JPM

270 Park Ave.
New York, NY 10017
Phone: 212-270-6000
Fax: 212-270-1648
Web: www.jpmorganchase.com

CEO: James (Jamie) Dimon
CFO: Michael J. Cavanagh
HR: John L. Donnelly
FYE: December 31
Type: Public

JPMorgan Chase was born with a silver spoon in its mouth but that hasn't stopped it. One of the largest financial services firms in the US, the company has more than 5,100 bank branches in some two dozen states (and counting) and is also among the nation's top mortgage lenders and credit card issuers. Active in some 60 countries, it also boasts formidable investment banking and asset management operations. The company's subsidiaries include the prestigious JPMorgan Private Bank and institutional investment manager JPMorgan Asset Management (with some $1.7 trillion in assets under supervision). In 2008 JPMorgan Chase bought Bear Stearns and the operations of failed thrift Washington Mutual (WaMu).

	Annual Growth	12/05	12/06	12/07	12/08	12/09
Assets ($ mil.)	14.1%	1,198,942.0	1,351,520.0	1,562,147.0	2,175,052.0	2,031,989.0
Net income ($ mil.)	8.3%	8,483.0	14,444.0	15,365.0	3,699.0	11,652.0
Market value ($ mil.)	1.2%	157,914.4	192,170.9	173,670.0	125,448.2	165,792.2
Employees	7.1%	168,847	174,360	180,667	224,961	222,316

JPS HEALTH NETWORK

1500 S. Main St.
Fort Worth, TX 76104
Phone: 817-921-3431
Fax: 817-924-1207
Web: www.jpshealthnet.org

CEO: Robert Earley
CFO: Randy Rogers
HR: Rose Thomason
FYE: September 30
Type: Not-for-profit

Residents of Cowtown don't suffer from gunshot wounds as much as they did back in the day; however, if they're searching for health care, they still need look no further than JPS Health Network. Founded in 1906 in Fort Worth, Texas, flagship facility John Peter Smith Hospital has approximately 460 beds and provides specialty services including orthopedics, cardiology, and women's health. JPS Health Network also includes behavioral health treatment center Trinity Springs Pavilion and the JPS Diagnostic & Surgery Hospital of Arlington. The company provides pediatrics, family medicine, and dental care through dozens of health care centers in northern Texas.

	Annual Growth	9/04	9/05	9/06	9/07	9/08
Est. sales ($ mil.)	—	—	—	—	—	140.7
Employees	—	—	—	—	—	3,000

JPS INDUSTRIES, INC.

Pink Sheets: JPST

55 Beattie Place, Ste. 1510
Greenville, SC 29601
Phone: 864-239-3900
Fax: 864-271-9939
Web: www.jpselastomerics.com

CEO: Michael L. Fulbright
CFO: Charles R. (Chuck) Tutterow
HR: —
FYE: October 31
Type: Public

JPS Industries' plastic products can be found surfing the waves and saving lives. Its JPS Composite Materials subsidiary makes high-strength fiberglass and synthetic fabrics for the aeronautics, military, and other industries. The company's products are used in a range of applications including body armor, insulation, plasma display screens, and even surfboards. JPS Industries also is the parent of JPS Elastomerics, which operates Stevens Urethane, maker of polyurethane film, sheet, tubing, and cords used to make athletic shoes, medical products, and auto parts. In 2008 JPS narrowed its focus and sold Stevens Geomembranes and Stevens Roofing to Dow Building Solutions, a part of The Dow Chemical Company.

⊞ J.R. SIMPLOT COMPANY

999 Main St., Ste. 1300
Boise, ID 83702
Phone: 208-336-2110
Fax: 208-389-7515
Web: www.simplot.com

CEO: Bill Whitacre
CFO: —
HR: —
FYE: August 31
Type: Private

J.R. Simplot hopes you'll have fries with that. Potato potentate J. R. "Jack" Simplot simply shook hands with McDonald's pioneer Ray Kroc in the mid-1960s and his company's french fry sales have sizzled ever since. Simplot still remains the major french fry supplier for McDonald's and supplies Burger King, and Wendy's as well. Along with potatoes, J.R. Simplot produces fruits and vegetables under the RoastWorks and Simplot Classic labels. It owns and operates more than 80,000 acres on 30 farms located in Idaho, Oregon, and Washington. It produces more than 1.5 million pounds of french fries annually, making it one of the world's largest processors of frozen potatoes.

JSP INTERNATIONAL, LLC

1285 Drummers Ln., Ste. 301
Wayne, PA 19087
Phone: 610-651-8600
Fax: 610-651-8601
Web: www.jsp.com

CEO: Carl Moyer
CFO: Dan Doyle
HR: —
FYE: March 31
Type: Subsidiary

Don't tell JSP International that a fender bender will ruin an automobile's aesthetic appeal. Its expanded polypropylene (EPP) and expanded polyethylene (EPE) beads make the kind of car bumpers that bend right back. Among the world's leading manufacturers of EPP, the company is the US arm of Japan's JSP Corporation. From sales and manufacturing offices in Illinois, Michigan, Pennsylvania, and Tennessee, JSP International makes EPP for the automotive industry; the packaging of sensitive materials such as computers and other electronics; recreational products (including protective athletic gear and sports equipment and surfaces); military gear; and acoustic walls.

JTEKT AUTOMOTIVE TENNESSEE-MORRISTOWN, INC.

5932 Commerce Blvd.
Morristown, TN 37814
Phone: 423-585-0999
Fax: 423-585-2941
Web: www.jtekt-na.com

CEO: Mike Davidson
CFO: Joe Cronin
HR: Clayton Chambers
FYE: December 31
Type: Subsidiary

JTEKT Automotive Tennessee-Morristown (formerly Toyoda-Koki Automotive North America) is a manufacturer of complete automotive steering systems — both electric and hydraulic power — as well as steering components, including power steering hydraulic pumps and reservoirs, steering gears, columns, shafts, pressure hoses, and return hoses. The company was founded in 1941 and is a subsidiary of JTEKT Corporation (formerly Koyo Seiko), a Japan-based manufacturer of steering systems, bearings, driveline components, and machine tools. JTEKT operates other steering system manufacturing subsidiaries in Michigan, Tennessee (Vonore), Virginia, and Texas.

JT3 LLC

821 Grier Dr.
Las Vegas, NV 89119
Phone: 702-492-2100
Fax: 702-361-0905
Web: www.jt3.com

CEO: Alan Hunter
CFO: Daniel (Dan) Wild
HR: Jack Pollock
FYE: December 31
Type: Joint venture

Consumer Reports can try out cars and toasters, but it can't test new weapons platforms: That's where JT3 (Joint Test, Tactics, and Training) comes in to play. A joint venture between URS Corporation and Raytheon Technical Services, JT3 provides engineering and technical support services for aerospace and military customers. Areas of operation include mission and project planning, flight test engineering and development, modeling and simulation services, and hardware and software support. JT3 has been involved in testing such high-flying projects as the F-35 Lightning II, F-117 Nighthawk, the B-2 Spirit, and F-22 Raptor.

JTH TAX, INC.

1716 Corporate Landing Pkwy.
Virginia Beach, VA 23454
Phone: 757-493-8855
Fax: 800-880-6432
Web: www.libertytax.com

CEO: John T. Hewitt
CFO: Mark Baumgartner
HR: —
FYE: April 30
Type: Private

JTH Tax wants to free you from those tax preparation shackles. Doing business as Liberty Tax Service, it is now the third-largest income tax preparation chain (behind H&R Block and Jackson Hewitt). Liberty Tax Service provides computerized tax preparation services to clients through some 3,200 offices throughout the US and in Canada. More than 1,700 franchisees operate the locations, which are known to have costumed Uncle Sams or Lady Liberties waving out front. The company's eSmart Tax product allows customers to file their taxes online. Liberty Tax Service also offers tax-preparation courses, IRS forms, tax calculators, and related programs and services.

	Annual Growth	4/04	4/05	4/06	4/07	4/08
Est. sales ($ mil.)	—	—	—	—	—	87.6
Employees	—	—	—	—	—	280

JTB HAWAII, INC.

2155 Kalakaua Ave., 9th Fl.
Honolulu, HI 96815
Phone: 808-922-0200
Fax: 808-926-9200
Web: www.jtb-hawaii.com

CEO: Takashi Sugi
CFO: Makiko Dickinson
HR: —
FYE: March 31
Type: Subsidiary

JTB Hawaii wants travelers to say "sayonara" to Japan and "aloha" to Hawaii. The company sells and provides tours to Japanese travelers visiting Hawaii. JTB Hawaii has field offices that facilitate tours, lodging, and activities at locations throughout Hawaii. The company, which is one of the largest Japanese-owned businesses in the Aloha State, is a subsidiary of travel agency JTB. Travel businesses have been affected by the global economic recession, but travel from Japan to Hawaii remains steady. Founded in 1964, JTB Hawaii has offices on Waikiki, Kauai, Maui, and Hawaii's Big Island.

JUGOS DEL VALLE USA, INC.

6633 Portwest Dr., Ste. 100
Houston, TX 77024
Phone: 713-622-2203
Fax: 713-622-2620
Web: www.jvalle.com

CEO: Miguel Longoria Villarreal
CFO: —
HR: —
FYE: December 31
Type: Subsidiary

Jugos del Valle USA, more commonly known as Del Valle, sells fruit juices and nectars. The company's customers range from national supermarket chains to mom-and-pop convenience stores. It also sells to foodservice operators, including restaurants. The company is the American subsidiary of Mexico's juice giant, Jugos Del Valle, which expanded its supply area to the US in 1996 in order to bring its products to the country's growing Mexican and other Latino populations. In 2007 Jugos Del Valle was jointly acquired by Coca-Cola FEMSA (a Mexican Coca-Cola bottler) and The Coca-Cola Company. The deal included the company's US operations.

	Annual Growth	12/04	12/05	12/06	12/07	12/08
Est. sales ($ mil.)	—	—	—	—	—	4.1
Employees	—	—	—	—	—	30

An in-depth profile of this company is available to Hoover's Online members at hoovers.com.

875

JUICY COUTURE, INC.

12723 Wentworth St.
Arleta, CA 91331
Phone: 818-767-0849
Fax: 818-767-1587
Web: www.juicycouture.com

CEO: Edgar O. Huber
CFO: Rob Trauber
HR: Andrew Romeo
FYE: December 31
Type: Subsidiary

Madonna and J-Lo have a Juicy secret. Both have been known to wear the ubiquitous Juicy Couture track suit. The Juicy Couture company, formed by two So-Cal scenesters and originally named Travis Jeans, makes women's T-shirts and other casual attire with a glamorous flair — claiming that women want to be comfortable and feel gorgeous. The apparel firm, owned by Liz Claiborne, has been expanding into swimwear, beachwear, watches, children's and infants' wear, fragrances, and footwear. Juicy Couture brand clothes are distributed throughout the US, Europe, and Asia in about 60 of its own stores, as well as through specialty and high-end department stores, such as Bergdorf Goodman.

THE JUILLIARD SCHOOL

60 Lincoln Center Plaza
New York, NY 10023
Phone: 212-799-5000
Fax: 212-724-0263
Web: www.juilliard.edu

CEO: Joseph W. Polisi
CFO: Christine Todd
HR: Alison Scott-Williams
FYE: June 30
Type: School

The Juilliard School educates some of the top performers from around the world. Students can earn undergraduate and graduate degrees in dance, drama, and music. The school also has an Evening Division that is geared toward working adults as well as a Pre-College Division that meets on Saturdays between September and May. Primarily a performing arts conservatory, the school also enriches the community through outreach and other special programs. Juilliard was founded in 1905 in Greenwich Village and took up residence at Lincoln Center in 1969. Famed alumni include William Hurt, Val Kilmer, Kevin Kline, Laura Linney, Winton Marsalis, Christopher Reeve, Ving Rhames, Nadja Salerno-Sonnenberg, and Robin Williams.

	Annual Growth	6/04	6/05	6/06	6/07	6/08
Est. sales ($ mil.)	—	—	—	—	—	94.8
Employees	—	—	—	—	—	550

JUNIATA VALLEY FINANCIAL CORP.

OTC: JUVF

Bridge and Main Streets
Mifflintown, PA 17059
Phone: 717-436-8211
Fax: 717-436-7551
Web: www.jvbonline.com

CEO: Francis J. Evanitsky
CFO: JoAnn N. McMinn
HR: —
FYE: December 31
Type: Public

Need a bank in Pennsylvania? Juniata Valley Financial may be the place for you. The institution is the holding company for Juniata Valley Bank, which serves central Pennsylvania from about a dozen banking locations. The bank offers standard deposit products and services, including checking and savings accounts, money market accounts, IRAs, and CDs. It also provides credit card services and originates a variety of consumer and business loans. Consumer loans make about 70% of its loan portfolio. Additionally, Juniata Valley Bank sells insurance and investment products. Juniata Valley Bank was established in 1867.

	Annual Growth	12/05	12/06	12/07	12/08	12/09
Assets ($ mil.)	1.9%	410.8	415.9	420.1	428.1	442.1
Net income ($ mil.)	2.6%	4.6	5.0	5.4	5.7	5.1
Market value ($ mil.)	(7.6%)	103.2	90.5	88.2	81.7	75.3
Employees	(1.2%)	145	153	150	150	138

JUNIPER GROUP, INC.

OTC: JUNP

20283 State Rd. 400, Ste. 400
Boca Raton, FL 33498
Phone: 561-482-9327
Fax: —
Web: www.junipergroup.com

CEO: Vlado P. Hreljanovic
CFO: Vlado P. Hreljanovic
HR: —
FYE: December 31
Type: Public

The Juniper Group is hoping to turn over a new leaf. The company primarily provides broadband installation and wireless infrastructure construction services through its Tower West Communications subsidiary, including tower erection and construction, site installation and surveying, and antenna installation. Its clients include national providers of wireless voice, messaging, and data services. Juniper also is involved in film distribution, acquiring motion picture rights from independent producers; that business line accounted for less than 2% of revenues in fiscal 2008.

	Annual Growth	12/05	12/06	12/07	12/08	12/09
Sales ($ mil.)	16.4%	0.6	4.7	1.9	0.6	1.1
Net income ($ mil.)	—	(4.9)	(1.7)	(9.8)	(55.0)	45.7
Market value ($ mil.)	(95.3%)	426,474.8	426,474.8	28,431.7	106.6	2.1
Employees	3.2%	15	15	—	9	17

JUNIPER NETWORKS, INC.

NYSE: JNPR

1194 N. Mathilda Ave.
Sunnyvale, CA 94089
Phone: 408-745-2000
Fax: 408-745-2100
Web: www.juniper.net

CEO: Kevin R. Johnson
CFO: Robyn M. Denholm
HR: Steven Rice
FYE: December 31
Type: Public

Juniper Networks has managed to grow in a landscape dominated by Cisco. The company designs and sells network infrastructure for private and public access networks. Customers use its products to securely deploy and manage services and applications across Internet protocol (IP) networks. The company's product portfolio includes routers, network traffic management software, virtual private network and firewall devices, data center and WAN acceleration tools, intrusion detection and prevention systems, and support services. Juniper sells directly and through resellers to network service providers, enterprises, government agencies, and schools. Customers outside the US account for more than half of Juniper's revenues.

	Annual Growth	12/05	12/06	12/07	12/08	12/09
Sales ($ mil.)	12.6%	2,064.0	2,303.6	2,836.1	3,572.4	3,315.9
Net income ($ mil.)	(24.2%)	354.0	(1,001.4)	360.8	511.7	117.0
Market value ($ mil.)	4.6%	11,732.9	9,965.1	17,467.8	9,212.7	14,032.1
Employees	14.9%	4,145	4,833	5,879	7,014	7,231

JUNO LIGHTING, INC.

1300 S. Wolf Rd.
Des Plaines, IL 60017
Phone: 847-827-9880
Fax: 847-296-4056
Web: www.junolighting.com

CEO: John Mabbott
CFO: John Vitacco
HR: Edward Laginess
FYE: November 30
Type: Subsidiary

Sharing its name with Jupiter's wife, Juno Lighting can bask in the light of its own glow. Juno Lighting makes light fixtures for commercial, institutional, and residential buildings under eight brand names. Its key product lines comprise showcase lighting fixtures, fiber optic lighting products, and emergency and exit lighting signs using light-emitting diode (LED) technology. Juno's other products include recessed and track-lighting systems. Under the Juno and Danalite labels the company offers LED undercabinet and casework lighting products. Juno counts contractors and remodelers as its chief customers. Founded in 1976, the company is a subsidiary of Paris-based giant Schneider Electric.

JUPITER BAND INSTRUMENTS, INC.

11310 Hwy. 290 West
Austin, TX 78737
Phone: 512-288-7400
Fax: 512-288-6445
Web: www.jupitermusic.com

CEO: Tabor Stamper
CFO: Tom Lawdenski
HR: Tina Peterson
FYE: December 31
Type: Subsidiary

A band of sixth-graders playing musical instruments together for the first time is music to Jupiter Band Instruments' ears. A subsidiary of musical instrument maker K.H.S. Musical Instruments Co. of Taiwan, Jupiter Band Instruments is the US distributor for Jupiter brand woodwinds and brass instruments, including flutes, trumpets, saxophones, and trombones, Mapex Drums, and Majestic Percussion. The firm's target markets are primarily students participating in school music programs or music training centers. Jupiter Band Instruments operates its Ross Mallet Instruments subsidiary (a maker of chimes, bells, xylophones, and marimbas) in Wisconsin.

JUPITER MARINE INTERNATIONAL HOLDINGS

Pink Sheets: JMIH

1103 12th Ave. East
Palmetto, FL 34221
Phone: 941-729-5000
Fax: 941-729-5005
Web: www.jupitermarine.com

CEO: Carl Herndon Sr.
CFO: Lawrence S. Tierney
HR: Carisa Albrecht
FYE: July 31
Type: Public

Women are from Venus, men are from Mars, and fishing boats are from Jupiter, as in Jupiter Marine International Holdings, Inc. (JMIH). The company designs and manufactures offshore sport fishing boats under the Jupiter brand name; the nine model lineup ranges in size from a 29-foot forward seating outboard to a 39-foot cruiser. JMIH offers open center console and forward cabin models, as well as yacht-like amenities. A build-a-boat option allows color selection. The company builds all of its boats at its plant in Palmetto, Florida. Products are sold through US dealers, primarily on the East and Gulf Coast. President and CEO Carl Herndon, his family, and CFO Lawrence Tierney collectively own more than half of JMIH.

JUST BORN, INC.

1300 Stefko Blvd.
Bethlehem, PA 18017
Phone: 610-867-7568
Fax: 610-867-9931
Web: www.justborn.com

CEO: David N. Shaffer
CFO: Ronald J. (Ron) Izewski
HR: Mark McLaughlin
FYE: December 31
Type: Private

Just Born gave birth to marshmallow treats for all occasions. The company makes the popular Easter candy, Marshmallow Peeps; these little chick-ettes and bunnies appear in Easter baskets everywhere. The seasonal candy comes in such colors as blue, lavender, pink, white, green, yellow, and orange. In addition, moviegoers will recognize the company's Hot Tamales and Mike and Ike brands. Other candy treats include Just Born Jelly Beans, Teanee Beanee Gourmet jelly beans, and Peanut Chews. Sam Born founded the company in 1923. The family-owned and -operated firm is run by co-CEOs Ross Born (Sam Born's grandson) and David Shaffer (Sam's nephew).

J.W. CHILDS ASSOCIATES, L.P.

111 Huntington Ave., Ste. 2900
Boston, MA 02199
Phone: 617-753-1100
Fax: 617-753-1101
Web: www.jwchilds.com

CEO: John W. Childs
CFO: Jodie Urquhart
HR: —
FYE: December 31
Type: Partnership

J.W. Childs Associates (JWC) makes private equity investment look like mere child's play. The firm, created by four former Thomas H. Lee partners, conducts friendly leveraged buyouts (LBOs) and recapitalizations of middle-market companies with strong brands and prospects for growth. Founded in 1995, it focuses on the consumer products, specialty retail, asset management, and health care sectors. JWC's portfolio includes about a dozen firms, including Advantage Sales and Marketing, CHG Healthcare Services, NutraSweet, Mattress Firm, Sunny Delight Beverages, specialty retailer Brookstone, and menswear line Joseph Abboud.

J. W. MAYS, INC.

NASDAQ (CM): MAYS

9 Bond St.
Brooklyn, NY 11201
Phone: 718-624-7400
Fax: 718-935-0378

CEO: Lloyd J. Shulman
CFO: Mark S. Greenblatt
HR: —
FYE: July 31
Type: Public

J. W. Mays can get you space in Brooklyn, as long as you're interested in offices and not bridges. The company owns and leases about 10 properties in and around New York City — mostly former MAYS department stores — and a warehouse in central Ohio. It leases its properties to retail, restaurant, commercial, and other tenants. The MAYS department store chain, founded in 1924 by Russian immigrant Joe Weinstein, closed in 1989 when management realized the New York real estate it occupied was worth more than the struggling discount retail business. Weinstein's descendants, including CEO Lloyd Shulman, control more than half of the company, although relations among the heirs have not always been harmonious.

	Annual Growth	7/05	7/06	7/07	7/08	7/09
Sales ($ mil.)	6.5%	12.9	13.7	18.2	14.6	16.6
Net income ($ mil.)	27.8%	0.3	1.4	2.1	(0.1)	0.8
Market value ($ mil.)	(1.6%)	32.3	36.3	45.7	36.5	30.2
Employees	(1.1%)	31	30	29	30	—

JWT

466 Lexington Ave.
New York, NY 10017
Phone: 212-210-7000
Fax: 212-210-7770
Web: www.jwt.com

CEO: Bob Jeffrey
CFO: —
HR: —
FYE: December 31
Type: Subsidiary

If you call on this advertising firm, don't bother asking for J. Walter. JWT, formerly J. Walter Thompson, is a leading advertising agency in the US and one of the largest in the world (along with McCann Worldgroup and BBDO Worldwide). It provides creative ad development, campaign management, and strategic planning services to such clients as Ford, Kimberly-Clark, and Shell. JWT also offers brand development and specialized marketing services, including customer relationship marketing, event marketing, and sponsorships. The firm operates in almost 90 countries through more than 200 offices. Founded in 1864, it is one of the flagship agency networks of UK-based media conglomerate WPP Group.

	Annual Growth	12/04	12/05	12/06	12/07	12/08
Est. sales ($ mil.)	—	—	—	—	—	3,725.8
Employees	—	—	—	—	—	9,000

An in-depth profile of this company is available to Hoover's Online members at hoovers.com.

877

K12 INC.

NYSE Arca: LRN

2300 Corporate Park Dr.
Herndon, VA 20171
Phone: 703-483-7000
Fax: 703-483-7330
Web: www.k12.com

CEO: Ronald J. (Ron) Packard
CFO: Keith T. Haas
HR: Howard Allentoff
FYE: June 30
Type: Public

K12 isn't a missing element from the periodic table, but it could help kids learn the periodic table. The "virtual public school" offers online educational programs for some some 40,000 students in kindergarten through 12th grade. Products include online public schools (in 24 states and overseas), course material and product sales directly to parents, and individualized supplemental programs offered through traditional public schools. Web courses cover core subjects such as English, math, science, history and art. K12 targets kids who underperform in public school or can't attend public school because of travel, disabilities, or because they are athletes or performers. CEO Ron Packard founded K12 in 2000.

	Annual Growth	6/05	6/06	6/07	6/08	6/09
Sales ($ mil.)	38.7%	85.3	116.9	140.6	226.2	315.6
Net income ($ mil.)	—	(3.5)	1.4	3.9	33.8	12.3
Market value ($ mil.)	0.2%	—	—	—	654.9	656.1
Employees	21.2%	—	558	636	763	993

KADANT INC.

NYSE: KAI

1 Technology Park Dr.
Westford, MA 01886
Phone: 978-776-2000
Fax: 978-635-1593
Web: www.kadant.com

CEO: Jonathan W. (Jon) Painter
CFO: Thomas M. O'Brien
HR: —
FYE: December 31
Type: Public

Seeking to hear the "Ka-ching" of increased profits, Kadant makes recycling equipment that turns wastepaper into white and brown grades of recycled paper. The company's main products are stock preparation equipment, including pulping and trash removal systems; cleaning, screening, and de-inking systems; accessories to clean the rolls of paper-making equipment and to cut and remove sheets of paper; and equipment that recycles water from pulp slurry and processes reusable fiber. Kadant was spun off from Thermo Electron (now Thermo Fisher Scientific) in 2001. The company gets more than half of its sales outside the US.

	Annual Growth	12/05	12/06	12/07	12/08	12/09
Sales ($ mil.)	(1.9%)	243.7	341.6	366.5	329.2	225.6
Net income ($ mil.)	—	6.9	17.1	22.7	(22.6)	(6.0)
Market value ($ mil.)	(3.6%)	229.9	302.9	368.7	167.5	198.3
Employees	3.4%	1,400	2,000	2,000	1,800	1,600

⊞ KAHALA CORP.

9311 E. Via De Ventura, Ste. 104
Scottsdale, AZ 85258
Phone: 480-362-4800
Fax: —
Web: www.kahalacorp.com

CEO: Kevin Blackwell
CFO: Walt Schultz
HR: —
FYE: December 31
Type: Private

Life is a quick-service beach at Kahala Corp. The company is a leading multi-concept franchisor with about a dozen restaurant brands encompassing about 3,500 locations across the US and in a small number of other countries. Its flagship brands include ice cream purveyor Cold Stone Creamery, the Taco Time Mexican fast-food chain, and Blimpie sub sandwiches. Other concepts include Great Steak & Potato Co. (cheesesteak sandwiches), Surf City Squeeze (smoothies), and Samurai Sam's (Asian-inspired cuisine). Most of Kahala's eateries are typically found in mall food courts, airports, and other high-traffic areas. The company is controlled by chairman Kevin Blackwell and former CFO David Guarino.

KAISER ALUMINUM CORPORATION

NASDAQ (GM): KALU

27422 Portola Pkwy., Ste. 350
Foothill Ranch, CA 92610
Phone: 949-614-1740
Fax: 949-614-1930
Web: www.kaiseral.com

CEO: Jack A. Hockema
CFO: Daniel J. Rinkenberger
HR: James E. McAuliffe
FYE: December 31
Type: Public

Kaiser Aluminum went on a diet, slimmed down considerably, and now operates just 12 fabricated products manufacturing plants in the US and Canada. Kaiser's main customers are in the aerospace, engineering, and transportation markets. The company manufactures more than 500 million pounds of fabricated aluminum products annually. Diversified metal services center Reliance Steel & Aluminum is the company's largest customer, representing almost 20% of sales. It had also participated in a joint venture with Rio Tinto plc called Anglesey Aluminum, which operated a UK aluminum smelting facility. (Kaiser got 49% of Anglesey's production.) The smelter was converted to a secondary remelt and casting operation in 2009.

	Annual Growth	12/05	12/06	12/07	12/08	12/09
Sales ($ mil.)	(2.4%)	1,089.7	667.5	1,504.5	1,508.2	987.0
Net income ($ mil.)	—	(749.0)	26.2	101.0	(68.5)	70.5
Market value ($ mil.)	(9.4%)	—	1,075.4	1,526.3	432.5	799.3
Employees	(3.3%)	2,400	2,425	2,600	2,500	2,100

⊞ KAISER FOUNDATION HEALTH PLAN, INC.

1 Kaiser Plaza
Oakland, CA 94612
Phone: 510-271-5800
Fax: 510-271-6493
Web: www.kaiserpermanente.org

CEO: George C. Halvorson
CFO: Kathy Lancaster
HR: Paul Records
FYE: December 31
Type: Subsidiary

Kaiser Foundation Health Plan aims to be the emperor of the HMO universe. With more than 8.6 million members in nine states and the District of Columbia, it is one of the largest not-for-profit managed health care companies in the US. Kaiser has an integrated care model, offering both hospital and physician care through a network of hospitals and physician practices operating under the Kaiser Permanente name. Members of Kaiser health plans have access to hospitals and hundreds of other health care facilities operated by Kaiser Foundation Hospitals and Permanente Medical Groups; these associations consist of about 14,000 doctors.

	Annual Growth	12/04	12/05	12/06	12/07	12/08
Sales ($ mil.)	9.5%	28,000.0	31,100.0	34,400.0	37,800.0	40,300.0
Employees	3.6%	—	—	156,000	159,766	167,300

KAISER FOUNDATION HEALTH PLAN OF COLORADO

10350 E. Dakota Ave.
Denver, CO 80231
Phone: 303-338-3800
Fax: 303-344-7277
Web: www.kaiserpermanente.org

CEO: Donna Lynne
CFO: James E. (Rick) Newsome
HR: Robin Sadler
FYE: December 31
Type: Subsidiary

Kaiser Foundation Health Plan of Colorado has high hopes for the health of those living in the Mile High City. Also known as Kaiser Permanente Colorado, the division of Kaiser Foundation Health Plan provides health care plans and related services to nearly half a million members living in and around the cities of Colorado Spring, Denver, and Boulder. One of the leading health plan providers in the state, Kaiser Permanente Colorado offers its plans to individuals and businesses large and small. Kaiser Foundation Health Plans have an integrated care model, offering both hospital and physician care through a vast network of hospitals and physician practices operating under the Kaiser and Exempla name.

KAISER PERMANENTE

1 Kaiser Plaza
Oakland, CA 94612
Phone: 510-271-5800
Fax: 510-267-7524
Web: www.kaiserpermanente.org

CEO: George C. Halvorson
CFO: Kathy Lancaster
HR: Ronald Knox
FYE: December 31
Type: Not-for-profit

Kaiser Permanente is out to be a permanent leader in US health care. The not-for-profit entity is among the largest integrated health care systems in the US. The company offers health care services through a network of more than 14,500 physicians belonging to Permanente Medical Groups. Kaiser Permanente also operates about three dozen hospitals and more than 400 medical offices that form the Kaiser Foundation Hospitals. Additionally, the Kaiser Foundation Health Plan covers millions of people with a range of health plans, most of which are in California. Founded in 1945, the company operates nationwide, though its business operations are largely concentrated along the West Coast.

	Annual Growth	12/04	12/05	12/06	12/07	12/08
Sales ($ mil.)	9.5%	28,000.0	31,100.0	34,400.0	37,800.0	40,300.0
Employees	4.5%	140,356	148,884	156,853	159,766	167,300

KAISER-FRANCIS OIL COMPANY

6733 S. Yale Ave.
Tulsa, OK 74136
Phone: 918-494-0000
Fax: 918-491-4694
Web: www.kfoc.net

CEO: George B. Kaiser
CFO: Don Millican
HR: Gwen Johnson
FYE: June 30
Type: Private

King of the Tulsa oil patch, oil and gas exploration and production independent Kaiser-Francis Oil Company buys, sells, and develops oil and gas properties, primarily in Arkansas, Colorado, Kansas, Nebraska, New Mexico, North Dakota, Oklahoma, Oregon, Texas, West Virginia, and Wyoming. The company teamed up with fellow Tulsa-based energy firm SemGas LP to help build the Wyckoff Gas Storage facility (6 billion cu. ft. of working gas storage) in Steuben County, New York. Local billionaire George Kaiser owns and manages Kaiser-Francis Oil. In 2009 Forbes pegged George Kaiser's estimated wealth at $9.5 billion.

	Annual Growth	6/04	6/05	6/06	6/07	6/08
Est. sales ($ mil.)	—	—	—	—	—	247.1
Employees	—	—	—	—	—	2,067

KAJIMA USA INC.

395 W. Passaic St.
Rochelle Park, NJ 07662
Phone: 201-518-2100
Fax: 201-518-1539
Web: www.kajimausa.com

CEO: Keisuke (KC) Koshijima
CFO: —
HR: —
FYE: March 31
Type: Subsidiary

US businesses are saying *konichiwa* to Kajima USA. The planning, design, construction, and real estate development company is the North American arm of Japan-based Kajima, one of the world's largest global contractors. Established in 1961, Kajima USA has about 10 group companies, including The Austin Company, KBD Group, Hawaiian Dredging Construction, Anglebrook Golf Club, and KUD International. Its clients have included Costco, Federal Express, Hitachi, Mazda, and Mitsubishi Motors. In 2008 Kajima USA increased its presence in the Southeast by acquiring construction services firm Batson-Cook.

	Annual Growth	3/04	3/05	3/06	3/07	3/08
Est. sales ($ mil.)	—	—	—	—	—	1,479.9
Employees	—	—	—	—	—	1,005

KALAS MANUFACTURING, INC.

25 Main St.
Denver, PA 17517
Phone: 717-336-5575
Fax: 717-336-4248
Web: www.kalaswire.com

CEO: Richard P. (Paul) Witwer
CFO: Dennis M. Melnyk
HR: —
FYE: October 31
Type: Private

Calling it as it sees it for over half a century, Kalas Manufacturing makes a living out of cable and wire. Also known as Kalas Wire, the company produces and distributes an electrical wire and cable lineup integral to bulk and irrigation wire, engineered battery cable, and submersible pump cable applications. Operating through three plants in Denver, Pennsylvania, and one in Lancaster, the company touts flexible production capacity for making wire and cable used in a diversity of markets, from household appliances to industrial construction and marine equipment, and recreational vehicles. Customers are courted worldwide through authorized distributors. The founding Witwer family owns and leads Kalas.

KALIL BOTTLING CO.

931 S. Highland Ave.
Tucson, AZ 85719
Phone: 520-624-1788
Fax: 520-623-6662
Web: www.kalilbottling.com

CEO: George Kalil
CFO: William (Bill) Ourand
HR: —
FYE: December 31
Type: Private

Kalil Bottling has been all in the family since 1948. President George Kalil grew up learning the business from his father and grandfather. Today, Kalil oversees a company that serves Arizona and parts of Colorado, New Mexico, and west Texas, supplying retail customers with a variety of beverages. Among its offerings are thirst-quenchers such as AriZona teas, Arrowhead water, and Vernors ginger ale, along with more widely known brands, including Gatorade, Big Red, 7UP, Snapple, and Sunkist. The company operates out of its production facility in Tucson, Arizona, and has four distribution warehouses — one each in Tucson, Phoenix, and Flagstaff, Arizona, and El Paso, Texas.

KAMAN CORPORATION

NASDAQ (GM): KAMN

1332 Blue Hills Ave.
Bloomfield, CT 06002
Phone: 860-243-7100
Fax: 860-243-6365
Web: www.kaman.com

CEO: Neal J. Keating
CFO: William C. Denninger Jr.
HR: Lowell J. Hill
FYE: December 31
Type: Public

Kaman makes fixed and rotary wing aircraft, but it's the distribution of 3 million industrial items that makes the company fly. After reorganizing in 2009 the company operates through two segments. Industrial Distribution supplies power transmission/motion control industrial products, while the Aerospace segment manufactures Kaman-branded aircraft bearings and components, and metallic/composite aerostructures for commercial, military, and general aviation fixed and rotary wing aircraft. It also makes safety, arming, and fuzing devices for missile and bomb systems for the US and its allies. Customers include Airbus, Bell, BAE Systems, Boeing, Lockheed Martin, Raytheon, and Sikorsky.

	Annual Growth	12/05	12/06	12/07	12/08	12/09
Sales ($ mil.)	1.0%	1,101.2	1,206.2	1,086.0	1,253.6	1,146.2
Net income ($ mil.)	42.7%	13.0	31.8	55.9	35.6	53.9
Market value ($ mil.)	4.1%	510.5	580.5	954.3	470.0	598.6
Employees	2.1%	3,712	3,906	3,618	4,294	4,032

KANA SOFTWARE, INC.

181 Constitution Dr.
Menlo Park, CA 94025
Phone: 650-614-8300
Fax: 650-614-8301
Web: www.kana.com

CEO: Mark A. Duffell
CFO: Jay A. Jones
HR: —
FYE: December 31
Type: Private

Kana Software thinks good customer service can be just one click away. The company's customer relationship management (CRM) software is used by call centers and e-commerce websites. Kana's software capabilities include customer service interaction through live Web chat, e-mail, telephone, and self-serve portals. It also offers applications that assist with and guide agents through conversations with customers. Kana Software serves companies in the telecommunications, manufacturing, financial services, and health care industries. In 2009 the company's assets and liabilities were acquired by private equity firm Accel-KKR for about $40 million in cash.

	Annual Growth	12/05	12/06	12/07	12/08	12/09
Sales ($ mil.)	1.3%	43.1	54.0	60.8	65.2	45.3
Net income ($ mil.)	—	(18.0)	(2.4)	(8.0)	(3.7)	34.9
Employees	(71.6%)	306	181	225	229	2

K&G MEN'S COMPANY, INC

1225 Chattahoochee Ave. NW
Atlanta, GA 30318
Phone: 404-351-7987
Fax: 404-351-8038
Web: www.kgmens.com

CEO: Mary Beth Blake
CFO: —
HR: Lori Robinson
FYE: January 31
Type: Subsidiary

Well suited for its customers' shopping habits, K&G Men's Company operates about 105 deep-discount career apparel superstores in more than 25 states. Its stores feature brand-name and private-label tailored and casual clothing, footwear, and accessories. The bargain warehouse-type stores average about 23,000 sq. ft. and offer first-run merchandise at prices 30%-60% lower than department stores. Founded in 1989, The Men's Wearhouse purchased K&G in 1999, converted most of its value outlets to the K&G Fashion Superstores banner, and began adding women's apparel to stores.

K&L GATES LLP

Henry W. Oliver Bldg., 535 Smithfield St.
Pittsburgh, PA 15222
Phone: 412-355-6500
Fax: 412-355-6501
Web: www.klgates.com

CEO: Peter J. Kalis
CFO: Glenn H. Graner
HR: Rick Jones
FYE: December 31
Type: Partnership

With about 1,800 lawyers and more than 35 offices located in North America, Europe, and Asia, K&L Gates represents a number of major multinational companies, large banks and mutual funds, and public sector entities. The firm divides its wide array of practices into six main areas: corporate and transactional; intellectual property; financial services; litigation and dispute resolution; real estate; and regulatory and policy. Clients have included Garuda Indonesia and Leed Petroleum. K&L Gates took its current shape in 2007 when Kirkpatrick & Lockhart Nicholson Graham merged with Preston Gates & Ellis. In March 2009, K&L Gates bought Chicago-based Bell Boyd, & Lloyd, which added about 200 lawyers to its firm.

KANEMATSU USA INC.

75 Rockefeller Plaza, 22nd Fl.
New York, NY 10019
Phone: 212-704-9400
Fax: 212-704-9483
Web: www.kanematsuusa.com

CEO: Hiroshi Iwakuma
CFO: Yoshio Tajima
HR: —
FYE: March 31
Type: Subsidiary

Kanematsu is a *sogo shosa* American style. The general trading company helps global industries import and export goods, as well as locate suppliers. Its major business operations are electronics, steel and metals, food products, chemicals, textiles, and aerospace. It assists companies in unfamiliar markets and in finding high-quality suppliers. Kanematsu assists US manufacturers with such services as logistics, financing, marketing, and research and development. The company originated in Texas as a branch of the Gosho Company in 1910 and is a subsidiary of Japan-based Kanematsu Corporation; it has nine branches throughout the US. Kanematsu Corporation was established in 1889.

	Annual Growth	3/04	3/05	3/06	3/07	3/08
Est. sales ($ mil.)	—	—	—	—	—	415.5
Employees	—	—	—	—	—	150

KANSAS CITY LIFE INSURANCE COMPANY

NASDAQ (CM): KCLI

3520 Broadway
Kansas City, MO 64111
Phone: 816-753-7000
Fax: 816-753-0138
Web: www.kclife.com

CEO: R. Philip Bixby
CFO: Tracy W. Knapp
HR: Charles R. Duffy Jr.
FYE: December 31
Type: Public

They're not just standing on the corner of 12th Street and Vine! Kansas City Life Insurance and subsidiary Sunset Life provide insurance products throughout the US to individuals (life and disability coverage and annuities) and to groups (life, dental, vision, and disability insurance). The companies sell through independent agents, brokers, and third-party marketers. Subsidiary Old American Insurance focuses on burial and related insurance. Kansas City Life Insurance also offers brokerage and investment services through its Sunset Financial Services unit. CEO Philip Bixby and his family control the company.

	Annual Growth	12/05	12/06	12/07	12/08	12/09
Assets ($ mil.)	(2.2%)	4,559.0	4,460.4	4,352.1	3,967.1	4,176.2
Net income ($ mil.)	(26.3%)	36.2	36.9	35.7	(17.0)	10.7
Market value ($ mil.)	(12.2%)	575.7	575.7	501.1	498.4	342.0
Employees	(4.7%)	541	537	527	512	447

⊞ KANSAS CITY SOUTHERN

NYSE: KSU

427 W. 12th St.
Kansas City, MO 64105
Phone: 816-983-1303
Fax: 816-983-1108
Web: www.kcsi.com

CEO: Michael R. (Mike) Haverty
CFO: Michael W. (Mike) Upchurch
HR: John E. Derry
FYE: December 31
Type: Public

Kansas City Southern (KCS) rides the rails of a 6,000-mile network that stretches from Missouri to Mexico. The company's Kansas City Southern Railway (KCSR) owns and operates more than 3,200 miles of track in the midwestern and southern US. KCS offers rail freight service in Mexico through Kansas City Southern de México (KCSM, formerly TFM), which maintains more than 2,600 miles of track and serves three major ports. Another KCS unit, Texas Mexican Railway, connects the KCSR and KCSM systems. The KCS railroads transport such freight as industrial and consumer products, agricultural and mineral products, and chemical and petroleum products.

	Annual Growth	12/05	12/06	12/07	12/08	12/09
Sales ($ mil.)	2.3%	1,352.0	1,659.7	1,742.8	1,852.1	1,480.2
Net income ($ mil.)	(13.3%)	100.9	108.9	153.8	168.7	57.0
Market value ($ mil.)	8.0%	2,362.7	2,802.7	3,320.1	1,842.4	3,219.6
Employees	18.8%	3,060	6,470	6,485	6,400	6,100

THE KANSAS CITY SOUTHERN RAILWAY COMPANY

427 W. 12th St.
Kansas City, MO 64121
Phone: 816-983-1303
Fax: 816-983-1446
Web: www.kcsi.com

CEO: David L. Starling
CFO: Michael W. (Mike) Upchurch
HR: John E. Derry
FYE: December 31
Type: Subsidiary

The primary subsidiary of Kansas City Southern (KCS), Kansas City Southern Railway (KCSR) transports freight over a network of more than 3,200 miles of track in the midwestern and southern US. The company's system spans parts of Alabama, Arkansas, Illinois, Kansas, Louisiana, Mississippi, Missouri, Oklahoma, Tennessee, and Texas. Freight carried by KCSR includes general commodities (agricultural and mineral products, chemical and petroleum products, and forest products and minerals), coal, intermodal containers, and motor vehicles. Through another KCS unit, Texas Mexican Railway, KCSR connects with sister company Kansas City Southern de México (KCSM), a major Mexican rail carrier. KCSR was founded in 1887.

KANSAS STATE UNIVERSITY

105 Anderson Hall
Manhattan, KS 66506
Phone: 785-532-6226
Fax: 785-532-6693
Web: www.ksu.edu

CEO: Jon Wefald
CFO: —
HR: —
FYE: June 30
Type: School

K-State is a big deal in the Little Apple. Located in Manhattan, Kansas (aka the Little Apple), Kansas State University (K-State) is a land grant institution that has an enrollment of more than 23,000 students. It offers more than 250 undergraduate majors, 65 graduate degrees, 45 doctoral degrees, and more than 20 graduate certificate programs. Notable alumni include former White House press secretary Marlin Fitzwater and actor Gordon Jump. Along with the University of Kansas and other universities, technical schools, and community colleges in the state, K-State is governed by The Kansas Board of Regents.

	Annual Growth	6/04	6/05	6/06	6/07	6/08
Est. sales ($ mil.)	—	—	—	—	—	411.7
Employees	—	—	—	—	—	5,168

THE KANTAR GROUP

501 Kings Hwy. East, 4th Fl.
Fairfield, CT 06825
Phone: 203-330-5200
Fax: 203-330-5201
Web: www.kantargroup.com

CEO: Eric Salama
CFO: Robert Bowtell
HR: Chris Robinson
FYE: December 31
Type: Business segment

The Kantar Group, a division of advertising giant WPP Group, is one of the world's largest market research organizations. It operates across 160 offices through some 20 specialist companies in 80 countries, including Millward Brown, Lightspeed Research, Cannondale Associates, The Futures Company, The Ziment Group, and Research International. The group offers a wide range of custom and syndicated research services covering such sectors as business-to-business, financial services, health care, and retail. Kantar also encompasses brand consultancies, demographics firms, and media researchers. In late 2008, WPP acquired TNS (formerly Taylor Nelson Sofres) and folded it under Kantar's operations.

KANTHAL CORPORATION

1 Commerce Blvd.
Palm Coast, FL 32164
Phone: 386-445-2000
Fax: 386-446-2244
Web: www.kanthalpalmcoast.com

CEO: Phil Yu
CFO: —
HR: —
FYE: December 31
Type: Subsidiary

Kanthal Corporation wants to get you heated up. Kanthal (dba Kanthal Palm Coast) is a part of Kanthal AB, itself a subsidiary of Sandvik's Materials Technology unit. Kanthal has four lines of wire products: heating/resistance (used to regulate electricity), conductive alloys (aluminum, beryllium, and copper wire), medical (gold and platinum plated for use in catheters, implants, and sensor coils), and specialty (custom designs). Its precision and ultra-fine wire products are used in electronics, aerospace applications, disk drives, and medical devices. Kanthal's manufacturing facility is located in Florida; capabilities include wire drawing, annealing, plating, anodizing, and roll milling.

KANTHAL GLOBAR

495 Commerce Dr., Ste. 7
Amherst, NY 14228
Phone: 716-691-4010
Fax: 716-691-7850
Web: www.globar.com

CEO: Brian Tierney
CFO: —
HR: —
FYE: December 31
Type: Subsidiary

Kanthal Globar markets high-temperature ceramic products for industrial and residential applications. The company's product lines serve two main categories including electronic components, such as resistors (produce charges), capacitors (store charges), and thermistors; electric heating elements for furnaces comprise the second category. Kanthal Globar is a subsidiary of Sweden's Kanthal AB, which in turn is a part of Sandvik AB, a manufacturer of tools and materials for the mining and construction industries. Kanthal Globar is part of Sandvik's Materials Technology business area.

KANZAKI SPECIALTY PAPERS INC.

20 Cummings St.
Ware, MA 01082
Phone: 413-967-6204
Fax: 413-967-5723
Web: www.kanzakiusa.com

CEO: Stephen P. Hefner
CFO: Alan Livingston
HR: Kevin D. Moriarty
FYE: March 31
Type: Subsidiary

Kanzaki Specialty Papers manufactures surface-coated materials and specialty papers. The company primarily uses thermal technology, which applies a coating to paper that makes for a high-definition image when heat is applied. The process also results in a longer-lasting product that is more resistant to decay from environmental elements (heat, humidity, and water) that can damage paper over time. The company's products include imaging paper used in computer printers, copiers, and fax machines. Kanzaki also produces adhesive labels for retail and postage use, prescription labels, and tickets for public transportation applications. The company, established in 1986, is a subsidiary of Tokyo-based Oji Paper Co.

KAO BRANDS COMPANY

2535 Spring Grove Ave.
Cincinnati, OH 45214
Phone: 513-421-1400
Fax: 513-263-7328
Web: www.kaobrands.com

CEO: William J. (Bill) Gentner
CFO: Joe Workman
HR: —
FYE: March 31
Type: Subsidiary

Kao Brands wants to keep its customers clean and feeling fresh. The company, pronounced "cow," formulates and manufactures personal care products for men and women. Its brand portfolio includes Jergens and Curél creams and lotions, John Frieda and Guhl hair care products, Bioré facial cleansers and strips, and Ban antiperspirants and deodorants. Kao Brands maintains operations in North America, Europe, Australia, and the Middle East, marketing its products in more than 50 countries. It was founded in 1882 as the Jergens Soap Company and primarily made coconut oil soap. More than a century later the firm became a subsidiary of Japan's Kao Corporation and adopted the Kao Brands name.

KAPLAN, INC.

888 7th Ave.
New York, NY 10106
Phone: 212-492-5800
Fax: 212-492-5933
Web: www.kaplan.com

CEO: Andrew S. (Andy) Rosen
CFO: Matthew C. Seelye
HR: Alison Rutledge-Parisi
FYE: December 31
Type: Subsidiary

Kaplan will put you to the test. The Washington Post subsidiary is perhaps best known for its test-preparation publications, which help students prepare for college and graduate school entrance exams, including the SAT, GRE, LSAT, and MCAT. Kaplan also offers prep courses at some 160 locations in North America and Europe. The bigger story for the company, though, is higher education, which accounts for more than half of its revenues. Kaplan University provides online undergraduate, graduate, and professional (including law) degrees in the US and abroad, primarily through Kaplan University. Additionally, Kaplan offers professional development and compliance training for the financial services, real estate, and IT sectors.

THE KAPLAN THALER GROUP, LTD.

Worldwide Plaza, 825 8th Ave., 34th Fl.
New York, NY 10019
Phone: 212-474-5000
Fax: 212-474-5702
Web: www.kaplanthaler.com

CEO: Linda Kaplan
CFO: Kevin Sweeney
HR: Susan Lauher
FYE: December 31
Type: Subsidiary

Customers call on ad agencies to create buzz, but only this one can create KTG Buzz. The Kaplan Thaler Group is a leading creative advertising agency that not only develops ad campaigns but helps promote those ads in the media through its KTG Buzz unit. The initiative creates public interest in its campaigns and also scores free media time for its clients. In addition to creative development, the firm offers planning and campaign management services, as well as branded entertainment development. CEO Linda Kaplan Thaler started the agency in 1997. It is now a subsidiary of Paris-based advertising conglomerate Publicis.

KAPSTONE PAPER AND PACKAGING CORPORATION

NYSE: KS

1101 Skokie Blvd., Ste. 300
Northbrook, IL 60062
Phone: 847-239-8800
Fax: 847-205-7551
Web: www.kapstonepaper.com

CEO: Roger W. Stone
CFO: Andrea K. Tarbox
HR: —
FYE: December 31
Type: Public

For KapStone Paper and Packaging's customers, it's a wrap! Focused mainly on producing unbleached kraft paper (strong wrapping paper) and linerboard (a type of paperboard), the company serves customers that convert its paper products into grocery bags and packaging for pet food, agricultural products, and cement and chemicals, among other materials. Graphic Packaging accounts for about 11% of sales. KapStone's pulp and paper mill in North Carolina operates with an annual capacity of about 440,000 tons. The company also markets dimensional lumber. About two-thirds of sales are made in the US. Established in 2005, KapStone has grown through acquisitions.

	Annual Growth	12/05	12/06	12/07	12/08	12/09
Sales ($ mil.)	56.9%	—	—	256.8	524.5	632.5
Net income ($ mil.)	72.5%	—	—	27.0	19.7	80.3
Market value ($ mil.)	18.5%	—	—	321.1	109.2	450.9
Employees	50.1%	—	—	710	1,750	1,600

KAR AUCTION SERVICES, INC.

NYSE: KAR

13085 Hamilton Crossing Blvd.
Carmel, IN 46032
Phone: 317-815-1100
Fax: 317-843-4898
Web: karauctionservices.com

CEO: James P. (Jim) Hallett
CFO: Eric M. Loughmiller
HR: —
FYE: December 31
Type: Public

KAR Auction Services is not a used car lot, but it sells more than 3 million used cars through subsidiaries. Formed in 2007, KAR is a holding company for ADESA, a wholesaler of used vehicles at auction; Insurance Auto Auctions, a salvage auto auction company; and Automotive Finance Corporation, a capital funding business, which serves used car dealers. In addition to some 215 physical auction sites throughout North America, KAR also hosts Internet auctions. The company makes money through auction fees extended to vehicle buyers and sellers and by providing add-on services such as inspections, storage, transportation, reconditioning, salvage recovery, and titling. KAR Auction Services went public in late 2009.

	Annual Growth	12/05	12/06	12/07	12/08	12/09
Sales ($ mil.)	6.3%	—	1,440.0	1,102.8	1,771.4	1,729.6
Net income ($ mil.)	—	—	—	(38.3)	(216.2)	23.2
Market value ($ mil.)	—	—	—	—	—	1,856.1
Employees	(1.1%)	—	13,076	11,000	13,102	12,648

KARSTEN MANUFACTURING CORPORATION

2201 W. Desert Cove
Phoenix, AZ 85029
Phone: 602-870-5000
Fax: 602-687-4482
Web: www.pinggolf.com

CEO: John A Solheim
CFO: Mike Trueblood
HR: Barry Woodbrey
FYE: December 31
Type: Private

If there's a PING in your putt, it's got to be Karsten Manufacturing. The company designs and produces customized PING golf clubs. (The clubs are named for the sound they make when striking the ball.) The company also makes golf bags, gloves, headwear, and related gear. It provides club-fitting services, systems, and training at golf courses and pro shops across the US, as well as an online fitting program. Professionals from all over the world swing with PING, including Phil Mickelson, Sherri Steinhauer, Angel Cabrera, and Lorena Ochoa. Karsten Manufacturing was founded in 1959 after Karsten Solheim designed a revolutionary putter in his garage. His youngest son, John, leads the family-owned company.

KASENNA, INC.

1196 Borregas Ave., Ste. 100
Sunnyvale, CA 94089
Phone: 650-943-8600
Fax: 408-747-1025
Web: www.kasenna.com

CEO: Vivek Pendharkar
CFO: Pablo Luther
HR: —
FYE: December 31
Type: Subsidiary

Need to send video content? Kasenna can help. The company develops and markets video delivery software for companies in such industries as broadcast, media, and telecommunications; it also serves systems integrators and developers. Kasenna's MediaBase and PortalTV products enable the delivery of video content across communications networks. It various functions include the acquisition, distribution, and management of video content. Customers include CNN in the US, NHK in Japan, and Sasktel in Canada. Kasenna also provides professional services such as consulting, training, and support. The company is a subsidiary of Canada-based IPTV specialist Espial Group.

	Annual Growth	12/04	12/05	12/06	12/07	12/08
Est. sales ($ mil.)	—	—	—	—	—	9.1
Employees	—	—	—	—	—	100

KATE SPADE LLC

48 W. 25th St.
New York, NY 10010
Phone: 212-739-6550
Fax: 212-739-6544
Web: www.katespade.com

CEO: Craig Leavitt
CFO: —
HR: Elyce Arons
FYE: July 31
Type: Subsidiary

kate spade's story is one of simplicity, like the bags it sells. Begun by designer Kate Spade and her husband, Andy, in 1993, signature kate spade bags were an instant success because of their uncomplicated design. Since then, the manufacturer has expanded into stationery, various functional bags (think diaper bags), and licensing — with lines of homewares (sheets, tabletop items, and wallpaper), as well as beauty products, eyewear, and shoes. Women's items are sold under the kate spade name while men's products carry the jack spade moniker. The company, which is owned by Liz Claiborne, distributes its products in Asia and sells them in the US through about 50 of its own shops and in upscale department stores.

KATY INDUSTRIES, INC.

OTC: KATY

305 Rock Industrial Park Dr.
Bridgeton, MO 63044
Phone: 314-656-4321
Fax: 314-656-4398
Web: www.katyindustries.com

CEO: David J. Feldman
CFO: James W. (Jim) Shaffer
HR: Joseph E. Mata
FYE: December 31
Type: Public

Katy Industries gives janitors the tools to clean up the acts of others. The firm makes and markets commercial cleaning products as well as plastic home storage products. Its Continental Commercial Products (CCP) subsidiary operates six divisions: Contico, Disco, Glit, Wilen, CCP Canada, and Gemtex. Its customers include janitorial/sanitary and food service distributors that supply restaurants, hotels, schools and other facilities. CCP operates in Missouri, California, and Georgia, as well as in Canada. Its products are sold under the Continental, Kleen Aire, Huskee, KingKan, Unibody, SuperKan, and Tilt-N-Wheel brand names. Since its 1967 founding, Katy Industries has sold everything from shrimp to shoes.

	Annual Growth	12/05	12/06	12/07	12/08	12/09
Sales ($ mil.)	(25.4%)	455.2	396.2	187.8	167.8	141.2
Net income ($ mil.)	—	(13.2)	(11.2)	(1.5)	(16.5)	(6.1)
Market value ($ mil.)	(13.3%)	24.6	21.3	15.9	9.1	13.9
Employees	(19.8%)	1,544	1,172	920	680	639

KAVLICO CORPORATION

14501 Princeton Ave.
Moorpark, CA 93021
Phone: 805-523-2000
Fax: 805-523-7125
Web: www.kavlico.com

CEO: Bob Ciurczak
CFO: —
HR: Angelo Vidalis
FYE: December 31
Type: Subsidiary

Kavlico manufactures sensors for pressure, position, force, level, tilt, and media quality systems. Its products are designed for use in a wide range of markets, including automotive, HVAC, industrial vehicles, marine, medical equipment, military/aerospace, and power generation. Other applications include wastewater monitoring and emission control. Kavlico is a subsidiary of Custom Sensors & Technologies and a global business unit of Schneider Electric. Kavlico was founded in 1958 by Norwegian immigrant Fred Kavli.

KAWASAKI RAIL CAR, INC.

29 Wells Ave., Bldg. 4
Yonkers, NY 10701
Phone: 914-376-4700
Fax: 914-376-4779
Web: www.kawasakirailcar.com

CEO: Matichi Sakai
CFO: —
HR: —
FYE: March 31
Type: Subsidiary

Like the Little Engine that Could, Kawasaki Rail's hard work and high hopes drive performance. The company manufactures passenger railcars including rapid transit and commuter cars, light rail and monorail cars, and high-speed (bullet) trains. Diesel and electric locomotives are made, as well as screen door systems that make transition from passenger platform to train safe and wind protected. Major customers are the Port Authority Trans-Hudson (PATH), MTA Metro-North and State of Connecticut, Maryland MTA, Virginia Railway Express, and the Massachusetts Bay Railroad. The company operates factories in Yonkers, New York, and Lincoln, Nebraska. Kawasaki Rail is a subsidiary of Japan-based Kawasaki Heavy Industries.

KAYDON CORPORATION

NYSE: KDN

315 E. Eisenhower Pkwy., Ste. 300
Ann Arbor, MI 48108
Phone: 734-747-7025
Fax: 734-747-6565
Web: www.kaydon.com

CEO: James O'Leary
CFO: Peter C. DeChants
HR: Anthony T. Behrman
FYE: December 31
Type: Public

Just about everything has a bearing on the business of Kaydon Corporation. The company custom designs, engineers, and manufactures bearings and bearing systems, slip rings, filtration products, and seals. Kaydon operates in three segments: friction and motion control products (anti-friction bearings, split roller bearings, and specialty balls), velocity control products (industrial shock absorbers and velocity controls), and sealing products (engine rings and shaft seals). Other products include metal alloys, machine tool components, presses, dies, and benders. These tap a diverse customer base — aerospace to defense and construction markets — for use in a range of robotics and material handling applications.

	Annual Growth	12/05	12/06	12/07	12/08	12/09
Sales ($ mil.)	5.6%	354.6	404.0	451.4	522.4	441.1
Net income ($ mil.)	(11.2%)	73.9	69.5	77.7	67.1	46.0
Market value ($ mil.)	2.7%	1,075.0	1,329.1	1,824.1	1,148.9	1,196.0
Employees	3.7%	1,800	1,900	2,125	2,420	2,084

KAZ, INC.

1775 Broadway, Ste. 2405
New York, NY 10019
Phone: 212-586-1630
Fax: 212-265-9248
Web: www.kaz.com

CEO: Richard Katzman
CFO: Jon Kosheff
HR: —
FYE: December 31
Type: Private

Kaz has built a business that allows its customers to blow off a little steam. The company makes humidifiers, vaporizers, air purifiers and filters, thermometers, heating pads, steam facial machines, and lawn and garden items. Its products, made under the Kaz, Honeywell, Stinger, Softheat, and Vicks brands, are sold worldwide through its website and through drug retailers and mass merchants such as CVS, Kmart, Target, and Wal-Mart. Vicks is licensed from Procter & Gamble, which in 2006 sold its Braun thermometers and blood pressure monitoring business to Kaz. Max Katzman invented the first electric vaporizer and founded Kaz in 1926; his grandson Richard is CEO.

	Annual Growth	12/04	12/05	12/06	12/07	12/08
Est. sales ($ mil.)	—	—	—	—	—	436.0
Employees	—	—	—	—	—	2,500

🎛 KB HOME

NYSE: KBH

10990 Wilshire Blvd.
Los Angeles, CA 90024
Phone: 310-231-4000
Fax: 310-231-4222
Web: www.kbhome.com

CEO: Jeffrey T. (Jeff) Mezger
CFO: Jeff Kaminski
HR: Thomas F. (Tom) Norton
FYE: November 30
Type: Public

For a dwelling done your way, you might turn to KB Home. KB builds houses mainly for first-time, trade-up, and active adult buyers primarily in the West, Southwest, and along the East Coast. The company markets houses under its Built to Order brand, which allows buyers to customize their homes by choosing a floor plan as well as exterior and interior features. The average selling price of a KB home is around $207,000. KB offers attached and detached single-family homes, in addition to townhomes and condos. It offers financing, mortgage assistance, title, and insurance through its KB Home Mortgage, a joint venture with Bank of America. KB has built more than a half a million homes since it was founded in 1957.

	Annual Growth	11/05	11/06	11/07	11/08	11/09
Sales ($ mil.)	(33.7%)	9,441.7	11,003.8	6,416.5	3,033.9	1,824.8
Net income ($ mil.)	—	842.4	482.4	(929.4)	(976.1)	(101.8)
Market value ($ mil.)	(33.6%)	6,141.6	4,550.1	1,838.9	1,023.7	1,192.8
Employees	(32.4%)	6,700	5,100	3,100	1,600	1,400

KBR, INC.

NYSE: KBR

601 Jefferson St., Ste. 3400
Houston, TX 77002
Phone: 713-753-3011
Fax: 713-753-5353
Web: www.kbr.com

CEO: William P. (Bill) Utt
CFO: Susan K. (Sue) Carter
HR: Klaudia J. Brace
FYE: December 31
Type: Public

If you thought KBR was only about government contracts in Iraq, think again. The construction and engineering company operates in more than 45 countries through six business units: upstream and downstream petrochemical and energy services, government and infrastructure, management services, technology, and ventures. Although its US government contracts in Iraq account for about 35% of its sales, the company is devoting more of its time to other civil engineering and construction operations. KBR builds, designs, and manages airports and energy and chemical plants; provides engineering, environmental, and transportation services; performs security and threat analyses; and designs and manages urban rail projects.

	Annual Growth	12/05	12/06	12/07	12/08	12/09
Sales ($ mil.)	4.4%	10,206.0	9,633.0	8,745.0	11,581.0	12,105.0
Net income ($ mil.)	11.0%	240.0	168.0	302.0	319.0	364.0
Market value ($ mil.)	(10.1%)	—	4,201.1	6,231.0	2,441.0	3,051.3
Employees	(5.0%)	62,500	56,000	52,000	57,000	51,000

KBW, INC.

NYSE: KBW

The Equitable Bldg., 787 7th Ave., 4th Fl.
New York, NY 10019
Phone: 212-887-7777
Fax: 212-541-6668
Web: www.kbw.com

CEO: John G. Duffy
CFO: Robert (Bob) Giambrone
HR: —
FYE: December 31
Type: Public

KBW is an investment bank for bankers. Clients of the firm include banks, insurance companies, broker/dealers, asset managers, and others in the financial services sector. The company specializes in investment banking; securities sales and trading; and research. Operating through subsidiary Keefe, Bruyette & Woods, KBW provides mergers and acquisitions advice, securities underwriting, and structured finance. KBW Asset Management offers investment advisory services to financial institutions and other institutional clients, as well as to wealthy individuals.

	Annual Growth	12/05	12/06	12/07	12/08	12/09
Sales ($ mil.)	5.4%	307.9	406.6	427.5	242.2	379.4
Net income ($ mil.)	7.9%	17.4	53.3	27.3	(62.3)	23.6
Market value ($ mil.)	(2.4%)	—	1,042.5	907.7	815.8	970.5
Employees	4.8%	430	455	529	529	518

🎛 KEANE INC.

100 City Square
Boston, MA 02129
Phone: 617-241-9200
Fax: 617-241-9507
Web: www.keane.com

CEO: John W. McCain
CFO: David A. Kaminsky
HR: Renee Southard
FYE: December 31
Type: Private

This company's customers are eager to have someone else look after their technology systems. Keane is a leading provider of information technology outsourcing and consulting services. It manages enterprise information systems and provides system integration services for both private and public sector. Keane also offers a range of business process outsourcing (BPO) services, as well as application development, consulting, project management, and strategic staffing. The company, which does much of its business in the US, counts agencies of the federal government among its top customers. Keane also operates internationally from about 30 offices in 11 countries in Europe and the Asia/Pacific region.

	Annual Growth	12/04	12/05	12/06	12/07	12/08
Sales ($ mil.)	(4.7%)	—	—	1,100.0	1,200.0	1,000.0
Employees	(7.4%)	—	—	14,000	13,600	12,000

KEARNY FINANCIAL CORP.

NASDAQ (GS): KRNY

120 Passaic Ave.
Fairfield, NJ 07004
Phone: 973-244-4500
Fax: —
Web: www.kearnyfederalsavings.com

CEO: Craig L. Montanaro
CFO: William C. (Bill) Ledgerwood
HR: —
FYE: June 30
Type: Public

Kearny Financial is the holding company for Kearny Federal Savings Bank, which has some two dozen branches in northern New Jersey. Kearny Federal Savings Bank offers such standard services as checking and savings accounts, CDs, ATM and debit cards, IRAs, and loans. Residential mortgages make up about two-thirds of its loan portfolio; multifamily and commercial mortgages and home equity loans round out most of the rest. Kearny also invests in mortgage-backed securities, government and municipal bonds, and other securities. The company is buying Central Jersey Bancorp for $72.3 million; the deal will add another 13 branches to Kearny's network. Mutual holding company Kearny MHC owns some 70% of Kearny Financial.

	Annual Growth	6/05	6/06	6/07	6/08	6/09
Assets ($ mil.)	0.2%	2,107.0	2,007.5	1,917.3	2,083.0	2,124.9
Net income ($ mil.)	(23.7%)	18.9	9.6	1.9	5.9	6.4
Market value ($ mil.)	(0.8%)	813.2	1,020.0	929.0	758.1	788.4
Employees	0.0%	284	287	292	286	284

KEHE DISTRIBUTORS, LLC

900 N. Schmidt Rd.
Romeoville, IL 60446
Phone: 630-343-0000
Fax: 815-886-1111
Web: www.kehefood.com

CEO: Brandon Barnholt
CFO: Christopher (Chris) Meyers
HR: Annette Roder
FYE: April 30
Type: Private

You might say this company plays a key role in getting food on grocery store shelves. KeHE Distributors is a leading wholesale supplier of ethnic and gourmet foods serving more than 15,000 retail grocery stores across the country. It distributes more than 40,000 items including such ethnic offerings as African-American, Asian, Hispanic, and Kosher food products, as well as a wide variety of organic and natural food products. Additionally, the company provides e-commerce services through subsidiary Eye Level Solutions. The company's KeHE Direct unit provides online ordering services for its customers. Arthur Kehe started the employee-owned company in 1952.

	Annual Growth	4/04	4/05	4/06	4/07	4/08
Sales ($ mil.)	—	—	—	—	—	750.0
Employees	—	—	—	—	—	2,500

KEIHIN NORTH AMERICA, INC.

400 W. New Rd.
Greenfield, IN 46140
Phone: 317-462-3015
Fax: 317-462-6379
Web: www.ipt-inc.com

CEO: Kentaro Kato
CFO: —
HR: —
FYE: December 31
Type: Subsidiary

A loyal part-ner, Keihin North America (formerly Keihin Indiana Precision Technology) is a leading manufacturer of automotive systems such as air and fuel management, HVAC, and electronic components used for engine control, supplemental restraint systems control (for airbag deployment), and ABS units for braking systems. Keihin North America (KNA) also makes mechanical parts such as fuel injectors, throttle bodies, and intake manifolds. It is the parent company of four business units: Keihin IPT Manufacturing, Keihin Aircon North America, Keihin Carolina System Technology, and Keihin Michigan Manufacturing. Major shareholders of KNA are Keihin Corp. (Tokyo), Honda Motor Company, and Honda Foundry.

	Annual Growth	12/04	12/05	12/06	12/07	12/08
Est. sales ($ mil.)	—	—	—	—	—	861.9
Employees	—	—	—	—	—	1,768

KEITHLEY INSTRUMENTS, INC.

NYSE: KEI

28775 Aurora Rd.
Solon, OH 44139
Phone: 440-248-0400
Fax: 440-248-6168
Web: www.keithley.com

CEO: Joseph P. Keithley
CFO: Mark J. Plush
HR: Philip R. Etsler
FYE: September 30
Type: Public

A wailing guitar? For the Rolling Stones, that's Keith's lead instrument. The company, Keithley Instruments, is more familiar to engineers, scientists, and technicians than to geezer rockers or their fans. Keithley makes some 500 different products, tools used to control, measure, and trace signals, whether they take the form of electrical current, light, or radio waves. Its portfolio includes digital multimeters, semiconductor parametric test and device characterization systems, signal analyzers and generators, and plug-in boards that enable PCs to be used for data acquisition. About 75% of Keithley's sales are to non-US customers. The semiconductor industry represents about 30% of sales.

	Annual Growth	9/05	9/06	9/07	9/08	9/09
Sales ($ mil.)	(7.8%)	141.6	155.2	143.7	152.5	102.5
Net income ($ mil.)	—	10.1	8.4	(0.3)	(2.6)	(50.5)
Market value ($ mil.)	(21.5%)	230.2	201.0	167.1	132.0	87.4
Employees	(3.8%)	651	673	698	696	557

KEKST AND COMPANY INCORPORATED

437 Madison Ave.
New York, NY 10022
Phone: 212-521-4800
Fax: —
Web: www.kekst.com

CEO: Gershon Kekst
CFO: —
HR: —
FYE: December 31
Type: Subsidiary

Kekst and Company provides public relations services, specifically corporate and financial communications. The agency's focus on helping clients communicate with the media, analysts, shareholders, employees, customers, and government officials has served it well since its founding in 1970. Kekst and Company's expertise includes such areas as restructuring support, crisis communications, litigation support, and issues advocacy. Industries served include the banking, defense, energy, health care, technology, business services, retail, and pharmaceutical sectors. In mid-2008, Kekst and Company was acquired by global advertising and media services conglomerate Publicis Groupe.

THE KELLER MANUFACTURING COMPANY, INC.

Pink Sheets: KMFI

124 N. First St.
Louisville, KY 40202
Phone: 502-814-1450
Fax: —
Web: www.kellerfurniture.com

CEO: Ronald W. Humin
CFO: —
HR: —
FYE: December 31
Type: Public

Keller Manufacturing Company thinks its products are the very model of what a door should be. Through its Paragon Door Designs subsidiary, the company makes decorative steel and fiberglass entry and storm doors, which are sold through dealers and home improvement companies in 20 states. Keller Manufacturing Company acquired 85% of Paragon Door Designs in 2006 after exiting the furniture business; Keller Manufacturing Company had specialized in wood bedroom and dining room furniture. Paragon Door Designs operates manufacturing facilities in Louisville, Kentucky. Keller Manufacturing Company was founded in 1885.

KELLOGG COMPANY

NYSE: K

1 Kellogg Sq.
Battle Creek, MI 49016
Phone: 269-961-2000
Fax: 269-961-2871
Web: www.kelloggcompany.com

CEO: A. D. David Mackay
CFO: Ronald L. (Ron) Dissinger
HR: Tammie Winnie
FYE: December 31
Type: Public

Location as irony — Battle Creek, Michigan-based Kellogg is in a constant battle for the #1 spot in the US cereal market with its main rival, General Mills. (In 2009 General Mills' sales were some $14.7 billion, compared to Kellogg's second place $12.6 billion.) But Kellogg's boasts many a familiar brand name, including Kellogg's Corn Flakes, Frosted Flakes, Corn Pops, and Rice Krispies. And while the company fills many a cereal bowl every morning, it puffs up its bottom line with snacks and cookies (Keebler, Cheez-It, and Famous Amos), along with convenience foods such as Eggo waffles and Nutri-Grain and Bear Naked cereal bars. Its products are sold in more than 180 countries worldwide.

	Annual Growth	12/05	12/06	12/07	12/08	12/09
Sales ($ mil.)	5.4%	10,177.2	10,906.7	11,776.0	12,822.0	12,575.0
Net income ($ mil.)	5.4%	980.4	1,004.1	1,103.0	1,148.0	1,212.0
Market value ($ mil.)	5.3%	16,451.9	19,055.6	19,957.8	16,691.8	20,250.9
Employees	4.8%	25,600	26,000	26,000	32,400	30,900

KELLWOOD COMPANY

600 Kellwood Pkwy.
Chesterfield, MO 63017
Phone: 314-576-3100
Fax: 314-576-3460
Web: www.kellwood.com

CEO: Michael W. Kramer
CFO: —
HR: —
FYE: January 31
Type: Private

Who would be one of the largest US apparel makers? Kellwood would. The firm generates most of its sales from women's wear, including its Koret and Sag Harbor lines. It also produces men's and children's clothes and accessories. Its other brands include My Michelle, Baby Phat, Phat Farm, Rewind, Vince, and XOXO. The company is a major supplier to department stores, as well as mass retailers, specialty boutiques, and catalogs. Kellwood also operates Vince and Sag Harbor brand outlet stores across the US. Kellwood has gained a foothold in new niches and grown through acquisitions, including Vince, Briggs New York, and Phat Fashions. It was taken private in 2008 by Sun Capital Partners and has been restructuring.

KELLY SERVICES, INC.

NASDAQ (GS): KELYA

999 W. Big Beaver Rd.
Troy, MI 48084
Phone: 248-362-4444
Fax: —
Web: www.kellyservices.com

CEO: Carl T. Camden
CFO: Patricia Little
HR: Antonina M. (Nina) Ramsey
FYE: December 31
Type: Public

These days a lot of "Kelly Girls" are men. Once a business that supplied only female clerical help, Kelly Services has expanded to include male and female temporary employees in light industrial, technical, and professional sectors, including information technology specialists, engineers, and accountants. It also places lawyers (Kelly Law Registry), scientists (Kelly Scientific Resources), substitute teachers (Kelly Educational Staffing), nurses and other medical staff (Kelly Healthcare Resources), and teleservices personnel (KellyConnect). Kelly Services assigns some 480,000 temporary employees each year. Chairman Terence Adderley owns a controlling stake in the company.

	Annual Growth	12/05	12/06	12/07	12/08	12/09
Sales ($ mil.)	(5.0%)	5,289.8	5,605.8	5,667.6	5,517.3	4,314.8
Net income ($ mil.)	—	39.3	63.5	61.0	(82.2)	(104.5)
Market value ($ mil.)	(17.9%)	917.3	1,012.4	652.8	455.1	417.4
Employees	(8.9%)	708,600	750,000	760,000	660,100	487,900

KELLY-MOORE PAINT COMPANY, INC.

987 Commercial St.
San Carlos, CA 94070
Phone: 650-592-8337
Fax: 650-508-8563
Web: www.kellymoore.com

CEO: Steven (Steve) DeVoe
CFO: Dan Stritmatter
HR: Debbie Culmer
FYE: December 31
Type: Private

You'd call them red, yellow, and green. Kelly-Moore Paint Company calls them High Society, Feisty, and Center Field. But never mind silly names for paint colors, Kelly-Moore aims to show that the paint business isn't entirely run by multinational big brushes like Sherwin-Williams and DuPont. The regional firm produces approximately 20 million gallons of paint per year from three manufacturing facilities and has more than 160 stores in eight states west of the Mississippi River. Kelly-Moore sells about 400 types of paints, finishes, and sundries to professional contractors and painters and to the do-it-yourself market. The employee-owned company was formed by William Moore and William Kelly in 1946.

KEMET CORPORATION

OTC: KEME

2835 KEMET Way
Simpsonville, SC 29681
Phone: 864-963-6300
Fax: —
Web: www.kemet.com

CEO: Per-Olof Lööf
CFO: William M. Lowe Jr.
HR: Larry C. McAdams
FYE: March 31
Type: Public

It's not capacitance happenstance that KEMET is one of the world's largest makers of tantalum and multilayer ceramic capacitors — devices that store, filter, and regulate electrical energy and that are used in virtually all electronic devices. KEMET makes more than 30 billion units a year; its focus is on surface-mount capacitors, including specialized units for aerospace, automotive, communications systems, computers, and military equipment. The company also makes solid aluminum capacitors for high-frequency applications. KEMET gets about three-quarters of its sales outside the US.

	Annual Growth	3/06	3/07	3/08	3/09	3/10
Sales ($ mil.)	10.7%	490.1	658.7	850.1	804.4	736.3
Net income ($ mil.)	—	0.4	6.9	(17.6)	(276.9)	(69.4)
Market value ($ mil.)	(38.0%)	768.3	620.7	327.8	19.9	113.6
Employees	3.7%	9,000	9,100	11,600	9,100	10,400

KEMIRA CHEMICALS, INC.

1950 Vaughn Rd.
Kennesaw, GA 30144
Phone: 770-436-1542
Fax: 770-436-3432
Web: www.kemirachemicals.com

CEO: Hannu Melarti
CFO: —
HR: —
FYE: December 31
Type: Subsidiary

Kemira Chemicals is the North American subsidiary of the Finnish international specialty chemical maker Kemira Oyj. The company manufactures specialty and process chemicals for the pulp and paper, water treatment, mineral slurries, and chemical industries. Products include biocides, colloidal silica, defoamers, dispersants, hazardous waste stabilizers, polishing slurries, sodium aluminate, and water treatment polymers. Kemira North America provides about a quarter of its parent's total sales.

KEMIRA WATER SOLUTIONS, INC.

808 E. Main St.
Lakeland, FL 33801
Phone: 800-533-5990
Fax: 863-797-1087
Web: www.kemirawatersolutions.com

CEO: Joseph W. Richey
CFO: Jerry Tenny
HR: —
FYE: December 31
Type: Subsidiary

Kemira Water Solutions hopes to make rivers flow cleaner. The company manufactures a wide range of iron and aluminum coagulants for the wastewater and potable water industries. Kemira Water Solutions provides customer-specific sewage treatment, odor control, and soil erosion and related services for municipalities, industrial companies, and agricultural operations. The company, which has offices in the US and Canada is one of North America's largest suppliers of inorganic coagulants. Kemira Water Solutions is the US subsidiary of leading Finnish chemical company Kemira Oyj.

THE KENAN ADVANTAGE GROUP, INC.

4366 Mt. Pleasant St., NW
North Canton, OH 44720
Phone: 330-491-0474
Fax: 330-491-1471
Web: www.kenanadvantagegroup.com

CEO: Dennis A. Nash
CFO: Carl H. Young
HR: Glenn Garson
FYE: December 31
Type: Private

Not only do the trucking subsidiaries of The Kenan Advantage Group (KAG) burn diesel fuel, but they also haul it. The group transports gasoline, diesel fuel, other petroleum and petrochemical products, and food throughout the US. The company operates a fleet of some 3,300 tractors and 4,300 tank trailers from a network of about 100 terminals in more than 35 states, mainly in the eastern half of the US. Customers include major oil companies and other petroleum marketers, along with food manufacturers. In addition to trucking, KAG provides fuel-related logistics services. Investment firm Littlejohn & Co. owns the company.

	Annual Growth	12/04	12/05	12/06	12/07	12/08
Sales ($ mil.)	—	—	—	—	—	800.0
Employees	—	—	—	—	—	—

KENDLE INTERNATIONAL INC.

NASDAQ (GS): KNDL

1200 Carew Tower, 441 Vine St.
Cincinnati, OH 45202
Phone: 513-381-5550
Fax: 513-381-5870
Web: www.kendle.com

CEO: Candace Kendle
CFO: Keith A. Cheesman
HR: Karen L. Crone
FYE: December 31
Type: Public

When it comes to research and development, few can hold a candle to Kendle International. A leading contract research organization (CRO) for the biotechnology and pharmaceutical industries, the company provides services that facilitate Phase I through Phase IV clinical trials; those services include patient recruitment, clinical monitoring, statistical analysis, and consulting on regulatory issues. Additionally, Kendle's TrialWare software helps customers manage research and clinical trial data. The company has expertise in a range of therapeutic areas, including oncology, the central nervous system, cardiovascular disease, and inflammation. Kendle provides services in about 100 countries around the globe.

	Annual Growth	12/05	12/06	12/07	12/08	12/09
Sales ($ mil.)	21.8%	250.6	373.9	568.8	678.6	551.9
Net income ($ mil.)	9.2%	10.7	8.5	18.7	29.4	15.2
Market value ($ mil.)	(8.2%)	383.5	468.5	728.8	383.2	272.8
Employees	17.6%	1,900	3,050	3,325	4,275	3,640

KENEXA CORPORATION

NASDAQ (GM): KNXA

650 E. Swedesford Rd., 2nd Fl.
Wayne, PA 19087
Phone: 610-971-9171
Fax: 610-971-9181
Web: www.kenexa.com

CEO: Nooruddin S. (Rudy) Karsan Sr.
CFO: Donald F. (Don) Volk
HR: Tim Geisert
FYE: December 31
Type: Public

Kenexa wants to streamline your HR processes. The company markets Web-based applications that automate human resources activities, such as recruitment, skills testing, and tracking of employee development. Kenexa also offers outsourcing options to clients, taking over part or all of the recruitment and hiring process. In addition, the company conducts employee surveys for its customers. Kenexa sells its services and software products mostly on a subscription basis to about 4,400 large and medium-sized corporations. The company was founded in 1987.

	Annual Growth	12/05	12/06	12/07	12/08	12/09
Sales ($ mil.)	24.5%	65.6	112.1	181.9	203.7	157.7
Net income ($ mil.)	—	6.1	15.9	23.5	(104.7)	(31.1)
Market value ($ mil.)	(11.4%)	476.7	751.5	438.8	180.3	294.4
Employees	20.5%	693	1,220	1,373	1,535	1,459

KENNAMETAL INC.

NYSE: KMT

1600 Technology Way
Latrobe, PA 15650
Phone: 724-539-5000
Fax: 724-539-6657
Web: www.kennametal.com

CEO: Carlos M. Cardoso
CFO: Frank P. Simpkins
HR: Kevin R. Walling
FYE: June 30
Type: Public

Kennametal welcomes your cutting-edge remarks. The company offers a host of metal-cutting tools and tooling systems for machining steel, equipment for mining and highway construction, and engineering services for production processes, across two business divisions: Metalworking Solutions and Services, and Advanced Materials Solutions. Its multi-trademark lineup includes cutting, milling, and drilling tools used in metalworking; drums, bits, and accessories used in mining; and bits, grader blades, and snowplow blades used in construction. Kennametal and its subsidiaries sell products and services worldwide, directly and through a distributor network. More than half of sales come from outside of North America.

	Annual Growth	6/05	6/06	6/07	6/08	6/09
Sales ($ mil.)	(3.5%)	2,304.2	2,329.6	2,385.5	2,705.1	1,999.9
Net income ($ mil.)	—	119.3	256.3	174.2	167.8	(119.7)
Market value ($ mil.)	(4.4%)	1,873.8	2,544.0	3,352.3	2,660.4	1,567.7
Employees	(4.6%)	14,000	13,300	13,947	13,673	11,600

KENNECOTT UTAH COPPER CORPORATION

8362 W. 10200 South
Bingham Canyon, UT 84006
Phone: 801-569-6000
Fax: 801-569-6045
Web: www.kennecott.com

CEO: Kelly Sanders
CFO: Patrick (Pat) Keenan
HR: Michael DeVolld
FYE: December 31
Type: Subsidiary

Kennecott Utah Copper, a subsidiary of mining giant Rio Tinto, operates Bingham Canyon, one of the world's biggest open pit mines. Annual production at Bingham Canyon is nearly 300,000 tons of copper, nearly 500,000 ounces of gold, 4 million ounces of silver, and 30 million pounds of molybdenum. In operation since 1903, Bingham Canyon has produced about 18 million tons of copper — more than any other mine in history. It has plenty of ore left, and Kennecott expects to continue open pit mining until 2018, followed by years of underground mining. The company has its own smelter and refinery; Kennecott also produces sulfuric acid as a by-product of the smelting process.

KENNEDY-WILSON HOLDINGS, INC.

NYSE: KW

9601 Wilshire Blvd., Ste. 220
Beverly Hills, CA 90210
Phone: 310-887-6400
Fax: 310-887-3410
Web: www.kennedywilson.com

CEO: William J. McMorrow
CFO: Freeman A. Lyle
HR: James C. (Jim) Ozello
FYE: December 31
Type: Public

Kennedy-Wilson isn't the latest presidential ticket, but it does its share of running offices. With more than 20 offices in the US and Japan, the firm operates through two core practices, real estate services and investments. KW Services division provides property and asset management, auction and residential sales, and brokerage, while KW Investments offers consulting and fund management for commercial and multifamily property acquisitions. Kennedy-Wilson manages more than 40 million sq. ft. of property across the US. It also looks to invest in and develop real estate on the West Coast. Kennedy-Wilson completed a reverse merger with acquisition vehicle Prospect Acquisition in 2009.

An in-depth profile of this company is available to Hoover's Online members at hoovers.com.

887

KENNETH COLE PRODUCTIONS, INC.

NYSE: KCP

603 W. 50th St.
New York, NY 10019
Phone: 212-265-1500
Fax: 866-741-5753
Web: www.kennethcole.com

CEO: Jill Granoff
CFO: David P. Edelman
HR: —
FYE: December 31
Type: Public

Kenneth Cole is a trendy old sole. Most known for its shoes, Kenneth Cole Productions also makes stylish apparel and accessories under the Kenneth Cole New York, Kenneth Cole Reaction, Unlisted, and Gentle Souls names. It licenses the Bongo and Le Tigre brands. Kenneth Cole licenses its name for hosiery, luggage, watches, and eyewear. It continues to expand, adding new lines for women and children, as well as men's and women's fragrances. About 5,500 department and specialty stores carry its products. Kenneth Cole operates more than 100 retail and outlet stores and sells through catalogs and websites. Chairman Kenneth Cole owns about 54% of the firm and controls almost all of the voting rights.

	Annual Growth	12/05	12/06	12/07	12/08	12/09
Sales ($ mil.)	(5.7%)	518.0	536.5	510.7	492.3	410.4
Net income ($ mil.)	—	33.5	26.8	7.1	(14.8)	(63.2)
Market value ($ mil.)	(21.6%)	461.5	434.1	316.5	128.1	174.6
Employees	1.4%	1,800	1,900	1,800	1,800	1,900

KENNYWOOD ENTERTAINMENT COMPANY, INC.

4800 Kennywood Blvd.
West Mifflin, PA 15122
Phone: 412-461-0500
Fax: 412-464-0719
Web: www.kennywoodentertainment.com

CEO: Harry Henninger
CFO: —
HR: —
FYE: December 31
Type: Subsidiary

Kennywood is not the *Islands in the Stream* counterpart to singer Dolly Parton's Dollywood. (Turn to Herschend Family Entertainment for that distinction). It does own and operate four amusement parks in Pennsylvania: Kennywood Park, Idlewild & Soak Zone, Sandcastle Waterpark, and Pittsburgh's Riverplex, a traditional picnic-type park located next to Sandcastle. The company markets its parks for group outings, and offers event planning and catering services. Kennywood Entertainment was founded in 1898. It is a subsidiary of Spanish theme park company Parques Reunidos.

KENSEY NASH CORPORATION

NASDAQ (GS): KNSY

735 Pennsylvania Dr.
Exton, PA 19341
Phone: 484-713-2100
Fax: 484-713-2900
Web: www.kenseynash.com

CEO: Joseph W. Kaufmann
CFO: Michael Celano
HR: —
FYE: June 30
Type: Public

Kensey Nash works not in vain — rather, in arteries. The firm developed the Angio-Seal, a bio-absorbable material to seal arterial punctures, which can occur during cardiovascular procedures. St. Jude Medical has licensed the rights to manufacture and market Angio-Seal worldwide. Other biomaterial products include tissue and bone grafting material and fixation devices for orthopedic surgeries, collagen-based burn treatments and wound dressings, and dental surgery aids. Kensey Nash also made a range of endovascular devices, including the QuickCat and ThromCat catheters for removing blood clots, but it sold the product line to Spectranetics in 2008.

	Annual Growth	6/05	6/06	6/07	6/08	6/09
Sales ($ mil.)	7.5%	61.4	60.4	69.5	79.8	82.1
Net income ($ mil.)	11.7%	12.9	3.7	3.6	4.8	20.1
Market value ($ mil.)	(3.5%)	294.2	287.0	260.9	311.8	255.0
Employees	(2.4%)	333	356	358	302	302

KENSINGTON PUBLISHING CORP.

119 W. 40th St.
New York, NY 10018
Phone: 212-407-1500
Fax: 212-935-0699
Web: www.kensingtonbooks.com

CEO: Steven (Steve) Zacharius
CFO: —
HR: —
FYE: December 31
Type: Private

Kensington Publishing holds court with readers. The independent publisher sells hardcover, trade, and mass market fiction and non-fiction books through its Kensington, Zebra, Pinnacle, and Citadel imprints. The company publishes about 600 titles a year and has a backlist of more than 3,000. Romance and women's fiction account for more than half of its titles published each year. Other niche topics covered include wicca, gambling, gay & lesbian, and military history. Readers can turn to the company's Rebel Base Books website to order titles such as *I Hope They Serve Beer in Hell* by Tucker Max, which sold more than 70,000 copies its first year and made the *New York Times Bestseller* list in 2006, 2007, and 2008.

	Annual Growth	12/04	12/05	12/06	12/07	12/08
Est. sales ($ mil.)	—	—	—	—	—	59.6
Employees	—	—	—	—	—	90

KENT FINANCIAL SERVICES, INC.

NASDAQ (CM): KENT

10911 Raven Ridge Rd., Ste. 103-45
Raleigh, NC 27614
Phone: 919-847-8710
Fax: —
Web: www.kentfinancialservices.com

CEO: Paul O. Koether
CFO: Bryan P. Healey
HR: —
FYE: December 31
Type: Public

Kent Financial Services (once known as Texas American Energy) has moved from the oil patch to the financial services field. The firm holds a majority stake in publicly traded Kent International Holdings (formerly Cortech), which scrapped its pharmaceutical research and is seeking new business opportunities in the US and China. The company in 2010 also scrapped subsidiary Kent Educational Services, which controlled The Academy for Teaching and Leadership, a provider of educational programs for school administrators and teachers. Chairman and CEO Paul Koether owns approximately 60% of Kent Financial Services.

	Annual Growth	12/05	12/06	12/07	12/08	12/09
Sales ($ mil.)	—	0.9	1.1	1.2	0.7	0.0
Net income ($ mil.)	—	(0.2)	(0.6)	(0.7)	(0.3)	(0.7)
Market value ($ mil.)	(11.4%)	6.8	6.5	5.8	4.1	4.2
Employees	(24.0%)	6	6	3	3	2

KENT INTERNATIONAL HOLDINGS, INC.

Pink Sheets: KNTH

211 Pennbrook Rd.
Far Hills, NJ 07931
Phone: 908-766-7222
Fax: 908-234-9355

CEO: Paul O. Koether
CFO: Bryan P. Healey
HR: —
FYE: December 31
Type: Public

Kent International Holdings (formerly Cortech) is a company without a core. The firm, which previously developed drugs for inflammatory disorders, lost its research partners because of disappointing test results and has discontinued its drug development operations. In 2006 Cortech merged with wholly owned subsidiary Kent International and took on the moniker of the latter to get a fresh start. It is looking for opportunities to merge with or acquire another business and, in the meantime, has set up an advertiser-supported social networking site aimed to promote interaction among Chinese and US users. Through his Kent Financial Services investment firm, chairman Paul Koether owns more than half of the firm.

	Annual Growth	12/05	12/06	12/07	12/08	12/09
Sales ($ mil.)	—	0.3	0.6	0.5	0.3	0.0
Net income ($ mil.)	—	(0.1)	(0.2)	(0.3)	(0.2)	(0.5)
Market value ($ mil.)	(10.0%)	10.0	9.4	9.2	5.3	6.6
Employees	0.0%	1	1	—	—	—

KENT STATE UNIVERSITY

Horning Rd.
Kent, OH 44242
Phone: 330-672-3000
Fax: 330-672-4023
Web: www.kent.edu

CEO: Lester A. Lefton
CFO: Gregg S. Floyd
HR: Barbara A. (Barb) Casher
FYE: June 30
Type: School

Kent State University (KSU) knows all about remembering history so as not to repeat it, but while it embraces its past it also moves beyond it. The school offers some 300 majors, minors, and certificates in arts and sciences, business, technology, and other fields. Through eight campuses located in Northeastern Ohio, KSU educates some 33,600 students, making it Ohio's second-largest public university (behind Ohio State). The school was founded in 1910 for teacher training. Its Center for Peaceful Change (later renamed the Center for Applied Conflict Management) was formed after four KSU students were killed and nine wounded by the Ohio National Guard in 1970 amidst a protest of the US invasion of Cambodia.

	Annual Growth	6/04	6/05	6/06	6/07	6/08
Est. sales ($ mil.)	—	—	—	—	—	346.8
Employees	—	—	—	—	—	5,466

KENTUCKY FIRST FEDERAL BANCORP

NASDAQ (GM): KFFB

479 Main St.
Hazard, KY 41702
Phone: 502-223-1638
Fax: —

CEO: Tony D. Whitaker
CFO: R. Clay Hulette
HR: —
FYE: June 30
Type: Public

Kentucky First Federal wants to be second to none for banking in the Bluegrass State. It was formed in 2005 to be the holding company for First Federal Savings and Loan of Hazard and First Federal Savings Bank of Frankfort (acquired in 2005), which operate three branches in the state's capital and one in the town of Hazard. The banks offer traditional deposit products, such as checking and savings accounts, NOW and money market accounts, and CDs. Lending is focused on residential mortgages, but the banks also offer loans secured by churches and commercial real estate, as well as consumer and construction loans. First Federal MHC, a mutual holding company, owns more than 60% of Kentucky First Federal.

	Annual Growth	6/05	6/06	6/07	6/08	6/09
Assets ($ mil.)	(3.2%)	273.9	261.9	268.9	247.7	240.9
Net income ($ mil.)	(15.9%)	1.6	1.6	0.9	0.9	0.8
Market value ($ mil.)	2.5%	86.2	82.4	79.6	73.3	95.3
Employees	0.0%	40	40	37	39	40

KENTUCKY INVESTORS, INC.

OTC: KINV

200 Capital Ave.
Frankfort, KY 40601
Phone: 502-223-2361
Fax: 502-875-7084
Web: www.investorsheritage.com

CEO: Harry Lee Waterfield II
CFO: Raymond L. Carr
HR: —
FYE: December 31
Type: Public

Forget coonskin caps and racehorses, these Kentucky investors put their money into insurance. Kentucky Investors' primary subsidiary, Investors Heritage Life Insurance, provides group and individual life insurance, burial insurance, credit insurance, and similar products, which are sold through independent agents and through funeral homes in about 30 states. Investor Heritage Life Insurance does most of its business in the East and Southeast. The company also owns non-insurance subsidiaries, which offer commercial printing, investment holding services, and funeral lending services. Chairman and president Harry Lee Waterfield controls 46% of the company's stock.

	Annual Growth	12/05	12/06	12/07	12/08	12/09
Assets ($ mil.)	(0.9%)	433.5	415.2	419.7	410.2	418.6
Net income ($ mil.)	(34.7%)	2.2	1.2	1.7	(1.4)	0.4
Market value ($ mil.)	(7.6%)	27.5	33.7	31.7	29.7	20.0
Employees	—	—	—	—	—	—

KENTUCKY LOTTERY CORPORATION

1011 W. Main St.
Louisville, KY 40202
Phone: 502-560-1500
Fax: 502-560-1670
Web: www.kylottery.com

CEO: Arthur L. (Arch) Gleason Jr.
CFO: Howard Kline
HR: Church Saufley
FYE: June 30
Type: Government-owned

Kentucky Lottery operates a variety of instant-win and numbers games for the benefit of state educational programs. The lottery offers scratch-off and pull-tab games, as well as Pick 3, Pick 4, and Win for Life lotteries. In addition, Kentucky Lottery is part of the Multi-State Lottery Association and participates in that organization's multi-state Powerball drawing. Proceeds from the games go to a variety of programs, including the College Access Program, the Kentucky Educational Excellence Scholarship Program, and the Kentucky Tuition Grants Program, as well as Kentucky's General Fund. The Kentucky Lottery was established in 1989.

KENWOOD USA CORPORATION

2201 E. Dominguez St.
Long Beach, CA 90810
Phone: 310-639-9000
Fax: 310-604-4488
Web: www.kenwoodusa.com

CEO: Junji Kobayashi
CFO: —
HR: —
FYE: March 31
Type: Subsidiary

Who in the world would provide stereo-gadget junkies with even more grist for the listening mill? Kenwood would. Kenwood USA, the largest subsidiary of Japan's Kenwood, designs, manufactures, and distributes consumer audio electronics products to customers in the US. Its home and car audio products are sold through electronics retailers, such as Best Buy, Fry's, Pep Boys, and Sears. Car and home audio products also may be purchased through specialized catalogs. The company's Kenwood Communications, based in Georgia, specializes in making and marketing mobile and portable two-way radios and custom systems. They're used by amateur radio users and civilian emergency responders.

KERR DRUG, INC.

3220 Spring Forest Rd.
Raleigh, NC 27616
Phone: 919-544-3896
Fax: 919-544-3796
Web: www.kerrdrug.com

CEO: Anthony N. (Tony) Civello
CFO: —
HR: —
FYE: December 31
Type: Private

Oh, you can buy knick-knacks and doo-dads at a Kerr Drug store, but the company that bills itself as "North Carolina's Drugstore" puts its primary focus on pharmacy operations, which account for about two-thirds of sales. Kerr Drug operates about 90 stores in North Carolina in several formats, ranging from large upscale stores featuring health care services and expanded general merchandise sections to the basic pharmacy format offering more cleaning supplies, health and beauty aids, and soft goods. Founded by Banks Kerr in 1951, the chain was sold in 1995 to retailer J. C. Penney. A management group led by Kerr CEO Anthony Civello and CFO Richard Johnson took Kerr Drug private in 1996.

An in-depth profile of this company is available to Hoover's Online members at hoovers.com.

KERYX BIOPHARMACEUTICALS, INC.

NASDAQ (GM): KERX

750 Lexington Ave., 20th Fl.
New York, NY 10022
Phone: 212-531-5965
Fax: 212-531-5961
Web: www.keryx.com

CEO: Ron Bentsur
CFO: James F. Oliviero
HR: —
FYE: December 31
Type: Public

Drugs are a life-or-death business for Keryx Biopharmaceuticals. The company specializes in developing treatments for life-threatening ailments, such as cancer and kidney disease. Its lead candidates are Zerenex, a compound that may reduce high phosphate levels in patients with end-stage renal disease, and KRX-0401 (also known as perifosine) to fight renal cell carcinoma and other cancers. Keryx suffered a major blow in 2008 when its previous lead candidate Sulonex failed in a pivotal clinical trial; the drug had been intended to treat diabetic nephropathy, a diabetes-related kidney disease.

	Annual Growth	12/05	12/06	12/07	12/08	12/09
Sales ($ mil.)	154.6%	0.6	0.5	1.0	1.3	25.2
Net income ($ mil.)	—	(26.9)	(73.8)	(90.1)	(52.9)	10.5
Market value ($ mil.)	(35.7%)	857.7	779.2	492.1	12.9	146.5
Employees	(15.2%)	29	40	50	17	15

KEWAUNEE SCIENTIFIC CORPORATION

NASDAQ (GM): KEQU

2700 W. Front St.
Statesville, NC 28677
Phone: 704-873-7202
Fax: 704-873-1275
Web: www.kewaunee.com

CEO: William A. Shumaker
CFO: D. Michael (Mike) Parker
HR: —
FYE: April 30
Type: Public

The nutty professor once wreaked havoc on furniture like that made by Kewaunee Scientific. The company makes furniture for laboratories, including wood and steel cabinets, fume hoods, and work surfaces. Its primary customers are labs (pharmaceutical, biotech, industrial, chemical, and commercial research), schools, and health care institutions. Kewaunee also makes technical workstations, workbenches, and computer enclosures for local area networking applications. The company's products are sold through VWR International, a school and lab products supplier (about 13% of sales), and through Kewaunee dealers.

	Annual Growth	4/05	4/06	4/07	4/08	4/09
Sales ($ mil.)	9.1%	73.5	84.1	81.4	89.5	104.0
Net income ($ mil.)	—	(0.1)	0.2	1.5	3.1	4.2
Market value ($ mil.)	5.7%	19.3	22.8	28.5	40.1	24.1
Employees	4.3%	484	566	554	569	572

⊞ KEY ENERGY SERVICES, INC.

NYSE: KEG

1301 McKinney St., Ste. 1800
Houston, TX 77010
Phone: 713-651-4300
Fax: 713-652-4005
Web: www.keyenergy.com

CEO: Richard J. (Dick) Alario
CFO: T.M. (Trey) Whichard III
HR: Kim B. Clarke
FYE: December 31
Type: Public

Energy is the key to growth for Key Energy Services, one of the US's largest well-servicing and workover companies. The company provides maintenance, workover, and recompletion of wells, primarily for onshore drilling. It also provides services such as contract drilling, well completion and abandonment, oil field fluid transportation, production testing, and storage and disposal services to major and independent oil companies. Key Energy Services has a fleet of 924 well service rigs, which operate primarily in the US, as well as in Argentina, Canada, and Mexico. It also has minority stakes in a Canada-based drilling and production services company and a Russia-based drilling and workover services firm.

	Annual Growth	12/05	12/06	12/07	12/08	12/09
Sales ($ mil.)	(2.4%)	1,190.4	1,546.2	1,662.0	1,972.1	1,078.7
Net income ($ mil.)	—	45.7	171.0	169.3	84.1	(156.1)
Market value ($ mil.)	(10.1%)	1,689.5	1,963.0	1,804.9	553.1	1,102.5
Employees	(3.7%)	9,400	9,400	9,820	8,582	8,100

KEY FOOD STORES CO-OPERATIVE, INC.

1200 South Ave.
Staten Island, NY 10314
Phone: 718-370-4200
Fax: 718-370-4225
Web: www.keyfoodstores.com

CEO: Dean Janeway
CFO: —
HR: —
FYE: April 30
Type: Cooperative

Key Food Stores Co-Operative is a friend to independent New York grocers. The co-op provides retail support and other services to 100-plus independently owned food retailers in the New York City area. Key Food's member-owners run stores mainly in Brooklyn and Queens, but also in the other boroughs and surrounding counties. It operates stores primarily under the Key Food banner, but it also has Key Food Marketplace locations that feature expanded meat, deli, and produce departments. In addition, the co-op supplies Key Foods-branded products to member stores. Among its members are Pick Quick Foods, Dan's Supreme Super Markets, Gemstone Supermarkets, and Queens Supermarkets. Key Foods was founded in 1937.

	Annual Growth	4/04	4/05	4/06	4/07	4/08
Est. sales ($ mil.)	—	—	—	—	—	29.9
Employees	—	—	—	—	—	425

⊞ KEY SAFETY SYSTEMS, INC.

7000 Nineteen Mile Rd.
Sterling Heights, MI 48314
Phone: 586-726-3800
Fax: —
Web: www.keysafetyinc.com

CEO: Jason Luo
CFO: Dave Smith
HR: Larry Casey
FYE: December 31
Type: Private

Key Safety Systems (KSS) won't start your car, but it can protect your occupants. The company is a leading maker and seller of air bags and air bag components, including sensors and inflators. It also makes seat belts, steering wheels, and air bag webbing fabric. The company supplies air bags to most of the world's carmakers, including Ford, GM, Hyundai, and Volkswagen. KSS also makes a line of automotive interior accessories, including automatic and manual shift knobs, parking brake handles, shift and brake boots, armrest covers, and pull handles. Non-automotive applicatons include military and commercial vehicles. The company is controlled by private investment firm Crestview Partners.

⊞ KEY TECHNOLOGY, INC.

NASDAQ (GM): KTEC

150 Avery St.
Walla Walla, WA 99362
Phone: 509-529-2161
Fax: 509-527-1331
Web: www.keyww.com

CEO: David M. Camp
CFO: John J. (Jack) Ehren
HR: —
FYE: September 30
Type: Public

When good french fries go bad, Key Technology comes to the rescue. The company makes food and material processing automation equipment. Its electro-optical automated inspection and sorting systems and product preparation systems can be used to evaluate fresh fruits and vegetables, beans, potato chips, and other snacks. Items can be sorted by color, size, and shape to identify defective or inconsistent products for removal. The company also makes conveyor and sorting systems for the tobacco, pharmaceutical, nutraceutical, and coffee industries. Key Technology gets about half of its sales outside the US.

	Annual Growth	9/05	9/06	9/07	9/08	9/09
Sales ($ mil.)	7.0%	80.3	84.8	107.5	134.1	105.4
Net income ($ mil.)	—	2.7	(0.8)	7.4	7.5	(0.5)
Market value ($ mil.)	(5.7%)	75.0	67.5	159.1	125.3	59.5
Employees	1.9%	478	486	532	612	515

[H] KEY TRONIC CORPORATION

NASDAQ (GM): KTCC

4424 N. Sullivan Rd., Lower Level
Spokane, WA 99216
Phone: 509-928-8000
Fax: 509-927-5383
Web: www.keytronic.com

CEO: Craig D. Gates
CFO: Ronald F. (Ron) Klawitter
HR: —
FYE: June 30
Type: Public

Contract electronics manufacturing holds the key for Key Tronic. The company, which does business as KeyTronicEMS to highlight its focus on electronics manufacturing services, provides printed circuit board assembly, tooling and prototyping, box build (completely built) systems, and plastic injection molding. In addition, Key Tronic offers such services as engineering, logistics, and testing. The company also makes customized and standard keyboards and mice for PCs, terminals, and workstations. Leading customers include Imation (10% of sales), International Game Technology (13%), Lexmark (14%), and Zebra Technologies.

	Annual Growth	6/05	6/06	6/07	6/08	6/09
Sales ($ mil.)	(2.3%)	202.9	187.7	201.7	204.1	184.9
Net income ($ mil.)	(29.3%)	4.4	9.8	5.2	5.6	1.1
Market value ($ mil.)	(17.2%)	34.8	40.0	52.2	35.9	16.4
Employees	(8.9%)	2,849	2,840	2,227	2,502	1,963

[H] KEYCORP

NYSE: KEY

127 Public Sq.
Cleveland, OH 44114
Phone: 216-689-6300
Fax: 216-689-0519
Web: www.key.com

CEO: Henry L. Meyer III
CFO: Jeffrey B. Weeden
HR: Thomas E. (Tom) Helfrich
FYE: December 31
Type: Public

Financial services giant KeyCorp has the clout of mean Henry Potter of Bedford Falls, but wants to be the sweet George Bailey of bankers. With a focus on retail operations, flagship subsidiary KeyBank operates about 1,000 branches in more than a dozen states scattered throughout the Northeast, the Midwest, the Rocky Mountains, and the Pacific Northwest (including Alaska). Its operations are divided into two groups: community banking offers traditional services such as deposits, loans, and financial planning, while national banking provides real estate capital, equipment financing, and capital markets services to large corporate clients nationwide.

	Annual Growth	12/05	12/06	12/07	12/08	12/09
Assets ($ mil.)	0.0%	93,126.0	92,337.0	99,983.0	104,531.0	93,287.0
Net income ($ mil.)	—	1,129.0	1,050.0	919.0	(1,468.0)	(1,311.0)
Market value ($ mil.)	(35.9%)	28,950.5	33,434.2	20,616.2	7,490.4	4,879.3
Employees	(3.8%)	19,485	20,006	18,934	18,095	16,698

KEYNOTE SYSTEMS, INC.

NASDAQ (GM): KEYN

777 Mariners Island Blvd.
San Mateo, CA 94404
Phone: 650-403-2400
Fax: 650-403-5500
Web: www.keynote.com

CEO: Umang Gupta
CFO: Curtis H. Smith
HR: —
FYE: September 30
Type: Public

Measuring website performance is the keystone of this company's operations. Keynote Systems provides software and services that evaluate Internet performance. Using a network of more than 2,000 computers connected to Internet backbones in more than 240 cities worldwide, Keynote monitors the speed of such activities as conducting e-commerce transactions, downloading Web pages, or using wireless applications to help clients identify information bottlenecks; clients purchase a subscription to access the data. It offers qualitative research and consulting services covering online behavior, industry trends, and customer satisfaction. Keynote also tests and measures the performance of mobile devices.

	Annual Growth	9/05	9/06	9/07	9/08	9/09
Sales ($ mil.)	10.5%	53.7	55.5	67.8	76.9	80.1
Net income ($ mil.)	(18.3%)	7.4	(7.5)	(4.7)	(3.1)	3.3
Market value ($ mil.)	(7.7%)	192.9	156.5	204.0	196.9	140.1
Employees	12.6%	191	270	285	300	307

KEYSTONE AUTOMOTIVE INDUSTRIES, INC.

700 E. Bonita Ave.
Pomona, CA 91767
Phone: 909-624-8041
Fax: 909-624-9136
Web: www.keystone-auto.com

CEO: Joseph M. Holsten
CFO: —
HR: —
FYE: March 31
Type: Subsidiary

Wonder why the gang at Keystone Automotive Industries salivates during the car chases from the old *Smokey and the Bandit* movies? The company is a leading distributor of unbranded new and recycled automotive parts used to repair damaged vehicles as well as materials used in painting. It also recycles bumpers and refurbishes alloy wheels. Keystone serves auto body shops through about 130 service centers in the US and Canada. The company operates wheel remanufacturing plants and bumper recycling facilities. Automobile recycling giant LKQ Corporation acquired Keystone Automotive Industries for approximately $807 million in 2007.

KEYSTONE AUTOMOTIVE OPERATIONS INC.

44 Tunkhannock Ave.
Exeter, PA 18643
Phone: 570-655-4514
Fax: 570-603-2003
Web: www.keystoneautomotive.com

CEO: Edward H. (Ed) Orzetti
CFO: —
HR: Deborah Branden
FYE: December 31
Type: Subsidiary

One of the largest automotive parts distributors in North America, Keystone Automotive Operations keeps a solid logistics plan locked in place. The company provides more than 700 lines of automotive parts and accessories to some 17,000 customers, mostly small specialty retailers and installers, in the US, Canada, and about 40 other countries. It operates four warehouses and about 20 stocking facilities in the US and Canada, as well as a fleet of more than 300 delivery trucks. In addition, the company runs about 25 retail stores in Pennsylvania under the A&A Auto Parts banner. Founded by the Amato family in 1971, Keystone Automotive is controlled by Bain Capital.

	Annual Growth	12/04	12/05	12/06	12/07	12/08
Est. sales ($ mil.)	—	—	—	—	—	566.3
Employees	—					1,800

KEYSTONE CONSOLIDATED INDUSTRIES, INC.

OTC: KYCN

5430 LBJ Fwy., Ste. 1740, 3 Lincoln Centre
Dallas, TX 75240
Phone: 972-458-0028
Fax: 972-448-1408
Web: www.keystonesteel.com

CEO: David L. Cheek
CFO: Bert E. Downing Jr.
HR: Ken Notaro
FYE: December 31
Type: Public

Keystone Consolidated Industries can wire your world. The company, mainly through its Keystone Steel & Wire division, makes fabricated wire products, including fencing, barbed wire, welded wire, and woven wire mesh for the agricultural, construction, and do-it-yourself markets. Many of its products are sold under the Red Brand label. A vertically integrated company with its own steel minimill, Keystone also makes industrial wire — used to make such items as barbecue grills, coat hangers, and nails — and carbon steel rod. Through holding company Contran, Dallas billionaire Harold Simmons (brother of Keystone chairman Glenn Simmons) is the largest investor in Keystone, holding almost two-thirds of its stock.

	Annual Growth	12/04	12/05	12/06	12/07	*12/08
Sales ($ mil.)	11.5%	364.3	367.5	440.5	451.2	562.7
Net income ($ mil.)	42.3%	16.1	39.2	57.7	64.8	66.1
Employees	(4.5%)	1,200	1,200	1,100	1,100	1,000

*Most recent year available

[H] An in-depth profile of this company is available to Hoover's Online members at hoovers.com.

891

KEYSTONE FOODS LLC

300 Barr Harbor Dr., Ste. 600
West Conshohocken, PA 19428
Phone: 610-667-6700
Fax: 610-667-1460
Web: www.keystonefoods.com

CEO: Jerry Dean
CFO: John Coggins
HR: Spence Jarnagin
FYE: December 31
Type: Private

Beef is just one of the cornerstones of this food company. Keystone Foods is one of the largest makers of hamburger patties and processed poultry with about 30 distribution and processing centers located throughout the world. A major supplier to McDonald's restaurants, Keystone serves about 30,000 restaurants worldwide with hamburgers, chicken wings, breast fillets, and chicken patties, as well as fish and pork products. Keystone also provides new product development services to its customers, as well as custom distribution and logistics services. Chairman Herb Lotman owns the company, which began as a beef-boning business in the 1960s.

	Annual Growth	12/04	12/05	12/06	12/07	12/08
Est. sales ($ mil.)	21.5%	3,000.0	3,119.0	3,310.0	5,580.0	6,540.0
Employees	15.1%	7,800	7,800	8,000	13,000	13,700

KEYSTONE GROUP, L.P.

201 Main St., Ste. 3100
Fort Worth, TX 76102
Phone: 817-390-8400
Fax: 817-338-2064

CEO: Robert M. Bass
CFO: —
HR: —
FYE: December 31
Type: Private

Keystone Group is owned and led by Texas financier Robert Bass, renowned for buying troubled businesses and making them profitable. (He also is among the richest men in America, a prominent philanthropist, and contributor to the Democratic Party.) His investment firm has holdings in real estate and the financial services, manufacturing, information services, and oil and gas industries. Keystone is a principal investor in Oak Hill Capital Partners, which manages approximately $8 billion in private equity capital and owns stakes in more than 20 companies.

	Annual Growth	12/04	12/05	12/06	12/07	12/08
Est. sales ($ mil.)	—	—	—	—	—	92.5
Employees	—	—	—	—	—	1,513

KEYSTONE RV COMPANY

2642 Hackberry Dr.
Goshen, IN 46526
Phone: 574-535-2100
Fax: 574-535-2199
Web: www.keystonerv.com

CEO: Ronald J. (Ron) Fenech
CFO: —
HR: —
FYE: July 31
Type: Subsidiary

Keystone RV Company wants to drive home a point: go RVing. The company, a subsidiary of RV and bus maker Thor Industries, is a manufacturer of towable travel trailers and fifth wheels. Keystone's brands include Everest, Fuzion, Laredo, Montana, Outback, and Sprinter, to name a few. The company also offers larger destination travel trailers and smaller travel trailers classified as "lite weight," as well as a line of "toy haulers" that feature living spaces and portable garages for housing and transporting motorcycles, ATVs, and other Big Boy Toys. Keystone has a network of more than 800 dealers and several manufacturing facilities located in Indiana and Oregon.

KFC CORPORATION

1441 Gardiner Ln.
Louisville, KY 40213
Phone: 502-874-8300
Fax: —
Web: www.kfc.com

CEO: Roger Eaton
CFO: —
HR: —
FYE: December 31
Type: Subsidiary

KFC rules the roost when it comes to serving chicken. One of the world's largest fast-food chains, the company owns and franchises more than 16,200 outlets in about 100 countries. (More than 5,100 locations are in the US.) The restaurants offer the Colonel's trademark fried chicken (in both Original Recipe and Extra Crispy varieties) along with chicken sandwiches, chicken pot pies, crispy chicken strips, mashed potatoes and gravy, and potato wedges. Its locations can be found operating as free-standing units and kiosks in high-traffic areas. More than 25% of the restaurants are company-operated. KFC is a unit of fast-food franchisor YUM! Brands, which also operates Pizza Hut and Taco Bell.

K-FED BANCORP

NASDAQ (GM): KFED

1359 N. Grand Ave.
Covina, CA 91724
Phone: 626-339-9663
Fax: —
Web: www.k-fed.com

CEO: Kay M. Hoveland
CFO: Dustin Luton
HR: —
FYE: June 30
Type: Public

K-Fed Bancorp had the name *before* a certain notorious baby-daddy did. K-Fed Bancorp is the holding company of Kaiser Federal Bank, a community thrift operating in Southern California and the San Francisco Bay area. With about 10 full-service branches and financial services offices, Kaiser Federal Bank offers such traditional retail deposit products as checking accounts, savings accounts, and CDs. The company uses deposit funds to originate or purchase a variety of loans; real estate loans make up the bulk of a lending portfolio that also includes automobile, home equity, and other consumer loans. K-Fed Mutual Holding Company owns more than half of K-Fed Bancorp.

	Annual Growth	6/05	6/06	6/07	6/08	6/09
Assets ($ mil.)	8.8%	639.9	738.9	799.6	849.0	895.1
Net income ($ mil.)	(1.5%)	5.0	4.9	4.7	3.9	4.7
Market value ($ mil.)	(6.8%)	162.0	192.6	210.3	144.2	122.0
Employees	1.3%	95	104	98	97	100

KFORCE INC.

NASDAQ (GS): KFRC

1001 E. Palm Ave.
Tampa, FL 33605
Phone: 813-552-5000
Fax: 813-254-9640
Web: www.kforce.com

CEO: David L. Dunkel
CFO: Joseph J. (Joe) Liberatore
HR: Peter M. Alonso
FYE: December 31
Type: Public

Kforce is a corporate matchmaker, placing highly skilled workers with the companies that need them. The specialty staffing firm provides primarily temporary staffing services (and to a lesser extent permanent placement) in such areas as information technology, accounting, health care, clinical research, and government. Kforce operates about 65 field offices across the US and serves *FORTUNE* 1000 corporations as well as small and midsized firms nationwide. Kforce also has two international offices in the Philippines. Formed in 1994, the company also offers Web-based services such as online resumes, job postings, career management information, and interactive interviews.

	Annual Growth	12/05	12/06	12/07	12/08	12/09
Sales ($ mil.)	3.2%	802.3	938.4	1,036.9	997.0	910.1
Net income ($ mil.)	(12.8%)	22.3	32.5	40.4	(84.1)	12.9
Market value ($ mil.)	2.9%	440.9	480.7	385.2	303.4	493.8
Employees	(1.4%)	11,193	12,460	12,297	10,729	10,600

KGB

655 Madison Ave., 21st Fl.
New York, NY 10021
Phone: 212-909-8282
Fax: 610-997-1050
Web: kgb.com

CEO: Robert A. Pines
CFO: —
HR: Kevin Gaugush
FYE: December 31
Type: Private

You don't need Cold War spies to find that phone number, thanks to this company. Formerly INFONXX, kgb is a provider of outsourced directory assistance services in the US and Europe. In addition to traditional directory assistance, it offers additional information services, such as movie listings, train schedules, and price comparisons. Through subsidiary The Number UK, kgb offers phone number lookup and other information services in the UK, primarily through its The Number 118 118 (akin to 411 in the US), as well as through its website (118.com). The company provides directory assistance in France through Le Numero 118 218. Chairman and CEO Robert Pines co-founded kgb in 1992.

KIA MOTORS AMERICA, INC.

111 Peters Canyon Rd.
Irvine, CA 92606
Phone: 949-468-4800
Fax: 949-468-4905
Web: www.kia.com

CEO: Byung Mo Ahn
CFO: N.K. (David) Kim
HR: John Yoon
FYE: December 31
Type: Subsidiary

With a growing stable of models and a generous 10-year/100,000 mile warranty, Kia is turning more and more heads in the US. Kia Motors America is the US marketing, sales, and service subsidiary of South Korea-based Kia Motors. Models sold in the US include the Amanti (premium sedan), Borrego (luxury SUV), Forte (two-door coupe), Optima (sedan), Sorento (compact SUV), Sedona (minivan), Sportage (SUV), Spectra (four-door and five-door), Rio (compact sedan), Rondo (crossover), and Soul (urban passenger vehicle). Kia Motors America has 640 dealerships all over the US. Fellow Korean automaker Hyundai Motor controls nearly 40% of Kia Motors.

	Annual Growth	12/04	12/05	12/06	12/07	12/08
Est. sales ($ mil.)	—	—	—	—	—	165.6
Employees	—	—	—	—	—	500

🆔 KID BRANDS, INC.

NYSE: KID

111 Bauer Dr.
Oakland, NJ 07436
Phone: 201-337-9000
Fax: —
Web: www.kidbrandsinc.com

CEO: Bruce G. Crain
CFO: Guy A. Paglinco
HR: —
FYE: December 31
Type: Public

Kid Brands looked the gift horse in the mouth and said "No thanks." The company, best known for its plush collectible bears, sold its gifts business in 2008 to focus on products for the youngest consumers: newborns to 2-year-olds. In September 2009, the manufacturer and marketer also changed its name from Russ Berrie and Company to Kid Brands. The company sells infant bedding and furniture, as well as related nursery accessories. It also peddles infant-development toys and teething, feeding, and bath and baby care products. Kid Brands' subsidiaries include Sassy, Kids Line, LaJobi, and CoCaLo. The late Russell Berrie founded the business in 1963.

	Annual Growth	12/05	12/06	12/07	12/08	12/09
Sales ($ mil.)	(4.3%)	290.2	294.8	331.2	229.2	243.9
Net income ($ mil.)	—	(35.1)	(9.4)	8.9	(111.6)	11.0
Market value ($ mil.)	(21.3%)	246.0	332.9	352.5	64.0	94.4
Employees	(27.3%)	1,220	1,034	1,036	386	340

KID GALAXY, INC.

150 Dow St., Tower 2, Unit 425B
Manchester, NH 03101
Phone: 603-645-6252
Fax: 603-647-9416
Web: www.kidgalaxy.com

CEO: James Markley
CFO: —
HR: —
FYE: March 31
Type: Subsidiary

Kid Galaxy wants kids to think its toys are outta this world. The company makes land (DRV, Morphibians), air (Hyper Flyer planes), and water toys (submarines), as well as foam toys and mini remote control vehicles known as KG Racers, as well as preschool lines called My First RC and Little Universe. Kid Galaxy sells its products in Australia, Canada, China, Japan, the UK, and the US, as well as through sales outlets in Hong Kong. The US is the biggest market for Kid Galaxy's toys. Founded in 1994, Kid Galaxy is a subsidiary of Lung Cheong International Holdings Limited, which acquired the toymaker in 2002.

KIEHL'S SINCE 1851 LLC

435 Hudson St., 5th Fl.
New York, NY 10014
Phone: 917-606-2740
Fax: 917-606-9536
Web: www.kiehls.com

CEO: Chris Salgardo
CFO: —
HR: —
FYE: December 31
Type: Subsidiary

Kiehl's Since 1851 makes natural hair and skin care products and lipstick and sells them strictly by word of mouth. Pretty strictly, anyway. Kiehl's doesn't advertise much or go door-to-door, and its rigid marketing policy keeps its products out of all but a few exclusive retailers — stores such as Barneys and Bergdorf Goodman. The company's East Village location in Manhattan is frequented by celebrity hairdressers, entertainers, and others willing to brave long checkout lines. Its products are also available at Kiehl's stores nationwide and overseas. Customers can order through its catalog and by phone. Cosmetics giant L'Oréal bought the company in 2000 and began expanding its reach beyond Manhattan.

KIEWIT POWER CONSTRUCTORS CO.

9401 Renner Blvd.
Lenexa, KS 66219
Phone: 913-928-7800
Fax: 913-689-4800
Web: www.kiewit.com/powerconstructors

CEO: Howard Barton
CFO: Dave Freeman
HR: Don Bendetti
FYE: December 31
Type: Subsidiary

Kiewit Power Constructors is plugged into the energy industry. The company, a part of Peter Kiewit Sons, has been working on complex building projects since it began with three Air Force bases in Greenland in 1951. Now the firm (working with sister company Kiewit Power Engineers) typically acts as a prime or general contractor for power and mechanical process facilities. Undertakings have included nuclear, fossil, geothermal, waste-to-energy, and gas turbine power projects; oil and process facilities; natural gas compressors; water and wastewater treatment plants; and nuclear fuel processing facilities in the US, Canada, and the Philippines.

An in-depth profile of this company is available to Hoover's Online members at hoovers.com.

KILLBUCK BANCSHARES, INC.

OTC: KLIB

165 N. Main St.
Killbuck, OH 44637
Phone: 330-276-2771
Fax: 330-276-0216
Web: www.killbuckbank.com

CEO: Luther E. Proper
CFO: Diane S. Knowles
HR: —
FYE: December 31
Type: Public

Interestingly enough, if you want to *save* a buck, you can take your *doe* to Killbuck. Killbuck Bancshares is the holding company for The Killbuck Savings Bank, which operates about 10 branches in northeast Ohio. It offers traditional retail products to individuals and small to midsized businesses, including checking and savings accounts, credit cards, and IRAs. Residential and commercial mortgages make up about two-thirds of its loan portfolio, which also includes business loans and consumer loans. Killbuck Bancshares is the #1 financial institution in Holmes County, where most of its offices are located. It also has branches in Knox and Tuscarawas counties.

	Annual Growth	12/05	12/06	12/07	12/08	12/09
Assets ($ mil.)	5.7%	298.0	313.2	336.3	341.3	372.0
Net income ($ mil.)	(7.3%)	4.2	5.2	4.9	4.5	3.1
Market value ($ mil.)	0.4%	62.6	68.3	70.9	70.6	63.5
Employees	0.6%	124	127	127	128	127

KILROY REALTY CORPORATION

NYSE: KRC

12200 W. Olympic Blvd., Ste. 200
Los Angeles, CA 90064
Phone: 310-481-8400
Fax: 310-481-6580
Web: www.kilroyrealty.com

CEO: John B. Kilroy Jr.
CFO: Tyler H. Rose
HR: —
FYE: December 31
Type: Public

Kilroy is *still* here, especially if you're referring to Southern California. A real estate investment trust (REIT), Kilroy Realty owns, manages, and develops office and industrial properties, mostly in suburban Orange County, San Diego, and Los Angeles. Its portfolio includes more than 90 office and 40 industrial properties, including the Kilroy Airport Center in Long Beach and the Westside Media Center in Los Angeles. Among its more than 285 tenants are large and small businesses including Intuit, Bridgepoint Education Scripps Health, and DIRECTV. The company also develops properties for itself and for other parties. It owns about 12 million sq. ft. of rentable space.

	Annual Growth	12/05	12/06	12/07	12/08	12/09
Sales ($ mil.)	3.5%	243.1	252.9	260.1	290.0	279.4
Net income ($ mil.)	3.0%	33.8	81.9	113.8	44.1	38.0
Market value ($ mil.)	(16.1%)	3,236.9	4,078.9	2,874.0	1,749.7	1,603.8
Employees	(1.3%)	139	143	148	134	132

KIMBALL INTERNATIONAL, INC.

NASDAQ (GS): KBALB

1600 Royal St.
Jasper, IN 47549
Phone: 812-482-1600
Fax: 812-482-8300
Web: www.kimball.com

CEO: James C. (Jim) Thyen
CFO: Robert F. Schneider
HR: Dean M. Vonderheide
FYE: June 30
Type: Public

These days, keyboards on Kimball products are used for entering data, not making music. Once a leader in the domestic piano business, Kimball International now makes more of its money from making navigation systems, HVAC controls, and defibrillators. Kimball boasts two business segments. Its Electronic Manufacturing Services (EMS) unit sells contract electronics and electro-mechanical assemblies primarily to the transportation, medical, and industrial markets. The company's Furniture segment makes and markets furniture and cabinets for the office, hospitality, and retail industries. Combined, the founding Habig and Thyen families own more than 50% of Kimball and fill its executive and board suites.

	Annual Growth	6/05	6/06	6/07	6/08	6/09
Sales ($ mil.)	1.8%	1,124.2	1,142.6	1,286.9	1,352.0	1,207.4
Net income ($ mil.)	1.0%	16.6	15.1	19.2	0.0	17.3
Market value ($ mil.)	(17.0%)	496.4	741.3	526.5	311.4	235.4
Employees	(5.6%)	7,750	7,512	7,560	7,195	6,164

KIMBERLY-CLARK CORPORATION

NYSE: KMB

351 Phelps Dr.
Irving, TX 75038
Phone: 972-281-1200
Fax: 972-281-1490
Web: www.kimberly-clark.com

CEO: Thomas J. (Tom) Falk
CFO: Mark A. Buthman
HR: Lizanne C. (Liz) Gottung
FYE: December 31
Type: Public

Nobody knows noses and diapering babies better than Kimberly-Clark, the world's top maker of personal paper products. The company operates through four business segments: personal care, consumer tissue, K-C Professional, and health care. Kimberly-Clark's largest unit, personal care, makes products such as diapers (Huggies, Pull-Ups), feminine care items (Kotex), and incontinence care products (Poise, Depend). Through its consumer tissue segment, the manufacturer offers facial and bathroom tissues, paper towels, and other household items under the names Cottonelle, Kleenex, Viva, and Scott. Kimberly-Clark's professional unit makes WypAll commercial wipes, among other items.

	Annual Growth	12/05	12/06	12/07	12/08	12/09
Sales ($ mil.)	4.7%	15,902.6	16,746.9	18,266.0	19,415.0	19,115.0
Net income ($ mil.)	6.0%	1,580.6	1,499.5	1,822.9	1,698.0	1,994.0
Market value ($ mil.)	1.7%	24,693.4	28,129.4	28,704.8	21,832.9	26,374.1
Employees	(0.4%)	57,000	55,000	53,000	53,000	56,000

KIMCO REALTY CORPORATION

NYSE: KIM

3333 New Hyde Park Rd.
New Hyde Park, NY 11042
Phone: 516-869-9000
Fax: 516-869-9001
Web: www.kimcorealty.com

CEO: David B. Henry
CFO: Michael V. Pappagallo
HR: —
FYE: December 31
Type: Public

Kimco Realty is the real deal. The self-managed and self-administered real estate investment trust (REIT) owns or has interests in more than 1,900 community shopping centers — totaling around 180 million sq. ft. of space — in 45 states, Canada, and Central and South America. Kimco is involved in land acquisition, development of new properties, and redevelopment of existing ones with a goal of long-term investment. It also offers related real estate services, including preferred equity and mezzanine debt financing, leasing and property services, and real estate investing. Kimco properties are usually anchored by a big-box store, such as Home Depot or Kohl's.

	Annual Growth	12/05	12/06	12/07	12/08	12/09
Sales ($ mil.)	10.8%	522.5	593.9	681.6	758.7	786.9
Net income ($ mil.)	(63.9%)	360.8	425.8	389.9	248.1	6.1
Market value ($ mil.)	(19.4%)	13,012.3	18,232.6	14,764.6	7,414.7	5,488.0
Employees	6.2%	503	618	682	680	640

KIMLEY-HORN AND ASSOCIATES, INC.

3001 Weston Pkwy.
Cary, NC 27513
Phone: 919-677-2000
Fax: 919-677-2050
Web: www.kimley-horn.com

CEO: John C. Atz
CFO: Nicholas L. (Nick) Ellis
HR: Barry Barber
FYE: December 31
Type: Private

Got land and need a plan? Kimley-Horn and Associates offers engineering and land planning services for environmental, water resource, wireless communications, landscape, transportation, urban development, and aviation projects. Founded by a pair of transportation engineers, the firm is a leading urban planning consultant and top intelligent transportation systems specialist. Kimley-Horn has worked on a variety of projects including parking and runway work at nation's busiest airports and hurricane damage investigations. It also specializes in residential, retail, and mixed-use land planning. Incorporated in 1967 by Bob Kimley, Bill Horn, and Ed Vick, the firm is now employee-owned.

	Annual Growth	12/04	12/05	12/06	12/07	12/08
Est. sales ($ mil.)	—	—	—	—	—	407.1
Employees	—	—	—	—	—	2,177

KIMPTON HOTEL & RESTAURANT GROUP, INC.

222 Kearney St., Ste. 200
San Francisco, CA 94108
Phone: 415-397-5572
Fax: 415-296-8031
Web: www.kimptongroup.com

CEO: Michael Depatie
CFO: Ben Rowe
HR: Alan Baer
FYE: December 31
Type: Private

Kimpton Hotel & Restaurant Group hopes a little style can help it stand out in the crowded leisure industry. The company targets business and leisure travelers at more than 40 boutique hotels in about 20 markets in the US and Canada. Kimpton buys older buildings in urban areas and transforms them into four-star hotels hotels that feature mostly smaller, European-style accommodations. Upscale Kimpton Restaurants are located next to most hotels. The company also offers management services, such as strategic planning, sales and marketing, human resources, and administration support. Investment banker and founder Bill Kimpton opened the company's first hotel, the Clarion Bedford, in San Francisco in 1981.

	Annual Growth	12/04	12/05	12/06	12/07	12/08
Est. sales ($ mil.)	—	—	—	—	—	600.0
Employees	—	—	—	—	—	6,000

KINDER MORGAN ENERGY PARTNERS, L.P.

NYSE: KMP

500 Dallas St., Ste. 1000
Houston, TX 77002
Phone: 713-369-9000
Fax: 713-369-9410
Web: www.kindermorgan.com

CEO: Richard D. (Rich) Kinder
CFO: Kimberly A. (Kim) Dang
HR: James E. Street
FYE: December 31
Type: Public

Kinder Morgan Energy Partners (KMP) keeps energy on the move throughout the US. The company holds stakes in or more than 28,000 miles of natural gas and petroleum product pipelines and owns 180 bulk terminals and rail transloading facilities that handle more than 87 million tons of coal, petroleum coke, and bulk products annually. KMP transports refined petroleum products (gasoline, diesel, and jet fuel) through 8,400 miles of pipelines and stores the products in 60 terminals in the US. Through its CO2 subsidiary, KMP transports carbon dioxide. Kinder Morgan owns 14% of KMP, and through its Kinder Morgan Management unit, acts as general partner.

	Annual Growth	12/05	12/06	12/07	12/08	12/09
Sales ($ mil.)	(8.0%)	9,787.1	8,954.6	9,217.7	11,740.3	7,003.4
Net income ($ mil.)	12.1%	812.2	972.1	590.3	1,304.8	1,283.8
Market value ($ mil.)	6.3%	9,913.6	9,930.2	11,192.7	9,484.5	12,641.8
Employees	—	0	0	7,600	7,800	7,931

KINDER MORGAN, INC.

500 Dallas St., Ste. 1000
Houston, TX 77002
Phone: 713-369-9000
Fax: 713-369-9100
Web: www.kindermorgan.com

CEO: Richard D. (Rich) Kinder
CFO: Kimberly A. (Kim) Dang
HR: James E. Street
FYE: December 31
Type: Private

Kinder Morgan (formerly Knight) pipes in profits by operating 36,000 miles of natural gas pipelines in the US and Canada. The company also distributes natural gas to more than 1.1 million customers, primarily in the Midwest, and it operates gas-fired power plants along its pipelines. Through Kinder Morgan Management, it controls Kinder Morgan Energy Partners, which transports refined products and operates 170 terminals that handle coal, petroleum coke, and other materials. In 2007 chairman and CEO Richard Kinder, who owns 31% of the company, led a group of investors in taking Kinder Morgan private and adopted the Knight name. To take advantage of its better-known brand, it reverted to Kinder Morgan in 2009.

	Annual Growth	12/04	12/05	12/06	12/07	12/08
Sales ($ mil.)	5.2%	—	—	—	11,500.0	12,094.8
Employees	2.6%	—	—	—	7,600	7,800

KINDER MORGAN MANAGEMENT, LLC

NYSE: KMR

500 Dallas St., Ste. 1000
Houston, TX 77002
Phone: 713-369-9000
Fax: 713-495-2817
Web: www.kindermorgan.com

CEO: Richard D. (Rich) Kinder
CFO: Kimberly A. (Kim) Dang
HR: James E. Street
FYE: December 31
Type: Public

This can get Kinder complicated: Kinder Morgan Management (KMM) was created by pipeline operator Kinder Morgan, Inc., to be the limited partner in Kinder Morgan Energy Partners (KMP). KMM oversees and manages KMP's business segments: pipelines that transport refined petroleum products (including gasoline, diesel, jet fuel, and natural gas liquids); natural gas pipelines; pipelines that transport carbon dioxide for oil field use; bulk terminals that handle coal, petroleum coke, and other products; and liquids terminals that handle refined petroleum products and chemicals.

	Annual Growth	12/05	12/06	12/07	12/08	12/09
Sales ($ mil.)	—	—	—	—	—	90.6
Net income ($ mil.)	—	—	—	—	—	59.0
Market value ($ mil.)	—	—	—	—	—	4,673.8
Employees	—	—	—	—	—	—

KINDRED HEALTHCARE, INC.

NYSE: KND

680 S. 4th St.
Louisville, KY 40202
Phone: 502-596-7300
Fax: 502-596-4170
Web: www.kindredhealthcare.com

CEO: Paul J. Diaz
CFO: Richard A. (Rich) Lechleiter
HR: —
FYE: December 31
Type: Public

Kindred Healthcare is one of the largest long-term health care providers in the US. Kindred operates some 220 nursing homes and more than 80 long-term acute care hospitals located in about 35 states. Its facilities have a combined capacity of about 34,000 beds. The company owns some of its facilities, but operates most of them under lease agreements with Ventas and other third parties. Kindred also operates a contract rehabilitation therapy business, which serves its own and other long-term care facilities, through its People-*first* Rehabilitation division.

	Annual Growth	12/05	12/06	12/07	12/08	12/09
Sales ($ mil.)	2.1%	3,924.0	4,266.7	4,220.3	4,151.4	4,270.0
Net income ($ mil.)	(27.5%)	144.9	146.0	(46.9)	36.3	40.1
Market value ($ mil.)	(1.8%)	784.1	768.6	986.2	514.0	728.8
Employees	1.2%	51,600	55,000	38,200	53,700	54,100

KINECTA FEDERAL CREDIT UNION

1440 Rosecrans Ave.
Manhattan Beach, CA 90266
Phone: 310-643-5458
Fax: 310-643-8350
Web: www.kinecta.org

CEO: Roger Ballard
CFO: Gregory Talbott
HR: Mark Steiman
FYE: December 31
Type: Mutual company

Kinecta Federal Credit Union provides banking services to more than 220,000 member-owners in Southern California. Its offerings include checking and savings accounts, money markets, IRAs, and savings bonds. Kinecta originates automobile, home equity, and residential mortgage loans; the company also offers credit card services. Kinecta has about two dozen branches; members have access to more than 4,000 branches around the world through a network of affiliated credit unions. The company provides check-cashing and other services through its Nix Check Cashing division. Nix operates about 50 branches in the greater Los Angeles area. Kinecta plans to merge with NuVision Federal Credit Union.

	Annual Growth	12/04	12/05	12/06	12/07	12/08
Est. sales ($ mil.)	—	—	—	—	—	172.1
Employees	—	—	—	—	—	450

An in-depth profile of this company is available to Hoover's Online members at hoovers.com.

895

KINETIC CONCEPTS, INC.

NYSE: KCI

8023 Vantage Dr.
San Antonio, TX 78230
Phone: 210-524-9000
Fax: 210-255-6998
Web: www.kci1.com

CEO: Catherine M. (Cathy) Burzik
CFO: Martin J. (Marty) Landon
HR: R. James (Jim) Cravens
FYE: December 31
Type: Public

Kinetic Concepts has made its bed and has no problems lying in it. The company's "therapeutic surfaces" (commonly known as hospital beds and specialized mattresses) treat and prevent complications associated with patient immobility, such as pressure sores and buildup of fluid in the lungs. The company also makes vacuum-assisted wound care systems and critical care therapy systems, which rotate immobilized patients to reduce the incidence of pulmonary complications and pressure sores. Its LifeCell business develops tissue regeneration products used in surgical procedures. Customers include acute and long-term care facilities, home health agencies, wound care clinics, and individuals in the US and abroad.

	Annual Growth	12/05	12/06	12/07	12/08	12/09
Sales ($ mil.)	13.3%	1,208.6	1,371.6	1,609.9	1,877.9	1,992.6
Net income ($ mil.)	17.0%	122.2	195.5	237.1	173.9	228.7
Market value ($ mil.)	(1.4%)	2,850.5	2,835.5	3,839.9	1,375.1	2,699.2
Employees	4.4%	5,735	6,300	6,400	6,900	6,800

KING & SPALDING LLP

1180 Peachtree St. NE
Atlanta, GA 30309
Phone: 404-572-4600
Fax: 404-572-5100
Web: www.kslaw.com

CEO: Robert D. Hays Jr.
CFO: Pete Nolan
HR: Christopher (Chris) Jackson
FYE: December 31
Type: Partnership

With a client list that has included Brown & Williamson Tobacco, Coca-Cola, and Scientific-Atlanta, law firm King & Spalding is well-established as one of the South's leading legal lights. The firm has more than 880 attorneys; counted among them have been such Georgia luminaries as former US Attorney General Griffin Bell and former US Senator Sam Nunn. Its leading practice area is litigation; others include corporate, energy, intellectual property, public finance, and tax law. Outside Atlanta, King & Spalding has about a dozen offices including locations in the United Arab Emirates and Saudi Arabia. Alex King and Jack Spalding founded the firm in 1885.

KING PHARMACEUTICALS, INC.

NYSE: KG

501 5th St.
Bristol, TN 37620
Phone: 423-989-8000
Fax: 423-274-8677
Web: www.kingpharm.com

CEO: Brian A. Markison
CFO: Joseph Squicciarino
HR: Janet Tuffy
FYE: December 31
Type: Public

King Pharmaceuticals might not rule the drug market, but it doesn't mind taking the reins on certain products under development. The company is engaged in marketing pain management drugs and developing late-stage pharmaceutical candidates in the areas of neuroscience and acute care. Already it has a portfolio of branded prescription products, including chronic pain drug Avinza, muscle relaxant Skelaxin, and blood-loss control aid Thrombin-JMI. It also produces emergency drug delivery devices through subsidiary Meridian Medical Technologies and medicated feed additives through Alpharma Animal Health; King acquired rival Alpharma for $1.6 billion in late 2008.

	Annual Growth	12/05	12/06	12/07	12/08	12/09
Sales ($ mil.)	0.1%	1,772.9	1,988.5	2,136.9	1,565.1	1,776.5
Net income ($ mil.)	(6.0%)	117.8	288.9	183.0	(333.1)	92.0
Market value ($ mil.)	(7.7%)	4,223.7	3,974.1	2,556.2	2,651.0	3,062.9
Employees	(1.3%)	2,795	2,800	2,052	3,392	2,649

KING RANCH, INC.

3 River Way, Ste. 1600
Houston, TX 77056
Phone: 832-681-5700
Fax: 832-681-5759
Web: www.king-ranch.com

CEO: Jack Hunt
CFO: —
HR: —
FYE: December 31
Type: Private

Meanwhile, back at the ranch . . . the sprawling King Ranch, to be exact. Founded in 1853, King Ranch's operations extend beyond its original 825,000 Texan cattle-raising acres. The ranch is still home to cattle and horses, of course. However, King Ranch oversees considerable farming interests in its home state and elsewhere (cotton, sorghum, sod, citrus, pecans, vegetables, and cane sugar). It also has varied retail operations (hardware, designer saddles and other leather goods, publishing and printing). In addition, King Ranch also beefs up revenues with tourist dollars from birdwatchers, hunters, and sightseers who visit its Texas ranch lands. The descendants of founder Richard King own King Ranch.

KINGSTON TECHNOLOGY COMPANY, INC.

17600 Newhope St.
Fountain Valley, CA 92708
Phone: 714-435-2600
Fax: 714-435-2699
Web: www.kingston.com

CEO: John Tu
CFO: —
HR: Daniel Hsu
FYE: December 31
Type: Private

Kingston Technology cuts a regal figure in the realm of memory. The company is a top maker of memory modules — printed circuit boards loaded with DRAM or other memory chips that increase the capacity and speed of printers and computers. Kingston also makes flash memory cards used in portable electronic devices, such as digital still cameras, MP3 players, and wireless phones. Kingston takes on some manufacturing chores for customers through its sister company Payton Technology, which runs a specialized factory in China that tests and packages memory chips before assembling them into customized memory modules. Founders John Tu (president) and David Sun (COO) own Kingston Technology.

	Annual Growth	12/04	12/05	12/06	12/07	12/08
Sales ($ mil.)	13.6%	2,400.0	3,000.0	3,700.0	4,500.0	4,000.0
Employees	19.7%	2,000	2,900	4,000	4,500	4,100

KINGSTONE COMPANIES, INC.

NASDAQ (CM): KINS

1158 Broadway
Hewlett, NY 11557
Phone: 516-374-7600
Fax: 516-295-7216
Web: kingstonecompanies.com

CEO: Barry B. Goldstein
CFO: Victor Brodsky
HR: —
FYE: December 31
Type: Public

Kingstone Companies (formerly DCAP Group) keeps things covered. While the company has transformed itself from a broker into an underwriter, its main business is still insurance. Its Kingstone Insurance Company (formerly Commercial Mutual Insurance Company) provides property/casualty insurance policies for individuals and businesses in New York State. Its products, including auto, business, and homeowners' policies, are sold through independent agents. The company has divested its former insurance brokerage business, which offered life and property/casualty policies through owned and franchised retail locations in New York and eastern Pennsylvania.

	Annual Growth	12/05	12/06	12/07	12/08	12/09
Assets ($ mil.)	23.7%	22.5	25.4	23.2	9.4	52.6
Net income ($ mil.)	76.0%	0.5	0.5	0.0	(1.0)	4.8
Market value ($ mil.)	(0.9%)	7.8	9.3	5.1	1.5	7.6
Employees	(20.7%)	101	87	68	46	40

KINGSWAY AMERICA INC.

150 Northwest Point Blvd.
Elk Grove Village, IL 60007
Phone: 847-871-6400
Fax: 847-264-2700
Web: www.kingswayamerica.com

CEO: Colin M. Simpson
CFO: Shelly Gobin
HR: —
FYE: December 31
Type: Subsidiary

It's Kingsway or *no* highway for some high-risk drivers. Kingsway America is the holding company for the US insurance subsidiaries of Canada-based Kingsway Financial Services. Kingsway America's group companies offer nonstandard personal automobile insurance for high-risk drivers, as well as specialty commercial auto coverage, including insurance for long-haul truckers, passenger transportation companies (taxis and limo drivers), and auto repair shops. Its subsidiaries include American Service Insurance, Mendota Insurance, and Universal Casualty.

KINRAY INC.

152-35 10th Ave.
Whitestone, NY 11357
Phone: 718-767-1234
Fax: 718-767-4388
Web: www.kinray.com

CEO: Stewart Rahr
CFO: Howard B. Hirsch
HR: —
FYE: December 31
Type: Private

Kinray, the US's top private wholesale drug distributor, is nothing if not independent. It provides generic, branded, and repackaged drugs, health and beauty products, medical equipment, vitamins, and diabetes-care products. The distributor also offers about 800 private-label products under the Preferred Plus Pharmacy brand. It serves more than 4,000 independent pharmacies, long-term care facilities, and specialty pharmacies in states stretching from Maine to Delaware; though Kinray is looking to supply generic drugs to pharmacies nationwide. The firm was founded in 1944 by Joseph Rahr. His son, CEO and president Stewart Rahr, has owned Kinray since 1975.

	Annual Growth	12/04	12/05	12/06	12/07	12/08
Sales ($ mil.)	9.8%	3,510.0	4,000.0	4,400.0	4,800.0	5,100.0
Employees	0.0%	1,000	800	1,000	1,000	1,000

KINTETSU WORLD EXPRESS (U.S.A.), INC.

100 Jericho Quadrangle, Ste. 326
Jericho, NY 11753
Phone: 516-933-7100
Fax: 516-933-7731
Web: www.kweusa.com

CEO: George Tomiyama
CFO: Katsumi Watanabe
HR: —
FYE: March 31
Type: Subsidiary

Kintetsu World Express (U.S.A.) helps move freight in and out of the US — and the rest of the world. The company specializes in international airfreight and ocean freight forwarding and customs brokerage services. (As a freight forwarder, Kintetsu World Express (U.S.A.) buys transportation capacity from carriers and resells it to customers.) Other services include consulting, inventory management, and warehousing and distribution as well as handling perishable or dangerous cargo. The company operates from a network of about 35 offices in major trade gateways throughout the US. Kintetsu World Express (U.S.A.) is a unit of Japan-based Kintetsu World Express, which launched its US operations in 1969.

	Annual Growth	3/04	3/05	3/06	3/07	3/08
Est. sales ($ mil.)	—	—	—	—	—	290.0
Employees	—	—	—	—	—	703

KION SPECIALTY POLYMERS

4331 Chesapeake Dr.
Charlotte, NC 28216
Phone: 800-585-2151
Fax: 704-395-6689
Web: www.kioncorp.com

CEO: Gregg McCraw
CFO: —
HR: —
FYE: December 31
Type: Subsidiary

KiON isn't the new low-budget, high-mileage car out of Detroit; it's an old high-performance polysilazane-based resin manufacturer based in North Carolina. The company's resins are used in coatings, electronics, and ceramics, and by the defense industry. Polysilazane resins are intermediates composed of alternating silicon and nitrogen atoms. The company was established in 1987 as Commodore Polymer Technologies. Swiss specialty chemical company Clariant, looking to bolster its own polysilazane manufacturing operations, acquired KiON in early 2006 from previous owners Blum Technology Trust.

THE KIRBY COMPANY

1920 W. 114th St.
Cleveland, OH 44102
Phone: 216-228-2400
Fax: 216-529-6146
Web: www.kirby.com

CEO: Mike Nichols
CFO: —
HR: Laurie Mueller
FYE: December 31
Type: Subsidiary

"At no cost to you, I'd like to vacuum and shampoo your carpet." Representatives of The Kirby Company have been sharing that sentiment since the first Kirby vacuum, the Model C, was manufactured in 1935. New Kirby machines have always been sold exclusively door-to-door; the upscale vacuums cost about $1,800 and come with a lifetime warranty. Kirby items are sold through independent dealers and distributors in the US and 70 other countries. The company, named for Jim Kirby, who designed his first vacuum cleaner in 1906, also sells a line of cleaning products. Kirby is part of Scott Fetzer Company, which operates more than 20 businesses.

KIRBY CORPORATION

55 Waugh Dr., Ste. 1000
Houston, TX 77007
Phone: 713-435-1000
Fax: 713-435-1464
Web: www.kirbycorp.com

NYSE: KEX
CEO: Joseph H. (Joe) Pyne
CFO: David W. Grzebinski
HR: Patrick C. Kelly
FYE: December 31
Type: Public

Where Kirby hauls cargo, the only curbs are riverbanks — the company is the largest inland tank barge operator in the US. Its fleet, operated by subsidiary Kirby Inland Marine, consists of more than 900 barges and about 240 towboats. The vessels are used to transport liquid bulk cargo: petrochemicals, crude and refined petroleum products, and agricultural chemicals. Major customers include Exxon Mobil affiliate SeaRiver Maritime and Dow Chemical, each of which accounts for about 10% of Kirby's sales. Its Marine Transportation segment (inland/offshore operations) is joined by its Engine Systems segment, which is a leading provider of diesel engine services and parts for marine, rail, and power generation customers.

	Annual Growth	12/05	12/06	12/07	12/08	12/09
Sales ($ mil.)	8.0%	795.7	984.2	1,172.6	1,360.2	1,082.2
Net income ($ mil.)	16.3%	68.8	95.5	123.3	157.2	125.9
Market value ($ mil.)	7.5%	1,409.5	1,844.2	2,511.5	1,478.4	1,882.0
Employees	2.2%	2,450	3,000	3,100	2,350	2,675

An in-depth profile of this company is available to Hoover's Online members at hoovers.com.

897

KIRIN BREWERY OF AMERICA, LLC

970 W. 190th St., Ste. 890
Torrance, CA 90404
Phone: 310-354-2400
Fax: 310-354-5955
Web: www.kirin.com

CEO: Kazuyasu Kato
CFO: —
HR: —
FYE: December 31
Type: Subsidiary

Kirin Brewery of America helps provide Americans with brews to wash down their sushi. Using Anheuser-Busch's facilities in Los Angeles, the wholly owned subsidiary of Japan's Kirin Brewery Company brews Kirin Lager (one of the world's biggest beer brands), Kirin Draft, Kirin Ichiban, and Kirin Light. The beers are most popular in the western US, home to many Japanese-Americans, and are distributed through Anheuser-Busch's network of wholesalers. Kirin agreed to outsource production, as well as distribution, to the US beer maker starting in 2007. Kirin Brewery of America was founded in 1996.

KIRKLAND & ELLIS LLP

300 N. LaSalle St.
Chicago, IL 60654
Phone: 312-862-2000
Fax: 312-862-2200
Web: www.kirkland.com

CEO: Douglas O. (Doug) McLemore
CFO: Nicholas J. (Nick) Willmott
HR: Wendy A. Cartland
FYE: January 31
Type: Partnership

Known for its work in cases that go to trial, law firm Kirkland & Ellis maintains a variety of practices aimed mainly at corporate clients. Besides litigation, the firm's core practice areas include corporate transactions, intellectual property, restructuring, and tax. Kirkland & Ellis represents public and private companies from a wide range of industries, as well as individuals and government agencies. Over the years its clients have included companies such as Bank of America, General Motors, McDonald's, Motorola, and Siemens. Overall, Kirkland & Ellis has more than 1,500 lawyers in about 10 offices, mostly in the US but also in Hong Kong, London, and Munich, Germany. The firm was founded in 1908.

KIRKLAND'S, INC.

NASDAQ (GM): KIRK

431 Smith Lane
Jackson, TN 38301
Phone: 731-988-3600
Fax: —
Web: www.kirklands.com

CEO: Robert E. Alderson
CFO: W. Michael (Mike) Madden
HR: Michelle R. Graul
FYE: January 31
Type: Public

When you just deplore your bare wood floor and feel the need to improve your home's décor, Kirkland's hopes you'll explore its stores for affordable rugs, art, lamps, and more. The company operates about 300 stores in some 35 states, which stock decorative home accessories and gifts, including framed art, mirrors, candles, lamps, picture frames, artificial flowers, rugs, garden accessories, and coffee-table books. Kirkland's also offers holiday items during Christmas and Easter. Stores operate under the names Kirkland's and Kirkland's Home. It phased out several Briar Patch by Kirkland's locations in 2008. Kirkland's was founded in 1966 by Carl Kirkland.

	Annual Growth	1/06	1/07	1/08	1/09	1/10
Sales ($ mil.)	(0.5%)	415.1	446.8	396.7	391.3	406.2
Net income ($ mil.)	262.7%	0.2	(0.1)	(25.9)	9.3	34.6
Market value ($ mil.)	27.9%	114.3	103.0	18.2	52.1	306.2
Employees	(6.9%)	4,878	4,312	3,843	3,455	3,667

KIRSHENBAUM BOND & PARTNERS LLC

160 Varick St., 4th Fl.
New York, NY 10013
Phone: 212-633-0080
Fax: 212-463-8643
Web: www.kb.com

CEO: Laurie Senecal
CFO: Chris Mozolewski
HR: —
FYE: December 31
Type: Subsidiary

Kirshenbaum Bond & Partners (aka kirshenbaum bond senecal + partners) provides a full range of marketing and advertising services, including traditional advertising, guerilla marketing, logo development, design, packaging, direct mail, collateral, interactive, multimedia, and website applications and development. The firm consists of several units, including lime public relations + promotion; the media kitchen (media buying/planning); open mind (qualitative/quantitative research); and dotglu (interactive/direct marketing). kirshenbaum bond has served such clients as The Andrew Jergens Company, Wendy's, Liberty Mutual, and the Target Corporation. Marketing communications services giant MDC Partners owns the agency.

K.I.S.S. INC.

13498 Pond Springs Rd., Bldg. A
Austin, TX 78729
Phone: 512-258-7003
Fax: 512-250-1225
Web: www.kisscleaning.com

CEO: Ginny Simpson
CFO: —
HR: —
FYE: December 31
Type: Private

If cleanliness is a turn-on, K.I.S.S. might prove successful in compelling you to pucker up. Standing for "Klean Image Service Specialist," K.I.S.S. is a janitorial services franchiser. Established in 1991 by company president Ginny Simpson, the woman-owned janitorial company provides custom-designed janitorial services such as window cleaning, wood floor restoration, carpet and tile cleaning, and recycling for all types of facilities, including airports, churches, country clubs, restaurants, schools, factories, and financial institutions. K.I.S.S. franchises will even replace light bulbs and filters in addition to other specialty services. The company mainly serves the south central Texas region.

	Annual Growth	12/04	12/05	12/06	12/07	12/08
Est. sales ($ mil.)	—	—	—	—	—	1.0
Employees	—	—	—	—	—	8

KIT DIGITAL, INC.

NASDAQ (GM): KITD

205 Hudson St., Ste. 802
New York, NY 10013
Phone: 212-661-4111
Fax: 646-619-4074
Web: www.kit-digital.com

CEO: Kaleil Isaza Tuzman
CFO: Robin Smyth
HR: —
FYE: December 31
Type: Public

A talking car won't help your company achieve its online goals, but maybe KIT digital can help. KIT digital operates an online platform that enables clients to publish, manage, and distribute Internet Protocol (IP)-based video content for marketing purposes. Its clients' video can be delivered through the Internet, set top boxes, and wireless devices. In its previous incarnation as ROO Group, the company was a syndicator of video-on-demand content for broadcast; in 2008 the firm refocused its operations on interactive marketing, and changed its name to KIT ("Knowledge, Imagination and Technology") digital. Chairman and CEO Kaleil Isaza Tuzman controls about 48% of KIT digital's voting power.

	Annual Growth	12/05	12/06	12/07	12/08	12/09
Sales ($ mil.)	63.6%	6.6	9.8	13.9	23.4	47.3
Net income ($ mil.)	—	(9.0)	(14.6)	(34.6)	(19.0)	(19.9)
Market value ($ mil.)	(44.4%)	2,668.8	2,466.6	137.5	121.3	254.2
Employees	40.7%	83	140	135	188	325

KITE REALTY GROUP TRUST

NYSE: KRG

30 S. Meridian St., Ste. 1100
Indianapolis, IN 46204
Phone: 317-577-5600
Fax: 317-577-5605
Web: www.kiterealty.com

CEO: John A. Kite
CFO: Daniel R. Sink
HR: Charlene (Charlie) Ehrlich
FYE: December 31
Type: Public

A real estate investment trust (REIT), Kite Realty Group Trust acquires, develops, and operates retail properties. It owns more than 50 strip malls and anchored shopping centers with some 8 million sq. ft. of leasable space in about 10 states, with a good chunk in Indiana. The REIT also has interests in three commercial properties, a parking garage, several retail sites under development, and nearly 100 acres of land held for possible future development. Kite Realty also provides third-party management, development, and construction services. Its largest tenants include Lowe's, Target, Publix, PetSmart, and Ross, though no single tenant accounts for more than 4% of the company's rental income.

	Annual Growth	12/05	12/06	12/07	12/08	12/09
Sales ($ mil.)	3.8%	99.4	131.9	138.8	142.7	115.3
Net income ($ mil.)	—	11.6	10.2	13.5	6.1	(1.2)
Market value ($ mil.)	(28.4%)	977.8	1,176.9	965.2	351.4	257.3
Employees	(1.3%)	95	109	137	107	90

KITZ CORP. OF AMERICA

10750 Corporate Dr.
Stafford, TX 77477
Phone: 281-491-7333
Fax: 281-491-9402
Web: www.kitz.com

CEO: James Walther
CFO: James Walther
HR: —
FYE: March 31
Type: Subsidiary

Kitz Corp. of America (KCA) promotes the free flow of anything *but* fluids. The subsidiary of Kitz Corp. sells and markets, as well as distributes, a slew of flow control valves. Through its divisions, KCA manufactures pressure seal and high-pressure valves and valve actuators, in chrome, carbon steel, and exotic alloys. The lineup is used in gas and oil pipelines, oil refineries, petrochemical processing plants, and power plants. Under such brands as Direct Seal, KCA products are promoted directly to engineering companies and end users, notably petrochemical plants. KCA was created to represent its Japan-based parent; KCA has evolved to also operate a network of valve modification shops in the US and Canada.

	Annual Growth	3/04	3/05	3/06	3/07	3/08
Est. sales ($ mil.)	—	—	—	—	—	60.7
Employees	—	—	—	—	—	32

KIWIBOX.COM, INC.

OTC: KIWB

330 W. 38th St., Ste. 1607
New York, NY 10018
Phone: 212-967-1953
Fax: —
Web: www.kiwiboxinc.com

CEO: Rudolph Hauke
CFO: Craig S. Cody
HR: —
FYE: December 31
Type: Public

KiwiBox.com (formerly Magnitude Information Systems) offered a line of ergonomic software tools that helped employees avoid repetitive stress injuries in their use of computers. Its flagship suite of software products, ErgoEnterprise, helped users modify their behavior by monitoring patterns during computer usage and warning them when they make repetitive use of input devices, such as keyboards and mice. In 2007 Magnitude acquired Kiwibox Media, which operates a social networking site for teenagers. In late 2009 the company changed its name to KiwiBox.com as part of a shifting strategy to focus on its social networking operations.

	Annual Growth	12/05	12/06	12/07	12/08	12/09
Sales ($ mil.)	(15.9%)	0.2	0.0	0.0	0.1	0.1
Net income ($ mil.)	—	(2.2)	(3.9)	(3.9)	(5.5)	(2.4)
Market value ($ mil.)	(29.5%)	38.3	14.4	17.4	11.9	9.5
Employees	(6.1%)	9	4	13	15	7

KKR & CO. L.P.

9 W. 57th St., Ste. 4200
New York, NY 10019
Phone: 212-750-8300
Fax: 212-750-0003
Web: www.kkr.com

CEO: Henry R. Kravis
CFO: William J. Janetschek
HR: Peter M. Fasolo
FYE: December 31
Type: Private

Have the barbarians at the gate become civilized? KKR & Co. (or KKR), the master of the leveraged buyout, has ditched its hostile takeover image for a kinder, gentler, buy-and-build strategy. KKR has more than $50 billion in assets under management, earning management fees as well as profiting from its direct interests. An active owner, KKR often supervises or installs new management and revamps strategy and corporate structure, selling underperforming units or adding new ones. KKR first filed an initial public offering in 2007 but now plans to take a somewhat more circuitous route to going public.

KKR FINANCIAL HOLDINGS LLC

NYSE: KFN

555 California St., 50th Fl.
San Francisco, CA 94104
Phone: 415-315-3620
Fax: 415-391-3077
Web: www.kkrfn.com

CEO: William C. (Bill) Sonneborn
CFO: Jeffrey B. Van Horn
HR: —
FYE: December 31
Type: Public

KKR Financial Holdings is a specialty finance company that invests in secured and unsecured corporate loans, including mezzanine loans, high-yield corporate bonds, asset-backed securities, and debt and equity securities. It has more than $18 billion of assets under management. The company is managed by KKR Financial Advisors; both companies are affiliates of private equity and leveraged buyout firm KKR & Co. Formerly a real estate investment trust (REIT), KKR Financial had significant investments in residential mortgages and related securities, but with the mortgage market melting down, the company restructured, dropped its REIT status, and stopped investing in residential mortgages in 2007.

	Annual Growth	12/05	12/06	12/07	12/08	12/09
Sales ($ mil.)	4.0%	407.5	976.5	740.2	987.8	476.5
Net income ($ mil.)	8.7%	55.1	135.3	(100.2)	(1,075.0)	76.9
Market value ($ mil.)	(29.9%)	3,799.1	4,242.5	2,225.0	250.2	918.5
Employees	20.5%	44	53	—	—	—

KLA-TENCOR CORPORATION

NASDAQ (GS): KLAC

1 Technology Dr.
Milpitas, CA 95035
Phone: 408-875-3000
Fax: 408-875-4144
Web: www.kla-tencor.com

CEO: Richard P. (Rick) Wallace
CFO: Mark P. Dentinger
HR: —
FYE: June 30
Type: Public

KLA-Tencor is hard-core when it comes to hunting down flaws in chips. The company — one of the world's largest makers of semiconductor equipment — offers yield management systems that monitor and analyze wafers at various stages of chip production, inspecting reticles (which make circuit patterns) and measuring crucial microscopic layers. The systems' feedback allows flaws to be corrected before they can ruin the costly wafers. KLA-Tencor has long dominated the market for equipment that inspects semiconductor photomasks and reticles. The company gets more than three-quarters of its sales from outside the US. Its customers are leading global semiconductor manufacturers, including Intel and Samsung Electronics.

	Annual Growth	6/05	6/06	6/07	6/08	6/09
Sales ($ mil.)	(7.6%)	2,085.2	2,070.6	2,731.2	2,521.7	1,520.2
Net income ($ mil.)	—	466.7	380.5	528.1	359.1	(523.4)
Market value ($ mil.)	(12.8%)	7,425.3	7,066.6	9,341.2	6,920.4	4,292.3
Employees	(2.8%)	5,500	5,900	6,000	6,000	4,900

An in-depth profile of this company is available to Hoover's Online members at hoovers.com.

KLAUSSNER FURNITURE INDUSTRIES, INC.

405 Lewallen Rd.
Asheboro, NC 27205
Phone: 336-625-6174
Fax: 336-626-0905
Web: www.klaussner.com

CEO: J. B. Davis
CFO: David O. (Dave) Bryant
HR: —
FYE: December 31
Type: Private

Klaussner Furniture Industries makes accoutrements for the couch potato in all of us. A leading US maker of furniture, Klaussner sells fabric- and leather-upholstered sofas and recliners, chairs, ottomans, occasional tables, home entertainment, and dining furniture under the Distinctions and Klaussner names. Its licensed brands include Sealy and Dick Idol. The furniture firm boasts manufacturing facilities in North Carolina and Iowa, as well as a handful of licensed Klaussnerhome stores and about 150 Klaussner Home Furnishings Galleries. It also owns 12% of furniture retailer Jennifer Convertibles. Chairman Hans Klaussner has owned the company since 1979; it was founded in 1964 as Stuart Furniture Industries.

KLEIN TOOLS, INC.

450 Bond St.
Lincolnshire, IL 60069
Phone: 847-821-5500
Fax: —
Web: www.klein-tools.com

CEO: Mathias A. (Mat) Klein III
CFO: Verne Tuite
HR: —
FYE: December 31
Type: Private

Five generations of Kleins have had a grip on Klein Tools, a maker of non-powered hand tools. The company's products can be found in the tool pouches of professionals in the construction, electronics, mining, telecommunications, and general industries. (Klein makes their pouches, too.) Its lineup includes cable cutters, chisels, drill bits, hammers, pliers, saws, screwdrivers, wire strippers, and wrenches. Klein also sells occupational protective gear and specialty chemicals. Products are distributed worldwide and sold by tool retailers and building supply stores, including Home Depot, Ace Hardware, and Grainger. Founded by Mathias Klein in 1857, the company is still owned by the Klein family.

KLEINER PERKINS CAUFIELD & BYERS

2750 Sand Hill Rd.
Menlo Park, CA 94025
Phone: 650-233-2750
Fax: 650-233-0300
Web: www.kpcb.com

CEO: Mark K. Allen
CFO: Susan Biglieri
HR: Juliet Flint
FYE: December 31
Type: Private

Let Kleiner Perkins Caufield & Byers (KPCB) beware — or, at the very least, be on the lookout. The venture capital firm invests money, time, and talent in early-stage innovative companies that sometimes become the foundations for new industries. KPCB has invested in such notable outfits as AOL, Amazon.com, Genentech, Google, Intuit, and Sun Microsystems. The firm focuses its investments in four main areas: information technology, life sciences, pandemic and bio-defense, and green technology. (Al Gore is one of its partners.) KPCB often forms networks among its investments so they can use one another to develop and expand. The company's current portolio includes stakes in about 100 companies.

KLEVER MARKETING, INC.

Pink Sheets: KLMK

2469 E. Ft. Union Blvd., Ste. 214
Cottonwood, UT 84121
Phone: 801-847-6444
Fax: 801-847-6442
Web: www.kleverkart.com

CEO: Paul G. Begum
CFO: —
HR: —
FYE: December 31
Type: Public

Klever Marketing wants to ride in your shopping cart. The company holds patents related to wireless advertising systems. It partnered with Fujitsu Transaction Solutions to develop advertising terminals that could be attached to shopping carts. The U-Scan Shopper provided advertisers with an opportunity to influence potential customers at the point of purchase. However, in 2007 Fujitsu underwent a restructuring that included the decision not to pursue the development of U-Scan shopping carts. The company's auditor has expressed doubt about Klever Marketing's ability to continue as a going concern. Klever, which underwent a debt restructuring in 2008, is now investigating merger and acquisition opportunities.

	Annual Growth	12/05	12/06	12/07	12/08	12/09
Sales ($ mil.)	—	—	0.0	0.0	0.0	0.0
Net income ($ mil.)	—	—	(0.9)	(0.7)	0.1	(0.6)
Market value ($ mil.)	25.1%	—	2.2	1.5	0.3	4.3
Employees	—	—	—	—	2	—

KLÖCKNER PENTAPLAST OF AMERICA, INC.

3585 Klöckner Rd.
Gordonsville, VA 22942
Phone: 540-832-3600
Fax: 540-832-5656
Web: www.kpafilms.com

CEO: Michael F. Tubridy
CFO: Markus Hölzl
HR: —
FYE: December 31
Type: Subsidiary

It's not a police force, but Klöckner Pentaplast of America is here to preserve and protect. The company is one of the largest manufactures of rigid plastic films and sheets for packaging and printing in North America. Uses for its products include pharmaceutical blister packaging, credit card production, food packaging, general-purpose packaging, shrink sleeve/label making, and stationery. The company has six manufacturing facilities in the US. Klöckner Pentaplast of America is a division of German plastic films producer Klöckner Pentaplast Group, which was founded in 1965 in Montabaur, Germany.

KMART CORPORATION

3333 Beverly Rd.
Hoffman Estates, IL 60179
Phone: 847-286-2500
Fax: 847-286-5500
Web: www.kmartcorp.com

CEO: W. Bruce Johnson
CFO: Michael D. (Mike) Collins
HR: —
FYE: January 31
Type: Subsidiary

Attention Kmart shoppers: Kmart is the #3 discount retailer in the US, behind Wal-Mart and Target. It sells name-brand and private-label goods (including its Joe Boxer and Jaclyn Smith labels), mostly to low- and mid-income families. It runs about 1,300 off-mall stores (including 35 Supercenters) in 49 US states, Puerto Rico, Guam, and the US Virgin Islands. About 275 Kmart stores sell home appliances (including Sears' Kenmore brand) and more than 1,020 locations house in-store pharmacies. The company also operates the kmart.com website, which includes merchandise from sister company Sears. Kmart is a subsidiary of Sears Holdings Corp., formed by the 2005 combination of ailing Sears, Roebuck and Kmart.

	Annual Growth	1/05	1/06	1/07	1/08	1/09
Sales ($ mil.)	(4.7%)	19,701.0	19,094.0	18,647.0	17,256.0	16,219.0
Employees	0.0%	133,000	133,000	133,000	133,000	133,000

KMG CHEMICALS, INC.

NASDAQ (GM): KMGB

9555 W. Sam Houston Pkwy. South, Ste. 600
Houston, TX 77099
Phone: 713-600-3800
Fax: 713-600-3850
Web: www.kmgb.com

CEO: J. Neal Butler
CFO: John V. Sobchak
HR: —
FYE: July 31
Type: Public

KMG Chemicals protects wood and helps make chips, though it has nothing to do with wood chips. Its wood preservatives are pentachlorophenol (penta), sodium penta, and creosote. KMG sells penta and creosote in the US, primarily to the railroad, construction, and utility industries. Sodium penta is sold in Latin America. Its electronic chemicals are used in the manufacture of semiconductors. The company makes herbicides to kill weeds and pesticides to keep insects from livestock and poultry. KMG's largest customer is silicon chip kingpin Intel, which accounts for about 10% of sales. Almost all of its sales are within the US. Chairman David Hatcher owns more than a third of KMG.

	Annual Growth	7/05	7/06	7/07	7/08	7/09
Sales ($ mil.)	34.0%	59.2	71.0	89.8	154.4	190.7
Net income ($ mil.)	34.7%	3.1	3.8	8.8	5.7	10.2
Market value ($ mil.)	(4.0%)	96.6	89.5	232.2	125.1	81.9
Employees	30.8%	93	110	118	274	272

KNAUF INSULATION

1 Knauf Dr.
Shelbyville, IN 46176
Phone: 317-398-4434
Fax: 317-398-3675
Web: www.knaufinsulation.com

CEO: Robert (Bob) Claxton
CFO: Warren Wise
HR: Mike Hudson
FYE: December 31
Type: Subsidiary

Knauf Insulation believes that an R rating is good for the family. (R-values are assigned by resistance to heat flow.) The company makes thermal and acoustical fiberglass insulation products for residential, commercial, industrial, marine, OEM, and metal building applications. Knauf also produces polystyrene custom shapes, insulation, panels, and other products. Established in 1978 as Knauf Fiber Glass, it is a member company of Knauf Gips KG, a multibillion-dollar family of building materials companies owned by the Germany-based Knauf family. Knauf Insulation has operations in some 50 countries.

KNIGHT TRANSPORTATION, INC.

NYSE: KNX

5601 W. Buckeye Rd.
Phoenix, AZ 85043
Phone: 602-269-2000
Fax: 602-269-8409
Web: www.knighttrans.com

CEO: Kevin P. Knight
CFO: David A. (Dave) Jackson
HR: —
FYE: December 31
Type: Public

Knight Transportation drivers don't drive long hours into the night. The truckload carrier instead focuses on short- to medium-haul trips, averaging about 500 miles. From some 35 regional operations centers, mainly in the southern, midwestern, and western US, Knight carries such cargo as consumer goods, food and beverages, and paper products. It has a fleet of about 3,700 tractors and 8,500 trailers, including about 700 refrigerated trailers. Besides for-hire hauling, Knight provides dedicated contract carriage, in which drivers and equipment are assigned to a customer long-term. It also offers freight brokerage services. Four members of the Knight family collectively own about 30% of the company.

	Annual Growth	12/05	12/06	12/07	12/08	12/09
Sales ($ mil.)	3.6%	566.8	664.4	713.6	766.9	651.7
Net income ($ mil.)	(4.8%)	61.7	73.0	63.1	56.3	50.6
Market value ($ mil.)	(1.8%)	1,730.8	1,423.5	1,236.5	1,345.9	1,610.6
Employees	5.7%	3,531	4,176	4,404	4,713	4,414

KNIGHTS OF COLUMBUS

1 Columbus Plaza
New Haven, CT 06510
Phone: 203-752-4000
Fax: 203-752-4100
Web: www.kofc.org

CEO: Carl A. Anderson
CFO: —
HR: —
FYE: December 31
Type: Not-for-profit

Good Knight! The Knights of Columbus is not only a formidable volunteer group, boasting about 13,000 councils made up of 1.7 million Roman Catholic male members in the US, Canada, Mexico, Poland, Puerto Rico, and several other countries; it's also a force to be reckoned with in the insurance world, providing life insurance, annuities, and long-term care insurance to its members and their families. The organization also manages the Knights of Columbus Museum in New Haven, Connecticut, featuring exhibits of religious art and history. The Knights of Columbus was founded in New Haven by Father Michael J. McGivney in 1882 and has been selling insurance since its founding.

⊞ KNIGHT CAPITAL GROUP, INC.

NYSE: KCG

545 Washington Blvd.
Jersey City, NJ 07310
Phone: 201-222-9400
Fax: 201-557-6853
Web: www.knighttradinggroup.com

CEO: Thomas M. (Tom) Joyce
CFO: Steven Bisgay
HR: Bronwen Bastone
FYE: December 31
Type: Public

A day trader is one thing, but a Knight trader is something altogether different. Knight Capital Group performs electronic and voice-activated trade execution services for US and foreign stocks, as well as futures, options, foreign exchange, and fixed income products, through subsidiaries such as Knight Equity Markets, Knight Capital Markets, Knight Direct, Hotspot, and Knight BondPoint. Active in the US, the UK, and Hong Kong, the company executes approximately four billion trades per day. Customers include brokerages, investment banks, institutional investors, private wealth managers, and corporate issuers of securities.

	Annual Growth	12/05	12/06	12/07	12/08	12/09
Sales ($ mil.)	16.4%	634.6	951.2	905.3	1,041.3	1,164.1
Net income ($ mil.)	15.2%	66.4	158.3	122.2	177.9	117.1
Market value ($ mil.)	11.7%	934.7	1,811.7	1,360.9	1,526.3	1,455.4
Employees	11.8%	720	844	868	1,045	1,126

⊞ KNOLL, INC.

NYSE: KNL

1235 Water St.
East Greenville, PA 18041
Phone: 215-679-7991
Fax: 215-679-1755
Web: www.knoll.com

CEO: Andrew B. Cogan
CFO: Barry L. McCabe
HR: Marcia A. Thompson
FYE: December 31
Type: Public

From the Bauhaus style to business chic, Knoll has designs on the furniture market. The company makes a variety of distinctively designed, curvilinear office furniture and related accessories, including office systems (a.k.a. cubicles). Its products are sold under such names as Equity, AutoStrada, Reff, and Currents. Other products include ergonomic seating, tables and desks, and filing systems. The firm, founded in 1938, offers an upscale line of designed furniture (KnollStudio), computer and desk accessories (KnollExtra), and fabric and leather upholstery (KnollTextiles). It sells its products primarily in North America, but also in Europe. Columbia Wanger Asset Management owns about 12% of Knoll.

	Annual Growth	12/05	12/06	12/07	12/08	12/09
Sales ($ mil.)	(0.9%)	808.0	982.2	1,055.8	1,120.1	780.0
Net income ($ mil.)	(6.5%)	35.9	58.6	71.4	84.9	27.4
Market value ($ mil.)	(11.9%)	804.1	1,034.0	772.2	423.9	485.5
Employees	(4.2%)	3,775	4,224	4,286	3,838	3,177

⊞ An in-depth profile of this company is available to Hoover's Online members at hoovers.com.

901

KNOLOGY, INC.

NASDAQ (GM): KNOL

1241 O. G. Skinner Dr.
West Point, GA 31833
Phone: 706-645-8553
Fax: 706-645-0148
Web: www.knology.com

CEO: Rodger L. Johnson
CFO: M. Todd Holt
HR: Brad M. Vanacore
FYE: December 31
Type: Public

Knology knows the way to a couch potato's heart is through its hybrid fiber-coaxial cable connection. The facilities-based telecommunications company provides integrated voice, video, and data services through its interactive broadband network. Knology offers bundled cable TV, local and long-distance phone, and high-speed Internet access to residential and business customers, primarily in midsized markets in the southeastern US. The company provides video, voice, and data services in Alabama, Florida, Georgia, Iowa, Minnesota, South Carolina, South Dakota, and Tennessee.

	Annual Growth	12/05	12/06	12/07	12/08	12/09
Sales ($ mil.)	16.5%	230.9	259.0	347.7	410.2	425.6
Net income ($ mil.)	—	(54.8)	(38.8)	(43.9)	(12.1)	(3.4)
Market value ($ mil.)	29.9%	141.5	392.0	470.9	190.1	402.3
Employees	4.3%	1,386	1,365	1,686	1,663	1,642

THE KNOT, INC.

NASDAQ (GM): KNOT

462 Broadway, 6th Fl.
New York, NY 10013
Phone: 212-219-8555
Fax: 212-219-1929
Web: www.theknot.com

CEO: David Liu
CFO: John P. Mueller
HR: —
FYE: December 31
Type: Public

Here comes the bride, surfing online. Where is the groom? He's in a chat room. The Knot is a leading online publisher serving the wedding market sector with content and services through TheKnot.com. The site offers advice and information on topics from engagement to honeymoon, as well as wedding planning tools (budget planner, gown finder), chat rooms, a directory of local resources, and an online gift store. The company's WeddingChannel.com offers online registry services. Other products target newlyweds and pregnant women. In addition to online content, The Knot produces branded TV content and national and local magazines, as well as books on lifestyle topics (published by Random House and Chronicle Books).

	Annual Growth	12/05	12/06	12/07	12/08	12/09
Sales ($ mil.)	19.9%	51.4	72.7	98.7	103.9	106.4
Net income ($ mil.)	—	4.0	23.4	11.9	4.1	(4.9)
Market value ($ mil.)	(3.1%)	386.2	885.9	538.2	280.9	340.0
Employees	18.7%	260	367	451	472	517

KNOUSE FOODS COOPERATIVE, INC.

800 Peach Glen Rd.
Peach Glen, PA 17375
Phone: 717-677-8181
Fax: 717-677-7069
Web: www.knouse.com

CEO: Kenneth E. (Ken) Guise Jr.
CFO: Thomas M. (Tom) DeNisco
HR: Scott Briggs
FYE: June 30
Type: Cooperative

Is there a Knouse in the house? Might be. With retail brand names such as Apple Time, Lucky Leaf, Musselman's, Lincoln, and Speas Farm, Knouse Foods Cooperative's apple products are in many a pantry. The company is a growers' co-op made up of some 125 Appalachian Mountain and Midwestern grower/members. It processes its members' apples for sale as canned and bottled applesauce, juice, cider, vinegar, apple butter, pie fillings, and snack packs, all of which are available nationwide. In addition to stocking supermarket shelves, Knouse, founded in 1949, supplies foodservice operators and industrial-ingredient companies with apple products. It also offers private-label and co-packing services.

	Annual Growth	6/04	6/05	6/06	6/07	6/08
Est. sales ($ mil.)	—	—	—	—	—	270.6
Employees	—	—	—	—	—	1,200

☐ KNOWLEDGE LEARNING CORPORATION

650 NE Holladay St., Ste. 1400
Portland, OR 97232
Phone: 503-872-1300
Fax: 503-872-1349
Web: www.knowledgelearning.com

CEO: Felicia Thornton
CFO: John A. (Jay) Muskovich
HR: Donna J. Lesch
FYE: December 31
Type: Private

Curious kids are learning while their parents are earning with the help of Knowledge Learning Corporation. The company operates more than 1,700 KinderCare, Knowledge Beginnings, and Children's Creative Learning early child care centers throughout the US; more than 300,000 students are enrolled in its centers. The group also offers before- and after-school care, summer camps, an online high school, and supplemental academic programs through its Champions division (formerly known as KLC School Partnerships). In 2007 Knowledge Learning Corporation acquired Children's Creative Learning Centers, an operator of onsite or adjacent child care centers for corporations, universities, and other entities.

KOBE STEEL USA INC

535 Madison Ave.
New York, NY 10022
Phone: 212-751-9400
Fax: 212-308-3116
Web: www.kobelco.co.jp/english/corp/group/united_states

CEO: Ryoji Hayashi
CFO: —
HR: —
FYE: March 31
Type: Subsidiary

A subsidiary of Kobe Steel Ltd., the diversified Kobe Steel USA is responsible for managing about a dozen companies that cover such operations as aluminum, copper, infrastructure and plant engineering. Other Kobe Steel USA Companies manufacture iron, machinery, real estate, silicon wafers, steel, and welding products; it also operates financial subsidiaries. Kobe Steel established the subsidiary in 1988.

	Annual Growth	3/04	3/05	3/06	3/07	3/08
Est. sales ($ mil.)	—	—	—	—	—	1.4
Employees	—	—	—	—	—	18

KOBELCO CONSTRUCTION MACHINERY AMERICA LLC

501 Richardson Rd.
Calhoun, GA 30701
Phone: 706-629-5572
Fax: 706-629-3952
Web: www.kobelcoamerica.com

CEO: Terence M. (Terry) Sheehan
CFO: Raymond Baloux
HR: —
FYE: December 31
Type: Subsidiary

If your job involves digging, Kobelco Construction Machinery America can help you get to the bottom of things. The company manufactures heavy duty small and full-size excavators and excavator-bulldozer combos. Products include compact, short radius, mid-size, and full-size units. Kobelco also sells used equipment and a limited number of "grey market" items, machines intended for sale overseas and lacking the usual aftermarket support and parts availability. Its machines are available through about 250 distribution locations. Kobelco is a joint venture owned by Dutch construction equipment giant CNH Global (a majority-owned subsidiary of Fiat) and Kobelco Construction Machinery USA.

KOCH ENTERPRISES, INC.

14 S. 11th Ave.
Evansville, IN 47744
Phone: 812-465-9800
Fax: 812-465-9613
Web: www.kochenterprises.com

CEO: Robert L. (Bob) Koch II
CFO: Susan E. Parsons
HR: —
FYE: December 31
Type: Private

KOCH gets straight A's. Indiana-based KOCH Enterprises is a diversified, private holding company active in aluminum, automotive finishing systems, air-conditioning equipment, and adhesives. Its global operations include subsidiaries George Koch Sons (engineers, installs, and services auto finishing systems), Koch Air (distributes heating and air-conditioning equipment), Gibbs Die Casting (supplies auto aluminum die castings), Brake Supply (repairs and replaces brakes and hydraulic systems for auto and mining operations), and Uniseal (makes structural adhesives, thermoplastics, and sealant systems for industrial and auto markets). President Bob Koch's great grandfather, George Koch, founded the firm in 1873.

	Annual Growth	12/04	12/05	12/06	12/07	12/08
Est. sales ($ mil.)	—	—	—	—	—	830.9
Employees	—	—	—	—	—	2,602

KOCH FOODS INCORPORATED

1300 W. Higgins Rd.
Park Ridge, IL 60068
Phone: 847-384-5940
Fax: 847-384-5961
Web: www.kochfoods.com

CEO: Joseph C. (Joe) Grendys
CFO: Mark Kaminsky
HR: —
FYE: December 31
Type: Private

Kids, always telling jokes that make their parents groan, ask why the chicken crossed the road. But it's you who should cross the road — to get to Koch Foods — because the company is ready with a whole henhouse full of poultry products. Its products include value-added fresh and frozen chicken, such as chicken tenderloins, tenders, strips, boneless breasts, and wings, along with diced and pulled white and dark meat, and whole and whole cut-up chickens. Koch's customers include companies in the retail food and foodservice sectors throughout the US, as well as overseas.

KOCH INDUSTRIES, INC.

4111 E. 37th St. North
Wichita, KS 67220
Phone: 316-828-5500
Fax: 316-828-5739
Web: www.kochind.com

CEO: Charles G. Koch
CFO: Steve Feilmeier
HR: —
FYE: December 31
Type: Private

Koch (pronounced "coke") Industries is the *real thing*, one of the largest (if not the largest) private companies in the US. Koch's operations are diverse, including refining and chemicals, process and pollution control equipment, and technologies; fibers and polymers; commodity and financial trading; and forest and consumer products (led by Georgia-Pacific LLC). Its Flint Hills Resources subsidiary owns three refineries that process more than 800,000 barrels of crude oil daily. Koch operates crude gathering systems and pipelines across North America as well as cattle ranches with a total of 15,000 head of cattle in Kansas, Montana, and Texas. Brothers Charles and David Koch control the company.

	Annual Growth	12/04	12/05	12/06	12/07	12/08
Sales ($ mil.)	25.7%	40,000.0	80,000.0	90,000.0	98,000.0	100,000.0
Employees	23.6%	30,000	80,000	80,000	80,000	70,000

KODAK IMAGING NETWORK, INC.

1480 64th St., Ste. 300
Emeryville, CA 94608
Phone: 510-229-1200
Fax: 510-229-2700
Web: www.kodakgallery.com

CEO: Victor Cho
CFO: —
HR: —
FYE: December 31
Type: Subsidiary

Kodak Imaging Network, doing business as Kodak Gallery, makes it easy to share digital photos. Formerly Ofoto, the Internet service lets registered users create online photo albums that friends and family members can view and download. The site also offers free editing tools and photo printing services, and it sells gifts (such as calendars, coffee mugs, and mouse pads) that users can personalize with their images. In addition to its US site, Kodak Gallery operates seven websites for consumers in Europe. All total, the service has more than 70 million members. Ofoto was founded in 1999 and acquired by Eastman Kodak in 2001. It was renamed in 2005 when Kodak rebranded the online service.

KODIAK OIL & GAS CORP.

NYSE Amex: KOG

1625 Broadway, Ste. 330
Denver, CO 80202
Phone: 303-592-8075
Fax: 303-592-8071
Web: www.kodiakog.com

CEO: Lynn A. Peterson
CFO: James P. Henderson
HR: —
FYE: December 31
Type: Public

Kodiak Oil & Gas bears the responsibility for exploration, development, and production of oil and natural gas in the Rockies. The company, which focuses on assets in the Vermillion Basin of the Green River Basin and the Williston Basin (located in Montana and North Dakota), reported proved reserves of 1.2 billion cu. ft. of natural gas and 344,000 barrels of oil in 2008. Kodiak Oil & Gas has 99,434 net acres of land holdings. In the Green River Basin it is exploring for unconventional gas through the exploitation of coalbed methane, over-pressured shales, and tight-gas-sands.

	Annual Growth	12/05	12/06	12/07	12/08	12/09
Sales ($ mil.)	118.0%	0.5	5.0	9.3	7.0	11.3
Net income ($ mil.)	—	(2.0)	(2.8)	(38.2)	(56.5)	(2.6)
Market value ($ mil.)	(17.3%)	—	467.8	262.4	37.0	264.8
Employees	23.0%	7	12	15	17	16

KOHLBERG & CO., L.L.C.

111 Radio Cir.
Mt. Kisco, NY 10549
Phone: 914-241-7430
Fax: 914-241-7476
Web: www.kohlberg.com

CEO: Samuel P. Frieder
CFO: —
HR: —
FYE: December 31
Type: Private

Call it the Kohlberg Variations: Kohlberg & Co. specializes in buyouts, recapitalizations, and equity investments of middle market companies (valued between $100 million and $500 million) in a variety of industries including machinery and equipment, food and consumer, and health care. The firm typically invests $50 million to $125 million, and works with the management teams of portfolio companies to guide their growth. It has raised some $3.7 billion of committed capital in a half-dozen private equity funds. Kohlberg was founded in 1987 by Jerome Kohlberg Jr., the senior founding partner of KKR (formerly Kohlberg Kravis Roberts), and James A. Kohlberg; it is not affiliated with KKR.

An in-depth profile of this company is available to Hoover's Online members at hoovers.com.

903

KOHLER CO.

444 Highland Dr.
Kohler, WI 53044
Phone: 920-457-4441
Fax: 920-457-1271
Web: kohlerco.com

CEO: Herbert V. Kohler Jr.
CFO: Jeffrey P. Cheney
HR: Laura Kohler
FYE: December 31
Type: Private

Kohler's profits are going down the drain, literally. The company makes bathroom and kitchen products — from toilets and baths to showers and sinks — under names including Kohler, Hytec, and Sterling. It also makes furniture under the Baker and McGuire brands and the Ann Sacks brand of ceramic, stone, and mosaic tile. Lesser-known operations include Kohler's manufacturing of small engines, generators, and power supplies for both consumer and industrial applications. Kohler's real estate operations include Destination Kohler, a resort in Wisconsin; and Old Course Hotel Golf Resort and Spa in Scotland. Chairman Herbert Kohler Jr. and his sister Ruth Kohler, grandchildren of the founder, control Kohler.

	Annual Growth	12/04	12/05	12/06	12/07	12/08
Est. sales ($ mil.)	16.4%	3,000.0	3,000.0	5,000.0	5,230.0	5,500.0
Employees	1.7%	28,000	31,000	33,000	32,000	30,000

KOHL'S CORPORATION

NYSE: KSS

N56 W17000 Ridgewood Dr.
Menomonee Falls, WI 53051
Phone: 262-703-7000
Fax: 262-703-6143
Web: www.kohlscorporation.com

CEO: Kevin B. Mansell
CFO: Wesley S. (Wes) McDonald
HR: —
FYE: January 31
Type: Public

Kohl's wants to be easy on shoppers and tough on competition. It operates 1,050-plus discount department stores in 49 states. More than a quarter of its stores are in the Midwest, where Kohl's continues to grow while rapidly expanding into other markets. Moderately priced name-brand and private-label apparel, shoes, accessories, and housewares are sold through centrally located cash registers, designed to expedite checkout and keep staff costs down. Kohl's competes with discount and mid-level department stores. Merchandising relationships allow Kohl's to carry top brands (NIKE, Levi's, OshKosh B'Gosh) not typically available to discounters; it sells them cheaper than department stores by controlling costs.

	Annual Growth	1/06	1/07	1/08	1/09	1/10
Sales ($ mil.)	6.4%	13,402.2	15,544.2	16,473.7	16,389.0	17,178.0
Net income ($ mil.)	4.2%	842.0	1,108.7	1,083.9	885.0	991.0
Market value ($ mil.)	3.2%	13,626.6	21,767.6	13,976.6	11,269.0	15,462.3
Employees	5.6%	107,000	125,000	125,000	126,000	133,000

KOLLSMAN, INC.

220 Daniel Webster Hwy.
Merrimack, NH 03054
Phone: 603-889-2500
Fax: 603-889-7966
Web: www.kollsman.com

CEO: Raanan I. Horowitz
CFO: —
HR: —
FYE: December 31
Type: Subsidiary

Kollsman develops advanced avionics and electro-optic (EO) instruments and systems for aerospace, defense, and medical applications. Its Commercial Aviation Systems division makes vision landing systems, cabin pressurization systems, cockpit instruments, and air data test equipment for commercial aircraft. Its Sensor Systems & EO unit develops infrared and laser-based optic systems, surveillance and reconnaissance systems, and armored vehicle systems for the defense industry, which accounts for about 40% of Kollman's business. Subsidiary KMC Systems makes private-label electromechanical devices for diagnostic and surgical use. Kollsman is owned by Israel-based defense concern Elbit Systems.

	Annual Growth	12/04	12/05	12/06	12/07	12/08
Est. sales ($ mil.)	—	—	—	—	—	75.0
Employees	—	—	—	—	—	550

KOMATSU AMERICA CORP.

1701 W. Golf Rd.
Rolling Meadows, IL 60008
Phone: 847-437-5800
Fax: 847-437-5814
Web: www.komatsuamerica.com

CEO: David W. (Dave) Grzelak
CFO: —
HR: Brian Risch
FYE: March 31
Type: Subsidiary

You would need a *very* big sandbox to play with Komatsu America's dump trucks and dozers. The company, a subsidiary of Japanese construction equipment giant Komatsu (#2 worldwide after Caterpillar), manufactures, sells, and maintains earthmoving machinery for the North American construction and mining markets. Komatsu America divides its operations into utility equipment (compact construction equipment) and mining systems. Its products include dump trucks, backhoes, crushers, graders, hydraulic excavators, crawler carriers, wheel loaders, bulldozers, and a computer-based mine management system. The company also provides financing, and rents and sells equipment through its sales subsidiaries and distributors.

KOMORI AMERICA CORPORATION

5520 Meadowbrook Industrial Ct.
Rolling Meadows, IL 60008
Phone: 847-806-9000
Fax: 847-806-0987
Web: www.komori-america.us

CEO: Kazuyoshi Miyao
CFO: Robert Rath
HR: —
FYE: March 31
Type: Subsidiary

Komori America thinks you'd be hard-pressed to find a better printing equipment manufacturer. The US subsidiary of Japan-based Komori Corporation makes and sells such products as sheetfed and web offset printing presses and precision printing machinery. Komori America has a sales force comprised of both direct and dealer representatives in North America. The company maintains headquarters, a technical product center, and a national parts center (stocking more than 260,000 parts) in Illinois, with additional regional sales, service, and parts distribution centers in California, Georgia, New Jersey, and Ohio. It offers financing on its printing systems through subsidiary Komori Leasing, Inc.

KONA GRILL, INC.

NASDAQ (GM): KONA

7150 E. Camelback Rd., Ste. 220
Scottsdale, AZ 85251
Phone: 480-922-8100
Fax: 480-991-6811
Web: www.konagrill.com

CEO: Marc A. Buehler
CFO: Mark S. Robinow
HR: —
FYE: December 31
Type: Public

This company is pinning its hopes on the flavor of the Big Island to draw a few mainlanders into its restaurants. Kona Grill operates about 20 upscale casual-dining restaurants offering both seafood and American dishes with an island twist. The restaurants serve both lunch and diner menus, and they offer a wide selection of sushi. In addition to dining, each location typically has a bar area for happy hour with margaritas and martinis. The restaurants are typically found near upscale shopping areas in Arizona, Texas, and about 20 other states. Former chairman and CEO Marcus Jundt and his family own about 20% of Kona Grill.

	Annual Growth	12/05	12/06	12/07	12/08	12/09
Sales ($ mil.)	21.8%	36.8	50.7	72.3	75.8	81.1
Net income ($ mil.)	—	(0.4)	(2.7)	(0.7)	(10.5)	(21.6)
Market value ($ mil.)	(23.4%)	77.9	188.3	133.8	20.2	26.9
Employees	14.6%	1,108	1,761	1,798	1,910	1,908

KONAMI GAMING, INC.

585 Trade Center Dr.
Las Vegas, NV 89119
Phone: 702-616-1400
Fax: 702-367-0007
Web: www.konamigaming.com

CEO: Satoshi Sakamoto
CFO: —
HR: Jennifer Martinez
FYE: March 31
Type: Subsidiary

You might say this company's reel business is real important to casinos. Konami Gaming is a leading manufacturer of casino gaming machines, including mechanical reel slot machines, video slots and video poker, and progressive payout games. In addition to casino gaming machines, the company markets information management systems designed to monitor player data, machine performance, and casino floor staff. Konami Gaming is the North American branch of Tokyo-based Konami Corporation, a global leader in the video game and casino gaming machine industry.

KONARKA TECHNOLOGIES, INC.

116 John St., 3rd Fl., Ste. 12
Lowell, MA 01852
Phone: 978-569-1400
Fax: 978-569-1401
Web: www.konarkatech.com

CEO: Rick D. Hess
CFO: Jerry Caruso
HR: —
FYE: December 31
Type: Private

Konarka Technologies has a future so bright, it's gotta use shades. The company (named after the Konarka temple of sun worship in Orissa, India) makes specialized photovoltaic materials used to convert light to energy. Its technology enables solar panels to be made from flexible plastic sheets called Power Plastic. Konarka Technologies has a broad portfolio of patents and technology licenses. Investors include 3i Group, Chevron, Draper Fisher Jurvetson, and New Enterprise Associates. The company has raised more than $150 million in private equity funding and has also received government research grants. Konarka Technologies has operations in Asia, Austria, Germany, and the US.

KONE INC.

1 Kone Ct.
Moline, IL 61265
Phone: 309-764-6771
Fax: 309-743-5469
Web: www.kone.com/en_US/main

CEO: Vance Tang
CFO: Kenneth E. Schmid Jr.
HR: Charles D. Moore
FYE: December 31
Type: Subsidiary

KONE began its elevator business on the ground floor and is working its way up. The US subsidiary of Finland's KONE sells, manufactures, upgrades, and maintains elevators, escalators, and automatic building doors. The KONE EcoSpace line of elevators is an environmentally friendly (using no oil) traction elevator that offers more space while conserving energy for residential, office, and public access use. Other brand names include the KONE HH Series and MX Series line of hydraulic elevators, as well as the KONE EcoSystem MR elevator. KONE USA accounts for about one-fifth of its parent company's elevator and escalator sales.

	Annual Growth	12/04	12/05	12/06	12/07	12/08
Est. sales ($ mil.)	—	—	—	—	—	289.8
Employees	—	—	—	—	—	4,115

KONGSBERG POWER PRODUCTS SYSTEMS

300 S. Cochran
Willis, TX 77378
Phone: 936-856-2971
Fax: 936-856-4328
Web: www.capro.com

CEO: Dan Hershberger
CFO: Garry Bingham
HR: Roger Dillon
FYE: December 31
Type: Subsidiary

Kongsberg Power Products Systems (formerly Capro) makes motion control systems and cable assemblies. Its automotive products include cables that operate hood and fuel door releases, heating and air conditioning controls, trunk releases, seat recliners, and door and window systems. The company also makes mechanical control systems and cable assemblies for power and industrial equipment OEMs. Kongsberg Power Products offers services that include engineering, design, and prototyping. A former subsidiary of diversified manufacturer Teleflex, Capro was sold in 2008 to global auto supplier Kongsberg Automotive Holding ASA, which changed the company's name but kept the Capro brand.

KONICA MINOLTA BUSINESS SOLUTIONS U.S.A., INC.

101 Williams Dr.
Ramsey, NJ 07446
Phone: 201-825-4000
Fax: 201-825-7605
Web: www.kmbs.konicaminolta.us

CEO: Nobuo (Ned) Umehara
CFO: Michael Leonczyk
HR: Donald Warwick
FYE: December 31
Type: Subsidiary

Konica Minolta Business Solutions U.S.A. (KMBS) is part of Konica Minolta Holdings, which was created from the merger of Konica and Minolta. KMBS offers copiers, fax machines, printers, and other office machines. In addition to standard customer support, it provides services such as document process streamlining and infrastructure management through its professional services group. KMBS serves organizations ranging from small offices to large production operations. The company operates branch offices and distribution centers throughout the US.

KONICA MINOLTA MEDICAL IMAGING U.S.A, INC.

411 Newark Pompton Tpke.
Wayne, NJ 07470
Phone: 973-633-1500
Fax: 973-523-7408
Web: www.konicaminolta.com/medicalusa

CEO: Henry Kobayashi
CFO: —
HR: Gill Saum
FYE: March 31
Type: Subsidiary

Konica Minolta Medical Imaging U.S.A. isn't interested in a snapshot of your pearly whites so much as your spine, skull, and chest. The company, a North American affiliate of Konica Minolta's medical and graphic imaging business unit, makes digital and traditional imaging products for diagnostic use by hospitals, imaging centers, private physicians, and veterinary clinics. Its products include computed radiography, digital radiography, and mammography imaging systems, as well as laser image printers and film processors. Customers have includes CHRISTUS Health, Tenet Healthcare, and Universal Health Services. The company sells products throughout the US, Canada, and Latin America.

	Annual Growth	3/04	3/05	3/06	3/07	3/08
Est. sales ($ mil.)	—	—	—	—	—	17.4
Employees	—	—	—	—	—	85

An in-depth profile of this company is available to Hoover's Online members at hoovers.com.

905

KOOS MANUFACTURING, INC.

2741 Seminole Ave.
South Gate, CA 90280
Phone: 323-564-2100
Fax: 323-567-8340

CEO: Yul Ku
CFO: —
HR: —
FYE: April 30
Type: Private

As long as the ladies continue shelling out the big bucks for denimwear, they may just find themselves "forever in blue jeans." Koos Manufacturing makes and distributes high-end denim jeans that retail for up to $350 a pair. The company has made jeans for The Buckle, Gap, Abercrombie & Fitch, and J. Crew, among others. In addition to its private-label business, Koos markets upscale denimwear through its AG Adriano Goldschmied business. It operates more than 10 AG stores and half a dozen AG Outlets. Other brands in Koos' portfolio include Big Star and Double A. The company operates manufacturing facilities in Los Angeles and Mexico. Founded in 1978, Koos Manufacturing is owned by president Yul Ku.

	Annual Growth	4/04	4/05	4/06	4/07	4/08
Est. sales ($ mil.)	—	—	—	—	—	35.8
Employees	—	—	—	—	—	700

KOOSHAREM CORPORATION

3820 State St.
Santa Barbara, CA 93105
Phone: 805-882-2200
Fax: 805-898-7111
Web: www.selectstaffing.com

CEO: Stephen Sorensen
CFO: Jeff R. Mitchell
HR: —
FYE: December 31
Type: Holding company

Doing business as the Select Family of Staffing Companies, Koosharem provides comprehensive staffing and workforce management services through its operating subsidiaries. Offerings include recruiting and screening of professional job candidates, payroll and attendance management, and specialty staffing. The Select Family of Staffing Companies serves a national clientele from a network of 300 offices operating under the Select Staffing, Remedy Intelligent Staffing, and RemX brands. Chairman and CEO Stephen Sorensen owns the company. In December 2009 Koosharem agreed to be acquired by Atlas Acquisition Holding Corp. and taken public in a deal worth $840 million. However, the deal fell through in February 2010.

KOPIN CORPORATION

NASDAQ (GM): KOPN

200 John Hancock Rd.
Taunton, MA 02780
Phone: 508-824-6696
Fax: 508-824-6958
Web: www.kopin.com

CEO: John C. C. Fan
CFO: Richard A. Sneider
HR: Joan Evans
FYE: December 31
Type: Public

Kopin's semiconductor wafers are good at copin' with high speeds. The company makes specialized gallium arsenide (GaAs) wafers with heterojunction bipolar transistors vertically engineered onto the surface (horizontal is the industry norm). Companies such as Skyworks Solutions (one-fifth of sales) use the specialized GaAs wafers — costlier than silicon but with higher performance — to make integrated circuits for wireless and fiber-optic gear that demands high speed or low power consumption. Kopin also makes tiny display devices used by Panasonic, Samsung Electronics, SANYO Electric, and Victor Company of Japan in digital camcorders. The company gets more than three-quarters of its sales in the Americas.

	Annual Growth	12/05	12/06	12/07	12/08	12/09
Sales ($ mil.)	6.2%	90.3	71.1	98.1	114.8	114.7
Net income ($ mil.)	12.5%	12.1	(2.1)	(6.6)	2.6	19.4
Market value ($ mil.)	(6.0%)	356.3	237.8	210.5	135.9	278.4
Employees	1.7%	317	299	363	302	339

KOPPERS HOLDINGS INC.

NYSE: KOP

436 7th Ave.
Pittsburgh, PA 15219
Phone: 412-227-2001
Fax: 412-227-2333
Web: www.koppers.com

CEO: Walter W. Turner
CFO: Brian H. McCurrie
HR: Steven R. (Steve) Lacy
FYE: December 31
Type: Public

Koppers Holdings treats wood right. The company makes carbon compounds and treated-wood products for the chemical, railroad, aluminum, utility, construction, and steel industries around the world. Its carbon materials and chemicals unit makes materials for producing aluminum, polyester resins, plasticizers, and wood preservatives. The railroad and utility products unit supplies treated crossties and utility poles and treats wood for vineyard, construction, and other uses. Koppers Holdings owns 50% of KSA Limited — subsidiaries of Heidelberg Cement own the other half — which produces concrete crossties. The company's manufacturing facilities are located in Asia, Australia, Europe, and North America.

	Annual Growth	12/05	12/06	12/07	12/08	12/09
Sales ($ mil.)	2.2%	1,030.2	1,159.5	1,327.9	1,364.8	1,124.4
Net income ($ mil.)	21.7%	9.9	15.2	56.6	52.1	21.7
Market value ($ mil.)	5.3%	—	535.6	888.3	442.2	625.4
Employees	(5.5%)	2,026	1,983	1,927	1,747	1,616

KORG USA, INC.

316 S. Service Rd.
Melville, NY 11747
Phone: 631-390-6500
Fax: 631-390-6501
Web: www.korg.com

CEO: Joseph Castronovo
CFO: —
HR: Susan F. Paris
FYE: March 31
Type: Subsidiary

Registers ringing up sales is music to Korg's ears. Korg USA is the US-based distribution operation of Korg Inc., a Japanese manufacturer of musical instruments and professional audio equipment. The subsidiary boasts a vast musical products portfolio and sells such items as drum machines, keyboard synthesizers, recording and sound equipment, tuners, metronomes, foot pedals, cases, and related accessories. The company primarily caters to customers in North America and counts Beyoncé and Whitesnake among its customers. Korg USA also is a distributor of instrument amplifiers made by Marshall and Vox, as well as the Vestax line of DJ mixers, turntables, and other equipment.

	Annual Growth	3/04	3/05	3/06	3/07	3/08
Est. sales ($ mil.)	—	—	—	—	—	90.0
Employees	—	—	—	—	—	112

🔲 KORN/FERRY INTERNATIONAL

NYSE: KFY

1900 Avenue of the Stars, Ste. 2600
Los Angeles, CA 90067
Phone: 310-552-1834
Fax: 310-553-6452
Web: www.kornferry.com

CEO: Gary D. Burnison
CFO: Michael A. DiGregorio
HR: Linda Hyman
FYE: April 30
Type: Public

High-level executives can jump ship via Korn/Ferry International. The world's largest executive recruitment firm, Korn/Ferry has almost 80 offices in more than 35 countries. The company's more than 600 consultants help prominent public and private companies, as well as government and not-for-profit organizations, find qualified job applicants for openings in a variety of executive level positions (including CEOs, CFOs, and other senior-level jobs). Through Futurestep, job seekers use the Internet and videotaped job interviews to find mid-level management positions. In addition, the company provides management assessment as well as coaching and executive development services. Korn/Ferry was founded in 1969.

	Annual Growth	4/05	4/06	4/07	4/08	4/09
Sales ($ mil.)	9.1%	476.4	551.8	689.2	835.6	676.1
Net income ($ mil.)	—	38.6	59.4	55.5	66.2	(10.1)
Market value ($ mil.)	(7.4%)	662.5	966.1	1,084.3	858.5	487.2
Employees	13.6%	1,256	1,841	1,705	1,894	2,090

KOSS CORPORATION

NASDAQ (GM): KOSS

4129 N. Port Washington Ave.
Milwaukee, WI 53212
Phone: 419-964-5000
Fax: —
Web: www.koss.com

CEO: Michael J. Koss
CFO: David Smith
HR: Cheryl Mike
FYE: June 30
Type: Public

Koss makes sure you can turn up the volume without disturbing the neighbors. It makes stereo headphones, or "stereophones," and related accessories. Koss products include headphones for home and on-the-go. It also sells headphones for communications purposes (DJ, home recording, telephone). It has two subsidiaries: Koss Classics and Bi-Audio. Koss products are sold through more than 15,000 US retail outlets, including audio specialty stores, catalogs, discount stores, and national retailers, as well as to fire and police units. It has an international office in Switzerland. The Koss family — including founder John Koss (inventor of stereo headphones) and his son, CEO Michael — owns about 75% of the firm.

	Annual Growth	6/05	6/06	6/07	6/08	6/09
Sales ($ mil.)	(1.3%)	40.3	50.9	46.2	46.9	38.2
Net income ($ mil.)	(18.4%)	4.5	6.2	5.2	4.5	2.0
Market value ($ mil.)	(6.7%)	63.3	91.7	69.3	58.4	48.0
Employees	(6.4%)	95	115	82	76	73

KPMG L.L.P.

3 Chestnut Ridge Rd.
Montvale, NJ 07645
Phone: 201-307-7000
Fax: 201-307-8617
Web: www.us.kpmg.com

CEO: John B. Veihmeyer
CFO: —
HR: Bruce N. Pfau
FYE: September 30
Type: Partnership

KPMG L.L.P. is the US member firm of KPMG International, a global network of accountancies with roots going back 300 years and one of the industry's Big Four (which also includes Deloitte Touche Tohmatsu, Ernst & Young, and PricewaterhouseCoopers). With approximately 90 offices across the US, KPMG offers accounting, audit, and tax-related services including valuation, regulatory, mergers and acquisitions, trade, and compliance services. The firm targets industries including financial services, media and entertainment, consumer products, health care providers, insurance, and pharmaceuticals.

	Annual Growth	9/04	9/05	9/06	9/07	9/08
Est. sales ($ mil.)	—	—	—	—	—	4,800.0
Employees	—	—	—	—	—	22,000

KPS CAPITAL PARTNERS, LP

200 Park Ave., 58th Fl.
New York, NY 10166
Phone: 212-338-5100
Fax: 212-867-7980
Web: www.kpsfund.com

CEO: Michael G. Psaros
CFO: Stephen E. Hoey
HR: —
FYE: December 31
Type: Private

KPS Capital Partners delivers a little CPR to struggling businesses. The firm manages the KPS Special Situations Funds, which are invested in troubled companies in the manufacturing, transportation, and service industries. Specializing in restructuring and turnaround situations, it has more than $1.8 billion of committed capital. KPS is a hands-on investor, often working with management and providing oversight and advice. Portfolio companies include Attends HealthCare Products, Bristol Compressors International, and automotive components manufacturers Cloyes Gear & Products, and Hephaestus Holdings, the parent company of Jernberg Industries and Impact Forge.

KRAFT FOODS INC.

NYSE: KFT

3 Lakes Dr.
Northfield, IL 60093
Phone: 847-646-2000
Fax: 847-646-6005
Web: www.kraft.com

CEO: Irene B. Rosenfeld
CFO: Timothy R. (Tim) McLevish
HR: Karen J. May
FYE: December 31
Type: Public

Mac & cheese if you please. Kraft Foods is the #1 US food company and #2 worldwide (after Nestlé). Its North America unit makes the world's largest-selling cheese brand (Kraft); cookie and cracker baker (Nabisco); and the milk-dunking favorite, Oreos. Its international business unit offers many of the same brands plus national favorites. Its Oscar Mayer, Kraft, Philadelphia, Maxwell House, Nabisco, Oreo, Jacobs, Milka, and LU brands all have revenues of at least $1 billion; more than 50 of its brands regularly hit the $100 million mark. Kraft's $19 billion offer to acquire Cadbury was accepted by a majority of Cadbury shareholders in 2010. Warren Buffett's Berkshire Hathaway owns about 9% of Kraft.

	Annual Growth	12/05	12/06	12/07	12/08	12/09
Sales ($ mil.)	4.3%	34,113.0	34,356.0	37,241.0	42,201.0	40,386.0
Net income ($ mil.)	3.6%	2,632.0	3,060.0	2,590.0	2,901.0	3,028.0
Market value ($ mil.)	(0.9%)	49,113.9	62,242.4	56,889.9	46,812.5	47,387.9
Employees	0.8%	94,000	90,000	103,000	98,000	97,000

KRASDALE FOODS INC.

65 W. Red Oak Ln.
White Plains, NY 10604
Phone: 914-694-6400
Fax: 914-697-5225
Web: www.krasdalefoods.com

CEO: Charles A. Krasne
CFO: Steve Silver
HR: Bernie Patton
FYE: December 31
Type: Private

Krasdale Foods is a leading independent grocery wholesaler that supplies more than 7,000 products to food retailers, mostly in the New York metropolitan area. From its distribution center in the Bronx, the company offers Krasdale-labeled, private-label, and regional brands, as well as ethnic and specialty food items. Krasdale also provides merchandising and marketing services to its customers. Abraham Krasne founded the company as A. Krasne Inc. in 1908. (The name was changed in 1972.) Led by his son and CEO, Charles Krasne, the family continues to own and operate the business.

KRATON PERFORMANCE POLYMERS, INC.

NYSE: KRA

15710 John F. Kennedy Blvd., Ste. 300
Houston, TX 77032
Phone: 281-504-4700
Fax: —
Web: www.kraton.com

CEO: Kevin M. Fogarty
CFO: Stephen E. (Steve) Tremblay
HR: Richard A. (Rick) Ott
FYE: December 31
Type: Public

If you brushed your teeth or shaved this morning, you probably touched Kraton Performance Polymers' products. Through operating subsidiary Kraton Polymers, the company makes styrenic block copolymers (SBCs), a material it invented in the 1960s. SBCs are used in adhesives, coatings, sealants, lubricants, packaging, and other applications across a range of industries such as roofing, medical, and personal care products (the rubbery grip on your toothbrush or razor handle, for example). Kraton sells some 800 products in more than 60 countries and has production facilities in the Americas and Europe.

	Annual Growth	12/05	12/06	12/07	12/08	12/09
Sales ($ mil.)	889.2%	—	1.0	1,089.6	1,226.0	968.0
Net income ($ mil.)	—	—	0.0	(43.7)	28.4	(0.3)
Market value ($ mil.)	—	—	—	—	—	417.3
Employees	(2.7%)	—	—	—	840	817

An in-depth profile of this company is available to Hoover's Online members at hoovers.com.

907

KRATON POLYMERS LLC

15710 John F. Kennedy Blvd., Ste. 300
Houston, TX 77032
Phone: 281-504-4700
Fax: 281-504-4817
Web: www.kraton.com

CEO: Kevin M. Fogarty
CFO: Stephen E. (Steve) Tremblay
HR: Richard A. (Rick) Ott
FYE: December 31
Type: Subsidiary

When the rubber meets the road, Kraton Polymers is responsible for both ends of the equation. Its styrenic block copolymers (SBCs) are important ingredients in both footwear and road building materials. SBCs are a kind of polymer used in a variety of plastic, rubber, and chemicals, as well as for improving the stability of asphalt. More specifically, the Kraton family of polymers is used in adhesives, toys, and packaging, and to make shoe soles. The company has manufacturing and R&D facilities in Asia, Europe, the US, and South America. Private investment firm Texas Pacific Group and a unit of JP Morgan Chase owned Kraton until parent company Kraton Performance Polymers went public in 2009.

KRATOS DEFENSE & SECURITY SOLUTIONS, INC.   NASDAQ (GS): KTOS

4810 Eastgate Mall
San Diego, CA 92121
Phone: 858-228-2000
Fax: 858-228-2001
Web: www.kratosdefense.com

CEO: Eric M. DeMarco
CFO: Deanna H. Lund
HR: —
FYE: December 31
Type: Public

Kratos Defense & Security Solutions designs technology systems and provides engineering, IT, and other technical services, primarily to intelligence, military, and security agencies of the federal government, as well as state and local agencies. The company also creates and maintains in-building IT networks that integrate voice, data, security, and building automation. Additionally, it provides program requirement development, operational testing, and software customization services. Customers include the US Department of Defense, particularly the US Navy (30% of sales).

	Annual Growth	12/05	12/06	12/07	12/08	12/09
Sales ($ mil.)	(2.8%)	375.3	327.8	193.6	297.3	334.5
Net income ($ mil.)	—	3.7	(57.9)	(40.8)	(111.1)	(41.5)
Market value ($ mil.)	(32.6%)	811.4	453.4	373.9	222.7	167.9
Employees	(5.9%)	2,300	2,180	1,500	2,000	1,800

KREISLER MANUFACTURING CORPORATION   Pink Sheets: KRSL

180 Van Riper Ave.
Elmwood Park, NJ 07407
Phone: 201-791-0700
Fax: 201-791-8015
Web: www.kreisler-ind.com

CEO: Michael D. Stern
CFO: Edward A. Stern
HR: Lisa Sibrel
FYE: June 30
Type: Public

Your Chrysler might have a hemi under the hood, but this Kreisler focuses on bigger engines. Kreisler Manufacturing, through subsidiary Kreisler Industrial, makes precision metal components for commercial and military aircraft engines and industrial gas turbines. Tube assemblies — used to transfer fuel for combustion, hydraulic fluid for thrust reversers, and oil for lubrication — account for most of the company's sales. A second subsidiary, Kreisler Polska, supplies machined components to Kreisler Industrial from a manufacturing plant in Krakow, Poland.

	Annual Growth	6/04	6/05	6/06	6/07	*6/08
Sales ($ mil.)	24.2%	12.3	14.4	19.7	23.9	29.3
Net income ($ mil.)	—	(0.7)	0.2	1.2	2.0	1.9
Employees	22.4%	110	124	155	201	247

*Most recent year available

KRISPY KREME DOUGHNUTS, INC.   NYSE: KKD

370 Knollwood St., Ste. 500
Winston-Salem, NC 27103
Phone: 336-725-2981
Fax: 336-733-3791
Web: www.krispykreme.com

CEO: James H. (Jim) Morgan
CFO: Douglas R. (Doug) Muir
HR: Kenneth J. Hudson
FYE: January 31
Type: Public

You might say these sweet treats are wholly delicious. Krispy Kreme Doughnuts operates a leading chain of doughnut outlets with about 580 locations throughout the US and in about 20 other countries. The shops are popular for their glazed doughnuts that are served fresh and hot out of the fryer. In addition to its original glazed variety, Krispy Kreme serves cake and filled doughnuts, crullers, and fritters, as well as hot coffee and other beverages. The chain includes about 270 doughnut shops and some 315 kiosks and satellite locations. The company owns and operates 80 locations and franchises the rest. Krispy Kreme also markets its doughnuts through grocery stores and supermarkets.

	Annual Growth	1/06	1/07	1/08	1/09	1/10
Sales ($ mil.)	(10.6%)	543.4	461.2	429.3	384.0	346.5
Net income ($ mil.)	—	(135.8)	(42.2)	(67.1)	(4.1)	(0.2)
Market value ($ mil.)	(18.8%)	438.4	831.6	184.8	93.7	190.2
Employees	(6.9%)	4,759	4,759	4,033	3,860	3,570

THE KROGER CO.   NYSE: KR

1014 Vine St.
Cincinnati, OH 45202
Phone: 513-762-4000
Fax: 513-762-1160
Web: www.kroger.com

CEO: David B. Dillon
CFO: J. Michael Schlotman
HR: Carver L. Johnson
FYE: January 31
Type: Public

Kroger is the nation's #1 pure grocery chain, but it still must watch out for falling prices; Wal-Mart has overtaken Kroger as the largest seller of groceries in the US. While Kroger has diversified through acquisitions, adding jewelry and general merchandise to its mix, food stores still account for about 85% of sales. The company operates about 3,620 stores, including some 2,465 supermarkets and multidepartment stores, under two dozen banners, in about 30 states. It also runs 775 convenience stores under names such as Quik Stop and Kwik Shop. Kroger's Fred Meyer Stores subsidiary (acquired in 1999) operates about 125 supercenters, which offer groceries, general merchandise, and jewelry, in the western US.

	Annual Growth	1/06	1/07	1/08	1/09	1/10
Sales ($ mil.)	6.1%	60,553.0	66,111.0	70,235.0	76,000.0	76,733.0
Net income ($ mil.)	(48.0%)	958.0	1,115.0	1,181.0	1,249.0	70.0
Market value ($ mil.)	3.9%	11,890.5	16,543.3	16,446.3	14,540.0	13,848.5
Employees	3.6%	290,000	310,000	323,000	326,000	334,000

KROLL INC.

1166 Avenue of the Americas
New York, NY 10036
Phone: 212-593-1000
Fax: 212-593-2631
Web: www.krollworldwide.com

CEO: Ben F. Allen
CFO: Michael C. (Mike) Hellriegel
HR: Jim Kelly
FYE: December 31
Type: Subsidiary

Kroll could tell you what it does, but then, it would have to charge you. The risk consulting company is made up of business units that operate under the Kroll brand, including Background Screening (pre-employment and credit screening, employment verification services); Investigations, Financial Advisory & Intelligence (corporate investigations, forensic accounting, compliance assessments); and Security Services (security consulting, crisis and emergency management, protective services). Founded in 1972 by Jules Kroll, the firm has offices in more than 55 cities in 27 countries. Insurance broker and parent company Marsh & McLennan Companies agreed to sell Kroll to Altegrity in mid-2010 for more than $1 billion.

KROLL ONTRACK INC.

9023 Columbine Rd.
Eden Prairie, MN 55347
Phone: 952-937-1107
Fax: 952-937-5750
Web: www.krollontrack.com

CEO: Kristin M. Nimsger
CFO: Thomas P. (Tom) Skiba
HR: —
FYE: December 31
Type: Subsidiary

Kroll Ontrack helps keep your data on the straight and narrow. The company, a subsidiary of Kroll, provides data recovery and legal technology products and services. With applications for document review, case management, interactive filing, and trial preparation, its legal division handles e-discovery, computer forensics, and consulting services. Its data recovery unit oversees e-mail and other data recovery, archive management, data erasure, and media disposal. The company also has a division devoted to search engine technology. Kroll Ontrack serves consumer and enterprise customers, law firms, and government agencies.

KRONES, INC.

9600 S. 58th St.
Franklin, WI 53132
Phone: 414-409-4000
Fax: 414-409-4140
Web: www.kronesusa.com

CEO: Holger Beckmann
CFO: Holger Beckmann
HR: Holger Beckmann
FYE: December 31
Type: Subsidiary

Krones is in the business of keeping things all bottled up. The company develops and manufactures packaging equipment and systems that design, clean, rinse, and fill bottles and other packaging products. Other products include labeling and sealing machines, inspection and monitoring systems, and mixing and carbonating systems. Krones caters to customers in the US, Canada, Central America, and the Caribbean in the food and beverage, beer, wine and spirits, health and beauty care, pharmaceutical, and household products industries. Krones was founded in 1966 as a subsidiary of KRONES AG.

	Annual Growth	12/04	12/05	12/06	12/07	12/08
Est. sales ($ mil.)	—	—	—	—	—	363.9
Employees	—	—	—	—	—	448

KRONOS INCORPORATED

297 Billerica Rd.
Chelmsford, MA 01824
Phone: 978-250-9800
Fax: 978-367-5900
Web: www.kronos.com

CEO: Aron J. Ain
CFO: Mark V. Julien
HR: David Almeda
FYE: September 30
Type: Private

You won't ever catch Kronos taking a nap in the company supply closet. The company's Workforce Central systems collect attendance data and automatically post it to payroll. Kronos data collection systems keep track of factory production and labor hours. It also makes labor management analysis software and payroll processing applications. Kronos sells its products through its own salesforce and through an alliance with payroll service company ADP. The company focuses on the health care, manufacturing, government, retail, and hospitality markets.

KRONOS WORLDWIDE, INC.

NYSE: KRO

5430 LBJ Fwy., Ste. 1700
Dallas, TX 75240
Phone: 972-233-1700
Fax: 972-448-1445
Web: www.kronostio2.com

CEO: Steven L. (Steve) Watson
CFO: Gregory M. (Greg) Swalwell
HR: —
FYE: December 31
Type: Public

Kronos can't take credit for Moby Dick being called the White Whale, but as for the brightly white paper the whale's tale is told on . . . that's a different story. Kronos, formerly a wholly owned subsidiary of NL Industries, is among the top manufacturers of titanium dioxide (TiO2 or Tioxide), the most-used whitening pigment for paper, paints, and plastic. With its six manufacturing plants in North America and Europe, Kronos has been able to carve out a place among the top companies in its industry. Kronos has 20% of the European market and about 15% in North America. In 2003 NL spun off Kronos to its own shareholders; NL and its parent company, Valhi, retain majority control of the company.

	Annual Growth	12/05	12/06	12/07	12/08	12/09
Sales ($ mil.)	(1.2%)	1,196.7	1,279.4	1,310.3	1,316.9	1,142.0
Net income ($ mil.)	—	71.0	82.0	(66.7)	9.0	(34.7)
Market value ($ mil.)	(13.5%)	1,420.6	1,594.5	854.5	570.5	795.8
Employees	0.3%	2,415	2,450	2,400	2,450	2,440

KRUEGER INTERNATIONAL, INC.

1330 Bellevue St.
Green Bay, WI 54302
Phone: 920-468-8100
Fax: 920-468-2270
Web: www.ki.com

CEO: Richard J. Resch
CFO: Mark Olsen
HR: —
FYE: December 31
Type: Private

Krueger International can be found in cubicles, classrooms, cafeterias, and college dorms. The company, which does business as KI, makes ergonomic seating, cabinets, and other furniture used by businesses, health care organizations, schools, and government agencies. The company offers everything from desks to daybeds, not to mention tables, filing systems, and trash cans. KI operates manufacturing facilities in Canada and the US, and markets its products through sales representatives, furniture dealers, architects, and interior designers worldwide. Founded in 1941, KI was purchased in the 1980s by its managers, who later allowed the company's employees to buy its stock. Today it is 100% employee owned.

	Annual Growth	12/04	12/05	12/06	12/07	12/08
Est. sales ($ mil.)	—	—	—	—	—	665.7
Employees	—	—	—	—	—	2,800

THE KRYSTAL COMPANY

1 Union Sq.
Chattanooga, TN 37402
Phone: 423-757-1550
Fax: 423-757-5610
Web: www.krystal.com

CEO: James F. (Fred) Exum Jr.
CFO: James W. (Jim) Bear
HR: Michael C. Bass
FYE: December 31
Type: Private

The Krystal Company is a fast-food gem of the South. The company's chain of about 400 restaurants in almost a dozen southern states are known for their petite, square hamburgers (what Northerners might call a Slyder). In addition, Krystal's menu features a larger-sized hamburger (B.A. Burger), chicken sandwiches (Krystal Chik), chili dogs (Chili Pup), and breakfast items. The company also sells its frozen burgers through grocery stores. More than 230 Krystal locations are company-owned, while the rest are franchised. The chain got its start in 1932 when R.B. Davenport Jr. and J. Glenn Sherrill opened up shop in Chattanooga, Tennessee. It is controlled today by former CEO Philip Sanford.

An in-depth profile of this company is available to Hoover's Online members at hoovers.com.

909

K-SEA GP HOLDINGS LP

1 Tower Center Blvd., 17th Fl.
East Brunswick, NJ 08816
Phone: 732-565-3818
Fax: —

CEO: Timothy J. Casey
CFO: John J. Nicola
HR: —
FYE: December 31
Type: Holding company

K-Sea GP Holdings helps transport the oil that makes the world go 'round. The company's assets consist of partnership interests in K-Sea Transportation Partners (KSP), which provides marine transportation and logistics services for petroleum products in the US. KSP has a fleet of almost 75 tank barges and 65 tugboats. Operating with a more than 4 million-barrel capacity, it serves clients such as Chevron, Exxon Mobil, BP, and ConocoPhillips. K-Sea GP Holdings had planned to go public but withdrew a proposed IPO in October 2008, citing market conditions.

K-SEA TRANSPORTATION PARTNERS L.P.

NYSE: KSP

1 Tower Center Blvd., 17th Fl.
East Brunswick, NJ 08816
Phone: 732-339-6100
Fax: 732-339-6140
Web: www.k-sea.com

CEO: Timothy J. Casey
CFO: Terrence Gill
HR: Dennis Luba
FYE: June 30
Type: Public

If you're transporting refined petroleum products, it's OK to go by K-Sea. K-Sea Transportation operates a fleet of about 75 tank barges and about 65 tugboats to propel them. Overall, the company's fleet has a carrying capacity of about 4.4 million barrels. K-Sea serves major oil companies, refiners, and oil traders, primarily along the east and west coasts of the US. About 80% of its business comes from one-year or longer contracts; major customers include BP, Chevron, ConocoPhillips, Exxon Mobil, and Tesoro. Investment funds managed by Jefferies Capital Partners, an affiliate of Jefferies Group, own K-Sea's general partner, which manages the company's operations.

	Annual Growth	6/05	6/06	6/07	6/08	6/09
Sales ($ mil.)	28.5%	121.4	182.8	226.6	326.3	330.5
Net income ($ mil.)	14.8%	8.0	5.9	15.8	25.7	13.9
Market value ($ mil.)	(13.0%)	655.1	614.9	898.2	607.7	375.1
Employees	19.3%	490	690	925	1,044	992

KSW, INC.

NASDAQ (GM): KSW

37-16 23rd St.
Long Island City, NY 11101
Phone: 718-361-6500
Fax: 718-784-1943
Web: www.kswmechanical.com

CEO: Floyd Warkol
CFO: Richard W. Lucas
HR: —
FYE: December 31
Type: Public

KSW may have a need to vent on occasion, but the company still knows how to keep its cool. Its KSW Mechanical Services subsidiary installs HVAC and process piping systems for large-scale industrial, commercial, institutional, public, and residential projects. The company also provides mechanical trade management services and engineering assistance. KSW primarily works in the New York metropolitan area but hopes to expand in the Northeast. Much of KSW's business comes from repeat customers; the company is an authorized bidder for agencies including the New York City Transit Authority and the Port Authority of New York and New Jersey.

	Annual Growth	12/05	12/06	12/07	12/08	12/09
Sales ($ mil.)	4.8%	53.4	77.1	77.3	93.0	64.5
Net income ($ mil.)	(16.7%)	2.7	2.8	3.7	4.2	1.3
Market value ($ mil.)	8.2%	16.8	44.3	43.8	18.7	23.0
Employees	0.0%	43	45	45	43	43

K-SWISS INC.

NASDAQ (GS): KSWS

31248 Oak Crest Dr.
Westlake Village, CA 91361
Phone: 818-706-5100
Fax: 818-706-5390
Web: www.kswiss.com

CEO: Steven Nichols
CFO: George Powlick
HR: Yvette Conen
FYE: December 31
Type: Public

K-Swiss refuses to remain neutral in the sports shoe wars. The company designs and sells running, tennis, and training shoes, including high-performance footwear for triathletes, for men, women, and children under the K-Swiss and Palladium brands. K-Swiss also sells sports apparel and accessories and lets visitors to its website design their own shoes. It's famous for the *K-Swiss Classic*, the white, all-weather, leather tennis shoe that was introduced in 1966 by K-Swiss' founders. K-Swiss products are marketed to upscale buyers and made by independent suppliers — almost entirely in China — and are sold in department and specialty retail stores, primarily in the US, as well as online.

	Annual Growth	12/05	12/06	12/07	12/08	12/09
Sales ($ mil.)	(17.1%)	508.6	501.1	410.4	340.2	240.7
Net income ($ mil.)	—	75.2	76.9	39.1	20.9	(28.0)
Market value ($ mil.)	(25.6%)	1,140.6	1,080.8	636.4	400.8	349.5
Employees	0.4%	510	236	572	584	519

K-TRON INTERNATIONAL, INC.

Rtes. 55 and 553
Pitman, NJ 08071
Phone: 856-589-0500
Fax: 856-589-8113
Web: www.ktron.com

CEO: Edward B. (Ed) Cloues II
CFO: Robert E. Wisniewski
HR: —
FYE: December 31
Type: Subsidiary

K-Tron International keeps manufacturers well fed. Through its K-Tron Process Group subsidiary, the company makes feeders that let manufacturers control the flow of solid bulk and liquid materials during manufacturing processes by weight and volume. It also makes pneumatic conveying systems, including vacuum and pressure systems that precisely control the flow of ingredients used by the pharmaceutical, food, chemical, and plastics industries. Its companies make size reduction equipment, too, used to crush coal and wood products. Subsidiary K-Tron Electronics produces and tests electronic assemblies for K-Tron, as well as sells to regional OEMs. Casket maker Hillenbrand acquired K-Tron in 2010 for $435 million.

	Annual Growth	12/05	12/06	12/07	12/08	12/09
Sales ($ mil.)	12.6%	118.9	148.1	201.7	243.0	190.8
Net income ($ mil.)	31.2%	7.3	12.9	21.3	25.8	21.6
Employees	8.6%	460	625	732	727	639

KUBOTA ENGINE AMERICA CORPORATION

505 Schelter Rd.
Lincolnshire, IL 60069
Phone: 847-955-2500
Fax: 847-955-2699
Web: www.kubotaengine.com

CEO: Joji Takizawa
CFO: —
HR: —
FYE: December 31
Type: Subsidiary

For Kubota Engine America (KEA) it is the little things in life that matter. The company, a subsidiary of Japan-based Kubota Corporation, makes compact diesel and gasoline engines for use in agricultural, construction, industrial, and power generation equipment. KEA's engines range in size from about 10 to 100 horsepower. KEA also manufactures 60 Hz generators. The company sells its products through more than 50 independent distributors throughout the US and a network of some 300 dealers worldwide. Although Kubota-branded compact engines first reached US shores in 1976, KEA was formed in 1998.

	Annual Growth	12/04	12/05	12/06	12/07	12/08
Est. sales ($ mil.)	—	—	—	—	—	10.3
Employees	—	—	—	—	—	66

KUBOTA TRACTOR CORPORATION

3401 Del Amo Blvd.
Torrance, CA 90503
Phone: 310-370-3370
Fax: 310-370-2370
Web: www.kubota.com

CEO: Satoshi Iida
CFO: Toby Anderson
HR: —
FYE: March 31
Type: Subsidiary

If you need a tractor but are worried about maneuvering it into a garden shed, the small but mighty products sold by Kubota Tractor Corporation (KTC) will fit the bill. The company acts as the American distribution arm of Japanese heavy equipment industry giant Kubota Corporation and specializes in compact tractors, construction equipment, and lawn and garden machinery. It is the leading marketer and distributor of under-40 horsepower tractors in the US, offering four lines of tractors and 80 models. Kubota Credit Corporation U.S.A. peddles financing options for the company's products, for both purchase and lease.

KUEHNE + NAGEL, INC.

10 Exchange Place, 19th Fl.
Jersey City, NJ 07302
Phone: 201-413-5500
Fax: 201-413-5777
Web: www.kn-portal.com/locations/north_america/united_states

CEO: Rolf Altorfer
CFO: Michael Schimpf
HR: Jamie Wood
FYE: December 31
Type: Subsidiary

Kuehne + Nagel, Inc. (pronounced KOO-nuh and NAH-gel) is the primary US-based unit of freight forwarding and logistics giant Kuehne + Nagel International AG. Kuehne + Nagel, Inc., specializes in contract logistics services, including warehousing and distribution. In addition, it participates in the parent company's international freight forwarding operations by coordinating air, sea, and ground transportation. Like other freight forwarders, Kuehne + Nagel doesn't own transportation assets; instead, it buys capacity from carriers and resells it to customers. In addition to more than 30 distribution centers spanning the US, the company owns about 45 offices specializing in import/export expertise.

	Annual Growth	12/04	12/05	12/06	12/07	12/08
Est. sales ($ mil.)	—	—	—	—	—	1,949.7
Employees	—	—	—	—	—	2,900

KULICKE AND SOFFA INDUSTRIES, INC.

NASDAQ (GM): KLIC

1005 Virginia Dr.
Fort Washington, PA 19034
Phone: 215-784-6000
Fax: 215-784-6001
Web: www.kns.com

CEO: C. Scott Kulicke
CFO: Michael J. Morris
HR: —
FYE: September 30
Type: Public

"Some assembly required" is music to Kulicke and Soffa Industries' ears. Kulicke and Soffa (K&S) is one of the world's top suppliers of assembly equipment for the semiconductor industry. Its die bonders and wire bonders use fine wires to connect an integrated circuit to its package leads, thereby completing the chip's electrical circuit. K&S also makes consumables for its chip assembly equipment, such as dicing blades. The company sells its products to such contractors and chip makers as Advanced Semiconductor Engineering, Amkor, Intel, Micron Technology, STMicroelectronics, and Texas Instruments. Customers in Asia account for about three-quarters of the company's sales.

	Annual Growth	9/05	9/06	9/07	9/08	9/09
Sales ($ mil.)	(20.4%)	561.3	696.3	700.4	328.0	225.2
Net income ($ mil.)	—	(104.1)	52.2	37.7	3.8	(36.0)
Market value ($ mil.)	(4.5%)	508.4	619.9	594.6	316.2	422.8
Employees	(12.0%)	3,610	2,454	2,903	2,573	2,167

KURT SALMON ASSOCIATES, INC.

1355 Peachtree St. NE, Ste. 900
Atlanta, GA 30309
Phone: 404-892-0321
Fax: 404-898-9590
Web: www.kurtsalmon.com

CEO: Mark Wietecha
CFO: David (Dave) Hetzel
HR: —
FYE: December 31
Type: Subsidiary

Retailers can call on Kurt Salmon Associates (KSA) when their cash registers stop ringing. The firm, a unit of UK-based Management Consulting Group, offers a range of consulting services aimed at streamlining supply chain and business operations for retailers and consumer products makers. Operating from about 10 offices in Asia, Europe, and North America, its consultants offer expertise in logistics, marketing and merchandising, and information technology. The firm also provides reports on industry and consumer trends. In addition, KSA has a health care unit that offers consulting services for hospitals and physician groups in the US. Textile engineer Kurt Salmon started the firm in 1935.

KURTZMAN CARSON CONSULTANTS LLC

2335 Alaska Ave.
El Segundo, CA 90245
Phone: 310-823-9000
Fax: 310-823-9133
Web: www.kccllc.com

CEO: Eric S. Kurtzman
CFO: Gerry Mullins
HR: —
FYE: —
Type: Subsidiary

The words "corporate restructuring" aren't thrown around lightly in the boardroom, but Kurtzman Carson Consultants (KCC) try to help soften the blow. The company is a claims and noticing agent for corporations undergoing Chapter 11 bankruptcy protection. It assists attorneys with administrative and technology services, such as collecting and analyzing data, filing documents, and administering claims through its proprietary software programs CaseView, ClearView, and DealView. Clients have included Skybus Airlines, Delphi, and NRG Energy. KCC was founded by attorneys Eric Kurtzman and Jonathan Carson in 2001. In April 2009, KCC was acquired by financial services company Computershare Limited.

K-V PHARMACEUTICAL COMPANY

NYSE: KV

2503 S. Hanley Rd.
St. Louis, MO 63144
Phone: 314-645-6600
Fax: 314-646-3751
Web: www.kvpharmaceutical.com

CEO: David A. Van Vliet
CFO: Stephen A. Stamp
HR: —
FYE: March 31
Type: Public

Just a spoonful of K-V Pharmaceutical might help the medicine go down. Historically the company has offered both branded and generic drugs, and drug delivery technologies used to make its drugs dissolve faster, release slower, or absorb better. Its generics unit, ETHEX, has specialized in generic versions of hard-to-copy branded drugs in a number of therapeutic categories, including pain management and respiratory disease. Its Ther-Rx subsidiary produced K-V's branded drugs, with a focus on women's health, cardiovascular, and anemia therapies. However, the company has suspended manufacturing operations subsequent to an FDA investigation.

	Annual Growth	3/05	3/06	3/07	3/08	3/09
Sales ($ mil.)	0.7%	303.5	367.6	443.6	601.9	312.3
Net income ($ mil.)	—	33.3	15.8	56.1	88.4	(313.6)
Market value ($ mil.)	(48.4%)	1,156.6	1,202.5	1,232.9	1,244.3	82.3
Employees	(10.8%)	1,072	1,145	1,414	1,590	680

K-VA-T FOOD STORES, INC.

201 Trigg St.
Abingdon, VA 24210
Phone: 276-628-5503
Fax: 276-623-5440
Web: www.foodcity.com

CEO: Steven C. (Steve) Smith
CFO: Robert L. Neeley
HR: Donnie Meadows
FYE: December 31
Type: Private

What do you call a chain of supermarkets in Kentucky, Virginia, and Tennessee? How about K-VA-T Food Stores? K-VA-T is one of the largest grocery chains in the region, with about 95 supermarkets under the Food City banner and another 10 Super Discount Foods locations. Originally a Piggly Wiggly franchise with three stores, K-VA-T was founded in 1955. It has expanded by acquiring stores from other regional food retailers, opening new stores, and adding services such as about 75 pharmacies, 55 Gas'N Go gasoline outlets, and banking. Its Food City Distribution Center provides warehousing and distribution services. The founding Smith family owns a majority of K-VA-T; employees own the rest of the company.

	Annual Growth	12/04	12/05	12/06	12/07	12/08
Sales ($ mil.)	8.3%	1,310.0	1,400.0	1,570.0	1,650.0	1,800.0
Employees	3.6%	10,400	11,000	11,500	12,000	12,000

KVH INDUSTRIES, INC.

NASDAQ (GM): KVHI

50 Enterprise Center
Middletown, RI 02842
Phone: 401-847-3327
Fax: 401-849-0045
Web: www.kvh.com

CEO: Martin A. Kits van Heyningen
CFO: Patrick J. Spratt
HR: —
FYE: December 31
Type: Public

KVH Industries makes products for people (or boats or armies) on the go. The company's mobile satellite communications products include antennas and compasses for yachts and commercial ships, mobile DIRECTV antennas for automobiles, and mobile satellite telephones (TracVision and TracPhone). KVH sells its satellite products to retailers and distributors, as well as boat and other vehicle manufacturers. The company's guidance and stabilization products — sold mainly to US and allied governments and defense contractors — include digital compasses, fiber optic gyros for tactical navigation (TACNAV), and guidance systems for torpedoes and unmanned aerial vehicles. KVH does business in Europe from an office in Denmark.

	Annual Growth	12/05	12/06	12/07	12/08	12/09
Sales ($ mil.)	5.7%	71.3	79.0	80.9	82.4	89.1
Net income ($ mil.)	—	2.9	3.7	2.5	3.1	(0.1)
Market value ($ mil.)	10.8%	140.6	152.4	115.8	74.4	211.7
Employees	4.5%	300	311	314	346	358

KWIK TRIP, INC.

1626 Oak St.
La Crosse, WI 54602
Phone: 608-781-8988
Fax: 608-781-8950
Web: www.kwiktrip.com

CEO: Donald P. (Don) Zietlow
CFO: Scott Teigen
HR: Tom Reinhart
FYE: September 30
Type: Private

Midwesterners who need to make a quick trip to get gas or groceries, cigarettes or donuts, race on over to Kwik Trip stores. Kwik Trip operates about 350 Kwik Trip and Kwik Star convenience stores throughout Iowa, Minnesota, and Wisconsin. The company also runs several Hearty Platter restaurants, about 40 Tobacco Outlet Plus (TOP) cigar stores, and car washes at some Kwik Trip store locations. All Kwik Trip stores built since 1990 are owned by Convenience Store Investments, a separate company, which leases the land and stores to Kwik Trip. Kwik Trip, which opened its first store in 1965 in Eau Claire, Wisconsin, is owned by the family of CEO Don Zietlow.

	Annual Growth	9/04	9/05	9/06	9/07	9/08
Est. sales ($ mil.)	—	—	—	—	—	3,640.4
Employees	—	—	—	—	—	8,400

KYOCERA INTERNATIONAL, INC.

8611 Balboa Ave.
San Diego, CA 92123
Phone: 858-576-2600
Fax: 858-492-1456
Web: americas.kyocera.com

CEO: John S. Rigby
CFO: William J. Edwards
HR: —
FYE: March 31
Type: Subsidiary

Kyocera International, the holding company for the North American operations of Japan's Kyocera Corporation, makes products ranging from semiconductor casings to knives and utensils. Having expanded through acquisitions beyond its origins in specialty ceramics, Kyocera International also makes LCD panels, thin-film devices, printers, industrial cutting tools, and solar energy systems. Its Kyocera Communications unit provides sales, marketing, and customer support for Kyocera and SANYO brand wireless phones in the US. Kyocera International's Kyocera Solar subsidiary is one of the world's largest producers of photovoltaic solar cells.

KYOCERA MITA AMERICA, INC.

225 Sand Rd.
Fairfield, NJ 07004
Phone: 973-808-8444
Fax: 973-882-6000
Web: usa.kyoceramita.com

CEO: Michael (Mike) Pietrunti
CFO: —
HR: —
FYE: March 31
Type: Subsidiary

Kyocera Mita America provides copiers, fax machines, printers, and multifunction devices. Its printer line includes monochrome, wide-format, and color devices, ranging from small desktop models to departmental models designed for large corporations. The company also provides document management software, as well as service and support services. It sells directly and through independent dealers and resellers to customers in the enterprise and government sectors. The company represents Kyocera Mita in the US; Kyocera Mita is the document imaging division of manufacturing giant Kyocera.

KYOCERA SOLAR, INC.

7812 E. Acoma Dr.
Scottsdale, AZ 85260
Phone: 480-948-8003
Fax: 480-483-6431
Web: www.kyocerasolar.com

CEO: Steven C. Hill
CFO: Mike Rennie
HR: —
FYE: March 31
Type: Subsidiary

Kyocera Solar turns daylight into more than night lights. The company, a subsidiary of Kyocera International, develops and sells solar-powered electric systems used to shed light on such dark spots as rural homes, recreational vehicle sites, remote telecom and pipeline monitoring equipment, and traffic signal locations. Its solar-powered water pumping systems can be used in areas where there is no sufficient water supply. Kyocera Solar sells integrated system packages directly to industrial users (product manufacturers, utilities, and corporate and government entities); it also provides products and support to a global network of more than 1,500 distributors and dealers, mostly in the US.

L-1 IDENTITY SOLUTIONS, INC. NYSE: ID

177 Broad St., 12th Fl.
Stamford, CT 06901
Phone: 203-504-1100
Fax: 203-504-1150
Web: www.l1id.com

CEO: Robert V. LaPenta
CFO: James (Jim) DePalma
HR: —
FYE: December 31
Type: Public

L-1 Identity Solutions takes a one-on-one approach to security. The company primarily develops face, finger, and iris recognition systems to protect and secure personal identities and assets. L-1 operates through two segments: Solutions drives a stable of secure credentialing and biometrics tools. Enrollment, consulting, training, and IT services are offered by a Services arm. L-1 produces driver's licenses, as well as voter, and other government and corporate-issued IDs. Its live scan systems are deployed by the Department of Homeland Security at US border crossings. L-1 serves US and foreign federal, state, and local governments, and commercial entities; government contracts represent some 95% of revenues.

	Annual Growth	12/05	12/06	12/07	12/08	12/09
Sales ($ mil.)	77.1%	66.2	164.4	389.5	562.9	650.9
Net income ($ mil.)	—	(7.4)	(31.0)	17.7	(548.7)	(4.2)
Market value ($ mil.)	(19.2%)	1,635.4	1,405.1	1,667.0	625.9	695.6
Employees	80.0%	223	1,047	1,819	2,264	2,339

L-3 COMMUNICATIONS HOLDINGS, INC. NYSE: LLL

600 3rd Ave.
New York, NY 10016
Phone: 212-697-1111
Fax: 212-805-5477
Web: www.l-3com.com

CEO: Michael T. Strianese
CFO: Ralph G. D'Ambrosio
HR: Sabrina J. Marotta
FYE: December 31
Type: Public

L-3's good defense is its best commercial offense. L-3 Communications Holdings makes secure and specialized systems for satellite, avionics, security, and marine communications. It also provides engineering and intelligence, surveillance, and reconnaissance products and services. The US government (primarily the Department of Defense) accounts for more than 80% of the company's business, but L-3 is using acquisitions to expand its commercial offerings. As a government contractor, the company is subject to the priorities of the Pentagon and other government agencies and faces potential cuts in military programs as defense priorities change. More than 85% of sales come from customers in the US.

	Annual Growth	12/05	12/06	12/07	12/08	12/09
Sales ($ mil.)	13.4%	9,444.7	12,476.9	13,960.5	14,901.0	15,615.0
Net income ($ mil.)	15.7%	508.5	526.1	756.1	929.0	911.0
Market value ($ mil.)	4.0%	8,605.4	9,465.3	12,261.6	8,539.4	10,063.7
Employees	3.0%	59,500	63,700	64,600	65,000	67,000

LA BREA BAKERY, INC.

15963 Strathern St.
Van Nuys, CA 91406
Phone: 818-742-4242
Fax: 818-742-4276
Web: www.labreabakery.com

CEO: John Yamin
CFO: —
HR: —
FYE: December 31
Type: Subsidiary

La Brea Bakery Holdings knows it takes some crust to win the hearts of foodies. The company is a leading US producer of partially baked artisan breads, which it supplies to restaurants and food stores throughout the US under the La Brea brand name. It also operates two casual dining restaurants, the La Brea Bakery Cafes, one in Los Angeles and one in Anaheim, California. As demand for upscale bread has continued to steadily grow, the company has expanded to two production facilities in California and New Jersey. La Brea is owned by the European specialty bakery firm ARYZTA. La Brea's baked goods are delivered daily to more than 1,350 grocery stores and restaurants in the greater Los Angeles area.

	Annual Growth	12/04	12/05	12/06	12/07	12/08
Est. sales ($ mil.)	—	—	—	—	—	200.0
Employees	—	—	—	—	—	1,200

LA JOLLA PHARMACEUTICAL COMPANY Pink Sheets: LJPC

6455 Nancy Ridge Dr.
San Diego, CA 92121
Phone: 858-452-6600
Fax: 858-626-2851
Web: www.ljpc.com

CEO: Deirdre Y. Gillespie
CFO: Gail A. Sloan
HR: Vicki Motte
FYE: December 31
Type: Public

La Jolla Pharmaceutical aimed to eliminate diseases. The development-stage firm was working with Toleragens, proprietary therapies that block the abnormal antibody production associated with certain autoimmune disorders without suppressing the entire immune system. Its lead drug candidate was Riquent, a treatment for renal disease associated with lupus. The drug would have been one of the few new drugs for lupus. However, the company ceased most of its operations after trials of Riquent failed in 2009. Adamis Pharmaceuticals announced plans to acquire La Jolla Pharmaceuticals, but when shareholders didn't respond, it dropped the plans.

	Annual Growth	12/05	12/06	12/07	12/08	12/09
Sales ($ mil.)	—	—	—	—	0.0	8.1
Net income ($ mil.)	—	—	—	—	(62.9)	(8.6)
Market value ($ mil.)	(71.2%)	—	—	—	38.1	11.0
Employees	(96.8%)	—	—	—	94	3

LA MESA R.V. CENTER, INC.

7430 Copley Park Pl.
San Diego, CA 92111
Phone: 858-874-8000
Fax: 858-874-8021
Web: www.lamesarv.com

CEO: James R. (Jim) Kimbrell
CFO: Timothy K. (Tim) O'Connor
HR: Yvette Broderick
FYE: December 31
Type: Private

The folks at La Mesa RV Center want to make everyone a happy camper. One of the world's largest Winnebago dealers, La Mesa RV also sells new and used campers and RVs from Tiffin Motorhomes, Gulf Stream, Rexhall, and Coachmen, among other brands at about 10 locations in California, Arizona, and Florida. It also has seasonal locations to service motorhomes in the spring and winter as they come out of or go into off-season storage. The company provides RV repair and sells parts for new and used vehicles at its service centers and online. La Mesa RV was founded in 1972.

LABARGE, INC. NYSE Amex: LB

9900 Clayton Rd.
St. Louis, MO 63124
Phone: 314-997-0800
Fax: 314-812-9438
Web: www.labarge.com

CEO: Craig E. LaBarge
CFO: Donald H. Nonnenkamp
HR: Tim LoGrasso
FYE: June 30
Type: Public

Despite its name, LaBarge is more spacecraft than boat. As a contract manufacturer, LaBarge designs, engineers, and produces complex electronics and interconnect systems that are able to withstand the physical extremes of combat, space, sea, and inner earth. The company's printed circuit boards, cables, electronic assemblies, and other products are used in demanding applications such as military communication systems, commercial aircraft, satellites, medical equipment, airport security, glass container fabrication systems, and oil drilling equipment. LaBarge's top customers include Owens-Illinois, Raytheon, and Schlumberger. More than 90% of sales are to customers in the US.

	Annual Growth	6/05	6/06	6/07	6/08	6/09
Sales ($ mil.)	10.7%	182.3	190.1	235.2	279.5	273.4
Net income ($ mil.)	(1.4%)	10.9	9.7	11.3	14.8	10.3
Market value ($ mil.)	(15.5%)	286.8	209.7	194.4	205.4	146.5
Employees	8.7%	1,050	1,200	1,260	1,350	—

An in-depth profile of this company is available to Hoover's Online members at hoovers.com.

LABORATORY CORPORATION OF AMERICA HOLDINGS
NYSE: LH

358 S. Main St.
Burlington, NC 27215
Phone: 336-229-1127
Fax: 336-436-1205
Web: www.labcorp.com

CEO: David P. (Dave) King
CFO: William B. (Brad) Hayes
HR: Lisa Hoffman Starr
FYE: December 31
Type: Public

This company pricks and prods for profit. Laboratory Corporation of America Holdings (LabCorp) is one of the top providers of clinical laboratory services in the world. LabCorp performs tests on some 440,000 patient specimens each day on behalf of managed care organizations, hospitals, doctors, government agencies, drug companies, and employers. Its services range from routine urinalyses, HIV tests, and Pap smears to specialty testing for diagnostic genetics, oncology diagnosis and monitoring, infectious diseases, clinical drug trials, and allergies. LabCorp operates about 1,500 service sites across the US that collect patient specimens and ship them to its 40 primary laboratories where tests are performed.

	Annual Growth	12/05	12/06	12/07	12/08	12/09
Sales ($ mil.)	9.0%	3,327.6	3,590.8	4,068.2	4,505.2	4,694.7
Net income ($ mil.)	8.9%	386.2	431.6	476.8	464.5	543.3
Market value ($ mil.)	8.6%	5,600.4	7,640.9	7,855.1	6,698.6	7,783.4
Employees	3.9%	24,000	25,000	26,000	28,000	28,000

LABRANCHE & CO INC.
NYSE: LAB

33 Whitehall St.
New York, NY 10004
Phone: 212-425-1144
Fax: 212-344-1469
Web: www.labranche.com

CEO: George M. L. (Michael) LaBranche IV
CFO: Jeffrey A. McCutcheon
HR: —
FYE: December 31
Type: Public

LaBranche family tree includes two primary branches — the market makers and the brokers. Subsidiary LaBranche Structured Holdings is a market-maker for derivatives including options, futures, and exchange-traded funds (ETFs). LaBranche provides brokerage and clearing services for institutional clients through LaBranche Financial Services. In 2010, LaBranche sold its NYSE-designated market-making business to Barclays Capital for some $25 million. (The deal did not include the company's specialist operations in the UK and Hong Kong.) Following that sale, LaBranche is focusing on its US derivatives and international equity businesses.

	Annual Growth	12/05	12/06	12/07	12/08	12/09
Sales ($ mil.)	(31.5%)	340.2	674.0	448.7	224.1	75.0
Net income ($ mil.)	—	37.5	136.8	(350.5)	(66.0)	(97.8)
Market value ($ mil.)	(27.2%)	428.0	416.1	213.4	202.8	120.2
Employees	(20.1%)	525	429	257	213	214

LACKS ENTERPRISES, INC.

5460 Cascade Rd. SE
Grand Rapids, MI 49546
Phone: 616-949-6570
Fax: 616-285-2367
Web: www.lacksenterprises.com

CEO: Richard Lacks Jr.
CFO: Brad Kirk
HR: Jim Green
FYE: July 31
Type: Private

It's not hipp if your car lacks a wheel cover or has a rusty grille. Lacks Enterprises makes high-impact plated plastic (HIPP) alternatives to die-cast and stainless steel automotive products such as wheel covers and grilles. The company's HIPP parts, plated with coppernickel chrome, are lighter and cheaper than all-metal alternatives, as well as more resistant to dents and rust. Other products include molding, rocker panels, and trim. Automotive OEM customers have included Chrysler, Ford, General Motors, Nissan, and Toyota. Its Plastic-Plate subsidiary makes items such as cell phone face plates for manufacturers of consumer electronics and telecommunications equipment. The Lacks family owns Lacks Enterprises.

THE LACLEDE GROUP, INC.
NYSE: LG

720 Olive St.
St. Louis, MO 63101
Phone: 314-342-0500
Fax: 314-421-1979
Web: www.thelacledegroup.com

CEO: Douglas H. Yaeger
CFO: Mark D. Waltermire
HR: Richard A. Skau
FYE: September 30
Type: Public

In the "Show Me" state, The Laclede Group is saying, "Show me the money." The group's main revenue source is utility Laclede Gas, which distributes natural gas to approximately 630,000 customers in eastern Missouri, including St. Louis. Laclede Group's nonregulated businesses provide gas transportation and other services and operate underground gas storage fields. Operations include wholesale gas marketing (Laclede Energy Resources), a propane pipeline (Laclede Pipeline), insurance (Laclede Gas Family Services), and real estate development (Laclede Development).

	Annual Growth	9/05	9/06	9/07	9/08	9/09
Sales ($ mil.)	4.4%	1,597.0	1,997.6	2,021.6	2,209.0	1,895.2
Net income ($ mil.)	12.5%	40.1	49.0	49.8	78.0	64.2
Market value ($ mil.)	(0.3%)	723.9	714.8	719.2	1,080.4	716.6
Employees	(2.3%)	1,933	1,874	1,835	1,807	1,762

LACROSSE FOOTWEAR, INC.
NASDAQ (GM): BOOT

17634 NE Airport Way
Portland, OR 97230
Phone: 503-262-0110
Fax: 503-262-0115
Web: www.lacrossefootwear.com

CEO: Joseph P. Schneider
CFO: David P. Carlson
HR: J. Gary Rebello
FYE: December 31
Type: Public

If customers are wearing its protective boots, LaCrosse Footwear doesn't care who steps on their toes. The company offers sturdy footwear for sporting, outdoors, and occupations such as farming, general utility, and construction. LaCrosse makes rubber, vinyl, and leather footwear, as well as rainwear and protective clothing, for adults and children. Its brands include LaCrosse, Danner, Burly, Camohide, and Iceman, among other names. LaCrosse's products are sold nationwide to catalog merchants, retailers, wholesalers, and the US government, as well as through company websites and outlet stores.

	Annual Growth	12/05	12/06	12/07	12/08	12/09
Sales ($ mil.)	8.8%	99.4	107.8	118.2	128.0	139.2
Net income ($ mil.)	1.4%	5.2	6.3	7.3	6.2	5.5
Market value ($ mil.)	3.7%	69.4	85.0	112.3	79.9	80.1
Employees	13.7%	276	303	306	359	462

LACTALIS USA, INC.

950 Third Ave., 22nd Fl.
New York, NY 10022
Phone: 212-758-6666
Fax: 212-758-7383
Web: www.lactalis-usa.com

CEO: Frédérick Bouisset
CFO: —
HR: —
FYE: December 31
Type: Business segment

Lactalis USA is not a party animal; the company is a party to cheese. The company is a leading maker of specialty cheeses in the US. It serves both the retail food and foodservice industries, including school lunch programs. It markets its cheeses under the Precious brand name. The company's cheese varieties include mozzarella (including fresh mozzarella), ricotta, and six different flavors of string cheese. In 2007 the company acquired California-based soft-cheese maker Mozzarella Fresca. Headquartered in New York City, Lactalis USA is part of the French dairy giant Groupe Lactalis.

	Annual Growth	12/04	12/05	12/06	12/07	12/08
Est. sales ($ mil.)	—	—	—	—	—	232.3
Employees	—	—	—	—	—	765

THELADDERS.COM, INC.

137 Varick St., 8th Fl.
New York, NY 10013
Phone: 646-453-1800
Fax: 646-453-1932
Web: www.theladders.com

CEO: Marc Cenedella
CFO: Harpeet Grewal
HR: Diana Kyser
FYE: December 31
Type: Private

You'll have to climb a few ladders to get to the top, and TheLadders.com can help you get the best view. Targeting high-level executive positions, the company lists job postings on its website (more than 35,000 jobs are typically featured). TheLadders.com only lists jobs that come with salaries of at least $100,000; industries covered include sales and marketing, finance, technology, and law. It charges companies to post available positions, and job hunters must buy a subscription to receive full access to the postings. TheLadders.com has signed more than 2 million members since it was founded in 2003 by former executives at HotJobs.

LADENBURG THALMANN FINANCIAL SERVICES

NYSE Amex: LTS

4400 Biscayne Blvd., 12th Fl.
Miami, FL 33137
Phone: 212-409-2000
Fax: 305-572-4199
Web: www.ladenburg.com

CEO: Richard J. (Dick) Lampen
CFO: Brett H. Kaufman
HR: —
FYE: December 31
Type: Public

Laden with cash? You might want to call Ladenburg Thalmann Financial Services, Inc. The company provides investment banking, trading, and asset management services to corporate, institutional, and individual clients throughout the US. Subsidiaries Triad Advisors (acquired in 2008) and Investacorp (2007) are independent broker-dealers serving primarily retail clients; together they have some 900 registered representatives and manage more than $15 billion in assets. Subsidiary Ladenburg Thalmann & Co. is a broker-dealer targeting mid-market and emerging companies and wealthy individuals. Ladenburg Thalmann Asset Management offers mutual funds, alternative investments, and third-party advisory services.

	Annual Growth	12/05	12/06	12/07	12/08	12/09
Sales ($ mil.)	48.8%	30.7	46.9	95.8	121.0	150.7
Net income ($ mil.)	—	(26.0)	4.7	9.4	(20.3)	(18.7)
Market value ($ mil.)	8.6%	77.3	204.9	356.1	120.9	107.5
Employees	1.1%	162	172	173	176	169

LADISH CO., INC.

NASDAQ (GM): LDSH

5481 S. Packard Ave.
Cudahy, WI 53110
Phone: 414-747-2611
Fax: 414-747-2963
Web: www.ladishco.com

CEO: Gary J. Vroman
CFO: Wayne E. Larsen
HR: Lawrence C. Hammond
FYE: December 31
Type: Public

Ladish got its start in 1905 when Herman Ladish bought a 1,500-pound steam hammer, and the company's been swinging ever since. Today the company designs and manufactures high-strength forged and cast metal components for aerospace and industrial markets. Jet engine parts, missile components, landing gear, helicopter rotors, and other aerospace products generate about 75% of the company's sales; general industrial components account for the remaining 25%. Aerospace industry giants Rolls-Royce (23%), United Technologies (15%), and General Electric (9%) together account for almost half of Ladish's sales. About 50% of its sales come from outside the US (the UK representing more than half of all foreign sales).

	Annual Growth	12/05	12/06	12/07	12/08	12/09
Sales ($ mil.)	7.0%	266.8	369.3	424.6	469.5	349.8
Net income ($ mil.)	(18.3%)	13.7	28.5	32.3	32.2	6.1
Market value ($ mil.)	(9.4%)	351.0	582.3	678.2	217.5	236.3
Employees	(12.6%)	1,950	1,200	1,270	1,380	1,137

LAFARGE NORTH AMERICA INC.

12950 Worldgate Dr., Ste. 500
Herndon, VA 20170
Phone: 703-480-3600
Fax: 703-796-2218
Web: www.lafargenorthamerica.com

CEO: Bruno Lafont
CFO: Eric C. Olsen
HR: —
FYE: December 31
Type: Subsidiary

Lafarge North America is at the foundation of buildings, roads, and bridges across US and Canada. One of North America's largest building materials manufacturers, the company operates around 600 concrete plants, aggregate plants, and cement plants in the US and Canada (through Lafarge Canada). Its products include asphalt, aggregates, gypsum wallboard, ready-mixed concrete, and concrete pipes and blocks. The products are used to build commercial, residential, transportation, public, and utilities projects. Lafarge North America is part of global building conglomerate Lafarge Group, based in France. It accounts for about 20% of its parent's sales.

LAGASSE, INC.

1 Parkway North Blvd.
Deerfield, IL 60015
Phone: 847-627-2400
Fax: —
Web: www.lagassesweet.com

CEO: Stephen A. (Steve) Schultz
CFO: Victoria Wright
HR: —
FYE: December 31
Type: Subsidiary

If a distributor needs food containers or the supplies used to clean up after the food has been consumed, Lagasse is ready. The company, which does business as LagasseSweet, acts as a wholesale distributor, offering more than 7,000 foodservice, janitorial, and paper products to other distributors, which in turn serve retailers and other customers. LagasseSweet stocks items from more than 100 manufacturers and distributes them from a network of about 30 facilities throughout the US. The company is a subsidiary of wholesale office products distributor United Stationers.

LAIRD TECHNOLOGIES, INC.

16401 Swingley Ridge Rd., Ste. 700
Chesterfield, MO 63017
Phone: 636-898-6000
Fax: 636-898-6100
Web: www.lairdtech.com

CEO: Martin L. Rapp
CFO: Roger Presley
HR: Carolyn Koenig
FYE: December 31
Type: Subsidiary

Laird Technologies knows that the shield is mightier than the sword, especially when it comes to shielding materials. Laird manufactures electromagnetic interference (EMI) shielding materials such as custom metal stampings, signal integrity components, thermal management products, wireless antennas, RF modules, and beryllium copper fingerstock for the aerospace, automotive, electronics, and medical equipment industries. The company also produces specialty applications such as metalized fabric and conductive tape and offers product engineering and testing services. Laird Technologies is the operating business of Laird PLC.

An in-depth profile of this company is available to Hoover's Online members at hoovers.com.

915

LAKE SHORE BANCORP, INC.

NASDAQ (GM): LSBK

125 E. 4th St.
Dunkirk, NY 14048
Phone: 716-366-4070
Fax: 716-366-2965
Web: www.lakeshoresavings.com

CEO: David C. Mancuso
CFO: Rachel A. Foley
HR: Janinne Fiegl Dugan
FYE: December 31
Type: Public

Money washes up along this shore. Lake Shore Bancorp is the holding company for Lake Shore Savings Bank, which serves consumers and businesses through about 10 branches in Chautauqua and Erie counties in western New York, near Lake Erie. Founded in 1891, the community oriented savings bank focuses on residential real estate lending, with one- to four-family mortgages accounting for a majority of its loan portfolio. Lake Shore Savings Bank also offers home equity loans and commercial and consumer loans, as well as checking and savings accounts, CDs, and IRAs. Mutual holding company Lake Shore, MHC owns about 60% of Lake Shore Bancorp.

	Annual Growth	12/05	12/06	12/07	12/08	12/09
Assets ($ mil.)	6.3%	333.7	354.2	357.8	407.8	425.7
Net income ($ mil.)	1.2%	2.1	1.8	1.8	1.5	2.2
Market value ($ mil.)	(14.5%)	—	76.3	52.3	42.5	47.7
Employees	0.7%	110	103	99	110	113

LAKELAND BANCORP, INC.

NASDAQ (GS): LBAI

250 Oak Ridge Rd.
Oak Ridge, NJ 07438
Phone: 973-697-2000
Fax: 973-697-8385
Web: www.lakelandbank.com

CEO: Thomas J. Shara Jr.
CFO: Joseph F. Hurley
HR: —
FYE: December 31
Type: Public

Lakeland Bancorp is shoring up in the Garden State. It's the holding company for Lakeland Bank, which serves northern New Jersey from about 50 branch offices. Targeting individuals and small to midsized businesses, the bank offers standard retail products such as checking and savings accounts, money market and NOW accounts, and CDs. It also offers financial planning and advisory services for consumers. The bank's lending activities primarily consist of commercial loans (about half of the company's loan portfolio) and residential mortgages (about a third of all loans). Its Lakeland Bank Equipment Leasing Division offers commercial equipment lease financing.

	Annual Growth	12/05	12/06	12/07	12/08	12/09
Assets ($ mil.)	5.4%	2,206.0	2,263.6	2,513.8	2,642.6	2,724.0
Net income ($ mil.)	—	20.2	17.0	18.0	15.2	(5.4)
Market value ($ mil.)	(16.8%)	320.1	340.7	278.2	270.3	153.4
Employees	(0.7%)	548	538	540	521	533

LAKELAND FINANCIAL CORPORATION

NASDAQ (GS): LKFN

202 E. Center St.
Warsaw, IN 46581
Phone: 574-267-6144
Fax: 574-267-6063
Web: www.lakecitybank.com

CEO: Michael L. Kubacki
CFO: David M. Findlay
HR: —
FYE: December 31
Type: Public

American dollars are preferred over Polish zloty in this Warsaw bank. Lakeland Financial is the holding company for Lake City Bank, which serves area business customers and individuals through more than 40 branches scattered across about a dozen northern Indiana counties. Founded in 1872 in Warsaw, Indiana, the bank offers such standard retail services as checking and savings accounts, money market accounts, and CDs. Commercial loans, including agricultural loans and mortgages, make up about 80% of the bank's loan portfolio. Lake City Bank also offers investment products and services such as corporate and personal trust, brokerage, employee benefit plans, and estate planning.

	Annual Growth	12/05	12/06	12/07	12/08	12/09
Assets ($ mil.)	12.0%	1,634.6	1,836.7	1,989.1	2,377.4	2,571.5
Net income ($ mil.)	1.4%	18.0	18.7	19.2	19.7	19.0
Market value ($ mil.)	(3.9%)	325.2	411.2	336.7	383.7	277.9
Employees	1.5%	434	449	447	446	461

LAKELAND INDUSTRIES, INC.

NASDAQ (GM): LAKE

701 Koehler Ave., Ste. 7
Ronkonkoma, NY 11779
Phone: 631-981-9700
Fax: 631-981-9751
Web: www.lakeland.com

CEO: Christopher J. (Chris) Ryan
CFO: Gary Pokrassa
HR: —
FYE: January 31
Type: Public

Lakeland Industries isn't your average haberdasher — it's like a love child of the EPA and OSHA. The company manufactures protective clothing for on-the-job hazards. Lakeland uses DuPont specialty fabrics such as Kevlar, TyChem, and Tyvek, as well as its own fabrics, to make industrial disposable garments, toxic-waste cleanup suits, fire- and heat-resistant apparel (including Fyrepel turnout gear for firefighters), industrial work gloves, and industrial and medical garments. Lakeland manufactures its products in Brazil, China, India, Mexico, and the US.

	Annual Growth	1/06	1/07	1/08	1/09	1/10
Sales ($ mil.)	(1.2%)	98.7	100.2	95.7	102.3	94.1
Net income ($ mil.)	(36.9%)	6.3	5.1	3.3	4.5	1.0
Market value ($ mil.)	(15.8%)	91.6	79.8	53.6	41.9	46.0
Employees	1.0%	1,634	1,667	1,782	2,238	1,700

LAKES ENTERTAINMENT, INC.

NASDAQ (GM): LACO

130 Cheshire Ln., Ste. 101
Minnetonka, MN 55305
Phone: 952-449-9092
Fax: 952-449-9353
Web: www.lakesgaming.com

CEO: Lyle Berman
CFO: Timothy J. Cope
HR: Dianne Stone
FYE: December 31
Type: Public

Even though Lakes Entertainment doesn't own a casino, it still keeps its eye on the slots. The company develops and manages Indian-owned casino properties, including the Cimarron Casino (Perkins, Oklahoma) for the Iowa Tribe of Oklahoma; the Four Winds Casino Resort (New Buffalo Township, Michigan) for the Pokagon Band of Potawatomi Indians; and the Red Hawk Casino for the Shingle Springs Band of Miwok Indians (El Dorado County, California). Lakes Entertainment also has agreements with tribes for casino development projects in Michigan, California, and Oklahoma, and is developing new casino table games to market and license to casinos. Chairman and CEO Lyle Berman owns about 20% of Lakes Entertainment.

	Annual Growth	12/05	12/06	12/07	12/08	12/09
Sales ($ mil.)	9.5%	18.2	29.9	28.5	24.3	26.2
Net income ($ mil.)	—	(11.9)	20.9	(13.6)	(86.3)	3.7
Market value ($ mil.)	(21.6%)	175.4	284.5	182.7	106.0	66.2
Employees	(24.5%)	123	50	49	50	40

LAKESHORE EQUIPMENT COMPANY

2695 E. Dominguez St.
Carson, CA 90895
Phone: 310-537-8600
Fax: 310-537-5403
Web: www.lakeshorelearning.com

CEO: Bo Kaplan
CFO: —
HR: —
FYE: December 31
Type: Private

Lakeshore Equipment Company aims to make learning fun. Through about 50 Lakeshore Learning Stores in two dozen states, the company sells educational toys and classroom tools, including art supplies, games, learning kits, textbooks, and teacher resource packets. It also offers products that address multicultural learning environments and special needs children, as well as in-store teacher workshops. In addition to its store network, Lakeshore Equipment markets learning materials via its two mail-order catalogs and website. Ethelyn Kaplan founded the company in 1954. Today it is run by her son Michael (chairman) and grandsons Bo (president and CEO) and Josh (VP of Merchandising).

	Annual Growth	12/04	12/05	12/06	12/07	12/08
Est. sales ($ mil.)	—	—	—	—	—	300.0
Employees	—	—	—	—	—	1,200

⊞ LAM RESEARCH CORPORATION

NASDAQ (GS): LRCX

4650 Cushing Pkwy.
Fremont, CA 94538
Phone: 510-572-0200
Fax: 510-572-2935
Web: www.lamrc.com

CEO: Stephen G. (Steve) Newberry
CFO: Ernest E. Maddock
HR: Sarah A. O'Dowd
FYE: June 30
Type: Public

It's not uncommon for chip makers in need of critical manufacturing equipment to go on the Lam. Lam Research is a top maker of semiconductor processing equipment. The company's products address two key steps in the chip-making process. Its plasma etch machines are used to create tiny circuitry patterns on silicon wafers. Lam also makes cleaning equipment that keeps unwanted particles from contaminating processed wafers. The company's customers include many large chip makers, such as Hynix Semiconductor, Samsung Electronics, STMicroelectronics, and Toshiba. Most of the company's sales are to customers outside of the US, primarily in the Asia/Pacific region.

	Annual Growth	6/05	6/06	6/07	6/08	6/09
Sales ($ mil.)	(7.2%)	1,502.5	1,642.2	2,566.6	2,474.9	1,115.9
Net income ($ mil.)	—	299.3	335.8	685.8	439.3	(302.1)
Market value ($ mil.)	(2.6%)	3,661.9	5,911.7	6,503.8	4,574.2	3,289.9
Employees	5.4%	2,200	2,430	3,000	3,800	2,711

⊞ LAMAR ADVERTISING COMPANY

NASDAQ (GS): LAMR

5551 Corporate Blvd., Ste 2-A
Baton Rouge, LA 70808
Phone: 225-926-1000
Fax: 225-926-1005
Web: www.lamar.com

CEO: Kevin P. Reilly Jr.
CFO: Keith A. Istre
HR: Tammy Duncan
FYE: December 31
Type: Public

Here's a company that shows all the signs of being a successful outdoor advertising business. Lamar Advertising is one of the top billboard operators in the US, along with CBS Outdoor and Clear Channel Outdoor. The company maintains about 160,000 billboards in about 45 states, plus Canada and Puerto Rico. It also sells advertising space on almost 30,000 signs placed on buses and at bus stops in more than 15 states, and it maintains some 100,000 logo signs (highway exit signs with logos of nearby hotels and restaurants) along interstates in about 20 states and Canada. Chairman, president, and CEO Kevin Reilly Jr., together with members of his family, controls a 67% voting stake in the company.

	Annual Growth	12/05	12/06	12/07	12/08	12/09
Sales ($ mil.)	0.8%	1,021.7	1,120.1	1,209.6	1,198.4	1,056.1
Net income ($ mil.)	—	41.8	43.9	46.2	9.7	(58.0)
Market value ($ mil.)	(9.4%)	4,252.6	6,028.1	4,431.4	1,157.9	2,866.1
Employees	(1.6%)	3,200	3,300	3,200	3,200	3,000

⊞ LANCASTER COLONY CORPORATION

NASDAQ (GS): LANC

37 W. Broad St.
Columbus, OH 43215
Phone: 614-224-7141
Fax: 614-469-8219
Web: www.lancastercolony.com

CEO: John B. (Jay) Gerlach Jr.
CFO: John L. Boylan
HR: Gary E. Thompson
FYE: June 30
Type: Public

Lancaster Colony provides three ingredients guaranteed to result in a romantic meal — caviar, candles, and wine glasses. The company makes specialty foods, including Marzetti salad dressings, Chatham Village croutons, Romanoff caviar, Texas Toast, and other bread, pasta, and sauce products. Lancaster's food products are available in food retailers throughout the US, as well as to foodservice operations including restaurants. It also offers private-label services. In addition to food, the company supplies other amenities for that special dinner mentioned above: Lancaster produces Candle-lite candles and candle accessories and glassware for the foodservice industry.

	Annual Growth	6/05	6/06	6/07	6/08	6/09
Sales ($ mil.)	(1.8%)	1,131.5	1,175.3	1,091.2	980.9	1,051.5
Net income ($ mil.)	(1.1%)	93.1	83.0	45.7	37.6	89.1
Market value ($ mil.)	0.7%	1,213.0	1,115.0	1,183.4	855.4	1,244.9
Employees	(12.7%)	5,500	5,600	4,800	3,500	3,200

⊞ LANCE, INC.

NASDAQ (GS): LNCE

8600 South Blvd.
Charlotte, NC 28273
Phone: 704-554-1421
Fax: 704-554-5562
Web: www.lance.com

CEO: David V. Singer
CFO: Richard D. (Rick) Puckett
HR: Kevin A. Henry
FYE: December 31
Type: Public

If you're familiar with the munchies named Toastchee, Cheese on Nipchee, and Captain's Wafers, Lance has undoubtedly helped you stave off a snack attack. The company produces single-serve, multi-pack, and family-sized packages of bakery products and sweet and savory snack foods, including cookies, crackers, nuts, and potato chips. Its snacks are sold primarily under the Lance, Cape Cod, and Tom's brand names at food retailers, mass merchandisers, and convenience, club, and discount stores in the US. It also supplies products to foodservice operators and manufactures private-label and branded-label snacks for other food manufacturers.

	Annual Growth	12/05	12/06	12/07	12/08	12/09
Sales ($ mil.)	7.8%	679.3	730.1	762.7	852.5	918.2
Net income ($ mil.)	17.9%	18.5	18.5	23.8	17.7	35.8
Market value ($ mil.)	9.0%	599.9	646.6	657.6	738.7	846.9
Employees	(3.3%)	5,500	4,800	4,700	4,800	4,800

LAND O'FROST, INC.

16850 Chicago Ave.
Lansing, IL 60438
Phone: 708-474-7100
Fax: 708-474-9329
Web: www.landofrost.com

CEO: Donna Van Eekeren
CFO: George Smolar
HR: —
FYE: December 31
Type: Private

Land O'Frost makes meat sandwich-worthy. The family-owned company manufactures lunch and deli meats (beef, chicken, turkey, Canadian bacon, and ham) under the DeliShaved, Land O'Frost, Taste Escapes, and Premium brand names. Land O'Frost customers include food retailers, food processors and foodservice companies across the US. It also provides meat-derived ingredients to other food manufacturers and bulk products to foodservice providers. The company operates three plants, one each in Illinois, Arkansas, and Kentucky. Land O'Frost was founded by Antoon Van Eekeren in the 1950s and is still owned and managed by his descendants.

	Annual Growth	12/04	12/05	12/06	12/07	12/08
Est. sales ($ mil.)	—	—	—	—	—	195.0
Employees	—	—	—	—	—	900

⊞ LAND O'LAKES, INC.

4001 Lexington Ave., North
Arden Hills, MN 55112
Phone: 651-481-2222
Fax: 651-481-2000
Web: www.landolakesinc.com

CEO: Christopher J. (Chris) Policinski
CFO: Daniel E. (Dan) Knutson
HR: Karen Grabow
FYE: December 31
Type: Cooperative

The people at Land O'Lakes cooperate in order to butter up customers. Owned by and serving more than 4,600 dairy farmer/members and some 980 smaller community cooperatives, Land O'Lakes is one of the largest dairy co-ops in the US. It provides its member/farmers with crop nutrient and protection products, seed, and animal feed. Its oldest and best known product, LAND O' LAKES butter, is the top butter brand in the US. The co-op offers more than 300 dairy-based food products from the 12.7 billion pounds of milk its member supply annually. Land O'Lakes operates 10 dairy product production sites in the US. Its Land O'Lakes Purina Feed division is a leading animal feed and pet food maker.

	Annual Growth	12/04	12/05	12/06	12/07	12/08
Sales ($ mil.)	11.9%	7,676.5	7,556.7	7,274.9	8,924.9	12,039.3
Net income ($ mil.)	65.3%	21.4	128.9	88.7	163.8	159.6
Employees	3.3%	8,000	7,500	8,500	8,700	9,100

⊞ An in-depth profile of this company is available to Hoover's Online members at hoovers.com.

917

LAND O'LAKES PURINA FEED LLC

1080 County Rd. F
Shoreview, MN 55126
Phone: 651-481-2222
Fax: —
Web: www.lolfeed.com

CEO: David R. (Dave) Hoogmoed
CFO: Daniel E. (Dan) Knutson
HR: —
FYE: December 31
Type: Subsidiary

Whether rodent, fowl, bovine, or swine, Land O'Lakes Purina Feed will have something for it to eat. As the largest US producer of animal feeds, the company addresses the dietary needs of livestock (poultry, swine, and dairy and beef cattle); specialty animals (such as llamas and emus); zoo and lab animals; wild birds; and companion animals (pets). In addition to feed, the company makes milk-replacer products for young animals, premixes, supplements, and custom-mixed feeds, along with offering farm-management advice and services. It is a subsidiary of dairy giant Land O'Lakes, Inc.

LANDAUER, INC.

NYSE: LDR

2 Science Rd.
Glenwood, IL 60425
Phone: 708-755-7000
Fax: 708-755-7016
Web: www.landauerinc.com

CEO: William E. Saxelby
CFO: Jonathon M. Singer
HR: —
FYE: September 30
Type: Public

If your employees are glowing — and not with joy — Landauer can tell you why. Landauer manufactures and markets dosimeters (radiation detection monitors) for use in nuclear plants, hospitals, and university and government laboratories. Landauer's services include radiation detection badge distribution, radiation monitoring, and reporting on exposures. Its HomeBuyer's Preferred subsidiary provides residential radon monitoring services primarily used for corporate employee relocation programs. The company operates worldwide from offices in France, the US, and the UK. It also operates through joint ventures in Australia, Brazil, China, Japan, and Mexico.

	Annual Growth	9/05	9/06	9/07	9/08	9/09
Sales ($ mil.)	5.7%	75.2	79.0	83.7	90.0	93.8
Net income ($ mil.)	8.0%	17.2	19.0	19.3	23.0	23.4
Market value ($ mil.)	2.9%	460.1	476.5	478.5	683.1	516.2
Employees	(1.1%)	450	420	400	430	430

LANDEC CORPORATION

NASDAQ (GS): LNDC

3603 Haven Ave.
Menlo Park, CA 94025
Phone: 650-306-1650
Fax: 650-368-9818
Web: www.landec.com

CEO: Gary T. Steele
CFO: Gregory S. (Greg) Skinner
HR: Shelley Hilt
FYE: May 31
Type: Public

Landec's products don't turn into pumpkins at midnight, but the changes are nearly as sudden and much more practical. The company has developed a technology that allows polymers to change physical characteristics when exposed to temperature changes. Its Intellipac permeable membrane packaging allows oxygen and carbon dioxide to enter and escape from sealed fresh-cut produce packages to keep produce fresh. It's used primarily by subsidiary Apio, which grows and packages fresh vegetables. The company also produces Intellicoat seed coatings, which allow early planting of crops by preventing germination until warm weather arrives. Landec has licensing deals with Monsanto and Air Products and Chemicals.

	Annual Growth	5/05	5/06	5/07	5/08	5/09
Sales ($ mil.)	3.5%	205.2	232.0	210.5	238.5	235.9
Net income ($ mil.)	9.3%	5.4	8.7	29.2	13.5	7.7
Market value ($ mil.)	3.1%	158.5	226.9	359.2	211.6	179.1
Employees	(9.9%)	167	186	107	118	110

LANDMARK BANCORP, INC.

NASDAQ (GM): LARK

701 Poyntz Ave.
Manhattan, KS 66505
Phone: 785-565-2000
Fax: 785-537-0619
Web: www.landmarkbancorpinc.com

CEO: Patrick L. Alexander
CFO: Mark A. Herpich
HR: Marsha Kemper
FYE: December 31
Type: Public

Landmark Bancorp is a tourist attraction for Kansas money. It is the holding company for Landmark National Bank, which has about 15 branches in communities in central, eastern, and southwestern Kansas. The bank provides standard commercial banking products including checking, savings, and money market accounts, as well as CDs and credit and debit cards. It primarily uses funds from deposits to write residential and commercial mortgages and business loans. Landmark National Bank offers non-deposit investment services through its affiliation with Investment Planners.

	Annual Growth	12/05	12/06	12/07	12/08	12/09
Assets ($ mil.)	5.9%	465.1	590.6	606.5	602.2	584.2
Net income ($ mil.)	(4.1%)	3.9	6.0	5.4	4.6	3.3
Market value ($ mil.)	(7.4%)	51.4	58.9	58.0	48.7	37.7
Employees	11.9%	142	207	203	195	223

⊞ LANDMARK GRAPHICS CORPORATION

2107 City West Blvd., Bldg. 2
Houston, TX 77042
Phone: 713-839-2000
Fax: 713-839-2015
Web: www.lgc.com

CEO: Paul Koeller
CFO: —
HR: —
FYE: December 31
Type: Subsidiary

As you look for oil, keep an eye out for Landmark Graphics. The company develops software that high-tech wildcatters use to find oil, drill for it, and analyze economic return. Databases built with Landmark software store information used by seismic analysis programs to simulate reservoirs and other geological structures. Well planning and drilling applications calculate how to get the oil, while reservoir management software tracks the amount left. Throughout the process, Landmark's production and economic applications manage risk and measure returns. Founded in 1982, Landmark Graphics is a subsidiary of Halliburton.

L&R DISTRIBUTORS, INC.

9301 Avenue D
Brooklyn, NY 11236
Phone: 718-272-2100
Fax: 631-254-0064
Web: www.alliedondemand.com

CEO: Mike Lucas
CFO: Art Walker
HR: —
FYE: December 31
Type: Private

Stocking shelves? L&R Distributors (formerly Allied Supply) is a wholesale distributor of a wide variety of household and personal care products, stationery items, toys, and sundries to supermarkets, independent pharmacies, and discount and stationery stores. Its offerings have ranged from ACE bandages to Zippo lighters and from Wiffle balls to baby wipes. The company operates throughout the US; among its key partners have been pharmaceutical distributors such as McKesson and Cardinal Health. L&R Distributors has been assembled via a string of transactions dating to the 1950s, including the 1986 merger of E&N Sales Corp. and Ortner Drug Co.

LANDRY'S RESTAURANTS, INC.

NYSE: LNY

1510 W. Loop South
Houston, TX 77027
Phone: 713-850-1010
Fax: 713-850-7205
Web: www.landrysseafood.com

CEO: Tilman J. Fertitta
CFO: Richard H. (Rick) Liem
HR: —
FYE: December 31
Type: Public

This company's empire stretches from surf to turf to Fremont Street. Landry's Restaurants is a leading operator of casual-dining places with more than 170 locations in Texas and about 30 other states. The company's portfolio of eateries is anchored by its flagship Landry's Seafood House chain; other concepts include Rainforest Cafe, Saltgrass Steak House, and the upscale Chart House. In addition to casual dining, Landry's owns and operates the iconic Golden Nugget Hotel & Casino in Las Vegas, along with a number of other entertainment properties, including aquariums, hotels, and other tourist attractions. CEO Tilman Fertitta, who owns a 55% stake in the company, has agreed to take Landry's private.

	Annual Growth	12/05	12/06	12/07	12/08	12/09
Sales ($ mil.)	(4.1%)	1,254.8	1,134.3	1,171.9	1,143.9	1,060.2
Net income ($ mil.)	—	44.8	(21.8)	18.1	2.9	(7.5)
Market value ($ mil.)	(5.5%)	433.7	488.6	319.9	188.3	345.7
Employees	(8.2%)	28,000	20,055	24,166	19,684	19,850

LANDS' END, INC.

1 Lands' End Ln.
Dodgeville, WI 53595
Phone: 608-935-9341
Fax: 608-935-4831
Web: www.landsend.com

CEO: Nick Coe
CFO: Susan Healy
HR: Kelly A. Ritchie
FYE: December 31
Type: Subsidiary

Lands' End has surrounded a number of sales channels. The firm markets casual apparel for men, women, and children through its flagship and specialty catalogs, website, and Sears department stores. It also has more than 290 in-store Lands' End Shops at Sears locations and operates more than a dozen free-standing retail stores in the US, UK, Germany, and Japan. Lands' End also offers home goods, luggage, school uniforms, and logoed business apparel and products. The company with the misplaced apostrophe in its name has been expanding its online presence, but catalogs continue to be its primary sales channel. Lands' End is a subsidiary of Sears, Roebuck, which is itself owned by Sears Holdings.

LANDSTAR SYSTEM, INC.

NASDAQ (GS): LSTR

13410 Sutton Park Dr., South
Jacksonville, FL 32224
Phone: 904-398-9400
Fax: 904-390-1437
Web: www.landstar.com

CEO: Henry H. Gerkens
CFO: James B. (Jim) Gattoni
HR: —
FYE: December 31
Type: Public

Truckload freight carrier Landstar System has hitched its star to an asset-light business model. The company's fleet of about 13,300 trailers (including flatbed, refrigerated, and standard dry vans) is operated primarily by independent contractors, and the company's services are marketed by sales agents. Landstar's freight carrier units transport general commodities and goods such as automotive products, building materials, chemicals, and machinery, as well as ammunition and explosives. Customers include third-party logistics providers and government agencies such as the US Department of Defense. In addition to truckload transportation, Landstar offers logistics and warehousing services.

	Annual Growth	12/05	12/06	12/07	12/08	12/09
Sales ($ mil.)	(5.5%)	2,517.8	2,513.8	2,487.3	2,646.4	2,010.1
Net income ($ mil.)	(12.5%)	120.0	113.1	109.7	110.9	70.4
Market value ($ mil.)	(1.8%)	2,093.3	1,914.8	2,113.9	1,927.3	1,944.4
Employees	1.7%	1,285	1,298	1,281	1,317	1,374

LANE BRYANT, INC.

3344 Morse Crossing
Columbus, OH 43219
Phone: 614-463-5200
Fax: 614-463-5240
Web: www.lanebryant.com

CEO: Brian P. Woolf
CFO: G. Scott Glaser
HR: Elizabeth Ackley
FYE: January 31
Type: Business segment

Lane Bryant is a big name in women's plus-size fashion. The nation's #1 plus-size retail chain operates about 890 full-line and outlet stores in some 45 states that offer moderately priced career and casual clothing (in sizes 14 to 28), accessories, hosiery, and intimate apparel targeted to women ages 35 to 55. Lane Bryant stores are found in malls and strip shopping centers and average about 5,900 sq. ft. Women can also shop online at lanebryant.com or by catalog. As the chain grows, Lane Bryant is moving its stores off the mall to strip shopping centers. Founded in 1904 by Lena Bryant (she misspelled her name on a bank loan), Lane Bryant is owned by specialty apparel retailer Charming Shoppes.

	Annual Growth	1/04	1/05	1/06	1/07	1/08
Sales ($ mil.)	8.1%	—	974.2	1,057.4	1,202.3	1,232.3
Employees	—	—	—	—	—	—

THE LANE CONSTRUCTION CORPORATION

90 Fieldstone Ct.
Cheshire, CT 06410
Phone: 203-235-3351
Fax: 203-237-4260
Web: www.laneconstruct.com

CEO: Robert E. (Bob) Alger
CFO: James M. (Jim) Ferrell
HR: Kristy L. Blackman
FYE: December 31
Type: Private

For more than a century Lane Construction has been a transportation specialist — building everything from horseless carriage lanes to airport runways. The heavy civil contractor evolved from a stone-crushing plant founded in 1890 by railroad engineer John S. Lane. The company and its 10 affiliates are known for building highways, roads, bridges, railroads, dams, and mass transit systems, primarily in the eastern and southern US. The group also produces bituminous concrete, precast concrete and mines aggregates at plants and quarries in the northeastern, mid-Atlantic, and southern US. Additionally, it sells and leases construction equipment. Lane Construction is owned by descendants of Lane and employees.

	Annual Growth	12/04	12/05	12/06	12/07	12/08
Est. sales ($ mil.)	—	—	—	—	—	969.5
Employees	—	—	—	—	—	3,500

LANE FURNITURE INDUSTRIES, INC.

5380 Hwy. 145
Tupelo, MS 38801
Phone: 662-566-7211
Fax: 662-566-3474
Web: www.lanefurniture.com

CEO: Gregory P. (Greg) Roy
CFO: Vaughn Howell
HR: Curtis Trawick
FYE: December 31
Type: Subsidiary

Nearly a century old, Lane Furniture Industries is a furniture maker, specializing in 18th-century reproductions and cedar chests. Its Lane home furnishings are sold nationwide through specialty retailers (such as Haverty's), as well as department stores (including Dillard's and J. C. Penney). Lane Furniture was established in 1912 when John Lane and his son Ed began a chest-manufacturing venture (incorporated as Standard Red Cedar Chest Company). Lane primarily makes mid-priced furniture, including recliners, motion furniture, and upholstered furniture. It also operates a mid-priced wood furniture unit. In addition, the company makes a line of primarily outdoor furniture under the Laneventure brand.

An in-depth profile of this company is available to Hoover's Online members at hoovers.com.

919

LANNETT COMPANY, INC.

NYSE Amex: LCI

9000 State Rd.
Philadelphia, PA 19136
Phone: 215-333-9000
Fax: 215-333-9004
Web: www.lannett.com

CEO: Arthur P. Bedrosian
CFO: Keith R. Ruck
HR: —
FYE: June 30
Type: Public

Lannett banks on the designation of "bioequivalent" for its products. The firm manufactures and markets generic prescription drugs such as painkillers (including two versions of Novartis' migraine treatment Fiorinal), anticonvulsants for epileptics, and Digoxin for congestive heart failure (a version of Lanoxin). The company has also developed a generic version of Abbott Laboratories' Synthroid. While it manufactures some of its products, Jerome Stevens Pharmaceuticals manufactures a significant portion of Lannett's inventories. Lannett prefers to focus on products with few generic competitors. Chairman William Farber and his family own more than half of the company.

	Annual Growth	6/05	6/06	6/07	6/08	6/09
Sales ($ mil.)	27.6%	44.9	64.1	82.6	72.4	119.0
Net income ($ mil.)	—	(32.8)	5.0	(6.9)	(2.3)	6.5
Market value ($ mil.)	7.0%	131.6	143.5	153.5	98.3	172.7
Employees	12.7%	172	193	198	222	277

LANTRONIX, INC.

NASDAQ (CM): LTRX

167 Technology Dr.
Irvine, CA 92618
Phone: 949-453-3990
Fax: 949-450-7249
Web: www.lantronix.com

CEO: Jerry D. Chase
CFO: Reagan Y. Sakai
HR: Allison Garcia
FYE: June 30
Type: Public

Lantronix gets electronics online. The company designs console servers that allow electronic devices such as bar code scanners, vending machines, thermostats, point-of-sale terminals, and security cameras to be accessed and controlled over networks. It also provides products for remote management of data centers and IT equipment. Lantronix, which outsources its manufacturing, sells primarily through OEMs, resellers, systems integrators, and distributors. Mega-distributors Ingram Micro and Tech Data together account for about 20% of sales. The company gets more than half of its sales in the Americas.

	Annual Growth	6/05	6/06	6/07	6/08	6/09
Sales ($ mil.)	0.3%	48.5	51.9	55.3	57.6	49.1
Net income ($ mil.)	—	(7.0)	(3.0)	(1.7)	(2.5)	(0.8)
Market value ($ mil.)	(23.0%)	81.1	135.0	87.3	42.7	28.5
Employees	(3.9%)	144	157	161	157	123

LANXESS CORPORATION

111 RIDC Park West Dr.
Pittsburgh, PA 15275
Phone: 412-809-1000
Fax: 412-809-3599
Web: www.us.lanxess.com

CEO: Randall S. (Randy) Dearth
CFO: —
HR: —
FYE: December 31
Type: Subsidiary

LANXESS Corporation's synthetic rubber products are used by the tire, auto, and industrial goods industries, while its plastics are marketed toward makers of medical and electronic communications products. LANXESS Corp.'s largest unit is its performance chemicals division, which supplies the textiles, pharmaceutical, and automobile industries, among others. The company's other units are performance polymers (the synthetic rubber operations) and advanced intermediates (basic and fine chemicals). Subsidiaries include Rhein Chemie (rubber chemicals), Sybron Chemicals (ion exchange resins), and Saltigo (fine, agro-, and pharmaceutical chemicals). Parent company LANXESS AG was spun off from Bayer in 2004.

LAPOLLA INDUSTRIES, INC.

OTC: LPAD

15402 Vantage Pkwy. East, Ste. 322
Houston, TX 77032
Phone: 281-219-4100
Fax: 281-219-4102
Web: www.lapollaindustries.com

CEO: Douglas J. Kramer
CFO: Charles Zajaczkowski
HR: —
FYE: December 31
Type: Public

LaPolla Industries would hate for its customers to have leaky roofs over their heads or insufficiently protected exterior walls. The company makes foam products used to protect roofs and the "building envelope," which is the separation of the exterior and interior parts of a building. It also makes coatings for weatherproofing concrete and metal roofing and other materials. The company changed its name in 2005 when it absorbed subsidiary LaPolla Industries, a provider of roof coatings and polyurethane foam construction systems. The former IFT Corp., which had previously been called Urecoats, acquired LaPolla in 2005. Chairman Richard Kurtz owns 57% of LaPolla.

	Annual Growth	12/05	12/06	12/07	12/08	12/09
Sales ($ mil.)	25.4%	20.2	30.3	31.8	47.6	50.0
Net income ($ mil.)	—	(1.5)	(3.0)	(5.1)	(3.5)	(2.8)
Market value ($ mil.)	(0.3%)	31.3	35.8	32.6	32.6	31.0
Employees	10.9%	39	48	41	66	59

LAPORTE BANCORP, INC.

NASDAQ (CM): LPSB

710 Indiana Ave.
LaPorte, IN 46350
Phone: 219-362-7511
Fax: 219-324-2269
Web: www.laportesavingsbank.com

CEO: Lee A. Brady
CFO: Michele M. Thompson
HR: —
FYE: December 31
Type: Public

LaPorte Bancorp hopes to be the door to savings. It was formed in 2007 to be the holding company for The LaPorte Savings Bank, which serves individuals and businesses through nearly 10 branches in northwestern Indiana. Founded in 1871, the bank offers standard deposit services such as checking and savings accounts, CDs, and IRAs. Real estate loans, including residential and commercial mortgages, account for about three-quarters of the bank's loan portfolio. Business loans and consumer loans such as home equity and auto loans round out its lending activities. The bank also offers trust and investment services. Mutual holding company LaPorte Savings Bank, MHC owns a majority of LaPorte Bancorp's stock.

	Annual Growth	12/05	12/06	12/07	12/08	12/09
Assets ($ mil.)	12.1%	256.9	266.5	367.3	368.6	405.8
Net income ($ mil.)	29.1%	0.9	1.1	0.7	(0.4)	2.5
Market value ($ mil.)	(19.3%)	—	—	31.0	24.1	20.2
Employees	7.8%	—	87	116	116	109

LAS VEGAS SANDS CORP.

NYSE: LVS

3355 Las Vegas Blvd. South
Las Vegas, NV 89109
Phone: 702-414-1000
Fax: 702-414-4884
Web: www.lasvegassands.com

CEO: Sheldon G. Adelson
CFO: Kenneth J. (Ken) Kay
HR: —
FYE: December 31
Type: Public

Rising from the ashes of the bulldozed Sands Hotel, the Venetian Casino Resort (owned by Las Vegas Sands) brings a touch of Venice to the Las Vegas Strip. Replete with gondoliers and a replica of the Rialto Bridge, the Venetian offers a 120,000-sq.-ft. casino and a 4,000-suite hotel, as well as a shopping, dining, and entertainment complex. Las Vegas Sands also operates The Palazzo Casino next door to the Venetian, and the nearby Sands Expo Center trade show and convention center. In addition to its Vegas holdings, the firm has a handful of properties in China through its Sands China subsidiary. Chairman and CEO Sheldon Adelson and trusts for his family own more than 50% of Las Vegas Sands.

	Annual Growth	12/05	12/06	12/07	12/08	12/09
Sales ($ mil.)	27.2%	1,740.9	2,236.9	2,950.6	4,389.9	4,563.1
Net income ($ mil.)	—	283.7	442.0	116.7	(163.6)	(354.5)
Market value ($ mil.)	(21.6%)	26,063.5	59,087.0	68,047.7	3,915.8	9,865.4
Employees	21.9%	12,230	15,280	28,000	28,500	27,000

LASALLE BRANDS CORPORATION
Pink Sheets: LSAL

7702 E. Doubletree Ranch Rd., Ste. 300
Scottsdale, AZ 85258
Phone: 480-905-5550
Fax: 480-945-3472
Web: www.lasalleicecream.com

CEO: Medhat (Tony) Mohamed
CFO: Scott Campbell
HR: —
FYE: December 31
Type: Public

LaSalle Brands (formerly Diners Acquisition Corp.) owns LaSalle Ice Cream, a premium frozen dairy brand that is distributed primarily in pints throughout the New York City area. LaSalle is popular for its variety of ice cream flavors, as well as gelato and fruit sorbet. The company also sells branded coffee and imported cookies. LaSalle Brands was founded in 1972. The company opened its first retail location in New York in 2005; it has since announced a franchising plan that calls for more than 30 dessert cafes to be operating throughout the US by the end of 2009.

LASALLE BRISTOL CORPORATION

601 County Rd. 17
Elkhart, IN 46516
Phone: 574-295-4400
Fax: 574-295-5290
Web: www.lasallebristol.com

CEO: Richard (Rick) Karcher
CFO: —
HR: —
FYE: December 31
Type: Subsidiary

LaSalle Bristol Corporation is a leading manufacturer and full-service supplier of home furnishing products for the manufactured housing, modular home, and recreational vehicle industries. Its key products include ventilation systems, ceiling fans, and lighting components. The company also carries a range of building, decorative, and plumbing products from a variety of vendors, including Moen, Delta Faucet, Ashley Furniture, and ClosetMaid. LaSalle Bristol, a subsidiary of holding company Heywood Williams Group, distributes its products through a network of about 20 branch locations and affiliates across the US.

	Annual Growth	12/04	12/05	12/06	12/07	12/08
Est. sales ($ mil.)	—	—	—	—	—	86.4
Employees	—	—	—	—	—	550

LASALLE HOTEL PROPERTIES
NYSE: LHO

3 Bethesda Metro Center, Ste. 1200
Bethesda, MD 20814
Phone: 301-941-1500
Fax: 301-941-1553
Web: www.lasallehotels.com

CEO: Michael D. (Mike) Barnello
CFO: Hans S. Weger
HR: Hans S. Weger
FYE: December 31
Type: Public

LaSalle Hotel Properties is a self-administered and self-managed real estate investment trust (REIT) that invests in, renovates, and leases luxury full-service hotel properties in the US. It owns more than 30 hotels in about a dozen states. Its hotels, which together have about 8,500 rooms, are typically located in major urban markets near convention centers, business districts, and resorts. The properties are managed by outside hotel operators under such brand names as Marriott, Sheraton, and Hilton. Among its properties are Hilton San Diego Resort and Spa and Hotel Deca in Seattle. LaSalle Hotel Properties became self-managing in 2001 after three years under the wing of Jones Lang LaSalle.

	Annual Growth	12/05	12/06	12/07	12/08	12/09
Sales ($ mil.)	11.3%	396.2	667.3	663.8	683.5	607.1
Net income ($ mil.)	(31.1%)	35.4	99.1	89.8	33.1	8.0
Market value ($ mil.)	(12.8%)	2,563.2	3,200.5	2,226.8	771.3	1,481.9
Employees	(0.9%)	27	31	31	30	26

LASERCARD CORPORATION
NASDAQ (GM): LCRD

1875 N. Shoreline Blvd.
Mountain View, CA 94043
Phone: 650-969-4428
Fax: 650-969-3140
Web: www.lasercard.com

CEO: Robert T. (Bob) DeVincenzi
CFO: Steven G. Larson
HR: —
FYE: March 31
Type: Public

Green cards are no longer green — but they are high-tech, thanks to LaserCard. The company makes wallet-sized, recordable optical data cards that permanently store electronic text, graphics, photos, and security marks such as fingerprints and holograms. The tamper-resistant cards, which store data and interface with personal computers, are used for such purposes as identification, security, and vehicle registration. US green cards and border crossing cards account for about 20% of sales, while Saudi Arabia's national ID card represents 23%. Other applications include health record storage, security access, and e-commerce transactions. LaserCard also offers optical card drives and card system software.

	Annual Growth	3/05	3/06	3/07	3/08	3/09
Sales ($ mil.)	15.0%	28.5	39.9	32.3	37.0	49.8
Net income ($ mil.)	—	(8.9)	0.8	(12.4)	(7.2)	(0.9)
Market value ($ mil.)	(16.6%)	60.9	275.3	144.2	103.9	29.5
Employees	17.4%	122	261	219	227	232

LASERSIGHT INCORPORATED
Pink Sheets: LRST

931 S. Semoran Blvd., Ste. 204
Winter Park, FL 32792
Phone: 407-678-9900
Fax: 407-678-4542
Web: www.lase.com

CEO: Danghui (David) Liu
CFO: Zhaokai (Art) Tang
HR: —
FYE: December 31
Type: Public

LaserSight has an eye for vision care. The company's LaserSight Technologies subsidiary makes excimer lasers, which surgically correct nearsightedness, farsightedness, and astigmatism. LaserSight's LaserScan LSX system is approved by the FDA for photorefractive keratectomy (PRK) and laser-in-situ keratomileusis (LASIK) vision correction procedures. The company also sells ophthalmic equipment including forceps, scissors, and needle holders. Subsidiary TechnicaLaser sells laser products for industrial, laboratory, and other applications. LaserSight has facilities in China and the US and markets its products in more than 30 countries worldwide.

LATHAM & WATKINS LLP

885 3rd Ave.
New York, NY 10022
Phone: 212-906-1200
Fax: 212-751-4864
Web: www.lw.com

CEO: Robert M. (Bob) Dell
CFO: Grant Johnson
HR: Mimi A. Krumholz
FYE: December 31
Type: Partnership

Latham & Watkins' founders Dana Latham and Paul Watkins flipped a coin in 1934 to determine which of their names would go first on the law firm's shingle. From that coin toss, the firm has grown into one of the largest in the US and boasts more than 2,100 lawyers in almost 30 offices around the world, from Europe to Asia. Latham & Watkins organizes its practices into five main areas: corporate; environment, land, and resources; finance; litigation; and tax. The firm has counted companies such as Amgen, Time Warner Inc., and Morgan Stanley among its clients.

	Annual Growth	12/04	12/05	12/06	12/07	12/08
Sales ($ mil.)	10.8%	—	1,413.0	1,624.0	2,005.0	1,923.0
Employees	6.3%	—	4,234	4,500	—	—

An in-depth profile of this company is available to Hoover's Online members at hoovers.com.

921

LATTICE INCORPORATED

OTC: LTTC

7150 N. Park Dr., Ste. 500
Pennsauken, NJ 08109
Phone: 856-910-1166
Fax: 856-910-1811
Web: www.latticeincorporated.com

CEO: Paul Burgess
CFO: Joseph (Joe) Noto
HR: —
FYE: December 31
Type: Public

Lattice has constructed a diverse product framework. The company provides communications products and services to corporate and government clients. Deriving the majority of its revenue through contracts with the federal government, it develops applications related to business management, geographic information systems (GIS), Web services, and geospatial systems. The company also provides technology that allows prison officials to monitor and control inmate collect-only phone calls. Formerly called Science Dynamics, the company changed its name to Lattice in 2007.

	Annual Growth	12/05	12/06	12/07	12/08	12/09
Sales ($ mil.)	38.8%	4.2	7.5	15.2	16.3	15.6
Net income ($ mil.)	—	(0.9)	(16.3)	3.7	0.9	(1.3)
Market value ($ mil.)	(47.3%)	14.9	11.5	8.0	1.5	1.1
Employees	12.6%	28	59	51	42	45

LATTICE SEMICONDUCTOR CORPORATION

NASDAQ (GM): LSCC

5555 NE Moore Ct.
Hillsboro, OR 97124
Phone: 503-268-8000
Fax: 503-268-8347
Web: www.latticesemi.com

CEO: Bruno Guilmart
CFO: Michael G. Potter
HR: Clay Miller
FYE: December 31
Type: Public

Lattice Semiconductor provides a latticework of programmable-chip products. The company is a top supplier of programmable logic devices (PLDs), including in-system programmable (ISP) devices that electronics manufacturers can configure and reconfigure after the chips are attached to a printed circuit board. Lattice also makes low-density logic devices, and sells the software needed to customize its chips, which are used in communications, computing, industrial, and military applications. The fabless semiconductor company also expanded into the market for field-programmable gate arrays (FPGAs), another type of programmable chip. More than three-quarters of its sales comes from customers outside the US.

	Annual Growth	12/05	12/06	12/07	12/08	12/09
Sales ($ mil.)	(2.0%)	211.1	245.5	228.7	222.3	194.4
Net income ($ mil.)	—	(49.1)	3.1	(239.8)	(38.2)	(7.0)
Market value ($ mil.)	(11.1%)	500.9	751.3	376.8	175.1	313.0
Employees	(6.1%)	909	960	883	753	708

LAUREATE EDUCATION, INC.

650 S. Exeter St.
Baltimore, MD 21202
Phone: 410-843-6100
Fax: —
Web: www.laureate-inc.com

CEO: Douglas L. (Doug) Becker
CFO: Eilif Serck-Hanssen
HR: —
FYE: December 31
Type: Private

If higher education is a matter of degrees, Laureate must be hot. The company provides adult career education through online and campus-based programs in 20 countries in Asia, the Americas, and Europe. Laureate Education's 50 institutions offer more than 130 bachelor's, master's, and doctoral degree programs and specializations to a combined enrollment of more than 550,000 students. It awards degrees in areas such as art, business, education, hospitality, law, engineering, and health sciences. An investment group headed by chairman and CEO Douglas Becker (who skipped college and went straight into business) owns the company.

LAUREL GROCERY COMPANY, LLC

129 Barbourville Rd.
London, KY 40744
Phone: 606-878-6601
Fax: 606-864-5693
Web: www.laurelgrocery.com

CEO: James K. (Jim) Buchanan
CFO: Doug George
HR: —
FYE: June 30
Type: Private

Some small grocers might be inclined to bestow a wreath on this company. Laurel Grocery Company is a broadline grocery wholesaler that supplies independent grocers in more than half a dozen states, including Georgia, Indiana, Kentucky, Ohio, Tennessee, and West Virginia. It distributes more than 23,000 items such as bakery foods, cigarettes, eggs, fluid milk, meat, and produce. In addition to wholesale distribution, the company provides a variety of business services, including accounting, insurance, and other financial services to customers, as well as advertising and merchandising programs. The family-owned business was founded in 1922.

	Annual Growth	6/04	6/05	6/06	6/07	6/08
Est. sales ($ mil.)	—	—	—	—	—	350.0
Employees	—	—	—	—	—	411

LAW ENFORCEMENT ASSOCIATES CORPORATION

NYSE Amex: AID

100 Hunter Place
Youngsville, NC 27596
Phone: 919-554-4700
Fax: 919-556-6240
Web: www.leacorp.com

CEO: Paul Briggs
CFO: —
HR: —
FYE: December 31
Type: Public

Criminals can run, but they can't hide. At least not if Law Enforcement Associates (LEA) has anything to say about it. The company makes surveillance equipment for law enforcement agencies worldwide. Its products include transmitters, receivers, video recording systems, and global positioning tracking systems. Law Enforcement Associates also makes audio surveillance equipment that lets law enforcement agencies monitor conversations. The company's under-vehicle inspection system (UVIS) is used to view the underside of vehicles entering and exiting secure areas in order to detect explosives or contraband.

	Annual Growth	12/05	12/06	12/07	12/08	12/09
Sales ($ mil.)	9.8%	8.2	7.5	6.7	9.2	11.9
Net income ($ mil.)	—	(0.3)	0.0	(1.0)	0.1	0.1
Market value ($ mil.)	(52.0%)	58.5	21.7	14.2	3.1	3.1
Employees	1.0%	25	35	33	33	26

LAWRENCE BERKELEY NATIONAL LABORATORY

1 Cyclotron Rd.
Berkeley, CA 94720
Phone: 510-486-4000
Fax: 510-486-6720
Web: www.lbl.gov

CEO: A. Paul Alivisatos
CFO: Jeffrey A. Fernandez
HR: Vera Potapenko
FYE: September 30
Type: Government-owned

Lawrence Berkeley National Laboratory is one of the leading government-sponsored research centers in the US. It performs basic and applied research in such areas as environmental studies, nanoscience, and quantitative biology, as well as physics and nuclear energy. During its history, 11 of the lab's scientists have won the Nobel Prize while 13 have won the National Medal of Science. The lab is funded by the US Department of Energy and managed by the University of California. Former director Steven Chu left the lab in 2009 to become the US energy secretary. Berkeley Lab was started in 1931 by Ernest Orlando Lawrence, a Nobel Prize-winning physicist in the area of high-energy physics.

An in-depth profile of this company is available to Hoover's Online members at hoovers.com.

LAWRENCE LIVERMORE NATIONAL LABORATORY

7000 East Ave.
Livermore, CA 94550
Phone: 925-422-1100
Fax: 925-422-1370
Web: www.llnl.gov

CEO: George H. Miller
CFO: Linda Rakow
HR: —
FYE: September 30
Type: Government-owned

Science and national security are brought together at Lawrence Livermore National Laboratory (LLNL). The facility directs its science and engineering work toward the goal of making sure US nuclear weapons are safe, secure, and reliable. LLNL also conducts research in such areas as national security, basic science and advanced technology, bioscience and biotechnology, and energy and the environment. Part of the National Nuclear Security Administration of the US Department of Energy, LLNL was founded at the height of the Cold War in 1952 as a companion to Los Alamos National Laboratory.

LAWSON PRODUCTS, INC.

NASDAQ (GS): LAWS

1666 E. Touhy Ave.
Des Plaines, IL 60018
Phone: 847-827-9666
Fax: —
Web: www.lawsonproducts.com

CEO: Thomas J. Neri
CFO: Ronald J. (Ron) Knutson
HR: Harry Dochelli
FYE: December 31
Type: Public

Lawson Products' stock in trade may sound boring to some, but to manufacturing companies it's positively riveting. The company offers approximately 240,000 items besides just rivets, screws, and nuts. It manufactures and distributes services and products to the industrial, commercial, institutional, and governmental MROs through its Rutland Tools subsidiary (85% of sales). It also manufactures, sells, and distributes specialized component parts to OEMs in the automotive, appliance, aerospace, construction, and transportation industries. Sales are generated through approximately 1,300 independent sales agents, as well as through printed catalogs. The US accounts for most of sales.

	Annual Growth	12/05	12/06	12/07	12/08	12/09
Sales ($ mil.)	(4.2%)	450.2	518.2	509.7	485.2	378.9
Net income ($ mil.)	—	26.7	13.0	10.6	(27.6)	(2.7)
Market value ($ mil.)	(17.3%)	321.6	391.1	323.2	194.7	150.4
Employees	(9.2%)	1,630	1,540	1,400	1,350	1,110

LAWSON SOFTWARE, INC.

NASDAQ (GS): LWSN

380 St. Peter St.
St. Paul, MN 55102
Phone: 651-767-7000
Fax: —
Web: www.lawson.com

CEO: Harry Debes
CFO: Stefan B. Schulz
HR: Kristin Trecker
FYE: May 31
Type: Public

Lawson Software just wants to bring a little law and order to managing enterprises. The company makes enterprise resource planning software for the health care, professional services, retail, public sector, telecommunications, and other industries. Its applications handle such tasks as distribution, procurement, human resources, customer service, professional services automation, and accounting. The company also offers consulting, implementation, and maintenance services. Lawson markets its products and services worldwide through offices located in more than two dozen countries. Brothers Richard and Bill Lawson and associate John Cerullo co-founded the company in 1975.

	Annual Growth	5/05	5/06	5/07	5/08	5/09
Sales ($ mil.)	22.6%	335.2	390.8	750.4	851.9	757.3
Net income ($ mil.)	37.4%	5.3	16.0	(20.9)	13.7	18.9
Market value ($ mil.)	(2.9%)	957.3	1,091.6	1,484.5	1,410.1	850.6
Employees	27.5%	1,400	3,400	3,800	4,200	3,700

LAYNE CHRISTENSEN COMPANY

NASDAQ (GS): LAYN

1900 Shawnee Mission Pkwy.
Mission Woods, KS 66205
Phone: 913-677-6800
Fax: 913-362-0133
Web: www.laynechristensen.com

CEO: Andrew B. Schmitt
CFO: Jerry W. Fanska
HR: John Wright
FYE: January 31
Type: Public

Layne Christensen cuts its way through the upper crust. The company provides drilling and construction services related to water, wastewater treatment, and mineral exploration. The company serves such clients as public and private water utilities, industrial companies, mining firms, and heavy civil construction contractors. It has operations throughout the Americas, as well as Africa, Australia, Europe, and Brazil. Layne Christensen's Water and Wastewater Infrastructure segment accounts for about two-thirds of company sales. Mineral exploration work accounts for most of the rest. The group has also entered the energy field, producing coal bed methane. The firm has some 80 sales and operations offices worldwide.

	Annual Growth	1/06	1/07	1/08	1/09	1/10
Sales ($ mil.)	17.0%	463.0	722.8	868.3	1,008.1	866.4
Net income ($ mil.)	(44.4%)	14.7	26.3	37.3	26.5	1.4
Market value ($ mil.)	(4.2%)	587.2	683.2	719.6	307.7	494.0
Employees	2.4%	3,551	3,919	4,300	3,600	3,900

LAZARD LTD

NYSE: LAZ

30 Rockefeller Plaza
New York, NY 10020
Phone: 212-632-6000
Fax: 212-632-6060
Web: www.lazard.com

CEO: Kenneth M. (Ken) Jacobs
CFO: Mathieu Bucaille
HR: —
FYE: December 31
Type: Public

With origins going back to 1848 New Orleans, the venerable House of Lazard has grown up alongside the investment banking industry. The firm offers financial advisory and asset management services from some 40 offices in the Americas, Europe, and Australasia. Its advisory arm provides M&A and other corporate advisory services; industry specialties include consumer, health care, energy, real estate, media, and telecommunications. Lazard has some $134 billion in assets under management; it serves primarily institutional investors as well as governments and wealthy individuals. Subsidiaries include asset manager Lazard Frères Gestion and Lazard Frères Banque, which manages the group's operations in France.

	Annual Growth	12/05	12/06	12/07	12/08	12/09
Sales ($ mil.)	4.4%	1,379.8	1,597.8	2,054.8	1,697.1	1,638.4
Net income ($ mil.)	—	161.1	93.0	155.0	3.1	(130.2)
Market value ($ mil.)	4.5%	3,234.1	4,799.5	4,124.3	3,015.2	3,849.5
Employees	1.2%	2,191	2,200	735	2,434	2,294

LAZARD MIDDLE MARKET

225 S. 6th St., 46th Fl.
Minneapolis, MN 55402
Phone: 612-339-0500
Fax: 612-339-0507
Web: www.agio.com

CEO: Jack P. Helms
CFO: Kyle A. Pecha
HR: —
FYE: December 31
Type: Subsidiary

How's Lazard Middle Market doing? Fair to middling, it seems. The investment bank focuses on mid-sized companies in the US and abroad, providing mergers and acquisitions support, private placements, distressed advisory and restructurings, and other financial advisory services. The company's industry areas of expertise include business services, retail, natural resources, health care, and media. Lazard Middle Market has offices in California, Illinois, New York, North Carolina, and Minnesota. Founded in 1978 as Goldsmith Agio Helms, the firm was acquired by international financial group Lazard in 2007.

	Annual Growth	12/04	12/05	12/06	12/07	12/08
Est. sales ($ mil.)	—	—	—	—	—	11.0
Employees	—	—	—	—	—	110

An in-depth profile of this company is available to Hoover's Online members at hoovers.com.

LAZARE KAPLAN INTERNATIONAL INC.

NYSE Amex: LKI

19 W. 44th St.
New York, NY 10036
Phone: 212-972-9700
Fax: 212-972-8561
Web: lazarediamonds.com

CEO: Leon Tempelsman
CFO: William H. Moryto
HR: —
FYE: May 31
Type: Public

Sometimes plain old diamonds just aren't good enough. Lazare Kaplan International specializes in cutting, polishing, and marketing premium-priced diamonds, as well as diamond jewelry. The company buys rough diamonds (primarily from Diamond Trading Company, a sales arm of behemoth De Beers), cuts and polishes the gems for maximum sparkle, and laser-inscribes the branded Lazare Diamonds with the company's logo and an ID number. Lazare boasts manufacturing plants in Puerto Rico, Russia (in Moscow and Barnaul), and South Africa (specifically Namibia) to handle processing of the diamonds. As part of its business, Lazare sells to wholesalers, manufacturers, and authorized jewelry retailers worldwide.

	Annual Growth	5/04	5/05	5/06	5/07	*5/08
Sales ($ mil.)	11.9%	235.8	421.4	528.0	434.4	369.7
Net income ($ mil.)	31.6%	2.4	5.2	1.5	(3.0)	7.2
Market value ($ mil.)	0.8%	72.6	71.1	70.0	71.8	75.1
Employees	(7.1%)	199	214	223	178	148

*Most recent year available

⊞ LA-Z-BOY INCORPORATED

NYSE: LZB

1284 N. Telegraph Rd.
Monroe, MI 48162
Phone: 734-242-1444
Fax: 734-457-2005
Web: www.lazboy.com

CEO: Kurt L. Darrow
CFO: Louis M. (Mike) Riccio Jr.
HR: Steven P. (Steve) Rindskopf
FYE: April 30
Type: Public

The kickback that La-Z-Boy gives its customers is perfectly legal. The top US maker of upholstered furniture, La-Z-Boy sells its ubiquitous recliners, plus chairs, sofas, tables, and modular seating units. One recliner has sported a drink cooler, phone, and massage and heat system. La-Z-Boy sells through about 70 company-owned stores, some 250 independent La-Z-Boy Furniture Galleries, and about 220 in-store galleries at furniture dealers, department stores, and other outlets. La-Z-Boy also makes wood furniture (desks, cabinets, and bedroom items) and licenses its name for use on furniture for the health care industry. Its brands include La-Z-Boy, Bauhaus USA, Hammary, American Drew/Lea, and Kincaid.

	Annual Growth	4/05	4/06	4/07	4/08	4/09
Sales ($ mil.)	(12.0%)	2,048.4	1,916.8	1,617.3	1,450.9	1,226.7
Net income ($ mil.)	—	35.1	(3.0)	4.1	(13.5)	(121.3)
Market value ($ mil.)	(31.2%)	610.3	789.7	602.6	328.3	137.1
Employees	(15.0%)	14,822	13,404	11,729	10,057	7,730

LAZY DAYS' R.V. CENTER, INC.

6130 Lazy Days Blvd.
Seffner, FL 33584
Phone: 813-246-4999
Fax: 813-246-4408
Web: www.lazydays.com

CEO: John Horton
CFO: Randall R. (Randy) Lay
HR: Debbie Dube
FYE: December 31
Type: Private

Plenty of hard work has turned Lazy Days' R.V. Center into one of the largest dealers of recreational vehicles in the US. At its 126-acre site, Lazy Days' sells about 15 brands of new and used RVs. The dealership also has some 230 service bays for repair and maintenance. Besides the RV dealership, the Lazy Days' location includes RallyPark, a 300-lot RV campground that includes a Cracker Barrel restaurant, Camping World retail store, and RV gas station. The company was founded in 1976 by Don Wallace and his late father, H. K. Wallace, and brother, Ron Wallace. It is controlled by Minnesota-based Wayzata Investment Partners. After a stint in Chapter 11, Lazy Days' completed its reorganization in December 2009.

	Annual Growth	12/04	12/05	12/06	12/07	12/08
Est. sales ($ mil.)	—	—	—	—	—	778.0
Employees	—	—	—	—	—	680

L. B. FOSTER COMPANY

NASDAQ (GS): FSTR

415 Holiday Dr.
Pittsburgh, PA 15220
Phone: 412-928-3417
Fax: 412-928-7891
Web: www.lbfoster.com

CEO: Stan L. Hasselbusch
CFO: David J. Russo
HR: Brian Kelly
FYE: December 31
Type: Public

L. B. Foster can help keep you on track whether you're riding the rails, or cruising the open road. The company manufactures new and relay rail and trackwork used in railroad and mass transit systems, as well as in industrial markets such as mining. L. B. Foster also supplies pipe coatings for oil and natural gas industries and pipe products for industrial, utility, and agricultural water wells. It taps federal, state, and local infrastructure markets, too, selling and renting steel sheet piling and earth wall systems necessary in highway and levee construction and repair. H-bearing piling is made to support bridges and high-rise buildings. US sales account for a majority of the company's operations.

	Annual Growth	12/05	12/06	12/07	12/08	12/09
Sales ($ mil.)	2.0%	353.5	389.8	509.0	512.6	382.0
Net income ($ mil.)	30.6%	5.4	13.5	110.7	27.7	15.7
Market value ($ mil.)	19.0%	151.5	263.9	526.8	318.6	303.6
Employees	(1.9%)	641	665	655	641	593

LCA-VISION INC.

NASDAQ (GS): LCAV

7840 Montgomery Rd.
Cincinnati, OH 45236
Phone: 513-792-9292
Fax: 513-792-5620
Web: www.lasikplus.com

CEO: David L. (Dave) Thomas
CFO: Michael J. Celebrezze
HR: Rhonda S. Sebastian
FYE: December 31
Type: Public

LCA-Vision thinks its services are a sight better than glasses. The company provides laser vision correction procedures at some 60 LasikPlus freestanding facilities. LCA-Vision's facilities treat nearsightedness, farsightedness, and astigmatism, primarily using laser-assisted in situ keratomileusis (LASIK), which reshapes the cornea with a computer-guided excimer laser. Additionally, the company's centers offer photorefractive keratectomy (PRK) and other corrective procedures. LCA-Vision operates through centers located in major cities across North America.

	Annual Growth	12/05	12/06	12/07	12/08	12/09
Sales ($ mil.)	(9.5%)	192.4	256.9	292.6	205.2	129.2
Net income ($ mil.)	—	31.7	38.3	32.5	(6.6)	(33.2)
Market value ($ mil.)	(42.7%)	886.7	641.3	372.7	76.7	95.6
Employees	(5.9%)	574	700	784	568	450

LCC INTERNATIONAL, INC.

4800 Westfields Blvd., Ste. 200
Chantilly, VA 20151
Phone: 703-873-2000
Fax: 703-873-2100
Web: www.lcc.com

CEO: Kenneth M. (Kenny) Young
CFO: Simone Delli Carri
HR: —
FYE: December 31
Type: Private

In the war of wireless standards, LCC International plays all sides — from CDMA to GSM. The radio-frequency engineering and consulting firm serves wireless carriers in every stage of operations. It helps aspiring carriers apply for licenses, buy cell sites, and design and deploy networks; it aids established carriers in expanding and upgrading technology; and it helps mature wireless firms streamline their operations. It also provides outsourced daily operations and maintenance of networks. In addition to wireless service providers, the company serves telecommunications equipment vendors, systems integrators, and tower operators. Riley Investment Management owns more than 40% of LCC International.

LCNB CORP.

OTC: LCNB

2 N. Broadway
Lebanon, OH 45036
Phone: 513-932-1414
Fax: 513-933-5262
Web: www.lcnb.com

CEO: Stephen P. Wilson
CFO: Robert C. Haines II
HR: —
FYE: December 31
Type: Public

It just makes *cents* that LCNB counts bucks in the Buckeye State. The firm is the holding company for LCNB National Bank, which operates some two dozen branches in southwestern Ohio. The bank offers personal and commercial banking services such as checking and savings accounts, money markets, IRAs, and CDs. Residential mortgages account for nearly half of the company's loan book. Other offerings include commercial mortgages, consumer loans including credit cards, and business loans. Trust services are also provided; subsidiary Dakin Insurance Agency sells commercial and personal property/casualty insurance. In 2007 LCNB acquired Sycamore National Bank, which allowed for financial growth and branch expansion.

	Annual Growth	12/05	12/06	12/07	12/08	12/09
Assets ($ mil.)	8.0%	539.5	548.2	604.1	649.7	734.4
Net income ($ mil.)	3.9%	6.7	6.5	6.0	6.6	7.8
Market value ($ mil.)	(13.3%)	124.2	120.4	76.9	60.2	70.2
Employees	3.0%	226	226	241	246	254

LEA INTERNATIONAL

4726 Eisenhower Blvd.
Tampa, FL 33634
Phone: 813-621-1324
Fax: 813-621-8980
Web: www.leaintl.com

CEO: Shawn Thompson
CFO: David Stimmel
HR: Colleen Krajack
FYE: July 31
Type: Business segment

LEA International, a subsidiary of Smiths Group plc, makes surge suppression equipment. Its products range from large-scale equipment for telecom and utilities applications to protectors for home electronics. Other applications include broadcast, data center, medical, and manufacturing operations. LEA International was founded in 1971. Smiths Group acquired the company in 2000 and made it part of the Smiths Interconnect segment.

LEADIS TECHNOLOGY, INC.

NASDAQ (GM): LDIS

800 W. California Ave., Ste. 200
Sunnyvale, CA 94086
Phone: 408-331-8600
Fax: 408-331-8601
Web: www.leadis.com

CEO: Antonio R. (Tony) Alvarez
CFO: John Allen
HR: —
FYE: December 31
Type: Public

In the race to market semiconductors for mobile and consumer electronics, Leadis Technology is neither leading nor following — it is getting out of the way, liquidating its assets and technologies. The global recession has eroded electronics demand, rippling to sales for chip developers and suppliers. The company has slashed product lines and its workforce. Leadis' remaining portfolio includes color display drivers with integrated controllers, used in MP3 players, personal navigation devices, and wireless phones. Customers in the Asia/Pacific once dominated sales, with China accounting for 40%.

	Annual Growth	12/04	12/05	12/06	12/07	*12/08
Sales ($ mil.)	(40.7%)	150.3	64.2	101.2	39.6	18.6
Net income ($ mil.)	—	17.6	(11.4)	(12.1)	(30.9)	(51.5)
Market value ($ mil.)	(58.0%)	320.1	154.8	140.7	86.0	9.9
Employees	16.0%	89	139	141	184	161
					*Most recent year available	

LEAP WIRELESS INTERNATIONAL, INC.

NASDAQ (GS): LEAP

10307 Pacific Center Ct.
San Diego, CA 92121
Phone: 858-882-6000
Fax: 858-882-6010
Web: www.leapwireless.com

CEO: Stewart D. (Doug) Hutcheson
CFO: Walter Z. Berger
HR: Leonard C. (Len) Stephens
FYE: December 31
Type: Public

Leap Wireless International wants to hurdle the competition. Through its Cricket Communications subsidiary, as well as affiliates LCW Wireless and Denali Operations, the company provides wireless telephone service to nearly 4 million customers in 30 US states. Leap Wireless targets the youth and minority markets with the flexible payment plans that are a key component of its marketing message. Its service features unlimited flat-rate local calling, a prepaid roaming option, multimedia, and wireless data, as well as mobile Web access through its Cricket Broadband service. The company makes sales both through its chain of retail locations and via partnerships with distributors and resellers.

	Annual Growth	12/05	12/06	12/07	12/08	12/09
Sales ($ mil.)	27.0%	914.7	1,136.7	1,630.8	1,958.9	2,383.2
Net income ($ mil.)	—	30.0	(4.8)	(75.9)	(147.8)	(239.5)
Market value ($ mil.)	(17.5%)	2,962.8	4,651.5	3,648.0	2,103.2	1,372.7
Employees	29.2%	1,507	2,034	2,425	3,423	4,202

LEAPFROG ENTERPRISES, INC.

NYSE: LF

6401 Hollis St.
Emeryville, CA 94608
Phone: 510-420-5000
Fax: 510-420-5001
Web: www.leapfrog.com

CEO: William B. (Bill) Chiasson
CFO: Mark A. Etnyre
HR: Sarah C. Shin
FYE: December 31
Type: Public

If putting pen to interactive paper helps your little Einstein learn, LeapFrog Enterprises wants to spend some time with your pint-sized genius. The toy maker develops interactive reading systems, educational games, books, and learning toys in four languages, covering subjects from math to music. Its bestselling brands include LeapPad, Leapster, Learning Path, Didj, and Tag. Products are sold to retailers, distributors, and schools worldwide, as well as to consumers via the company's website. Former vice chairman and CEO Michael Wood founded LeapFrog in 1995 because the toy market offered nothing to help his 3-year-old learn phonics.

	Annual Growth	12/05	12/06	12/07	12/08	12/09
Sales ($ mil.)	(12.6%)	649.8	502.3	442.3	459.1	379.8
Net income ($ mil.)	—	17.5	(145.1)	(101.3)	(68.3)	(2.7)
Market value ($ mil.)	(23.9%)	748.6	609.1	432.4	224.9	251.2
Employees	(10.3%)	837	916	844	626	541

🔲 LEAR CORPORATION

NYSE: LEA

21557 Telegraph Rd.
Southfield, MI 48033
Phone: 248-447-1500
Fax: 248-447-1772
Web: www.lear.com

CEO: Robert E. (Bob) Rossiter
CFO: Matthew J. (Matt) Simoncini
HR: Rick Van Heukelom
FYE: December 31
Type: Public

Lear doesn't take a back seat to anyone when it comes to manufacturing automotive seats. The company is a leader in the global market for car seat systems and a supplier of automotive electronics. In addition to seating systems and their components, Lear manufactures wire harnesses, junction boxes, terminals and connectors, and body control modules. It has some 200 facilities in 35 countries and sells to automakers such as BMW, Fiat, Ford, General Motors, Renault-Nissan, and VW. Lear gets about 70% of its sales outside North America. Struggling with debt and the effects of the global automotive industry downturn, Lear filed for Chapter 11 bankruptcy protection in July 2009 and emerged that November.

	Annual Growth	12/05	12/06	12/07	12/08	12/09
Sales ($ mil.)	(13.1%)	17,089.2	17,838.9	15,995.0	13,570.5	9,739.6
Net income ($ mil.)	—	(1,381.5)	(710.4)	241.5	(689.9)	814.4
Employees	(10.1%)	115,000	104,000	91,000	80,000	75,000

🔲 An in-depth profile of this company is available to Hoover's Online members at hoovers.com.

LEARJET INC.

1 Learjet Way
Wichita, KS 67209
Phone: 316-946-2000
Fax: 316-946-2200
Web: www.learjet.com

CEO: David Coleal
CFO: —
HR: Justin Welner
FYE: January 31
Type: Subsidiary

A pioneer in the aerospace industry, Learjet Inc. builds high-performance business jets — the limos of the sky. The company has built more than 2,000 aircraft at its Wichita, Kansas, plant since its first jet rolled off the assembly line in 1964. Current Learjet models — from light jets to midsize and super midsize jets — tout superior cruise velocity, ascent rates and operating maximums, and competitive operating costs. Since 1990 Learjet has operated as a subsidiary of Bombardier.

	Annual Growth	1/04	1/05	1/06	1/07	1/08
Est. sales ($ mil.)	—	—	—	—	—	328.6
Employees	—	—	—	—	—	4,482

LEARNING CARE GROUP, INC.

21333 Haggerty Rd., Ste. 300
Novi, MI 48375
Phone: 248-697-9000
Fax: 248-697-9002
Web: learningcaregroup.com

CEO: William D. (Bill) Davis
CFO: Robert T. VanHees
HR: Scott W. Smith
FYE: June 30
Type: Private

Take your seats and pay attention, class: Learning Care Group (formerly Childtime Learning Centers) takes care of children who are between the ages of six weeks and 12 years. The company provides both full-time and part-time child care, educational and developmental programs, and workplace child care. Most of its more than 1,100 sites in the US (operated under brand names The Children's Courtyard, Childtime Learning Centers, La Petite Academy, Montessori Unlimited, and Tutor Time Child Care) are in suburban areas, but some centers are on or near company work sites. In 2008 the private equity arm of Morgan Stanley acquired a 60% stake in Learning Care Group from A.B.C. Learning Centres for about $420 million.

⊞ LEARNING TREE INTERNATIONAL, INC.

NASDAQ (GM): LTRE

1805 Library St.
Reston, VA 20190
Phone: 703-709-9119
Fax: 703-709-6405
Web: www.learningtree.com

CEO: Nicholas R. (Nick) Schacht
CFO: Charles R. (Bob) Waldron
HR: Nancy J. McKinley
FYE: September 30
Type: Public

Learning Tree International says, "Leave no IT professional behind." The company offers more than 200 courses, including about 30 professional certification programs, to IT managers in corporations and government agencies. The bulk of the company's course library focuses on information technology topics such as Web development, programming languages, network security, and operating systems. Learning Tree has a growing list of management training offerings, however, with courses in business skills, leadership development, and project management. The company offers its classes in Japan, Europe, and North America.

	Annual Growth	9/05	9/06	9/07	9/08	9/09
Sales ($ mil.)	(3.3%)	151.6	154.0	167.2	181.3	132.6
Net income ($ mil.)	—	(0.7)	(3.1)	17.0	13.8	1.2
Market value ($ mil.)	(3.6%)	181.6	111.8	244.4	171.2	156.7
Employees	(1.7%)	457	481	495	535	427

LECG CORPORATION

NASDAQ (GS): XPRT

2000 Powell St., Ste. 600
Emeryville, CA 94608
Phone: 510-985-6700
Fax: 510-653-9898
Web: www.lecg.com

CEO: Steve Samek
CFO: Warren D. Barratt
HR: Tina M. Bussone
FYE: December 31
Type: Public

You ask, "Can I get a witness?" and LECG answers, "Yes!" The firm provides expert testimony to a wide range of corporate clients and government agencies on issues such as competition and antitrust, intellectual property, labor and employment, and mergers and acquisitions. In addition, LECG offers in-depth studies and consulting services. Clients typically come from industries such as energy, financial services, health care and pharmaceuticals, and telecommunications. LECG operates primarily in the US; the firm also has offices elsewhere in the Americas and in Europe and the Asia/Pacific region. Altogether it owns about 30 offices worldwide.

	Annual Growth	12/05	12/06	12/07	12/08	12/09
Sales ($ mil.)	(2.1%)	286.7	353.9	370.4	335.7	263.2
Net income ($ mil.)	—	22.4	21.5	11.4	(86.7)	(74.1)
Market value ($ mil.)	(35.6%)	641.3	681.9	555.7	247.6	110.3
Employees	(6.7%)	1,151	1,196	1,134	865	874

⊞ LECROY CORPORATION

NASDAQ (GM): LCRY

700 Chestnut Ridge Rd.
Chestnut Ridge, NY 10977
Phone: 845-425-2000
Fax: 845-578-5985
Web: www.lecroy.com

CEO: Thomas H. (Tom) Reslewic
CFO: Sean B. O'Connor
HR: —
FYE: June 30
Type: Public

If only LeCroy made an instrument to analyze signals exchanged between the sexes. The company makes high-performance, real-time oscilloscopes under the WaveAce, WaveExpert, WaveJet, WaveMaster, WavePro, WaveRunner, and WaveSurfer brand names that capture electronic signals, convert them to digital form, and perform measurements and analysis. LeCroy makes such other products as differential amplifiers, electrical probes, production test digitizers and analyzers, serial data analyzers, and waveform generators. The company also provides technical support, maintenance, and recalibration services. Customers include BAE, IBM, and Siemens. About two-thirds of the company's sales come from outside North America.

	Annual Growth	6/05	6/06	6/07	6/08	6/09
Sales ($ mil.)	(5.1%)	165.0	160.5	151.3	160.5	134.0
Net income ($ mil.)	—	2.1	6.6	(13.2)	1.7	(106.7)
Market value ($ mil.)	(27.7%)	174.1	174.1	123.0	112.9	47.5
Employees	(0.8%)	402	458	433	455	389

LECTEC CORPORATION

OTC: LECT

1407 South Kings Highway
Texarkana, TX 75501
Phone: 903-832-0993
Fax: 903-832-0997
Web: www.lectec.com

CEO: Judd A. Berlin
CFO: Judd A. Berlin
HR: —
FYE: December 31
Type: Public

It's all a skin game at LecTec. The company licenses topical patches that deliver over-the-counter drugs through the skin. Its patents, used by pharmaceutical companies, include adhesive patches, wound dressings, and inhalation therapies. LecTec formerly made its products, but ceased manufacturing a few years ago and is now an intellectual property licensing and holding company. LecTec licenses its technology to Novartis for that company's Triaminic Vapor Patch, a cough suppressant for adults and children. LecTec is pursuing additional licensing agreements with Novartis, as well as seeking other licensing partners. It's also looking to expand its product portfolio through research and development opportunities.

	Annual Growth	12/05	12/06	12/07	12/08	12/09
Sales ($ mil.)	180.9%	0.4	0.1	0.1	0.1	24.9
Net income ($ mil.)	—	(0.5)	(0.4)	(0.7)	(1.0)	15.0
Market value ($ mil.)	67.6%	2.2	2.8	5.6	11.8	17.3
Employees	(9.1%)	—	4	4	1	3

⊞ LEE ENTERPRISES, INCORPORATED

NYSE: LEE

201 N. Harrison St., Ste. 600	CEO: Mary E. Junck
Davenport, IA 52801	CFO: Carl G. Schmidt
Phone: 563-383-2100	HR: Vytenis P. (Vito) Kuraitis
Fax: 563-323-9609	FYE: September 30
Web: www.lee.net	Type: Public

This Lee commands an army of newspapers. Lee Enterprises owns or has stakes in about 50 daily newspapers and more than 300 weekly papers and niche publications serving primarily small and midsized markets in more than 20 states. Its portfolio is anchored by the *St. Louis Post Dispatch*, which boasts a daily circulation of more than 210,000. Lee also owns 50% of Madison Newspapers, publisher of the *Wisconsin State Journal*. In addition to traditional publishing, Lee operates a number of websites in conjunction with its newspapers, and it has about 10 commercial printing units in a half dozen states. Former chairman Lloyd Schermer and his family have nearly 30% voting control of the company.

	Annual Growth	9/05	9/06	9/07	9/08	9/09
Sales ($ mil.)	(0.6%)	860.9	1,128.6	1,127.7	1,028.9	842.0
Net income ($ mil.)	—	76.9	70.8	81.0	(879.9)	(180.2)
Market value ($ mil.)	(49.6%)	1,906.3	1,132.6	698.7	157.1	123.4
Employees	(4.8%)	10,000	9,400	9,250	8,200	8,200

LEE HECHT HARRISON LLC

50 Tice Blvd.	CEO: Peter Alcide
Woodcliff Lake, NJ 07677	CFO: Karine Storm
Phone: 201-930-9333	HR: Andrea R. Huff
Fax: 201-307-0878	FYE: December 31
Web: www.lhh.com	Type: Subsidiary

Lee Hecht Harrison, a unit of the world's #1 employment services firm Adecco, provides career and leadership consulting through its more than 240 offices around the globe. The company offers services in areas such as career and leadership development, outplacement, and executive coaching. Clients include organizations, individuals, and recruiters. It additionally offers clients the opportunity to access career information from home. Lee Hecht Harrison sponsors events featuring experts on human resources topics. The company was founded in 1974 and resides within its parent company's Human Capital Solutions division.

LEGACY BANCORP, INC.

NASDAQ (GM): LEGC

99 North St.	CEO: J. Williar (Bill) Dunlaevy
Pittsfield, MA 01202	CFO: Paul H. Bruce
Phone: 413-443-4421	HR: Amy Sullivan Thompson
Fax: 413-442-8155	FYE: December 31
Web: www.legacy-banks.com	Type: Public

A name change, demutualization, and a listing on Nasdaq will be this bancorp's Legacy. In 2005, Legacy Bancorp (formerly Mutual Bancorp of the Berkshires) shed its mutual status, through which depositors owned stakes in the bank, and offered its shares to the public. It is the holding company for Legacy Banks, which has nearly 20 branches in western Massachusetts' Berkshire County and eastern New York. In addition to traditional deposit accounts, the bank and other subsidiaries offer trust services, insurance, investment products, and portfolio management. Legacy Bancorp traces its history to 1835.

	Annual Growth	12/05	12/06	12/07	12/08	12/09
Assets ($ mil.)	5.0%	778.3	808.3	924.5	944.7	946.3
Net income ($ mil.)	—	(2.2)	2.8	1.2	1.4	(7.8)
Market value ($ mil.)	(7.3%)	116.2	138.0	115.4	93.0	85.8
Employees	3.9%	151	160	183	182	176

LEGACY RESERVES LP

NASDAQ (GS): LGCY

303 W. Wall St., Ste. 1400	CEO: Cary D. Brown
Midland, TX 79701	CFO: Steven H. (Steve) Pruett
Phone: 432-689-5200	HR: —
Fax: 432-689-5299	FYE: December 31
Web: www.legacylp.com	Type: Public

Legacy Reserves has its sights set on creating its very own prosperous legacy. The independent oil and gas company explores for oil and gas deposits in the Permian Basin of West Texas and southeast New Mexico and exploits those resources. In 2009 Legacy Reserves reported proved reserves of 37.1 million barrels of oil equivalent (72% oil and natural gas liquids; 84% proved developed). The company was formed in 2005 to own and operate the oil and natural gas properties that it acquired from the Moriah Group, the Brothers Group, and MBN Properties. These investors, along with the firm's directors and executive officers, own about 24% of Legacy Reserves.

	Annual Growth	12/05	12/06	12/07	12/08	12/09
Sales ($ mil.)	63.1%	19.4	69.1	112.2	215.4	137.3
Net income ($ mil.)	—	5.9	4.4	(55.7)	158.2	(92.8)
Market value ($ mil.)	(2.5%)	—	—	829.5	373.1	788.2
Employees	41.1%	24	23	58	98	95

LEGAL CLUB OF AMERICA CORPORATION

Pink Sheets: LEGL

7771 W. Oakland Park Blvd., Ste. 217	CEO: Brett Merl
Sunrise, FL 33351	CFO: Linda Friedman
Phone: 954-377-0222	HR: Elaine Gonzales
Fax: 954-267-0401	FYE: June 30
Web: www.legalclub.com	Type: Public

Like insurance, you would probably prefer not to need the services of Legal Club of America. The company offers legal services plans that allow its members to receive free or discounted legal advice from its network of more than 22,000 lawyers. Founded in 1993, Legal Club of America markets its products and services directly to potential clients as part of corporate benefits packages. Its flagship product, the Legal Club Family Legal Plan, offers members services in legal care, as well as financial education and credit counseling, tax advice, life events counseling, and identity theft restoration and insurance.

⊞ LEGG MASON, INC.

NYSE: LM

100 International Dr.	CEO: Mark R. Fetting
Baltimore, MD 21202	CFO: Charles J. (C. J.) Daley Jr.
Phone: 410-539-0000	HR: —
Fax: —	FYE: March 31
Web: www.leggmason.com	Type: Public

Legg Mason's feats include wealth management and mutual fund management. The financial services firm has several subsidiaries that offer asset management, trust services, and annuities to retail and institutional investors. The company manages about 140 mutual funds under the Legg Mason, Western Asset, and The Royce Funds banners. Other offerings include closed-end funds and separately managed accounts. Legg Mason distributes its products through its own offices, retirement plans, and financial intermediaries, as well as through an agreement with Morgan Stanley Smith Barney. The company operates primarily in North America and the UK, but also has offices in about 15 other countries.

	Annual Growth	3/06	3/07	3/08	3/09	3/10
Assets ($ mil.)	(1.9%)	9,302.5	9,604.5	11,830.4	9,321.4	8,613.7
Net income ($ mil.)	(35.0%)	1,144.2	646.8	267.6	(1,947.9)	204.4
Market value ($ mil.)	(30.8%)	20,496.1	15,406.8	9,154.8	2,600.2	4,688.6
Employees	(1.7%)	3,800	4,030	4,220	3,890	3,550

⊞ An in-depth profile of this company is available to Hoover's Online members at hoovers.com.

927

LEGGETT & PLATT, INCORPORATED

NYSE: LEG

No. 1 Leggett Rd.
Carthage, MO 64836
Phone: 417-358-8131
Fax: 417-358-5840
Web: www.leggett.com

CEO: David S. (Dave) Haffner
CFO: Matthew C. (Matt) Flanigan
HR: John A. Hale
FYE: December 31
Type: Public

That spring in your step after a good night's sleep may be there courtesy of Leggett & Platt (L&P) — the pioneer of coiled bedsprings. Primarily using aluminum and steel, the company makes residential furnishings (such as innersprings and bed frames) and commercial fixtures (store displays, shelves, furniture components). It also produces industrial materials (wire, steel tubing) and specialized items (quilting machines, automotive seating, docking stations for electronic devices). Customers include furniture retailers, telecommunications firms, and makers of automobiles, construction products, bedding, and lawn gear. The firm operates production, distribution, and warehousing facilities in about 20 countries.

	Annual Growth	12/05	12/06	12/07	12/08	12/09
Sales ($ mil.)	(12.9%)	5,299.3	5,505.4	4,306.4	4,076.1	3,055.1
Net income ($ mil.)	(17.8%)	251.3	300.3	(11.2)	104.4	115.0
Market value ($ mil.)	(2.9%)	3,400.0	3,539.2	2,582.6	2,249.4	3,020.9
Employees	(13.5%)	33,000	32,828	24,000	20,600	18,500

LEHIGH CEMENT COMPANY

7660 Imperial Way
Allentown, PA 18195
Phone: 610-366-4600
Fax: 610-366-4851
Web: www.lehighcement.com

CEO: Richard Manning
CFO: —
HR: —
FYE: December 31
Type: Subsidiary

Lehigh Cement Company has built a solid foundation in the cement business. One of the largest cement producers in North American, the company produces ready-mix concrete; concrete pipe and block; precast concrete; portland, blended and specialty cements; and aggregates. Other products include prestressed cement products, custom-color portland and masonry cement, fly ash, and other pozzolanic materials. Lehigh has about a dozen cement plants and more than 40 distribution terminals in North America. It serves customers who use its products in highway, architectural, industrial, and marine applications. Founded in 1897, the company is a subsidiary of Germany-based HeidelbergCement.

	Annual Growth	12/04	12/05	12/06	12/07	12/08
Est. sales ($ mil.)	—	—	—	—	—	300.0
Employees	—	—	—	—	—	2,249

LEHIGH HANSON COMPANY

300 E. John Carpenter Fwy.
Irving, TX 75062
Phone: 972-653-5500
Fax: 972-653-6146
Web: www.hanson.biz/hansonus

CEO: Richard Manning
CFO: —
HR: —
FYE: December 31
Type: Subsidiary

Lehigh Hanson Company has a big crush on the concrete materials business. The company's Hanson Pipe & Precast division makes concrete pipes, manholes, and precast concrete products. Hanson Brick & Tile makes clay bricks and roofing tiles and is the largest brick manufacturer in the US. Its Hardscapes division makes decorative paving stones for landscaping. Lehigh Hanson has nearly 700 facilities in operation in the US and Canada. German construction materials firm HeidelbergCement acquired Lehigh Hanson Company's UK-based parent Hanson in 2007, creating one of the world's largest cement makers.

	Annual Growth	12/04	12/05	12/06	12/07	12/08
Est. sales ($ mil.)	—	—	—	—	—	3,516.4
Employees	—	—	—	—	—	14,937

LEHMAN BROTHERS HOLDINGS INC.

Pink Sheets: LEHMQ

1271 Avenue of the Americas
New York, NY 10020
Phone: 646-285-9000
Fax: —
Web: www.lehman.com

CEO: Bryan P. Marsal
CFO: William J. (Bill) Fox
HR: —
FYE: November 30
Type: Public

In what could be called the collapse heard 'round the world, venerable investment bank Lehman Brothers declared bankruptcy in September 2008, ending a reign of some 160 years in financial services. One of the top bulge-bracket firms and perennially among the industry leaders in M&A advice, debt and equity underwriting, and global finance suffered a knockout punch and reported nearly $7 billion in losses after becoming embroiled in the global credit crisis of 2007 and 2008. After acquisition talks with foreign investors fell through, Lehman attempted to restructure itself, including selling off operations for cash. The plan was too little too late, though, and Lehman filed for Chapter 11 bankruptcy protection.

LEHMAN TRIKES, INC.

TSX Venture: LHT

125 Industrial Dr.
Spearfish, SD 57783
Phone: 605-642-2111
Fax: 605-642-1184
Web: www.lehmantrikes.com

CEO: Kennon D. (Ken) Hines
CFO: Timothy Kling
HR: —
FYE: November 30
Type: Public

Lehman Trikes proudly proclaims that it is the "leader of the three-world." The company builds motorized tricycles by converting heavy-cruiser motorcycles manufactured by the likes of Honda, Victory, and Suzuki. Lehman Trikes also sells the kits needed for do-it-yourselfers to convert traditional two-wheelers into motor trikes. Lehman Trikes offers a complete line of accessories, including pinstriping, light bars, heel guards, trailer hitches, and trunk liners, too. The company's products are sold primarily in Canada and the US.

	Annual Growth	11/05	11/06	11/07	11/08	11/09
Sales ($ mil.)	30.3%	11.6	14.3	19.8	22.6	33.4
Net income ($ mil.)	—	(0.8)	0.1	(1.0)	(0.6)	0.6
Market value ($ mil.)	(18.1%)	6.9	21.6	11.3	6.9	3.1
Employees	—	—	—	—	—	—

LEICA GEOSYSTEMS HDS LLC

4550 Norris Canyon Rd.
San Ramon, CA 94583
Phone: 925-790-2300
Fax: 925-790-2309
Web: hds.leica-geosystems.com

CEO: Erwin Frei
CFO: Mark Gullans
HR: —
FYE: March 31
Type: Subsidiary

Leica Geosystems HDS is the High-Definition Surveying (HDS) division of Switzerland-based Leica Geosystems Holdings AG. The division develops and manufactures 3D laser-scanning hardware and software products for as-built, detail, engineering, and topographic surveys for 2D and 3D mapping and modeling applications. The unit markets its products under the Leica ScanStation 2 and Leica HDS6000 names, along with the related Cyclone and CloudWorx software packages. The company has customers and representatives in over 40 countries. Leica Geosystems HDS was founded as Cyra Technologies in 1993 and was acquired by Leica Geosystems in 2001.

	Annual Growth	3/04	3/05	3/06	3/07	3/08
Est. sales ($ mil.)	—	—	—	—	—	10.5
Employees	—	—	—	—	—	72

LEIFHEIT INTERNATIONAL USA, INC.

510 Broadhollow Rd., Ste. 201
Melville, NY 11747
Phone: 631-501-1054
Fax: 631-396-0010
Web: www.leifheitusa.com

CEO: Mari O'Connor
CFO: —
HR: —
FYE: December 31
Type: Subsidiary

Leifheit International USA is the US distribution arm of German housewares maker LEIFHEIT. The company sells a range of household products, including kitchen tools and gadgets (carafes, canning supplies, graters), laundry room utensils (ironing, drying boards), cleaning necessities (swivel brooms, spray mops), and ladders and step stools. It also distributes Birambeau kitchen tools, Dr. Oetker bakeware, and Soehnle kitchen and bathroom scales. Leifheit (pronouced "life height") International USA was formed in 1996.

LEMAITRE VASCULAR, INC.

NASDAQ (GM): LMAT

63 2nd Ave.
Burlington, MA 01803
Phone: 781-221-2266
Fax: 781-425-5049
Web: www.lemaitre.com

CEO: George W. LeMaitre
CFO: Joseph P. Pellegrino Jr.
HR: Cornelia W. (Connie) LeMaitre
FYE: December 31
Type: Public

LeMaitre Vascular makes the veins run on time. The company makes both disposable and implanted surgical vascular devices, including catheters and stents, under such brands as AnastoClip, EndoFit, and Pruitt-Inahara. LeMaitre was founded in 1983 by vascular surgeon George D. LeMaitre, who developed a valvulotome used to prepare veins for arterial bypass. The company has since expanded its offerings to include a device to create dialysis access sites and another to treat aortic aneurysms. Its products are sold to hospitals in North America, Europe, and Japan through a direct sales force. Dr. LeMaitre's son George W. LeMaitre (the company's chairman, president, and CEO) holds a controlling stake in the company.

	Annual Growth	12/05	12/06	12/07	12/08	12/09
Sales ($ mil.)	13.5%	30.7	34.6	41.4	48.7	50.9
Net income ($ mil.)	100.0%	0.1	(1.2)	(2.9)	(3.3)	1.6
Market value ($ mil.)	(5.9%)	—	93.6	96.7	36.0	78.0
Employees	2.5%	206	218	251	200	227

LEMANS CORPORATION

3501 Kennedy Rd.
Janesville, WI 53545
Phone: 608-758-1111
Fax: 608-758-4677
Web: www.parts-unlimited.com

CEO: Fred Fox
CFO: Mark Scharenbroch
HR: —
FYE: September 30
Type: Private

Lemans has a role to play with plenty of parts for those who live to ride (and ride to live). As part of its Parts Unlimited division, Lemans distributes parts and accessories for street and off-road motorcycles, snowmobiles, personal watercraft, and all-terrain vehicles (ATVs). The company also manufactures and distributes boots, gloves, goggles, helmets, jackets, jerseys, safety gear, and other riding apparel and accessories for motorcyclists. Lemans does so through its Thor and Drag Specialties subsidiaries. The company's Moose Utility Division specializes in parts for ATVs and apparel for their riders.

LENDER PROCESSING SERVICES, INC.

NYSE: LPS

601 Riverside Ave.
Jacksonville, FL 32204
Phone: 904-854-5100
Fax: 904-854-4124
Web: www.lpsvcs.com

CEO: Jeffrey S. Carbiener
CFO: Francis K. Chan
HR: —
FYE: December 31
Type: Public

Lender Processing Services (LPS) is making a go of it on its own. The company (which was spun off from Fidelity National Information Services in 2008) provides the mortgage industry with technology to assist lenders from start to finish, from checking credit and applying for mortgages to processing and closing services. LPS also offers data and analytics for the mortgage and capital markets industries and provides default management services to the secondary mortgage market. More than 1,000 banks use its Mortgage Servicing Package (MSP); LPS processes more than half of all mortgages in the US. Customers include Bank of America, Wells Fargo, and National City Mortgage.

	Annual Growth	12/05	12/06	12/07	12/08	12/09
Sales ($ mil.)	14.4%	1,382.5	1,485.0	1,690.6	1,861.9	2,370.5
Net income ($ mil.)	9.0%	195.7	201.1	256.8	230.9	276.7
Market value ($ mil.)	38.1%	—	—	—	2,792.4	3,855.3
Employees	12.8%	—	—	7,000	7,200	8,900

LENDMARK FINANCIAL SERVICES, INC.

2118 Usher St.
Covington, GA 30014
Phone: 678-625-6500
Fax: 678-625-6515
Web: www.lendmarkfinancial.com

CEO: Robert W. (Bobby) Aiken
CFO: Wayne Taylor
HR: —
FYE: December 31
Type: Subsidiary

Lendmark Financial Services is a subsidiary of southeastern banking bigwig BB&T. The company provides consumer, auto, and nonconforming or subprime mortgage loans to customers who do not meet its parent company's lending requirements. Launched in the mid-1990s to serve clients in Georgia who couldn't qualify for loans through traditional channels, Lendmark Financial Services today operates more than 100 branches in about 10 eastern states ranging from Delaware to Florida. It became a subsidiary of BB&T in 2000 when its former parent, First Liberty Bank, was acquired by the financial services concern.

⊞ LENNAR CORPORATION

NYSE: LEN

700 NW 107th Ave.
Miami, FL 33172
Phone: 305-559-4000
Fax: 305-228-8383
Web: www.lennar.com

CEO: Stuart A. Miller
CFO: Bruce E. Gross
HR: —
FYE: November 30
Type: Public

Lennar is one of the largest homebuilding, land-owning, loan-making leviathans in the US, along with D.R. Horton and Pulte Homes. The company builds single-family attached and detached homes in 14 states under brand names including Lennar, Cambridge, NuHome, and Greystone. Lennar targets first-time, move-up, and active adult buyers and markets its homes as "everything included." The company also provides financial services including mortgage financing, title, and closing services. In fiscal 2009 Lennar delivered some 11,500 homes at an average price of $243,000 — a steep drop from the 33,000 homes delivered just two years earlier. CEO Stuart Miller controls 46% of the company.

	Annual Growth	11/05	11/06	11/07	11/08	11/09
Sales ($ mil.)	(31.1%)	13,867.0	16,266.7	10,186.8	4,575.4	3,119.4
Net income ($ mil.)	—	1,355.2	593.9	(1,941.1)	(1,109.1)	(417.1)
Market value ($ mil.)	(31.5%)	10,666.5	9,708.6	2,929.2	1,314.8	2,343.0
Employees	(27.2%)	13,687	12,605	6,934	4,704	3,835

⊞ An in-depth profile of this company is available to Hoover's Online members at hoovers.com.

929

LENNOX INTERNATIONAL INC.

NYSE: LII

2140 Lake Park Blvd.	CEO: Todd M. Bluedorn
Richardson, TX 75080	CFO: Robert W. (Bob) Hau
Phone: 972-497-5000	HR: Daniel M. Sessa
Fax: 972-497-5292	FYE: December 31
Web: www.lennoxinternational.com	Type: Public

Lennox International makes sure the temperature is just right. The company makes climate control equipment such as heating, ventilation, air conditioning, and refrigeration units for residential and commercial uses. It sells furnaces, heat pumps, fireplaces, and air conditioners under such brands as Lennox, Armstrong Air, and Aire-Flo; chillers and condensing units are sold under the Bohn and Larkin names. Products are sold to some 7,000 dealers in the US and Canada. Lennox also owns and operates 100 service and installation centers. The company has operations in Asia, Australia, Europe, and South America. Named after inventor Dave Lennox, the company was acquired in 1904 by newspaper publisher D.W. Norris.

	Annual Growth	12/05	12/06	12/07	12/08	12/09
Sales ($ mil.)	(4.1%)	3,366.2	3,671.1	3,749.7	3,481.4	2,847.5
Net income ($ mil.)	(23.7%)	150.6	166.0	169.0	122.8	51.1
Market value ($ mil.)	8.5%	1,573.3	1,707.7	2,310.8	1,801.4	2,178.0
Employees	(7.7%)	16,000	16,000	15,000	13,500	11,600

LENOX CORPORATION

1414 Radcliffe St.	CEO: Peter B. Cameron
Bristol, PA 19007	CFO: Steve O'Connell
Phone: 267-525-7800	HR: —
Fax: —	FYE: December 31
Web: www.lenox.com	Type: Private

As the first American brand of china to be used in the White House, Lenox sets the table like no other. The company sells tabletop and giftware products under the Lenox, Dansk, and Gorham brand names. Customers include independent gift retailers, department stores, and catalog firms. Lenox also sells its products online and by catalog. Walter Scott Lenox founded the business in 1889 as the Ceramic Art Company. Investment firm Clarion Capital Partners acquired Lenox Group's assets in 2009 after it filed for Chapter 11 bankruptcy protection. As the firm reorganized, it boxed up its Department 56 giftware brand, selling it to collectibles marketer Enesco.

LENSCRAFTERS, INC.

4000 Luxottica Place	CEO: Kerry Bradley
Mason, OH 45040	CFO: Jack S. Dennis
Phone: 513-765-6000	HR: Mildred Curtis
Fax: 513-765-6249	FYE: December 31
Web: www.lenscrafters.com	Type: Subsidiary

LensCrafters brings eyewear and malls together. Part of the growing retail arm (Luxottica Retail) of Italy's Luxottica Group, LensCrafters is North America's largest retailer of eyewear and related services, with about 965 stores in the US, Canada, and Puerto Rico. The company-owned stores, mainly located in shopping malls, offer prescription frames and sunglasses (most made by Luxottica), contact lenses, and vision exams by an on-site optometrist. Most of the locations house in-store lens finishing labs. Outside North America, Luxottica operates about 165 LensCrafters stores in China and Hong Kong. LensCrafters was founded in 1983 and acquired by Luxottica in 1995.

LEO BURNETT COMPANY, INC.

35 W. Wacker Dr.	CEO: Thomas (Tom) Bernardin
Chicago, IL 60601	CFO: Paul Eichelman
Phone: 312-220-5959	HR: Veronika Borbas
Fax: 312-220-3299	FYE: December 31
Web: www.leoburnett.com	Type: Subsidiary

This company has come up with some gr-r-reat ideas to promote brands. The #2 ad agency in the US (behind WPP Group's JWT), Leo Burnett has helped create some of the top consumer brands, including Kellogg's Frosted Flakes cereal and its Tony the Tiger icon. It offers creative development and campaign planning services through about 95 offices in almost 85 countries. Its Arc Worldwide subsidiary provides promotional and direct marketing services, as well as multimedia and interactive marketing development. Vigilante acts as an urban marketing firm, while Lápiz Integrated Hispanic Marketing targets Spanish-speakers. The company, which does business as Leo Burnett Worldwide, is owned by ad conglomerate Publicis.

LEONARD GREEN & PARTNERS, L.P.

11111 Santa Monica Blvd., Ste. 2000	CEO: Jonathan D. Sokoloff
Los Angeles, CA 90025	CFO: Cody L. Franklin
Phone: 310-954-0444	HR: —
Fax: 310-954-0404	FYE: December 31
Web: www.leonardgreen.com	Type: Private

This private equity firm has a green thumb for growing businesses. Leonard Green & Partners (LGP) specializes in long-term investments in friendly buyouts, focusing on established retailers and consumer products companies such as Neiman Marcus, Varsity Brands, The Sports Authority, and Rite Aid. The investment firm, which was founded in 1989, generally doesn't participate in the day-to-day operations of its holdings. However, it does take seats on boards to help direct strategic and financial development. Currently investing its fifth private equity fund, LGP owns stakes in about 20 firms and manages some $9 billion in equity capital.

LEPRINO FOODS COMPANY

1830 W. 38th Ave.	CEO: Larry Jensen
Denver, CO 80211	CFO: Ron Klump
Phone: 303-480-2600	HR: Bradley (Brad) Olsen
Fax: 303-480-2605	FYE: October 31
Web: www.leprinofoods.com	Type: Private

Don't try to butter up Leprino Foods — it's into mozzarella with a capital "M." The company is a worldwide leader in mozzarella making. It sells its mozzarella to pizza purveyors large and small, including powerhouses like Domino's, Papa John's, and Pizza Hut, as well as to food manufacturing companies. In addition to mozzarella, the company makes reduced-fat cheddar, reduced-fat Monterey Jack, string, and queso cheeses. Leprino's other products include dairy powders, such as whey protein concentrate and lactose for use in animal feeds, yogurt, baby formula, and baked goods. It is supplied by the nation's large dairy co-ops.

An in-depth profile of this company is available to Hoover's Online members at hoovers.com.

LES SCHWAB TIRE CENTERS

20900 Cooley Rd.
Bend, OR 97701
Phone: 541-447-4136
Fax: —
Web: www.lesschwab.com

CEO: Dick Borgman
CFO: Tom Freedman
HR: Jodie Hueske
FYE: December 31
Type: Private

If you need new tires or a brake job after heading out West, roll into Les Schwab Tire Centers. The company offers tires by name-brand and private-label manufacturers, custom wheels, and batteries at some 400 stores in Alaska, California, Idaho, Montana, Nevada, Oregon, Utah, and Washington. It also provides alignment, brake, and shock work. Les Schwab Tire Centers prides itself on customer service, and it doesn't hurt that the chain's namesake wrote the bible of tire retailing: *Pride in Performance: Keep It Going.* The company's roots reach back to 1952, when founder Les Schwab started his business with a single tire shop. Today the firm is owned by Schwab's family.

LESCARDEN INC.

OTC: LCAR

420 Lexington Ave., Ste. 212
New York, NY 10170
Phone: 212-687-1050
Fax: 212-687-1051
Web: www.catrix.com

CEO: William E. (Bill) Luther
CFO: William E. (Bill) Luther
HR: —
FYE: May 31
Type: Public

Lescarden lessens scarring when it can. The company develops clinical dermatological, osteoarthritis, and wound care products. Lescarden focuses on developing natural therapies. Many of its products utilize bovine cartilage, which is said to possess beneficial healing qualities. Its lead product, the bovine-based and FDA-approved Catrix, is sold as a dressing for non-healing wounds such as diabetic ulcers. Lescarden also markets a line of Catrix-based skin care products targeting the plastic surgery, dermatology, and medical spa markets. Other products include Poly-Nag, an anti-arthritic compound made from chitin, a material found in the shells of invertebrates, and BIO-CARTILAGE, a nutritional supplement.

	Annual Growth	5/05	5/06	5/07	5/08	5/09
Sales ($ mil.)	(32.4%)	2.4	1.6	1.1	0.4	0.5
Net income ($ mil.)	—	0.4	0.1	0.1	(0.4)	(0.2)
Market value ($ mil.)	(43.0%)	11.8	7.7	5.6	2.8	1.2
Employees	(24.0%)	3	3	3	3	1

LESCO, INC.

1301 E. 9th St., Ste. 1300
Cleveland, OH 44114
Phone: 216-706-9250
Fax: 800-673-3030
Web: www.lesco.com

CEO: David P. (Dave) Werning
CFO: Michael A. Weisbarth
HR: Kathleen M. Minahan
FYE: December 31
Type: Subsidiary

When LESCO sees a golf course or a lawn, it sees green. The company sells fertilizer, grass seed, and turf-protection products used on golf courses and lawns, primarily under the LESCO name, but also under brands such as NOVEX (a longer-acting turf fertilizer). Customers include landscapers, municipalities, and country clubs. Consumable goods (fertilizer, grass seed, herbicides, insecticides, and fungicides) account for most of LESCO's sales, but it also sells hard goods like rotary mowers, spreaders, and sprayers. It is a subsidiary of the John Deere Landscapes unit of Deere & Company; that unit sells its products through about 600 service centers and a fleet of 100 tractor-trailer-based stores.

LESLIE'S POOLMART, INC.

3925 E. Broadway Rd., Ste. 100
Phoenix, AZ 85040
Phone: 602-366-3999
Fax: 602-366-3934
Web: www.lesliespool.com

CEO: Lawrence H. Hayward
CFO: Steven L. Ortega
HR: —
FYE: September 30
Type: Private

Leslie's Poolmart is the big fish of pool product retailers. The company sells pool and spa chemicals, cleaning and testing equipment, pumps, covers, and recreational items through some 620 stores in some 35 states, mostly in Arizona, California, Florida, Georgia, and Texas. The company also sells its products through catalogs and its website. Leslie's makes chlorine tablets and repackages other chemicals to be sold under the Leslie name, as well. Pool chemicals, major equipment, and parts account for a majority of the company's sales. Founded in 1963, Leslie's is majority owned by affiliates of Leonard Green & Partners.

LETICA CORPORATION

52585 Dequindre Rd.
Rochester, MI 48308
Phone: 248-652-0557
Fax: 248-608-2153
Web: www.letica.com

CEO: Ilija Letica
CFO: Albert (Al) Gustafson
HR: Anne Ventimiglio-Esser
FYE: June 30
Type: Private

Letica has plastic containers by the gallon — and other sizes as well. Owned and run by the Letica family, Letica Corp. is a nationwide maker of plastic packaging, from buckets to cups, some of which use recycled material. The company produces one- to seven-gallon commercial containers, often with multi-color labels. In addition to a rigid packaging segment, Letica's Maui foodservice packaging offers plastic injection-molded, thin-wall containers and lids, as well as paper containers. Products are transported to customers and backhauled by a freightlines segment. Customizing containers for specific applications, Letica caters to building material suppliers, hardware stores, and retail and restaurant outlets.

LEUCADIA NATIONAL CORPORATION

NYSE: LUK

315 Park Ave. South
New York, NY 10010
Phone: 212-460-1900
Fax: 212-598-4869
Web: www.leucadia.com

CEO: Joseph S. Steinberg
CFO: Joseph A. Orlando
HR: —
FYE: December 31
Type: Public

Holding company Leucadia National owns stakes in firms involved in manufacturing, auto finance, medical products, gaming, oil and gas drilling, and real estate. The investment firm typically seeks out troubled companies that it believes are undervalued; its holdings include Idaho Timber, Conwed Plastics, Goober Drilling, and medical products firm Sangart, which develops blood transfusion technology and products. Leucadia also holds stakes in several US wineries and vineyard developments along the West Coast (Pine Ridge, Archery Summit, and Chamisal vineyards). It also owns a 30% stake in a copper mine in Spain.

	Annual Growth	12/05	12/06	12/07	12/08	12/09
Sales ($ mil.)	13.2%	682.5	450.9	877.8	1,080.7	1,119.0
Net income ($ mil.)	(23.9%)	1,636.0	189.4	484.3	(2,535.4)	548.6
Market value ($ mil.)	0.1%	5,773.8	6,861.4	11,460.0	4,817.6	5,788.4
Employees	(4.2%)	3,969	1,323	4,057	3,584	3,340

LEVCOR INTERNATIONAL, INC.

151 W. 40th St.
New York, NY 10018
Phone: 212-354-8500
Fax: 212-354-4938

CEO: Robert A. Levinson
CFO: Pramila Devi (Devi) Shaheed
HR: —
FYE: December 31
Type: Private

Button. Button. Who's got the button? Levcor does. Buttons and other accoutrements are the core of Levcor International's business. The company makes and sells buttons, decorations, craft products, and complementary product lines, including iron-ons, kits, and fashion and jewelry accessories. Levcor's products are sold to the home sewing and craft markets through mass merchandisers and retailers, such as Wal-Mart and Jo-Ann Stores. Levcor operated a textile division that made women's coordinated apparel but it exited the unprofitable business in mid-2006 after several years of tweaking it. Chairman, president, and CEO Robert Levinson controls about 30% of Levcor.

LEVITON MANUFACTURING CO., INC.

201 North Service Road
Melville, NY 11747
Phone: 631-812-6000
Fax: 800-832-9538
Web: www.leviton.com

CEO: Donald J. Hendler
CFO: Mark Baydarian
HR: Mark Fogel
FYE: December 31
Type: Private

Its more than 25,000 products make Leviton Manufacturing a leviathan of electrical and electronic components. The company makes switches, plugs, connectors, and integrated networks designed for home, commercial, and industrial uses. The company's divisions also produce lighting controls and voice and data equipment. Its Wiring Device division makes everything from basic switches to receptacles, including the designer Decora and Acenti collections. Its products are sold in North America to distributors, manufacturers, and retail outlets, such as Home Depot, Sears, and Wal-Mart. The Leviton family owns the company, which started out making tip mantles for gaslights in 1906.

LEVEL 3 COMMUNICATIONS, INC.

NASDAQ (GS): LVLT

1025 Eldorado Blvd.
Broomfield, CO 80021
Phone: 720-888-1000
Fax: 720-888-5085
Web: www.level3.com

CEO: James Q. (Jim) Crowe
CFO: Sunit S. Patel
HR: Thomas C. (Tom) Stortz
FYE: December 31
Type: Public

Level 3 Communications owns a piece of the communications networking market. The company operates one of the world's largest Internet protocol (IP)-based fiber-optic networks, connecting customers in 22 countries. Its services include broadband Internet access, wholesale voice origination and termination, enterprise voice, content distribution, broadband transport, and colocation. Level 3's wholesale customers include ISPs, telecom carriers, cable TV operators, wireless providers, and the US government. The company markets directly to businesses, state agencies, and schools. Its content delivery unit targets video distributors, Web portals, online gaming and software companies, and social networking sites.

	Annual Growth	12/05	12/06	12/07	12/08	12/09
Sales ($ mil.)	1.0%	3,613.0	3,378.0	4,269.0	4,301.0	3,762.0
Net income ($ mil.)	—	(638.0)	(744.0)	(1,114.0)	(290.0)	(618.0)
Market value ($ mil.)	(14.6%)	4,753.9	9,275.9	5,035.5	1,159.5	2,534.3
Employees	2.0%	4,800	7,400	6,680	5,300	5,200

LEVY RESTAURANTS, INC.

980 N. Michigan Ave., Ste. 400
Chicago, IL 60611
Phone: 312-664-8200
Fax: 312-280-2739
Web: www.levyrestaurants.com

CEO: Andrew J. (Andy) Lansing
CFO: Bob Seiffert
HR: Cindy Noble
FYE: December 31
Type: Subsidiary

This company's menu of operations feeds people out on the town and at the game. Levy Restaurants is a leading restaurant operator and contract foodservices provider. Its fine dining spots, found mostly in Chicago, include Bistro 110, Fulton's on the River, and Spiaggia. Most of the company's business, though, comes from running foodservice operations at more than 75 sports stadiums, convention centers, and race tracks, including Churchill Downs (Louisville, Kentucky), Lambeau Field (Green Bay, Wisconsin), and Wrigley Field (Chicago). Levy Restaurants also runs dining locations at Walt Disney's Disney World resort and theme park in Orlando. The company is a subsidiary of UK-based Compass Group.

LEVI STRAUSS & CO.

1155 Battery St.
San Francisco, CA 94111
Phone: 415-501-6000
Fax: 415-501-7112
Web: www.levistrauss.com

CEO: R. John Anderson
CFO: Blake J. Jorgensen
HR: Cathleen L. Unruh
FYE: November 30
Type: Private

Levi Strauss & Co. (LS&CO.) strives to provide the world's casual workday wardrobe, inside and out. LS&CO., a top manufacturer of brand-name clothing globally, sells jeans and sportswear under the Levi's, Dockers, and Levi Strauss Signature names in more than 110 countries. It also markets men's and women's underwear and loungewear. Levi's jeans — department store staples — were once the uniform of American youth, but LS&CO. has been working to reconnect with the niche and expand outside the US. It has transformed its products portfolio to include wrinkle-free and stain-resistant fabrics used in making some of its Levi's and Dockers slacks. The Haas family (relatives of founder Levi Strauss) owns LS&CO.

	Annual Growth	11/04	11/05	11/06	11/07	11/08
Sales ($ mil.)	1.4%	4,072.5	4,125.2	4,106.6	4,266.1	4,303.1
Net income ($ mil.)	65.7%	30.4	155.9	239.0	460.4	229.3
Employees	6.5%	8,850	9,635	10,680	11,550	11,400

LEXICON PHARMACEUTICALS, INC

NASDAQ (GM): LXRX

8800 Technology Forest Place
The Woodlands, TX 77381
Phone: 281-863-3000
Fax: 281-863-8088
Web: www.lexpharma.com

CEO: Arthur T. Sands
CFO: James F. Tessmer
HR: Mary McKinney
FYE: December 31
Type: Public

Lexicon Pharmaceuticals works with some of the biggest words in the dictionary — words like deoxyribonucleic acid. The drug development company is focused on a handful of candidates in clinical and pre-clinical research, identified by its gene knockout technology. Its leading candidates include LX1031 for irritable bowel syndrome and LX1032 for carcinoid syndrome. Other products in its pipeline include potential treatments for rheumatoid arthritis, diabetes, and glaucoma. The company got its start with the development of knockout mice — mice whose DNA has been modified to disrupt, or "knock out" certain gene functions — to study the potential effects of drugs on various genetic targets.

	Annual Growth	12/05	12/06	12/07	12/08	12/09
Sales ($ mil.)	(38.7%)	75.7	72.8	50.1	32.3	10.7
Net income ($ mil.)	—	(36.3)	(54.3)	(58.8)	(76.9)	(82.8)
Market value ($ mil.)	(17.4%)	1,231.5	1,218.0	1,022.3	472.4	573.6
Employees	(17.8%)	755	585	550	347	345

LEXINGTON HOME BRANDS

1300 National Highway
Thomasville, NC 27360
Phone: 336-474-5300
Fax: 336-474-5491
Web: www.lexington.com

CEO: Philip D. (Phil) Haney
CFO: Craig Spooner
HR: Chris Little
FYE: December 31
Type: Private

Lexington Home Brands wants to outfit your abode in high style. The company makes and markets upscale upholstered, leather, wooden, and wicker furniture for the bedroom, dining room, and living room. Lexington's portfolio of brands includes Bob Timberlake, Lexington, and Tommy Bahama Home. It also produces collections inspired by professional golfer Arnold Palmer and real estate mogul and reality TV personality Donald Trump. Lexington's wares are sold through independent home furnishings retailers, department stores, galleries, and designer showrooms in the US, Mexico, India, and other countries. Founded in 1901, the furniture maker is owned by the private equity firm Sun Capital Partners.

LEXINGTON INSURANCE COMPANY

100 Summer St.
Boston, MA 02110
Phone: 617-330-1100
Fax: 617-951-0067
Web: www.lexingtoninsurance.com

CEO: Peter J. Eastwood
CFO: —
HR: —
FYE: December 31
Type: Subsidiary

Business itself can be a tricky business, but Lexington Insurance wants to reduce the risk. Lexington Insurance provides commercial property/casualty insurance and risk management services. The company also offers specialty coverages that include boiler and machinery, professional liability, inland marine, and terrorism coverage. The company caters to clients with unusual or high-risk coverage needs. Its products are distributed through surplus (specialty insurance) brokers. Lexington Insurance is a subsidiary of American International Group (AIG), and has been placed within its Chartis group.

	Annual Growth	12/04	12/05	12/06	12/07	12/08
Est. sales ($ mil.)	—	—	—	—	—	3,797.6
Employees	—	—	—	—	—	312

LEXINGTON PRECISION CORPORATION

Pink Sheets: LEXPQ

800 3rd. Ave
New York, NY 10022
Phone: 212-319-4657
Fax: 212-319-4659
Web: www.lexingtonprecision.com

CEO: Warren Delano
CFO: Dennis J. Welhouse
HR: —
FYE: December 31
Type: Public

Lexington Precision may be wired to the auto industry, but it has injected itself into the medical industry as well. The company makes rubber and metal component parts used mostly in automotive and medical applications. Lexington Precision's Rubber Group manufactures rubber components such as rubber wire seals and insulators for ignition wiring, as well as rubber parts for medical products such as syringes and catheters. The company's Metals Group produces machined aluminum, brass, and steel components. Lexington Precision filed for Chapter 11 protection from creditors in April 2008.

	Annual Growth	12/04	12/05	12/06	12/07	*12/08
Sales ($ mil.)	(9.8%)	110.4	96.8	87.9	88.4	73.0
Net income ($ mil.)	—	1.6	(3.8)	(7.3)	(7.0)	(10.3)
Market value ($ mil.)	(29.3%)	3.0	3.5	2.1	1.3	0.8
Employees	(16.2%)	978	797	706	666	482

*Most recent year available

LEXINGTON REALTY TRUST

NYSE: LXP

1 Penn Plaza, Ste. 4015
New York, NY 10119
Phone: 212-692-7200
Fax: 212-594-6600
Web: www.lxp.com

CEO: T. Wilson Eglin
CFO: Patrick Carroll
HR: Lisa Soares
FYE: December 31
Type: Public

Lexington Realty Trust (formerly Lexington Corporate Properties Trust) lays down the law when it comes to commercial real estate. The self-managed real estate investment trust (REIT) owns interests in more than 200 single-tenant commercial properties throughout some 40 US states and the Netherlands. Its properties include offices, warehouses, manufacturing facilities, and retail sites totaling approximately 38 million sq. ft. of rentable space. Most properties are rented under triple net leases, in which tenants are responsible for expenses such as real estate taxes and repairs. Prominent clients include Bank of America, Dana Holding, and Food Lion.

	Annual Growth	12/05	12/06	12/07	12/08	12/09
Sales ($ mil.)	17.6%	197.1	207.4	431.7	441.2	376.6
Net income ($ mil.)	—	32.7	7.8	76.9	8.5	(211.3)
Market value ($ mil.)	(26.9%)	2,848.9	2,998.7	1,944.8	668.8	813.2
Employees	3.2%	52	56	65	65	59

LEXISNEXIS GROUP

9443 Springboro Pike
Dayton, OH 45342
Phone: 937-865-6800
Fax: 937-847-3090
Web: www.lexisnexis.com

CEO: Andrew (Andy) Prozes
CFO: Carolyn Ullerick
HR: Robert Rigby-Hall
FYE: December 31
Type: Subsidiary

Users in more than 100 countries count on LexisNexis Group to flex its information muscle. A unit of publishing giant Reed Elsevier Group, the company offers subscribers access to thousands of sources — including newspaper, magazine, and journal articles, and public records — through the Internet, CD-ROMs, and books. The bulk of its content focuses on legal, tax, business, government, academic, and risk management information. The company's flagship legal research service, Lexis.com, offers online access to legal documents from some 45,000 sources. LexisNexis launched the Nexis news and business information research service in 1980; the company became part of Reed Elsevier Group in 1994.

LEXMARK INTERNATIONAL, INC.

NYSE: LXK

740 W. New Circle Rd.
Lexington, KY 40550
Phone: 859-232-2000
Fax: 859-232-2403
Web: www.lexmark.com

CEO: Paul J. Curlander
CFO: John W. Gamble Jr.
HR: Jeri L. Isbell
FYE: December 31
Type: Public

Lexmark International attacks printing with a host of jets and lasers. A leading maker of printers and related supplies, the company provides color, monochrome, and multifunction laser printers; color and multifunction ink jet printers; dot matrix printers; and ink cartridges. Lexmark markets to customers ranging from individual consumers to large organizations in the financial services, government, health care, manufacturing, and retail sectors. It sells its products in more than 150 countries through distributors, resellers, and retailers; Lexmark also sells its products through partnerships with other equipment vendors. The company gets more than half of its sales outside the US.

	Annual Growth	12/05	12/06	12/07	12/08	12/09
Sales ($ mil.)	(7.2%)	5,221.5	5,108.1	4,973.9	4,528.4	3,879.9
Net income ($ mil.)	(20.0%)	356.3	338.4	300.8	240.2	145.9
Market value ($ mil.)	(12.7%)	3,519.2	5,746.3	2,736.6	2,111.7	2,039.5
Employees	(3.3%)	13,600	14,900	13,800	14,000	11,900

An in-depth profile of this company is available to Hoover's Online members at hoovers.com.

LFP, INC.

8484 Wilshire Blvd., Ste. 900
Beverly Hills, CA 90211
Phone: 323-651-5400
Fax: 323-651-3525
Web: hustler.com

CEO: Larry Flynt
CFO: —
HR: Steve Shaw
FYE: December 31
Type: Private

The founding fathers probably never imagined anything like this company when they wrote the First Amendment. LFP (which also does business as Larry Flynt Publications) runs the adult entertainment empire owned by infamous porn purveyor Larry Flynt, including his flagship magazine *Hustler*. The company's publishing portfolio includes two additional magazine titles (*Barely Legal* and *Taboo*). LFP also produces and distributes adult videos (through its Hustler Video), and has a number of adult websites. In addition, the company runs about ten Hustler Hollywood retail stores. Flynt started publishing *Hustler* magazine in 1974 and founded Larry Flynt Publications two years later.

LG ELECTRONICS MOBILECOMM U.S.A., INC.

10101 Old Grove Rd.
San Diego, CA 92131
Phone: 858-635-5300
Fax: 858-635-5225
Web: us.lge.com/about/company/us_mobile.jsp

CEO: Jeff Hwang
CFO: —
HR: —
FYE: December 31
Type: Subsidiary

LG Electronics Mobilecomm USA sums it up pretty well: the company, which also operates as LG Mobile Phones, manufactures and markets mobile phones and related accessories. The company also provides sales and marketing support in North America for its parent company, LG Electronics, a Korea-based manufacturer of consumers electronics, information technology, and communications products. LG Mobile Phones also has marketing partnerships with wireless carriers, including AT&T Mobility, Verizon, and US Cellular, as well as retail outlets such as Best Buy.

THE LGL GROUP, INC.

NYSE Amex: LGL

2525 Shader Rd.
Orlando, FL 32804
Phone: 407-298-2000
Fax: 407-293-2979
Web: www.lynchcorp.com

CEO: Greg P. Anderson
CFO: Howard D. Castle
HR: —
FYE: December 31
Type: Public

The LGL Group is hoping that one isn't the loneliest number. Previously made up of two separate businesses, the company has a sole remaining line of business: its MtronPTI subsidiary, which produces frequency control devices, such as crystals and oscillators, used primarily in communications equipment. MtronPTI was formed in the 2004 merger of M-tron Industries and Piezo Technology, Inc. In 2007 The LGL Group sold certain assets of its unprofitable Lynch Systems subsidiary for about $3 million. The company gets the majority of its sales from outside the US.

	Annual Growth	12/05	12/06	12/07	12/08	12/09
Sales ($ mil.)	(9.3%)	46.2	49.3	39.5	40.2	31.3
Net income ($ mil.)	—	1.2	0.9	(2.6)	(1.3)	(2.5)
Market value ($ mil.)	(20.5%)	18.4	15.6	15.2	4.4	7.3
Employees	(11.5%)	355	386	303	280	218

LHC GROUP, INC.

NASDAQ (GM): LHCG

420 W. Pinhook Rd., Ste. A
Lafayette, LA 70503
Phone: 337-233-1307
Fax: 337-235-8037
Web: www.lhcgroup.com

CEO: Keith G. Myers
CFO: Peter J. (Pete) Roman
HR: Lolanda B. Brown
FYE: December 31
Type: Public

LHC Group operates care facilities and provides home health care services to rural markets in select US regions. The company's some 230 home health nursing agencies provide care to Medicare beneficiaries, offering such services as private duty nursing, physical therapy, and medically oriented social services. LHC also operates around 20 hospices that provide palliative care for terminal patients, as well as several long-term, acute-care hospital facilities (mostly within host hospitals) that serve patients who no longer need intensive care but still require complex care in a hospital setting. The company also operates a handful of rehabilitation, disease management, and other specialty health facilities.

	Annual Growth	12/05	12/06	12/07	12/08	12/09
Sales ($ mil.)	34.5%	162.5	215.2	298.0	383.3	532.0
Net income ($ mil.)	54.7%	10.1	20.6	19.6	30.2	57.8
Market value ($ mil.)	17.8%	327.5	535.6	469.3	676.3	631.4
Employees	19.6%	3,415	3,959	4,498	5,376	6,998

LIBBEY INC.

NYSE: LBY

300 Madison Ave.
Toledo, OH 43604
Phone: 419-325-2100
Fax: —
Web: www.libbey.com

CEO: John F. Meier
CFO: Gregory T. Geswein
HR: —
FYE: December 31
Type: Public

The sound of breaking glass is music to Libbey's ears. It signals potential sales for the firm, which is a leading maker and seller of glassware, tablewear, and flatware to the foodservice industry and to retailers in the US and Canada. Libbey's products are made in five countries and exported to more than 100 countries. Its brands include Libbey, Crisa, Royal Leerdam, and Traex, among others. Subsidiary World Tableware imports metal flatware, serveware and ceramic dinnerware for resale. Libbey owns Vitrocrisa, the largest Mexican glass tableware maker. Libbey was founded in 1818 as the New England Glass Company.

	Annual Growth	12/05	12/06	12/07	12/08	12/09
Sales ($ mil.)	7.1%	570.1	692.4	816.4	812.6	750.2
Net income ($ mil.)	—	(19.4)	(20.9)	(2.3)	(80.5)	(28.8)
Market value ($ mil.)	(7.0%)	165.2	199.4	256.0	20.2	123.6
Employees	18.3%	3,500	7,150	7,442	7,306	6,857

LIBERTY BANCORP, INC.

OTC: LBCP

16 W. Franklin St.
Liberty, MO 64068
Phone: 816-781-4822
Fax: 816-781-6851
Web: www.banklibertykc.com

CEO: Brent M. Giles
CFO: Marc J. Weishaar
HR: —
FYE: September 30
Type: Public

Liberty Bancorp was formed in 2006 to be the holding company for BankLiberty (formerly Liberty Savings Bank), which operates ten branches in the Kansas City area. It offers traditional deposit services such as checking and savings accounts, CDs, and IRAs, in addition to newfangled offerings like Internet banking, bill payment, and cash management services. Commercial real estate loans account for the largest portion of the company's loan portfolio (around 40%), followed by construction loans, mainly to custom homebuilders. However, citing depressed market conditions, the bank has decreased its volume of construction loans. It also offers business, residential real estate, and consumer loans.

	Annual Growth	9/05	9/06	9/07	9/08	9/09
Assets ($ mil.)	13.4%	237.6	287.6	333.2	336.2	392.4
Net income ($ mil.)	4.7%	1.5	1.5	1.9	1.9	1.8
Market value ($ mil.)	(9.8%)	—	36.8	38.6	32.4	27.0
Employees	10.7%	74	67	74	84	111

LIBERTY BELL BANK

NASDAQ (CM): LBBB

2099 Rte. 70 East
Cherry Hill, NJ 08003
Phone: 856-489-8401
Fax: 856-489-8405
Web: www.libertybellbank.com

CEO: Kevin L. Kutcher
CFO: Dennis Costa
HR: —
FYE: December 31
Type: Public

You won't find Liberty Bell Bank in Philadelphia, but rather across the Delaware River in South Jersey. It serves businesses and individuals from three branches in Cherry Hill, Evesham, Moorestown, and Mount Laurel. The bank offers traditional retail deposit products, including checking, savings, and money market accounts, and certificates of deposit. The bank's lending activities focus on area real estate; commercial mortgages account for the largest percentage of its loan portfolio, followed by one- to four-family residential mortgages. Business loans help to round out its portfolio.

	Annual Growth	12/06	12/07	12/08	12/09	12/10
Sales ($ mil.)	—	—	—	—	—	8.9
Net income ($ mil.)	—	—	—	—	—	(0.4)
Employees	—	—	—	—	—	39

LIBERTY CAPITAL GROUP

NASDAQ (GS): LCAPA

12300 Liberty Blvd.
Englewood, CO 80112
Phone: 720-875-5400
Fax: 720-875-7469
Web: www.libertymedia.com

CEO: Gregory B. (Greg) Maffei
CFO: Christopher W. (Chris) Shean
HR: —
FYE: December 31
Type: Public

Liberty Capital Group is a tracking stock of Liberty Media, a holding company controlled by John Malone with interests in media, retail, and telecommunications. Liberty Capital includes holdings related to cable television programming and telecommunications services, including Starz Media (media production and distribution) and TruePosition (wireless positioning applications). Liberty Capital also owns the Atlanta Braves professional baseball team, as well as stakes in SIRIUS XM Radio, Time Warner, and Sprint Nextel Corporation. Liberty Capital, formed in 2006, operates alongside two other Liberty Media tracking stocks: Liberty Interactive Group and Liberty Starz (formerly Liberty Entertainment).

	Annual Growth	12/05	12/06	12/07	12/08	12/09
Sales ($ mil.)	(18.3%)	1,459.0	1,287.0	1,621.0	617.0	649.0
Net income ($ mil.)	—	(362.0)	331.0	1,673.0	(590.0)	127.0
Market value ($ mil.)	6.8%	—	1,868.4	2,221.4	449.1	2,276.9
Employees	—	—	—	—	—	23,073

LIBERTY DIVERSIFIED INDUSTRIES INC.

5600 N. Hwy. 169
New Hope, MN 55428
Phone: 763-536-6600
Fax: 763-536-6685
Web: www.libertydiversified.com

CEO: Michael (Mike) Fiterman
CFO: Steve Richardson
HR: —
FYE: May 31
Type: Private

Freedom means — among many things — diversity; Liberty Diversified Industries (LDI) pushes just that, worldwide! It designs, manufactures, markets, and distributes corrugated paper, plastic, and metal packaging, through businesses Diversi-Plast, Liberty Carton, Presentation Packaging (specialty displays), Liberty Paper (recycled containers), and material handling equipment maker Valley Craft. The LDI family includes office storage supplier, SAFCO, Ergolet, a lift maker for the elderly, and LDI Transport, a 200-plus trailer fleet. LDI also owns Milltronics CNC (computer numerically controlled) Machines, and high-speed machine maker Takumi. Family-owned, LDI is led by its founder's grandson, CEO Mike Fiterman.

	Annual Growth	5/04	5/05	5/06	5/07	5/08
Est. sales ($ mil.)	—	—	—	—	—	219.0
Employees	—	—	—	—	—	1,820

LIBERTY GLOBAL, INC.

NASDAQ (GS): LBTYA

12300 Liberty Blvd.
Englewood, CO 80112
Phone: 303-220-6600
Fax: 303-220-6601
Web: www.lgi.com

CEO: Michael T. (Mike) Fries
CFO: Charles H. R. (Charlie) Bracken
HR: Amy M. Blair
FYE: December 31
Type: Public

Liberty Global may call the US home, but most of its subscribers enjoy the company's services from international living rooms. Through its operating subsidiaries, the company provides cable TV programming and content distribution, telephone service, and Internet access to more than 16 million subscribers in 15 European, Asian, and Latin American countries. Its core market is western Europe, where it does more than half of its business through subsidiary UPC Holding, and in Belgium, through a controlling stake in Telenet Holding. Chellomedia is the company's European programming business; the company also offers satellite TV in select markets.

	Annual Growth	12/05	12/06	12/07	12/08	12/09
Sales ($ mil.)	21.1%	5,151.3	6,487.5	9,003.3	10,561.1	11,080.2
Net income ($ mil.)	—	(80.1)	706.2	(422.6)	(788.9)	14.1
Market value ($ mil.)	(0.7%)	5,891.5	7,632.8	10,261.7	4,168.6	5,731.8
Employees	1.6%	21,600	20,500	22,000	22,300	23,000

LIBERTY HOMES, INC.

Pink Sheets: LIBHA

1101 Eisenhower Dr. North
Goshen, IN 46526
Phone: 574-533-0431
Fax: 574-533-0438
Web: www.libertyhomesinc.com

CEO: Edward J. Hussey
CFO: Marc A. Dosmann
HR: Brian L. Christner
FYE: December 31
Type: Public

Liberty Homes gives home buyers the freedom to move about the land. The company builds modular homes for the US and Canada from seven manufacturing facilities. The company's floor plans range from two to five bedrooms and cost from $35,000 to about $125,000. Options include kitchen islands, utility rooms, and front porches. The company builds homes under the Liberty Homes, Waverlee Homes, and Badger Built Homes brand names. Independent dealers and company-owned retail centers sell the company's products. CEO Edward Hussey and his family control Liberty Homes.

LIBERTY INTERACTIVE GROUP

NASDAQ (GS): LINTA

12300 Liberty Blvd.
Englewood, CO 80112
Phone: 720-875-5400
Fax: 720-875-7469
Web: www.libertymedia.com

CEO: Gregory B. (Greg) Maffei
CFO: Christopher W. (Chris) Shean
HR: —
FYE: December 31
Type: Public

Liberty Interactive Group stands by your right to shop from home and online. One of three tracking stocks of Liberty Media, it includes home shopping network QVC, perishable goods e-tailer Provide Commerce (Proflowers.com), and online costume shop Buyseasons. Liberty Interactive also owns a stake in Barry Diller's Internet conglomerate IAC/InterActiveCorp, QVC rival HSN, as well as several companies IAC/InterActiveCorp spun off in 2008. Liberty Media spun off Liberty Interactive in 2006 along with Liberty Capital, a similar tracking stock that includes Starz Media, True Position, and the Atlanta Braves baseball team. (A third tracking stock, Liberty Starz, formerly Liberty Entertainment, was created in 2008.)

	Annual Growth	12/05	12/06	12/07	12/08	12/09
Sales ($ mil.)	6.3%	6,501.0	7,326.0	7,802.0	8,079.0	8,305.0
Net income ($ mil.)	(0.1%)	298.0	598.0	441.0	(781.0)	297.0
Market value ($ mil.)	(20.5%)	—	12,884.9	11,397.5	1,863.7	6,475.3
Employees	—	—	—	—	—	23,073

An in-depth profile of this company is available to Hoover's Online members at hoovers.com.

935

LIBERTY MEDIA CORPORATION

12300 Liberty Blvd.	CEO: Gregory B. (Greg) Maffei
Englewood, CO 80112	CFO: David J. A. Flowers
Phone: 720-875-5400	HR: —
Fax: 720-875-5401	FYE: December 31
Web: www.libertymedia.com	Type: Holding company

Liberty Media takes the liberty of arranging its varied businesses as it pleases. The holding company comprises publicly traded Liberty Capital Group, Liberty Starz (formerly Liberty Entertainment), and Liberty Interactive Group. The arrangement effectively splits the fast-growing video and online commerce operations and the company's less robust telecommunications and entertainment businesses. Liberty Media's biggest holding, the QVC home-shopping network, falls under the Liberty Interactive umbrella, as does e-tailer Provide Commerce. Movie producer and distributor Starz Media and the Atlanta Braves both belong to Liberty Capital. In 2009 the company spun off most of its Liberty Entertainment unit, merging it with DIRECTV.

	Annual Growth	12/04	12/05	12/06	12/07	12/08
Est. sales ($ mil.)	—	—	—	—	—	10,084.0
Employees	—	—	—	—	—	22,075

LIBERTY MUTUAL HOLDING COMPANY INC.

175 Berkeley St.	CEO: Edmund F. (Ted) Kelly
Boston, MA 02116	CFO: Dennis J. Langwell
Phone: 617-357-9500	HR: Helen E. R. Sayles
Fax: 617-350-7648	FYE: December 31
Web: www.libertymutual.com	Type: Mutual company

Boston boasts of baked beans, the Red Sox, and the Liberty Mutual Group. Liberty Mutual Holding is the parent company for the Liberty Mutual Group and its operating subsidiaries. Liberty Mutual is one of the top property/casualty insurers in the US and among the top 10 providers of automobile insurance. The company also offers homeowners' insurance and commercial lines for small to large companies. Liberty Mutual Group operates through four business divisions: Personal Markets, Commercial Markets, Agency Markets, and Liberty International. It distributes its products through a diversified blend of independent and exclusive agents, brokers, and direct sales.

	Annual Growth	12/04	12/05	12/06	12/07	12/08
Assets ($ mil.)	9.6%	72,359.0	78,824.0	85,498.0	94,679.0	104,300.0
Net income ($ mil.)	(2.2%)	1,245.0	1,027.0	1,626.0	1,518.0	1,140.0
Employees	4.3%	38,000	39,000	39,000	41,000	45,000

LIBERTY NATIONAL LIFE INSURANCE COMPANY

2001 3rd Ave. South	CEO: Anthony L. McWhorter
Birmingham, AL 35233	CFO: Danny H. Almond
Phone: 205-325-4200	HR: Patricia Herring
Fax: 205-325-4198	FYE: December 31
Web: www.libnat.com	Type: Subsidiary

Liberty National Life Insurance certainly carries a torch for financial security. The flagship subsidiary of Torchmark provides life and supplemental health insurance products throughout the US. Its products are targeted at middle-income families. It also sells directly to individuals and through workplace plans, using thousands of agents and more than 200 branch offices located in the majority of US states, with the exception of the most northern portions of the country. Liberty National Life Insurance's health insurance offerings include coverage for cancer and critical illness, hospital intensive care, and accident protection. Its life insurance offerings include group and whole life coverage.

	Annual Growth	12/04	12/05	12/06	12/07	12/08
Est. sales ($ mil.)	—	—	—	—	—	906.7
Employees	—	—	—	—	—	1,090

LIBERTY PROPERTY TRUST

	NYSE: LRY
Great Valley Corporate Center, 500 Chesterfield Pkwy.	CEO: William P. Hankowsky
Malvern, PA 19355	CFO: George J. Alburger Jr.
Phone: 610-648-1700	HR: Caren P. Hosansky
Fax: 610-644-4129	FYE: December 31
Web: www.libertyproperty.com	Type: Public

There's the "Land of the Free" but no such thing as "free land" to Liberty Property Trust. The self-managed real estate investment trust (REIT) owns leases, manages, and has interests in about 350 office buildings and more than 400 industrial properties, including distribution, warehouse, light manufacturing, and research and development facilities. The company's properties encompass more than 70 million sq. ft. of space, mainly in the mid-Atlantic, southeast, and midwest regions of the US. The Vanguard Group and GlaxoSmithKline are the REIT's top tenants.

	Annual Growth	12/05	12/06	12/07	12/08	12/09
Sales ($ mil.)	2.3%	680.7	666.7	698.7	748.5	744.3
Net income ($ mil.)	(25.0%)	249.4	266.6	164.8	151.9	79.0
Market value ($ mil.)	(7.0%)	4,852.7	5,565.0	3,262.7	2,585.4	3,625.1
Employees	(0.1%)	470	474	488	481	469

LIBERTY STARZ

	NASDAQ (GS): LSTZA
12300 Liberty Blvd.	CEO: Gregory B. (Greg) Maffei
Englewood, CO 80112	CFO: Christopher W. (Chris) Shean
Phone: 720-875-5400	HR: —
Fax: 720-875-7469	FYE: December 31
Web: www.libertymedia.com	Type: Public

Liberty Starz (formerly Liberty Entertainment) is a tracking stock of Liberty Media that includes Starz Entertainment, a leading pay-TV operator with about 15 cable movie channels branded under the Encore and Starz banners. Encore reaches about 30 million US homes, while the Starz channels boast more than 16 million subscribers. Other business assets attributed to the Liberty Starz tracking stock include online fantasy sports sites Fanball and PicksPal. Liberty Media is a holding company controlled by John Malone with interests in telecommunications, cable television, online media, and retailing.

	Annual Growth	12/05	12/06	12/07	12/08	12/09
Sales ($ mil.)	11.8%	6,501.0	7,326.0	7,802.0	10,084.0	10,158.0
Net income ($ mil.)	116.1%	298.0	598.0	441.0	3,479.0	6,501.0
Employees	14.0%	13,660	14,700	19,000	22,075	23,075

LIBERTY TRAVEL, INC.

69 Spring St.	CEO: Billy McDonough
Ramsey, NJ 07446	CFO: —
Phone: 201-934-3500	HR: —
Fax: 201-934-3651	FYE: December 31
Web: www.libertytravel.com	Type: Private

Give me liberty, or give me . . . travel? Liberty Travel gives you both. The company offers leisure and corporate travel services to consumers mainly in the Northeast and Florida. Travel agents can book customized land-only and air-inclusive travel packages through Liberty's wholesale travel business GOGO Worldwide Vacations, which has almost 45 offices in about 20 states. From its more than 200 offices, Liberty offers trips including Colorado Rockies ski excursions, Alaskan cruises, and family vacations to Walt Disney World. The company was founded in 1951 and was acquired by Australian-based travel agency Flight Centre in early 2008 for about $135 million.

LICT CORPORATION

Pink Sheets: LICT

401 Theodore Fremd Ave.
Rye, NY 10580
Phone: 914-921-8821
Fax: 914-921-6410
Web: www.lictcorp.com

CEO: Robert E. Dolan
CFO: Robert E. Dolan
HR: —
FYE: December 31
Type: Public

LICT (formerly Lynch Interactive) is a holding company that operates through 12 small (mostly rural) local-exchange phone companies located primarily in the Midwestern and Western US; it also has a limited presence in the Northeast. The company provides local telephone service over nearly 60,000 access lines while dial-up and broadband Internet service lines number about 50,000. Subsidiaries include JBN Telephone, Haviland Telephone, and Giant Communications in Kansas; CentraCom Interactive in Utah; and Bretton Woods Telephone in New Hampshire. Chairman Mario Gabelli owns 24% of LICT.

LIEBERT CORPORATION

1050 Dearborn Dr.
Columbus, OH 43085
Phone: 614-841-6700
Fax: 614-841-6022
Web: www.liebert.com

CEO: Robert P. (Bob) Bauer
CFO: —
HR: —
FYE: September 30
Type: Subsidiary

Liebert keeps its cool in the face of a power meltdown. The company designs, makes and markets surge suppressors, uninterruptable power supply (UPS) units, precision cooling equipment, enclosures, and monitoring equipment that protect and support IT environments. Its products are used by companies in the communications, government, industrial, and utilities sectors. Liebert, which also provides support services, sells directly and through independent and factory-direct representatives, distributors, and resellers. Customers include BancaPromex, Bruker Instruments, and SunTrust Service Corp. Founded in 1965, Liebert operates as a subsidiary of the Emerson Network Power Company, a segment of Emerson Electric.

LIFE CARE CENTERS OF AMERICA

3570 Keith St. NW
Cleveland, TN 37312
Phone: 423-472-9585
Fax: 423-476-5974
Web: www.lcca.com

CEO: Beecher Hunter
CFO: Steve Ziegler
HR: Jennie McClaren
FYE: December 31
Type: Private

If you or a loved one has reached the Golden Age of retirement, there's a good chance Life Care Centers of America offers a service you can use. The company is a privately owned operator of more than 200 retirement and health care centers in 28 states. Its offerings include retirement communities, assisted-living facilities, and nursing homes (and even some campuses that provide all three in a continuum of care). In addition, Life Care operates centers specifically for people with Alzheimer's disease or related dementia. Some of Life Care's specialized services include home health care, adult day care, hospice, and wound care. Founder Forrest Preston opened his first center in 1970.

	Annual Growth	12/04	12/05	12/06	12/07	12/08
Sales ($ mil.)	6.2%	1,800.0	1,957.0	2,050.0	2,120.0	2,290.0
Employees	(6.2%)	40,000	30,000	30,000	31,153	31,000

LIFE INSURANCE COMPANY OF NORTH AMERICA

2 Liberty Place, 1601 Chestnut St.
Philadelphia, PA 19192
Phone: 215-761-1000
Fax: 215-761-5004

CEO: H. Edward (Ed) Hanway
CFO: —
HR: —
FYE: December 31
Type: Subsidiary

CIGNA, the parent company of Life Insurance Company of North America (LINA), is sort of like the old woman who lived in a shoe. You know, she had so many children she didn't know what to do? Life Insurance Company of North America is one of CIGNA's many, many children. The subsidiary offers group life, accident, and disability insurance. LINA was formed in 1956 by Insurance Company of North America (INA), a CIGNA predecessor company. Philadelphia-based CIGNA is one of the top health insurers in North America, with medical plans covering nearly 12 million people.

	Annual Growth	12/04	12/05	12/06	12/07	12/08
Est. sales ($ mil.)	—	—	—	—	—	1,933.4
Employees	—	—	—	—	—	1,500

THE LIFE IS GOOD COMPANY

283 Newbury St.
Boston, MA 02115
Phone: 617-266-4160
Fax: 617-266-4260
Web: www.lifeisgood.com

CEO: Bert Jacobs
CFO: Bob Romano
HR: Stephanie Manners
FYE: December 31
Type: Private

Life certainly sounds good for brothers Bert and John Jacobs, who went from living in their van and subsisting on peanut butter and jelly sandwiches to running a $100-million-plus company in just a few short years. The Life is good co-founders sold T-shirts to college students up and down the East Coast before creating the firm's stick-figure mascot, Jake. Life is good got its official start in 1994 and, today, the unconventional company sells casual apparel (T-shirts, lounge pants, boxers) and accessories, caps, backpacks, jewelry, pet gear, and home goods through a handful of company stores, its website, and through some 4,500 specialty and sporting goods stores in the US and more than 25 other countries.

LIFE PARTNERS HOLDINGS, INC.

NASDAQ (GM): LPHI

204 Woodhew
Waco, TX 76712
Phone: 254-751-7797
Fax: 254-751-1025
Web: www.lphi.net

CEO: Brian D. Pardo
CFO: David M. Martin
HR: —
FYE: February 28
Type: Public

Life Partners Holdings, parent company of Life Partners, Inc., makes its bucks by helping its customers make a buck. The company facilitates viatical and life settlement transactions, in which an institution or wealthy investor purchases individual life insurance policies (at a discount) and becomes the beneficiary of those policies when they mature. Viatical settlements involve terminally ill policyholders with only a couple of years to live; life settlement transactions involve sellers with longer life expectancies. Life Partners makes its money from fees earned by facilitating viatical and life settlements.

	Annual Growth	2/06	2/07	2/08	2/09	2/10
Assets ($ mil.)	56.9%	12.0	16.6	31.9	52.4	72.7
Net income ($ mil.)	127.4%	1.1	3.4	18.8	27.2	29.4
Market value ($ mil.)	53.8%	54.7	95.9	178.9	254.2	305.8
Employees	13.8%	37	37	40	56	62

An in-depth profile of this company is available to Hoover's Online members at hoovers.com.

937

LIFE QUOTES, INC.

NASDAQ (CM): QUOT

8205 S. Cass Ave., Ste. 102
Darien, IL 60561
Phone: 630-515-0170
Fax: 630-515-0270
Web: www.lifequotes.com

CEO: Robert S. Bland
CFO: Phillip A. Perillo
HR: —
FYE: December 31
Type: Public

No pithy or inspirational sentiments here, Life Quotes is in the insurance business. Formerly known as Insure.com, the company offers comparative shopping for insurance products from more than a dozen carriers through its Life Quotes and Consumer Insurance Guide brands. Life Quotes provides information on personal and commercial life and property/casualty insurance coverage. The company earns commissions on the policies it sells through its website and, for some lines of insurance, receives fees for passing on qualified leads to insurance companies. CEO Robert Bland owns a controlling stake in Life Quotes and is working to acquire the remaining shares.

	Annual Growth	12/05	12/06	12/07	12/08	12/09
Sales ($ mil.)	(3.7%)	17.1	17.2	18.0	15.7	14.7
Net income ($ mil.)	—	(4.9)	(3.6)	(0.2)	(1.0)	14.2
Market value ($ mil.)	0.0%	20.3	26.4	27.1	19.1	20.3
Employees	1.7%	99	108	107	151	106

LIFE SCIENCES RESEARCH INC.

NYSE Arca: LSR

Mettlers Road
East Millstone, NJ 08875
Phone: 201-525-1819
Fax: —
Web: www.lsrinc.net

CEO: Andrew H. Baker
CFO: Richard A. Michaelson
HR: —
FYE: December 31
Type: Public

Life Sciences Research stands ready to test everything that humans, animals, and the environment eat, use, and are exposed to. The contract research organization (CRO) performs safety and efficacy tests on pharmaceutical and chemical compounds used in products being developed by drug, agricultural, industrial, and veterinary companies. Life Sciences Research and its subsidiaries provide both large and start-up drugmaker clients worldwide with toxicology, metabolism, and stability studies for preclinical candidates that are applying for product approval. The company was taken private in 2009 after being acquired by Lion Holdings.

LIFE TECHNOLOGIES CORPORATION

NASDAQ (GS): LIFE

5791 Van Allen Way
Carlsbad, CA 92008
Phone: 760-603-7200
Fax: 760-602-6500
Web: www.lifetechnologies.com

CEO: Gregory T. (Greg) Lucier
CFO: David F. Hoffmeister
HR: Peter M. Leddy
FYE: December 31
Type: Public

Need to make a quick clone? Life Technologies (formerly Invitrogen) makes instrument systems, reagents, software, and other laboratory products that speed up and simplify gene cloning, expression, and analysis. Its products are also used to advance personalized (gene-based) medicine and environmental research. Life Technologies' broad product lineup includes cloning kits, chemical reagents, and cell culture products, as well as mass spectrometry systems and laboratory software. The company operates in more than 100 countries around the world, serving life sciences researchers, drugmakers, and other customers in the forensics, biosecurity, food testing, and agricultural industries.

	Annual Growth	12/05	12/06	12/07	12/08	12/09
Sales ($ mil.)	28.6%	1,198.5	1,263.5	1,281.7	1,620.3	3,280.3
Net income ($ mil.)	2.3%	132.0	(191.0)	143.2	31.3	144.6
Market value ($ mil.)	11.9%	6,025.2	5,116.5	8,445.5	4,215.1	9,442.8
Employees	(27.9%)	4,800	4,835	4,300	9,700	1,300

LIFE TIME FITNESS, INC.

NYSE: LTM

2902 Corporate Place
Chanhassen, MN 55317
Phone: 952-947-0000
Fax: 952-947-9137
Web: www.lifetimefitness.com

CEO: Bahram Akradi
CFO: Michael R. (Mike) Robinson
HR: —
FYE: December 31
Type: Public

Life Time Fitness wants to help you keep your New Year's resolutions. The company operates more than 85 exercise and recreation centers in some 20 states, including Illinois, Indiana, Michigan, Texas, and Virginia. Life Time Fitness facilities offer swimming pools, basketball and racquet courts, child care centers, spas, dining services, and climbing walls, in addition to some 400 pieces of exercise equipment. Most facilities are open 24 hours a day, seven days a week, and average about 100,000 sq. ft. in size. They target a membership of about 5,500 to 11,500, and are designed to serve as an all-in-one sports and athletic club, professional fitness facility, family recreation center, and spa and resort.

	Annual Growth	12/05	12/06	12/07	12/08	12/09
Sales ($ mil.)	21.0%	390.1	511.9	655.8	769.6	837.0
Net income ($ mil.)	15.1%	41.2	50.6	68.0	71.8	72.4
Market value ($ mil.)	(10.1%)	1,590.4	2,025.4	2,074.3	540.7	1,040.9
Employees	16.3%	9,500	12,350	15,000	16,700	17,400

LIFECELL CORPORATION

1 Millennium Way
Branchburg, NJ 08876
Phone: 908-947-1100
Fax: 908-947-1200
Web: www.lifecell.com

CEO: Lisa N. Colleran
CFO: Steven T. Sobieski
HR: —
FYE: December 31
Type: Subsidiary

LifeCell puts new life into the tissue graft market. The firm makes skin graft materials processed from cadaver skin, a category of products known as allografts. Its products include AlloDerm, used in reconstructive plastic, dental, and burn surgeries and Strattice Reconstructive Tissue Matrix, for plastic and reconstructive surgery and wound healing. LifeCell markets a series of other products for additional applications, including one called Cymetra for grafting and head and neck plastic reconstruction. The company markets its products in the US and abroad through a direct sales force and distributors, including Stryker and Boston Scientific. LifeCell is owned by wound care company Kinetic Concepts.

LIFEPOINT HOSPITALS, INC.

NASDAQ (GS): LPNT

103 Powell Ct., Ste. 200
Brentwood, TN 37027
Phone: 615-372-8500
Fax: 615-372-8575
Web: www.lifepointhospitals.com

CEO: William F. (Bill) Carpenter III
CFO: Jeffrey S. (Jeff) Sherman
HR: Todd Wiltsie
FYE: December 31
Type: Public

Folks who get sick in the country but are sick of the city can go to one of LifePoint's hospitals. The company, a spinoff of hospital giant HCA, operates some 50 hospitals (with about 6,000 total beds) that are located in non-urban areas where they are, in most cases, the only available acute care facilities. LifePoint's hospitals are located in 17 states, with the heaviest concentrations in Alabama, Kentucky, Louisiana, New Mexico, and Virginia. The company participates in the HealthTrust Purchasing Group, a group purchasing organization that negotiates competitive contracts on medical supplies and equipment.

	Annual Growth	12/05	12/06	12/07	12/08	12/09
Sales ($ mil.)	12.4%	1,855.1	2,439.7	2,630.1	2,700.8	2,962.7
Net income ($ mil.)	17.0%	72.9	145.5	102.0	114.5	136.6
Market value ($ mil.)	(3.5%)	2,073.0	1,863.0	1,644.1	1,262.6	1,798.3
Employees	3.7%	19,000	20,000	21,000	21,000	22,000

LIFEQUEST WORLD CORPORATION

OTC: LQWC

1181 Grier Dr., Ste. C
Las Vegas, NV 89119
Phone: 702-914-9688
Fax: 702-914-9625
Web: www.lifequestworld.com

CEO: Anthony C. Jurak
CFO: —
HR: Maria J. Guedes
FYE: May 31
Type: Public

Tired? Run-down? Listless? Do you poop out at parties? Time to call Tonic-man! LifeQuest World uses its Tonicman radio shows to help get the word out about its Jurak Classic Whole Body Tonic, but its main distribution is through multilevel marketing. The company's primary product is a liquid herbal formula created in 1943 by Carl Jurak, father of CEO Anthony Jurak (who owns 41% of the company). LifeQuest has acquired ImmunXT for about $2 million and since has invested heavily in marketing the immune stimulating dietary supplement (even hiring actor and body builder Peter Lupus as its spokesman). The company expects ImmunXT — which is an algae-based botanical complex — to become its flagship product.

	Annual Growth	5/05	5/06	5/07	5/08	5/09
Sales ($ mil.)	(24.0%)	2.4	1.4	1.0	1.0	0.8
Net income ($ mil.)	—	(0.5)	(1.1)	(1.4)	(1.5)	(1.2)
Market value ($ mil.)	(51.4%)	216.8	54.2	92.2	20.5	12.0
Employees	(19.1%)	7	8	9	5	3

LIFESCAN, INC.

1000 Gibraltar Dr.
Milpitas, CA 95035
Phone: 408-263-9789
Fax: 408-942-6070
Web: www.lifescan.com

CEO: Tom West
CFO: —
HR: —
FYE: December 31
Type: Subsidiary

LifeScan is sugar sweet for diabetes patients. A subsidiary of health care giant Johnson & Johnson, the company is a leading supplier of blood glucose monitoring systems, sold under the OneTouch brand name, that help diabetes patients monitor and manage their disease. Many of the company's products — including meters, test strips, lancing devices, and software — allow users to test with tiny amounts of blood taken from the forearm or palm rather than using painful finger pricks. In addition to products for home use, LifeScan sells glucose monitoring systems (branded SureStep and OneTouch Flexx) that are used in hospitals and other institutional settings.

LIFESIZE COMMUNICATIONS, INC.

901 S. Mopac Expwy., Bldg. 3, Ste. 300
Austin, TX 78746
Phone: 512-347-9300
Fax: 512-347-9301
Web: www.lifesize.com

CEO: Craig B. Malloy
CFO: William R. (Bill) Paape
HR: Alise Mullins
FYE: December 31
Type: Subsidiary

LifeSize Communications puts people in the same room, even when there's an ocean between them. The company offers high-definition video systems, audioconferencing equipment, and video management software for educators, enterprises, and the public sector. With product packages designed for varying group sizes, it provides systems that include cameras, phones, and wireless remotes. The company also sells tech infrastructure, such as firewalls and gateways. LifeSize counts Adena Health System, Case Western Reserve University, Cozen O'Connor, and National Geographic among its customers. In 2009 Logitech acquired LifeSize Communications for $405 million in cash.

	Annual Growth	12/04	12/05	12/06	12/07	12/08
Est. sales ($ mil.)	—	—	—	—	—	15.8
Employees	—	—	—	—	—	80

LIFESPAN CORPORATION

167 Point St.
Providence, RI 02903
Phone: 401-444-3500
Fax: 401-444-5433
Web: www.lifespan.org

CEO: George A. Vecchione
CFO: Mary A. Wakefield
HR: Brandon Melton
FYE: September 30
Type: Private

Lifespan Corporation helps to increase the longevity of the residents of Rhode Island. Founded in 1994, the multi-hospital health system includes the state's largest acute care facility, Rhode Island Hospital. Rhode Island Hospital has about 720 beds and provides general and advanced medical-surgical care in a wide range of specialties, including organ transplantation, neurosurgery, and orthopedics. It also performs biomedical research in areas such as cancer and vascular disease. Rhode Island Hospital and its sister facility The Miriam Hospital serve as teaching facilities for Brown University's medical school.

	Annual Growth	9/04	9/05	9/06	9/07	9/08
Est. sales ($ mil.)	—	—	—	—	—	1,473.1
Employees	—	—	—	—	—	8,000

LIFESTORE FINANCIAL GROUP

Pink Sheets: LSFG

21 E. Ashe St.
West Jefferson, NC 28694
Phone: 336-246-4344
Fax: 336-246-3966
Web: www.golifestore.com

CEO: Robert E. Washburn
CFO: —
HR: —
FYE: June 30
Type: Public

LifeStore helps you prepeare for whatever life has in store. Formerly AF Financial Group, LifeStore Financial Group provides good ol' traditional banking and insurance services through subsidiaries LifeStore Bank and LifeStore Insurance Services. The bank operates seven offices in northwestern North Carolina's Alleghany, Ashe, and Watauga counties. It provides standard deposit products such as checking and savings accounts and CDs. Residential mortgages make up about half of its loan portfolio. The bank also offers investment products and services through a pact with a third-party provider. LifeStore Insurance Services sells bonds and auto, homeowners, health, and life insurance.

	Annual Growth	6/05	6/06	6/07	6/08	6/09
Sales ($ mil.)	7.2%	16.0	18.1	20.6	21.9	21.1
Net income ($ mil.)	7.5%	0.6	1.0	1.5	1.5	0.8
Employees	(3.8%)	120	111	111	—	—

LIFETIME BRANDS, INC.

NASDAQ (GS): LCUT

1000 Stewart Ave.
Garden City, NY 11530
Phone: 516-683-6000
Fax: 516-683-6116
Web: www.lifetimebrands.com

CEO: Jeffrey (Jeff) Siegel
CFO: Laurence Winoker
HR: —
FYE: December 31
Type: Public

Take-out meals eaten from the carton? Not in this lifetime. Lifetime Brands designs and distributes cutlery, cutting boards, cookware, dinnerware, and home décor under 30-plus brands including Cuisinart, Farberware, KitchenAid, Mikasa, Pfaltzgraff, and Salton. The company also offers items under licensed brands and sells its varied lines in the US, Canada, and Europe through high-end retailers, supermarkets, department (Macy's) and discount stores, including Wal-Mart and Target, as well as online and by catalog. The firm closed all of its money-losing retail stores in 2008. The family of company founder Milton Cohen owns about 15% of the firm. CEO Jeffrey Siegel and SVP Craig Phillips together own 17%.

	Annual Growth	12/05	12/06	12/07	12/08	12/09
Sales ($ mil.)	7.7%	307.9	457.4	493.7	487.9	415.0
Net income ($ mil.)	(33.8%)	14.1	15.5	8.9	(49.0)	2.7
Market value ($ mil.)	(23.3%)	248.4	197.4	156.0	42.5	85.9
Employees	(11.1%)	1,686	1,199	1,469	1,168	1,051

An in-depth profile of this company is available to Hoover's Online members at hoovers.com.

939

LIFETIME ENTERTAINMENT SERVICES, LLC

309 W. 49th St.
New York, NY 10019
Phone: 212-424-7000
Fax: 212-957-4449
Web: www.lifetimetv.com

CEO: Abbe Raven
CFO: James Wesley
HR: Patricia (Pat) Langer
FYE: December 31
Type: Subsidiary

Lifetime Entertainment Services hopes viewers make a long-term commitment to its television programs. The company operates three cable-TV networks (Lifetime, Lifetime Movie Network, Lifetime Real Women) focused on serving female viewers with original movies, talk shows, and syndicated shows. Its Lifetime network, #1 among women's channels, reaches nearly 100 million US households. Lifetime Entertainment also offers lifestyle and entertainment content online. Formed through the merger of channels Daytime and Cable Health Network in 1984, the company is a subsidiary of A&E Television Networks (AETN).

THE LIFETIME HEALTHCARE, INC.

165 Court St.
Rochester, NY 14647
Phone: 585-454-1700
Fax: 585-238-4233
Web: www.lifethc.com/index.shtml

CEO: David H. Klein
CFO: Emil D. Duda
HR: Ginger E. Parysek
FYE: December 31
Type: Holding company

The Lifetime Healthcare Companies is a not-for-profit holding company that provides health insurance and related services to more than 2 million members in New York State through its various subsidiaries. The company's core products are the health insurance plans offered through its Excellus BlueCross BlueShield subsidiary. Long-term care insurance is provided through the company's MedAmerica subsidiary. Primary care is provided to members via the company's Lifetime Health Medical Group. The company also provides third-party administration services through its EBS Benefit Solutions and RMSCO subsidiaries.

	Annual Growth	12/04	12/05	12/06	12/07	12/08
Est. sales ($ mil.)	—	—	—	—	—	3.2
Employees	—	—	—	—	—	25

LIFETOUCH INC.

11000 Viking Dr., Ste. 400
Eden Prairie, MN 55344
Phone: 952-826-4000
Fax: 952-826-4557
Web: www.lifetouch.com

CEO: Paul Harmel
CFO: Randolph (Randy) Pladson
HR: Ted Koenecke
FYE: June 30
Type: Private

When it's picture day at school and the kids are all lined up with new haircuts and scrubbed faces, odds are good that their toothy grins are directed at someone from Lifetouch. One of the largest US portrait photographers, employee-owned Lifetouch also runs about 700 photography studios inside J. C. Penney and Target stores across the nation. In addition, Lifetouch takes baby, family, business, and sports portraits; publishes church directories and yearbooks; and offers event digital imaging (which combines photography, graphics, and text), CD business imaging, and video production services. The firm operates in the US and Canada. Lifetouch was founded in 1936 as National School Studios.

LIFEWATCH CORP.

10255 W. Higgins Rd. St. 100
Rosemont, IL 60018
Phone: 877-774-9846
Fax: 847-720-2111
Web: www.lifewatch.com

CEO: Yacov Geva
CFO: —
HR: Michael Maultz
FYE: December 31
Type: Joint venture

LifeWatch is not a reality show, but its transmissions are a matter of life and death for its audience. The company sells electronic heart monitors that wirelessly transmit patient data to technicians and physicians for remote evaluation. Its revenue comes from signal monitoring, data evaluation, and notification services as well as cardiac event monitoring devices sold under the LifeStar and King of Hearts brands. The company also offers clinical research services. LifeWatch monitors about 250,000 patients from three facilities in Illinois, Pennsylvania, and Florida. Customers include cardiologists, diagnostic clinics, and hospitals. LifeWatch is a subsidiary of Switzerland-based health products provider Card Guard.

	Annual Growth	12/04	12/05	12/06	12/07	12/08
Est. sales ($ mil.)	—	—	—	—	—	47.0
Employees	—	—	—	—	—	344

LIFEWAY CHRISTIAN RESOURCES OF THE SOUTHERN BAPTIST CONVENTION

1 LifeWay Plaza, MSN 146
Nashville, TN 37234
Phone: 615-251-2000
Fax: 615-251-3899
Web: www.lifeway.com

CEO: Thom S. Rainer
CFO: Jerry Rhyne
HR: —
FYE: September 30
Type: Not-for-profit

LifeWay Christian Resources of the Southern Baptist Convention helps to spread the teachings of Jesus. The company is a not-for-profit Christian publisher; it also sells Bibles and other books, CDs, gifts, software, church furniture, signs, and other supplies through more than 150 LifeWay Christian Stores in 25 US states, online, and through its catalog. In addition, LifeWay operates two of the nation's largest Christian conference facilities (and summer camps). LifeWay Ridgecrest Conference Center in North Carolina and LifeWay Glorieta Conference Center in New Mexico together welcome about 2,000 guests per year. LifeWay was founded in 1891 by Dr. J.M. Frost.

	Annual Growth	9/04	9/05	9/06	9/07	9/08
Est. sales ($ mil.)	—	—	—	—	—	476.6
Employees	—	—	—	—	—	4,000

⊞ LIFEWAY FOODS, INC.

NASDAQ (GM): LWAY

6431 W. Oakton St.
Morton Grove, IL 60053
Phone: 847-967-1010
Fax: 847-967-6558
Web: lifeway.net

CEO: Julie Smolyansky
CFO: Edward P. (Ed) Smolyansky
HR: —
FYE: December 31
Type: Public

Kefir is not milk with a pedigree, but it *is* cultured and it's the lifeblood of Lifeway Foods. In addition to the yogurt-like dairy beverage called kefir, the company's products include Farmer's Cheese, Sweet Kiss (a sweetened cheese spread), and Soy-Treat, a soy-based kefir. A drinkable yogurt product is aimed at the Hispanic market under the brand name La Fruta. Its Probugs offering, a flavored drink with live kefir cultures packaged in pouches, is aimed at children. A longtime staple in the dairy cases of health-food stores, Lifeway's products are available throughout the US, as well as internationally.

	Annual Growth	12/05	12/06	12/07	12/08	12/09
Sales ($ mil.)	30.4%	20.1	27.7	38.7	44.5	58.1
Net income ($ mil.)	22.3%	2.5	2.9	3.2	1.9	5.6
Market value ($ mil.)	17.6%	104.2	156.6	198.2	150.4	199.0
Employees	23.5%	86	120	120	200	200

An in-depth profile of this company is available to Hoover's Online members at hoovers.com.

☐ LIGAND PHARMACEUTICALS

NASDAQ (GM): LGND

10275 Science Center Dr.
San Diego, CA 92121
Phone: 858-550-7500
Fax: 858-550-7506
Web: www.ligand.com

CEO: John L. Higgins
CFO: John P. Sharp
HR: Audrey Warfield
FYE: December 31
Type: Public

Ligand Pharmaceuticals Incorporated is receptive to new ideas. The drug development company works with gene transcription technology to address assorted illnesses. The company sold off its commercial operations, including its FDA-approved pain drug Avinza, and has refocused on developing a pipeline of new compounds. Its research and development projects include treatments for thrombocytopenia (low platelet count), osteoporosis, menopausal conditions, hepatitis C, cancers, and chronic liver disease, developed internally and in collaboration with larger drug companies. Ligand is expanding its development pipeline through acquisitions.

	Annual Growth	12/05	12/06	12/07	12/08	12/09
Sales ($ mil.)	(31.5%)	176.6	141.0	12.9	27.3	38.9
Net income ($ mil.)	—	(36.4)	(31.7)	281.7	(98.1)	(1.9)
Market value ($ mil.)	(33.6%)	1,311.0	1,287.5	567.9	322.2	255.1
Employees	(38.2%)	493	122	59	96	72

LIGHTING SCIENCE GROUP CORPORATION

Pink Sheets: LSCG

2100 McKinney Ave., Ste. 1515
Dallas, TX 75201
Phone: 214-382-3630
Fax: 214-382-3631
Web: www.lsgc.com

CEO: Zachary S. (Zach) Gibler
CFO: Jonathan T. Cohen
HR: Lynn Vera
FYE: December 31
Type: Public

Going green turns on Lighting Science (LSGC). LSGC designs, manufactures, and markets eco-friendly, light-emitting diode (LED) technologies that conserve energy and eliminate the use of hazardous materials. The company sells optimized digital lighting (ODL) and LED replacement lamps, fixtures, and bulbs for streets, garages, stages, and retail displays. While most of its customers are in retail, commercial, industrial, and public sectors, LSGC also customizes ambiance and lighting systems for entertainment venues and nightclubs. Pegasus Capital Advisors controls more than two-thirds of LSGC's voting rights.

	Annual Growth	12/05	12/06	12/07	12/08	12/09
Sales ($ mil.)	321.0%	0.1	0.4	2.8	20.8	31.4
Net income ($ mil.)	—	(3.1)	(9.8)	(13.1)	(95.0)	(48.1)
Market value ($ mil.)	(47.6%)	323.8	256.6	262.7	11.3	24.4
Employees	114.1%	6	13	13	145	126

LIGHTPATH TECHNOLOGIES, INC.

NASDAQ (CM): LPTH

2603 Challenger Tech Ct., Ste. 100
Orlando, FL 32826
Phone: 407-382-4003
Fax: 407-382-4007
Web: www.lightpath.com

CEO: J. James (Jim) Gaynor
CFO: Dorothy M. Cipolla
HR: —
FYE: June 30
Type: Public

LightPath Technologies is lighting the optical networking way. The company, which has traditionally used its patented GRADIUM glass to make distortion-reducing lenses for inspection equipment, is developing new applications for its technologies in the optoelectronics and fiber-optic communications fields. Its optoelectronics products include collimators (optical network components) and optical isolators (filters that prevent light waves from reflecting backward). LightPath serves such customers as CyOptics, Intel, Santur, ThorLabs, and T-Networks. The company targets aerospace, telecommunications, health care, instrumentation, and the military. LightPath gets about two-thirds of its sales in the US.

	Annual Growth	6/05	6/06	6/07	6/08	6/09
Sales ($ mil.)	(10.7%)	11.8	12.2	13.4	8.8	7.5
Net income ($ mil.)	—	(3.5)	(3.4)	(2.6)	(5.5)	(3.8)
Market value ($ mil.)	(18.9%)	26.4	35.7	42.9	13.2	11.4
Employees	1.9%	115	207	214	174	124

THE LIGHTSTONE GROUP LLC

326 3rd St.
Lakewood, NJ 08701
Phone: 732-367-0129
Fax: 732-363-7183
Web: www.lightstonegroup.com

CEO: Peyton (Chip) Owen Jr.
CFO: —
HR: Pamela Z. (Pam) Meadows
FYE: December 31
Type: Private

Like a beacon in the night, Lightstone will lead you to lodging, food, and more. The company owns a portfolio of residential, commercial, retail, and industrial properties throughout the US, Canada, and Puerto Rico. It owns more than 19,000 residential units and about 700 hotel properties as well as a total of approximately 25 million sq. ft. of commercial space. Subsidiary Beacon Management operates a portfolio of more than 30 apartment communities, primarily located in the Southeast and mid-Atlantic. Its Park Avenue Funding unit provides real estate financing for commercial properties of all types. Chairman David Lichtenstein (German for "lightstone") founded the company in 1988.

LIMCO-PIEDMONT INC.

5304 S. Lawton Ave.
Tulsa, OK 74107
Phone: 918-445-4300
Fax: —
Web: www.limcopiedmont.com

CEO: Avraham (Avi) Ortal
CFO: Mary Dowdy
HR: —
FYE: December 31
Type: Subsidiary

Limco-Piedmont wants to keep planes out of limbo while waiting for repairs. The company performs aircraft component maintenance, repair, and overhaul (MRO) services for commercial and military planes, as well as air cargo carriers. Limco-Piedmont makes heat transfer equipment used in airplanes and offers inventory management and parts procurement for airlines. Parts services account for about one-quarter of the company's business. Major customers include the US government, KLM Royal Dutch Airlines, Lufthansa, and Bell Helicopter. TAT Technologies, which previously owned about 62% of Limco-Piedmont, acquired the remainder of Limco-Piedmont's common stock in 2009.

LIME ENERGY CO.

NASDAQ (CM): LIME

1280 Landmeier Rd.
Elk Grove Village, IL 60007
Phone: 847-437-1666
Fax: 847-437-4969
Web: www.lime-energy.com

CEO: David R. Asplund
CFO: Jeffrey R. Mistarz
HR: Jeffrey R. Mistarz
FYE: December 31
Type: Public

Lime Energy wants to shine a little less light for a lot less money. The company's Energy Services segment installs energy efficient lighting upgrades for commercial and industrial customers. It works with each customer to determine the best lighting set-up given several factors, such as hours of operation, energy costs, and building environment. It also provides energy engineering services, including energy management planning and assistance with applying for energy rebates. The company serves government, commercial, and industrial clients; top customers include Honeywell International and Johnson Controls.

	Annual Growth	12/05	12/06	12/07	12/08	12/09
Sales ($ mil.)	95.0%	4.9	8.1	19.5	57.2	70.8
Net income ($ mil.)	—	(6.9)	(16.4)	(15.6)	(13.0)	(17.3)
Market value ($ mil.)	(48.5%)	1,485.9	148.7	223.0	109.7	104.3
Employees	73.3%	41	77	33	329	370

LIMELIGHT NETWORKS, INC.

NASDAQ (GM): LLNW

2220 W. 14th St.
Tempe, AZ 85281
Phone: 602-850-5000
Fax: 602-850-5001
Web: www.limelightnetworks.com

CEO: Jeffrey W. (Jeff) Lunsford
CFO: Douglas S. (Doug) Lindroth
HR: —
FYE: December 31
Type: Public

Limelight Networks wants to be the center of attention for digital content providers. The company offers services for delivering media files such as video, music, games, software, and social media, via the Internet. Limelight Networks also provides on-demand and live streaming services for content in all major formats, including Adobe Flash, MP3 audio, QuickTime, RealNetworks RealPlayer, and Windows Media. Its more than 1,300 customers include social network site Facebook, video game company Electronic Arts, and software giant Microsoft, which accounts for some 15% of sales. Limelight Networks' clients provide content through a variety of devices, including PCs, mobile phones, and digital video recorders.

	Annual Growth	12/05	12/06	12/07	12/08	12/09
Sales ($ mil.)	57.7%	21.3	64.3	103.1	129.5	131.7
Net income ($ mil.)	205.6%	0.4	(3.7)	(73.0)	(63.1)	34.9
Market value ($ mil.)	(24.6%)	—	—	608.1	216.2	346.0
Employees	18.2%	168	158	239	294	328

LIMITED BRANDS, INC.

NYSE: LTD

3 Limited Pkwy.
Columbus, OH 43216
Phone: 614-415-7000
Fax: 614-415-7440
Web: www.limitedbrands.com

CEO: Leslie H. Wexner
CFO: Stuart B. Burgdoerfer
HR: Jane L. Ramsey
FYE: January 31
Type: Public

Limited Brands is as much of a shopping-mall mainstay as food courts and teenagers. The company operates about 2,970 stores throughout North America under the Victoria's Secret, Bath & Body Works (BBW), and La Senza (in Canada) banners, as well as corresponding websites and catalogs. Originally focused on apparel, Limited Brands sold its ailing Limited Stores and Express chains — leaving the company free to focus on two core businesses: Victoria's Secret and BBW. Limited Brands also owns apparel importer MAST Industries, luxe department store operator Henri Bendel, and The White Barn Candle Co. Limited Brands was founded in 1963 by its chairman Leslie Wexner.

	Annual Growth	1/06	1/07	1/08	1/09	1/10
Sales ($ mil.)	(2.9%)	9,699.0	10,671.0	10,134.0	9,043.0	8,632.0
Net income ($ mil.)	(9.4%)	666.0	675.0	718.0	220.0	448.0
Market value ($ mil.)	(5.3%)	7,694.0	9,085.8	6,201.4	2,575.5	6,185.1
Employees	(4.3%)	110,000	125,500	97,500	90,900	92,100

LIN TV CORP.

NYSE: TVL

4 Richmond Sq., Ste. 200
Providence, RI 02906
Phone: 401-454-2880
Fax: 401-454-0089
Web: www.lintv.com

CEO: Vincent L. Sadusky
CFO: Richard J. Schmaeling
HR: Dan Donohue
FYE: December 31
Type: Public

This company spells success with TV call letters. Doing business as LIN Media, LIN TV owns and operates about 30 stations serving nearly 20 markets in about a dozen states. Its portfolio of stations includes affiliates with all the major networks — mostly CBS and FOX — as well as stations affiliated with smaller networks The CW Network and MyNetworkTV. Many of the company's stations operate as duopolies with two stations serving a single market. In addition, LIN Media owns 20% of a joint venture with NBC Universal parent General Electric that operates NBC stations in Dallas and San Diego. Dallas-based private equity firm HM Capital Partners controls 35% of the company.

	Annual Growth	12/05	12/06	12/07	12/08	12/09
Sales ($ mil.)	(2.8%)	380.4	426.1	395.9	399.8	339.5
Net income ($ mil.)	—	(26.1)	(234.5)	53.7	(830.4)	9.1
Market value ($ mil.)	(20.5%)	589.4	526.4	643.9	57.7	236.0
Employees	(6.6%)	2,414	2,119	2,100	2,098	1,840

LINCARE HOLDINGS INC.

NASDAQ (GS): LNCR

19387 US 19 North
Clearwater, FL 33764
Phone: 727-530-7700
Fax: 727-532-9692
Web: www.lincare.com

CEO: John P. Byrnes
CFO: Paul G. Gabos
HR: Shelia Dilley
FYE: December 31
Type: Public

Lincare Holdings doesn't take breathing for granted. With more than 1,000 offices across the US, the company helps some 700,000 patients with chronic obstructive pulmonary diseases (including emphysema and severe asthma) by providing oxygen therapy services. Through its local service centers, Lincare delivers oxygen equipment to patients in their homes, and it trains them and monitors their use of the equipment. The company offers positive airway pressure machines for patients with sleep apnea and supplies other home medical equipment. In some markets the company also provides home infusion services, such as chemotherapy, pain management, parenteral nutrition, and other procedures.

	Annual Growth	12/05	12/06	12/07	12/08	12/09
Sales ($ mil.)	5.2%	1,266.6	1,409.8	1,596.0	1,664.6	1,550.5
Net income ($ mil.)	(10.7%)	213.7	213.0	226.1	237.2	136.1
Market value ($ mil.)	(3.0%)	2,776.7	2,639.5	2,329.5	1,784.2	2,460.3
Employees	4.6%	8,258	9,070	9,450	9,957	9,867

LINCOLN BENEFIT LIFE COMPANY

2940 S. 84th St.
Lincoln, NE 68506
Phone: 402-475-4061
Fax: 402-328-6124
Web: www.accessallstate.com/Anon/CompanyInfoLBL1.aspx

CEO: Fredrick F. Cripe
CFO: —
HR: —
FYE: December 31
Type: Subsidiary

It may not be a hot rod, but this Lincoln does help auto insurance giant Allstate get on down the road. A subsidiary of unit Allstate Life Insurance, Lincoln Benefit Life produces a variety of life insurance, annuities, and other retirement and investment products (primarily deferred and immediate fixed annuities, interest sensitive life, and traditional life insurance) that are sold by Allstate's exclusive agents, as well as by independent agents and through securities dealers. Lincoln Benefit Life is authorized to offer its products in all US states except New York.

	Annual Growth	12/04	12/05	12/06	12/07	12/08
Est. sales ($ mil.)	—	—	—	—	—	19.9
Employees	—	—	—	—	—	19

LINCOLN EDUCATIONAL SERVICES

NASDAQ (GS): LINC

200 Executive Dr., Ste. 340
West Orange, NJ 07052
Phone: 973-736-9340
Fax: 973-736-1750
Web: www.lincolnedu.com

CEO: Shaun E. McAlmont
CFO: Cesar Ribeiro
HR: –
FYE: December 31
Type: Public

Lincoln hopes its graduates are better "Abe-l" to get a career. Lincoln Educational Services Corporation provides vocational programs from schools including Lincoln Technical Group, Nashville Auto-Diesel College, and Southwestern College. It offers programs in automotive technology, health sciences, skilled trades (including HVAC and electronics), hospitality services, and IT/business. Some 31,000 students are enrolled at more than 40 campuses throughout the US. Lincoln has expanded by buying smaller schools and by opening campuses in new markets. It has also expanded its campus facilities to accommodate higher enrollments.

	Annual Growth	12/05	12/06	12/07	12/08	12/09
Sales ($ mil.)	16.6%	299.2	321.5	327.8	376.9	552.5
Net income ($ mil.)	27.4%	18.7	15.6	8.3	20.2	49.2
Market value ($ mil.)	11.0%	371.4	351.3	383.4	345.1	564.1
Employees	17.0%	2,270	2,862	2,671	3,206	4,250

An in-depth profile of this company is available to Hoover's Online members at hoovers.com.

⊞ LINCOLN ELECTRIC HOLDINGS, INC.

NASDAQ (GS): LECO

22801 St. Clair Ave.	CEO: John M. Stropki Jr.
Cleveland, OH 44117	CFO: Vincent K. Petrella
Phone: 216-481-8100	HR: Gretchen A. Farrell
Fax: 216-486-1751	FYE: December 31
Web: www.lincolnelectric.com	Type: Public

With this thing, I thee weld. Lincoln Electric, the world's largest manufacturer of arc welders and welding gear by sales, is a global manufacturer of welding and cutting products, including arc welding power sources, consumable electrodes, fluxes, fume extraction equipment, robotic welding systems, and wire feeders; other welding products include regulators and torches. In North America, which geographically accounts for more than 40% of its sales, products are sold primarily through a network of industrial distributors. Outside of North America, the company has manufacturing facilities and an international sales organization that serve customers in Asia/Pacific, Europe, and South America.

	Annual Growth	12/05	12/06	12/07	12/08	12/09
Sales ($ mil.)	1.9%	1,601.2	1,971.9	2,280.8	2,479.1	1,729.3
Net income ($ mil.)	(20.6%)	122.3	175.0	202.7	212.3	48.6
Market value ($ mil.)	7.8%	1,689.0	2,573.1	3,031.3	2,168.9	2,276.7
Employees	4.6%	7,485	8,430	8,992	9,329	8,950

⊞ LINCOLN NATIONAL CORPORATION

NYSE: LNC

150 N. Radnor Chester Rd.	CEO: Dennis R. Glass
Radnor, PA 19807	CFO: Frederick J. (Fred) Crawford
Phone: 484-583-1400	HR: Lisa M. Buckingham
Fax: 484-583-1421	FYE: December 31
Web: www.lfg.com	Type: Public

Who better to trust with your nest egg than the company that took its name from Honest Abe? Lincoln National, which operates as Lincoln Financial Group, provides retirement planning and life insurance to individuals and employers in the form of annuities, 401K savings plans, and a variety of life, dental, and disability insurance products. It does business through such subsidiaries as Lincoln National Life Insurance and Lincoln Life & Annuity Company of New York. The company is also active in the investment management business, offering individual and institutional clients such financial services as pension plans, trusts, and mutual funds through its subsidiaries.

	Annual Growth	12/05	12/06	12/07	12/08	12/09
Assets ($ mil.)	9.2%	124,787.6	178,494.0	191,435.0	163,136.0	177,433.0
Net income ($ mil.)	—	831.1	1,316.0	1,215.0	57.0	(485.0)
Market value ($ mil.)	(17.2%)	16,040.7	20,084.9	17,610.5	5,698.8	7,525.8
Employees	11.8%	5,259	10,744	10,870	9,696	8,208

THE LINCOLN NATIONAL LIFE INSURANCE COMPANY

350 Church St.	CEO: Dennis R. Glass
Hartford, CT 06103	CFO: —
Phone: 260-455-2000	HR: —
Fax: 860-466-2835	FYE: December 31
Web: www.lfg.com	Type: Subsidiary

Lincoln National Life Insurance is the primary insurance subsidiary of Lincoln National Corporation (which operates as Lincoln Financial Group) — honest. Lincoln National Life Insurance sells term life, universal life, variable universal life, and whole life insurance policies to individuals. It also provides corporate-owned life insurance policies to businesses seeking insurance on their key employees. The company distributes its life insurance policies through Lincoln Financial Distributors, a network of agents, financial planners, and associates of Lincoln Financial Advisors. Founded in 1905, Lincoln National Life Insurance was the first affiliate in the Lincoln Financial Group to bear the Lincoln name.

LINCOLN PROPERTY COMPANY

3300 Lincoln Plaza, 500 N. Akard	CEO: A. Mack Pogue
Dallas, TX 75201	CFO: Dennis Streit
Phone: 214-740-3300	HR: Louann Hudson
Fax: 214-740-3441	FYE: June 30
Web: www.lincolnproperty.com	Type: Private

Lincoln Property is one of the largest diversified real estate companies in the US — honest! The company began by building garden apartments in the Southwest, then expanded into commercial and retail projects. It owns, leases, and manages nearly 300 residential communities consisting of some 130,000 units throughout the US. Its commercial division provides third-party management and leasing services for residential and commercial properties. Also one of the largest developers and managers of military housing, Lincoln Property has arrangements with the US Army, Navy, and Marines.

	Annual Growth	6/04	6/05	6/06	6/07	6/08
Est. sales ($ mil.)	—	—	—	—	—	80.7
Employees	—	—	—	—	—	3,985

LINDER INDUSTRIAL MACHINERY COMPANY

1601 S. Frontage Rd.	CEO: Jeffrey G. (Jeff) Cox
Plant City, FL 33563	CFO: Peggy Smith
Phone: 813-754-2727	HR: Polly Van Valkenburg
Fax: 813-754-6090	FYE: March 31
Web: www.linderco.com	Type: Subsidiary

Need to dig yourself out of a big hole? Linder Industrial Machinery can offer the right dozers, excavators, crushers, and loaders. Part of SMS International, a construction machinery distribution subsidiary of Sumitomo, Linder provides heavy, off-road machinery made by major OEMs such as Esco, Atlas Copco, Hensley, and Komatsu. The company supplies new, rebuilt, and rental utility and construction equipment, in addition to providing 24/7 parts and repair services to commercial, construction, and municipal markets. An exclusive Komatsu distributor, Linder Industrial is given sole rights to introducing new equipment like the Komatsu hydraulic excavator to customers in Florida, North Carolina, and South Carolina.

⊞ LINDSAY CORPORATION

NYSE: LNN

2222 N. 111th St.	CEO: Richard W. (Rick) Parod
Omaha, NE 68164	CFO: David B. Downing
Phone: 402-829-6800	HR: Dan G. Keller
Fax: 402-428-7232	FYE: August 31
Web: www.lindsaymanufacturing.com	Type: Public

Liquid resources are big assets at Lindsay Corp. The company designs and manufactures irrigation systems primarily for agricultural use. The Zimmatic brand irrigation systems, its self-propelled center-pivot and lateral-move lineup, is designed to use water, energy, and labor more efficiently than traditional flood or surface irrigation. Touting better to bumper crop yields, a global dealer network sells to farmers in more than 90 countries. (The US accounts for about two-thirds of sales.) Lindsay also plies water pumping stations (through subsidiary Watertronics), as well as replacement parts. An infrastructure division makes movable barriers for traffic control and crash cushions for road safety.

	Annual Growth	8/05	8/06	8/07	8/08	8/09
Sales ($ mil.)	17.3%	177.3	226.0	281.9	475.1	336.2
Net income ($ mil.)	30.2%	4.8	11.7	15.6	39.4	13.8
Market value ($ mil.)	13.2%	315.9	356.1	506.1	1,022.7	518.3
Employees	4.4%	645	763	899	1,239	766

⊞ An in-depth profile of this company is available to Hoover's Online members at hoovers.com.

LINEAR TECHNOLOGY CORPORATION

NASDAQ (GS): LLTC

1630 McCarthy Blvd.
Milpitas, CA 95035
Phone: 408-432-1900
Fax: 408-434-0507
Web: www.linear.com

CEO: Lothar Maier
CFO: Paul Coghlan
HR: —
FYE: June 30
Type: Public

Linear Technology's chips keep real-world information right in line. The company's high performance linear integrated circuits (ICs) transform analog signals — which convey information about real-world phenomena such as temperature, pressure, sound, or speed — into digital form, receivable by electronic devices. The company also makes linear devices that control power and regulate voltage in electronic systems. Its products are used in a myriad of equipment, including PCs and notebooks, cell phones, radar systems, auto navigation, satellite, and scientific and industrial instruments. Linear caters largely to communications and industrial markets, followed by computers, consumer goods, auto and space/military.

	Annual Growth	6/05	6/06	6/07	6/08	6/09
Sales ($ mil.)	(2.0%)	1,049.7	1,093.0	1,083.1	1,175.2	968.5
Net income ($ mil.)	(7.8%)	434.0	428.7	411.7	387.6	313.5
Market value ($ mil.)	(10.7%)	8,223.6	7,506.4	8,109.3	7,300.2	5,233.6
Employees	4.4%	3,217	3,755	3,837	4,173	3,821

LINKEDIN CORPORATION

2029 Stierlin Ct.
Mountain View, CA 94043
Phone: 650-687-3600
Fax: 650-687-0505
Web: www.linkedin.com

CEO: Jeff Weiner
CFO: Steven J. (Steve) Sordello
HR: Steve Cadigan
FYE: December 31
Type: Private

Feeling a bit disconnected? LinkedIn wants to help. The company is an online business network designed to help professionals find jobs, people, and service providers. The company has grown to reach more than 40 million users in some 200 countries since its inception in 2003. LinkedIn is free to join; it also offers paid accounts and sells advertising. The company is backed by venture capital firms including Sequoia Capital, Greylock, and Bessemer Venture Partners, as well as individuals such as Marc Andreessen (co-founder of Netscape and chairman of Opsware), Joe Kraus (co-founder of Excite), and Peter Thiel (co-founder of PayPal).

	Annual Growth	12/04	12/05	12/06	12/07	12/08
Est. sales ($ mil.)	—	—	—	—	—	17.0
Employees	—	—	—	—	—	320

LINKSHARE CORPORATION

215 Park Ave. South, 8th Fl.
New York, NY 10003
Phone: 646-654-6000
Fax: 646-602-0160
Web: www.linkshare.com

CEO: Jonathan Levine
CFO: —
HR: —
FYE: June 30
Type: Subsidiary

Turning clicks into commerce has been LinkShare's plan since 1996. The company operates The LinkShare Network, a performance-based affiliate marketing network. Its clients, which have included retailers Dell and Land's End, market their products through promotional links placed on affiliate websites. LinkShare charges its clients based on volume of traffic and purchases made. The company also offers tools that help clients manage, track, and analyze affiliate, search, and e-mail marketing campaigns. Headquartered in New York City, LinkShare owns additional offices in Chicago; London; San Francisco; Tampa, Florida; and Tokyo. The company is a subsidiary of Japanese online retailer Rakuten.

LINN ENERGY, LLC

NASDAQ (GS): LINE

J P Morgan Chase Tower, 600 Travis, Ste. 7000
Houston, TX 77002
Phone: 281-840-4000
Fax: —
Web: www.linnenergy.com

CEO: Mark E. Ellis
CFO: Kolja Rockov
HR: —
FYE: December 31
Type: Public

It's a Linn-Linn situation. Founder and chairman Michael Linn's namesake company Linn Energy has successfully drilled for natural gas across the US. The natural gas exploration and production company has made 25 property acquisitions in California, New York, Oklahoma, Pennsylvania, Texas, Virginia, and West Virginia since its founding in 2003. The company has proved reserves of 1,660 billion cu. ft. of natural gas equivalent. Linn Energy has focused on shallow drilling (2,500 to 5,500 ft.). In 2008 the company operated some 66% of its almost 6,720 gross productive wells.

	Annual Growth	12/05	12/06	12/07	12/08	12/09
Sales ($ mil.)	53.1%	49.7	191.1	338.3	1,435.0	273.1
Net income ($ mil.)	—	(56.4)	79.2	(364.3)	999.6	(298.2)
Market value ($ mil.)	(4.4%)	—	4,722.9	3,699.9	2,212.9	4,121.2
Employees	43.4%	130	220	525	505	550

LION GABLES RESIDENTIAL TRUST

2859 Paces Ferry Rd., Ste. 1450
Atlanta, GA 30339
Phone: 770-436-4600
Fax: 770-435-7434
Web: www.gables.com

CEO: David D. Fitch
CFO: Dawn H. Severt
HR: Philip E. Altschuler
FYE: December 31
Type: Subsidiary

Lion Gables Residential Trust (LGRT) is a privately owned real estate investment trust (REIT) that owns, develops, and manages apartment complexes, mainly in the southern US. The company, which also manages properties for third parties, oversees approximately 35,000 apartment homes and more than 60 apartment communities with some 17,000 units. The company targets "affluent renters-by-choice" through its focus on luxury properties in upscale, high-growth urban areas, rather than outlying suburban complexes. In 2005 Gables Residential was acquired by a private partnership sponsored by ING Clarion Partners, a part of Dutch financial giant ING Groep.

	Annual Growth	12/04	12/05	12/06	12/07	12/08
Est. sales ($ mil.)	—	—	—	—	—	30.6
Employees	—	—	—	—	—	1,494

LIONBRIDGE TECHNOLOGIES, INC.

NASDAQ (GM): LIOX

1050 Winter St.
Waltham, MA 02451
Phone: 781-434-6000
Fax: 781-434-6034
Web: www.lionbridge.com

CEO: Rory J. Cowan
CFO: Donald M. (Don) Muir
HR: Michele Erwin
FYE: December 31
Type: Public

Lionbridge Technologies wants to be king of the jungle at bridging the language gap. The company offers translation, or localization, of software, user manuals, Web content, and other materials, preparing them for international use by tailoring them to individual languages and cultures. The firm also supplies human interpreters to government agencies and businesses. Additionally Lionbridge provides testing services: Under its VeriTest brand, the company checks websites, software, and hardware to ensure their quality. Microsoft accounts for about 20% of sales, and other clients have included Google, Volvo, and Nikon. CEO Rory Cowan owns about 8% of Lionbridge.

	Annual Growth	12/05	12/06	12/07	12/08	12/09
Sales ($ mil.)	13.3%	236.3	418.9	452.0	461.4	389.3
Net income ($ mil.)	—	(3.9)	(4.9)	(4.2)	(119.3)	(4.0)
Market value ($ mil.)	(24.3%)	418.3	383.8	211.5	74.5	137.1
Employees	1.7%	3,921	4,295	4,600	4,500	4,200

An in-depth profile of this company is available to Hoover's Online members at hoovers.com.

LIONS GATE ENTERTAINMENT CORP.

NYSE: LGF

2700 Colorado Ave.
Santa Monica, CA 90404
Phone: 310-449-9200
Fax: 310-255-3870
Web: www.lionsgatefilms.com

CEO: Jon Feltheimer
CFO: James (Jim) Keegan
HR: —
FYE: March 31
Type: Public

Independent films are the cat's meow at Lions Gate Entertainment. The firm, which operates as Lionsgate, is the leading producer and distributor of independent films — such as Academy Award winner *Juno* and romantic comedy *Nick and Norah's Infinite Playlist* — through its Mandate Pictures division. It produces TV programming (including *Nurse Jackie* for Showtime Networks) through Lionsgate Television. Lionsgate also releases films under the Trimark brand and owns a library of more than 8,000 movie titles. In addition, it owns production studio Roadside Attractions. Lionsgate's 2003 purchase of rival Artisan Entertainment for $160 million created the industry's largest indie studio.

	Annual Growth	3/05	3/06	3/07	3/08	3/09
Sales ($ mil.)	14.9%	842.6	951.2	976.7	1,361.0	1,466.4
Net income ($ mil.)	—	20.3	6.1	27.5	(74.0)	(163.0)
Market value ($ mil.)	(17.8%)	1,302.1	1,196.0	1,345.7	1,148.9	595.1
Employees	26.7%	311	354	400	444	802

LIPPINCOTT WILLIAMS & WILKINS

530 Walnut St.
Philadelphia, PA 19106
Phone: 215-521-8300
Fax: 215-521-8902
Web: www.lww.com

CEO: Rick Perry
CFO: —
HR: —
FYE: December 31
Type: Subsidiary

A division of Wolters Kluwer, Lippincott Williams & Wilkins is a publisher of health care information for the medical industry and students. The company publishes the information in print format (textbooks, journals), as well as electronic formats (CD-ROM, Internet, and Intranet). Titles include *Stedman's Medical Dictionary* and *Griffith's 5-Minute Clinical Consult*. The company also publishes more than 275 medical journals, newsletters, and loose-leaf products with such titles as *Implant Dentistry*, *Journal of Immunotherapy*, and *American Nursing Student*. Lippincott Williams & Wilkins has offices in the US, Australia, Hong Kong, and the UK.

LIQUIDITY SERVICES, INC.

NASDAQ (GS): LQDT

1920 L St. NW, 6th Fl.
Washington, DC 20036
Phone: 202-467-6868
Fax: 202-467-5475
Web: www.liquidityservicesinc.com

CEO: William P. (Bill) Angrick III
CFO: James M. Rallo
HR: —
FYE: September 30
Type: Public

Hey, bidder, bidder. Take a swing at Liquidity Services (LSI). The online auction firm provides manufacturers, retailers, corporations, and governments with an electronic marketplace to dispose of, liquidate, and track goods in the reverse supply chain. More than 1 million professional buyers are registered on the firm's online marketplaces, through which they can bid for wholesale, surplus, and salvage items like retail customer returns, overstock products, and end-of-life goods. LSI, founded in 1999, also offers valuation, appraisal, inventory, marketing, sale, and logistical management of assets; warehousing and inspection of inventory; and transaction support such as collections and dispute mediation.

	Annual Growth	9/05	9/06	9/07	9/08	9/09
Sales ($ mil.)	27.5%	89.4	147.8	198.6	263.9	236.3
Net income ($ mil.)	8.6%	4.1	8.0	11.0	11.6	5.7
Market value ($ mil.)	(12.8%)	—	421.0	296.8	293.0	278.7
Employees	23.1%	304	378	533	621	698

LIQUIDNET HOLDINGS, INC.

498 7th Ave., 12th Fl.
New York, NY 10018
Phone: 646-674-2000
Fax: 646-674-2003
Web: www.liquidnet.com

CEO: Seth Merrin
CFO: William (Bill) Maw
HR: Jerilyn Medrea
FYE: December 31
Type: Private

Liquidity is the byword at Liquidnet Holdings, an institution where loose lips are not tolerated. Through its Liquidnet H20 platform, the company has created an electronic marketplace for institutional trading that brings buyers and sellers together and lets them anonymously negotiate trades without intermediaries or information leaks. Subsidiary Miletus Trading provides analytics and other services to institutional investors. Liquidnet's global membership community of institutional firms today represents some $16 trillion in equity assets under management. The company operates mostly in the US as well as in Africa, Asia, Australia, Canada, and Europe. Liquidnet filed to go public in 2008.

LITHIA MOTORS, INC.

NYSE: LAD

360 E. Jackson St.
Medford, OR 97501
Phone: 541-776-6401
Fax: 541-774-7617
Web: www.lithia.com

CEO: Sidney B. (Sid) DeBoer
CFO: Jeffrey B. (Jeff) DeBoer
HR: Barbara Perkins
FYE: December 31
Type: Public

Lithia Motors is encountering potholes on the acquisition and economic autobahns. The company operates about 90 stores in select markets in about a dozen states. The firm sells more than 25 brands of domestic and imported new and used cars and trucks through its stores and online. Chrysler (Dodge, Jeep) and GM (Buick, Chevrolet, Cadillac, GMC) are the top sellers. Lithia Motors also offers financing and parts, and operates about 15 collision-repair service centers. Unlike most consolidators, it prefers to pay cash (rather than stock) for dealerships in smaller markets. Chairman and CEO Sidney DeBoer, through Lithia Holding Co., controls Lithia Motors, which was founded in 1946 by his father Walt.

	Annual Growth	12/05	12/06	12/07	12/08	12/09
Sales ($ mil.)	(12.1%)	2,935.4	3,172.9	3,219.0	2,137.8	1,749.3
Net income ($ mil.)	(34.4%)	49.8	37.3	21.5	(252.6)	9.2
Market value ($ mil.)	(28.5%)	816.7	747.1	356.7	84.7	213.5
Employees	(8.8%)	5,692	6,261	5,828	4,868	3,930

LITHIUM TECHNOLOGY CORPORATION

Pink Sheets: LTHU

5115 Campus Dr.
Plymouth Meeting, PA 19462
Phone: 610-940-6090
Fax: 610-940-6091
Web: www.lithiumtech.com

CEO: Theo M. Kremers
CFO: Timothy J. Ryder
HR: —
FYE: December 31
Type: Public

Lithium Technology is engaged in the development of large-format rechargeable lithium-ion batteries for aerospace, automotive, stationary power, and national security applications. Customers include Lockheed Martin Space Systems and the UK Ministry of Defense. Lithium Technology acquired lithium polymer battery maker GAIA Holding from Arch Hill Capital in a 2002 share exchange transaction that gave Arch Hill Capital 61% control of Lithium Technology. Lithium's auditor has expressed doubt about the company's ability to continue as a going concern, due to its accumulated deficit of $131 million and its need for additional financing.

	Annual Growth	12/05	12/06	12/07	12/08	12/09
Sales ($ mil.)	76.2%	—	—	—	4.2	7.4
Net income ($ mil.)	—	—	—	—	(6.4)	(10.5)
Market value ($ mil.)	(18.4%)	—	—	—	102.8	83.9
Employees	5.4%	—	—	—	74	78

An in-depth profile of this company is available to Hoover's Online members at hoovers.com.

945

LITTELFUSE, INC.

NASDAQ (GS): LFUS

8755 W. Higgins Rd., Ste. 500
Chicago, IL 60631
Phone: 773-628-1000
Fax: 800-522-7697
Web: www.littelfuse.com

CEO: Gordon B. Hunter
CFO: Philip G. (Phil) Franklin
HR: Ryan K. Stafford
FYE: December 31
Type: Public

Littelfuse is big on circuit protection. The company is the world's #1 fuse maker. In addition to its fuses, Littelfuse's other circuit protection devices include positive temperature coefficient devices that limit current when too much is being supplied and electrostatic discharge suppressors that redirect transient high voltage. The company's thyristors protect telecommunications circuits from transient voltage caused by lightning strikes. Littelfuse's 4,000-plus customers include electronics manufacturers (Hewlett-Packard and Samsung), automakers (Ford, GM, Honda, and Toyota), and the automotive aftermarket (AutoZone and Pep Boys). The company gets about two-thirds of its sales outside the US.

	Annual Growth	12/05	12/06	12/07	12/08	12/09
Sales ($ mil.)	(2.0%)	467.1	534.9	536.1	530.9	430.1
Net income ($ mil.)	(14.6%)	17.7	23.8	36.8	8.0	9.4
Market value ($ mil.)	4.2%	597.3	698.8	722.4	363.8	704.7
Employees	(0.7%)	5,646	6,550	6,200	6,300	5,500

LITTLE CAESAR ENTERPRISES, INC.

2211 Woodward Ave.
Detroit, MI 48201
Phone: 313-983-6000
Fax: 313-983-6390
Web: www.littlecaesars.com

CEO: Michael (Mike) Ilitch
CFO: Darrel Snygg
HR: Joni C. Nelson
FYE: December 31
Type: Subsidiary

I came, I saw, I bought a pizza. Little Caesar Enterprises operates and franchises more than 2,500 Little Caesars carryout pizza restaurants throughout the US and in about ten other countries. The chain offers a variety of original and deep-dish pizzas along with cheese bread, salads, and sandwiches. While some stores are stand-alone units, many Little Caesars locations can be found in strip malls and other high-traffic areas; the units typically do not offer dine-in seating. About 80% of the chain's outlets are run by franchisees. Little Caesars was founded in 1959 by Mike and Marian Ilitch, who also control a sports and entertainment empire through Ilitch Holdings.

LITTLE LEAGUE BASEBALL, INCORPORATED

539 Rt. 15 Hwy.
Williamsport, PA 17702
Phone: 570-326-1921
Fax: 570-326-1074
Web: www.littleleague.org

CEO: Stephen D. (Steve) Keener
CFO: David B. Houseknecht
HR: Carol Kester
FYE: September 30
Type: Not-for-profit

Little League Baseball's players might be small, but the organization's reach is anything but. Little League Baseball oversees more than 7,000 baseball and softball programs for about 3 million children in more than 100 countries worldwide, including the US, China, Israel, Russia, and Venezuela. On the local level, Little League Baseball programs are organized and operated by volunteers. The season ends with the annual Little League World Series played in Williamsport, Pennsylvania. The organization also runs the Peter J. McGovern Little League Museum in Pennsylvania, the Little League Foundation, and summer baseball camps. Little League Baseball was founded by Carl Stotz with only three teams in 1939.

	Annual Growth	9/04	9/05	9/06	9/07	9/08
Est. sales ($ mil.)	—	—	—	—	—	19.4
Employees	—	—	—	—	—	105

THE LITTLE TIKES COMPANY

2180 Barlow Rd.
Hudson, OH 44236
Phone: 330-650-3000
Fax: 330-287-2864
Web: www.littletikes.com

CEO: Isaac Larian
CFO: —
HR: —
FYE: December 31
Type: Subsidiary

With a reach that spans the globe, The Little Tikes Company is anything but miniature. Founded in 1970 the firm makes infant and preschool products, including development toys, creative arts, ride-on toys, sandboxes, activity gyms, climbers, and juvenile furniture. Primarily it makes and markets molded plastic items. It's known for its Cozy Coupe, which celebrated its 30th anniversary in 2009, and its sturdy Sports Car beds. Little Tikes' products are sold through retailers such as Target, JCPenney, Toys "R" Us, and Wal-Mart, as well as specialty retailers. Little Tikes is owned by MGA Entertainment, maker of the Moxie Girlz line of dolls and the Electronic Hot Hoops.

LITTLEFIELD CORPORATION

OTC: LTFD

2501 N. Lamar Blvd.
Austin, TX 78705
Phone: 512-476-5141
Fax: 512-476-5680
Web: www.littlefield.com

CEO: Jeffrey L. (Jeff) Minch
CFO: Richard S. (Rich) Chilinski
HR: —
FYE: December 31
Type: Public

A fun game of bingo is serious business for this company. Littlefield Corporation owns and operates nearly 40 bingo halls in Texas, South Carolina, Alabama, and Florida. Its gaming locations generate revenue by renting out the space to charitable organizations that use the halls for fund raising activities, such as charity bingo and other events. More than 100 charities utilize Littlefield's properties. President and CEO Jeffrey Minch and his family own about 20% of the company.

	Annual Growth	12/05	12/06	12/07	12/08	12/09
Sales ($ mil.)	(4.0%)	11.3	13.4	13.4	11.2	9.6
Net income ($ mil.)	(34.7%)	1.1	0.8	0.3	(4.3)	0.2
Market value ($ mil.)	8.9%	8.7	14.5	26.3	6.3	12.2
Employees	(47.0%)	405	425	215	80	32

LITTON LOAN SERVICING, LP

4828 Loop Central Dr.
Houston, TX 77081
Phone: 713-960-9676
Fax: 713-966-8830
Web: www.littonloan.com

CEO: Larry B. Litton Jr.
CFO: —
HR: —
FYE: December 31
Type: Subsidiary

Litton Loan Servicing collects principal and interest payments on prime and subprime residential mortgages, including Federal Housing Administration, Veterans Administration, and manufactured home loans. The company's loan portfolio includes approximately 400,000 mortgages worth more than $55 billion. Troubled former parent company Credit-Based Asset Servicing and Securitization (C-BASS for short) sold the firm to Goldman Sachs for some $430 million in late 2007 in order to raise capital. Litton Loan Servicing was founded in 1988 as a subservicer of problem loans in the wake of the Texas real estate bust by Larry Litton Sr. His son, Larry Jr., has since taken over the president and CEO reins.

LIVE NATION ENTERTAINMENT, INC.

NYSE: LYV

9348 Civic Center Dr.
Beverly Hills, CA 90210
Phone: 310-867-7000
Fax: 310-867-7001
Web: www.livenation.com

CEO: Michael (Mike) Rapino
CFO: Kathy Willard
HR: —
FYE: December 31
Type: Public

Live Nation Entertainment holds center stage as the world's largest ticket seller and promoter of live entertainment. In 2010 the company significantly expanded its ticketing services with the purchase of Ticketmaster Entertainment. The deal, worth some $889 million, created a powerful live-music conglomerate. The firm also owns or operates more than 140 venues in North America and Europe. Annually, more than 52 million people attend some 22,000 Live Nation events. Live Nation also owns House of Blues venues through HOB Entertainment. In addition, through deals with pop stars such as Madonna and U2, Live Nation owns a stake in various artists' music, including albums, tours, and merchandise.

	Annual Growth	12/05	12/06	12/07	12/08	12/09
Sales ($ mil.)	9.2%	2,936.8	3,691.6	4,185.0	4,166.8	4,181.0
Net income ($ mil.)	—	(130.6)	(31.4)	(11.9)	(231.8)	(49.7)
Market value ($ mil.)	(10.2%)	2,264.3	3,871.8	2,509.8	992.1	1,470.9
Employees	9.4%	3,000	4,400	4,700	4,700	4,300

LIVEDEAL, INC.

NASDAQ (CM): LIVE

2490 E. Sunset Rd., Ste. 100
Las Vegas, NV 89120
Phone: 702-939-0230
Fax: 702-939-0246
Web: www.livedeal.com

CEO: Kevin A. Hall
CFO: Lawrence W. Tomsic
HR: Kevin A. Hall
FYE: September 30
Type: Public

LiveDeal (formerly YP Corp.) is an Internet yellow pages and local online classifieds provider. The company offers goods and services listed for sale through its online classified marketplace at classifieds.livedeal.com; LiveDeal also publishes about 17 million business listings via its business directory at yellowpages.livedeal.com. Sources of revenue include advertising sales, a pay-per-lead program with major auto dealers, and optional listing upgrade and e-commerce/fraud prevention fees. The company changed its name from YP Corp. after its 2007 purchase of online local classifieds marketplace LiveDeal.

	Annual Growth	9/05	9/06	9/07	9/08	9/09
Sales ($ mil.)	(14.6%)	25.2	36.9	26.3	25.3	13.4
Net income ($ mil.)	—	(0.7)	(1.1)	1.8	(1.5)	(22.6)
Market value ($ mil.)	(34.7%)	53.4	55.2	42.4	9.1	9.7
Employees	(2.2%)	128	79	86	223	117

LIVEPERSON, INC.

NASDAQ (CM): LPSN

462 7th Ave., 3rd Fl.
New York, NY 10018
Phone: 212-609-4200
Fax: 212-609-4201
Web: www.liveperson.com

CEO: Robert P. LoCascio
CFO: Timothy E. (Tim) Bixby
HR: —
FYE: December 31
Type: Public

LivePerson wants to inject some life into your customer service operations. The company provides online, hosted software applications that enable retailers and other companies selling goods online to communicate with customers. LivePerson's software enables communications through multiple channels, including text-based chat, e-mail, and customer self-service tools. Clients install an icon on their websites that, when clicked, opens a dialogue window with customer service representatives. As part of its services, LivePerson also maintains transcripts of customer interactions and offers the option of conducting user exit surveys.

	Annual Growth	12/05	12/06	12/07	12/08	12/09
Sales ($ mil.)	40.7%	22.3	33.5	52.2	74.7	87.5
Net income ($ mil.)	32.9%	2.5	2.2	5.8	(23.8)	7.8
Market value ($ mil.)	5.6%	285.4	266.1	271.7	92.6	354.6
Employees	39.1%	111	178	314	349	416

LIVEWIRE MOBILE, INC.

Pink Sheets: LVWR

1 Monarch Dr., Ste. 203
Littleton, MA 01460
Phone: 978-742-3100
Fax: 978-742-6965
Web: www.livewiremobile.com

CEO: Matthew Stecker
CFO: Todd Donahue
HR: —
FYE: December 31
Type: Public

LiveWire Mobile takes mobile communications personally. The company provides mobile content and subscriber management products to wireless service providers. Its caller personalization applications provide such functionality as musical ringback service. The company markets its services to mobile network operators worldwide. Previously a telecom equipment provider called NMS Communications, the company sold its platforms business (voice quality and echo cancellation systems) to Dialogic for $28 million in cash in 2008. NMS then changed its name to LiveWire Mobile. The company gets about two-thirds of its sales outside the Americas.

	Annual Growth	12/05	12/06	12/07	12/08	12/09
Sales ($ mil.)	(37.4%)	109.5	99.6	82.5	15.6	16.8
Net income ($ mil.)	—	5.0	(15.8)	(8.6)	(38.2)	(2.8)
Employees	(21.3%)	344	425	347	168	—

LIVEWORLD, INC.

OTC: LVWD

4340 Stevens Creek Blvd., Ste. 101
San Jose, CA 95129
Phone: 408-871-5200
Fax: 408-871-5300
Web: www.liveworld.com

CEO: Peter H. Friedman
CFO: David S. Houston
HR: —
FYE: December 31
Type: Public

LiveWorld hopes that online collaboration is the key to its livelihood. Promoting itself as an "online community agency", LiveWorld creates custom communities that are targeted at three distinct areas: loyalty marketing (community of enthusiasts loyal to the clients' business), customer support (used for directly supporting and answering customer questions), and business intelligence (analysis on participating customers' behavior). LiveWorld has created online communities for such prominent companies as AOL, eBay, The Campbell Soup Company, and Warner Brothers. Chairman and CEO Peter Friedman and EVP Jenna Woodul founded LiveWorld in 1996 from remnants of Apple's now-defunct eWorld online service.

	Annual Growth	12/04	12/05	12/06	12/07	*12/08
Sales ($ mil.)	22.7%	5.2	9.6	9.8	10.9	11.8
Net income ($ mil.)	—	(0.5)	0.6	(0.3)	(2.4)	(1.6)
Employees	5.6%	62	63	63	73	—

*Most recent year available

LIZ CLAIBORNE, INC.

NYSE: LIZ

1441 Broadway
New York, NY 10018
Phone: 212-354-4900
Fax: 212-626-3416
Web: www.lizclaiborneinc.com

CEO: William L. McComb
CFO: Andrew C. (Andy) Warren
HR: Lisa Piovano Machacek
FYE: December 31
Type: Public

Liz Claiborne is dressed for success as a leading US seller of clothes and accessories for women. It markets its products as designer items but prices them for a broader market. Its brands — including Liz & Co., Concepts by Claiborne, kate spade, Juicy Couture, and Lucky — are sold worldwide in department stores, more than 450 specialty stores, about 300 outlets, and more than a handful of branded websites. Liz Claiborne also makes men's clothing and licenses its name for shoes, sunglasses, swimwear, formalwear, home furnishings, and stationery. Amid the downturn in the economy and department store sales, the firm restructured its business in 2009 and hired a turnaround specialist.

	Annual Growth	12/05	12/06	12/07	12/08	12/09
Sales ($ mil.)	(11.2%)	4,847.8	4,994.3	4,577.3	3,984.9	3,011.9
Net income ($ mil.)	—	317.4	254.7	(372.8)	(951.8)	(306.4)
Market value ($ mil.)	(37.0%)	3,385.0	4,107.0	1,923.1	245.7	532.0
Employees	(7.0%)	15,400	17,000	16,500	15,000	11,500

An in-depth profile of this company is available to Hoover's Online members at hoovers.com.

947

LKQ CORPORATION

NASDAQ (GS): LKQX

120 N. LaSalle St., Ste. 3300
Chicago, IL 60602
Phone: 312-621-1950
Fax: 312-621-1969
Web: www.lkqcorp.com

CEO: Joseph M. Holsten
CFO: John S. Quinn
HR: —
FYE: December 31
Type: Public

Ever wonder what happens to a car once the insurance company declares it "totaled"? Enter LKQ. A nationwide recycler of damaged cars, LKQ buys wrecked cars at auction and salvages reusable parts including engines, front-end assemblies, doors, fenders, grilles, and mirrors. It then distributes those parts to collision repair and mechanical repair shops, or directly to the customer; mechanical parts that can't be reused are sold as-is to parts reconditioners, and items such as fluids, batteries, and tires are marketed to other recyclers. The company refurbishes wheels, bumpers, and lights. LKQ, which also distributes supplies to paint and body shops, operates from about 300 locations across North America.

	Annual Growth	12/05	12/06	12/07	12/08	12/09
Sales ($ mil.)	39.1%	547.4	789.4	1,126.8	1,937.3	2,047.9
Net income ($ mil.)	42.5%	30.9	44.4	65.9	99.9	127.5
Market value ($ mil.)	22.7%	1,236.3	1,641.9	3,002.4	1,665.5	2,798.2
Employees	31.2%	3,370	4,270	9,100	9,600	10,000

L.L. BEAN, INC.

3 Campus Dr.
Freeport, ME 04033
Phone: 207-552-3028
Fax: 207-552-3080
Web: www.llbean.com

CEO: Christopher J. (Chris) McCormick
CFO: Mark Fasold
HR: Martha Cyr
FYE: February 28
Type: Private

With L.L. Bean, you can tame the great outdoors — or just look as if you could. The outdoor apparel and gear maker mails more than 200 million catalogs per year. L.L. Bean's library includes about 10 specialty catalogs offering products in categories such as children's clothing, fly-fishing, outerwear, sportswear, housewares, footwear, camping and hiking gear, and the Maine hunting shoe upon which the company was built. L.L. Bean also operates about 15 retail stores and an equal number of outlets throughout the Northeast, Illinois, and China. In addition, it sells online through English- and Japanese-language websites. L.L. Bean was founded in 1912 by Leon Leonwood Bean and is controlled by his descendants.

LL&E ROYALTY TRUST

Pink Sheets: LRTR

919 Congress Ave.
Austin, TX 78701
Phone: 512-236-6599
Fax: 512-479-2553

CEO: Michael J. (Mike) Ulrich
CFO: —
HR: —
FYE: December 31
Type: Public

LL&E Royalty Trust owns royalty interests in oil and gas properties located in Alabama, Florida, Texas, and offshore Louisiana. Formed in 1983, the trust receives and distributes royalties to shareholders based on the amount of oil and gas sold either to affiliates or on the spot market. Royalty trusts distribute essentially all royalties received to their shareholders, but their profitability is dependent upon the price of oil and gas and the productivity of the properties. LL&E Royalty Trust has proved reserves of 294,000 barrels of oil and 319 million cu. ft. of natural gas.

LLOYD'S AMERICA INC.

The Museum Office Building, 25 W. 53rd St., 14th Fl.
New York, NY 10019
Phone: 212-382-4060
Fax: 212-382-4070
Web: us.lloyds.com

CEO: Hank Watkins
CFO: —
HR: —
FYE: December 31
Type: Subsidiary

Lloyd's America, the US subsidiary of the famed Lloyd's of London, is the liaison between the London-based specialty insurance market and its US producers (brokers who bring business to Lloyd's syndicates). The company provides information on the market, including statistical information, and on insurance requirements. It also provides lists of approved brokers and correspondents in the US and UK so US brokers not affiliated with Lloyd's can contact it to place insurance business, all of which is underwritten in London. That the US is Lloyd's largest market (about a third of sales) makes this an important function. Lloyd's America operates offices in California, Illinois, Kentucky, and New York.

LMI AEROSPACE, INC.

NASDAQ (GS): LMIA

411 Fountain Lakes Blvd.
St. Charles, MO 63301
Phone: 636-946-6525
Fax: 636-949-1576
Web: www.lmiaerospace.com

CEO: Ronald S. (Ron) Saks
CFO: Lawrence E. (Ed) Dickinson
HR: Cindy Maness
FYE: December 31
Type: Public

It don't mean a thing if it ain't got a wing. LMI Aerospace makes key airplane structures such as door and cockpit window frames, wing leading-edge skins, fuselage skins, and interior components. The Aerostructures segment fabricates, machines, finishes, and integrates more than 30,000 aluminum and specialty alloy components for commercial, corporate, and military aircraft. The Engineering Services segment (D3 Technologies) provides design, engineering, and program management services for aircraft. The Tempco Engineering unit serves the medical and semiconductor industries, as well as aircraft manufacturers. Customers include Boeing, Gulfstream, and Sikorsky. CEO Ronald Saks owns about 17% of the company.

	Annual Growth	12/05	12/06	12/07	12/08	12/09
Sales ($ mil.)	24.3%	101.1	123.0	168.5	239.5	241.2
Net income ($ mil.)	18.3%	5.2	10.7	13.2	15.3	10.2
Market value ($ mil.)	(1.6%)	166.6	182.2	312.0	133.8	156.5
Employees	17.1%	673	916	1,457	1,350	1,266

LNB BANCORP, INC.

NASDAQ (GM): LNBB

457 Broadway
Lorain, OH 44052
Phone: 440-244-6000
Fax: 440-244-4815
Web: www.4lnb.com

CEO: Daniel E. (Dan) Klimas
CFO: Gary J. Elek
HR: Mary E. Miles
FYE: December 31
Type: Public

LNB Bancorp is the holding company for The Lorain National Bank, which operates more than 20 branches in Ohio's Cuyahoga, Erie, Lorain, and Summit counties. The bank serves local businesses and individuals, offering such deposit products as checking and savings accounts, money market accounts, CDs, and IRAs. It also offers trust services and credit cards. The bank's lending activities primarily consist of commercial loans (approximately 60% of its portfolio) and real estate mortgages, as well as installment and home equity loans. The Lorain National Bank offers brokerage and investment services to customers through an agreement with Investment Centers of America.

	Annual Growth	12/05	12/06	12/07	12/08	12/09
Assets ($ mil.)	9.4%	801.1	851.1	1,056.6	1,136.1	1,149.5
Net income ($ mil.)	—	6.4	5.4	5.5	3.4	(2.0)
Market value ($ mil.)	(30.0%)	132.2	118.2	107.9	38.7	31.7
Employees	1.4%	257	243	270	277	272

LNR PROPERTY CORPORATION

1601 Washington Ave., Ste. 800
Miami Beach, FL 33139
Phone: 305-695-5500
Fax: 305-695-5589
Web: www.lnrproperty.com

CEO: Thomas J. (Tom) Hughes
CFO: Stephen Ferguson
HR: Illeanne Rukes
FYE: November 30
Type: Private

LNR is a real estate investment and management company spun off from homebuilding giant Lennar in 1997. LNR owns and manages a portfolio of real estate properties and real estate finance investments (unrated and junk-grade commercial mortgage-backed securities and collateralized debt obligations, high-yield mortgage loans, and mezzanine financing). Its LandSource Communities Development joint venture with Lennar develops and sells homes as well as land for residential or commercial use; it owns Newhall Land and Farming. LandSource declared bankruptcy in 2008, a victim of the housing downturn. LNR is a subsidiary of Cerberus Capital Management, which owns a 75% stake in the company through LNR Property Holdings.

LOCAL.COM CORPORATION

NASDAQ (CM): LOCM

1 Technology Dr., Bldg. G
Irvine, CA 92618
Phone: 949-784-0800
Fax: 949-784-0880
Web: corporate.local.com

CEO: Heath B. Clarke
CFO: Brenda Agius
HR: Heather A. Dilley
FYE: December 31
Type: Public

Local.com, formerly Interchange, traffics in keywords. Specializing in paid-search advertising, the company connects businesses hawking their wares to consumers surfing the Web via its distribution network of more than 700 media websites and search engines. It makes money from direct advertisers who bid for placement (based on keywords) and pay for click-throughs, and from indirect advertisers that gain inclusion on the network through paid-search firms that have partnered with Local.com (such as LookSmart and Yahoo!). In an effort to capitalize on the awareness of its primary search engine, which it bought in 2005, the company changed its name to Local.com from Interchange in late 2006.

	Annual Growth	12/05	12/06	12/07	12/08	12/09
Sales ($ mil.)	32.8%	18.1	14.2	21.5	38.3	56.3
Net income ($ mil.)	—	(6.5)	(13.3)	(18.2)	(8.6)	(6.3)
Market value ($ mil.)	1.2%	88.4	64.8	76.9	24.9	92.9
Employees	6.4%	67	58	68	74	86

LOCATEPLUS HOLDINGS CORPORATION

Pink Sheets: LPHC

100 Cummings Center, Ste. 235M
Beverly, MA 01915
Phone: 978-921-2727
Fax: 978-524-8767
Web: www.locateplus.com

CEO: Ronald Lifton
CFO: Brian McHugh
HR: —
FYE: December 31
Type: Public

LocatePLUS Holdings provides databases of public and non-public background information for law enforcement agencies, government agencies, law firms, private investigators, and insurance companies. Its Internet-based LocatePLUS database provides searchable and cross-referenced data about individuals, including names, addresses, birth dates, social security numbers, court records, and motor vehicle records. Its Worldwide Information CD-ROM databases provide motor vehicle and driver's license information. Its Certifion Corporation unit, operating under the Entersect name, provides screening for resume and online dating services. LocatePLUS also offers information on phone numbers through its Dataphant unit.

LOCKHEED MARTIN CORPORATION

NYSE: LMT

6801 Rockledge Dr.
Bethesda, MD 20817
Phone: 301-897-6000
Fax: 301-897-6704
Web: www.lockheedmartin.com

CEO: Robert J. Stevens
CFO: Bruce L. Tanner
HR: John T. Lucas
FYE: December 31
Type: Public

Lockheed Martin takes flight in times of crisis — the company is one of the world's top military contractors (along with Boeing and Northrop Grumman). Lockheed is firmly on the defense/government side of the aerospace industry; in fact, the US government accounts for about 85% of sales. This reliance on the US government is a double-edged sword: Lockheed can largely avoid turbulence in the commercial aerospace sector, but the company is vulnerable to military spending cuts. The Electronic Systems and Information Systems & Global Services segments account for more than half of Lockheed's sales. The US Department of Defense (DoD), US Army, and US Navy are among its many customers.

	Annual Growth	12/05	12/06	12/07	12/08	12/09
Sales ($ mil.)	5.0%	37,213.0	39,620.0	41,862.0	42,731.0	45,189.0
Net income ($ mil.)	13.5%	1,825.0	2,529.0	3,033.0	3,217.0	3,024.0
Market value ($ mil.)	4.3%	23,606.6	34,157.8	39,051.2	31,193.5	27,954.7
Employees	0.9%	135,000	140,000	140,000	146,000	140,000

LOCKHEED MARTIN LOGISTICS SERVICES

400 Brookfield Pkwy.
Greenville, SC 29607
Phone: 864-422-6240
Fax: —
Web: www.lockheedmartin.com/capabilities/air_power/logistics

CEO: Michael A. Grasso
CFO: —
HR: John Slipke
FYE: December 31
Type: Subsidiary

With such craft as the F-16 Fighting Falcon, the F/A-22 Raptor, and the F-35 Joint Strike Fighter (officially named Lightning II), Lockheed Martin is the US's leading maker of military jet fighters. Those craft and other jets don't take care of themselves, so Lockheed created a unit to tackle logistics, maintenance, repair, and overhaul chores. Lockheed Martin Logistics Services (formerly Lockheed Martin Aircraft & Logistics Centers), part of the Aeronautics division of parent Lockheed Martin, repairs and maintains aircraft and aircraft engines and provides related logistics services for government customers. The Department of Defense — particularly the US Air Force — accounts for most of the unit's sales.

THE LOCKTON COMPANIES, LLC

444 W. 47th St., Ste. 900
Kansas City, MO 64112
Phone: 816-960-9000
Fax: 816-960-9099
Web: www.lockton.com

CEO: John L. Lumelleau
CFO: Alan L. Salts
HR: Jo-Ann Gastin
FYE: April 30
Type: Private

The world's largest privately held insurance brokerage, Lockton offers risk management services, commercial property/casualty insurance, surety bonds, mergers and acquisition support services, and employee benefit planning services. Initially targeting construction businesses, Lockton has expanded its expertise to other industries including energy, health care, hospitality, manufacturing, retail, and transportation. The company operates from about 20 domestic offices and more than 25 international offices in Latin America, Asia, and Europe. It serves corporate clients operating worldwide. Lockton was founded in 1966 by Jack Lockton, brother of chairman David Lockton; it is owned by company executives.

	Annual Growth	4/04	4/05	4/06	4/07	4/08
Sales ($ mil.)	29.2%	—	343.8	409.2	667.1	742.0
Employees	41.2%	—	1,350	3,700	3,825	3,800

An in-depth profile of this company is available to Hoover's Online members at hoovers.com.

949

LODGENET INTERACTIVE CORPORATION

NASDAQ (GM): LNET

3900 W. Innovation St.
Sioux Falls, SD 57107
Phone: 605-988-1000
Fax: 605-988-1511
Web: www.lodgenet.com

CEO: Scott C. Petersen
CFO: Frank P. Elsenbast
HR: —
FYE: December 31
Type: Public

Enjoy your stay: Watch a movie, play Nintendo, surf the Internet, use the shampoo, but please don't steal the towels. LodgeNet Interactive provides free and fee-based guest services, including cable TV, on-demand movies, Nintendo video games, DIRECTV broadcast satellite TV programming, and Internet access to more than 10,000 hotels, serving about 2 million rooms. The company installs broadband networks to enable its Internet and interactive services, which include video checkout and room service menus. LodgeNet is spreading its system architecture and technology through licensing partners outside North America, where the company gets almost all of its sales.

	Annual Growth	12/05	12/06	12/07	12/08	12/09
Sales ($ mil.)	15.1%	275.8	288.2	485.6	533.9	484.5
Net income ($ mil.)	—	(7.0)	1.8	(65.2)	(48.4)	(10.2)
Market value ($ mil.)	(20.6%)	349.2	627.1	436.9	17.5	138.5
Employees	7.8%	809	803	1,459	1,202	1,091

LODGIAN, INC.

3445 Peachtree Rd. NE, Ste. 700
Atlanta, GA 30326
Phone: 404-364-9400
Fax: 404-364-0088
Web: www.lodgian.com

CEO: Daniel E. (Dan) Ellis
CFO: James A. MacLennan
HR: Carol L. Mayne
FYE: December 31
Type: Private

If you're living in hotel lodgings, does that make you a Lodgian? Lodgian is a multi-brand hospitality franchisee that operates some 35 hotels in more than 20 US states and one hotel in Windsor, Canada. The company's portfolio is focused mostly on the mid-market segment serving both leisure and business travels with full-service brands franchised from InterContinental Hotels (including Crowne Plaza and Holiday Inn) and Marriott (Courtyard by Marriott, Fairfield Inn by Marriott, Residence Inn by Marriott, SpringHill Suites by Marriott). It also runs a handful of unaffiliated and other branded hotels (Hilton, Carlson, Starwood, and Wyndham).

	Annual Growth	12/05	12/06	12/07	12/08	12/09
Sales ($ mil.)	(12.3%)	319.3	261.8	278.1	240.4	188.5
Net income ($ mil.)	—	12.3	(15.2)	(8.4)	(12.0)	(53.9)
Employees	(18.2%)	5,277	3,534	3,444	3,046	2,362

LOEHMANN'S HOLDINGS INC.

2500 Halsey St.
Bronx, NY 10461
Phone: 718-409-2000
Fax: 718-518-2766
Web: www.loehmanns.com

CEO: Jerald (Jerry) Politzer
CFO: Richard Morretta
HR: Nancy Straface
FYE: January 31
Type: Private

Humorist Erma Bombeck claimed that *All I Know About Animal Behavior I Learned in Loehmann's Dressing Room* — and if you've ever tussled over the last discounted Donna Karan blouse at one of this retailer's stores, you know what she was talking about. With some 60-plus Loehmann's stores in more than 15 states (nearly a third are in California), Loehmann's Holdings sells designer and brand-name women's and men's apparel, accessories, intimate apparel, fragrances, shoes, and gifts at deep discounts. But caution to the shy: Loehmann's is famous for its communal dressing rooms. Founded in Brooklyn in 1921 by Frieda Loehmann, the company was acquired by Dubai-based Istithmar PJSC in mid-2006 for about $300 million.

LOEWS CORPORATION

NYSE: L

667 Madison Ave.
New York, NY 10065
Phone: 212-521-2000
Fax: 212-521-2525
Web: www.loews.com

CEO: James S. Tisch
CFO: Peter W. Keegan
HR: Alan Momeyer
FYE: December 31
Type: Public

When it comes to diversification, Loews definitely has the low-down. The holding company's main interest is insurance through publicly traded subsidiary CNA Financial, which offers commercial property/casualty coverage. Other wholly owned and partially owned holdings include hotels in the US and Canada through its Loews Hotels subsidiary. Its energy holdings include contract oil-drilling operator Diamond Offshore Drilling (which operates roughly 50 offshore oil rigs), interstate natural gas transmission pipeline systems operator Boardwalk Pipelines, and HighMount Exploration & Production (also natural gas).

	Annual Growth	12/05	12/06	12/07	12/08	12/09
Assets ($ mil.)	1.2%	70,675.6	76,880.9	76,079.0	69,857.0	74,070.0
Net income ($ mil.)	3.4%	1,211.6	2,491.3	2,489.0	4,530.0	1,383.0
Market value ($ mil.)	3.5%	13,231.5	17,355.1	21,067.1	11,822.5	15,212.4
Employees	(3.8%)	21,600	21,600	21,700	19,100	18,500

LOEWS HOTELS HOLDING CORPORATION

667 Madison Ave.
New York, NY 10021
Phone: 212-521-2000
Fax: 212-521-2525
Web: www.loewshotels.com

CEO: Jonathan M. Tisch
CFO: —
HR: —
FYE: December 31
Type: Subsidiary

Loews Hotels is high on the list for luxury accommodations. The company operates about 20 upscale hotels located in prime business and travel locations in the US and Canada. In addition to offering amenities such as fine dining options, spas, and golf courses, the properties also feature facilities for weddings, meetings, and other events. Loews' hotels include The Regency in New York City, The Santa Monica Beach Hotel in California, and Quebec City's Le Concorde. The company also has resort locations and hotels operated in conjunction with such tourist destination brands as Hard Rock Cafe and Universal Studios' theme parks. Loews Hotels is a subsidiary of diversified holding company Loews Corporation.

LOGAN ALUMINUM, INC.

6920 Lewisburg Rd.
Russellville, KY 42276
Phone: 270-755-6000
Fax: 270-755-6573
Web: www.logan-aluminum.com

CEO: Randy W. Schumaker
CFO: Gary W. Grohovsky
HR: Stacey Hughes
FYE: December 31
Type: Joint venture

Those folks who like to crush beer cans against their foreheads owe a lot to Logan Aluminum. Formed in 1983, Logan manufactures aluminum sheet that is used primarily by the beverage industry. A joint-venture of ARCO Aluminum (60%) and Novelis (40%), Logan Aluminum consists of one production facility that also manufactures products for makers of building products and rigid containers as well as for the automotive industry. Its technology includes ingot casting, hot and cold rolling, and finishing. Logan also operates an aluminum recycling facility that opened in 2008. ARCO Aluminum is a part of energy giant BP, and Novelis is owned by Indian aluminum producer Hindalco.

LOGIC DEVICES INCORPORATED

NASDAQ (GM): LOGC

395 W. Java Dr.
Sunnyvale, CA 94089
Phone: 408-542-5400
Fax: 408-542-0080
Web: www.logicdevices.com

CEO: William J. (Bill) Volz
CFO: Kimiko Milheim
HR: —
FYE: September 30
Type: Public

LOGIC Devices doesn't produce philosophical machines. Rather, LOGIC specializes in high-end digital signal processor (DSP) chips used in applications including medical imaging, instrumentation, telecommunications, and military weapons systems. The company outsources production of its chips to Asian foundries, primarily Taiwan Semiconductor Manufacturing. LOGIC works with sales representatives and international distributors, and also sells directly to OEMs, including Lockheed Martin, QUALCOMM, Raytheon, Sony, Teradyne, and Texas Instruments.

	Annual Growth	9/05	9/06	9/07	9/08	9/09
Sales ($ mil.)	(3.8%)	3.5	4.6	4.7	3.4	3.0
Net income ($ mil.)	—	(1.4)	0.1	(1.5)	(4.0)	(0.8)
Market value ($ mil.)	(5.0%)	7.4	18.1	14.0	6.8	6.1
Employees	(3.3%)	16	20	21	15	14

LOGICALIS, INC.

1750 S. Telegraph Rd., Ste. 300
Bloomfield Hills, MI 48302
Phone: 248-745-5400
Fax: 248-335-8715
Web: www.us.logicalis.com

CEO: Terrence (Terry) Flood
CFO: Greg Baker
HR: —
FYE: February 28
Type: Subsidiary

Logicalis believes that your enterprise technology should operate in a straightforward, logical fashion. The company provides a variety of information technology (IT) services such as consulting, implementation, systems integration, staffing, network design, and training. Logicalis also offers managed services for tasks such as network security, IT infrastructure management and monitoring, and application management. Customers come from a variety of fields including manufacturing, financial services, and health care. The company is the US operating subsidiary of UK-based Logicalis Group.

	Annual Growth	2/04	2/05	2/06	2/07	2/08
Est. sales ($ mil.)	—	—	—	—	—	409.3
Employees	—	—	—	—	—	650

LOGMEIN, INC.

NASDAQ (GM): LOGM

500 Unicorn Park Dr.
Woburn, MA 01801
Phone: 781-638-9050
Fax: 781-998-7792
Web: secure.logmein.com

CEO: Michael K. Simon
CFO: James F. (Jim) Kelliher
HR: —
FYE: December 31
Type: Public

LogMeIn helps you stay productive even when on the go. The company provides remote access software and services to consumers, small and midsized businesses, and IT service providers. Consumers and remote workers can access their computers' desktops, files, applications, and network resources. Businesses and IT service providers use LogMeIn's technology to provide remote management and support. LogMeIn offers both free and subscription-based services. Its paid services add advanced features such as file transfer, remote printing, and drive mapping. LogMeIn's corporate customers include 3M, AMD, and IBM. The company was founded in 2003.

	Annual Growth	12/05	12/06	12/07	12/08	12/09
Sales ($ mil.)	114.7%	3.5	11.3	27.0	51.7	74.4
Net income ($ mil.)	—	(5.9)	(6.7)	(9.1)	(5.4)	8.8
Market value ($ mil.)	—	—	—	—	—	458.6
Employees	47.7%	71	126	262	287	338

LOJACK CORPORATION

NASDAQ (GS): LOJN

200 Lowder Brook Dr., Ste. 1000
Westwood, MA 02090
Phone: 781-251-4700
Fax: 781-251-4649
Web: www.lojack.com

CEO: Richard T. Riley
CFO: Timothy P. O'Connor
HR: Mark Bornemann
FYE: December 31
Type: Public

LoJack's signature product helps police recover stolen vehicles — a chilling thought for those driving hot cars. When a car equipped with a LoJack transmitter is stolen, its radio signal is activated and tracked by police. LoJack rents tracking computers to law enforcement agencies, then markets transponders to dealers and operators in about 25 states and the District of Columbia, and some 30 countries internationally. The company also markets products for cargo and equipment tracking and recovery. LoJack provides installation and maintenance of its units, which are manufactured by third parties. Canada-based subsidiary Boomerang Tracking uses cellular technology to track stolen vehicles.

	Annual Growth	12/05	12/06	12/07	12/08	12/09
Sales ($ mil.)	(8.3%)	190.7	213.3	222.7	198.7	135.0
Net income ($ mil.)	—	18.4	16.5	21.4	(32.5)	(34.7)
Market value ($ mil.)	(36.0%)	442.3	313.1	308.2	75.5	74.1
Employees	(5.8%)	890	913	925	837	700

⊞ LONE STAR STEAKHOUSE & SALOON, INC.

224 E. Douglas, Ste. 700
Wichita, KS 67202
Phone: 316-264-8899
Fax: 316-264-5988
Web: www.lonestarsteakhouse.com

CEO: Ryan Franklin
CFO: Ed Barton
HR: Pat Barth
FYE: December 31
Type: Private

There are actually two stars in this steakhouse constellation. Lone Star Steakhouse & Saloon owns and operates more than 140 steakhouse restaurants offering mesquite-grilled steaks, ribs, chicken, and fish dishes. The casual dining spots, found in more than 30 states, are punctuated by Texas paraphernalia, neon beer signs, and country music. The company also runs the Texas Land & Cattle Steak House chain, which has about 30 locations in Texas and five other states. Started in 1992, Lone Star Steakhouse is owned by Dallas-based private equity firm Lone Star Funds.

THE LONGABERGER COMPANY

1 Market Sq., 1500 E. Main St.
Newark, OH 43055
Phone: 740-322-5588
Fax: 740-322-5240
Web: www.longaberger.com

CEO: Tami Longaberger
CFO: Rusty Deaton
HR: Tom Coles
FYE: December 31
Type: Private

A tisket, a tasket, a Longaberger basket. The Longaberger Company is the #1 maker of handmade baskets in the US, selling nearly 10 million a year. The baskets are sold through in-home shows conducted by Longaberger's about 45,000 independent sales associates. Baskets account for about half of sales, but the company also sells fabrics, pottery, and wrought-iron home accessories. Longaberger's home office is a seven-story rendition of a basket with two 75-ton handles on top. The company also owns a golf course, a hotel, and Longaberger Homestead (an events area with shops and restaurants). The family-owned firm is run by the daughters of the late Dave Longaberger, who founded the company in 1973.

⊞ An in-depth profile of this company is available to Hoover's Online members at hoovers.com.

951

LONGVIEW FIBRE COMPANY

300 Fibre Way
Longview, WA 98632
Phone: 360-425-1550
Fax: 360-575-5934
Web: www.longviewfibre.com

CEO: Frank V. McShane
CFO: Heidi Pozzo
HR: Sally Nelson
FYE: December 31
Type: Subsidiary

"Paper or plastic?" is not an option at Longview Fibre. The company owns and manages tree farms, one of the largest pulp and paper mills in North America, and a network of seven converting plants. Its paper mill and converting plants produce specialty kraft paper, containerboard, and converted goods such as corrugated containers and point-of-purchase displays. No shortage of lumber, Longview Fibre's timberland spans 588,000 acres in Oregon and Washington. Its unprocessed logs are sold to saw mills and plywood plants, and exported to Japan. In 2006 the company restructured to qualify for real estate investment trust (REIT) tax treatment. Longview Fibre was acquired by Brookfield Asset Management in 2007.

LONZA INC

90 Boroline Rd.
Allendale, NJ 07401
Phone: 201-316-9200
Fax: 201-785-9973
Web: www.lonza.com

CEO: Jeanne Thoma
CFO: Vincent L. DiVito
HR: Terry Krezmer
FYE: December 31
Type: Subsidiary

From disinfecting workplaces to exfoliating dry skin, Lonza puts itself in the middle of things. As the North American operations of its parent company, Lonza accounts for more than a third of the Switzerland-based Lonza Group's roughly $4 billion in annual sales. While Lonza doesn't actually make consumer products, the company provides chemical ingredients and intermediates for the biocide, nutrition, personal care, pharmaceutical, plastics, and water treatment industries from its ten manufacturing and R&D locations throughout the eastern half of the US.

	Annual Growth	12/04	12/05	12/06	12/07	12/08
Est. sales ($ mil.)	—	—	—	—	—	433.6
Employees	—	—	—	—	—	536

LOOKSMART, LTD.

NASDAQ (GM): LOOK

625 2nd St.
San Francisco, CA 94107
Phone: 415-348-7000
Fax: 415-348-7050
Web: www.looksmart.com

CEO: Jean-Yves Dexmier
CFO: Stephen Markowski
HR: Stacey A. Giamalis
FYE: December 31
Type: Public

It's hard to find anything online without looking unless you're talking about ads. LookSmart helps publishers, advertisers, and consumers see what they want when it comes to online advertising. The company earns most of its revenue through its Advertiser Networks offering, which provide advertisers with targeted, pay-per-click (PPC) search advertising, contextual advertising, and banner products. It also offers Publisher Solutions that help content publishers maintain advertiser relationships online. LookSmart sold most of its consumer website operations in 2007. It initially retained its Wisenut search engine technology and Furl.net social bookmarking service, but shut down those businesses in 2008.

	Annual Growth	12/05	12/06	12/07	12/08	12/09
Sales ($ mil.)	5.8%	41.4	48.7	56.2	65.0	51.8
Net income ($ mil.)	—	(17.9)	(13.7)	3.4	(14.8)	(6.2)
Market value ($ mil.)	(27.8%)	64.5	76.6	54.7	27.8	17.5
Employees	(15.4%)	127	120	93	90	65

LOOPNET, INC.

NASDAQ (GS): LOOP

185 Berry St., Ste. 4000
San Francisco, CA 94107
Phone: 415-243-4200
Fax: 415-764-1622
Web: www.loopnet.com

CEO: Richard J. (Rich) Boyle Jr.
CFO: Brent Stumme
HR: —
FYE: December 31
Type: Public

Feeling out of the loop when it comes to commercial real estate? LoopNet provides information services to the commercial real estate market through its namesake website, LoopNet.com, an online marketplace that includes approximately 652,000 property listings. The company offers a free basic membership, as well as a subscription-based premium membership. LoopNet has about 4 million registered members and more than 77,000 premium members. The company also offers LoopLink, which helps real estate brokers integrate LoopNet listings into their own websites; BizBuySell, an online marketplace for operating businesses that are for sale; and commercial real estate network CityFeet.com.

	Annual Growth	12/05	12/06	12/07	12/08	12/09
Sales ($ mil.)	25.3%	31.0	48.4	70.7	86.1	76.5
Net income ($ mil.)	(11.1%)	18.9	15.5	21.1	18.3	11.8
Market value ($ mil.)	(12.8%)	—	515.6	483.6	234.7	341.8
Employees	18.8%	138	198	266	305	275

LORAL SPACE & COMMUNICATIONS INC.

NASDAQ (GM): LORL

600 3rd Ave.
New York, NY 10016
Phone: 212-697-1105
Fax: 212-338-5662
Web: www.loral.com

CEO: Michael B. (Mickey) Targoff
CFO: Harvey B. Rein
HR: —
FYE: December 31
Type: Public

Loral Space & Communications has a higher purpose. The company's main business unit, Space Systems/Loral (SS/L), makes satellites and related systems and components for digital broadcasters, data distribution, commercial weather forecasting, and digital audio service providers. The company also holds a majority stake in fixed satellite services provider Telesat Canada. The unit leases satellite transponder capacity to cable and satellite broadcasters, voice and data networks, and other users. SS/L's customers include DIRECTV, DISH Network, and SIRIUS XM Radio. Telesat counts the US and Canadian governments among its customers. Loral Space & Communications gets more than half of its sales in the US.

	Annual Growth	12/05	12/06	12/07	12/08	12/09
Sales ($ mil.)	49.8%	197.2	797.3	882.5	869.4	993.4
Net income ($ mil.)	—	(15.3)	(22.7)	29.7	(692.9)	231.7
Market value ($ mil.)	2.8%	845.4	1,217.2	1,023.8	434.3	944.9
Employees	10.7%	1,700	2,100	2,140	2,300	2,550

LORD & TAYLOR LLC

424 5th Ave.
New York, NY 10018
Phone: 212-391-3344
Fax: 212-768-0743
Web: www.lordandtaylor.com

CEO: Brendan L. Hoffman
CFO: Michael Cuhlane
HR: —
FYE: December 31
Type: Private

Venerable Lord & Taylor is a Fifth Avenue institution trying not to become a retail industry dinosaur. The department store chain operates about 45 stores in nine states and the District of Columbia, as well as an online shopping site. Its stores sell better women's, men's, and children's apparel and accessories, and cosmetics. Services include personal shopping and in-store restaurants at some locations. Its Fifth Avenue flagship (more than 10% of annual sales) store's Christmas windows are a New York holiday tradition. Founded in 1826, the firm has changed hands through consolidation. In 2006 Macy's sold Lord & Taylor for nearly $1.1 billion to NRDC Equity Partners, owner of Hudson's Bay Trading Company.

An in-depth profile of this company is available to Hoover's Online members at hoovers.com.

LORD CORPORATION

111 Lord Dr.
Cary, NC 27511
Phone: 919-468-5979
Fax: 919-469-5777
Web: www.lordcorp.com

CEO: Richard L. McNeel
CFO: Tesa L. Oechsle
HR: Mark Boris
FYE: December 31
Type: Private

When it comes to adhesives and vibration control products, LORD knows. LORD is a leading maker of adhesives (for rubber-to-metal bonding for engine mounts, bushings, and hoses, and automotive body panel assembly, as well as circuit assembly); coatings (protect metal, rubber, plastic, ceramic, and wood against corrosion control, severe temperatures, chemical attack, and abrasion); and vibration, motion, and noise control devices and systems (aerospace, automotive engine mounts, and industrial applications). Its magneto-rheological (MR) technology alters fluids for better lubricity and viscosity in mechanical management. LORD has 15 facilities in nine countries. It was founded in 1924 by Hugh Lord.

	Annual Growth	12/04	12/05	12/06	12/07	12/08
Est. sales ($ mil.)	—	—	—	—	—	727.0
Employees	—	—	—	—	—	2,583

L'ORÉAL USA, INC.

575 5th Ave.
New York, NY 10017
Phone: 212-818-1500
Fax: 212-984-4999
Web: www.lorealusa.com

CEO: Frédéric Rozé
CFO: Arnaud Legain
HR: Sarah Hibberson
FYE: December 31
Type: Subsidiary

The changes made by L'Oréal USA since its 1953 founding have been anything but cosmetic. The US arm of L'Oréal (the world's #1 cosmetics firm), L'Oréal USA boasts a host of big-name brands, including Maybelline and Redken. It also owns salon product makers Matrix and Kérastase, as well as consumer-focused SoftSheen/Carson and perfume brands Ralph Lauren and Gloria Vanderbilt. The unit's upscale Lancôme (makeup, skin care) and Biotherm (skin care) lines are sold nationwide in department stores. Its parent bought Dallas-based SkinCeuticals. The company agreed to acquire Essie Cosmetics in 2010.

LORILLARD, INC.

NYSE: LO

714 Green Valley Rd.
Greensboro, NC 27408
Phone: 336-335-7000
Fax: 336-335-7550
Web: www.lorillard.com

CEO: Martin L. (Marty) Orlowsky
CFO: David H. Taylor
HR: William G. Crump
FYE: December 31
Type: Public

Newport news provides the best read on Lorillard, the #3 cigarette maker in the US (behind Philip Morris USA and Reynolds American). Newport, Lorillard's flagship brand, is the best-selling menthol cigarette and second-largest cigarette brand in the US. It generates more than 90% of Lorillard's sales by volume. Other brands include the premium and discount lines of Kent, Max, Old Gold, True, and Maverick. The company sells its products primarily to wholesale distributors. Lorillard was named the Carolina Group until 2008, when it split from former parent Loews. Founded in 1760 by French immigrant Pierre Lorillard, it is the nation's oldest continuously operating tobacco firm.

	Annual Growth	12/05	12/06	12/07	12/08	12/09
Sales ($ mil.)	10.0%	3,568.0	3,755.0	3,969.0	4,204.0	5,233.0
Net income ($ mil.)	7.6%	706.0	826.0	898.0	887.0	948.0
Market value ($ mil.)	42.4%	—	—	—	8,613.4	12,263.5
Employees	(1.8%)	—	—	2,800	2,800	2,700

LOS ANGELES CITY COLLEGE

855 N. Vermont Ave.
Los Angeles, CA 90029
Phone: 323-953-4000
Fax: 323-953-4013
Web: www.lacitycollege.edu

CEO: Jamillah Moore
CFO: —
HR: —
FYE: August 31
Type: School

Los Angeles City College (LACC) is a community college that offers certificate and associate's degree programs. The school concentrates its curriculum on arts and sciences and vocational coursework. Many of its students transfer to UC or USC after completing LACC's curriculum, designed in preparation for transfer to a four-year university. Enrollment is at about 17,000 students, more than 50% of which are over the age of 55. The primary language for nearly half of LACC's students is something other than English. LACC was founded as Los Angeles Junior College in 1929 by the Los Angeles Board of Education.

LOS ANGELES COUNTY METROPOLITAN TRANSPORTATION AUTHORITY

1 Gateway Plaza
Los Angeles, CA 90012
Phone: 213-922-6000
Fax: 213-922-2704
Web: www.metro.net

CEO: Arthur T. (Art) Leahy
CFO: Terry Matsumoto
HR: —
FYE: June 30
Type: Government-owned

Thanks to the bus and rail systems of the Los Angeles County Metropolitan Transportation Authority, known to Angelenos as Metro, millions of passenger journeys involve modes of transportation other than cars on freeways. On its own and through contractors, Metro maintains a fleet of more than 2,600 buses that serve about 190 routes. About 1.2 million passenger boardings take place on a typical weekday. Metro's rail system spans about 75 miles and incorporates more than 60 stations; weekday boardings average about 260,000. In addition, Metro helps pay for car pool lanes and bicycle paths. A board made up of elected officials and appointees oversees the agency.

LOST ARROW CORPORATION

259 W. Santa Clara St.
Ventura, CA 93001
Phone: 805-643-8616
Fax: 805-653-6355

CEO: Casey Sheahan
CFO: Martha Groszewski
HR: —
FYE: April 30
Type: Holding company

Lost Arrow Corporation knows exactly what its targets are — the Great Outdoors, and the consumers that love it. Known best as the parent holding company of Patagonia, its group of companies focuses on clothing and activewear for outdoor sports and activities. Other subsidiaries include Water Girl, a women's clothing and swimwear manufacturer, and Lotus Designs, which makes clothing and accessories for kayakers and whitewater paddlers. The group also owns Point Blanks, a surfboard manufacturer. Founder Yvon Chouinard, a legendary rock climber and mountaineer, and his wife, Malinda, own Lost Arrow.

An in-depth profile of this company is available to Hoover's Online members at hoovers.com.

953

LOUD TECHNOLOGIES INC.

16220 Wood-Red Rd. NE
Woodinville, WA 98072
Phone: 425-892-6500
Fax: 425-487-4337
Web: www.loudtechinc.com

CEO: Rodney E. Olson
CFO: David Olson
HR: Christina Foltz
FYE: December 31
Type: Private

LOUD Technologies helps musicians bring their music to the masses. Best known for its multi-channel mixing consoles, which allow sound engineers to combine some 100 sound channels, the company also makes loudspeakers, commercial audio systems, amplifiers, audio and music software, guitars, and orchestral string instruments. Brands include Alvarez, Ampeg, Crate, Mackie, Martin Audio, and TAPCO, among others. It also owns loudspeaker manufacturer Eastern Acoustic Works (EAW). LOUD Technologies' products are sold through thousands of retail outlets and a network of installed sound contractors in the US, as well as through distributors worldwide. LOUD Technolgoies is owned by private equity firm Sun Capital.

LOUIS VUITTON NORTH AMERICA, INC.

19 E. 57th St.
New York, NY 10022
Phone: 212-931-2000
Fax: 212-931-2903
Web: www.lvmh.com

CEO: Daniel Lalonde
CFO: Patrice Pfistner
HR: —
FYE: December 31
Type: Subsidiary

Louis Vuitton North America is the North American operations subsidiary of French luxury goods giant LVMH Moët Hennessy Louis Vuitton, which boasts more than 60 luxury brands including Clicquot, Dom Pérignon, Moët & Chandon, Christian Dior, Givenchy, Donna Karan (DKI), Sephora, and TAG Heuer. The firm specializes in wines and spirits, fashion and leather goods, perfumes and cosmetics, watches and jewelry, and duty free shopping. Louis Vuitton North America operates more than 540 stores — including a four-story emporium on New York's Fifth Avenue — throughout the US and contributes more than 20% of its parent company's sales.

LOUIS A. WEISS MEMORIAL HOSPITAL

4646 N. Marine Dr.
Chicago, IL 60640
Phone: 773-878-8700
Fax: 773-564-7203
Web: www.weisshospital.org

CEO: Frank Molinaro
CFO: Jeff Meigs
HR: Keoni Nader
FYE: June 30
Type: Joint venture

Louis A. Weiss Memorial Hospital serves the residents of Chicago's North Side. The facility has about 340 beds and a medical staff of some 400 physicians covering more than 25 specialties. It conducts medical research and education programs through its affiliation with the University of Chicago Medical Center. Weiss offers a complete range of services for adults, including orthopedics, cardiology, vascular health, rehabilitation, cancer care, geriatrics, and women's health care. Specialty divisions provide laboratory, radiology, wound healing, and hospice care. Vanguard Health Systems owns 80% of the hospital and the University of Chicago Medical Center owns the rest.

LOUISIANA BANCORP, INC.

NASDAQ (GM): LABC

1600 Veterans Blvd.
Metairie, LA 70005
Phone: 504-834-1190
Fax: —
Web: www.bankofneworleans.net

CEO: Lawrence J. LeBon III
CFO: John P. LeBlanc
HR: Lindsey Gordon
FYE: December 31
Type: Public

Louisiana Bancorp's vault isn't filled with Mardi Gras doublons, *chère*. The holding company owns the Bank of New Orleans, which offers standard retail banking products to individuals and small businesses, including deposit accounts, loans and mortgages, and credit cards. Residential mortgages represent about half of the bank's loan portfolio; commercial mortgages and land loans make up most of the rest. Bank of New Orleans operates three locations and a loan office in the Crescent City; a fourth branch has been closed since being damaged by Hurricane Katrina in 2005. The bank was founded in 1909 as Greater New Orleans Homestead.

	Annual Growth	12/05	12/06	12/07	12/08	12/09
Assets ($ mil.)	8.2%	240.9	219.7	270.9	327.4	329.8
Net income ($ mil.)	88.0%	0.2	2.0	2.6	2.7	2.5
Market value ($ mil.)	17.6%	—	—	48.0	58.5	66.3
Employees	5.4%	—	58	60	65	68

THE LOUIS BERGER GROUP, INC.

412 Mount Kemble Ave.
Morristown, NJ 07960
Phone: 973-407-1000
Fax: 973-267-6468
Web: www.louisberger.com

CEO: Nicholas J. (Nick) Masucci
CFO: Luke McKinnon
HR: —
FYE: June 30
Type: Private

An architect, an engineer, and an environmentalist walked into a bar. Turns out it wasn't a joke — it was The Louis Berger Group, a New Jersey-based engineering firm. The company, which provides civil, structural, mechanical, electrical, and environmental engineering services, has worked on high-profile projects such as the Pennsylvania Turnpike, the first toll expressway in the US. Louis Berger and its family of companies also has a significant overseas presence. It has built highways, airports, seaports, and dams and contributed to cultural and environmental preservation for projects in 140 countries. The group also has worked on reconstruction projects in Iraq and Afghanistan.

LOUISIANA LOTTERY CORPORATION

555 Laurel St.
Baton Rouge, LA 70801
Phone: 225-297-2000
Fax: 225-297-2005
Web: www.lalottery.com

CEO: Rose J. Hudson
CFO: —
HR: Robin Schooling
FYE: June 30
Type: Government-owned

Louisiana Lottery likes it when people get an itch to scratch. The company operates the state's lottery activities, which include both instant scratch-off games and lotto. Louisiana also participates in the Multi-State Lottery Association's Powerball game. Half of the company's annual $180 million in revenue goes to prize winners, while the rest goes to the state treasury (35%), lottery operations funding (10%), and lottery retailers (5%). A state amendment requires that the treasury funds go into state education coffers. The Louisiana Lottery Corporation was formed in 1991 by the state legislature; it is a true corporation, not a state entity.

LOUISIANA STATE UNIVERSITY SYSTEM

3810 W. Lakeshore Dr.
Baton Rouge, LA 70808
Phone: 225-578-2111
Fax: 225-578-5524
Web: www.lsusystem.edu

CEO: John V. Lombardi
CFO: John Antolik
HR: Sharyon Lipscomb
FYE: June 30
Type: School

The Louisiana State University System, like a good pot of gumbo, offers something that appeals to every taste. The system is composed of 10 campuses and a public hospital system spanning the state. Student enrollment exceeds 57,000 and the system boasts about 2,100 faculty members. Campuses include flagship institution LSU Agricultural and Mechanical College (LSU) located in Baton Rouge, LSU Agricultural Center, the LSU Health Sciences Center, LSU at Alexandria, LSU at Eunice, LSU in Shreveport, the Pennington Biomedical Research Center, and the University of New Orleans. Notable alumni include political strategist James Carville, actress Joanne Woodward, and basketball player Shaquille O'Neal.

LOUISIANA-PACIFIC CORPORATION   NYSE: LPX

414 Union St., Ste. 2000
Nashville, TN 37219
Phone: 615-986-5600
Fax: 615-986-5666
Web: www.lpcorp.com

CEO: Richard W. (Rick) Frost
CFO: Curtis M. (Curt) Stevens
HR: Ann P. Harris
FYE: December 31
Type: Public

Louisiana-Pacific (LP) has you surrounded. The building materials company specializes in manufacturing products for floors, walls, and roofs. LP produces oriented strand board (OSB), siding products, and engineered/composite wood products. LP also makes decorative molding and cellulose insulation. Products are used in new home and manufactured housing construction, and for repair and remodeling. The company sells its products to residential builders and homeowners through wholesale distributors and home centers. Home Depot and Taiga Building Products make up abut 10% of sales. LP operates about 24 manufacturing facilities in the US, Canada, and South America.

	Annual Growth	12/05	12/06	12/07	12/08	12/09
Sales ($ mil.)	(20.2%)	2,598.9	2,235.1	1,704.9	1,376.2	1,054.7
Net income ($ mil.)	—	456.6	123.7	(179.9)	(578.8)	(122.3)
Market value ($ mil.)	(29.0%)	3,483.4	2,730.2	1,734.7	197.8	885.1
Employees	(8.1%)	5,600	5,600	5,100	4,700	4,000

LOVEJOY INDUSTRIES, INC.

194 S. Main St.
Versailles, KY 40383
Phone: 859-873-6828
Fax: 859-873-5927
Web: www.lovejoyindustries.com

CEO: Matthew A. Lovejoy
CFO: Mark J. Kepf
HR: —
FYE: December 31
Type: Holding company

Lovejoy Industries finds both love and joy in working with metals. The holding company does business primarily in metal die casting, industrial molding manufacturing, and nonferrous metal foundries. It has bought and sold a number of industrial and manufacturing operations over the past 40-plus years. Touting competitive "lean" business practices in casting of aluminum, magnesium, and zinc, Lovejoy's affiliates are Acme Die Casting, Elkton Die Casting, Pichinin Die Casting (Brazil concern), and Acme Alliance (raw basic industrial services to technology companies, and the power tool industry). The company targets customers in automotive, telecommunications, gasoline distribution, and electric equipment markets.

	Annual Growth	12/04	12/05	12/06	12/07	12/08
Est. sales ($ mil.)	—	—	—	—	—	33.6
Employees	—	—	—	—	—	400

LOVE'S TRAVEL STOPS & COUNTRY STORES, INC.

10601 N. Pennsylvania Ave.
Oklahoma City, OK 73120
Phone: 405-751-9000
Fax: 405-749-9110
Web: www.loves.com

CEO: Tom Love
CFO: Doug Stussi
HR: Kevin Asbury
FYE: December 31
Type: Private

If you're a trucker or RVer on the road, all you need is Love's. Love's Travel Stops & Country Stores operates more than 220 travel stop locations throughout a swath of about 35 states from California to Virginia, including convenience stores in Colorado, Kansas, New Mexico, Oklahoma, and Texas. Each travel stop includes a convenience store; a fast-food restaurant, such as Taco Bell or Subway; and gas outlets for cars, trucks, and RVs. The travel stops also provide shower rooms, laundry facilities, game rooms, and mail drops. Love's Travel Stops & Country Stores is owned by the family of CEO Tom Love, who founded the company in 1964.

	Annual Growth	12/04	12/05	12/06	12/07	12/08
Sales ($ mil.)	65.3%	2,210.0	3,807.0	6,330.0	7,000.0	16,500.0
Employees	14.4%	3,800	4,400	5,600	6,000	6,500

LOWER COLORADO RIVER AUTHORITY

3700 Lake Austin Blvd.
Austin, TX 78703
Phone: 512-473-3200
Fax: —
Web: www.lcra.org

CEO: Thomas G. Mason
CFO: Brady Edwards
HR: Christopher Kennedy
FYE: June 30
Type: Government-owned

The stars at night may be big and bright, but more than 1 million people deep in the heart of Texas still need electricity from the Lower Colorado River Authority (LCRA). Serving more than 50 counties along the lower Colorado River from Central Texas' Hill Country to the Gulf of Mexico, the not-for-profit, state-run entity supplies wholesale electricity to more than 40 retail utilities (primarily municipalities and cooperatives). It operates three fossil-fuel powered plants and six hydroelectric dams that give it a production capacity of about 2,300 megawatts; it also purchases electricity from Texas wind farms. The LCRA provides water and wastewater utility services to more than 30 communities as well.

	Annual Growth	6/04	6/05	6/06	6/07	6/08
Sales ($ mil.)	14.4%	694.4	802.6	1,045.4	1,079.4	1,187.8
Net income ($ mil.)	10.3%	34.4	41.4	26.2	43.6	50.9
Employees	1.1%	2,224	2,200	2,200	2,244	2,325

LOWE'S COMPANIES, INC.   NYSE: LOW

1000 Lowe's Blvd.
Mooresville, NC 28117
Phone: 704-758-1000
Fax: 336-658-4766
Web: www.lowes.com

CEO: Robert A. Niblock
CFO: Robert F. (Bob) Hull Jr.
HR: Cedric T. Coco
FYE: January 31
Type: Public

No longer a low-profile company, Lowe's Companies has evolved from a regional hardware store operator into a nationwide chain of home improvement superstores bent on international expansion. The #2 US home improvement chain (after The Home Depot), Lowe's has about 1,700 superstores in 50 states and more than 15 locations in Canada and Mexico, as well as an e-commerce site. Its stores sell some 40,000 products for do-it-yourselfers and professionals for home improvement and repair projects, such as lumber, paint, plumbing and electrical supplies, tools, and gardening products, as well as appliances, lighting, and furniture. Lowe's is the second-largest US home appliance retailer after Sears.

	Annual Growth	1/06	1/07	1/08	1/09	1/10
Sales ($ mil.)	2.2%	43,243.0	46,927.0	48,283.0	48,230.0	47,220.0
Net income ($ mil.)	(10.4%)	2,771.0	3,105.0	2,809.0	2,195.0	1,783.0
Market value ($ mil.)	(9.1%)	45,863.7	48,656.7	38,148.8	26,370.7	31,249.4
Employees	6.6%	185,000	210,000	216,000	229,000	239,000

An in-depth profile of this company is available to Hoover's Online members at hoovers.com.

LOYOLA UNIVERSITY NEW ORLEANS

6363 St. Charles Ave.
New Orleans, LA 70118
Phone: 504-865-3847
Fax: 504-865-3851
Web: www.loyno.edu

CEO: Rev Kevin W. Wildes
CFO: —
HR: —
FYE: July 31
Type: School

Loyola University New Orleans is part of the Jesuit network of universities and enrolls roughly 3,000 students. The university offers some 60 degree programs through five colleges: Arts and Sciences, Business Administration, City College, Music, and School of Law. The Louisiana State Legislature granted the charter to Loyola University in 1912. After Hurricane Katrina struck New Orleans in 2005, the university cancelled its fall semester for the first time in Loyola's history. The school's estimated property damage totaled $4 million. Classes reconvened in January of 2006 and in April the school announced a restructuring plan that would eliminate several degree programs and 17 faculty positions.

	Annual Growth	7/04	7/05	7/06	7/07	7/08
Est. sales ($ mil.)	—	—	—	—	—	113.4
Employees	—	—	—	—	—	1,000

LPL INVESTMENT HOLDINGS INC.

1 Beacon St., Fl. 22
Boston, MA 02108
Phone: 617-423-3644
Fax: —
Web: lplfinancial.lpl.com

CEO: Mark S. Casady
CFO: Robert J. Moore
HR: Denise M. Abood
FYE: December 31
Type: Private

LPL Investment is the holding company for LPL Financial, one of the largest brokerage firms in the US. The company offers technology, training, infrastructure, and research, as well as stocks, bonds, mutual funds, annuities, insurance, and other investment products and services to approximately 12,000 independent financial advisors at more than 6,500 locations across the US. It doesn't create or sell its own investment products, but provides access to those of other firms. LPL provides similar services to about 750 community banks and credit unions across the US. It also performs clearing and custody services for financial professionals and institutions. LPL filed to go public in 2010.

	Annual Growth	12/05	12/06	12/07	12/08	12/09
Sales ($ mil.)	18.2%	1,407.3	1,739.9	2,717.6	3,117.1	2,749.5
Net income ($ mil.)	2.5%	43.1	33.6	61.1	45.5	47.5
Employees	19.9%	1,200	2,200	2,621	2,800	2,480

LQ MANAGEMENT LLC

909 Hidden Ridge, Ste. 600
Irving, TX 75038
Phone: 214-492-6600
Fax: 214-492-6616
Web: www.lq.com

CEO: Wayne B. Goldberg
CFO: Temple H. Weiss
HR: Dixie Sweeney
FYE: December 31
Type: Subsidiary

La Quinta . . . Spanish for "Next to Denny's?" LQ Management is owner of the La Quinta (which is Spanish for the villa) hotel brand. The company has hotels throughout the US (about 45 states), Canada, and Mexico under the La Quinta Inns and La Quinta Inn & Suites brands. LQ Management franchises the majority of its properties. The growing company has more than 750 hotels, which encompass some 65,000 guest rooms; in addition, it has some 250 properties in the development pipeline. La Quinta hotels operate in the limited service, midscale segment. It targets a mix of corporate and leisure travelers. LQ Management is owned by investment firm The Blackstone Group.

	Annual Growth	12/04	12/05	12/06	12/07	12/08
Est. sales ($ mil.)	—	—	—	—	—	307.4
Employees	—	—	—	—	—	9,130

LRAD CORPORATION

NASDAQ (CM): LRAD

15378 Avenue of Science, Ste. 100
San Diego, CA 92128
Phone: 858-676-1112
Fax: 858-676-1120
Web: www.lradx.com

CEO: Thomas R. (Tom) Brown
CFO: Katherine H. (Kathy) McDermott
HR: —
FYE: September 30
Type: Public

High-tech sound may drive development for LRAD (formerly American Technology Corporation), but the firm is also banking on it to drive its bottom line. LRAD, whose past sales largely came from its portable radios, discontinued its portable consumer electronics division to make products that transmit sound over short and long distances. The company's Long Range Acoustic Devices generate the majority of revenues nowadays, and they have been deployed by the US military and used by public safety agencies worldwide. To strengthen its identity as a global provider of long-range acoustic technology systems, the company changed its name to LRAD in 2010.

	Annual Growth	9/05	9/06	9/07	9/08	9/09
Sales ($ mil.)	11.6%	10.2	8.9	9.9	11.2	15.8
Net income ($ mil.)	—	(9.1)	(7.7)	(5.6)	(6.4)	(1.0)
Market value ($ mil.)	(23.2%)	155.5	116.9	116.3	16.8	54.2
Employees	(5.9%)	46	41	38	33	36

THE L.S. STARRETT COMPANY

NYSE: SCX

121 Crescent St.
Athol, MA 01331
Phone: 978-249-3551
Fax: 978-249-8495
Web: www.starrett.com

CEO: Douglas A. Starrett
CFO: Francis J. O¿Brien
HR: Joel Shaughnessy
FYE: June 30
Type: Public

L.S. Starrett has forged its business inch by inch. The company makes more than 5,000 products, including hand measuring tools (Evans Rule tape measures, steel rules, combination squares, micrometers) and precision instruments (vernier calipers and height and depth gauges). Starrett, which as part of its business boasts major subsidiaries in Brazil, Scotland, and China, sells its products in more than 100 countries. The manufacturer also makes levels, vises, lubricants, saw blades, and vocational and educational materials. Starrett primarily sells its products to machinists in the metalworking industry but serves the DIY, automotive, aviation, construction, marine, and farm equipment industries, as well.

	Annual Growth	6/05	6/06	6/07	6/08	6/09
Sales ($ mil.)	1.0%	195.9	200.9	222.4	242.4	203.7
Net income ($ mil.)	—	4.0	(3.8)	6.7	10.8	(3.2)
Market value ($ mil.)	(21.9%)	121.7	91.1	122.3	158.8	45.4
Employees	(5.5%)	2,219	2,129	2,113	2,221	1,768

LSB CORPORATION

NASDAQ (GM): LSBX

30 Massachusetts Ave.
North Andover, MA 01845
Phone: 978-725-7500
Fax: 978-725-7593
Web: www.riverbk.com

CEO: Gerald T. Mulligan
CFO: Diane L. Walker
HR: Teresa K. Flynn
FYE: December 31
Type: Public

LSB Corporation helps those with common (and uncommon) wealth in Massachusetts. It owns RiverBank (formerly Lawrence Savings Bank), which has about a half dozen offices in northeastern Massachusetts and nearby southern New Hampshire. Founded in 1868, RiverBank offers checking and savings accounts, NOW and money market accounts, CDs, and IRAs. Commercial mortgages dominate the company's lending activities — they account for some 50% of all loans. Residential mortgages account for more than 20%; home equity, construction, business, and consumer loans round out its loan book.

	Annual Growth	12/05	12/06	12/07	12/08	12/09
Assets ($ mil.)	11.8%	521.8	543.0	621.7	761.3	816.6
Net income ($ mil.)	4.5%	4.2	0.1	3.7	(2.7)	5.0
Market value ($ mil.)	(13.5%)	78.2	74.7	72.1	32.9	43.8
Employees	2.2%	101	101	91	94	110

LSB FINANCIAL CORP.

NASDAQ (GM): LSBI

101 Main St.
Lafayette, IN 47901
Phone: 765-742-1064
Fax: 765-742-1507
Web: www.lsbank.com

CEO: Randolph F. (Randy) Williams
CFO: Mary Jo David
HR: —
FYE: December 31
Type: Public

There's nothing psychedelic about LSB. Straight-laced LSB Financial is the holding company for Lafayette Savings Bank, which has been serving northern Indiana since 1869. Today the bank has a handful of branches in the communities of Lafayette and West Lafayette, offering checking, savings, and money market accounts, NOW accounts, and CDs. It primarily writes real estate loans, with residential mortgages making up about half of the company's loan portfolio. It also writes commercial and multifamily residential mortgages, real estate construction loans, and land development loans.

	Annual Growth	12/05	12/06	12/07	12/08	12/09
Assets ($ mil.)	(0.1%)	372.7	368.4	342.0	373.0	371.0
Net income ($ mil.)	(37.6%)	3.3	3.3	1.6	1.7	0.5
Market value ($ mil.)	(21.9%)	40.8	38.1	29.8	15.4	15.2
Employees	1.6%	91	96	97	91	97

LSB INDUSTRIES, INC.

NYSE: LXU

16 S. Pennsylvania Ave.
Oklahoma City, OK 73107
Phone: 405-235-4546
Fax: 405-235-5067
Web: www.lsbindustries.com

CEO: Jack E. Golsen
CFO: Tony M. Shelby
HR: —
FYE: December 31
Type: Public

LSB Industries makes a wide variety of chemicals (including nitric acid) and climate-control products. Its chemicals segment makes nitrate fertilizers and acids for agricultural, mining, and industrial markets. The climate-control division makes hydronic fan coils and a variety of heat pumps. Additionally, its industrial products segment distributes industrial milling, drilling, turning, and fabricating machines. The company's chemical unit accounts for more than half of sales; geographically, pretty much all of its sales are within the US. CEO Jack Golsen and family members own about 40% of the firm, which conducts most of its business through subsidiary ThermaClime.

	Annual Growth	12/05	12/06	12/07	12/08	12/09
Sales ($ mil.)	7.6%	396.7	492.0	586.4	749.0	531.8
Net income ($ mil.)	43.5%	5.1	15.9	46.9	36.6	21.6
Market value ($ mil.)	23.1%	130.6	245.9	599.1	176.6	299.4
Employees	8.4%	1,267	1,565	1,788	1,878	1,749

⊞ LSI CORPORATION

NYSE: LSI

1621 Barber Ln.
Milpitas, CA 95035
Phone: 408-433-8000
Fax: 408-954-3220
Web: www.lsi.com

CEO: Abhijit Y. (Abhi) Talwalkar
CFO: Bryon Look
HR: Gautam Srivastava
FYE: December 31
Type: Public

LSI can show you around the circuit. The fabless semiconductor developer provides standard integrated circuits (ICs) and custom-designed application-specific ICs (ASICs), focusing on broadband and wireless communications, data storage, and networking markets. LSI was a pioneer of system-on-a-chip (SoC) devices, which combine elements of an electronic system — especially a microprocessor, memory, and logic — onto a single chip. LSI's top customers include Hewlett-Packard, IBM (about 19% of sales), and Seagate (around 15%). LSI also provides hardware and software for storage area networks. The Asia/Pacific region accounts for approximately half of the company's sales.

	Annual Growth	12/05	12/06	12/07	12/08	12/09
Sales ($ mil.)	3.7%	1,919.3	1,982.1	2,603.6	2,677.1	2,219.2
Net income ($ mil.)	—	(5.6)	169.6	(2,486.8)	(622.3)	(47.7)
Market value ($ mil.)	(6.9%)	5,228.9	5,882.5	3,470.7	2,150.4	3,928.2
Employees	5.7%	4,322	4,010	6,193	5,488	5,397

⊞ LSI INDUSTRIES INC.

NASDAQ (GS): LYTS

10000 Alliance Rd.
Cincinnati, OH 45242
Phone: 513-793-3200
Fax: 513-984-1335
Web: www.lsi-industries.com

CEO: Robert J. (Bob) Ready
CFO: Ronald S. Stowell
HR: Stan Adams
FYE: June 30
Type: Public

LSI Industries will dance, sing, do anything, just to get your name in lights. The company and its subsidiaries make lighting, graphics, and menu boards for a range of corporate arenas, primarily in the US and Canada. LSI bridges three activities. Its lighting unit makes LED light fixtures for outdoor/indoor/landscape use, from convenience store illumination to chain store lighting. A graphics segment produces indoor/outdoor graphics lighting and menu boards, including digital signage, canopy graphics, and shelf talkers. Design and production of LED video screens is led by a technology segment. Regional managers, national sales reps, and distributors cater to clients Exxon Mobil, Burger King, Ford, and Wal-Mart.

	Annual Growth	6/05	6/06	6/07	6/08	6/09
Sales ($ mil.)	(4.6%)	282.4	280.5	337.5	305.3	233.8
Net income ($ mil.)	—	14.6	14.4	20.8	(13.7)	(13.4)
Market value ($ mil.)	(20.9%)	335.0	408.6	430.5	195.3	131.1
Employees	(6.8%)	1,640	1,764	1,740	1,500	1,240

LTC PROPERTIES INC.

NYSE: LTC

31365 Oak Crest Dr., Ste. 200
Westlake Village, CA 91361
Phone: 805-981-8655
Fax: 805-981-8663
Web: www.ltcproperties.com

CEO: Wendy L. Simpson
CFO: Pamela (Pam) Shelley-Kessler
HR: —
FYE: December 31
Type: Public

Specializing in TLC, LTC Properties sees real estate as a healthy investment. The self-administered real estate investment trust (REIT) primarily invests in health care and long-term care facilities. Its portfolio includes more than 80 assisted living centers (homes for elderly residents not requiring constant supervision), about 60 skilled nursing facilities (which provide rehabilitative and restorative nursing care), and a New Jersey charter school. It owns properties in some two-dozen states. Major tenants include Extendicare, Brookdale Senior Living, and MVP Health Care; together, the three firms account for more than half of LTC Properties' rental revenue.

	Annual Growth	12/05	12/06	12/07	12/08	12/09
Sales ($ mil.)	(3.1%)	79.2	73.7	74.8	69.4	69.9
Net income ($ mil.)	(4.2%)	52.7	78.8	47.8	43.0	44.4
Market value ($ mil.)	6.2%	500.4	649.8	596.1	482.6	636.5
Employees	2.0%	12	12	13	13	13

LTD COMMODITIES LLC

2800 Lakeside Dr.
Bannockburn, IL 60015
Phone: 847-295-5532
Fax: 847-604-7600
Web: www.ltdcommodities.com

CEO: Michael Hara
CFO: —
HR: —
FYE: December 31
Type: Private

You won't find soybeans or pork bellies, but you can buy a little silver (as in a pair of sterling silver earrings) from LTD Commodities. The company, which also does business under the ABC Distributing name, is a business-to-business supplier of apparel for women, men, and children, as well as home and garden accessories, jewelry, electronics, luggage, toys, furniture, gift items, and other general merchandise. LTD Commodities sells its products through numerous catalogs as well as the Internet. It ships only to US business addresses. LTD Commodities was founded in 1963 as a small mail-order business.

⊞ An in-depth profile of this company is available to Hoover's Online members at hoovers.com.

957

LTX-CREDENCE CORPORATION

NASDAQ (GM): LTXC

1355 California Cir.
Milpitas, CA 95035
Phone: 408-635-4300
Fax: 408-635-4985
Web: www.ltx.com

CEO: David G. (Dave) Tacelli
CFO: Mark J. Gallenberger
HR: Jill Barres
FYE: July 31
Type: Public

LTX-Credence isn't John Fogerty's latest band. The company makes automated test equipment used by makers of wireless, computer, automotive, and consumer electronics chips to test semiconductors as they're being manufactured. In 2008 LTX Corp. merged with rival Credence Systems to form LTX-Credence Corporation. The company consolidated the respective predecessors' product lines into four basic test equipment families — ASL, Sapphire, Diamond, and X-Series — following the combination. The company sells its wares worldwide through a direct sales force and distributors. More than 60% of sales come from outside the US.

	Annual Growth	7/05	7/06	7/07	7/08	7/09
Sales ($ mil.)	0.5%	134.5	216.5	147.6	135.8	137.4
Net income ($ mil.)	—	(132.7)	12.2	(10.7)	(0.6)	(137.3)
Market value ($ mil.)	(39.3%)	967.9	789.2	672.1	319.2	131.8
Employees	5.9%	499	438	454	482	627

THE LUBRIZOL CORPORATION

NYSE: LZ

29400 Lakeland Blvd.
Wickliffe, OH 44092
Phone: 440-943-4200
Fax: 440-943-5337
Web: www.lubrizol.com

CEO: James L. Hambrick
CFO: Charles P. Cooley
HR: C. Lawrence Miller
FYE: December 31
Type: Public

Lubrizol is a smooth operator — the company is the world's #1 maker of additives for lubricants and fuels. Its Lubrizol Additives segment includes engine oil additives that fight sludge buildup, viscosity breakdown, and component wear; fuel additives designed to control deposits and improve combustion; and additives for paints, inks, greases, metalworking, and other markets. Lubrizol's Advanced Materials segment (performance coatings and chemicals) delivers its products to the personal care and rubber and plastics markets. The company markets nearly 3,000 products in more than 100 countries; operates research facilities and testing labs in Europe, Asia, and North America; and has plants in 17 countries.

	Annual Growth	12/05	12/06	12/07	12/08	12/09
Sales ($ mil.)	3.2%	4,042.7	4,040.8	4,499.0	5,027.8	4,586.3
Net income ($ mil.)	27.5%	189.3	105.6	283.4	(66.1)	500.8
Market value ($ mil.)	13.8%	2,962.4	3,419.4	3,694.3	2,482.2	4,976.0
Employees	(2.8%)	7,500	6,700	6,900	6,970	6,700

LUBY'S, INC.

NYSE: LUB

13111 NW Fwy., Ste. 600
Houston, TX 77040
Phone: 713-329-6800
Fax: 713-329-6809
Web: www.lubys.com

CEO: Christopher J. (Chris) Pappas
CFO: K. Scott Gray
HR: Paulette Gerukos
FYE: August 31
Type: Public

When Mom wants a salad, Dad craves fried chicken, and little Johnny is screaming for enchiladas, what's an all-American family to do? A simple trip to the cafeteria line at Luby's may do the trick. Luby's owns and operates about 95 cafeteria-style restaurants that offer dozens of different entrees, salads, vegetable dishes, and desserts. The chain's menu is heavy on such comfort foods as mashed potatoes, macaroni and cheese, and fried chicken. Nearly all of the restaurants are found in Texas; Luby's has a small number of eateries in three other states. In addition to its core restaurant business, Luby's offers contract foodservices to a small number of clients in the health care and education industries.

	Annual Growth	8/05	8/06	8/07	8/08	8/09
Sales ($ mil.)	(2.4%)	322.2	324.6	320.4	317.7	292.9
Net income ($ mil.)	—	3.4	19.6	10.9	2.3	(26.4)
Market value ($ mil.)	(24.1%)	368.4	266.6	321.3	208.0	122.0
Employees	(6.7%)	7,680	8,210	7,500	7,807	5,826

LUCAS ENERGY, INC.

NYSE Amex: LEI

3000 Richmond Ave., Ste. 400
Houston, TX 77098
Phone: 713-528-1881
Fax: —
Web: www.lucasenergy.com

CEO: William A. Sawyer
CFO: Don L. Sytsma
HR: —
FYE: March 31
Type: Public

Lucas Energy puts a good amount of energy into drilling. The independent crude oil and gas company owns and operates about 35 production wells and holds more than 1.5 million barrels of oil in proved reserves. Its operations are spread over some 11,000 acres primarily in the Austin Chalk region of Texas. The company leases its well-producing properties from local landowners and small operators and is building up its reserve base by acquiring and re-drilling older or underperforming wells that have been overlooked by larger oil and gas companies. Most of Lucas Energy's revenue comes from sales of crude oil to customers such as Gulfmart and Texon, with the remainder derived from natural gas sales.

	Annual Growth	3/05	3/06	3/07	3/08	3/09
Sales ($ mil.)	61.7%	—	—	1.3	3.1	3.4
Net income ($ mil.)	—	—	—	0.3	0.0	(2.1)
Market value ($ mil.)	(84.4%)	—	—	—	34.6	5.4
Employees	15.5%	—	—	3	5	4

LUCAS GROUP

3384 Peachtree Rd., Ste. 700
Atlanta, GA 30326
Phone: 404-239-5620
Fax: 404-260-7290
Web: www.lucasgroup.com

CEO: Andrea (Andi) Jennings
CFO: Bob Prather
HR: Kelly Stewart
FYE: September 30
Type: Private

Lucas Group recruits senior-level management in the US and Europe for mid-sized companies, multinational corporations, and startups. The company makes placements in a number of functional areas — including advertising, sales, accounting and finance, manufacturing, legal, and technical — across all major industries. It also operates a specialty practice focused on recruiting former military personnel for corporate leadership positions. Founded in 1970, the firm operates more than a dozen offices throughout the US and two in Germany; it has served such clients as Johnson Controls and Ciena.

	Annual Growth	9/04	9/05	9/06	9/07	9/08
Est. sales ($ mil.)	—	—	—	—	—	52.6
Employees	—	—	—	—	—	339

LUCASFILM ENTERTAINMENT COMPANY LTD.

1110 Gorgas Ave.
San Francisco, CA 94129
Phone: 415-746-8000
Fax: —
Web: www.lucasarts.com

CEO: Darrell Rodriguez
CFO: Kevin Parker
HR: —
FYE: April 30
Type: Subsidiary

Not so long ago, in a galaxy not so far away, filmmaker George Lucas founded a software company to entertain audiences with something other than movies. Lucasfilm Entertainment (which does business as LucasArts) produces interactive games for computers and home video game consoles. Much of that source material is, of course, the *Star Wars* films created by the company's owner, George Lucas. LucasArts has more *Star Wars* games than you can shake a lightsaber at and it also produces games based on Lucasfilm's successful trilogy of *Indiana Jones* films, as well as other titles. LucasArts' games blend 3-D animation, interactive digital sound, live-action video, and visual effects.

LUCASFILM LTD.

1110 Gorgas Ave.
San Francisco, CA 94129
Phone: 415-662-1800
Fax: —
Web: www.lucasfilm.com

CEO: Micheline (Mich) Chau
CFO: Steve Condiotti
HR: —
FYE: March 31
Type: Private

The Force is definitely with Emperor George Lucas. The brains behind the *Star Wars* and *Indiana Jones* series, Lucasfilm is one of the most successful independent movie studios in the history of film. Owned by filmmaker George Lucas, the company's productions have won a total of about 20 Academy Awards. Its most recent live action feature film is 2008's *Indiana Jones and the Kingdom of the Crystal Skull* (released in partnership with Paramount); 1999's *Episode I — The Phantom Menace* is Lucasfilm's biggest money-maker, with a gross of more than $920 million worldwide. Other subsidiaries in the Lucas empire are responsible for licensing, special effects, and software. Lucasfilm was created in 1971.

LUCY ACTIVEWEAR, INC.

222 SW Columbia St.
Portland, OR 97201
Phone: 503-228-2142
Fax: —
Web: www.lucy.com

CEO: Shaz Kahng
CFO: —
HR: Corey Routh
FYE: December 31
Type: Subsidiary

If you're an avid outdoorswoman or a yoga devotee, you're likely to end up loving *this* Lucy. Lucy Activewear sells women's activewear (tops, bottoms, jackets, bras, maternity wear, and related accessories) through some 60 company-owned stores (primarily located in California, but also in a dozen other states and the District of Columbia). Lucy Activewear, founded in 1999, also sells merchandise through its website. VF Corporation acquired the fast-growing company for $110 million in mid-2007 to lay a foundation for a contemporary brands division (or what VF calls a "coalition"), which also includes the premium-denim brand 7 For All Mankind.

LUFKIN INDUSTRIES, INC.

NASDAQ (GS): LUFK

601 S. Raguet St.
Lufkin, TX 75904
Phone: 936-634-2211
Fax: 936-637-5272
Web: www.lufkin.com

CEO: John F. (Jay) Glick
CFO: Christopher L. (Chris) Boone
HR: —
FYE: December 31
Type: Public

Lufkin Industries is all geared up to help pump oil. Through its Oil Field division the company manufactures and services pumping units, automation equipment, and foundry castings. It also provides computer control equipment and analytical services used to maximize well efficiency. As part of Lufkin Industries' vertical integration, the Oil Field segment also operates an iron foundry to produce castings for new pumping units, and for third parties. Through its Power Transmission unit, Lufkin Industries manufactures and services gearboxes (in power levels from 20 to 85,000 horsepower) used in large-scale industrial applications. The company operates manufacturing plants in Argentina, Canada, France and the US.

	Annual Growth	12/05	12/06	12/07	12/08	12/09
Sales ($ mil.)	1.5%	492.2	605.5	597.2	741.2	521.4
Net income ($ mil.)	(16.1%)	44.5	73.0	74.2	88.2	22.0
Market value ($ mil.)	10.1%	746.3	869.1	857.3	516.3	1,095.4
Employees	(0.9%)	2,700	3,000	2,700	3,000	2,600

LUITPOLD PHARMACEUTICALS, INC.

1 Luitpold Dr.
Shirley, NY 11967
Phone: 631-924-4000
Fax: 631-924-1731
Web: www.luitpold.com

CEO: Mary Jane Helenek
CFO: Mary Lent
HR: —
FYE: December 31
Type: Subsidiary

Luitpold Pharmaceuticals earns its gold from the businesses of drugs and medical devices. Luitpold markets and manufactures injectable products used to treat an array of ailments including kidney disease. Luitpold also manufactures materials used in dental bone grafting and bone regeneration and treatments for equine and canine joint diseases. The company, which targets its products primarily to hospitals and clinics in US and Canadian markets, operates through four divisions: American Regent, Luitpold Animal Health, Osteohealth, and Contract Manufacturing. Originally a German company named after a Bavarian prince, Luitpold is a subsidiary of one of Japan's largest pharmaceutical companies, Daiichi Sankyo.

	Annual Growth	12/04	12/05	12/06	12/07	12/08
Est. sales ($ mil.)	—	—	—	—	—	400.0
Employees	—	—	—	—	—	470

LUK USA LLC

3401 Old Airport Rd.
Wooster, OH 44691
Phone: 330-264-4383
Fax: 330-264-4333
Web: www.lukusa.com

CEO: Andreas Schick
CFO: —
HR: —
FYE: December 31
Type: Subsidiary

Need a little more torque in your converter? As luck — make that LuK — would have it, there's a solution. LuK USA makes torque converters, clutches, flywheels, gearboxes, and other related transmission products for both the automobile and agriculture machinery industries. Its manufacturing facility measures 500,000 sq. ft. The company's customers include Ford, General Motors, Honda, Nissan, and Toyota Motor. Established in 1977, LuK USA is a unit of German parts manufacturer LuK GmbH, which in turn is part of the Schaeffler manufacturing conglomerate.

LUMBER LIQUIDATORS, INC.

NYSE: LL

3000 John Deere Rd.
Toano, VA 23168
Phone: 757-259-4280
Fax: —
Web: www.lumberliquidators.com

CEO: Jeffrey W. (Jeff) Griffiths
CFO: Daniel E. Terrell
HR: E. Jean Matherne
FYE: December 31
Type: Public

Thanks to the resurgence of hardwoods, Lumber Liquidators is in the money. The nation's largest specialty retailer of hardwood flooring, Lumber Liquidators sells more than 25 domestic and exotic wood species of both prefinished and unfinished hardwood flooring from about 200 stores in 45 states. It also sells antique and reclaimed boards, laminate flooring, and installation accessories. Brands include Bellawood, Builder's Pride, Schön, and more. The company also sells its products online, by catalog, and from its Virginia call center. Homeowners represent about 90% of Lumber Liquidators' customer base. The company was founded in 1993 by its chairman, Tom Sullivan.

	Annual Growth	12/05	12/06	12/07	12/08	12/09
Sales ($ mil.)	22.1%	244.9	332.1	405.3	482.2	544.6
Net income ($ mil.)	25.9%	10.7	12.9	11.3	22.1	26.9
Market value ($ mil.)	72.7%	—	—	245.8	288.8	732.8
Employees	17.5%	490	490	670	788	934

An in-depth profile of this company is available to Hoover's Online members at hoovers.com.

959

LUMBERMENS MUTUAL CASUALTY COMPANY

1 Kemper Dr.
Long Grove, IL 60049
Phone: 847-320-2000
Fax: 847-320-3818
Web: www.kemperinsurance.com

CEO: David B. Mathis
CFO: Fredrick T. Griffith
HR: —
FYE: December 31
Type: Mutual company

Lumbermens Mutual Casualty, the flagship member of the Kemper Insurance Companies family, is waiting for the axe to fall. No longer writing new policies, the once-proud Kemper Insurance Companies traditionally offered a wide array of personal, risk management, and commercial property/casualty products, mostly through Lumbermens. It stopped writing new business in 2003 and is voluntarily liquidating by running off all of its remaining property/casualty business, a process begun in 2004. James Kemper founded Lumbermens Mutual in 1912.

	Annual Growth	12/04	12/05	12/06	12/07	12/08
Est. sales ($ mil.)	—	—	—	—	—	19.2
Employees	—	—	—	—	—	9,000

LUMILEDS LIGHTING U.S., LLC

370 W. Trimble Rd.
San Jose, CA 95131
Phone: 408-964-2900
Fax: 408-435-6855
Web: www.lumileds.com

CEO: Michael C. (Mike) Holt
CFO: —
HR: —
FYE: December 31
Type: Subsidiary

Lumileds Lighting is helping the world take a shine to LEDs. A subsidiary of Philips Lighting, Lumileds designs and produces LED core materials and packaging that can be integrated into general lighting products. Its red, amber, blue, green, and white light-emitting diodes (LEDs), including its high-brightness LUXEON line, are used in indoor and outdoor lighting, LCD displays, traffic signals, automotive lighting, and camera flashes. Lumileds has manufacturing operations in Asia, Australia, India, and the US; it has R&D labs in California and the Netherlands. Lumileds started as a joint venture between Agilent Technologies and Philips Lighting; in 2005 Agilent sold its stake in Lumileds to Philips.

LUMINEX CORPORATION

NASDAQ (GM): LMNX

12212 Technology Blvd.
Austin, TX 78727
Phone: 512-219-8020
Fax: 512-219-5195
Web: www.luminexcorp.com

CEO: Patrick J. Balthrop Sr.
CFO: Harriss T. Currie
HR: Eddie Chien
FYE: December 31
Type: Public

Luminex Corporation sheds new light on genetic mysteries. The company's xMAP technology — which consists of instruments, software, and disposable microspheres, or tiny beads on which tests are performed — allows users to run up to 100 bioassays on one drop of fluid. Luminex licenses the technology to other life sciences companies, which develop reagent-based tests to go with the instrumentation systems and then distribute them to end users, or use them to perform testing services for their customers. Luminex also develops some assays of its own. Its strategic partners include companies focused on drug discovery and biomedical research (Millipore) and clinical diagnostics (Bio-Rad, Inverness Medical).

	Annual Growth	12/05	12/06	12/07	12/08	12/09
Sales ($ mil.)	29.9%	42.3	53.0	75.0	104.4	120.6
Net income ($ mil.)	—	(2.7)	1.5	(2.7)	3.1	17.7
Market value ($ mil.)	6.5%	486.6	531.9	680.1	894.5	625.2
Employees	24.0%	185	303	344	384	437

LUMMUS TECHNOLOGY INC.

1515 Broad St.
Bloomfield, NJ 07003
Phone: 973-893-1515
Fax: 973-893-2000
Web: www.cbi.com/lummus

CEO: Daniel M. McCarthy
CFO: John Albanese
HR: Kaye Bell-Reiter
FYE: December 31
Type: Subsidiary

Lummus Technology (formerly ABB Lummus Global) looms large across the globe in engineering projects. The company provides engineering, procurement, and construction-related services for the petrochemical, refining, and gas processing industries. It oversees the construction of process plants and offshore facilities, performing a range of services, including process design, project management, project financing, engineer training, and technical support. Its Lummus Heat Transfer unit supplies and designs specialized heat transfer equipment. Major clients include Chevron, Shell, and Sinopec. Chicago Bridge & Iron Company (CB&I) acquired the company from Swiss ABB for some $950 million in 2007.

	Annual Growth	12/05	12/06	12/07	12/08	12/09
Sales ($ mil.)	(24.0%)	1,087.8	988.4	104.6	438.7	363.4
Net income ($ mil.)	100.6%	5.0	(80.0)	10.4	110.8	80.9
Employees	(4.0%)	2,500	2,400	—	—	—

LUNA INNOVATIONS INCORPORATED

NASDAQ (GM): LUNA

1 Riverside Cir., Ste. 400
Roanoke, VA 24016
Phone: 540-769-8400
Fax: 540-769-8401
Web: www.lunainnovations.com

CEO: Kent A. Murphy
CFO: Dale E. Messick
HR: —
FYE: December 31
Type: Public

R&D firm Luna Innovations endeavors to make practical use of cutting-edge technologies in the areas of molecular technology and sensing. Its molecular technology efforts focus on materials (including polymers, reagents, and nanomaterials) with enhanced performance characteristics; Luna has developed contrast agents for MRI testing, nanomaterials used in solar cells, and protective coatings. It has also created sensing technologies used in medical monitoring equipment, as well as wireless and fiber-optic monitoring systems for defense and industrial instrumentation. Luna Innovations emerged from Chapter 11 bankruptcy protection in January 2010. The firm voluntarily filed in July 2009.

	Annual Growth	12/05	12/06	12/07	12/08	12/09
Sales ($ mil.)	20.3%	16.5	23.5	33.7	36.9	34.6
Net income ($ mil.)	—	(2.0)	(9.4)	(7.8)	(6.3)	(20.4)
Market value ($ mil.)	(15.8%)	—	46.2	110.6	24.8	27.5
Employees	4.5%	161	193	200	196	192

LUNDBECK INC.

4 Parkway North, Ste. 200
Deerfield, IL 60015
Phone: 847-282-1000
Fax: 847-282-1001
Web: www.lundbeckinc.com

CEO: Sean Nolan
CFO: Curtis R. Rhine
HR: Lance D. Williams
FYE: December 31
Type: Subsidiary

Lundbeck Inc. (formerly Ovation Pharmaceuticals) hopes to earn its applause by staying on the look-out for niche pharmaceuticals that larger drugmakers cast aside. The company's focus is on developing drugs for central nervous system (CNS) disorders, as well as cancer drugs and hospital-based therapies. Its FDA-approved products for neurological conditions include treatments for ADHD, anxiety, and seizures; the company has several CNS products in its development pipeline, such as epilepsy drugs, drug addiction therapies, and seizure medications. Among its other marketed products are several oncology drugs, as well as a treatment for lead poisoning. The company was acquired by Denmark-based H. Lundbeck in 2009.

	Annual Growth	12/04	12/05	12/06	12/07	12/08
Est. sales ($ mil.)	—	—	—	—	—	25.0
Employees	—	—	—	—	—	300

LUXOTTICA RETAIL

4000 Luxottica Place
Mason, OH 45040
Phone: 513-765-6000
Fax: 513-765-6249
Web: www.luxottica.com

CEO: Kerry Bradley
CFO: Jack S. Dennis
HR: —
FYE: December 31
Type: Business segment

If you need glasses, Luxottica Retail has you in its sights. The retail arm of Italian eyewear giant Luxottica Group, Luxottica Retail is one of the world's leading operators of optical stores. The company has more than 6,250 locations in North America, Europe, the Asia/Pacific region, the Middle East, and Africa. Its chains include LensCrafters, Oakley, Oliver Peoples, Pearle Vision, and Sunglass Hut, as well as more than 1,200 in-store businesses Sears Optical and Target Optical. About 5,700 of Luxottica Retail's stores are company-owned; the rest are franchised. In addition, Luxottica Retail oversees a leading US managed vision care plan, EyeMed Vision Care, which serves some 3,4000 corporations.

LYDALL, INC.

NYSE: LDL

1 Colonial Rd.
Manchester, CT 06042
Phone: 860-646-1233
Fax: 860-646-4917
Web: www.lydall.com

CEO: Dale G. Barnhart
CFO: Erika H. Turner
HR: Mona G. Estey
FYE: December 31
Type: Public

Lydall's products help to beat the heat, nix the noise, and filter the rest. The company makes thermal and acoustical barriers, automotive heat shields, and insulation products that offer protection in temperatures ranging from near absolute zero to 3,000 degrees Fahrenheit. Lydall's thermal and acoustical products are used by the appliance and automotive industries, and in industrial kilns and furnaces. The company rounds out its offerings with industrial and commercial air and liquid filtration products and — through its subsidiary Charter Medical — fluid management systems for the medical and biopharmaceutical markets. Export sales represent over 50% of the company's annual net sales.

	Annual Growth	12/05	12/06	12/07	12/08	12/09
Sales ($ mil.)	(5.1%)	306.5	326.4	338.9	305.7	248.9
Net income ($ mil.)	—	5.4	10.2	9.1	(5.0)	(14.2)
Market value ($ mil.)	(10.6%)	139.0	184.4	179.4	98.1	88.9
Employees	(5.4%)	1,500	1,400	1,400	1,200	1,200

LYKES BROS. INC.

400 N. Tampa St.
Tampa, FL 33602
Phone: 813-470-5000
Fax: 813-470-5082
Web: www.lykesranch.com

CEO: Howell L. Ferguson
CFO: Frederick J. (Fred) Bennett
HR: Richard (Rich) Hetherton
FYE: September 30
Type: Private

This bunch of Florida siblings Lykes land, lots o' land. Family-owned Lykes Bros. concentrates its efforts on its 337,000 acres of land holdings — which is home to the company's diverse operations, which include cattle ranching (20,000 head), forestry, and sod and sugarcane farms. The company also grows landscaping trees, leases grazing and farm land, oversees pine and eucalyptus forests, and offers hunting (deer, quail, turkey) and fishing tours on its 1,867-acre Silver Lake Preserve. The company was founded by Dr. Howell Tyson Lykes in 1900 and is owned by the descendants of his seven sons.

LYONDELLBASELL NORTH AMERICA INC.

1 Houston Center, 1221 McKinney St., Ste. 700
Houston, TX 77010
Phone: 713-652-7200
Fax: —
Web: www.lyondellbasell.com

CEO: James L. (Jim) Gallogly
CFO: —
HR: —
FYE: December 31
Type: Subsidiary

LyondellBasell North America is North America's leading producer of polypropylene. It is the American division of global petrochemical giant LyondellBasell and also makes polyethylene and other advanced polyolefin materials. The company operates about 30 manufacturing plants, technical centers, and R&D facilities in the US and Mexico. It also operates a petroleum refinery in Houston and acts as the exclusive marketer of polypropylene resins manufactured at a plant owned by ConocoPhillips. LyondellBasell's US unit emerged from Chapter 11 bankruptcy protection in 2010 under a new parent holding company, LyondellBasell Industries NV.

	Annual Growth	12/04	12/05	12/06	12/07	12/08
Est. sales ($ mil.)	—	—	—	—	—	27,674.0
Employees	—	—	—	—	—	7,340

LYRIS, INC.

OTC: LYRI

103 Foulk Rd., Ste. 205Q
Wilmington, DE 19803
Phone: 302-691-6189
Fax: —
Web: www.lyrisinc.com

CEO: Luis A. Rivera
CFO: Heidi Mackintosh
HR: —
FYE: June 30
Type: Public

Lyris is a firm believer in the far-reaching power of e-mail. The company provides a variety of e-mail marketing software and services. Clients use the company's products to manage e-mail lists and to create and monitor e-mail marketing campaigns. Its customers come from a wide range of industries including financial services, consumer goods, health care, retail, media, and transportation. The company also provides professional services such as consulting, support, and training. Formerly called J. L. Halsey, the company changed its name in 2007.

	Annual Growth	6/05	6/06	6/07	6/08	6/09
Sales ($ mil.)	110.6%	2.2	24.4	39.0	43.2	43.3
Net income ($ mil.)	—	(0.2)	2.6	0.3	(5.5)	(18.6)
Market value ($ mil.)	(12.4%)	61.9	111.7	97.1	81.3	36.4
Employees	52.1%	48	113	162	250	257

An in-depth profile of this company is available to Hoover's Online members at hoovers.com.

961